Lee Ahlstrom

SPHERICAL COORDINATES: $u = u(\rho, \phi, \theta)$, $\mathbf{v} = v_\rho \hat{\mathbf{e}}_\rho + v$

$$\nabla u = \left(\hat{\mathbf{e}}_\rho \frac{\partial}{\partial \rho} + \hat{\mathbf{e}}_\phi \frac{1}{\rho}\frac{\partial}{\partial \phi} + \hat{\mathbf{e}}_\theta \frac{1}{\rho \sin\phi}\frac{\partial}{\partial \theta}\right) u$$

$$= \frac{\partial u}{\partial \rho}\hat{\mathbf{e}}_\rho + \frac{1}{\rho}\frac{\partial u}{\partial \phi}\hat{\mathbf{e}}_\phi + \frac{1}{\rho \sin\phi}\frac{\partial u}{\partial \theta}\hat{\mathbf{e}}_\theta$$

$$\nabla^2 u = \frac{1}{\rho^2}\left[\frac{\partial}{\partial \rho}\left(\rho^2 \frac{\partial u}{\partial \rho}\right) + \frac{1}{\sin\phi}\frac{\partial}{\partial \phi}\left(\sin\phi \frac{\partial u}{\partial \phi}\right) + \frac{1}{\sin^2\phi}\frac{\partial^2 u}{\partial \theta^2}\right]$$

$$\nabla \cdot \mathbf{v} = \frac{1}{\rho^2}\frac{\partial}{\partial \rho}(\rho^2 v_\rho) + \frac{1}{\rho \sin\phi}\frac{\partial}{\partial \phi}(v_\phi \sin\phi) + \frac{1}{\rho \sin\phi}\frac{\partial v_\theta}{\partial \theta}$$

$$\nabla \times \mathbf{v} = \frac{1}{\rho \sin\phi}\left[\frac{\partial}{\partial \phi}(v_\theta \sin\phi) - \frac{\partial v_\phi}{\partial \theta}\right]\hat{\mathbf{e}}_\rho$$

$$+ \frac{1}{\rho}\left[\frac{1}{\sin\phi}\frac{\partial v_\rho}{\partial \theta} - \frac{\partial(\rho v_\theta)}{\partial \rho}\right]\hat{\mathbf{e}}_\phi + \frac{1}{\rho}\left[\frac{\partial(\rho v_\phi)}{\partial \rho} - \frac{\partial v_\rho}{\partial \phi}\right]\hat{\mathbf{e}}_\theta$$

$$= \frac{1}{\rho^2 \sin\phi}\begin{vmatrix} \hat{\mathbf{e}}_\rho & \rho\hat{\mathbf{e}}_\phi & \rho\sin\phi\,\hat{\mathbf{e}}_\theta \\ \dfrac{\partial}{\partial \rho} & \dfrac{\partial}{\partial \phi} & \dfrac{\partial}{\partial \theta} \\ v_\rho & \rho v_\phi & \rho \sin\phi\, v_\theta \end{vmatrix}$$

$$\mathbf{R} = \rho\hat{\mathbf{e}}_\rho, \quad d\mathbf{R} = d\rho\,\hat{\mathbf{e}}_\rho + \rho\, d\phi\,\hat{\mathbf{e}}_\phi + \rho \sin\phi\, d\theta\,\hat{\mathbf{e}}_\theta$$

$$dA = \begin{cases} \rho^2 |\sin\phi|\, d\phi\, d\theta & \text{(constant-}\rho\text{ surface)} \\ \rho|\sin\phi|\, d\rho\, d\theta & \text{(constant-}\phi\text{ surface)}, \\ \rho\, d\rho\, d\phi & \text{(constant-}\theta\text{ surface)} \end{cases} \quad dV = \rho^2 |\sin\phi|\, d\rho\, d\phi\, d\theta$$

GAUSS DIVERGENCE THEOREM: $\int_{\mathcal{V}} \operatorname{div} \mathbf{v}\, dV = \int_{\mathcal{S}} \hat{\mathbf{n}} \cdot \mathbf{v}\, dA$

GREEN'S FIRST IDENTITY: $\int_{\mathcal{V}} (\nabla u \cdot \nabla v + u\nabla^2 v)\, dV = \int_{\mathcal{S}} u \frac{\partial v}{\partial n}\, dA$

GREEN'S SECOND IDENTITY: $\int_{\mathcal{V}} (u\nabla^2 v - v\nabla^2 u)\, dV = \int_{\mathcal{S}} \left(u\frac{\partial v}{\partial n} - v\frac{\partial u}{\partial n}\right) dA$

STOKES' THEOREM: $\int_{\mathcal{S}} \hat{\mathbf{n}} \cdot \operatorname{curl} \mathbf{v}\, dA = \oint_{\mathcal{C}} \mathbf{v} \cdot d\mathbf{R}$

GREEN'S THEOREM: $\int_{\mathcal{S}} \left(\frac{\partial Q}{\partial x} - \frac{\partial P}{\partial y}\right) dA = \oint_{\mathcal{C}} (P\, dx + Q\, dy)$

MICHAEL D. GREENBERG
Department of Mechanical Engineering
University of Delaware

Advanced Engineering Mathematics

PRENTICE HALL, ENGLEWOOD CLIFFS, NEW JERSEY 07632

Library of Congress Cataloging-in-Publication Data

Greenberg, Michael D, 1935–
Advanced engineering mathematics.

Includes bibliographies and index.
1. Engineering mathematics. I. Title.
TA330.G725 1988 620'.001'51 87-25877
ISBN 0-13-010505-8

This book is dedicated, with appreciation, to my students

Editorial/production supervision: *Virginia Huebner*
Interior design: *Lorraine Mullaney*
Cover design: *Lorraine Mullaney*
Manufacturing buyer: *Paula Massenaro*
Cover photo: *Cliff Feulner, The Image Bank*

Printed in the United States of America

10 9 8 7 6 5 4 3 2 1

ISBN 0-13-010505-8

Prentice-Hall International (U.K.) Ltd., *London*
Prentice-Hall of Australia Pty. Limited, *Sydney*
Prentice-Hall Canada Inc., *Toronto*
Prentice-Hall Hispanoamericana, S.A., *Mexico*
Prentice-Hall of India Private Limited, *New Delhi*
Prentice-Hall of Japan, Inc., *Tokyo*
Simon & Schuster Asia Pte. Ltd., *Singapore*
Editora Prentice-Hall do Brasil, Ltda., *Rio de Janeiro*

Contents

Preface

Purpose.

This book is intended primarily as a text for a single- or multi-semester course in applied mathematics for students in engineering or science. Beyond such a course, or courses, it is intended that the book be useful for reference and for self-study. Thus, explanations are sometimes more detailed than they might have been, common difficulties are anticipated and discussed, and the writing is somewhat conversational.

It should be emphasized that by "self-study" we do not necessarily mean outside the context of a formal course. Rather, we are interested in possibilities even within course settings. For if the text can be understood through self-study, then the instructor has more instructional options available. For instance, in a given lecture one might answer questions on the reading, highlight a few points, and then take a detailed look at some pedagogically-interesting exercises, rather than present a complete discussion of the assigned reading.

Topic Coverage.

Topic coverage is traditional, with one exception. Most texts of this type assume only a knowledge of the calculus, and begin with a detailed treatment of ordinary differential equations (ODEs). Here, we begin, instead, with linear algebra. Thus, prerequisites for this book include the usual calculus sequence, together with a course, or at least a part of a course, on ordinary differential equations. Nevertheless, there is ODE material included: The needed elementary theory and solution techniques are reviewed, for convenient reference, in Appendix A, matrix methods are employed for systems of coupled equations in Chapter 4, the Fourier and Laplace transforms are used to solve ODEs in Chapters 11 and 12, and series solutions of the Bessel and Legendre equations are studied in Chapter 17.

Some important topics have *not* been included: qualitative (phase plane and existence/uniqueness) and quantitative (numerical integration) discussions of nonlinear ODEs, linear programming, nondeterministic methods, variational methods and optimization, fast Fourier transform, numerical integration, and the finite-element method. A number of these topics could be grouped under the heading "numerical methods." Numerical methods were not omitted due to any lack of importance. On the contrary, it was felt that they are now so extensive and pervasive that they demand more attention than could be accommodated in the present text. It is true that we do include sections, in Part IV, on the finite-difference solution of partial differential equations (PDEs), but we do so for the following reasons. First, that discussion provides an important and convincing application of matrix theory, which was the subject of Part I. Second, there is a "hands-on" flavor to the numerical solution methods which nicely complements the more theoretical looking methods of separation of variables and integral transforms. Finally, the finite-difference methods discussed are at least a modest representative of the larger domain of numerical methods.

Organization.

Since there are more than 20 chapters, the book is organized into five parts in order to provide a logical framework. These parts are as follows:

Part I: Linear Algebra
Part II: Multivariable Calculus and Field Theory
Part III: Fourier Series; Fourier and Laplace Transforms
Part IV: Partial Differential Equations
Part V: Complex Variable Theory

Roughly speaking, Parts I, II, III, and V are rather independent, whereas Part IV draws heavily on Parts II and III and, in the finite-difference sections, also on Part I.

A number of sections are listed as OPTIONAL. The point here is not that these sections *should* be omitted, but rather that they *can* be omitted in a shorter course. For example, whereas non-Cartesian coordinates are of great importance in engineering and science, it is possible that in a briefer discussion of field theory an instructor might wish to limit discussion to the Cartesian case. Thus plane polar, cylindrical, and spherical polar coordinates are split off as optional "parallel" sections in both Parts II and IV. Further, Chapter 9 can be studied without having first studied the optional sections in Chapter 8 on surfaces and volumes. As one more example, Sections 3.7 (Change of Basis) and 3.8 (Vector Transformation) are listed as optional simply because they are not drawn on subsequently in Part I.

In my own course, a junior-level course for mechanical and electrical engineers, which follows three semesters of calculus and one semester of differential equations, the twenty-five 1-hour-and-20-minute classes (excluding examinations) are allotted as follows:

Linear Algebra: 6 classes, covering Sections 1.1 to 4.3, with Sections 2.6, 3.7, and 3.8 omitted

Field Theory: 9 classes, covering Sections 7.1 to 7.6, 8.2, and Chapter 9

Fourier Series and PDEs: 10 classes, covering Sections 10.1 to 10.3, 13.1 to 13.3, 14.1, 14.2, 14.5, 15.1 to 15.3, 15.5, 16.1, and 16.2

Finally, it should be mentioned that special functions—such as the delta, gamma, Bessel, and Legendre functions—are introduced when needed, rather than in a separate chapter.

Exercises.

Exercises listed at the end of a section cover material presented in that section. These exercises serve a number of purposes. First, it is occasionally stated in the text that "it can be shown," with the details left to the exercises. Second, there are numerous "drill"-type exercises. These are complemented by exercises which are more thought provoking and/or deal with applications. Finally, in most sections there is important supplementary information introduced in the exercises. The idea here was to keep the text part relatively lean and to include supplementary material as part of the exercises. This material is also intended to increase the value of the text in terms of subsequent reference. To illustrate, consider Sections 17.2 and 17.3, on Bessel and Legendre functions. For a text of this type, the Bessel function discussion is a bit long (as is felt to be justified not only because of the importance of Bessel functions but also because consideration of the Bessel equation is somewhat representative of other special functions as well). Thus it is important to have the follow-up section on Legendre functions be especially crisp and to the point. To accomplish that goal, considerable information about Legendre functions is relegated to the exercises, including Rodriques' formula, the generating function, integral representation, Legendre functions of the second kind, associated Legendre functions, and applications to electrostatics.

As mentioned above, it is recommended that the instructor consider the option of lecturing on text material rather selectively, and balancing that against self-study. In that event, it is hoped that the exercises may be used as a source of interesting material for lecture and class discussion.

Finally, answers are given at the end of the book for exercises indicated by asterisks. In addition, a Solutions Manual is available to instructors, and can be obtained either through the Prentice-Hall sales representative or by contacting the College Book Division, Prentice-Hall, Englewood Cliffs, NJ 07632.

References.

References to other books appear in three different ways. First, there are one or two suggested references for each of the five parts, as follows:

PART I: HOWARD ANTON, *Elementary Linear Algebra,* 2nd ed. New York: Wiley, 1977.

BEN NOBLE, *Applications of Undergraduate Mathematics in Engineering.* New York: Macmillan, 1967.

PART II: J. E. MARSDEN AND A. J. TROMBA, *Vector Calculus,* San Francisco: W. H. Freeman, 1976.

H. M. SCHEY, *Div, Grad, Curl, and All That.* New York: W. W. Norton, 1973.

PART III: W. E. BOYCE AND R. C. DIPRIMA, *Elementary Differential Equations and Boundary Value Problems,* 3rd ed. New York: Wiley, 1977.

R. V. CHURCHILL AND J. W. BROWN, *Fourier Series and Boundary Value Problems,* 3rd ed. New York: McGraw-Hill, 1978.

PART IV: R. V. CHURCHILL AND J. W. BROWN, *Fourier Series and Boundary Value Problems,* 3rd ed. New York: McGraw-Hill, 1978.

DAVID L. POWERS, *Boundary Value Problems,* 2nd ed. New York: Academic Press, 1977.

PART V: E. B. SAFF AND A. D. SNIDER, *Fundamentals of Complex Analysis,* Englewood Cliffs, NJ: Prentice-Hall, 1976.

References to these texts are capitalized: for instance, ANTON, and SAFF AND SNIDER. The instructor may wish to place these suggested references on library reserve for the class. I generally also include Morris Kline's *Mathematical Thought From Ancient to Modern Times* (New York, Oxford University Press: 1972) among the reserve reading as an excellent historical source. Second, rather specific references are footnoted. Finally, additional general references are listed at the end of each part.

Acknowledgements.

Most of all, this book has benefitted from an excellent review process organized by Mr. Robert Sickles and Mr. David Ostrow of Prentice-Hall. In particular, I am happy to acknowledge the following reviewers for their thoughtful and detailed comments: Professors Edward Beltrami (State University of New York at Stony Brook), John A. Burns (Virginia Polytechnic Institute and State University), J. M. Cushing (University of Arizona), Michael Ecker (Pennsylvania State University), Stuart Goldenberg (California Polytechnic State University), Wilfred Greenlee (University of Arizona), John Hildebrant (Louisiana State University), Joseph Jasiulek (Case Western Reserve University), Ronald J. Lomax (The University of Michigan, Ann Arbor), John T. Scheick (Ohio State University), and Pan-Tai Liu (University of Rhode Island).

Also serving as a reviewer was Professor Leslie A. Month (Mills College), and I extend special thanks to her not only for her help in this project but also for her constant support.

I'm also grateful to Ms. Virginia Huebner for expert handling of the editorial and production phase, and to the many students who took the time to provide me with lists of errors in the early drafts, and with suggestions for improvement.

Closure.

In spite of all precautions, errors will no doubt be found in using this book, and I encourage you to let me know about them, so they can be corrected in subsequent printings. Beyond that, any comments, suggestions for improvement, or ideas that you wish to share would be most appreciated, especially regarding the choice of topics.

Michael D. Greenberg

Systems of Linear Equations; Introduction 1

INTRODUCTION 1.1

Although linear algebra has occupied an important place in applied mathematics and science since the late nineteenth century, the subject has gained greater prominence since around 1960 with the rise of digital computer technology. Our approach to the subject, in Part I, stresses foundations, concepts, and applications. Patience is asked of the applications-oriented reader during those sections in which the emphasis is on foundations and concepts.

Chapter 1 introduces systems of linear algebraic equations; Gauss elimination is discussed both as a solution technique and as a path to information concerning the existence and uniqueness of solutions; matrices appear, though briefly. *Chapters 2* and *3* take us from vectors in n-space to matrices and determinants; linear systems are considered again, in the second half of Chapter 3, in terms of rank, inverse matrix, Cramer's rule, and linear transformation. *Chapter 4* introduces the eigenvalue problem, diagonalization, the Jordan form, and quadratic forms; areas of application include vibration theory, chemical kinetics, buckling, and systems of ordinary differential equations. *Chapter 5* is optional and brief. It provides an extension to complex spaces, as encountered especially in the study of physics and chemistry.

1.2 BASIC IDEAS

The problem of finding solutions of equations of the form

$$f(x) = 0 \tag{1}$$

occupies a place of both practical and historical importance.* Equation (1) is said to be **algebraic,** or **polynomial,** if $f(x)$ is expressible in the form $a_n x^n + a_{n-1}x^{n-1} + \cdots + a_1 x + a_0$, where $a_n \neq 0$ for definiteness [i.e., if $f(x)$ is a polynomial of finite degree n], and it is said to be **transcendental** otherwise.

EXAMPLE 1

$$3x^4 - 2x^3 + x + 5 = 0 \quad \text{and} \quad 6x - 5 = 0 \tag{2a,b}$$

are algebraic, whereas

$$x^3 - 5\sin x = 0 \quad \text{and} \quad e^x - 2 = 0 \tag{3a,b}$$

are transcendental, since $\sin x$ and e^x, we state without proof, cannot be expressed as polynomials of finite degree.† ◀

Besides the algebraic versus transcendental distinction, we say that (1) is either linear or nonlinear, **linear** if $f(x)$ is a first-degree polynomial, in which case (1) is of the simple form

$$a_1 x + a_0 = 0, \tag{4}$$

and **nonlinear** otherwise. Thus (2b) is linear and (2a), (3a), and (3b) are nonlinear.

While (1) is one equation in one unknown, we often encounter problems involving more than one equation and/or more than one unknown, i.e., a *system* of equations, say m equations in n unknowns, where $m \geq 1$ and $n \geq 1$,

$$\begin{aligned} f_1(x_1, x_2, \ldots, x_n) &= 0 \\ f_2(x_1, x_2, \ldots, x_n) &= 0 \\ &\vdots \\ f_m(x_1, x_2, \ldots, x_n) &= 0, \end{aligned} \tag{5}$$

such as

$$\begin{aligned} x_1 - \sin(x_1 + x_2) &= 0 \\ x_2 - \cos(x_1 - x_2) &= 0. \end{aligned} \tag{6}$$

One may feel that m must equal n, as is the case in (6), so that there are as many equations as unknowns. Although that is often the case, systems with $m > n$ and $m < n$ arise also, and will be included here.

As the titles of Chapter 1 and Part I imply, we will limit ourselves to the (extremely important) special case where the system (5) is **linear,** i.e., of the form

* Not many students of applied mathematics consider collateral reading on the history of mathematics, yet such reading can substantially enrich one's mathematical experience. Along these lines we recommend Morris Kline's *Mathematical Thought from Ancient to Modern Times* (New York: Oxford University Press, 1972).

† We shall use the symbols ◀ and ■ to mark the end of examples and proofs, respectively.

$$
\begin{aligned}
a_{11}x_1 + a_{12}x_2 + \cdots + a_{1n}x_n &= c_1 \quad \text{(eq.1)}\\
a_{21}x_1 + a_{22}x_2 + \cdots + a_{2n}x_n &= c_2 \quad \text{(eq.2)}\\
&\ \vdots\\
a_{m1}x_1 + a_{m2}x_2 + \cdots + a_{mn}x_n &= c_m; \quad \text{(eq.m)}
\end{aligned}
\tag{7}
$$

we also restrict it to be *finite* in that m and n are both finite, and *real* in that the a_{ij} coefficients ($i = 1, \ldots, m$ and $j = 1, \ldots, n$) and the c_j ($j = 1, \ldots, m$) constants are real numbers. Of course, if $m = n = 1$, then (7) is equivalent to (4).

The subscript notation adopted in (7) is not essential in principle, but will be helpful in holding the nomenclature to a minimum, in rendering the inherent patterns more visible, and in permitting a natural transition to the subsequently introduced matrix notation. The first subscript on the a_{ij}'s indicates the equation, and the second indicates the x_j variable that it multiplies; for example, a_{21} appears in the second equation and multiplies the x_1 variable. Some authors write $a_{2,1}$ in place of a_{21}, so that one does not mistakenly read the subscript as twenty-one, but we will omit commas except when such ambiguity is not easily resolved from the context.

Thus the problem that forms the subject of Chapter 1 is the system (7). In the next section we introduce one important solution technique, Gauss elimination, and at the same time, explore the questions "Do solutions *exist*?" and "If so, *how many*?"

1.2 EXERCISES

1. True or false? If false, give a counterexample.
(a) An algebraic equation is necessarily linear.
(b) An algebraic equation is necessarily nonlinear.
(c) A transcendental equation is necessarily linear.
(d) A transcendental equation is necessarily nonlinear.
(e) A linear equation is necessarily algebraic.
(f) A nonlinear equation is necessarily algebraic.
(g) A linear equation is necessarily transcendental.
(h) A nonlinear equation is necessarily transcendental.

GAUSS ELIMINATION 1.3

As indicated in Section 1.2, we wish to consider the task of solving a given linear system:

$$
\boxed{
\begin{aligned}
a_{11}x_1 + a_{12}x_2 + \cdots + a_{1n}x_n &= c_1 \quad \text{(eq.1)}\\
a_{21}x_1 + a_{22}x_2 + \cdots + a_{2n}x_n &= c_2 \quad \text{(eq.2)}\\
&\ \vdots\\
a_{m1}x_1 + a_{m2}x_2 + \cdots + a_{mn}x_n &= c_m \quad \text{(eq.m)}
\end{aligned}}
\tag{1}
$$

of m equations in the n unknowns x_1 through x_n.

First, we say that a sequence of numbers $s_1, s_2, \ldots, s_n$ is a **solution** of (1) if and only if each of the m equations is satisfied numerically when we substitute s_1 for x_1, s_2 for x_2, and so on. If there exist *one or more* solutions to (1), we say that the system is **consistent;** if there is precisely *one* solution, that solution is **unique;** and if there is more than one, the solution is **nonunique.** If, on the other hand, there are *no* solutions to (1), the system is said to be **inconsistent.**

The collection of all solutions to (1) is called its **solution set.** Hence, by "solving" (1) we mean finding its solution set.

Beginning modestly, let $m = n = 2$, in which case (1) is simply

$$a_{11}x_1 + a_{12}x_2 = c_1 \quad \text{(eq.1)} \tag{2a}$$

$$a_{21}x_1 + a_{22}x_2 = c_2. \quad \text{(eq.2)} \tag{2b}$$

If we assume that a_{11}, a_{12} are not both zero, then (eq.1) defines a straight line, say L1, in a cartesian x_1, x_2 plane; similarly, if a_{21}, a_{22} are not both zero, then (eq.2) defines a straight line, L2. There exist three possibilities regarding the lines L1 and L2 (Fig 1.1):

1. They may intersect at precisely one point, say P, in which case there is evidently a *unique* solution, namely the coordinate pair x_1, x_2 of the point P.
2. They may be parallel, in which case there is evidently *no* solution; (2) is inconsistent, its solution set is empty.
3. They may actually coincide, in which case the coordinate pair of each point on the line is a solution; hence there is an *infinite* number of solutions.

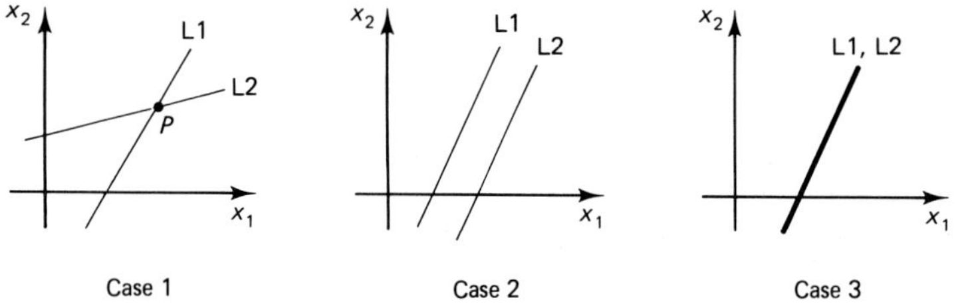

Fig. 1.1 Existence and uniqueness for the system (2).

EXAMPLE 1

$$2x_1 - x_2 = 5 \tag{3a}$$

$$x_1 + 3x_2 = -1. \tag{3b}$$

From (3a), $x_2 = 2x_1 - 5$. Thus (3b) becomes $x_1 + 3(2x_1 - 5) = -1$, or $x_1 = 2$. Hence the system (3) is of type 1, with the unique solution $x_1 = 2$, $x_2 = -1$. Further, the system

$$\begin{aligned} x_1 + 3x_2 &= 1 \\ x_1 + 3x_2 &= 0 \end{aligned} \tag{4}$$

is evidently of type 2, with no solution, and the system

$$\begin{aligned} x_1 + 3x_2 &= 1 \\ 2x_1 + 6x_2 &= 2 \end{aligned} \tag{5}$$

is of type 3. ◀

As we shall see shortly, the general system (1) admits exactly the same possibilities: a unique solution, no solution, or an infinite number of solutions. In other words, we shall see that a linear system cannot have precisely six solutions; if it has more than one, it must have an infinite number of them.

Turning to the general case (1), solution procedures amount to a systematic application of arithmetic steps that reduce (1) to simpler and simpler forms, until the solution(s), or lack of a solution, is evident.

Let us illustrate one such procedure.

EXAMPLE 2

$$\begin{aligned} x_1 + x_2 - x_3 &= 1 \\ 3x_1 + x_2 + x_3 &= 9 \\ x_1 - x_2 + 4x_3 &= 8. \end{aligned} \tag{6}$$

Keeping the first equation intact, add -3 times the first equation to the second, and add -1 times the first equation to the third. This yields a new "indented" system,

$$\begin{aligned} x_1 + x_2 - x_3 &= 1 \\ -2x_2 + 4x_3 &= 6 \\ -2x_2 + 5x_3 &= 7. \end{aligned} \tag{7}$$

Next, keep the first two of these equations intact, and add -1 times the second equation to the third. Thus

$$\begin{aligned} x_1 + x_2 - x_3 &= 1 \\ -2x_2 + 4x_3 &= 6 \\ x_3 &= 1, \end{aligned} \tag{8}$$

and multiplying the second of these by $-\frac{1}{2}$ to normalize (i.e., change to unity) the leading coefficient, we have

$$\begin{aligned} x_1 + x_2 - x_3 &= 1 \quad \text{(eq.1)} \\ x_2 - 2x_3 &= -3 \quad \text{(eq.2)} \\ x_3 &= 1. \quad \text{(eq.3)} \end{aligned} \tag{9}$$

If we regard the original system (6) as a tangle of string that we wish to unravel, the first step is to find a loose end; that is, in effect, what the foregoing process of "successive indentations" has done for us.* Specifically, (eq.3) in (9) is the "loose end," and with that in hand we may unravel (9) by what is known as **back substitution.** Putting $x_3 = 1$ into (eq.2) we may solve for x_2; thus $x_2 = -1$. And putting $x_3 = 1$ and $x_2 = -1$ into (eq.1) we may solve for x_1.

RESULT Unique solution,

$$x_1 = 3, \qquad x_2 = -1, \qquad x_3 = 1. \tag{10}$$

* The process leading from (6) to (9) was one of successive elimination: We eliminated x_1 from the last two equations in (6), and then we eliminated x_2 from the last equation in (7). In fact, the procedure is known in the literature by that name, *successive elimination*. Here, we occasionally refer to it as *successive indentation* since that name carries with it a visual image of the process.

COMMENT To solve (6) we transformed that system, through a sequence of arithmetic operations, to the indented or "triangular" form (9), which was then solved. But was it obvious that the solution set of (9), given by (10), was necessarily identical to that of the original system (6)? In other words, is it not conceivable that in applying the arithmetic steps that carried us from (6) to (9) we might, inadvertently, have altered the solution set? For example, $x + 1 = 4$ has the unique solution $x = 3$, but if we innocently square both sides, the resulting equation, $(x + 1)^2 = 16$, admits the *two* solutions $x = 3$ and $x = -5$. ◀

The question just raised applies to linear systems in general. It will be answered in Theorem 1 below, but first we need to define two terms: "equivalent systems" and "elementary operations."

Two linear systems in n unknowns, x_1 through x_n, are said to be **equivalent** *if their solution sets are identical.*

The following operations on linear systems are known as **elementary operations:**

1. Addition of a multiple of one equation to another
   Symbolically: (eq. j) $\to$ (eq. j) + α(eq. k)*
2. Multiplication of an equation by a nonzero constant
   Symbolically: (eq. j) $\to$ α(eq. j)
3. Interchange of two equations
   Symbolically: (eq. j) $\to$ (eq. k) and (eq. k) $\to$ (eq. j)

Then we can state the following important result.

Theorem 1 *Equivalent Systems*

Two linear systems are equivalent if one can be obtained from the other by a finite number of elementary operations.

Outline of Proof The truth of this claim for elementary operations of types 2 and 3 should be evident, so we will confine our remarks to operations of type 1. It will suffice to look at the effect of one such operation. Thus, suppose that a given linear system A is altered by replacing its jth equation by its jth plus α times its kth, its other equations being kept intact. Let us call the new system A'. Surely, every solution of A will also be a solution of A', since we have merely added equal quantities to equal quantities. That is, *if A' results from A by the application of an elementary operation of type 1, then every solution of A is also a solution of A'*. Further, we can convert A' back to A by an elementary operation of type 1, namely, by replacing the jth equation of A' by the jth equation of A' plus $-\alpha$ times the kth equation of A'. Consequently, it follows from the italicized result (two sentences back) that every solution of A' is also a solution of A. Then A and A' are equivalent, as claimed. ■

In Example 2, we saw that each step was an elementary operation: Three elementary operations of type 1 took us from (6) to (8), and one of type 2 took us from (8) to (9); finally, the back substitution amounted to several operations of type 1.

* That is, the jth equation is replaced by the jth plus α times the kth.

Thus, according to Theorem 1, equivalence was maintained throughout, so we can be sure that (10) is the solution set of the original system (6) (as can be verified by direct substitution).

The system in Example 2 admitted a unique solution. To see how the method of successive elimination works out when there is no solution, or a nonunique solution, let us work two more examples.

EXAMPLE 3 Consider

$$\begin{aligned} 2x_1 + x_2 - 2x_3 &= 4 \\ x_1 + 2x_2 + x_3 &= 4 \\ 3x_1 + 3x_2 - x_3 &= c, \end{aligned} \tag{11}$$

where c is a parameter.* Applying successive elimination, we have

$$\begin{aligned} 2x_1 + x_2 - 2x_3 &= 4 \\ \tfrac{3}{2}x_2 + 2x_3 &= 2 \\ \tfrac{3}{2}x_2 + 2x_3 &= c - 6, \end{aligned}$$

and then

$$2x_1 + x_2 - 2x_3 = 4 \tag{12a}$$

$$\tfrac{3}{2}x_2 + 2x_3 = 2 \tag{12b}$$

$$0 = c - 8. \tag{12c}$$

Finally, multiplying (12a) by $\frac{1}{2}$ and (12b) by $\frac{2}{3}$, we have

$$\begin{aligned} x_1 + \tfrac{1}{2}x_2 - x_3 &= 2 \\ x_2 + \tfrac{4}{3}x_3 &= \tfrac{4}{3} \\ 0 &= c - 8. \end{aligned} \tag{13}$$

There are two possibilities:

1. $c \neq 8$. If $c \neq 8$, the third equation in (13) is a contradiction, i.e., its solution set is empty; it cannot be satisfied by any choice of x_1, x_2, x_3. Thus there is no solution to (13). And since (13) is equivalent to (11), there is *no solution* to (11).
2. $c = 8$. In this case the third equation is merely $0 = 0$ and can be discarded. The solution of the remaining two equations is

$$x_3 = \alpha \text{ (arbitrary)}, \qquad x_2 = \frac{4(1-\alpha)}{3}, \qquad x_1 = \frac{4+5\alpha}{3}. \tag{14}$$

* If c is a **parameter,** that means it is to be regarded as a *constant* in the course of the solution. (The *value* of that constant is important; it may even affect the existence and uniqueness of the solution, as in the present example.) It is to be appreciated that the role of c is a matter of viewpoint, and that different viewpoints may be appropriate at different stages of the analysis. For example, regarding c as fixed, the (unique) solution of the system

$$\begin{aligned} x + y &= 4 \\ x - 2y &= c \end{aligned}$$

is found to be $x = (8 + c)/3$, $y = (4 - c)/3$; with that in hand, we may then wish to free c and consider how the solution $x = x(c)$, $y = y(c)$ varies with c.

Since α is arbitrary, we say that (14) constitutes a *one-parameter family of solutions*. [Of course, the presence of an infinite number of solutions does not mean that *every* sequence x_1, x_2, x_3 is a solution; e.g. $x_1 = x_2 = x_3 = 1$ is not of the form (14), and is *not* a solution.]

RESULT No solution if $c \neq 8$; one-parameter family of solutions if $c = 8$. ◀

EXAMPLE 4 Consider the system of four equations ($m = 4$) in six unknowns ($n = 6$)

$$\begin{aligned} x_1 - x_2 + x_3 \qquad\qquad + 2x_6 &= 0 \\ x_1 + x_2 + 2x_3 + 4x_4 + x_5 + 2x_6 &= 3 \\ 2x_2 + x_3 + 4x_4 + 3x_5 + x_6 &= 2 \\ x_1 - 3x_2 \qquad - 4x_4 - 2x_5 + x_6 &= 0. \end{aligned} \tag{15}$$

Add -1 times the first equation to the second and fourth equations:

$$\begin{aligned} x_1 - x_2 + x_3 \qquad\qquad + 2x_6 &= 0 \\ 2x_2 + x_3 + 4x_4 + x_5 \qquad &= 3 \\ 2x_2 + x_3 + 4x_4 + 3x_5 + x_6 &= 2 \\ -2x_2 - x_3 - 4x_4 - 2x_5 - x_6 &= 0. \end{aligned} \tag{16}$$

Add -1 times the second to the third, and add the second to the fourth:

$$\begin{aligned} x_1 - x_2 + x_3 \qquad\qquad + 2x_6 &= 0 \\ 2x_2 + x_3 + 4x_4 + x_5 \qquad &= 3 \\ 2x_5 + x_6 &= -1 \\ -x_5 - x_6 &= 3. \end{aligned}$$

Add $\frac{1}{2}$ times the third to the fourth:

$$\begin{aligned} x_1 - x_2 + x_3 \qquad\qquad + 2x_6 &= 0 \\ 2x_2 + x_3 + 4x_4 + x_5 \qquad &= 3 \\ 2x_5 + x_6 &= -1 \\ -\tfrac{1}{2}x_6 &= \tfrac{5}{2}. \end{aligned} \tag{17}$$

Finally, multiply the second and third by $\frac{1}{2}$, and the fourth by -2, to normalize the leading coefficients:

$$\begin{aligned} x_1 - x_2 + x_3 \qquad\qquad + 2x_6 &= 0 \\ x_2 + \tfrac{1}{2}x_3 + 2x_4 + \tfrac{1}{2}x_5 \qquad &= \tfrac{3}{2} \\ x_5 + \tfrac{1}{2}x_6 &= -\tfrac{1}{2} \\ x_6 &= -5, \end{aligned} \tag{18}$$

and by back substitution we arrive at the *two-parameter family of solutions*

$$\begin{aligned} &x_6 = -5, \qquad x_5 = 2, \qquad x_4 = \alpha_1(\text{arbitrary}), \qquad x_3 = \alpha_2(\text{arbitrary}), \\ &x_2 = \tfrac{1}{2} - 2\alpha_1 - \tfrac{1}{2}\alpha_2, \qquad x_1 = \tfrac{21}{2} - 2\alpha_1 - \tfrac{3}{2}\alpha_2. \end{aligned} \tag{19}$$ ◀

Having introduced the notion of a "p-parameter family of solutions" in the examples, let us elaborate a bit. Suppose that the system (1) is consistent, that arbitrary values $\alpha_1, \ldots, \alpha_p$ may be assigned to a certain set of p unknowns, and that the remaining $n - p$ unknowns can be expressed uniquely in terms of these α's. The solution set of (1) will then be said to consist of a *p-parameter family of solutions*. Each choice of values for $\alpha_1, \ldots, \alpha_p$ yields a so-called *particular solution*. For example, in Example 4 the two-parameter family of solutions (19) was obtained; if we assign the values $\alpha_1 = 2$ and $\alpha_2 = -1$, say, then (19) reduces to the particular solution $x_1 = 8$, $x_2 = -3$, $x_3 = -1$, $x_4 = 2$, $x_5 = 2$, $x_6 = -5$.

The process of successive elimination employed in the foregoing examples is due to Gauss.* Various refinements are possible, but the procedure is essentially as follows.

GAUSS ELIMINATION

For the system (1) of m equations in n unknowns:

STEP 1 Let the numbering of the equations and the unknowns be such that $a_{11} \neq 0$. Eliminate the x_1 variable from the second through mth equations by adding

- $-a_{21}/a_{11}$ times the first equation to the second equation,

  ⋮
- $-a_{m1}/a_{11}$ times the first equation to the mth equation.†

This step produces an (equivalent) indented system of the form

$$\begin{aligned} a_{11}x_1 + a_{12}x_2 + \cdots + a_{1n}x_n &= c_1 \\ a'_{22}x_2 + \cdots + a'_{2n}x_n &= c'_2 \\ &\;\vdots \\ a'_{m2}x_2 + \cdots + a'_{mn}x_n &= c'_m, \end{aligned} \tag{20}$$

where the primes call attention to the revisions.

STEP 2 Suppose that the coefficients $a'_{22}, a'_{32}, \ldots, a'_{m2}$ are not all zero. Then we may assume that $a'_{22} \neq 0$; for if it were zero, we could interchange the second equa-

* *Karl Friedrich Gauss* (1777–1855), generally regarded as the foremost mathematician of the nineteenth century, and often referred to as the "prince of mathematicians."

† The multiples $a_{21}/a_{11}, \ldots, a_{m1}/a_{11}$ are finite since $a_{11} \neq 0$.

tion [of (20)] with a subsequent equation such that the new value of a'_{22} were nonzero. We eliminate x_2 from the third through mth equations by adding

- $-a'_{32}/a'_{22}$ times the second equation to the third,

  ⋮

- $-a'_{m2}/a'_{22}$ times the second equation to the mth.

Continuing in this manner, we eliminate x_3 from the fourth through mth equations, and so on. The result is a system of the form

$$
\begin{aligned}
a_{11}x_1 + a_{12}x_2 + \cdots\cdots\cdots + a_{1n}x_n &= c_1 \\
a'_{22}x_2 + \cdots\cdots\cdots + a'_{2n}x_n &= c'_2 \\
&\ \vdots \\
a''_{qq}x_q + \cdots + a''_{qn}x_n &= c''_q \\
0 &= c''_{q+1} \\
&\ \vdots \\
0 &= c''_m,
\end{aligned}
\tag{21}
$$

where $1 \le q \le m$. Here we have designated as the qth equation the last equation, which is not a "wipe-out" on the left-hand side; i.e., $a''_{qq}, \ldots, a''_{qn}$ are not all zero.

Recall that we supposed that $a'_{22}, \ldots, a'_{m2}$, in (20), were not all zero. Consequently, there is but a single indentation between the first and second equations of (21). If they *were* all zero, but $a'_{23}, \ldots, a'_{m3}$ were not, then a double indentation, of the form

$$
\begin{aligned}
a_{11}x_1 + a_{12}x_2 + a_{13}x_3 + \cdots \\
a'_{23}x_3 + \cdots,
\end{aligned}
$$

would have obtained. In other words, there is *at least* one indentation, but perhaps more, as we move from the first equation in (21) to the second, from the second to the third, . . ., and from the $(q-1)$th to the qth.

STEP 3 Multiply each of the first through qth equations in (21) by the inverse of the leading coefficient to normalize the leading coefficient, and then apply back substitution.

Results (Existence and Uniqueness of Solution)

There are precisely three possibilities:

1. If $q < m$ and $c''_{q+1}, \ldots, c''_m$ are not all zero, the system is inconsistent.
   Result: No solution.
   Example: See (13) for the case where $c \neq 8$.
2. If $q < m$ and $c''_{q+1}, \ldots, c''_m$ are all zero, there is an $(n-q)$-parameter family of solutions if $q < n$, and a unique solution if $q = n$.
   Result: Unique solution or an infinity of solutions.
   Example: In (12) we have $n = 3$ and $q = 2$. Thus if $c = 8$, there exists a one-parameter family of solutions.

3. If $q = m$, there is an $(n - q)$-parameter family of solutions if $q < n$, and a unique solution if $q = n$.
Result: Unique solution or an infinity of solutions.
Examples: In (8) we have $q = m = n = 3$, and there is a unique solution. In (17) we have $q = m = 4$ and $n = 6$; thus $n - q = 2$, and there is a two-parameter family of solutions.

Comparing the italicized results, we can state the following important result.

> ***Theorem 2*** *Existence/Uniqueness for Linear Systems*
> Every system of linear algebraic equations admits no solution, a unique solution, or an infinity of solutions.

A special case of great importance occurs when all of the c_j's in (1) are zero; (1) is then said to be **homogeneous.** (If the system is *not* homogeneous, then it is **nonhomogeneous.**) Since c_1 through c''_m in (21) are linear combinations of the original c_j's, they too must be zero; thus if (1) is homogeneous, so is (21). In particular, if $q < m$, then $c''_{q+1}, \dots, c''_m$ are all zero, so case 1 cannot occur. Furthermore, it should be clear that $x_1 = x_2 = \cdots = x_n = 0$ is necessarily a solution of every homogeneous system, the so-called **trivial solution.** Thus, while Theorem 2 holds for *all* linear systems, homogeneous systems admit the following more specific statement.

> ***Theorem 3*** *Existence/Uniqueness for Homogeneous Systems*
> Every homogeneous linear system is consistent; either it admits the unique trivial solution, or else it admits an infinity of nontrivial solutions in addition to the trivial solution.

In summary, not only did the Gauss method provide us with a systematic solution procedure, it also led us to some solid information regarding the existence and uniqueness of solutions.

MATRIX NOTATION

In applying Gauss elimination, we quickly discover that writing the variables $x_1, \dots, x_n$ over and over is inefficient, and even tends to upstage the more central role of the a_{ij}'s and c_j's. It is therefore preferable to omit the x_j's altogether and to work directly with the rectangular array

$$\begin{pmatrix} a_{11} & a_{12} & \cdots & a_{1n} & c_1 \\ a_{21} & a_{22} & \cdots & a_{2n} & c_2 \\ \vdots & \vdots & & \vdots & \vdots \\ a_{m1} & a_{m2} & \cdots & a_{mn} & c_m \end{pmatrix}, \tag{22}$$

known as the **augmented matrix** of the system (1), i.e., the **coefficient matrix**

$$\begin{pmatrix} a_{11} & a_{12} & \cdots & a_{1n} \\ a_{21} & a_{22} & \cdots & a_{2n} \\ \vdots & \vdots & & \vdots \\ a_{m1} & a_{m2} & \cdots & a_{mn} \end{pmatrix}, \tag{23}$$

augmented by the column of c_j's. By *matrix* we simply mean a rectangular array of numbers, called *elements*; it is customary to enclose the elements between parentheses to emphasize that the entire matrix is regarded as a single entity. A horizontal line of elements is called a *row*, and a vertical line is called a *column*. Counting rows from the top, and columns from the left,

$$a_{21} \quad a_{22} \quad \cdots \quad a_{2n} \quad c_2 \quad \text{and} \quad \begin{matrix} c_1 \\ c_2 \\ \vdots \\ c_m \end{matrix},$$

say, are the second row and $(n + 1)$th column, respectively, of the augmented matrix (22).

In terms of the abbreviated matrix notation, the calculation in Example 2 (page 5) would look like this:

Original system

$$\begin{pmatrix} 1 & 1 & -1 & 1 \\ 3 & 1 & 1 & 9 \\ 1 & -1 & 4 & 8 \end{pmatrix}.$$

Add -3 times first row to second row, and add -1 times first row to third row:

$$\begin{pmatrix} 1 & 1 & -1 & 1 \\ 0 & -2 & 4 & 6 \\ 0 & -2 & 5 & 7 \end{pmatrix}.$$

Add -1 times second row to third row, and multiply second row by $-\frac{1}{2}$:

$$\begin{pmatrix} 1 & 1 & -1 & 1 \\ 0 & 1 & -2 & -3 \\ 0 & 0 & 1 & 1 \end{pmatrix}. \tag{24}$$

Thus, corresponding to the so-called elementary operations on members of a system of linear equations (page 6) there are **elementary row operations** on the augmented matrix, as follows:

1. Addition of a multiple of one row to another
   Symbolically: (jth row) $\to$ (jth row) + α(kth row)
2. Multiplication of a row by a nonzero constant
   Symbolically: (jth row) $\to$ α(jth row)
3. Interchange of two rows
   Symbolically: (jth row) $\to$ (kth row), and (kth row) $\to$ (jth row)

And we say that two matrices are **row equivalent** if one can be obtained from the other by finitely many elementary row operations.

Finally, we point out that the back-substitution steps are elementary row operations, too. With these steps included, the entire process is generally known as **Gauss–Jordan reduction,** after Gauss and *Camille Jordan* (1838–1922). The final result is to be a matrix that is in **reduced row-echelon form.** That is,

1. In each row not made up entirely of zeros, the first nonzero element is a 1, a so-called *leading 1*.
2. In any two consecutive rows, not made up entirely of zeros, the leading 1 in the lower row is to the right of the leading 1 in the upper row.
3. If a column contains a leading 1, every other element in that column is a zero.
4. All rows made up entirely of zeros are grouped together at the bottom of the matrix.

For example, the matrices

$$\begin{pmatrix} \textcircled{1} & 0 & 0 \\ 0 & \textcircled{1} & 0 \\ 0 & 0 & \textcircled{1} \end{pmatrix}, \quad \begin{pmatrix} \textcircled{1} & 0 & 2 \\ 0 & \textcircled{1} & 6 \\ 0 & 0 & 0 \end{pmatrix}, \quad \begin{pmatrix} \textcircled{1} & 5 & 0 & 0 \\ 0 & 0 & \textcircled{1} & 2 \\ 0 & 0 & 0 & 0 \\ 0 & 0 & 0 & 0 \end{pmatrix},$$

$$\begin{pmatrix} \textcircled{1} & 1 & 0 & 0 & 0 & 6 \\ 0 & 0 & \textcircled{1} & 0 & 0 & -1 \\ 0 & 0 & 0 & \textcircled{1} & 0 & 3 \\ 0 & 0 & 0 & 0 & \textcircled{1} & 1 \end{pmatrix} \tag{25}$$

are all in reduced row-echelon form. The leading 1's are enclosed in circles for emphasis.

EXAMPLE 5 Let us illustrate these final steps of the Gauss–Jordan reduction by returning to (18), which was in Gauss-eliminated form, and completing the back-substitution part of the Gauss-Jordan process. Beginning with the augmented matrix corresponding to (18), we have

$$\begin{pmatrix} 1 & -1 & 1 & 0 & 0 & 2 & 0 \\ 0 & 1 & \frac{1}{2} & 2 & \frac{1}{2} & 0 & \frac{3}{2} \\ 0 & 0 & 0 & 0 & 1 & \frac{1}{2} & -\frac{1}{2} \\ 0 & 0 & 0 & 0 & 0 & 1 & -5 \end{pmatrix} \to \begin{pmatrix} 1 & 0 & \frac{3}{2} & 2 & \frac{1}{2} & 2 & \frac{3}{2} \\ 0 & 1 & \frac{1}{2} & 2 & \frac{1}{2} & 0 & \frac{3}{2} \\ 0 & 0 & 0 & 0 & 1 & \frac{1}{2} & -\frac{1}{2} \\ 0 & 0 & 0 & 0 & 0 & 1 & -5 \end{pmatrix} \to$$
$$\begin{pmatrix} 1 & 0 & \frac{3}{2} & 2 & 0 & \frac{7}{4} & \frac{7}{4} \\ 0 & 1 & \frac{1}{2} & 2 & 0 & -\frac{1}{4} & \frac{7}{4} \\ 0 & 0 & 0 & 0 & 1 & \frac{1}{2} & -\frac{1}{2} \\ 0 & 0 & 0 & 0 & 0 & 1 & -5 \end{pmatrix} \to \begin{pmatrix} 1 & 0 & \frac{3}{2} & 2 & 0 & 0 & \frac{21}{2} \\ 0 & 1 & \frac{1}{2} & 2 & 0 & 0 & \frac{1}{2} \\ 0 & 0 & 0 & 0 & 1 & 0 & 2 \\ 0 & 0 & 0 & 0 & 0 & 1 & -5 \end{pmatrix}. \tag{26}$$

The last of the matrices above is in reduced row-echelon form, and once again, yields the solution (19).

That is, we *obtain zeros above each of the leading 1's, beginning at the left and working toward the right*. There are no numbers above the leading 1 in the first column, of course, so we started with the second column. With that done we moved on to the fifth column (since there were no leading 1's in the third and fourth columns) and finally, to the sixth column. ◀

EXAMPLE 6 As our final example, consider the system

$$\begin{aligned} x_1 + 2x_2 - x_3 - 2x_4 &= 1 \\ 2x_1 + x_2 + 3x_3 - 4x_4 &= 4. \end{aligned} \tag{27}$$

The Gauss-Jordan reduction:

Original system:	$\begin{pmatrix} 1 & 2 & -1 & -2 & 1 \\ 2 & 1 & 3 & -4 & 4 \end{pmatrix}$	Gauss elimination	Gauss–Jordan reduction
Add -2 times first row to second:	$\begin{pmatrix} 1 & 2 & -1 & -2 & 1 \\ 0 & -3 & 5 & 0 & 2 \end{pmatrix}$		
Multiply second row by $-\frac{1}{3}$:	$\begin{pmatrix} 1 & 2 & -1 & -2 & 1 \\ 0 & 1 & -\frac{5}{3} & 0 & -\frac{2}{3} \end{pmatrix}$		
Add -2 times second row to first:	$\begin{pmatrix} 1 & 0 & \frac{7}{3} & -2 & \frac{7}{3} \\ 0 & 1 & -\frac{5}{3} & 0 & -\frac{2}{3} \end{pmatrix}$	back substitution	

From the last of these four matrices we obtain the solution

$$\begin{aligned} &x_4 = \alpha_1 \text{ (arbitrary)}, \qquad x_3 = \alpha_2 \text{ (arbitrary)}, \\ &x_2 = \tfrac{5}{3}\alpha_2 - \tfrac{2}{3}, \qquad x_1 = 2\alpha_1 - \tfrac{7}{3}\alpha_2 + \tfrac{7}{3}. \end{aligned} \tag{28}$$ ◀

Observe that matrices have been introduced here as a notational shorthand in solving linear systems by Gauss elimination and by Gauss-Jordan reduction. In later chapters we turn our attention to the matrices themselves.

Finally, we must emphasize that whereas the elimination procedures described in this section are exact in principle, in practice they generally involve *round-off errors* because computing machines carry only a finite number of significant figures. Unfortunately, rather small round-off errors can, under certain circumstances, lead to intolerably large errors in the solution. Thus, a great deal of research has focused on such error generation, and Gauss elimination software standardly includes some form of "pivoting" to render the user relatively safe from the catastrophic effects of round-off. Important as this subject is, it is best reserved for a course in numerical methods. Here our discussion has been geared more toward fundamental theory than toward software implementation, although some rather brief remarks about round-off error disasters are contained in Exercise 9.

1.3 EXERCISES

1. Can four linear equations in six unknowns have no solution? A unique solution? A one-, two-, three-, four-, five-, or six-parameter family of solutions? For each affirmative answer give one illustrative example. [If you give the system in the form (21), no further solution is necessary.]

2. Derive the solution set for each of the following systems, using the Gauss-Jordan reduction. Document each elementary operation used.

*(a)
$$\begin{aligned} 2x_1 - x_2 - x_3 - 3x_4 &= 0 \\ x_1 - x_2 + 4x_3 \qquad &= 2 \end{aligned}$$

(b)
$$\begin{aligned} x + 2y + 3z &= 4 \\ 5x + 6y + 7z &= 8 \\ 9x + 10y + 11z &= 12 \end{aligned}$$

(c)
$$\begin{aligned} x_1 + x_2 - 2x_3 &= 3 \\ x_1 - x_2 - 3x_3 &= 1 \\ x_1 - 3x_2 - 4x_3 &= -1 \end{aligned}$$

(d)
$$\begin{aligned} 2x_1 - x_2 &= 6 \\ 3x_1 + 2x_2 &= 4 \\ x_1 + 10x_2 &= -12 \\ 6x_1 + 11x_2 &= -2 \end{aligned}$$

*(e)
$$\begin{aligned} x_1 - x_2 + 2x_3 + x_4 &= -1 \\ 2x_1 + x_2 + x_3 - x_4 &= 4 \\ x_1 + 2x_2 - x_3 - 2x_4 &= 5 \\ x_1 \qquad + x_3 \qquad &= 1 \end{aligned}$$

(f)
$$\begin{aligned} x_1 \qquad + x_3 \qquad &= 1 \\ x_1 + 2x_2 - x_3 - 2x_3 &= 5 \\ x_1 - x_2 + 2x_3 + x_4 &= 0 \\ 2x_1 + x_2 + x_3 - x_4 &= 4 \end{aligned}$$

(g)
$$\begin{aligned} x_3 + x_4 &= 2 \\ 4x_2 - x_3 + x_4 &= 0 \\ x_1 - x_2 + 2x_3 + x_4 &= 4 \end{aligned}$$

(h)
$$\begin{aligned} x + 2y + 3z &= 5 \\ 2x + 3y + 4z &= 8 \\ 3x + 4y + 5z &= c \\ x + y \qquad &= 2 \end{aligned}$$

*(i)
$$\begin{aligned} 2x + y + z &= 10 \\ 3x + y - z &= 6 \\ x - 2y - 4z &= -10 \end{aligned}$$

(j)
$$\begin{aligned} 2x_1 + x_2 \qquad &= 1 \\ x_1 + 2x_2 + x_3 \qquad &= 1 \\ x_2 + 2x_3 + x_4 &= 1 \\ x_3 + 2x_4 &= 1 \end{aligned}$$

(k)
$$\begin{aligned} 2x_1 + x_2 \qquad &= c \\ x_1 + 2x_2 + x_3 &= -1 \\ x_2 + 2x_3 &= -4 \end{aligned}$$

(l)
$$\begin{aligned} 2x_1 + x_2 \qquad + x_4 + 2x_5 &= 0 \\ x_1 + x_2 - x_3 \qquad &= 0 \\ x_1 + x_2 + x_3 - 3x_4 + 2x_5 &= 0 \\ 2x_1 + 2x_2 - x_3 \qquad + c x_5 &= 0 \end{aligned}$$

3. (*DC circuit*) If Kirchhoff's *current law* (namely, that at any point of an electrical circuit the sum of the incoming currents must equal the sum of the outgoing currents) is applied to each of the junction points a, c, and his *voltage law* (namely, that the algebraic sum of the voltage rises around each closed loop of a circuit must equal zero) is applied to each loop of the DC circuit shown, we obtain the equations

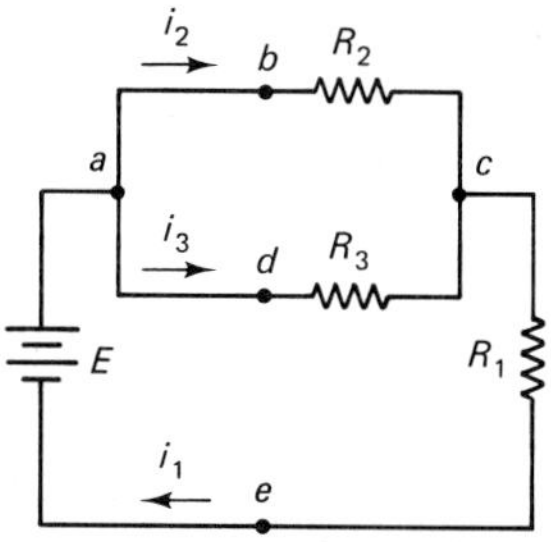

Junction a: $i_1 = i_2 + i_3$

Junction c: $i_2 + i_3 = i_1$

Loop $abcda$: $-R_2 i_2 + R_3 i_3 = 0$

Loop $abcea$: $-R_2 i_2 - R_1 i_1 + E = 0$

Loop $adcea$: $-R_3 i_3 - R_1 i_1 + E = 0$

or

$$\begin{aligned} i_1 - i_2 - i_3 &= 0 \\ i_1 - i_2 - i_3 &= 0 \\ R_2 i_2 - R_3 i_3 &= 0 \\ R_1 i_1 + R_2 i_2 &= E \\ R_1 i_1 + R_3 i_3 &= E, \end{aligned} \qquad \text{(a)}$$

* An asterisk preceding an exercise letter denotes those exercises for which an answer is given at the back of the book.

where i_1, i_2, i_3 are the three currents (measured as positive in the directions assumed in the figure), R_1, R_2, R_3 are the resistances of the three resistors, and E is the voltage rise (from e to a) induced by the battery or other source. [Evidently, we did not need to apply the current law to both junctions since the resulting equations are identical. Similarly, it may be that not all of the loop equations are needed. But rather than try to decide which of equations (a) to keep and which to discard, let us merely keep them all.] We now state the problem: Obtain the solution set of equations (a) by Gauss-Jordan reduction. Take

*(a) $R_1 = R_2 = R_3 \equiv R$
(b) $R_1 = R_2 \equiv R$, $R_3 = 2R$
(c) $R_1 \equiv R$, $R_2 = R_3 = 2R$
(d) $R_1 \equiv R$, $R_2 = 4R$, $R_3 = 6R$

4. (*Statically indeterminate structures*) (a) Consider the static equilibrium of the system shown below, consisting of three (weightless) coplanar cables connected at P, at which point a vertical load F is applied. A vertical force balance at P gives the equation $T_1 \cos 45 + T_2 \cos 30 + T_3 \cos 60 = F$, or $\sqrt{2}T_1 + \sqrt{3}T_2 + T_3 = 2F$, on the unknown tensions T_1, T_2, T_3. Applying a horizontal force balance, derive a second equation on T_1, T_2, T_3. Show that the result is a linear system of two equations in the three unknowns T_1, T_2, T_3, and that this system admits a one-parameter family of solutions. (We say that such a structure is *statically indeterminate* because the forces in it cannot be uniquely determined by the laws of statics. To complete the solution for T_1, T_2, T_3 we would need to consider also the dimensions and elastic properties of the three cables. For such a discussion we refer the interested reader to NOBLE, Sec. 10.2. Finally, note that if one of the cables, say the middle one, is removed, then the system admits a unique solution—independent of the dimensions and elastic properties of the cables—and the system is statically *determinate*.)

(b) Applying horizontal and vertical force balances at P and Q, derive a system of equations governing the tensions $T_1, \ldots, T_5$ for the coplanar system of five weightless cables shown. (You need not solve.)

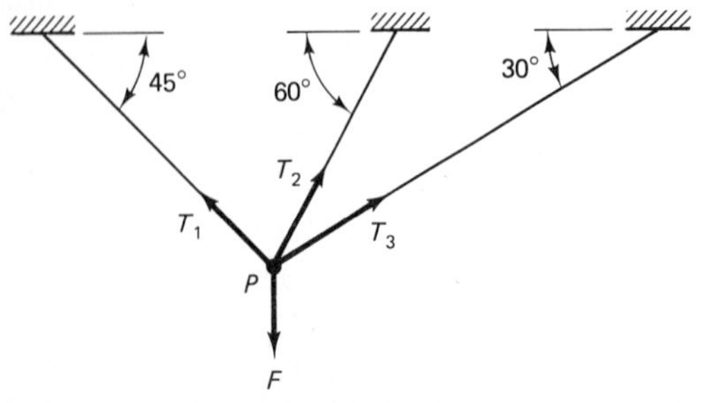

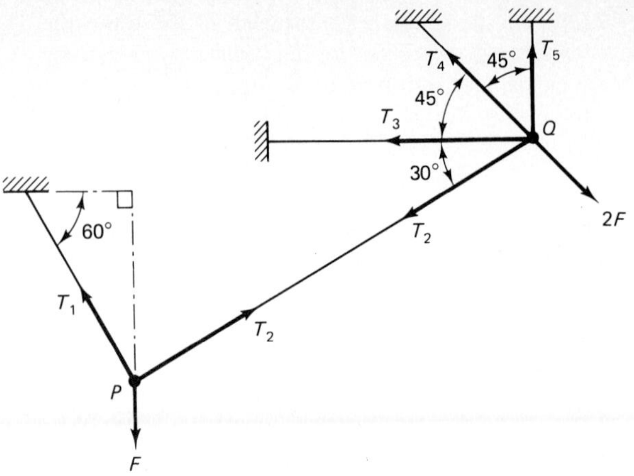

5. Give a geometrical interpretation, in words and/or pictures, of the nonexistence, unique existence, and nonunique existence of solutions of the following systems.

(a)
$$\begin{aligned} a_{11}x_1 + a_{12}x_2 &= c_1 \\ a_{21}x_1 + a_{22}x_2 &= c_2 \\ a_{31}x_1 + a_{32}x_2 &= c_3 \end{aligned}$$

(b)
$$\begin{aligned} a_{11}x_1 + a_{12}x_2 + a_{13}x_3 &= c_1 \\ a_{21}x_1 + a_{22}x_2 + a_{23}x_3 &= c_2 \\ a_{31}x_1 + a_{32}x_2 + a_{33}x_3 &= c_3 \end{aligned}$$

HINT In part (b), recall from calculus and analytic geometry that if a, b, c are not all zero, then $ax + by + cz = d$ is the equation of a *plane* in Cartesian x, y, z space.

6. If possible, adapt the methods of this section to solve the following *nonlinear* systems; if it is *not* possible, say so.

*(a)
$$\begin{aligned} x_1^2 + 2x_2^2 - x_3^2 &= 29 \\ x_1^2 + x_2^2 + x_3^2 &= 19 \\ 3x_1^2 + 4x_2^2 \qquad &= 67 \end{aligned}$$

(b)
$$\begin{aligned} x + 3y &= 13 \\ \sin x + 2y &= 5 \end{aligned}$$

(c)
$$\begin{aligned} \sin x + \sin y \qquad\qquad &= 1 \\ \sin x - \sin y + 4\cos z &= 1.2 \\ \sin x + \sin y + 2\cos z &= 1.6, \end{aligned}$$
where $-\pi/2 \le x \le \pi/2$, $-\pi/2 \le y \le \pi/2$, and $0 \le z \le 2\pi$.

7. For what values of the parameter λ do the following homogeneous (do you agree that they are homogeneous?) systems admit *non*trivial solutions? Find the nontrivial solutions corresponding to each such λ.

*(a)
$$\begin{aligned} 2x + y &= \lambda x \\ x + 2y &= \lambda y \end{aligned}$$

(b)
$$\begin{aligned} 2x - y &= \lambda x \\ -x + 2y &= \lambda y \end{aligned}$$

(c) $\begin{aligned} x - 2y &= \lambda x \\ 4x - 8y &= \lambda y \end{aligned}$ (d) $\begin{aligned} z &= \lambda x \\ z &= \lambda y \\ x + y + z &= \lambda z \end{aligned}$

(e) $\begin{aligned} x + y + z &= \lambda x \\ y + z &= \lambda y \\ 2z &= \lambda z \end{aligned}$ (f) $\begin{aligned} 2x + y + z &= \lambda x \\ x + 2y + z &= \lambda y \\ x + y + 2z &= \lambda z \end{aligned}$

8. If the system (1) has an r-parameter family of solutions, what is the largest possible value of r (in terms of m and n)?

9. (*Ill-conditioned systems*) Practically speaking, our numerical calculations are normally carried out on computers, be they hand-held calculators or large digital computers. Such machines carry only a finite number of significant figures and thus introduce *round-off error* into most calculations. One might expect (or hope) that such slight deviations will lead to answers that are only slightly in error. For example, the solution of

$$\begin{aligned} x + y &= 2 \\ x - 1.014y &= 0 \end{aligned} \tag{a}$$

is $x \approx 1.007$, $y \approx 0.993$, whereas the solution of the rounded-off version

$$\begin{aligned} x + y &= 2 \\ x - 1.01y &= 0 \end{aligned}$$

is very much the same, namely $x \approx 1.005$, $y \approx 0.995$. In sharp contrast, the solutions of

$$\begin{aligned} x + y &= 2 \\ x + 1.014y &= 0 \end{aligned} \tag{b}$$

and the rounded-off version

$$\begin{aligned} x + y &= 2 \\ x + 1.01y &= 0 \end{aligned}$$

are $x \approx 144.9$, $y \approx -142.9$ and $x = 202$, $y = -200$, respectively; (b) is an example of a so-called **ill-conditioned** system, ill-conditioned in the sense that small changes in the coefficients lead to large changes in the solution. Reduction of round-off error can be effected by modifying the Gauss method so as to include *pivotal condensation,** although not very much for ill-conditioned systems. An introductory discussion of these ideas, as well as further references, can be found in ANTON. (See also Exercise 9 on page 116.) Here we ask only the following: Explain why (b) is much more sensitive to round-off than (a) by exploring the two cases graphically, i.e., in the x, y plane.

10. Show that m linear homogeneous equations in n unknowns always admit an infinity of nontrivial solutions if $n > m$.

11. Evaluate these excerpts from examination papers.

(a) "Given the system

$$\begin{aligned} x_1 - 2x_2 &= 0 \\ 2x_1 - 4x_2 &= 0, \end{aligned}$$

add -2 times the first equation to the second and add $-\frac{1}{2}$ times the second equation to the first. By these Gauss elimination steps we obtain the equivalent system $0 = 0$ and $0 = 0$, and hence the two-parameter family of solutions $x_1 = \alpha_1$ (arbitrary), $x_2 = \alpha_2$ (arbitrary)."

(b) "Given the system

$$\begin{aligned} x_1 + x_2 - 4x_3 &= 0 \\ 2x_1 - x_2 + x_3 &= 0, \end{aligned}$$

since both left-hand sides equal zero, they must equal each other. Hence we have the equivalent system

$$x_1 + x_2 - 4x_3 = 2x_1 - x_2 + x_3."$$

12. Let

$$\begin{aligned} a_1x_1 + a_2x_2 + a_3x_3 &= 0 \\ b_1x_1 + b_2x_2 + b_3x_3 &= 0 \end{aligned}$$

represent any two planes through the origin in a Cartesian x_1, x_2, x_3 space. For the case where the planes intersect along a line, show whether or not that line necessarily passes through the origin.

* That is, rearranging the order of the unknowns and/or the equations so that the pivots (i.e., the divisors) are as large as possible.

2 Vector Space

2.1 INTRODUCTION

Normally, one meets vectors for the first time within some physical context—in studying mechanics, electric and magnetic fields, and so on. There, the vectors exist within two- or three-dimensional space and correspond to such entities as force, velocity, position, magnetic field, and so on. They have both *magnitude* and *direction;* they can be *scaled* by multiplicative factors, *added* according to the parallelogram law; *dot* and *cross product* operations are defined between vectors; the *angle* between two vectors is defined; vectors can be *expanded* as linear combinations of *base vectors;* and so on.

Alternatively, there exists a highly formalized axiomatic approach to vectors known as *linear vector space* or *abstract vector space*. Although this generalized vector concept is essentially an outgrowth of the more primitive system of "arrow vectors" in 2-space and 3-space, it extends well beyond that system in scope and applicability.

For pedagogical reasons, we break the transition from 2-space and 3-space to abstract vector space into two steps: in Sections 2.4 and 2.5 we introduce a generalization to "n-space," and in Section 2.6 we complete the extension to general vector space. But whereas our discussion of generalized vector space will be rather brief, n-space will be considered in some detail, because it is the n-space concept that will form the backbone of Part I.

2.2 VECTORS; GEOMETRICAL REPRESENTATION

Some quantities that we encounter may be completely defined by a single real number, or magnitude; the mass or kinetic energy of a given particle, and the temperature or salinity at some point in the ocean, are examples. Others are not defined solely by a magnitude, but rather by a magnitude *and* a direction, examples being force, velocity, momentum, and acceleration. Such quantities are called **vectors.**

The defining features of a vector being magnitude and direction suggests the geometric representation of a vector as a directed line segment, or "arrow," where the length of the arrow is scaled according to the magnitude of the vector. For example, if the wind is blowing at 8 meters/second from the northeast, that defines a wind-velocity vector **v**, where we adopt boldface type to signify that the quantity is a vector; alternative notations include the use of an overhead arrow, as in $\vec{v}$. Choosing, according to convenience, a scale of 5 meters/second per centimeter, say, the geometric representation of **v** is as shown in Fig. 2.1. Denoting the magnitude, or **norm,** of any vector **v** as $\|\mathbf{v}\|$, we have $\|\mathbf{v}\| = 8$ for the **v** vector in Fig. 2.1.

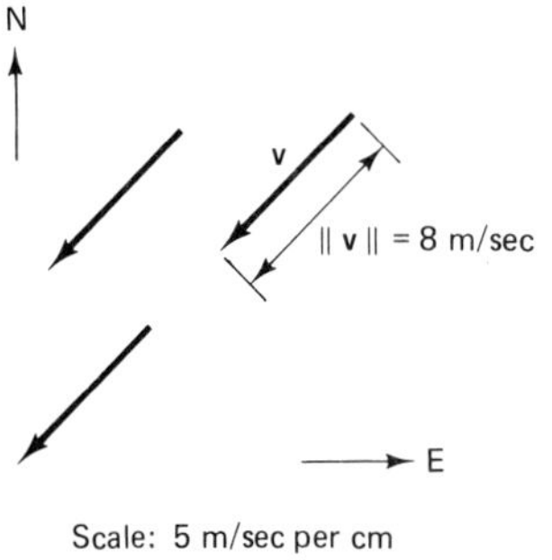

Fig. 2.1 Geometric representation of **v**.

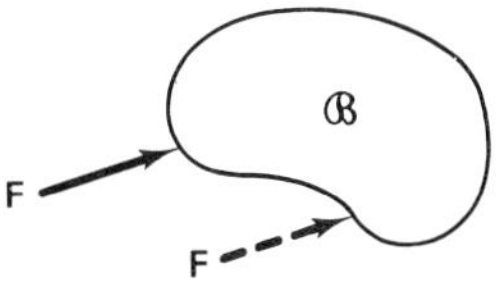

Fig. 2.2. Position of a vector.

Observe that the *location* of a vector is not specified, only its magnitude and direction. Thus the two unlabeled arrows in Fig. 2.1 are equally valid alternative representations of **v**. That is not to say that the physical *effect* of the vector will be entirely independent of its position; for example, it should be apparent that the motion of the body $\mathcal{B}$ induced by a force **F** (Fig. 2.2) will certainly depend on the point of application of **F**,* as will the stress field induced in $\mathcal{B}$. Nevertheless, the two vectors in Fig. 2.2 are still regarded as equal, as are the three in Fig. 2.1.

Like numbers, vectors do not become truly useful until we introduce rules for their manipulation, i.e., a vector algebra. Having elected the arrow representation of vectors, the vector algebra that we now introduce will be essentially geometric.

First, as noted above, we say that two vectors are *equal* if and only if their lengths are identical, and if their directions are identical as well.

Next, we define a process of **addition** between any two vectors **u** and **v**. The first step is to move **v** (if necessary), parallel to itself, so that its tail coincides with the head of **u**. Then the *resultant* **u** + **v** is defined as the arrow from the tail of **u** to the head of **v**, as in Fig. 2.3a. Reversing the order, **v** + **u** is as shown in Fig. 2.3b.

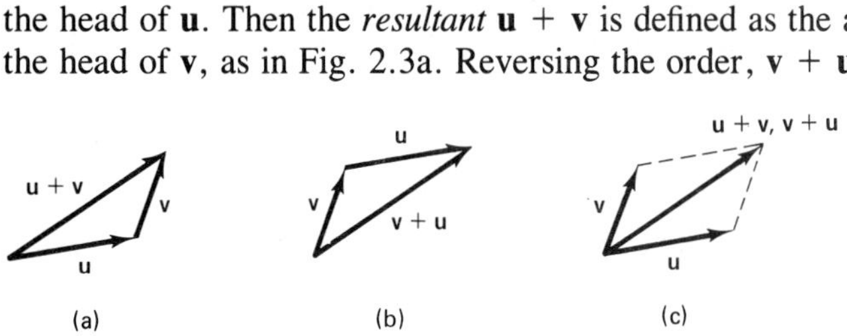

Fig. 2.3. Vector addition.

* Students of mechanics may recall that the point of application of **F** will affect the *rotational* part of the motion, but not the *translational* part.

Equivalently, we may place **u** and **v** tail to tail, as in Fig. 2.3c. Comparing Fig. 2.3c with Fig. 2.3a and b, we see that the diagonal of the parallelogram, (Fig. 2.3c) is both $\mathbf{u} + \mathbf{v}$ and $\mathbf{v} + \mathbf{u}$. Thus

$$\mathbf{u} + \mathbf{v} = \mathbf{v} + \mathbf{u}, \tag{1}$$

so addition is commutative. One may show (Exercise 3) that it is associative as well,

$$(\mathbf{u} + \mathbf{v}) + \mathbf{w} = \mathbf{u} + (\mathbf{v} + \mathbf{w}). \tag{2}$$

Next, we define any vector of zero length to be a **zero vector,** denoted as **0**. Its length being zero, its direction is immaterial; any direction may be assigned if desired. From the definition of addition above, it follows that

$$\mathbf{u} + \mathbf{0} = \mathbf{0} + \mathbf{u} = \mathbf{u} \tag{3}$$

for each vector **u**.

Corresponding to **u** we define a **negative inverse** "$-\mathbf{u}$" such that if **u** is any nonzero vector, then $-\mathbf{u}$ is determined uniquely, as shown in Fig. 2.4a; i.e., it is of the same length as **u**, but is directed in the opposite direction (again, **u** and $-\mathbf{u}$ have the same length, the length of $-\mathbf{u}$ is *not* negative); for the zero vector we have $-\mathbf{0} = \mathbf{0}$. We denote $\mathbf{u} + (-\mathbf{v})$ as $\mathbf{u} - \mathbf{v}$ ("**u** minus **v**"), but emphasize that it is really the addition of **u** and $-\mathbf{v}$, as in Fig. 2.4b.

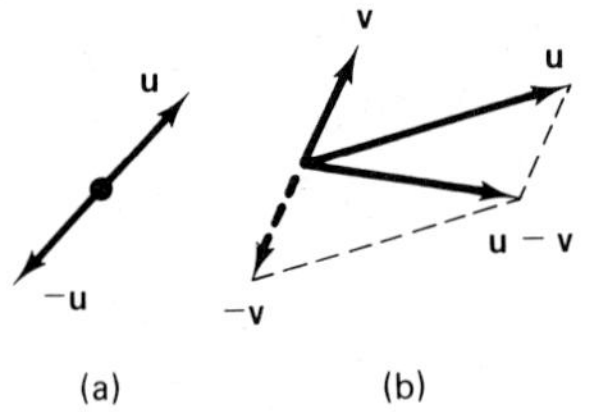

Fig. 2.4 $-\mathbf{u}$ and vector subtraction.

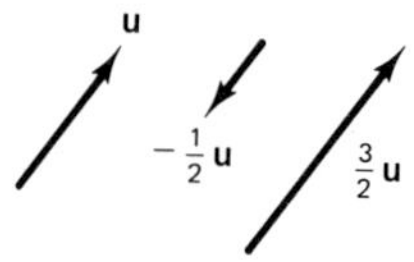

Fig. 2.5 Scalar multiplication.

Finally, we introduce another operation, called **scalar multiplication,** between any vector **u** and any scalar (i.e, a real number) α: If $\alpha \neq 0$ and $\mathbf{u} \neq \mathbf{0}$, then $\alpha\mathbf{u}$ is a vector whose length is $|\alpha|$ times the length of **u** and whose direction is the same as that of **u** if $\alpha > 0$, and the opposite if $\alpha < 0$; if $\alpha = 0$ and/or $\mathbf{u} = \mathbf{0}$, then $\alpha\mathbf{u} = \mathbf{0}$. This definition is illustrated in Fig. 2.5. It follows from this definition that scalar multiplication has the following algebraic properties:

$$\alpha(\beta\mathbf{u}) = (\alpha\beta)\mathbf{u}, \tag{4a}$$

$$(\alpha + \beta)\mathbf{u} = \alpha\mathbf{u} + \beta\mathbf{u}, \tag{4b}$$

$$\alpha(\mathbf{u} + \mathbf{v}) = \alpha\mathbf{u} + \alpha\mathbf{v}, \tag{4c}$$

$$1\mathbf{u} = \mathbf{u}, \tag{4d}$$

where α, β are any scalars and **u**, **v** are any vectors.

Observe that the important parallelogram rule of vector addition is a definition, so it does not need to be proved. Nevertheless, definitions are not necessarily fruitful, so it is worthwhile to reflect for a moment on why the parallelogram rule has proved so important and useful. Basically, if we say that "the sum of **u** and **v** is **w**," and thereby pass from the two vectors **u, v** to the single vector **w**, it seems fair to expect some sort of equivalence to exist between the action of **w** and the joint action of **u** and **v**. For example, if $\mathbf{F}_1$ and $\mathbf{F}_2$ are two forces acting on a body $\mathcal{B}$, as shown in Fig. 2.6, it is known from fundamental principles of mechanics that their combined effect will be the same as that due to the single force **F**, so it seems reasonable and natural to say that **F** is the *sum* of $\mathbf{F}_1$ and $\mathbf{F}_2$. This concept goes back at least as far as Aristotle (384–322 B.C.). Thus while the algebra of vectors is developed here as an essentially mathematical matter, it is important to appreciate the role of physics and physical motivation.

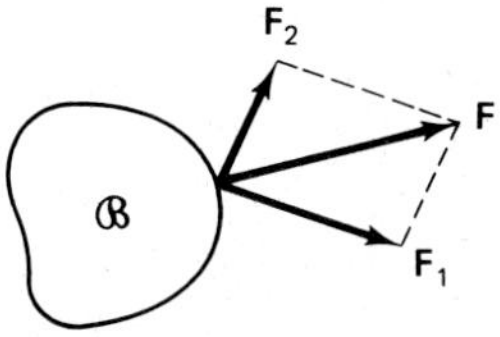

Fig. 2.6 Physical motivation for parallelogram addition.

In closing this section, let us remark that our foregoing discussion should not be construed to imply that objects of physical interest are necessarily vectors (as are force and velocity) or scalars [as are temperature, mass, and speed (i.e., the *magnitude of the velocity vector*)]. For example, in the study of mechanics one finds that more than a magnitude and a direction are needed to fully define the state of stress at a point; in fact, a "second-order tensor" is needed—a quantity that is more exotic than a vector in much the same way that a vector is more exotic than a scalar.*

2.2 EXERCISES

1. Trace the vectors **A**, **B**, **C**, shown where **A** is twice as long as **B**. Then determine each of the following, by graphical means.

(a) $\mathbf{A} + \mathbf{B} + \mathbf{C}$ (b) $\mathbf{B} - \mathbf{A}$
(c) $\mathbf{A} - \mathbf{C} + 3\mathbf{B}$ (d) $2(\mathbf{B} - \mathbf{A}) + 6\mathbf{0}$
(e) $\mathbf{A} + (4\mathbf{B} - \mathbf{C})$ (f) $\mathbf{A} + 2\mathbf{B} - 2\mathbf{C}$

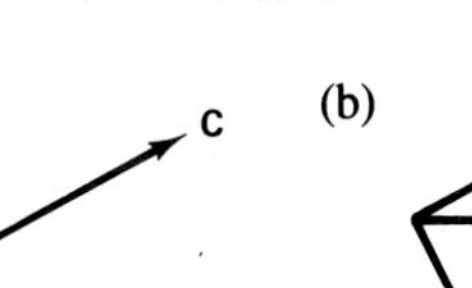

2. In each case, **C** can be expressed as a linear combination of **A** and **B**, that is, as $\mathbf{C} = \alpha\mathbf{A} + \beta\mathbf{B}$. Trace the three vectors and, by graphical means, determine α and β.

(a)

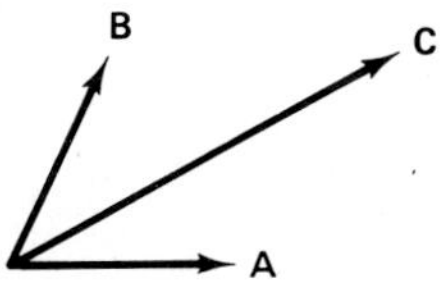

(b)

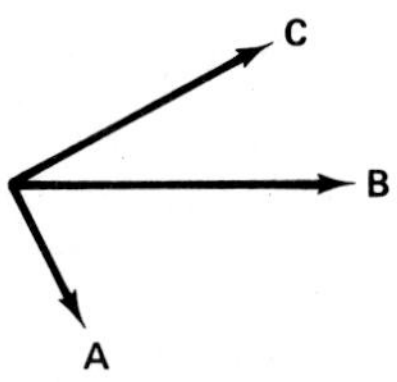

(c)

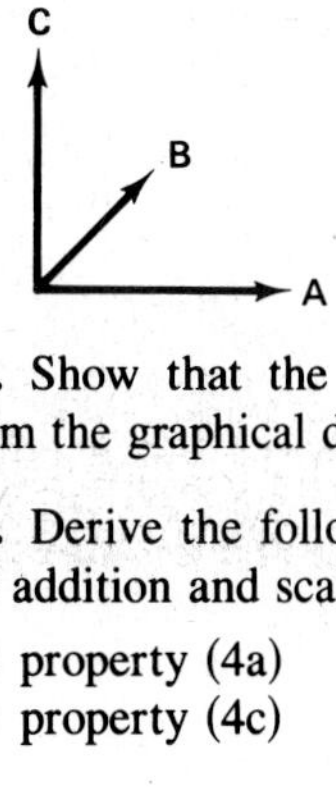

(d)

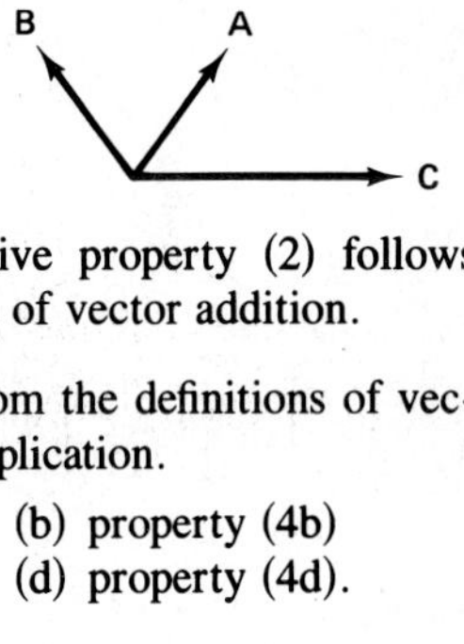

3. Show that the associative property (2) follows from the graphical definition of vector addition.

4. Derive the following from the definitions of vector addition and scalar multiplication.

(a) property (4a) (b) property (4b)
(c) property (4c) (d) property (4d).

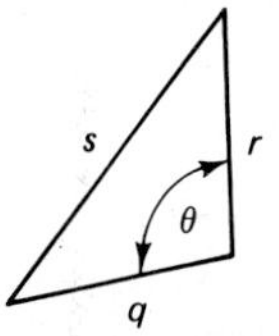

5. (a) If $\|\mathbf{A}\| = 1$, $\|\mathbf{B}\| = 2$, and $\|\mathbf{C}\| = 5$, can

*For an introduction to tensors, we highly recommend to the interested reader the 68-page book *Tensor Analysis* by H. D. Block (Columbus, Ohio: Charles E. Merrill, 1962), but we suggest that all or most of Part I in this book be studied first.

$\mathbf{A} + \mathbf{B} + \mathbf{C} = \mathbf{0}$? *Hint:* Use the *law of cosines* $s^2 = q^2 + r^2 - 2qr \cos \theta$ (see the accompanying figure) or the Euclidean proposition that the length of any one side of a triangle cannot exceed the sum of the lengths of the other two sides.
(b) Repeat part (a), with "$\|\mathbf{A}\| = 1$" changed to $\|\mathbf{A}\| = 4$.

6. Use the definitions and properties given in the reading to show that $\mathbf{A} + \mathbf{B} = \mathbf{C}$ implies that $\mathbf{A} = \mathbf{C} - \mathbf{B}$.

7. (a) Show that if $\mathbf{A} + \mathbf{B} = \mathbf{0}$ and $\mathbf{A}$ and $\mathbf{B}$ are not aligned (i.e., parallel), then each of $\mathbf{A}$ and $\mathbf{B}$ must be $\mathbf{0}$.
(b) Vectors are often of help in deriving geometrical relationships. For example, to show that *the diagonals of a parallelogram bisect each other,* one may proceed as follows. From the accompanying figure, $\mathbf{A} + \mathbf{B} = \mathbf{C}$, $\mathbf{A} - \alpha\mathbf{D} = \beta\mathbf{C}$, and $\mathbf{A} = \mathbf{B} + \mathbf{D}$. Eliminating $\mathbf{A}$ and $\mathbf{B}$, we obtain $(2\beta - 1)\mathbf{C} = (1 - 2\alpha)\mathbf{D}$, and since $\mathbf{C}$ and $\mathbf{D}$ are not aligned, it must be true [per part (a)] that $2\beta - 1 = 1 - 2\alpha = 0$ (i.e., $\alpha = \beta = \frac{1}{2}$), which completes the proof. We now state the problem: Use this sort of procedure to show that *a line from one vertex of a parallelogram to the midpoint of a nonadjacent side trisects a diagonal.*

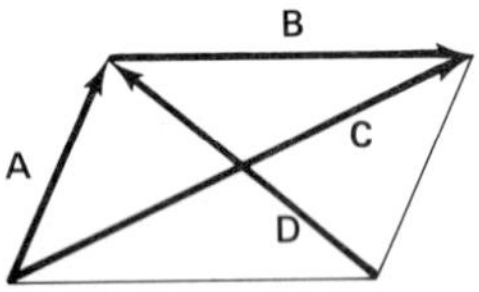

8. If (see the accompanying figure) the vector $\mathbf{A} + \alpha\mathbf{B}$ is placed with its tail at point P, show the line generated by its head as α varies between $-\infty$ and $+\infty$.

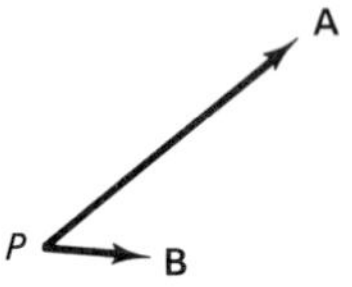

9. If (see the accompanying figure) $\|\mathbf{AB}\|/\|\mathbf{AC}\| = \alpha$, show that $\mathbf{OB} = \alpha\mathbf{OC} + (1 - \alpha)\mathbf{OA}$.

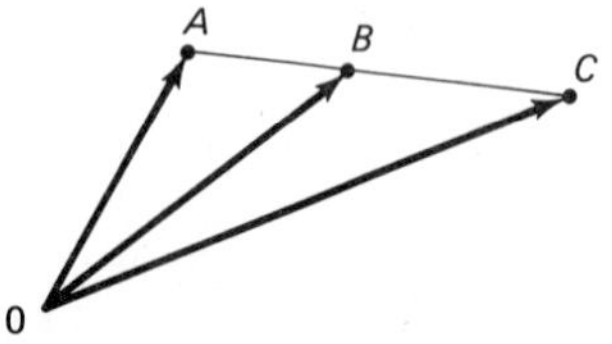

10. One may express *linear displacement* as a vector: If a particle moves from point A to point B, the displacement vector is the directed line segment, say $\mathbf{u}$, from A to B. For example, observe that a displacement $\mathbf{u}$ from A to B, followed by a displacement $\mathbf{v}$ from B to C, is equivalent to a single displacement $\mathbf{w}$ from A to C: $\mathbf{u} + \mathbf{v} = \mathbf{w}$ [part (a) in the accompanying figure].

(a) (b)

Reversing the order, displacements $\mathbf{v}$ and then $\mathbf{u}$ also carry us from A to C: $\mathbf{v} + \mathbf{u} = \mathbf{w}$ [part (b) in the figure]. Thus $\mathbf{u} + \mathbf{v} = \mathbf{v} + \mathbf{u}$, so that the commutativity axiom (1) is indeed satisfied. How about *angular* displacements? Suppose that we express the angular displacement of a rigid body about an axis as $\boldsymbol{\theta}$, where the magnitude of $\boldsymbol{\theta}$ is equal to the angle of rotation, and the orientation of $\boldsymbol{\theta}$ is along the axis of rotation, in the direction specified by the "right-hand rule"; i.e., if we curl the fingers of our right hand about the axis of rotation, in the direction of rotation, then the direction $\boldsymbol{\theta}$ along the axis of rotation is the direction in which our thumb points. The problem is to show that $\boldsymbol{\theta}$, defined in this way, is not a proper vector quantity. *Hint:* Considering the unit cube shown below, say, show (by keeping track of the coordinates of the corner A) that the orientation that results from a rotation of $\pi/2$ about the x axis, followed by a rotation of $\pi/2$ about the y axis, is *not* the same as that which results when the order of the rotations is reversed. *Note:* If you have encountered *angular velocity* vectors (usually denoted as $\boldsymbol{\omega}$ or $\boldsymbol{\Omega}$), in mechanics, it may seem strange to you that *finite rotations* (assigned a vector direction by the right-hand rule) are not true vectors. The idea is that angular velocity involves *infinitesimal* rotations, and infinitesimal rotations (assigned a vector direction by the right-hand rule) *are* true vectors. This is a subtle point, and is discussed in many sources—e.g., Robert R. Long, *Engineering Science Mechanics,* (Englewood Cliffs, N.J.: Prentice-Hall, 1963), pp. 31–36.

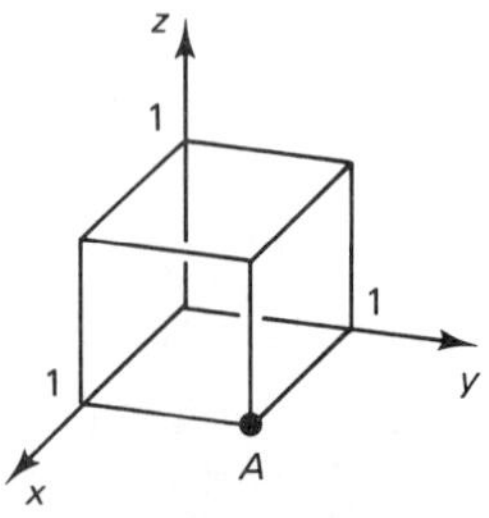

Continuing our discussion, we define here the angle between two vectors, and a "dot product" operation between two vectors. The angle θ between two nonzero vectors **u** and **v** will be understood to mean the ordinary angle between the two vectors when they are arranged tail to tail, as in Fig. 2.7. (We will not attempt to define θ if one or both of the vectors is **0**.) Of course, this definition of θ is ambiguous in that there are *two* such angles, an interior angle ($\leq\pi$) and an exterior angle ($\geq\pi$); for definiteness, we choose θ to be the interior angle,

$$0 \leq \theta \leq \pi, \tag{1}$$

as in Fig. 2.7. Unless explicitly stated otherwise, angular measure will be understood to be in *radians*.

Next, we define the so-called **dot product, u · v,** between two vectors **u** and **v** as

$$\mathbf{u}\cdot\mathbf{v} \equiv \begin{cases} \|\mathbf{u}\|\,\|\mathbf{v}\|\cos\theta & \text{if } \mathbf{u}, \mathbf{v} \neq \mathbf{0} \quad (2a) \\ 0 & \text{if } \mathbf{u} = \mathbf{0} \text{ or } \mathbf{v} = \mathbf{0}; \quad (2b) \end{cases}$$

$\|\mathbf{u}\|$, $\|\mathbf{v}\|$, and $\cos\theta$ are scalars, so $\mathbf{u}\cdot\mathbf{v}$ is a scalar, too.*

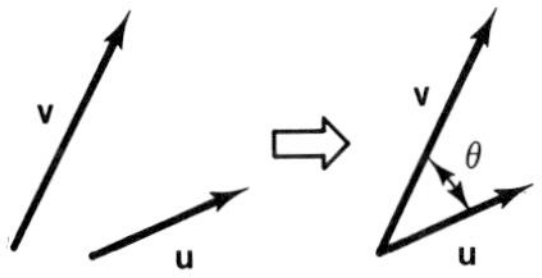

Fig. 2.7 The angle θ between **u** and **v**.

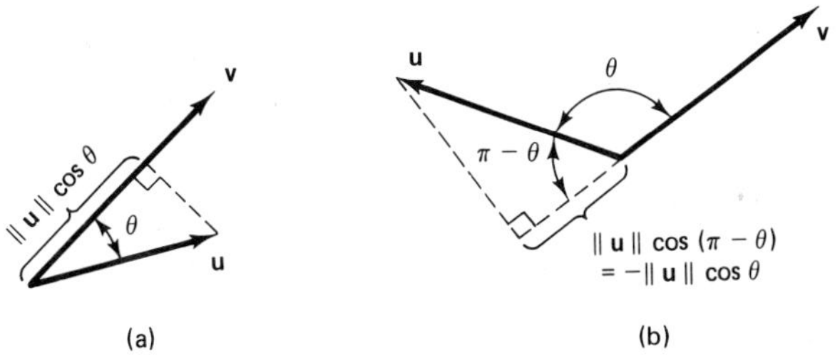

Fig. 2.8 Projection of **u** on **v**.

By way of geometrical interpretation, observe (Fig. 2.8a) that $\|\mathbf{u}\|\cos\theta$ is the length of the orthogonal projection of **u** on the line of action of **v,** so that $\mathbf{u}\cdot\mathbf{v} = \|\mathbf{u}\|\|\mathbf{v}\|\cos\theta = (\|\mathbf{v}\|)(\|\mathbf{u}\|\cos\theta)$ is the length of **v** times the length of the orthogonal projection of **u** on the line of action of **v**.[†] Actually, that statement holds if $0 \leq \theta \leq \pi/2$; if $\pi/2 < \theta \leq \pi$, the cosine is negative, and $\mathbf{u}\cdot\mathbf{v} = \|\mathbf{u}\|\|\mathbf{v}\|\cos\theta$ is the *negative* of the length of **v** times the length of the orthogonal projection of **u** on the line of action of **v**.

* One may wonder why (2b) is needed, since if $\mathbf{u} = \mathbf{0}$, say, then $\|\mathbf{u}\| = 0$ and $\|\mathbf{u}\|\|\mathbf{v}\|\cos\theta$ is apparently zero anyway. But the point is that if **u** and/or **v** are **0**, then θ is undefined; hence $\cos\theta$ (and even zero times $\cos\theta$) is undefined, too.

[†] Alternatively, we could decompose $\mathbf{u}\cdot\mathbf{v} = \|\mathbf{u}\|\|\mathbf{v}\|\cos\theta$ as $(\|\mathbf{u}\|)(\|\mathbf{v}\|\cos\theta)$, i.e., as the length of **u** times the length of the orthogonal projection of **v** on the line of action of **u.**

EXAMPLE 1 Work Done by a Force. In mechanics, the *work* W done when a particle undergoes a linear displacement from an initial point A to a final point B, under the action of a constant force $\mathbf{F}$ (Fig. 2.9), is defined as the length of the orthogonal projection of $\mathbf{F}$ on the line of displacement—positive if $0 \leq \theta < \pi/2$ (i.e., if $\mathbf{F}$ is assisting the motion, as in Fig. 2.9a), and negative if $\pi/2 < \theta \leq \pi$ (i.e., if $\mathbf{F}$ is opposing the motion, as in Fig. 2.9b)—times the displacement, i.e., the length of the displacement vector $\mathbf{AB}$ with its head at B and its tail at A. But that is precisely the dot product $\mathbf{F} \cdot \mathbf{AB}$. Thus

$$W = \mathbf{F} \cdot \mathbf{AB}. \quad ◀ \tag{3}$$

An important special case of the dot product occurs when $\theta = \pi/2$. Then $\mathbf{u}$ and $\mathbf{v}$ are *perpendicular*, and

$$\mathbf{u} \cdot \mathbf{v} = \|\mathbf{u}\| \|\mathbf{v}\| \cos \frac{\pi}{2} = 0. \tag{4}$$

Also of importance is the case where $\mathbf{u} = \mathbf{v}$. Then, according to (2),

$$\mathbf{u} \cdot \mathbf{u} = \begin{cases} \|\mathbf{u}\| \, \|\mathbf{u}\| \cos 0 = \|\mathbf{u}\|^2 & \text{if } \mathbf{u} \neq \mathbf{0} \\ 0 & \text{if } \mathbf{u} = \mathbf{0} \end{cases} \tag{5}$$

so that we have

$$\boxed{\|\mathbf{u}\| = \sqrt{\mathbf{u} \cdot \mathbf{u}}} \tag{6}$$

whether $\mathbf{u} = \mathbf{0}$ or not. The relationship (6) between the dot product and the norm will be useful in subsequent sections.

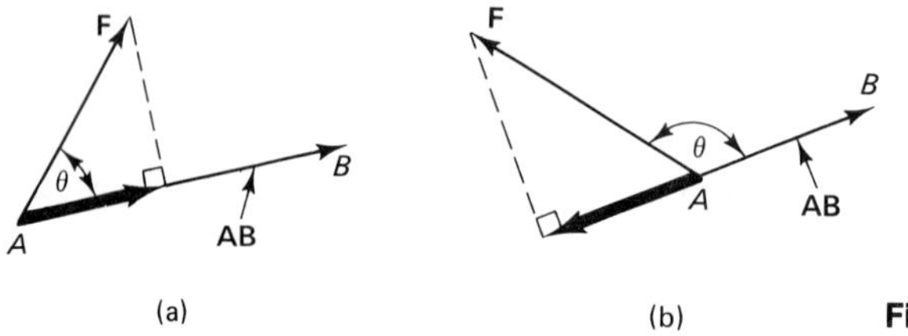

Fig. 2.9 Work done by **F**.

2.3 EXERCISES

1. Evaluate $\mathbf{u} \cdot \mathbf{v}$ in each case.

(a)

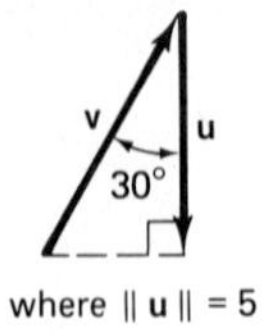

(b)

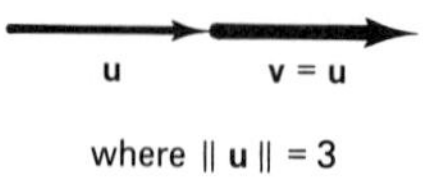

(c)

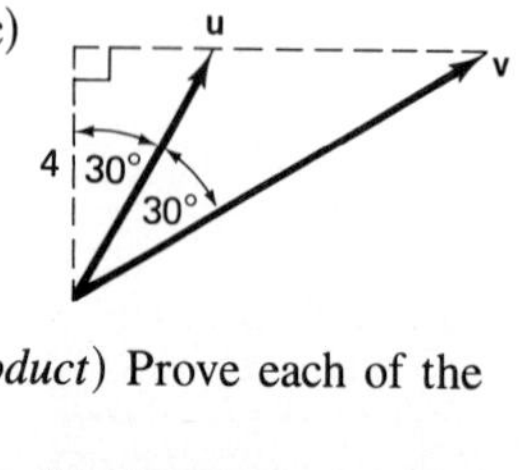

2. (*Properties of the dot product*) Prove each of the following properties of the dot product, where α, β are any scalars, and $\mathbf{u}$, $\mathbf{v}$, $\mathbf{w}$ are any vectors.

(a) $\mathbf{u} \cdot \mathbf{v} = \mathbf{v} \cdot \mathbf{u}$ (commutativity)

(b) $\mathbf{u} \cdot \mathbf{u} > 0$ for all $\mathbf{u} \neq \mathbf{0}$; $= 0$ for $\mathbf{u} = \mathbf{0}$ (nonnegativeness)

(c) $(\alpha \mathbf{u} + \beta \mathbf{v}) \cdot \mathbf{w} = \alpha (\mathbf{u} \cdot \mathbf{w}) + \beta (\mathbf{v} \cdot \mathbf{w})$ (linearity)

Hint: In proving part (c), you may wish to show, first, that part (c) is equivalent to the two conditions $(\mathbf{u} + \mathbf{v}) \cdot \mathbf{w} = \mathbf{u} \cdot \mathbf{w} + \mathbf{v} \cdot \mathbf{w}$ and $(\alpha \mathbf{u}) \cdot \mathbf{v} = \alpha (\mathbf{u} \cdot \mathbf{v})$.

3. Using the properties given in Exercise 2, show

that

$(\mathbf{u} + \mathbf{v}) \cdot (\mathbf{w} + \mathbf{x}) = \mathbf{u} \cdot \mathbf{w} + \mathbf{u} \cdot \mathbf{x} + \mathbf{v} \cdot \mathbf{w} + \mathbf{v} \cdot \mathbf{x}$. (a)

4. Consider the unit cube shown, where P is the midpoint of the right-hand face. Evaluate each of the following.

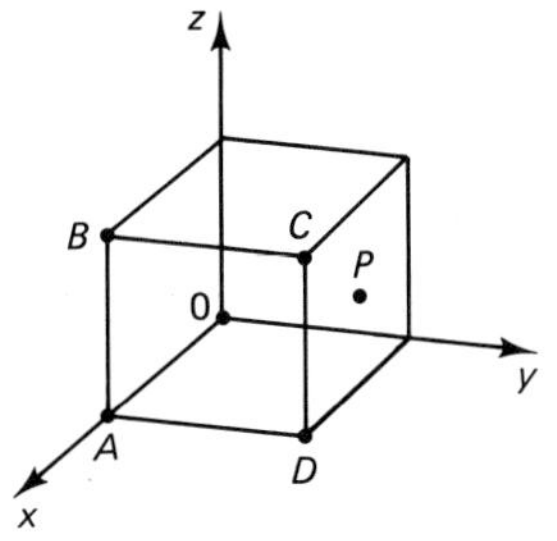

*(a) $\mathbf{OC} \cdot \mathbf{AB}$	(b) $\mathbf{BA} \cdot \mathbf{OP}$	(c) $\mathbf{AC} \cdot \mathbf{OP}$
*(d) $\mathbf{OC} \cdot \mathbf{CP}$	(e) $\mathbf{OC} \cdot \mathbf{OP}$	(f) $\mathbf{BC} \cdot \mathbf{OP}$
*(g) $\mathbf{AO} \cdot \mathbf{OP}$	(h) $\mathbf{CP} \cdot \mathbf{DP}$	(i) $\mathbf{BP} \cdot \mathbf{DB}$
(j) $\mathbf{PB} \cdot \mathbf{CO}$	(k) $\mathbf{AP} \cdot \mathbf{PB}$	(l) $\mathbf{AO} \cdot \mathbf{PA}$

Hint: In evaluating $\mathbf{AC} \cdot \mathbf{OP}$, for example, it may be convenient to write $\mathbf{AC} \cdot \mathbf{OP} = (\mathbf{AD} + \mathbf{DC}) \cdot (\mathbf{OD} + \mathbf{DP})$, and then to apply (a) in Exercise 3.

5. Referring to the figure in Exercise 4, use the dot product to compute the following angles. (See the hint in Exercise 4.)

*(a) APO	(b) APB	(c) APC	(d) APD
(e) ABP	(f) ACP	*(g) BPO	(h) BPC
(i) BPD	(j) BOP	(k) CPO	(l) DPO

6. If $\mathbf{u}$ and $\mathbf{v}$ are nonzero, show that $\mathbf{w} = \|\mathbf{v}\|\mathbf{u} + \|\mathbf{u}\|\mathbf{v}$ bisects the angle between $\mathbf{u}$ and $\mathbf{v}$. (You may use any of the properties given in Exercise 2.)

n-SPACE 2.4

Here we move away from our dependence on the arrow representation of vectors, in 2-space and 3-space, by introducing an alternative representation in terms of 2-tuples and 3-tuples. This will lead us to a more general notion of vectors in "n-space".

The idea is simple and is based on the familiar representation of *points* in cartesian 1-, 2-, and 3-space as 1-, 2-, and 3-tuples of real numbers. For example, the 2-tuple (a_1, a_2) denotes the point P indicated in Fig. 2.10a, where a_1, a_2 are the x, y coordinates, respectively. But it can also serve to denote the vector $\mathbf{OP}$ in Fig. 2.10b, or indeed, any equivalent vector $\mathbf{QR}$.

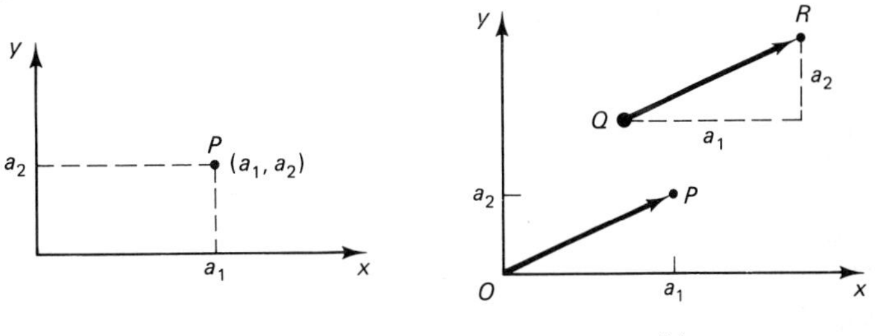

Fig. 2.10 2-tuple representation.

Thus the vector is now represented as the 2-tuple (a_1, a_2) rather than as an arrow, and while pictures may still be drawn, as in Fig. 2.10b, they are no longer essential and can be discarded if we wish—at least once the algebra of 2-tuples is established (in the next paragraph). The set of all such real 2-tuple vectors will be called **2-space** and will be denoted by the symbol $\mathbb{R}^2$; i.e.,

$$\mathbb{R}^2 = \{(a_1, a_2) \mid a_1, a_2 \text{ real numbers*}\}. \tag{1}$$

* When we say that a_1, a_2 are real numbers, we mean *finite* real numbers, i.e., excluding $+\infty$ and $-\infty$, the finiteness of quantities normally being implicit.

Vectors $\mathbf{u} = (u_1, u_2)$ and $\mathbf{v} = (v_1, v_2)$ in $\mathbb{R}^2$ are defined to be *equal* if $u_1 = v_1$ and $u_2 = v_2$; if their sum is defined as*

$$\mathbf{u} + \mathbf{v} \equiv (u_1 + v_1, u_2 + v_2), \tag{2}$$

as follows from the geometric representation in Fig. 2.11; the *scalar multiple* $\alpha\mathbf{u}$ is defined (Exercise 2), for any scalar α, as

$$\alpha\mathbf{u} \equiv (\alpha u_1, \alpha u_2); \tag{3}$$

the *zero vector* is

$$\mathbf{0} \equiv (0, 0); \tag{4}$$

and the *negative of* $\mathbf{u}$ is

$$-\mathbf{u} \equiv (-u_1, -u_2). \tag{5}$$

Similarly for $\mathbb{R}^3$:

$$\mathbb{R}^3 = \{(a_1, a_2, a_3) \mid a_1, a_2, a_3 \text{ real numbers}\}, \tag{6}$$

$$\mathbf{u} + \mathbf{v} \equiv (u_1 + v_1, u_2 + v_2, u_3 + v_3), \tag{7}$$

and so on.†

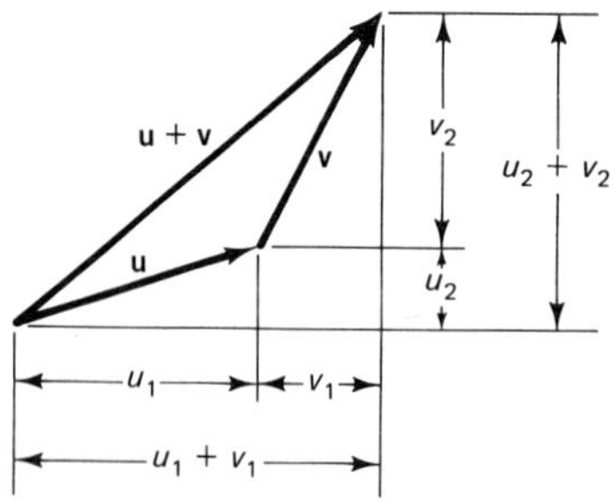

Fig. 2.11 Establishing (2).

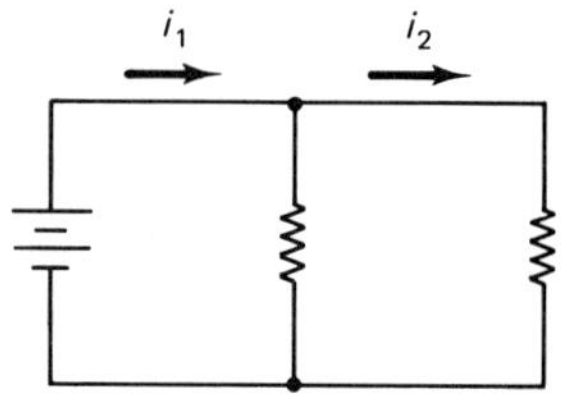

Fig. 2.12 Electrical system.

It may not be evident that we have gained much, since the arrow and n-tuple representations are essentially equivalent. But in fact, the n-tuple format begins to open doors. For example, the instantaneous state of the electrical circuit (consisting of a battery and two resistors) shown in Fig. 2.12 may be defined by the two currents i_1 and i_2 or, equivalently, by the single 2-tuple vector (i_1, i_2). Thus, even though "magnitudes," "directions," and "arrow vectors" may not leap to mind, in describing the system shown in Fig. 2.12, a vector representation *is* quite natural within the n-tuple framework, and that puts us in a position, in dealing with that electrical system, to make use of whatever vector theorems and techniques are available, as developed in the next several sections and chapters.

Indeed, why stop at 3-tuples? One may introduce the set of all ordered real ***n*-tuple** vectors, even if n is greater than 3; we call this ***n*-space,** and denote it as $\mathbb{R}^n$, i.e.,

* We use the $\equiv$ equal sign to mean *equal to by definition*.

† The space $\mathbb{R}^1$ of 1-tuples will not be of interest here.

$$\mathbb{R}^n = \{(a_1, \ldots, a_n) \mid a_1, \ldots, a_n \text{ real numbers}\}. \tag{8}$$

Consider two vectors, $\mathbf{u} = (u_1, \ldots, u_n)$ and $\mathbf{v} = (v_1, \ldots, v_n)$, in $\mathbb{R}^n$. The scalars $u_1, \ldots, u_n$ and $v_1, \ldots, v_n$ are called the **components** (or elements) of **u** and **v**. As you may well expect, based on our foregoing discussion of $\mathbb{R}^2$ and $\mathbb{R}^3$, **u** and **v** are said to be *equal* if $u_1 = v_1, \ldots, u_n = v_n$, and we define

$$\mathbf{u} + \mathbf{v} \equiv (u_1 + v_1, \ldots, u_n + v_n), \tag{9a}$$

$$\alpha \mathbf{u} \equiv (\alpha u_1, \ldots, \alpha u_n), \tag{9b}$$

$$\mathbf{0} \equiv (0, \ldots, 0), \tag{9c}$$

$$-\mathbf{u} \equiv (-1)\mathbf{u}, \tag{9d}$$

$$\mathbf{u} - \mathbf{v} \equiv \mathbf{u} + (-\mathbf{v}). \tag{9e}$$

From these definitions we may deduce the following properties:

$$\mathbf{u} + \mathbf{v} = \mathbf{v} + \mathbf{u}, \qquad \text{(commutativity)} \tag{10a}$$

$$(\mathbf{u} + \mathbf{v}) + \mathbf{w} = \mathbf{u} + (\mathbf{v} + \mathbf{w}), \qquad \text{(associativity)} \tag{10b}$$

$$\mathbf{u} + \mathbf{0} = \mathbf{u}, \tag{10c}$$

$$\mathbf{u} + (-\mathbf{u}) = \mathbf{0}, \tag{10d}$$

$$\alpha(\beta \mathbf{u}) = (\alpha\beta)\mathbf{u}, \qquad \text{(associativity)} \tag{10e}$$

$$(\alpha + \beta)\mathbf{u} = \alpha \mathbf{u} + \beta \mathbf{u}, \qquad \text{(distributivity)} \tag{10f}$$

$$\alpha(\mathbf{u} + \mathbf{v}) = \alpha \mathbf{u} + \alpha \mathbf{v}, \qquad \text{(distributivity)} \tag{10g}$$

$$1\mathbf{u} = \mathbf{u}, \tag{10h}$$

$$0\mathbf{u} = \mathbf{0}. \tag{10i}$$

To illustrate how such n-tuples might arise, observe that the state of the electrical system shown in Fig. 2.13, at any instant, may be defined by the four currents i_1, i_2, i_3, i_4, and that these may be regarded as the components of a single vector $\mathbf{i} = (i_1, i_2, i_3, i_4)$ in $\mathbb{R}^4$.

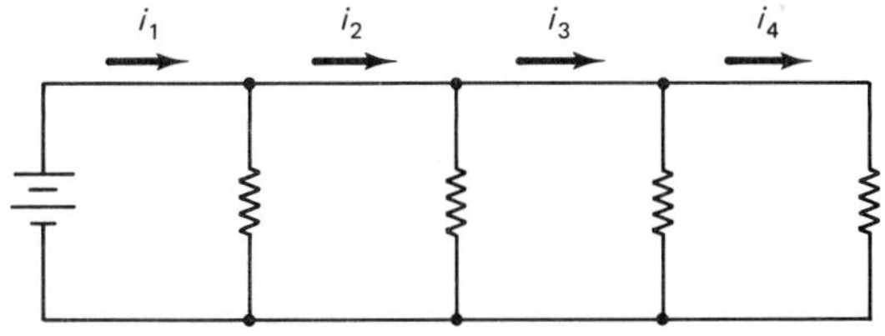

Fig. 2.13 Another electrical circuit.

Of course, the notation of $(u_1, \ldots, u_n)$ as a *point* or *arrow* in an "n-dimensional space" can be realized graphically only if $n \leq 3$; if $n > 3$, the interpretation is valid only in an abstract or schematic sense. However, our inability to carry out traditional cartesian graphical constructions for $n > 3$ will be no hindrance. Indeed, part of the idea here is to move *away* from a dependence on graphical constructions.

Having extended the vector concept to $\mathbb{R}^n$, the reader may well wonder if further extension is possible. Such extension is not only possible, it constitutes an important step in modern mathematics. More about this in Section 2.6.

2.4 EXERCISES

1. If $\mathbf{t} = (5, 0, 1, 2)$, $\mathbf{u} = (2, -1, 3, 4)$, $\mathbf{v} = (4, -5, 1)$, $\mathbf{w} = (-1, -2, 5, 6)$, evaluate each of the following (as a single vector); if the operation is undefined, state that. At each step cite the equation number of the definition or property being used.

(a) $2\mathbf{t} + 7\mathbf{u}$ (b) $3\mathbf{t} - 5\mathbf{u}$
(c) $4[\mathbf{u} + 5(\mathbf{w} - 2\mathbf{u})]$ (d) $4\mathbf{tu} + \mathbf{w}$
(e) $-\mathbf{w} + \mathbf{t}$ (f) $2\mathbf{t}/\mathbf{u}$
(g) $\mathbf{t} + 2\mathbf{u} + 3\mathbf{w}$ (h) $\mathbf{t} - 2\mathbf{u} - 4\mathbf{v}$
(i) $\mathbf{u}(3\mathbf{t} + \mathbf{w})$ (j) $\mathbf{u}^2 + 2\mathbf{t}$
(k) $2\mathbf{t} + 7\mathbf{u} - 4$ (l) $\mathbf{u} + \mathbf{wt}$
(m) $\sin \mathbf{u}$ (n) $\mathbf{w} + \mathbf{t} - 2\mathbf{u}$

2. Let $\mathbf{u} = (1, 3, 0, -2)$, $\mathbf{v} = (2, 0, -5, 0)$, and $\mathbf{w} = (4, 3, 2, -1)$.

(a) If $3\mathbf{u} - \mathbf{x} = 4(\mathbf{v} + 2\mathbf{x})$, solve for $\mathbf{x}$ (i.e., find its components.)
(b) If $\mathbf{x} + \mathbf{u} + \mathbf{v} + \mathbf{w} = \mathbf{0}$, solve for $\mathbf{x}$.

3. Let $\mathbf{u}$, $\mathbf{v}$, and $\mathbf{w}$ be as given in Exercise 2. Citing the definition or property used, at each step, solve each of the following for $\mathbf{x}$. *Note:* Besides the definitions and properties stated in this section, it should be clear that if $\mathbf{x} = \mathbf{y}$, then $\mathbf{x} + \mathbf{z} = \mathbf{y} + \mathbf{z}$ for any $\mathbf{z}$, and $\alpha\mathbf{x} = \alpha\mathbf{y}$ for any α (adding and multiplying equals by equals.)

(a) $3\mathbf{x} + 2(\mathbf{u} - 5\mathbf{v}) = \mathbf{w}$
(b) $3\mathbf{x} = 4\mathbf{0} + (1, 0, 0, 0)$
(c) $\mathbf{u} - 4\mathbf{x} = \mathbf{0}$
(d) $\mathbf{u} + \mathbf{v} - 2\mathbf{x} = \mathbf{w}$

4. If $\mathbf{t} = (2, 1, 3)$, $\mathbf{u} = (1, 2, -4)$, $\mathbf{v} = (0, 1, 1)$, $\mathbf{w} = (-2, 1, -1)$, solve each of the following for the scalars α_1, α_2, α_3. If no such scalars exist, state that.

(a) $\alpha_1\mathbf{t} + \alpha_2\mathbf{u} + \alpha_3\mathbf{v} = \mathbf{0}$
(b) $\alpha_1\mathbf{t} + \alpha_2\mathbf{v} + \alpha_3\mathbf{w} = \mathbf{0}$
(c) $\alpha_1\mathbf{t} + \alpha_2\mathbf{u} + \alpha_3\mathbf{w} = (1, 3, 2)$
(d) $\alpha_1\mathbf{t} + \alpha_2\mathbf{v} + \alpha_3\mathbf{w} = (2, 0, -1)$
(e) $\alpha_1\mathbf{u} + \alpha_2\mathbf{v} = \mathbf{0}$
(f) $\alpha_1\mathbf{u} + \alpha_2\mathbf{v} = \alpha_3\mathbf{w} - (2, 0, 0)$

5. (a) If $\mathbf{u}$ and $\mathbf{v}$ are given 4-tuples and $\mathbf{0} = (0, 0, 0, 0)$, does the vector equation $\alpha_1\mathbf{u} + \alpha_2\mathbf{v} = \mathbf{0}$ necessarily have nontrivial solutions for the scalars α_1 and α_2? Explain. (If the answer is "no," a counterexample will suffice.)
(b) Repeat part (a), but where $\mathbf{u}$, $\mathbf{v}$ are 3-tuples and $\mathbf{0} = (0, 0, 0)$.
(c) Repeat part (a), but where $\mathbf{u}$, $\mathbf{v}$ are 2-tuples and $\mathbf{0} = (0, 0)$.

2.5 NORM, DOT PRODUCT, AND ANGLE FOR n-SPACE

We wish to define the norm of an n-tuple vector, and the dot product and angle between two n-tuple vectors, just as we did for "arrow vectors". These definitions should be expressed in terms of the *components* of the n-tuples, since the graphical and geometrical arguments used for arrow vectors will not be possible here for $n > 3$. Thus if $\mathbf{u} = (u_1, \ldots, u_n)$, we wish to define the *norm* or "length" of $\mathbf{u}$, denoted as $\|\mathbf{u}\|$, in terms of the components $u_1, \ldots, u_n$ of $\mathbf{u}$; and given another vector $\mathbf{v} = (v_1, \ldots, v_n)$, we wish to define the *angle* θ between $\mathbf{u}$ and $\mathbf{v}$, and the *dot product* $\mathbf{u} \cdot \mathbf{v}$, in terms of $u_1, \ldots, u_n$ and $v_1, \ldots, v_n$.

Furthermore, we would like these definitions to be reasonable; specifically, we would like them to reduce to the definitions given in Sections 2.2 and 2.3 in the event that $n = 2$ or 3.

Let us begin with the dot product. Our plan is to go back to the arrow vector formula

$$\mathbf{u} \cdot \mathbf{v} = \|\mathbf{u}\|\|\mathbf{v}\|\cos\theta, \tag{1}$$

to reexpress it in terms of vector components for $\mathbb{R}^2$ and $\mathbb{R}^3$, and then to generalize those forms to $\mathbb{R}^n$.

If $\mathbf{u}$ and $\mathbf{v}$ are vectors in $\mathbb{R}^2$, as shown in Fig. 2.14, formula (1) may be ex-

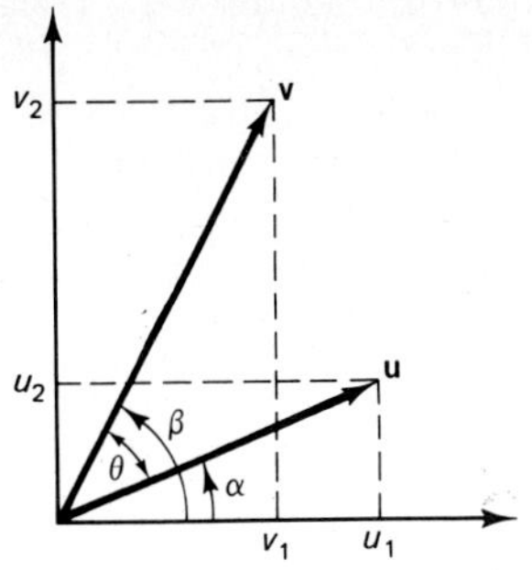

Fig. 2.14 u·v in terms of components.

pressed in terms of the components of **u** and **v** as follows:

$$\begin{aligned} \mathbf{u}\cdot\mathbf{v} &= \|\mathbf{u}\|\|\mathbf{v}\|\cos\theta \\ &= \|\mathbf{u}\|\|\mathbf{v}\|\cos(\beta-\alpha) \\ &= \|\mathbf{u}\|\|\mathbf{v}\|(\cos\beta\cos\alpha+\sin\beta\sin\alpha) \\ &= (\|\mathbf{u}\|\cos\alpha)(\|\mathbf{v}\|\cos\beta)+(\|\mathbf{u}\|\sin\alpha)(\|\mathbf{v}\|\sin\beta) \\ &= u_1v_1+u_2v_2. \end{aligned} \tag{2}$$

We state, without derivation, that the analogous result for $\mathbb{R}^3$ is

$$\mathbf{u}\cdot\mathbf{v} = u_1v_1+u_2v_2+u_3v_3. \tag{3}$$

Generalizing (2) and (3) to $\mathbb{R}^n$, it is eminently reasonable to define the (scalar-valued) dot product of two n-tuple vectors $\mathbf{u}=(u_1,\ldots,u_n)$ and $\mathbf{v}=(v_1,\ldots,v_n)$ as

$$\boxed{\mathbf{u}\cdot\mathbf{v} \equiv u_1v_1+u_2v_2+\cdots+u_nv_n = \sum_{j=1}^{n} u_jv_j.} \tag{4}$$

Observe that we have not proved (4); it is a definition.

Defining the dot product is the key, for now $\|\mathbf{u}\|$ and θ follow easily. Specifically, we define

$$\boxed{\|\mathbf{u}\| \equiv \sqrt{\mathbf{u}\cdot\mathbf{u}} = \sqrt{\sum_{j=1}^{n} u_j^2}} \tag{5}$$

in accordance with equation (6) on page 24, and

$$\boxed{\theta \equiv \cos^{-1}\left(\frac{\mathbf{u}\cdot\mathbf{v}}{\|\mathbf{u}\|\|\mathbf{v}\|}\right),} \tag{6}$$

directly from (1), where the inverse cosine is understood to be in the interval $[0, \pi]$.* Notice the generalized-Pythagorean-theorem nature of (5).

Other dot products and norms are sometimes defined for n-space, but we choose

* By the "interval $[a, b]$ on a real x axis," we mean the points $a \le x \le b$; such an interval is said to be *closed* since it includes the two endpoints. To denote the *open* interval $a < x < b$, we write (a, b). Similarly, $[a, b)$ means $a \le x < b$, and $(a, b]$ means $a < x \le b$. Implicit in the closed-interval notation $[a, b]$ is the finiteness of a and b.

to use (4) and (5), which are known as the **Euclidean dot product** and **Euclidean norm,** respectively. To signify that the Euclidean dot product and norm have been adopted, we henceforth refer to the space as **Euclidean n-space,** rather than just n-space. We will still denote it by the symbol $\mathbb{R}^n$ (although some authors prefer the notation $\mathbb{E}^n$).

EXAMPLE 1 Let $\mathbf{u} = (1, 0)$ and $\mathbf{v} = (2, -2)$. Then

$$\mathbf{u}\cdot\mathbf{v} = (1)(2) + (0)(-2) = 2,$$
$$\|\mathbf{u}\| = \sqrt{(1)^2 + (0)^2} = 1,$$
$$\|\mathbf{v}\| = \sqrt{(2)^2 + (-2)^2} = 2\sqrt{2},$$
$$\theta = \cos^{-1}\left(\frac{2}{2\sqrt{2}}\right) = \frac{\pi}{4} \quad (\text{or } 45°),$$

as is easily verified if we sketch $\mathbf{u}$ and $\mathbf{v}$ as arrow vectors in a cartesian plane. ◀

EXAMPLE 2 Let $\mathbf{u} = (2, -2, 4, -1)$ and $\mathbf{v} = (5, 9, -1, 0)$. Then

$$\mathbf{u}\cdot\mathbf{v} = (2)(5) + (-2)(9) + (4)(-1) + (-1)(0) = -12, \tag{7}$$
$$\|\mathbf{u}\| = \sqrt{(2)^2 + (-2)^2 + (4)^2 + (-1)^2} = 5, \tag{8}$$
$$\|\mathbf{v}\| = \sqrt{(5)^2 + (9)^2 + (-1)^2 + (0)^2} = \sqrt{107}, \tag{9}$$
$$\theta = \cos^{-1}\left(\frac{-12}{5\sqrt{107}}\right) \approx \cos^{-1}(-0.232) \approx 1.805 \ (\text{or } 103.4°). \tag{10}$$

In this case n (= 4) is greater than 3, so (7) through (10) are not to be understood in any physical or graphical sense, merely in terms of the definitions (4) to (6).

COMMENT The dot product of $\mathbf{u} = (2, -2, 4)$ and $\mathbf{v} = (5, 9, -1, 0)$, on the other hand, is *not defined,* since here $\mathbf{u}$ and $\mathbf{v}$ are members of different spaces, $\mathbb{R}^3$ and $\mathbb{R}^4$, respectively. It is *not* legitimate to augment $\mathbf{u}$ to the form $(2, -2, 4, 0)$ on the grounds that "surely adding a zero can't hurt"; "$(2, -2, 4) = (2, -2, 4, 0)$" is *false*. ◀

There is one catch that you may have noticed: (6) serves to define a (real) θ only if the argument of the arccosine is less than or equal to unity in magnitude. For 2- and 3-space this should be the case in view of the equivalence between 2- and 3-tuple vectors and arrow vectors, but for n-space with $n > 3$ it is not so obvious. That

$$-1 \le \frac{\mathbf{u}\cdot\mathbf{v}}{\|\mathbf{u}\|\|\mathbf{v}\|} \le 1 \quad \text{or} \quad |\mathbf{u}\cdot\mathbf{v}| \le \|\mathbf{u}\|\|\mathbf{v}\| \tag{11}$$

does necessarily hold will, nevertheless, be proved in a moment.

PROPERTIES OF THE DOT PRODUCT

The dot product defined by (4) possesses the following important properties:

1. *Commutativity:*

$$\mathbf{u} \cdot \mathbf{v} = \mathbf{v} \cdot \mathbf{u}. \tag{12a}$$

2. *Nonnegativeness:*

$$\begin{aligned} \mathbf{u} \cdot \mathbf{u} &> 0 \quad \text{for all } \mathbf{u} \neq \mathbf{0} \\ &= 0 \quad \text{for } \mathbf{u} = \mathbf{0}. \end{aligned} \tag{12b}$$

3. *Linearity:*

$$(\alpha \mathbf{u} + \beta \mathbf{v}) \cdot \mathbf{w} = \alpha (\mathbf{u} \cdot \mathbf{w}) + \beta (\mathbf{v} \cdot \mathbf{w}), \tag{12c}$$

for any scalars α, β and any vectors $\mathbf{u}$, $\mathbf{v}$, $\mathbf{w}$. The single linearity condition (12c) is equivalent to the two conditions $(\mathbf{u} + \mathbf{v}) \cdot \mathbf{w} = \mathbf{u} \cdot \mathbf{w} + \mathbf{v} \cdot \mathbf{w}$ and $(\alpha \mathbf{u}) \cdot \mathbf{v} = \alpha (\mathbf{u} \cdot \mathbf{v})$. Verification of these claims is easy and is left for the exercises.

EXAMPLE 3 Expand the dot product $(6\mathbf{t} - 2\mathbf{u}) \cdot (\mathbf{v} + 4\mathbf{w})$. Using (12), we obtain

$$\begin{aligned} (6\mathbf{t} - 2\mathbf{u}) \cdot (\mathbf{v} + 4\mathbf{w}) &= 6[\mathbf{t} \cdot (\mathbf{v} + 4\mathbf{w})] - 2[\mathbf{u} \cdot (\mathbf{v} + 4\mathbf{w})] && \text{by (12c)} \\ &= 6[(\mathbf{v} + 4\mathbf{w}) \cdot \mathbf{t}] - 2[(\mathbf{v} + 4\mathbf{w}) \cdot \mathbf{u}] && \text{by (12a)} \\ &= 6(\mathbf{v} \cdot \mathbf{t}) + 24(\mathbf{w} \cdot \mathbf{t}) - 2(\mathbf{v} \cdot \mathbf{u}) - 8(\mathbf{w} \cdot \mathbf{u}) && \text{by (12c)} \end{aligned}$$

in much the same way that we obtain $(a - b)(c + d) = ac + ad - bc - bd$ in scalar arithmetic. ◀

As a consequence of (12) we are in a position to prove the promised inequality (11), namely the **Schwarz inequality***:

$$\boxed{|\mathbf{u} \cdot \mathbf{v}| \leq \|\mathbf{u}\| \|\mathbf{v}\|.} \tag{13}$$

To derive this result, we start with the inequality

$$(\mathbf{u} + \alpha \mathbf{v}) \cdot (\mathbf{u} + \alpha \mathbf{v}) \geq 0, \tag{14}$$

which is guaranteed by (12b), for any scalar α and any vectors $\mathbf{u}$ and $\mathbf{v}$. Expanding the left-hand side and noting that $\mathbf{u} \cdot \mathbf{u} = \|\mathbf{u}\|^2$ and $\mathbf{v} \cdot \mathbf{v} = \|\mathbf{v}\|^2$, (14) becomes†

$$\|\mathbf{u}\|^2 + 2\alpha \mathbf{u} \cdot \mathbf{v} + \alpha^2 \|\mathbf{v}\|^2 \geq 0. \tag{15}$$

Regarding $\mathbf{u}$ and $\mathbf{v}$ as fixed and α as variable, the left-hand side is then a quadratic function of α. If we choose α so as to minimize the left-hand side, then (15) will be

* After *Hermann Amandus Schwarz* (1843–1921). The names Cauchy and Bunyakovsky are also associated with this well-known inequality.

† Does a term such as $\alpha \mathbf{u} \cdot \mathbf{v}$ in (15) mean $(\alpha \mathbf{u}) \cdot \mathbf{v}$, or $\alpha (\mathbf{u} \cdot \mathbf{v})$? It does not matter; by virtue of (12c) (with $\beta = 0$ and $\mathbf{w}$ changed to $\mathbf{v}$), $(\alpha \mathbf{u}) \cdot \mathbf{v} = \alpha (\mathbf{u} \cdot \mathbf{v})$, so the parentheses are not needed.

as close to an equality as possible, and hence as informative as possible. Thus setting $d(\text{left-hand side})/d\alpha = 0$, we obtain

$$2\mathbf{u}\cdot\mathbf{v} + 2\alpha\|\mathbf{v}\|^2 = 0 \qquad \text{or} \qquad \alpha = -\frac{\mathbf{u}\cdot\mathbf{v}}{\|\mathbf{v}\|^2}.$$

Putting this value of α back into (15) gives us

$$\|\mathbf{u}\|^2 - 2\frac{(\mathbf{u}\cdot\mathbf{v})^2}{\|\mathbf{v}\|^2} + \frac{(\mathbf{u}\cdot\mathbf{v})^2}{\|\mathbf{v}\|^2} \geq 0,$$

$$\|\mathbf{u}\|^2\|\mathbf{v}\|^2 - 2(\mathbf{u}\cdot\mathbf{v})^2 + (\mathbf{u}\cdot\mathbf{v})^2 \geq 0,$$

$$\|\mathbf{u}\|^2\|\mathbf{v}\|^2 \geq (\mathbf{u}\cdot\mathbf{v})^2,$$

and taking square roots of both sides yields the Schwarz inequality (13).

Thus it was not merely a matter of luck that the arguments of the arccosines were smaller than unity in magnitude in Examples 1 and 2; it was guaranteed in advance by the Schwarz inequality (13).

PROPERTIES OF THE NORM

Since the norm is related to the dot product according to

$$\|\mathbf{u}\| = \sqrt{\mathbf{u}\cdot\mathbf{u}}, \tag{16}$$

the properties (12) of the dot product should imply certain corresponding properties of the norm. These properties are as follows:

1.

$$\|\alpha\mathbf{u}\| = |\alpha|\,\|\mathbf{u}\|. \tag{17a}$$

2. *Nonnegativeness*:

$$\begin{aligned} \|\mathbf{u}\| &> 0 \qquad \text{for all } \mathbf{u} \neq \mathbf{0} \\ &= 0 \qquad \text{for } \mathbf{u} = \mathbf{0}. \end{aligned} \tag{17b}$$

3. *Triangle inequality*:

$$\|\mathbf{u} + \mathbf{v}\| \leq \|\mathbf{u}\| + \|\mathbf{v}\|. \tag{17c}$$

For example, (17a) simply says that $\alpha\mathbf{u}$ is $|\alpha|$ times as long as $\mathbf{u}$; and for arrow representations of 2-tuples or 3-tuples the triangle inequality (17c) amounts to the Euclidean proposition that the length of any one side of a triangle cannot exceed the sum of the lengths of the other two sides (Fig. 2.15). Less obvious, however, is the fact that (17c) holds for n-tuples for n's > 3.

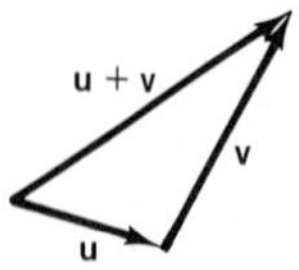

Fig. 2.15 Triangle inequality.

Let us prove only (17a) and (17c), since (17b) follows easily from (16) and (12b). First (17a):

$$\begin{aligned}
\|\alpha \mathbf{u}\| &= \sqrt{(\alpha \mathbf{u}) \cdot (\alpha \mathbf{u})} && \text{by (16)} \\
&= \sqrt{\alpha \mathbf{u} \cdot (\alpha \mathbf{u})} && \text{by (12c) with } \beta = 0 \text{ and } \mathbf{w} = \alpha \mathbf{u} \\
&= \sqrt{\alpha (\alpha \mathbf{u}) \cdot \mathbf{u}} && \text{by (12a)} \\
&= \sqrt{\alpha^2 \mathbf{u} \cdot \mathbf{u}} && \text{by (12c) with } \beta = 0 \text{ and } \mathbf{w} = \mathbf{u} \\
&= |\alpha| \sqrt{\mathbf{u} \cdot \mathbf{u}} = |\alpha| \|\mathbf{u}\|.
\end{aligned}$$

Turning to (17c), we find that

$$\begin{aligned}
\|\mathbf{u} + \mathbf{v}\|^2 &= (\mathbf{u} + \mathbf{v}) \cdot (\mathbf{u} + \mathbf{v}) \qquad \text{by (16)} \\
&= \mathbf{u} \cdot \mathbf{u} + \mathbf{v} \cdot \mathbf{u} + \mathbf{u} \cdot \mathbf{v} + \mathbf{v} \cdot \mathbf{v} \\
&= \|\mathbf{u}\|^2 + 2\mathbf{u} \cdot \mathbf{v} + \|\mathbf{v}\|^2, \\
\|\mathbf{u} + \mathbf{v}\|^2 &\le \|\mathbf{u}\|^2 + 2|\mathbf{u} \cdot \mathbf{v}| + \|\mathbf{v}\|^2, \\
\|\mathbf{u} + \mathbf{v}\|^2 &\le \|\mathbf{u}\|^2 + 2\|\mathbf{u}\|\|\mathbf{v}\| + \|\mathbf{v}\|^2 \qquad \text{by (13)} \\
&= (\|\mathbf{u}\| + \|\mathbf{v}\|)^2,
\end{aligned}$$

so that

$$\|\mathbf{u} + \mathbf{v}\| \le \|\mathbf{u}\| + \|\mathbf{v}\|,$$

as claimed. A key step was the use of the Schwarz inequality (13), but we also used the simple inequality $\mathbf{u} \cdot \mathbf{v} \le |\mathbf{u} \cdot \mathbf{v}|$, which holds since $\mathbf{u} \cdot \mathbf{v}$ is a (positive, zero, or negative) real number; i.e., if $\mathbf{u} \cdot \mathbf{v}$ is negative, then the $<$ holds, and if $\mathbf{u} \cdot \mathbf{v}$ is zero or positive, then the $=$ holds.

EXAMPLE 4 Let us verify the triangle inequality for a specific example, say the vectors $\mathbf{u} = (2, 1, 3, -1)$ and $\mathbf{v} = (0, 4, 2, 1)$. Then $\mathbf{u} + \mathbf{v} = (2, 5, 5, 0)$, so (17c) becomes

$$\sqrt{54} \le \sqrt{15} + \sqrt{21}$$

or $7.348 \le 3.873 + 4.583$, which *is* true. ◀

ORTHOGONALITY

If $\mathbf{u}$ and $\mathbf{v}$ are nonzero vectors such that $\mathbf{u} \cdot \mathbf{v} = 0$, then

$$\theta = \cos^{-1}\left(\frac{\mathbf{u} \cdot \mathbf{v}}{\|\mathbf{u}\|\|\mathbf{v}\|}\right) = \cos^{-1}\left(\frac{0}{\|\mathbf{u}\|\|\mathbf{v}\|}\right) = \cos^{-1}(0) = \frac{\pi}{2}, \tag{18}$$

and we say that $\mathbf{u}$ and $\mathbf{v}$ are *perpendicular*. [Here we have used the nonzeroness of $\mathbf{u}$ and $\mathbf{v}$ in the third equality in (18); if $\mathbf{u}$ and/or $\mathbf{v}$ *were* $\mathbf{0}$, we would have had $\cos^{-1}(0/\|\mathbf{u}\|\|\mathbf{v}\|) = \cos^{-1}(0/0)$, which is not defined.]

But to equate the condition $\mathbf{u} \cdot \mathbf{v} = 0$ to perpendicularity ($\theta = \pi/2$) would not be proper since $\mathbf{u} \cdot \mathbf{v}$ will also be zero in the event that $\mathbf{u}$ and/or $\mathbf{v}$ are $\mathbf{0}$, in which case θ is not defined. Let us therefore make a distinction between perpendicularity and "orthogonality." Specifically, we will say that $\mathbf{u}$ and $\mathbf{v}$ are **orthogonal** if and only if

$$\mathbf{u} \cdot \mathbf{v} = 0. \tag{19}$$

Only if $\mathbf{u}$ and $\mathbf{v}$ are both nonzero does orthogonality imply perpendicularity (i.e., $\theta = \pi/2$). Within this definition, we see that the zero vector, $\mathbf{0}$, is orthogonal to *every* vector, including itself (Exercise 14).

Finally, we say that a *set* of vectors, say $\{\mathbf{u}_1, \ldots, \mathbf{u}_k\}$, is an **orthogonal set** if every vector in the set is orthogonal to every other one:

$$\mathbf{u}_i \cdot \mathbf{u}_j = 0 \qquad \text{if } i \neq j. \tag{20}$$

EXAMPLE 5 $\mathbf{u}_1 = (2, 3, -1, 0)$, $\mathbf{u}_2 = (1, 2, 8, 3)$, $\mathbf{u}_3 = (9, -6, 0, 1)$ is an orthogonal set because $\mathbf{u}_1 \cdot \mathbf{u}_2 = \mathbf{u}_1 \cdot \mathbf{u}_3 = \mathbf{u}_2 \cdot \mathbf{u}_3 = 0$. ◀

EXAMPLE 6 $\mathbf{u}_1 = (1, 3)$, $\mathbf{u}_2 = (0, 0)$ is an orthogonal set since $\mathbf{u}_1 \cdot \mathbf{u}_2 = 0$. ◀

NORMALIZATION

If $\mathbf{u}$ is any nonzero vector, then $\mathbf{u}/\|\mathbf{u}\|$ is said to be its **normalized** version,* i.e., the vector is scaled so as to have unit length. That it does have unit length is easily verified:

$$\begin{aligned} \left\| \frac{1}{\|\mathbf{u}\|}\mathbf{u} \right\| &= \left| \frac{1}{\|\mathbf{u}\|} \right| \|\mathbf{u}\| && \text{by (17a)} \\ &= \frac{1}{\|\mathbf{u}\|}\|\mathbf{u}\| && \text{by (17b)} \\ &= 1. \end{aligned}$$

We will frequently use the notation

$$\frac{1}{\|\mathbf{u}\|}\mathbf{u} \equiv \hat{\mathbf{u}}, \tag{21}$$

where the caret indicates that $\mathbf{u}$ has been normalized. A vector of unit length is called a **unit vector.**

EXAMPLE 7 If $\mathbf{u} = (1, -1, 0, 2)$, say, then $\|\mathbf{u}\| = \sqrt{6}$, so

$$\hat{\mathbf{u}} = \frac{1}{\sqrt{6}}(1, -1, 0, 2) = \left(\frac{1}{\sqrt{6}}, -\frac{1}{\sqrt{6}}, 0, \frac{2}{\sqrt{6}}\right). \quad ◀$$

* By $\mathbf{u}/\|\mathbf{u}\|$ we mean the scalar multiplication of $\mathbf{u}$ by $1/\|\mathbf{u}\|$.

1. Given the following vectors $\mathbf{u}$ and $\mathbf{v}$, determine $\|\mathbf{u}\|$, $\|\mathbf{v}\|$ and θ (in radians and degrees). If $\mathbf{u}$ and $\mathbf{v}$ are orthogonal, state that.

*(a) $\mathbf{u} = (4, 3)$, $\mathbf{v} = (2, -1)$
(b) $\mathbf{u} = (1, 2, 3, 4)$, $\mathbf{v} = (-4, -3, -2, -1)$
(c) $\mathbf{u} = (3, 0, 1)$, $\mathbf{v} = (-2, 3, 6)$
(d) $\mathbf{u} = (2, 2, 2)$, $\mathbf{v} = (-4, -4, -4)$
(e) $\mathbf{u} = (2, 5)$, $\mathbf{v} = (10, -4)$
(f) $\mathbf{u} = (1, 2, 3, 4)$, $\mathbf{v} = (4, 3, 2, 1)$
*(g) $\mathbf{u} = (3, 2, 0, -1, 1)$, $\mathbf{v} = (-5, 0, 0, 2, 4)$

2. State whether or not each of the following expressions is defined.

(a) $\|\mathbf{u}\|\mathbf{u}$
(b) $\mathbf{u}\cdot(\mathbf{v}\cdot\mathbf{w})$
(c) $\|(\mathbf{u}\cdot\mathbf{v})\mathbf{v}\|$
(d) $(\mathbf{u}+\mathbf{v})\cdot\mathbf{w}$
(e) $(\mathbf{u}+\mathbf{v})\cdot(\mathbf{u}-\mathbf{v})$
(f) $\mathbf{u}+6(\mathbf{v}\cdot\mathbf{w})$
(g) $\cos^{-1}(2\mathbf{u}+\mathbf{v})$
(h) $\mathbf{u}/\|\mathbf{u}\|^2$
(i) $(7\mathbf{u})\cdot(2\mathbf{u})$
(j) $\|\mathbf{u}+3\mathbf{u}^2\|$

3. Let us denote, as points in 2- and 3-space, $A = (2, 0)$, $B = (3, -1)$, $C = (5, 0)$, $D = (4, 2)$, $E = (2, 2)$, $F = (1, 3, -2)$, $G = (2, 0, 4)$, $H = (5, 4, 3)$, $I = (-3, -1, 0)$, $J = (0, 0, 0)$. Determine, by vector methods, all interior angles and their sum, in degrees, for each of the following polygons.

(a) *ABCA*
(b) *ABCDA*
*(c) *ABCDEA*
(d) *BCDB*
(e) *BCDEB*
(f) *FGHF*
(g) *FGIF*
(h) *GHIG*
(i) *FGJF*
(j) *GHJG*
(k) *HIJH*
(l) *FIJF*

4. (a)–(g) Normalize each pair of $\mathbf{u}$, $\mathbf{v}$ vectors in Exercise 1; i.e., obtain $\hat{\mathbf{u}}$ and $\hat{\mathbf{v}}$.

5. If vectors $\mathbf{A}$, $\mathbf{B}$, $\mathbf{C}$, represented as arrows, form a triangle such that $\mathbf{A} = \mathbf{B} + \mathbf{C}$, derive the *law of cosines* $C^2 = A^2 + B^2 - 2AB\cos\alpha$, where α is the interior angle between $\mathbf{A}$ and $\mathbf{B}$, and where A, B, C are the lengths of $\mathbf{A}$, $\mathbf{B}$, $\mathbf{C}$, respectively, by starting with the identity $\mathbf{C}\cdot\mathbf{C} = (\mathbf{A}-\mathbf{B})\cdot(\mathbf{A}-\mathbf{B})$.

6. (*Orthogonalization*) In each of the following, find scalars α, β, γ and vectors $\mathbf{u}_1$, $\mathbf{u}_2$, $\mathbf{u}_3$, such that $\mathbf{u}_1 = \mathbf{u}$, $\mathbf{u}_2 = \mathbf{u} + \alpha\mathbf{v}$, $\mathbf{u}_3 = \mathbf{u} + \beta\mathbf{v} + \gamma\mathbf{w}$ is a nonzero orthogonal set, i.e., $\mathbf{u}_1\cdot\mathbf{u}_2 = 0$, $\mathbf{u}_1\cdot\mathbf{u}_3 = 0$, and $\mathbf{u}_2\cdot\mathbf{u}_3 = 0$, where $\mathbf{u}_1, \mathbf{u}_2, \mathbf{u}_3 \neq \mathbf{0}$. If this is *not* possible, state that.

*(a) $\mathbf{u} = (1, 3, 0)$, $\mathbf{v} = (2, 3, 0)$, $\mathbf{w} = (2, 1, -3)$
(b) $\mathbf{u} = (2, 0, -1)$, $\mathbf{v} = (1, 2, 3)$, $\mathbf{w} = (3, -2, -5)$
(c) $\mathbf{u} = (1, 0, 0)$, $\mathbf{v} = (2, 1, 0)$, $\mathbf{w} = (3, 2, -1)$
(d) $\mathbf{u} = (1, 2, 0, 1)$, $\mathbf{v} = (1, 0, 1, 1)$, $\mathbf{w} = (2, -1, 1, 1)$
(e) $\mathbf{u} = (1, 0, 0, 0)$, $\mathbf{v} = (1, 1, 0, 0)$, $\mathbf{w} = (1, 1, 1, 0)$
(f) $\mathbf{u} = (1, -1, 1, -1)$, $\mathbf{v} = (1, 2, 0, 1)$, $\mathbf{w} = (0, 2, 1, 0)$
(g) $\mathbf{u} = (1, 2)$, $\mathbf{v} = (0, 2)$, $\mathbf{w} = (1, -1)$
(h) $\mathbf{u} = (3, 0)$, $\mathbf{v} = (1, 1)$, $\mathbf{w} = (-1, 2)$

7. If $\mathbf{u} = (1, 3, -4, 2)$ and $\mathbf{v} = (2, 0, 0, 3)$, evaluate the following.

*(a) $\|\mathbf{u}-\mathbf{v}\|$
(b) $\|3\mathbf{u}-2\mathbf{v}\| + \|-\mathbf{v}\|$
(c) $\left\|\dfrac{1}{\|\mathbf{u}\|}\mathbf{u}\right\|$
(d) $\|\mathbf{u}\| + \|\mathbf{v}\|$

8. Derive the following identities.

(a) $\|\mathbf{u}+\mathbf{v}\|^2 + \|\mathbf{u}-\mathbf{v}\|^2 = 2\|\mathbf{u}\|^2 + 2\|\mathbf{v}\|^2$
(b) $\|\mathbf{u}+\mathbf{v}\|^2 - \|\mathbf{u}-\mathbf{v}\|^2 = 4\mathbf{u}\cdot\mathbf{v}$
(c) Verify parts (a) and (b) for the case $\mathbf{u} = (2, 0, 1, 1,)$ and $\mathbf{v} = (1, -3, 0, 2)$.

9. Find all vectors (if any) orthogonal to the following vectors.

*(a) $(3, 0, -1)$
(b) $(2, 1, 1)$ and $(1, 2, 3)$
(c) $(1, 1, 0, -1)$
(d) $(1, 3, 4, 0)$ and $(2, -1, 0, 5)$
(e) $(6, -1, 2, 2)$, $(1, 4, 3, 0)$, and $(4, -9, -4, 2)$
(f) $(6, -1, 2, 2)$, $(1, 4, 3, 0)$, and $(4, -5, -4, 2)$
(g) $(1, -2, 0)$, $(2, 3, 1)$, and $(7, 0, 2)$
(h) $(2, 1, -1)$, $(1, 1, 1)$, and $(3, 2, 1)$

10. (*Orthogonal separation*) It is often desired to separate a given nonzero vector $\mathbf{u}$ into the sum of two orthogonal vectors, one parallel and one perpendicular to some other nonzero vector $\mathbf{v}$, as sketched in part (a) of the accompanying figure. That is, $\mathbf{u} = \mathbf{u}_1 + \mathbf{u}_2$, where $\mathbf{u}_1$ is of the form $\alpha\mathbf{v}$, and $\mathbf{u}_2\cdot\mathbf{u}_1 = 0$. We call $\mathbf{u}_1$ the *orthogonal projection of* **u** *on* **v**, and we call $\mathbf{u}_2$ the *component of* **u** *orthogonal to* **v**. (Clearly, the separation is not uniquely determined by $\mathbf{u}$ alone; see, for example, the two different separations of $\mathbf{u}$ sketched here. But evidently it *is* unique once $\mathbf{v}$ is specified.)

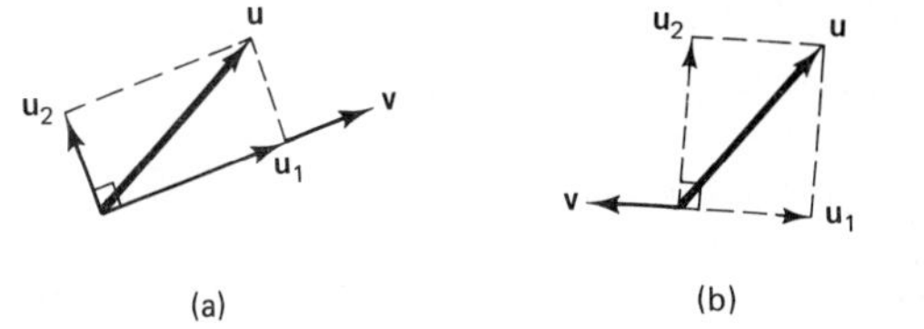

(a) Show that $\mathbf{u}_1$ and $\mathbf{u}_2$ can be found, in terms of $\mathbf{u}$ and $\mathbf{v}$, as

$$\mathbf{u}_1 = (\mathbf{u} \cdot \hat{\mathbf{v}})\hat{\mathbf{v}} \qquad \text{where} \quad \hat{\mathbf{v}} = \mathbf{v}/\|\mathbf{v}\|, \qquad \text{(a)}$$
$$\mathbf{u}_2 = \mathbf{u} - \mathbf{u}_1.$$

Is (a) valid only for 2- and 3-space (as in the sketch), or does it hold, without modification, for n-space as well?

(b) Use equations (a) to carry out the separation for the cases $\mathbf{u} = (1, 3)$, $\mathbf{v} = (2, 4)$ and $\mathbf{u} = (1, 3)$, $\mathbf{v} = (-1, -2)$. Interpret graphically.
*(c) Use equations (a) to carry out the separation for $\mathbf{u} = (2, 3, 1)$, $\mathbf{v} = (0, 2, 3)$.
(d) Repeat part (c), for $\mathbf{u} = (1, 2, -1)$, $\mathbf{v} = (3, -1, 1)$.
(e) Repeat part (c), for $\mathbf{u} = (3, 0, 5, 6)$, $\mathbf{v} = (1, -2, 0, 4)$.
(f) Repeat part (c), for $\mathbf{u} = (2, 1, 0, 0, 3)$, $\mathbf{v} = (0, 0, 1, -2, 1)$.

11. (a) Prove the associative property $(\alpha\mathbf{u}) \cdot \mathbf{v} = \alpha(\mathbf{u} \cdot \mathbf{v})$.
(b) Prove the distributive property $(\mathbf{u} + \mathbf{v}) \cdot \mathbf{w} = \mathbf{u} \cdot \mathbf{w} + \mathbf{v} \cdot \mathbf{w}$.
(c) Prove that the linearity property (12c) is equivalent to the *two* properties given in parts (a) and (b).

12. (*Direction cosines*) The **direction cosines** of a vector $\mathbf{u} = (u_1, u_2, u_3)$ in 3-space are defined as $l_1 \equiv \cos\alpha$, $l_2 \equiv \cos\beta$, $l_3 \equiv \cos\gamma$, where α, β, γ are the angles between $\mathbf{u}$ and the positive coordinate axes, as shown.

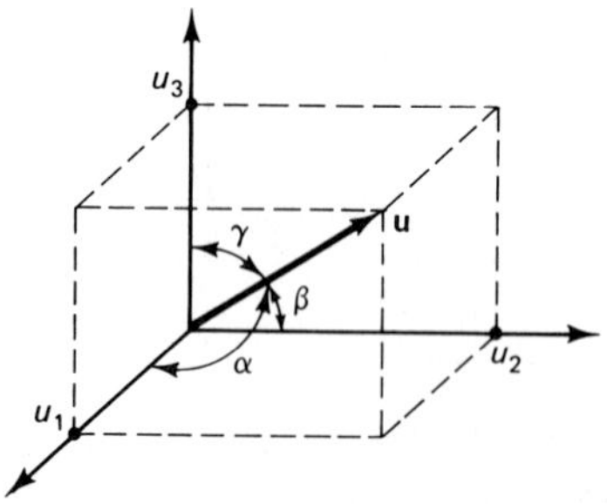

(a) Obtain general expressions for l_1, l_2, l_3 in terms of the components u_1, u_2, u_3.
*(b) Evaluate l_1, l_2, l_3 for $\mathbf{u} = (2, -1, 5)$.
(c) Evaluate l_1, l_2, l_3 for $\mathbf{u} = (2, -4, 1)$.
(d) Evaluate l_1, l_2, l_3 for $\mathbf{u} = (4, 0, -3)$.
(e) Show that $l_1^2 + l_2^2 + l_3^2 = 1$.

13. If $\mathbf{u} \cdot \mathbf{v} = 0$ and $\mathbf{v} \cdot \mathbf{w} = 0$, does that imply that $\mathbf{u} \cdot \mathbf{w} = 0$? Prove or disprove. *Hint:* If a claim is true, it needs to be proved in general, i.e., for all possible cases. But if it is false, it can be disproved merely by putting forward a single counterexample.

14. Determine whether or not each set of vectors is orthogonal.
*(a) (1, 3), (−6, 2), (0, 0)
(b) (2, 3, 0), (−3, 2, 1), (1, 1, 1), (1, −3, 1)
(c) (1, 0, 0, 0), (0, 1, 0, 0), (0, 0, 1, 0), (0, 0, 0, 1)
(d) (1, 1, 1, 1), (1, −1, 1, −1), (0, 1, 0, −1), (2, 0, −2, 0)
(e) (2, 1, −1, 1), (1, 1, 3, 0), (1, −1, 0, −1), (2, 1, 1, 1)

15. Determine a unit vector along the line of intersection of the following two planes in $\mathbb{R}^3$. *Note: Do not use "cross products," since this topic has not yet been discussed here.*

*(a) $x_1 + 2x_2 - x_3 = 8$
$x_1 - x_2 + x_3 = 0$
(b) $x_1 + 4x_2 = 0$
$x_1 - x_2 + 2x_3 = 0$
(c) $x_1 - x_2 - 5x_3 = 0$
$x_2 + 4x_3 = 6$
(d) $2x_1 + x_3 = 1$
$x_1 + 4x_2 = 1$
(e) $x_1 - 5x_2 + x_3 = 4$
$2x_1 - x_2 - x_3 = 3$
(f) $x_1 + x_2 + 12x_3 = 0$
$x_1 + 2x_2 + 12x_3 = 5$

2.6 GENERALIZED VECTOR SPACE

Looking back at our generalization to n-space it is natural to wonder if further generalization is possible. The answer is yes, and the idea is as follows. In preceding sections we introduced the vectors and arithmetic rules for their manipulation, and *then* derived the various properties, such as $\mathbf{u} + \mathbf{v} = \mathbf{v} + \mathbf{u}$, $\mathbf{u} + \mathbf{0} = \mathbf{u}$, $\alpha(\beta\mathbf{u}) = (\alpha\beta)\mathbf{u}$, and so on. In generalizing, the essential idea is to reverse the cart and the horse. Specifically, we elevate the derived properties to axioms, or requirements, and regard the vectors as "objects," the nature of which is not restricted in advance. They may be chosen to be n-tuples, or whatever; all that we ask is that a + operation, a zero vector, a negative inverse, and scalar multiplication be defined such that all of the vector space axioms are satisfied. Thus:

***Definition 1** Vector Space*

We call a (nonempty) set $\mathscr{S}$ of "objects," which shall be denoted by boldface type and referred to as *vectors,* a **vector space** if the following requirements are met:

(i) An operation, which will be called vector *addition* and denoted as +, is defined between any two vectors in $\mathscr{S}$ in such a way that if **u** and **v** are in $\mathscr{S}$, then **u** + **v** is, too (i.e., $\mathscr{S}$ is *closed under addition*). Furthermore,

$$\mathbf{u} + \mathbf{v} = \mathbf{v} + \mathbf{u} \qquad (commutativity) \tag{1}$$

$$(\mathbf{u} + \mathbf{v}) + \mathbf{w} = \mathbf{u} + (\mathbf{v} + \mathbf{w}) \qquad (associativity) \tag{2}$$

(ii) $\mathscr{S}$ contains a unique *zero vector* **0** such that

$$\mathbf{u} + \mathbf{0} = \mathbf{u} \tag{3}$$

for each **u** in $\mathscr{S}$.

(iii) For each **u** in $\mathscr{S}$ there is a unique vector "−**u**" in $\mathscr{S}$, called the *negative of* **u**, such that

$$\mathbf{u} + (-\mathbf{u}) = \mathbf{0}. \tag{4}$$

We denote $\mathbf{u} + (-\mathbf{v})$ as $\mathbf{u} - \mathbf{v}$ for brevity, but emphasize that it is actually the + operation between **u** and −**v**.

(iv) Another operation, called *scalar multiplication,* is defined such that if **u** is any vector in $\mathscr{S}$ and α is any scalar,* then the scalar multiple $\alpha\mathbf{u}$ is in $\mathscr{S}$, too (i.e., $\mathscr{S}$ is *closed under scalar multiplication*). Further, we require that

$$\alpha(\beta\mathbf{u}) = (\alpha\beta)\mathbf{u}, \qquad (associativity) \tag{5}$$

$$(\alpha + \beta)\mathbf{u} = \alpha\mathbf{u} + \beta\mathbf{u}, \qquad (distributivity) \tag{6}$$

$$\alpha(\mathbf{u} + \mathbf{v}) = \alpha\mathbf{u} + \alpha\mathbf{v}, \qquad (distributivity) \tag{7}$$

$$1\mathbf{u} = \mathbf{u}, \tag{8}$$

if the vectors **u**, **v** are in $\mathscr{S}$, and α, β are scalars.

Observe that if we write $\mathbf{u} + \mathbf{v} + \mathbf{w}$, it is not clear whether we mean $(\mathbf{u} + \mathbf{v}) + \mathbf{w}$ (i.e., first add **u** and **v**, and then add the result to **w**) or $\mathbf{u} + (\mathbf{v} + \mathbf{w})$. However, the associative property (2) guarantees that it does not matter, so the parentheses can be omitted without ambiguity. Similarly, $\alpha\beta\mathbf{u}$ is unambiguous by virtue of (5).

EXAMPLE 1 $\mathbb{R}^n$*-Space*. Certainly, the *n-space* $\mathbb{R}^n$, defined earlier, does constitute a vector space since, as noted above, the vector space axioms listed above were,

* We continue to restrict all scalars to be (finite) *real* numbers; hence we describe the vector space as a **real vector space.** The complex case is introduced later, in Chapter 5.

after all, extracted from Section 2.4 (on n-tuples). But let us perturb things a bit to better appreciate the role of the axioms.

Suppose that we chose to define the addition of n-tuples according to

$$\mathbf{u} + \mathbf{v} \equiv (u_1 + 2v_1, u_2 + 2v_2, \ldots, u_n + 2v_n), \tag{9}$$

instead of $\mathbf{u} + \mathbf{v} \equiv (u_1 + v_1, u_2 + v_2, \ldots, u_n + v_n)$. Would we still have a vector space? Well, according to (9),

$$\mathbf{v} + \mathbf{u} = (v_1 + 2u_1, v_2 + 2u_2, \ldots, v_n + 2u_n). \tag{10}$$

Thus axiom (1), that $\mathbf{u} + \mathbf{v} = \mathbf{v} + \mathbf{u}$, holds only in the event that $u_j + 2v_j = v_j + 2u_j$ for each $j = 1, \ldots, n$, i.e., only if $u_j = v_j$ or, in other words, only if $\mathbf{u} = \mathbf{v}$. Since (1) does not hold for *all* possible $\mathbf{u}$'s and $\mathbf{v}$'s, we conclude that we would *not* have a vector space if we adopted the definition (9). [Are any other axioms, besides (1), violated by (9)? See Exercise 2.] ◀

$\mathbb{R}^n$ is but one example of a vector space. Many other useful spaces can be introduced by using objects other than n-tuples as the vectors. For example, the vectors may be functions, matrices, kumquats, or whatever, provided that addition, a zero vector, a negative inverse, and scalar multiplication are defined such that all of the vector space axioms are satisfied. For nowhere, in Definition 1, is the *nature* of the vectors specified or in any way restricted.

We choose not to discuss other such spaces here, because $\mathbb{R}^n$ is all that we will need in Part I. However, *function space* (i.e., vector space in which the vectors are functions) will be used in Part III, when we develop the important subject of Fourier series.

Let us close this section by noting three useful vector properties.

> ***Theorem 1*** *Properties of Scalar Multiplication*
> If $\mathbf{u}$ is any vector in a vector space $\mathcal{S}$ and α is any scalar, then
>
> $$0\mathbf{u} = \mathbf{0}, \tag{11}$$
>
> $$(-1)\mathbf{u} = -\mathbf{u}, \tag{12}$$
>
> $$\alpha\mathbf{0} = \mathbf{0}. \tag{13}$$

Proof These results follow from our definition of vector space. To prove the first, one line of approach is as follows:

$$\begin{aligned} 0\mathbf{u} + \mathbf{u} &= 0\mathbf{u} + 1\mathbf{u} && \text{by (8)} \\ &= (0 + 1)\mathbf{u} && \text{by (6)} \\ &= 1\mathbf{u} \\ &= \mathbf{u} && \text{by (8).} \end{aligned}$$

Then

$$0\mathbf{u} + \mathbf{u} + (-\mathbf{u}) = \mathbf{u} + (-\mathbf{u})$$

$$0\mathbf{u} + \mathbf{0} = \mathbf{0} \qquad \text{by (4),}$$
$$0\mathbf{u} = \mathbf{0} \qquad \text{by (3).}$$

The remaining two, (12) and (13), are left for the exercises. ■

We do appreciate that you may be tempted to deny any *need* for proving such assertions as (11) to (13), since they seem to be so obvious. But appearing to be obvious is not always the same as being true. In any event, such practice will be helpful in acquiring a working understanding of the axiomatic nature of vector space.

One final comment: Observe that in Definition 1 there is no mention of a dot product or a norm. In fact, a vector space $\mathcal{S}$ *need not have* a dot product or a norm defined for it. If we do define a norm for $\mathcal{S}$, we say that $\mathcal{S}$ is a *normed vector space*. How is the norm to be defined? Any way that is convenient, provided that it satisfies properties 1 to 3 on page 32. (Do you recall our comment on reversing the cart and the horse in the opening paragraph of this section? Well, properties 1 to 3 were derived as *properties* for the Euclidean norm that we defined for n-space. In defining generalized vector space we now take those properties and elevate them to axioms, or requirements.) For example, Struble,* in working with n-space, finds the *taxicab norm* (Exercise 6)†

$$\|\mathbf{u}\| = |u_1| + |u_2| + \cdots + |u_n| \tag{14}$$

algebraically simpler to use than the Euclidean norm, and furthermore, he defines no dot product whatsoever.

If we do define a dot product (also called an *inner product*) for $\mathcal{S}$, we say that $\mathcal{S}$ is an *inner product space,* and the dot product needs to satisfy requirements 1 to 3 on page 31. If we define both a dot product *and* a norm, we say that $\mathcal{S}$ is a *normed inner product space*. In doing so, suppose that we first define a dot product (in accordance with the requirements on page 31). In selecting a convenient norm we can either derive our norm from the already defined dot product as $\|\mathbf{u}\| \equiv \sqrt{\mathbf{u}\cdot\mathbf{u}}$, which is called the *natural norm,* or we can introduce the norm independently, satisfying the requirements on page 32. For example, if we choose the Euclidean dot product $\mathbf{u}\cdot\mathbf{v} = u_1v_1 + \cdots + u_nv_n$, for $\mathbb{R}^n$, we may use the natural norm $\|\mathbf{u}\| = \sqrt{\mathbf{u}\cdot\mathbf{u}} = (\sum_{j=1}^n u_j^2)^{1/2}$ or we may use a different norm, such as the taxicab norm (14).

2.6 EXERCISES

1. Recall that $\mathbb{R}^n$ is the vector space ("real" vector space since all scalars are to be real numbers) in which the vectors are n-tuples $\mathbf{u} = (u_1, \ldots, u_n)$, with the definitions

$$\mathbf{u} + \mathbf{v} = (u_1, \ldots, u_n) + (v_1, \ldots, v_n)$$
$$\equiv (u_1 + v_1, \ldots, u_n + v_n), \tag{a}$$
$$\mathbf{0} \equiv (0, \ldots, 0), \tag{b}$$
$$-\mathbf{u} \equiv (-u_1, \ldots, -u_n), \tag{c}$$
$$\alpha\mathbf{u} \equiv (\alpha u_1, \ldots, \alpha u_n). \tag{d}$$

*R. A. Struble, *Nonlinear Differential Equations* (New York: McGraw-Hill, 1962).

†The name *taxicab norm,* adopted by Struble, is apt, inasmuch as a cab driver judges the distance from the corner of 2nd Avenue and 34th Street to the corner of 5th Avenue and 36th Street to be 5 blocks, not $\sqrt{13}$ blocks.

If we make the following modifications, do we still have a vector space? If not, specify all requirements, within Definition 1, that fail to be met.

*(a) definition (d) changed to $\alpha\mathbf{u} \equiv (\alpha^2 u_1, \ldots, \alpha^2 u_n)$
*(b) only vectors of the form $\mathbf{u} = (u, u, \ldots, u)$ admitted, where $-\infty < u < \infty$
(c) only vectors of the form $\mathbf{u} = (u, 2u, 3u, \ldots, nu)$ admitted, where $-\infty < u < \infty$
(d) definition (a) changed to $\mathbf{u} + \mathbf{v} \equiv (u_1 - v_1, \ldots, u_n - v_n)$
(e) definition (a) changed to $\mathbf{u} + \mathbf{v} \equiv (v_1 + u_1, \ldots, v_n + u_n)$
(f) definition (a) changed to $\mathbf{u} + \mathbf{v} = (0, \ldots, 0)$ (for all $\mathbf{u}$, $\mathbf{v}$)
(g) only the vector $(0, 0, \ldots, 0)$ admitted (This is an example of a **zero vector space,** i.e., a vector space containing but a single vector, the zero vector.)

***2.** We noted, in Example 1, that definition (9) of vector addition violates axiom (1). Does it violate any other axioms as well? Explain.

3. Prove (12), namely, that $(-1)\mathbf{u} = -\mathbf{u}$.

4. Prove (13), namely, that $\alpha\mathbf{0} = \mathbf{0}$.

5. Prove that if $\alpha\mathbf{u} = \mathbf{0}$, then $\alpha = 0$ and/or $\mathbf{u} = \mathbf{0}$.

6. Verify that the taxicab norm (14) satisfies requirements 1 to 3 on page 32.

7. (a) Does the choice $\|\mathbf{u}\| = \max_{1 \le j \le n} |u_j|$, for $\mathbb{R}^n$, satisfy requirements 1 to 3 on page 32?
(b) How about $\|\mathbf{u}\| = \min_{1 \le j \le n} |u_j|$?

8. Show that if we define a legitimate dot product $\mathbf{u} \cdot \mathbf{v}$ for $\mathscr{S}$ (i.e., satisfying 1 to 3 on page 31), the natural norm $\|\mathbf{u}\| = \sqrt{\mathbf{u} \cdot \mathbf{u}}$ will automatically be a legitimate norm (i.e., it will satisfy 1 to 3 on page 32).

9. Let $\mathscr{S}$ be the set of real-valued polynomial functions, of degree n, defined on $a \le x \le b$. If $\mathbf{f} = a_0 + a_1 x + \cdots + a_n x^n$ and $\mathbf{g} = b_0 + b_1 x + \cdots + b_n x^n$ are any two such functions, and α is any (real) scalar, define the sum $\mathbf{f} + \mathbf{g}$ and the scalar multiple $\alpha\mathbf{f}$ as

$$(\mathbf{f} + \mathbf{g})(x) = (a_0 + b_0) + (a_1 + b_1)x + \cdots + (a_n + b_n)x^n,$$

$$(\alpha\mathbf{f})(x) = \alpha a_0 + \alpha a_1 x + \cdots + \alpha a_n x^n,$$

respectively. Show that $\mathscr{S}$ is a vector space.

2.7 SUBSPACE AND SPAN

Here we begin a sequence of closely related ideas: span, linear dependence, basis, and dimension. The ideas, definitions, and theorems will hold for *any* vector space, but our illustrative examples will be restricted to the n-space $\mathbb{R}^n$, this being the vector space of interest in Part I.

We begin with the idea of the "span" of a set of vectors.

> ***Definition 1** Span*
>
> If $\mathbf{u}_1, \mathbf{u}_2, \ldots, \mathbf{u}_k$ are vectors in some vector space $\mathscr{S}$, then the set of all linear combinations of these vectors, i.e., all vectors of the form
>
> $$\mathbf{u} = \alpha_1\mathbf{u}_1 + \alpha_2\mathbf{u}_2 + \cdots + \alpha_k\mathbf{u}_k, \tag{1}$$
>
> where $\alpha_1, \ldots, \alpha_k$ are arbitrary scalars, is called the **span** of $\mathbf{u}_1, \mathbf{u}_2, \ldots, \mathbf{u}_k$, and is denoted as*
>
> $$\text{span}\,\{\mathbf{u}_1, \ldots, \mathbf{u}_k\}.$$

Let us illustrate with some vector sets in $\mathbb{R}^n$ for $n \le 3$, since for $n \le 3$ we will

*Other common notations for the span of $\mathbf{u}_1, \ldots, \mathbf{u}_k$ include "lin$\{\mathbf{u}_1, \ldots, \mathbf{u}_k\}$" and "sp$\{\mathbf{u}_1, \ldots, \mathbf{u}_k\}$."

be able to support the discussion with pictures, i.e., diagrams of the arrow vector representations of the n-tuple vectors.

EXAMPLE 1 Consider the single vector

$$\mathbf{u}_1 = (4, 2) \tag{2}$$

in $\mathbb{R}^2$. Then span$\{\mathbf{u}_1\}$ is the set of all vectors that are scalar multiples of $\mathbf{u}_1$. Hence span$\{\mathbf{u}_1\}$ is the set of all vectors on the line L in Fig. 2.16, such as $\mathbf{u} = 2\mathbf{u}_1 = (8, 4)$, $\mathbf{v} = -\frac{1}{2}\mathbf{u}_1 = (-2, -1)$, and $\mathbf{0} = 0\mathbf{u}_1 = (0, 0)$. We say that $\mathbf{u}_1$ *generates* the line L. ◀

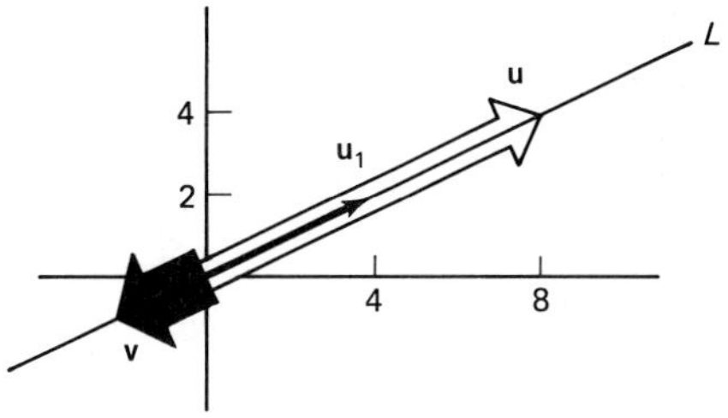

Fig. 2.16 Span $\{\mathbf{u}_1\}$.

EXAMPLE 2 Observe that if

$$\mathbf{u}_1 = (4, 2), \qquad \mathbf{u}_2 = (-2 -1), \tag{3}$$

then span$\{\mathbf{u}_1, \mathbf{u}_2\}$ is the same as in Example 1, namely, all vectors on the line L, for both $\mathbf{u}_1$ and $\mathbf{u}_2$ lie along L, and so surely any linear combination of them, $\alpha_1\mathbf{u}_1 + \alpha_2\mathbf{u}_2$, does too. Unlike Example 1, however, this time it turns out that the representation (1) is not *uniquely* determined. For example, the vector $\mathbf{u} = (8, 4)$ can be expressed as $\mathbf{u} = 2\mathbf{u}_1$, $\mathbf{u} = -4\mathbf{u}_2$, $\mathbf{u} = \mathbf{u}_1 - 2\mathbf{u}_2$, and so on. [In fact, it is easily verified that $\mathbf{u} = (\alpha + 2)\mathbf{u}_1 + 2\alpha\mathbf{u}_2$ for *any* α.] ◀

It happened, in Examples 1 and 2, that the span was only a small subset of the given space $\mathbb{R}^2$, namely the subset consisting of all vectors lying on L. Observe carefully that that subset of $\mathbb{R}^2$ is itself a vector space, a so-called "subspace" of $\mathbb{R}^2$. For if $\mathbf{u}$ and $\mathbf{v}$ are any two vectors on L, then $\mathbf{u} + \mathbf{v}$ is on L, too, so the set *is* closed under addition; similarly, if $\mathbf{u}$ is on L, so is $\alpha\mathbf{u}$, for any scalar α, so the set *is* closed under scalar multiplication; L *does* contain the zero vector [since we can set all the α's in (1) equal to zero]; and for each $\mathbf{u}$ on L there is a (unique) vector $-\mathbf{u}$ on L such that $\mathbf{u} + (-\mathbf{u}) = \mathbf{0}$.

> ***Definition 2*** *Subspace*
> If a subset $\mathcal{T}$ of a vector space $\mathcal{S}$ is itself a vector space (under the same rules of addition and scalar multiplication as $\mathcal{S}$), then $\mathcal{T}$ is a **subspace** of $\mathcal{S}$.

> ***Theorem 1*** *Span as a Subspace*
> If $\mathbf{u}_1, \ldots, \mathbf{u}_k$ are vectors in a vector space $\mathcal{S}$, then span$\{\mathbf{u}_1, \ldots, \mathbf{u}_k\}$ is itself a vector space, a subspace of $\mathcal{S}$.

Thus we say that the line L (i.e., the set of all vectors lying on L), in Fig. 2.16, is a subspace of $\mathbb{R}^2$. (The proof of Theorem 1 is left for the exercises.)

EXAMPLE 3 Let

$$\mathbf{u}_1 = (5, 1), \qquad \mathbf{u}_2 = (1, 3). \tag{4}$$

To determine the extent of span $\{\mathbf{u}_1, \mathbf{u}_2\}$, let $\mathbf{v} = (v_1, v_2)$ be any given vector in $\mathbb{R}^2$, and try to express

$$\mathbf{v} = \alpha_1 \mathbf{u}_1 + \alpha_2 \mathbf{u}_2. \tag{5}$$

That is,

$$\begin{aligned}(v_1, v_2) &= \alpha_1(5, 1) + \alpha_2(1, 3)\\ &= (5\alpha_1, \alpha_1) + (\alpha_2, 3\alpha_2)\\ &= (5\alpha_1 + \alpha_2, \alpha_1 + 3\alpha_2).\end{aligned} \tag{6}$$

Equating components, we obtain the linear equations

$$\begin{aligned}5\alpha_1 + \alpha_2 &= v_1\\ \alpha_1 + 3\alpha_2 &= v_2\end{aligned} \tag{7}$$

in α_1, α_2. Applying Gauss elimination, (7) becomes

$$\begin{aligned}\alpha_1 + \tfrac{1}{5}\alpha_2 &= \tfrac{1}{5}v_1\\ \alpha_2 &= \tfrac{5}{14}v_2 - \tfrac{1}{14}v_1.\end{aligned} \tag{8}$$

Now, it is clear from the Gauss-reduced form (8) that the system is *consistent* (solvable for α_1, α_2) for *every* vector $\mathbf{v}$ in $\mathbb{R}^2$. Hence we may conclude that span $\{\mathbf{u}_1, \mathbf{u}_2\}$ is all of $\mathbb{R}^2$; we say that $\{\mathbf{u}_1, \mathbf{u}_2\}$ spans $\mathbb{R}^2$. (Here we use "span" as a verb.)

Thus, every $\mathbf{v}$ in $\mathbb{R}^2$ can be expressed as a linear combination of $\mathbf{u}_1$ and $\mathbf{u}_2$. As representative, let $\mathbf{v} = (6, -4)$, i.e., $v_1 = 6$ and $v_2 = -4$. Then (8) gives $\alpha_2 = -\frac{13}{7}$ and $\alpha_1 = \frac{11}{7}$, so that (5) becomes

$$\mathbf{v} = \tfrac{11}{7}\mathbf{u}_1 - \tfrac{13}{7}\mathbf{u}_2. \tag{9}$$

To see this in graphical terms, observe, from Fig. 2.17, that $\mathbf{v} = \mathbf{OA} + \mathbf{OB}$, where (with the aid of a scale) $\mathbf{OA} \approx 1.6\mathbf{u}_1$ and $\mathbf{OB} \approx -1.9\mathbf{u}_2$. Thus $\mathbf{v} \approx 1.6\mathbf{u}_1 - 1.9\mathbf{u}_2$, in agreement with (9).

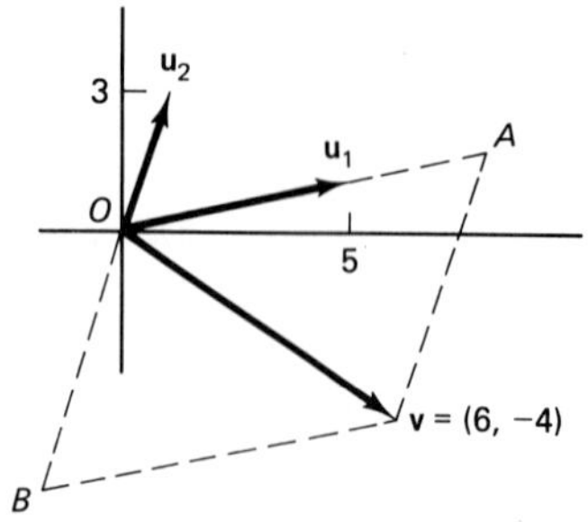

Fig. 2.17 Representation of **v**.

COMMENT Suppose that we add $\mathbf{u}_3 = (2, 2)$ to the set. It should be evident that $\text{span}\{\mathbf{u}_1, \mathbf{u}_2, \mathbf{u}_3\}$ is all of $\mathbb{R}^2$, again, since $\{\mathbf{u}_1, \mathbf{u}_2\}$ spanned $\mathbb{R}^2$ even "without any help" from $\mathbf{u}_3$. But in case this is not clear, let us go through steps analogous to steps (5) to (8):

$$\mathbf{v} = \alpha_1 \mathbf{u}_1 + \alpha_2 \mathbf{u}_2 + \alpha_3 \mathbf{u}_3, \tag{10}$$

so $(v_1, v_2) = (5\alpha_1 + \alpha_2 + 2\alpha_3, \alpha_1 + 3\alpha_2 + 2\alpha_3)$. Thus

$$\begin{aligned} 5\alpha_1 + \alpha_2 + 2\alpha_3 &= v_1 \\ \alpha_1 + 3\alpha_2 + 2\alpha_3 &= v_2, \end{aligned}$$

or

$$\begin{aligned} \alpha_1 + \tfrac{1}{5}\alpha_2 + \tfrac{2}{5}\alpha_3 &= \tfrac{1}{5}v_1 \\ \alpha_2 + \tfrac{4}{7}\alpha_3 &= \tfrac{5}{14}v_2 - \tfrac{1}{14}v_1. \end{aligned} \tag{11}$$

Like (8), (11) is *consistent* for *every* $\mathbf{v}$ in $\mathbb{R}^2$, so $\{\mathbf{u}_1, \mathbf{u}_2, \mathbf{u}_3\}$ spans $\mathbb{R}^2$, as claimed. Whereas (8) had a unique solution, so that the representation (5) was unique, (11) happens to have an infinity of solutions, so that the representation (10) is *not* unique. ◀

EXAMPLE 4 As a final example, consider the span of

$$\mathbf{u}_1 = (1, 2, 2), \qquad \mathbf{u}_2 = (-1, 0, 2) \tag{12}$$

in $\mathbb{R}^3$. Setting

$$\mathbf{v} = \alpha_1 \mathbf{u}_1 + \alpha_2 \mathbf{u}_2, \tag{13}$$

we have

$$\begin{aligned} \alpha_1 - \alpha_2 &= v_1 \\ 2\alpha_1 \quad\quad &= v_2 \\ 2\alpha_1 + 2\alpha_2 &= v_3, \end{aligned}$$

or, after Gauss elimination,

$$\begin{aligned} \alpha_1 - \alpha_2 &= v_1 \\ \alpha_2 &= \tfrac{1}{2}v_2 - v_1 \\ 0 &= v_3 - 2v_2 + 2v_1. \end{aligned} \tag{14}$$

Now, $\text{span}\{\mathbf{u}_1, \mathbf{u}_2\}$ is the set of all possible vectors $\mathbf{v}$ given by (13), i.e., all vectors $\mathbf{v}$ for which the system (14) is consistent, i.e., all vectors $\mathbf{v} = (v_1, v_2, v_3)$ such that

$$2v_1 - 2v_2 + v_3 = 0 \tag{15}$$

[so that the last of equations (14) is $0 = 0$ rather than a contradiction].

In geometrical terms, on the other hand, $\text{span}\{\mathbf{u}_1, \mathbf{u}_2\}$ should be the subset of $\mathbb{R}^3$ consisting of the *plane* that passes through $\mathbf{u}_1$ and $\mathbf{u}_2$ ($\mathbf{u}_1$ and $\mathbf{u}_2$ are shown in Fig. 2.18). How does that fact correlate with (15)? As a matter of fact, (15) *is* the equation of a plane in 3-space, and that plane does pass through the origin, through

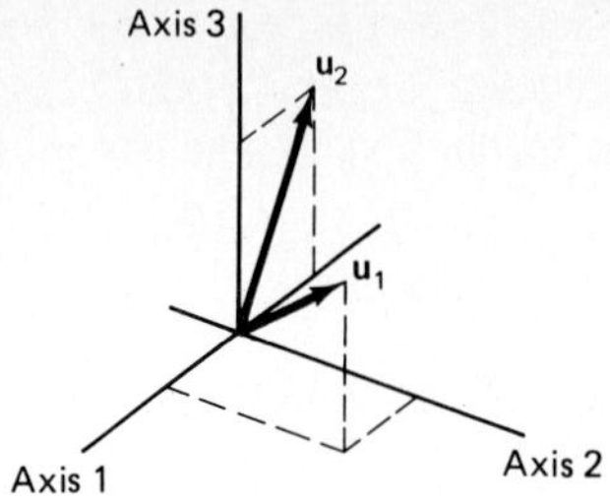

Fig. 2.18 $\mathbf{u}_1$ and $\mathbf{u}_2$.

the tip of $\mathbf{u}_1$ [i.e., the point (1, 2, 2)], and through the tip of $\mathbf{u}_2$ [the point (−1, 0, 2)]. Hence it *is* the plane through $\mathbf{u}_1$ and $\mathbf{u}_2$, so the analytical approach, namely steps (13) to (15), and our geometrical interpretation, are in agreement.

RESULT Span$\{\mathbf{u}_1, \mathbf{u}_2\}$ is not all of $\mathbb{R}^3$; it is only the subspace of $\mathbb{R}^3$ consisting of the plane (i.e., all vectors in the plane) containing the given vectors $\mathbf{u}_1$ and $\mathbf{u}_2$.

WATCH OUT Students sometimes call that plane $\mathbb{R}^2$ and hence conclude that span$\{\mathbf{u}_1, \mathbf{u}_2\}$ is $\mathbb{R}^2$. That is incorrect; $\mathbb{R}^2$ is made up of *two*-tuples, while the vectors in the above-mentioned plane are *three*-tuples. Thus $\mathbb{R}^2$ space is not relevant in this problem. All that can be said here is that span$\{\mathbf{u}_1, \mathbf{u}_2\}$ is the subspace of $\mathbb{R}^3$ consisting of the plane containing the vectors $\mathbf{u}_1$ and $\mathbf{u}_2$, i.e., the plane defined by (15). ◀

2.7 EXERCISES

1. Show whether or not the vectors

*(a) (1, 0, . . . , 0), (0, 1, 0, . . . , 0), . . . , (0, . . . , 0, 1) span $\mathbb{R}^n$

(b) (0, 0, 0, 1), (0, 0, 1, 1), (0, 1, 1, 1), (1, 1, 1, 1) span $\mathbb{R}^4$

(c) (1, 2, 0, 4), (2, 3, 1, −1), (0, 1, 0, 1), (0, 0, 0, 0), (1, 1, 2, 3) span $\mathbb{R}^4$

*(d) (1, 3, 2, 2), (5, 7, 1, 0), (−1, −2, −4, 3) span $\mathbb{R}^4$

(e) (1, 0, 1), (2, 1, −1), (1, 2, −5) span $\mathbb{R}^3$

(f) (1, 1, 2), (0, 0, 0), (2, 1, 0), (−1, 0, 3) span $\mathbb{R}^3$

(g) (2, 0, 3), (−1, 2, 4), (−5, 2, −2) span $\mathbb{R}^3$

*(h) (1, 3, 0), (2, −1, 1), (1, 1, 4) span $\mathbb{R}^3$

(i) (−1, 2, 4), (−5, 2, −2), (2, 0, 3), (1, 2, 3) span $\mathbb{R}^3$

(j) (0, 0, 0), (2, 1, 4), (−1, 3, 5) span $\mathbb{R}^3$

(k) (2, 1, 3), (1, −1, 2) span $\mathbb{R}^3$

(l) (2, 1, −1), (1, 3, 1), (5, 5, −1), (0, 5, 3) span $\mathbb{R}^3$

(m) (−4, 1, 0), (2, 2, 2), (1, 2, 3) span $\mathbb{R}^3$

(n) (−3, 1, 0), (1, 1, 1), (−1, 7, 5) span $\mathbb{R}^3$

(o) (1, 2), (2, 1) span $\mathbb{R}^2$

(p) (1, 2), (2, 1), (4, 5) span $\mathbb{R}^2$

(q) (1, 2), (2, 1), (2, 3), (2, −4) span $\mathbb{R}^2$

2. (a) Sketch any two vectors that span the space of all vectors in the plane of the paper.

(b) Sketch any three such vectors.

(c) Sketch any four such vectors.

3. Are the following vector sets subspaces of $\mathbb{R}^2$? Explain.

*(a) the straight line L that extends from the origin to infinity; see below left

(b) the wedge-shaped region (including its boundary lines) that extends to infinity in both directions; see below right

(c) the upper half plane $x_2 \geq 0$; see below center.

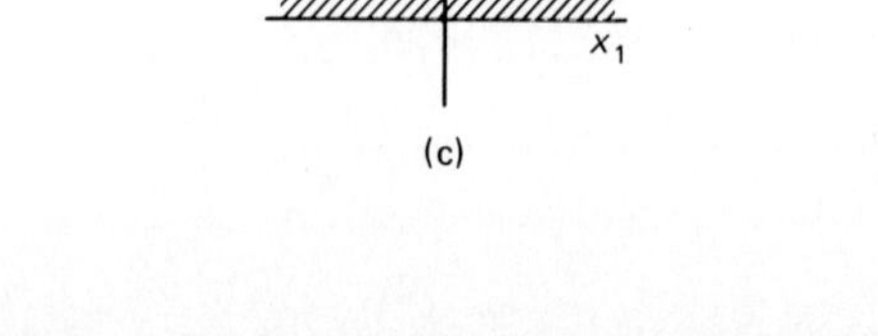

4. (*Solution space*) Consider a set of m homogeneous linear equations in the n unknowns $x_1, \ldots, x_n$,

$$\begin{aligned} a_{11}x_1 + a_{12}x_2 + \cdots + a_{1n}x_n &= 0 \\ &\vdots \\ a_{m1}x_1 + a_{m2}x_2 + \cdots + a_{mn}x_n &= 0, \end{aligned} \tag{a}$$

and denote each solution of this system as an n-tuple vector $\mathbf{x} = (x_1, \ldots, x_n)$ in $\mathbb{R}^n$. Show that the set of all such vectors (for any prescribed values of m, n, and the coefficients a_{11} through a_{mn}) is a vector space [called the **solution space** of (a)], and that this space is a subspace of $\mathbb{R}^n$. *Hint:* To show that the set of such vectors is indeed a vector space, you need to verify that the requirements listed in Definition 1 (page 37) are all met. However, a number of these can be ignored. For example, look at item (i). Here, you need merely show that the set is closed under addition [i.e., if $\mathbf{x} = (x_1, \ldots, x_n)$ and $\mathbf{y} = (y_1, \ldots, y_n)$ are solutions of (a), then so is $\mathbf{x} + \mathbf{y}$]; i.e., you need not bother verifying that $\mathbf{u} + \mathbf{v} = \mathbf{v} + \mathbf{u}$ and that $(\mathbf{u} + \mathbf{v}) + \mathbf{w} = \mathbf{u}(\mathbf{v} + \mathbf{w})$ since we know that these rules will be satisfied because our vectors are n-tuples, with the "usual" rules of addition, scalar multiplication, ... Thus under item (i) you need merely show that the set is closed under vector addition. Under item (ii) you need merely show that the set does indeed contain the zero vector $\mathbf{0} = (0, \ldots, 0)$ [i.e., that $\mathbf{x} = (0, \ldots, 0)$ is a solution of (a)]. Under (iii) you need merely show that if $\mathbf{x}$ is in the set [of solutions of (a)], then so is $-\mathbf{x}$. And under (iv) you need merely show that the set is closed under scalar multiplication, i.e. , if $\mathbf{x}$ is a solution of (a), then so is $\alpha\mathbf{x}$, for any scalar α.

5. As an illustration of the ideas contained in Exercise 4, consider the simple system $x_1 + 3x_2 = 0$; i.e., $m = 1$, $n = 2$, $a_{11} = 1$, and $a_{12} = 3$. The solution is $x_2 = \alpha$ (arbitrary), $x_1 = -3\alpha$, or $\mathbf{x} = (x_1, x_2) = \alpha(-3, 1)$, so the solution space is the span of the vector $(-3, 1)$, i.e., span$\{(-3, 1)\}$. In this manner, determine the solution space for each of the following examples.

*(a) $x_1 - x_2 + 4x_3 = 0$

(b) $x_1 + x_2 + x_3 - x_4 = 0$

(c) $x_1 - x_2 = 0$
$x_1 - 2x_2 = 0$

(d) $x_1 - x_2 + x_3 - 2x_4 = 0$
$x_1 - x_2 + x_4 + 2x_5 = 0$

(e) $x_1 + x_2 - x_3 + x_4 = 0$
$x_1 + 2x_2 - x_4 = 0$
$x_2 + x_3 = 0$

(f) $x_1 + x_2 + 2x_3 - 2x_4 = 0$
$x_1 + x_2 + 2x_3 + x_5 = 0$
$2x_4 + x_5 = 0$

6. Find any two vectors in $\mathbb{R}^3$ that span the plane

*(a) $x_1 - 2x_2 + 4x_3 = 0$

(b) $2x_1 + x_2 - 6x_3 = 0$

(c) $x_1 + 5x_3 = 0$

(d) $x_1 + 4x_2 + x_3 = 0$

7. Prove Theorem 1.

LINEAR DEPENDENCE 2.8

The reader may recall, from a first course in differential equations, that "linear dependence" and "linear independence" play an important role in establishing the general solution of a linear ordinary differential equation. The definition of linear dependence given below, in terms of vectors, will be essentially identical to that encountered in the study of ordinary differential equations.

> ***Definition 1** Linear Dependence and Linear Independence*
> A finite set of vectors $\{\mathbf{u}_1, \ldots, \mathbf{u}_k\}$ is **linearly dependent** (LD for short) if at least one of the vectors can be expressed as a linear combination of the others. If none of the vectors can be so expressed, the set is **linearly independent** (LI for short).

EXAMPLE 1 Let $\mathbf{u}_1 = (1, 0)$, $\mathbf{u}_2 = (1, 1)$, and $\mathbf{u}_3 = (5, 4)$. These are LD since, by inspection, we can express $\mathbf{u}_3$ as a linear combination of $\mathbf{u}_1$ and $\mathbf{u}_2$: $\mathbf{u}_3 = \mathbf{u}_1 + 4\mathbf{u}_2$. (Alternatively, we could express $\mathbf{u}_2 = \frac{1}{4}\mathbf{u}_3 - \frac{1}{4}\mathbf{u}_1$, or $\mathbf{u}_1 = -4\mathbf{u}_2 + \mathbf{u}_3$.) ◀

EXAMPLE 2 Let $\mathbf{u}_1 = (1, 0)$ and $\mathbf{u}_2 = (1, 1)$. These are LI since $\mathbf{u}_1$ cannot be expressed as a "linear combination of the others," namely, as a scalar multiple of $\mathbf{u}_2$, nor can $\mathbf{u}_2$ be expressed as a scalar multiple of $\mathbf{u}_1$. ◀

EXAMPLE 3 Let $\mathbf{u}_1 = (2, -1)$, $\mathbf{u}_2 = (0, 0)$, and $\mathbf{u}_3 = (0, 1)$. These are LD since we can express $\mathbf{u}_2 = 0\mathbf{u}_1 + 0\mathbf{u}_3$. (The fact that we *cannot* express $\mathbf{u}_1$ as a linear combination of $\mathbf{u}_2$ and $\mathbf{u}_3$, nor $\mathbf{u}_3$ as a linear combination of $\mathbf{u}_1$ and $\mathbf{u}_2$, does not alter our conclusion, for recall the words "at least one" in the definition.) ◀

It is implicit in Definition 1 that $\mathbf{u}_1, \ldots, \mathbf{u}_k$ are all members of the same vector space; in Examples 1 to 3 that space was $\mathbb{R}^2$. Thus it would simply make no sense to ask whether $\mathbf{u}_1 = (2, 5)$ and $\mathbf{u}_2 = (4, 3, 0, 1)$ are linearly dependent or not, since $\mathbf{u}_1$ is a member of $\mathbb{R}^2$ while $\mathbf{u}_2$ is a member of $\mathbb{R}^4$.

The preceding examples were simple enough to be worked by inspection. In more complicated cases, the following theorem provides a systematic approach for determining whether a given vector set is linearly dependent or linearly independent.

Theorem 1 *Test for Linear Dependence/Independence*

A finite set of vectors $\{\mathbf{u}_1, \ldots, \mathbf{u}_k\}$ is LD if and only if there exist scalars α_j, not all zero, such that

$$\boxed{\alpha_1\mathbf{u}_1 + \alpha_2\mathbf{u}_2 + \cdots + \alpha_k\mathbf{u}_k = \mathbf{0};} \tag{1}$$

otherwise, the set is LI.

Proof Because of the "if and only if" we need to prove the statement in both directions. First, suppose that the set is LD. Then one of the vectors, say $\mathbf{u}_j$, can be expressed as a linear combination of the others:

$$\mathbf{u}_j = \alpha_1\mathbf{u}_1 + \cdots + \alpha_{j-1}\mathbf{u}_{j-1} + \alpha_{j+1}\mathbf{u}_{j+1} + \cdots + \alpha_k\mathbf{u}_k \tag{2}$$

or

$$\alpha_1\mathbf{u}_1 + \cdots + \alpha_{j-1}\mathbf{u}_{j-1} - \mathbf{u}_j + \alpha_{j+1}\mathbf{u}_{j+1} + \cdots + \alpha_k\mathbf{u}_k = \mathbf{0}. \tag{3}$$

Now, no matter what the values of $\alpha_1, \ldots, \alpha_{j-1}$ and $\alpha_{j+1}, \ldots, \alpha_k$ are, the coefficient of $\mathbf{u}_j$ in (3), namely -1, is not zero, so there *do* exist scalars $\alpha_1, \ldots, \alpha_k$ not *all* zero, such that (1) holds. Conversely, suppose that (1) holds, with the α's not all zero. Thus we may suppose that α_m, say, is nonzero. Then we can multiply (1) through by $1/\alpha_m$ (since $\alpha_m \neq 0$), and transpose $\mathbf{u}_m$, to obtain

$$\mathbf{u}_m = -\left(\frac{\alpha_1}{\alpha_m}\right)\mathbf{u}_1 - \cdots - \left(\frac{\alpha_{m-1}}{\alpha_m}\right)\mathbf{u}_{m-1} - \left(\frac{\alpha_{m+1}}{\alpha_m}\right)\mathbf{u}_{m+1} - \cdots - \left(\frac{\alpha_k}{\alpha_m}\right)\mathbf{u}_k. \tag{4}$$

Here $\mathbf{u}_m$ is expressed as a linear combination of the other vectors, so the set must be LD. This completes the proof. ■

EXAMPLE 4 Consider the 4-tuples

$$\mathbf{u}_1 = (2, 0, 1, -3), \quad \mathbf{u}_2 = (0, 1, 1, 1), \quad \mathbf{u}_3 = (2, 2, 3, 0). \tag{5}$$

To see if these vectors are LI or LD, appeal directly to (1):

$$\alpha_1(2, 0, 1, -3) + \alpha_2(0, 1, 1, 1) + \alpha_3(2, 2, 3, 0) = (0, 0, 0, 0) \tag{6}$$

or $(2\alpha_1 + 2\alpha_3, \alpha_2 + 2\alpha_3, \alpha_1 + \alpha_2 + 3\alpha_3, -3\alpha_1 + \alpha_2) = (0, 0, 0, 0)$. Thus

$$\begin{aligned} 2\alpha_1 \qquad\quad + 2\alpha_3 &= 0 \\ \alpha_2 + 2\alpha_3 &= 0 \\ \alpha_1 + \alpha_2 + 3\alpha_3 &= 0 \\ -3\alpha_1 + \alpha_2 \qquad\quad &= 0. \end{aligned} \tag{7}$$

Applying Gauss elimination yields

$$\begin{aligned} 2\alpha_1 \qquad\quad + 2\alpha_3 &= 0 \\ \alpha_2 + 2\alpha_3 &= 0 \\ \alpha_3 &= 0 \\ 0 &= 0. \end{aligned} \tag{8}$$

This system admits only the trivial solution, $\alpha_1 = \alpha_2 = \alpha_3 = 0$, so $\mathbf{u}_1, \mathbf{u}_2, \mathbf{u}_3$ are LI. ◀

EXAMPLE 5 Consider the 3-tuples

$$\mathbf{u}_1 = (1, 0, 1), \quad \mathbf{u}_2 = (1, 1, 1), \quad \mathbf{u}_3 = (1, 1, 2), \quad \mathbf{u}_4 = (1, 2, 1). \tag{9}$$

Working from (1), as in Example 4, we have

$$\begin{aligned} \alpha_1 + \alpha_2 + \alpha_3 + \alpha_4 &= 0 \\ \alpha_2 + \alpha_3 + 2\alpha_4 &= 0 \\ \alpha_1 + \alpha_2 + 2\alpha_3 + \alpha_4 &= 0 \end{aligned} \tag{10}$$

or, after Gauss elimination,

$$\begin{aligned} \alpha_1 + \alpha_2 + \alpha_3 + \alpha_4 &= 0 \\ \alpha_2 + \alpha_3 + 2\alpha_4 &= 0 \\ \alpha_3 \qquad\quad &= 0. \end{aligned} \tag{11}$$

This time, there exist nontrivial solutions for the α_j's, so the vectors $\mathbf{u}_1, \mathbf{u}_2, \mathbf{u}_3, \mathbf{u}_4$ are LD. [Specifically, (11) gives $\alpha_3 = 0$, $\alpha_4 = \alpha$, $\alpha_2 = -2\alpha$, $\alpha_1 = \alpha$, where α is arbitrary. With $\alpha = 1$, say, (1) becomes

$$\mathbf{u}_1 - 2\mathbf{u}_2 + 0\mathbf{u}_3 + \mathbf{u}_4 = \mathbf{0}.]$$ ◀

We conclude this section with three useful theorems.

> ***Theorem 2***
> *Two* vectors are LD if and only if one is a scalar multiple of the other.

Proof This theorem follows immediately from Definition 1. ■

Thus $\mathbf{u}_1$ and $\mathbf{u}_2$, shown in Fig. 2.19, are LI, since $\mathbf{u}_1$ is evidently not a scalar multiple of $\mathbf{u}_2$, and $\mathbf{u}_2$ is not a scalar multiple of $\mathbf{u}_1$.

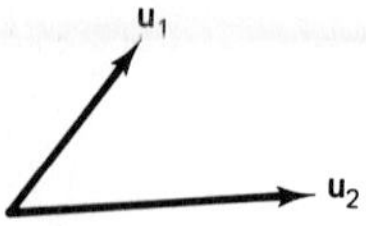

Fig. 2.19 Two LI vectors.

WATCH OUT Observe that $\mathbf{u}_1$ and $\mathbf{u}_2$ in Example 5 are LI. Similarly, $\mathbf{u}_1$ and $\mathbf{u}_3$ are LI, $\mathbf{u}_1$ and $\mathbf{u}_4$ are LI, $\mathbf{u}_2$ and $\mathbf{u}_3$ are LI, $\mathbf{u}_2$ and $\mathbf{u}_4$ are LI, and $\mathbf{u}_3$ and $\mathbf{u}_4$ are LI. Does it not follow that the set $\{\mathbf{u}_1, \mathbf{u}_2, \mathbf{u}_3, \mathbf{u}_4\}$ is LI? It does not. Linear independence of the vectors, taken two at a time, is not the same as linear independence of the vectors taken all together.

> ***Theorem 3***
> Every finite set of vectors $\{\mathbf{u}_1, \ldots, \mathbf{u}_k\}$ containing the zero vector is LD.

Proof Our proof is a generalization of the ideas contained in Example 3. For suppose that $\mathbf{u}_m = \mathbf{0}$ for some $m (1 \le m \le k)$. Then

$$0\mathbf{u}_1 + \cdots + 0\mathbf{u}_{m-1} + \alpha_m \mathbf{u}_m + 0\mathbf{u}_{m+1} + \cdots + 0\mathbf{u}_k = \mathbf{0} \tag{12}$$

for any $\alpha_m \neq 0$, since $\mathbf{u}_m$ is $\mathbf{0}$. Since the scalar coefficients on the left-hand side of (12) (namely, $0, \ldots, 0, \alpha_m, 0, \ldots, 0$) are not all zero, it follows that the vector set $\{\mathbf{u}_1, \ldots, \mathbf{u}_k\}$ is LD. ■

> ***Theorem 4***
> Every finite *orthogonal* set of (nonzero) vectors is LI.

Proof Dot $\mathbf{u}_1$ into

$$\alpha_1 \mathbf{u}_1 + \alpha_2 \mathbf{u}_2 + \cdots + \alpha_k \mathbf{u}_k = \mathbf{0}. \tag{13}$$

In other words,

$$\begin{aligned} \mathbf{u}_1 \cdot (\alpha_1 \mathbf{u}_1 + \alpha_2 \mathbf{u}_2 + \cdots + \alpha_k \mathbf{u}_k) &= \mathbf{u}_1 \cdot \mathbf{0}, \\ \alpha_1 \mathbf{u}_1 \cdot \mathbf{u}_1 + \alpha_2 \mathbf{u}_1 \cdot \mathbf{u}_2 + \cdots + \alpha_k \mathbf{u}_1 \cdot \mathbf{u}_k &= 0, \\ \alpha_1 \|\mathbf{u}_1\|^2 + 0 + \cdots + 0 &= 0. \end{aligned} \tag{14}$$

Now $\mathbf{u}_1 \neq \mathbf{0}$ implies that $\|\mathbf{u}_1\| \neq 0$, so it follows from (14) that $\alpha_1 = 0$. Similarly, dotting $\mathbf{u}_2$ into (13) gives $\alpha_2 = 0$, and so on. Since $\alpha_1 = \alpha_2 = \cdots = \alpha_k = 0$, the $\mathbf{u}_j$'s must be LI, as claimed. ∎

EXAMPLE 6 As is easily verified, the (nonzero) vectors

$$\mathbf{u}_1 = (1, 0, 1), \quad \mathbf{u}_2 = (0, 3, 0), \quad \mathbf{u}_3 = (2, 0, -2)$$

are mutually orthogonal. Then it follows from Theorem 4 that they are LI. ◀

2.8 EXERCISES

1. Determine whether the following sets of vectors are LI or LD.

*(a) (1, 3), (2, 0), (−1, 3), (7, 3)
(b) (1, 3), (2, 0), (1, 2), (−1, 5)
(c) (2, 3, 0), (1, −2, 3)
(d) (2, 3, 0), (1, −2, 4), (1, 1, 0), (1, 1, 1)
(e) (0, 0, 2), (0, 0, 3), (2, −1, 5), (1, 2, 4), (7, 9, 1), (2, 0, −4)
(f) (2, 3, 0, 0), (1, −5, 0, 2), (3, 1, 2, 2)
*(g) (1, 3, 2, 0), (4, 1, −2, −2), (0, 2, 0, 3), (4, 7, 1, 2)
(h) (2, 0, 1, −1, 0), (1, 2, 0, 3, 1), (4, −4, 3, −9, −2)
(i) (1, 3, 0), (0, 1, −1), (0, 0, 0)
(j) (1, 1, 0, 0), (1, −1, 0, 0), (0, 0, −2, 2), (0, 0, 1, 1)
(k) (1, −3, 0, 2, 1), (−2, 6, 0, −4, −2)
(l) (5, 4, 1, 1), (0, 0, 0, 0), (1, 9, −7, 2)
*(m) (1, 2, 3, 4), (2, 3, 4, 5)
(n) (2, 1, −1), (1, 4, 2), (3, −2, −4)
(o) (7, 1, 0), (−1, 1, 4), (2, 3, 5)
(p) (1, 2, −1), (1, 0, 1), (3, −2, 5)
(q) (3, 1, 0, 0), (1, −2, 4, 1), (2, 1, 6, 5)
(r) (2, 4, 0, 1), (1, 0, 1, 2), (1, −3, 1, 2), (1, 1, −1, −1)

2. Prove that if

$$\sum_1^n \alpha_j \mathbf{u}_j = \sum_1^n \beta_j \mathbf{u}_j,$$

where $\mathbf{u}_1, \ldots, \mathbf{u}_n$ are LI, then $\alpha_j = \beta_j$ for $j = 1, \ldots, n$.

3. Show, by graphical means that the vector sets shown below, and lying in the plane of the paper, are LD. (The emphasis here is on the method and ideas, not on graphical precision.)

(a)

(b)
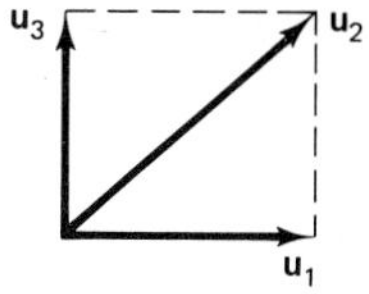

(c)
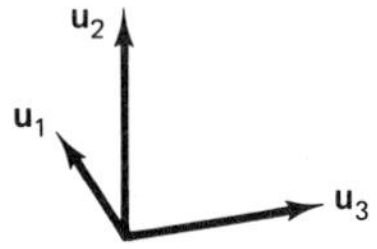

(d)
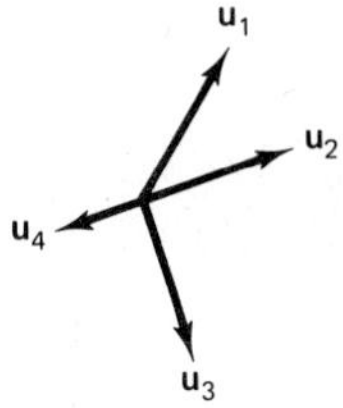

(e)
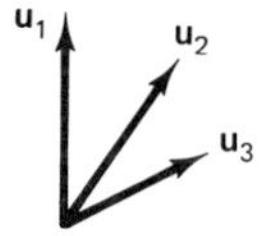

4. To clarify further the "watch out" comment preceding Theorem 3, show that for a vector set $\{\mathbf{u}_1, \mathbf{u}_2, \mathbf{u}_3, \mathbf{u}_4\}$, say, to be LI it is *necessary*, but *not sufficient*, that each of the subsets $\{\mathbf{u}_1, \mathbf{u}_2\}$, $\{\mathbf{u}_1, \mathbf{u}_3\}$, $\{\mathbf{u}_1, \mathbf{u}_4\}$, $\{\mathbf{u}_2, \mathbf{u}_3\}$, $\{\mathbf{u}_2, \mathbf{u}_4\}$, and $\{\mathbf{u}_3, \mathbf{u}_4\}$ be LI.

5. Prove or disprove:

(a) $\mathbf{v}$ is in span$\{\mathbf{u}_1, \ldots, \mathbf{u}_k\}$ if $\{\mathbf{v}, \mathbf{u}_1, \ldots, \mathbf{u}_k\}$ is LD.
(b) $\mathbf{v}$ is not in span$\{\mathbf{u}_1, \ldots, \mathbf{u}_k\}$ if $\{\mathbf{v}, \mathbf{u}_1, \ldots, \mathbf{u}_k\}$ is LI.
(c) $\mathbf{v}$ is not in span$\{\mathbf{u}_1, \ldots, \mathbf{u}_k\}$ if and only if $\{\mathbf{v}, \mathbf{u}_1, \ldots, \mathbf{u}_k\}$ is LI.

2.9 BASES AND EXPANSIONS

Beginning simply, consider the vector space $\mathbb{R}^2$, that is, the set of all vectors in a plane. In particular, consider the vectors $\mathbf{e}_1$ and $\mathbf{e}_2$ shown in Fig. 2.20a. It should be evident that $\mathbf{e}_1$, $\mathbf{e}_2$ are LI (Theorem 2, page 48) and that they *span* the space (of vectors lying in the plane). Since they span the space, any given vector in the space, such as $\mathbf{u}$ in Fig. 2.20b and $\mathbf{v}$ in Fig. 2.20c, can be expressed as a linear combination of $\mathbf{e}_1$ and $\mathbf{e}_2$.

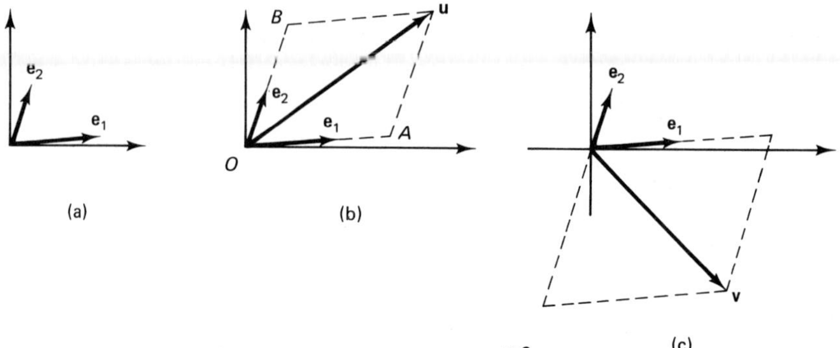

Fig. 2.20 Vector expansion in $\mathbb{R}^2$.

For the vector $\mathbf{u}$, for example, $\mathbf{u} = \mathbf{OA} + \mathbf{OB}$; with the aid of a scale, $\mathbf{OA} = 1.6\mathbf{e}_1$ and $\mathbf{OB} = 2\mathbf{e}_2$, so that

$$\mathbf{u} = 1.6\mathbf{e}_1 + 2\mathbf{e}_2. \tag{1}$$

Similarly (Fig. 2.20c),

$$\mathbf{v} = 2\mathbf{e}_1 - 2.5\mathbf{e}_2, \tag{2}$$

and so on, for any given vector in the plane. Of course, the zero vector is simply $\mathbf{0} = 0\mathbf{e}_1 + 0\mathbf{e}_2$.

The formulas (1) and (2) are examples of the *expansion* of a given vector [$\mathbf{u}$ in (1), $\mathbf{v}$ in (2)] in terms of a set of *base vectors* [the set $\{\mathbf{e}_1, \mathbf{e}_2\}$].

> ***Definition 1** Basis*
>
> A finite set of vectors $\{\mathbf{e}_1, \ldots, \mathbf{e}_k\}$ in a vector space $\mathcal{S}$ is a **basis** for $\mathcal{S}$ if every vector $\mathbf{u}$ in $\mathcal{S}$ can be expanded uniquely in the form
>
> $$\mathbf{u} = \alpha_1\mathbf{e}_1 + \alpha_2\mathbf{e}_2 + \cdots + \alpha_k\mathbf{e}_k = \sum_{j=1}^{k} \alpha_j\mathbf{e}_j. \tag{3}$$

By the expansion (3) being unique, we mean that the α_j *expansion coefficients* are uniquely determined.

> ***Theorem 1** Test for Basis*
>
> A finite set $\{\mathbf{e}_1, \ldots, \mathbf{e}_k\}$ is a basis for $\mathcal{S}$ if and only if it spans $\mathcal{S}$ and is LI.

Proof First it follows from the definition of the verb span that every vector **u** in $\mathcal{S}$ can be expanded as in (3) if and only if the set $\{\mathbf{e}_1, \ldots, \mathbf{e}_k\}$ spans $\mathcal{S}$. Turning to the question of the uniqueness of the expansion, suppose that both

$$\mathbf{u} = \alpha_1\mathbf{e}_1 + \cdots + \alpha_k\mathbf{e}_k \tag{4}$$

and

$$\mathbf{u} = \beta_1\mathbf{e}_1 + \cdots + \beta_k\mathbf{e}_k \tag{5}$$

hold for any given vector **u** in $\mathcal{S}$. Subtracting (5) from (4) gives us

$$(\alpha_1 - \beta_1)\mathbf{e}_1 + \cdots + (\alpha_k - \beta_k)\mathbf{e}_k = \mathbf{0}. \tag{6}$$

Now the coefficients $(\alpha_1 - \beta_1), \ldots, (\alpha_k - \beta_k)$ in (6) must each be zero, in which case $\alpha_1 = \beta_1, \ldots, \alpha_k = \beta_k$ and expansions (4) and (5) are identical, if and only if the set $\{\mathbf{e}_1, \ldots, \mathbf{e}_k\}$ is LI. Hence the expansion (3) is unique if and only if the set is LI, and this completes the proof. ■

The key idea, revealed in the proof above, is that a basis needs to contain *enough* vectors, but *not too many*: enough so that the set spans the space and can therefore be used to expand any given vector in the space, but not too many, in order that such expansions will be unique.

EXAMPLE 1 Consider the vectors

$$\mathbf{e}_1 = (-2, 1), \qquad \mathbf{e}_2 = (2, 4). \tag{7}$$

As may be verified, the set (7) is LI and spans $\mathbb{R}^2$ and is therefore a basis for $\mathbb{R}^2$. Using that set to expand the vector $\mathbf{u} = (6, 2)$, say, we express

$$\mathbf{u} = \alpha_1\mathbf{e}_1 + \alpha_2\mathbf{e}_2 \tag{8}$$

or $(6, 2) = (-2\alpha_1, \alpha_1) + (2\alpha_2, 4\alpha_2)$. Hence

$$\begin{aligned} -2\alpha_1 + 2\alpha_2 &= 6 \\ \alpha_1 + 4\alpha_2 &= 2. \end{aligned} \tag{9}$$

Solving (9), $\alpha_1 = -2$ and $\alpha_2 = 1$, so the expansion (8) is

$$\mathbf{u} = -2\mathbf{e}_1 + \mathbf{e}_2, \tag{10}$$

as displayed in Fig. 2.21a.

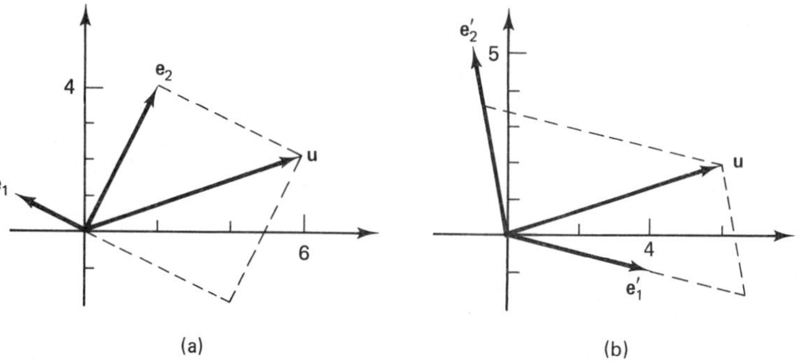

Fig. 2.21 Two bases for $\mathbb{R}^2$.

It is to be emphasized that the basis (7) shown in Fig. 2.21a is by no means the *only* basis for $\mathbb{R}^2$; there are slews of them. For example, it is easily verified that another is

$$\mathbf{e}_1' = (4, -1), \qquad \mathbf{e}_2' = (-1, 5), \tag{11}$$

and in this case the expansion of $\mathbf{u} = (6, 2)$ is found to be

$$\mathbf{u} = \tfrac{32}{19}\mathbf{e}_1' + \tfrac{14}{19}\mathbf{e}_2', \tag{12}$$

as depicted in Fig. 2.21b.

COMMENT The difference between the expansions (10) and (12) is *not* at odds with the notion of uniqueness, since the two expansions are with respect to different bases. In other words, (10) *is* the unique expansion of $\mathbf{u}$ in terms of the $\mathbf{e}_1$, $\mathbf{e}_2$ basis, and (12) *is* the unique expansion of $\mathbf{u}$ in terms of the $\mathbf{e}_1'$, $\mathbf{e}_2'$ basis. ◀

If, as in Example 1, there are many bases for a given space, it would be natural to wonder how we know which one to use. In some applications, we will find that the simplest or most natural basis to use will often be apparent from the mathematical context; in other applications we may need to work hard to find the best basis. This point is discussed later, in Chapter 4.

Observe that to obtain the expansion (10) we needed to solve the linear system (9) for α_1 and α_2. Similarly, it turns out that the expansion of $\mathbf{u} = (3, -2, 0, 4)$ in terms of the basis

$$\mathbf{e}_1 = (2, 1, 1, 1), \quad \mathbf{e}_2 = (1, 0, 3, 0), \quad \mathbf{e}_3 = (1, -2, 0, 4), \quad \mathbf{e}_4 = (5, 3, 2, 2) \tag{13}$$

for $\mathbb{R}^4$ requires the solution of the linear system

$$\begin{aligned}
2\alpha_1 + \alpha_2 + \alpha_3 + 5\alpha_4 &= 3\\
\alpha_1 - 2\alpha_3 + 3\alpha_4 &= -2\\
\alpha_1 + 3\alpha_2 + 2\alpha_4 &= 0\\
\alpha_1 + 4\alpha_3 + 2\alpha_4 &= 4,
\end{aligned} \tag{14}$$

and so on. In other words, the expansion process can be quite tedious.

On the other hand, suppose that $\{\mathbf{e}_1, \ldots, \mathbf{e}_k\}$ is an *orthogonal* basis for $\mathscr{S}$, i.e., it is not only a basis but also happens to be an orthogonal set:

$$\mathbf{e}_i \cdot \mathbf{e}_j = 0 \quad \text{if} \quad i \neq j. \tag{15}$$

Suppose that we wish to expand a given vector $\mathbf{u}$ in $\mathscr{S}$ in terms of that basis; i.e., we wish to determine the coefficients $\alpha_1, \ldots, \alpha_k$ in the expansion

$$\mathbf{u} = \alpha_1\mathbf{e}_1 + \alpha_2\mathbf{e}_2 + \cdots + \alpha_k\mathbf{e}_k. \tag{16}$$

To accomplish this, dot (16) with $\mathbf{e}_1, \mathbf{e}_2, \ldots, \mathbf{e}_k$, in turn. Doing so, and using (15), we obtain the linear system

$$\begin{aligned}
\mathbf{u}\cdot\mathbf{e}_1 &= (\mathbf{e}_1\cdot\mathbf{e}_1)\alpha_1 + 0\alpha_2 + \cdots + 0\alpha_k\\
\mathbf{u}\cdot\mathbf{e}_2 &= 0\alpha_1 + (\mathbf{e}_2\cdot\mathbf{e}_2)\alpha_2 + 0\alpha_3 + \cdots + 0\alpha_k\\
&\;\vdots
\end{aligned} \tag{17}$$

$$\mathbf{u}\cdot\mathbf{e}_k = 0\alpha_1 + \cdots + 0\alpha_{k-1} + (\mathbf{e}_k\cdot\mathbf{e}_k)\alpha_k$$

of k equations in the k unknowns $\alpha_1, \ldots, \alpha_k$. (Observe that all of the quantities $\mathbf{u}\cdot\mathbf{e}_1, \ldots, \mathbf{u}\cdot\mathbf{e}_k$, $\mathbf{e}_1\cdot\mathbf{e}_1, \ldots, \mathbf{e}_k\cdot\mathbf{e}_k$ are computable since $\mathbf{u}$, $\mathbf{e}_1, \ldots, \mathbf{e}_k$ are known.) The crucial point is that the equations (17) are *uncoupled* (i.e., each equation contains only one of the unknowns), and easily yield

$$\alpha_1 = \frac{\mathbf{u}\cdot\mathbf{e}_1}{\mathbf{e}_1\cdot\mathbf{e}_1}, \quad \alpha_2 = \frac{\mathbf{u}\cdot\mathbf{e}_2}{\mathbf{e}_2\cdot\mathbf{e}_2}, \quad \ldots, \quad \alpha_k = \frac{\mathbf{u}\cdot\mathbf{e}_k}{\mathbf{e}_k\cdot\mathbf{e}_k}, \tag{18}$$

provided, of course, that none of the denominators $\mathbf{e}_1\cdot\mathbf{e}_1, \ldots, \mathbf{e}_k\cdot\mathbf{e}_k$ vanish. But these quantities cannot vanish since $\mathbf{e}_j\cdot\mathbf{e}_j = \|\mathbf{e}_j\|^2$, which is zero if and only if $\mathbf{e}_j = \mathbf{0}$, and this cannot be since if any $\mathbf{e}_j$ were $\mathbf{0}$, then the set $\{\mathbf{e}_1, \ldots, \mathbf{e}_k\}$ would be LD (per Theorem 3 on page 48), and hence not a basis.

Thus, *if the* $\{\mathbf{e}_1, \ldots, \mathbf{e}_k\}$ *basis is orthogonal, the expansion of any given* $\mathbf{u}$ *is simply*

$$\boxed{\mathbf{u} = \left(\frac{\mathbf{u}\cdot\mathbf{e}_1}{\mathbf{e}_1\cdot\mathbf{e}_1}\right)\mathbf{e}_1 + \cdots + \left(\frac{\mathbf{u}\cdot\mathbf{e}_k}{\mathbf{e}_k\cdot\mathbf{e}_k}\right)\mathbf{e}_k = \sum_{j=1}^{k}\left(\frac{\mathbf{u}\cdot\mathbf{e}_j}{\mathbf{e}_j\cdot\mathbf{e}_j}\right)\mathbf{e}_j.} \tag{19}$$

If, further, the $\mathbf{e}_j$'s are *normalized*, i.e., scaled such that

$$\|\mathbf{e}_j\| = 1 \qquad \text{for} \qquad j = 1, \ldots, k, \tag{20}$$

then $\mathbf{e}_j\cdot\mathbf{e}_j = \|\mathbf{e}_j\|^2 = 1$ in (19), for each j, so (19) simplifies slightly to

$$\boxed{\mathbf{u} = (\mathbf{u}\cdot\hat{\mathbf{e}}_1)\hat{\mathbf{e}}_1 + \cdots + (\mathbf{u}\cdot\hat{\mathbf{e}}_k)\hat{\mathbf{e}}_k = \sum_{j=1}^{k}(\mathbf{u}\cdot\hat{\mathbf{e}}_j)\hat{\mathbf{e}}_j,} \tag{21}$$

where we recall that carets denote unit vectors.

A set of vectors that is both orthogonal *and* normalized is said to be **orthonormal,** or ON for short. Thus (21) holds for ON bases.

Formulas (19) and (21) are important.

EXAMPLE 2 Looking back at Example 1, observe that the basis (7) happened to be orthogonal (although not normalized) since $\mathbf{e}_1\cdot\mathbf{e}_2 = -4 + 4 = 0$. [Accordingly, the angle between $\mathbf{e}_1$ and $\mathbf{e}_2$ *is* seen, in Fig. 2.21a, to be 90°.] Thus to expand $\mathbf{u} = (6, 2)$ by means of (19), we compute

$$\mathbf{u}\cdot\mathbf{e}_1 = -10, \qquad \mathbf{u}\cdot\mathbf{e}_2 = 20, \qquad \mathbf{e}_1\cdot\mathbf{e}_1 = 5, \qquad \mathbf{e}_2\cdot\mathbf{e}_2 = 20.$$

Then (19) gives

$$\mathbf{u} = -\tfrac{10}{5}\mathbf{e}_1 + \tfrac{20}{20}\mathbf{e}_2 = -2\mathbf{e}_1 + \mathbf{e}_2,$$

in agreement with (10). ◀

EXAMPLE 3 We state without proof (Exercise 6) that the orthogonal set

$$\mathbf{e}_1 = (1, 0, 2, 0)$$
$$\mathbf{e}_2 = (0, 1, 0, 0) \tag{22}$$

$$\mathbf{e}_3 = (-2, 0, 1, 5)$$

$$\mathbf{e}_4 = (-2, 0, 1, -1)$$

is a basis for $\mathbb{R}^4$. To expand $\mathbf{u} = (4, 3, -3, 6)$, say, we compute $\mathbf{u}\cdot\mathbf{e}_1 = -2$, $\mathbf{e}_1 \cdot \mathbf{e}_1 = 5$, and so on, so that (19) yields

$$\mathbf{u} = -\tfrac{2}{5}\mathbf{e}_1 + 3\mathbf{e}_2 + \tfrac{19}{30}\mathbf{e}_3 - \tfrac{17}{6}\mathbf{e}_4. \quad \blacktriangleleft \tag{23}$$

The set

$$\hat{\mathbf{i}}_1 = (1, 0, \dots, 0), \quad \hat{\mathbf{i}}_2 = (0, 1, 0, \dots, 0), \quad \dots, \quad \hat{\mathbf{i}}_n = (0, \dots, 0, 1) \tag{24}$$

in $\mathbb{R}^n$ is of special interest. It is ON, and hence *LI* (Theorem 4 on page 48). Furthermore, it *spans* $\mathbb{R}^n$ since any vector $\mathbf{u} = (u_1, \dots, u_n)$ in $\mathbb{R}^n$ can be expanded in terms of $\hat{\mathbf{i}}_1, \dots, \hat{\mathbf{i}}_n$ as

$$\begin{aligned}\mathbf{u} &= (u_1, u_2, \dots, u_n)\\ &= u_1(1, 0, \dots, 0) + u_2(0, 1, 0, \dots, 0) + \cdots + u_n(0, \dots, 0, 1)\end{aligned}$$

or

$$\mathbf{u} = u_1\hat{\mathbf{i}}_1 + u_2\hat{\mathbf{i}}_2 + \cdots + u_n\hat{\mathbf{i}}_n. \tag{25}$$

Thus (24) is a basis for $\mathbb{R}^n$, an ON basis, in fact. It is frequently used, and is generally known as the **standard basis** for $\mathbb{R}^n$.

For the particular case where $n = 3$, the symbols $\hat{\mathbf{i}}, \hat{\mathbf{j}}, \hat{\mathbf{k}}$ are often used in place of $\hat{\mathbf{i}}_1, \hat{\mathbf{i}}_2, \hat{\mathbf{i}}_3$, respectively, so that (25) becomes*

$$\mathbf{u} = u_1\hat{\mathbf{i}} + u_2\hat{\mathbf{j}} + u_3\hat{\mathbf{k}}. \tag{26}$$

To illustrate graphically, suppose that $\mathbf{u} = (2, 5, 6)$, as shown in Fig. 2.22. By our definition of the addition of arrow vectors, we may decompose $\mathbf{u}$ as $\mathbf{OD} + \mathbf{DE}$. And if we then decompose $\mathbf{OD}$, in turn, as $\mathbf{OA} + \mathbf{OB}$, we have $\mathbf{u} = \mathbf{OE} = \mathbf{OD} + \mathbf{DE} = \mathbf{OA} + \mathbf{OB} + \mathbf{DE} = \mathbf{OA} + \mathbf{OB} + \mathbf{OC}$. But $\mathbf{OA} = 2\hat{\mathbf{i}}$, $\mathbf{OB} = 5\hat{\mathbf{j}}$, and $\mathbf{OC} = 6\hat{\mathbf{k}}$, so that

$$\mathbf{u} = 2\hat{\mathbf{i}} + 5\hat{\mathbf{j}} + 6\hat{\mathbf{k}}, \tag{27}$$

in agreement with (26).

Now, suppose that we have a basis $\{\mathbf{e}_1, \dots, \mathbf{e}_k\}$ for some vector space $\mathcal{S}$, and that this basis is *not orthogonal*. Since orthogonal bases are especially convenient, as we have noted, we may wish to "trade in" the given basis for one that is orthogonal. This can be accomplished by a systematic procedure known as *Gram–Schmidt orthogonalization,* whereby we convert the given LI set to an orthogonal set (Exercise 11). Alternatively, if we *do* wish to work with the nonorthogonal basis it is still possible to achieve computational simplicity equal to that offered by an orthogonal basis

* Recall that if $\mathbf{u} = (u_1, \dots, u_n)$, then $u_1, \dots, u_n$ are called the *components* (or *coordinates*) of $\mathbf{u}$. Observe from (25) that $u_1, \dots, u_n$ also happen to be the expansion coefficients in the expansion of $\mathbf{u}$ with respect to the standard basis $\{\hat{\mathbf{i}}_1, \dots, \hat{\mathbf{i}}_n\}$. More generally, if $\{\mathbf{e}_1, \dots, \mathbf{e}_k\}$ is a basis for a vector space $\mathcal{S}$, and a given vector $\mathbf{u}$ in $\mathcal{S}$ is expanded as $\mathbf{u} = \alpha_1\mathbf{e}_1 + \cdots + \alpha_k\mathbf{e}_k$, then the expansion coefficients $\alpha_1, \dots, \alpha_k$ are called the *components (or coordinates) of* $\mathbf{u}$ *with respect to the basis* $\{\mathbf{e}_1, \dots, \mathbf{e}_k\}$.

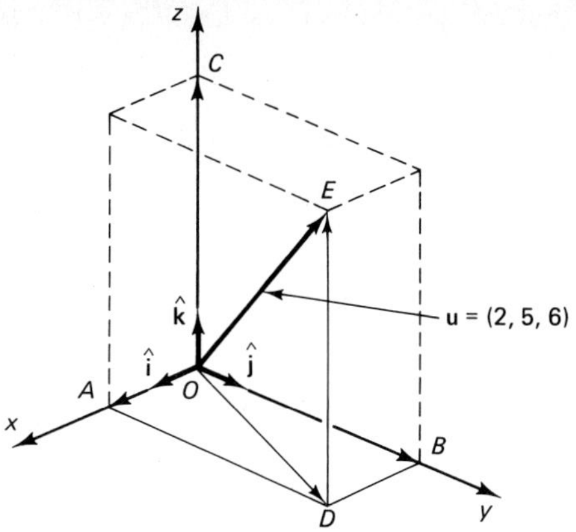

Fig. 2.22 $\hat{i}$, $\hat{j}$, $\hat{k}$.

if we are willing first to compute the so-called *dual* or *reciprocal vectors* corresponding to the given basis. This procedure is described in Exercise 13.

2.9 EXERCISES

1. Show whether or not the following are bases. *Note:* For parts (a)–(n) you may use either Theorem 1 or Definition 1. Using Theorem 1, you need to see whether or not the set is LI and spans the given space; equivalently, using Definition 1 you need to see whether or not $\alpha_1\mathbf{e}_1 + \cdots + \alpha_n\mathbf{e}_n = \mathbf{u}$ has a unique solution for $\alpha_1, \ldots, \alpha_n$ for every given $\mathbf{u}$ in the space. For parts (o)–(r) we leave you to your own devices.

*(a) (1, 0), (1, 1), (1, 2) for $\mathbb{R}^2$
(b) (3, 2), (−1, −5) for $\mathbb{R}^2$
(c) (1, 1) for $\mathbb{R}^2$
(d) (2, 0, 1), (5, −1, 2), (1, −1, 0) for $\mathbb{R}^3$
(e) (5, −1, 2), (2, 0, 1), (1, −1, 1) for $\mathbb{R}^3$
(f) (2, 1, 0, 6), (7, −1, −2, 3), (4, 3, 2, 1) for $\mathbb{R}^4$
*(g) (4, 3, −2, 1), (5, 0, 0, 0), (2, 1, −3, 0), (1, 2, 4, 5) for $\mathbb{R}^4$
(h) (4, 2, 0, 0), (1, 2, 3, 0), (5, −2, 3, 1), (0, −6, 0, 1) for $\mathbb{R}^4$
(i) (1, 0, 0, 0), (1, 1, 0, 0), (1, 1, 1, 0), (1, 1, 1, 1) for $\mathbb{R}^4$
(j) (3, 0, 0, 1), (2, 0, 0, 1), (1, 3, 5, 6), (4, −2, 1, 3) for $\mathbb{R}^4$
(k) (1, 3, −1, 2), (1, 2, 4, 3), (2, 5, 3, 5), (3, 7, 7, 8) for $\mathbb{R}^4$
(l) (2, 3, 5, 0), (1, −1, 2, 3), (4, 1, 2, 3), (5, 4, 1, 0), (1, 2, 4, 6) for $\mathbb{R}^4$
(m) (1, 0, 0, 0), (0, 1, 0, 0), (0, 0, 1, 0), (0, 0, 0, 1), (0, 0, 0, 0) for $\mathbb{R}^4$
(n) (1, 0, 0, 0), (0, 1, 0, 0), (0, 0, 1, 0), (0, 0, 0, 0) for $\mathbb{R}^4$
(o) (1, 1, 2), (4, −2, −1) for span{(2, −4, −5), (1, −1, −1)}
*(p) (1, 1, 2), (4, −2, −1) for span{(3, −5, −6), (1, 2, 1)}
(q) (1, 1, 1), (1, −1, 2) for span{(2, 4, 1), (1, 7, −2)}
(r) (1, 2, 3), (1, 0, 4) for span{(3, 2, 0), (1, 1, −1)}

2. Expand each vector $\mathbf{u}$ in terms of the orthogonal basis $\{\mathbf{e}_1, \mathbf{e}_2, \mathbf{e}_3\}$ of $\mathbb{R}^3$, where $\mathbf{e}_1 = (2, 1, 3)$, $\mathbf{e}_2 = (1, -2, 0)$, $\mathbf{e}_3 = (6, 3, -5)$.

*(a) $\mathbf{u} = (1, 0, 0)$ (b) $\mathbf{u} = (9, -2, 4)$
(c) $\mathbf{u} = (0, 1, 5)$ (d) $\mathbf{u} = (3, -1, 1)$
(e) $\mathbf{u} = (0, 5, 0)$ (f) $\mathbf{u} = (1, 2, 3)$

3. *(a)–(f) Expand each of the $\mathbf{u}$ vectors in Exercise 2 in terms of the ON basis $\{\hat{\mathbf{e}}_1, \hat{\mathbf{e}}_2, \hat{\mathbf{e}}_3\}$ of $\mathbb{R}^3$, where $\hat{\mathbf{e}}_1 = (1/\sqrt{14})(2, 1, 3)$, $\hat{\mathbf{e}}_2 = (1/\sqrt{5})(1, -2, 0)$, $\hat{\mathbf{e}}_3 = (1/\sqrt{70})(6, 3, -5)$.

4. Expand each vector $\mathbf{u}$ in terms of the orthogonal basis $\{\mathbf{e}_1, \ldots, \mathbf{e}_4\}$ of $\mathbb{R}^4$, where $\mathbf{e}_1 = (2, 0, -1, -5)$, $\mathbf{e}_2 = (2, 0, -1, 1)$, $\mathbf{e}_3 = (0, 1, 0, 0)$, $\mathbf{e}_4 = (1, 0, 2, 0)$.

*(a) $\mathbf{u} = (1, 0, 0, 0)$ (b) $\mathbf{u} = (0, 6, 0, 0)$
(c) $\mathbf{u} = (2, 5, 1, -3)$ (d) $\mathbf{u} = (4, 3, -2, 0)$
(e) $\mathbf{u} = (1, 2, 0, 5)$ (f) $\mathbf{u} = (2, -7, 4, 1)$
(g) $\mathbf{u} = (0, 0, 0, 9)$ (h) $\mathbf{u} = (2, 3, -2, 1)$
(i) $\mathbf{u} = (0, 0, 5, 0)$

5. Show that the set (13) is a basis for $\mathbb{R}^4$, as claimed.

6. Show that the set (22) is a basis for $\mathbb{R}^4$, as claimed.

7. If $\{\mathbf{e}_1, \ldots, \mathbf{e}_k\}$ is an orthogonal set in a vector space $\mathscr{S}$, is it necessarily a basis for $\mathscr{S}$? Explain.

8. (a) How many different bases may be found for $\mathbb{R}^n$?

(b) How many different orthogonal bases may be found for $\mathbb{R}^n$?

9. (*Equation of a plane*) (a) To obtain the equation of a given plane in cartesian x, y, z space, suppose that $\mathbf{r}_0$ is a position vector $\mathbf{OP}_0$ which is normal to the plane, and let $\hat{\mathbf{n}}$ be a unit vector normal to the plane, as shown in the figure. Further, let P be any point (x, y, z) in the plane. (Think of P_0 as a fixed point, and of P as a variable point.) Then the set of all points P in the plane will be the set of all points such that $(\mathbf{P}_0\mathbf{P}) \cdot \hat{\mathbf{n}} = 0$. Use this result and the accompanying sketch to show that the equation of the plane may be expressed as

$$\hat{\mathbf{n}} \cdot \mathbf{r} = c, \tag{a}$$

and show that c happens to be the shortest (i.e., perpendicular) distance from the origin to the plane.

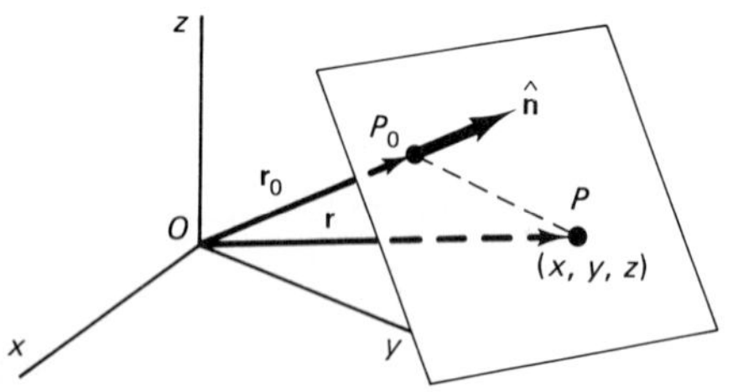

*(b) Determine the shortest distance from the origin to the plane, and a unit normal vector to the plane, for the plane defined by the equation $2x + 3y - z = 5$.
(c) Repeat part (b), for $6x - 5y = -2$.
(d) Repeat part (b), for $3x - 4y + 8z = 0$.
(e) Repeat part (b), for $x + y - 2z = -4$.

10. (*Zero vector space*) Show that a **zero vector space,** i.e., a vector space consisting of the zero vector alone, has no basis.

11. (*Gram–Schmidt orthogonalization process*) Given k LI vectors $\mathbf{v}_1, \ldots, \mathbf{v}_k$, it is possible to obtain from them k ON vectors, say $\hat{\mathbf{e}}_1, \ldots, \hat{\mathbf{e}}_k$, in span$\{\mathbf{v}_1, \ldots, \mathbf{v}_k\}$ by the **Gram–Schmidt process,** after *Jörgen P. Gram* (1850–1916) and *Erhardt Schmidt* (1876–1959), by taking $\mathbf{e}_1$ equal to $\mathbf{v}_1$, taking $\mathbf{e}_2$ equal to a suitable linear combination of $\mathbf{v}_1$, $\mathbf{v}_2$, taking $\mathbf{e}_3$ equal to a suitable linear combination of $\mathbf{v}_1$, $\mathbf{v}_2$, $\mathbf{v}_3$, and so on, and then normalizing the results. The resulting ON set is as follows:

$$\begin{aligned}
\hat{\mathbf{e}}_1 &= \frac{\mathbf{v}_1}{\|\mathbf{v}_1\|},\\
\hat{\mathbf{e}}_2 &= \frac{\mathbf{v}_2 - (\mathbf{v}_2 \cdot \hat{\mathbf{e}}_1)\hat{\mathbf{e}}_1}{\|\mathbf{v}_2 - (\mathbf{v}_2 \cdot \hat{\mathbf{e}}_1)\hat{\mathbf{e}}_1\|},\\
&\;\vdots\\
\hat{\mathbf{e}}_j &= \frac{\mathbf{v}_j - \sum_{i=1}^{j-1} (\mathbf{v}_j \cdot \hat{\mathbf{e}}_i)\hat{\mathbf{e}}_i}{\|\mathbf{v}_j - \sum_{i=1}^{j-1} (\mathbf{v}_j \cdot \hat{\mathbf{e}}_i)\hat{\mathbf{e}}_i\|} \qquad \text{through } j = k.
\end{aligned} \tag{a}$$

We now state the problem: Verify that each $\hat{\mathbf{e}}_j$ defined by (a) is a linear combination of $\mathbf{v}_1, \ldots, \mathbf{v}_j$, and that the $\hat{\mathbf{e}}_j$'s are ON. [In verifying that $\|\hat{\mathbf{e}}_j\| = 1$, be sure to show that each denominator in (a) is nonzero.]

12. In each case use the Gram–Schmidt formula (a) in Exercise 11 to obtain an ON set from the given LI set.

*(a) (4, 0), (2, 1)
(b) (1, −2), (3, 4)
(c) (1, 0, 0), (1, 1, 0), (1, 1, 1)
*(d) (1, 1, 0), (2, −1, 1), (1, 0, 3)
(e) (1, 1, 1), (2, 0, −1)
(f) (1, 1, 1), (1, 0, 1), (1, 1, 0)
(g) (1, 2, 1), (1, −1, 2), (−1, 3, 1)
(h) (2, 0, 1), (1, 1, 1), (−2, 0, 3)
(i) (2, 1, 1, 0), (1, 5, −1, 2)
(j) (6, −1, 1, 2, 1), (2, 3, −1, 1, 4)

13. (*The dual or reciprocal vectors*) For definiteness, consider our vector space $\mathscr{S}$ to be $\mathbb{R}^n$.

(a) If $\{\hat{\mathbf{e}}_1, \ldots, \hat{\mathbf{e}}_n\}$ is an ON basis for $\mathbb{R}^n$, and $\mathbf{u}$ is in $\mathbb{R}^n$, then by dotting $\hat{\mathbf{e}}_i$ into both sides of the equation $\mathbf{u} = \sum_{j=1}^n \alpha_j \hat{\mathbf{e}}_j$, we find that $\alpha_i = \mathbf{u} \cdot \hat{\mathbf{e}}_i$, so that the expansion of $\mathbf{u}$ in terms of the given basis is

$$\mathbf{u} = \sum_{j=1}^{n} (\mathbf{u} \cdot \hat{\mathbf{e}}_j)\, \hat{\mathbf{e}}_j. \tag{a}$$

If, instead, we have a basis $\{\mathbf{e}_1, \ldots, \mathbf{e}_n\}$ which is *not* ON, then, as noted in the text, the expansion process is not so simple. However, suppose that we can find a set $\{\mathbf{e}_1^*, \ldots, \mathbf{e}_n^*\}$ such that

$$\mathbf{e}_i \cdot \mathbf{e}_j^* = \begin{cases} 1, & i = j \\ 0, & i \neq j. \end{cases} \tag{b}$$

Then show that dotting $\mathbf{e}_i^*$ into $\mathbf{u} = \sum_{j=1}^n \alpha_j \mathbf{e}_j$ gives $\alpha_i = \mathbf{u} \cdot \mathbf{e}_i^*$, so that

$$\mathbf{u} = \textstyle\sum_{j=1}^n (\mathbf{u} \cdot \mathbf{e}_j^*)\mathbf{e}_j. \tag{c}$$

The set $\{\mathbf{e}_1^*, \ldots, \mathbf{e}_n^*\}$ is called the *dual* or *reciprocal* set corresponding to the original set $\{\mathbf{e}_1, \ldots, \mathbf{e}_n\}$. (We will see in Exercise 18 on page 119 that the dual set exists, is unique, and is itself a basis for $\mathbb{R}^n$, the so-called *dual* or *reciprocal basis*.)

(b) Given the basis $\mathbf{e}_1 = (1, 0)$, $\mathbf{e}_2 = (1, 1)$ for $\mathbb{R}^2$, use equation (b) to determine the dual vectors $\mathbf{e}_1^*, \mathbf{e}_2^*$. Then use equation (c) to expand $\mathbf{u} = (3, 1)$. Sketch $\mathbf{e}_1, \mathbf{e}_2, \mathbf{e}_1^*, \mathbf{e}_2^*, \mathbf{u}$ to scale, and verify the expansion graphically, i.e., by means of the parallelogram rule of vector addition.

(c) Repeat part (b), for $\mathbf{e}_1 = (2, 1)$, $\mathbf{e}_2 = (0, 2)$, $\mathbf{u} = (-3, 2)$.

(d) Repeat part (b), for $\mathbf{e}_1 = (-1, 1)$, $\mathbf{e}_2 = (2, 1)$, $\mathbf{u} = (0, 4)$.

*(e) Given the basis $\mathbf{e}_1 = (1, 0, 0)$, $\mathbf{e}_2 = (1, 1, 0)$, $\mathbf{e}_3 = (1, 1, 1)$ for $\mathbb{R}^3$, use equation (b) to determine the dual vectors $\mathbf{e}_1^*, \mathbf{e}_2^*, \mathbf{e}_3^*$. Then use equation (c) to expand each of the vectors $\mathbf{u} = (4, -1, 5)$, $\mathbf{v} = (0, 0, 2)$, and $\mathbf{w} = (5, -2, 3)$. Be sure to see that the dual vectors get computed once and for all, for a given basis $\{\mathbf{e}_1, \ldots, \mathbf{e}_n\}$; once we have got them, expansions of the form (c) are simple.

(f) Repeat part (e) for $\mathbf{e}_1 = (2, 0, 1)$, $\mathbf{e}_2 = (1, 1, 0)$, $\mathbf{e}_3 = (1, -1, 3)$, and $\mathbf{u} = (6, 1, 0)$, $\mathbf{v} = (1, 2, 4)$, $\mathbf{w} = (0, 3, 0)$.

(g) Show that if the $\{\mathbf{e}_1, \ldots, \mathbf{e}_n\}$ basis does happen to be ON, then the dual vectors coalesce with the $\mathbf{e}_j$'s, i.e., $\mathbf{e}_j^* = \mathbf{e}_j$ for $j = 1, 2, \ldots, n$.

DIMENSION 2.10

If we always worked in 3-space, the notion of dimension would hardly need elaboration; e.g., 3-space is three-dimensional, any plane within it is two-dimensional, and any line within it is one-dimensional. However, having extended our vector concept beyond 3-space, we need to clarify the idea of "dimension," and that is the object of this final section of Chapter 2.

Definition 1 *Dimension*
If the greatest number of LI vectors that can be found in a vector space $\mathcal{S}$ is k, where $1 \le k < \infty$, then $\mathcal{S}$ is ***k*-dimensional,** and we write

$$\dim \mathcal{S} = k. \tag{1}$$

If $\mathcal{S}$ is the zero vector space (i.e., if it contains only the zero vector), we define $\dim \mathcal{S} = 0$. If an arbitrarily large number of LI vectors can be found in $\mathcal{S}$, we say that $\mathcal{S}$ is infinite-dimensional.*

To determine the dimension of a given vector space, if that dimension turns out to be finite, we may rely on the following theorem rather than working directly from Definition 1.

Theorem 1 *Dimension*
If for a vector space $\mathcal{S}$, a basis can be found consisting of k vectors, where $1 \le k < \infty$, then $\mathcal{S}$ is k-dimensional.

Proof Let $\{\mathbf{e}_1, \ldots, \mathbf{e}_k\}$ be a basis for $\mathcal{S}$. Because these vectors form a basis, they must be LI. Hence we have *at least* k LI vectors in $\mathcal{S}$, and it remains to show that *no*

* The infinite-dimensional case will be encountered later when we discuss Fourier series.

more than k LI vectors can be found in $\mathcal{S}$. Well, suppose that vectors $\mathbf{e}_1', \ldots, \mathbf{e}_{k+1}'$, in $\mathcal{S}$, *are* LI. Each of these can be expanded in terms of the given base vectors, as

$$\begin{aligned} \mathbf{e}_1' &= a_{11}\mathbf{e}_1 + \cdots + a_{1k}\mathbf{e}_k \\ &\vdots \\ \mathbf{e}_{k+1}' &= a_{k+1,1}\mathbf{e}_1 + \cdots + a_{k+1,k}\mathbf{e}_k, \end{aligned} \tag{2}$$

say. Putting these expressions into the equation

$$\alpha_1\mathbf{e}_1' + \alpha_2\mathbf{e}_2' + \cdots + \alpha_{k+1}\mathbf{e}_{k+1}' = \mathbf{0}, \tag{3}$$

and grouping terms, gives

$$(\alpha_1 a_{11} + \cdots + \alpha_{k+1}a_{k+1,1})\mathbf{e}_1 + \cdots + (\alpha_1 a_{1k} + \cdots + \alpha_{k+1}a_{k+1,k})\mathbf{e}_k = \mathbf{0}.$$

But the set $\{\mathbf{e}_1, \ldots, \mathbf{e}_k\}$ is LI, since it is a basis, so each coefficient in the preceding equation must be zero:

$$\begin{aligned} a_{11}\alpha_1 + \cdots + a_{k+1,1}\alpha_{k+1} &= 0 \\ &\vdots \\ a_{1k}\alpha_1 + \cdots + a_{k+1,k}\alpha_{k+1} &= 0. \end{aligned} \tag{4}$$

These are k linear homogeneous equations in the $k + 1$ unknowns α_1 through α_{k+1}, and such a system necessarily admits nontrivial solutions (Exercise 10, page 17). Thus the α's in (3) are not all necessarily zero, so the vectors $\mathbf{e}_1', \ldots, \mathbf{e}_{k+1}'$ could not have been LI after all. Hence it is not possible to find more that k LI vectors in $\mathcal{S}$, and this completes the proof. ■

Now the spaces of concern in Part I are the n-tuple spaces $\mathbb{R}^n$, and subspaces thereof. For $\mathbb{R}^n$ we have:

> ***Theorem 2*** *Dimension of* $\mathbb{R}^n$
> The dimension of $\mathbb{R}^n$ is n.

Proof We have already seen in Section 2.9 that the *standard basis* contains n vectors. Thus it follows, from Theorem 1, that $\dim \mathbb{R}^n = n$. ■

Indeed, we might well have questioned the reasonableness of our definition of dimension if $\mathbb{R}^n$ had turned out to be other than n-dimensional!

Finally, what about the dimension of a *subspace,* for example, the subspace of $\mathbb{R}^3$ that is spanned by two given vectors?

> ***Theorem 3*** *Dimension of span* $\{\mathbf{u}_1, \ldots, \mathbf{u}_k\}$
> The dimension of span $\{\mathbf{u}_1, \ldots, \mathbf{u}_k\}$, where the $\mathbf{u}$'s are not all zero, denoted as dim [span $\{\mathbf{u}_1, \ldots, \mathbf{u}_k\}$], is equal to the greatest number of LI vectors within the generating set $\{\mathbf{u}_1, \ldots, \mathbf{u}_k\}$.

Proof Denote the generating set $\{\mathbf{u}_1, \ldots, \mathbf{u}_k\}$ as U. Let the greatest number of LI vectors in U be N, where $1 \leq N \leq k$. It may be assumed, without loss of generality, that the members of U have been numbered so that $\mathbf{u}_1, \ldots, \mathbf{u}_N$ are LI; then each of the remaining members of U, namely $\mathbf{u}_{N+1}, \ldots, \mathbf{u}_k$, can be expressed as a linear combination of $\mathbf{u}_1, \ldots, \mathbf{u}_N$. Surely, then, each vector in span U can similarly be expressed as a linear combination of $\mathbf{u}_1, \ldots, \mathbf{u}_N$. Now $\{\mathbf{u}_1, \ldots, \mathbf{u}_N\}$ is LI and spans span U. According to Theorem 1, then, the dimension of span U is N, i.e. , it is the same as the greatest number of LI vectors in U, as was to be proved. ■

EXAMPLE 1 What is the dimension of the subspace of $\mathbb{R}^3$ that is spanned by

$$\mathbf{u}_1 = (1, 0, 2), \qquad \mathbf{u}_2 = (3, -1, 0)? \tag{5}$$

These vectors are LI since neither one is a scalar multiple of the other. Hence there are two LI vectors within the generating set, and, according to Theorem 3, $\dim[\text{span}\{\mathbf{u}_1, \mathbf{u}_2\}] = 2$.

COMMENT It does *not* follow that span$\{\mathbf{u}_1, \mathbf{u}_2\}$ is $\mathbb{R}^2$; $\mathbf{u}_1$, $\mathbf{u}_2$, and hence all linear combinations of $\mathbf{u}_1$, $\mathbf{u}_2$, are *3-tuples,* not 2-tuples. It just happens that span$\{\mathbf{u}_1, \mathbf{u}_2\}$ is a two-dimensional subspace of $\mathbb{R}^3$, namely the *plane* containing $\mathbf{u}_1$ and $\mathbf{u}_2$. ◀

EXAMPLE 2 Let

$$\mathbf{u}_1 = (3, -1, 2, 1), \qquad \mathbf{u}_2 = (1, 1, 0, -1), \qquad \mathbf{u}_3 = (4, 0, 2, 0). \tag{6}$$

These vectors are, of course, members of $\mathbb{R}^4$. But since $\mathbf{u}_1$, $\mathbf{u}_2$, $\mathbf{u}_3$ are only three vectors, $\dim[\text{span}\{\mathbf{u}_1, \mathbf{u}_2, \mathbf{u}_3\}]$ is *at most* three. In fact, it is *not* three, since we see (by inspection) that $\mathbf{u}_3 = \mathbf{u}_1 + \mathbf{u}_2$. But $\mathbf{u}_1$ and $\mathbf{u}_2$, say, are LI, since neither is a scalar multiple of the other. Thus there are only two LI vectors within the generating set, so $\dim[\text{span}\{\mathbf{u}_1, \mathbf{u}_2, \mathbf{u}_3\}] = 2$. ◀

Admittedly, we have not spelled out a standard procedure for determining the greatest number of LI vectors in a given set $\{\mathbf{u}_1, \ldots, \mathbf{u}_k\}$. Such a procedure will emerge in Section 3.5 when we discuss the notion of "rank." Meanwhile, in the present section, we will "get by" by keeping the examples and exercises simple enough so that fundamentals will suffice.

THE KRONECKER DELTA

There is a useful bit of notation that might well be introduced at this point, namely, the **Kronecker delta*** δ_{ij}, defined as

$$\delta_{ij} \equiv \begin{cases} 1 & \text{if } i = j \\ 0 & \text{if } i \neq j \end{cases}, \tag{7}$$

* After *Leopold Kronecker* (1823–1891), who contributed to algebra and the theory of equations. It was Kronecker who said "God made the integers; all else is the work of man."

where the subscripted i and j are normally positive integers. Clearly, δ_{ij} is symmetric in i and j, that is,

$$\delta_{ij} = \delta_{ji}. \tag{8}$$

To illustrate its use, recall that $\{\hat{\mathbf{e}}_1, \ldots, \hat{\mathbf{e}}_k\}$ is ON if and only if

$$\hat{\mathbf{e}}_i \cdot \hat{\mathbf{e}}_j = \begin{cases} 1 & \text{if } i = j \\ 0 & \text{if } i \neq j \end{cases} \tag{9}$$

i.e., if and only if

$$\boxed{\hat{\mathbf{e}}_i \cdot \hat{\mathbf{e}}_j = \delta_{ij}.} \tag{10}$$

Further, suppose that $\{\hat{\mathbf{e}}_1, \ldots, \hat{\mathbf{e}}_k\}$ is an ON basis for some space $\mathscr{S}$ and that we wish to expand a given vector $\mathbf{u}$ in $\mathscr{S}$ as

$$\mathbf{u} = \sum_{i=1}^{k} \alpha_i \hat{\mathbf{e}}_i, \tag{11}$$

i.e., we wish to evaluate the expansion coefficients α_i. Dotting $\hat{\mathbf{e}}_j$ (where j is any integer such that $1 \leq j \leq k$) into (11),

$$\mathbf{u} \cdot \hat{\mathbf{e}}_j = \left(\sum_{i=1}^{k} \alpha_i \hat{\mathbf{e}}_i\right) \cdot \hat{\mathbf{e}}_j = \sum_{i=1}^{k} \alpha_i \hat{\mathbf{e}}_i \cdot \hat{\mathbf{e}}_j = \sum_{i=1}^{k} \alpha_i \delta_{ij} = \alpha_j. \tag{12}$$

Thus the expansion coefficients are given by $\alpha_j = \mathbf{u} \cdot \hat{\mathbf{e}}_j$ or, equivalently, $\alpha_i = \mathbf{u} \cdot \hat{\mathbf{e}}_i$, so (11) becomes

$$\mathbf{u} = \sum_{i=1}^{k} (\mathbf{u} \cdot \hat{\mathbf{e}}_i)\, \hat{\mathbf{e}}_i. \tag{13}$$

This formula agrees with our earlier result, equation (21) on page 53; the only difference is in our use, here, of the more compact Kronecker delta notation.

2.10 EXERCISES

1. Let $\mathbf{u}_1 = (1, 0, 0)$, $\mathbf{u}_2 = (0, 1, 0)$, $\mathbf{u}_3 = (0, 0, 1)$, $\mathbf{u}_4 = (1, 1, 0)$, $\mathbf{u}_5 = (0, 1, 1)$, $\mathbf{u}_6 = (1, 1, 1)$, and $\mathbf{u}_7 = (3, 2, 2)$. Evaluate each of the following.

*(a) dim [span $\{\mathbf{u}_1\}$]
(b) dim [span $\{\mathbf{u}_1, \mathbf{u}_2\}$]
(c) dim [span $\{\mathbf{u}_1, \mathbf{u}_2, \mathbf{u}_3\}$]
*(d) dim [span $\{\mathbf{u}_1, \mathbf{u}_2, \mathbf{u}_3, \mathbf{u}_4\}$]
(e) dim [span $\{\mathbf{u}_1, \mathbf{u}_2, \mathbf{u}_4\}$]
(f) dim [span $\{\mathbf{u}_1, \mathbf{u}_4, \mathbf{u}_5\}$]
(g) dim [span $\{\mathbf{u}_5, \mathbf{u}_6, \mathbf{u}_7\}$]
(h) dim [span $\{\mathbf{u}_1, \mathbf{u}_5, \mathbf{u}_6, \mathbf{u}_7\}$]

2. Let $\mathbf{u}_1 = (1, 0, 0, 0)$, $\mathbf{u}_2 = (1, 1, 0, 0)$, $\mathbf{u}_3 = (1, 1, 1, 0)$, $\mathbf{u}_4 = (1, 1, 1, 1)$, $\mathbf{u}_5 = (0, 0, 0, 1)$, and $\mathbf{u}_6 = (3, 3, 3, 3)$. Evaluate each of the following.

*(a) dim [span $\{\mathbf{u}_1, \mathbf{u}_3, \mathbf{u}_5\}$]
(b) dim [span $\{\mathbf{u}_1, \mathbf{u}_4, \mathbf{u}_6\}$]
(c) dim [span $\{\mathbf{u}_2, \mathbf{u}_4, \mathbf{u}_6\}$]
*(d) dim [span $\{\mathbf{u}_5\}$]
(e) dim [span $\{\mathbf{u}_3, \mathbf{u}_4\}$]
(f) dim [span $\{\mathbf{u}_3, \mathbf{u}_4, \mathbf{u}_5, \mathbf{u}_6\}$]
(g) dim [span $\{\mathbf{u}_4, \mathbf{u}_6\}$]
(h) dim [span $\{\mathbf{u}_2, \mathbf{u}_3, \mathbf{u}_4, \mathbf{u}_5, \mathbf{u}_6\}$]

3. *(a)–(f) (*Solution space*) First, read Exercises 4 and 5 on page 45. We now state the problem: Determine the dimension of the solution space in Exercise 5 on page 45.

4. Show that if $\mathscr{S}$ is k-dimensional, and $\mathbf{e}_1, \ldots, \mathbf{e}_k$ are LI vectors in $\mathscr{S}$, then $\{\mathbf{e}_1, \ldots, \mathbf{e}_k\}$ is a basis for $\mathscr{S}$.

5. Show that if $\{\mathbf{e}_1, \ldots, \mathbf{e}_k\}$ and $\{\mathbf{f}_1, \ldots, \mathbf{f}_l\}$ are two bases for a given space $\mathscr{S}$, then k must equal l.

6. Verify the last step in (12), namely, that $\sum_{i=1}^{k} \alpha_i \delta_{ij} = \alpha_j$.

7. Verify the following identities, where all indices (i, j, k, l) are understood to run from 1 to N.

(a) $\sum_j \delta_{ij} = 1$

(b) $\sum_j \delta_{ij} \delta_{jk} = \delta_{ik}$

(c) $\sum_j \sum_k \delta_{ij} \delta_{jk} \delta_{kl} = \delta_{il}$

8. Determine the dimension of each "hyperplane."

*(a) $x_1 - 3x_2 + 5x_3 + x_4 = 0$ in $\mathbb{R}^4$
(b) $x_1 + 2x_4 = 0$ in $\mathbb{R}^4$
(c) $2x_1 - x_2 + x_3 = 0$ in $\mathbb{R}^3$
(d) $x_1 - 3x_2 + 2x_5 = 0$ in $\mathbb{R}^5$
(e) $x_1 - 2x_4 + x_6 = 0$ in $\mathbb{R}^6$

3 Matrices, Determinants, and Linear Equations

3.1 INTRODUCTION

In this chapter we provide a systematic introduction first to matrices and matrix algebra, and then to determinants. This rather natural order of presentation is the reverse of the historical order, with determinants dating back to the middle of the eighteenth century, but with matrices not being formalized until Cayley's first major paper on the subject in 1858.* Vectors, matrices, and determinants will be the principal objects of interest throughout the remainder of Part I.

3.2 MATRICES AND MATRIX ALGEBRA

A **matrix** is a rectangular array of quantities that are called the *elements* (or *entries*) of the matrix. Normally, the elements will be real numbers,† although they may occasionally be other objects, such as differential operators or even matrices themselves. Some of these cases will be met as we go along; for the present, however, let us consider the elements to be *real numbers*.

Specifically, any matrix **A** may be expressed as

**Arthur Cayley* (1821–1895). In fact, the paper mentioned above was one of around 200 produced by Cayley in a 15-year period during which he was engaged in the practice of law. This period ended in 1863, when he accepted a professorship of mathematics at Cambridge.

†Occasionally, the elements will be *complex*; extension to that case is contained in Chapter 5.

$$\mathbf{A} = \begin{pmatrix} a_{11} & a_{12} & \cdots & a_{1n} \\ a_{21} & a_{22} & \cdots & a_{2n} \\ \vdots & \vdots & & \vdots \\ a_{m1} & a_{m2} & \cdots & a_{mn} \end{pmatrix}, \tag{1}$$

where the parentheses are used to emphasize that the entire array is to be regarded as a single entity. A horizontal line of elements is called a **row**, and a vertical one is called a **column**. Counting rows from the top and columns from the left, then

$$a_{21} \quad a_{22} \quad \cdots \quad a_{2n} \quad \text{and} \quad \begin{matrix} a_{13} \\ a_{23} \\ \vdots \\ a_{m3}, \end{matrix}$$

say, are the second row and third column, respectively. Thus we call the first subscript on a_{ij} the *row index*, and the second subscript the *column index*.

We usually use boldface capital letters to denote matrices and lightface lowercase letters to denote their elements. The matrix $\mathbf{A}$ in (1) is seen to have m rows and n columns and is therefore said to be $m \times n$ (read "m by n"); we shall refer to this as the *form* of $\mathbf{A}$. In some applications m and/or n may be infinite, but here we shall consider only matrices of finite size: $1 \leq m < \infty$, $1 \leq n < \infty$. Furthermore, m and n may, but need not, be equal. If $\mathbf{A}$ is small (e.g., m and n both less that 4) we may wish to dispense with the subscript notation for the elements. For example, if $m = n = 2$, we may prefer

$$\mathbf{A} = \begin{pmatrix} a & b \\ c & d \end{pmatrix} \quad \text{to} \quad \mathbf{A} = \begin{pmatrix} a_{11} & a_{12} \\ a_{21} & a_{22} \end{pmatrix}, \tag{2}$$

but if $\mathbf{A}$ is large this becomes inconvenient. What is more, the double-subscript notation employed in (1) is convenient in digital computer calculations.

In view of the subscript notation in (1), one also writes

$$\mathbf{A} = \{a_{ij}\} \tag{3}$$

for short, where a_{ij} is called the *ij element* and $i = 1, \ldots, m$ and $j = 1, \ldots, n$. Some authors write $a_{i,j}$ in place of a_{ij} to avoid ambiguity—for example, to prevent us from reading a_{21} as a-sub-twenty-one, but we choose to omit the commas, except when such ambiguity is not easily resolved from the context.

EXAMPLE 1

$$\mathbf{A} = \begin{pmatrix} 3 & -2 \\ 0 & 1 \\ 5 & 4 \end{pmatrix}, \qquad \mathbf{B} = \begin{pmatrix} 3 & -2 & 0 \\ 0 & 1 & 0 \\ 5 & 4 & 0 \end{pmatrix}, \qquad \mathbf{C} = (8, -7, 0, 4, 3),$$

$$\mathbf{D} = \begin{pmatrix} 6 & 0 & 2 & \sqrt{5} \\ 3 & 1 & -1 & 0 \\ -1 & 2 & 3 & 0 \\ \pi & 0 & 5 & -2 \end{pmatrix}, \quad \mathbf{E} = \begin{pmatrix} 3 \\ 2 \\ 12 \\ -9 \end{pmatrix}, \quad \mathbf{F} = \begin{pmatrix} 3 & -2 \\ 0 & 1 \\ 5 & 4 \end{pmatrix}, \quad \mathbf{G} = (4).$$

These matrices are 3×2, 3×3, 1×5, 4×4, 4×1, 3×2, and 1×1, respectively. If we denote $\mathbf{D} = \{d_{ij}\}$, $\mathbf{E} = \{e_{ij}\}$, and $\mathbf{G} = \{g_{ij}\}$, then $d_{14} = \sqrt{5}$, $d_{43} = 5$, $d_{44} = -2$, $e_{31} = 12$, $g_{11} = 4$, and so on. **C** happens to be a single row; in that case we frequently separate the elements by commas, but the commas are not essential. ◀

Two matrices are said to be **equal** if they are of the same form, and if their corresponding elements are equal. Thus the only matrices in Example 1 that are equal are **A** and **F**; i.e., $\mathbf{A} = \mathbf{F}$. It is to be emphasized that $\mathbf{A} \neq \mathbf{B}$; the third column (of zeros) in **B** *cannot* be ignored or discarded and, by the same token, we cannot simply add a column of zeros to **A**; **A** is 3×2, **B** is 3×3, so there is no way they can be equal.

One may be tempted to identify matrix **C** above as a 5-tuple vector. That would be a bit premature, since vectors are not merely objects; they have rules for vector addition and scalar multiplication defined, whereas our matrices are, thus far, just mathematical "objects." In fact, our next step is to define some arithmetic operations for matrices so that they may be manipulated in useful ways. For vectors we defined two arithmetic operations, vector addition and scalar multiplication; for matrices we define three: matrix addition, scalar multiplication, *and* the multiplication of matrices.

MATRIX ADDITION

If $\mathbf{A} = \{a_{ij}\}$ and $\mathbf{B} = \{b_{ij}\}$ are any two matrices of the same form, say $m \times n$, then their *sum* $\mathbf{A} + \mathbf{B}$ is defined as

$$\boxed{\mathbf{A} + \mathbf{B} \equiv \{a_{ij} + b_{ij}\}} \tag{4}$$

and is itself an $m \times n$ matrix. If **A** and **B** are of the same form, they are said to be *conformable for addition*; if they are not of the same form, the sum $\mathbf{A} + \mathbf{B}$ is *not defined.*

EXAMPLE 2 If

$$\mathbf{A} = \begin{pmatrix} 2 & 0 & -6 \\ 1 & 3 & 4 \end{pmatrix}, \quad \mathbf{B} = \begin{pmatrix} -1 & 2 & 0 \\ 15 & 6 & 3 \end{pmatrix}, \quad \mathbf{C} = \begin{pmatrix} 4 & 2 \\ -1 & 0 \end{pmatrix}, \tag{5}$$

then

$$\mathbf{A} + \mathbf{B} = \begin{pmatrix} 1 & 2 & -6 \\ 16 & 9 & 7 \end{pmatrix}, \tag{6}$$

but $\mathbf{A} + \mathbf{C}$ and $\mathbf{B} + \mathbf{C}$ are not defined since **A** and **B** are 2×3 while **C** is 2×2. ◀

SCALAR MULTIPLICATION

If $\mathbf{A} = \{a_{ij}\}$ is any $m \times n$ matrix and c is any scalar, the product $c\mathbf{A}$ is defined as

$$\boxed{c\mathbf{A} \equiv \{ca_{ij}\},} \tag{7}$$

and is itself an $m \times n$ matrix; we do not distinguish between $c\mathbf{A}$ and $\mathbf{A}c$. Furthermore, we denote

$$-\mathbf{A} \equiv (-1)\mathbf{A}. \tag{8}$$

In place of $\mathbf{A} + (-\mathbf{B})$, we simply write $\mathbf{A} - \mathbf{B}$, and call it the *difference* of **A** and **B**, or **A** *minus* **B**.

EXAMPLE 3 If **A** and **E** are the matrices in Example 1, then 3**A** and −**E**, say, are

$$3\mathbf{A} = \begin{pmatrix} 9 & -6 \\ 0 & 3 \\ 15 & 12 \end{pmatrix} \quad \text{and} \quad -\mathbf{E} = \begin{pmatrix} -3 \\ -2 \\ -12 \\ 9 \end{pmatrix}. \blacktriangleleft \tag{9}$$

We shall list the important properties of matrix addition and scalar multiplication in a moment, but first let us define the so-called **zero matrix 0** to be any $m \times n$ matrix all the elements of which are zero. For example,

$$\begin{pmatrix} 0 & 0 & 0 \\ 0 & 0 & 0 \end{pmatrix} = \mathbf{0} \quad \text{and} \quad \begin{pmatrix} 0 \\ 0 \\ 0 \end{pmatrix} = \mathbf{0},$$

the first being 2×3, the second being 3×1.

Theorem 1 *Properties of Matrix Addition and Scalar Multiplication*
If **A**, **B**, and **C** are any $m \times n$ matrices, **0** is an $m \times n$ zero matrix, and α, β are any scalars, then

$$\mathbf{A} + \mathbf{B} = \mathbf{B} + \mathbf{A} \qquad \text{(commutativity)} \tag{10a}$$

$$(\mathbf{A} + \mathbf{B}) + \mathbf{C} = \mathbf{A} + (\mathbf{B} + \mathbf{C}) \qquad \text{(associativity)} \tag{10b}$$

$$\mathbf{A} + \mathbf{0} = \mathbf{A} \tag{10c}$$

$$\mathbf{A} + (-\mathbf{A}) = \mathbf{0} \tag{10d}$$

$$\alpha(\beta\mathbf{A}) = (\alpha\beta)\mathbf{A} \qquad \text{(associativity)} \tag{10e}$$

$$(\alpha + \beta)\mathbf{A} = \alpha\mathbf{A} + \beta\mathbf{A} \qquad \text{(distributivity)} \tag{10f}$$

$$\alpha(\mathbf{A} + \mathbf{B}) = \alpha\mathbf{A} + \alpha\mathbf{B} \qquad \text{(distributivity)} \tag{10g}$$

$$1\mathbf{A} = \mathbf{A}$$

$$0\mathbf{A} = \mathbf{0} \tag{10h}$$

$$\alpha\mathbf{0} = \mathbf{0}. \tag{10i}$$

The proof follows easily from the foregoing definitions, and is left for the exercises.

Observe that there are no surprises in (10); the usual rules of arithmetic are seen to apply. For the special case where **A** consists of a single row (or column), we see that the definitions of addition and scalar multiplication above are identical to those introduced in Section 2.4 for n-tuple vectors. Thus we may properly refer to the matrices

$$\mathbf{A} = (a_{11}, a_{12}, \ldots, a_{1n}) \quad \text{and} \quad \mathbf{A} = \begin{pmatrix} a_{11} \\ a_{21} \\ \cdot \\ \cdot \\ \cdot \\ a_{n1} \end{pmatrix} \tag{11}$$

as n-dimensional **row** and **column vectors**, respectively.

MATRIX MULTIPLICATION

Judging from the rather natural way in which matrix addition and scalar multiplication are defined, by (4) and (7), one might well expect the multiplication of two matrices $\mathbf{A} = \{a_{ij}\}$ and $\mathbf{B} = \{b_{ij}\}$ to be defined only if $\mathbf{A}$ and $\mathbf{B}$ are of the same form, with the definition $\mathbf{AB} \equiv \{a_{ij}b_{ij}\}$. In fact, this is *not* the case. Instead, the standard definition of matrix multiplication is the one suggested by Cayley. Called the *Cayley product*, it is as follows: If $\mathbf{A} = \{a_{ij}\}$ is any $m \times n$ matrix and $\mathbf{B} = \{b_{ij}\}$ is any $n \times p$ matrix (so that the number of columns of $\mathbf{A}$ is equal to the number of rows of $\mathbf{B}$), then the product $\mathbf{AB}$ is defined as

$$\boxed{\mathbf{AB} \equiv \left\{ \sum_{k=1}^{n} a_{ik}b_{kj} \right\};} \tag{12}$$

i.e., if we denote $\mathbf{AB} = \mathbf{C} = \{c_{ij}\}$, then

$$c_{ij} = \sum_{k=1}^{n} a_{ik}b_{kj}. \tag{13}$$

If the number of columns of $\mathbf{A}$ is equal to the number of rows of $\mathbf{B}$, then $\mathbf{A}$ and $\mathbf{B}$ are said to be *conformable for multiplication*; if not, the product $\mathbf{AB}$ is *not defined*. *Note:* The relative forms of $\mathbf{A}$, $\mathbf{B}$ and their product $\mathbf{C}$ are important and, as stated above, are as follows:

$$\underset{m \times n}{\mathbf{A}} \quad \text{times} \quad \underset{n \times p}{\mathbf{B}} = \underset{m \times p}{\mathbf{C}}. \tag{14}$$

(the two n's: equal)

EXAMPLE 4 Suppose that

$$\mathbf{A} = \begin{pmatrix} 2 & 0 & -5 \\ 1 & 3 & 2 \\ 4 & 1 & -1 \\ 0 & 2 & 7 \end{pmatrix} \quad \text{and} \quad \mathbf{B} = \begin{pmatrix} 5 & 1 \\ -2 & 3 \\ 1 & 0 \end{pmatrix}.$$

Then $\mathbf{A}$ is 4×3 and $\mathbf{B}$ is 3×2. Since the number of columns of $\mathbf{A}$ (namely, 3) is the same as the number of rows of $\mathbf{B}$, the product $\mathbf{AB}$ is defined and, according to (14), will be 4×2. According to the definition (13),

$$\mathbf{AB} = \begin{pmatrix} 2 & 0 & -5 \\ 1 & 3 & 2 \\ 4 & 1 & -1 \\ 0 & 2 & 7 \end{pmatrix} \begin{pmatrix} 5 & 1 \\ -2 & 3 \\ 1 & 0 \end{pmatrix} = \begin{pmatrix} 5 & 2 \\ 1 & 10 \\ 17 & \boxed{7} \\ 3 & 6 \end{pmatrix} = \mathbf{C}. \tag{15}$$

$$4 \times 3 \qquad\qquad 3 \times 2 \qquad\qquad 4 \times 2$$

Looking at c_{32}, for example, (13) gives

$$c_{32} = \sum_{k=1}^{3} a_{3k} b_{k2} = (4)(1) + (1)(3) + (-1)(0) = 7,$$

(a_{3k}: 3rd row of **A**; b_{k2}: 2nd column of **B**)

as indicated by the arrows in (15).* One more:

$$c_{11} = \sum_{k=1}^{3} a_{1k} b_{k1} = (2)(5) + (0)(-2) + (-5)(1) = 5.$$

We move across the rows of the first matrix, and down the columns of the second. ◀

EXAMPLE 5 As two additional examples,

$$\underset{3 \times 3}{\begin{pmatrix} 5 & 0 & -1 \\ 2 & 3 & 4 \\ 1 & 0 & 6 \end{pmatrix}} \underset{3 \times 1}{\begin{pmatrix} 3 \\ 2 \\ 5 \end{pmatrix}} = \underset{3 \times 1}{\begin{pmatrix} (5)(3) + (0)(2) + (-1)(5) \\ (2)(3) + (3)(2) + (4)(5) \\ (1)(3) + (0)(2) + (6)(5) \end{pmatrix}} = \begin{pmatrix} 10 \\ 32 \\ 33 \end{pmatrix}$$

and

$$\underset{2 \times 2}{\begin{pmatrix} -3 & 1 \\ 10 & 2 \end{pmatrix}} \underset{2 \times 2}{\begin{pmatrix} 1 & 0 \\ 2 & 4 \end{pmatrix}} = \underset{2 \times 2}{\begin{pmatrix} (-3)(1) + (1)(2) & (-3)(0) + (1)(4) \\ (10)(1) + (2)(2) & (10)(0) + (2)(4) \end{pmatrix}} = \begin{pmatrix} -1 & 4 \\ 14 & 8 \end{pmatrix}. \quad ◀$$

EXAMPLE 6 *Linear Algebraic Equations.* It is an important fact that the system of m linear algebraic equations

$$\begin{aligned} a_{11}x_1 + a_{12}x_2 + \cdots + a_{1n}x_n &= c_1 \\ a_{21}x_1 + a_{22}x_2 + \cdots + a_{2n}x_n &= c_2 \\ &\ \vdots \\ a_{m1}x_1 + a_{m2}x_2 + \cdots + a_{mn}x_n &= c_m \end{aligned} \tag{16}$$

in the n unknowns $x_1, \ldots, x_n$ is equivalent to the single compact matrix equation

$$\mathbf{Ax} = \mathbf{c}, \tag{17}$$

* Observe that c_{32} is the *dot product* of the third row of **A**, considered as a 3-tuple vector, with the second column of **B**. More generally, if $\mathbf{AB} = \mathbf{C} = \{c_{ij}\}$, then c_{ij} is the dot product of the ith row of **A** with the jth column of **B**.

where

$$\mathbf{A} = \begin{pmatrix} a_{11} & a_{12} & \cdots & a_{1n} \\ a_{21} & a_{22} & \cdots & a_{2n} \\ \vdots & \vdots & & \vdots \\ a_{m1} & a_{m2} & \cdots & a_{mn} \end{pmatrix}, \quad \mathbf{x} = \begin{pmatrix} x_1 \\ x_2 \\ \vdots \\ x_n \end{pmatrix}, \quad \text{and} \quad \mathbf{c} = \begin{pmatrix} c_1 \\ c_2 \\ \vdots \\ c_m \end{pmatrix}. \tag{18}$$

A is called the **coefficient matrix**, and **x** is the unknown; i.e., its components, or elements, are the unknowns $x_1, \ldots, x_n$. To verify this equivalence, work out the product **Ax**, and set the result equal to **c**. This step gives

$$\underset{m \times 1}{\begin{pmatrix} a_{11}x_1 + \cdots + a_{1n}x_n \\ a_{21}x_1 + \cdots + a_{2n}x_n \\ \vdots \\ a_{m1}x_1 + \cdots + a_{mn}x_n \end{pmatrix}} = \underset{m \times 1}{\begin{pmatrix} c_1 \\ c_2 \\ \vdots \\ c_m \end{pmatrix}}. \tag{19}$$

These two $m \times 1$ matrices (or m-dimensional column vectors) will be equal if and only if each of their corresponding m elements (or components) are equal. Thus (19) is equivalent to the m scalar equations (16), so (16) and (17) are equivalent, as claimed. This important result is of course a consequence of (12), and provides strong support for adopting that definition of matrix multiplication in the first place. ◀

It is extremely important to see that *matrix multiplication is not, in general, commutative*; i.e.,

$$\mathbf{AB} \neq \mathbf{BA}, \tag{20}$$

except in exceptional cases. For suppose that **A** is $m \times n$ and **B** is $n \times p$, so that **AB** is indeed defined. On the other hand, $\mathbf{BA} = (n \times p)(m \times n)$* is not even defined, let alone equal to **AB**, unless $p = m$. Assuming that this is the case,

$$\mathbf{BA} = (n \times m)(m \times n) = n \times n, \tag{21}$$

whereas

$$\mathbf{AB} = (m \times n)(n \times m) = m \times m. \tag{22}$$

Comparing (21) and (22), we see that we must also have $m = n$ if **AB** and **BA** are to be of the same form and hence possibly be equal to each other. Thus *a necessary condition for* **AB** *to equal* **BA**, *i.e., for* **A** *and* **B** *to commute, is that* **A** *and* **B** *both be* $n \times n$. Consider two such examples:

EXAMPLE 7 If

$$\mathbf{A} = \begin{pmatrix} 2 & 3 \\ 3 & 0 \end{pmatrix} \quad \text{and} \quad \mathbf{B} = \begin{pmatrix} -2 & 3 \\ 3 & -4 \end{pmatrix},$$

*This and the next several equalities are understood in terms of *form*; for example, $\mathbf{BA} = (n \times p)(m \times n)$ since **B** is $n \times p$ and **A** is $m \times n$.

then

$$\mathbf{AB} = \begin{pmatrix} 2 & 3 \\ 3 & 0 \end{pmatrix}\begin{pmatrix} -2 & 3 \\ 3 & -4 \end{pmatrix} = \begin{pmatrix} 5 & -6 \\ -6 & 9 \end{pmatrix}$$

and

$$\mathbf{BA} = \begin{pmatrix} -2 & 3 \\ 3 & -4 \end{pmatrix}\begin{pmatrix} 2 & 3 \\ 3 & 0 \end{pmatrix} = \begin{pmatrix} 5 & -6 \\ -6 & 9 \end{pmatrix} = \mathbf{AB},$$

so that **A** and **B** do commute. ◀

EXAMPLE 8 On the other hand, if

$$\mathbf{A} = \begin{pmatrix} 2 & 3 \\ 1 & 0 \end{pmatrix} \quad \text{and} \quad \mathbf{B} = \begin{pmatrix} -2 & 1 \\ 5 & 8 \end{pmatrix}$$

then

$$\mathbf{AB} = \begin{pmatrix} 2 & 3 \\ 1 & 0 \end{pmatrix}\begin{pmatrix} -2 & 1 \\ 5 & 8 \end{pmatrix} = \begin{pmatrix} 11 & 26 \\ -2 & 1 \end{pmatrix}$$

and

$$\mathbf{BA} = \begin{pmatrix} -2 & 1 \\ 5 & 8 \end{pmatrix}\begin{pmatrix} 2 & 3 \\ 1 & 0 \end{pmatrix} = \begin{pmatrix} -3 & -6 \\ 18 & 15 \end{pmatrix} \neq \mathbf{AB},$$

so that **A** and **B** do not commute even though they are both $n \times n$. ◀

Thus the condition that **A** and **B** must both be $n \times n$, for **A** and **B** to commute, is *necessary but not sufficient.*

In view of the importance of which factor is first and which is second, in a matrix product **AB**, we sometimes say that **B** is *premultiplied* by **A**, and **A** is *postmultiplied* by **B**, so as to leave no doubt as to which factor is first and which is second.

Any $n \times n$ matrix $\mathbf{A} = \{a_{ij}\}$ is said to be **square**, and of **order** n,* and the elements $a_{11}, a_{22}, \ldots, a_{nn}$ are said to lie on the **main diagonal** of **A**, i.e., the diagonal from the upper left corner to the lower right corner. Notice that to be able to multiply any matrix **A** with itself, **A** needs to be square. For suppose that **A** is $m \times n$; then we have

$$\underset{m \times n}{\mathbf{A}} \qquad \underset{m \times n}{\mathbf{A}}$$

and we need n (the number of columns in the first matrix) to equal m (the number of rows in the second) for the multiplication to be defined. If **A** *is* square, and p is any positive integer, we define

$$\underbrace{\mathbf{AA}\cdots\mathbf{A}}_{p \text{ factors}} \equiv \mathbf{A}^p; \tag{23}$$

* Thus we distinguish between form and order: The *form* of an $m \times n$ matrix is $m \times n$, the *order* of an $n \times n$ matrix is n.

the familiar laws of exponents,

$$\mathbf{A}^p\mathbf{A}^q = \mathbf{A}^{p+q}, \qquad (\mathbf{A}^p)^q = \mathbf{A}^{pq} \tag{24}$$

follow for any positive integers p and q.

If, in particular, the only nonzero elements of a square matrix lie on the main diagonal, $\mathbf{A}$ is said to be a **diagonal matrix**. For example,

$$\mathbf{A} = \begin{pmatrix} 3 & 0 \\ 0 & -2 \end{pmatrix}, \qquad \mathbf{B} = \begin{pmatrix} 7 & 0 & 0 \\ 0 & 0 & 0 \\ 0 & 0 & 0 \end{pmatrix}, \quad \text{and} \quad \mathbf{C} = \begin{pmatrix} 1 & 0 & 0 & 0 \\ 0 & 0 & 0 & 0 \\ 0 & 0 & 2 & 0 \\ 0 & 0 & 0 & 5 \end{pmatrix}$$

are all diagonal, and any diagonal matrix of order n can be denoted as

$$\mathbf{D} = \begin{pmatrix} d_{11} & & & \bigcirc \\ & d_{22} & & \\ & & \ddots & \\ \bigcirc & & & d_{nn} \end{pmatrix}, \tag{25}$$

where not all of the d_{jj}'s are zero,* and the two large zeros mean that all of the off-diagonal elements are zero, i.e., $d_{ij} = 0$ if $i \neq j$. It is easy to show [Exercise 18(a)] that

$$\mathbf{D}^p = \begin{pmatrix} d_{11}^p & & & \bigcirc \\ & d_{22}^p & & \\ & & \ddots & \\ \bigcirc & & & d_{nn}^p \end{pmatrix} \tag{26}$$

for any positive integer p.

If, furthermore, $d_{11} = d_{22} = \cdots = d_{nn} = 1$, then (25) is called the **identity matrix I**. Thus

$$\mathbf{I} = \begin{pmatrix} 1 & & & \bigcirc \\ & 1 & & \\ & & \ddots & \\ \bigcirc & & & 1 \end{pmatrix} = \{\delta_{ij}\}, \tag{27}$$

where δ_{ij} is the **Kronecker delta** symbol defined in Chapter 2, namely

$$\delta_{ij} \equiv \begin{cases} 1 & \text{if } i = j \\ 0 & \text{if } i \neq j. \end{cases} \tag{28}$$

It is sometimes convenient to include a subscript n to indicate the order of **I**. For example,

$$\begin{pmatrix} 1 & 0 \\ 0 & 1 \end{pmatrix} = \mathbf{I}_2 \quad \text{and} \quad \begin{pmatrix} 1 & 0 & 0 \\ 0 & 1 & 0 \\ 0 & 0 & 1 \end{pmatrix} = \mathbf{I}_3.$$

* If all of the diagonal elements were zero as well, then *all* the elements would be zero, and it would be more appropriate to describe **D** as a zero matrix, **0**.

A basic property of the identity matrix is that if **A** is any square matrix of the same order as **I**, then [Exercise 18(b)]

$$\mathbf{IA} = \mathbf{AI} = \mathbf{A}. \tag{29}$$

In other words, **I** is the matrix analog of the number 1 in scalar arithmetic. Comparing (29) with (20), observe that one case in which commutativity *does* hold is when one of the matrices is the identity matrix **I**.

Finally, it is convenient to extend our definition of $\mathbf{A}^p$ [recall (23)] to the case where $p = 0$. If **A** is any $n \times n$ matrix, we define

$$\mathbf{A}^0 \equiv \mathbf{I}, \tag{30}$$

where **I** is an $n \times n$ identity matrix.

Perhaps we should take a moment to recall that whereas the identity matrix **I** is always square, the zero matrix **0** is simply $m \times n$, not necessarily square. It is easily seen [Exercise 18(c)] that

$$\mathbf{0A} = \mathbf{0} \quad \text{and} \quad \mathbf{A0} = \mathbf{0} \tag{31}$$

for any matrix **A**. In the first of these equations, suppose that the **0** on the left is $m \times n$ and that **A** is $n \times p$; then the **0** on the right is $m \times p$, i.e., it is not necessarily of the same form as the one on the left.

In view of the general failure of commutativity, as stated in (20), we may well wonder if any other familiar arithmetic rules fail to hold for the multiplication of matrices. The answer is yes; the following rules for real numbers (a, b, c) do *not* carry over to matrices:

1. $ab = ba$ (*commutativity*).
2. If $ab = ac$ and $a \neq 0$, then $b = c$ (*cancellation rule*).
3. If $ab = 0$, then $a = 0$ and/or $b = 0$.

To add emphasis, we state these difficulties as a theorem.

***Theorem 2** "Exceptional" Properties of Matrix Multiplication*

(i) $\mathbf{AB} \neq \mathbf{BA}$ in general.
(ii) Even if $\mathbf{A} \neq \mathbf{0}$, $\mathbf{AB} = \mathbf{AC}$ does not imply that $\mathbf{B} = \mathbf{C}$.
(iii) $\mathbf{AB} = \mathbf{0}$ does not imply that $\mathbf{A} = \mathbf{0}$ and/or $\mathbf{B} = \mathbf{0}$.

The first of these has already been discussed. To illustrate property (ii), let

$$\mathbf{A} = \begin{pmatrix} 1 & 1 \\ 1 & 1 \end{pmatrix}, \quad \mathbf{B} = \begin{pmatrix} 1 & 5 \\ 4 & -1 \end{pmatrix}, \quad \text{and} \quad \mathbf{C} = \begin{pmatrix} 2 & 3 \\ 3 & 1 \end{pmatrix}.$$

Then

$$\mathbf{AB} = \begin{pmatrix} 5 & 4 \\ 5 & 4 \end{pmatrix} \quad \text{and} \quad \mathbf{AC} = \begin{pmatrix} 5 & 4 \\ 5 & 4 \end{pmatrix},$$

so that $\mathbf{AB} = \mathbf{AC}$, even though $\mathbf{B} \neq \mathbf{C}$. [By the way, in contrast with property (ii), note that the *additive* cancellation rule *does* hold, i.e., $\mathbf{A} + \mathbf{B} = \mathbf{A} + \mathbf{C}$ does imply that $\mathbf{B} = \mathbf{C}$.]

To illustrate property (iii), let

$$\mathbf{A} = \begin{pmatrix} 1 & 2 \\ 0 & 0 \end{pmatrix} \quad \text{and} \quad \mathbf{B} = \begin{pmatrix} 2 & -6 \\ -1 & 3 \end{pmatrix}.$$

Then

$$\mathbf{AB} = \begin{pmatrix} 1 & 2 \\ 0 & 0 \end{pmatrix}\begin{pmatrix} 2 & -6 \\ -1 & 3 \end{pmatrix} = \begin{pmatrix} 0 & 0 \\ 0 & 0 \end{pmatrix} = \mathbf{0}$$

even though $\mathbf{A} \neq \mathbf{0}$ and $\mathbf{B} \neq \mathbf{0}$.

Nonetheless, several important properties do carry over from the multiplication of real numbers to the multiplication of matrices:

***Theorem 3** "Ordinary" Properties of Matrix Multiplication*

If α, β are scalars, and the matrices $\mathbf{A}$, $\mathbf{B}$, $\mathbf{C}$ are suitably conformable, then

$$(\alpha\mathbf{A})\mathbf{B} = \mathbf{A}(\alpha\mathbf{B}) = \alpha(\mathbf{AB}) \qquad \text{(associativity)} \tag{32a}$$

$$\mathbf{A}(\mathbf{BC}) = (\mathbf{AB})\mathbf{C} \qquad \text{(associativity)} \tag{32b}$$

$$(\mathbf{A} + \mathbf{B})\mathbf{C} = \mathbf{AC} + \mathbf{BC} \qquad \text{(distributivity)} \tag{32c}$$

$$\mathbf{C}(\mathbf{A} + \mathbf{B}) = \mathbf{CA} + \mathbf{CB} \qquad \text{(distributivity)} \tag{32d}$$

$$\mathbf{A}(\alpha\mathbf{B} + \beta\mathbf{C}) = \alpha\mathbf{AB} + \beta\mathbf{AC}. \qquad \text{(linearity)} \tag{32e}$$

Proof is easy and is left for the exercises.

Let us close this section with a discussion of the **partitioning** of matrices. The idea is that any matrix $\mathbf{A}$ (which is larger than 1×1) may be partitioned into a number of smaller matrices called **blocks** (or **cells**) by vertical lines that extend from bottom to top, and horizontal lines that extend from left to right.

EXAMPLE 9

$$\mathbf{A} = \begin{pmatrix} 2 & 0 & -3 \\ 5 & 2 & 7 \\ 1 & 3 & 0 \\ 0 & 4 & 6 \end{pmatrix} = \left(\begin{array}{cc:c} 2 & 0 & -3 \\ 5 & 2 & 7 \\ \hdashline 1 & 3 & 0 \\ \hdashline 0 & 4 & 6 \end{array}\right) = \begin{pmatrix} \mathbf{A}_{11} & \mathbf{A}_{12} \\ \mathbf{A}_{21} & \mathbf{A}_{22} \\ \mathbf{A}_{31} & \mathbf{A}_{32} \end{pmatrix}, \tag{33}$$

where the blocks are

$$\mathbf{A}_{11} = \begin{pmatrix} 2 & 0 \\ 5 & 2 \end{pmatrix}, \quad \mathbf{A}_{12} = \begin{pmatrix} -3 \\ 7 \end{pmatrix}, \quad \mathbf{A}_{21} = (1, 3), \quad \mathbf{A}_{22} = (0), \quad \text{etc.}$$

Clearly, the partition is not unique. In the present example we could also have set

$$\mathbf{A} = \begin{pmatrix} 2 & 0 & -3 \\ 5 & 2 & 7 \\ 1 & 3 & 0 \\ 0 & 4 & 6 \end{pmatrix} = \left(\begin{array}{c|c|c} 2 & 0 & -3 \\ 5 & 2 & 7 \\ 1 & 3 & 0 \\ 0 & 4 & 6 \end{array}\right) = (\mathbf{A}_{11}, \mathbf{A}_{12}, \mathbf{A}_{13}), \tag{34}$$

say. In the latter case the blocks are column vectors, and since we normally use boldface lowercase letters for column vectors, we may prefer to express (34) as

$$\mathbf{A} = (\mathbf{a}_1, \mathbf{a}_2, \mathbf{a}_3), \tag{35}$$

where we have discarded the row subscripts since there is, after all, only one row in $(\mathbf{a}_1, \mathbf{a}_2, \mathbf{a}_3)$. ◀

While the matrices used here as illustrations are kept small for convenience, those encountered in modern applications may be quite large, e.g., 300 × 300. Even with the availability of large digital computers, such large matrices create special computational problems, and it is often advantageous to work instead with a number of smaller matrices through the use of partitioning. Such advantages might well prove illusory, however, were it not for the fact that the usual matrix arithmetic *can* be carried out with partitioned matrices.

Specifically, if $\mathbf{A}$ and $\mathbf{B}$ are partitioned as

$$\mathbf{A} = \begin{pmatrix} \mathbf{A}_{11} & \mathbf{A}_{12} & \cdots & \mathbf{A}_{1n} \\ \vdots & & & \vdots \\ \mathbf{A}_{m1} & \mathbf{A}_{m2} & \cdots & \mathbf{A}_{mn} \end{pmatrix} \quad \text{and} \quad \mathbf{B} = \begin{pmatrix} \mathbf{B}_{11} & \mathbf{B}_{12} & \cdots & \mathbf{B}_{1q} \\ \vdots & & & \vdots \\ \mathbf{B}_{p1} & \mathbf{B}_{p2} & \cdots & \mathbf{B}_{pq} \end{pmatrix}, \tag{36}$$

then

$$\alpha\mathbf{A} = \begin{pmatrix} \alpha\mathbf{A}_{11} & \alpha\mathbf{A}_{12} & \cdots & \alpha\mathbf{A}_{1n} \\ \vdots & & & \vdots \\ \alpha\mathbf{A}_{m1} & \alpha\mathbf{A}_{m2} & \cdots & \alpha\mathbf{A}_{mn} \end{pmatrix}; \tag{37}$$

if $m = p$ and $n = q$ and each $\mathbf{A}_{ij}$ block is of the same form as the corresponding $\mathbf{B}_{ij}$ block, then

$$\mathbf{A} + \mathbf{B} = \begin{pmatrix} \mathbf{A}_{11} + \mathbf{B}_{11} & \mathbf{A}_{12} + \mathbf{B}_{12} & \cdots & \mathbf{A}_{1n} + \mathbf{B}_{1n} \\ \vdots & \vdots & & \vdots \\ \mathbf{A}_{m1} + \mathbf{B}_{m1} & \mathbf{A}_{m2} + \mathbf{B}_{m2} & \cdots & \mathbf{A}_{mn} + \mathbf{B}_{mn} \end{pmatrix}; \tag{38}$$

and if $n = p$ and we denote $\mathbf{AB} = \mathbf{C}$, then

$$\mathbf{C}_{ij} = \sum_{k=1}^{n} \mathbf{A}_{ik}\mathbf{B}_{kj}, \tag{39}$$

provided that the number of columns in each of $\mathbf{A}_{ik}$ is the same as the number of rows in the corresponding $\mathbf{B}_{kj}$, so that the products in (39) are in fact defined.

Verification of these three claims, (37) to (39), is left for the exercises.

EXAMPLE 10 If

$$\mathbf{A} = \left(\begin{array}{cc|c} 2 & 4 & 1 \\ -1 & 3 & 0 \\ \hline 5 & 4 & 6 \end{array}\right) = \begin{pmatrix} \mathbf{A}_{11} & \mathbf{A}_{12} \\ \mathbf{A}_{21} & \mathbf{A}_{22} \end{pmatrix} \tag{40}$$

and

$$\mathbf{B} = \left(\begin{array}{cc|c} 0 & 1 & 3 \\ 2 & -4 & -1 \\ \hline 5 & 8 & 2 \end{array}\right) = \begin{pmatrix} \mathbf{B}_{11} & \mathbf{B}_{12} \\ \mathbf{B}_{21} & \mathbf{B}_{22} \end{pmatrix}, \tag{41}$$

then

$$\mathbf{AB} = \begin{pmatrix} \mathbf{A}_{11}\mathbf{B}_{11} + \mathbf{A}_{12}\mathbf{B}_{21} & \mathbf{A}_{11}\mathbf{B}_{12} + \mathbf{A}_{12}\mathbf{B}_{22} \\ \mathbf{A}_{21}\mathbf{B}_{11} + \mathbf{A}_{22}\mathbf{B}_{21} & \mathbf{A}_{21}\mathbf{B}_{12} + \mathbf{A}_{22}\mathbf{B}_{22} \end{pmatrix}. \tag{42}$$

But

$$\begin{aligned}
\mathbf{A}_{11}\mathbf{B}_{11} + \mathbf{A}_{12}\mathbf{B}_{21} &= \begin{pmatrix} 2 & 4 \\ -1 & 3 \end{pmatrix}\begin{pmatrix} 0 & 1 \\ 2 & -4 \end{pmatrix} + \begin{pmatrix} 1 \\ 0 \end{pmatrix}(5 \quad 8) \\
&= \begin{pmatrix} 8 & -14 \\ 6 & -13 \end{pmatrix} + \begin{pmatrix} 5 & 8 \\ 0 & 0 \end{pmatrix} = \begin{pmatrix} 13 & -6 \\ 6 & -13 \end{pmatrix}, \\
\mathbf{A}_{11}\mathbf{B}_{12} + \mathbf{A}_{12}\mathbf{B}_{22} &= \begin{pmatrix} 2 & 4 \\ -1 & 3 \end{pmatrix}\begin{pmatrix} 3 \\ -1 \end{pmatrix} + \begin{pmatrix} 1 \\ 0 \end{pmatrix}(2) \\
&= \begin{pmatrix} 2 \\ -6 \end{pmatrix} + \begin{pmatrix} 2 \\ 0 \end{pmatrix} = \begin{pmatrix} 4 \\ -6 \end{pmatrix}, \\
\mathbf{A}_{21}\mathbf{B}_{11} + \mathbf{A}_{22}\mathbf{B}_{21} &= (5 \quad 4)\begin{pmatrix} 0 & 1 \\ 2 & -4 \end{pmatrix} + (6)(5 \quad 8) \\
&= (8 \quad -11) + (30 \quad 48) = (38 \quad 37)
\end{aligned}$$

and

$$\mathbf{A}_{21}\mathbf{B}_{12} + \mathbf{A}_{22}\mathbf{B}_{22} = (5 \quad 4)\begin{pmatrix} 3 \\ -1 \end{pmatrix} + (6)(2) = (23),$$

so

$$\mathbf{AB} = \left(\begin{array}{cc|c} 13 & -6 & 4 \\ 6 & -13 & -6 \\ \hline 38 & 37 & 23 \end{array}\right) = \begin{pmatrix} 13 & -6 & 4 \\ 6 & -13 & -6 \\ 38 & 37 & 23 \end{pmatrix}. \tag{43}$$

The partition

$$\mathbf{B} = \left(\begin{array}{c|cc} 0 & 1 & 3 \\ 2 & -4 & -1 \\ \hline 5 & 8 & 2 \end{array}\right) = \begin{pmatrix} \mathbf{B}_{11} & \mathbf{B}_{12} \\ \mathbf{B}_{21} & \mathbf{B}_{22} \end{pmatrix}, \tag{44}$$

in place of (41), would also be conformable with (40) for the multiplication **AB**, and would lead to the same result, (43). On the other hand, neither of the partitions

$$\mathbf{B} = \left(\begin{array}{c|cc} 0 & 1 & 3 \\ \hline 2 & -4 & -1 \\ 5 & 8 & 2 \end{array}\right) \quad \text{or} \quad \mathbf{B} = \left(\begin{array}{cc|c} 0 & 1 & 3 \\ \hline 2 & -4 & -1 \\ 5 & 8 & 2 \end{array}\right) \tag{45}$$

would be conformable with (40) for the product **AB**; for example, the first term, $\mathbf{A}_{11}\mathbf{B}_{11}$, in (42) would not be defined then, since $\mathbf{A}_{11}$ has two columns whereas the $\mathbf{B}_{11}$'s in (45) have only one row. ◀

Looking back at this section, observe that once we defined the three arithmetic operations for matrices—multiplication by a scalar, addition, and multiplication—things went rather smoothly except for the difficulties associated with matrix multiplication, as listed in Theorem 2. Those three setbacks notwithstanding, the Cayley definition of multiplication does possess the important properties given in Theorem 3, and turns out to be virtually indispensable in linear analysis.

3.2 EXERCISES

1. Given the matrices

$$\mathbf{A} = \begin{pmatrix} 0 & 3 \\ 2 & -5 \\ 1 & 10 \\ 1 & 2 \end{pmatrix}, \qquad \mathbf{B} = \begin{pmatrix} 5 & -1 \\ 0 & 2 \end{pmatrix},$$

$$\mathbf{x} = \begin{pmatrix} 4 \\ 3 \end{pmatrix}, \qquad \mathbf{y} = (-1, 2),$$

work out whichever of the products **AB**, **BA**, **Ax**, **xA**, **Bx**, **xB**, **yB**, $\mathbf{A}^2$, $\mathbf{B}^2$, $\mathbf{x}^2$, **xy**, and **yx** are defined.

2. Let **A** be 6×4, **B** be 4×4, **C** be 4×3, and **D** and **E** be 3×1. Determine which of the following are defined, and for those that are, give the form of the resulting matrix.

*(a) $\mathbf{A}^{10}$
(b) $\mathbf{B}^{10}$
(c) **ABC**
*(d) **ABCD**
(e) **ACBD**
(f) **CD** + **E**
(g) **C**(2**D** − **E**)
(h) **AB** + **AC**
(i) **BC** + **CB**

3. Evaluate the products

$$\begin{pmatrix} 1 & 0 & 0 \\ 0 & 2 & 0 \\ 0 & 0 & 3 \end{pmatrix}\begin{pmatrix} 1 & 1 & 1 \\ 1 & 1 & 1 \\ 1 & 1 & 1 \end{pmatrix} \text{ and } \begin{pmatrix} 1 & 1 & 1 \\ 1 & 1 & 1 \\ 1 & 1 & 1 \end{pmatrix}\begin{pmatrix} 1 & 0 & 0 \\ 0 & 2 & 0 \\ 0 & 0 & 3 \end{pmatrix}.$$

4. Suppose that **A** is $n \times n$, **x** is $n \times 1$, and c is a scalar. Can we reexpress $\mathbf{Ax} = c\mathbf{x}$ as $(\mathbf{A} - c)\mathbf{x} = \mathbf{0}$? Explain.

5. If **A** and **B** are square matrices of the same order, are the following correct? Explain.

*(a) $(\mathbf{A} + \mathbf{B})^2 = \mathbf{A}^2 + 2\mathbf{AB} + \mathbf{B}^2$
(b) $(\mathbf{A} + \mathbf{B})(\mathbf{A} - \mathbf{B}) = \mathbf{A}^2 - \mathbf{B}^2$
(c) $(\mathbf{AB})^2 = \mathbf{A}^2\mathbf{B}^2$
(d) $(\mathbf{AB})^3 = \mathbf{A}^3\mathbf{B}^3$

6. If p is a positive integer, does **A** need to be square for $\mathbf{A}^p$ to be defined? Explain.

7. Expand each of the following, assuming that all of the matrices are suitably conformable. Justify each step by citing the relevant equation number in Theorem 1 or 3.

(a) (2**A** + **B**)(**A** + 2**B**)
(b) (**A** + **B**)**C**(**D** + **E**)
(c) $(\mathbf{A} + \mathbf{B})^3$
(d) (**A** − 3**I**)(2**A** + **I**)

8. Given

$$\mathbf{A} = \begin{pmatrix} 1 & 1 \\ 1 & 1 \end{pmatrix}, \qquad \mathbf{B} = \begin{pmatrix} 1 & 1 \\ 0 & 1 \end{pmatrix}, \qquad \mathbf{C} = \begin{pmatrix} 1 & 2 \\ -3 & 2 \end{pmatrix},$$

$$\text{and} \quad \mathbf{D} = \begin{pmatrix} 0 & 5 & 7 \\ 0 & 0 & 8 \\ 0 & 0 & 0 \end{pmatrix},$$

evaluate each of the following.

*(a) $\mathbf{A}^{100}$ (b) $\mathbf{B}^{100}$ (c) $\mathbf{C}^{8}$ (d) $\mathbf{D}^{2}$ *(e) $\mathbf{D}^{100}$ (f) $(\mathbf{ABC})^4$ (g) $(\mathbf{CBA})^4$ (h) $\mathbf{B}^4\mathbf{C}^4$ and $(\mathbf{BC})^4$ (i) $\mathbf{C}^3\mathbf{B}^3$ and $(\mathbf{CB})^3$

9. Any diagonal matrix whose diagonal elements are all equal is called a **scalar matrix**. If

$$\mathbf{S} = \begin{pmatrix} k & & & \\ & k & & 0 \\ & & \ddots & \\ 0 & & & k \end{pmatrix}$$

is $n \times n$, and $\mathbf{A}$ is any $n \times n$ matrix, show that

$$\mathbf{AS} = \mathbf{SA} = k\mathbf{A}.$$

What can be said if, instead, $\mathbf{A}$ is $m \times n$ $(m \neq n)$?

10. If for any given vector

$$\mathbf{x} = \begin{pmatrix} x_1 \\ \vdots \\ x_4 \end{pmatrix},$$

the product $\mathbf{Ax}$ is the column vector given below, find $\mathbf{A}$.

*(a) $\mathbf{Ax} = \begin{pmatrix} 0 \\ x_1 \\ x_2 \end{pmatrix}$

(b) $\mathbf{Ax} = \begin{pmatrix} x_2 \\ x_3 + 5x_4 \end{pmatrix}$

(c) $\mathbf{Ax} = \begin{pmatrix} x_3 - x_4 \\ 0 \\ 2x_1 \\ x_2 + 4x_3 + x_4 \\ -x_2 \end{pmatrix}$

(d) $\mathbf{Ax} = \begin{pmatrix} x_2 + x_3 - x_4 \\ x_1 - 3x_2 \\ 0 \\ x_2 + x_4 \end{pmatrix}$

11. Make up a specific pair of matrices, $\mathbf{A}$ and $\mathbf{B}$, both nonzero, such that $\mathbf{AB} = \mathbf{0}$, where

(a) $\mathbf{A}$ is 4×3 and $\mathbf{B}$ is 3×1
(b) $\mathbf{A}$ is 5×2 and $\mathbf{B}$ is 2×2
(c) $\mathbf{A}$ is 1×2 and $\mathbf{B}$ is 2×4
(d) $\mathbf{A}$ is 4×3 and $\mathbf{B}$ is 3×2

12. Given the partitioned matrices $\mathbf{A}$ and $\mathbf{B}$, below, carry out the products $\mathbf{A}^2$ and $\mathbf{AB}$ for those cases in which the partitioning is suitable, i.e., conformable.

(a) $\mathbf{A} = \left(\begin{array}{cc|c} 2 & 0 & -1 \\ 1 & -1 & 0 \\ \hline 5 & 2 & 4 \end{array}\right)$, $\quad \mathbf{B} = \left(\begin{array}{cc|c} 3 & 6 & 2 \\ 0 & 1 & 0 \\ \hline 3 & -4 & 7 \end{array}\right)$

(b) $\mathbf{A} = \left(\begin{array}{cc|c} 2 & 0 & -1 \\ 1 & -1 & 0 \\ \hline 5 & 2 & 4 \end{array}\right)$, $\quad \mathbf{B} = \left(\begin{array}{c|cc} 3 & 6 & 2 \\ 0 & 1 & 0 \\ \hline 3 & -4 & 7 \end{array}\right)$

(c) $\mathbf{A} = \left(\begin{array}{c|cc} 2 & 0 & -1 \\ \hline 1 & -1 & 0 \\ 5 & 2 & 4 \end{array}\right)$, $\quad \mathbf{B} = \left(\begin{array}{cc|c} 3 & 6 & 2 \\ 0 & 1 & 0 \\ \hline 3 & -4 & 7 \end{array}\right)$

13. (a) If $\mathbf{AB}$ is defined, and $\mathbf{B}$ is partitioned into columns as $\mathbf{B} = (\mathbf{b}_1, \mathbf{b}_2, \ldots, \mathbf{b}_p)$, show from the definition of matrix multiplication that $\mathbf{AB} = (\mathbf{Ab}_1, \mathbf{Ab}_2, \ldots, \mathbf{Ab}_p)$.
(b) Show that $c_1\mathbf{x}_1 + c_2\mathbf{x}_2 + \cdots + c_n\mathbf{x}_n$ can be expressed in the form

$$(\mathbf{x}_1, \mathbf{x}_2, \ldots, \mathbf{x}_n)\begin{pmatrix} c_1 \\ \vdots \\ c_n \end{pmatrix}.$$

14. (a) If two unpartitioned matrices are not conformable for addition, can they be rendered conformable by suitable partitioning? Explain.
(b) Repeat part (a), for multiplication.

15. If there is some positive integer p such that $\mathbf{A}^p = \mathbf{0}$, then $\mathbf{A}$ is said to be **nilpotent** (mnemonic: "potentially nil"). A square matrix $\mathbf{A} = \{a_{ij}\}$ such that $a_{ij} = 0$ for all $i > j$ is said to be an **upper triangular matrix**; if $a_{ij} = 0$ for all $i < j$, then $\mathbf{A}$ is a **lower triangular matrix**. A matrix is said to be **triangular** if it is either upper triangular or lower triangular.

(a) Every upper triangular matrix with null main diagonal (so that $a_{ij} = 0$ for all $i \geq j$) is nilpotent. Verify this result for second-, third-, and fourth-order matrices.
(b) In fact, show that *every* upper triangular matrix (of finite order) with null main diagonal is nilpotent. *Hint:* Use partitioning and induction.
(c) Is every lower diagonal matrix with null main diagonal nilpotent? Explain.
(d) If $\mathbf{A}^p = \mathbf{0}$, show that $(\mathbf{I} + \mathbf{A} + \mathbf{A}^2 + \cdots + \mathbf{A}^{p-1})(\mathbf{I} - \mathbf{A}) = (\mathbf{I} - \mathbf{A})(\mathbf{I} + \mathbf{A} + \mathbf{A}^2 + \cdots + \mathbf{A}^{p-1}) = \mathbf{I}$.

16. If $\mathbf{A}^2 = \mathbf{I}$, then $\mathbf{A}$ is called **involutory**.

(a) Show, using Theorems 1 to 3 and (29), that $\mathbf{A}$ is involutory if and only if

$$(\mathbf{I} - \mathbf{A})(\mathbf{I} + \mathbf{A}) = \mathbf{0}.$$

*(b) Give an example of an involutory matrix other than $\mathbf{I}$ and $-\mathbf{I}$. Thus, observe that $\mathbf{A}^2 = \mathbf{I}$ does *not* imply that $\mathbf{A} = \pm\mathbf{I}$.

17. (a) Prove (10a) to (10c).
(b) Prove (10d) to (10f).
(c) Prove (10g) to (10j).

18. (a) Verify (26). (b) Verify (29).
(c) Verify (31). (d) Verify (32a) and (32b)
(e) Verify (32c) and (32d). (f) Show that (32e) follows from (32a) to (32d).

19. Show that the most general matrix that commutes with $\begin{pmatrix} 1 & 2 \\ 3 & 4 \end{pmatrix}$ is $\begin{pmatrix} \alpha - \beta & 2\beta/3 \\ \beta & \alpha \end{pmatrix}$, where α and β are arbitrary.

20. Given $\mathbf{A}$, find the most general matrix $\mathbf{B}$ such that $\mathbf{AB} = \mathbf{0}$.

*(a) $\mathbf{A} = \begin{pmatrix} 1 & 2 \\ 3 & 4 \end{pmatrix}$ (b) $\mathbf{A} = \begin{pmatrix} 2 & 3 \\ 0 & 0 \end{pmatrix}$

*(c) $\mathbf{A} = \begin{pmatrix} 0 & 0 \\ 5 & 0 \end{pmatrix}$ (d) $\mathbf{A} = \begin{pmatrix} 2 & 3 \\ 4 & 6 \end{pmatrix}$

21. Explore and discuss the advantages and disadvantages of defining $c_{ij} = a_{ij}b_{ij}$ in place of the Cayley product (13).

***22.** (*Transition probability matrix*) Selling their valuables, professors A and B raise \$2 apiece, and proceed to match coins at \$1 per match. There arise five possible states:

S_1	S_2	S_3	S_4	S_5
04	13	22	31	40

In state S_2, for example, A has \$1 and B has \$3. If either player is bankrupted (A is bankrupt in state S_1, B in state S_5), the game is over. Let $p_{ij}^{(n)}$ be the n-step transition probability, i.e., the probability of changing from state S_i to state S_j in n matches. For $n = 1$ we see that

$$\mathbf{P}^{(1)} = \{p_{ij}^{(1)}\} = \begin{pmatrix} 1 & 0 & 0 & 0 & 0 \\ \frac{1}{2} & 0 & \frac{1}{2} & 0 & 0 \\ 0 & \frac{1}{2} & 0 & \frac{1}{2} & 0 \\ 0 & 0 & \frac{1}{2} & 0 & \frac{1}{2} \\ 0 & 0 & 0 & 0 & 1 \end{pmatrix}.$$

For example, beginning in S_2, say, one match will necessarily move us to S_1 or S_3, with 50% probability in each case; thus $p_{21}^{(1)} = p_{23}^{(1)} = \frac{1}{2}$. Precisely \$1 will change hands, so that $p_{22}^{(1)} = p_{24}^{(1)} = p_{25}^{(1)} = 0$. Further, once in S_1 (or S_5) we remain there (according to the rules), so $p_{11}^{(1)} = 1$, $p_{12}^{(1)} = p_{13}^{(1)} = p_{14}^{(1)} = p_{15}^{(1)} = 0$. Show, by any convincing arguments or discussion, that

$$p_{ij}^{(2)} = \sum_{k=1}^{5} p_{ik}^{(1)} p_{kj}^{(1)}, \quad p_{ij}^{(3)} = \sum_{k=1}^{5} p_{ik}^{(2)} p_{kj}^{(1)}, \quad \text{etc.}$$

or, in matrix notation, $\mathbf{P}^{(2)} = [\mathbf{P}^{(1)}]^2$, $\mathbf{P}^{(3)} = [\mathbf{P}^{(1)}]^3$, etc. Use this result to determine $\mathbf{P}^{(2)}$ and $\mathbf{P}^{(3)}$. What is the probability that A is bankrupt after (at most) 3 matches if she starts with \$2? If she starts with \$3? If she starts with \$1? *Note:* $\mathbf{P}^{(1)}$ is an example of a *Markov matrix*. Markov matrices are also encountered in Exercises 13 and 14 on page 144.

THE TRANSPOSE MATRIX 3.3

Here we continue the development of Section 3.2. Given an $m \times n$ matrix $\mathbf{A} = \{a_{ij}\}$, one defines the **transpose** of $\mathbf{A}$, denoted as $\mathbf{A}^\mathrm{T}$ (and read as $\mathbf{A}$-transpose), as

$$\mathbf{A}^\mathrm{T} \equiv \{a_{ji}\} = \begin{pmatrix} a_{11} & a_{21} & \cdots & a_{m1} \\ a_{12} & a_{22} & \cdots & a_{m2} \\ \vdots & & & \vdots \\ a_{1n} & a_{2n} & \cdots & a_{mn} \end{pmatrix}, \tag{1}$$

i.e., the $n \times m$ matrix obtained by interchanging the rows and columns of $\mathbf{A}$; the first row of $\mathbf{A}$ becomes the first column of $\mathbf{A}^\mathrm{T}$, the first column of $\mathbf{A}$ becomes the first row of $\mathbf{A}^{\mathrm{T}}$, and so on.* Or, denoting the i, j element of $\mathbf{A}^{\mathrm{T}}$ as a_{ij}^{T}, we have the relation

$$a_{ij}^{\mathrm{T}} \equiv a_{ji} \tag{2}$$

between the elements of $\mathbf{A}^{\mathrm{T}}$ and $\mathbf{A}$.

EXAMPLE 1 Given

$$\underset{3 \times 3}{\mathbf{A} = \begin{pmatrix} 2 & -5 & 3 \\ 0 & 1 & 2 \\ 6 & 5 & 2 \end{pmatrix}}, \quad \underset{3 \times 1}{\mathbf{B} = \begin{pmatrix} 5 \\ 3 \\ 6 \end{pmatrix}}, \quad \text{and} \quad \underset{1 \times 4}{\mathbf{C} = (4 \quad 1 \quad -3 \quad 2)},$$

then

$$\underset{3 \times 3}{\mathbf{A}^{\mathrm{T}} = \begin{pmatrix} 2 & 0 & 6 \\ -5 & 1 & 5 \\ 3 & 2 & 2 \end{pmatrix}}, \quad \underset{1 \times 3}{\mathbf{B}^{\mathrm{T}} = (5 \quad 3 \quad 6)}, \quad \text{and} \quad \underset{4 \times 1}{\mathbf{C}^{\mathrm{T}} = \begin{pmatrix} 4 \\ 1 \\ -3 \\ 2 \end{pmatrix}}. \quad ◀$$

Besides the above-mentioned interchanging of the rows and columns, it is worth observing that $\mathbf{A}^{\mathrm{T}}$ is formed by "flipping" the elements of $\mathbf{A}$ about the main diagonal. For example,

$$\begin{pmatrix} 9 & 12 & 0 \\ 1 & -3 & 2 \end{pmatrix}^{\mathrm{T}} = \begin{pmatrix} 9 & 1 \\ 12 & -3 \\ 0 & 2 \end{pmatrix}. \tag{3}$$

Theorem 1 *Properties of the Transpose*

$$(\mathbf{A}^{\mathrm{T}})^{\mathrm{T}} = \mathbf{A} \tag{4a}$$

$$(\mathbf{A} + \mathbf{B})^{\mathrm{T}} = \mathbf{A}^{\mathrm{T}} + \mathbf{B}^{\mathrm{T}} \tag{4b}$$

$$(\alpha\mathbf{A})^{\mathrm{T}} = \alpha\mathbf{A}^{\mathrm{T}} \tag{4c}$$

$$(\mathbf{A}\mathbf{B})^{\mathrm{T}} = \mathbf{B}^{\mathrm{T}}\mathbf{A}^{\mathrm{T}}, \tag{4d}$$

where it is assumed in (4b) that $\mathbf{A}$ and $\mathbf{B}$ are conformable for addition, and in (4d) that they are conformable for multiplication.

Proof Proof of (4a) to (4c) is simple and is left as an exercise. To prove (4d), let $\mathbf{AB} \equiv \mathbf{C} = \{c_{ij}\}$. By the definition of matrix multiplication, then

* Thus, $\mathbf{A}^{\mathrm{T}}$ is *not* $\mathbf{A}$ to the Tth power; it is the transpose of $\mathbf{A}$.

$$c_{ij} = \sum_{k=1}^{n} a_{ik} b_{kj}. \tag{5}$$

Thus

$$\begin{aligned} c_{ij}^{\mathrm{T}} = c_{ji} &= \sum_{k=1}^{n} a_{jk} b_{ki} \qquad \text{[interchanging } i \text{ and } j \text{ in (5)]} \\ &= \sum_{k=1}^{n} b_{ki} a_{jk} = \sum_{k=1}^{n} b_{ik}^{\mathrm{T}} a_{kj}^{\mathrm{T}}. \end{aligned} \tag{6}$$

Having returned to the subscript pattern $(\cdot)_{ij} = \Sigma(\cdot)_{ik}(\cdot)_{kj}$, as in (5), we may conclude from (6) that

$$\mathbf{C}^{\mathrm{T}} = \mathbf{B}^{\mathrm{T}}\mathbf{A}^{\mathrm{T}} \quad \text{or} \quad (\mathbf{AB})^{\mathrm{T}} = \mathbf{B}^{\mathrm{T}}\mathbf{A}^{\mathrm{T}},$$

as claimed. It should be clearly understood that the third equality in (6) is *not* equivalent to the matrix statement $\mathbf{AB} = \mathbf{BA}$, which, of course, would not necessarily be true; it is simply the *scalar* statement that $a_{jk}b_{ki} = b_{ki}a_{jk}$, which is certainly true since the multiplication of scalars *is* commutative [for example, (2)(6) = (6)(2) = 12]. ■

The striking feature of (4d) is the reversal in the order: $(\mathbf{AB})^{\mathrm{T}}$ on the left, $\mathbf{B}^{\mathrm{T}}\mathbf{A}^{\mathrm{T}}$ on the right. Notice how (4d) checks "dimensionally":

$$\begin{aligned} [(m \times n)(n \times p)]^{\mathrm{T}} &= (n \times p)^{\mathrm{T}}(m \times n)^{\mathrm{T}} \\ (m \times p)^{\mathrm{T}} &= (p \times n)(n \times m) \\ p \times m &= p \times m. \end{aligned} \tag{7}$$

Naturally, (7) does not *prove* (4d), but it provides a useful check, just as we check the *physical* units (such as force, mass, length, and time) of an equation to be sure that they are consistent.

EXAMPLE 2 Given

$$\mathbf{A} = \begin{pmatrix} 4 & 2 & -5 \\ 0 & 1 & 3 \end{pmatrix} \quad \text{and} \quad \mathbf{B} = \begin{pmatrix} 6 \\ 0 \\ -1 \end{pmatrix},$$

then

$$\mathbf{AB} = \begin{pmatrix} 4 & 2 & -5 \\ 0 & 1 & 3 \end{pmatrix}\begin{pmatrix} 6 \\ 0 \\ -1 \end{pmatrix} = \begin{pmatrix} 29 \\ -3 \end{pmatrix}, \quad \text{so} \quad (\mathbf{AB})^{\mathrm{T}} = (29, -3) \tag{8}$$

and

$$\mathbf{B}^{\mathrm{T}}\mathbf{A}^{\mathrm{T}} = (6 \quad 0 \quad -1)\begin{pmatrix} 4 & 0 \\ 2 & 1 \\ -5 & 3 \end{pmatrix} = (29, -3),$$

in agreement with (8). ◀

Furthermore, it follows from (4d) that

$$(\mathbf{ABC})^{\mathrm{T}} = \mathbf{C}^{\mathrm{T}}\mathbf{B}^{\mathrm{T}}\mathbf{A}^{\mathrm{T}}, \tag{9a}$$

$$(\mathbf{ABCD})^{\mathrm{T}} = \mathbf{D}^{\mathrm{T}}\mathbf{C}^{\mathrm{T}}\mathbf{B}^{\mathrm{T}}\mathbf{A}^{\mathrm{T}}, \tag{9b}$$

and so on (Exercise 2).

Using lowercase boldface letters for matrices that happen to be column vectors, let

$$\mathbf{x} = \begin{pmatrix} x_1 \\ x_2 \\ \vdots \\ x_n \end{pmatrix} \quad \text{and} \quad \mathbf{y} = \begin{pmatrix} y_1 \\ y_2 \\ \vdots \\ y_n \end{pmatrix}.$$

Then the standard dot product

$$\mathbf{x} \cdot \mathbf{y} = x_1 y_1 + x_2 y_2 + \cdots + x_n y_n = \sum_{j=1}^{n} x_j y_j$$

can be expressed compactly, in matrix language, as*

$$\boxed{\mathbf{x} \cdot \mathbf{y} = \mathbf{x}^{\mathrm{T}}\mathbf{y}} \quad \text{or as} \quad \mathbf{y}^{\mathrm{T}}\mathbf{x}, \tag{10}$$

although *not* as $\mathbf{xy}^{\mathrm{T}}$ or $\mathbf{yx}^{\mathrm{T}}$, which expressions represent $n \times n$ matrices!

EXAMPLE 3 If

$$\mathbf{x} = \begin{pmatrix} 3 \\ 1 \\ -2 \end{pmatrix} \quad \text{and} \quad \mathbf{y} = \begin{pmatrix} 5 \\ 0 \\ 4 \end{pmatrix},$$

then

$$\mathbf{x} \cdot \mathbf{y} = \mathbf{x}^{\mathrm{T}}\mathbf{y} = (3 \quad 1 \quad -2)\begin{pmatrix} 5 \\ 0 \\ 4 \end{pmatrix} = 15 + 0 - 8 = 7$$

or

$$\mathbf{x} \cdot \mathbf{y} = \mathbf{y}^{\mathrm{T}}\mathbf{x} = (5 \quad 0 \quad 4)\begin{pmatrix} 3 \\ 1 \\ -2 \end{pmatrix} = 15 + 0 - 8 = 7,$$

whereas

$$\mathbf{xy}^{\mathrm{T}} = \begin{pmatrix} 3 \\ 1 \\ -2 \end{pmatrix}(5 \quad 0 \quad 4) = \begin{pmatrix} 15 & 0 & 12 \\ 5 & 0 & 4 \\ -10 & 0 & -8 \end{pmatrix} \neq \mathbf{x} \cdot \mathbf{y}$$

* There is a slight difficulty here: $\mathbf{x} \cdot \mathbf{y}$ is to be a scalar, whereas $\mathbf{x}^{\mathrm{T}}\mathbf{y}$ is a 1×1 matrix. Thus what we really intend, by $\mathbf{x}^{\mathrm{T}}\mathbf{y}$ in (10), is not the 1×1 matrix, but rather the scalar element inside it. That could be noted by writing $\mathbf{x} \cdot \mathbf{y} = (\mathbf{x}^{\mathrm{T}}\mathbf{y})_{11}$ instead, but it will be simpler to leave (10) intact, with the *understanding* that the right-hand side is a scalar.

and

$$\mathbf{y}\mathbf{x}^{\mathrm{T}} = \begin{pmatrix} 5 \\ 0 \\ 4 \end{pmatrix} (3 \quad 1 \quad -2) = \begin{pmatrix} 15 & 5 & -10 \\ 0 & 0 & 0 \\ 12 & 4 & -8 \end{pmatrix} \neq \mathbf{x} \cdot \mathbf{y}.$$

Thus remember that the transpose "T" belongs on the first of the two vectors. ◀

Finally, two more definitions: If

$$\mathbf{A}^{\mathrm{T}} = \mathbf{A} \tag{11}$$

we say that **A** is **symmetric**, and if

$$\mathbf{A}^{\mathrm{T}} = -\mathbf{A}, \tag{12}$$

we say that it is **skew-symmetric** (or antisymmetric). For either of these properties to apply, obviously **A** must be square, since otherwise $\mathbf{A}^{\mathrm{T}}$ and **A** would be of different form. And for **A** to be skew symmetric all of its diagonal elements must be zero, since (12) implies that $a_{ji} = -a_{ij}$, or if we set $i = j$, $a_{ii} = -a_{ii}$; thus $2a_{ii} = 0$, so $a_{ii} = 0$ for each i.

It would be reasonable to imagine that the likelihood of encountering, in practical applications, purely symmetric or skew-symmetric matrices would be rather slim. Quite the contrary, it turns out—as we shall see later—that symmetric matrices arise frequently, and that their symmetry is often a consequence of fundamental physical principles, rather than chance.

EXAMPLE 4 Given

$$\mathbf{A} = \begin{pmatrix} 2 & 4 & 1 \\ 4 & 0 & 5 \\ 1 & 5 & -3 \end{pmatrix}, \quad \mathbf{B} = \begin{pmatrix} 0 & -2 & -5 \\ 2 & 0 & 1 \\ 5 & -1 & 0 \end{pmatrix}, \quad \mathbf{C} = \begin{pmatrix} 3 & 1 & 4 \\ 2 & 6 & 2 \\ 5 & -2 & 0 \end{pmatrix},$$

then

$$\mathbf{A}^{\mathrm{T}} = \begin{pmatrix} 2 & 4 & 1 \\ 4 & 0 & 5 \\ 1 & 5 & -3 \end{pmatrix}, \quad \mathbf{B}^{\mathrm{T}} = \begin{pmatrix} 0 & 2 & 5 \\ -2 & 0 & -1 \\ -5 & 1 & 0 \end{pmatrix}, \quad \mathbf{C}^{\mathrm{T}} = \begin{pmatrix} 3 & 2 & 5 \\ 1 & 6 & -2 \\ 4 & 2 & 0 \end{pmatrix};$$

A is symmetric, **B** is skew symmetric, and **C** is neither. ◀

Even if a square matrix is neither symmetric nor skew symmetric, it can be separated into the sum of a symmetric matrix and a skew-symmetric matrix, for if **A** is square, then

$$\begin{aligned} \mathbf{A} &= \tfrac{1}{2}(\mathbf{A} + \mathbf{A}^{\mathrm{T}}) + \tfrac{1}{2}(\mathbf{A} - \mathbf{A}^{\mathrm{T}}) \\ &\equiv \quad \mathbf{A}_1 \quad + \quad \mathbf{A}_2, \end{aligned} \tag{13}$$

where $\mathbf{A}_1$ is symmetric, since [using (4a), (4b), and (4c)]

$$\mathbf{A}_1^{\mathrm{T}} = [\tfrac{1}{2}(\mathbf{A} + \mathbf{A}^{\mathrm{T}})]^{\mathrm{T}} = \tfrac{1}{2}(\mathbf{A}^{\mathrm{T}} + \mathbf{A}) = \mathbf{A}_1, \tag{14}$$

and $\mathbf{A}_2$ is skew symmetric since

$$\mathbf{A}_2^{\mathrm{T}} = [\tfrac{1}{2}(\mathbf{A} - \mathbf{A}^{\mathrm{T}})]^{\mathrm{T}} = \tfrac{1}{2}(\mathbf{A}^{\mathrm{T}} - \mathbf{A}) = -\mathbf{A}_2. \tag{15}$$

Where did we get (13)? It is merely a suitably arranged identity.

EXAMPLE 5 For the $\mathbf{C}$ matrix of Example 4, the separation (13) is

$$\mathbf{C} = \tfrac{1}{2}(\mathbf{C} + \mathbf{C}^{\mathrm{T}}) + \tfrac{1}{2}(\mathbf{C} - \mathbf{C}^{\mathrm{T}})$$

$$= \begin{pmatrix} 3 & \frac{3}{2} & \frac{9}{2} \\ \frac{3}{2} & 6 & 0 \\ \frac{9}{2} & 0 & 0 \end{pmatrix} + \begin{pmatrix} 0 & -\frac{1}{2} & -\frac{1}{2} \\ \frac{1}{2} & 0 & 2 \\ \frac{1}{2} & -2 & 0 \end{pmatrix}. \blacktriangleleft \tag{16}$$

The expression (13) is but one of many such separations. For example, a vector $\mathbf{v}$ in 3-space can be separated into the sum of two vectors, one lying in a given plane (the "projection of $\mathbf{v}$" onto that plane) and the other perpendicular to that plane; a function $f(x)$ can be separated, as we shall see in Chapter 10, into the sum of an *even* function and an *odd* function; a vector field can be separated, as we shall see in Chapter 9, into the sum of two vector fields, one *irrotational* and the other *solenoidal*, and so on.

Finally, we again caution the reader that notation is not always the same from one writer to another. In the case of the transpose matrix, for example, we use the symbol $\mathbf{A}^{\mathrm{T}}$, but another common symbol for this quantity is $\mathbf{A}'$.

In summary, three items in this section that will be of special importance to us are the definition (2) of the transpose matrix, the property (4d), and the expression (10) of the dot product in matrix notation.

3.3 EXERCISES

1. *(a)If $\mathbf{x} = (3, -3)^{\mathrm{T}}$ and $\mathbf{y} = (1, 2)^{\mathrm{T}}$, work out $\mathbf{x}^{\mathrm{T}}\mathbf{y}$ and $\mathbf{x}\mathbf{y}^{\mathrm{T}}$.
(b) If $\mathbf{x} = (4, -1, 0)^{\mathrm{T}}$ and $\mathbf{y} = (1, 2, 3)^{\mathrm{T}}$, work out $\mathbf{x}^{\mathrm{T}}\mathbf{y}$ and $\mathbf{x}\mathbf{y}^{\mathrm{T}}$.
(c) If $\mathbf{x} = (0, 4, -2, 1)^{\mathrm{T}}$ and $\mathbf{y} = (3, 0, 1, -2)^{\mathrm{T}}$, work out $\mathbf{x}^{\mathrm{T}}\mathbf{y}$ and $\mathbf{x}\mathbf{y}^{\mathrm{T}}$.
Note: It is more convenient to write a vector $\mathbf{x} = \begin{pmatrix} 5 \\ 2 \end{pmatrix}$, say, as $\mathbf{x} = (5, 2)^{\mathrm{T}}$ since the latter takes up less vertical space on the page and is easier to typeset.

2. Show that (9a) and (9b) follow directly from (4d).

3. Recall that in general $\mathbf{AB} \neq \mathbf{BA}$, and that a *necessary* (but not sufficient) condition for equality to hold is that both $\mathbf{A}$ and $\mathbf{B}$ be square and of the same order. Perhaps a *sufficient* condition is that $\mathbf{A}$ and $\mathbf{B}$ both be of the same order and *symmetric*. Prove or disprove this tentative claim.

4. Verify $(\mathbf{ABC})^{\mathrm{T}} = \mathbf{C}^{\mathrm{T}}\mathbf{B}^{\mathrm{T}}\mathbf{A}^{\mathrm{T}}$ directly, for

(a) $\mathbf{A} = \begin{pmatrix} 5 & -2 \\ 0 & 1 \\ -1 & 3 \end{pmatrix}$, $\mathbf{B} = \begin{pmatrix} 0 \\ 7 \end{pmatrix}$,
$\mathbf{C} = (3 \quad -1 \quad 2 \quad 9)$

(b) $\mathbf{A} = \begin{pmatrix} 1 & 2 \\ 5 & 4 \end{pmatrix}$, $\mathbf{B} = \begin{pmatrix} 0 & 0 \\ 1 & 1 \end{pmatrix}$, $\mathbf{C} = \begin{pmatrix} 4 & -1 & 5 \\ 0 & 3 & 0 \end{pmatrix}$

(c) $\mathbf{A} = (5 \quad 3 \quad 0)$, $\mathbf{B} = \begin{pmatrix} -2 & 1 \\ 6 & 4 \\ 5 & 3 \end{pmatrix}$, $\mathbf{C} = \begin{pmatrix} 4 \\ 8 \end{pmatrix}$

5. (a) *If* $\mathbf{x} = (x_1, x_2, x_3)^{\mathrm{T}}$ and $\mathbf{A} = \{a_{ij}\}$ is a symmetric 3×3 matrix, write out the quantity $\mathbf{x}^{\mathrm{T}}\mathbf{A}\mathbf{x}$, which is said to be a *quadratic form* in x_1, x_2, x_3. Quadratic forms will be discussed in Chapter 4.
*(b) Determine $\mathbf{A}$ if $\mathbf{x}^{\mathrm{T}}\mathbf{A}\mathbf{x} = x_1^2 + 6x_1x_2 + 5x_1x_3 + 4x_2^2 + 7x_3^2$.
(c) Determine $\mathbf{A}$ if $\mathbf{x}^{\mathrm{T}}\mathbf{A}\mathbf{x} = x_1x_2 - x_2x_3 + x_2^2 + 6x_3^2$.

6. Express each of these square matrices as the sum of a symmetric matrix and a skew-symmetric matrix.

*(a) $\begin{pmatrix} 0 & 7 \\ 3 & 0 \end{pmatrix}$ (b) $\begin{pmatrix} 1 & 2 \\ 3 & 4 \end{pmatrix}$

(c) $\begin{pmatrix} 6 & 0 & -1 \\ 2 & 0 & 3 \\ -4 & 2 & 1 \end{pmatrix}$ (d) $\begin{pmatrix} 6 & 5 & 3 \\ 5 & 2 & -1 \\ 4 & -1 & 9 \end{pmatrix}$

7. Show that if $\mathbf{A}$ is an $m \times n$ matrix, then $\mathbf{A}\mathbf{A}^{\mathrm{T}}$ is symmetric. *Hint:* There is often an inclination to work out a problem like this using "brute force," i.e., by actually writing out the $\mathbf{A}$ and $\mathbf{A}^{\mathrm{T}}$ matrices, multiplying them, and examining the resulting matrix to see if it is symmetric. Wherever possible, we advise against such a procedure. In this problem, for example, we wish to show that $\mathbf{C}^{\mathrm{T}} = \mathbf{C}$, where $\mathbf{C}$ is short for $\mathbf{A}\mathbf{A}^{\mathrm{T}}$; i.e., we wish to show that $(\mathbf{A}\mathbf{A}^{\mathrm{T}})^{\mathrm{T}} = \mathbf{A}\mathbf{A}^{\mathrm{T}}$, and this can be done (in one or two short lines) using the properties stated in Theorem 1.

8. Prove that *the product* **AB** *need not be symmetric, even if* **A** *and* **B** *are both symmetric and of the same order*.

9. Prove the properties (4a), (4b), and (4c).

DETERMINANTS 3.4

In this section we introduce a scalar quantity associated with every square matrix, the so-called "determinant" of the matrix. If the matrix is **A**, we denote its determinant as either

$$\det \mathbf{A} \quad \text{or} \quad |\mathbf{A}|. \tag{1}$$

Note carefully that the latter notation, $|\mathbf{A}|$, means the determinant of **A**, *not* the absolute value of **A**. (This should not be confusing because the absolute value of a matrix has not been, and will not be, defined.)

In terms of the full matrix, the notations corresponding to (1) are

$$\det \begin{pmatrix} a_{11} & a_{12} & \cdots & a_{1n} \\ a_{21} & a_{22} & \cdots & a_{2n} \\ \vdots & & & \vdots \\ a_{n1} & a_{n2} & \cdots & a_{nn} \end{pmatrix} \quad \text{and} \quad \begin{vmatrix} a_{11} & a_{12} & \cdots & a_{1n} \\ a_{21} & a_{22} & \cdots & a_{2n} \\ \vdots & & & \vdots \\ a_{n1} & a_{n2} & \cdots & a_{nn} \end{vmatrix}, \tag{2}$$

respectively.

Rather than begin with the general $(n \times n)$ case, we state that for 1×1 and 2×2 matrices the definitions are as follows:

$$1 \times 1: \quad \boxed{|a_{11}| \equiv a_{11}} \tag{3}$$

$$2 \times 2: \quad \boxed{\begin{vmatrix} a_{11} & a_{12} \\ a_{21} & a_{22} \end{vmatrix} \equiv a_{11}a_{22} - a_{21}a_{12}.} \tag{4}$$

EXAMPLE 1 If $\mathbf{A} = (-6)$ and $\mathbf{B} = \begin{pmatrix} 5 & 1 \\ 0 & -2 \end{pmatrix}$, then

$$\det \mathbf{A} = -6 \quad \text{and} \quad \det \mathbf{B} = \begin{vmatrix} 5 & 1 \\ 0 & -2 \end{vmatrix} = (5)(-2) - (1)(0) = -10. \quad ◀$$

More generally, we define the determinant of an $n \times n$ matrix $\mathbf{A} = \{a_{ij}\}$ according to the **cofactor expansion**,

$$\boxed{\det \mathbf{A} \equiv \sum_{1}^{n} a_{jk} A_{jk},} \tag{5}$$

where *the summation is on j for any fixed value of k* ($1 \le k \le n$), **or** *on k for any fixed value of j* ($1 \le j \le n$). A_{jk}, called the **cofactor** of the a_{jk} element, is defined as

$$A_{jk} \equiv (-1)^{j+k} M_{jk}, \tag{6}$$

where M_{jk} is called the **minor** of a_{jk}, i.e., the determinant of the $(n-1) \times (n-1)$ matrix that survives when the row and column containing a_{jk} (namely, the jth row and the kth column) are struck out.

For example, if

$$\mathbf{A} = \begin{pmatrix} 4 & 0 & -2 & 3 \\ 1 & 6 & 3 & 3 \\ 5 & 0 & 4 & 12 \\ 2 & -1 & 7 & 9 \end{pmatrix}, \quad \text{then} \quad M_{23} = \begin{vmatrix} 4 & 0 & 3 \\ 5 & 0 & 12 \\ 2 & -1 & 9 \end{vmatrix}.$$

Thus, if $\mathbf{A}$ is $n \times n$, then the right-hand side of (5) is a linear combination of n determinants, each of which is $(n-1) \times (n-1)$. These, in turn, may be expressed as a linear combination of $(n-2) \times (n-2)$ determinants, and so on, until we have a (perhaps large) number of small determinants, say 2×2, which are readily evaluated by means of (4).

EXAMPLE 2 Let

$$\mathbf{A} = \begin{pmatrix} 0 & 2 & -1 \\ 4 & 3 & 5 \\ 2 & 0 & -4 \end{pmatrix}. \tag{7}$$

Using (5) with $j = 1$, say,

$$\left.\begin{aligned} \det \mathbf{A} = \sum_{k=1}^{3} a_{1k} A_{1k} &= a_{11}A_{11} + a_{12}A_{12} + a_{13}A_{13} \\ &= a_{11}(-1)^2 M_{11} + a_{12}(-1)^3 M_{12} + a_{13}(-1)^4 M_{13} \\ &= a_{11}M_{11} - a_{12}M_{12} + a_{13}M_{13} \\ &= (0)\begin{vmatrix} 3 & 5 \\ 0 & -4 \end{vmatrix} - (2)\begin{vmatrix} 4 & 5 \\ 2 & -4 \end{vmatrix} + (-1)\begin{vmatrix} 4 & 3 \\ 2 & 0 \end{vmatrix} \\ &= 0 - (2)(-16 - 10) + (-1)(0 - 6) = 58. \end{aligned}\right\} \tag{8}$$

This particular choice ($j = 1$, summing on k) is said to be a *cofactor expansion about the first row*, since (8) is the sum of the first-row elements a_{11}, a_{12}, a_{13}, multiplied by their cofactors.

According to (5), we can expand about *any* row or column. Let us illustrate that the same answer is indeed obtained if we expand about other rows or columns.

Expansion about second row [i.e., set $j = 2$ in (5), and sum on k]:

$$\begin{aligned}
\det \mathbf{A} = \sum_{k=1}^{3} a_{2k}A_{2k} &= a_{21}A_{21} + a_{22}A_{22} + a_{23}A_{23} \\
&= a_{21}(-1)^3 M_{21} + a_{22}(-1)^4 M_{22} + a_{23}(-1)^5 M_{23} \\
&= -(4)\begin{vmatrix} 2 & -1 \\ 0 & -4 \end{vmatrix} + (3)\begin{vmatrix} 0 & -1 \\ 2 & -4 \end{vmatrix} - (5)\begin{vmatrix} 0 & 2 \\ 2 & 0 \end{vmatrix} \\
&= -(4)(-8) + (3)(2) - (5)(-4) = 58,
\end{aligned}$$

again.

Expansion about third column ($k = 3$, sum on j):

$$\begin{aligned}
\det \mathbf{A} = \sum_{j=1}^{3} a_{j3}A_{j3} &= a_{13}A_{13} + a_{23}A_{23} + a_{33}A_{33} \\
&= a_{13}(-1)^4 M_{13} + a_{23}(-1)^5 M_{23} + a_{33}(-1)^6 M_{33} \\
&= (-1)\begin{vmatrix} 4 & 3 \\ 2 & 0 \end{vmatrix} - (5)\begin{vmatrix} 0 & 2 \\ 2 & 0 \end{vmatrix} + (-4)\begin{vmatrix} 0 & 2 \\ 4 & 3 \end{vmatrix} \\
&= (-1)(-6) - (5)(-4) + (-4)(-8) = 58,
\end{aligned}$$

once more. ◀

Example 2 *illustrates* that the cofactor expansion (5) yields the same value, independent of which row or column is chosen for the expansion. For *proof* of the claim that that is always true, we refer the interested reader to Kreyszig.*

Since we may expand about any row or column, it is convenient, in hand calculations, to choose the row or column with the most zeros in it since those terms in the expansion then drop out.

EXAMPLE 3 Let

$$\mathbf{A} = \begin{pmatrix} 4 & 0 & -2 & 0 \\ 1 & 0 & 2 & 0 \\ 1 & 3 & 5 & 6 \\ 1 & 0 & 0 & -3 \end{pmatrix}.$$

If we expand about the first row, say, then

$$\begin{aligned}
\det \mathbf{A} = &+(4)\begin{vmatrix} 0 & 2 & 0 \\ 3 & 5 & 6 \\ 0 & 0 & -3 \end{vmatrix} - (0)\begin{vmatrix} 1 & 2 & 0 \\ 1 & 5 & 6 \\ 1 & 0 & -3 \end{vmatrix} \\
&+(-2)\begin{vmatrix} 1 & 0 & 0 \\ 1 & 3 & 6 \\ 1 & 0 & -3 \end{vmatrix} - (0)\begin{vmatrix} 1 & 0 & 2 \\ 1 & 3 & 5 \\ 1 & 0 & 0 \end{vmatrix}. \qquad (9)
\end{aligned}$$

* Erwin Kreyszig, *Advanced Engineering Mathematics*, 4th ed. (New York: Wiley, 1979), p. 336.

The second and fourth terms on the right are zero, so it remains to work out the two remaining 3×3 determinants in (9).

However, it would have been easier to notice that the second column of the $\mathbf{A}$ matrix has several zeros in it. Thus if we expand about that column instead, then

$$\det \mathbf{A} = 0 + 0 - (3)\begin{vmatrix} 4 & -2 & 0 \\ 1 & 2 & 0 \\ 1 & 0 & -3 \end{vmatrix} + 0, \tag{10}$$

and we have only one 3×3 determinant to evaluate, whereas in (9) we had two. In the same spirit, let us evaluate the 3×3 determinant in (10) by expanding about its third column (since it contains two zeros). Then

$$\det \mathbf{A} = -(3)(-3)\begin{vmatrix} 4 & -2 \\ 1 & 2 \end{vmatrix} = 9(8 + 2) = 90. \quad ◀$$

In carrying out such expansions, it is helpful to realize that the $(-1)^{j+k}$ factor in (6) imposes the following "field of signs":

$$\begin{pmatrix} + & - & + & \cdots \\ - & + & - & \cdots \\ + & - & + & \cdots \\ \vdots & \vdots & \vdots & \end{pmatrix}; \tag{11}$$

that is, + at the upper left-hand corner, and then alternating in checkerboard fashion as we move away from that location. For example, (9) is an expansion about the first row, and the signs obtained are the same as those present in the first row of (11).

Before continuing, let us introduce the idea of a "triangular" matrix. A square matrix $\mathbf{A} = \{a_{ij}\}$ is **upper triangular** if $a_{ij} = 0$ for all $j < i$, and **lower triangular** if $a_{ij} = 0$ for all $i < j$. Thus

$$\begin{pmatrix} a_{11} & a_{12} & \cdots & a_{1n} \\ 0 & a_{22} & & \vdots \\ 0 & 0 & \ddots & \vdots \\ \vdots & & & \\ 0 & 0 & \cdots & a_{nn} \end{pmatrix} \quad \text{or} \quad \begin{pmatrix} a_{11} & a_{12} & \cdots & a_{1n} \\ & a_{22} & & \vdots \\ & & \ddots & \vdots \\ & \bigcirc & & a_{nn} \end{pmatrix} \quad \text{for short,}$$

is upper triangular, and

$$\begin{pmatrix} a_{11} & & & \bigcirc \\ a_{21} & a_{22} & & \\ \vdots & & \ddots & \\ a_{n1} & \cdots & & a_{nn} \end{pmatrix}$$

is lower triangular. If a matrix is either upper triangular or lower triangular, it is said to be **triangular**.

We now list, without proof, a number of important and useful properties of determinants, for any $n \times n$ matrix $\mathbf{A}$.

Properties

D1. *If A is triangular* $\det \mathbf{A}$ *is simply the product of the diagonal elements,* $\det \mathbf{A} = a_{11}a_{22} \cdots a_{nn}$.

D2. *If all the elements of any row or any column are zero, then* $\det \mathbf{A} = 0$.

D3. *The determinants of* **A** *and its transpose are the same,*

$$\det \mathbf{A} = \det(\mathbf{A}^{\mathrm{T}}). \tag{12}$$

D4. *If any two rows or columns of* **A** *are interchanged, to yield a new matrix* **B**, *then* $\det \mathbf{A} = -\det \mathbf{B}$.

D5. *If all the elements of any row or any column of* **A** *are multiplied by a scalar* α, *to yield a new matrix* **B**, *then* $\det \mathbf{B} = \alpha \det \mathbf{A}$.

D6. *If any two rows or columns are proportional to each other, then* $\det \mathbf{A} = 0$.

D7. *If any row (or column) is modified by adding* α *times the corresponding elements of another row (or column) to it, yielding a new matrix* **B**, *then* $\det \mathbf{B} = \det \mathbf{A}$.

D8. *If* **A** *and* **B** *are both* $n \times n$, *then*

$$\det(\mathbf{AB}) = (\det \mathbf{A})(\det \mathbf{B}). \tag{13}$$

D9. $\det(\alpha \mathbf{A}) = \alpha^n \det \mathbf{A}$. (14)

D10. *Even if* **A** *and* **B** *are both* $n \times n$, *then in general,*

$$\det(\mathbf{A} + \mathbf{B}) \neq \det \mathbf{A} + \det \mathbf{B}. \tag{15}$$

D11. *If any one row (or column)* $\mathbf{a}$ *of* **A** *is separated as* $\mathbf{a} = \mathbf{b} + \mathbf{c}$, *then*

$$\det \mathbf{A}\big|_{\mathbf{a}} = \det \mathbf{A}\big|_{\mathbf{b}} + \det \mathbf{A}\big|_{\mathbf{c}}, \tag{16}$$

where we have written $\mathbf{A}|_{\mathbf{a}}$ *to denote the* **A** *matrix with* $\mathbf{a}$ *intact,* $\mathbf{A}|_{\mathbf{b}}$ *to denote the* **A** *matrix with* $\mathbf{b}$ *in place of* $\mathbf{a}$, *and similarly for* $\mathbf{A}|_{\mathbf{c}}$. *For example,*

$$\begin{vmatrix} 6+2 & -3+1 & 5+4 \\ 3 & 0 & 2 \\ 1 & -6 & 7 \end{vmatrix} = \begin{vmatrix} 6 & -3 & 5 \\ 3 & 0 & 2 \\ 1 & -6 & 7 \end{vmatrix} + \begin{vmatrix} 2 & 1 & 4 \\ 3 & 0 & 2 \\ 1 & -6 & 7 \end{vmatrix}.$$

These properties are not independent of each other; for example, D6 follows from D4 and D5, D2 follows from D5, and so on (Exercise 15).

Bear in mind that det is not linear, i.e., if α, β are scalars and $\mathbf{A}, \mathbf{B}$ are $n \times n$ matrices, then

$$\det(\alpha \mathbf{A} + \beta \mathbf{B}) \neq \alpha \det \mathbf{A} + \beta \det \mathbf{B} \tag{17}$$

in general. For instance, if $\beta = 0$, is $\det(\alpha \mathbf{A}) = \alpha \det \mathbf{A}$? No, according to (14) it is $\alpha^n \det \mathbf{A}$. Or, with $\alpha = \beta = 1$, does $\det(\mathbf{A} + \mathbf{B}) = \det \mathbf{A} + \det \mathbf{B}$? Not in general, according to property D10. In studying linear analysis it is easy to take the linearity of "everything in sight" for granted, so (17) may come as a bit of a surprise. Equally surprising is the truth of (13) when one contrasts the complexity of the matrix multiplication **AB** on the left with the simple outcome on the right. This result was proved by Cauchy in 1815.*

**Augustin-Louis Cauchy* (1789–1857) is surely among the greatest mathematicians. Unlike his contemporary, Gauss, who published little of his work, Cauchy published more than 700 papers, second only to Euler in number. Among the subjects on which he worked were determinants, ordinary and partial differential equations, complex variable theory, and the wave theory of light.

The properties D1 to D11 can be particularly helpful in hand calculations. Let us illustrate with an example, in which we use D1 and D7.

EXAMPLE 4

$$\begin{vmatrix} 2 & -4 & 0 & 3 \\ 1 & 1 & 3 & 5 \\ 4 & 1 & -6 & 2 \\ 8 & 2 & -5 & 1 \end{vmatrix} = \begin{vmatrix} 2 & -4 & 0 & 3 \\ 0 & 3 & 3 & \frac{7}{2} \\ 0 & 9 & -6 & -4 \\ 0 & 18 & -5 & -11 \end{vmatrix} = \begin{vmatrix} 2 & -4 & 0 & 3 \\ 0 & 3 & 3 & \frac{7}{2} \\ 0 & 0 & -15 & -\frac{29}{2} \\ 0 & 0 & -23 & -32 \end{vmatrix} \tag{18}$$

$$= \begin{vmatrix} 2 & -4 & 0 & 3 \\ 0 & 3 & 3 & \frac{7}{2} \\ 0 & 0 & -15 & -\frac{29}{2} \\ 0 & 0 & 0 & -\frac{293}{30} \end{vmatrix}$$

$$= (2)(3)(-15)\left(-\frac{293}{30}\right) = 879.$$

In the first equality we added $-\frac{1}{2}$ times the first row to the second, -2 times the first row to the third, and -4 times the first row to the fourth; according to property D7, these steps do not change the determinant. In the second equality we added -3 times the second row to the third, and -6 times the second row to the fourth. In the third equality we added $-\frac{23}{15}$ times the third row to the fourth. Having thus attained a triangular form, we then applied property D1.

Although the answer is unique, the solution procedure certainly is not; many different approaches are possible. ◀

A practical consideration of great importance is the *computing time* (and hence expense) entailed in the digital computer evaluation of a determinant. As representative of current high-speed digital computers, consider the Burroughs B7700, which (using Fortran) takes on the order of 1 microsecond to do one multiplication, and about the same for one addition or subtraction. If we count each multiplication, addition, and subtraction as one "calculation," it can be shown (Exercise 17a) that the number of calculations $N(n)$ required in the evaluation (by cofactor expansion) of an $n \times n$ determinant behaves like

$$N(n) \sim en! \tag{19}$$

as $n \to \infty$, where $e \approx 2.718$ is the base of the natural logarithm, and $n!$ is n factorial. And if each calculation takes approximately 1 microsecond, some time estimates are as follows:

n	*Computing Time*
5	3×10^{-4} sec
10	10 sec
15	4×10^{6} sec $\approx$ 40 days
20	7×10^{12} sec $\approx$ 210,000 years
25	4×10^{19} sec $\approx$ 10^{12} years

Here we have a problem. In fact, determinants encountered in applications may be of much higher order than 25. However, "there are formulas and there are formulas," and some are more efficient than others. For example, while the cofactor expansion of an $n \times n$ determinant requires approximately $2.7n!$ calculations, the triangularization method employed in Example 4 (which, as you may have noted, is reminiscent of the Gauss elimination method discussed in Section 1.3) requires only

$$N(n) \sim \frac{2n^3}{3} \tag{20}$$

calculations for large n's (Exercise 17b), and hence about $2n^3/3$ microseconds altogether. For $n = 20$, say, this is about 0.005 second, which, compared with 210,000 years, represents a significant saving.

Such difficulties with large systems will again be encountered when, in subsequent sections, we discuss matrix inversion and the solution of the linear equation $\mathbf{Ax} = \mathbf{c}$.

Thus far in this section we have not indicated how determinants are *used.* We shall see, in the sections to follow, that they play a key role in the theory of systems of linear equations. Meanwhile, a number of specialized applications, such as the Routh–Hurwitz criteria, are included in the exercises to follow.

3.4 EXERCISES

1. Show that the cofactor expansion of $\begin{vmatrix} a_{11} & a_{12} \\ a_{21} & a_{22} \end{vmatrix}$, together with the definition (3), does yield the result $a_{11}a_{22} - a_{21}a_{12}$, as given in (4).

2. Evaluate the following determinants by expanding about each row and about each column.

(a) $\begin{vmatrix} 2 & 1 \\ 4 & 3 \end{vmatrix}$ (b) $\begin{vmatrix} 3 & -1 \\ 4 & 2 \end{vmatrix}$

(c) $\begin{vmatrix} 1 & 2 \\ 3 & 6 \end{vmatrix}$ (d) $\begin{vmatrix} 0 & 1 \\ 1 & 5 \end{vmatrix}$

(e) $\begin{vmatrix} 0 & 1 & 2 \\ 0 & 0 & 1 \\ 3 & 0 & -1 \end{vmatrix}$ (f) $\begin{vmatrix} -1 & 2 & 0 \\ 0 & 4 & 0 \\ 1 & 0 & 3 \end{vmatrix}$

*(g) $\begin{vmatrix} 2 & 0 & 0 \\ 0 & -4 & 0 \\ 0 & 0 & 5 \end{vmatrix}$ (h) $\begin{vmatrix} 1 & 2 & 3 \\ 0 & 4 & 5 \\ 0 & 0 & 6 \end{vmatrix}$

3. Evaluate the following.

*(a) $\begin{vmatrix} 2 & 1 & -1 \\ 0 & 0 & 3 \\ 0 & 0 & 5 \end{vmatrix}$ (b) $\begin{vmatrix} 0 & 0 & -2 \\ 0 & 2 & -1 \\ 4 & 3 & 1 \end{vmatrix}$

(c) $\begin{vmatrix} 0 & 0 & 4 \\ 0 & 3 & 0 \\ 2 & 0 & 0 \end{vmatrix}$ (d) $\begin{vmatrix} 1 & 2 & -3 \\ 4 & 5 & 6 \\ 7 & 8 & 9 \end{vmatrix}$

(e) $\begin{vmatrix} 1 & 1 & 1 & 1 \\ 1 & 2 & 4 & 8 \\ 1 & 3 & 9 & 27 \\ 1 & 4 & 16 & 64 \end{vmatrix}$ (f) $\begin{vmatrix} 1 & -3 & 0 & 1 \\ 2 & 4 & 0 & 1 \\ 0 & 0 & 2 & 0 \\ 1 & 0 & 0 & 5 \end{vmatrix}$

*(g) $\begin{vmatrix} 0 & 0 & 0 & 3 \\ 0 & 0 & 2 & 0 \\ 0 & -1 & 0 & 0 \\ 4 & 0 & 0 & 0 \end{vmatrix}$ (h) $\begin{vmatrix} 2 & 1 & 0 & 0 \\ 1 & 2 & 1 & 0 \\ 0 & 1 & 2 & 1 \\ 0 & 0 & 1 & 2 \end{vmatrix}$

(i) $\begin{vmatrix} 1 & 0 & 0 & 0 \\ 0 & 2 & 0 & 0 \\ 0 & 0 & 3 & 0 \\ 5 & 0 & 0 & 4 \end{vmatrix}$ (j) $\begin{vmatrix} 2 & 3 & 1 & 1 \\ 1 & 0 & 2 & 1 \\ 3 & 3 & 3 & 2 \\ 1 & 4 & 1 & 0 \end{vmatrix}$

(k) $\begin{vmatrix} 0 & 0 & 0 & 2 \\ 0 & 0 & -1 & 6 \\ 0 & 3 & 2 & 1 \\ 1 & 5 & 4 & -2 \end{vmatrix}$ (l) $\begin{vmatrix} 1 & 0 & 0 & 1 \\ 0 & 1 & 0 & 0 \\ 2 & 0 & 0 & 0 \\ 0 & 0 & 3 & 0 \end{vmatrix}$

*(m) $\begin{vmatrix} 0 & 3 & 0 & 1 \\ 0 & 2 & 0 & 1 \\ 0 & 0 & 1 & 0 \\ 5 & 0 & 0 & 0 \end{vmatrix}$

4. Show that

(a) $$\begin{vmatrix} 1 & 5 & 9 & 13 \\ 2 & 6 & 10 & 14 \\ 3 & 7 & 11 & 15 \\ 4 & 8 & 12 & 16 \end{vmatrix} = 0$$

(b) $$\begin{vmatrix} 1 & 2 & 3 & 4 & 5 \\ 6 & 7 & 8 & 9 & 10 \\ 11 & 12 & 13 & 14 & 15 \\ 16 & 17 & 18 & 19 & 20 \\ 21 & 22 & 23 & 24 & 25 \end{vmatrix} = 0$$

5. Evaluate.

(a) $$\begin{vmatrix} 0 & 0 & 0 & 0 & 0 & a \\ 0 & 0 & 0 & 0 & b & c \\ 0 & 0 & 0 & d & e & f \\ 0 & 0 & g & h & i & j \\ 0 & k & l & m & n & o \\ p & q & r & s & t & u \end{vmatrix}$$

(b) $$\begin{vmatrix} a & b & c & d & e & f \\ g & h & i & j & k & 0 \\ l & m & n & o & 0 & 0 \\ p & q & r & 0 & 0 & 0 \\ s & t & 0 & 0 & 0 & 0 \\ u & 0 & 0 & 0 & 0 & 0 \end{vmatrix}$$

6. Evaluate the following using the triangularization method employed in Example 4.

(a) $\begin{vmatrix} 1 & 2 & 4 \\ 1 & 3 & 9 \\ 1 & 4 & 16 \end{vmatrix}$ (b) $\begin{vmatrix} 1 & 0 & 1 \\ 0 & 1 & 0 \\ 2 & 0 & 1 \end{vmatrix}$

(c) $\begin{vmatrix} 2 & -1 & 5 \\ 4 & 2 & 3 \\ 1 & 6 & -1 \end{vmatrix}$ (d) $\begin{vmatrix} 4 & 3 & 4 \\ 2 & 1 & 2 \\ 1 & 0 & 1 \end{vmatrix}$

7. A mnemonic device often put forward for evaluating 2×2 and 3×3 determinants is as shown below.

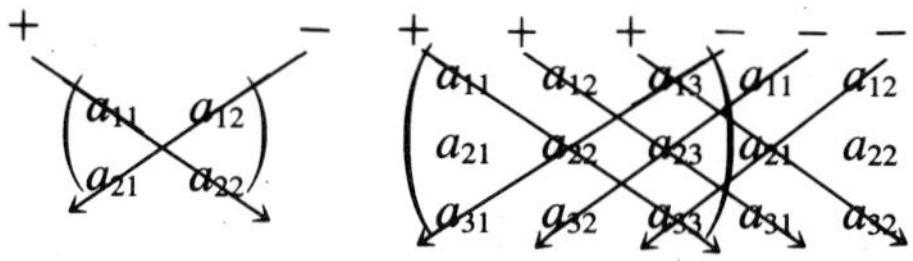

In other words, the determinants are the sums of the indicated products, with each product carrying the indicated sign. For example, in the 2×2 case this device gives

$$\begin{vmatrix} a_{11} & a_{12} \\ a_{21} & a_{22} \end{vmatrix} = +(a_{11}a_{22}) - (a_{21}a_{12}),$$

which does agree with (4). We now state the problem: Write out the mnemonic result for the 3×3 case, and verify (by cofactor expansion) that it is correct. *Caution:* This device does *not* hold, in general, for $n \times n$ determinants if $n \geq 4$.

8. Let $\mathbf{A} = \{a_{ij}\}$ be diagonal. Show, by cofactor expansion and also be means of property D1, that

$$\det \mathbf{A} = a_{11}a_{22} \cdots a_{nn}. \qquad \text{(a)}$$

9. (a) Suppose that an $n \times n$ matrix $\mathbf{A}$ can be partitioned into the **block-diagonal** form

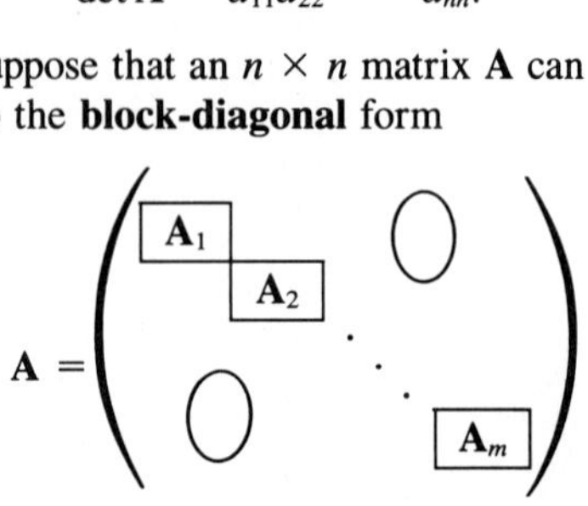

where $\mathbf{A}_1, \ldots, \mathbf{A}_m$ are all square, although not necessarily all of the same order. Show that

$$\det \mathbf{A} = (\det \mathbf{A}_1)(\det \mathbf{A}_2) \cdots (\det \mathbf{A}_m). \qquad \text{(a)}$$

This result may be regarded as an extension of formula (a) in Exercise 8, wherein $\mathbf{A}_1, \ldots, \mathbf{A}_m$ were all 1×1's.
(b) Does equation (a) hold for the cases

$\mathbf{A} =$ 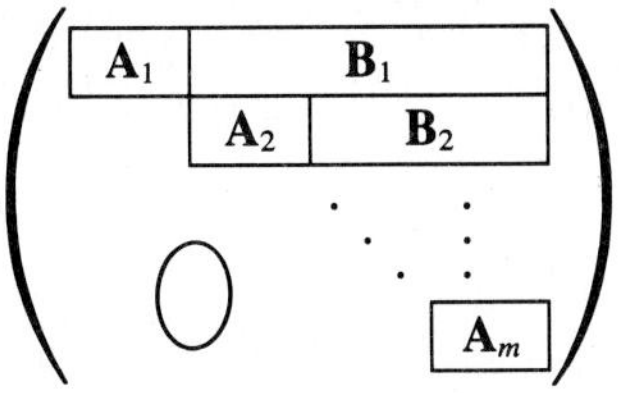 and

$\mathbf{A} =$ 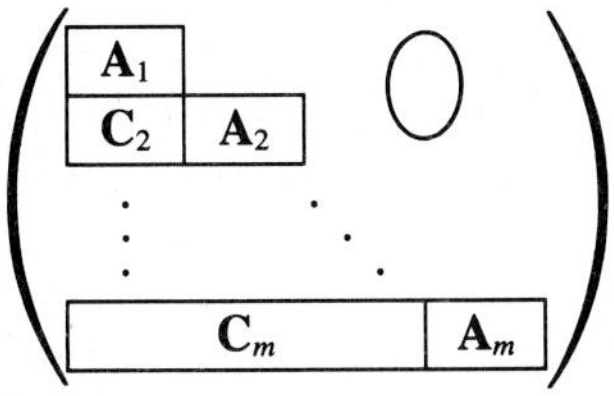

where $\mathbf{B}_1, \ldots, \mathbf{B}_{m-1}$ and $\mathbf{C}_2, \ldots, \mathbf{C}_m$ are not necessarily zero matrices? Explain.

10. Evaluate each of the following determinants, with the help of the results given in Exercise 9.

*(a) $\begin{vmatrix} 5 & 7 & 0 & 0 \\ 2 & -3 & 0 & 0 \\ 0 & 0 & 1 & 5 \\ 0 & 0 & 2 & 2 \end{vmatrix}$ (b) $\begin{vmatrix} 6 & 8 & 0 & 0 \\ 3 & 4 & 0 & 0 \\ 0 & 0 & 1 & 2 \\ 0 & 0 & 3 & 4 \end{vmatrix}$

(c) $\begin{vmatrix} 2 & 0 & 0 & 0 \\ 0 & 3 & 5 & 0 \\ 0 & 1 & 4 & 0 \\ 0 & 0 & 0 & 6 \end{vmatrix}$ (d) $\begin{vmatrix} 6 & 0 & 0 & 0 & 0 \\ 0 & 4 & 2 & 7 & 0 \\ 0 & 3 & 1 & 1 & 0 \\ 0 & 2 & 2 & 2 & 0 \\ 0 & 0 & 0 & 0 & 9 \end{vmatrix}$

(e) $\begin{vmatrix} 3 & -1 & 0 & 0 & 0 \\ 2 & 4 & 0 & 0 & 0 \\ 0 & 0 & 5 & 0 & 0 \\ 0 & 0 & 1 & 2 & 7 \\ 0 & 0 & 3 & -6 & 1 \end{vmatrix}$

11. Deduce, from (13), that if $\mathbf{A}, \mathbf{B}, \mathbf{C}, \mathbf{D}$ are $n \times n$ matrices, then

$$\det(\mathbf{ABCD}) = (\det \mathbf{A})(\det \mathbf{B})(\det \mathbf{C})(\det \mathbf{D}).$$

12. (a) Verify that the equation of a straight line through the distinct points (x_1, y_1) and (x_2, y_2) is

$$\begin{vmatrix} x & y & 1 \\ x_1 & y_1 & 1 \\ x_2 & y_2 & 1 \end{vmatrix} = 0. \qquad \text{(a)}$$

(b) Verify that the equation of a plane through the distinct points (x_1, y_1, z_1), (x_2, y_2, z_2), and (x_3, y_3, z_3) is

$$\begin{vmatrix} x & y & z & 1 \\ x_1 & y_1 & z_1 & 1 \\ x_2 & y_2 & z_2 & 1 \\ x_3 & y_3 & z_3 & 1 \end{vmatrix} = 0. \qquad \text{(b)}$$

13. Prove the determinant property D11. *Hint:* Write out the cofactor expansion about the row (or column) $\mathbf{a}$.

14. (a) Derive property D1.
(b) Derive property D9.

15. (a) Show that property D6 follows from properties D4 and D5.
(b) Show that property D2 follows from property D5.

16. Verify properties D8 and D10 for the following cases.

(a) $\mathbf{A} = \begin{pmatrix} 1 & 2 \\ 3 & 2 \end{pmatrix}$, $\mathbf{B} = \begin{pmatrix} 6 & 3 \\ 4 & 8 \end{pmatrix}$

(b) $\mathbf{A} = \begin{pmatrix} 1 & 2 \\ 3 & 2 \end{pmatrix}$, $\mathbf{B} = \begin{pmatrix} 6 & 4 \\ 4 & 8 \end{pmatrix}$

(c) $\mathbf{A} = \begin{pmatrix} 0 & 3 & 5 \\ 1 & -1 & 2 \\ 0 & 2 & 2 \end{pmatrix}$, $\mathbf{B} = \begin{pmatrix} 2 & -1 & 0 \\ 2 & 1 & -2 \\ 5 & 4 & 3 \end{pmatrix}$

17. (a) Derive (19). *Hint:* Show that $N(n) = nN(n-1) + 2n - 1$. Then, seeking $N(n)$ in the form $n!Q_n$, show that $Q_n - Q_{n-1} = (2n-1)/n!$, which admits the solution

$$Q_n = \frac{3}{2} + 2\sum_{j=2}^{n-1} \frac{1}{j!} - \sum_{j=3}^{n} \frac{1}{j!} \sim e \quad \text{as} \quad n \to \infty.$$

(b) Derive (20). *Hint:* $n(n-1) + (n-1)(n-2) + \cdots + (2)(1) = n(n^2-1)/3$.

18. (*Routh–Hurwitz criterion*) Consider the general nth-degree algebraic equation in λ,

$$a_0\lambda^n + a_1\lambda^{n-1} + \cdots + a_{n-1}\lambda + a_n = 0, \qquad \text{(a)}$$

where the coefficients $a_0, \ldots, a_n$ are real and

$a_0 > 0$. Such an equation arises, for example, when one seeks solutions of the differential equation

$$a_0 \frac{d^n x}{dt^n} + a_1 \frac{d^{n-1}x}{dt^{n-1}} + \cdots + a_{n-1}\frac{dx}{dt} + a_n x = 0 \quad \text{(b)}$$

in the form $x = e^{\lambda t}$. It is known from the theory of equations that (a) possesses exactly n roots if one counts multiple roots according to their multiplicity; for example, if $\lambda^3 + 2\lambda^2 + \lambda = 0$, then $\lambda(\lambda + 1)(\lambda + 1) = 0$, and we have the "three" roots $\lambda = 0, -1, -1$. In general, the roots may be *complex*, i.e., of the form $a + ib$, where $i \equiv \sqrt{-1}$, and where a, b are called the *real* and *imaginary* parts, respectively. The solution of (b) and indeed the physical system that it represents, is said to be **stable** if and only if the real part of every root of (a) is negative (i.e., if all of its roots lie in the left half of the "complex plane"). One is often more interested in whether or not the system is stable than in the solution itself. Thus it is important, in applications, to be able to test for stability directly, by a suitable assessment of the $a_0, \ldots, a_n$ coefficients, without actually having to compute the n roots (which can be time consuming and costly if n is large). A useful criterion is as follows:

(*Routh–Hurwitz criterion*) *Necessary and sufficient* conditions for stability of the system governed by (b) [or, equivalently, for all of the roots of (a) to have negative real parts] are that $a_j > 0$ for each $j = 0, \ldots, n$, and that $\Delta_j > 0$ for each $j = 1, \ldots, n$, where

$$\Delta_j = \begin{vmatrix} a_1 & a_0 & 0 & 0 & 0 & \cdots & 0 \\ a_3 & a_2 & a_1 & a_0 & 0 & \cdots & 0 \\ a_5 & a_4 & a_3 & a_2 & a_1 & \cdots & 0 \\ \vdots & & & & & & \vdots \\ a_{2j-1} & a_{2j-2} & a_{2j-3} & a_{2j-4} & & \cdots & a_j \end{vmatrix}.$$

Zeros are entered for any a_k's that are called for where $k > n$. For example, if $n = 3$, then

$$\Delta_1 = a_1, \quad \Delta_2 = \begin{vmatrix} a_1 & a_0 \\ a_3 & a_2 \end{vmatrix}, \quad \Delta_3 = \begin{vmatrix} a_1 & a_0 & 0 \\ a_3 & a_2 & a_1 \\ 0 & 0 & a_3 \end{vmatrix};$$

expanding Δ_3 about the third row yields the simplification $\Delta_3 = a_3\Delta_2$. We now state the problem: Use the Routh–Hurwitz criterion to determine whether or not the following systems are stable.

*(a) $2\lambda^7 + 8\lambda^6 + 4\lambda^5 + 3\lambda^4 + \lambda^2 + \lambda + 6 = 0$
*(b) $\lambda^5 + \lambda^4 + \lambda^3 + \lambda^2 + \lambda + 1 = 0$
*(c) $\lambda^5 + 2\lambda^4 + 5\lambda^3 + 7\lambda^2 + 6\lambda + 4 = 0$
(d) $\lambda^4 + 4\lambda^3 + 5\lambda^2 + 4\lambda + 1 = 0$
(e) $2\lambda^4 + 3\lambda^3 + 4\lambda^2 + \lambda + 2 = 0$
(f) $\lambda^6 + \lambda^5 - 3\lambda^4 + 2\lambda^3 - \lambda^2 + 10\lambda + 6 = 0$
(g) $\lambda^4 + \lambda^3 + \lambda^2 + \lambda + 2 = 0$

19. It can be shown that the equations

$$a_0x^2 + a_1x + a_2 = 0 \qquad (a_0 \neq 0)$$

$$b_0x^2 + b_1x + b_2 = 0 \qquad (b_0 \neq 0)$$

have a common root if and only if

$$\begin{vmatrix} a_0 & a_1 & a_2 & 0 \\ 0 & a_0 & a_1 & a_2 \\ b_0 & b_1 & b_2 & 0 \\ 0 & b_0 & b_1 & b_2 \end{vmatrix} = 0.$$

[Similar results for two algebraic equations of degrees m and n, say, were put forward by *James Joseph Sylvester* (1814–1897).] Use this result to determine whether or not the following equation pairs have any common roots.

*(a) $3x^2 + 2x - 5 = 0$, $3x^2 + 3x - 2 = 0$
(b) $3x^2 + 2x - 5 = 0$, $x^2 + x + 1 = 0$

20. (a) Suppose that the elements a_{ij} of an $n \times n$ matrix $\mathbf{A}$ are differentiable functions of some parameter t. Regarding det $\mathbf{A}$ as a function of the n^2 variables $a_{11}, a_{12}, \ldots, a_{nn}$, show that

$$\frac{\partial}{\partial a_{ij}}(\det \mathbf{A}) = A_{ij}, \qquad \text{(a)}$$

where A_{ij} is the cofactor of a_{ij}. Use (a) and chain differentiation to show that

$$\frac{d}{dt}(\det \mathbf{A}) = \sum_{i=1}^{n}\sum_{j=1}^{n} A_{ij}\frac{da_{ij}}{dt}, \qquad \text{(b)}$$

a formula first given by *Carl Gustav Jacob Jacobi* (1804–1851) in 1841. By the $\Sigma\Sigma$ notation we mean

$$\sum_{i=1}^{n}\sum_{j=1}^{n} c_{ij} \equiv \sum_{i=1}^{n}\left(\sum_{j=1}^{n} c_{ij}\right);$$

for example, if $n = 2$, then

$$\sum_{i=1}^{2}\sum_{j=1}^{2} c_{ij} = \sum_{i=1}^{2}\left(\sum_{j=1}^{2} c_{ij}\right) = \sum_{i=1}^{2}(c_{i1} + c_{i2})$$
$$= c_{11} + c_{21} + c_{12} + c_{22}.$$

Observe that (b) is equivalent to the statement

$$\frac{d}{dt}(\det \mathbf{A}) = \begin{vmatrix} \frac{da_{11}}{dt} & \cdots & \frac{da_{1n}}{dt} \\ a_{21} & \cdots & a_{2n} \\ \vdots & & \vdots \\ a_{n1} & \cdots & a_{nn} \end{vmatrix} \tag{c}$$

$$+ \cdots + \begin{vmatrix} a_{11} & \cdots & a_{1n} \\ \vdots & & \vdots \\ a_{n-1,1} & \cdots & a_{n-1,n} \\ \frac{da_{n1}}{dt} & \cdots & \frac{da_{nn}}{dt} \end{vmatrix}.$$

(b) Apply equation (b) to

$$\mathbf{A} = \begin{pmatrix} t & t & 0 \\ t & 1 & 2 \\ 0 & 3 & 2+t \end{pmatrix}.$$

(c) Apply equation (b) to

$$\mathbf{A} = \begin{pmatrix} 1+t & 1 & 1 \\ t & t & 2 \\ 3 & 1-t & 0 \end{pmatrix}.$$

21. (*Vandermonde determinant*) Verify the formula

$$\begin{vmatrix} x_1^{n-1} & x_1^{n-2} & \cdots & x_1 & 1 \\ x_2^{n-1} & x_2^{n-2} & \cdots & x_2 & 1 \\ \vdots & & & & \vdots \\ x_n^{n-1} & x_n^{n-2} & \cdots & x_n & 1 \end{vmatrix} = \prod_{1 \le i < j \le n} (x_i - x_j), \tag{a}$$

which holds for $n \ge 2$, for the cases $n = 2$ and $n = 3$, by actually working out both sides. The left-hand side is known as the **Vandermonde determinant**. Just as Σ is used to denote sums, Π is used for *products*:

$$\prod_{i=1}^{n} c_i \left(\text{or} \prod_{1 \le i \le n} c_i \right) \equiv c_1 c_2 \cdots c_n.$$

The notation under the Π in (a) means that we are to include all factors of the form $(x_i - x_j)$ as i and j range from 1 to n, subject to the restriction that i be less than j. For example.

$$\prod_{1 \le i < j \le 4} (x_i - x_j) = (x_1 - x_2)(x_1 - x_3)(x_1 - x_4)$$
$$(x_2 - x_3)(x_2 - x_4)(x_3 - x_4).$$

Note: The important and useful property of the Vandermonde determinant is that it is nonzero, unless $x_i = x_j$ for at least one i,j pair such that $i \neq j$.

22. Surely, it is a simple matter to express any given square matrix $\mathbf{A}$ as $\mathbf{A} = \mathbf{A}_1 + \mathbf{A}_2$, where $\mathbf{A}_1$ and $\mathbf{A}_2$ are both triangular. Writing $\det \mathbf{A} = \det(\mathbf{A}_1 + \mathbf{A}_2) = \det \mathbf{A}_1 + \det \mathbf{A}_2$, $\det \mathbf{A}_1$ and $\det \mathbf{A}_2$ are readily computed by means of property D1, and we seem to have found an extremely simple method of computing $\det \mathbf{A}$. Is the proposed procedure sound? Explain.

23. (*Effect of elementary row operations*) *Do elementary row operations* (defined on page 12) *preserve the determinant of a matrix*? That is, if $\mathbf{A}'$ is the matrix that results from the application of an elementary row operation to a given (square) matrix $\mathbf{A}$, is it necessarily true that $\det \mathbf{A}' = \det \mathbf{A}$? *Note:* Treat each of the three types of elementary row operation separately.

24. Given a square matrix $\mathbf{A}$, we obtain a new matrix $\mathbf{A}'$ by carrying out the indicated elementary row operation. How does $\det \mathbf{A}'$ compare with $\det \mathbf{A}$? (For example, $\det \mathbf{A}' = \det \mathbf{A}$, $\det \mathbf{A}' = -\det \mathbf{A}$, $\det \mathbf{A}' = 3 \det \mathbf{A}$, or whatever.)

*(a) Interchange the second and fourth rows.
(b) Interchange the second and fifth rows.
(c) Add twice the second row to the third.
*(d) Add the second row to twice the third.
(e) Multiply the second row by −5.
(f) Add −4 times the first row to the second.
(g) Add −3 times the first row to twice the second.

RANK; APPLICATIONS TO LINEAR DEPENDENCE AND TO EXISTENCE AND UNIQUENESS FOR THE LINEAR SYSTEM Ax = c 3.5

Having just introduced determinants, we may now add one more important definition, the "rank" of a matrix. We shall then be in a position to formulate an extremely useful theorem regarding the existence and uniqueness of solutions to the problem of

m simultaneous linear equations in n unknowns, i.e., to the linear equation $\mathbf{Ax} = \mathbf{c}$, where $\mathbf{A}$ is an $m \times n$ matrix, the unknown $\mathbf{x}$ is an $n \times 1$ column vector, and $\mathbf{c}$ is an $m \times 1$ column vector; and we shall also be able to make a useful connection between the rank of a matrix and the linear dependence of a set of vectors, a subject introduced back in Chapter 2.

First some terminology. We say that any matrix obtained from a given $m \times n$ matrix $\mathbf{A}$ by deleting at most $m - 1$ rows and at most $n - 1$ columns from $\mathbf{A}$ is a **submatrix** of $\mathbf{A}$.

EXAMPLE 1 Consider a 2×3 matrix

$$\mathbf{A} = \begin{pmatrix} a_{11} & a_{12} & a_{13} \\ a_{21} & a_{22} & a_{23} \end{pmatrix}. \tag{1}$$

If we delete *no* rows and *no* columns, we obtain the submatrix $\mathbf{A}$ itself; if we delete the first row and the second column, we obtain the submatrix $(a_{21} \quad a_{23})$, and so on. Altogether, the matrix $\mathbf{A}$ given in (1) admits the following submatrices:

$$\begin{pmatrix} a_{11} & a_{12} & a_{13} \\ a_{21} & a_{22} & a_{23} \end{pmatrix} \quad \begin{pmatrix} a_{11} & a_{12} \\ a_{21} & a_{22} \end{pmatrix} \quad \begin{pmatrix} a_{11} & a_{13} \\ a_{21} & a_{23} \end{pmatrix} \quad \begin{pmatrix} a_{12} & a_{13} \\ a_{22} & a_{23} \end{pmatrix}$$

$$(a_{11} \quad a_{12} \quad a_{13}), \quad (a_{21} \quad a_{22} \quad a_{23}), \quad \begin{pmatrix} a_{11} \\ a_{21} \end{pmatrix}, \quad \begin{pmatrix} a_{12} \\ a_{22} \end{pmatrix}, \quad \begin{pmatrix} a_{13} \\ a_{23} \end{pmatrix},$$

$$(a_{11} \quad a_{12}), \quad (a_{11} \quad a_{13}), \quad (a_{12} \quad a_{13}), \quad (a_{21} \quad a_{22}), \quad (a_{21} \quad a_{23}),$$

$$(a_{22} \quad a_{23}), \quad (a_{11}), \quad (a_{12}), \quad (a_{13}), \quad (a_{21}), \quad (a_{22}), \quad \text{and} \quad (a_{23}).$$

We deleted at most one row and at most two columns; if we deleted two rows and/or three columns, there would have been nothing left! In other words, a submatrix is itself a matrix, so it must have at least one row and at least one column. ◀

We are ready to define the rank of a matrix.

> ***Definition 1** Rank*
>
> A matrix $\mathbf{A}$, not necessarily square, is of **rank** r, or $r(\mathbf{A})$, if it contains at least one $r \times r$ submatrix with nonzero determinant, but no square submatrix larger than $r \times r$ with nonzero determinant. A matrix is of rank 0 if it is a zero matrix.

EXAMPLE 2

$$\mathbf{A} = \begin{pmatrix} 2 & -1 & 1 & 0 \\ 0 & 3 & 3 & 6 \\ 1 & 4 & 5 & 9 \end{pmatrix}. \tag{2}$$

Certainly, r is at most 3 in this case since the largest possible square submatrix of $\mathbf{A}$ is 3×3. (More generally, if $\mathbf{A}$ is $m \times n$, then r is at most equal to the smaller of m

and n.) However, upon calculation, we find that all four of the 3×3 submatrices have zero determinant, so that r is at most 2. In fact, there are a number of 2×2 submatrices with nonzero determinant, such as

$$\begin{vmatrix} 2 & -1 \\ 0 & 3 \end{vmatrix} = 6 \neq 0,$$

but even if there were only one such submatrix that would still be all we need to conclude that $r = 2$. ◀

EXAMPLE 3 The ranks of

$$\mathbf{A} = \begin{pmatrix} 5 \\ 6 \\ 0 \end{pmatrix}, \quad \mathbf{B} = \begin{pmatrix} 5 & -2 \\ 6 & 3 \\ 0 & 1 \end{pmatrix}, \quad \mathbf{C} = \begin{pmatrix} 5 & -2 & 0 \\ 6 & 3 & 0 \\ 0 & 1 & 0 \end{pmatrix}, \quad \mathbf{D} = \begin{pmatrix} 3 & 1 & 0 & 0 \\ 0 & 1 & 0 & 0 \\ 9 & 3 & 0 & 0 \end{pmatrix}$$

are 1, 2, 2, and 2, respectively. In $\mathbf{D}$, for example, every 3×3 submatrix contains a column of zeros and hence has a vanishing determinant, but the 2×2 submatrix $\begin{pmatrix} 3 & 1 \\ 0 & 1 \end{pmatrix}$ has a nonvanishing determinant, so $r(\mathbf{D}) = 2$. ◀

There is an important connection to be made between the rank of a matrix and the linear dependence of a set of vectors, namely:

> ***Theorem 1***
> For any matrix $\mathbf{A}$, the number of LI row vectors is equal to the number of LI column vectors.

> ***Theorem 2*** *Rank and Linear Dependence*
> The rank of a matrix $\mathbf{A}$ is equal to the number of LI row (or column) vectors in $\mathbf{A}$.

For proofs of Theorems 1 and 2, the interested reader is referred to ANTON (Section 4.6) and Kreyszig,* respectively.

EXAMPLE 4 Let us illustrate these two theorems with the matrix $\mathbf{A}$ of Example 2. Denote the row vectors as $\mathbf{r}_1, \mathbf{r}_2, \mathbf{r}_3$ and the column vectors as $\mathbf{c}_1, \mathbf{c}_2, \mathbf{c}_3, \mathbf{c}_4$; for example, $\mathbf{r}_3 = (1, 4, 5, 9)$. Now, the first two rows, $\mathbf{r}_1$ and $\mathbf{r}_2$, are LI since neither one is a scalar multiple of the other. But, as is easily verified, $\mathbf{r}_3 = \frac{1}{2}\mathbf{r}_1 + \frac{3}{2}\mathbf{r}_2$, so that $\mathbf{r}_1, \mathbf{r}_2, \mathbf{r}_3$ are not LI; thus there are two LI row vectors in $\mathbf{A}$. Turning to the

* E. Kreyszig, *Advanced Engineering Mathematics*, 3rd ed. (New York: Wiley, 1972), Sec. 6.10. Of the two authors, Kreyszig defines rank in the same way that we do, but ANTON chooses to define the rank of $\mathbf{A}$ as the number of LI row (or column) vectors in $\mathbf{A}$; according to Theorem 2, the two definitions are equivalent.

columns, $\mathbf{c}_1$ and $\mathbf{c}_2$ are LI, since neither one is a scalar multiple of the other, but then $\mathbf{c}_3 = \mathbf{c}_1 + \mathbf{c}_2$ and $\mathbf{c}_4 = \mathbf{c}_1 + 2\mathbf{c}_2$; thus there are two LI column vectors in **A**. We see that the number of LI row vectors *is* equal to the number of LI column vectors (namely two), in accordance with Theorem 1. According to Theorem 2, then, the rank of **A** must be two, in agreement with the result obtained in Example 2. ◀

In Example 4, we interpreted the rank of a given matrix **A** in terms of the number of LI row (or column) vectors in **A**. Instead, suppose that we were not given **A**, but rather the vector set $\{\mathbf{u}_1, \mathbf{u}_2, \mathbf{u}_3\}$, where

$$\mathbf{u}_1 = \begin{pmatrix} 2 \\ -1 \\ 1 \\ 0 \end{pmatrix}, \qquad \mathbf{u}_2 = \begin{pmatrix} 0 \\ 3 \\ 3 \\ 6 \end{pmatrix}, \qquad \mathbf{u}_3 = \begin{pmatrix} 1 \\ 4 \\ 5 \\ 9 \end{pmatrix},$$

and were asked to find the number of LI vectors in the set. This sort of question arose in Section 2.8, and to answer it we could, of course, proceed as in Section 2.8. Now an alternative approach presents itself. Namely, construct a matrix **A** with $\mathbf{u}_1^T, \mathbf{u}_2^T, \mathbf{u}_3^T$ as its rows (or with $\mathbf{u}_1, \mathbf{u}_2, \mathbf{u}_3$ as its columns), and compute the rank $r(\mathbf{A})$ since, according to Theorem 2, $r(\mathbf{A})$ is equal to the number of LI vectors in **A**.

Unfortunately, calculating the rank of a given matrix can be tedious since, either directly or indirectly, it entails the evaluation of determinants, and determinants larger than 3×3 are not much fun. Thus it would be helpful if we could perform certain operations on the given matrix **A** such that the resulting matrix **B** would be simpler (i.e., containing more zeros) but of the same rank as **A**. Such operations are, in fact, the **elementary row operations** defined on page 12, namely:

1. Addition of a multiple of one row to another
2. Multiplication of a row by a nonzero constant
3. Interchange of two rows

Furthermore, we defined (on page 13) two matrices to be **row equivalent** if one can be obtained from the other by finitely many row operations.

> ***Theorem 3*** *Elementary Row Operations and Rank*
> Row-equivalent matrices have the same rank; i.e., the rank of a matrix is not altered by elementary row operations.

Proof. Proof of this theorem can be cumbersome if we use the definition of rank given on page 94, but is simple if we use the relationship between rank and linear independence given in Theorem 2. Consider an elementary row operation of type 1. Let the original $m \times n$ matrix be **A**, and let **A′** be the the $m \times n$ matrix that results when c times the kth row of **A** is added to the jth row of **A**. If we denote the rows of **A** as $\mathbf{r}_1, \ldots, \mathbf{r}_m$, and the rows of **A′** as $\mathbf{r}_1', \ldots, \mathbf{r}_m'$, then

$$\mathbf{r}_1' = \mathbf{r}_1, \quad \mathbf{r}_2' = \mathbf{r}_2, \quad \ldots, \quad \mathbf{r}_j' = \mathbf{r}_j + c\mathbf{r}_k, \quad \ldots, \quad \mathbf{r}_{m-1}' = \mathbf{r}_{m-1}, \quad \mathbf{r}_m' = \mathbf{r}_m. \tag{3}$$

Finally, let the ranks of **A** and **A′** be r and r', respectively. Then (Exercise 8)

$$\begin{aligned} r &= \dim[\operatorname{span}\{\mathbf{r}_1, \ldots, \mathbf{r}_m\}] \\ r' &= \dim[\operatorname{span}\{\mathbf{r}'_1, \ldots, \mathbf{r}'_m\}]. \end{aligned} \tag{4}$$

Now each vector $\mathbf{v}'$ in span$\{\mathbf{r}'_1, \ldots, \mathbf{r}'_m\}$ can be expressed as

$$\begin{aligned} \mathbf{v}' &= \alpha_1\mathbf{r}'_1 + \alpha_2\mathbf{r}'_2 + \cdots + \alpha_m\mathbf{r}'_m \\ &= \alpha_1\mathbf{r}_1 + \cdots + \alpha_j(\mathbf{r}_j + c\mathbf{r}_k) + \cdots + \alpha_k\mathbf{r}_k + \cdots + \alpha_m\mathbf{r}_m \\ &= \alpha_1\mathbf{r}_1 + \cdots + (\alpha_k + c\alpha_j)\mathbf{r}_k + \cdots + \alpha_m\mathbf{r}_m, \end{aligned}$$

namely, as a linear combination of $\mathbf{r}_1, \ldots, \mathbf{r}_m$. Thus each vector $\mathbf{v}'$ in span$\{\mathbf{r}'_1, \ldots, \mathbf{r}'_m\}$ is also in span$\{\mathbf{r}_1, \ldots, \mathbf{r}_m\}$. In the same way, it is found that each vector $\mathbf{v}$ in span$\{\mathbf{r}_1, \ldots, \mathbf{r}_m\}$ is also in span$\{\mathbf{r}'_1, \ldots, \mathbf{r}'_m\}$. Hence span$\{\mathbf{r}_1, \ldots, \mathbf{r}_m\}$ and span$\{\mathbf{r}'_1, \ldots, \mathbf{r}'_m\}$ are identical, so it follows from (4) that $r' = r$.

For row operations of types 2 and 3 the proof is trivial and will be omitted. ■

EXAMPLE 5 How many LI vectors are there in the set $\{\mathbf{u}_1, \mathbf{u}_2, \mathbf{u}_3\}$, where $\mathbf{u}_1 = (3, 2, 5, -1)^{\mathrm{T}}$, $\mathbf{u}_2 = (-3, 2, -1, 2)^{\mathrm{T}}$, and $\mathbf{u}_3 = (6, -4, 14, 1)^{\mathrm{T}}$?* According to Theorem 1, the answer may be found as the rank of the matrix the rows of which are the given vectors. To compute the rank, let us apply a sequence of elementary row operations, as follows:

$$\mathbf{A} = \begin{pmatrix} 3 & 2 & 5 & -1 \\ -3 & 2 & -1 & 2 \\ 6 & -4 & 14 & -1 \end{pmatrix} \blacktriangleright \mathbf{A}' = \begin{pmatrix} 3 & 2 & 5 & -1 \\ 0 & 4 & 4 & 1 \\ 0 & -8 & 4 & 1 \end{pmatrix}$$

$$\blacktriangleright \mathbf{A}'' = \begin{pmatrix} 3 & 2 & 5 & -1 \\ 0 & 4 & 4 & 1 \\ 0 & 0 & 12 & 3 \end{pmatrix}.$$

Here we obtained **A′** by adding the first row of **A** to the second, and -2 times the first row of **A** to the third; and we obtained **A″** by adding twice the second row of **A′** to the third. The procedure is essentially a matricized version of Gauss elimination, and its object is the "triangularization" of as much of the matrix as possible, since determinants of triangular matrices are simple (recall property D1 on page 87). In the present case, the first three columns of **A″** constitute a triangular 3×3 matrix with nonvanishing determinant, so $r(\mathbf{A}'') = 3$. But according to Theorem 3, $r(\mathbf{A}'') = r(\mathbf{A}') = r(\mathbf{A})$, so $r(\mathbf{A}) = 3$. Hence the number of LI vectors in the set $\{\mathbf{u}_1, \mathbf{u}_2, \mathbf{u}_3\}$ is three. ◀

EXAMPLE 6 Leaving the in-between elementary row operations to the reader,

$$\mathbf{A} = \begin{pmatrix} 2 & 1 & -3 & 4 \\ 2 & 4 & -2 & 5 \\ 0 & 3 & 1 & 3 \\ 2 & 1 & -3 & 2 \end{pmatrix} \blacktriangleright \mathbf{A}' = \begin{pmatrix} 2 & 1 & -3 & 4 \\ 0 & 3 & 1 & 1 \\ 0 & 0 & 0 & 2 \\ 0 & 0 & 0 & 0 \end{pmatrix}.$$

* Recall that to save space, we often write column vectors as transposes of row vectors.

Evidently, $r(\mathbf{A}') = 3$ as seen by deleting the fourth row and third column of $\mathbf{A}'$. Hence $r(\mathbf{A}) = 3$. This is certainly much easier than computing determinants, as we did in Example 2. ◀

We have already mentioned the utility of the concept of rank in determining the number of LI vectors within a given set. A second important application of rank is in connection with the existence and uniqueness of solutions of systems of linear algebraic equations, as encountered in Chapter 1. Specifically, we have the following fundamental theorem.

Theorem 4 *Existence/Uniqueness for Linear Systems*
Consider a linear system of m equations in n unknowns or, in matrix notation,

$$\mathbf{Ax} = \mathbf{c}, \tag{5}$$

where $\mathbf{A}$ is the $m \times n$ coefficient matrix, $\mathbf{x}$ is the n-dimensional unknown column vector, $\mathbf{c}$ is the given m-dimensional column vector, and $\mathbf{A}|\mathbf{c}$ is the augmented matrix (defined on page 12). Such a system is consistent (i.e., has at least one solution) if and only if the rank of the coefficient matrix $\mathbf{A}$, $r(\mathbf{A})$, is equal to the rank of the augmented matrix, $r(\mathbf{A}|\mathbf{c})$. More specifically, (5) has

(i) no solution if and only if $r(\mathbf{A}) \neq r(\mathbf{A}|\mathbf{c})$;
(ii) a unique solution if and only if $r(\mathbf{A}) = r(\mathbf{A}|\mathbf{c}) = n$;
(iii) an $(n - r)$-parameter family of solutions if and only if $r(\mathbf{A}) = r(\mathbf{A}|\mathbf{c}) \equiv r$ is less than n.

Proof The idea is first to simplify (5) by applying Gauss elimination. The result is an equivalent indented system of the form

$$\begin{aligned}
a_{11}x_1 + a_{12}x_2 + \cdots\cdots\cdots\cdots + a_{1n}x_n &= c_1 \\
a'_{22}x_2 + \cdots\cdots\cdots\cdots + a'_{2n}x_n &= c'_2 \\
&\ \ \vdots \\
a''_{qq}x_q + \cdots + a''_{qn}x_n &= c''_q \\
0 &= c''_{q+1} \\
&\ \ \vdots \\
0 &= c''_m,
\end{aligned} \tag{6}$$

where $1 \leq q \leq m$, as on page 10. In matrix form, denote (6) as

$$\mathbf{A}'\mathbf{x} = \mathbf{c}'. \tag{7}$$

Then (Exercise 9) $r(\mathbf{A}') = q$, and $r(\mathbf{A}'|\mathbf{c}')$ is either q or $q + 1$: q if $c''_{q+1}, \ldots, c''_m$ are all zero or if $q = m$, and $q + 1$ if $q < m$ and $c''_{p+1}, \ldots, c''_m$ are *not* all zero. If we combine this result with the results 1 to 3 on page 10 and note that $r(\mathbf{A}') = r(\mathbf{A})$ and $r(\mathbf{A}'|\mathbf{c}') = r(\mathbf{A}|\mathbf{c})$, since (7) follows from (5) through a finite sequence of elementary row operations, we obtain the results (i) to (iii), stated above. ■

EXAMPLE 7 Consider the system

$$\begin{pmatrix} 3 & 1 & 0 & -1 \\ 2 & 1 & -4 & 1 \\ -1 & -1 & 8 & -3 \end{pmatrix} \begin{pmatrix} x_1 \\ x_2 \\ x_3 \\ x_4 \end{pmatrix} = \begin{pmatrix} 5 \\ 0 \\ c \end{pmatrix}, \tag{8}$$

where c is a parameter. Then

$$\mathbf{A}\,|\,\mathbf{c} = \begin{pmatrix} 3 & 1 & 0 & -1 & 5 \\ 2 & 1 & -4 & 1 & 0 \\ -1 & -1 & 8 & -3 & c \end{pmatrix}. \tag{9}$$

Applying elementary row operations, the resulting (simpler) matrix is

$$\begin{pmatrix} 3 & 1 & 0 & -1 & 5 \\ 0 & 1 & -12 & 5 & -10 \\ 0 & 0 & 0 & 0 & c-5 \end{pmatrix}. \tag{10}$$

Evidently, the rank of this matrix is 3 if $c - 5 \neq 0$, and 2 if $c - 5 = 0$. Thus

$$r(\mathbf{A}\,|\,\mathbf{c}) = \begin{cases} 3 & \text{if } c \neq 5 \\ 2 & \text{if } c = 5\,. \end{cases} \tag{11}$$

And if we cover up the fifth column, in (10), it is seen that

$$r(\mathbf{A}) = 2. \tag{12}$$

Comparing (11) and (12) in the light of Theorem 4, we distinguish two cases: If $c \neq 5$, then $r(\mathbf{A}) \neq r(\mathbf{A}\,|\,\mathbf{c})$, and there is no solution of (8). If $c = 5$, then $r(\mathbf{A}) = r(\mathbf{A}\,|\,\mathbf{c}) = 2$, whereas $n = 4$, so $n - r = 4 - 2 = 2$, and there exists a two-parameter family of solutions of (8), namely,

$$x_4 = \text{arbitrary} = \alpha_1, \qquad x_3 = \text{arbitrary} = \alpha_2,$$

$$x_2 = 12\alpha_2 - 5\alpha_1 - 10, \qquad x_1 = 2\alpha_1 - 4\alpha_2 + 5,$$

or, in column vector form,

$$\mathbf{x} = \begin{pmatrix} x_1 \\ x_2 \\ x_3 \\ x_4 \end{pmatrix} = \begin{pmatrix} 5 + 2\alpha_1 - 4\alpha_2 \\ -10 - 5\alpha_1 + 12\alpha_2 \\ \alpha_2 \\ \alpha_1 \end{pmatrix} = \begin{pmatrix} 5 \\ -10 \\ 0 \\ 0 \end{pmatrix} + \alpha_1 \begin{pmatrix} 2 \\ -5 \\ 0 \\ 1 \end{pmatrix} + \alpha_2 \begin{pmatrix} -4 \\ 12 \\ 1 \\ 0 \end{pmatrix}. \tag{13}$$ ◀

Naturally, the **homogeneous** system

$$\mathbf{Ax} = \mathbf{0} \tag{14}$$

is but a special case of (5), and hence it is governed by Theorem 4. However, it is such an important case that it deserves a theorem of its own. In (14), the augmented matrix $\mathbf{A}\,|\,\mathbf{c}$ is the $\mathbf{A}$ matrix augmented by a column of zeros, so it must surely be true that $r(\mathbf{A}\,|\,\mathbf{c}) = r(\mathbf{A})$ and, according to Theorem 4, it must further be true that (14) is consistent. This should be no great surprise since (14) must always admit the trivial solution $\mathbf{x} = \mathbf{0}$. Hence the significant question about (14) is whether $\mathbf{x} = \mathbf{0}$ is its *only* solution, or whether it admits nontrivial solutions as well. This question is answered by parts (ii) and (iii) of Theorem 4, so we can state the following more specialized theorems:

> ***Theorem 5** Homogeneous Case*
>
> If $\mathbf{A}$ is $m \times n$ and $\mathbf{x}$ is $n \times 1$, the homogeneous system
>
> $$\mathbf{Ax} = \mathbf{0} \tag{15}$$
>
> **(i)** is consistent,
> **(ii)** admits the trivial solution $\mathbf{x} = \mathbf{0}$,
> **(iii)** admits the unique solution $\mathbf{x} = \mathbf{0}$ if and only if $r(\mathbf{A}) = n$,
> **(iv)** admits an $(n - r)$-parameter family of nontrivial solutions, in addition to the trivial solution, if and only if $r(\mathbf{A}) \equiv r < n$.

> ***Theorem 6** Homogeneous Case, **A** Square*
>
> If $\mathbf{A}$ is $n \times n$ and $\mathbf{x}$ is $n \times 1$, the homogeneous system $\mathbf{Ax} = \mathbf{0}$ admits nontrivial solutions if and only if $\det \mathbf{A} = 0$.

Theorems 5 and 6 will be especially useful in Chapter 4.

In summary, we have defined the *rank* of a matrix and have illustrated the relevance of this concept in two important applications—in determining the number of LI vectors in a given set, and in connection with the existence and uniqueness of solutions of linear systems of the form $\mathbf{Ax} = \mathbf{c}$.

Looking back at what has been accomplished in this section, it is natural to point at the several important theorems; certainly, Theorems 4 and 5 are fundamental in linear analysis. However, equally significant is the concept of rank, i.e., the *definition* of the rank of a matrix, to which these theorems are indebted. No doubt there is an infinity of mathematical definitions which *could* be put forward but which are not to be found in the literature. The idea, then, is that *fruitful* definitions, such as the definitions of vectors, matrices, determinants, and rank, represent major steps in themselves.

3.5 EXERCISES

1. Determine the rank of each of the following matrices.

*(a) $\begin{pmatrix} 0 & 0 & 2 & 0 \end{pmatrix}$ (b) $\begin{pmatrix} 5 & 1 & 8 \end{pmatrix}$

(c) $\begin{pmatrix} 5 & 3 \\ -10 & -6 \end{pmatrix}$ (d) $\begin{pmatrix} 5 \\ 0 \\ 0 \end{pmatrix}$

(e) $\begin{pmatrix} -1 \\ 2 \\ 5 \end{pmatrix}$ (f) $\begin{pmatrix} 0 & 0 \\ 0 & 0 \\ 0 & 0 \end{pmatrix}$

*(g) $\begin{pmatrix} 1 & 2 & 5 \\ 2 & 4 & 4 \end{pmatrix}$ (h) $\begin{pmatrix} 0 & 2 \\ 0 & 0 \\ 0 & 0 \end{pmatrix}$

(i) $\begin{pmatrix} 1 & 2 & 3 \\ 4 & 5 & 6 \\ 7 & 8 & 9 \end{pmatrix}$ (j) $\begin{pmatrix} 4 & 0 & 1 & -2 \\ 0 & 0 & 1 & 1 \\ 3 & 2 & 2 & 5 \end{pmatrix}$

(k) $\begin{pmatrix} 6 & 5 & 1 & 0 \\ 0 & 2 & 3 & 0 \\ 0 & 0 & 0 & 6 \end{pmatrix}$ (l) $\begin{pmatrix} 1 & 0 & 3 & 0 \\ 0 & 1 & 0 & 3 \\ 1 & 1 & 2 & 2 \end{pmatrix}$

*(m) $\begin{pmatrix} 2 & 0 & 0 \\ 0 & 0 & 1 \\ 3 & 4 & 5 \end{pmatrix}$

(n) $\begin{pmatrix} 1 & 0 & 0 & 0 & 1 \\ 2 & 1 & 0 & -1 & 3 \\ 1 & 2 & -1 & -1 & 4 \\ 2 & -1 & 1 & 0 & 0 \end{pmatrix}$ (o) $\begin{pmatrix} 1 & 2 & 3 \\ 4 & 5 & 6 \\ 7 & 8 & 9 \\ 10 & 11 & 12 \end{pmatrix}$

(p) $\begin{pmatrix} 1 & 0 & 2 \\ 2 & 1 & -1 \\ 0 & 1 & 3 \\ 1 & 2 & 4 \end{pmatrix}$

(q) $\begin{pmatrix} 1 & 1 & 1 & 1 & 1 & 0 \\ 0 & 1 & 1 & 1 & 1 & 0 \\ 0 & 0 & 1 & 1 & 1 & 0 \\ 0 & 0 & 0 & 1 & 1 & 0 \\ 0 & 0 & 0 & 0 & 1 & 0 \end{pmatrix}$

(r) $\begin{pmatrix} 1 & 3 & 0 & 2 & 1 & 1 & 0 \\ 0 & 4 & 2 & 0 & 5 & 6 & 2 \\ 0 & 0 & -3 & 1 & 2 & 2 & 0 \\ 0 & 0 & 0 & 0 & 0 & 0 & 0 \\ 0 & 0 & 0 & 0 & 0 & 0 & 4 \end{pmatrix}$

2. Determine the number of LI rows and columns in each matrix.

*(a) $\begin{pmatrix} 0 & 0 & 2 & 0 \\ -1 & 0 & 0 & 0 \\ 0 & 0 & 0 & 7 \\ 0 & 4 & 0 & 0 \end{pmatrix}$ (b) $\begin{pmatrix} 1 & 2 \\ 3 & 4 \\ 5 & 6 \\ 7 & 8 \end{pmatrix}$

(c) $\begin{pmatrix} 3 & 1 & -4 & 4 \\ 0 & 2 & 2 & 9 \\ 2 & 2 & 1 & 0 \\ -1 & 3 & 7 & 5 \end{pmatrix}$ (d) $\begin{pmatrix} 2 & 1 & 0 & 0 \\ 1 & 2 & 1 & 0 \\ 0 & 1 & 2 & 1 \end{pmatrix}$

(e) $\begin{pmatrix} 2 & -1 & 0 & 1 \\ 0 & 3 & 4 & 5 \\ 1 & 1 & 2 & 3 \end{pmatrix}$ (f) $\begin{pmatrix} 0 & 1 & 3 \\ 1 & 3 & 1 \\ 3 & 1 & 0 \end{pmatrix}$

3. If two matrices of the same form have the same rank, need they be row equivalent? Prove or disprove.

4. Show, by carrying out suitable row operations, that the following pairs of matrices are row equivalent.

(a) $\begin{pmatrix} 1 & 3 & -3 & 0 \\ 2 & 1 & 0 & 4 \end{pmatrix}$ and $\begin{pmatrix} 4 & 2 & 0 & 8 \\ 3 & 4 & -3 & 4 \end{pmatrix}$

(b) $\begin{pmatrix} 2 & 1 & 0 \\ 2 & 2 & 3 \\ 4 & 4 & 9 \\ 4 & 4 & 6 \end{pmatrix}$ and $\begin{pmatrix} 2 & 1 & 0 \\ 0 & 1 & 3 \\ 0 & 0 & 3 \\ 0 & 0 & 0 \end{pmatrix}$

(c) $\begin{pmatrix} 5 & 2 \\ 0 & -3 \\ 1 & 4 \end{pmatrix}$ and $\begin{pmatrix} 9 & 2 \\ -6 & -3 \\ 9 & 4 \end{pmatrix}$

5. Show that the following pairs of matrices are *not* row equivalent.

(a) $\begin{pmatrix} 1 & 2 \\ 3 & 4 \end{pmatrix}$ and $\begin{pmatrix} 1 & 2 \\ 2 & 4 \end{pmatrix}$

(b) $\begin{pmatrix} 0 & 2 & 0 \\ 0 & 0 & 4 \\ 6 & 0 & 0 \end{pmatrix}$ and $\begin{pmatrix} 3 & -1 & 5 \\ 1 & 5 & -5 \\ 2 & 2 & 0 \end{pmatrix}$

6. Prove that $r(\mathbf{A}^T) = r(\mathbf{A})$ for every $m \times n$ matrix $\mathbf{A}$.

7. (*Elementary matrices*) An $n \times n$ matrix is said to be an **elementary matrix** if it can be obtained from the $n \times n$ identity matrix $\mathbf{I}_n$ by a single elementary row operation. For example,

$$\begin{pmatrix} 0 & 0 & 1 & 0 \\ 0 & 1 & 0 & 0 \\ 1 & 0 & 0 & 0 \\ 0 & 0 & 0 & 1 \end{pmatrix}, \quad \begin{pmatrix} 1 & 0 \\ 0 & 4 \end{pmatrix}, \quad \text{and} \quad \begin{pmatrix} 1 & 0 & 0 \\ -2 & 1 & 0 \\ 0 & 0 & 1 \end{pmatrix}$$

are all elementary; the first is obtained by interchanging the first and third rows of $\mathbf{I}_4$, the second is obtained by multiplying the second row of $\mathbf{I}_2$ by 4, and the third is obtained by adding -2 times the first row of $\mathbf{I}_3$ to the second. It is not hard to show that *if* $\mathbf{E}$ *is an* $m \times m$ *elementary matrix that results from carrying out a certain elementary row operation on* $\mathbf{I}_m$, *and* $\mathbf{A}$ *is an* $m \times n$ *matrix, the product* $\mathbf{EA}$ *yields the matrix that results from carrying out the same row operation on* $\mathbf{A}$. For example,

$$\underbrace{\begin{pmatrix} 0 & 0 & 1 & 0 \\ 0 & 1 & 0 & 0 \\ 1 & 0 & 0 & 0 \\ 0 & 0 & 0 & 1 \end{pmatrix}}_{\substack{\text{first and third} \\ \text{rows of } \mathbf{I}_4 \\ \text{interchanged}}} \begin{pmatrix} 1 & 2 \\ 3 & 4 \\ 5 & 6 \\ 7 & 8 \end{pmatrix} = \underbrace{\begin{pmatrix} 5 & 6 \\ 3 & 4 \\ 1 & 2 \\ 7 & 8 \end{pmatrix}}_{\substack{\text{first and third} \\ \text{rows of } \mathbf{A} \\ \text{interchanged}}}.$$

We now state the problem: For each of the following systems, carry out the Gauss–Jordan procedure by premultiplying the left and right sides by a suitable sequence of elementary matrices; thus obtain the solution (if any) in each case.

*(a) $\begin{pmatrix} 1 & 2 \\ 2 & -1 \end{pmatrix}\begin{pmatrix} x_1 \\ x_2 \end{pmatrix} = \begin{pmatrix} 4 \\ -1 \end{pmatrix}$

(b) $\begin{pmatrix} 1 & -1 \\ 1 & 1 \end{pmatrix}\begin{pmatrix} x_1 \\ x_2 \end{pmatrix} = \begin{pmatrix} 0 \\ 5 \end{pmatrix}$

(c) $\begin{pmatrix} 2 & 3 \\ 1 & -1 \end{pmatrix}\begin{pmatrix} x_1 \\ x_2 \end{pmatrix} = \begin{pmatrix} 8 \\ 5 \end{pmatrix}$

(d) $\begin{pmatrix} 1 & 2 \\ 3 & 4 \end{pmatrix}\begin{pmatrix} x_1 \\ x_2 \end{pmatrix} = \begin{pmatrix} 1 \\ 1 \end{pmatrix}$

(e) $\begin{pmatrix} 1 & 0 & 1 \\ 2 & 1 & 2 \\ 1 & -1 & 0 \end{pmatrix}\begin{pmatrix} x_1 \\ x_2 \\ x_3 \end{pmatrix} = \begin{pmatrix} 0 \\ 2 \\ 0 \end{pmatrix}$

(f) $\begin{pmatrix} 1 & 1 & 0 \\ 0 & 1 & -1 \\ 1 & 1 & 1 \end{pmatrix}\begin{pmatrix} x_1 \\ x_2 \\ x_3 \end{pmatrix} = \begin{pmatrix} 0 \\ 0 \\ 6 \end{pmatrix}$

8. Identify the two theorems from which equations (4) follow. One is in this section, and one is in Chapter 2.

9. (*Completion of proof to Theorem 4*) Show that $r(\mathbf{A}') = p$ and that $r(\mathbf{A}' \mid \mathbf{c}')$ is either p or $p + 1$, as claimed in the proof to Theorem 4. *Note:* There is at least one indentation, but perhaps more, as we move from the first equation in (6) to the second, from the second to the third, . . . , and from the $(p - 1)$th to the pth. Also, it is implicit that not all of the coefficients $a''_{pp}, \ldots, a''_{pn}$ are zero in the pth equation; if they were, the left-hand side would simply have been denoted by a zero. *Hint:* To show that $r(\mathbf{A}') = p$, show that $\mathbf{A}'$ must contain a $p \times p$ submatrix which is upper triangular, with all its diagonal elements nonzero.

10. In each system, of the form $\mathbf{Ax} = \mathbf{c}$, evaluate $r(\mathbf{A})$ and $r(\mathbf{A} \mid \mathbf{c})$ and use Theorem 4 (or 5) to determine how many solutions (if any) exist—for example, none, one, a three-parameter family, and so on (but you need not *find* those solutions).

(a) $\begin{pmatrix} 2 & 5 & 0 \\ 1 & 0 & -3 \\ 4 & 5 & -6 \end{pmatrix}\begin{pmatrix} x_1 \\ x_2 \\ x_3 \end{pmatrix} = \begin{pmatrix} 2 \\ 2 \\ 8 \end{pmatrix}$

(b) $\begin{pmatrix} 2 & 5 & 0 \\ 1 & 0 & -3 \\ 4 & 5 & -6 \end{pmatrix}\begin{pmatrix} x_1 \\ x_2 \\ x_3 \end{pmatrix} = \begin{pmatrix} 2 \\ 3 \\ 8 \end{pmatrix}$

*(c) $\begin{pmatrix} 4 & 3 & 0 & -2 \\ -8 & -6 & 0 & 4 \end{pmatrix}\begin{pmatrix} x_1 \\ x_2 \\ x_3 \\ x_4 \end{pmatrix} = \begin{pmatrix} 3 \\ c \end{pmatrix}$

(d) $\begin{pmatrix} 2 & 3 \\ -1 & 0 \\ 1 & 3 \\ 6 & 3 \end{pmatrix}\begin{pmatrix} x_1 \\ x_2 \end{pmatrix} = \begin{pmatrix} 4 \\ 1 \\ 5 \\ 0 \end{pmatrix}$

(e) $\begin{pmatrix} 4 & 1 & 2 \\ 2 & 0 & 3 \\ 2 & 1 & -1 \end{pmatrix}\begin{pmatrix} x_1 \\ x_2 \\ x_3 \end{pmatrix} = \begin{pmatrix} 0 \\ 0 \\ 0 \end{pmatrix}$

(f) $\begin{pmatrix} 4 & 1 & 3 \\ 2 & 0 & 3 \\ 2 & 1 & -1 \end{pmatrix}\begin{pmatrix} x_1 \\ x_2 \\ x_3 \end{pmatrix} = \begin{pmatrix} 0 \\ 0 \\ 0 \end{pmatrix}$

11. Determine all possible values of λ such that the following homogeneous systems admit *nontrivial* solutions. *Note:* $\mathbf{Ax} = \mathbf{Bx}$, say, is homogeneous since it is equivalent to $(\mathbf{A} - \mathbf{B})\mathbf{x} = \mathbf{0}$.

*(a) $\begin{pmatrix} 2 - \lambda & 1 \\ 1 & 2 - \lambda \end{pmatrix}\begin{pmatrix} x_1 \\ x_2 \end{pmatrix} = \mathbf{0}$

(b) $\begin{pmatrix} 0 & 0 & 1 \\ 0 & 0 & 1 \\ 1 & 1 & 1 \end{pmatrix}\begin{pmatrix} x_1 \\ x_2 \\ x_3 \end{pmatrix} = \lambda\begin{pmatrix} x_1 \\ x_2 \\ x_3 \end{pmatrix}$

(c) $\begin{pmatrix} 1 & 2 \\ 2 & 0 \end{pmatrix}\begin{pmatrix} x_1 \\ x_2 \end{pmatrix} = \lambda\begin{pmatrix} 4 & -3 \\ -3 & 5 \end{pmatrix}\begin{pmatrix} x_1 \\ x_2 \end{pmatrix}$

(d) $\begin{pmatrix} 5 & \lambda \\ 2 & -4 \end{pmatrix}\begin{pmatrix} x_1 \\ x_2 \end{pmatrix} = \begin{pmatrix} 0 \\ 0 \end{pmatrix}$

12. (*Dimensional analysis*) Consider a rectangular flat plate in steady motion through otherwise-undisturbed air, as shown in the figure; V is the flight speed, θ is the "angle of attack" or incidence of the plate, A is the chord length, and B is the span (i.e., the dimension of the plate normal to the paper). We wish to undertake an experimental determination of the lift force l in which the following variables are taken into account:

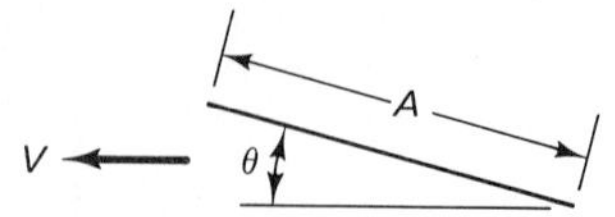

Variable	Symbol	Fundamental Units
Chord	A	L
Span	B	L
Incidence	θ	$M^0L^0T^0$
Flight velocity	V	LT^{-1}
Velocity of sound in air	V_0	LT^{-1}
Air density	ρ	ML^{-3}
Absolute viscosity	μ	$ML^{-1}T^{-1}$
Lift	l	MLT^{-2}

Here M, L, T stand for mass, length, and time; since θ is measured in radians it is dimensionless and therefore has the units $M^0L^0T^0$. [Recall the relation $s = r\theta$, where s is the length of arc of a circle of radius r subtended by the angle θ (measured in radians); thus $\theta = s/r$ = length/length = dimensionless.] As we shall see, it is important to determine the relevant *dimensionless parameters*. In the present case that means determining dimensionless products of the form

$$A^aB^b\theta^cV^dV_0^e\rho^f\mu^g l^h. \tag{a}$$

That is, we seek the exponents $a, \ldots, h$ such that

$$(L)^a(L)^b(M^0L^0T^0)^c(LT^{-1})^d(LT^{-1})^e(ML^{-3})^f(ML^{-1}T^{-1})^g(MLT^{-2})^h = M^0L^0T^0.$$

Equating exponents of L, T, M on both sides, we see that $a, \ldots, h$ must satisfy the homogeneous linear system

$$\begin{aligned} a + b + d + e - 3f - g + h &= 0 \\ -d - e - g - 2h &= 0 \\ f + g + h &= 0. \end{aligned} \tag{b}$$

(a) Solve system (b) for $a, \ldots, h$, and show that the solution can be expressed (as in Example 7) in the vector form

$$\begin{pmatrix} a \\ b \\ c \\ d \\ e \\ f \\ g \\ h \end{pmatrix} = \alpha_1 \begin{pmatrix} -2 \\ 0 \\ 0 \\ -2 \\ 0 \\ -1 \\ 0 \\ 1 \end{pmatrix} + \alpha_2 \begin{pmatrix} -1 \\ 0 \\ 0 \\ -1 \\ 0 \\ -1 \\ 1 \\ 0 \end{pmatrix} + \alpha_3 \begin{pmatrix} 0 \\ 0 \\ 0 \\ -1 \\ 1 \\ 0 \\ 0 \\ 0 \end{pmatrix} + \alpha_4 \begin{pmatrix} 0 \\ 0 \\ 1 \\ 0 \\ 0 \\ 0 \\ 0 \\ 0 \end{pmatrix} + \alpha_5 \begin{pmatrix} -1 \\ 1 \\ 0 \\ 0 \\ 0 \\ 0 \\ 0 \\ 0 \end{pmatrix}, \tag{c}$$

where $\alpha_1, \ldots, \alpha_5$ are arbitrary constants.

(b) Show that the five column vectors on the right-hand side of equation (c) are LI. (Later, in Theorem 3 of Section 3.8, we will see that it is *always* true that if $\mathbf{Ax} = \mathbf{0}$ admits a p-parameter family of solutions $\mathbf{x} = \alpha_1\mathbf{x}_1 + \cdots + \alpha_p\mathbf{x}_p$, then the set $\{\mathbf{x}_1 \ldots, \mathbf{x}_p\}$ is LI. For the present, however, we only ask you to verify, directly, that the five column vectors in (c) are LI.)

(c) Choosing $\alpha_1 = 1$, $\alpha_2 = \alpha_3 = \alpha_4 = \alpha_5 = 0$ in (c) put the solution (c) into (b) and obtain the dimensionless lift $l/(\rho V^2A^2)$. Similarly, set $\alpha_2 = -1$ and the other α_j's $= 0$ and obtain the *Reynolds number* $\text{Re} = \rho AV/\mu$; set $\alpha_3 = -1$ and the other α_j's $= 0$ and obtain the *Mach number* $M = V/V_0$; set $\alpha_4 = 1$ and the other α_j's $= 0$ and obtain the *incidence* θ; set $\alpha_5 = 1$ and the other α_j's $= 0$ and obtain the *aspect ratio* $\mathcal{A} = B/A$.

Note 1: An experimentalist would assume that there exists some functional relationship among these quantities $[l/(\rho V^2A^2), \text{Re}, M, \theta, \mathcal{A}]$. Being specifically concerned with the lift, the dimensionless lift $l/(\rho V^2A^2)$ would be singled out and expressed as some function of the others. That is, one would express

$$\frac{l}{\rho V^2 A^2} = f(\text{Re}, M, \theta, \mathcal{A}), \tag{d}$$

and would seek to generate curves of f versus Re, for instance, by keeping M, θ, $\mathcal{A}$ fixed, varying Re through a number of values and experimentally determining the dimensionless lift $l/(\rho V^2A^2)$. Observe that it is far more efficient to work with dimensionless quantities since there are fewer of them. Specifically, if we express l in terms of the dimensional quantities, instead, as

$$l = f(A, B, \theta, V, V_0, \rho, \mu), \tag{e}$$

then we are confronted with a function of seven variables rather than a function of four variables.

Note 2: Although an infinite number of dimensionless parameters can be obtained (by assigning values to $\alpha_1, \ldots, \alpha_5$), those obtained above (Re, M, θ, $\mathcal{A}$) will suffice. For example, $\alpha_1 = 0$, $\alpha_2 = 1$, $\alpha_3 = -3$, $\alpha_4 = \alpha_5 = 0$ gives the combination M^3/Re.

13. (*Dimensional analysis*) First read all of Exercise 12. Now, in studying the drag force on a sphere moving beneath a water surface, the following variables are deemed relevant:

Variable	*Symbol*	*Fundamental Units*
Radius of sphere	R	L
Depth below water surface	d	L
Velocity of sphere	V	LT^{-1}
Water density	ρ	ML^{-3}
Absolute viscosity	μ	$ML^{-1}T^{-1}$
Gravity	g	LT^{-2}
Wavelength of free surface waves	λ	L
Drag force	D	MLT^{-2}

Proceeding along the same lines as in Exercise 12, obtain the following relevant dimensionless parameters: the dimensionless drag force $D/(\rho V^2R^2)$, the *Reynolds number* $\text{Re} = \rho RV/\mu$, the *Froude number* $V^2/(Rg)$, and the two length ratios λ/R and d/R.

14. Determine whether the following sets of vectors are LI or LD by computing the rank of a suitable matrix and using Theorem 1.

*(a) (2, 0, 1, −1), (0, 3, 0, 3), (4, 3, 2, 1)
(b) (4, 1, 2), (2, 2, 1), (2, −1, 1), (4, 7, 2), (0, 1, 0)
(c) (1, 3, 2, 4, 5), (2, 3, 1, 5, 4), (4, 5, 3, 1, 2)
(d) (2, 1, 1), (4, 2, 2), (0, 1, 2), (1, 0, 0)
(e) (1, −2, 0, 1), (0, 1, 1, 2), (1, 0, 2, 5), (2, −7, −3, −4).

***15.** (*Stoichiometry*) Listing all possible equilibrium reactions among H_2, O_2, H_2O, H, O, and OH, we have

$$H_2 + O_2 \rightleftharpoons 2OH$$
$$H_2 + \tfrac{1}{2}O_2 \rightleftharpoons H_2O$$
$$H + OH \rightleftharpoons H_2 + O$$
$$H_2 \rightleftharpoons 2H$$
$$O_2 \rightleftharpoons 2O.$$

The question we pose is: How many of these reactions are linearly independent? It is convenient to reexpress them symbolically as

$$H_2 + O_2 - 2OH = 0$$
$$H_2 + \tfrac{1}{2}O_2 - H_2O = 0$$
$$H_2 - H + O - OH = 0$$
$$H_2 - 2H = 0$$
$$O_2 - 2O = 0.$$

The elements in the coefficient matrix

$$\begin{array}{cccccc} H_2 & O_2 & H_2O & H & O & OH \end{array}$$
$$\mathbf{A} = \begin{pmatrix} 1 & 1 & 0 & 0 & 0 & -2 \\ 1 & 1/2 & -1 & 0 & 0 & 0 \\ 1 & 0 & 0 & -1 & 1 & -1 \\ 1 & 0 & 0 & -2 & 0 & 0 \\ 0 & 1 & 0 & 0 & -2 & 0 \end{pmatrix}$$

are the so-called stoichiometric coefficients. The number of linearly independent reactions is equal to the rank $r(\mathbf{A})$. Determine such a set of linearly independent reactions by applying elementary row operations to **A**. *Note:* Here the original stoichiometry problem has been recast, by the author, in terms of matrix theory. In practice, of course, one needs to be able to look at a problem, such as this one, and recognize that it can, in fact, be expressed in terms of matrix theory.

16. (*Stoichiometry*) Repeat Exercise 15, for the reactions

$$H_2 + Cl_2 \rightleftharpoons 2HCl$$
$$Cl + H_2 \rightleftharpoons HCl + H$$
$$H_2 \rightleftharpoons 2H$$
$$Cl_2 \rightleftharpoons 2Cl.$$

17. (*Stoichiometry*) Repeat Exercise 15 for the reactions

$$O_2 + CH_3 \rightarrow CH_3OO$$
$$CH_4 + CH_3OO \rightarrow CH_3 + CH_3OOH$$
$$CH_3OOH \rightarrow CO + 2H_2 + O$$
$$CH_4 + O \rightarrow CH_3 + OH$$
$$CH_4 + O_2 \rightarrow CH_3OOH$$

describing the combustion of methane (CH_4) in air.

18. (*Complementary and particular solutions of* $\mathbf{Ax} = \mathbf{c}$) Suppose that the linear system $\mathbf{Ax} = \mathbf{c}$ admits a p-parameter family of solutions

$$\mathbf{x} = \mathbf{x}_0 + \alpha_1\mathbf{x}_1 + \cdots + \alpha_p\mathbf{x}_p, \tag{a}$$

where $\alpha_1, \ldots, \alpha_p$ are arbitrary constants, and $\mathbf{x}_1, \ldots, \mathbf{x}_p$ are LI vectors. In Example 7, for example, p is 2, $\mathbf{x}_0 = (5, -10, 0, 0)^{\mathrm{T}}$, $\mathbf{x}_1 = (2, -5, 0, 1)^{\mathrm{T}}$, and $\mathbf{x}_2 = (-4, 12, 1, 0)^{\mathrm{T}}$.

(a) Show that (in the language of the theory of linear, ordinary differential equations) $\mathbf{x}_0$ is necessarily a *particular solution* (i.e., $\mathbf{Ax}_0 = \mathbf{c}$) and that $\mathbf{x}_1, \ldots, \mathbf{x}_p$ are *complementary solutions* (i.e., $\mathbf{Ax}_1 = \mathbf{0}, \ldots, \mathbf{Ax}_p = \mathbf{0}$).
(b) Express the solution (19) on page 9 in the vector form (a). Verify that $\mathbf{x}_0$ is a particular solution and that $\mathbf{x}_1$, $\mathbf{x}_2$ are complementary solutions.

19. (*Gramian test for linear dependence*) Given a set of vectors $\{\mathbf{v}_1, \ldots, \mathbf{v}_n\}$, let its **Gram determinant** [after *Jörgen P. Gram* (1850–1916)], or the **Gramian** of $\mathbf{v}_1, \ldots, \mathbf{v}_n$, be defined as

$$G \equiv \begin{vmatrix} \mathbf{v}_1\cdot\mathbf{v}_1 & \mathbf{v}_1\cdot\mathbf{v}_2 & \cdots & \mathbf{v}_1\cdot\mathbf{v}_n \\ \mathbf{v}_2\cdot\mathbf{v}_1 & \mathbf{v}_2\cdot\mathbf{v}_2 & \cdots & \mathbf{v}_2\cdot\mathbf{v}_n \\ \vdots & \vdots & & \vdots \\ \mathbf{v}_n\cdot\mathbf{v}_1 & \mathbf{v}_n\cdot\mathbf{v}_2 & \cdots & \mathbf{v}_n\cdot\mathbf{v}_n \end{vmatrix}. \tag{a}$$

There is a useful theorem that states that *the set* $\{\mathbf{v}_1, \ldots, \mathbf{v}_n\}$ *is LD if and only if its Gramian is zero.*

(a) Prove that if $\{\mathbf{v}_1, \ldots, \mathbf{v}_n\}$ is LD, then $G = 0$. *Hint:* If the set is LD, there exist c's not all zero such that $c_1\mathbf{v}_1 + \cdots + c_n\mathbf{v}_n = \mathbf{0}$. Taking suitable dot products, obtain the $n \times n$ system

$$\begin{aligned}(\mathbf{v}_1 \cdot \mathbf{v}_1)c_1 + (\mathbf{v}_1 \cdot \mathbf{v}_2)c_2 + \cdots + (\mathbf{v}_1 \cdot \mathbf{v}_n)c_n &= 0\\ (\mathbf{v}_2 \cdot \mathbf{v}_1)c_1 + (\mathbf{v}_2 \cdot \mathbf{v}_2)c_2 + \cdots + (\mathbf{v}_2 \cdot \mathbf{v}_n)c_n &= 0\\ &\vdots\\ (\mathbf{v}_n \cdot \mathbf{v}_1)c_1 + (\mathbf{v}_n \cdot \mathbf{v}_2)c_2 + \cdots + (\mathbf{v}_n \cdot \mathbf{v}_n)c_n &= 0\end{aligned} \tag{b}$$

on the c_j's, and then apply a relevant theorem from this section.

(b) Prove the converse, that $G = 0$ implies that $\{\mathbf{v}_1, \ldots, \mathbf{v}_n\}$ is LD. *Hint:* Consider the following approach for $n = 2$, and generalize it to the case of n vectors. For $n = 2$,

$$G = \begin{vmatrix} \mathbf{v}_1 \cdot \mathbf{v}_1 & \mathbf{v}_1 \cdot \mathbf{v}_2 \\ \mathbf{v}_2 \cdot \mathbf{v}_1 & \mathbf{v}_2 \cdot \mathbf{v}_2 \end{vmatrix} = 0$$

implies (by what theorem?) that the system

$$(\mathbf{v}_1 \cdot \mathbf{v}_1)c_1 + (\mathbf{v}_1 \cdot \mathbf{v}_2)c_2 = 0 \tag{c}$$

$$(\mathbf{v}_2 \cdot \mathbf{v}_1)c_1 + (\mathbf{v}_2 \cdot \mathbf{v}_2)c_2 = 0 \tag{d}$$

admits a nontrivial solution for c_1, c_2. Multiplying (c) by c_1 and (d) by c_2, and adding, show that $\|c_1\mathbf{v}_1 + c_2\mathbf{v}_2\|^2 = 0$. Thus $c_1\mathbf{v}_1 + c_2\mathbf{v}_2 = \mathbf{0}$ with c_1, c_2 not both zero, so $\mathbf{v}_1, \mathbf{v}_2$ are LD.

THE INVERSE MATRIX AND CRAMER'S RULE 3.6

Besides using Gauss elimination, how might we solve a linear system

$$\mathbf{Ax} = \mathbf{c}? \tag{1}$$

Well, if $\mathbf{A}$, $\mathbf{x}$, and $\mathbf{c}$ were *scalars*, we would divide both sides of (1) by $\mathbf{A}$, and obtain

$$\mathbf{x} = \frac{\mathbf{c}}{\mathbf{A}}, \tag{2}$$

provided that $\mathbf{A} \neq 0$. Unfortunately, this method does not carry over to the matrix case since the division of one matrix by another is not defined. However, matrix multiplication *is* defined, so instead of dividing both sides of (1) by $\mathbf{A}$, suppose that we *multiply* both sides by a matrix "$\mathbf{A}^{-1}$" which has the property that

$$\mathbf{A}^{-1}\mathbf{A} = \mathbf{I}. \tag{3}$$

Then

$$\mathbf{A}^{-1}\mathbf{Ax} = \mathbf{A}^{-1}\mathbf{c},$$

or

$$\mathbf{Ix} = \mathbf{A}^{-1}\mathbf{c}, \tag{4}$$

and we appear to have "the solution"

$$\mathbf{x} = \mathbf{A}^{-1}\mathbf{c}. \tag{5}$$

Consider an exploratory example.

EXAMPLE 1 Let $\mathbf{Ax} = \mathbf{c}$ be the system

$$\begin{aligned} -x_1 - 2x_2 &= 1 \\ x_1 + x_2 &= 1 \\ x_2 &= 1 \end{aligned} \quad \text{or} \quad \begin{pmatrix} -1 & -2 \\ 1 & 1 \\ 0 & 1 \end{pmatrix} \begin{pmatrix} x_1 \\ x_2 \end{pmatrix} = \begin{pmatrix} 1 \\ 1 \\ 1 \end{pmatrix}. \tag{6}$$

We find, for example by trial and error, that

$$\begin{pmatrix} 1 & 2 & 0 \\ 1 & 1 & 2 \end{pmatrix} \begin{pmatrix} -1 & -2 \\ 1 & 1 \\ 0 & 1 \end{pmatrix} = \begin{pmatrix} 1 & 0 \\ 0 & 1 \end{pmatrix} = \mathbf{I}, \tag{7}$$

so that premultiplication of (6) by the matrix $\begin{pmatrix} 1 & 2 & 0 \\ 1 & 1 & 2 \end{pmatrix}$ yields

$$\begin{pmatrix} 1 & 0 \\ 0 & 1 \end{pmatrix} \begin{pmatrix} x_1 \\ x_2 \end{pmatrix} = \begin{pmatrix} 1 & 2 & 0 \\ 1 & 1 & 2 \end{pmatrix} \begin{pmatrix} 1 \\ 1 \\ 1 \end{pmatrix},$$

and hence the (tentative) solution

$$\begin{pmatrix} x_1 \\ x_2 \end{pmatrix} = \begin{pmatrix} 3 \\ 4 \end{pmatrix}. \tag{8}$$

Yet it is easily seen that (8) does *not* satisfy the original system (6). In fact, application of Gauss elimination to (6) reveals that (6) is inconsistent; it has no solution. Hence (8) is an erroneous result. ◀

In other words, we must proceed with caution. The idea is that *the premultiplication of* $\mathbf{Ax} = \mathbf{c}$ *by a matrix* $\mathbf{A}^{-1}$ *having the property that* $\mathbf{A}^{-1}\mathbf{A} = \mathbf{I}$ *does not necessarily lead to an equivalent system.*

As will be shown next, however, if $\mathbf{A}$ is *square*, say $n \times n$, and a matrix $\mathbf{A}^{-1}$ can be found such that $\mathbf{A}^{-1}\mathbf{A} = \mathbf{I}$, the premultiplication of $\mathbf{Ax} = \mathbf{c}$ by $\mathbf{A}^{-1}$ *does* lead to an equivalent system, namely, the unique solution $\mathbf{x} = \mathbf{A}^{-1}\mathbf{c}$.

First, assuming that $\mathbf{A}$ is $n \times n$, observe from

$$\underset{m\times p}{\mathbf{A}^{-1}} \; \underset{n\times n}{\mathbf{A}} = \mathbf{I} \tag{9}$$

that p (the number of columns in $\mathbf{A}^{-1}$) must equal n for $\mathbf{A}^{-1}$ to be conformable for multiplication with $\mathbf{A}$, and that m (the number of rows in $\mathbf{A}^{-1}$) must equal n for the product $\mathbf{A}^{-1}\mathbf{A}$ to be square. Thus $\mathbf{A}^{-1}$ is necessarily square too, of order n.

Second, it follows from (9) that

$$\det(\mathbf{A}^{-1}\mathbf{A}) = \det \mathbf{I} = 1,$$

or, recalling property D8 on page 87,

$$\det \mathbf{A}^{-1} \det \mathbf{A} = 1. \tag{10}$$

Equation (10) cannot possibly be satisfied if $\det \mathbf{A} = 0$. Hence if a matrix $\mathbf{A}^{-1}$, satisfying (9), is to exist, it is *necessary* that $\det \mathbf{A} \neq 0$.

Assuming that that is the case, that $\det \mathbf{A} \neq 0$, let us seek to determine $\mathbf{A}^{-1}$. Our starting point is the cofactor expansion from page 84,

$$\det \mathbf{A} = \Sigma\, a_{jk} A_{jk}, \tag{11}$$

where A_{jk} is the cofactor of the a_{jk} element, and the sum is either on j (for any fixed value of k) or on k (for any fixed value of j). Let us take the sum to be on j. Observe that

$$\sum_j a_{jk} A_{ji} = \begin{cases} \det \mathbf{A} & \text{if } i = k \\ 0 & \text{if } i \neq k \end{cases}, \tag{12}$$

since if $i = k$, then (11) applies, and if $i \neq k$, then the left-hand side of (12) is again a cofactor expansion, this time an expansion about the ith column—but with the ith column replaced by the kth column; thus it is a determinant containing two identical columns and according to property D6 on page 87, it must therefore be zero. Rearranging (12) by dividing through by $\det \mathbf{A}$ (which is permissible since we have assumed that $\det \mathbf{A} \neq 0$) and using the Kronecker delta notation,

$$\sum_j \left(\frac{A_{ji}}{\det \mathbf{A}}\right) a_{jk} = \delta_{ik}. \tag{13}$$

This scalar statement (which holds for $1 \leq i \leq n$ and $1 \leq j \leq n$) is equivalent, according to the definition of matrix multiplication,* to the matrix equation

$$\mathbf{A}^{-1}\mathbf{A} = \mathbf{I}, \tag{14}$$

where the desired **inverse matrix** $\mathbf{A}^{-1}$ (read as $\mathbf{A}$-inverse) is†

$$\mathbf{A}^{-1} = \{\alpha_{ij}\} = \left\{\frac{A_{ji}}{\det \mathbf{A}}\right\}. \tag{15}$$

Or, written out,

$$\boxed{\mathbf{A}^{-1} = \frac{1}{\det \mathbf{A}} \begin{pmatrix} A_{11} & A_{21} & \cdots & A_{n1} \\ A_{12} & A_{22} & \cdots & A_{n2} \\ \vdots & & & \vdots \\ A_{1n} & A_{2n} & \cdots & A_{nn} \end{pmatrix}.} \tag{16}$$

The "A_{ji}" in (15) is not a misprint; the j, i indices simply turn out to be in the reverse order of those in α_{ij}.

* Recall that if $\mathbf{BC} = \mathbf{D}$, then $d_{ij} = \Sigma_k b_{ik} c_{kj}$ or, what is equivalent, $d_{ik} = \Sigma_j b_{ij} c_{jk}$.

† It is tempting to let the i, j element of $\mathbf{A}^{-1}$ be denoted as a_{ij}^{-1}, but this quantity could easily be misunderstood to be $1/a_{ij}$. Thus let us use α_{ij}.

Besides having $\mathbf{A}^{-1}\mathbf{A} = \mathbf{I}$, as stated in (14), it is crucial, as we shall see, that $\mathbf{A}\mathbf{A}^{-1} = \mathbf{I}$ as well. To show that $\mathbf{A}\mathbf{A}^{-1} = \mathbf{I}$ holds, write

$$\begin{aligned} \mathbf{A}\mathbf{A}^{-1} &= \left\{\sum_k a_{ik}\alpha_{kj}\right\} && \text{(definition of matrix multiplication)} \\ &= \left\{\sum_k a_{ik}\frac{A_{jk}}{\det \mathbf{A}}\right\} && \text{[by (15)].} \end{aligned} \tag{17}$$

But

$$\sum_k a_{ik}A_{jk} = \begin{cases} \det \mathbf{A} & \text{if } i = j \\ 0 & \text{if } i \neq j \end{cases} \tag{18}$$

since if $i = j$, then (11) applies, and if $i \neq j$, then the left-hand side of (18) is again a cofactor expansion, this time an expansion about the jth row—but with the jth row replaced by the ith row; thus it is a determinant containing two identical rows, and according to property D6 on page 87, it must therefore be zero. Hence (17) becomes

$$\mathbf{A}\mathbf{A}^{-1} = \{\delta_{ij}\} = \mathbf{I}, \tag{19}$$

as claimed.

Returning to the linear equation

$$\mathbf{A}\mathbf{x} = \mathbf{c}, \tag{20}$$

observe that premultiplication of the left- and right-hand sides by $\mathbf{A}^{-1}$ gives

$$\begin{aligned} \mathbf{A}^{-1}\mathbf{A}\mathbf{x} &= \mathbf{A}^{-1}\mathbf{c}, \quad \text{or} \\ \mathbf{I}\mathbf{x} &= \mathbf{A}^{-1}\mathbf{c} \qquad \text{[by (14)],} \quad \text{or} \\ \mathbf{x} &= \mathbf{A}^{-1}\mathbf{c} \end{aligned}$$

since $\mathbf{I}\mathbf{x} = \mathbf{x}$. To verify that $\mathbf{x} = \mathbf{A}^{-1}\mathbf{c}$ does indeed satisfy the original system (20), put it into (20): Does

$$\mathbf{A}(\mathbf{A}^{-1}\mathbf{c}) = \mathbf{c}?$$

Well,

$$\begin{aligned} \mathbf{A}(\mathbf{A}^{-1}\mathbf{c}) &= (\mathbf{A}\mathbf{A}^{-1})\mathbf{c} && \text{(associativity)} \\ &= \mathbf{I}\mathbf{c} && \text{[by (19)]} \\ &= \mathbf{c}. \end{aligned}$$

Pulling these results together, we can state the following:

> ***Theorem 1*** *Inverse Matrix*
>
> Let $\mathbf{A}$ be $n \times n$. If $\det \mathbf{A} \neq 0$, then there exists a matrix $\mathbf{A}^{-1}$, also $n \times n$, called the **inverse** of $\mathbf{A}$, such that
>
> $$\boxed{\mathbf{A}^{-1}\mathbf{A} = \mathbf{A}\mathbf{A}^{-1} = \mathbf{I}.} \tag{21}$$
>
> $\mathbf{A}$ is then said to be **invertible**, and the inverse $\mathbf{A}^{-1}$ is given by (15). If $\det \mathbf{A} = 0$, then $\mathbf{A}^{-1}$ does not exist, and $\mathbf{A}$ is said to be **singular**.*

We have called $\mathbf{A}^{-1}$, given by (15), "the" inverse of $\mathbf{A}$. But perhaps $\mathbf{A}$ can have *more than one* inverse. In fact, this is impossible:

> ***Theorem 2*** *Uniqueness of $\mathbf{A}^{-1}$*
>
> If $\mathbf{A}$ is invertible, then $\mathbf{A}^{-1}$ is unique.

Proof Let $\mathbf{B}$ and $\mathbf{C}$ both be inverses of $\mathbf{A}$. Then $\mathbf{BA} = \mathbf{I}$ and $\mathbf{CA} = \mathbf{I}$. Subtracting, $\mathbf{BC} - \mathbf{CA} = \mathbf{0}$ or $(\mathbf{B} - \mathbf{C})\mathbf{A} = \mathbf{0}$. And postmultiplying this last equation by $\mathbf{A}^{-1}$ (which exists by assumption), we have $(\mathbf{B} - \mathbf{C})\mathbf{A}\mathbf{A}^{-1} = \mathbf{0}\mathbf{A}^{-1}$, or $(\mathbf{B} - \mathbf{C})\mathbf{I} = \mathbf{0}$. Thus $\mathbf{B} - \mathbf{C} = \mathbf{0}$, and hence $\mathbf{B} = \mathbf{C}$. ■

Finally, we return to the application of $\mathbf{A}^{-1}$ in the solution of $\mathbf{Ax} = \mathbf{c}$.

> ***Theorem 3*** *Solution of $\mathbf{Ax} = \mathbf{c}$*
>
> If $\mathbf{A}$ is $n \times n$ and $\det \mathbf{A} \neq 0$, then $\mathbf{Ax} = \mathbf{c}$ admits the unique solution $\mathbf{x} = \mathbf{A}^{-1}\mathbf{c}$.

Proof That $\mathbf{x} = \mathbf{A}^{-1}\mathbf{c}$ satisfies $\mathbf{Ax} = \mathbf{c}$ was shown just above Theorem 1. That the solution is unique follows from Theorem 4 on page 98, since $\det \mathbf{A} \neq 0$ implies that $r(\mathbf{A}) = r(\mathbf{A}|\mathbf{c}) = n$. ■

EXAMPLE 2 Consider the problem

$$\begin{aligned} x_1 + 3x_2 \phantom{{}+x_3} &= 5 \\ -2x_1 + 3x_2 + x_3 &= 1 \\ x_2 + x_3 &= -2, \end{aligned} \tag{22}$$

* There exist interesting generalizations of the notion of the inverse matrix for matrices that are not strictly invertible (perhaps not even square). Such are the *Moore–Penrose generalized inverse* and the *pseudoinverse*. See, for example, Gilbert Strang, *Linear Algebra and Its Applications* (New York: Academic Press, 1976), Chap. 3.

or, equivalently, the problem $\mathbf{Ax} = \mathbf{c}$, where

$$\mathbf{A} = \begin{pmatrix} 1 & 3 & 0 \\ -2 & 3 & 1 \\ 0 & 1 & 1 \end{pmatrix}, \qquad \mathbf{x} = \begin{pmatrix} x_1 \\ x_2 \\ x_3 \end{pmatrix}, \quad \text{and} \quad \mathbf{c} = \begin{pmatrix} 5 \\ 1 \\ -2 \end{pmatrix}. \tag{23}$$

We find that $\det \mathbf{A} = 8 \neq 0$, so that $\mathbf{A}$ is invertible and $\mathbf{A}^{-1}$ is given by (16). Recalling that $A_{ij} = (-1)^{i+j} M_{ij}$, where M_{ij} is the minor determinant of a_{ij}, we compute

$$\begin{aligned}
M_{11} &= \begin{vmatrix} 3 & 1 \\ 1 & 1 \end{vmatrix} = 3 - 1 = 2, & A_{11} &= (-1)^{1+1}(2) = 2 \\
M_{12} &= -2, & A_{12} &= 2 \\
M_{13} &= -2, & A_{13} &= -2 \\
M_{21} &= 3, & A_{21} &= -3 \\
M_{22} &= 1, & A_{22} &= 1 \\
M_{23} &= 1, & A_{23} &= -1 \\
M_{31} &= 3, & A_{31} &= 3 \\
M_{32} &= 1, & A_{32} &= -1 \\
M_{33} &= 9, & A_{33} &= 9,
\end{aligned}$$

so

$$\mathbf{A}^{-1} = \frac{1}{8}\begin{pmatrix} 2 & -3 & 3 \\ 2 & 1 & -1 \\ -2 & -1 & 9 \end{pmatrix}. \tag{24}$$

It is easiiy verified that $\mathbf{AA}^{-1} = \mathbf{A}^{-1}\mathbf{A} = \mathbf{I}$. In hand calculations such a check is important because it is quite easy to slip up on at least one entry or, as is more likely, to forget the noted index reversal in (15), for example, to take the 1,2 element in $\mathbf{A}^{-1}$ to be $A_{12}/\det \mathbf{A}$ instead of $A_{21}/\det \mathbf{A}$.

Thus the unique solution of the given problem $\mathbf{Ax} = \mathbf{c}$ is

$$\mathbf{x} = \mathbf{A}^{-1}\mathbf{c} = \frac{1}{8}\begin{pmatrix} 2 & -3 & 3 \\ 2 & 1 & -1 \\ -2 & -1 & 9 \end{pmatrix}\begin{pmatrix} 5 \\ 1 \\ -2 \end{pmatrix} = \begin{pmatrix} \frac{1}{8} \\ \frac{13}{8} \\ -\frac{29}{8} \end{pmatrix}. \quad \blacktriangleleft \tag{25}$$

EXAMPLE 3 The matrix

$$\mathbf{A} = \begin{pmatrix} 1 & 4 \\ 1 & 2 \end{pmatrix}$$

is invertible, since $\det \mathbf{A} = 2 - 4 = -2 \neq 0$. Furthermore,

$$\begin{aligned}
M_{11} &= 2, & A_{11} &= 2 \\
M_{12} &= 1, & A_{12} &= -1
\end{aligned}$$

$$M_{21} = 4, \qquad A_{21} = -4$$

$$M_{22} = 1, \qquad A_{22} = 1,$$

so that

$$\mathbf{A}^{-1} = \frac{1}{-2}\begin{pmatrix} 2 & -4 \\ -1 & 1 \end{pmatrix} = \begin{pmatrix} -1 & 2 \\ \frac{1}{2} & -\frac{1}{2} \end{pmatrix}. \quad \blacktriangleleft$$

EXAMPLE 4 The matrix

$$\mathbf{A} = \begin{pmatrix} 2 & 4 \\ 1 & 2 \end{pmatrix}$$

is singular, since $\det \mathbf{A} = 4 - 4 = 0$, so $\mathbf{A}^{-1}$ does not exist. ◀

There are a number of properties and formulas related to inverses. None of these is difficult to prove, and in the interest of brevity, we shall merely list them for future reference, with their proof left for the exercises.

PROPERTIES

I1 *If* **A** *and* **B** *are of the same order, and invertible, then* **AB** *is too, and*

$$(\mathbf{AB})^{-1} = \mathbf{B}^{-1}\mathbf{A}^{-1}. \tag{26}$$

I2 *If* **A** *is invertible, then* $\mathbf{A}^{-1}$ *and* $\mathbf{A}^n$ ($n = 1, 2, \ldots$) are too, and

$$(\mathbf{A}^{-1})^{-1} = \mathbf{A} \tag{27}$$

$$(\mathbf{A}^{n})^{-1} = (\mathbf{A}^{-1})^{n}. \tag{28}$$

I3 *If* **A** *is invertible, then*

$$\mathbf{A}^m\mathbf{A}^n = \mathbf{A}^{m+n} \tag{29}$$

and

$$(\mathbf{A}^m)^n = \mathbf{A}^{mn} \tag{30}$$

for any integers m and n, positive, negative, or zero.

I4 *If* **A** *is invertible, then* **AB** = **AC** *implies that* **B** = **C**. *Equivalently, if* **A** *is invertible, then* **AB** = **0** *implies that* **B** = **0**.

I5 If **A** *is invertible, then*

$$(\mathbf{A}^{\mathrm{T}})^{-1} = (\mathbf{A}^{-1})^{\mathrm{T}} \tag{31}$$

and

$$\det(\mathbf{A}^{-1}) = \frac{1}{\det \mathbf{A}}. \tag{32}$$

Of these, (26) is reminiscent of the formula $(\mathbf{AB})^{\mathrm{T}} = \mathbf{B}^{\mathrm{T}}\mathbf{A}^{\mathrm{T}}$ for transposes. Finally, although we did not list it explicitly as a property, observe that every invertible matrix commutes, under multiplication, with its inverse, since, according to

(21), $\mathbf{AA}^{-1} = \mathbf{A}^{-1}\mathbf{A}$. This is noteworthy in view of the general failure of multiplicative commutativity.

Before using (16) to derive the well-known Cramer's rule, let us emphasize that the formula (16) is by no means the only way to calculate $\mathbf{A}^{-1}$; it is an *explicit* expression for $\mathbf{A}^{-1}$ and is therefore of great theoretical importance, but in terms of computation, it leaves much to be desired, except for small (say, $n \leq 3$) calculations. The reason is that (16) requires the evaluation of n^2 cofactor determinants of order $n - 1$, as well as det $\mathbf{A}$, and as discussed in Section 3.4, large determinants pose a major computational problem. Thus considerable effort has been devoted to the development of more streamlined methods, and there now exist a variety of alternative algorithms. Discussion of these would carry us beyond our present scope, but one or two of these methods are included in the exercises.

CRAMER'S RULE

We have seen that if $\mathbf{A}$ is invertible, and we know $\mathbf{A}^{-1}$, then the solution of the linear equation $\mathbf{Ax} = \mathbf{c}$ is

$$\mathbf{x} = \mathbf{A}^{-1}\mathbf{c}. \tag{33}$$

This gives the entire $\mathbf{x}$ vector, and hence all of the components $x_1, \ldots, x_n$ at once. Suppose that we focus, instead, on the individual components of $\mathbf{x}$. Writing out (33),

$$\begin{pmatrix} x_1 \\ \vdots \\ x_n \end{pmatrix} = \begin{pmatrix} \alpha_{11} & \alpha_{12} & \cdots & \alpha_{1n} \\ \vdots & & & \vdots \\ \alpha_{n1} & \alpha_{n2} & \cdots & \alpha_{nn} \end{pmatrix} \begin{pmatrix} c_1 \\ \vdots \\ c_n \end{pmatrix} = \begin{pmatrix} \Sigma_j \, \alpha_{1j} c_j \\ \vdots \\ \Sigma_j \, \alpha_{nj} c_j \end{pmatrix}, \tag{34}$$

and equating the ith component on the left with the ith component on the right, we have the scalar statement

$$x_i = \sum_j \alpha_{ij} c_j \tag{35}$$

for any desired i $(1 \leq i \leq n)$; or, recalling (15),

$$x_i = \sum_j \left(\frac{A_{ji}}{\det \mathbf{A}} \right) c_j = \frac{\Sigma_j A_{ji} c_j}{\det \mathbf{A}}. \tag{36}$$

Now if the numerator on the right-hand side were $\Sigma_j A_{ji} a_{ji}$, instead, it would be recognizable as the determinant of $\mathbf{A}$, namely the cofactor expansion about the ith column. But the a_{ji}'s are replaced, in (36), by the c_j's, so the numerator of (36) amounts to a determinant, but not the determinant of $\mathbf{A}$; rather, it is the determinant of the $\mathbf{A}$ matrix with its ith column replaced by the column of c_j's (or the $\mathbf{c}$ vector, if you like).

The upshot, known as **Cramer's rule**, after *Gabriel Cramer* (1704–1752), is as follows.

> ***Theorem 4*** *Cramer's Rule*
> If $\mathbf{Ax} = \mathbf{c}$ where $\mathbf{A}$ is invertible, then each component x_i of $\mathbf{x}$ may be computed as the ratio of two determinants; the denominator is $\det \mathbf{A}$, and the numerator is also the determinant of the $\mathbf{A}$ matrix, but with the ith column replaced by $\mathbf{c}$.

EXAMPLE 5 Let us reconsider the system (24),

$$\begin{pmatrix} 1 & 3 & 0 \\ -2 & 3 & 1 \\ 0 & 1 & 1 \end{pmatrix} \begin{pmatrix} x_1 \\ x_2 \\ x_3 \end{pmatrix} = \begin{pmatrix} 5 \\ 1 \\ -2 \end{pmatrix}. \tag{37}$$

Here $\det \mathbf{A} = 8$, and, according to Cramer's rule,

$$x_1 = \frac{\begin{vmatrix} \boxed{\begin{matrix} 5 \\ 1 \\ -2 \end{matrix}} & \begin{matrix} 3 \\ 3 \\ 1 \end{matrix} & \begin{matrix} 0 \\ 1 \\ 1 \end{matrix} \end{vmatrix}}{8} = \frac{1}{8}, \qquad x_2 = \frac{\begin{vmatrix} \begin{matrix} 1 \\ -2 \\ 0 \end{matrix} & \boxed{\begin{matrix} 5 \\ 1 \\ -2 \end{matrix}} & \begin{matrix} 0 \\ 1 \\ 1 \end{matrix} \end{vmatrix}}{8} = \frac{13}{8},$$

$$x_3 = \text{etc.} = -\frac{29}{8},$$

where we have framed the replacement columns for emphasis; we recommend that you fill in the "etc." calculation of x_3. Of course, the results above do agree with those given by (25). ◀

In closing, we should mention that Cramer's rule for the solution of $\mathbf{Ax} = \mathbf{c}$ is generally inefficient, computationally, and is not widely used for systems containing many equations. It is, however, of theoretical importance as an *explicit* expression of the solution.

3.6 EXERCISES

1. In each case use (16) to evaluate the inverse matrix. If the matrix is not invertible, state that.

*(a) $\begin{pmatrix} a & b \\ c & d \end{pmatrix}$ where $ad - bc \neq 0$

(b) $\begin{pmatrix} d_1 & & & \bigcirc \\ & d_2 & & \\ & & \ddots & \\ \bigcirc & & & d_n \end{pmatrix}$ where $d_1, \dots, d_n \neq 0$

(c) $\begin{pmatrix} 2 & 1 \\ 2 & -1 \end{pmatrix}$

(d) $\begin{pmatrix} 3 & 0 \\ 0 & 4 \end{pmatrix}$

(e) $\begin{pmatrix} 0 & 1 \\ 1 & 0 \end{pmatrix}$

(f) $\begin{pmatrix} 1 & 2 \\ 3 & 6 \end{pmatrix}$

*(g) $\begin{pmatrix} 1 & 1 & 1 \\ 0 & 1 & 1 \\ 0 & 0 & 1 \end{pmatrix}$

(h) $\begin{pmatrix} 0 & 0 & 2 \\ 0 & -1 & 0 \\ 1 & 0 & 0 \end{pmatrix}$

(i) $\begin{pmatrix} 3 & 1 & -2 \\ 1 & 2 & 1 \\ 1 & -3 & -3 \end{pmatrix}$

(j) $\begin{pmatrix} 7 & 1 & 3 \\ 2 & -1 & 1 \\ 0 & 1 & 4 \end{pmatrix}$

(k) $\begin{pmatrix} 1 & 0 & 2 \\ 0 & 3 & 0 \\ 4 & 0 & 5 \end{pmatrix}$ (l) $\begin{pmatrix} 2 & 3 & -5 \\ 12 & 1 & 0 \\ 3 & 4 & 1 \end{pmatrix}$

(m) $\begin{pmatrix} 2 & 0 & 0 & 0 \\ 0 & 1 & 3 & 0 \\ 0 & 0 & 1 & 0 \\ 0 & 0 & 4 & 1 \end{pmatrix}$ (n) $\begin{pmatrix} 2 & 3 & 0 & 0 \\ 1 & 1 & 0 & 0 \\ 0 & 0 & 1 & 0 \\ 0 & 0 & 4 & 1 \end{pmatrix}$

(o) $\begin{pmatrix} 7 & 1 & 3 & 0 \\ 2 & -1 & 1 & 0 \\ 0 & 1 & 4 & 0 \\ 0 & 0 & 0 & 1 \end{pmatrix}$ (p) $\begin{pmatrix} \cos\theta & -\sin\theta \\ \sin\theta & \cos\theta \end{pmatrix}$

(q) $\begin{pmatrix} \cos\theta & -\sin\theta & 0 \\ \sin\theta & \cos\theta & 0 \\ 0 & 0 & 1 \end{pmatrix}$ (r) $\begin{pmatrix} \cos\theta & 0 & -\sin\theta \\ 0 & 1 & 0 \\ \sin\theta & 0 & \cos\theta \end{pmatrix}$

2. *(Block-diagonal matrices)* If an $n \times n$ matrix $\mathbf{A}$ can be partitioned as

$$\mathbf{A} = \begin{pmatrix} \mathbf{A}_1 & & & \bigcirc \\ & \mathbf{A}_2 & & \\ & & \ddots & \\ \bigcirc & & & \mathbf{A}_k \end{pmatrix} \qquad (k \le n)$$

it is said to be **block diagonal**; all of the $\mathbf{A}_j$ submatrices need to be square, although not necessarily of equal order, with their main diagonals coinciding with the main diagonal of $\mathbf{A}$. For example,

$$\mathbf{B} = \left(\begin{array}{cc|cc} 2 & 1 & 0 & 0 \\ 3 & 1 & 0 & 0 \\ \hline 0 & 0 & 1 & 2 \\ 0 & 0 & 4 & -1 \end{array}\right) = \begin{pmatrix} \mathbf{B}_1 & \mathbf{0} \\ \mathbf{0} & \mathbf{B}_2 \end{pmatrix}$$

and

$$\mathbf{C} = \left(\begin{array}{cc|ccc|c} 2 & 1 & 0 & 0 & 0 & 0 \\ 1 & 2 & 0 & 0 & 0 & 0 \\ \hline 0 & 0 & -1 & 0 & 3 & 0 \\ 0 & 0 & 2 & 5 & 1 & 0 \\ 0 & 0 & 3 & 1 & 0 & 0 \\ \hline 0 & 0 & 0 & 0 & 0 & 4 \end{array}\right) = \begin{pmatrix} \mathbf{C}_1 & \mathbf{0} & \mathbf{0} \\ \mathbf{0} & \mathbf{C}_2 & \mathbf{0} \\ \mathbf{0} & \mathbf{0} & \mathbf{C}_3 \end{pmatrix}$$

are both block diagonal. Such matrices exhibit essentially the same simple features as diagonal matrices.

(a) Show that $\mathbf{A}$ is invertible if and only if $\mathbf{A}_1, \ldots, \mathbf{A}_k$ are. *Hint:* Recall equation (a) in Exercise 9 on p. 9.
(b) Assuming that $\mathbf{A}_1, \ldots, \mathbf{A}_k$ are invertible, verify that

$$\mathbf{A}^{-1} = \begin{pmatrix} \mathbf{A}_1^{-1} & & \bigcirc \\ & \ddots & \\ \bigcirc & & \mathbf{A}_k^{-1} \end{pmatrix}.$$

(c) Use part (b) to find $\mathbf{B}^{-1}$, where $\mathbf{B}$ is given above.
(d) Use part (b) to find $\mathbf{C}^{-1}$, where $\mathbf{C}$ is given above.

3. Solve for x_1 and x_2 by Cramer's rule.

*(a) $\begin{aligned} x_1 + 4x_2 &= 0 \\ 3x_1 - x_2 &= 6 \end{aligned}$ (b) $\begin{aligned} ax_1 + bx_2 &= c \\ dx_1 + ex_2 &= f \end{aligned}$

(c) $\begin{aligned} x_1 - 2x_2 + x_3 &= 4 \\ 2x_1 + 3x_2 + x_3 &= -7 \\ 4x_1 + x_2 + 2x_3 &= 0 \end{aligned}$

(d) $\begin{aligned} x_1 + 2x_2 + 3x_3 &= 9 \\ x_1 + 4x_2 \qquad &= 6 \\ x_1 \qquad - 5x_3 &= 2 \end{aligned}$

(e) $\begin{aligned} 2x_1 + x_2 \qquad\qquad &= 1 \\ x_1 + 2x_2 + x_3 \qquad &= 0 \\ x_2 + 2x_3 + x_4 &= 0 \\ x_3 + 2x_4 &= 0 \end{aligned}$

(f) $\begin{aligned} x_1 + x_2 + x_3 &= 1 \\ x_1 + 2x_2 + 3x_3 &= 0 \\ x_1 - x_2 + 4x_3 &= 0 \end{aligned}$

4. Suppose that $\mathbf{Ax} = \mathbf{c}$ is a linear system of order 3, and that to the $\mathbf{c}$ vectors

$$\mathbf{c} = \begin{pmatrix} 1 \\ 0 \\ 0 \end{pmatrix}, \begin{pmatrix} 0 \\ 1 \\ 0 \end{pmatrix}, \begin{pmatrix} 0 \\ 0 \\ 1 \end{pmatrix}$$

there correspond unique solutions

$$\mathbf{x} = \begin{pmatrix} 2 \\ 5 \\ -1 \end{pmatrix}, \begin{pmatrix} 1 \\ 1 \\ 2 \end{pmatrix}, \begin{pmatrix} 3 \\ 0 \\ 4 \end{pmatrix},$$

respectively. Then what is the solution $\mathbf{x}$ corresponding to $\mathbf{c} = (4, 3, -1)^{\mathrm{T}}$? Is it unique? Explain.

5. (*Polynomial fit*) Show that it is always possible to fit a unique nth-degree polynomial $y(x) = a_0 + a_1x + a_2x^2 + \cdots + a_nx^n$ through any $n + 1$ distinct points $(x_1, y_1), \ldots, (x_{n+1}, y_{n+1})$ in the cartesian (x, y) plane. *Hint:* Recall the properties of the Vandermonde determinant (Exercise 21, page 93).

6. (*A^{-1} by elementary row operations*) We have already noted, separately, that *if A is invertible,* then $\mathbf{Ax} = \mathbf{c}$ yields the unique solution $\mathbf{x} = \mathbf{A}^{-1}\mathbf{c}$, and that this solution is obtainable by Gauss elimination, i.e., by a finite number of successive elementary row operations. Combining the two ideas, we should be able to use row operations to compute $\mathbf{A}^{-1}$. The idea is to rewrite $\mathbf{Ax} = \mathbf{c}$ and $\mathbf{Ax} = \mathbf{Ic}$ and to apply a suitable sequence of row operations to $\mathbf{A}$ and $\mathbf{I}$; when $\mathbf{A}$ is reduced to $\mathbf{I}$ on the left, $\mathbf{I}$ will be converted to $\mathbf{A}^{-1}$ on the right. $\mathbf{x}$ and $\mathbf{c}$ are not involved in the row operations, and we can dispense with them and focus upon $\mathbf{A}$ and $\mathbf{I}$. Let us illustrate, using the $\mathbf{A}$ matrix of Example 2. Placing $\mathbf{A}$ and $\mathbf{I}$ side by side yields

$$\mathbf{A}|\mathbf{I} = \left(\begin{array}{ccc|ccc} 1 & 3 & 0 & 1 & 0 & 0 \\ -2 & 3 & 1 & 0 & 1 & 0 \\ 0 & 1 & 1 & 0 & 0 & 1 \end{array}\right) \to$$

$$\left(\begin{array}{ccc|ccc} 1 & 3 & 0 & 1 & 0 & 0 \\ 0 & 9 & 1 & 2 & 1 & 0 \\ 0 & 1 & 1 & 0 & 0 & 1 \end{array}\right) \to$$

$$\left(\begin{array}{ccc|ccc} 1 & 3 & 0 & 1 & 0 & 0 \\ 0 & 9 & 1 & 2 & 1 & 0 \\ 0 & 0 & \frac{8}{9} & -\frac{2}{9} & -\frac{1}{9} & 1 \end{array}\right) \to$$

$$\left(\begin{array}{ccc|ccc} 1 & 3 & 0 & 1 & 0 & 0 \\ 0 & 9 & 1 & 2 & 1 & 0 \\ 0 & 0 & 1 & -\frac{1}{4} & -\frac{1}{8} & \frac{9}{8} \end{array}\right) \to$$

$$\left(\begin{array}{ccc|ccc} 1 & 3 & 0 & 1 & 0 & 0 \\ 0 & 9 & 0 & \frac{9}{4} & \frac{9}{8} & -\frac{9}{8} \\ 0 & 0 & 1 & -\frac{1}{4} & -\frac{1}{8} & \frac{9}{8} \end{array}\right) \to$$

$$\left(\begin{array}{ccc|ccc} 1 & 3 & 0 & 1 & 0 & 0 \\ 0 & 1 & 0 & \frac{1}{4} & \frac{1}{8} & -\frac{1}{8} \\ 0 & 0 & 1 & -\frac{1}{4} & -\frac{1}{8} & \frac{9}{8} \end{array}\right) \to$$

$$\left(\begin{array}{ccc|ccc} 1 & 0 & 0 & \frac{1}{4} & -\frac{3}{8} & \frac{3}{8} \\ 0 & 1 & 0 & \frac{1}{4} & \frac{1}{8} & -\frac{1}{8} \\ 0 & 0 & 1 & -\frac{1}{4} & -\frac{1}{8} & \frac{9}{8} \end{array}\right)$$

so

$$\mathbf{A}^{-1} = \begin{pmatrix} \frac{1}{4} & -\frac{3}{8} & \frac{3}{8} \\ \frac{1}{4} & \frac{1}{8} & -\frac{1}{8} \\ -\frac{1}{4} & -\frac{1}{8} & \frac{9}{8} \end{pmatrix},$$

in agreement with (24). Use this technique to invert the following matrices.

*(a) $\begin{pmatrix} 3 & 7 \\ 1 & 2 \end{pmatrix}$ (b) $\begin{pmatrix} 5 & 4 \\ -1 & 3 \end{pmatrix}$

(c) $\begin{pmatrix} 1 & 1 \\ 2 & 3 \end{pmatrix}$ *(d) $\begin{pmatrix} 0 & 1 & 3 \\ 2 & -1 & 1 \\ 0 & 1 & 4 \end{pmatrix}$

(e) $\begin{pmatrix} 1 & 0 & 2 \\ 0 & 3 & 0 \\ 4 & 0 & 5 \end{pmatrix}$ (f) $\begin{pmatrix} 2 & 3 & 1 \\ 1 & 1 & -2 \\ 0 & 1 & 4 \end{pmatrix}$

(g) $\begin{pmatrix} 1 & 1 & 1 \\ 1 & 1 & 0 \\ 1 & 0 & 0 \end{pmatrix}$ (h) $\begin{pmatrix} 1 & 1 & 1 \\ 0 & 1 & 1 \\ 2 & 0 & 1 \end{pmatrix}$

(i) $\begin{pmatrix} 0 & 0 & 1 \\ 4 & 1 & 1 \\ 2 & 1 & 2 \end{pmatrix}$ (j) $\begin{pmatrix} 1 & 0 & 1 & 1 \\ 0 & 1 & 3 & -1 \\ 2 & 1 & 0 & 4 \\ 1 & 1 & 2 & 1 \end{pmatrix}$

(k) $\begin{pmatrix} 1 & 1 & 1 & 1 \\ 0 & 1 & 1 & 1 \\ 0 & 0 & 1 & 1 \\ 0 & 0 & 0 & 1 \end{pmatrix}$ (l) $\begin{pmatrix} 2 & 1 & 0 & 0 \\ 1 & 2 & 1 & 0 \\ 0 & 1 & 2 & 1 \\ 0 & 0 & 1 & 2 \end{pmatrix}$

7. (*More about elementary operations*) Besides elementary row operations one may carry out the analogous operations on columns; we will call these *elementary column operations,* and by an *elementary operation* we will mean either an elementary row operation or an elementary column operation. As noted in Exercise 7 on page 101, any elementary row operation on a matrix $\mathbf{A}$ can be effected by the *pre*multiplication of $\mathbf{A}$ by a suitable elementary matrix $\mathbf{E}$, i.e., by the product $\mathbf{EA}$.

(a) Show that any elementary column operation on $\mathbf{A}$ can be effected by the *post*multiplication of $\mathbf{A}$ by a suitable elementary matrix $\mathbf{E}$, i.e., by the product $\mathbf{AE}$.

(b) Evidently, any elementary matrix $\mathbf{E}$ is invertible, with its inverse $\mathbf{E}^{-1}$ corresponding to the reverse operation. Verify this claim in each of the following representative cases by writing down the corresponding elementary matrices and showing that their product is $\mathbf{I}$. In each case let $\mathbf{A}$ be 3×4.

1. *Elementary operation:* Add 4 times row 2 to row 3. *Reverse elementary operation:* Add -4 times row 2 to row 3.
2. *Elementary operation:* Multiply row 2 by 4. *Reverse elementary operation:* Multiply row 2 by $\frac{1}{4}$.
3. *Elementary operation:* Interchange rows 2 and 3. *Reverse elementary operation:* Interchange rows 2 and 3.

4. Same as case 1, with "row" changed to "column."
5. Same as case 2, with "row" changed to "column."
6. Same as case 3, with "row" changed to "column."

(c) We noted in Exercise 6 that if $\mathbf{A}$ is invertible, there exists a finite sequence of elementary row operations that reduce $\mathbf{A}$ to $\mathbf{I}$. Thus there must exist a finite sequence of elementary matrices $\mathbf{E}_1, \ldots, \mathbf{E}_k$ such that $\mathbf{E}_k \cdots \mathbf{E}_2\mathbf{E}_1\mathbf{A} = \mathbf{I}$. Solving this equation for $\mathbf{A}$, show that $\mathbf{A}$ (i.e., any invertible matrix) can necessarily be expressed as the product of a finite number of elementary matrices.

8. *($\mathbf{A}^{-1}$ and the solution of $\mathbf{Ax} = \mathbf{c}$, by partitioning)* Consider $\mathbf{Ax} = \mathbf{c}$, where $\mathbf{A}$ is $n \times n$ and invertible. Let us partition according to

$$\mathbf{A} = \left(\begin{array}{c|c} \mathbf{A}_{11} & \mathbf{A}_{12} \\ \hline \mathbf{A}_{21} & \mathbf{A}_{22} \end{array}\right), \qquad \mathbf{x} = \left(\begin{array}{c} \mathbf{x}_1 \\ \hline \mathbf{x}_2 \end{array}\right), \qquad \mathbf{c} = \left(\begin{array}{c} \mathbf{c}_1 \\ \hline \mathbf{c}_2 \end{array}\right),$$

where $\mathbf{A}_{11}$ is $(n-1) \times (n-1)$ and hence $\mathbf{A}_{22}$ is 1×1, namely a_{nn}; $\mathbf{x}_1$ and $\mathbf{c}_1$ are $(n-1) \times 1$, and $\mathbf{x}_2$ and $\mathbf{c}_2$ are 1×1. Then $\mathbf{Ax} = \mathbf{c}$ becomes

$$\mathbf{A}_{11}\mathbf{x}_1 + \mathbf{A}_{12}\mathbf{x}_2 = \mathbf{c}_1 \tag{a}$$

$$\mathbf{A}_{21}\mathbf{x}_1 + \mathbf{A}_{22}\mathbf{x}_2 = \mathbf{c}_2. \tag{b}$$

Assuming that $\mathbf{A}_{11}$ is invertible, (a) yields

$$\mathbf{x}_1 = \mathbf{A}_{11}^{-1}\mathbf{c}_1 - \mathbf{A}_{11}^{-1}\mathbf{A}_{12}\mathbf{x}_2. \tag{c}$$

(a) Putting (c) into (b), show that

$$\mathbf{x}_2 = \kappa(\mathbf{c}_2 - \mathbf{A}_{21}\mathbf{A}_{11}^{-1}\mathbf{c}_1), \tag{d}$$

where

$$\kappa = \frac{1}{\mathbf{A}_{22} - \mathbf{A}_{21}\mathbf{A}_{11}^{-1}\mathbf{A}_{12}} \tag{e}$$

and where we further assume that the (scalar) denominator on the right side of (e) is nonzero, so that κ is finite. Then the solution $\mathbf{Ax} = \mathbf{c}$ is given by (c) to (e). The only inverse in these is $\mathbf{A}_{11}^{-1}$, where $\mathbf{A}_{11}$ is of the order $n-1$. Thus we achieve a reduction in order from n to $n-1$.

(b) Use equations (c) to (e) to solve

$$\begin{pmatrix} 1 & 3 & 0 \\ -2 & 3 & 1 \\ 0 & 1 & 1 \end{pmatrix}\begin{pmatrix} x_1 \\ x_2 \\ x_3 \end{pmatrix} = \begin{pmatrix} 5 \\ 1 \\ -2 \end{pmatrix}.$$

(c) Use equations (c) to (e) to solve

$$\begin{pmatrix} 2 & 1 & 1 \\ 1 & 1 & 3 \\ 4 & 1 & 2 \end{pmatrix}\begin{pmatrix} x_1 \\ x_2 \\ x_3 \end{pmatrix} = \begin{pmatrix} 1 \\ 0 \\ 0 \end{pmatrix}.$$

(d) Deduce from equations (c) to (e) that

$$\mathbf{A}^{-1} = \begin{pmatrix} \mathbf{A}_{11}^{-1}(\mathbf{I} - \kappa\mathbf{A}_{12}\mathbf{A}_{21}\mathbf{A}_{11}^{-1}) & \kappa\mathbf{A}_{11}^{-1}\mathbf{A}_{12} \\ \kappa\mathbf{A}_{21}\mathbf{A}_{11}^{-1} & -\kappa \end{pmatrix}. \tag{f}$$

(e) Use equation (f) to invert

$$\mathbf{A} = \begin{pmatrix} 1 & 1 & 0 \\ 0 & 1 & 1 \\ 0 & 0 & 1 \end{pmatrix}.$$

(f) Use equation (f) to invert

$$\mathbf{A} = \begin{matrix} 2 & 1 & 0 & 0 \\ 1 & 2 & 1 & 0 \\ 0 & 1 & 2 & 1 \\ 0 & 0 & 1 & 2 \end{matrix}.$$

Here you may wish to apply (f) twice: first to the 3×3 submatrix $\mathbf{A}_{11}$, and then to $\mathbf{A}$ itself, i.e., in steps.

9. (*Ill-conditioned systems*) Consider the system

$$\begin{pmatrix} 1 & \frac{1}{2} & \frac{1}{3} \\ \frac{1}{2} & \frac{1}{3} & \frac{1}{4} \\ \frac{1}{3} & \frac{1}{4} & \frac{1}{5} \end{pmatrix}\begin{pmatrix} x_1 \\ x_2 \\ x_3 \end{pmatrix} = \begin{pmatrix} 1 \\ 2 \\ 2 \end{pmatrix} \quad \text{or} \quad \mathbf{Ax} = \mathbf{c}. \tag{a}$$

Here $\mathbf{A}$ happens to be a third-order **Hilbert matrix.***

(a) Evaluate det $\mathbf{A}$ and $\mathbf{A}^{-1}$ exactly, and thus show that the exact solution of (a) is $\mathbf{x} = (-3, -12, 30)^{\mathrm{T}}$.

(b) To simulate the effects of round-off error, consider, in place of (a) the "rounded-off" system

$$\begin{pmatrix} 1 & 0.5 & 0.33 \\ 0.5 & 0.33 & 0.25 \\ 0.33 & 0.25 & 0.2 \end{pmatrix}\begin{pmatrix} x_1 \\ x_2 \\ x_3 \end{pmatrix} = \begin{pmatrix} 1 \\ 2 \\ 2 \end{pmatrix}. \tag{b}$$

Solving (b), show that $\mathbf{x} \approx (11.1, -84.1, 96.8)^{\mathrm{T}}$. [Thus only a slight error in the coefficient matrix led to a disproportionately large error in the solution, and hence (a) is said to be **ill conditioned**.† In practice it is important to know if a given system is ill conditioned so that steps may be taken to achieve a

**David Hilbert* (1862–1943), a leading mathematician of this century.

† Ill-conditioned systems were also mentioned in Exercise 9 on page 17.

sufficiently accurate solution. According to one criterion that has been suggested in the literature, an $n \times n$ matrix $\mathbf{A}$ may be considered ill conditioned if

$$\frac{|\det \mathbf{A}|}{\sqrt{\sum_{i=1}^{n}\sum_{j=1}^{n} a_{ij}^2}} \ll 1. \tag{c}$$

In the case of the Hilbert matrix, in equation (a), the left-hand side of the inequality (c) is found to be 0.00033, which is indeed much smaller than unity.]

***10.** Prove that *a square matrix* $\mathbf{A}$ *is invertible if and only if its columns (rows) are LI.*

11. Derive the following properties, listed in the text.
(a) property I1 (b) property I4 (c) property I5

12. Suppose that the complete solution of $\mathbf{Ax} = \mathbf{c}$ is $\mathbf{x} = \mathbf{x}_0 + \alpha_1\mathbf{z}_1 + \cdots + \alpha_p\mathbf{z}_p$, where the α_j's are arbitrary and where $\mathbf{A}$ is square. Is $\mathbf{A}$ invertible? Is $\mathbf{A}$ necessarily $p \times p$? Explain.

***13.** Is it legitimate to cancel the $\mathbf{A}$ and the $\mathbf{A}^{-1}$ in $\mathbf{A}^{-1}\mathbf{BA}$, on the grounds that $\mathbf{A}^{-1}\mathbf{A} = \mathbf{I}$, and thus obtain $\mathbf{A}^{-1}\mathbf{BA} = \mathbf{B}$? Explain.

14. (*Nilpotent matrices*) If there is some positive integer p such that $\mathbf{A}^p = \mathbf{0}$, then $\mathbf{A}$ is said to be **nilpotent**.
(a) Show that a nilpotent matrix is singular.
(b) If $\mathbf{A}$ is nilpotent, with $\mathbf{A}^p = \mathbf{0}$, show that $(\mathbf{I} - \mathbf{A})^{-1} = \mathbf{I} + \mathbf{A} + \mathbf{A}^2 + \cdots + \mathbf{A}^{p-1}$.

***15.** Show that *if* $\mathbf{A}$ *is symmetric (and invertible), then* $\mathbf{A}^{-1}$ *is symmetric, too.* You may use properties I1 to I5.

16. (*Stiffness and elasticity matrices*) A mechanical spring is said to be linear, or Hookean, if it obeys *Hooke's law,** namely that the force f required to extend it (as shown below) is proportional to the extension x; taking the constant of proportionality to be k, called the *stiffness* or *modulus* of the spring, we have

$$f = kx. \tag{a}$$

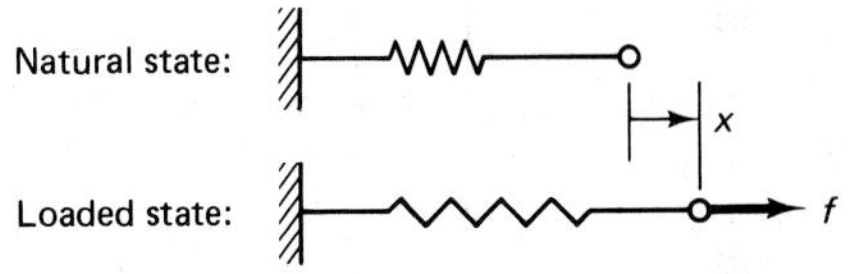

Here k is positive; f and x are positive in extension and negative in compression. Now, consider the static equilibrium of the mass–spring system shown below.† All five springs are linear. The three masses m_1, m_2, m_3 are acted on by the forces f_1, f_2, f_3, and the result-

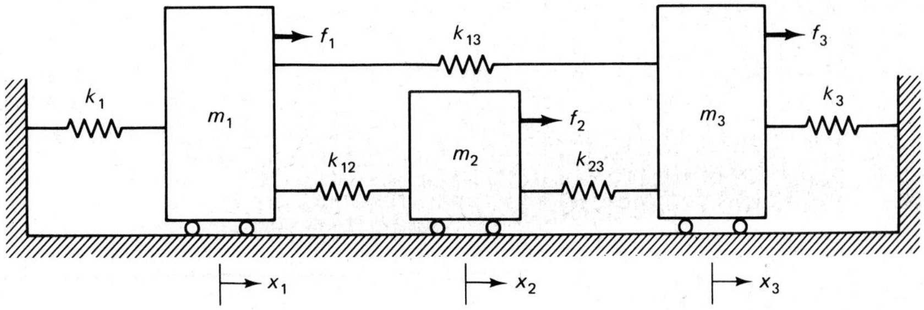

**Robert Hooke* (1635–1703). Hooke's law (a) is a fundamental empirical fact. In spirit, it followed *Galileo Galilei* (1564-1642), who, in breaking with lines established by the ancient Greeks, sought to establish a descriptive and quantitative science, expressed in formulas. For example, whereas Aristotle explained the increasing speed of a falling body in terms of the body moving more and more jubilantly as it approaches its natural place (the center of the earth), Galileo sidestepped the question of cause entirely, and put forward instead the key formula $v = 32t$, where v is the speed (in feet/second) and t is the time (in seconds). It may be argued that this momentous break with the less productive Greek tradition marked the beginning of modern science.

†It is to be appreciated that the figure is intended as schematic. For instance, the end deflection of a cantilever beam subjected to a lateral end load is proportional to the load, so the beam is *equivalent* to a simple lateral spring. Thus we are considering a physical system that can be *modeled* by the mass–spring arrangement shown in the figure; in reality, the system may look quite different.

ing displacements, measured positive to the right, are x_1, x_2, x_3; when $x_1 = x_2 = x_3 = 0$ the springs are neither stretched nor compressed. We desire the relationship between the applied forces f_1, f_2, f_3 and the resulting displacements x_1, x_2, x_3. For definiteness, suppose that

$$x_1 > x_2 > x_3 > 0. \tag{b}$$

Then the leftmost spring is stretched while all the rest are compressed, and the horizontal forces on m_1 are as follows:

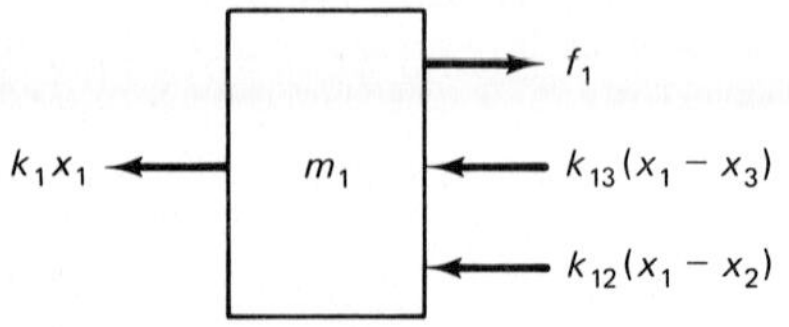

Thus for the horizontal equilibrium of m_1 we must have

$$f_1 = k_1x_1 + k_{12}(x_1 - x_2) + k_{13}(x_1 - x_3). \tag{c}$$

In fact, (c) holds whether or not x_1, x_2, x_3 satisfy (b). For example, if $x_3 > x_2 > x_1 > 0$, instead, then all springs are *stretched,* except for the rightmost one, and the revised force diagram for m_1 becomes

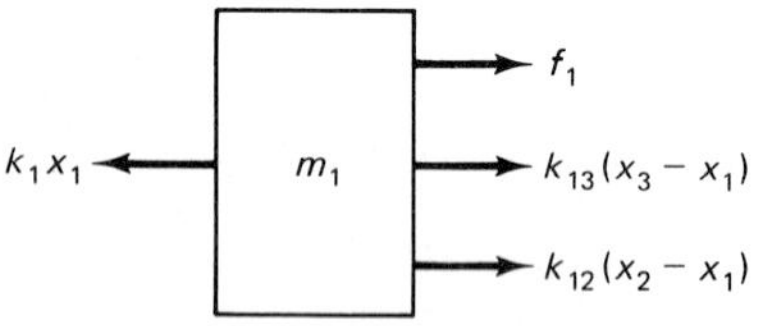

from which it follows that

$$\begin{aligned} f_1 &= k_1x_1 - k_{12}(x_2 - x_1) - k_{13}(x_3 - x_1) \\ &= k_1x_1 + k_{12}(x_1 - x_2) + k_{13}(x_1 - x_3), \end{aligned}$$

as in (c). Thus the idea is to make any assumption on x_1, x_2, x_3, such as (b), in order to proceed.

(a) Determine the equilibrium equations for m_2 and m_3 as well, and show that

$$\begin{pmatrix} f_1 \\ f_2 \\ f_3 \end{pmatrix} = \tag{d}$$

$$\begin{pmatrix} k_1 + k_{12} + k_{13} & -k_{12} & -k_{13} \\ -k_{12} & k_{12} + k_{23} & -k_{23} \\ -k_{13} & -k_{23} & k_{13} + k_{23} + k_3 \end{pmatrix} \begin{pmatrix} x_1 \\ x_2 \\ x_3 \end{pmatrix},$$

or $\mathbf{f} = \mathbf{Kx}$ for short, where $\mathbf{K}$ is usually called the *stiffness matrix*.

(b) Physically, one may expect that given $\mathbf{f}$, there should exist a unique response $\mathbf{x}$. But that will be the case if and only if $\det \mathbf{K} \neq 0$, and it is hard to imagine that the physical parameters $k_1, k_{12}, k_{13}, k_{23}, k_3$ cannot be adjusted so as to render $\det \mathbf{K} = 0$. To resolve this question, work out $\det \mathbf{K}$ and thus determine whether or not $\mathbf{K}$ is necessarily invertible. Naturally, the spring stiffnesses are all positive.

*(c) Taking $k_1 = k_{12} = k_{13} = k_{23} = k_3 \equiv k$, say, evaluate the *elasticity matrix* $\mathbf{K}^{-1}$, and thus solve for $\mathbf{x}$ as $\mathbf{x} = \mathbf{K}^{-1}\mathbf{f}$.

(d) Repeat part (c), with $k_1 = k_{12} = k_{23} = k_3 \equiv k$ and $k_{13} = 0$.

(e) Repeat part (c), with $k_1 = k_{12} = k_{13} = k_3 \equiv k$ and $k_{23} = 0$.

(f) Repeat part (c), with $k_1 = k_{12} = k_{13} = k_{23} \equiv k$ and $k_3 = 0$.

(g) Continuing the consideration begun in part (b), show that even if we are allowed to remove any one spring (hence, to set its stiffness equal to zero), $\mathbf{K}$ is still inevitably invertible. Next, show that if we are allowed to remove any *two* springs, we can render $\mathbf{K}$ singular in two different ways, one of which is to set $k_1 = k_3 = 0$. For that case the inverse matrix method does not apply because $\det \mathbf{K} = 0$. Thus, proceed by Gauss elimination and show that two possibilities exist: (1) there is *no* solution if f_1, f_2, f_3 do not satisfy a certain "compatibility" relation, and (2) if f_1, f_2, f_3 *do* satisfy that relation, there exists a one-parameter infinity of solutions. Interpret both of these results in *physical* terms.

(h) Observe that $\mathbf{K}$, given in equation (d), is *symmetric*. (This symmetry is rather striking because the *physical* system, shown in the figure, does not display any particular symmetry; e.g., k_1 need not equal k_3 and k_{12} need not equal k_{23}.) According to Exercise 15, if the inverse matrix $\mathbf{K}^{-1}$ (called the *elasticity matrix*) exists, it is symmetric, too. Denoting $\mathbf{K}^{-1} = \{\alpha_{ij}\}$, show that the α_{ij} element has the physical significance of being the displacement x_i of the ith mass due to a unit load $f_j = 1$ on the jth mass (i.e., with *no* load on either of the other two masses). Thus the symmetry of $\mathbf{K}^{-1}$, which means that $\alpha_{ij} = \alpha_{ji}$, can be interpreted physically as follows: *The displacement x_i of the ith mass due to a unit load $f_j = 1$ on the jth mass is equal to the displacement x_j of the jth mass due to a unit load $f_i = 1$ on the ith mass. Note:* This result is but one example of the rather general Maxwell–Rayleigh–Betti reciprocity theorem of solid mechanics. In case the italicized reciprocity result above is not clearly understood, let us illustrate the Maxwell–Rayleigh–Betti reciprocity in a different setting. Specifically, the two deflections δ of the beam shown in the figure are equal. A counterpart of the above-mentioned reciprocity theorem exists in electrical circuit theory. Finally, we recommend looking back at the paragraph preceding Example 4 on page 81.

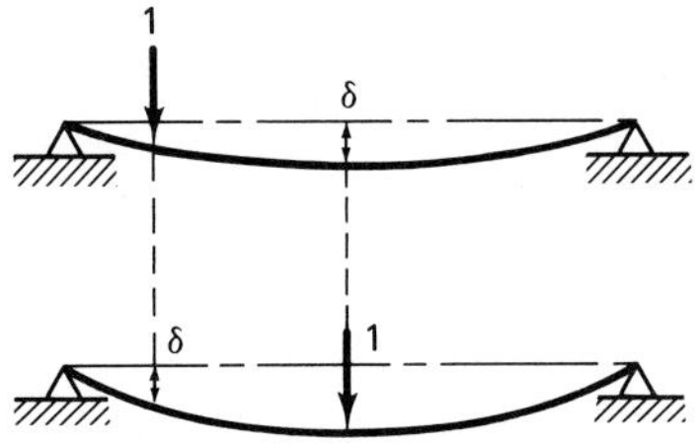

17. (*A dc circuit*) Application of Kirchhoff's laws to the circuit shown on page 15 produced the linear equations

$$\begin{aligned} i_1 - i_2 - i_3 &= 0 \\ i_1 - i_2 - i_3 &= 0 \\ R_2 i_2 - R_3 i_3 &= 0 \\ R_1 i_1 + R_2 i_2 \qquad &= E \\ R_1 i_1 \qquad + R_3 i_3 &= E \end{aligned}$$

on the currents i_1, i_2, i_3. The second equation may be discarded because it is the same as the first; similarly, the fifth may be discarded since it is merely the fourth equation minus the third.

(a) Solve the resulting system,

$$\begin{aligned} i_1 - i_2 - i_3 &= 0 \\ R_2 i_2 - R_3 i_3 &= 0 \\ R_1 i_1 + R_2 i_2 \qquad &= E, \end{aligned} \tag{a}$$

by the inverse matrix method.
(b) Show that the coefficient matrix, in part (a), is necessarily invertible. That is, show that the determinant of the coefficient matrix cannot possibly vanish. Note that the resistances are positive: $R_1 > 0$, $R_2 > 0$, $R_3 > 0$.
(c) Suppose, instead, that we allow one or more of the resistances to be zero, so that $R_1 \geq 0$, $R_2 \geq 0$, $R_3 \geq 0$. Show that if any two, or all three, of the resistances are zero, then the determinant *does* vanish, so that equations (a) admit either no solution or an infinity of solutions. For each of these four "singular" cases determine whether there is no solution or an infinity of solutions by applying Gauss elimination. State the *physical* significance of each of these results insofar as possible.

18. (*Dual or reciprocal basis*) First, read Exercise 13 on page 56. Show that
(a) if base vectors $\mathbf{e}_1, \ldots, \mathbf{e}_n$ of $\mathbb{R}^n$ are arranged as the rows of a matrix $\mathbf{B}$, say, then $\mathbf{B}$ is invertible and the columns of $\mathbf{B}^{-1}$ are the dual vectors $\mathbf{e}_1^*, \ldots, \mathbf{e}_n^*$
(b) $\{\mathbf{e}_1^*, \ldots, \mathbf{e}_n^*\}$ is itself a basis for $\mathbb{R}^n$, the so-called **dual** or **reciprocal basis** corresponding to the basis $\{\mathbf{e}_1, \ldots, \mathbf{e}_n\}$.

CHANGE OF BASIS 3.7

[Optional Section]

In a given problem one selects what appears to be the most convenient basis, but at some stage of the analysis it may be desirable to switch to some other basis. For example, in studying the aerodynamics of a propeller it is generally most convenient to carry out the analysis (of the propeller-induced pressure field, for example) with respect to a propeller-fixed basis, i.e., one that rotates with the propeller, although eventually we may wish to relate quantities back to a stationary (nonrotating) basis. How do the coordinates of a given vector change as we change the basis? It is that question which we address in this section.

Let $B = \{\mathbf{e}_1, \ldots, \mathbf{e}_n\}$ be a given basis for the vector space V under consideration, so that any given vector $\mathbf{x}$ in V can be expanded as

$$\mathbf{x} = x_1\mathbf{e}_1 + \cdots + x_n\mathbf{e}_n. \tag{1}$$

If we switch to some other basis $B' = \{\mathbf{e}_1', \ldots, \mathbf{e}_n'\}$, then we may, similarly, expand the same vector $\mathbf{x}$ as

$$\mathbf{x} = x_1'\mathbf{e}_1' + \cdots + x_n'\mathbf{e}_n'. \tag{2}$$

The question that we pose is: How are the x_j' coordinates related to the x_j coordinates? Well, since B' is a basis, we may expand each of the $\mathbf{e}_j$'s in terms of B':

$$\begin{aligned} \mathbf{e}_1 &= q_{11}\mathbf{e}_1' + \cdots + q_{n1}\mathbf{e}_n' \\ &\vdots \\ \mathbf{e}_n &= q_{1n}\mathbf{e}_1' + \cdots + q_{nn}\mathbf{e}_n'. \end{aligned} \tag{3}$$

Then, if we put (3) into (1), we have

$$\mathbf{x} = \underbrace{(x_1 q_{11} + \cdots + x_n q_{1n})}_{x_1'}\mathbf{e}_1' + \cdots + \underbrace{(x_1 q_{n1} + \cdots + x_n q_{nn})}_{x_n'}\mathbf{e}_n', \tag{4}$$

so that

$$\begin{aligned} x_1' &= q_{11}x_1 + \cdots + q_{1n}x_n \\ &\vdots \\ x_n' &= q_{n1}x_1 + \cdots + q_{nn}x_n. \end{aligned} \tag{5}$$

or

$$\boxed{[\mathbf{x}]_{B'} = \mathbf{Q}[\mathbf{x}]_B,} \tag{6}$$

where $\mathbf{Q} = \{q_{ij}\}$ and

$$[\mathbf{x}]_B = \begin{pmatrix} x_1 \\ \vdots \\ x_n \end{pmatrix}, \qquad [\mathbf{x}]_{B'} = \begin{pmatrix} x_1' \\ \vdots \\ x_n' \end{pmatrix}. \tag{7}$$

We call $[\mathbf{x}]_B$ the **coordinate vector** of the vector $\mathbf{x}$ with respect to the ordered basis B, and similarly for $[\mathbf{x}]_{B'}$; and we call $\mathbf{Q}$ the **coordinate transformation matrix** from B to B'. If we partition $\mathbf{Q}$ into columns,

$$\mathbf{Q} = \left(\begin{array}{c|c|c|c} q_{11} & q_{12} & & q_{1n} \\ \vdots & \vdots & \cdots & \vdots \\ q_{n1} & q_{n2} & & q_{nn} \end{array}\right), \tag{8}$$

we see that the columns are themselves coordinate vectors: The jth column is the coordinate vector $[\mathbf{e}_j]_{B'}$, so we may reexpress (6) as

$$\boxed{[\mathbf{x}]_{B'} = ([\mathbf{e}_1]_{B'}, \ldots, [\mathbf{e}_n]_{B'})\,[\mathbf{x}]_B.} \tag{9}$$

Thus far our results apply whether the bases are orthogonal or not. *In the remainder of this section we assume that both bases B and B' are ON.* In that case we have

$$
\mathbf{Q}^{\mathrm{T}}\mathbf{Q} = \begin{pmatrix} q_{11} & \cdots & q_{n1} \\ \hdashline q_{12} & \cdots & q_{n2} \\ \hdashline & \vdots & \\ \hdashline q_{1n} & \cdots & q_{nn} \end{pmatrix} \left(\begin{array}{c:c:c:c} q_{11} & q_{12} & & q_{1n} \\ \vdots & \vdots & \cdots & \vdots \\ q_{n1} & q_{n2} & & q_{nn} \end{array}\right) \tag{10}
$$

$$
= \begin{pmatrix} \hat{\mathbf{e}}_1 \cdot \hat{\mathbf{e}}_1 & \cdots & \hat{\mathbf{e}}_1 \cdot \hat{\mathbf{e}}_n \\ \vdots & & \vdots \\ \hat{\mathbf{e}}_n \cdot \hat{\mathbf{e}}_1 & \cdots & \hat{\mathbf{e}}_n \cdot \hat{\mathbf{e}}_n \end{pmatrix} = \begin{pmatrix} 1 & & & 0 \\ & 1 & & \\ & & \ddots & \\ 0 & & & 1 \end{pmatrix} = \mathbf{I},
$$

where the carets above the $\mathbf{e}_j$'s remind us that the $\mathbf{e}_j$'s are normalized, i.e., have unit length. It follows from (10) that

$$
\boxed{\mathbf{Q}^{\mathrm{T}} = \mathbf{Q}^{-1}.} \tag{11}
$$

This property of the $\mathbf{Q}$ matrix makes it easy to reverse equation (6), i.e., to solve for $[\mathbf{x}]_B$ in terms of $[\mathbf{x}]_{B'}$, for then

$$
[\mathbf{x}]_B = \mathbf{Q}^{-1}[\mathbf{x}]_{B'} = Q^{\mathrm{T}}[\mathbf{x}]_{B'}. \tag{12}
$$

In other words, we do not need to face up to a perhaps-tedious matrix inversion, since $\mathbf{Q}^{-1}$ is merely $\mathbf{Q}^{\mathrm{T}}$.

It also follows from (11) that

$$
\boxed{\det \mathbf{Q} = \pm 1,} \tag{13}
$$

since $\mathbf{QQ}^{\mathrm{T}} = \mathbf{I}$, so that $\det(\mathbf{QQ}^{\mathrm{T}}) = \det \mathbf{I} = 1$; but $\det(\mathbf{QQ}^{\mathrm{T}}) = (\det \mathbf{Q})(\det \mathbf{Q}^{\mathrm{T}}) = (\det \mathbf{Q})(\det \mathbf{Q}) = (\det \mathbf{Q})^2$, so that $(\det \mathbf{Q})^2 = 1$. Hence $\det \mathbf{Q} = \pm 1$.

Finally, observe that if we dot $\hat{\mathbf{e}}_i'$ into the jth equation in (3) we have $\hat{\mathbf{e}}_i' \cdot \hat{\mathbf{e}}_j = \hat{\mathbf{e}}_i' \cdot (q_{1j}\hat{\mathbf{e}}_1' + \cdots + q_{nj}\hat{\mathbf{e}}_n')$, and since B' is ON, the right-hand side reduces to q_{ij}. Thus

$$
q_{ij} = \hat{\mathbf{e}}_i' \cdot \hat{\mathbf{e}}_j; \tag{14}
$$

(14) tells us how to compute the elements of the $\mathbf{Q}$ matrix.

Any matrix with the property (11), whether it arises as a coordinate transformation matrix or not, is called an **orthogonal matrix** because it follows from (11) that the set of column vectors in $\mathbf{Q}$ is orthogonal—orthonormal, in fact; similarly for the row vectors in $\mathbf{Q}$.

EXAMPLE 1 *Rotation in the Plane*. Consider the vector space $V = \mathbb{R}^2$ with the ON bases $B = \{\hat{\mathbf{e}}_1, \hat{\mathbf{e}}_2\}$ and $B' = \{\hat{\mathbf{e}}_1', \hat{\mathbf{e}}_2'\}$ shown in Fig. 3.1; we may imagine B' as obtained from B by a counterclockwise rotation through an angle θ (or clockwise if θ is negative). Given any vector $\mathbf{x}$, how do its coordinates x_1', x_2' relative to B' relate to its coordinates x_1, x_2 relative to B?

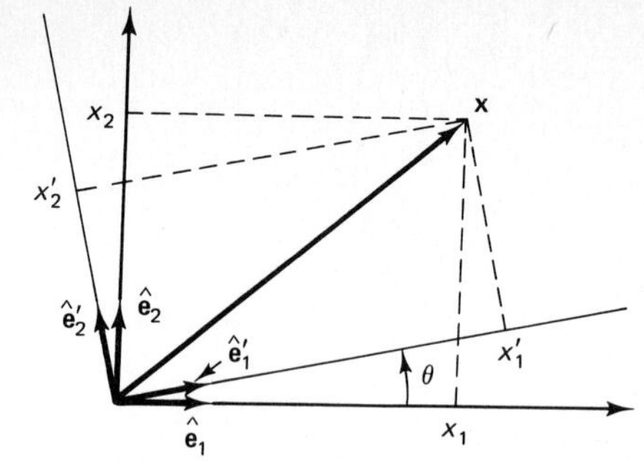

Fig. 3.1 Rotation in the plane.

They relate according to (6), where the elements of $\mathbf{Q}$ can be computed from (14). Thus

$$q_{11} = \hat{\mathbf{e}}_1' \cdot \hat{\mathbf{e}}_1 = (1)(1)\cos\theta = \cos\theta$$

$$q_{12} = \hat{\mathbf{e}}_1' \cdot \hat{\mathbf{e}}_2 = (1)(1)\cos\left(\frac{\pi}{2} - \theta\right) = \sin\theta$$

$$q_{21} = \hat{\mathbf{e}}_2' \cdot \hat{\mathbf{e}}_1 = (1)(1)\cos\left(\frac{\pi}{2} + \theta\right) = -\sin\theta$$

$$q_{22} = \hat{\mathbf{e}}_2' \cdot \hat{\mathbf{e}}_2 = (1)(1)\cos\theta = \cos\theta,$$

so that the coordinate transformation matrix is

$$\mathbf{Q} = \begin{pmatrix} \cos\theta & \sin\theta \\ -\sin\theta & \cos\theta \end{pmatrix}. \tag{15}$$

Hence

$$\begin{pmatrix} x_1' \\ x_2' \end{pmatrix} = \begin{pmatrix} \cos\theta & \sin\theta \\ -\sin\theta & \cos\theta \end{pmatrix} \begin{pmatrix} x_1 \\ x_2 \end{pmatrix}. \tag{16}$$

Or, the other way around,

$$\begin{pmatrix} x_1 \\ x_2 \end{pmatrix} = \begin{pmatrix} \cos\theta & \sin\theta \\ -\sin\theta & \cos\theta \end{pmatrix}^{-1} \begin{pmatrix} x_1' \\ x_2' \end{pmatrix} = \begin{pmatrix} \cos\theta & \sin\theta \\ -\sin\theta & \cos\theta \end{pmatrix}^{\mathrm{T}} \begin{pmatrix} x_1' \\ x_2' \end{pmatrix},$$

so

$$\begin{pmatrix} x_1 \\ x_2 \end{pmatrix} = \begin{pmatrix} \cos\theta & -\sin\theta \\ \sin\theta & \cos\theta \end{pmatrix} \begin{pmatrix} x_1' \\ x_2' \end{pmatrix}. \tag{17}$$

COMMENT 1 We recommend the practice of checking results, both to detect errors and to increase understanding. In the present case it is easy to check (16) for one or two special cases. For example, if $\theta = 0$, the two bases are identical, so we should have $x_1 = x_1'$, $x_2 = x_2'$; that is precisely what (16) gives. Also, if $\theta = \pi/2$, say, we should have $x_1 = -x_2'$, $x_2 = x_1'$ (Fig. 3.2), and that is precisely what (16) gives. We do not claim that one or two such special cases serve to prove the correctness of (16). Rather, we suggest that if there *were* an error in (16), it might well have surfaced in this check.

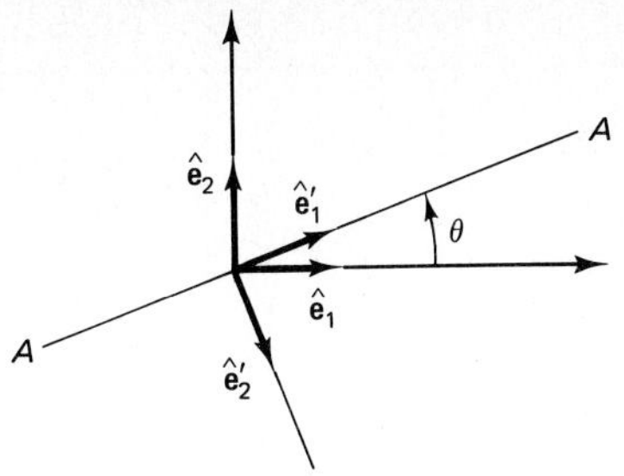

Fig. 3.2 Rotation-plus-reflection in a plane.

COMMENT 2 Notice that the columns of $\mathbf{Q}$ are the coordinate vectors of $\hat{\mathbf{e}}_1$, $\hat{\mathbf{e}}_2$ with respect to the $B' = \{\hat{\mathbf{e}}_1', \hat{\mathbf{e}}_2'\}$, basis, as promised by (9):

$$\mathbf{Q} = \left(\begin{array}{c|c} \cos\theta & \sin\theta \\ -\sin\theta & \cos\theta \end{array}\right) = ([\hat{\mathbf{e}}_1]_{B'}, [\hat{\mathbf{e}}_2]_{B'}). \tag{18}$$

Reversing the story, the columns of $\mathbf{Q}^{-1}$ ($= \mathbf{Q}^{\mathrm{T}}$) are the coordinate vectors of $\hat{\mathbf{e}}_1'$, $\hat{\mathbf{e}}_2'$ with respect to the $B = \{\hat{\mathbf{e}}_1, \hat{\mathbf{e}}_2\}$ basis:

$$\mathbf{Q}^{-1} = \mathbf{Q}^{\mathrm{T}} = \left(\begin{array}{c|c} \cos\theta & -\sin\theta \\ \sin\theta & \cos\theta \end{array}\right) = ([\hat{\mathbf{e}}_1']_B, [\hat{\mathbf{e}}_2']_B). \tag{19}$$

COMMENT 3 We should note that a change from one ON basis to another, in a plane, is not necessarily a rotation. For instance, if, in this example, we reverse the direction of $\hat{\mathbf{e}}_2'$, then $\{\hat{\mathbf{e}}_1', \hat{\mathbf{e}}_2'\}$ is still ON (Fig. 3.2), but it is evidently not obtainable from $\{\hat{\mathbf{e}}_1, \hat{\mathbf{e}}_2\}$ by means of a rotation alone; rather, it is obtainable through a rotation *and* a reflection, i.e., a counterclockwise rotation through an angle θ and then a reflection about the axis AA (Fig. 3.2). In this case

$$q_{11} = \hat{\mathbf{e}}_1' \cdot \hat{\mathbf{e}}_1 = \cos\theta$$

$$q_{12} = \hat{\mathbf{e}}_1' \cdot \hat{\mathbf{e}}_2 = \cos\left(\frac{\pi}{2} - \theta\right) = \sin\theta$$

$$q_{21} = \hat{\mathbf{e}}_2' \cdot \hat{\mathbf{e}}_1 = \cos\left(\frac{\pi}{2} - \theta\right) = \sin\theta$$

$$q_{22} = \hat{\mathbf{e}}_2' \cdot \hat{\mathbf{e}}_2 = \cos(\pi - \theta) = -\cos\theta,$$

so that $\mathbf{Q}$ is the orthogonal matrix

$$\mathbf{Q} = \begin{pmatrix} \cos\theta & \sin\theta \\ \sin\theta & -\cos\theta \end{pmatrix}. \tag{20}$$

Observe that for pure rotation, in which case $\mathbf{Q}$ is given by (15), we have $\det\mathbf{Q} = +1$, whereas for rotation plus reflection, in which case $\mathbf{Q}$ is given by (20), we have $\det\mathbf{Q} = -1$. For elaboration of this point, see Exercise 7. ◀

3.7 EXERCISES

***1.** Given that $\mathbf{e}_1 = \mathbf{e}_1' + 2\mathbf{e}_2'$ and $\mathbf{e}_2 = \mathbf{e}_1' - \mathbf{e}_2'$, find the coordinate transformation matrix $\mathbf{Q}$. Is $\mathbf{Q}$ orthogonal? If $[\mathbf{x}]_B = (5, -1)^T$, find $[\mathbf{x}]_{B'}$. If $[\mathbf{x}]_{B'} = (2, 3)^T$, find $[\mathbf{x}]_B$.

2. Given that $\mathbf{e}_1 = \mathbf{e}_1' + \mathbf{e}_2' - \mathbf{e}_3'$, $\mathbf{e}_2 = \mathbf{e}_1' - \mathbf{e}_2' + \mathbf{e}_3'$, and $\mathbf{e}_3 = -\mathbf{e}_1' + \mathbf{e}_2' + \mathbf{e}_3'$, find the coordinate transformation matrix $\mathbf{Q}$. Is $\mathbf{Q}$ orthogonal? If $[\mathbf{x}]_B = (4, 1, -2)^T$, find $[\mathbf{x}]_{B'}$. If $[\mathbf{x}]_{B'} = (1, 0, 2)^T$, find $[\mathbf{x}]_B$.

3. Let $\hat{\mathbf{e}}_1 = (1, 0)^T$, $\hat{\mathbf{e}}_2 = (0, 1)^T$, and $\hat{\mathbf{e}}_1' = \frac{1}{\sqrt{5}}(2, 1)^T$, $\hat{\mathbf{e}}_2' = \frac{1}{\sqrt{5}}(1, -2)^T$.

*(a) Find the coordinate transformation matrix $\mathbf{Q}$. Is $\mathbf{Q}$ orthogonal?

(b) If $[\mathbf{x}]_B = (8, -6)^T$, find $[\mathbf{x}]_{B'}$.

(c) If $[\mathbf{x}]_{B'} = (1, 3)^T$, find $[\mathbf{x}]_B$.

4. Let $\hat{\mathbf{e}}_1 = (1, 0, 0, 0)^T$, $\hat{\mathbf{e}}_2 = (0, 1, 0, 0)^T$, $\hat{\mathbf{e}}_3 = (0, 0, 1, 0)^T$, $\hat{\mathbf{e}}_4 = (0, 0, 0, 1)^T$, and $\hat{\mathbf{e}}_1' = \frac{1}{\sqrt{2}}(1, 1, 0, 0)^T$, $\hat{\mathbf{e}}_2' = (0, 0, 1, 0)^T$, $\hat{\mathbf{e}}_3' = \frac{1}{\sqrt{3}}(1, -1, 0, 1)^T$, and $\hat{\mathbf{e}}_4' = \frac{1}{\sqrt{6}}(1, -1, 0, -2)^T$.

(a) Find the coordinate transformation matrix $\mathbf{Q}$. Is $\mathbf{Q}$ orthogonal?

*(b) If $[\mathbf{x}]_B = (1, 1, 2, 5)^T$, find $[\mathbf{x}]_{B'}$.

(c) If $[\mathbf{x}]_{B'} = (1, 1, 2, 5)^T$, find $[\mathbf{x}]_B$.

5. Show whether or not these matrices are orthogonal.

*(a) $\begin{pmatrix} 1 & 1 \\ 1 & -1 \end{pmatrix}$ (b) $\begin{pmatrix} 1 & 0 & 0 \\ 0 & 0 & -1 \\ 0 & 1 & 0 \end{pmatrix}$

(c) $\begin{pmatrix} 1 & 1 & 1 \\ 1 & 1 & 0 \\ 1 & 0 & 0 \end{pmatrix}$

*(d) $\begin{pmatrix} 1 & 0 & 0 & 0 \\ 0 & 0 & \frac{1}{\sqrt{2}} & \frac{1}{\sqrt{2}} \\ 0 & 1 & 0 & 0 \\ 0 & 0 & -\frac{1}{\sqrt{2}} & \frac{1}{\sqrt{2}} \end{pmatrix}$

(e) $\begin{pmatrix} 0 & 2 & 0 & 0 \\ 0 & 0 & 1 & 0 \\ 0 & 0 & 0 & -1 \\ 1 & 0 & 0 & 0 \end{pmatrix}$

(f) $\begin{pmatrix} \frac{1}{\sqrt{2}} & \frac{1}{\sqrt{3}} & \frac{1}{\sqrt{6}} \\ \frac{1}{\sqrt{2}} & -\frac{1}{\sqrt{3}} & -\frac{1}{\sqrt{6}} \\ 0 & \frac{1}{\sqrt{3}} & -\frac{2}{\sqrt{6}} \end{pmatrix}$

6. For the case of rotation in a plane, the transformation $\mathbf{Q}$ corresponded to a counterclockwise rotation of the basis through an angle θ. Does $\mathbf{Q}^{-1}$ correspond to the reverse of this, a *clockwise* rotation θ? Prove or disprove.

7. (*Rotation and reflection*) (a) Show that *every* orthogonal coordinate transformation matrix of order 2 is of one of the following two types:

$$\mathbf{Q}_1 = \begin{pmatrix} \cos\theta & \sin\theta \\ -\sin\theta & \cos\theta \end{pmatrix}, \qquad \mathbf{Q}_2 = \begin{pmatrix} \cos\theta & \sin\theta \\ \sin\theta & -\cos\theta \end{pmatrix},$$

i.e., as given by the pure rotation (15), or by the rotation plus reflection (18).

(b) Show that these two cases can be distinguished by the sign of the determinant, specifically, that $\det\mathbf{Q} = +1$ if $\mathbf{Q}$ corresponds to pure rotation, and that $\det\mathbf{Q} = -1$ if $\mathbf{Q}$ corresponds to rotation plus reflection.

8. (a) Prove that if $\mathbf{Q}$ is orthogonal, so is $\mathbf{Q}^T$.

(b) Prove that if $\mathbf{Q}$ is orthogonal, so is $\mathbf{Q}^{-1}$.

***9.** Evaluate $\begin{pmatrix} \cos\theta & \sin\theta \\ -\sin\theta & \cos\theta \end{pmatrix}^n$.

[Optional Section]

In Section 3.7 the vector stayed put while the basis changed; in the present section it is the *vector* that changes. Specifically, we consider a vector-valued function **F** of a vector variable **x.** That is, to each vector **x** in a vector space V the function **F** assigns a uniquely determined vector **F**(**x**) in some vector space W (which may, but need not, be identical to V). We call **F** a **transformation** (or **mapping**) from V into W, and denote it as

$$\mathbf{F}: V \rightarrow W.$$

Further, we call V the **domain** of **F** and W the **range of definition** of **F.** Some authors also call **F** an "operator." More commonly, however, the term "operator" is reserved for those cases in which W is identical to V; thus, one normally speaks of $\mathbf{F}: V \rightarrow V$ as an **operator** on V. In this book we follow the latter convention.

Two transformations, say **F** and **G**, are said to be *equal* (**F** = **G**) if their domains V are the same and if **F**(**x**) = **G**(**x**) for each **x** in V.

It is helpful, and picturesque, to regard **x** as an "input" vector, **F**(**x**) as the "output" vector, and **F** as the transformation that converts **x** into **F**(**x**), as indicated schematically in Fig. 3.3.

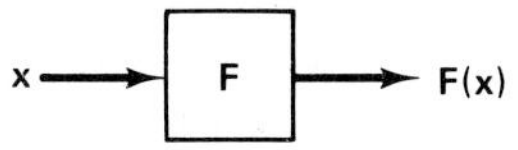

Fig. 3.3 Input/output.

EXAMPLE 1 To illustrate, consider the transformation $\mathbf{F}: \mathbb{R}^4 \rightarrow \mathbb{R}^3$ defined by

$$\mathbf{F}(\mathbf{x}) = \begin{pmatrix} x_1 - 2x_2 + x_4 \\ x_1 + x_3 \\ x_1 + 2x_2 + 2x_3 - x_4 \end{pmatrix}. \tag{1}$$

Here V is $\mathbb{R}^4$, W is $\mathbb{R}^3$, and we have:

$$\text{input: } \mathbf{x} = \begin{pmatrix} x_1 \\ x_2 \\ x_3 \\ x_4 \end{pmatrix} \text{ in } \mathbb{R}^4; \quad \text{output: } \mathbf{F}(\mathbf{x}) = \begin{pmatrix} x_1 - 2x_2 + x_4 \\ x_1 + x_3 \\ x_1 + 2x_2 + 2x_3 - x_4 \end{pmatrix} \text{ in } \mathbb{R}^3. \tag{2}$$

For example, if $\mathbf{x} = (2, 3, 6, -1)^{\mathrm{T}}$, then $\mathbf{F}(\mathbf{x}) = (-5, 8, 21)^{\mathrm{T}}$. Observe that the transformation **F** is not an operator since $W = \mathbb{R}^3$, whereas $V = \mathbb{R}^4$. ◀

Introducing a bit more terminology, we say that the vector **F**(**x**) in W is the **image** of the vector **x** in V under the transformation **F**. More generally, if S_V is a subset* of V, then the set of all vectors **F**(**x**) in W, for which **x** is in S_V, is called the im-

* S_V is a *subset* of V if every member of S_V is a member of V.

age of S_V under **F**. Conversely, if S_W is a subset of W, then the set of all vectors **x** in V, for which $\mathbf{F}(\mathbf{x})$ is in S_W, is called the **inverse image** of S_W.

Since V and W are vector spaces, each must contain a zero vector. We will denote these zero vectors as $\mathbf{0}_V$ and $\mathbf{0}_W$, respectively, unless $W = V$, in which case we use the single symbol **0**. Finally, we define the image of V in W as the **range** R of **F**, and we define the inverse image of $\mathbf{0}_W$ in V as the **nullspace** or **kernel** K of **F**.

EXAMPLE 2 Let us find the range and kernel of the transformation **F** given in Example 1. First the range: The range of **F** is the set of all vectors **c** in W for which the equation $\mathbf{F}(\mathbf{x}) = \mathbf{c}$ is consistent, i.e., has at least one solution **x** in V. In the present case $\mathbf{F}(\mathbf{x}) = \mathbf{c}$ is

$$\begin{pmatrix} x_1 - 2x_2 + x_4 \\ x_1 + x_3 \\ x_1 + 2x_2 + 2x_3 - x_4 \end{pmatrix} = \begin{pmatrix} c_1 \\ c_2 \\ c_3 \end{pmatrix} \tag{3}$$

or, equivalently,

$$\begin{aligned} x_1 - 2x_2 \qquad\quad + x_4 &= c_1 \\ x_1 \qquad\quad + x_3 \qquad\quad &= c_2 \\ x_1 + 2x_2 + 2x_3 - x_4 &= c_3. \end{aligned} \tag{4}$$

Applying elementary operations to (4), we obtain the equivalent system

$$x_1 - 2x_2 \qquad\quad + x_4 = c_1 \tag{5a}$$

$$2x_2 + x_3 - x_4 = c_2 - c_1 \tag{5b}$$

$$0 = c_3 - 2c_2 + c_1. \tag{5c}$$

This system is consistent if and only if **c** lies in the plane (through the origin) defined by $c_3 - 2c_2 + c_1 = 0$. That plane is a two-dimensional subspace of $\mathbb{R}^3$; it is the range R of **F**.

Turning to the kernel K of **F**, i.e., the inverse image of $(0, 0, 0)^{\mathrm{T}}$ in $\mathbb{R}^4$, we need merely set $c_1 = c_2 = c_3 = 0$ in (5) and solve for **x**. That solution gives

$$\mathbf{x} = \alpha_1 \begin{pmatrix} 0 \\ 1 \\ 0 \\ 2 \end{pmatrix} + \alpha_2 \begin{pmatrix} -2 \\ -1 \\ 2 \\ 0 \end{pmatrix} \equiv \alpha_1 \mathbf{x}_1 + \alpha_2 \mathbf{x}_2, \tag{6}$$

where α_1, α_2 are arbitrary constants, and where $\mathbf{x}_1$, $\mathbf{x}_2$ are seen to be LI. Thus $K = \operatorname{span}\{\mathbf{x}_1, \mathbf{x}_2\}$ and $\dim K = 2$. The situation is summarized, schematically, in Fig. 3.4. ◀

We define two more terms: The **rank of F** is the dimension of the range R, and the **nullity of F** is the dimension of the kernel K, i.e.,

$$\operatorname{rank} \mathbf{F} = \dim R, \tag{7a}$$

$$\operatorname{nullity} \mathbf{F} = \dim K. \tag{7b}$$

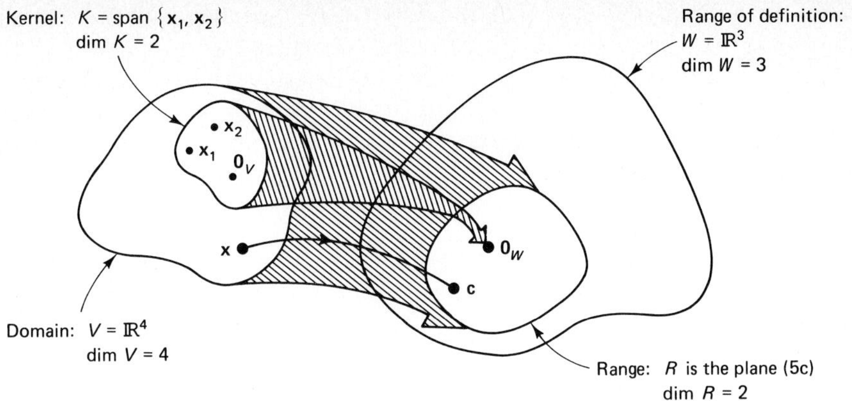

Fig. 3.4 The transformation **F**.

For example, for the transformation in Example 2 we see that rank $\mathbf{F} = \dim R = 2$, and nullity $\mathbf{F} = \dim K = 2$, as well.

Next, we distinguish transformations as either "linear" or "nonlinear."

> ***Definition 1*** *Linear Transformation*
> We say that $\mathbf{F}: V \to W$ is a **linear** transformation if
> $$\mathbf{F}(\alpha\mathbf{u} + \beta\mathbf{v}) = \alpha\mathbf{F}(\mathbf{u}) + \beta\mathbf{F}(\mathbf{v}) \tag{8}$$
> for every choice of vectors **u**, **v** in V, and scalars α, β; otherwise, **F** is said to be **nonlinear.**

EXAMPLE 3 To illustrate, consider the transformation $\mathbf{F}: \mathbb{R}^3 \to \mathbb{R}^2$, where

$$\mathbf{F}(\mathbf{x}) = \begin{pmatrix} x_1 - 2x_2 + x_3 \\ x_2 + 5x_3 \end{pmatrix}. \tag{9}$$

Is **F** linear? Well,

$$\begin{aligned} \mathbf{F}(\alpha\mathbf{u} + \beta\mathbf{v}) &= \begin{pmatrix} (\alpha u_1 + \beta v_1) - 2(\alpha u_2 + \beta v_2) + (\alpha u_3 + \beta v_3) \\ (\alpha u_2 + \beta v_2) + 5(\alpha u_3 + \beta v_3) \end{pmatrix} \\ &= \alpha\begin{pmatrix} u_1 - 2u_2 + u_3 \\ u_2 + 5u_3 \end{pmatrix} + \beta\begin{pmatrix} v_1 - 2v_2 + v_3 \\ v_2 + 5v_3 \end{pmatrix} \\ &= \alpha\mathbf{F}(\mathbf{u}) + \beta\mathbf{F}(\mathbf{v}), \end{aligned} \tag{10}$$

for every choice of **u**, **v**, α, β, so that **F** is indeed linear. Notice that the key step in (10), the second equality, follows from the definitions of the addition and scalar multiplication of matrices [(4) and (7) on page 64]. ◀

EXAMPLE 4 Consider $\mathbf{F}: \mathbb{R}^2 \to \mathbb{R}^2$, where

$$\mathbf{F}(\mathbf{x}) = \begin{pmatrix} x_1^2 \\ x_1 + 2x_2 \end{pmatrix}. \tag{11}$$

Then

$$
\begin{aligned}
\mathbf{F}(\alpha\mathbf{u}+\beta\mathbf{v})\\
&= \begin{pmatrix} (\alpha u_1+\beta v_1)^2 \\ (\alpha u_1+\beta v_1)+2(\alpha u_2+\beta v_2) \end{pmatrix}\\
&= \alpha\begin{pmatrix} u_1^2 \\ u_1+2u_2 \end{pmatrix} + \beta\begin{pmatrix} v_1^2 \\ v_1+2v_2 \end{pmatrix} + \begin{pmatrix} (\alpha^2-\alpha)u_1^2+(\beta^2-\beta)v_1^2+2\alpha\beta u_1 v_1 \\ 0 \end{pmatrix}\\
&= \alpha\mathbf{F}(\mathbf{u})+\beta\mathbf{F}(\mathbf{v})+\text{"deviation,"}
\end{aligned}
$$

where the "deviation,"

$$\mathbf{F}(\alpha\mathbf{u}+\beta\mathbf{v})-\alpha\mathbf{F}(\mathbf{u})-\beta\mathbf{F}(\mathbf{v}) = \begin{pmatrix} (\alpha^2-\alpha)u_1^2+(\beta^2-\beta)v_1^2+2\alpha\beta u_1 v_1 \\ 0 \end{pmatrix}$$

is obviously not equal to zero for all choices of α, β, $\mathbf{u}$, $\mathbf{v}$; e.g., if $\alpha=\beta=u_1=v_1=1$, then (for any u_2 and v_2) the deviation vector is $\begin{pmatrix} 2 \\ 0 \end{pmatrix}$. Thus (8) does not hold for all choices of α, β, $\mathbf{u}$, $\mathbf{v}$, so $\mathbf{F}$ is *nonlinear*. ◀

If $\mathbf{F}$ is linear, then besides (8) we have

$$
\begin{aligned}
\mathbf{F}(\alpha\mathbf{u}+\beta\mathbf{v}+\gamma\mathbf{w}) &= \mathbf{F}(\alpha\mathbf{u}+(\beta\mathbf{v}+\gamma\mathbf{w}))\\
&= \alpha\mathbf{F}(\mathbf{u})+\mathbf{F}(\beta\mathbf{v}+\gamma\mathbf{w}) = \alpha\mathbf{F}(\mathbf{u})+\beta\mathbf{F}(\mathbf{v})+\gamma\mathbf{F}(\mathbf{w})
\end{aligned}
$$

or, more generally,

$$\boxed{\mathbf{F}(\alpha_1\mathbf{u}_1+\cdots+\alpha_n\mathbf{u}_n) = \alpha_1\mathbf{F}(\mathbf{u}_1)+\cdots+\alpha_n\mathbf{F}(\mathbf{u}_n).} \tag{12}$$

In the remainder of this section we consider only linear transformations. Observe that (9) can be expressed in matrix notation as

$$\mathbf{F}(\mathbf{x}) = \begin{pmatrix} 1 & -2 & 1 \\ 0 & 1 & 5 \end{pmatrix}\begin{pmatrix} x_1 \\ x_2 \\ x_3 \end{pmatrix}; \tag{13}$$

i.e., the action of $\mathbf{F}$ on $\mathbf{x}$ is equivalent to multiplication by $\mathbf{A}$, where $\mathbf{A}$ is the matrix $\begin{pmatrix} 1 & -2 & 1 \\ 0 & 1 & 5 \end{pmatrix}$:

$$\mathbf{F}(\mathbf{x}) = \mathbf{A}\mathbf{x}. \tag{14}$$

Note that we do *not* say that "the transformation $\mathbf{F}$ is the matrix $\mathbf{A}$"; rather, we say that $\mathbf{F}$ is the transformation *multiplication by* $\mathbf{A}$. For that reason we call $\mathbf{F}$ a **matrix transformation.** The point that we wish to make here is that the linear transformation given in Example 3 happens to be a matrix transformation. We now show that that correspondence is no accident.

> ***Theorem 1*** A transformation $\mathbf{F}: \mathbb{R}^n \to \mathbb{R}^m$ is linear if and only if it is a matrix transformation.

Proof First, we show that if **F** is a matrix transformation [i.e., if there is an $m \times n$ matrix **A** such that $\mathbf{F}(\mathbf{x}) = \mathbf{A}\mathbf{x}$ for each **x** in $\mathbb{R}^n$], then **F** is linear. That is easy, since $\mathbf{F}(\alpha\mathbf{u} + \beta\mathbf{v}) = \mathbf{A}(\alpha\mathbf{u} + \beta\mathbf{v}) = \alpha\mathbf{A}\mathbf{u} + \beta\mathbf{A}\mathbf{v} = \alpha\mathbf{F}(\mathbf{u}) + \beta\mathbf{F}(\mathbf{v})$ for all **u**, **v** in $\mathbb{R}^n$ and for all scalars α, β. To prove the converse, let $\{\hat{\mathbf{i}}_1, \ldots, \hat{\mathbf{i}}_n\}$ and $\{\hat{\mathbf{I}}_1, \ldots, \hat{\mathbf{I}}_m\}$ be standard bases for $\mathbb{R}^n$ and $\mathbb{R}^m$, respectively. We may express

$$\mathbf{x} = \sum_{j=1}^{n} x_j \hat{\mathbf{i}}_j \quad \text{and} \quad \mathbf{y} = \sum_{k=1}^{m} y_k \hat{\mathbf{I}}_k.$$

Then

$$\mathbf{F}(\mathbf{x}) = \mathbf{F}\left(\sum_{j=1}^{n} x_j \hat{\mathbf{i}}_j\right) = \sum_{j=1}^{n} x_j \mathbf{F}(\hat{\mathbf{i}}_j)$$

by (12). Since $\mathbf{F}(\hat{\mathbf{i}}_j)$ is in $\mathbb{R}^m$, it can be expressed in the form

$$\mathbf{F}(\hat{\mathbf{i}}_j) = \sum_{k=1}^{m} a_{kj} \hat{\mathbf{I}}_k,$$

so

$$\mathbf{F}(\mathbf{x}) = \sum_{j=1}^{n} x_j \sum_{k=1}^{m} a_{kj} \hat{\mathbf{I}}_k = \sum_{k=1}^{m} \left(\sum_{j=1}^{n} a_{kj} x_j\right) \hat{\mathbf{I}}_k. \tag{15}$$

But we also have

$$\mathbf{F}(\mathbf{x}) = \mathbf{y} = \sum_{k=1}^{m} y_k \hat{\mathbf{I}}_k, \tag{16}$$

and it follows from (15) and (16), and the linear independence of the $\hat{\mathbf{I}}_k$'s, that

$$y_k = \sum_{j=1}^{n} a_{kj} x_j$$

or $\mathbf{y} = \mathbf{A}\mathbf{x}$, where $\mathbf{A} = \{a_{kj}\}$ is $m \times n$, as was to be proved. ■

We now introduce some additional terminology. First, recall that **F** is understood to be single valued; i.e., to each vector **x** in the domain V of **F** there corresponds a unique image $\mathbf{F}(\mathbf{x})$ in the range R of **F**. If, in addition to each vector in R there corresponds a unique inverse image in V, then **F** is said to be **one-to-one.** Notice that we do not say "to each vector in W there corresponds a unique inverse image in V" since R may not be all of W, in which case those vectors which are in W but not in R have no inverse image at all. If R does turn out to be all of W, then **F** is said to be **onto**; i.e., **F** maps V "onto" W rather than "into" W. Finally, if **F** is both one-to-one and onto, it is said to be **invertible**, for then every vector in W has a unique image in V. This inverse transformation, from W onto V, is called the **inverse of F** and is denoted as $\mathbf{F}^{-1}$.

EXAMPLE 5 Consider the matrix transformation **F** in Example 2; there, $\mathbf{F}(\mathbf{x}) = \mathbf{A}\mathbf{x}$, with

$$\mathbf{A} = \begin{pmatrix} 1 & -2 & 0 & 1 \\ 1 & 0 & 1 & 0 \\ 1 & 2 & 2 & -1 \end{pmatrix}. \tag{17}$$

From (5c) we see that R is only the two-dimensional subspace of $W\,(=\mathbb{R}^3)$ consisting of the plane $c_3 - 2c_2 + c_1 = 0$, so that **F** is not *onto*. That result is illustrated schematically in Fig. 3.4, where R is shown to be only a part of W. Furthermore, if **c** *is* in R [i.e., if (5c) is satisfied], then (5) yields a nonunique solution for **x**, so that **F** is not one-to-one. Summarizing, **F** is neither one-to-one nor onto, and is therefore not invertible. ◀

EXAMPLE 6 Consider the matrix transformation $\mathbf{F}: \mathbb{R}^2 \to \mathbb{R}^3$ associated with the matrix

$$\mathbf{A} = \begin{pmatrix} 1 & -2 \\ 1 & 1 \\ 2 & -1 \end{pmatrix}. \tag{18}$$

Applying elementary operations to the system $\mathbf{Ax} = \mathbf{c}$, namely, to

$$\begin{pmatrix} 1 & -2 \\ 1 & 1 \\ 2 & -1 \end{pmatrix}\begin{pmatrix} x_1 \\ x_2 \end{pmatrix} = \begin{pmatrix} c_1 \\ c_2 \\ c_3 \end{pmatrix}, \tag{19}$$

we obtain the equivalent system

$$x_1 - 2x_2 = c_1 \tag{20a}$$

$$3x_2 = c_2 - c_1 \tag{20b}$$

$$0 = c_3 - c_2 - c_1, \tag{20c}$$

from which it is seen that **F** is *not* onto (why not?), although it *is* one-to-one (why?). Thus **F** is not invertible. ◀

EXAMPLE 7 Consider the matrix transformation $\mathbf{F}: \mathbb{R}^3 \to \mathbb{R}^2$ associated with the matrix

$$\mathbf{A} = \begin{pmatrix} 1 & 1 & 2 \\ 2 & 0 & -3 \end{pmatrix}. \tag{21}$$

Applying elementary operations to the system $\mathbf{Ax} = \mathbf{c}$, namely, to

$$\begin{pmatrix} 1 & 1 & 2 \\ 2 & 0 & -3 \end{pmatrix}\begin{pmatrix} x_1 \\ x_2 \\ x_3 \end{pmatrix} = \begin{pmatrix} c_1 \\ c_2 \end{pmatrix}, \tag{22}$$

we obtain the equivalent system

$$x_1 + x_2 + 2x_3 = c_1 \tag{23a}$$

$$2x_2 + 7x_3 = 2c_1 - c_2, \tag{23b}$$

from which it is seen that **F** *is* onto (why?), although *not* one-to-one (why not?). Thus **F** is not invertible. ◀

EXAMPLE 8 Consider the matrix transformation $\mathbf{F}: \mathbb{R}^3 \to \mathbb{R}^3$ associated with the matrix

$$\mathbf{A} = \begin{pmatrix} 2 & -1 & 1 \\ 0 & 3 & 1 \\ 1 & 1 & 0 \end{pmatrix}. \tag{24}$$

Applying elementary operations to the system $\mathbf{Ax} = \mathbf{c}$, we obtain

$$2x_1 - x_2 + x_3 = c_1 \tag{25a}$$

$$3x_2 + x_3 = c_2 \tag{25b}$$

$$-2x_3 = 2c_3 - c_2 - c_1, \tag{25c}$$

from which it is seen that $\mathbf{F}$ is both onto (so that $\mathbf{F}$ is an operator) and one-to-one, and is therefore invertible; completion of the Gauss–Jordan reduction of (25) reveals that the inverse operator $\mathbf{F}^{-1}$ is the matrix operator associated with the matrix

$$\begin{pmatrix} \frac{1}{6} & -\frac{1}{6} & \frac{2}{3} \\ -\frac{1}{6} & \frac{1}{6} & \frac{1}{3} \\ \frac{1}{2} & \frac{1}{2} & -1 \end{pmatrix} \tag{26}$$

which, of course, is the inverse of the $\mathbf{A}$ matrix, $\mathbf{A}^{-1}$. ◀

For the case of matrix transformations, we can make an interesting observation about the range R, for if we partition $\mathbf{A}$ into columns, say $\mathbf{a}_1, \ldots, \mathbf{a}_n$, then

$$\mathbf{F}(\mathbf{x}) = \mathbf{Ax} = \begin{pmatrix} a_{11} & a_{12} & \cdots & a_{1n} \\ \vdots & & & \vdots \\ a_{m1} & a_{m2} & \cdots & a_{mn} \end{pmatrix} \begin{pmatrix} x_1 \\ \vdots \\ x_n \end{pmatrix} = (\mathbf{a}_1, \mathbf{a}_2, \ldots, \mathbf{a}_n) \begin{pmatrix} x_1 \\ \vdots \\ x_n \end{pmatrix} \tag{27}$$
$$= x_1 \mathbf{a}_1 + \cdots + x_n \mathbf{a}_n,$$

from which it follows that *the range R is the span of* $\{\mathbf{a}_1, \ldots, \mathbf{a}_n\}$,

$$R = \operatorname{span}\{\mathbf{a}_1, \ldots, \mathbf{a}_n\}. \tag{28}$$

We call $\operatorname{span}\{\mathbf{a}_1, \ldots, \mathbf{a}_n\}$ the **column space** of $\mathbf{A}$. It follows from (28) that the dimension of R is equal to the number of LI column vectors in $\mathbf{A}$. But the number of LI column vectors in $\mathbf{A}$ is, by definition, the rank of the $\mathbf{A}$ matrix, $r(\mathbf{A})$. Thus we can say that if $\mathbf{F}$ is a matrix transformation, with matrix $\mathbf{A}$, then

$$\boxed{\dim R = r(\mathbf{A}).} \tag{29}$$

We come now to an important theorem which expresses a sort of "conservation of dimension."

> ***Theorem 2** Dimension*
> If $\mathbf{F}: V \to W$ is a linear transformation on a finite-dimensional vector space V, then
>
> $$\boxed{\dim R + \dim K = \dim V.} \tag{30}$$
>
> Or since $\dim R = \operatorname{rank} \mathbf{F}$ and $\dim K = \text{nullity } \mathbf{F}$,
>
> $$\operatorname{rank} \mathbf{F} + \operatorname{nullity} \mathbf{F} = \dim V.$$

Proof The case where $\dim V = 0$ is simple and is left for the exercises. Thus we assume that $\dim V > 0$. Let $\dim V = n$ and $\dim K = k$, and let $\{\mathbf{x}_1, \ldots, \mathbf{x}_k\}$ be a basis for K. (Of course, if $k = 0$, then K has no basis.) Surely, $k \leq n$. If $k = n$, then that basis is also a basis for V. Thus every vector in V is sent by $\mathbf{F}$ into $\mathbf{0}_W$. Hence the range R is the single vector $\mathbf{0}_W$; thus R is of dimension zero, so that $\dim R + \dim K = 0 + n = n = \dim V$, in accordance with (30). If $k < n$, then choose vectors $\mathbf{x}_{k+1}, \ldots, \mathbf{x}_n$ in V so that $\{\mathbf{x}_1, \ldots, \mathbf{x}_k, \mathbf{x}_{k+1}, \ldots, \mathbf{x}_n\}$ is a basis for V. We wish to show that the image of $\mathbf{x}_{k+1}, \ldots, \mathbf{x}_n$ is a basis for R, for since there are $n - k$ vectors in this basis for R, then R must be $(n - k)$-dimensional, so that $\dim R = n - k = \dim V - \dim K$, as was to be shown. To see that the image of the set $\{\mathbf{x}_{k+1}, \ldots, \mathbf{x}_n\}$ is indeed a basis for R, observe first that it spans R since, for any α's,

$$\begin{aligned}
\mathbf{F}(\alpha_1 \mathbf{x}_1 + \cdots + \alpha_k \mathbf{x}_k + \alpha_{k+1}\mathbf{x}_{k+1} + \cdots + \alpha_n \mathbf{x}_n)& \\
&= \alpha_1 \mathbf{F}(\mathbf{x}_1) + \cdots + \alpha_k \mathbf{F}(\mathbf{x}_k) + \alpha_{k+1} \mathbf{F}(\mathbf{x}_{k+1}) + \cdots + \alpha_n \mathbf{F}(\mathbf{x}_n) \\
&= \mathbf{0}_W + \cdots + \mathbf{0}_W + \alpha_{k+1} \mathbf{F}(\mathbf{x}_{k+1}) + \cdots + \alpha_n \mathbf{F}(\mathbf{x}_n) \\
&= \alpha_{k+1} \mathbf{F}(\mathbf{x}_{k+1}) + \cdots + \alpha_n \mathbf{F}(\mathbf{x}_n),
\end{aligned}$$

so that

$$R = \operatorname{span}\{\mathbf{F}(\mathbf{x}_{k+1}), \ldots, \mathbf{F}(\mathbf{x}_n)\}.$$

Thus it remains to show that $\{\mathbf{F}(\mathbf{x}_{k+1}), \ldots, \mathbf{F}(\mathbf{x}_n)\}$ is LI. Well, if

$$\beta_{k+1} \mathbf{F}(\mathbf{x}_{k+1}) + \cdots + \beta_n \mathbf{F}(\mathbf{x}_n) = \mathbf{0}_W, \tag{31}$$

then, since $\mathbf{F}$ is linear, we may reexpress (31) as

$$\mathbf{F}(\beta_{k+1}\mathbf{x}_{k+1} + \cdots + \beta_n \mathbf{x}_n) = \mathbf{0}_W. \tag{32}$$

By definition of the kernel, the argument of $\mathbf{F}$, in (32), must be in K, which is spanned by $\{\mathbf{x}_1, \ldots, \mathbf{x}_k\}$, so that we can express

$$\beta_{k+1}\mathbf{x}_{k+1} + \cdots + \beta_n \mathbf{x}_n = \gamma_1 \mathbf{x}_1 + \cdots + \gamma_k \mathbf{x}_k$$

or

$$\beta_{k+1}\mathbf{x}_{k+1} + \cdots + \beta_n \mathbf{x}_n - \gamma_1 \mathbf{x}_1 - \cdots - \gamma_k \mathbf{x}_k = \mathbf{0}_V. \tag{33}$$

By the assumed linear independence of $\{\mathbf{x}_1, \ldots, \mathbf{x}_k, \mathbf{x}_{k+1}, \ldots, \mathbf{x}_n\}$ it follows from (33) that $\beta_{k+1}, \ldots, \beta_n, \gamma_1, \ldots, \gamma_k$ must all be zero. Thus (31) holds only if the β's are all zero, so the set $\{\mathbf{F}(\mathbf{x}_{k+1}), \ldots, \mathbf{F}(\mathbf{x}_n)\}$ is LI. This completes the proof. ■

Let us illustrate the truth of (30) for the matrix transformations in Examples 5 to 8:

	$\dim R + \dim K$	$= \dim V$	
Example 5:	$2 + 2$	$= 4$	✓
Example 6:	$2 + 0$	$= 2$	✓
Example 7:	$2 + 1$	$= 3$	✓
Example 8:	$3 + 0$	$= 3$	✓

In each of those four examples **F** was a matrix transformation. But while our emphasis, here, on matrix transformations is consistent with our emphasis, in Part I, on n-space, we note that Theorem 2 is not limited to matrix transformations.

Finally, Theorem 2 enables us to resolve an important point regarding the solution of the homogeneous linear equation

$$\mathbf{Ax} = \mathbf{0}, \tag{34}$$

where **A** is $m \times n$ and **x** is $n \times 1$. For let us suppose that the Gauss–Jordan reduction yields, as the general solution of (34), a p-parameter family of solutions*

$$\mathbf{x} = \alpha_1 \mathbf{x}_1 + \cdots + \alpha_p \mathbf{x}_p. \tag{35}$$

There is a nagging question which, in fact, we have not even enunciated until now: Are the $\mathbf{x}_1, \ldots, \mathbf{x}_p$ necessarily LI? That is, is the nullspace of **A** p-dimensional?† We certainly hope so, for if only k of the vectors $\mathbf{x}_1, \ldots, \mathbf{x}_p$ were LI, where $k < p$, then the right-hand side of (35) could be reexpressed as a linear combination of $\mathbf{x}_1, \ldots, \mathbf{x}_k$, and it would then seem more appropriate to call the solution of (34) a k-parameter family of solutions. Well, Theorem 2 tells us that $\dim K = \dim V - \dim R = n - r(\mathbf{A})$, and Theorem 5 on page 100 tells us that $n - r(\mathbf{A}) = p$. Comparison of these results reveals that $\dim K = p$, i.e., the nullspace of **A** *is* p-dimensional. With this result established, it is easy to show, further, that $\{\mathbf{x}_1, \ldots, \mathbf{x}_p\}$ is indeed necessarily LI. For we see from (35) that the nullspace of **A** is $\operatorname{span}\{\mathbf{x}_1, \ldots, \mathbf{x}_p\}$, and since we have established that the nullspace is p-dimensional, we have $\dim[\operatorname{span}\{\mathbf{x}_1, \ldots, \mathbf{x}_p\}] = p$. It then follows from Theorem 3 on page 58 that the set $\{\mathbf{x}_1, \ldots, \mathbf{x}_p\}$ is LI. Let us state this result as a theorem, for reference.

Theorem 3

If $\mathbf{Ax} = \mathbf{0}$, where **A** is an $m \times n$ matrix and **x** is an $n \times 1$ column vector, admits a p-parameter family of solutions

$$\mathbf{x} = \alpha_1 \mathbf{x}_1 + \cdots + \alpha_p \mathbf{x}_p, \tag{36}$$

then the set $\{\mathbf{x}_1, \ldots, \mathbf{x}_p\}$ is LI, and the nullspace of **A** is p-dimensional, i.e.,

$$\boxed{\dim K = p.} \tag{37}$$

* By (35) being the *general solution* of (34), we mean that every solution of (34) can be expressed in the form (35).

† By "nullspace of **A**," what we really mean is the nullspace of the matrix transformation **F**, where $\mathbf{F}(\mathbf{x}) = \mathbf{Ax}$.

Summarizing, recall that we developed n-space in Chapter 2, and then generalized the vector space concept in Section 2.6. The role of the present section, in Chapter 3, is analogous to that of Section 2.6 in that we have generalized the notion of matrix, developed earlier in the chapter, to that of *transformations on vector spaces*. Those transformations may, but need not, be matrix transformations and they may, but need not, be linear. However, the linear case received heavy emphasis here because it is both more tractable and more useful in applications. Some additional concepts have been relegated to the exercises in order to render the text portion a bit more compact.

3.8 EXERCISES

1. In general, the effect of a transformation on the input vector varies from one input vector to another. For example, let F: $\mathbb{R}^2 \to \mathbb{R}^2$ be a matrix transformation $\mathbf{F}(\mathbf{x}) = \mathbf{A}\mathbf{x}$, where $\mathbf{A} = \begin{pmatrix} 3 & 2 \\ 0 & 1 \end{pmatrix}$. In 2-space the "effect" of a transformation on a nonzero vector $\mathbf{x}$ amounts to the resulting rotation in the plane, and the dilation (i.e., $\|\mathbf{Ax}\|/\|\mathbf{x}\|$). For the transformation $\mathbf{F}$ given above, show that these effects are as follows for the given input vectors, and notice that the effect of $\mathbf{F}$ varies from one $\mathbf{x}$ to another.

Input	Effect of F
(a) $\mathbf{x} = \begin{pmatrix} 1 \\ 0 \end{pmatrix}$	rotation = 0 radians dilation = 3
(b) $\mathbf{x} = \begin{pmatrix} 0 \\ 1 \end{pmatrix}$	rotation ≈ 1.1 radians clockwise dilation = $\sqrt{5}$
(c) $\mathbf{x} = \begin{pmatrix} 1 \\ -1 \end{pmatrix}$	rotation = 0 radians dilation = 1

2. Determine whether $\mathbf{F}$ is linear or nonlinear by determining whether or not the deviation $\mathbf{F}(\alpha\mathbf{u} + \beta\mathbf{v}) - \alpha\mathbf{F}(\mathbf{u}) - \beta\mathbf{F}(\mathbf{v})$ is necessarily zero.

*(a) $\mathbf{F}: \mathbb{R}^2 \to \mathbb{R}^2$, $\quad \mathbf{F}(\mathbf{x}) = \begin{pmatrix} x_1^2 \\ x_1 + x_2 \end{pmatrix}$

(b) $\mathbf{F}: \mathbb{R}^2 \to \mathbb{R}^2$, $\quad \mathbf{F}(\mathbf{x}) = \begin{pmatrix} 3x_1 \\ x_1 + x_2 \end{pmatrix}$

(c) $\mathbf{F}: \mathbb{R}^3 \to \mathbb{R}^2$, $\quad \mathbf{F}(\mathbf{x}) = \begin{pmatrix} x_1x_2 \\ x_3 \end{pmatrix}$

*(d) $\mathbf{F}: \mathbb{R}^2 \to \mathbb{R}^1$, $\quad \mathbf{F}(\mathbf{x}) = (3x_2)$

(e) $\mathbf{F}: \mathbb{R}^2 \to \mathbb{R}^2$, $\quad \mathbf{F}(\mathbf{x}) = \begin{pmatrix} 6 \\ -5 \end{pmatrix}$

(f) $\mathbf{F}: \mathbb{R}^2 \to \mathbb{R}^2$, $\quad \mathbf{F}(\mathbf{x}) = \begin{pmatrix} x_1 + 3 \\ x_2 + 5 \end{pmatrix}$

(g) $\mathbf{F}: \mathbb{R}^2 \to \mathbb{R}^2$, $\quad \mathbf{F}(\mathbf{x}) = \begin{pmatrix} \sin x_2 \\ 4x_1 \end{pmatrix}$

(h) $\mathbf{F}: \mathbb{R}^2 \to \mathbb{R}^2$, $\quad \mathbf{F}(\mathbf{x}) = \begin{pmatrix} x_1 + 1 \\ x_2 + 1 \end{pmatrix}$

3. Show that if $\mathbf{F}: V \to W$ is linear, then $\mathbf{F}(\mathbf{0}) = \mathbf{0}$.

4. (*Identity operator*) We say that $\mathbf{I}: V \to V$ is an **identity operator** if $\mathbf{I}(\mathbf{x}) = \mathbf{x}$ for each $\mathbf{x}$ in V.

(a) Suppose that $\mathbf{F}: V \to V$ is linear and that $\{\mathbf{v}_1, \ldots, \mathbf{v}_n\}$ is a basis for V. Show that if $\mathbf{F}(\mathbf{v}_1) = \mathbf{v}_1, \ldots, \mathbf{F}(\mathbf{v}_n) = \mathbf{v}_n$, then $\mathbf{F} = \mathbf{I}$.

*(b) Determine the matrix $\mathbf{A}$ corresponding to the identity operator $\mathbf{I}$: $\mathbb{R}^n \to \mathbb{R}^n$, i.e., such that $\mathbf{I}(\mathbf{x}) = \mathbf{Ax}$.

5. (*Zero transformation*) We say that $\boldsymbol{\phi}: V \to W$ is a **zero transformation** if $\boldsymbol{\phi}(\mathbf{x}) = \mathbf{0}$ for all $\mathbf{x}$'s in V.

(a) Suppose that $\mathbf{F}: V \to W$ is linear and that $\{\mathbf{v}_1, \ldots, \mathbf{v}_n\}$ is a basis for V. Show that if $\mathbf{F}(\mathbf{v}_1) = \mathbf{0}, \ldots, \mathbf{F}(\mathbf{v}_n) = \mathbf{0}$, then $\mathbf{F} = \boldsymbol{\phi}$.

(b) Determine the matrix $\mathbf{A}$ corresponding to the zero transformation $\boldsymbol{\phi}$: $\mathbb{R}^n \to \mathbb{R}^m$, i.e., such that $\boldsymbol{\phi}(\mathbf{x}) = \mathbf{Ax}$.

6. In each case $\mathbf{F}$: $\mathbb{R}^n \to \mathbb{R}^m$ is the matrix transformation corresponding to the given $m \times n$ matrix $\mathbf{A}$. Determine $\dim R$ [recall (29)], $\dim K$ [recall (37)], and $\dim V$, and verify the dimension theorem (30). Is $\mathbf{F}$ onto? One-to-one? Invertible? Explain. Put forward any basis for K and any basis for R (if, indeed, they *have* bases; for recall Exercise 10 on page 56).

*(a) $\begin{pmatrix} 2 & 1 & 1 \\ 1 & 1 & 1 \end{pmatrix}$ $\qquad$ (b) $\begin{pmatrix} 2 & 1 & 1 \\ 1 & 1 & 1 \\ 4 & 3 & 3 \end{pmatrix}$

(c) $\begin{pmatrix} 2 & 1 & 1 \\ 1 & 1 & 1 \\ 1 & 1 & 2 \end{pmatrix}$ $\qquad$ *(d) $\begin{pmatrix} 4 & 1 \\ 3 & 2 \\ 0 & -1 \end{pmatrix}$

(e) $\begin{pmatrix} 1 & 2 & 3 \\ 0 & 4 & 5 \\ 0 & 0 & 6 \end{pmatrix}$ (f) $\begin{pmatrix} 0 & 0 & 6 & 0 \\ 0 & -2 & 0 & 0 \\ 1 & 0 & 0 & 0 \end{pmatrix}$

(g) $\begin{pmatrix} 2 & -1 & 1 \\ 0 & 0 & 3 \\ 1 & 1 & 1 \\ 1 & 2 & 3 \end{pmatrix}$ (h) $\begin{pmatrix} 1 & 4 \\ 2 & 1 \\ 0 & 1 \\ 0 & 3 \end{pmatrix}$

(i) $\begin{pmatrix} 1 & -1 & 0 & 2 \\ 0 & 1 & 1 & 2 \\ 3 & 0 & 1 & 0 \\ 1 & 2 & -1 & 1 \end{pmatrix}$

7. Make up any example of a matrix transformation $\mathbf{F}: \mathbb{R}^n \to \mathbb{R}^m$ that is one-to-one but not onto, one that is onto but not one-to-one, one that is neither one-to-one nor onto, and one that is both one-to-one and onto. If such an example is impossible, explain why that is so.

*(a) $n = 2, m = 2$ (b) $n = 3, m = 2$
(c) $n = 2, m = 3$ (d) $n = 3, m = 3$
(e) $n = 2, m = 4$ (f) $n = 4, m = 2$
(g) $n = 3, m = 4$ (h) $n = 4, m = 3$
(i) $n = 4, m = 4$ (j) $n = 2, m = 5$
(k) $n = 3, m = 5$ (l) $n = 4, m = 5$

8. (a) Show that a linear transformation $\mathbf{F}: V \to W$ is one-to-one if and only if $\dim K = 0$.
(b) Use Theorem 2 to show that a linear transformation $\mathbf{F}: V \to W$ cannot be invertible if $\dim V \neq \dim W$.

***9.** (*Projection operators*) Let $\mathbf{F}$: $\mathbb{R}^3 \to \mathbb{R}^3$ be the transformation

$$\mathbf{F}(\mathbf{x}) = (\mathbf{x} \cdot \hat{\mathbf{v}})\hat{\mathbf{v}}, \tag{a}$$

where $\hat{\mathbf{v}} = (v_1, v_2, v_3)^{\mathrm{T}}$ is a prescribed unit vector. In geometric terms, $\mathbf{F}(\mathbf{x})$ is the vector orthogonal projection of $\mathbf{x}$ onto the line of action of $\hat{\mathbf{v}}$, as illustrated below. Hence $\mathbf{F}$ in (a) is known as a **projection operator**. We now state the problem: Show that $\mathbf{F}$ is linear, so that one can express $\mathbf{F}(\mathbf{x})$ as $\mathbf{Ax}$. Then determine the nine elements of the $\mathbf{A}$ matrix. (They will depend on v_1, v_2, v_3.)

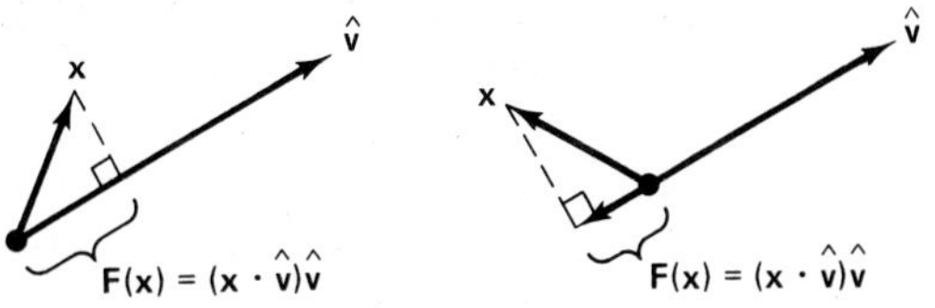

(a) (b)

10. (*More about projection operators*) This time, let $\mathbf{F}: \mathbb{R}^3 \to \mathbb{R}^3$ be the transformation

$$\mathbf{F}(\mathbf{x}) = (\mathbf{x} \cdot \hat{\mathbf{v}}_1)\hat{\mathbf{v}}_1 + (\mathbf{x} \cdot \hat{\mathbf{v}}_2)\hat{\mathbf{v}}_2, \tag{a}$$

where $\hat{\mathbf{v}}_1$, $\hat{\mathbf{v}}_2$ are prescribed ON vectors. Then $\mathbf{F}(\mathbf{x})$ is the vector orthogonal projection of $\mathbf{x}$ onto the *plane* spanned by $\{\hat{\mathbf{v}}_1, \hat{\mathbf{v}}_2\}$.

(a) Given that $\hat{\mathbf{v}}_1 = (1, 0, 0)^{\mathrm{T}}$ and $\hat{\mathbf{v}}_2 = (0, 1, 0)^{\mathrm{T}}$, work out $\mathbf{F}(\mathbf{x})$ for $\mathbf{x} = (2, 3, 4)^{\mathrm{T}}$, and draw an informative, labeled picture, analogous to the one shown in Exercise 9.
(b) Show that $\mathbf{F}$ is linear, so that one can express $\mathbf{F}(\mathbf{x})$ as $\mathbf{Ax}$. Then determine the nine elements of the $\mathbf{A}$ matrix, in terms of the components v_{11}, v_{12}, v_{13} of $\hat{\mathbf{v}}_1$ and v_{21}, v_{22}, v_{23} of $\hat{\mathbf{v}}_2$.

11. Show that $\mathbf{F}(\alpha\mathbf{u} + \beta\mathbf{v}) = \alpha\mathbf{F}(\mathbf{u}) + \beta\mathbf{F}(\mathbf{v})$, in Definition 1, is equivalent to the two conditions $\mathbf{F}(\mathbf{u} + \mathbf{v}) = \mathbf{F}(\mathbf{u}) + \mathbf{F}(\mathbf{v})$ and $\mathbf{F}(\alpha\mathbf{u}) = \alpha\mathbf{F}(\mathbf{u})$.

12. (*Reflection about a line*) Let $\mathbf{F}: \mathbb{R}^2 \to \mathbb{R}^2$ reflect any given vector $\mathbf{x}$ about the line L, as shown in the accompanying figure.

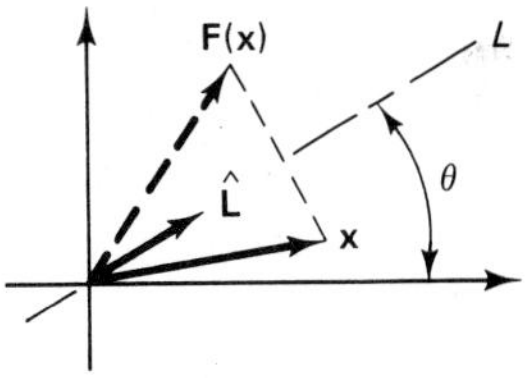

(a) Show that $\mathbf{F}(\mathbf{x}) = \mathbf{x} + 2[(\mathbf{x} \cdot \hat{\mathbf{L}})\hat{\mathbf{L}} - \mathbf{x}]$.
*(b) Show that $\mathbf{F}$ is linear and determine the matrix $\mathbf{A}$ such that $\mathbf{F}(\mathbf{x}) = \mathbf{Ax}$.
(c) Work out $\mathbf{A}^2$ and show that $\mathbf{A}^2 = \mathbf{I}$ (Exercise 4). Why should it have been obvious, without working out $\mathbf{A}^2$, that $\mathbf{A}^2 = \mathbf{I}$?

13. (*Linear combination and composition*) If $\mathbf{F}$ and $\mathbf{G}$ are transformations from V into W, then we define the **linear combination** of $\mathbf{F}$ and $\mathbf{G}$, $(\alpha\mathbf{F} + \beta\mathbf{G})$: $V \to W$, by

$$(\alpha\mathbf{F} + \beta\mathbf{G})(\mathbf{x}) \equiv \alpha\mathbf{F}(\mathbf{x}) + \beta\mathbf{G}(\mathbf{x}) \tag{a}$$

for all $\mathbf{x}$ in V. Given transformations $\mathbf{F}$: $U \to V$ and $\mathbf{G}$: $V \to W$, we define the **composition** of $\mathbf{F}$ and $\mathbf{G}$, $(\mathbf{GF})$: $U \to W$, by

$$(\mathbf{GF})(\mathbf{x}) \equiv \mathbf{G}(\mathbf{F}(\mathbf{x})) \tag{b}$$

for all $\mathbf{x}$ in U.

*(a) Let $\mathbf{F}$: $\mathbb{R}^4 \to \mathbb{R}^2$ and $\mathbf{G}$: $\mathbb{R}^2 \to \mathbb{R}^2$ be matrix transformations with matrices

$$\mathbf{A} = \begin{pmatrix} 1 & 5 & 3 & -2 \\ 2 & 5 & 0 & 0 \end{pmatrix} \quad \text{and} \quad \mathbf{B} = \begin{pmatrix} 2 & 0 \\ 4 & 0 \end{pmatrix},$$

respectively. Evaluate $(\mathbf{GF})(\mathbf{x})$ for $\mathbf{x} = (3, 1, -2, 6)^{\mathrm{T}}$. Find a single matrix corresponding to the composite transformation $\mathbf{GF}$.

(b) Let $\mathbf{F}: V \to V$ be a linear operator, and define the composite transformation $\mathbf{F}^2: V \to V$ by $\mathbf{F}^2(\mathbf{x}) \equiv \mathbf{F}(\mathbf{F}(\mathbf{x}))$. Show that $\mathbf{F}^2$ is linear, too.

14. Show that the *translation operator* $\mathbf{F}(\mathbf{x}) = \mathbf{x} + \mathbf{c}$, where $\mathbf{c}$ is a constant vector, is nonlinear.

15. (*Applications to computer graphics*) It is basic, in computer graphics, to be able to move points about, in 3-space, by combinations of translations and rotations. Translation is easily accomplished by the operator

$$\mathbf{F}(\mathbf{X}) = \mathbf{X} + \mathbf{\Delta X}, \tag{a}$$

where $\mathbf{X} = (x, y, z)^{\mathrm{T}}$ is the position vector to the point and $\mathbf{\Delta X} = (\Delta x, \Delta y, \Delta z)^{\mathrm{T}}$ is the translation. However, whereas it is convenient, in the computer software, to express all translations and rotations as matrix transformations, the operator $\mathbf{F}: \mathbb{R}^3 \to \mathbb{R}^3$ is not linear (Exercise 14), and hence not expressible as a matrix transformation. To circumvent this difficulty we define $\mathbf{X} = (x, y, z, 1)^{\mathrm{T}}$, instead, where the fourth component, unity, is included for convenience. Then we can express

$$\mathbf{F}(\mathbf{x}) = \mathbf{TX}$$
$$= \begin{pmatrix} 1 & 0 & 0 & \Delta x \\ 0 & 1 & 0 & \Delta y \\ 0 & 0 & 1 & \Delta z \\ 0 & 0 & 0 & 1 \end{pmatrix} \begin{pmatrix} x \\ y \\ z \\ 1 \end{pmatrix} = \begin{pmatrix} x + \Delta x \\ y + \Delta y \\ z + \Delta z \\ 1 \end{pmatrix}, \tag{b}$$

which, if we pay attention to only the first three components, effects the translation by means of multiplication by $\mathbf{T}$, where $\mathbf{T}$ is the 4×4 matrix in (b).

(a) Show that

$$\mathbf{F}(\mathbf{X}) = \mathbf{R}_z \mathbf{X} = \begin{pmatrix} c_z & -s_z & 0 & 0 \\ s_z & c_z & 0 & 0 \\ 0 & 0 & 1 & 0 \\ 0 & 0 & 0 & 1 \end{pmatrix} \begin{pmatrix} x \\ y \\ z \\ 1 \end{pmatrix} \tag{c}$$

effects a rotation about the z axis through an angle θ_z, taken according to the right-hand rule, where c_z, s_z are shorthand for $\cos\theta_z$, $\sin\theta_z$, respectively. *Hint:* Letting $x = r\cos\theta$, $y = r\sin\theta$, show that

$$\mathbf{F}(\mathbf{X}) = \mathbf{R}_z \mathbf{X} = \begin{pmatrix} r\cos(\theta + \theta_z) \\ r\sin(\theta + \theta_z) \\ z \\ 1 \end{pmatrix}.$$

Note: Similarly, rotations about the x axis through an angle θ_x, and about the y axis through an angle θ_y, are effected by

$$\mathbf{F}(\mathbf{X}) = \mathbf{R}_y \mathbf{X} = \begin{pmatrix} c_y & 0 & -s_y & 0 \\ 0 & 1 & 0 & 0 \\ s_y & 0 & c_y & 0 \\ 0 & 0 & 0 & 1 \end{pmatrix} \begin{pmatrix} x \\ y \\ z \\ 1 \end{pmatrix} \tag{d}$$

and

$$\mathbf{F}(\mathbf{x}) = \mathbf{R}_x \mathbf{X} = \begin{pmatrix} 1 & 0 & 0 & 0 \\ 0 & c_x & -s_x & 0 \\ 0 & s_x & c_x & 0 \\ 0 & 0 & 0 & 1 \end{pmatrix} \begin{pmatrix} x \\ y \\ z \\ 1 \end{pmatrix}, \tag{e}$$

respectively, where c_x, s_x, c_y, s_y denote $\cos\theta_x$, $\sin\theta_x$, $\cos\theta_y$, $\sin\theta_y$.

(b) Show that a rotation about the z axis, followed by a translation, is effected by the composite transformation (see Exercise 13)

$$\mathbf{F}(\mathbf{x}) = \mathbf{TR}_z \mathbf{X} = \begin{pmatrix} c_z & -s_z & 0 & \Delta x \\ s_z & c_z & 0 & \Delta y \\ 0 & 0 & 1 & \Delta z \\ 0 & 0 & 0 & 1 \end{pmatrix} \begin{pmatrix} x \\ y \\ z \\ 1 \end{pmatrix}.$$

Does the order of the operations matter? That is, is $\mathbf{TR}_z = \mathbf{R}_z\mathbf{T}$?

*(c) Compute $\mathbf{F}(\mathbf{X}) = \mathbf{TR}_x\mathbf{R}_y\mathbf{R}_z\mathbf{X}$ for $\mathbf{X} = (1, 1, 0, 1)^{\mathrm{T}}$, $\theta_z = -\pi/4$, $\theta_y = \pi/2$, $\theta_x = \pi$, $\Delta x = 2$, $\Delta y = 1$, $\Delta z = -3$. Verify the result by drawing the coordinate axes, identifying the initial point $\mathbf{X}$, and then carrying out each rotation and translation graphically in a neat sketch.

*(d) Let the point and eraser of a pencil be located, initially, by $\mathbf{X}_p = (0, 1, 1, 1)^{\mathrm{T}}$ and $\mathbf{X}_e = (0, 1, 0, 1)^{\mathrm{T}}$, respectively. Locate the point and the eraser following the composite transformation

$$\mathbf{F}(\mathbf{X}) = \mathbf{TR}_x\mathbf{R}_y\mathbf{R}_z\mathbf{X},$$

where $\theta_x = 0.2$, $\theta_y = 0.3$, $\theta_z = -0.6$, $\Delta x = 1$, $\Delta y = 3$, $\Delta z = 1$. In a neat sketch, show the pencil in its initial and final configurations, and verify that its length has remained the same.

(e) Repeat part (d), with $\theta_x = \pi/2$, $\theta_y = 0$, $\theta_z = -\pi$, $\Delta x = \Delta y = \Delta z = 1$.

(f) Repeat part (d), with $\theta_x = -\pi/2$, $\theta_y = \theta_z = \pi/2$, $\Delta x = \Delta y = 1$, $\Delta z = 0$.

16. Prove Theorem 2 for the case where $\dim V = 0$.

The Eigenvalue Problem 4

INTRODUCTION 4.1

There exists an important class of homogeneous equations, known as eigenvalue problems. They arise not only in theoretical considerations, but also in a wide variety of applications, such as vibration theory, chemical kinetics, stability of equilibria, buckling of structures, convergence of iterative techniques, and coupled systems of ordinary differential equations. In fact, even if the problem at hand is not itself an eigenvalue problem, it may be true that the solution is best expressed in terms of the solution to a related eigenvalue problem.

THE EIGENVALUE PROBLEM 4.2

In applications, we often encounter systems of the form

$$\mathbf{A}\mathbf{x} = \lambda \mathbf{x}, \tag{1}$$

where $\mathbf{A}$ is an $n \times n$ matrix and λ is a scalar that is not known in advance.* Certainly, $\mathbf{x} = \mathbf{0}$ is a solution of (1), but our interest will be found to lie in the *nontrivial* solutions. Such solutions are called characteristic vectors, or **eigenvectors,** of $\mathbf{A}$. Schematically, the situation is as shown in Fig. 4.1. Given any vector $\mathbf{x} \neq \mathbf{0}$, suppose that $\mathbf{A}\mathbf{x}$ is as shown in Fig. 4.1a. Since this $\mathbf{A}\mathbf{x}$ is not aligned with $\mathbf{x}$, the chosen $\mathbf{x}$ does not satisfy (1) and is not an eigenvector. Selecting some other $\mathbf{x}$, suppose

* Throughout this chapter, **A** will be understood to be square.

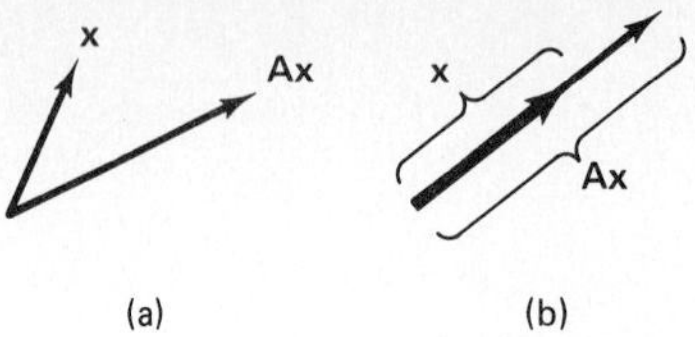

Fig. 4.1 Eigenvalue problem.

that **Ax** *is* aligned with **x**, as in Fig. 4.1b. Such an **x** is an eigenvector of **A**, and the ratio of **Ax** to **x** is called the characteristic value, or **eigenvalue, λ**, corresponding to that eigenvector. With the help of a scale, we see from Fig. 4.1b that $\lambda \approx 1.5$ in this case. (In other cases, λ may be negative, zero, or even complex, as we shall see.)

Proceeding more systematically, let us rewrite the *eigenvalue problem* (1) as*

$$(\mathbf{A} - \lambda\mathbf{I})\mathbf{x} = \mathbf{0}. \tag{2}$$

Because this system is homogeneous, we know from Theorem 6 (page 100) that it will have nontrivial solutions if and only if the determinant of the coefficient matrix is zero:

$$\boxed{\det(\mathbf{A} - \lambda\mathbf{I}) = 0.} \tag{3}$$

Expanding the determinant, it will be found that the left-hand side of (3) is an nth-degree polynomial in λ, the so-called **characteristic polynomial** corresponding to **A**. Hence (3) is an algebraic equation of nth degree in λ, the so-called **characteristic equation** corresponding to **A**. Its solutions are the eigenvalues of **A**; for each of these values of λ the nontrivial solutions of (2) are the corresponding eigenvectors.

> ***Theorem 1***
>
> The eigenvalues of **A** are the roots of the characteristic equation $\det(\mathbf{A} - \lambda\mathbf{I}) = 0$, and the corresponding eigenvectors are the nontrivial solutions of $(\mathbf{A} - \lambda\mathbf{I})\mathbf{x} = \mathbf{0}$.

EXAMPLE 1 Find the eigenvalues and eigenvectors† of the matrix

$$\mathbf{A} = \begin{pmatrix} 1 & -2 \\ 4 & -8 \end{pmatrix}. \tag{4}$$

The characteristic equation is

$$\det(\mathbf{A} - \lambda\mathbf{I}) = \begin{vmatrix} 1 - \lambda & -2 \\ 4 & -8 - \lambda \end{vmatrix} = \lambda^2 + 7\lambda = 0, \tag{5}$$

or

$$\lambda(\lambda + 7) = 0; \qquad \lambda = 0, \quad \lambda = -7. \tag{6}$$

Thus there are two eigenvalues, $\lambda = 0$ and $\lambda = -7$. To determine the eigenvectors corresponding to $\lambda = 0$, set $\lambda = 0$ in (2) and find the nontrivial solutions, say

* Observe that we do *not* write $(\mathbf{A} - \lambda)\mathbf{x} = \mathbf{0}$ because **A** is a matrix and λ is a scalar, so $\mathbf{A} - \lambda$ is not defined. Instead, we express $\mathbf{Ax} = \lambda\mathbf{x} = \lambda\mathbf{Ix}$, where **I** is $n \times n$, so that $(\mathbf{A} - \lambda\mathbf{I})\mathbf{x} = \mathbf{0}$, where $\mathbf{A} - \lambda\mathbf{I}$ *is* defined.

† Professor Ralph Palmer Agnew has suggested the term "eigens" as a colorful and concise substitute for the more ponderous, and often repeated, phrase "eigenvalues and eigenvectors."

by Gauss elimination:

$$x_1 - 2x_2 = 0$$
$$4x_1 - 8x_2 = 0$$

or, after Gauss elimination,

$$x_1 - 2x_2 = 0$$
$$0 = 0,$$

so that $x_2 =$ arbitrary $\equiv \alpha$ and $x_1 = 2\alpha$. If we use the letter **e** in place of **x** to denote the eigenvector, then

$$\mathbf{e} = \begin{pmatrix} 2\alpha \\ \alpha \end{pmatrix} = \alpha\begin{pmatrix} 2 \\ 1 \end{pmatrix}, \tag{7}$$

where the scalar α is arbitrary—except that we cannot allow it to be zero; for if $\alpha = 0$, then $\mathbf{e} = \mathbf{0}$, whereas eigenvectors are to be *nontrivial* solutions. The presence of the arbitrary scale factor α in (7) is not surprising, for if **e** is a solution of the homogeneous equation (2), so is any scalar multiple of **e**.

Turning to the eigenvalue $\lambda = -7$, set $\lambda = -7$ in (2) and again apply Gauss elimination:

$$\begin{aligned} 8x_1 - 2x_2 &= 0 \\ 4x_1 - x_2 &= 0, \end{aligned} \qquad \begin{aligned} 8x_1 - 2x_2 &= 0 \\ 0 &= 0, \end{aligned}$$

so that $x_2 =$ arbitrary $\equiv \beta$ and $x_1 = \beta/4$. Hence

$$\mathbf{e} = \beta\begin{pmatrix} \frac{1}{4} \\ 1 \end{pmatrix} \qquad (\beta \neq 0). \tag{8}$$

Summarizing, the eigenvalues and corresponding eigenvectors of **A** are

$$\lambda = 0, \quad \mathbf{e} = \begin{pmatrix} 2 \\ 1 \end{pmatrix}; \qquad \lambda = -7, \quad \mathbf{e} = \begin{pmatrix} 1 \\ 4 \end{pmatrix}, \tag{9}$$

where we have set $\alpha = 1$ and $\beta = 4$ [to remove the fraction $\frac{1}{4}$ in (8)], for definiteness. *Although we may refer to* $(2, 1)^T$ *and* $(1, 4)^T$ *as "the" eigenvectors, it should be remembered that each of them may be scaled by any (nonzero) factor.*

COMMENT Note carefully that it is the eigen*vectors* that are to be nontrivial. There is nothing improper about $\lambda = 0$, as occurs in this example. In fact, $\lambda = 0$ will be an eigenvalue if the determinant of **A** happens to be zero, as should be clear from (3). ◀

For a given eigenvalue λ of an $n \times n$ matrix **A**, the set of all solutions to $(\mathbf{A} - \lambda\mathbf{I})\mathbf{x} = \mathbf{0}$ is a subspace of $\mathbb{R}^n$,† and is known as the **eigenspace** corresponding to that eigenvalue. Each vector in that eigenspace, *except for the zero vector,* is an eigenvector corresponding to the given eigenvalue λ. For instance, in Example 1 the eigenspace corresponding to $\lambda = -7$ is the set of all multiples of $(1, 4)^{\mathrm{T}}$. This eigenspace amounts to a one-dimensional line through the origin; the vector $(1, 4)^{\mathrm{T}}$ is

* Indeed, neither the inverse matrix method of solution nor Cramer's rule can be used because the coefficient matrix $\mathbf{A} - \lambda\mathbf{I}$ is singular: $\det(\mathbf{A} - \lambda\mathbf{I}) = 0$.

† Recall Exercise 4 on page 45.

a *basis* for this eigenspace corresponding to the eigenvalue $\lambda = -7$. Similarly, $(2, 1)^T$ is a basis for the one-dimensional eigenspace corresponding to the eigenvalue $\lambda = 0$.

EXAMPLE 2 Find the eigenvalues and eigenvectors of

$$\mathbf{A} = \begin{pmatrix} 2 & 1 & 1 \\ 1 & 2 & 1 \\ 1 & 1 & 2 \end{pmatrix}. \tag{10}$$

Then

$$\det(\mathbf{A} - \lambda\mathbf{I}) = \begin{vmatrix} 2-\lambda & 1 & 1 \\ 1 & 2-\lambda & 1 \\ 1 & 1 & 2-\lambda \end{vmatrix} = -\lambda^3 + 6\lambda^2 - 9\lambda + 4 = 0. \tag{11}$$

By inspection, one root of (11) is $\lambda = 1$, so $\lambda - 1$ must be a factor of the characteristic polynomial $-\lambda^3 + 6\lambda^2 - 9\lambda + 4$. Dividing $\lambda - 1$ into $-\lambda^3 + 6\lambda^2 - 9\lambda + 4$ by long division yields $-\lambda^2 + 5\lambda - 4$, so

$$\det(\mathbf{A} - \lambda\mathbf{I}) = (\lambda - 1)(-\lambda^2 + 5\lambda - 4) = 0.$$

Finally, the quadratic formula (or inspection) may be used to factor $-\lambda^2 + 5\lambda - 4$, so that

$$\det(\mathbf{A} - \lambda\mathbf{I}) = -(\lambda - 1)(\lambda - 1)(\lambda - 4) = -(\lambda - 1)^2(\lambda - 4) = 0. \tag{12}$$

Thus the eigenvalues are $\lambda = 1$ and $\lambda = 4$; $\lambda = 1$ is said to be a *repeated eigenvalue*—specifically, it is said to be of *multiplicity* 2 since $\lambda - 1$ is a factor of degree 2 of the characteristic polynomial. More generally, an eigenvalue λ_j is said to be of *multiplicity* k if $\lambda - \lambda_j$ is a factor of degree k of the characteristic polynomial.

Let us find the eigenvectors.

$\lambda = 4$: (2) becomes

$$\begin{aligned} -2x_1 + x_2 + x_3 &= 0 \\ x_1 - 2x_2 + x_3 &= 0 \\ x_1 + x_2 - 2x_3 &= 0 \end{aligned}$$

or, after Gauss elimination,

$$\begin{aligned} -2x_1 + x_2 + x_3 &= 0 \\ x_2 - x_3 &= 0 \\ 0 &= 0. \end{aligned}$$

Thus

$$\mathbf{e} = \alpha\begin{pmatrix} 1 \\ 1 \\ 1 \end{pmatrix} \qquad (\alpha \neq 0), \tag{13}$$

so that $(1, 1, 1)^T$ is a basis for the eigenspace corresponding to $\lambda = 4$.

$\lambda = 1$: Putting $\lambda = 1$ into (2) and applying Gauss elimination,

$$\begin{aligned} x_1 + x_2 + x_3 &= 0 \\ 0 &= 0 \\ 0 &= 0, \end{aligned} \tag{14}$$

so that x_3 = arbitrary $\equiv \beta$, x_2 = arbitrary $\equiv \gamma$, and $x_1 = -\beta - \gamma$. Thus

$$\mathbf{e} = \begin{pmatrix} -\beta - \gamma \\ \gamma \\ \beta \end{pmatrix} = \beta \begin{pmatrix} -1 \\ 0 \\ 1 \end{pmatrix} + \gamma \begin{pmatrix} -1 \\ 1 \\ 0 \end{pmatrix}, \tag{15}$$

where β and γ are arbitrary provided that they are not both zero. This eigenspace is evidently the two-dimensional subspace of $\mathbb{R}^3$ consisting of the plane spanned by the LI (linearly independent) vectors $(-1, 0, 1)^T$ and $(-1, 1, 0)^T$. The latter two vectors constitute a basis for the eigenspace. ◀

EXAMPLE 3 For

$$\mathbf{A} = \begin{pmatrix} 2 & -2 & 0 \\ 3 & 1 & 0 \\ 0 & 0 & 2 \end{pmatrix} \tag{16}$$

we obtain the characteristic equation

$$(\lambda^2 - 3\lambda + 8)(2 - \lambda) = 0,$$

with roots

$$\lambda = 2, \quad \frac{3}{2} + i\frac{\sqrt{23}}{2}, \quad \frac{3}{2} - i\frac{\sqrt{23}}{2}, \tag{17}$$

where $i \equiv \sqrt{-1}$. Having elected to confine our attention to *real* systems, i.e., where *all* scalars (including the elements of our matrices) are real, consistency dictates that we disallow the two complex roots. Thus the only (real) eigenvalue of $\mathbf{A}$ is $\lambda = 2$, and the corresponding eigenvector is found from (2):

$$\begin{aligned} -2x_2 &= 0 \\ 3x_1 - x_2 &= 0 \\ 0 &= 0, \end{aligned}$$

or $x_1 = x_2 = 0$, x_3 = arbitrary = α, say. Thus

$$\lambda = 2, \qquad \mathbf{e} = \alpha \begin{pmatrix} 0 \\ 0 \\ 1 \end{pmatrix}. \tag{18}$$

However, while the exclusion of the two complex roots is logical and consistent, it represents a view that is somewhat narrow. (For example, the development of mathematics was certainly not speeded by those who refused to admit the complex roots of algebraic equations.) Rather, if complex numbers insist on entering, it behooves us to make room for them.

Within this spirit, we obtain the additional eigenvalues and eigenvectors:

$$\lambda = \frac{3}{2} + i\frac{\sqrt{23}}{2}, \quad \mathbf{e} = \beta\begin{pmatrix} 4 \\ 1 - i\sqrt{23} \\ 0 \end{pmatrix};$$
$$\lambda = \frac{3}{2} - i\frac{\sqrt{23}}{2}, \quad \mathbf{e} = \gamma\begin{pmatrix} 4 \\ 1 + i\sqrt{23} \\ 0 \end{pmatrix}. \tag{19}$$

However, if we are to admit complex scalars, we need to go back and see what modifications need to be introduced in this and preceding chapters. Such discussion will be postponed until Chapter 5. ◀

Here we have emphasized the basic mechanics of *solving* eigenvalue proglems. In subsequent sections, and in the exercises, we not only expand on the theory, but we also formulate and solve a number of diverse and interesting applications.

4.2 EXERCISES

1. Determine the eigenvalues and a basis for each eigenspace.

*(a) $\begin{pmatrix} 0 & 0 & 0 \\ 0 & 0 & 0 \\ 0 & 0 & 0 \end{pmatrix}$ (b) $\begin{pmatrix} 1 & 0 & 0 \\ 0 & 1 & 0 \\ 0 & 0 & 1 \end{pmatrix}$

(c) $\begin{pmatrix} 2 & 0 & 0 \\ 0 & 1 & 1 \\ 0 & 1 & 1 \end{pmatrix}$ (d) $\begin{pmatrix} 1 & 1 \\ 0 & 2 \end{pmatrix}$

(e) $\begin{pmatrix} 2 & -5 \\ 0 & 0 \end{pmatrix}$ (f) $\begin{pmatrix} 2 & 4 \\ -1 & -2 \end{pmatrix}$

*(g) $\begin{pmatrix} a & b & c \\ a & b & c \\ a & b & c \end{pmatrix}$ $\begin{matrix} a \neq 0 \\ b \neq 0 \\ c \neq 0 \end{matrix}$ (h) $\begin{pmatrix} 1 & 2 & 3 \\ 0 & 4 & 5 \\ 0 & 0 & 6 \end{pmatrix}$

(i) $\begin{pmatrix} 0 & 1 & 1 \\ 0 & 0 & 1 \\ 0 & 0 & 1 \end{pmatrix}$ (j) $\begin{pmatrix} 1 & 0 & 0 & 0 \\ 0 & -2 & 0 & 0 \\ 0 & 0 & 4 & 0 \\ 0 & 0 & 0 & 4 \end{pmatrix}$

(k) $\begin{pmatrix} 0 & 0 & 1 \\ 0 & 0 & 1 \\ 1 & 1 & 1 \end{pmatrix}$ (l) $\begin{pmatrix} 1 & 0 & 1 \\ 0 & 1 & 0 \\ 0 & 0 & 1 \end{pmatrix}$

*(m) $\begin{pmatrix} 1 & 0 & 1 \\ 1 & 1 & 0 \\ 0 & 0 & 1 \end{pmatrix}$ (n) $\begin{pmatrix} -2 & 1 & 2 \\ 1 & -2 & 2 \\ 2 & 2 & 1 \end{pmatrix}$

(o) $\begin{pmatrix} -1 & 0 & 0 & 0 \\ 0 & 0 & 0 & 1 \\ 0 & 0 & 0 & 1 \\ 0 & 1 & 1 & 1 \end{pmatrix}$ (p) $\begin{pmatrix} a & 1 \\ 1 & a \end{pmatrix}$

(q) $\begin{pmatrix} a & -1 \\ -1 & a \end{pmatrix}$ (r) (6)

2. If λ, $\mathbf{e}$ are an eigenvalue and corresponding eigenvector of a matrix $\mathbf{A}$, show that $\lambda = (\mathbf{e}^T\mathbf{A}\mathbf{e})/(\mathbf{e}^T\mathbf{e})$. *Hint:* Recall that the dot product of two column vectors $\mathbf{u}$ and $\mathbf{v}$ is $\mathbf{u}\cdot\mathbf{v} = \mathbf{u}^T\mathbf{v}$.

3. Show that the eigenvalues of $\mathbf{A}^T$ are the same as those of $\mathbf{A}$. Is the eigenspace corresponding to an eigenvalue λ of $\mathbf{A}$ the same as the eigenspace corresponding to the same eigenvalue λ of $\mathbf{A}^T$? Prove or disprove.

4. Show that the eigenvalues of $k\mathbf{A}$, for any scalar k, are k times those of $\mathbf{A}$. Are the corresponding eigenspaces the same?

5. Show that if $\mathbf{A}$ is triangular, its eigenvalues are simply the diagonal elements of $\mathbf{A}$.

6. Show that if λ is an eigenvalue of $\mathbf{A}$, with a corresponding eigenvector $\mathbf{e}$, then λ^n is an eigenvalue of $\mathbf{A}^n$, with the same eigenvector $\mathbf{e}$, for any integer n.

(Of course, if n is negative, $\mathbf{A}$ needs to be nonsingular if $\mathbf{A}^n$ is to exist in the first place.) *Hint:* Premultiply $\mathbf{Ae} = \lambda\mathbf{e}$ by $\mathbf{A}, \mathbf{A}^2, \ldots$.

7. Use the results stated in the preceding two exercises to determine the eigenvalues and eigenspaces of $\mathbf{A}^{10}$ for each of the following $\mathbf{A}$ matrices. Check your results by working out $\mathbf{A}^{10}$ and its eigenvalues and eigenvectors.

*(a) $\begin{pmatrix} 1 & 1 & 2 \\ 0 & -1 & 2 \\ 0 & 0 & 2 \end{pmatrix}$ (b) $\begin{pmatrix} 3 & 0 & 1 \\ 0 & 0 & 0 \\ 0 & 0 & 0 \end{pmatrix}$

(c) $\begin{pmatrix} 1 & 0 & 1 \\ 0 & 0 & 0 \\ 0 & 0 & 1 \end{pmatrix}$

8. (*Similar matrices*) (a) Suppose that $\mathbf{Ax} = \mathbf{y}$ where $\mathbf{A}$ is square. Setting $\mathbf{x} = \mathbf{Qx}'$ and $\mathbf{y} = \mathbf{Qy}'$, where $\mathbf{Q}$ is invertible, show that

$$\mathbf{A}'\mathbf{x}' = \mathbf{y}', \tag{a}$$

where

$$\mathbf{A}' = \mathbf{Q}^{-1}\mathbf{AQ}. \tag{b}$$

(b) Given any invertible matrix $\mathbf{Q}$, matrices $\mathbf{A}$ and $\mathbf{A}'$, related by (b), are said to be **similar**. Show that if $\mathbf{A}$ and $\mathbf{A}'$ are similar, they have the same characteristic polynomials, and hence the same eigenvalues.

9. (*The characteristic polynomial*) Let us write the characteristic equation $\det(\mathbf{A} - \lambda\mathbf{I}) = 0$ in the standard form

$$\det(\mathbf{A} - \lambda\mathbf{I}) = \begin{vmatrix} a_{11} - \lambda & a_{12} & \cdots & a_{1n} \\ a_{21} & a_{22} - \lambda & \cdots & a_{2n} \\ \vdots & & & \vdots \\ a_{n1} & a_{n2} & \cdots & a_{nn} - \lambda \end{vmatrix}$$
$$\equiv (-1)^n[\lambda^n - \beta_1\lambda^{n-1} + \beta_2\lambda^{n-2} - \cdots + (-1)^n\beta_n] = 0. \tag{a}$$

If we denote the n roots (not all of which need to be real) as $\lambda_1, \lambda_2, \ldots, \lambda_n$, numbering repeated roots separately, we may factor

$$\lambda^n - \beta_1\lambda^{n-1} + \cdots + (-1)^n\beta_n = (\lambda - \lambda_1)(\lambda - \lambda_2)\cdots(\lambda - \lambda_n). \tag{b}$$

Multiplying out the right-hand side of (b) and equating coefficients of like powers of λ, on both sides of the equation, yields the relations

$$\begin{aligned} \beta_1 &= \lambda_1 + \lambda_2 + \cdots + \lambda_n, \\ \beta_2 &= \lambda_1\lambda_2 + \lambda_1\lambda_3 + \cdots + \lambda_{n-1}\lambda_n, \\ \beta_3 &= \lambda_1\lambda_2\lambda_3 + \cdots + \lambda_{n-2}\lambda_{n-1}\lambda_n, \\ &\vdots \\ \beta_n &= \lambda_1\lambda_2\cdots\lambda_n. \end{aligned} \tag{c}$$

For example, if $n = 4$, then $\beta_2 = \lambda_1\lambda_2 + \lambda_1\lambda_3 + \lambda_1\lambda_4 + \lambda_2\lambda_3 + \lambda_2\lambda_4 + \lambda_3\lambda_4$ and $\beta_3 = \lambda_1\lambda_2\lambda_3 + \lambda_1\lambda_2\lambda_4 + \lambda_1\lambda_3\lambda_4 + \lambda_2\lambda_3\lambda_4$.

Alternatively, one may expand the determinant in (a) directly, and identify the coefficients of the various powers of λ in terms of certain subdeterminants of $\mathbf{A}$, and hence determine the β_j's in terms of these subdeterminants. The result, we state without proof, is that β_j (for $j = 1, \ldots, n$) *is the sum of all the jth-order principal minors of* $\mathbf{A}$. (By a "principal minor" we mean the determinant of a submatrix of $\mathbf{A}$, whose main diagonal lies along that of $\mathbf{A}$.) Thus

$$\begin{aligned} \beta_1 &= a_{11} + a_{22} + \cdots + a_{nn} \equiv \operatorname{tr}\mathbf{A} \\ &\vdots \\ \beta_n &= \det\mathbf{A}, \end{aligned} \tag{d}$$

where the sum $a_{11} + a_{22} + \cdots + a_{nn}$ is called the **trace** of $\mathbf{A}$ and is denoted here as $\operatorname{tr}\mathbf{A}$.

(a) Verify equations (d) for $n = 2$, by expanding $\det(\mathbf{A} - \lambda\mathbf{I})$.

(b) Verify equations (d) for $n = 3$, by expanding $\det(\mathbf{A} - \lambda\mathbf{I})$; i.e., verify that

$$\beta_1 = a_{11} + a_{22} + a_{33},$$

$$\beta_2 = \begin{vmatrix} a_{11} & a_{12} \\ a_{21} & a_{22} \end{vmatrix} + \begin{vmatrix} a_{11} & a_{13} \\ a_{31} & a_{33} \end{vmatrix} + \begin{vmatrix} a_{22} & a_{23} \\ a_{32} & a_{33} \end{vmatrix},$$

$$\beta_3 = \begin{vmatrix} a_{11} & a_{12} & a_{13} \\ a_{21} & a_{22} & a_{23} \\ a_{31} & a_{32} & a_{33} \end{vmatrix}.$$

(c) Finally, comparing equations (c) with equations (d), show that

$$\begin{aligned} \lambda_1 + \lambda_2 + \cdots + \lambda_n &= \operatorname{tr}\mathbf{A} \\ &\vdots \\ \lambda_1\lambda_2\cdots\lambda_n &= \det\mathbf{A}, \end{aligned} \tag{e}$$

and hence that $\mathbf{A}$ is singular if and only if at least one of its eigenvalues is zero.

***10.** If $\mathbf{A}$ and $\mathbf{B}$, both $n \times n$, have the same eigenvalues, need it be true that $\mathbf{A} = \mathbf{B}$? Prove or disprove.

11. Show that if $\mathbf{e}_1, \ldots, \mathbf{e}_n$ are LI eigenvectors of matrices $\mathbf{A}$ and $\mathbf{B}$, both $n \times n$, then $\mathbf{A}$ and $\mathbf{B}$ must be equal.

12. Can an $n \times n$ matrix have more than n LI eigenvectors? Explain.

13. (*Markov matrix*) An $n \times n$ matrix $\mathbf{A} = \{a_{ij}\}$ is called a **Markov** (or **stochastic**) **matrix** if

$$a_{ij} \geq 0 \qquad \text{for each } i, j,$$

and if either

$$\sum_{j=1}^{n} a_{ij} = 1 \qquad \text{for each } i,$$

or if

$$\sum_{i=1}^{n} a_{ij} = 1 \qquad \text{for each } j.$$

It can be shown that $\lambda = 1$ is an eigenvalue of every Markov matrix. You may use that fact below.

(a) Find the eigenvalues of

$$\mathbf{A} = \begin{pmatrix} 0 & \frac{1}{2} & \frac{1}{2} \\ \frac{1}{2} & \frac{1}{2} & 0 \\ 0 & 1 & 0 \end{pmatrix}.$$

(b) Find one eigenvalue of each of the matrices

$$\mathbf{A} = \begin{pmatrix} 8 & 10 & 12 \\ 9 & 10 & 11 \\ 10 & 10 & 10 \end{pmatrix} \quad \text{and} \quad \mathbf{B} = \begin{pmatrix} 3 & 1 & 2 \\ 2 & 2 & 1 \\ 0 & 2 & 2 \end{pmatrix}$$

Hint: Recall Exercise 4.

(c) Determine the eigenvalues and a basis for each eigenspace for the 20×20 matrix $\mathbf{A}$ having unity for each of its 400 elements.

14. (*Example of a Markov process*) Suppose that at a given initial time there are x_0 people in Delaware and y_0 people in Maryland, where x_0 and y_0 are not both zero. Each year, 30% of the people in Delaware move to Maryland, and 10% of the people in Maryland move to Delaware. For simplicity, we assume that no other population exchanges occur and that there are no births or deaths. Thus we have a closed system, with the total number of people remaining constant.

(a) If x_n, y_n denote the populations in Delaware and Maryland, respectively, after n years, show that

$$\mathbf{p}_{n+1} = \mathbf{A}\mathbf{p}_n, \tag{a}$$

where

$$\mathbf{p}_n = \begin{pmatrix} x_n \\ y_n \end{pmatrix} \quad \text{and} \quad \mathbf{A} = \begin{pmatrix} 0.7 & 0.1 \\ 0.3 & 0.9 \end{pmatrix},$$

and that

$$\mathbf{p}_n = \mathbf{A}^n \mathbf{p}_0. \tag{b}$$

(b) Show that $\mathbf{A}$ is a Markov matrix (see Exercise 13), so that the population distribution is governed by a so-called "Markov process."

*(c) Of interest is the possible existence of an *equilibrium state,* i.e., a population distribution that remains constant with time. By definition, then, $\mathbf{p}_{n+1} = \mathbf{p}_n$, so that equation (a) becomes

$$\mathbf{A}\mathbf{p}_n = \mathbf{p}_n. \tag{c}$$

Since equation (c) is an eigenvalue problem with $\lambda = 1$ it follows that there exists an equilibrium state if and only if unity happens to be an eigenvalue of $\mathbf{A}$. But since $\mathbf{A}$ is a Markov matrix we know in advance that that will be the case. Thus there exists an equilibrium state, and that state is given by the eigenvector corresponding to the eigenvalue $\lambda = 1$. Find that equilibrium state, say, $\mathbf{p}_{eq}$.

(d) Having found the equilibrium state, we are interested in whether that state is stable or unstable. Show that it is, in fact, stable. Specifically, show that for every possible $\mathbf{p}_0$ [i.e., for every $\mathbf{p}_0 = (x_0, y_0)^T$, where $x_0 \geq 0$ and $y_0 \geq 0$], $\mathbf{p}_n \rightarrow \mathbf{p}_{eq}$ as $n \rightarrow \infty$. *Hint:* Expand $\mathbf{p}_0$ as $\mathbf{p}_0 = \alpha \mathbf{e}_1 + \beta \mathbf{e}_2$, where $\mathbf{e}_1$ and $\mathbf{e}_2$ are the already computed eigenvectors of $\mathbf{A}$, then multiply this equation repeatedly by $\mathbf{A}$.

(e) This time, suppose that we have three neighboring states, say X, Y, Z, with initial populations $x_0 =$ 10,000, $y_0 =$ 40,000, $z_0 =$ 20,000, respectively. In each subsequent year 20% of the population of X moves to Y and 10% of the population of Y moves to X; 20% of the population of Y moves to Z and 10% of the population of Z moves to Y; 10% of the population of X moves to Z and no one from Z moves to X. Assuming that there are no births and no deaths, we have a closed system, with the total population remaining constant. Denoting the population vector after n years as $\mathbf{p}_n = (x_n, y_n, z_n)^T$, show that $\mathbf{p}_{n+1} = \mathbf{A}\mathbf{p}_n$ and determine the $\mathbf{A}$ matrix. Determine the equilibrium population vector, say, $\mathbf{p}_{eq}$, and show that $\mathbf{p}_n$ inevitably tends to $\mathbf{p}_{eq}$ as $n \rightarrow \infty$.

15. (*Cayley–Hamilton theorem*) The **Cayley–Hamilton theorem** states that if the characteristic equation of any square matrix $\mathbf{A}$ is $\lambda^n + \alpha_1 \lambda^{n-1} + \cdots +$

$\alpha_{n-1}\lambda + \alpha_n = 0$, then $\mathbf{A}^n + \alpha_1 \mathbf{A}^{n-1} + \cdots + \alpha_{n-1}\mathbf{A} + \alpha_n \mathbf{I} = \mathbf{0}$; i.e., "**A** satisfies its characteristic equation."

(a) Prove this theorem for the general 2 × 2 case, $\mathbf{A} = \begin{pmatrix} a & b \\ c & d \end{pmatrix}$.

(b) If $\mathbf{A} = \begin{pmatrix} 2 & 1 \\ 1 & 2 \end{pmatrix}$, show that $\mathbf{A}^2 - 4\mathbf{A} + 3\mathbf{I} = \mathbf{0}$, so that

$$\mathbf{A}^{-1} = \tfrac{4}{3}\mathbf{I} - \tfrac{1}{3}\mathbf{A} = \begin{pmatrix} \frac{2}{3} & -\frac{1}{3} \\ -\frac{1}{3} & \frac{2}{3} \end{pmatrix}.$$

16. (*Generalized eigenvalue problem*) If $\mathbf{B} \neq \mathbf{I}$, then $\mathbf{Ax} = \lambda \mathbf{Bx}$ is called a **generalized eigenvalue problem.** It should be easy to see that in this case the characteristic equation is $\det(\mathbf{A} - \lambda \mathbf{B}) = 0$, and that the eigenvectors then follow as the nontrivial solutions of $(\mathbf{A} - \lambda\mathbf{B})\mathbf{x} = \mathbf{0}$. Find the eigenvalues and eigenspaces in each case.

*(a) $\begin{pmatrix} 5 & 1 \\ 1 & 5 \end{pmatrix}\begin{pmatrix} x_1 \\ x_2 \end{pmatrix} = \lambda \begin{pmatrix} 8 & -4 \\ -4 & 8 \end{pmatrix}\begin{pmatrix} x_1 \\ x_2 \end{pmatrix}$

(b) $\begin{pmatrix} x_1 \\ x_2 \end{pmatrix} = \lambda \begin{pmatrix} 1 & 0 \\ 1 & 1 \end{pmatrix}\begin{pmatrix} x_1 \\ x_2 \end{pmatrix}$

(c) $\begin{pmatrix} 2 & -1 \\ -1 & 2 \end{pmatrix}\begin{pmatrix} x_1 \\ x_2 \end{pmatrix} = \lambda \begin{pmatrix} 1 & 0 \\ 0 & 2 \end{pmatrix}\begin{pmatrix} x_1 \\ x_2 \end{pmatrix}$

(d) $\begin{pmatrix} x_1 \\ x_2 \\ x_3 \end{pmatrix} = \lambda \begin{pmatrix} 2 & 1 & 1 \\ 1 & 2 & 1 \\ 1 & 1 & 2 \end{pmatrix}\begin{pmatrix} x_1 \\ x_2 \\ x_3 \end{pmatrix}$

17. We have seen that a given eigenvalue can have more than one LI eigenvector. In Example 2, for instance, the LI eigenvectors $(-1, 0, 1)^{\mathrm{T}}$ and $(-1, 1, 0)^{\mathrm{T}}$ both correspond to the eigenvalue $\lambda = 1$. Is the reverse possible? That is, can an eigenvector **e** correspond to two or more different eigenvalues? Prove or disprove.

18. In seeking the eigenvalues and eigenvectors of a given matrix **A**, is it permissible first to simplify **A** by means of some elementary row operations? (That is, are the eigenvalues and eigenvectors of **A** invariant with respect to elementary row operations?) Explain.

SYMMETRIC MATRICES 4.3

It has been mentioned* that matrices arising in applications are often, although not always, symmetric; i.e.,†

$$\mathbf{A}^{\mathrm{T}} = \mathbf{A}. \tag{1}$$

It turns out, as we shall see, that such symmetry leads to a number of special and useful properties concerning the eigenvalues and eigenvectors of **A**.

> ***Theorem 1** Real Characteristic Roots*
> If **A** is symmetric, then all roots of its characteristic equation are real.

> ***Theorem 2** Dimension of Eigenspace*
> If an eigenvalue λ of a symmetric matrix **A** is of multiplicity k, then the eigenspace corresponding to λ is of dimension k.

Proofs of Theorems 1 and 2 are left for the exercises.

* See, for example, Exercise 16(g) on page 118.

† Recall that we have chosen to limit our consideration to *real* systems, i.e., where all scalars, including matrix elements, are real numbers. Thus when we say that **A** is symmetric, we mean real and symmetric, or *real-symmetric,* for short.

> ***Theorem 3*** *Orthogonality of Eigenvectors*
>
> If $\mathbf{A}$ is a symmetric, then eigenvectors corresponding to distinct eigenvalues are orthogonal.

Proof Let $\mathbf{e}_j$ and $\mathbf{e}_k$ be eigenvectors corresponding to distinct eigenvalues λ_j and λ_k, respectively. Thus

$$\mathbf{A}\mathbf{e}_j = \lambda_j \mathbf{e}_j \tag{2a}$$

and

$$\mathbf{A}\mathbf{e}_k = \lambda_k \mathbf{e}_k. \tag{2b}$$

Next, recall from (10) on page 80 that the dot product of two n-dimensional column vectors $\mathbf{x}$, $\mathbf{y}$ is $\mathbf{x} \cdot \mathbf{y} = \mathbf{x}^{\mathrm{T}}\mathbf{y}$. Then, if we dot both sides of (2a) with $\mathbf{e}_k$, and both sides of (2b) with $\mathbf{e}_j$, we have

$$\begin{array}{rl|rl} \mathbf{e}_k \cdot (\mathbf{A}\mathbf{e}_j) = & \mathbf{e}_k \cdot (\lambda_j \mathbf{e}_j) & (\mathbf{A}\mathbf{e}_k) \cdot \mathbf{e}_j = & (\lambda_k \mathbf{e}_k) \cdot \mathbf{e}_j \\ \mathbf{e}_k^{\mathrm{T}} \mathbf{A}\mathbf{e}_j = & \lambda_j \mathbf{e}_k^{\mathrm{T}} \mathbf{e}_j, & (\mathbf{A}\mathbf{e}_k)^{\mathrm{T}} \mathbf{e}_j = & \lambda_k \mathbf{e}_k^{\mathrm{T}} \mathbf{e}_j \\ & & \mathbf{e}_k^{\mathrm{T}} \mathbf{A}^{\mathrm{T}} \mathbf{e}_j = & \lambda_k \mathbf{e}_k^{\mathrm{T}} \mathbf{e}_j. \end{array} \tag{3}$$

But $\mathbf{A}^{\mathrm{T}} = \mathbf{A}$ by assumption, so if we subtract the bottom equations on the left and right, we obtain

$$0 = (\lambda_j - \lambda_k)\mathbf{e}_k^{\mathrm{T}} \mathbf{e}_j. \tag{4}$$

Finally, $\lambda_j - \lambda_k \neq 0$ since λ_j and λ_k are distinct, by assumption, so it follows from (4) that

$$\mathbf{e}_k^{\mathrm{T}} \mathbf{e}_j = 0, \qquad \text{i.e., } \mathbf{e}_k \cdot \mathbf{e}_j = 0, \tag{5}$$

as claimed. ■

Let us look back at the results found in Examples 1 and 2 of Section 4.2 in the light of these three theorems.

EXAMPLE 1 Recall, from Example 1 on page 138, that

$$\mathbf{A} = \begin{pmatrix} 1 & -2 \\ 4 & -8 \end{pmatrix}; \qquad \lambda_1 = 0, \quad \mathbf{e}_1 = \begin{pmatrix} 2 \\ 1 \end{pmatrix}; \quad \text{and} \quad \lambda_2 = -7, \quad \mathbf{e}_2 = \begin{pmatrix} 1 \\ 4 \end{pmatrix}, \tag{6}$$

where we have numbered the eigenvalues and eigenvectors, with subscripts, for convenient reference. Here $\mathbf{A}$ is *not* symmetric, so Theorems 1, 2, and 3 simply do not apply. Theorem 1, for example, does *not* say that the roots are real *if and only if* $\mathbf{A}$ is symmetric. In fact, both roots turn out, in this case, to be real even though $\mathbf{A}$ is not symmetric. ◀

EXAMPLE 2 Recall, from Example 2 on page 140, that

$$\mathbf{A} = \begin{pmatrix} 2 & 1 & 1 \\ 1 & 2 & 1 \\ 1 & 1 & 2 \end{pmatrix}; \qquad \lambda_1 = 4, \qquad \mathbf{e}_1 = \begin{pmatrix} 1 \\ 1 \\ 1 \end{pmatrix}; \tag{7}$$

$$\lambda_2 = \lambda_3 = 1, \quad \mathbf{e} = \beta \begin{pmatrix} -1 \\ 0 \\ 1 \end{pmatrix} + \gamma \begin{pmatrix} -1 \\ 1 \\ 0 \end{pmatrix},$$

where β and γ are arbitrary, provided that they are not both zero. Here $\mathbf{A}$ is symmetric, so the theorems do apply: In accordance with Theorem 1 the roots are all real; in accordance with Theorem 3 $\mathbf{e}_1 \cdot \mathbf{e} = 0$ (for all choices of β, γ); and in accordance with Theorem 2, the eigenspace corresponding to $\lambda = 1$ [i.e., the span of $(-1, 0, 1)^{\mathrm{T}}$ and $(-1, 1, 0)^{\mathrm{T}}$] is two-dimensional since $(-1, 0, 1)^{\mathrm{T}}$ and $(-1, 1, 0)^{\mathrm{T}}$ are LI, and the eigenspace corresponding to $\lambda = 4$ [i.e., the span of $(1, 1, 1)^{\mathrm{T}}$] is one-dimensional.

Since the eigenspace corresponding to $\lambda = 1$ is two-dimensional we must be able to find two orthogonal vectors within it. [Although $(-1, 0, 1)^{\mathrm{T}}$ and $(-1, 1, 0)^{\mathrm{T}}$ are LI, they are not orthogonal.] We shall label these orthogonal vectors as $\mathbf{e}_2$ and $\mathbf{e}_3$, respectively, and think of $\mathbf{e}_2$ as associated with λ_2, and $\mathbf{e}_3$ with λ_3. For example, letting $\beta = 1$, $\gamma = 0$, choose

$$\mathbf{e}_2 \equiv \begin{pmatrix} -1 \\ 0 \\ 1 \end{pmatrix}, \tag{8}$$

and seek $\mathbf{e}_3$ as a linear combination

$$\mathbf{e}_3 = \beta \begin{pmatrix} -1 \\ 0 \\ 1 \end{pmatrix} + \gamma \begin{pmatrix} -1 \\ 1 \\ 0 \end{pmatrix} = \begin{pmatrix} -\beta - \gamma \\ \gamma \\ \beta \end{pmatrix} \tag{9}$$

such that $\mathbf{e}_3$ is orthogonal to $\mathbf{e}_2$. Then

$$\mathbf{e}_3 \cdot \mathbf{e}_2 = (-1)(-\beta - \gamma) + (0)(\gamma) + (1)(\beta) = 2\beta + \gamma = 0 \tag{10}$$

gives $\gamma = -2\beta$. Choosing $\beta = 1$, say, then $\gamma = -2$, and (9) gives*

$$\mathbf{e}_3 = \begin{pmatrix} 1 \\ -2 \\ 1 \end{pmatrix}. \tag{11}$$

The orthogonal vectors (8) and (11) are indeed both of the form

$$\beta \begin{pmatrix} -1 \\ 0 \\ 1 \end{pmatrix} + \gamma \begin{pmatrix} -1 \\ 1 \\ 0 \end{pmatrix}, \tag{12}$$

* The procedure used here to obtain the orthogonal set $\mathbf{e}_2$, $\mathbf{e}_3$ from the LI set $(-1, 0, 1)^{\mathrm{T}}$, $(-1, 1, 0)^{\mathrm{T}}$ is essentially the Gram–Schmidt orthogonalization procedure given in Exercise 11 on page 56.

and hence they are in the eigenspace corresponding to $\lambda = 1$; in one case $\beta = 1$, $\gamma = 0$, and in the other case $\beta = 1$, $\gamma = -2$. Of course, (8) and (11) are not the *only* pair of orthogonal eigenvectors within the eigenspace corresponding to $\lambda = 1$; for example, another such pair is

$$\mathbf{e}_2 = (-2, 1, 1)^{\mathrm{T}} \qquad (\beta = 1, \gamma = 1),$$

$$\mathbf{e}_3 = (0, -1, 1)^{\mathrm{T}} \qquad (\beta = 1, \gamma = -1).$$

In any case, the result is that the eigenvectors $\mathbf{e}_1$, $\mathbf{e}_2$, $\mathbf{e}_3$ are mutually orthogonal and hence provide an *orthogonal basis* for the space. ◀

Generalization of the ideas contained in the preceding example yield the following important theorem.

***Theorem 4** Orthogonal Basis*

If an $n \times n$ matrix $\mathbf{A}$ is symmetric, then its eigenvectors provide an orthogonal basis for n-space.

Proof Let us outline the proof. First, $\mathbf{A}$ has precisely n (real) eigenvalues, since its characteristic equation is of nth degree and, according to Theorem 1, all of the n characteristic roots (counting multiplicities, if present) are necessarily real. If all of the n eigenvalues are distinct, the corresponding n eigenvectors are orthogonal (Theorem 3), and n orthogonal vectors in an n-dimensional space constitute an orthogonal basis for that space. What if the n eigenvalues are *not* distinct? Suppose that all are distinct except for one, say λ, which is of multiplicity k. Then the $n - k$ eigenvectors corresponding to the *other* eigenvalues are orthogonal to each other, and also to all vectors in the eigenspace corresponding to λ—further, that eigenspace is k-dimensional (Theorem 2) and hence contains k orthogonal vectors. Altogether, then, we have $(n - k) + k = n$ orthogonal eigenvectors, and hence an orthogonal basis. A similar argument holds if there is more than one repeated eigenvalue. ■

We close this section with an application to vibration theory.

EXAMPLE 3 *Vibration of a Two-Mass System.** Consider the mass–spring system shown in Fig. 4.2. The displacements of the two masses, m_1 and m_2, measured positive to the right, are x_1 and x_2; when $x_1 = x_2 = 0$, the springs, of stiffness k_1, k_{12}, and k_2, are neither stretched nor compressed. Our object is to determine the motion $x_1(t)$ and $x_2(t)$ that results from the application of some combination of initial disturbance and applied force. By an "initial disturbance" we shall mean a set of prescribed initial conditions $x_1(0)$, $\dot{x}_1(0)$, $x_2(0)$, $\dot{x}_2(0)$, where the dots denote differentiation with respect to the time t, and by "forcing functions" we shall mean the forces $F_1(t)$, $F_2(t)$ applied to m_1, m_2, as shown in Fig. 4.2.

The governing physical principle is *Newton's second law* "$f = ma$," applied

*The reader may wish to review Example 4 in Section A.5, and Example 2 in Section A.7 of Appendix A, before proceeding.

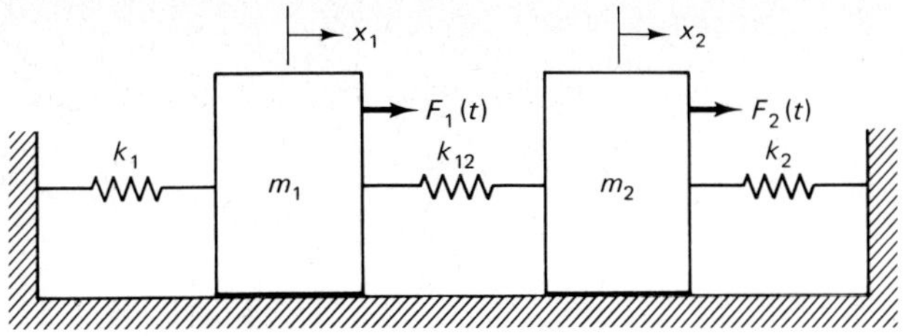

Fig. 4.2 Two-mass system.

separately to each of the two masses.* Neglecting both friction and air resistance, the only forces acting on m_1 and m_2 are F_1, F_2, and the spring forces, as shown in Fig. 4.3. Thus we have[†]

$$m_1\ddot{x}_1 = -k_1x_1 - k_{12}(x_1 - x_2) + F_1(t) \tag{13a}$$

$$m_2\ddot{x}_2 = -k_2x_2 + k_{12}(x_1 - x_2) + F_2(t), \tag{13b}$$

or, if we rearrange the equations and append the initial conditions,

$$m_1\ddot{x}_1 + (k_1 + k_{12})x_1 - k_{12}x_2 = F_1(t); \qquad x_1(0),\ \dot{x}_1(0) \text{ given} \tag{14a}$$

$$m_2\ddot{x}_2 - k_{12}x_1 + (k_{12} + k_2)x_2 = F_2(t); \qquad x_2(0),\ \dot{x}_2(0) \text{ given.} \tag{14b}$$

Observe that the equations (14a) and (14b) are *coupled* through the $k_{12}x_2$ term in (14a) and the $k_{12}x_1$ term in (14b). The presence of this mathematical coupling is due, of course, to the *physical* coupling of m_1 and m_2 by the middle spring.

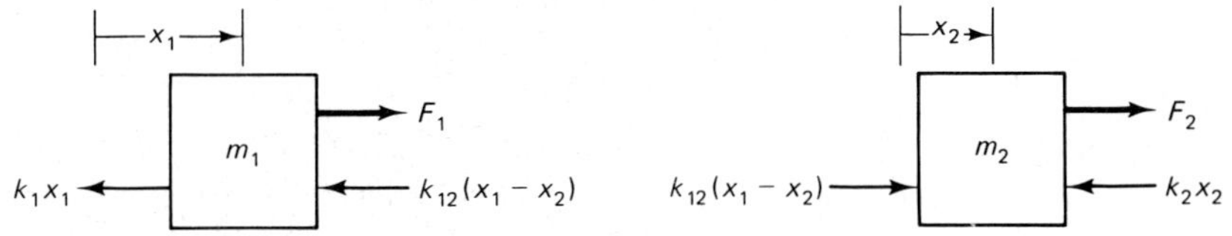

Fig. 4.3 Forces on m_1 and m_2.

Now, we recall from the elementary theory of ordinary differential equations that to solve (14) for x_1 and x_2, the idea is to find complementary and particular solutions, separately, combine them to form the general solution, and then to apply the initial conditions to evaluate the constants of integration. Rather than develop that line of approach, it will prove more instructive to split (14) into two separate problems, the so-called *free* and *forced* vibrations. That is, we observe that the input disturbance in the problem formulated above consists of two parts, the initial conditions $x_1(0)$, $\dot{x}_1(0)$, $x_2(0)$, $\dot{x}_2(0)$, and the forcing functions $F_1(t)$, $F_2(t)$, and we propose to consider their effects separately: the *free*, or *natural*, vibration is the motion caused by the initial conditions $x_1(0)$, $\dot{x}_1(0)$, $x_2(0)$, $\dot{x}_2(0)$ (in the absence of the forces F_1 and F_2), and the *forced* vibration is the motion caused by $F_1(t)$, $F_2(t)$.

* More accurately, Newton's second law states that $f = d/dt$ (momentum), but since each mass is constant, in this problem, we have

$$\frac{d}{dt}(\text{momentum}) = m\frac{d}{dt}(\text{velocity}) = ma.$$

† If the origin of the "spring terms" on the right-hand side of (13) is not clear, you may wish to read the introduction to Exercise 16 on page 117.

Free Vibration Thus, setting $F_1(t) = F_2(t) = 0$, we consider the problem

$$m_1\ddot{x}_1 + (k_1 + k_{12})x_1 - k_{12}x_2 = 0; \qquad x_1(0),\ \dot{x}_1(0) \text{ given} \tag{15a}$$

$$m_2\ddot{x}_2 - k_{12}x_1 + (k_{12} + k_2)x_2 = 0; \qquad x_2(0),\ \dot{x}_2(0) \text{ given.} \tag{15b}$$

Anticipating a vibratory motion, let us seek a solution to (15) of the form

$$x_1(t) = \xi_1 \sin(\omega t + \phi) \tag{16a}$$

$$x_2(t) = \xi_2 \sin(\omega t + \phi), \tag{16b}$$

where the *amplitudes* ξ_1, ξ_2, the *frequency* ω, and the *phase angle* ϕ are as-yet-unknown constants. Putting (16) into (15), we obtain the algebraic equations

$$\begin{aligned} -m_1\omega^2\xi_1 + (k_1 + k_{12})\xi_1 - k_{12}\xi_2 &= 0 \\ -m_2\omega^2\xi_2 - k_{12}\xi_1 + (k_{12} + k_2)\xi_2 &= 0, \end{aligned} \tag{17}$$

or, in matrix form,

$$\begin{pmatrix} \dfrac{k_1 + k_{12}}{m_1} & -\dfrac{k_{12}}{m_1} \\ -\dfrac{k_{12}}{m_2} & \dfrac{k_{12} + k_2}{m_2} \end{pmatrix} \begin{pmatrix} \xi_1 \\ \xi_2 \end{pmatrix} = \omega^2 \begin{pmatrix} \xi_1 \\ \xi_2 \end{pmatrix}. \tag{18}$$

Surely, $\xi_1 = \xi_2 = 0$ is a solution of (18), the trivial solution. However, this solution is of no interest here, not because it is beneath our dignity by virtue of being so simple, but because it gives $x_1(t) = x_2(t) = 0$, which cannot possibly satisfy nonzero initial conditions. In other words, we are interested in a vibratory motion, not in a state of rest. Furthermore, ω has not yet been specified, and is at our disposal. Thus (18) is really an *eigenvalue problem,* *

$$\mathbf{A}\boldsymbol{\xi} = \lambda\boldsymbol{\xi}, \tag{19a}$$

where

$$\mathbf{A} = \begin{pmatrix} \dfrac{k_1 + k_{12}}{m_1} & -\dfrac{k_{12}}{m_1} \\ -\dfrac{k_{12}}{m_2} & \dfrac{k_{12} + k_2}{m_2} \end{pmatrix}, \qquad \boldsymbol{\xi} = \begin{pmatrix} \xi_1 \\ \xi_2 \end{pmatrix}, \quad \text{and} \quad \lambda = \omega^2; \tag{19b}$$

the appropriate values of ω (or λ) are those that permit *non*trivial solutions of (19a).

For definiteness, and algebraic simplicity, let us set

$$m_1 = m_2 = k_1 = k_{12} = k_2 = 1. \tag{20}$$

* Observe that we could, alternatively, have expressed (17) as $\mathbf{A}\boldsymbol{\xi} = \lambda\mathbf{B}\boldsymbol{\xi}$, where $\lambda = \omega^2$, and where

$$\mathbf{A} = \begin{pmatrix} k_1 + k_{12} & -k_{12} \\ -k_{12} & k_{12} + k_2 \end{pmatrix}, \qquad \mathbf{B} = \begin{pmatrix} m_1 & 0 \\ 0 & m_2 \end{pmatrix}$$

are both symmetric. In this form we have a *generalized* eigenvalue problem, as introduced in the exercises at the end of Section 4.2.

Then

$$\mathbf{A} = \begin{pmatrix} 2 & -1 \\ -1 & 2 \end{pmatrix}, \tag{21}$$

the characteristic equation of which is

$$\det(\mathbf{A} - \lambda\mathbf{I}) = \lambda^2 - 4\lambda + 3 = 0. \tag{22}$$

Thus the eigenvalues are $\lambda = 1$ and 3. The corresponding eigenvectors are easily found, and the results are as follows:

$$\lambda_1 = 1, \quad \mathbf{e}_1 = \begin{pmatrix} 1 \\ 1 \end{pmatrix}; \qquad \lambda_2 = 3, \quad \mathbf{e}_2 = \begin{pmatrix} 1 \\ -1 \end{pmatrix}. \tag{23}$$

What does (23) do for us? Well, each "eigenpair" (eigenvalue and corresponding eigenvector) gives us ω, ξ_1, and ξ_2 in (16), with ϕ remaining arbitrary. For example, the first eigenpair gives $\omega = \sqrt{\lambda_1} = 1$* and $\xi_1 = \xi_2 = 1$, so that (in column vector form)

$$\mathbf{x} = \begin{pmatrix} x_1(t) \\ x_2(t) \end{pmatrix} = \begin{pmatrix} 1 \sin(t + \phi_1) \\ 1 \sin(t + \phi_1) \end{pmatrix}, \tag{24}$$

where ϕ_1 is arbitrary. Similarly, the second eigenpair yields the solution

$$\mathbf{x} = \begin{pmatrix} x_1(t) \\ x_2(t) \end{pmatrix} = \begin{pmatrix} 1 \sin(\sqrt{3}\, t + \phi_2) \\ -1 \sin(\sqrt{3}\, t + \phi_2) \end{pmatrix}, \tag{25}$$

where ϕ_2 is arbitrary and not necessarily equal to ϕ_1. Since the differential equations (15) are linear, their general solution is an arbitrary linear combination of the two solutions (24) and (25), namely

$$\mathbf{x} = A_1 \begin{pmatrix} \sin(t + \phi_1) \\ \sin(t + \phi_1) \end{pmatrix} + A_2 \begin{pmatrix} \sin(\sqrt{3}\, t + \phi_2) \\ -\sin(\sqrt{3}\, t + \phi_2) \end{pmatrix}, \tag{26a}$$

$$\mathbf{x} = A_1 \begin{pmatrix} \sin(t + \phi_1) \\ \sin(t + \phi_1) \end{pmatrix} + A_2 \begin{pmatrix} \sin(\sqrt{3}\, t + \phi_2) \\ \sin(\sqrt{3}\, t + \phi_2 + \pi) \end{pmatrix}. \tag{26b}$$

In the terminology of vibration theory, we call the two vectors on the right-hand side of (26) the two **natural modes** of vibration, "natural" in that they represent the free, or natural, vibration. We also call them **orthogonal modes** since the components $x_1(t)$, $x_2(t)$ in each mode are in the same ratio as the components of the corresponding orthogonal eigenvectors, $\mathbf{e}_1$ and $\mathbf{e}_2$, namely $1 : 1$ for the first mode and $1 : -1$ for the second. The orthogonality of the two natural modes is not a coincidence; it is a consequence of the symmetry of the **A** matrix, given by (21) (see Exercise 14). Some comments:

COMMENT 1 Note the central role of the eigenvalue problem. Each eigenpair defines a natural mode; the eigenvalue gives us the vibrational frequency, and the eigenvector gives us the mode "shape." More precisely, the frequencies are the square roots of the eigenvalues and are called the **eigenfrequencies, characteristic frequencies,** or **natural frequencies.**

* The negative root, $\omega = -1$, would be found to yield no additional information.

COMMENT 2 Referring to the low-frequency ($\omega = 1$ radian per unit time) mode as the "low mode," and the high-frequency ($\omega = \sqrt{3}$) mode as the "high mode," note that in the low mode $x_1(t) = x_2(t)$, so that the two masses move in unison, while in the high mode $x_1(t) = -x_2(t)$, so that the two masses move in exact opposition. Thus in the low mode the middle spring is inactive—it is neither stretched nor compressed—whereas in the high mode it is active. Hence there is more stiffness in the system in the high mode (since all three springs are active) than in the low mode (wherein only two are active), so it is not surprising that the frequency of the high mode exceeds that of the low mode.

COMMENT 3 The constants A_1, A_2, ϕ_1, ϕ_2 in (26) are, essentially, the usual "integration constants"; they are determined from the initial conditions. To illustrate, suppose that

$$x_1(0) = x_2(0) = a \quad \text{and} \quad \dot{x}_1(0) = \dot{x}_2(0) = 0, \tag{27}$$

where a is prescribed. Imposing these conditions upon (26a),

$$\left.\begin{aligned} x_1(0) &= a = A_1 \sin \phi_1 + A_2 \sin \phi_2 \\ x_2(0) &= a = A_1 \sin \phi_1 - A_2 \sin \phi_2 \end{aligned}\right\} \tag{28a}$$

$$\left.\begin{aligned} \dot{x}_1(0) &= 0 = A_1 \cos \phi_1 + \sqrt{3}\, A_2 \cos \phi_2 \\ \dot{x}_2(0) &= 0 = A_1 \cos \phi_1 - \sqrt{3}\, A_2 \cos \phi_2 \end{aligned}\right\}. \tag{28b}$$

Adding and subtracting the equations (28a), and also (28b), we obtain the simpler equations

$$\begin{aligned} A_1 \sin \phi_1 &= a \\ A_2 \sin \phi_2 &= 0 \\ A_1 \cos \phi_1 &= 0 \\ A_2 \cos \phi_2 &= 0, \end{aligned} \tag{29}$$

so that $A_1 = a$, $\phi_1 = \pi/2$, $A_2 = 0$, and ϕ_2 is immaterial since $A_2 = 0$.* Putting these values into (26a) yields

$$\mathbf{x} = a\begin{pmatrix} \sin\left(t + \dfrac{\pi}{2}\right) \\ \sin\left(t + \dfrac{\pi}{2}\right) \end{pmatrix} + 0\begin{pmatrix} \sin(\sqrt{3}\, t + \phi_2) \\ -\sin(\sqrt{3}\, t + \phi_2) \end{pmatrix}$$

or

$$\mathbf{x} = a\begin{pmatrix} \cos t \\ \cos t \end{pmatrix} + 0\begin{pmatrix} \sin(\sqrt{3}\, t + \phi_2) \\ -\sin(\sqrt{3}\, t + \phi_2) \end{pmatrix}. \tag{30}$$

In this case the motion is entirely in the low mode, as should not be surprising, in view of (27), since $x_1(0) = x_2(0)$ and $\dot{x}_1(0) = \dot{x}_2(0)$, and the low mode has already been noted to be the "together" motion $x_1(t) = x_2(t)$.

*Other solutions exist, such as $A_1 = -a$, $\phi_1 = -\pi/2$, $A_2 = 0$, $\phi_2 =$ arbitrary, but they would lead to the same final result, as given by (30).

In contrast, the initial conditions

$$x_1(0) = a, \qquad x_2(0) = -a, \qquad \dot{x}_1(0) = \dot{x}_2(0) = 0 \tag{31}$$

will be found to produce the high-mode motion

$$\mathbf{x} = 0\begin{pmatrix} \sin(t + \phi_1) \\ \sin(t + \phi_1) \end{pmatrix} + a\begin{pmatrix} \cos\sqrt{3}\,t \\ -\cos\sqrt{3}\,t \end{pmatrix}, \tag{32}$$

and conditions such as

$$x_1(0) = a, \qquad x_2(0) = \dot{x}_1(0) = \dot{x}_2(0) = 0$$

and

$$x_1(0) = 2, \qquad x_2(0) = 3, \qquad \dot{x}_1(0) = 1, \qquad \dot{x}_2(0) = -2$$

will lead to motions that are *combinations* of the two modes, i.e., where both A_1 and A_2 in (26) are nonzero.

COMMENT 4 In this case the motion of the system was found to consist of a linear combination of *two* natural modes. Correspondingly, the single-mass oscillator (Fig. 4.4) exhibits only one mode, the three-mass oscillator (Fig. 4.5) exhibits three, and so on.

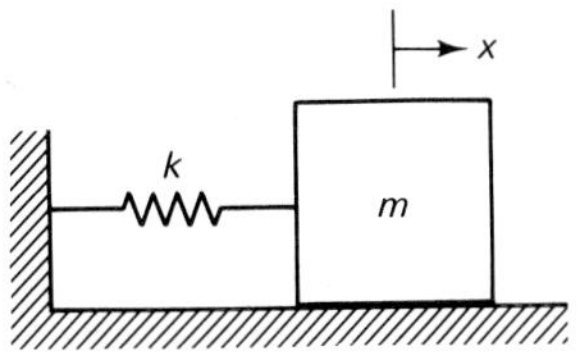

Fig. 4.4 Single-mass oscillator.

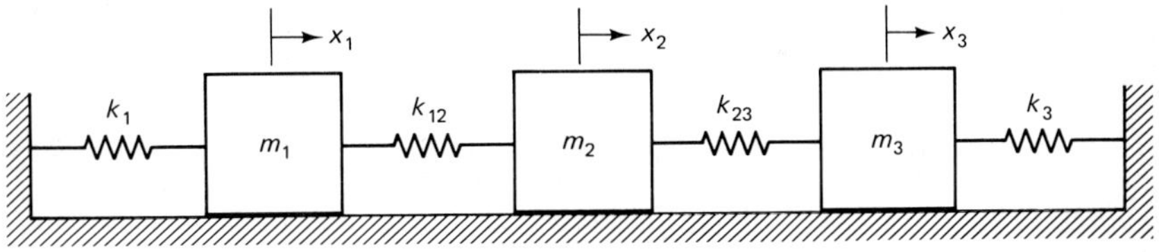

Fig. 4.5 Three-mass oscillator.

Forced Vibration Here we are interested in the "driven response"* $x_1(t)$, $x_2(t)$ to impressed forces $F_1(t)$, $F_2(t)$, say $F_1(t) = F_1 \sin \Omega t$, $F_2(t) = F_2 \sin \Omega t$, where F_1, F_2 are the force amplitudes and Ω is the prescribed frequency. Then the governing equations (14) are

$$\begin{aligned} m_1\ddot{x}_1 + (k_1 + k_{12})x_1 - k_{12}x_2 &= F_1 \sin \Omega t \\ m_2\ddot{x}_2 - k_{12}x_1 + (k_{12} + k_2)x_2 &= F_2 \sin \Omega t. \end{aligned} \tag{33}$$

We will not specify initial conditions. Nor will we seek the general solution of (33). Rather, our interest here will be more focused and will lie in the particular solution of the form

$$\begin{aligned} x_1(t) &= \xi_1 \sin \Omega t \\ x_2(t) &= \xi_2 \sin \Omega t. \end{aligned} \tag{34}$$

* See Example 2 in Section A.7.

Putting (34) into (33), we obtain the equations

$$\begin{aligned} -m_1\Omega^2\xi_1 + (k_1 + k_{12})\xi_1 - k_{12}\xi_2 &= F_1 \\ -m_2\Omega^2\xi_2 - k_{12}\xi_1 + (k_{12} + k_2)\xi_2 &= F_2 \end{aligned} \tag{35}$$

on ξ_1, ξ_2; or, in matrix form,

$$\begin{pmatrix} k_1 + k_{12} - m_1\Omega^2 & -k_{12} \\ -k_{12} & k_{12} + k_2 - m_2\Omega^2 \end{pmatrix}\begin{pmatrix} \xi_1 \\ \xi_2 \end{pmatrix} = \begin{pmatrix} F_1 \\ F_2 \end{pmatrix}. \tag{36}$$

Observe carefully that in the case of the free vibration the differential equations were homogeneous and led to an eigenvalue problem, i.e., of the form "$\mathbf{Ax} = \lambda\mathbf{x}$." In contrast, the forced vibration is governed by nonhomogeneous differential equations, and these lead to the system (36), which is of the form "$\mathbf{Ax} = \mathbf{c}$"; this is *not* an eigenvalue problem, it is simply a nonhomogeneous linear system.

The system (36) is simple since it is merely of order 2. Setting

$$k_1 = k_{12} = k_2 = m_1 = m_2 = 1, \qquad F_1 = F, \qquad F_2 = 0, \tag{37}$$

say, for the sake of illustration, (36) becomes

$$\begin{pmatrix} 2 - \Omega^2 & -1 \\ -1 & 2 - \Omega^2 \end{pmatrix}\begin{pmatrix} \xi_1 \\ \xi_2 \end{pmatrix} = \begin{pmatrix} F \\ 0 \end{pmatrix} \tag{38}$$

and solving (by Cramer's rule, Gauss elimination, inverse matrix, or whatever method you wish), we obtain

$$\xi_1 = \frac{F(2 - \Omega^2)}{(\Omega^2 - 1)(\Omega^2 - 3)}, \qquad \xi_2 = \frac{F}{(\Omega^2 - 1)(\Omega^2 - 3)}, \tag{39}$$

provided that $\Omega \neq 1, \sqrt{3}$. [If $\Omega = 1$ or $\Omega = \sqrt{3}$, the expressions in (39) are undefined. The problem is that if $\Omega = 1$ or $\sqrt{3}$, the determinant of the coefficient matrix vanishes. Hence there must be either no solution of (38), or an infinity of solutions; in fact, there is *no* solution, since the rank of the coefficient matrix is then 1, while the rank of the augmented matrix is 2.]

In fact, 1 and $\sqrt{3}$ are the natural frequencies of the system. Thus the case in which the driving frequency Ω is set at one of the natural frequencies is somewhat singular, and that condition is known as *resonance*. Observe that the nonexistence of solutions of (35), in that case, does not mean that solutions of (33) do not exist, but only that the assumed form (34) is inappropriate.

Finally, of important interest to the engineer are the so-called *response curves*, i.e., graphs of the amplitudes $|\xi_1|$ and $|\xi_2|$ versus the driving frequency Ω. These are sketched, from (39) (for $\Omega \neq 1, \sqrt{3}$), in Fig. 4.6. Noteworthy features of these curves are the unbounded growth of both $|\xi_1|$ and $|\xi_2|$ as Ω approaches either of the two natural frequencies, the tending to zero of both $|\xi_1|$ and $|\xi_2|$ as $\Omega \to \infty$, and the at-first-glance-curious result that $|\xi_1| = 0$, and hence $x_1(t) \equiv 0$, for $\Omega = \sqrt{2}$. (Regarding the latter, do you see how the mass m_1 manages to remain motionless even though it is subjected to a sinusoidal driving force?)

In summary, the free vibration gives rise to an eigenvalue problem, the eigenvalues yielding the natural frequencies, and the eigenvectors yielding the corre-

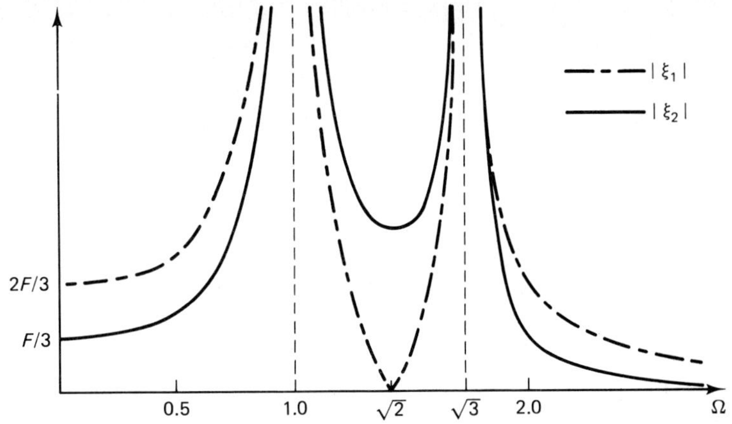

Fig. 4.6 Response curves.

sponding mode shapes, while the forced vibration gives rise to a nonhomogeneous problem of the form $\mathbf{Ax} = \mathbf{c}$. ◀

As can be seen from the preceding example, the eigenvalue problem plays a prominent role in the analysis of vibrating systems—be they mechanical, electrical, or whatever. However, it has many other diverse and important applications as well. Some—involving principal axes and principal inertias, chemical kinetics, the buckling of structures, and the solution of coupled linear systems of ordinary differential equations—are treated in the remaining sections of this chapter. Others arise later in the text, for example, in our study of maxima and minima of functions of several variables (Section 6.8), and in connection with the numerical solution of partial differential equations (Section 14.5).

4.3 EXERCISES

1. For each $n \times n$ matrix obtain n ON eigenvectors.

*(a) $\begin{pmatrix} 2 & 0 & 0 & 0 \\ 0 & 1 & 1 & 0 \\ 0 & 1 & 1 & 0 \\ 0 & 0 & 0 & 2 \end{pmatrix}$ (b) $\begin{pmatrix} 1 & 0 & 0 & 0 \\ 0 & 1 & 0 & 0 \\ 0 & 0 & 1 & 0 \\ 0 & 0 & 0 & 1 \end{pmatrix}$

(c) $\begin{pmatrix} 1 & 0 & 0 & 0 \\ 0 & 2 & 1 & 1 \\ 0 & 1 & 2 & 1 \\ 0 & 1 & 1 & 2 \end{pmatrix}$ (d) $\begin{pmatrix} 0 & 0 & 1 \\ 0 & 1 & 0 \\ 1 & 0 & 0 \end{pmatrix}$

(e) $\begin{pmatrix} 0 & 1 & 0 \\ 1 & 0 & 0 \\ 0 & 0 & 0 \end{pmatrix}$ (f) $\begin{pmatrix} 2 & 1 \\ 1 & 0 \end{pmatrix}$

2. To put the "orthogonal basis" result, in Theorem 4, in perspective, consider some *non*symmetric matrices. In each of the following cases, compute the eigenvectors of $\mathbf{A}$ and determine whether or not they provide an orthogonal basis for $\mathbb{R}^2$.

*(a) $\mathbf{A} = \begin{pmatrix} 1 & 1 \\ 0 & 0 \end{pmatrix}$ (b) $\mathbf{A} = \begin{pmatrix} 1 & 1 \\ 0 & 1 \end{pmatrix}$

(c) $\mathbf{A} = \begin{pmatrix} 1 & 4 \\ 1 & 1 \end{pmatrix}$ (d) $\mathbf{A} = \begin{pmatrix} 0 & 1 \\ 0 & 0 \end{pmatrix}$

3. (*Proof of Theorem 1*) (a) Prove Theorem 1 for the simple case where $\mathbf{A}$ is merely 2×2, i.e., of the form $\begin{pmatrix} a & b \\ b & d \end{pmatrix}$. *Hint:* Solve the characteristic equation, and show that the roots are necessarily real.
(b) We will now supply the "skeleton" of a general proof of Theorem 1. We ask that you copy it down and fill in the logic, in words, that carries us from one step to the next. (Elementary knowledge of complex arithmetic is presumed. We will denote the complex conjugate by an overhead bar. Thus, if $z = x + iy$, then $\bar{z} = x - iy$.) "Skeleton proof":

$$\mathbf{Ax} = \lambda \mathbf{x}, \quad \text{so} \quad \mathbf{A\bar{x}} = \bar{\lambda}\mathbf{\bar{x}}.$$

Then $(\mathbf{Ax})\cdot\overline{\mathbf{x}} = \lambda(\mathbf{x}\cdot\overline{\mathbf{x}})$ and $\mathbf{x}\cdot(\mathbf{A}\overline{\mathbf{x}}) = \overline{\lambda}(\mathbf{x}\cdot\overline{\mathbf{x}})$ or $\mathbf{x}^{\mathrm{T}}\mathbf{A}^{\mathrm{T}}\overline{\mathbf{x}} = \lambda\mathbf{x}^{\mathrm{T}}\overline{\mathbf{x}}$ and $\mathbf{x}^{\mathrm{T}}\mathbf{A}\overline{\mathbf{x}} = \overline{\lambda}\mathbf{x}^{\mathrm{T}}\overline{\mathbf{x}}$. Thus $(\lambda - \overline{\lambda})\mathbf{x}^{\mathrm{T}}\overline{\mathbf{x}} = 0$, so $\lambda = \overline{\lambda}$. Thus λ is real.

4. (*Proof of Theorem 2*) Here we provide a rough outline of a proof of Theorem 2 in which, for simplicity, we assume that $\mathbf{A}$ is 3×3, with an eigenvalue λ_1 of multiplicity 2. We ask you to write out the proof in more detail, i.e., filling in the "gaps" so that every step is clearly understandable. To begin, we construct an orthogonal matrix $\mathbf{Q}$ (i.e., its columns are ON, so that $\mathbf{Q}^{-1} = \mathbf{Q}^{\mathrm{T}}$) with any eigenvector $\hat{\mathbf{e}}_1$ corresponding to λ_1 as its first column:

$$\mathbf{Q} = \left(\hat{\mathbf{e}}_1 \;\vdots\; \text{etc.} \;\vdots\; \text{etc.}\right).$$

Then

$$\mathbf{Q}^{-1}\mathbf{AQ} = \begin{pmatrix} \hat{\mathbf{e}}_1^{\mathrm{T}} \\ \hdashline \text{etc.} \\ \hdashline \text{etc.} \end{pmatrix}\left(\lambda_1\hat{\mathbf{e}}_1^{\mathrm{T}} \;\vdots\; \text{etc.} \;\vdots\; \text{etc.}\right)$$

$$= \begin{pmatrix} \lambda_1 & a & b \\ 0 & c & d \\ 0 & e & f \end{pmatrix}$$

But $\mathbf{Q}^{-1}\mathbf{AQ}$ is symmetric (why?), so that we must have $a = b = 0$. Thus

$$\mathbf{Q}^{-1}\mathbf{AQ} - \lambda\mathbf{I} = \begin{pmatrix} \lambda_1 - \lambda & 0 & 0 \\ 0 & g & h \\ 0 & i & j \end{pmatrix}.$$

Now $|\mathbf{Q}^{-1}\mathbf{AQ} - '\lambda\mathbf{I}| = |\mathbf{A} - \lambda\mathbf{I}|$ (why?), which, by assumption, has a $(\lambda - \lambda_1)^2$ factor. Thus $\begin{vmatrix} g & h \\ i & j \end{vmatrix}$ must be zero when $\lambda = \lambda_1$, so that $r(\mathbf{Q}^{-1}\mathbf{AQ} - \lambda\mathbf{I})$ is at most 1 when $\lambda = \lambda_1$. But $\mathbf{Q}^{-1}\mathbf{AQ} - \lambda\mathbf{I} = \mathbf{Q}^{-1}(\mathbf{A} - \lambda\mathbf{I})\mathbf{Q}$ and $\mathbf{A} - \lambda\mathbf{I}$ are similar (Exercise 8, page 143), so their ranks are the same. (Let $\mathbf{B} \equiv \mathbf{A} - \lambda\mathbf{I}$. To see that similar matrices $\mathbf{Q}^{-1}\mathbf{BQ}$ and $\mathbf{B}$ are of the same rank note, from Exercise 7 on page 115, that $\mathbf{Q}^{-1}\mathbf{BQ}$ can be expressed as the $\mathbf{B}$ matrix both pre- and postmultiplied by a finite number of elementary matrices.) Thus $r(\mathbf{A} - \lambda\mathbf{I})$ is at most 1, when $\lambda = \lambda_1$, so (Theorem 2, page 132) $(\mathbf{A} - \lambda\mathbf{I})\mathbf{x} = \mathbf{0}$ admits at least two LI eigenvectors corresponding to λ_1. (Thus we can find an $\hat{\mathbf{e}}_2$, in λ_1's eigenspace, which is orthogonal to $\hat{\mathbf{e}}_1$, and we can let $\hat{\mathbf{e}}_2$ be the second column in $\mathbf{Q}$, thus advancing the argument one step in the event that the multiplicity of λ_1 were *greater* than 2. You need not pursue this argument.) We cannot find *more* than two since then the dimension of the span of all of the eigenvectors of $\mathbf{A}$ would exceed 3. Thus if λ_1 is of multiplicity 2, its eigenspace is of dimension 2, as was to be shown.

5. Referring to (19), determine the eigenfrequencies and corresponding mode shapes (i.e., the corresponding eigenvectors). We suggest that you carry four or five significant figures.

*(a) $m_1 = m_2 = k_1 = k_{12} = 1,\ k_2 = 20$
(b) $m_1 = m_2 = k_{12} = 1,\ k_1 = 16,\ k_2 = 36$
(c) $m_1 = m_2 = k_1 = 1,\ k_{12} = 0,\ k_2 = 9$
(d) $m_1 - m_2 = k_1 = k_{12} = 1,\ k_2 = 0$

6. (a) Solve for the constants A_1, A_2, ϕ_1, ϕ_2 in (26) for the general initial conditions

$$x_1(0) = a, \qquad x_2(0) = b,$$
$$\dot{x}_1(0) = c, \qquad \dot{x}_2(0) = d.$$

*(b) What conditions on a, b, c, d imply a purely low-mode motion?
(c) What conditions on a, b, c, d imply a purely high-mode motion?

7. (*Beats*) Suppose, in place of (20), that $m_1 = m_2 = k_{12} = 1$, $k_1 = k_2 = 20$, so that the "coupling" of m_1 and m_2 is weak since k_{12} is much smaller than k_1 and k_2. (In the limit, if k_{12} were zero, there would be no coupling at all, and the motions of m_1 and m_2 would be entirely independent.) Supposing further that $x_1(0) = 1$, $x_2(0) = \dot{x}_1(0) = \dot{x}_2(0) = 0$, proceed as in Example 3 and show, for the free vibration, that

$$x_1(t) = \tfrac{1}{2}(\cos\sqrt{20}\,t + \cos\sqrt{22}\,t) \qquad \text{(a)}$$
$$x_2(t) = \tfrac{1}{2}(\cos\sqrt{20}\,t - \cos\sqrt{22}\,t). \qquad \text{(b)}$$

Next, use the trigonometric identities

$$\left.\begin{aligned} \cos A + \cos B &= 2\cos\tfrac{1}{2}(A + B)\cos\tfrac{1}{2}(A - B) \\ \cos A - \cos B &= -2\sin\tfrac{1}{2}(A + B)\sin\tfrac{1}{2}(A - B) \end{aligned}\right. \qquad \text{(c)}$$

to show that

$$\left.\begin{aligned} x_1(t) &\approx \cos 4.58t\,\cos 0.11t \\ x_2(t) &\approx \sin 4.58t\,\sin 0.11t. \end{aligned}\right. \qquad \text{(d)}$$

Use (d) to sketch $x_1(t)$ and $x_2(t)$ versus t in separate graphs, one below the other, labeling key values. Observe the slow transfer of energy, back and forth, betweem m_1 and m_2. In vibration theory this phenomenon is known as **beats.**

***8.** Suppose, in place of (20), that $m_1 = k_1 = 1$, $m_2 = k_{12} = k_2 = 4$. Obtain a modal solution for $\mathbf{x}$, analogous to (26). What are the eigenfrequencies? Are the modes orthogonal?

9. Find the eigenfrequencies and mode shapes (the eigenvectors) for

(a) the single-mass system in Fig. 4.4
(b) the three-mass system in Fig. 4.5, with $m_1 = m_2 = m_3 = k_1 = k_{12} = k_{23} = k_3 = 1$

10. (*Rayleigh's quotient*) Let $\mathbf{A}$ be a symmetric matrix of order n, with orthogonal eigenvectors $\mathbf{e}_1, \ldots, \mathbf{e}_n$, and corresponding eigenvalues $\lambda_1, \ldots, \lambda_n$, ordered such that $|\lambda_1| \geq |\lambda_2| \geq \cdots \geq |\lambda_n|$. Then any $\mathbf{x}$ in n-space can be expanded as

$$\mathbf{x} = \sum_{j=1}^{n} a_j \mathbf{e}_j. \qquad \text{(a)}$$

(a) Using equation (a) and recalling that $\mathbf{x} \cdot \mathbf{y} = \mathbf{x}^{\mathrm{T}}\mathbf{y}$, show that

$$\left| \frac{\mathbf{x}^{\mathrm{T}}\mathbf{A}\mathbf{x}}{\mathbf{x}^{\mathrm{T}}\mathbf{x}} \right| \leq |\lambda_1| \qquad (\mathbf{x} \neq \mathbf{0}). \qquad \text{(b)}$$

Thus the left-hand side of equation (b), which may also be expressed as $\left| \frac{\mathbf{Ax} \cdot \mathbf{x}}{\mathbf{x} \cdot \mathbf{x}} \right|$, provides a *lower bound* on the magnitude of the largest eigenvalue of $\mathbf{A}$. Such bounds are of importance since it is often only the largest (sometimes the smallest) eigenvalue that is of interest.
(b) Illustrate equation (b), using $\mathbf{x} = (0, 1, 2)^{\mathrm{T}}$, say, for the matrix

$$\mathbf{A} = \begin{pmatrix} 2 & 0 & 0 \\ 0 & -1 & -2 \\ 0 & -2 & -1 \end{pmatrix}.$$

That is, compare the bound equation (b) with the exact value of $|\lambda_1|$. Repeat for $\mathbf{x} = (0, 1, 1.4)^{\mathrm{T}}$, $(0, 1, 1.1)^{\mathrm{T}}$, $(0, 1, 1)^{\mathrm{T}}$.
(c) Derive the equality

$$\frac{\mathbf{e}_j^{\mathrm{T}}\mathbf{A}\mathbf{e}_j}{\mathbf{e}_j^{\mathrm{T}}\mathbf{e}_j} = \lambda_j \qquad (j = 1, 2, \ldots, n). \qquad \text{(c)}$$

Summary: The ratio

$$R(\mathbf{x}) = \frac{\mathbf{x}^{\mathrm{T}}\mathbf{A}\mathbf{x}}{\mathbf{x}^{\mathrm{T}}\mathbf{x}} \qquad \text{(d)}$$

is known as **Rayleigh's quotient,** after *Lord Rayleigh* (*John William Strutt;* 1842–1919). Imagine putting randomly chosen $\mathbf{x}$ vectors, one after another, into Rayleigh's quotient. If $\mathbf{x}$ happens to coincide with an eigenvector of $\mathbf{A}$, then, according to (c), $R(\mathbf{x})$ gives the corresponding eigenvalue. In any case, (b) indicates that $|R(\mathbf{x})|$ is always less than or equal to the magnitude of the largest eigenvalue.

11. (*An enclosure theorem*) Let $\mathbf{A}$ be a symmetric matrix of order n. Given any nonzero (n-dimensional column) vector $\mathbf{x}$, define the n ratios

$$r_j = \frac{j\text{th element of } \mathbf{Ax}}{j\text{th element of } \mathbf{x}} \qquad (j = 1, 2, \ldots, n). \qquad \text{(a)}$$

If any ratio is 0/0, it is to be discarded. Certainly if $\mathbf{x}$ happens to be an eigenvector $\mathbf{e}$, with corresponding eigenvalue λ, then $r_1 = r_2 = \cdots = r_n = \lambda$. If $\mathbf{x}$ is *not* an eigenvector, not all of the r_j's will be the same, and we denote the algebraically smallest and largest of these as $r_{\min}$ and $r_{\max}$, respectively. We state, without proof, that there must be an eigenvalue λ of $\mathbf{A}$ enclosed by these values, i.e.,*

$$r_{\min} \leq \lambda \leq r_{\max}. \qquad \text{(b)}$$

As a simple illustration let

$$\mathbf{A} = \begin{pmatrix} 2 & 1 & 1 \\ 1 & 0 & 3 \\ 1 & 3 & 0 \end{pmatrix},$$

and work out the inequality (b) using $\mathbf{x} = (3, 1, 1)^{\mathrm{T}}$, $(2, 1, 1)^{\mathrm{T}}$, $(1.1, 1, 1)^{\mathrm{T}}$, and $(1, 1, 1)^{\mathrm{T}}$, in turn. What is the *exact* value of the enclosed eigenvalue?

12. (*The power method*) There exists a simple *iterative* procedure for calculating eigenvalues and eigenvectors which is known as the **power method.** To begin, one selects any nonzero vector $\mathbf{x}^{(0)}$ and then computes $\mathbf{x}^{(1)} \equiv \mathbf{A}\mathbf{x}^{(0)}$, $\mathbf{x}^{(2)} \equiv \mathbf{A}\mathbf{x}^{(1)}$, and so on. That is,

$$\mathbf{x}^{(k+1)} \equiv \mathbf{A}\mathbf{x}^{(k)} \qquad (k = 0, 1, 2, \ldots). \qquad \text{(a)}$$

Before analyzing the situation, let us apply (a) and see what happens. Let

$$\mathbf{A} = \begin{pmatrix} 2 & 0 & 0 \\ 0 & -2 & 1 \\ 0 & 1 & -2 \end{pmatrix}. \qquad \text{(b)}$$

* What if one or more elements of $\mathbf{x}$ are zero and the corresponding elements of $\mathbf{Ax}$ are nonzero? If all of the corresponding elements of $\mathbf{Ax}$ are positive (or negative), then (b) is to be replaced by $r_{\min} \leq \lambda < \infty$ and $-\infty < \lambda \leq r_{\max}$; i.e., there is an eigenvalue in each of those two intervals. If some of the corresponding elements of $\mathbf{Ax}$ are positive and some are negative, then (b) is to be replaced by the (uninformative) statement $-\infty < \lambda < \infty$.

Apply (a): Choosing $\mathbf{x}^{(0)} = (0, 0, 1)^T$, say, we obtain

$$\begin{matrix} \mathbf{A} & \mathbf{x}^{(0)} & \mathbf{x}^{(1)} \\ \begin{pmatrix} 2 & 0 & 0 \\ 0 & -2 & 1 \\ 0 & 1 & -2 \end{pmatrix} & \begin{pmatrix} 0 \\ 0 \\ 1 \end{pmatrix} & \begin{pmatrix} 0 \\ 1 \\ -2 \end{pmatrix} \end{matrix}$$

$$\begin{matrix} \mathbf{x}^{(2)} & \mathbf{x}^{(3)} & \mathbf{x}^{(4)} & \mathbf{x}^{(5)} \\ \begin{pmatrix} 0 \\ -4 \\ 5 \end{pmatrix} & \begin{pmatrix} 0 \\ 13 \\ -14 \end{pmatrix} & \begin{pmatrix} 0 \\ -40 \\ 41 \end{pmatrix} & \begin{pmatrix} 0 \\ 121 \\ -122 \end{pmatrix}, \end{matrix} \tag{c}$$

and so on. Now, observe, from the very nature of the eigenvalue problem $\mathbf{Ax} = \lambda\mathbf{x}$, that if $\mathbf{x}^{(0)}$ were an eigenvector of $\mathbf{A}$, then $\mathbf{Ax}^{(0)}$ would be some scalar multiple of $\mathbf{x}^{(0)}$. But $\mathbf{Ax}^{(0)} \equiv \mathbf{x}^{(1)}$, and $\mathbf{x}^{(1)}$ is seen from (c) *not* to be a scalar multiple of $\mathbf{x}^{(0)}$. Hence $\mathbf{x}^{(0)}$ is not an eigenvector of $\mathbf{A}$. Similarly, $\mathbf{x}^{(1)}$ is not an eigenvector because $\mathbf{x}^{(2)}$ is not a multiple of $\mathbf{x}^{(1)}$, and so on. Nevertheless, we see that with each successive step $\mathbf{x}^{(k+1)}$ draws closer and closer to being a multiple of $\mathbf{x}^{(k)}$, so that the sequence $\mathbf{x}^{(k)}$ is evidently *approaching* an eigenvector of $\mathbf{A}$. In fact, $\mathbf{x}^{(5)}$ is very close to being a multiple of $\mathbf{x}^{(4)}$, so that

$$\mathbf{e} \approx \begin{pmatrix} 0 \\ 121 \\ -122 \end{pmatrix}. \tag{d}$$

According to (b) in Exercise 11, there is an eigenvalue bracketed by

$$\frac{121}{-40} \le \lambda \le \frac{-122}{41} \quad \text{or}$$

$$-3.025 \le \lambda \le -2.97560\ldots.$$

Alternatively, application of the Rayleigh quotient (c) in Exercise 10 gives

$$\lambda \approx \frac{\mathbf{x}^{(4)\mathrm{T}}\mathbf{Ax}^{(4)}}{\mathbf{x}^{(4)\mathrm{T}}\mathbf{x}^{(4)}} = \frac{\mathbf{x}^{(4)\mathrm{T}}\mathbf{x}^{(5)}}{\mathbf{x}^{(4)\mathrm{T}}\mathbf{x}^{(4)}} = \frac{-9842}{3281} \approx -2.9997. \tag{e}$$

How do (d) and (e) compare with the *exact* values? These are

$$\lambda_1 = -3, \quad \mathbf{e}_1 = \begin{pmatrix} 0 \\ 1 \\ -1 \end{pmatrix};$$

$$\lambda_2 = 2, \quad \mathbf{e}_2 = \begin{pmatrix} 1 \\ 0 \\ 0 \end{pmatrix}; \quad \lambda_3 = -1, \quad \mathbf{e}_3 = \begin{pmatrix} 0 \\ 1 \\ 1 \end{pmatrix}, \tag{f}$$

so (d) and (e) are evidently approximations to the "eigenpair" λ_1, $\mathbf{e}_1$. [It is striking that whereas $\mathbf{e}$ agrees with $\mathbf{e}_1$ to only around 1 part in 100, λ agrees with λ_1 to 1 part in 10,000. This situation is typical: If the elements of $\mathbf{x}^{(k)}$ agree with those in $\mathbf{e}$ to 1 part in N, then $\lambda^{(k)} = \mathbf{x}^{(k)\mathrm{T}}\mathbf{Ax}^{(k)}/\mathbf{x}^{(k)\mathrm{T}}\mathbf{x}^{(k)} = \mathbf{x}^{(k)\mathrm{T}}\mathbf{x}^{(k+1)}/\mathbf{x}^{(k)\mathrm{T}}\mathbf{x}^{(k)}$ can be expected to agree with λ to 1 part in approximately N^2. For discussion of this point, as well as additional information concerning these last three exercises, we refer you to Stephen H. Crandall, *Engineering Analysis* (New York: McGraw-Hill, 1956), Chap. 2.]

To see what is going on, suppose that $\mathbf{A}$ is a symmetric matrix of order n (although symmetry is more than we need; it would suffice for $\mathbf{A}$ to have n LI eigenvectors), and let its eigenvalues be ordered so that $|\lambda_1| \ge |\lambda_2| \ge \cdots \ge |\lambda_n|$, as in (f). Since $\mathbf{A}$ is symmetric, its eigenvectors $\mathbf{e}_1, \ldots, \mathbf{e}_n$ are an orthogonal basis for n-space. Hence our initial vector $\mathbf{x}^{(0)}$ must be expressible as

$$\mathbf{x}^{(0)} = \sum_{j=1}^{n} a_j\mathbf{e}_j. \tag{g}$$

Of course, we cannot *compute* the a_j's since we do not know the $\mathbf{e}_j$'s yet, but that is no problem; it is the *form* of (g) that will be important here. It follows from (a) and (g) that

$$\begin{aligned} \mathbf{x}^{(1)} &= \mathbf{Ax}^{(0)} = \mathbf{A}\sum_1^n a_j\mathbf{e}_j = \sum_1^n a_j\lambda_j\mathbf{e}_j \\ \mathbf{x}^{(2)} &= \mathbf{Ax}^{(1)} = \mathbf{A}\sum_1^n a_j\lambda_j\mathbf{e}_j = \sum_1^n a_j\lambda_j^2\mathbf{e}_j \\ &\vdots \\ \mathbf{x}^{(k)} &= \sum_1^n a_j\lambda_j^k\mathbf{e}_j \\ &= \lambda_1^k\left[a_1\mathbf{e}_1 + a_2\left(\frac{\lambda_2}{\lambda_1}\right)^k\mathbf{e}_2 + \cdots + a_n\left(\frac{\lambda_n}{\lambda_1}\right)^k\mathbf{e}_n\right]. \end{aligned} \tag{h}$$

Now, if λ_1 is in fact *dominant*, i.e., $|\lambda_1| > |\lambda_2| \ge \cdots \ge |\lambda_n|$, then $(\lambda_2/\lambda_1)^k, \ldots, (\lambda_n/\lambda_1)^k$ all tend to zero as $k \to \infty$, so that $\mathbf{x}^{(k)} \sim \lambda_1^k a_1\mathbf{e}_1$ as $k \to \infty$ (provided that $a_1 \neq 0$, i.e., provided that $\mathbf{x}^{(0)}$ does not happen to be orthogonal to $\mathbf{e}_1$). Eigenvectors can be scaled arbitrarily, so the $\lambda_1^k a_1$ factor is of little interest; the point is that $\mathbf{x}^{(k)}$ converges to $\mathbf{e}_1$, the eigenvector corresponding to the dominant eigenvalue. That is precisely what was found in the preceding illustration, wherein the dominant eigenvalue was $\lambda_1 = -3$.

(a) Determine the dominant eigenvalue, and corresponding eigenvector, by the power method, for

$$\mathbf{A} = \begin{pmatrix} 0 & 0 & 1 \\ 0 & 0 & 1 \\ 1 & 1 & 1 \end{pmatrix}.$$

Note: Observe that even though your iteration converges, you cannot be certain that the eigenvalue obtained is the *dominant* one, λ_1, since your chosen $\mathbf{x}^{(0)}$ may (without your knowing it) be orthogonal to $\mathbf{e}_1$, as mentioned in the sentence following (h). Hence we recommend that you carry out the iteration three times, once with $\mathbf{x}^{(0)} = (1, 0, 0)^T$, once with $\mathbf{x}^{(0)} = (0, 1, 0)^T$, and once with $\mathbf{x}^{(0)} = (0, 0, 1)^T$, since there is no way that all *three* of these $\mathbf{x}^{(0)}$'s can be orthogonal to $\mathbf{e}_1$ (do you see why this is so?). Go as far as $\mathbf{x}^{(5)}$, in each case, and use the Rayleigh quotient to estimate λ, as in (e).

*(b) Repeat part (a), for

$$\mathbf{A} = \begin{pmatrix} 2 & 1 & -1 \\ 1 & 4 & 3 \\ -1 & 3 & 4 \end{pmatrix}.$$

(c) Repeat part (a), for

$$\mathbf{A} = \begin{pmatrix} 2 & 1 & 1 \\ 1 & 2 & 1 \\ 1 & 1 & 2 \end{pmatrix}.$$

*(d) Repeat part (a), for

$$\mathbf{A} = \begin{pmatrix} 0 & -1 & 1 \\ -1 & -3 & -4 \\ 1 & -4 & -3 \end{pmatrix}.$$

(e) Repeat part (a), for

$$\mathbf{A} = \begin{pmatrix} 4 & 1 & 3 \\ 1 & 0 & -1 \\ 3 & -1 & 4 \end{pmatrix}.$$

(f) Repeat part (a), for

$$\mathbf{A} = \begin{pmatrix} 1 & 1 & 1 \\ 1 & 1 & 1 \\ 1 & 1 & 3 \end{pmatrix}.$$

(g) Repeat part (a), for

$$\mathbf{A} = \begin{pmatrix} 2 & 3 & 1 & 1 \\ 3 & 3 & 1 & 1 \\ 1 & 1 & 3 & 1 \\ 1 & 1 & 1 & 2 \end{pmatrix}.$$

(h) Returning to the $\mathbf{A}$ matrix given by equation (b), work out $\mathbf{A}^4$. Then apply the power method to $\mathbf{A}^4$, beginning with $\mathbf{x}^{(0)} = (0, 0, 1)^T$. Can you explain the improvement in the *rate* of convergence [compared with that in equation (c)]? Show how to recover the eigenvalues and eigenvectors of $\mathbf{A}$ from those of $\mathbf{A}^4$.

*(i) Apply the power method to the matrix $\mathbf{A} = \begin{pmatrix} 2 & 1 & 0 \\ 1 & 2 & 0 \\ 0 & 0 & 3 \end{pmatrix}$. *Note:* The eigenvalues of $\mathbf{A}$ happen to be 3, 3, 1, so that λ_1 and λ_2 are equal.

13. (*Solution of $\mathbf{A}x = \Lambda x + c$ by eigenvector expansion method*) Techniques for solving linear systems were considered at length in Chapters 1 and 3. The material in the present section now provides an important alternative line of approach which we call the **eigenvector expansion method.** To illustrate the method, let us return to the linear system

$$\begin{pmatrix} 2-\Omega^2 & -1 \\ -1 & 2-\Omega^2 \end{pmatrix}\begin{pmatrix} \xi_1 \\ \xi_2 \end{pmatrix} = \begin{pmatrix} F \\ 0 \end{pmatrix} \tag{a}$$

encountered in Example 3.

(a) First, reexpress (a), as

$$\begin{pmatrix} 2 & -1 \\ -1 & 2 \end{pmatrix}\begin{pmatrix} \xi_1 \\ \xi_2 \end{pmatrix} = \Omega^2\begin{pmatrix} \xi_1 \\ \xi_2 \end{pmatrix} + \begin{pmatrix} F \\ 0 \end{pmatrix}, \tag{b}$$

i.e., in the form

$$\mathbf{Ax} = \Lambda\mathbf{x} + \mathbf{c}, \tag{c}$$

where $\mathbf{A} = \begin{pmatrix} 2 & -1 \\ -1 & 2 \end{pmatrix}$, $\mathbf{x} = (\xi_1, \xi_2)^T$, $\Lambda = \Omega^2$, and $\mathbf{c} = (F, 0)^T$. Now $\mathbf{A}$ is symmetric, so its eigenvectors $\mathbf{e}_1$, $\mathbf{e}_2$ necessarily constitute an orthogonal basis for 2-space. Adopting that basis, expand

$$\mathbf{x} = a_1\mathbf{e}_1 + a_2\mathbf{e}_2 \tag{d}$$

and

$$\mathbf{c} = c_1\mathbf{e}_1 + c_2\mathbf{e}_2, \tag{e}$$

where c_1 and c_2 can be computed, as in (19) on page 53, and a_1, a_2 are our unknowns; if we can determine

a_1, a_2, then (d) gives **x**. Putting (d) and (e) into (c), and recalling that $\mathbf{A}\mathbf{e}_1 = \lambda_1\mathbf{e}_1$ and $\mathbf{A}\mathbf{e}_2 = \lambda_2\mathbf{e}_2$, show that

$$a_j(\lambda_j - \Lambda) = c_j \qquad (j = 1, 2). \tag{f}$$

(b) Solving (f) for a_j, provided that Λ does not coincide with either of the eigenvalues λ_1 or λ_2, show that the desired solution to (c) is

$$\mathbf{x} = \sum_{j=1}^{2} \frac{c_j}{\lambda_j - \Lambda}\mathbf{e}_j. \tag{g}$$

(c) Compute c_1, c_2, as mentioned in part (a), evaluate the right-hand side of (g), and show that the resulting solution is in agreement with that given, componentwise, in (39).

(d) Suppose that Λ *does* coincide with one of the eigenvalues; e.g., suppose that $\Lambda = \lambda_1$ ($\neq \lambda_2$). Then (g) does not hold. Backing up to (f), show that there are two possibilities: (1) If $c_1 \neq 0$, there is *no* solution to (c). (2) If $c_1 = 0$, equation (c) admits the one-parameter family of solutions

$$\mathbf{x} = \alpha_1\mathbf{e}_1 + \frac{c_2}{\lambda_2 - \Lambda}\mathbf{e}_2, \tag{h}$$

where α_1 is arbitrary.

(e) Generalizing the ideas in parts (a) to (d), consider equation (c), where **A** is *any* given symmetric $n \times n$ matrix, where **c** is any given $n \times 1$ column vector, and where Λ is a parameter. Show that if Λ coincides with an eigenvalue of multiplicity p, say λ_1, then (c) admits the p-parameter family of solutions

$$\mathbf{x} = \alpha_1\mathbf{e}_1 + \cdots + \alpha_p\mathbf{e}_p + \sum_{j=p+1}^{n} \frac{c_j}{\lambda_j - \Lambda}\mathbf{e}_j, \tag{i}$$

where $\alpha_1, \ldots, \alpha_p$ are arbitrary if c_1 through c_p are 0, and admits no solution otherwise. Show that the advantage of using the eigenvectors of **A** as our base vectors, in the expansions

$$\mathbf{x} = \sum_{j=1}^{n} a_j\mathbf{e}_j, \qquad \mathbf{c} = \sum_{j=1}^{n} c_j\mathbf{e}_j, \tag{j}$$

is that the resulting system of equations on the a_j's is *uncoupled*. (Of course, this advantage is not "free of charge"; we do need to take the trouble to compute the eigenvalues and eigenvectors.)

14. (*Generalized eigenvalue problem*) The symmetry of the **A** matrix (21) resulted in the orthogonality of the eigenvectors; hence the natural modes were referred to as *orthogonal*. However, notice from (19) that **A** is symmetric only in the event that $m_1 = m_2$ (or $k_{12} = 0$). What can be said regarding the orthogonality of the natural modes in the more general case? Well, observe that (18) can be reexpressed as

$$\begin{pmatrix} k_1 + k_{12} & -k_{12} \\ -k_{12} & k_{12} + k_2 \end{pmatrix}\begin{pmatrix} \xi_1 \\ \xi_2 \end{pmatrix} = \omega^2\begin{pmatrix} m_1 & 0 \\ 0 & m_2 \end{pmatrix}\begin{pmatrix} \xi_1 \\ \xi_2 \end{pmatrix}, \tag{a}$$

or, more compactly, as

$$\mathbf{K}\boldsymbol{\xi} = \lambda\mathbf{M}\boldsymbol{\xi}, \tag{b}$$

where

$$\mathbf{K} = \begin{pmatrix} k_1 + k_{12} & -k_{12} \\ -k_{12} & k_{12} + k_2 \end{pmatrix},$$
$$\mathbf{M} = \begin{pmatrix} m_1 & 0 \\ 0 & m_2 \end{pmatrix}, \tag{c}$$
$$\lambda = \omega^2.$$

Observe, further, that **K** and **M** are each symmetric. We now state the problem: Consider the generalized eigenvalue problem (b) (see Exercise 16 on page 145), where **K** and **M** are each symmetric $n \times n$ matrices. Show that if $\mathbf{e}_j$ and $\mathbf{e}_k$ are eigenvectors corresponding to distinct eigenvalues λ_j and λ_k, respectively, then $\mathbf{e}_j$, $\mathbf{e}_k$ satisfy the "generalized" orthogonality relation

$$\mathbf{e}_j \cdot (\mathbf{M}\mathbf{e}_k) = 0; \tag{d}$$

i.e., $\mathbf{e}_j$ is orthogonal to $\mathbf{e}_k$ "relative to **M**." Show, further, that

$$\mathbf{e}_j \cdot (\mathbf{K}\mathbf{e}_k) = 0 \tag{e}$$

as well. *Hint:* What is needed here is a generalization of our proof of Theorem 3.

4.4 DIAGONALIZATION

[Optional Section]

We have seen that diagonal matrices are especially simple from both computational and theoretical points of view. For example, the solution of $\mathbf{A}\mathbf{x} = \mathbf{c}$, where **A** is $n \times n$, is generally quite tedious if n is large, but is trivial if **A** is diagonal. Similarly, the raising of an $n \times n$ matrix $\mathbf{A}$ to a large power (for example, computing $\mathbf{A}^{100}$) is generally quite cumbersome by direct calculation, but is trivial if $\mathbf{A}$ is diagonal. Thus the diagonalization of a given matrix $\mathbf{A}$, i.e., its reduction to diagonal form, should prove to be of considerable interest.

We say that a square matrix $\mathbf{A}$ is **diagonalizable** if there exists an invertible matrix $\mathbf{Q}$ such that $\mathbf{Q}^{-1}\mathbf{A}\mathbf{Q}$ is diagonal, say,

$$\mathbf{Q}^{-1}\mathbf{A}\mathbf{Q} = \mathbf{D}. \tag{1}$$

If so, $\mathbf{Q}$ is said to **diagonalize** $\mathbf{A}$. How we make use of (1) will be demonstrated shortly. First, we need to say something about conditions on $\mathbf{A}$ which guarantee that it is diagonalizable, and we need to show how to find $\mathbf{Q}$.

Theorem 1 *Diagonalization*

Let $\mathbf{A}$ be $n \times n$.

(i) $\mathbf{A}$ is diagonalizable if and only if it has **n** LI eigenvectors.

(ii) If $\mathbf{A}$ has n LI eigenvectors $\mathbf{q}_1, \ldots, \mathbf{q}_n$, and $\mathbf{Q} = (\mathbf{q}_1, \ldots, \mathbf{q}_n)$, then $\mathbf{Q}^{-1}\mathbf{A}\mathbf{Q} = \mathbf{D}$ is diagonal, with the jth diagonal element of $\mathbf{D}$ equal to the jth eigenvalue of $\mathbf{A}$.

Proof First let us prove that if $\mathbf{A}$ is diagonalizable, it has n LI eigenvectors. If $\mathbf{A}$ is diagonalizable, there exists an invertible matrix

$$\mathbf{Q} = \begin{pmatrix} q_{11} & q_{12} & \cdots & q_{1n} \\ q_{21} & q_{22} & \cdots & q_{2n} \\ \vdots & & & \vdots \\ q_{n1} & q_{n2} & \cdots & q_{nn} \end{pmatrix} \tag{2}$$

such that

$$\mathbf{Q}^{-1}\mathbf{A}\mathbf{Q} = \mathbf{D} = \begin{pmatrix} d_1 & & & 0 \\ & d_2 & & \\ & & \ddots & \\ 0 & & & d_n \end{pmatrix}. \tag{3}$$

Premultiplying (3) by $\mathbf{Q}$ yields

$$\mathbf{A}\mathbf{Q} = \begin{pmatrix} q_{11} & \cdots & q_{1n} \\ \vdots & & \vdots \\ q_{n1} & \cdots & q_{nn} \end{pmatrix} \begin{pmatrix} d_1 & & 0 \\ & \ddots & \\ 0 & & d_n \end{pmatrix} = \begin{pmatrix} d_1 q_{11} & d_2 q_{12} & \cdots & d_n q_{1n} \\ \vdots & \vdots & & \vdots \\ d_1 q_{n1} & d_2 q_{n2} & \cdots & d_n q_{nn} \end{pmatrix} \tag{4}$$

$$\equiv (d_1\mathbf{q}_1, d_2\mathbf{q}_2, \ldots, d_n\mathbf{q}_n),$$

where we have defined the vector $\mathbf{q}_j$ as the jth column of $\mathbf{Q}$. Alternatively,

$$\mathbf{A}\mathbf{Q} = \mathbf{A}(\mathbf{q}_1, \mathbf{q}_2, \ldots, \mathbf{q}_n) = (\mathbf{A}\mathbf{q}_1, \mathbf{A}\mathbf{q}_2, \ldots, \mathbf{A}\mathbf{q}_n) \tag{5}$$

and, comparing (4) and (5), we have

$$\begin{aligned} \mathbf{Aq} &= d_1\mathbf{q}_1 \\ &\vdots \\ \mathbf{Aq}_n &= d_n\mathbf{q}_n. \end{aligned} \tag{6}$$

Now $\mathbf{q}_1, \ldots, \mathbf{q}_n$ are necessarily nonzero, since otherwise $\mathbf{Q}$ would be singular. This fact, together with the form of the equations in (6), indicates that the d_j's and $\mathbf{q}_j$'s are eigenvalues and eigenvectors of $\mathbf{A}$. Furthermore, the rank of $\mathbf{Q}$ must be n since $\mathbf{Q}$ is to be invertible, so (Theorem 2, page 95) the columns of $\mathbf{Q}$ must be LI. Hence we have proved "half" of property (i), namely, that if $\mathbf{A}$ is diagonalizable, then it has n LI eigenvectors. In doing so, we have also proved property (ii).

It remains to prove the rest of (i), namely that if $\mathbf{A}$ has n LI eigenvectors, it is diagonalizable. Let the eigenvalues of $\mathbf{A}$ be $d_1, \ldots, d_n$, and let the corresponding (LI) eigenvectors be $\mathbf{q}_1, \ldots, \mathbf{q}_n$. Then

$$\begin{aligned} \mathbf{AQ} &= (\mathbf{Aq}_1, \ldots, \mathbf{Aq}_n) = (d_1\mathbf{q}_1, \ldots, d_n\mathbf{q}_n) \\ &= \begin{pmatrix} d_1 q_{11} & \cdots & d_n q_{1n} \\ \vdots & & \vdots \\ d_1 q_{n1} & \cdots & d_n q_{nn} \end{pmatrix} = \begin{pmatrix} q_{11} & \cdots & q_{1n} \\ \vdots & & \vdots \\ q_{n1} & \cdots & q_{nn} \end{pmatrix} \begin{pmatrix} d_1 & & 0 \\ & \ddots & \\ 0 & & d_n \end{pmatrix} \equiv \mathbf{QD}. \end{aligned} \tag{7}$$

Now $\mathbf{Q}$ is invertible since its columns are LI, so premultiplying (7) by $\mathbf{Q}^{-1}$, we obtain $\mathbf{Q}^{-1}\mathbf{AQ} = \mathbf{D}$. Hence $\mathbf{A}$ is diagonalizable, and the proof is complete. ■

An $n \times n$ matrix $\mathbf{Q}$, the columns of which are n LI eigenvectors of $\mathbf{A}$, is called a **modal matrix** of $\mathbf{A}$.

Theorem 1 relates the diagonalizability of $\mathbf{A}$ to the eigenvectors of $\mathbf{A}$. With the help of Theorem 2, to follow, we will be in a position to relate the diagonalizability of $\mathbf{A}$ to the eigenvalues of $\mathbf{A}$ as well. With that done, we will then turn to some physical applications.

***Theorem 2** Distinct Eigenvalues, LI Eigenvectors*

If $\lambda_1, \ldots, \lambda_k$ are k distinct eigenvalues of an $n \times n$ matrix $\mathbf{A}$, and $\mathbf{e}_1, \ldots, \mathbf{e}_k$ are corresponding eigenvectors, then $\mathbf{e}_1, \ldots, \mathbf{e}_k$ are LI.*

Proof We need to demonstrate that

$$c_1\mathbf{e}_1 + c_2\mathbf{e}_2 + \cdots + c_k\mathbf{e}_k = \mathbf{0} \tag{8}$$

holds only if $c_1 = c_2 = \cdots = c_n = 0$. Multiplying (8) by $\mathbf{A}$ and noting that $\mathbf{Ae}_j = \lambda_j\mathbf{e}_j$, we have

$$c_1\lambda_1\mathbf{e}_1 + c_2\lambda_2\mathbf{e}_2 + \cdots + c_k\lambda_k\mathbf{e}_k = \mathbf{0}.$$

Repeating the process, we have

*Observe that if $\mathbf{A}$ is *symmetric*, then $\mathbf{e}_1, \ldots, \mathbf{e}_k$ are not only LI, they are *orthogonal*.

$$c_1\lambda_1^2\mathbf{e}_1 + c_2\lambda_2^2\mathbf{e}_2 + \cdots + c_k\lambda_k^2\mathbf{e}_k = \mathbf{0}$$
$$\vdots$$
$$c_1\lambda_1^{k-1}\mathbf{e}_1 + c_2\lambda_2^{k-1}\mathbf{e}_2 + \cdots + c_k\lambda_k^{k-1}\mathbf{e}_k = \mathbf{0}.$$

Combining these equations, in matrix form, gives us

$$\begin{pmatrix} \lambda_1^{k-1} & \lambda_2^{k-1} & \cdots & \lambda_k^{k-1} \\ \vdots & \vdots & & \vdots \\ \lambda_1^2 & \lambda_2^2 & \cdots & \lambda_k^2 \\ \lambda_1 & \lambda_2 & \cdots & \lambda_k \\ 1 & 1 & \cdots & 1 \end{pmatrix} \begin{pmatrix} c_1\mathbf{e}_1 \\ c_2\mathbf{e}_2 \\ \vdots \\ c_k\mathbf{e}_k \end{pmatrix} = \mathbf{0}. \tag{9}$$

But since the λ_j's are distinct, it follows from (a) in Exercise 21 on page 93 [plus the fact that $\det(\mathbf{A}^{\mathrm{T}}) = \det\mathbf{A}$] that the determinant of the coefficient matrix is nonzero, so (9) admits only the trivial solution $c_1\mathbf{e}_1 = c_2\mathbf{e}_2 = \cdots = c_k\mathbf{e}_k = \mathbf{0}$. Finally, the $\mathbf{e}_j$'s are nonzero since they are eigenvectors, and hence $c_1, c_2, \ldots, c_k$ are necessarily zero. ■

From Theorems 1 and 2 we may draw the following important conclusion.

> ***Theorem 3*** *Diagonalizability*
> If an $n \times n$ matrix has n distinct eigenvalues, then it is diagonalizable.

EXAMPLE 1 *A Problem in Chemical Kinetics.* We consider, here, a special class of chemical reactions known as *first-order reactions*. These reactions are governed by systems of linear, coupled, first-order ordinary differential equations. Specifically, suppose that $X_1, \ldots, X_n$ are the chemical names of n reacting species (elements or molecules), that $x_j(t)$ denotes the concentration of X_j (in suitable units) as a function of the time t, and that the *rate constant* for the conversion of X_i to X_j is the positive constant k_{ji}. For a two-component reaction, for example, denoted schematically in Fig. 4.7, this means that

$$\dot{x}_1 = -k_{21}x_1 + k_{12}x_2 \tag{10a}$$

$$\dot{x}_2 = k_{21}x_1 - k_{12}x_2, \tag{10b}$$

where the dots denote d/dt. The first term on the right-hand side of (10a) accounts for the rate of loss of X_1 due to the $X_1 \rightarrow X_2$ reaction; it is proportional to the concentration of X_1, namely x_1, and the constant of proportionality is the relevant rate constant k_{21}. The second term on the right-hand side of (10a) accounts for the rate of gain of X_1 due to the reverse reaction $X_2 \rightarrow X_1$. A similar accounting holds for the terms in (10b).

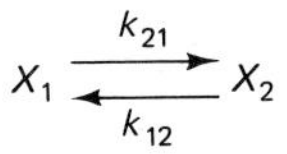

Fig. 4.7 Two-component reaction.

For the three-component reaction shown in Fig. 4.8, we have

$$\dot{x}_1 = -(k_{21} + k_{31})x_1 + k_{12}x_2 + k_{13}x_3 \tag{11a}$$

$$\dot{x}_2 = k_{21}x_1 - (k_{12} + k_{32})x_2 + k_{23}x_3 \tag{11b}$$

$$\dot{x}_3 = k_{31}x_1 + k_{32}x_2 - (k_{13} + k_{23})x_3. \tag{11c}$$

The difficulty in solving (10), (11), and similar systems for n-component reactions where $n > 3$ is due to the *coupling*; the equations (10) are coupled by virtue of the $k_{12}x_2$ term in (10a) and the $k_{21}x_1$ term in (10b), and similarly for (11).

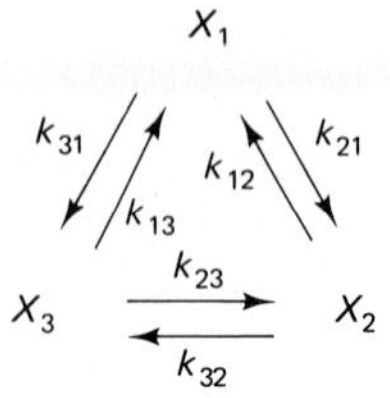

Fig. 4.8 Three-component reaction.

Changing to more compact matrix notation, observe that these systems are of the form

$$\dot{\mathbf{x}} = \mathbf{A}\mathbf{x}, \tag{12}$$

where the coupling is due to the fact that $\mathbf{A}$ is not diagonal. Our object will be to convert (12) to a system in which the matrix *is* diagonal. To accomplish that, we introduce a linear change of variables, from $\mathbf{x}$ to $\mathbf{x}'$ say, per

$$\mathbf{x} = \mathbf{Q}\mathbf{x}', \tag{13}$$

where $\mathbf{Q}$ is to be a suitable chosen invertible matrix; the primes indicate the new variables, *not* differentiation. Written out, (13) is merely the linear change of variables

$$\begin{aligned} x_1 &= q_{11}x_1' + q_{12}x_2' + \cdots + q_{1n}x_n' \\ x_2 &= q_{21}x_1' + q_{22}x_2' + \cdots + q_{2n}x_n' \\ &\vdots \\ x_n &= q_{n1}x_1' + q_{n2}x_2' + \cdots + q_{nn}x_n' \end{aligned}$$

from $x_1, \ldots, x_n$ to $x_1', \ldots, x_n'$. Let all of the elements of the $\mathbf{Q}$ matrix be constants, i.e., independent of t.

Putting (13) into (12) and noting that $d\mathbf{x}/dt = d(\mathbf{Q}\mathbf{x}')/dt = \mathbf{Q}\,d\mathbf{x}'/dt = \mathbf{Q}\dot{\mathbf{x}}'$ yields

$$\mathbf{Q}\dot{\mathbf{x}}' = \mathbf{A}\mathbf{Q}\mathbf{x}', \tag{14}$$

and premultiplying both sides by $\mathbf{Q}^{-1}$ gives

$$\dot{\mathbf{x}}' = \mathbf{Q}^{-1}\mathbf{A}\mathbf{Q}\mathbf{x}'. \tag{15}$$

Thus if $\mathbf{A}$ is diagonalizable, we can choose $\mathbf{Q}$ so that $\mathbf{Q}^{-1}\mathbf{A}\mathbf{Q} \equiv \mathbf{D}$ is diagonal;

specifically [Theorem 1(ii)], we choose the columns of **Q** to be the eigenvectors of **A**. Then

$$\dot{\mathbf{x}}' = \mathbf{D}\mathbf{x}'. \tag{16}$$

or

$$\begin{aligned} \dot{x}_1' &= d_1 x_1' \\ &\vdots \\ \dot{x}_n' &= d_n x_n', \end{aligned} \tag{17}$$

and since these are *not* coupled they are easily integrated, to give

$$\begin{aligned} x_1' &= C_1 e^{d_1 t} \\ &\vdots \\ x_n' &= C_n e^{d_n t}, \end{aligned} \tag{18}$$

where $C_1, \ldots, C_n$ are the constants of integration. Finally, we return to the unprimed x_j's via (13):

$$\mathbf{x} = \mathbf{Q}\mathbf{x}', \tag{19}$$

so

$$\begin{aligned} x_1 &= C_1 q_{11} e^{d_1 t} + C_2 q_{12} e^{d_2 t} + \cdots + C_n q_{1n} e^{d_n t} \\ &\vdots \\ x_n &= C_1 q_{n1} e^{d_1 t} + C_2 q_{n2} e^{d_2 t} + \cdots + C_n q_{nn} e^{d_n t}. \end{aligned} \tag{20}$$

Let us carry out these steps for the case where $n = 2$, i.e., for the system (10). It is easily found that the eigenvalues and eigenvectors of the "rate matrix"

$$\mathbf{A} = \begin{pmatrix} -k_{21} & k_{12} \\ k_{21} & -k_{12} \end{pmatrix} \tag{21}$$

are

$$\lambda_1 = 0, \quad \mathbf{e}_1 = \begin{pmatrix} k_{12} \\ k_{21} \end{pmatrix}; \qquad \lambda_2 = -(k_{12} + k_{21}), \quad \mathbf{e}_2 = \begin{pmatrix} 1 \\ -1 \end{pmatrix}. \tag{22}$$

Since the 2×2 matrix **A** has two distinct eigenvalues, it follows from Theorem 3 that **A** is diagonalizable. According to Theorem 1(ii), we choose the diagonalizing matrix **Q** as

$$\mathbf{Q} = (\mathbf{e}_1, \mathbf{e}_2) = \begin{pmatrix} k_{12} & 1 \\ k_{21} & -1 \end{pmatrix}, \tag{23}$$

in which case

$$\mathbf{D} = \begin{pmatrix} \lambda_1 & 0 \\ 0 & \lambda_2 \end{pmatrix} = \begin{pmatrix} 0 & 0 \\ 0 & -(k_{12} + k_{21}) \end{pmatrix}. \tag{24}$$

Thus (17) is

$$\begin{aligned} \dot{x}_1' &= 0x_1' \\ \dot{x}_2' &= -(k_{12} + k_{21})x_2', \end{aligned} \tag{25}$$

so

$$\begin{aligned} x_1' &= C_1 \\ x_2' &= C_2 e^{-(k_{12} + k_{21})t}, \end{aligned} \tag{26}$$

and (19) then yields

$$\begin{pmatrix} x_1 \\ x_2 \end{pmatrix} = \begin{pmatrix} k_{12} & 1 \\ k_{21} & -1 \end{pmatrix} \begin{pmatrix} C_1 \\ C_2 e^{-(k_{12}+k_{21})t} \end{pmatrix} \tag{27}$$

or

$$\begin{aligned} x_1 &= C_1 k_{12} + C_2 e^{-(k_{12} + k_{21})t} \\ x_2 &= C_1 k_{21} - C_2 e^{-(k_{12} + k_{21})t}. \end{aligned} \tag{28}$$

COMMENT 1 Here we have emphasized the mathematics rather than the chemistry, but we should note that while we have taken the rate constants, i.e., the k_{ij}'s, as known, one problem of importance to the chemist is the determination of these constants. Such determination normally involves a blend of the foregoing theory with suitable experiments, as discussed in Chap. 12 of NOBLE.

COMMENT 2 Transition from (12) to (16) was effected by introducing the change of variables (13). A variation of this approach, which you may prefer, is as follows. If **A** is diagonalizable, there is a **Q** such that

$$\mathbf{Q}^{-1}\mathbf{A}\mathbf{Q} = \mathbf{D}. \tag{29}$$

Premultiplying (29) by **Q** gives **AQ** = **QD**, and then postmultiplying this equation by $\mathbf{Q}^{-1}$ gives

$$\mathbf{A} = \mathbf{Q}\mathbf{D}\mathbf{Q}^{-1}. \tag{30}$$

Putting (30) into (12) gives us

$$\dot{\mathbf{x}} = \mathbf{Q}\mathbf{D}\mathbf{Q}^{-1}\mathbf{x}.$$

Hence

$$\mathbf{Q}^{-1}\dot{\mathbf{x}} = \mathbf{D}\mathbf{Q}^{-1}\mathbf{x},$$

or

$$\frac{d}{dt}(\mathbf{Q}^{-1}\mathbf{x}) = \mathbf{D}(\mathbf{Q}^{-1}\mathbf{x}), \tag{31}$$

and if we let $\mathbf{Q}^{-1}\mathbf{x} \equiv \mathbf{x}'$, we obtain (16), as before. ◀

We saw, in Section 4.3, that symmetry of a matrix carries with it certain useful properties as regards the eigenvalue problem, and it seems reasonable to expect that we might benefit from these properties in diagonalization. Thus, in the rest of this section, let us suppose that the matrix **A**, under consideration, is *symmetric*.

> ***Theorem 4*** *Diagonalizability*
>
> If **A** is symmetric, then it is diagonalizable (whether or not its eigenvalues are distinct).

Proof. The proof is simple. According to Theorem 1(i), an $n \times n$ matrix **A** is diagonalizable if and only if it has n LI eigenvectors. But according to Theorem 4 on page 148, a *symmetric* $n \times n$ matrix **A** has n orthogonal (and hence LI) eigenvectors. ■

There is an additional bonus. If, for a symmetric matrix **A**, we use *normalized* eigenvectors of **A**, say $\hat{\mathbf{e}}_1, \ldots, \hat{\mathbf{e}}_n$, in the modal matrix **Q**, in which case **Q** is called a **normalized modal matrix**, it turns out that

$$\mathbf{Q}^{-1} = \mathbf{Q}^{\mathrm{T}}. \tag{32}$$

Thus the inverse matrix $\mathbf{Q}^{-1}$, if we need it, is simply the tranpose of **Q**, no tedious inversion being needed. To verify (32), observe, from the definitions of matrix multiplication and the dot product, that

$$\mathbf{Q}^{\mathrm{T}}\mathbf{Q} = \begin{pmatrix} \hat{\mathbf{e}}_1^{\mathrm{T}} \\ \vdots \\ \hat{\mathbf{e}}_n^{\mathrm{T}} \end{pmatrix} (\hat{\mathbf{e}}_1, \ldots, \hat{\mathbf{e}}_n)$$
$$= \begin{pmatrix} \hat{\mathbf{e}}_1 \cdot \hat{\mathbf{e}}_1 & \hat{\mathbf{e}}_1 \cdot \hat{\mathbf{e}}_2 & \cdots & \hat{\mathbf{e}}_1 \cdot \hat{\mathbf{e}}_n \\ \hat{\mathbf{e}}_2 \cdot \hat{\mathbf{e}}_1 & \hat{\mathbf{e}}_2 \cdot \hat{\mathbf{e}}_2 & \cdots & \hat{\mathbf{e}}_2 \cdot \hat{\mathbf{e}}_n \\ \vdots & & & \vdots \\ \hat{\mathbf{e}}_n \cdot \hat{\mathbf{e}}_1 & \hat{\mathbf{e}}_n \cdot \hat{\mathbf{e}}_2 & \cdots & \hat{\mathbf{e}}_n \cdot \hat{\mathbf{e}}_n \end{pmatrix} = \begin{pmatrix} 1 & & & 0 \\ & 1 & & \\ & & \ddots & \\ 0 & & & 1 \end{pmatrix} = \mathbf{I}. \tag{33}$$

Now we know that $\mathbf{Q}^{-1}$ exists (since the columns of **Q** are LI), so if we postmultiply (33) by $\mathbf{Q}^{-1}$, we obtain

$$\mathbf{Q}^{\mathrm{T}}\mathbf{Q}\mathbf{Q}^{-1} = \mathbf{I}\mathbf{Q}^{-1},$$

or

$$\mathbf{Q}^{\mathrm{T}} = \mathbf{Q}^{-1}. \tag{34}$$

Since $\mathbf{Q}^{\mathrm{T}} = \mathbf{Q}^{-1}$, **Q** is an *orthogonal* matrix. Such matrices were met in Section 3.7 in connection with change of basis.

Let us close this section with one more application.

EXAMPLE 2 *A Free-Vibration Problem.* Consider a mass m constrained by two mechanical springs, of stiffnesses k_1 and k_2, as sketched in Fig. 4.9. Imagine Fig. 4.9 as a view looking down on the apparatus, which lies in a horizontal plane on a frictionless table. In the configuration shown, the springs are neither stretched nor compressed, and m is at rest in static equilibrium. However, if some initial displacement and/or velocity is imparted to m, some motion, apparently vibrational, will result, and it is that motion that we wish to consider.

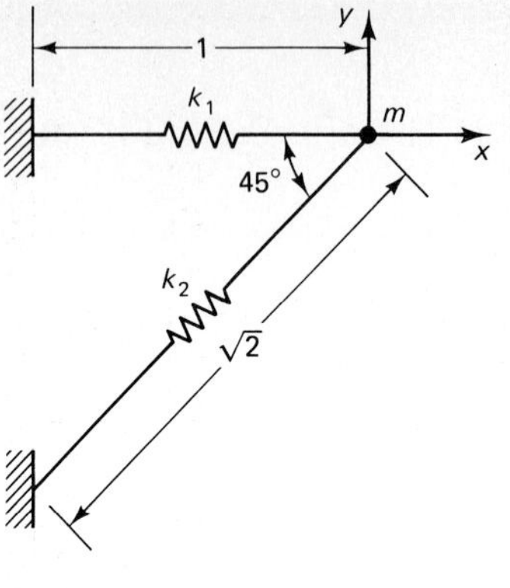

Fig. 4.9 Mass–spring system; view from above.

Formulation The first step is to introduce a coordinate system. An apparently reasonable choice is the Cartesian x,y system shown in Fig. 4.9, with its origin at the equilibrium position of the mass m. (It will be convenient to regard m as a "point mass.")

Now, if m is at some point x, y other than the origin, then one or both springs will be stretched or compressed, and will exert forces $\mathbf{F}_1$ and $\mathbf{F}_2$ on m, as shown in Fig. 4.10. The magnitude of $\mathbf{F}_1$ is

$$\begin{aligned} \|\mathbf{F}_1\| &= k_1 \text{ times the stretch in spring 1} \\ &= k_1\{\sqrt{[x-(-1)]^2+(y-0)^2}-1\} \\ &= k_1\{\sqrt{(x+1)^2+y^2}-1\}. \end{aligned} \tag{35}$$

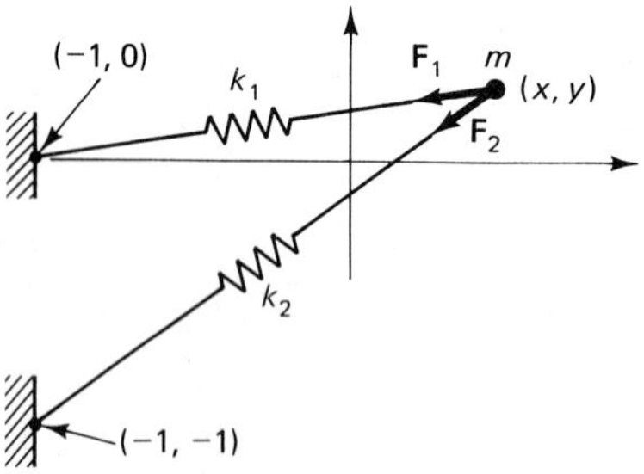

Fig. 4.10 Forces on m.

If we multiply this magnitude by a unit vector directed from (x, y) toward $(-1, 0)$, we will have $\mathbf{F}_1$. Well, the vector from (x, y) to $(-1, 0)$ is

$$(-1-x)\hat{\mathbf{i}}+(0-y)\hat{\mathbf{j}}, \tag{36}$$

where $\hat{\mathbf{i}}, \hat{\mathbf{j}}$ are unit base vectors in the x, y directions, respectively. Normalizing (36) yields the desired unit vector

$$-\frac{(1+x)\hat{\mathbf{i}}+y\hat{\mathbf{j}}}{\sqrt{(1+x)^2+y^2}} \equiv \hat{\mathbf{F}}_1, \tag{37}$$

say, so

$$\mathbf{F}_1 = \|\mathbf{F}_1\|\hat{\mathbf{F}}_1 = -k_1\left\{\frac{\sqrt{(x+1)^2+y^2}-1}{\sqrt{(x+1)^2+y^2}}\right\}[(x+1)\hat{\mathbf{i}}+y\hat{\mathbf{j}}]. \tag{38}$$

In the same manner, we find that

$$\mathbf{F}_2 = \|\mathbf{F}_2\|\hat{\mathbf{F}}_2 = -k_2\left\{\frac{\sqrt{(x+1)^2+(y+1)^2}-\sqrt{2}}{\sqrt{(x+1)^2+(y+1)^2}}\right\}[(x+1)\hat{\mathbf{i}}+(y+1)\hat{\mathbf{j}}]. \tag{39}$$

Now, the governing physical principle is the following version (for constant mass) of *Newton's second law of motion*,

$$\begin{aligned} m\ddot{x} &= F_x \\ m\ddot{y} &= F_y, \end{aligned} \tag{40}$$

where the double dots are short for d^2/dt^2, and F_x and F_y are the net x and y components of the forces acting on m. If we denote

$$\mathbf{F}_1 = F_{1x}\hat{\mathbf{i}} + F_{1y}\hat{\mathbf{j}} \quad \text{and} \quad \mathbf{F}_2 = F_{2x}\hat{\mathbf{i}} + F_{2y}\hat{\mathbf{j}},$$

then

$$\begin{aligned} F_x &= F_{1x} + F_{2x} \\ F_y &= F_{1y} + F_{2y}, \end{aligned} \tag{41}$$

so the differential equations of motion, governing the motion $x(t), y(t)$ of the mass m, are

$$\begin{aligned} m\ddot{x} = &-k_1\left\{\frac{\sqrt{(x+1)^2+y^2}-1}{\sqrt{(x+1)^2+y^2}}\right\}(x+1) \\ &- k_2\left\{\frac{\sqrt{(x+1)^2+(y+1)^2}-\sqrt{2}}{\sqrt{(x+1)^2+(y+1)^2}}\right\}(x+1) \end{aligned} \tag{42a}$$

$$\begin{aligned} m\ddot{y} = &-k_1\left\{\frac{\sqrt{(x+1)^2+y^2}-1}{\sqrt{(x+1)^2+y^2}}\right\}y \\ &- k_2\left\{\frac{\sqrt{(x+1)^2+(y+1)^2}-\sqrt{2}}{\sqrt{(x+1)^2+(y+1)^2}}\right\}(y+1). \end{aligned} \tag{42b}$$

These equations are evidently rather intractable because of the complicated functions of x and y on the right-hand sides. To render them tractable, let us back off a bit and limit our discussion to the case of *small* motions, i.e., wherein m remains within some small neighborhood of the origin. Thus

$$|x| \ll 1 \quad \text{and} \quad |y| \ll 1. \tag{43}$$

The idea, then, will be to expand the functions on the right-hand side of (42) in Taylor series about $x = y = 0$ and retain only the lowest-order terms, in essentially the same way that one often approximates

$$\begin{aligned} \sin x &= x - \frac{x^3}{3!} + \frac{x^5}{5!} - \cdots \quad &\text{(Taylor series about } x = 0) \\ &\approx x \quad &\text{(retaining only the lowest-order term)} \end{aligned} \tag{44}$$

for $|x| \ll 1$. However, while the reader has, no doubt, studied Taylor series for functions of a single variable, such as the function $f(x) = \sin x$ in (44), the right-hand sides of (42) are functions of *two* variables, x and y.* Without getting into a discussion of Taylor series of functions of more than one variable, it should suffice to point out that we need merely expand in one variable at a time. Thus, to expand a given (sufficiently well-behaved) function $f(x, y)$ about $(0, 0)$, we write

$$\begin{aligned} f(x,y) &= f(0,y) + f_x(0,y)x + \frac{1}{2!}f_{xx}(0,y)x^2 + \cdots \quad &&\text{(holding } y \text{ fixed and expanding in } x) \\ &\approx f(0,y) + f_x(0,y)x. \quad &&\text{(retaining terms only through first order)}^\dagger \end{aligned} \tag{45}$$

Next we expand the coefficients $f(0, y)$ and $f_x(0, y)$, in (45), in terms of y; we will expand $f(0, y)$ through first order, but need to expand $f_y(0, y)$ only through zeroth order since $f_x(0, y)$ already multiplies the first-order quantity x, and we have decided to keep terms only through first order. Thus

$$f(0,y) \approx f(0,0) + f_y(0,0)y$$
$$f_x(0,y) \approx f_x(0,0),$$

and (45) becomes

$$f(x,y) \approx f(0,0) + f_x(0,0)x + f_y(0,0)y. \tag{46}$$

Letting $f(x, y)$ be the right-hand side of (42a), we have

$$\begin{aligned} f(x,y) &= 0 + (-k_1 - \frac{k_2}{2})x + (-\frac{k_2}{2})y + \cdots \\ &\approx -(k_1 + \frac{k_2}{2})x - \frac{k_2}{2}y. \end{aligned} \tag{47a}$$

Here we have used the assumption (44) to justify the neglect of second- and higher-order terms. In the same way, we obtain for the right-hand side of (42b),

$$f(x,y) \approx -\frac{k_2}{2}x - \frac{k_2}{2}y. \tag{47b}$$

With the approximations (47a) and (47b), (42a) and (42b) simplify (considerably!) to

$$m\ddot{x} = -(k_1 + \frac{k_2}{2})\,x - \frac{k_2}{2}y \tag{48a}$$

$$m\ddot{y} = -\frac{k_2}{2}x - \frac{k_2}{2}y. \tag{48b}$$

* One may argue that $x = x(t)$ and $y = y(t)$, so that the right-hand sides of (42) are functions of the single variable t. True, but here we are regarding them as functions of the two independent variables x and y.

† A term $x^m y^n$ is said to be of *order* (or degree) $m + n$.

We have reverted to equal signs in (48), but it is of course to be understood that (48) is only an approximation to the original system (42). While (48) is coupled, just as (42) was, it is *linear*, and hence tractable.*

Solution by diagonalization The system (48) could be solved by the method employed in Example 3 on page 148, but we choose to use the notion of diagonalization instead. The only difficulty in (48) is the coupling, namely the presence of the y term in (48a) and the x term in (48b). Or if we set

$$\begin{pmatrix} x \\ y \end{pmatrix} \equiv \mathbf{q} \quad \text{and} \quad \begin{pmatrix} \dfrac{2k_1 + k_2}{2m} & \dfrac{k_2}{2m} \\ \dfrac{k_2}{2m} & \dfrac{k_2}{2m} \end{pmatrix} \equiv \mathbf{A}, \tag{49}$$

and express (48) compactly as

$$\ddot{\mathbf{q}} + \mathbf{A}\mathbf{q} = \mathbf{0}, \tag{50}$$

the difficulty is that $\mathbf{A}$ is not diagonal. But $\mathbf{A}$ is symmetric, and hence diagonalizable (Theorem 4). Thus proceeding as in Example 1, we introduce a linear change of variables

$$\mathbf{q} = \mathbf{Q}\mathbf{q}', \tag{51}$$

so that (50) becomes

$$\mathbf{Q}\ddot{\mathbf{q}}' + \mathbf{A}\mathbf{Q}\mathbf{q}' = \mathbf{0}$$

or, if $\mathbf{Q}$ is invertible,

$$\ddot{\mathbf{q}}' + (\mathbf{Q}^{-1}\mathbf{A}\mathbf{Q})\mathbf{q}' = \mathbf{0}. \tag{52}$$

The eigenvalues of $\mathbf{A}$ are easily found to be

$$\lambda = \frac{k_1 + k_2 \pm \sqrt{k_1^2 + k_2^2}}{2m}.$$

To simplify the writing, let us sacrifice a bit of generality and set

$$m = 1, \qquad k_1 = 3, \qquad k_2 = 4$$

from this point on. In that case the eigenvalues and eigenvectors of $\mathbf{A}$ are found to be

$$\lambda_1 = 1, \quad \hat{\mathbf{e}}_1 = \frac{1}{\sqrt{5}}\begin{pmatrix} 1 \\ -2 \end{pmatrix}; \qquad \lambda_2 = 6, \quad \hat{\mathbf{e}}_2 = \frac{1}{\sqrt{5}}\begin{pmatrix} 2 \\ 1 \end{pmatrix}. \tag{53}$$

*There are some questions of rigor here that we have played down. For example, the neglect of higher-order terms in (47a) has not been given rigorous support. Furthermore, even if we are agreed that the right-hand sides of (42) are closely approximated, for $|x| \ll 1$ and $|y| \ll 1$, by the right-hand sides of (48), does that really imply that the *solutions* $x(t), y(t)$ of (42) are closely approximated by the solutions $x(t), y(t)$ of (48)? However, our principal concern, here, is in the solution of (48) by diagonalization, and we hope that our heuristic approach in the *formulation* of (48) will be acceptable to the more rigorous reader.

Hence if we set

$$\mathbf{Q} = (\hat{\mathbf{e}}_1, \hat{\mathbf{e}}_2) = \begin{pmatrix} \frac{1}{\sqrt{5}} & \frac{2}{\sqrt{5}} \\ -\frac{2}{\sqrt{5}} & \frac{1}{\sqrt{5}} \end{pmatrix}, \tag{54}$$

then

$$\mathbf{Q}^{-1}\mathbf{A}\mathbf{Q} = \begin{pmatrix} \lambda_1 & 0 \\ 0 & \lambda_2 \end{pmatrix} = \begin{pmatrix} 1 & 0 \\ 0 & 6 \end{pmatrix}, \tag{55}$$

so (52), rewritten in scalar form, is the *uncoupled*, and hence simpler, pair of equations

$$\begin{aligned} \ddot{x}' + x' &= 0 \\ \ddot{y}' + 6y' &= 0. \end{aligned} \tag{56}$$

The general solution of these equations is

$$\begin{aligned} x' &= A_1 \sin(t + \phi_1) \\ y' &= A_2 \sin(\sqrt{6}t + \phi_2), \end{aligned} \tag{57}$$

where the magnitudes of A_1, A_2 and phase angles ϕ_1, ϕ_2 are the four constants of integration.

If we wish to return to the original variables, x, y, we use the connection $\mathbf{q} = \mathbf{Q}\mathbf{q}'$, namely,

$$\begin{aligned} \begin{pmatrix} x \\ y \end{pmatrix} &= \begin{pmatrix} \frac{1}{\sqrt{5}} & \frac{2}{\sqrt{5}} \\ -\frac{2}{\sqrt{5}} & \frac{1}{\sqrt{5}} \end{pmatrix} \begin{pmatrix} x' \\ y' \end{pmatrix} \\ &= A_1 \begin{pmatrix} \frac{1}{\sqrt{5}} \sin(t + \phi_1) \\ -\frac{2}{\sqrt{5}} \sin(t + \phi_1) \end{pmatrix} + A_2 \begin{pmatrix} \frac{2}{\sqrt{5}} \sin(\sqrt{6}\,t + \phi_2) \\ \frac{1}{\sqrt{5}} \sin(\sqrt{6}\,t + \phi_2) \end{pmatrix}. \end{aligned} \tag{58}$$

Or, in scalar form,

$$\begin{aligned} x(t) &= C_1 \sin(t + \phi_1) + 2C_2 \sin(\sqrt{6}\,t + \phi_2) \\ y(t) &= -2C_1 \sin(t + \phi_1) + C_2 \sin(\sqrt{6}\,t + \phi_2), \end{aligned} \tag{59}$$

where $A_1/\sqrt{5} \equiv C_1$ and $A_2/\sqrt{5} \equiv C_2$, for short.

COMMENT 1 As in Example 3 on page 148, we see that the general solution (58) is a linear combination of two orthogonal modes, where the orthogonality follows from the symmetry of **A**. The mode "shapes," or directions, are dictated by the eigenvectors, and the frequencies are the square roots of the corresponding eigenvalues, as summarized in Fig. 4.11.

COMMENT 2 The linear change of variables $\mathbf{q} = \mathbf{Q}\mathbf{q}'$, where **Q** is an orthogonal matrix, may be regarded in terms of change of basis, as discussed in Section 3.7.

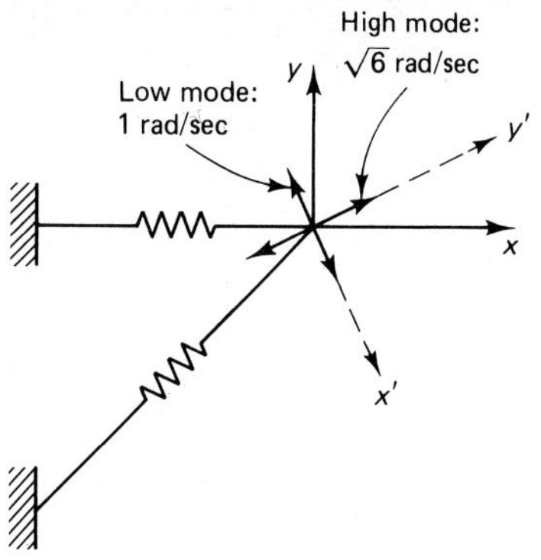

Fig. 4.11 Orthogonal modes.

[Comparing $\mathbf{q}' = \mathbf{Q}^{-1}\mathbf{q}$ with (6) on page 120, we see that $\mathbf{Q}^{-1}$ of the present section corresponds to $\mathbf{Q}$ of Section 3.7.] From the discussion of "Rotation in the Plane" in that section, it follows that the $\mathbf{Q}$ matrix given here in (54) corresponds to a clockwise rotation, from x, y to x', y', through an angle $\cos^{-1}(1/\sqrt{5})$, as shown in Fig. 4.11.

COMMENT 3 In principle, it would have been best to choose the x', y' coordinate system in the first place. But its orientation was not known a priori, so our procedure was to select *any* x, y system to get started; with equation (50) in hand, we were *then* in a position to change over to the optimal coordinates x', y'. ◀

We have seen that an $n \times n$ matrix $\mathbf{A}$ is diagonalizable if and only if it has n LI eigenvectors, and that a *sufficient* condition for $\mathbf{A}$ to have n LI eigenvectors is that it have n distinct eigenvalues. But if $\mathbf{A}$ is *symmetric*, it is diagonalizable whether or not its eigenvalues are distinct.

4.4 EXERCISES

1. Diagonalize each of the following $\mathbf{A}$ matrices, i.e., determine matrices $\mathbf{Q}$ and $\mathbf{D}$ such that $\mathbf{Q}^{-1}\mathbf{A}\mathbf{Q} = \mathbf{D}$ is diagonal. If not possible, state that.

*(a) $\begin{pmatrix} 2 & -3 \\ 0 & 0 \end{pmatrix}$ (b) $\begin{pmatrix} 2 & 4 \\ -1 & -2 \end{pmatrix}$

(c) $\begin{pmatrix} 1 & 0 \\ 1 & 0 \end{pmatrix}$ *(d) $\begin{pmatrix} 0 & 0 & 1 \\ 0 & 0 & 1 \\ 1 & 1 & 1 \end{pmatrix}$

(e) $\begin{pmatrix} 0 & 1 & 1 \\ 0 & 0 & 1 \\ 0 & 0 & 0 \end{pmatrix}$ (f) $\begin{pmatrix} 2 & 0 & 0 \\ 0 & 1 & 1 \\ 0 & 1 & 1 \end{pmatrix}$

(g) $\begin{pmatrix} 2 & 1 & -1 \\ 1 & 4 & 3 \\ -1 & 3 & 4 \end{pmatrix}$ (h) $\begin{pmatrix} 0 & 1 & 0 \\ 1 & 0 & 0 \\ 0 & 0 & 0 \end{pmatrix}$

(i) $\begin{pmatrix} 4 & 0 & 0 & 0 \\ 0 & 1 & 1 & 0 \\ 0 & 1 & 1 & 0 \\ 0 & 0 & 0 & 2 \end{pmatrix}$

2. Let $\mathbf{A}$ be the matrix in Exercise 1(d). Compute $\mathbf{A}^{100}$. *Hint:* Show that if $\mathbf{Q}^{-1}\mathbf{A}\mathbf{Q} = \mathbf{D}$, then $\mathbf{A} = \mathbf{Q}\mathbf{D}\mathbf{Q}^{-1}$. Then $\mathbf{A}^2 = \mathbf{Q}\mathbf{D}\mathbf{Q}^{-1}\mathbf{Q}\mathbf{D}\mathbf{Q}^{-1} = \mathbf{Q}\mathbf{D}^2\mathbf{Q}^{-1}$, and so on.

3. Obtain the general solution of the following systems of differential equations [in which $(\dot{\ }) \equiv d()/dt$] by the methods of this section.

*(a) $\dot{x} = x + y$
$\dot{y} = x + y$

(b) $\dot{x} = x + 4y$
$\dot{y} = x + y$

(c) $\ddot{x} = 2x + 4y$
$\ddot{y} = x - y$
(d) $\dot{x} + 2x + y = 0$
$\dot{y} + x + 2y + z = 0$
$\dot{z} + y + 2z = 0$
*(e) $\dot{x} = 4x + y + 3z$
$\dot{y} = x - z$
$\dot{z} = 3x - y + 4z$
(f) $\ddot{x} = -y + z$
$\ddot{y} = -x - 3y - 4z$
$\ddot{z} = x - 4y - 3z$

***4.** Can a singular matrix be diagonalized? Explain.

5. Refer to Fig. 4.11.
(a) What is the angle between the x axis and the x' axis?
(b) We see from the figure that the line of action of the high mode falls between the two springs. Show that that situation holds for all possible combinations of (positive) spring stiffnesses k_1 and k_2.

6. In Example 2 there are two orthogonal modes. How many would there be if there were three springs instead of two? Two masses instead of one? Explain.

7. Determine (as in Example 2) the natural frequencies and mode shapes, for each of the systems shown below. You need carry only three or four significant figures. Each spring is of unit length.

*(a)

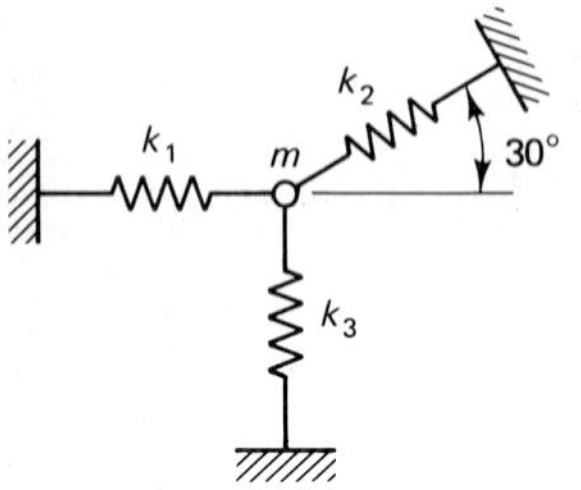

$m = k_1 = k_2 = 1,\ k_3 = 10$

(b)

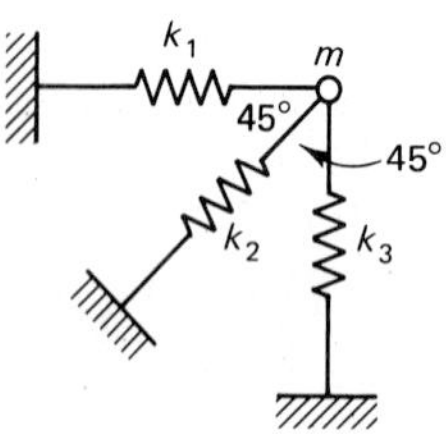

$n_{/} = k_1 = 4,\ k_2 = 3,\ k_3 = 1$

8. (*Principal inertias, principal axes*) Two vectors of importance in studying the dynamics of a rigid body $\mathcal{B}$ are the *moment of momentum*, $\mathbf{H}_p$, and the *angular velocity*, $\boldsymbol{\omega}$, of $\mathcal{B}$. These are related according to $\mathbf{H}_p = \mathcal{I}\boldsymbol{\omega}$, where $\mathcal{I}$ is the *inertia matrix*. Written out, we have

$$\begin{pmatrix} (H_p)_x \\ (H_p)_y \\ (H_p)_z \end{pmatrix} = \begin{pmatrix} I_{xx} & -I_{xy} & -I_{xz} \\ -I_{yx} & I_{yy} & -I_{yz} \\ -I_{zx} & -I_{zy} & I_{zz} \end{pmatrix} \begin{pmatrix} \omega_x \\ \omega_y \\ \omega_z \end{pmatrix}, \qquad \text{(a)}$$

where P is the origin of a Cartesian x,y,z coordinate system (see the figure), and

$$\begin{aligned} I_{xx} &= \int_{\mathcal{B}} (y^2 + z^2)\, dm, & I_{xy} &= I_{yx} = \int_{\mathcal{B}} xy\, dm \\ I_{yy} &= \int_{\mathcal{B}} (x^2 + z^2)\, dm, & I_{xz} &= I_{zx} = \int_{\mathcal{B}} xz\, dm \qquad \text{(b)} \\ I_{zz} &= \int_{\mathcal{B}} (x^2 + y^2)\, dm, & I_{yz} &= I_{zy} = \int_{\mathcal{B}} yz\, dm. \end{aligned}$$

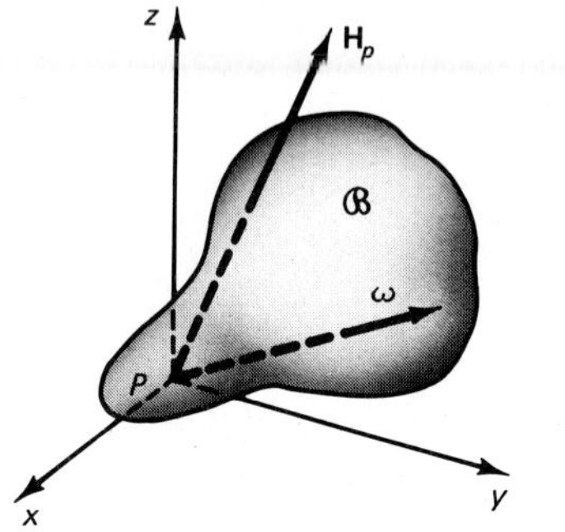

I_{xx}, I_{yy}, I_{zz} are known as the *moments of inertia* of $\mathcal{B}$ about the x, y, z axes, respectively, and I_{xy}, I_{xz}, I_{yz} are known as the *products of inertia* of $\mathcal{B}$; dm in (b) is "d(mass)." Now the relation (a) and hence the subsequent dynamic analysis (which will be of no concern here) will be simplest if $\mathcal{I}$ is diagonal, i.e., if all of the products of inertia are zero. In general, it is too difficult to see, by inspection, how to orient the coordinate axes to achieve this result. Instead, we go ahead and choose *some* x, y, z reference frame, compute the nine inertia components, and then rotate to a new cartesian x', y', z' frame so as to diagonalize $\mathcal{I}$. That is, if $\mathbf{x} = \mathbf{Q}\mathbf{x}'$, where $\mathbf{x} = (x, y, z)^{\mathrm{T}}$ and $\mathbf{x}' = (x', y', z')^{\mathrm{T}}$, then $\mathbf{H}_p = \mathbf{Q}\mathbf{H}_p'$ and $\boldsymbol{\omega} = \mathbf{Q}\boldsymbol{\omega}'$, so that $\mathbf{H}_p = \mathcal{I}\boldsymbol{\omega}$ becomes

$$\mathbf{Q}\mathbf{H}_p' = \mathcal{I}\mathbf{Q}\boldsymbol{\omega}' \quad \text{or} \quad \mathbf{H}_p' = (\mathbf{Q}^{-1}\mathcal{I}\mathbf{Q})\boldsymbol{\omega}', \qquad \text{(c)}$$

where $\mathbf{Q}^{-1}\mathcal{I}\mathbf{Q} \equiv \mathcal{I}'$ is diagonal. That such diagonalization is possible follows from the fact that $\mathcal{I}$ is *symmetric*, since $I_{xy} = I_{yx}$, $I_{xz} = I_{zx}$, and $I_{yz} = I_{zy}$. $I_{x'x'}$, $I_{y'y'}$, and $I_{z'z'}$ are called the **principal inertias** of $\mathcal{B}$ (with respect to coordinates with origin at P), and the x', y', z' axes are called the **principal axes**. We now state the problem: Compute the principal inertias and determine the principal axes for each of the following bodies; sketch the principal axes. In each case $\mathcal{B}$ can be assumed, for simplicity, to be infinitely thin, with mass density σ mass units per unit area.

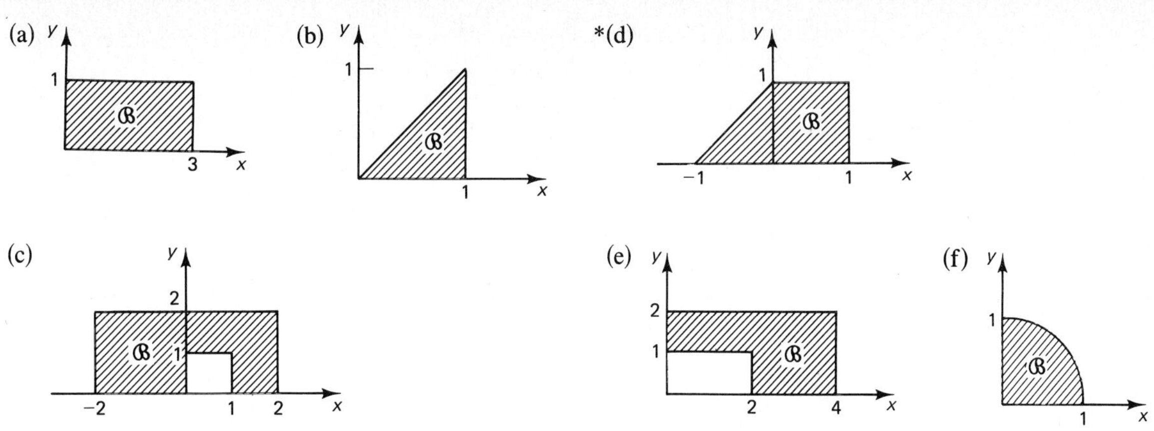

JORDAN FORM 4.5

[Optional Section]

In Section 4.4 we saw that any $n \times n$ matrix $\mathbf{A}$ is diagonalizable (by a suitable similarity transformation $\mathbf{Q}^{-1}\mathbf{A}\mathbf{Q} = \mathbf{D}$) if and only if $\mathbf{A}$ has n LI eigenvectors. Unfortunately, an $n \times n$ matrix does not necessarily have n LI eigenvectors. For example,

$$\mathbf{A} = \begin{pmatrix} 1 & 4 \\ -1 & 5 \end{pmatrix}$$

has the characteristic equation $(\lambda - 3)^2 = 0$, so $\lambda = 3, 3$. Since the λ's are not distinct, it follows from Theorem 2 (page 162) that the corresponding eigenvectors need not be LI. In fact, we find that the eigenspace corresponding to $\lambda = 3$ is only one-dimensional, with $\mathbf{e} = \alpha(2, 1)^{\mathrm{T}}$, so that one, but no more than one, LI eigenvector can be found. We conclude that $\mathbf{A}$ is not diagonalizable.

Thus the sad fact is that *not all matrices* are diagonalizable*. However, it turns out that *every* matrix is "*almost diagonalizable*," in a sense that will be made clear shortly.

Normally, we present theory, then examples and applications. Here, however, it seems best to reverse the order since an example will make it much easier for us to see our way into the general theory.

EXAMPLE 1 Consider

$$\mathbf{A} = \begin{pmatrix} 2 & -1 & 2 & 0 \\ 0 & 3 & -1 & 0 \\ 0 & 1 & 1 & 0 \\ 0 & 1 & -3 & 5 \end{pmatrix}. \tag{1}$$

* It will be understood, in this section, that **A** is square.

Calculation reveals that the eigenvalues are $\lambda = 2, 2, 2, 5$, with the eigenvectors

$$\lambda_1 = \lambda_2 = \lambda_3 = 2: \qquad \mathbf{e} = (1, 0, 0, 0)^{\mathrm{T}} \equiv \mathbf{e}_1, \text{say} \tag{2a}$$

$$\lambda_4 = 5: \qquad \mathbf{e} = (0, 0, 0, 1)^{\mathrm{T}} \equiv \mathbf{e}_4. \tag{2b}$$

In this case, the eigenvalue of multiplicity 3, $\lambda = 2$, contributes only one LI eigenvector, instead of three, so we end up with only two LI eigenvectors, $\mathbf{e}_1$ and $\mathbf{e}_4$ given above, instead of the four that are needed for $\mathbf{A}$ to be diagonalizable. Thus $\mathbf{A}$ cannot be diagonalized.

But we *can* find so-called *generalized eigenvectors* $\mathbf{e}_2$ and $\mathbf{e}_3$, associated with $\lambda = 2$, such that $\mathbf{e}_1, \mathbf{e}_2, \mathbf{e}_3, \mathbf{e}_4$ are LI. Noting that $\mathbf{e}_1$ satisfies

$$(\mathbf{A} - \lambda_1 \mathbf{I})\mathbf{e}_1 = \mathbf{0}, \tag{3a}$$

we introduce $\mathbf{e}_2, \mathbf{e}_3$ so as to satisfy the conditions

$$(\mathbf{A} - \lambda_1 \mathbf{I})\mathbf{e}_2 = \mathbf{e}_1, \tag{3b}$$

$$(\mathbf{A} - \lambda_1 \mathbf{I})\mathbf{e}_3 = \mathbf{e}_2. \tag{3c}$$

With $\mathbf{e}_1$ known, the idea is to solve (3b) for $\mathbf{e}_2$ and then, putting this $\mathbf{e}_2$ into (3c), to solve (3c) for $\mathbf{e}_3$. Not wishing to be distracted by the details of those calculations, let us suppose, for the moment, that $\mathbf{e}_2$ and $\mathbf{e}_3$ are in hand. We will show that $\mathbf{e}_1, \mathbf{e}_2, \mathbf{e}_3, \mathbf{e}_4$ are necessarily LI. For suppose that

$$\alpha_1 \mathbf{e}_1 + \alpha_2 \mathbf{e}_2 + \alpha_3 \mathbf{e}_3 + \alpha_4 \mathbf{e}_4 = \mathbf{0}. \tag{4}$$

Multiplying each term in (4) by $\mathbf{A} - \lambda_1 \mathbf{I}$, and recalling equations (3) and the fact that $\mathbf{A}\mathbf{e}_4 = \lambda_4 \mathbf{e}_4$, we obtain

$$\alpha_2 \mathbf{e}_1 + \alpha_3 \mathbf{e}_2 + \alpha_4 (\lambda_4 - \lambda_1) \mathbf{e}_4 = \mathbf{0}. \tag{5}$$

Repeating the process, we multiply (5) by $\mathbf{A} - \lambda_1 \mathbf{I}$ and obtain

$$\alpha_3 \mathbf{e}_1 + \alpha_4 (\lambda_4 - \lambda_1)^2 \mathbf{e}_4 = \mathbf{0}. \tag{6}$$

Repeating the process once more gives

$$\alpha_4 (\lambda_4 - \lambda_1)^3 \mathbf{e}_4 = \mathbf{0}. \tag{7}$$

Now $\mathbf{e}_4 \neq \mathbf{0}$ and $\lambda_4 - \lambda_1 \neq 0$, so it follows from (7) that $\alpha_4 = 0$. With $\alpha_4 = 0$, (6) then gives $\alpha_3 = 0$. Then (5) gives $\alpha_2 = 0$, and (4) gives $\alpha_1 = 0$, so that $\alpha_1, \alpha_2, \alpha_3, \alpha_4$ are all necessarily zero in (4). Hence $\mathbf{e}_1, \mathbf{e}_2, \mathbf{e}_3, \mathbf{e}_4$ are LI, as claimed.

Staying as close as possible to the modal matrix approach discussed in Section 4.4, let us construct a 4×4 matrix

$$\mathbf{P} = (\mathbf{e}_1, \mathbf{e}_2, \mathbf{e}_3, \mathbf{e}_4). \tag{8}$$

Since its columns are the eigenvectors $\mathbf{e}_1, \mathbf{e}_4$ and the *generalized* eigenvectors $\mathbf{e}_2, \mathbf{e}_3$, we will refer to $\mathbf{P}$ as a *generalized modal matrix* associated with $\mathbf{A}$. Recall that if $\mathbf{P}$ were a true modal matrix, $\mathbf{P}^{-1}\mathbf{A}\mathbf{P}$ would be diagonal. We plan to show, next, that although $\mathbf{P}^{-1}\mathbf{A}\mathbf{P}$ is not diagonal, it is *almost* diagonal.

First, observe that $\mathbf{P}^{-1}$ does indeed exist since the columns of $\mathbf{P}$ (namely, $\mathbf{e}_1, \mathbf{e}_2, \mathbf{e}_3, \mathbf{e}_4$) are LI. Let us suppose that $\mathbf{P}^{-1}$ has now been computed, and let us denote its rows as $\mathbf{r}_1, \mathbf{r}_2, \mathbf{r}_3, \mathbf{r}_4$:

$$\mathbf{P}^{-1} = \begin{pmatrix} \mathbf{r}_1 \\ \mathbf{r}_2 \\ \mathbf{r}_3 \\ \mathbf{r}_4 \end{pmatrix}. \tag{9}$$

Since $\mathbf{P}^{-1}\mathbf{P} = \mathbf{I}$, it follows that

$$\mathbf{r}_i\mathbf{e}_j = \delta_{ij}, \tag{10}$$

where δ_{ij} is the Kronecker delta.

We are now ready to show that $\mathbf{P}^{-1}\mathbf{A}\mathbf{P}$ is almost diagonal.

$$\begin{aligned}
\mathbf{P}^{-1}\mathbf{A}\mathbf{P} &= \mathbf{P}^{-1}\mathbf{A}(\mathbf{e}_1, \mathbf{e}_2, \mathbf{e}_3, \mathbf{e}_4) \\
&= \mathbf{P}^{-1}(\mathbf{A}\mathbf{e}_1, \mathbf{A}\mathbf{e}_2, \mathbf{A}\mathbf{e}_3, \mathbf{A}\mathbf{e}_4) \\
&= \mathbf{P}^{-1}(\lambda_1\mathbf{e}_1, \mathbf{e}_1 + \lambda_1\mathbf{e}_2, \mathbf{e}_2 + \lambda_1\mathbf{e}_3, \lambda_4\mathbf{e}_4) \qquad (11) \\
&= \begin{pmatrix} \mathbf{r}_1 \\ \mathbf{r}_2 \\ \mathbf{r}_3 \\ \mathbf{r}_4 \end{pmatrix}(\lambda_1\mathbf{e}_1, \lambda_1\mathbf{e}_2, \lambda_1\mathbf{e}_3, \lambda_4\mathbf{e}_4) + \begin{pmatrix} \mathbf{r}_1 \\ \mathbf{r}_2 \\ \mathbf{r}_3 \\ \mathbf{r}_4 \end{pmatrix}(\mathbf{0}, \mathbf{e}_1, \mathbf{e}_2, \mathbf{0}) \\
&= \begin{pmatrix} \lambda_1 & 0 & 0 & 0 \\ 0 & \lambda_1 & 0 & 0 \\ 0 & 0 & \lambda_1 & 0 \\ 0 & 0 & 0 & \lambda_4 \end{pmatrix} + \begin{pmatrix} 0 & 1 & 0 & 0 \\ 0 & 0 & 1 & 0 \\ 0 & 0 & 0 & 0 \\ 0 & 0 & 0 & 0 \end{pmatrix},
\end{aligned}$$

so

$$\mathbf{P}^{-1}\mathbf{A}\mathbf{P} = \begin{pmatrix} \lambda_1 & 1 & 0 & 0 \\ 0 & \lambda_1 & 1 & 0 \\ 0 & 0 & \lambda_1 & 0 \\ 0 & 0 & 0 & \lambda_4 \end{pmatrix} = \begin{pmatrix} 2 & 1 & 0 & 0 \\ 0 & 2 & 1 & 0 \\ 0 & 0 & 2 & 0 \\ 0 & 0 & 0 & 5 \end{pmatrix} \equiv \mathbf{J}, \tag{12}$$

where $\mathbf{J}$ is known as a *Jordan form* for $\mathbf{A}$. Although $\mathbf{J}$ is not diagonal, it is as close to diagonal as we are able to get. Further, $\mathbf{J}$ is seen to be a *triangular* matrix (upper triangular), and this form is convenient in applications.

It remains to determine $\mathbf{e}_2$, $\mathbf{e}_3$, and $\mathbf{P}^{-1}$. Notice that among all the steps in obtaining the Jordan form (12), the only possible weak link is in the calculation of the generalized eigenvectors $\mathbf{e}_2$ and $\mathbf{e}_3$ for, after all, (3b) is of the general form "$\mathbf{A}\mathbf{X} = \mathbf{c}$" and may, conceivably, have no solution. Similarly for (3c). We supply general comments on this point a bit later. For the present, let us at least *try* to find $\mathbf{e}_2$ and $\mathbf{e}_3$. Expressing $\mathbf{e}_2 = (x_1^{(2)}, \ldots, x_4^{(2)})^{\mathrm{T}}$, (3b) becomes

$$\begin{pmatrix} 0 & -1 & 2 & 0 \\ 0 & 1 & -1 & 0 \\ 0 & 1 & -1 & 0 \\ 0 & 1 & -3 & 3 \end{pmatrix}\begin{pmatrix} x_1^{(2)} \\ x_2^{(2)} \\ x_3^{(2)} \\ x_4^{(2)} \end{pmatrix} = \begin{pmatrix} 1 \\ 0 \\ 0 \\ 0 \end{pmatrix} \tag{13}$$

Not only is (13) consistent, it admits the one-parameter family of solutions $\mathbf{e}_2 = (\alpha, 1, 1, 2/3)^{\mathrm{T}}$, where α is arbitrary. We do not need all possible $\mathbf{e}_2$'s; one will suffice. Thus we might as well choose $\alpha = 0$ for simplicity. Then (3c) becomes

$$\begin{pmatrix} 0 & -1 & 2 & 0 \\ 0 & 1 & -1 & 0 \\ 0 & 1 & -1 & 0 \\ 0 & 1 & -3 & 3 \end{pmatrix}\begin{pmatrix} x_1^{(3)} \\ x_2^{(3)} \\ x_3^{(3)} \\ x_4^{(3)} \end{pmatrix} = \begin{pmatrix} 0 \\ 1 \\ 1 \\ \frac{2}{3} \end{pmatrix}, \tag{14}$$

with the solution $\mathbf{e}_3 = (\beta, 2, 1, 5/9)^T$, where β is arbitrary. With $\beta = 0$, for simplicity, we have

$$\mathbf{P} = (\mathbf{e}_1, \mathbf{e}_2, \mathbf{e}_3, \mathbf{e}_4) = \begin{pmatrix} 1 & 0 & 0 & 0 \\ 0 & 1 & 2 & 0 \\ 0 & 1 & 1 & 0 \\ 0 & \frac{2}{3} & \frac{5}{9} & 1 \end{pmatrix}. \tag{15}$$

CONCLUSION **A** is reduced to the Jordan form (12) by the similarity transformation $\mathbf{P}^{-1}\mathbf{A}\mathbf{P}$, where **P** is given by (15).

COMMENT 1 While we have not bothered to compute $\mathbf{P}^{-1}$, we should warn you that $\mathbf{P}^{-1} \neq \mathbf{P}^T$. In Section 4.4 the normalized modal matrix **Q** *was* orthogonal (i.e., $\mathbf{Q}^{-1} = \mathbf{Q}^T$) since its columns constituted an orthonormal set. Here, however, the columns of **P** are not orthonormal, they are merely LI.

COMMENT 2 It is tempting to scale $\mathbf{e}_2$ by a factor of 3 and $\mathbf{e}_3$ by a factor of 9 so that **P** [given by (15)] contains no fractions. Is such scaling permissible? Well, we can certainly scale $\mathbf{e}_1$ by any nonzero factor since it is an eigenvector. That is, if $\mathbf{e}_1$ satisfies the *homogeneous* equation (3a), so does any scalar multiple of $\mathbf{e}_1$. But $\mathbf{e}_2$ and $\mathbf{e}_3$ are not eigenvectors, they are *generalized* eigenvectors, and they satisfy the *nonhomogeneous* equations (3b) and (3c). From (3c) we see that if we wish to scale $\mathbf{e}_3$ by a factor of 9, we also need to scale $\mathbf{e}_2$ by 9, and from (3b) we see that if we scale $\mathbf{e}_2$ by 9, we also need to scale $\mathbf{e}_1$ by 9. Thus, if we want **P** to contain only integer elements, we can change $\mathbf{e}_1, \mathbf{e}_2, \mathbf{e}_3$ to $\mathbf{e}_1 = (9, 0, 0, 0)^T$, $\mathbf{e}_2 = (0, 9, 9, 6)^T$, and $\mathbf{e}_3 = (0, 18, 9, 5)^T$, respectively. ◀

To generalize the ideas developed in the foregoing example, we begin with some definitions.

Let λ be an eigenvalue (of **A**) of multiplicity K, and let the eigenspace corresponding to λ be of dimension k, where $k < K$. Within that eigenspace there can be found k LI eigenvectors of **A**, say, $\mathbf{e}_1$ through $\mathbf{e}_k$. Vectors $\mathbf{e}_{k+1}$ through $\mathbf{e}_K$, such that

$$\begin{aligned} (\mathbf{A} - \lambda\mathbf{I})\mathbf{e}_{k+1} &= \mathbf{e}_k, \\ (\mathbf{A} - \lambda\mathbf{I})\mathbf{e}_{k+2} &= \mathbf{e}_{k+1}, \\ &\vdots \\ (\mathbf{A} - \lambda\mathbf{I})\mathbf{e}_K &= \mathbf{e}_{K-1} \end{aligned} \tag{16}$$

will be called **generalized eigenvectors** corresponding to the eigenvalue λ. We speak of $\mathbf{e}_k, \mathbf{e}_{k+1}, \ldots, \mathbf{e}_K$ as a **chain of vectors** headed by the eigenvector $\mathbf{e}_k$.

Next, we define a **Jordan block** $\mathbf{J}_i$ to be a matrix of the type

$$\mathbf{J}_i = \begin{pmatrix} \lambda_i & 1 & & & \bigcirc \\ & \lambda_i & 1 & & \\ & & \ddots & \ddots & \\ & & & \lambda_i & 1 \\ \bigcirc & & & & \lambda_i \end{pmatrix}. \tag{17}$$

Finally, suppose that **A** is $n \times n$ and that $\mathbf{e}_1, \mathbf{e}_2, \ldots, \mathbf{e}_n$ are eigenvectors and generalized eigenvectors of **A**, with all chains kept intact.

EXAMPLE 2 For example, if **A** is 9×9 and has eigenvalues with the multiplicities shown in column 1 of Table 4.1, with the dimension of the corresponding eigenspaces as shown in column 2, the distribution of eigenvectors and generalized eigenvectors (assuming that these do exist) will be as shown in columns 3 and 4. Then $\mathbf{e}_1, \mathbf{e}_2, \ldots, \mathbf{e}_n$ may be grouped as follows:

TABLE 4.1 Example of Distribution of Eigenvectors and Generalized Eigenvectors

	Multiplicity	*Dimension of Eigenspace*	*Eigenvectors*	*Generalized Eigenvectors*
λ_1	1	1	$\mathbf{e}_1$	None
λ_2	5	2	$\mathbf{e}_2, \mathbf{e}_3$	$\mathbf{e}_4, \mathbf{e}_5, \mathbf{e}_6$
λ_7	3	1	$\mathbf{e}_7$	$\mathbf{e}_8, \mathbf{e}_9$

$$\overbrace{\underbrace{\mathbf{e}_1}_{\text{chain}}}^{\lambda_1},\ \overbrace{\underbrace{\mathbf{e}_2}_{\text{chain}},\ \underbrace{\mathbf{e}_3, \mathbf{e}_4, \mathbf{e}_5, \mathbf{e}_6}_{\text{chain}}}^{\lambda_2},\ \overbrace{\underbrace{\mathbf{e}_7, \mathbf{e}_8, \mathbf{e}_9}_{\text{chain}}}^{\lambda_7}. \quad \blacktriangleleft \tag{18}$$

If **P** is the generalized modal matrix $\mathbf{P} = (\mathbf{e}_1, \ldots, \mathbf{e}_n)$, then $\mathbf{P}^{-1}\mathbf{AP}$ will be *block diagonal*, with each chain leading to a Jordan block on the main diagonal. We call this matrix a **Jordan form** for **A** and denote it as $\mathbf{J} = \mathbf{P}^{-1}\mathbf{AP}$. For instance, in Example 1 we had

$$\mathbf{J} = \begin{pmatrix} \boxed{\begin{matrix} \lambda_1 & 1 & 0 \\ 0 & \lambda_1 & 1 \\ 0 & 0 & \lambda_1 \end{matrix}}_{\,\mathbf{J}_1} & \bigcirc \\ \bigcirc & \boxed{\lambda_4}_{\,\mathbf{J}_2} \end{pmatrix}, \tag{19}$$

and in Example 2 **J** would look like this:

$$\mathbf{J} = \begin{pmatrix} \boxed{\lambda_1}_{\,\mathbf{J}_1} & & & \bigcirc \\ & \boxed{\lambda_2}_{\,\mathbf{J}_2} & & \\ & & \boxed{\begin{matrix} \lambda_2 & 1 & 0 & 0 \\ 0 & \lambda_2 & 1 & 0 \\ 0 & 0 & \lambda_2 & 1 \\ 0 & 0 & 0 & \lambda_2 \end{matrix}}_{\,\mathbf{J}_3} & \\ \bigcirc & & & \boxed{\begin{matrix} \lambda_3 & 1 & 0 \\ 0 & \lambda_3 & 1 \\ 0 & 0 & \lambda_3 \end{matrix}}_{\,\mathbf{J}_4} \end{pmatrix}, \tag{20}$$

Theorem 1 *Jordan Form*

If an $n \times n$ matrix $\mathbf{A}$ has s LI eigenvectors, then it has a generalized modal matrix $\mathbf{P}$, and

$$\mathbf{J} = \mathbf{P}^{-1}\mathbf{A}\mathbf{P} = \begin{pmatrix} \mathbf{J}_1 & & & \bigcirc \\ & \mathbf{J}_2 & & \\ & & \ddots & \\ \bigcirc & & & \mathbf{J}_s \end{pmatrix}, \tag{21}$$

where the Jordan block $\mathbf{J}_i$ corresponds to the ith chain.

Whereas $s \leq n$ in Theorem 1 it is, of course, only the case where $s < n$ that is of concern in this section since if $s = n$, then $\mathbf{A}$ is diagonalizable, as discussed in Section 4.4. Or, in terms of the present discussion, if $s = n$, then $\mathbf{J}_1, \ldots, \mathbf{J}_s$ are all 1×1, $\mathbf{J}$ is diagonal, and $\mathbf{P}$ is the modal matrix $\mathbf{Q}$ discussed in Section 4.4.

The part of Theorem 1 that we have *not* proved is that the generalized eigenvectors can indeed be found. Looking back at (16), we see that solutions $\mathbf{e}_{k+1}, \ldots, \mathbf{e}_K$ of (16) can be found if and only if $r(\mathbf{A} - \lambda\mathbf{I}) = r((A - \lambda\mathbf{I}), \mathbf{e}_k) = \cdots = r((\mathbf{A} - \lambda\mathbf{I}), \mathbf{e}_{K-1})$. Proof of this point lies beyond our present scope, and will be omitted.*

Now we look at one last example, this time an application to a system of differential equations.

EXAMPLE 3 Consider the system of differential equations

$$\begin{aligned} \dot{x}_1 &= 3x_1 - x_3 \\ \dot{x}_2 &= -x_1 + 2x_2 + x_3 \\ \dot{x}_3 &= x_1 + x_3, \end{aligned} \tag{22}$$

or, in matrix form,

$$\dot{\mathbf{x}} = \mathbf{A}\mathbf{x}; \qquad \mathbf{x} = \begin{pmatrix} x_1 \\ x_2 \\ x_3 \end{pmatrix}, \qquad \mathbf{A} = \begin{pmatrix} 3 & 0 & -1 \\ -1 & 2 & 1 \\ 1 & 0 & 1 \end{pmatrix}, \tag{23}$$

where $(\dot{\ }) = d(\ )/dt$. The equations (22) are coupled (i.e., $\mathbf{A}$ is not diagonal), and we wish to uncouple them—insofar as possible—in order to solve them for $x_1(t)$, $x_2(t)$, $x_3(t)$. Thus, if possible, we wish to diagonalize $\mathbf{A}$; if not possible, we will settle for a reduction to Jordan form.

The eigenvalues and eigenvectors of $\mathbf{A}$ are found to be

$$\lambda_1 = \lambda_2 = \lambda_3 = 2: \qquad \mathbf{e} = \begin{pmatrix} \alpha \\ \beta \\ \alpha \end{pmatrix} = \alpha\begin{pmatrix} 1 \\ 0 \\ 1 \end{pmatrix} + \beta\begin{pmatrix} 0 \\ 1 \\ 0 \end{pmatrix}, \tag{24}$$

* For two different lines of proof, we refer the interested reader to Gilbert Strang, *Linear Algebra and Its Applications* (New York: Academic Press, 1976); and D. Faddeev and V. Faddeeva, *Computational Methods of Linear Algebra* (San Francisco: W. H. Freeman, 1963).

so we set

$$\mathbf{e}_1 = \begin{pmatrix} 1 \\ 0 \\ 1 \end{pmatrix}, \qquad \mathbf{e}_2 = \begin{pmatrix} 0 \\ 1 \\ 0 \end{pmatrix}, \tag{25}$$

say, and seek a generalized eigenvector $\mathbf{e}_3$ per $(\mathbf{A} - 2\mathbf{I})\mathbf{e}_3 = \mathbf{e}_2$, or

$$\begin{pmatrix} 1 & 0 & -1 \\ -1 & 0 & 1 \\ 1 & 0 & -1 \end{pmatrix} \begin{pmatrix} x_1^{(3)} \\ x_2^{(3)} \\ x_3^{(3)} \end{pmatrix} = \begin{pmatrix} 0 \\ 1 \\ 0 \end{pmatrix}. \tag{26}$$

Unfortunately, this system is inconsistent! Yet, we know, from Theorem 1, that a generalized eigenvector $\mathbf{e}_3$ *can* be found. So we go back to the eigenspace $\mathbf{e} = (\alpha, \beta, \alpha)^{\mathrm{T}}$ and select a better eigenvector to head the chain. Setting $\mathbf{e}_2 = (\alpha, \beta, \alpha)^{\mathrm{T}}$, but this time without any priori specification of α and β, we find that the consistency of $(\mathbf{A} - 2\mathbf{I})\mathbf{e}_3 = \mathbf{e}_2$ requires that $\beta = -\alpha$. Thus, in place of (25), we choose

$$\mathbf{e}_1 = \begin{pmatrix} 1 \\ 0 \\ 1 \end{pmatrix}, \qquad \mathbf{e}_2 = \begin{pmatrix} 1 \\ -1 \\ 1 \end{pmatrix}, \tag{27}$$

and this time $(\mathbf{A} - 2\mathbf{I})\mathbf{e}_3 = \mathbf{e}_2$ becomes*

$$\begin{pmatrix} 1 & 0 & -1 \\ -1 & 0 & 1 \\ 1 & 0 & -1 \end{pmatrix} \begin{pmatrix} x_1^{(3)} \\ x_2^{(3)} \\ x_3^{(3)} \end{pmatrix} = \begin{pmatrix} 1 \\ -1 \\ 1 \end{pmatrix}, \tag{28}$$

which *is* consistent. In fact, (28) admits a two-parameter family of solutions. But one solution is all we need, and we select the simple solution $\mathbf{e}_3 = (1, 0, 0)^{\mathrm{T}}$. Thus,

$$\mathbf{P} = \begin{pmatrix} 1 & 1 & 1 \\ 0 & -1 & 0 \\ 1 & 1 & 0 \end{pmatrix}. \tag{29}$$

Now set $\mathbf{x} = \mathbf{P}\mathbf{x}'$ in (23), so $\dot{\mathbf{x}} = \mathbf{A}\mathbf{x}$ becomes $\mathbf{P}\dot{\mathbf{x}}' = \mathbf{A}\mathbf{P}\mathbf{x}'$, or

$$\dot{\mathbf{x}}' = \mathbf{P}^{-1}\mathbf{A}\mathbf{P}\mathbf{x}' = \mathbf{J}\mathbf{x}' = \begin{pmatrix} 2 & 0 & 0 \\ 0 & 2 & 1 \\ 0 & 0 & 2 \end{pmatrix} \mathbf{x}'. \tag{30}$$

Denoting $\mathbf{x}' = (x_1', x_2', x_3')^{\mathrm{T}}$, we therefore have the system

$$\dot{x}_1 = 2x_1 \tag{31a}$$

$$\dot{x}_2 = 2x_2 + x_3 \tag{31b}$$

$$\dot{x}_3 = 2x_3. \tag{31c}$$

* Having come up with a new $\mathbf{e}_2$, as given in (27), we need to go back and make sure that $\mathbf{e}_1$ [which we chose by arbitrarily setting $\alpha = 1$ and $\beta = 0$ in (24)] and $\mathbf{e}_2$ are LI. They are. If they were not, $\mathbf{e}_1$ would need to be rechosen as any vector $(\alpha, \beta, \alpha)^{\mathrm{T}}$ which is linearly independent of $\mathbf{e}_2 = (1, -1, 1)^{\mathrm{T}}$.

Observe (and this is the point) that (30) is simpler than (23) inasmuch as **J** is triangular. Thus, as in Gauss elimination, we may "unravel" the tangle by starting at the bottom and working up:* (31c) gives $x_3' = Ae^{2t}$; putting this expression into (31b) and solving, $x_2' = (B + At)e^{2t}$; and (31a) gives $x_1' = Ce^{2t}$, where A, B, C are integration constants. Returning to **x**,

$$\mathbf{x} = \mathbf{P}\mathbf{x}' = \begin{pmatrix} 1 & 1 & 1 \\ 0 & -1 & 0 \\ 1 & 1 & 0 \end{pmatrix}\begin{pmatrix} Ce^{2t} \\ (B+At)e^{2t} \\ Ae^{2t} \end{pmatrix} = \begin{pmatrix} [(A+B+C)+At]e^{2t} \\ -(B+At)e^{2t} \\ [(B+C)+At]e^{2t} \end{pmatrix}, \tag{32}$$

so we have

$$\begin{aligned} x_1(t) &= [(A + B + C) + At]e^{2t} \\ x_2(t) &= -(B + At)e^{2t} \\ x_3(t) &= [(B + C) + At]e^{2t} \end{aligned} \tag{33}$$

as the general solution to (22). ◀

To summarize, if an $n \times n$ matrix **A** has n LI eigenvectors, then it is diagonalizable, i.e., $\mathbf{Q}^{-1}\mathbf{A}\mathbf{Q} = \mathbf{D}$, where **Q** is the modal matrix of **A** and **D** is diagonal. That story was presented in Section 4.4. In the present section we looked at the case where **A** has *less than n* LI eigenvectors and is therefore not diagonalizable. We found that **A** is, nonetheless, *almost diagonalizable*. Specifically, $\mathbf{P}^{-1}\mathbf{A}\mathbf{P} = \mathbf{J}$, where **P** is a *generalized modal matrix* of **A** and **J** is a *Jordan form* of **A**.

4.5 EXERCISES

1. Compute the inverse of **P**, given by (15), and verify that $\mathbf{P}^{-1}\mathbf{A}\mathbf{P}$ equals the **J** matrix given in (12).

2. Reduce each of the following matrices to Jordan form; i.e., determine a generalized modal matrix **P** and the corresponding Jordan form **J**.

*(a) $\begin{pmatrix} 1 & 4 \\ 0 & 1 \end{pmatrix}$ (b) $\begin{pmatrix} 3 & 1 \\ 0 & -1 \end{pmatrix}$

(c) $\begin{pmatrix} 0 & 2 \\ 0 & 0 \end{pmatrix}$ (d) $\begin{pmatrix} 2 & 4 \\ -1 & 6 \end{pmatrix}$

(e) $\begin{pmatrix} 1 & 4 \\ -1 & 5 \end{pmatrix}$ (f) $\begin{pmatrix} -4 & -4 \\ 1 & -8 \end{pmatrix}$

*(g) $\begin{pmatrix} 2 & -4 \\ 1 & -2 \end{pmatrix}$ (h) $\begin{pmatrix} 3 & 1 & -1 \\ -1 & 1 & 1 \\ 0 & 0 & 2 \end{pmatrix}$

(i) $\begin{pmatrix} 1 & 1 & 1 \\ 0 & 1 & 1 \\ 0 & 0 & 1 \end{pmatrix}$ (j) $\begin{pmatrix} -1 & 1 & -3 \\ 1 & 0 & 2 \\ 2 & -1 & 4 \end{pmatrix}$

(k) $\begin{pmatrix} 3 & 1 & -1 & 1 \\ -1 & 1 & 1 & 0 \\ 0 & 0 & 2 & 0 \\ 0 & 0 & 0 & 2 \end{pmatrix}$ (l) $\begin{pmatrix} 1 & 0 & 0 & 0 \\ 1 & 1 & 0 & 0 \\ 1 & 1 & 1 & 0 \\ 1 & 1 & 1 & 1 \end{pmatrix}$

*(m) $\begin{pmatrix} -1 & 1 & 1 & 1 \\ 0 & -2 & 1 & -2 \\ 0 & 0 & -2 & 1 \\ 0 & 1 & -1 & 1 \end{pmatrix}$ (n) $\begin{pmatrix} -1 & 0 & 0 & 0 \\ 0 & -2 & 0 & -1 \\ 0 & 0 & -1 & 0 \\ 0 & 1 & 0 & 0 \end{pmatrix}$

*Recall (from an introductory course in differential equations, or from Appendix A) that $\dot{x} + M(t)x = N(t)$ admits the general solution

$$x(t) = e^{-\int M dt}\left(\int N e^{\int M dt} dt + \text{constant}\right).$$

(o) $\begin{pmatrix} -1 & 0 & 0 & 0 \\ 0 & 8 & 5 & 4 \\ 0 & -5 & -1 & -5 \\ 0 & -4 & -5 & 0 \end{pmatrix}$ (p) $\begin{pmatrix} 1 & 0 & 0 & 0 \\ 0 & 3 & 0 & -1 \\ 0 & 0 & 4 & 0 \\ 0 & 1 & 0 & 5 \end{pmatrix}$

3. Derive the general solution, in each case, following essentially the same procedure as in Example 2.

*(a) $\dot{x} = 3x + y$
$\dot{y} = -4x - y$

(b) $\dot{x} = \left(\frac{13 + \sqrt{3}}{4}\right) x + \frac{1}{4} y$

$\dot{y} = -\left(\frac{3 + \sqrt{3}}{4}\right) x + \left(\frac{12 - \sqrt{3}}{4}\right) y$

(c) $\ddot{x} = 4x + 2y + 3$
$\ddot{y} = -8x - 4y$

(d) $\ddot{x} = -\frac{19}{3} x + \frac{25}{3} y$
$\ddot{y} = -\frac{4}{3} x + \frac{1}{3} y$

(e) $\dot{x} - 13x + 7y + 3z = 0$
$\dot{y} - 12x + 7y + 2z = 0$
$\dot{z} - 16x + 8y + 5z = 0$

*(f) $\dot{x} = -15x + 9y + 5z$
$\dot{y} = -20x + 13y + 6z$
$\dot{z} = -16x + 8y + 7z$

(g) $\dot{x} = -2x + 2y + z + 1$
$\dot{y} = -5x + 4y + 2z + 2$
$\dot{z} = -x + y + z - 3$

(h) $\ddot{x} = 10x - 3y - 4z$
$\ddot{y} = 7x - 4z$
$\ddot{z} = 15x - 7y - 5z + 2$

4. If **J** is a Jordan form for **A**, is α**J** a Jordan form for α**A**? Prove or disprove.

5. Prove that if **J** is a Jordan form for **A**, and **A** is similar to **B**, then **J** is a Jordan form for **B**. *Note:* The term "similar" was defined in Exercise 8 on page 143.

APPLICATION TO FIRST-ORDER SYSTEMS WITH CONSTANT COEFFICIENTS 4.6

[Optional Section]

In Sections 4.4 and 4.5 we focused on diagonalization and Jordan forms, and systems of ordinary differential equations entered in some of the applications. In the present section we focus more systematically on the differential equation part of the story.

A system of first-order linear differential equations of the form

$$\begin{aligned} \dot{x}_1 &= a_{11}(t)x_1 + a_{12}(t)x_2 + \cdots + a_{1n}(t)x_n + f_1(t) \\ \dot{x}_2 &= a_{21}(t)x_1 + a_{22}(t)x_2 + \cdots + a_{2n}(t)x_n + f_2(t) \\ &\vdots \\ \dot{x}_n &= a_{n1}(t)x_1 + a_{n2}(t)x_2 + \cdots + a_{nn}(t)x_n + f_n(t), \end{aligned} \tag{1a}$$

in which the $a_{ij}(t)$ coefficients and the $f_i(t)$'s are prescribed functions and the overhead dots denote d/dt, is called a **first-order linear differential system** in n unknowns or, for brevity, a **first-order system**. By choosing the independent variable to be t we do not mean to imply that it necessarily represents "the time," although in a given application that may be the case. A system of this form occurred in Section 4.4 in connection with a problem in chemical kinetics (page 163); in that example we had $\mathbf{f}(t) = \mathbf{0}$.

If we ask $x_1(t), \ldots, x_n(t)$ to satisfy not only the differential equations above but also a set of **initial conditions**,

$$x_1(t_0) = c_1, \quad x_2(t_0) = c_2, \quad \ldots, \quad x_n(t_0) = c_n, \tag{1b}$$

then the combined problem (1a) and (1b) is known as an **initial-value problem**. The latter can be expressed more compactly in matrix notation as

$$\dot{\mathbf{x}} = \mathbf{A}(t)x + \mathbf{f}(t); \qquad \mathbf{x}(t_0) = \mathbf{c}, \tag{2}$$

where $\mathbf{x} = (x_1, \ldots, x_n)^{\mathrm{T}}$, $\mathbf{f} = (f_1, \ldots, f_n)^{\mathrm{T}}$, $\mathbf{c} = (c_1, \ldots, c_n)^{\mathrm{T}}$, and $\mathbf{A} = \{a_{ij}\}$.

Notice that (2) includes problems of the form

$$\frac{d^n x}{dt^n} + a_1(t)\frac{d^{n-1}x}{dt^{n-1}} + \cdots + a_{n-1}(t)\frac{dx}{dt} + a_n(t)x = f(t); \tag{3a}$$

$$x(t_0) = b_1, \quad \frac{dx}{dt}(t_0) = b_2, \quad \ldots, \quad \frac{d^{n-1}x}{dt^{n-1}}(t_0) = b_n, \tag{3b}$$

as explained in Section A.9 of Appendix A.

From this point forward, we limit our attention to the special case of *constant coefficients*, i.e. , where the a_{ij}'s are constants. Thus let us rewrite (2) as

$$\boxed{\dot{\mathbf{x}} = \mathbf{A}\mathbf{x} + \mathbf{f}(t); \qquad \mathbf{x}(t_0) = \mathbf{c}.} \tag{4}$$

Our object is to solve (4) using diagonalization and Jordan forms.

Following the distinction established in Sections 4.4 and 4.5, we break our discussion into two parts: First, we consider the case where **A** is diagonalizable; the prerequisite for this case is Section 4.4. Second, we consider the case where **A** is *not* diagonalizable; the prerequisite for this case is Section 4.5.

CASE 1: A DIAGONALIZABLE

To begin, suppose that **A** has n LI eigenvectors, so that it is diagonalizable. Thus if **Q** is a modal matrix of **A**, then $\mathbf{Q}^{-1}\mathbf{A}\mathbf{Q} = \mathbf{D}$ is diagonal. Or, solving for **A**, $\mathbf{A} = \mathbf{Q}\mathbf{D}\mathbf{Q}^{-1}$. Putting this expression into (4), we have

$$\dot{\mathbf{x}} = \mathbf{Q}\mathbf{D}\mathbf{Q}^{-1}\mathbf{x} + \mathbf{f}(t); \qquad \mathbf{x}(t_0) = \mathbf{c}. \tag{5}$$

Premultiplying by $\mathbf{Q}^{-1}$ yields

$$\mathbf{Q}^{-1}\dot{\mathbf{x}} = \mathbf{D}\mathbf{Q}^{-1}\mathbf{x} + \mathbf{Q}^{-1}\mathbf{f}(t); \qquad \mathbf{Q}^{-1}\mathbf{x}(t_0) = \mathbf{Q}^{-1}\mathbf{c}. \tag{6}$$

Thus, if we set $\mathbf{Q}^{-1}\mathbf{x} = \mathbf{x}'$, say, and note that **Q** is a constant matrix [so that $\frac{d}{dt}(\mathbf{Q}^{-1}\mathbf{x}) = \mathbf{Q}^{-1}\dot{\mathbf{x}}$], we have*

$$\dot{\mathbf{x}}' = \mathbf{D}\mathbf{x}' + \mathbf{f}'(t); \qquad \mathbf{x}'(t_0) = \mathbf{c}', \tag{7}$$

where $\mathbf{f}'(t) = \mathbf{Q}^{-1}\mathbf{f}(t)$ and $\mathbf{c}' = \mathbf{Q}^{-1}\mathbf{c}$.

The point, of course, is that (7) is simpler than (4) inasmuch as **D** is diagonal—for then the n scalar differential equations within (7) are uncoupled. By the way, notice that the systems (5) and (7) are indeed equivalent; i.e., if **x** is a solution of (5), then $\mathbf{x}' = \mathbf{Q}^{-1}\mathbf{x}$ is a solution of (7), and if $\mathbf{x}'$ is a solution of (7), then $\mathbf{x} = \mathbf{Q}\mathbf{x}'$ is a

* The prime, in $\mathbf{x}'$, does *not* denote differentiation, it denotes the vector $\mathbf{Q}^{-1}\mathbf{x}$.

solution of (5). This equivalence follows from the fact that the foregoing derivation of (7) from (5) is "reversible." That is, if we premultiply all terms in (7) by **Q**, then we recover (5).

Continuing with our solution, let us write out (7):

$$\begin{aligned} \dot{x}_1' &= \lambda_1 x_1' + f_1'(t); \qquad x_1'(t_0) = c_1' \\ &\vdots \\ \dot{x}_n' &= \lambda_n x_n' + f_n'(t); \qquad x_n'(t_0) = c_n'. \end{aligned} \tag{8}$$

If the $f_j'(t)$'s are sufficiently well behaved, say continuous over the interval I of interest containing the "initial" point t_0, then each initial-value problem in (8) has a unique solution over I, namely,*

$$\begin{aligned} x_1'(t) &= c_1' e^{\lambda_1 t} + \int_{t_0}^{t} e^{\lambda_1 (t-\tau)} f_1'(\tau)\, d\tau \\ &\vdots \\ x_n'(t) &= c_n' e^{\lambda_n t} + \int_{t_0}^{t} e^{\lambda_n (t-\tau)} f_n'(\tau)\, d\tau, \end{aligned} \tag{9}$$

or, in matrix form,

$$\mathbf{x}'(t) = e^{\mathbf{D}t}\mathbf{c}' + \int_{t_0}^{t} e^{\mathbf{D}(t-\tau)}\mathbf{f}'(\tau)\, d\tau, \tag{10}$$

where we have defined

$$e^{\mathbf{D}t} \equiv \begin{pmatrix} e^{\lambda_1 t} & & & 0 \\ & e^{\lambda_2 t} & & \\ & & \ddots & \\ 0 & & & e^{\lambda_n t} \end{pmatrix}. \tag{11}$$

Note the order $e^{\mathbf{D}t}\mathbf{c}'$, not $\mathbf{c}'e^{\mathbf{D}t}$, in (10).

Finally, we return to $\mathbf{x}$ by putting $\mathbf{x}' = \mathbf{Q}^{-1}\mathbf{x}$, $\mathbf{f}' = \mathbf{Q}^{-1}\mathbf{f}$, $\mathbf{c}' = \mathbf{Q}^{-1}\mathbf{c}$ in (10), and premultiplying each term by **Q**. This step yields

$$\boxed{\mathbf{x}(t) = \mathbf{Q}e^{\mathbf{D}t}\mathbf{Q}^{-1}\mathbf{c} + \int_{t_0}^{t} \mathbf{Q}e^{\mathbf{D}(t-\tau)}\mathbf{Q}^{-1}\mathbf{f}(\tau)\, d\tau} \tag{12}$$

as the unique solution of (4). Now (12) is in a computationally useful form. First, we compute the eigenvalues and eigenvectors of **A**. The eigenvalues give us **D**, and the eigenvectors give us **Q**. Putting these results into (12), and recalling the definition (11), yields the desired solution for $\mathbf{x}(t)$.

EXAMPLE 1 Consider the problem

$$\ddot{x} + \dot{x} - 6x = -7 + 6t; \qquad x(0) = 6, \quad \dot{x}(0) = 4. \tag{13}$$

* See (29) in Section A.8, with x, y changed to t, x', respectively.

First, reexpress (13) as

$$\frac{dx_1}{dt} = x_2; \qquad x_1(0) = 6$$
$$\frac{dx_2}{dt} = 6x_1 - x_2 - 7 + 6t; \qquad x_2(0) = 4, \tag{14}$$

or, as $\dot{\mathbf{x}} = \mathbf{A}\mathbf{x} + \mathbf{f}$ and $\mathbf{x}(0) = \mathbf{c}$, where

$$\mathbf{A} = \begin{pmatrix} 0 & 1 \\ 6 & -1 \end{pmatrix}, \qquad \mathbf{f}(t) = \begin{pmatrix} 0 \\ -7 + 6t \end{pmatrix}, \qquad \mathbf{c} = \begin{pmatrix} 6 \\ 4 \end{pmatrix}. \tag{15}$$

The eigenvalues and eigenvectors of $\mathbf{A}$ are found to be

$$\lambda_1 = 2, \quad \mathbf{e}_1 = \begin{pmatrix} 1 \\ 2 \end{pmatrix}; \qquad \lambda_2 = -3, \quad \mathbf{e}_2 = \begin{pmatrix} 1 \\ -3 \end{pmatrix} \tag{16}$$

and since these $\mathbf{e}_j$'s are LI it follows that $\mathbf{A}$ is diagonalizable and that (12) applies. Thus with

$$\mathbf{D} = \begin{pmatrix} 2 & 0 \\ 0 & -3 \end{pmatrix}, \qquad \mathbf{Q} = \begin{pmatrix} 1 & 1 \\ 2 & -3 \end{pmatrix}, \qquad \mathbf{Q}^{-1} = \frac{1}{5}\begin{pmatrix} 3 & 1 \\ 2 & -1 \end{pmatrix}, \tag{17}$$

(12) gives

$$\begin{aligned} \mathbf{x} &= \begin{pmatrix} 1 & 1 \\ 2 & -3 \end{pmatrix}\begin{pmatrix} e^{2t} & 0 \\ 0 & e^{-3t} \end{pmatrix}\begin{pmatrix} \frac{3}{5} & \frac{1}{5} \\ \frac{2}{5} & -\frac{1}{5} \end{pmatrix}\begin{pmatrix} 6 \\ 4 \end{pmatrix} \\ &\qquad + \int_0^t \begin{pmatrix} 1 & 1 \\ 2 & 3 \end{pmatrix}\begin{pmatrix} e^{2(t-\tau)} & 0 \\ 0 & e^{-3(t-\tau)} \end{pmatrix}\begin{pmatrix} \frac{3}{5} & \frac{1}{5} \\ \frac{2}{5} & -\frac{1}{5} \end{pmatrix}\begin{pmatrix} 0 \\ -7 + 6\tau \end{pmatrix} d\tau \\ &= \begin{pmatrix} 4e^{2t} + e^{-3t} - t + 1 \\ 8e^{2t} - 3e^{-3t} - 1 \end{pmatrix}, \end{aligned} \tag{18}$$

so that

$$x(t) = x_1(t) = 4e^{2t} + e^{-3t} - t + 1 \tag{19}$$

is the desired solution. ◀

In deriving (12), an interesting quantity arose—the **exponential matrix function** $e^{\mathbf{B}}$, where $\mathbf{B} = \{b_{ij}\}$ is an $n \times n$ matrix. Thus far, $\mathbf{B}$ has been diagonal, and for that case we have defined

$$\boxed{e^{\mathbf{B}} \equiv \begin{pmatrix} e^{b_{11}} & & & 0 \\ & e^{b_{22}} & & \\ & & \ddots & \\ 0 & & & e^{b_{nn}} \end{pmatrix}.} \qquad (\mathbf{B} \text{ diagonal}) \tag{20}$$

More generally, suppose that $\mathbf{B}$ is *any* $n \times n$ matrix, not necessarily diagonal. Following the well-known Taylor series formula

$$e^x = 1 + \frac{x}{1!} + \frac{x^2}{2!} + \cdots,$$

it seems reasonable to define

$$\boxed{e^{\mathbf{B}} \equiv \mathbf{I} + \frac{1}{1!}\mathbf{B} + \frac{1}{2!}\mathbf{B}^2 + \cdots.} \tag{21}$$

Fine, but observe that the right-hand side of (21) is an *infinite series of matrices*, and such series have not yet been defined. Mimicking the usual definition of convergence for series of scalars, we define an infinite series of matrices $\Sigma_{k=1}^{\infty} \mathbf{A}_k$ as the limit of the sequence of partial sums $\mathbf{S}_N$, where $\mathbf{S}_N = \Sigma_{k=1}^{N} \mathbf{A}_k$. Thus

$$\sum_{k=1}^{\infty} \mathbf{A}_k \equiv \lim_{N\to\infty} \mathbf{S}_N. \tag{22}$$

The infinite series on the left is said to **converge** if the limit on the right exists, and to **diverge** if the limit does not exist. Finally, note that $\lim_{N\to\infty} \mathbf{S}_N$ is the *limit of a sequence of matrices*, and such limits have not yet been defined, so we are not yet out of the woods. Thus suppose that $\mathbf{C}_1, \mathbf{C}_2, \ldots$ is a sequence of $m \times n$ matrices and that the i, j element of $\mathbf{C}_n$ is $(c_{ij})_n$. We say that the sequence **converges** to a matrix $\mathbf{C}$, the i, j element of which is c_{ij}, if

$$\lim_{n\to\infty} (c_{ij})_n = c_{ij} \tag{23}$$

for each i, j, and we denote such convergence by writing either

$$\lim_{n\to\infty} \mathbf{C}_n = \mathbf{C} \quad \text{or} \quad \mathbf{C}_n \to \mathbf{C}. \tag{24}$$

If the sequence does not converge, it is said to **diverge**.

EXAMPLE 2

$$\begin{pmatrix} 1 + \dfrac{2}{n} & 0 \\ 2 - \dfrac{3}{n} & 5 \end{pmatrix} \to \begin{pmatrix} 1 & 0 \\ 2 & 5 \end{pmatrix}, \tag{25}$$

but

$$\begin{pmatrix} 7 + 2n & \dfrac{1}{n} \\ 5 & -2 \end{pmatrix} \tag{26}$$

diverges because $\lim_{n\to\infty} (7 + 2n)$ does not exist. ◀

With (21) in hand, let us return to (12) and consider the combination $\mathbf{Q}e^{\mathbf{D}t}\mathbf{Q}^{-1}$:

$$\begin{aligned} \mathbf{Q}e^{\mathbf{D}t}\mathbf{Q}^{-1} &= \mathbf{Q}\left(\mathbf{I} + \mathbf{D}t + \frac{1}{2!}\mathbf{D}^2t^2 + \cdots\right)\mathbf{Q}^{-1} \\ &= \mathbf{I} + \mathbf{QDQ}^{-1}t + \frac{1}{2!}\mathbf{QD}^2\mathbf{Q}^{-1}t^2 + \cdots \\ &= \mathbf{I} + \mathbf{QDQ}^{-1}t + \frac{1}{2!}\mathbf{QDQ}^{-1}\mathbf{QDQ}^{-1}t^2 + \cdots, \end{aligned} \tag{27}$$

and recalling that $\mathbf{QDQ}^{-1} = \mathbf{A}$, this series gives

$$\mathbf{Q}e^{\mathbf{D}t}\mathbf{Q}^{-1} = \mathbf{I} + \mathbf{A}t + \frac{1}{2!}\mathbf{A}^2t^2 + \cdots = e^{\mathbf{A}t}. \tag{28}$$

Similarly, $\mathbf{Q}e^{\mathbf{D}(t-\tau)}\mathbf{Q}^{-1} = e^{\mathbf{A}(t-\tau)}$, so (12) can be expressed in the equivalent form

$$\boxed{\mathbf{x}(t) = e^{\mathbf{A}t}\mathbf{c} + \int_{t_0}^{t} e^{\mathbf{A}(t-\tau)}\mathbf{f}(\tau)\,d\tau,} \tag{29}$$

which is of exactly the same form as the solution

$$x(t) = e^{At}c + \int_{t_0}^{t} e^{A(t-\tau)}f(\tau)\,d\tau \tag{30}$$

to the initial-value problem

$$\dot{x} = Ax + f(t); \qquad x(t_0) = c. \tag{31}$$

Naturally, the exponentials $e^{\mathbf{A}t}$ and $e^{\mathbf{A}(t-\tau)}$ in (29) can be evaluated using the expansions

$$e^{\mathbf{A}t} = \mathbf{I} + \mathbf{A}t + \frac{1}{2!}\mathbf{A}^2t^2 + \cdots, \tag{32}$$

$$e^{\mathbf{A}(t-\tau)} = \mathbf{I} + \mathbf{A}(t-\tau) + \frac{1}{2!}\mathbf{A}^2(t-\tau)^2 + \cdots,$$

or, practically speaking, the approximations

$$e^{\mathbf{A}t} \approx \mathbf{I} + \mathbf{A}t + \frac{1}{2!}\mathbf{A}^2t^2 + \cdots + \frac{1}{M!}\mathbf{A}^Mt^M,$$

$$e^{\mathbf{A}(t-\tau)} \approx \mathbf{I} + \mathbf{A}(t-\tau) + \frac{1}{2!}\mathbf{A}^2(t-\tau)^2 + \cdots + \frac{1}{M!}\mathbf{A}^M(t-\tau)^M, \tag{33}$$

for some finite M, although this approach is not generally recommended. Instead, we suggest computing the eigenvalues and eigenvectors of $\mathbf{A}$, and hence the $\mathbf{D}$, $\mathbf{Q}$, and $\mathbf{Q}^{-1}$ matrices, and then obtaining the desired exponentials as

$$e^{\mathbf{A}t} = \mathbf{Q}e^{\mathbf{D}t}\mathbf{Q}^{-1}, \qquad e^{\mathbf{A}(t-\tau)} = \mathbf{Q}e^{\mathbf{D}(t-\tau)}\mathbf{Q}^{-1}, \tag{34}$$

where $e^{\mathbf{D}t}$ and $e^{\mathbf{D}(t-\tau)}$ are simply

$$e^{\mathbf{D}t} = \begin{pmatrix} e^{\lambda_1 t} & & 0 \\ & \ddots & \\ 0 & & e^{\lambda_n t} \end{pmatrix},$$

and

$$e^{\mathbf{D}(t-\tau)} = \begin{pmatrix} e^{\lambda_1(t-\tau)} & & 0 \\ & \ddots & \\ 0 & & e^{\lambda_n(t-\tau)} \end{pmatrix}, \tag{35}$$

because **D** is diagonal. This procedure amounts to using (12) as the "computational version" of (29).

CASE 2: A NOT DIAGONALIZABLE

Recall that we derived (29) under the original assumption **A** is diagonalizable. We state, without proof, that (29) is still correct even if **A** is *not* diagonalizable. In that case we might well expect (34) to be replaced by

$$e^{\mathbf{A}t} = \mathbf{P}e^{\mathbf{J}t}\mathbf{P}^{-1} \quad \text{and} \quad e^{\mathbf{A}(t-\tau)} = \mathbf{P}e^{\mathbf{J}(t-\tau)}\mathbf{P}^{-1}, \tag{36}$$

where **P** and **J** are **A**'s generalized modal matrix and Jordan form, respectively. Well, let's see. Recalling, from Theorem 1 on page 180, that

$$\mathbf{P}^{-1}\mathbf{A}\mathbf{P} = \mathbf{J}, \tag{37}$$

it follows, from premultiplication by **P** and postmultiplication by $\mathbf{P}^{-1}$, that

$$\mathbf{A} = \mathbf{P}\mathbf{J}\mathbf{P}^{-1}.$$

Thus,

$$\begin{aligned} e^{\mathbf{A}t} &= \mathbf{I} + \mathbf{A}t + \frac{1}{2!}\mathbf{A}^2t^2 + \cdots \\ &= \mathbf{I} + \mathbf{P}\mathbf{J}\mathbf{P}^{-1}t + \frac{1}{2!}\mathbf{P}\mathbf{J}\mathbf{P}^{-1}\mathbf{P}\mathbf{J}\mathbf{P}^{-1}t^2 + \cdots \\ &= \mathbf{I} + \mathbf{P}\mathbf{J}\mathbf{P}^{-1}t + \frac{1}{2!}\mathbf{P}\mathbf{J}^2\mathbf{P}^{-1}t^2 + \cdots \\ &= \mathbf{P}\left(\mathbf{I} + \mathbf{J}t + \frac{1}{2!}\mathbf{J}^2t^2 + \cdots\right)\mathbf{P}^{-1} \\ &= \mathbf{P}e^{\mathbf{J}t}\mathbf{P}^{-1}, \end{aligned} \tag{38}$$

as claimed. Similarly, $e^{\mathbf{A}(t-\tau)} = \mathbf{P}e^{\mathbf{D}(t-\tau)}\mathbf{P}^{-1}$ merely by changing t to $t - \tau$ in (38), so that the analog of (12), for the case where **A** is *not* diagonalizable, is

$$\boxed{\mathbf{x}(t) = \mathbf{P}e^{\mathbf{J}t}\mathbf{P}^{-1}\mathbf{c} + \int_{t_0}^{t} \mathbf{P}e^{\mathbf{J}(t-\tau)}\mathbf{P}^{-1}\mathbf{f}(\tau)\,d\tau.} \tag{39}$$

Let us illustrate this case, i.e., where **A** is nondiagonalizable.

EXAMPLE 3 Consider the problem

$$\begin{pmatrix} \dot{x}_1 \\ \dot{x}_2 \\ \dot{x}_3 \\ \dot{x}_4 \end{pmatrix} = \begin{pmatrix} 2 & -1 & 2 & 0 \\ 0 & 3 & -1 & 0 \\ 0 & 1 & 1 & 0 \\ 0 & 1 & -3 & 5 \end{pmatrix}\begin{pmatrix} x_1 \\ x_2 \\ x_3 \\ x_4 \end{pmatrix}; \quad \begin{pmatrix} x_1(0) \\ x_2(0) \\ x_3(0) \\ x_4(0) \end{pmatrix} = \begin{pmatrix} -1 \\ 1 \\ 1 \\ 0 \end{pmatrix}. \tag{40}$$

This **A** matrix was considered in Example 1 on page 175. There we found that

$$\mathbf{P} = \begin{pmatrix} 1 & 0 & 0 & 0 \\ 0 & 1 & 2 & 0 \\ 0 & 1 & 1 & 0 \\ 0 & \frac{2}{3} & \frac{5}{9} & 1 \end{pmatrix}, \quad \mathbf{P}^{-1} = \begin{pmatrix} 1 & 0 & 0 & 0 \\ 0 & -1 & 2 & 0 \\ 0 & 1 & -1 & 0 \\ 0 & \frac{1}{9} & -\frac{7}{9} & 1 \end{pmatrix},$$

$$\mathbf{J} = \begin{pmatrix} 2 & 1 & 0 & 0 \\ 0 & 2 & 1 & 0 \\ 0 & 0 & 2 & 0 \\ 0 & 0 & 0 & 5 \end{pmatrix}. \tag{41}$$

Unfortunately, $\mathbf{J}$ is not diagonal, so the simple formula (20) cannot be used to compute $e^{\mathbf{J}t}$. However, $\mathbf{J}$ differs from a diagonal matrix "only slightly." Specifically, let us split

$$\mathbf{J} = \mathbf{\Lambda} + \boldsymbol{\delta}; \qquad \mathbf{\Lambda} = \begin{pmatrix} 2 & 0 & 0 & 0 \\ 0 & 2 & 0 & 0 \\ 0 & 0 & 2 & 0 \\ 0 & 0 & 0 & 5 \end{pmatrix}, \qquad \boldsymbol{\delta} = \begin{pmatrix} 0 & 1 & 0 & 0 \\ 0 & 0 & 1 & 0 \\ 0 & 0 & 0 & 0 \\ 0 & 0 & 0 & 0 \end{pmatrix}. \tag{42}$$

Then (Exercise 3)

$$\begin{aligned} \mathbf{J}^n = (\mathbf{\Lambda} + \boldsymbol{\delta})^n &= \mathbf{\Lambda}^n + n\mathbf{\Lambda}^{n-1}\boldsymbol{\delta} + \frac{n(n-1)}{2!}\mathbf{\Lambda}^{n-2}\boldsymbol{\delta}^2 \\ &+ \frac{n(n-1)(n-2)}{3!}\mathbf{\Lambda}^{n-3}\boldsymbol{\delta}^3 + \cdots, \end{aligned} \tag{43}$$

so that

$$\begin{aligned} e^{\mathbf{J}t} &= \mathbf{I} + \mathbf{J}t + \frac{1}{2!}\mathbf{J}^2t^2 + \frac{1}{3!}\mathbf{J}^3t^3 + \cdots \\ &= \mathbf{I} + (\mathbf{\Lambda} + \boldsymbol{\delta})t + \frac{1}{2!}(\mathbf{\Lambda}^2 + 2\mathbf{\Lambda}\boldsymbol{\delta} + \boldsymbol{\delta}^2)t^2 + \frac{1}{3!}(\mathbf{\Lambda}^3 + 3\mathbf{\Lambda}^2\boldsymbol{\delta} + 3\mathbf{\Lambda}\boldsymbol{\delta}^2 + \boldsymbol{\delta}^3)t^3 \\ &+ \frac{1}{4!}(\mathbf{\Lambda}^4 + 4\mathbf{\Lambda}^3\boldsymbol{\delta} + 6\mathbf{\Lambda}^2\boldsymbol{\delta}^2 + 4\mathbf{\Lambda}\boldsymbol{\delta}^3 + \boldsymbol{\delta}^4)t^4 + \cdots \\ &= \left(\mathbf{I} + \mathbf{\Lambda}t + \frac{1}{2!}\mathbf{\Lambda}^2t^2 + \cdots\right) + \frac{t}{1!}\left(\mathbf{I} + \frac{1}{1!}\mathbf{\Lambda}t + \frac{1}{2!}\mathbf{\Lambda}^2t^2 + \cdots\right)\boldsymbol{\delta} \\ &+ \frac{t^2}{2!}\left(\mathbf{I} + \mathbf{\Lambda}t + \frac{1}{2!}\mathbf{\Lambda}^2t^2 + \cdots\right)\boldsymbol{\delta}^2 + \cdots. \end{aligned} \tag{44}$$

Thus

$$\boxed{e^{\mathbf{J}t} = e^{\mathbf{\Lambda}t}\left(\mathbf{I} + \frac{1}{1!}t\boldsymbol{\delta} + \frac{1}{2!}t^2\boldsymbol{\delta}^2 + \cdots\right),} \tag{45}$$

where $e^{\Lambda t}$ can be computed from (20) since $\mathbf{\Lambda}$ is diagonal. In the present example,

$$e^{\Lambda t} = \begin{pmatrix} e^{2t} & 0 & 0 & 0 \\ 0 & e^{2t} & 0 & 0 \\ 0 & 0 & e^{2t} & 0 \\ 0 & 0 & 0 & e^{5t} \end{pmatrix}. \tag{46}$$

Now, the series in (45) will always terminate after a finite number of terms since $\boldsymbol{\delta}$ will always be nilpotent. In this example,

$$\boldsymbol{\delta} = \begin{pmatrix} 0 & 1 & 0 & 0 \\ 0 & 0 & 1 & 0 \\ 0 & 0 & 0 & 0 \\ 0 & 0 & 0 & 0 \end{pmatrix}, \quad \boldsymbol{\delta}^2 = \begin{pmatrix} 0 & 0 & 1 & 0 \\ 0 & 0 & 0 & 0 \\ 0 & 0 & 0 & 0 \\ 0 & 0 & 0 & 0 \end{pmatrix}, \quad \boldsymbol{\delta}^3 = \boldsymbol{\delta}^4 = \cdots = \mathbf{0}, \tag{47}$$

so that

$$e^{\mathbf{J}t} = e^{\Lambda t}\left(\mathbf{I} + t\boldsymbol{\delta} + \frac{1}{2}t^2\boldsymbol{\delta}^2\right). \tag{48}$$

Putting (46) and (47) into (48) gives

$$e^{\mathbf{J}t} = \begin{pmatrix} e^{2t} & te^{2t} & \frac{1}{2}t^2e^{2t} & 0 \\ 0 & e^{2t} & te^{2t} & 0 \\ 0 & 0 & e^{2t} & 0 \\ 0 & 0 & 0 & e^{5t} \end{pmatrix}. \tag{49}$$

Finally, with $e^{\mathbf{J}t}$ given by (49), $\mathbf{P}$ and $\mathbf{P}^{-1}$ given by (41), $\mathbf{c} = (-1, 1, 1, 0)^{\mathrm{T}}$, and $\mathbf{f} = \mathbf{0}$, we have

$$\mathbf{x} = \mathbf{P}e^{\mathbf{J}t}\mathbf{P}^{-1}\mathbf{c} + \int_0^t \mathbf{P}e^{\mathbf{J}(t-\tau)}\mathbf{P}^{-1}\mathbf{f}(\tau)\,d\tau$$

$$= \begin{pmatrix} (-1 + t)e^{2t} \\ e^{2t} \\ e^{2t} \\ \frac{2}{3}(e^{2t} - e^{5t}) \end{pmatrix} \tag{50}$$

as the desired solution. ◀

In summary, we derived the unique solution to the initial-value problem (4). If $\mathbf{A}$ is diagonalizable, that solution is given by (12), where $e^{\mathbf{D}t}$ and $e^{\mathbf{D}(t-\tau)}$ are computed using (20). If $\mathbf{A}$ is *not* diagonalizable, that solution is given by (39), where $e^{\mathbf{J}t}$ and $e^{\mathbf{J}(t-\tau)}$ are evaluated using (45).

In the course of that discussion, there arose an interesting quantity—the exponential matrix function. Other functions of square matrices (sines, cosines, fractional powers, etc.) occur as well; for a systematic discussion of such functions we refer the interested reader to Wylie and Barrett.*

*C. R. Wylie and L. C. Barrett, *Advanced Engineering Mathematics*, 5th ed. (New York: McGraw-Hill, 1982), Sec. 12.7.

4.6 EXERCISES

1. Reexpress the following problems in the standard form (2). Identify **A**, **f**, and **c**.

*(a) $\ddot{x} + 6x = 2\sin t$; $x(0) = 5$, $\dot{x}(0) = -4$
(b) $\dddot{x} + t^2\dot{x} - (1 + 3t)x = e^{5t} + 2\cos t$; $x(1) = 0$, $\dot{x}(1) = 4$, $\ddot{x}(1) = -8$
(c) $\dddot{x} - e^t\ddot{x} + x = 0$; $x(0) = 1$, $\dot{x}(0) = 0$, $\ddot{x}(0) = 6$
(d) $\dddot{x} - x = \sin t$; $x(\pi) = 2$, $\dot{x}(\pi) = -1$, $\ddot{x}(\pi) = 0$
(e) $\ddot{x} = -2x - y$; $x(0) = 1$, $\dot{x}(0) = 3$
$\ddot{y} = -x - 5y$; $y(0) = 0$, $\dot{y}(0) = -1$
(f) $\dddot{x} = x + e^t y$; $x(0) = 1$, $\dot{x}(0) = 3$, $\ddot{x}(0) = 0$
$\dot{y} = tx - y$; $y(0) = 4$
(g) $\ddot{x} = x - y - z$; $x(1) = 2$, $\dot{x}(1) = 0$
$\ddot{y} = -x + y + 2z$; $y(1) = 0$, $\dot{y}(1) = 0$
$\ddot{z} = -x + 2y + 3z$; $z(1) = 0$, $\dot{z}(1) = 0$

2. Solve the following problems using (12) or (39), whichever is appropriate. You may need to first reexpress the problem in the standard form (2).

*(a) $\dot{x} = x + y$; $x(0) = 0$
$\dot{y} = x + y + e^{3t}$; $y(0) = 0$
(b) $\dot{x} = 2x + 4y + 1$; $x(1) = 0$
$\dot{y} = x - y$; $y(1) = 0$
(c) $\dot{x}_1 = 4x_1 + x_2 + 3x_3$; $x_1(0) = 1$
$\dot{x}_2 = x_1 - x_3 + 6$; $x_2(0) = 0$
$\dot{x}_3 = 3x_1 - x_2 + 4x_3$; $x_3(0) = 0$
(d) $\ddot{x} + 3\dot{x} + 2x = e^t$; $x(0) = 0$, $\dot{x}(0) = 0$
(e) $\ddot{x} + 2\dot{x} + x = 0$; $x(0) = 1$, $\dot{x}(0) = 0$
(f) $\dot{x} = 2x + 4y$; $x(0) = 5$
$\dot{y} = -x + 6y$; $y(0) = 0$
(g) $\dot{x} = -x + y - 3z$; $x(0) = 0$
$\dot{y} = x + 2z$; $y(0) = 0$
$\dot{z} = 2x - y + 4z$; $z(0) = 1$

3. In the second equality in (43) we use the fact that $\mathbf{\Lambda}$ and $\boldsymbol{\delta}$ necessarily commute. Prove that claim, namely, that $\mathbf{\Lambda\delta} = \boldsymbol{\delta}\mathbf{\Lambda}$.

4. Evaluate $e^{\mathbf{A}}$ for each given **A** matrix.

*(a) $\begin{pmatrix} 1 & 2 \\ 0 & 3 \end{pmatrix}$ (b) $\begin{pmatrix} 2 & 2 \\ 2 & 2 \end{pmatrix}$

(c) $\begin{pmatrix} 2 & -4 \\ 1 & -2 \end{pmatrix}$ (d) $\begin{pmatrix} 2 & 1 \\ 1 & 2 \end{pmatrix}$

(e) $\begin{pmatrix} 2 & 0 \\ 7 & 3 \end{pmatrix}$ *(f) $\begin{pmatrix} 0 & 5 \\ 0 & 0 \end{pmatrix}$

(g) $\begin{pmatrix} 0 & 0 & 1 \\ 0 & 0 & 1 \\ 1 & 1 & 1 \end{pmatrix}$ (h) $\begin{pmatrix} 2 & 1 & 0 \\ 1 & 2 & 1 \\ 0 & 1 & 2 \end{pmatrix}$

*(i) $\begin{pmatrix} -1 & 1 & -3 \\ 1 & 0 & 2 \\ 2 & -1 & 4 \end{pmatrix}$

(j) $\begin{pmatrix} 1 & 1 & 0 & 0 \\ 0 & 1 & 1 & 0 \\ 0 & 0 & 1 & 1 \\ 0 & 0 & 0 & 1 \end{pmatrix}$ (k) $\begin{pmatrix} 1 & 0 & 0 & 1 \\ 0 & 1 & 0 & 0 \\ 0 & 0 & 1 & 0 \\ 0 & 0 & 0 & 1 \end{pmatrix}$

4.7 QUADRATIC FORMS

Optional Section

An algebraic expression

$$F(x_1, x_2) = a_{11}x_1^2 + a_{22}x_2^2 + 2a_{12}x_1x_2, \tag{1}$$

wherein the 2 (that multiplies the last term) is included for subsequent convenience, is called a **quadratic form** in the two variables x_1 and x_2; similarly,

$$F(x_1, x_2, x_3) = a_{11}x_1^2 + a_{22}x_2^2 + a_{33}x_3^2 + 2a_{12}x_1x_2 + 2a_{13}x_1x_3 + 2a_{23}x_2x_3 \tag{2}$$

is a quadratic form in three variables, and so on for any finite number of variables. Such forms occur in a variety of applications, including the study of maxima and minima, stability of equilibria, vibrations of dynamical systems, and the conic sections, and these forms are the subject of this final section of Chapter 4.

First, observe that a quadratic form $F(x_1 \ldots, x_n)$ can be expressed concisely as

$$\boxed{F(x_1, \ldots, x_n) = \mathbf{x}^{\mathrm{T}}\mathbf{A}\mathbf{x},} \tag{3}$$

where $\mathbf{x} = (x_1, \ldots, x_n)^{\mathrm{T}}$, and $\mathbf{A} = \{a_{ij}\}$ is a symmetric $n \times n$ matrix. If $n = 2$, for example, then

$$\begin{aligned} F(x_1, x_2) &= (x_1 \quad x_2)\begin{pmatrix} a_{11} & a_{12} \\ a_{12} & a_{22} \end{pmatrix}\begin{pmatrix} x_1 \\ x_2 \end{pmatrix} \\ &= (x_1 \quad x_2)\begin{pmatrix} a_{11}x_1 + a_{12}x_2 \\ a_{12}x_1 + a_{22}x_2 \end{pmatrix} = a_{11}x_1^2 + a_{22}x_2^2 + 2a_{12}x_1x_2, \end{aligned}$$

as in (1).

EXAMPLE 1 If

$$F(x_1, x_2) = 2x_1^2 - x_2^2 + 6x_1x_2, \tag{4}$$

then, from (1), $a_{11} = 2$, $a_{22} = -1$, $2a_{12} = 6$, so $a_{12} = 3$, and hence the associated symmetric $\mathbf{A}$ matrix is

$$\mathbf{A} = \begin{pmatrix} 2 & 3 \\ 3 & -1 \end{pmatrix}.$$ ◀

EXAMPLE 2 If

$$F(x_1, \ldots, x_4) = x_2^2 + 5x_3^2 + 6x_1x_3 - x_2x_3 + 10x_3x_4, \tag{5}$$

then $a_{22} = 1$, $a_{33} = 5$, $2a_{13} = 6$, so $a_{13} = 3$, $2a_{23} = -1$, so $a_{23} = -\frac{1}{2}$, $2a_{34} = 10$, so $a_{34} = 5$, and all the other a_{ij}'s are zero. Thus

$$\mathbf{A} = \begin{pmatrix} 0 & 0 & 3 & 0 \\ 0 & 1 & -\frac{1}{2} & 0 \\ 3 & -\frac{1}{2} & 5 & 5 \\ 0 & 0 & 5 & 0 \end{pmatrix}.$$ ◀

Further, a quadratic form is said to be **canonical** if all "mixed" terms, such as x_1x_2, x_1x_3, x_2x_3, and so on, are absent, i.e., if all of the coefficients a_{12}, a_{13}, a_{23}, and so on, are zero. Thus,

$$F(x_1, \ldots, x_n) = a_{11}x_1^2 + a_{22}x_2^2 + \cdots + a_{nn}x_n^2 \tag{6}$$

is canonical, and its associated matrix,

$$\mathbf{A} = \begin{pmatrix} a_{11} & & & \text{\Large 0} \\ & a_{22} & & \\ & & \ddots & \\ \text{\Large 0} & & & a_{nn} \end{pmatrix},$$

is diagonal. For example, neither (4) nor (5) is canonical, but

$$F(x_1, x_2) = 4x_1^2 - 3x_2^2 \tag{7}$$

and

$$F(x_1, x_2, x_3, x_4) = x_1^2 + 8x_3^2 + 2x_4^2 \tag{8}$$

are.

There is interest in being able to reduce a given quadratic form to canonical form, i.e., to its simplest form, through a linear change of variables

$$\mathbf{x} = \mathbf{Q}\mathbf{x}' \tag{9}$$

from $x_1, \ldots, x_n$ to $x_1', \ldots, x_n'$. Putting (9) into (3),

$$F = (\mathbf{Q}\mathbf{x}')^{\mathrm{T}}\mathbf{A}(\mathbf{Q}\mathbf{x}') = \mathbf{x}'^{\mathrm{T}}(\mathbf{Q}^{\mathrm{T}}\mathbf{A}\mathbf{Q})\mathbf{x}'. \tag{10}$$

Thus, given $\mathbf{A}$, we wish to determine a $\mathbf{Q}$ matrix such that $\mathbf{Q}^{\mathrm{T}}\mathbf{A}\mathbf{Q}$ is *diagonal*, for then (10) will be canonical in the new variables $x_1', \ldots, x_n'$. As stated above, $\mathbf{A}$ is symmetric, so it follows from the preceding section that a normalized modal matrix of $\mathbf{A}$ (i.e., the columns of which are the normalized eigenvectors of $\mathbf{A}$) constitutes a suitable $\mathbf{Q}$.* In that case

$$\mathbf{Q}^T\mathbf{A}\mathbf{Q} = \begin{pmatrix} \lambda_1 & & 0 \\ & \ddots & \\ 0 & & \lambda_n \end{pmatrix} \equiv \boldsymbol{\Lambda}, \tag{11}$$

where the λ's are the eigenvalues of $\mathbf{A}$, so (10) is simply

$$F = \lambda_1 x_1'^2 + \cdots + \lambda_n x_n'^2. \tag{12}$$

This expression is the desired canonical form of F.

EXAMPLE 3 Reduce

$$F(x_1, x_2) = 3x_1^2 + 3x_2^2 + 2x_1x_2 \tag{13}$$

to canonical form. First, identify $\mathbf{A}$:

$$\mathbf{A} = \begin{pmatrix} 3 & 1 \\ 1 & 3 \end{pmatrix}.$$

Next, determine the eigenvalues and eigenvectors of $\mathbf{A}$. These are found to be

$$\lambda_1 = 4, \quad \hat{\mathbf{e}}_1 = \frac{1}{\sqrt{2}}\begin{pmatrix} 1 \\ 1 \end{pmatrix}; \quad \lambda_2 = 2, \quad \hat{\mathbf{e}}_2 = \frac{1}{\sqrt{2}}\begin{pmatrix} 1 \\ -1 \end{pmatrix}.$$

(Whether we call $\lambda_1 = 4$ and $\lambda_2 = 2$, or vice versa, will not matter.) According to (12), the desired canonical form of F is then

$$F = \lambda_1 x_1'^2 + \lambda_2 x_2'^2 = 4x_1'^2 + 2x_2'^2. \tag{14}$$

It looks like we are all done, so why do we need to know $\hat{\mathbf{e}}_1, \hat{\mathbf{e}}_2$? To know the connection between x_1, x_2 and x_1', x_2'. Specifically,

$$\mathbf{x} = \mathbf{Q}\mathbf{x}' = (\hat{\mathbf{e}}_1, \hat{\mathbf{e}}_2)\mathbf{x}',$$

* We do not claim that $\mathbf{Q}$ *must* be a modal matrix of $\mathbf{A}$ for $\mathbf{Q}^{\mathrm{T}}\mathbf{A}\mathbf{Q}$ to be diagonal; see Exercise 5.

or

$$\begin{pmatrix} x_1 \\ x_2 \end{pmatrix} = \frac{1}{\sqrt{2}} \begin{pmatrix} 1 & 1 \\ 1 & -1 \end{pmatrix} \begin{pmatrix} x_1' \\ x_2' \end{pmatrix},$$

so that

$$\begin{aligned} x_1 &= \frac{1}{\sqrt{2}} x_1' + \frac{1}{\sqrt{2}} x_2' \\ x_2 &= \frac{1}{\sqrt{2}} x_1' - \frac{1}{\sqrt{2}} x_2'. \end{aligned} \tag{15}$$

Or if we wish to have it the other way round, we can use $\mathbf{x}' = \mathbf{Q}^{-1}\mathbf{x} = \mathbf{Q}^{\mathrm{T}}\mathbf{x}$. (In the present example $\mathbf{Q}$ happens, by coincidence, to be symmetric, so that $\mathbf{Q}^{\mathrm{T}} = \mathbf{Q}$.) Thus

$$\begin{aligned} x_1' &= \frac{1}{\sqrt{2}} x_1 + \frac{1}{\sqrt{2}} x_2 \\ x_2' &= \frac{1}{\sqrt{2}} x_1 - \frac{1}{\sqrt{2}} x_2. \end{aligned}$$ ◀

The change of variables (15) was found by the systematic procedure spelled out above, which we now summarize:

Every quadratic form $F(x_1, \ldots, x_n) = \mathbf{x}^{\mathrm{T}}\mathbf{A}\mathbf{x}$ *can be reduced to the canonical form (12) by introducing the change of variables* $\mathbf{x} = \mathbf{Q}\mathbf{x}'$, *where the* λ*'s in (12) are the eigenvalues of* $\mathbf{A}$, *and the columns of* $\mathbf{Q}$ *are the corresponding normalized eigenvectors of* $\mathbf{A}$. *The reverse transformation is given by* $\mathbf{x}' = \mathbf{Q}^{\mathrm{T}}\mathbf{x}$.

One classifies quadratic forms as follows. A quadratic form $\mathbf{x}^{\mathrm{T}}\mathbf{A}\mathbf{x}$ associated with a symmetric matrix $\mathbf{A}$ is said to be **positive definite** if $\mathbf{x}^{\mathrm{T}}\mathbf{A}\mathbf{x} > 0$ for all $\mathbf{x} \neq \mathbf{0}$, and **negative definite** if $\mathbf{x}^{\mathrm{T}}\mathbf{A}\mathbf{x} < 0$ for all $\mathbf{x} \neq \mathbf{0}$. It is conventional, then, to say that the *matrix* $\mathbf{A}$, too, is positive definite, or negative definite, accordingly.

In applying this classification, it is simplest to work with the canonical version of the given form, namely $\mathbf{x}^{\mathrm{T}}\mathbf{A}\mathbf{x} = \mathbf{x}'^{\mathrm{T}}\mathbf{\Lambda}\mathbf{x}' = \lambda_1 x_1'^2 + \cdots + \lambda_n x_n'^2$. Since the latter is a sum of squares, it is evident that if $\lambda_1, \ldots, \lambda_n$ are all positive (negative), then $\mathbf{x}^{\mathrm{T}}\mathbf{A}\mathbf{x} > 0$ (<0) for all $\mathbf{x}' \neq \mathbf{0}$, so $\mathbf{x}^{\mathrm{T}}\mathbf{A}\mathbf{x}$ is positive (negative) definite—provided that $\mathbf{x}' \neq \mathbf{0}$ is equivalent to $\mathbf{x} \neq \mathbf{0}$. But $\mathbf{x}$ and $\mathbf{x}'$ are related through $\mathbf{x} = \mathbf{Q}\mathbf{x}'$, where $\mathbf{Q}$ is nonsingular; if $\mathbf{x}' = \mathbf{0}$, then $\mathbf{x} = \mathbf{Q}\mathbf{0} = \mathbf{0}$, and if $\mathbf{x} = \mathbf{0}$, then $\mathbf{x}' = \mathbf{Q}^{-1}\mathbf{x} = \mathbf{Q}^{-1}\mathbf{0} = \mathbf{0}$. Thus $\mathbf{x}' = \mathbf{0}$ if and only if $\mathbf{x} = \mathbf{0}$, so $\mathbf{x}' \neq \mathbf{0}$ is equivalent to $\mathbf{x} \neq \mathbf{0}$ Hence:

> ***Theorem 1*** *Definiteness*
> Let $\mathbf{A}$ be $n \times n$ and symmetric. Then $\mathbf{A}$ and its quadratic form $\mathbf{x}^{\mathrm{T}}\mathbf{A}\mathbf{x}$ are positive (negative) definite if each of the eigenvalues of $\mathbf{A}$ is positive (negative).*

* By positive eigenvalues we mean $\lambda_j > 0$ for $j = 1, \ldots, n$, *not* $\lambda_j \geq 0$ (similarly for negative eigenvalues). To see why this distinction is important, suppose that $\mathbf{A}$ is 3×3, with $\lambda_1 = 0$, $\lambda_2 = 3$, $\lambda_3 = 7$, say. Then $\mathbf{x}^{\mathrm{T}}\mathbf{A}\mathbf{x} = \mathbf{x}'^{\mathrm{T}}\mathbf{\Lambda}\mathbf{x}' = 0x_1'^2 + 3x_2'^2 + 7x_3'^2$ is *not* positive for all $\mathbf{x}' \neq \mathbf{0}$, since it is zero for $\mathbf{x}' = (\alpha, 0, 0)^{\mathrm{T}}$, where α is any nonzero number.

EXAMPLE 4

$$F(x_1, x_2, x_3) = 3x_1^2 + 4x_2^2 + 4x_3^2 - 4x_2x_3. \tag{16}$$

Then

$$\mathbf{A} = \begin{pmatrix} 3 & 0 & 0 \\ 0 & 4 & -2 \\ 0 & -2 & 4 \end{pmatrix}, \quad \text{and} \quad \lambda = 6, 3, 2.$$

Since all three λ's are positive, F is positive definite. ◀

EXAMPLE 5

$$F(x_1, x_2) = -2x_1^2 - 3x_2^2 + 2x_1x_2. \tag{17}$$

Then

$$\mathbf{A} = \begin{pmatrix} -2 & 1 \\ 1 & -3 \end{pmatrix}, \quad \text{and} \quad \lambda = \frac{-5 + \sqrt{5}}{2}, \frac{-5 - \sqrt{5}}{2}.$$

Since both λ's are negative, F is negative definite. ◀

EXAMPLE 6

$$F(x_1, x_2, x_3) = 2x_1^2 + 4x_2^2 + 4x_3^2 + 2x_1x_2 - 2x_1x_3 + 6x_2x_3. \tag{18}$$

Then

$$\mathbf{A} = \begin{pmatrix} 2 & 1 & -1 \\ 1 & 4 & 3 \\ -1 & 3 & 4 \end{pmatrix}, \quad \text{and} \quad \lambda = 7, 3, 0.$$

Here F is *not* positive definite, because of the presence of the zero eigenvalue; it is neither positive definite nor negative definite. In fact, it is said to be positive *semi*definite since at least one of the eigenvalues of $\mathbf{A}$ is zero, and the others are positive. (Similarly, if $\lambda = -7, -3, 0$, we would classify F as *negative* semidefinite.) ◀

We close this section with an interesting physical application.

EXAMPLE 7 *Buckling Load.* Three rigid rods, each of length l, are pinned at their ends, with the end A constrained to move in a frictionless vertical slot, as shown in Fig. 4.12. The three lateral springs, each of stiffness k, are unstretched and uncompressed when the system is undeflected (i.e., when $x = y = 0$), and the middle spring is attached at the middle of the middle rod. We find that as the load P is slowly increased the deflection remains zero ($x = y = z = 0$), so that $x = y = z = 0$ constitutes an "equilibrium state" of the system. Eventually, however, the system "buckles," i.e., collapses. The problem posed here is to determine P_{cr} in terms of the given quantities. It will be convenient to work with the potential en-

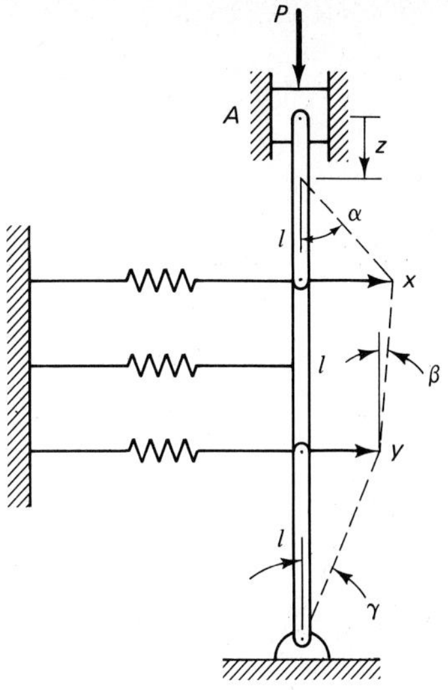

Fig. 4.12 Structure.

ergy V of the system, and to use the physical principle that the system will arrange itself so as to minimize its potential V.

Recall, from elementary physics, that the potential energy stored in a spring of stiffness k, deflected by an amount x, is $\frac{1}{2}kx^2$. Further, note that we may associate a potential with the load P by regarding it as being due to a weight P sitting on the slider. Then the gravitational potential of the weight is $-Pz$, if we define the potential to be zero when $z = 0$. Thus

$$V = \frac{1}{2}kx^2 + \frac{1}{2}ky^2 + \frac{1}{2}k\left(\frac{x+y}{2}\right)^2 - Pz. \tag{19}$$

But z can be expressed in terms of x and y, through the geometry. Specifically, if we introduce the angles α, β, γ shown in Fig. 4.12,

$$z + l\cos\alpha + l\cos\beta + l\cos\gamma = 3l. \tag{20}$$

For the onset of buckling, α, β, γ, x, y, z are all infinitesimal (arbitrarily small), so we may express

$$\begin{aligned} \cos\gamma &= 1 - \frac{1}{2!}\gamma^2 + \frac{1}{4!}\gamma^4 - \cdots \\ &\sim 1 - \frac{\gamma^2}{2} \sim 1 - \frac{1}{2}\left(\frac{y}{l}\right)^2, \end{aligned} \tag{21}$$

and similarly for $\cos\alpha$ and $\cos\beta$. Thus (20) becomes

$$z + l\left[1 - \frac{1}{2}\left(\frac{x}{l}\right)^2\right] + l\left[1 - \frac{1}{2}\left(\frac{x+y}{l}\right)^2\right] + l\left[1 - \frac{1}{2}\left(\frac{y}{l}\right)^2\right] \sim 3l$$

or,

$$z \sim \frac{x^2 - xy + y^2}{l},$$

so that

$$V(x, y) \sim \left(\frac{5k}{8} - \frac{P}{l}\right)x^2 + \left(\frac{5k}{8} - \frac{P}{l}\right)y^2 + \left(\frac{k}{4} + \frac{P}{l}\right)xy. \tag{22}$$

The right-hand side of (22) is seen to be a *quadratic form*, say

$$F(x, y) = \left(\frac{5k}{8} - \frac{P}{l}\right)x^2 + \left(\frac{5k}{8} - \frac{P}{l}\right)y^2 + \left(\frac{k}{4} + \frac{P}{l}\right)xy, \tag{23}$$

with associated matrix

$$\mathbf{A} = \begin{pmatrix} \frac{5k}{8} - \frac{P}{l} & \frac{k}{8} + \frac{P}{2l} \\ \frac{k}{8} + \frac{P}{2l} & \frac{5k}{8} - \frac{P}{l} \end{pmatrix}. \tag{24}$$

The crucial point is whether or not F is positive definite, for if $F(x, y)$ is positive definite, then $V(x, y)$ has a minimum at $x = y = 0$, so the undeflected equilibrium configuration $x = y = 0$ is stable. Otherwise, the equilibrium configuration will be *un*stable, and the system will buckle.

To assess the positive definiteness of F, we need merely evaluate the eigenvalues of $\mathbf{A}$. These are

$$\lambda_1 = \frac{3k}{2}\left(\frac{1}{3} - \frac{P}{kl}\right), \qquad \lambda_2 = \frac{k}{2}\left(\frac{3}{2} - \frac{P}{kl}\right), \tag{25}$$

so F is positive definite if and only if $P/kl < \frac{1}{3}$. Thus the critical load, or "buckling load," is $P_{cr} = kl/3$.

COMMENT 1 Physically, the idea is that as the system begins to deflect, the springs gain potential energy while the weight P loses potential energy. For instability (buckling) we need the loss to exceed the gain. Since the loss is proportional to P, one anticipates the existence of a critical value P_{cr} such that if $P = P_{cr}$, the loss just balances the gain, and if $P > P_{cr}$, the loss exceeds the gain.

COMMENT 2 If $P/kl < \frac{1}{3}$, the $V(x, y)$ graph is a "valley" (the bottom of which is at $x = y = 0$); if $P/kl > \frac{3}{2}$, it is a "hill"; and if $\frac{1}{3} < P/kl < \frac{3}{2}$, it is a so-called *saddle*. We have avoided this sort of geometric viewpoint, above, since such issues are not discussed in detail until Section 6.8. In that section we will apply these matrix methods to the theory of *maxima and minima of functions of more than one variable*. ◀

4.7 EXERCISES

1. For each of the following quadratic forms in n variables determine the associated symmetric $\mathbf{A}$ matrix (as in Examples 1 and 2).

*(a) $2x_1^2 + 4x_2^2 + x_1x_2 \quad (n = 2)$
(b) $x_3^2 + 2x_1x_3 + 2x_2x_3 \quad (n = 3)$
(c) $x_1^2 + x_2^2 + x_1x_2 \quad (n = 2)$
(d) $x_1^2 - 4x_3^2 + 3x_1x_2 \quad (n = 3)$
(e) $x_1^2 - 2x_3^2 + 5x_4^2 \quad (n = 4)$
(f) $x_1^2 - 4x_1x_2 \quad (n = 2)$
(g) $3x_1x_2 \quad (n = 2)$
(h) $x_2^2 + 3x_3^2 + 5x_4^2 - x_5^2 \quad (n = 5)$
(i) $-2x_1x_3 \quad (n = 3)$

*(j) $x_3^2 + x_1x_2 + x_1x_3 + x_2x_3 \quad (n = 3)$
(k) $6x_2x_3 \quad (n = 3)$
(l) $x_1^2 + 2x_4^2 - 4x_2x_3 \quad (n = 4)$

2. *(a)–(l) Reduce each quadratic form in Exercise 1 to the canonical form (12) by means of a normalized modal matrix transformation **Q**. Further, classify the quadratic form and the associated symmetric **A** matrix as positive definite, positive semidefinite, negative definite, or negative semidefinite, where applicable.

3. We state, without proof, that *a necessary and sufficient condition for a quadratic form* $F = \mathbf{x}^T\mathbf{A}\mathbf{x}$, *and its associated symmetric matrix* **A**, *to be positive definite is that*

$$a_{11} > 0, \quad \begin{vmatrix} a_{11} & a_{12} \\ a_{21} & a_{22} \end{vmatrix} > 0, \quad \begin{vmatrix} a_{11} & a_{12} & a_{13} \\ a_{21} & a_{22} & a_{23} \\ a_{31} & a_{32} & a_{33} \end{vmatrix} > 0, \quad \ldots, \quad \det \mathbf{A} > 0.$$

Apply this condition to each of the following **A** matrices, and compare your conclusion with that drawn from direct examination of the eigenvalues.

(a) $\begin{pmatrix} 4 & 1 \\ 1 & 4 \end{pmatrix}$ (b) $\begin{pmatrix} 1 & 1 \\ 1 & 1 \end{pmatrix}$

(c) $\begin{pmatrix} 2 & -1 \\ -1 & 2 \end{pmatrix}$ (d) $\begin{pmatrix} 0 & 1 & 1 \\ 1 & 0 & 1 \\ 1 & 1 & 0 \end{pmatrix}$

(e) $\begin{pmatrix} 6 & 0 & 0 \\ 0 & 2 & 0 \\ 0 & 0 & 3 \end{pmatrix}$ (f) $\begin{pmatrix} 0 & 0 & 8 \\ 0 & 0 & 0 \\ 8 & 0 & 0 \end{pmatrix}$

(g) $\begin{pmatrix} -2 & 1 & 2 \\ 1 & -2 & 2 \\ 2 & 2 & 1 \end{pmatrix}$ (h) $\begin{pmatrix} 0 & 0 & 1 & 0 \\ 0 & 0 & 1 & 0 \\ 1 & 1 & 1 & 0 \\ 0 & 0 & 0 & 9 \end{pmatrix}$

(i) $\begin{pmatrix} 2 & 1 & 0 & 0 \\ 1 & 2 & 0 & 0 \\ 0 & 0 & 4 & 1 \\ 0 & 0 & 1 & 4 \end{pmatrix}$

4. (*Completing squares*) It was mentioned (footnote, page 194) that the **Q** matrix in (9) does not *have* to be a modal matrix of **A**. Given $F = x_1^2 + x_2^2 + x_1x_2$, for example, suppose that we proceed, instead, by "completing squares":

$$\begin{aligned} F &= x_1^2 + x_2^2 + x_1x_2 \\ &= (x_1^2 + x_1x_2 + \tfrac{1}{4}x_2^2) + x_2^2 - \tfrac{1}{4}x_2^2 \qquad \text{(a)} \\ &= (x_1 + \tfrac{1}{2}x_2)^2 + \tfrac{3}{4}x_2^2, \end{aligned}$$

so the transformation

$$x_1' = x_1 + \tfrac{1}{2}x_2, \qquad x_2' = x_2 \qquad \text{(b)}$$

reduces F to the canonical form $F = x_1'^2 + \frac{3}{4}x_2'^2$.

*(a) Show that the matrix **Q** corresponding to (b) is *not* a modal matrix.
(b) Reduce $F = x_1^2 + x_2^2 + 4x_3^2 + 2x_1x_2 - x_1x_3$ to canonical form by completing squares.
(c) Repeat part (b), for $F = x_1^2 + 4x_1x_2 + x_2x_3$.
(d) Repeat part (b), for $F = 4x_1^2 + 2x_1x_3 + x_2x_3$.
*(e) Repeat part (b), for $F = x_3^2 + 2x_1x_3$.
(f) Does the method of completing squares work for $F = 2x_1x_2$? Explain.

5. Reduce the following quadratic equations to the canonical form $ax'^2 + by'^2 = c$, and hence decide whether they correspond to *ellipses*, or *hyperbolas*. Sketch their graphs, showing both the x, y and x', y' axes, as well as the intercepts on the x', y' axes. *Hint:* Recall that $(x'/A)^2 + (y'/B)^2 = 1$ is the equation of an ellipse with intercepts at $\pm A$ on the x' axis, and at $\pm B$ on the y' axis (or a circle of radius A if $A = B$). Further, $(x'/A)^2 - (y'/B)^2 = 1$ is the equation of a hyperbola with intercepts at $\pm A$ on the x' axis, and $(y'/B)^2 - (x'/A)^2 = 1$ is the equation of a hyperbola with intercepts at $\pm B$ on the y' axis.

(a) $3x^2 + 2y^2 - 2xy = 6$
(b) $xy = 1$
(c) $4y^2 + 3xy = 1$
(d) $x^2 + y^2 - 10xy = 4$
(e) $x^2 + y^2 + 2xy = 4$ (This case will be found to be "degenerate." Put forward a brief discussion of what this case has to do with ellipses and hyperbolas.)

***6.** Rework Example 7 for the case where the middle spring is removed. Show that the buckling load is then $P_{cr} = \frac{1}{3}kl$. Note that this result is the same as in Example 7, where the middle spring is included. Can you explain why this is so?

5 Extension to Complex Case*[Optional]

5.1 INTRODUCTION

In the first four chapters *all* scalars were understood to be real: the coefficients in systems of linear equations, the components of vectors, the elements of matrices, and so on. In some applications, however, perhaps more so in physics and chemistry than in engineering, complex numbers enter. For example, the reader may have met the *Euler angles* θ, ϕ, ψ used to specify the orientation of a rigid body such as a gyroscope. Alternatively, it is sometimes advantageous to employ so-called *Cayley–Klein parameters*, and in doing so one meets the *Pauli spin matrices*

$$\sigma_x = \begin{pmatrix} 0 & 1 \\ 1 & 0 \end{pmatrix}, \qquad \sigma_y = \begin{pmatrix} 0 & -i \\ i & 0 \end{pmatrix}, \qquad \sigma_z = \begin{pmatrix} 1 & 0 \\ 0 & -1 \end{pmatrix}, \tag{1}$$

of which σ_y is seen to have complex elements.

The purpose of this chapter, then, is to indicate the changes that need to be made in extending our vector and matrix systems so as to include complex numbers. Although this could have been done from the start, it was felt that the gain in simplicity, in the preceding chapters, more than offsets the need for this special chapter.

5.2 COMPLEX n-SPACE

All scalars in the vector space $\mathbb{R}^n$ defined in Section 2.4—namely, the scalars that multiplied vectors, and the scalar components of the vectors themselves—were real. If, instead, we allow these scalars to be complex, then in place of $\mathbb{R}^n$ we have the

* Prerequisite: Section 18.2.

complex n-space denoted here as $\mathbb{C}^n$:

$$\mathbb{C}^n = \{(a_1, \ldots, a_n) \mid a_1, \ldots, a_n \text{ complex numbers}\}. \tag{1}$$

The definitions $\mathbf{u} + \mathbf{v} \equiv (u_1 + v_1, \ldots, u_n + v_n)$, $\alpha\mathbf{u} \equiv (\alpha u_1, \ldots, \alpha u_n)$, $\mathbf{0} \equiv (0, \ldots, 0)$, and $-\mathbf{u} \equiv (-u_1, \ldots, -u_n)$ are the same as for $\mathbb{R}^n$, except that now the scalars are complex numbers, such as $3 - 2i$, 5 (i.e., $5 + 0i$), and so on. And from these definitions the same properties follow as for $\mathbb{R}^n$, namely $\mathbf{u} + \mathbf{v} = \mathbf{v} + \mathbf{u}, \ldots$, as in (10) on page 27.

However, the Euclidean dot product $\mathbf{u} \cdot \mathbf{v} = u_1 v_1 + \cdots + u_n v_n$, which we adopted for real vector space, is no longer convenient inasmuch as the resulting norm $\|\mathbf{u}\| = \sqrt{\mathbf{u} \cdot \mathbf{u}} = \sqrt{u_1^2 + \cdots + u_n^2}$ fails to display the key properties expected of a norm, in particular the nonnegativeness condition

$$\|\mathbf{u}\| \begin{array}{ll} > 0 & \text{for all } \mathbf{u} \neq \mathbf{0} \\ = 0 & \text{for } \mathbf{u} = \mathbf{0}. \end{array} \tag{2}$$

For example, if $\mathbf{u} = (2, 2i, 0, 0)$, then $\|\mathbf{u}\| = \sqrt{(2)^2 + (2i)^2 + (0)^2 + (0)^2} = 0$ even though $\mathbf{u} \neq \mathbf{0}$; and if $\mathbf{u} = (0, 2i, 0, 0)$, then $\|\mathbf{u}\| = \sqrt{0 - 4 + 0 + 0} = 2i$ is not even real!

To avoid this problem with the norm, we adopt the modified dot product

$$\boxed{\mathbf{u} \cdot \mathbf{v} \equiv u_1 \overline{v}_1 + u_2 \overline{v}_2 + \cdots + u_n \overline{v}_n = \sum_{j=1}^{n} u_j \overline{v}_j} \tag{3}$$

(where the overhead bar denotes complex conjugate), for then

$$\boxed{\|\mathbf{u}\| \equiv \sqrt{\mathbf{u} \cdot \mathbf{u}} = \sqrt{\sum_{j=1}^{n} u_j \overline{u}_j} = \sqrt{\sum_{j=1}^{n} |u_j|^2}} \tag{4}$$

does satisfy the nonnegativeness condition (2).

EXAMPLE 1 If $\mathbf{u} = (2, 3 - 5i, 0\ 4i)$, then

$$\begin{aligned} \|\mathbf{u}\| &= \sqrt{(2)(2) + (3 - 5i)(3 + 5i) + (0)(0) + (4i)(-4i)} \\ &= \sqrt{4 + 34 + 16} = \sqrt{54}, \end{aligned}$$

which *is* real and positive. ◀

PROPERTIES OF THE DOT PRODUCT

Observe that

$$\begin{aligned} \overline{\mathbf{v} \cdot \mathbf{u}} &= \overline{v_1 \overline{u}_1 + \cdots + v_n \overline{u}_n} \\ &= \overline{v_1 \overline{u}_1} + \cdots + \overline{v_n \overline{u}_n} \\ &= \overline{v}_1 \overline{\overline{u}}_1 + \cdots + \overline{v}_n \overline{\overline{u}}_n \\ &= \overline{v}_1 u_1 + \cdots + \overline{v}_n u_n \\ &= u_1 \overline{v}_1 + \cdots + u_n \overline{v}_n \\ &= \mathbf{u} \cdot \mathbf{v}. \end{aligned}$$

Thus, in place of the commutativity condition $\mathbf{u} \cdot \mathbf{v} = \mathbf{v} \cdot \mathbf{u}$, satisfied in the real case, we have the so-called conjugate commutativity $\mathbf{u} \cdot \mathbf{v} = \overline{\mathbf{v} \cdot \mathbf{u}}$ in the complex case. In fact, the properties

1. *Conjugate commutativity:*

$$\mathbf{u} \cdot \mathbf{v} = \overline{\mathbf{v} \cdot \mathbf{u}}, \tag{5a}$$

2. *Nonnegativeness:*

$$\mathbf{u} \cdot \mathbf{u} \begin{array}{ll} > 0 & \text{for all } \mathbf{u} \neq \mathbf{0} \\ = 0 & \text{for } \mathbf{u} = \mathbf{0}, \end{array} \tag{5b}$$

3. *Linearity:*

$$(\alpha \mathbf{u} + \beta \mathbf{v}) \cdot \mathbf{w} = \alpha (\mathbf{u} \cdot \mathbf{w}) + \beta (\mathbf{v} \cdot \mathbf{w}), \tag{5c}$$

of the complex dot product are the same as in the real case [(12) on page 31] except for the complex conjugate bar in (5a).

EXAMPLE 2 If $\mathbf{u} = (1 + 2i, -4, 0)$ and $\mathbf{v} = (3 + i, i, 2 - i)$, then $\mathbf{u} \cdot \mathbf{v} = (1 + 2i)(3 - i) + (-4)(-i) + (0)(2 + i) = 5 + 9i$, and $\mathbf{v} \cdot \mathbf{u} = (3 + i)(1 - 2i) + (i)(-4) + (2 - i)(0) = 5 - 9i$. ◀

The **Schwarz inequality**,

$$|\mathbf{u} \cdot \mathbf{v}| \leq \|\mathbf{u}\| \|\mathbf{v}\|, \tag{6}$$

is found to hold (Exercise 7), as in the real case, except that here $|\mathbf{u} \cdot \mathbf{v}|$ is the modulus of a complex number rather than the absolute value of a real number.

PROPERTIES OF THE NORM

The norm (4) admits the properties

1.

$$\|\alpha \mathbf{u}\| = |\alpha| \, \|\mathbf{u}\|, \tag{7a}$$

2. *Nonnegativeness:*

$$\|\mathbf{u}\| \begin{array}{ll} > 0 & \text{for all } \mathbf{u} \neq \mathbf{0} \\ = 0 & \text{for } \mathbf{u} = \mathbf{0}, \end{array} \tag{7b}$$

3. *Triangle inequality:*

$$\|\mathbf{u} + \mathbf{v}\| \leq \|\mathbf{u}\| + \|\mathbf{v}\|. \tag{7c}$$

These properties are identical to those given on page 32 for the real case, but here $|\alpha|$ is the modulus of a complex number rather than the absolute value of a real number. Also, the proofs are slightly different due to the presence of complex numbers. To illustrate, consider (7c):

$$
\begin{aligned}
\|\mathbf{u}+\mathbf{v}\|^2 &= (\mathbf{u}+\mathbf{v})\cdot(\mathbf{u}+\mathbf{v}) \\
&= \mathbf{u}\cdot\mathbf{u}+\mathbf{u}\cdot\mathbf{v}+\mathbf{v}\cdot\mathbf{u}+\mathbf{v}\cdot\mathbf{v} \\
&= \|\mathbf{u}\|^2+\mathbf{u}\cdot\mathbf{v}+\overline{\mathbf{u}\cdot\mathbf{v}}+\|\mathbf{v}\|^2 \\
&= \|\mathbf{u}\|^2+2\,\mathrm{Re}\,(\mathbf{u}\cdot\mathbf{v})+\|\mathbf{v}\|^2, \\
\|\mathbf{u}+\mathbf{v}\|^2 &\le \|\mathbf{u}\|^2+2|\mathrm{Re}\,(\mathbf{u}\cdot\mathbf{v})|+\|\mathbf{v}\|^2, \\
\|\mathbf{u}+\mathbf{v}\|^2 &\le \|\mathbf{u}\|^2+2|\mathbf{u}\cdot\mathbf{v}|+\|\mathbf{v}\|^2, \\
\|\mathbf{u}+\mathbf{v}\|^2 &\le \|\mathbf{u}\|^2+2\|\mathbf{u}\|\|\mathbf{v}\|+\|\mathbf{v}\|^2 \\
&= (\|\mathbf{u}\|+\|\mathbf{v}\|)^2,
\end{aligned}
$$

so that

$$\|\mathbf{u}+\mathbf{v}\| \le \|\mathbf{u}\|+\|\mathbf{v}\|;$$

(7a) and (7b) are left for the exercises.

Thus far, then, the only substantial change (beyond the fact that the scalars are now complex) is the change in the dot product from $\mathbf{u}\cdot\mathbf{v} \equiv u_1v_1 + \cdots + u_nv_n$ to $\mathbf{u}\cdot\mathbf{v} \equiv u_1\overline{v}_1 + \cdots + u_n\overline{v}_n$. Furthermore, whereas we defined the angle θ between $\mathbf{u}$ and $\mathbf{v}$ as $\theta = \cos^{-1}(\mathbf{u}\cdot\mathbf{v}/\|\mathbf{u}\|\|\mathbf{v}\|)$ in the real case, this definition is awkward in the complex case since $\mathbf{u}\cdot\mathbf{v}$ (and hence the argument of the arccosine) is complex. Instead of trying to patch things up, we simply choose not to define θ for the complex case, although we do retain a notion of perpendicularity; i.e., we still say that $\mathbf{u}$ and $\mathbf{v}$ are *orthogonal* if $\mathbf{u}\cdot\mathbf{v} = 0$.

Finally,

> ***Theorem 1** Dimension of $\mathbb{C}^n$*
> The dimension of $\mathbb{C}^n$ is n.

You may have expected the dimension to be $2n$, on the grounds that each vector component has both real and imaginary parts. However, observe that the ON set

$$
\begin{aligned}
\hat{\mathbf{i}}_1 &= (1, 0, \ldots, 0) \\
\hat{\mathbf{i}}_2 &= (0, 1, 0, \ldots, 0) \\
&\vdots \\
\hat{\mathbf{i}}_n &= (0, \ldots, 0, 1)
\end{aligned}
\tag{8}
$$

is a basis for $\mathbb{C}^n$, just as it was for $\mathbb{R}^n$, since the set is LI and spans the space. That it spans $\mathbb{C}^n$ follows from the fact that every vector $\mathbf{u} = (u_1, \ldots, u_n)$ in $\mathbb{C}^n$ can be expanded as $\mathbf{u} = u_1\hat{\mathbf{i}}_1 + \cdots + u_n\hat{\mathbf{i}}_n$. And since the basis (8), which we shall call the *standard basis* for $\mathbb{C}^n$, contains n vectors, it follows from the definition of dimension on page 57 that $\mathbb{C}^n$ is n-dimensional.

5.2 EXERCISES

1. Normalize each of the following vectors.

*(a) $(1, i)$ (b) $(1 + i, 1 - i)$
(c) $(1, 3, -2, 0)$ (d) $(2, 1 - 3i, 0, 5)$
(e) $(2 + 3i, 1 - i, 4i)$ (f) $(i, 0, 0, -i)$
(g) (x, y, z, ict) This vector (in which x, y, z are Cartesian coordinates, c is the speed of light, and t is the time) arises in the *special theory of relativity;* in that application, the space $\mathbb{C}^4$ is known as *world space* or *Minkowski space*.

2. Show whether or not the following vector sets are bases for $\mathbb{C}^3$.

*(a) $(i, 2, 1 + i)$, $(0, 1, 2 + i)$, $(4, 1, -i)$
(b) $(1, 0, 2)$, $(3, 2, -2)$, $(0, 0, 4)$
(c) $(4, 1 - 2i, 0)$, $(3 + i, i, -2i)$, $(-2 - 2i, 1 - 4i, 4i)$
(d) $(1, 0, 0)$, $(0, 1, 0)$, $(0, 0, i)$
(e) $(i, 1, 2)$, $(3, 1 - i, -i)$, $(3 + 2i, 3 - i, 4 - i)$, $(3 - i, -i, -2 - i)$

3. Show that the set $\mathbf{e}_1 = (i, 1, 0)$, $\mathbf{e}_2 = (2, 2i, 1)$, $\mathbf{e}_3 = (1, i, -4)$ is an orthogonal basis for $\mathbb{C}^3$.

4. Show that (19) on page 53 (with $k = n$) is valid for $\mathbb{C}^n$, and use it to expand each vector in terms of the bases given in Exercise 3.

*(a) $(2 + 4i, -3i, 2)$ (b) $(0, 0, 1)$
(c) $(1, 1, 1)$ (d) $(i, 2i, 3i)$
(e) $(0, i, 0)$ (f) $(1 - i, 0, 0)$

***5.** Show that $(\alpha \mathbf{x}) \cdot \mathbf{y} = \alpha(\mathbf{x} \cdot \mathbf{y})$, whereas $\mathbf{x} \cdot (\alpha \mathbf{y}) = \overline{\alpha}(\mathbf{x} \cdot \mathbf{y})$.

6. The property (5a) was proved in the text. Prove (5b) and (5c).

7. Prove the Schwarz inequality (6).

8. Prove the properties (7a) and (7b).

9. Vectors in $\mathbb{R}^1$, $\mathbb{R}^2$, and $\mathbb{R}^3$ can be displayed, graphically, as arrow vectors. Is the same true for $\mathbb{C}^1$, $\mathbb{C}^2$, $\mathbb{C}^3$? Explain.

5.3 COMPLEX MATRICES

All of Chapter 3—on matrices, determinants, and linear equations—holds even if the scalars are allowed to be complex. To illustrate, consider a representative example.

EXAMPLE 1 Given

$$\mathbf{A} = \begin{pmatrix} 2 & 1 + i \\ 0 & i \end{pmatrix}, \tag{1}$$

compute $\mathbf{A}^{-1}$. We proceed as usual, although the numbers are now complex:

$$\det \mathbf{A} = (2)(i) - (0)(1 + i) = 2i \quad (\neq 0, \text{ so } \mathbf{A}^{-1} \text{ exists})$$

$$\begin{aligned} \text{Minors: } M_{11} &= i & \text{Cofactors: } A_{11} &= i \\ M_{12} &= 0 & A_{12} &= 0 \\ M_{21} &= 1 + i & A_{21} &= -1 - i \\ M_{22} &= 2 & A_{22} &= 2, \end{aligned}$$

so

$$\mathbf{A}^{-1} = \frac{1}{2i}\begin{pmatrix} i & -1 - i \\ 0 & 2 \end{pmatrix} = \begin{pmatrix} \frac{1}{2} & \frac{-1 + i}{2} \\ 0 & -i \end{pmatrix}, \tag{2}$$

as is easily verified by showing that $\mathbf{A}^{-1}\mathbf{A} = \mathbf{I}$. ◀

However, in Chapter 4, on the eigenvalue problem, dot products begin to appear, so the impact of the change in the dot product (from $\mathbf{x} \cdot \mathbf{y} = x_1 y_1 + \cdots + x_n y_n$ to $\mathbf{x} \cdot \mathbf{y} = x_1 \overline{y}_1 + \cdots + x_n \overline{y}_n$) begins to be felt. Expressed in matrix form, the dot product is now

$$\boxed{\mathbf{x} \cdot \mathbf{y} = \mathbf{x}^{\mathrm{T}} \overline{\mathbf{y}}} \quad \text{or} \quad \overline{\mathbf{y}}^{\mathrm{T}} \mathbf{x}. \tag{3}$$

We begin with two definitions. Given an $m \times n$ matrix $\mathbf{A} = \{a_{ij}\}$, we define the **complex conjugate** of $\mathbf{A}$ as

$$\overline{\mathbf{A}} \equiv \{\overline{a}_{ij}\}, \tag{4}$$

and the **Hermitian conjugate**, or **adjoint**, of $\mathbf{A}$ as[†]

$$\mathbf{A}^* \equiv \{\overline{a}_{ji}\}, \qquad \text{i.e.,} \quad \boxed{\mathbf{A}^* \equiv \overline{\mathbf{A}}^{\mathrm{T}}.} \tag{5}$$

If $\overline{\mathbf{A}} = \mathbf{A}$, then $\mathbf{A}$ is **real**, and if $\mathbf{A}^* = \mathbf{A}$, then $\mathbf{A}$ is **Hermitian**, or **self-adjoint**; evidently, if $\mathbf{A}$ is to be self-adjoint, it must be square, and its diagonal elements must be real (since $\overline{a}_{ji} = a_{ij}$ becomes $\overline{a}_{jj} = a_{jj}$ on the main diagonal).

EXAMPLE 2 If

$$\mathbf{A} = \begin{pmatrix} 2+i & 0 & 3-5i \\ 7 & 1 & 4i \\ 2 & i & 3 \end{pmatrix},$$

then

$$\overline{\mathbf{A}} = \begin{pmatrix} 2-i & 0 & 3+5i \\ 7 & 1 & -4i \\ 2 & -i & 3 \end{pmatrix} \quad \text{and} \quad \mathbf{A}^* = \begin{pmatrix} 2-i & 7 & 2 \\ 0 & 1 & -i \\ 3+5i & -4i & 3 \end{pmatrix}.$$

Since $\mathbf{A}^* \neq \mathbf{A}$, $\mathbf{A}$ is not self-adjoint. ◀

EXAMPLE 3 If

$$\mathbf{A} = \begin{pmatrix} 3 & 1+4i \\ 1-4i & 0 \end{pmatrix},$$

then

$$\overline{\mathbf{A}} = \begin{pmatrix} 3 & 1-4i \\ 1+4i & 0 \end{pmatrix} \quad \text{and} \quad \mathbf{A}^* = \begin{pmatrix} 3 & 1+4i \\ 1-4i & 0 \end{pmatrix}.$$

Since $\mathbf{A}^* = \mathbf{A}$, $\mathbf{A}$ is self-adjoint. ◀

[†] Watch out: Some authors call $\mathbf{A}^* = \overline{\mathbf{A}}^{\mathrm{T}}$ the Hermitian conjugate of $\mathbf{A}$, as we do, but define the *adjoint* of (a square matrix) $\mathbf{A}$, differently, as

$$\text{Adj } \mathbf{A} \equiv \begin{pmatrix} A_{11} & \cdots & A_{n1} \\ \vdots & & \vdots \\ A_{1n} & \cdots & A_{nn} \end{pmatrix}$$

where the A_{ij}'s are the cofactors; then, recalling (16) on page 107, $\mathbf{A}^{-1} = (1/\det \mathbf{A})\text{Adj } \mathbf{A}$.

Some properties of the complex conjugate and adjoint matrices are as follows:

$$\overline{\overline{\mathbf{A}}} = \mathbf{A} \tag{6a}$$

$$\overline{\mathbf{A} + \mathbf{B}} = \overline{\mathbf{A}} + \overline{\mathbf{B}} \tag{6b}$$

$$\overline{\mathbf{AB}} = \overline{\mathbf{A}}\,\overline{\mathbf{B}} \tag{6c}$$

$$(\mathbf{A}^*)^* = \mathbf{A} \tag{6d}$$

$$(\mathbf{A} + \mathbf{B})^* = \mathbf{A}^* + \mathbf{B}^* \tag{6e}$$

$$(\mathbf{AB})^* = \mathbf{B}^*\mathbf{A}^*. \tag{6f}$$

These properties are easily verified. In addition, the key property of the adjoint matrix is that

$$\boxed{(\mathbf{Ax}) \cdot \mathbf{y} = \mathbf{x} \cdot (\mathbf{A}^*\mathbf{y})} \tag{7}$$

holds for all vectors **x** and **y**—specifically, if **A** is $m \times n$, **x** is any $n \times 1$ vector and **y** is any $m \times 1$ vector. To prove (7), observe that

$$(\mathbf{Ax}) \cdot \mathbf{y} = (\mathbf{Ax})^{\mathrm{T}}\overline{\mathbf{y}} = \mathbf{x}^{\mathrm{T}}\mathbf{A}^{\mathrm{T}}\overline{\mathbf{y}} = \mathbf{x}^{\mathrm{T}}\overline{\overline{\mathbf{A}}^{\mathrm{T}}\mathbf{y}} = \mathbf{x}^{\mathrm{T}}\overline{\mathbf{A}^*\mathbf{y}} = \mathbf{x} \cdot (\mathbf{A}^*\mathbf{y}). \tag{8}$$

SELF-ADJOINT MATRICES

Recall, from our study of *real* systems, that matrices arising in applications are often *symmetric*, i.e., $\mathbf{A}^{\mathrm{T}} = \mathbf{A}$, and that such matrices exhibit a number of special and useful properties concerning the eigenvalue problem, as spelled out in Theorems 1 to 4 on pages 145 to 148. Analogously, in the study of *complex* systems it is found that matrices arising in applications are often *self-adjoint*, i.e., $\mathbf{A}^* = \overline{\mathbf{A}}^{\mathrm{T}} = \mathbf{A}$, and that such matrices exhibit analogous special and useful properties.

EXAMPLE 4 *Lorentz Transformation*. In the special theory of relativity one considers the vector (x, y, z, ict), where x, y, z are Cartesian coordinates, c is the speed of light, and t is the time. If the corresponding vector, referred to an x', y', z' system which is translating in the z direction with constant speed v, is denoted as (x', y', z', ict'), it turns out that these vectors are related according to

$$\begin{pmatrix} x' \\ y' \\ z' \\ ict' \end{pmatrix} = \begin{pmatrix} 1 & 0 & 0 & 0 \\ 0 & 1 & 0 & 0 \\ 0 & 0 & \dfrac{1}{\sqrt{1-\beta^2}} & \dfrac{i\beta}{\sqrt{1-\beta^2}} \\ 0 & 0 & \dfrac{-i\beta}{\sqrt{1-\beta^2}} & \dfrac{1}{\sqrt{1-\beta^2}} \end{pmatrix} \begin{pmatrix} x \\ y \\ z \\ ict \end{pmatrix}, \tag{9}$$

where $\beta = v/c$ (<1). This is the important *Lorentz transformation*, and it is seen that the transformation matrix is self-adjoint. ◀

Next, we give four important theorems, which are the counterparts of Theorems 1 to 4 (for real matrices) in Section 4.3.

> ***Theorem 1*** *Real Eigenvalues*
> If $\mathbf{A}$ is self-adjoint, then all of its eigenvalues are real.

Proof. Let us both pre-dot and post-dot both sides of $\mathbf{Ax} = \lambda\mathbf{x}$ with $\mathbf{x}$; i.e.,*

$$\text{Pre-dot:} \quad \mathbf{x}\cdot(\mathbf{Ax}) = \mathbf{x}\cdot(\lambda\mathbf{x}) = \bar{\lambda}(\mathbf{x}\cdot\mathbf{x}) \tag{10a}$$

$$\text{Post-dot:} \quad (\mathbf{Ax})\cdot\mathbf{x} = (\lambda\mathbf{x})\cdot\mathbf{x} = \lambda(\mathbf{x}\cdot\mathbf{x}). \tag{10b}$$

But the left-hand sides are equal, by virtue of the property (7) and the assumption that $\mathbf{A}$ is self-adjoint. Thus subtracting (10b) from (10a) yields

$$(\bar{\lambda} - \lambda)(\mathbf{x}\cdot\mathbf{x}) = 0. \tag{11}$$

Now $\mathbf{x}\cdot\mathbf{x} = \|\mathbf{x}\|^2 \neq 0$ since $\mathbf{x}$ is an eigenvector, so it follows from (11) that $\bar{\lambda} - \lambda = 0$, or $\bar{\lambda} = \lambda$. Thus λ is real. ■

> ***Theorem 2*** *Dimension of Eigenspace*
> If an eigenvalue λ of a self-adjoint matrix $\mathbf{A}$ is of multiplicity k, then the span of the corresponding eigenvectors (called the eigenspace of $\mathbf{A}$ corresponding to λ) is of dimension k.

We state the foregoing theorem without proof.

> ***Theorem 3*** *Orthogonality of Eigenvectors*
> If $\mathbf{A}$ is self-adjoint, then eigenvectors corresponding to distinct eigenvalues are orthogonal.

Proof. Let $\mathbf{e}_j$ and $\mathbf{e}_k$ be eigenvectors corresponding to distinct eigenvalues λ_j and λ_k, respectively. Thus

$$\mathbf{Ae}_j = \lambda_j\mathbf{e}_j \tag{12a}$$

and

$$\mathbf{Ae}_k = \lambda_k\mathbf{e}_k. \tag{12b}$$

Pre-dotting both sides of (12a) with $\mathbf{e}_k$, and post-dotting both sides of (12b) with $\mathbf{e}_j$, and using the fact that $\bar{\lambda} = \lambda$, we have

$$\begin{aligned} \mathbf{e}_k\cdot(\mathbf{Ae}_j) &= \mathbf{e}_k\cdot(\lambda_j\mathbf{e}_j) & (\mathbf{Ae}_k)\cdot\mathbf{e}_j &= (\lambda_k\mathbf{e}_k)\cdot\mathbf{e}_j \\ &= \bar{\lambda}_j(\mathbf{e}_k\cdot\mathbf{e}_j) & &= \lambda_k(\mathbf{e}_k\cdot\mathbf{e}_j). \\ &= \lambda_j(\mathbf{e}_k\cdot\mathbf{e}_j) \end{aligned} \tag{13}$$

* Note Exercise 5 on page 204.

But $(\mathbf{Ae}_k)\cdot\mathbf{e}_j = \mathbf{e}_k\cdot(\mathbf{A}^*\mathbf{e}_j) = \mathbf{e}_k\cdot(\mathbf{Ae}_j)$, so if we subtract $(\mathbf{Ae}_k)\cdot\mathbf{e}_j = \lambda_k(\mathbf{e}_k\cdot\mathbf{e}_j)$ from $\mathbf{e}_k\cdot(\mathbf{Ae}_j) = \lambda_j(\mathbf{e}_k\cdot\mathbf{e}_j)$, we obtain

$$0 = (\lambda_j - \lambda_k)(\mathbf{e}_k\cdot\mathbf{e}_j). \tag{14}$$

Finally, $\lambda_j - \lambda_k \neq 0$ since λ_j and λ_k are distinct, by assumption, so it follows from (14) that $\mathbf{e}_j\cdot\mathbf{e}_k = 0$, as was to be shown. ■

> ***Theorem 4** Orthogonal Basis*
> If an $n \times n$ matrix $\mathbf{A}$ is self-adjoint, then its eigenvectors constitute an orthogonal basis for n-space.

Proof is essentially the same as for Theorem 4 on page 148.

EXAMPLE 5 Find the eigenvalues and eigenvectors of

$$\mathbf{A} = \begin{pmatrix} 3 & 2i \\ -2i & 0 \end{pmatrix}$$

Setting $\det(\mathbf{A} - \lambda\mathbf{I}) = 0$ gives the characteristic equation

$$(3-\lambda)(-\lambda) - (2i)(-2i) = \lambda^2 - 3\lambda - 4 = (\lambda+1)(\lambda-4) = 0.$$

Hence

$$\lambda_1 = -1, \quad \text{and} \quad \lambda_2 = 4.$$

Observe that $\mathbf{A}$ is self-adjoint and, sure enough, in accordance with Theorem 1, its λ's are real.

To find the eigenvectors, solve $(\mathbf{A} - \lambda\mathbf{I})\mathbf{x} = \mathbf{0}$.

$$\lambda = \lambda_1 = -1: \quad \begin{pmatrix} 4 & 2i \\ -2i & 1 \end{pmatrix}\begin{pmatrix} x_1 \\ x_2 \end{pmatrix} = \begin{pmatrix} 0 \\ 0 \end{pmatrix} \quad \text{or} \quad \begin{aligned} 4x_1 + 2ix_2 &= 0 \\ -2ix_1 + x_2 &= 0. \end{aligned}$$

Solving, $x_2 = 2ix_1$, so the eigenvector is (to within the usual arbitrary nonzero scale factor)

$$\mathbf{e}_1 = \begin{pmatrix} 1 \\ 2i \end{pmatrix}.$$

$$\lambda = \lambda_2 = 4: \quad \begin{pmatrix} -1 & 2i \\ -2i & -4 \end{pmatrix}\begin{pmatrix} x_1 \\ x_2 \end{pmatrix} = \begin{pmatrix} 0 \\ 0 \end{pmatrix} \quad \text{or} \quad \begin{aligned} -x_1 + 2ix_2 &= 0 \\ -2ix_1 - 4x_2 &= 0. \end{aligned}$$

Solving, $x_1 = 2ix_2$, so

$$\mathbf{e}_2 = \begin{pmatrix} 2i \\ 1 \end{pmatrix}.$$

Again, $\mathbf{A}$ is self-adjoint and λ_1 and λ_2 are distinct, and in accordance with Theorem 3, the eigenvectors are orthogonal: $\mathbf{e}_1\cdot\mathbf{e}_2 = (1)(\overline{2i}) + (2i)(\overline{1}) = (1)(-2i) + (2i)(1) = 0.$ ◀

HERMITIAN FORMS, DIAGONALIZATION, AND UNITARY MATRICES

The analog of the quadratic form $F(x_1, \ldots, x_n) = \mathbf{x}^{\mathrm{T}}\mathbf{A}\mathbf{x}$, where $\mathbf{A}$ is symmetric ($\mathbf{A}^{\mathrm{T}} = \mathbf{A}$) and $\mathbf{x} = (x_1, \ldots, x_n)^{\mathrm{T}}$, is the **Hermitian form***

$$F = \overline{\mathbf{x}}^{\mathrm{T}}\mathbf{A}\mathbf{x}, \tag{15}$$

where $\mathbf{A}$ is self-adjoint ($\overline{\mathbf{A}}^{\mathrm{T}} = \mathbf{A}$). For example, if $n = 2$, then (15) becomes

$$\begin{aligned} F &= (\overline{x}_1 \quad \overline{x}_2)\begin{pmatrix} a_{11} & a_{12} \\ \overline{a}_{12} & a_{22} \end{pmatrix}\begin{pmatrix} x_1 \\ x_2 \end{pmatrix} \\ &= a_{11}x_1\overline{x}_1 + a_{22}x_2\overline{x}_2 + a_{12}\overline{x}_1x_2 + \overline{a}_{12}x_1\overline{x}_2. \end{aligned} \tag{16}$$

The right-hand side of (16) is seen to be real since a_{11} and a_{22} are diagonal elements of a self-adjoint matrix, and hence are real, $x_1\overline{x}_1 = |x_1|^2$ and $x_2\overline{x}_2 = |x_2|^2$ are real, and the fourth term is the conjugate of the third term. In fact, F is real for *all* values $n \geq 1$:

$$\overline{F} = \overline{\overline{\mathbf{x}}^{\mathrm{T}}\mathbf{A}\mathbf{x}} = \mathbf{x}^{\mathrm{T}}\overline{\mathbf{A}\mathbf{x}} = \overline{(\mathbf{A}\mathbf{x})^{\mathrm{T}}}\mathbf{x} = \overline{\mathbf{x}}^{\mathrm{T}}\overline{\mathbf{A}}^{\mathrm{T}}\mathbf{x} = \overline{\mathbf{x}}^{\mathrm{T}}\mathbf{A}\mathbf{x} = F. \tag{17}$$

(See Exercise 7.)

To reduce F to canonical form, set $\mathbf{x} = \mathbf{U}\mathbf{x}'$ in (15). Then

$$F = \overline{(\mathbf{U}\mathbf{x}')^{\mathrm{T}}}\mathbf{A}\mathbf{U}\mathbf{x}' = \overline{\mathbf{x}}^{\mathrm{T}}(\mathbf{U}^*\mathbf{A}\mathbf{U})\mathbf{x}', \tag{18}$$

so $\mathbf{U}$ is to be chosen so that

$$\mathbf{U}^*\mathbf{A}\mathbf{U} = \mathbf{D} \tag{19}$$

is diagonal. Recalling our discussion of the *real* case (Section 4.5), it is not surprising that a suitable $\mathbf{U}$ matrix is a normalized modal matrix of $\mathbf{A}$ (Exercise 8); with that choice, the diagonal elements of $\mathbf{D}$ are the eigenvalues of $\mathbf{A}$, and F reduces to the canonical form

$$\begin{aligned} F &= \lambda_1 x_1'\overline{x}_1' + \lambda_2 x_2'\overline{x}_2' + \cdots + \lambda_n x_n'\overline{x}_n' \\ &= \lambda_1 |x_1'|^2 + \lambda_2 |x_2'|^2 + \cdots + \lambda_n |x_n'|^2. \end{aligned} \tag{20}$$

In the real case the normalized modal matrix was denoted as $\mathbf{Q}$, and it turned out that $\mathbf{Q}$ was orthogonal, i.e., $\mathbf{Q}^{\mathrm{T}} = \mathbf{Q}^{-1}$. Analogously, we find (Exercise 9), in the present case, that

$$\overline{\mathbf{U}}^{\mathrm{T}} = \mathbf{U}^{-1} \quad \text{or} \quad \boxed{\mathbf{U}^* = \mathbf{U}^{-1},} \tag{21}$$

and such a matrix is said to be **unitary**.

> ***Theorem 5** Eigenvalues of Unitary Matrix*
> If λ is an eigenvalue of a unitary matrix, then $|\lambda| = 1$.

* *Charles Hermite* (1822–1901), a professor at the Sorbonne and at the Ecole Polytechnique, contributed to the theory of elliptic functions, and is also well known for his introduction of the Hermite polynomials.

Proof Let $\mathbf{U}$ be unitary, with an eigenvalue λ and corresponding eigenvector $\mathbf{e}$:

$$\mathbf{Ue} = \lambda\mathbf{e} \qquad (\mathbf{e} \neq \mathbf{0}). \tag{22}$$

Seeking to employ (21), we take the conjugate transpose of both sides:

$$(\overline{\mathbf{Ue}})^{\mathrm{T}} = (\overline{\lambda\mathbf{e}})^{\mathrm{T}} \quad \text{or} \quad \overline{\mathbf{e}}^{\mathrm{T}}\,\mathbf{U}^{-1} = \overline{\lambda}\overline{\mathbf{e}}^{\mathrm{T}}. \tag{23}$$

And postmultiplying the left with $\mathbf{Ue}$ and the right with $\lambda\mathbf{e}$ [which are equal by (22), and nonzero], (23) gives

$$\overline{\mathbf{e}}^{\mathrm{T}}\mathbf{U}^{-1}\mathbf{Ue} = \overline{\lambda}\overline{\mathbf{e}}^{\mathrm{T}}\lambda\mathbf{e} \quad \text{or} \quad \overline{\mathbf{e}}^{\mathrm{T}}\mathbf{e} = |\lambda|^2\overline{\mathbf{e}}^{\mathrm{T}}\mathbf{e}. \tag{24}$$

But $\overline{\mathbf{e}}^{\mathrm{T}}\mathbf{e} = \|\mathbf{e}\|^2 \neq 0$, so (24) implies that $|\lambda|^2 = 1$, or $|\lambda| = 1$, as claimed. ■

EXAMPLE 6 Reduce

$$F = 3x_1\overline{x}_1 + 2i\overline{x}_1x_2 - 2ix_1\overline{x}_2 \tag{25}$$

to canonical form. Comparing (25) with (16), we see that $a_{11} = 3$, $a_{22} = 0$, and $a_{12} = 2i$, so that

$$\mathbf{A} = \begin{pmatrix} 3 & 2i \\ -2i & 0 \end{pmatrix}.$$

This is the same $\mathbf{A}$ as in Example 5, so

$$\lambda_1 = -1, \quad \hat{\mathbf{e}}_1 = \frac{1}{\sqrt{5}}\begin{pmatrix} 1 \\ 2i \end{pmatrix}; \qquad \lambda_2 = 4, \quad \hat{\mathbf{e}}_2 = \frac{1}{\sqrt{5}}\begin{pmatrix} 2i \\ 1 \end{pmatrix}.$$

Thus the desired canonical form is

$$F = \lambda_1|x_1'|^2 + \lambda_2|x_2'|^2 = -|x_1'|^2 + 4|x_2'|^2,$$

where x_1, x_2 and x_1', x_2' are related according to

$$\mathbf{x} = \mathbf{Ux}' = (\hat{\mathbf{e}}_1, \hat{\mathbf{e}}_2)\mathbf{x}',$$

or

$$\begin{pmatrix} x_1 \\ x_2 \end{pmatrix} = \frac{1}{\sqrt{5}}\begin{pmatrix} 1 & 2i \\ 2i & 1 \end{pmatrix}\begin{pmatrix} x_1' \\ x_2' \end{pmatrix}.$$

Or, if we prefer it the other way around,

$$\mathbf{x}' = \mathbf{U}^{-1}\mathbf{x} = \mathbf{U}^*\mathbf{x} \quad \text{or} \quad \begin{pmatrix} x_1' \\ x_2' \end{pmatrix} = \frac{1}{\sqrt{5}}\begin{pmatrix} 1 & -2i \\ -2i & 1 \end{pmatrix}\begin{pmatrix} x_1 \\ x_2 \end{pmatrix}.$$ ◀

5.3 EXERCISES

1. Invert each of the following matrices. If the matrix is not invertible (i.e., if it is singular), state that.

*(a) $\begin{pmatrix} 2 & i \\ 1 & 4 \end{pmatrix}$ (b) $\begin{pmatrix} 1+i & 3i \\ 1 & 2-i \end{pmatrix}$

(c) $\begin{pmatrix} 3 & 1+i \\ 1-i & 2 \end{pmatrix}$ (d) $\begin{pmatrix} 1 & 3 & i \\ 0 & 1+i & 1 \\ 0 & 0 & 2 \end{pmatrix}$

(e) $\begin{pmatrix} 0 & i & 0 \\ -i & 0 & 2+2i \\ 0 & 2-2i & 0 \end{pmatrix}$ (f) $\begin{pmatrix} 4 & 0 & -i \\ 0 & 4 & 0 \\ i & 0 & 4 \end{pmatrix}$

2. *(a)–(f) Determine the eigenvalues and eigenvectors of each of the matrices in Exercise 1, and show that the results are in accord with the relevent theorems in this section.

3. Determine the eigenvalues and eigenvectors in each case.

(a) $\begin{pmatrix} 1 & 2 \\ 1 & 0 \end{pmatrix}$ *(b) $\begin{pmatrix} 2 & 1 \\ -1 & 2 \end{pmatrix}$

(c) $\begin{pmatrix} 1 & 2 \\ 3 & 4 \end{pmatrix}$ (d) $\begin{pmatrix} 4 & -5 \\ 1 & 2 \end{pmatrix}$

***4.** Give necessary and sufficient conditions on a, b, c, d such that $\mathbf{A} = \begin{pmatrix} a & b \\ c & d \end{pmatrix}$ will have complex eigenvalues, i.e., such that $\operatorname{Im} \lambda \neq 0$.

5. Reduce the following to the canonical form (20), and give the matrix transformations from $\mathbf{x}$ to $\mathbf{x}'$, and from $\mathbf{x}'$ to $\mathbf{x}$.

*(a) $F = 2x_1\bar{x}_1 + 3x_2\bar{x}_2 + (1 + i)\bar{x}_1x_2 + (1 - i)x_1\bar{x}_2$
(b) $F = 2x_1\bar{x}_1 + 5x_2\bar{x}_2 - 2i\bar{x}_1x_2 + 2ix_1\bar{x}_2$
(c) $F = i\bar{x}_1x_2 - ix_1\bar{x}_2 + 2(1 + i)\,\bar{x}_2x_3 + 2(1 - i)\,x_2\bar{x}_3$
(d) $F = 4x_1\bar{x}_1 + 4x_2\bar{x}_2 + 4x_3\bar{x}_3 + ix_1\bar{x}_3 - i\bar{x}_1x_3$

6. Given each of the following $\mathbf{A}$ matrices, evaluate $\mathbf{A}^{1000}$.

(a) $\begin{pmatrix} 2 & 1 - i \\ 1 + i & 3 \end{pmatrix}$ *(b) $\begin{pmatrix} 2 & -2i \\ 2i & 5 \end{pmatrix}$

(c) $\begin{pmatrix} 0 & -i \\ i & 2 \end{pmatrix}$ (d) $\begin{pmatrix} 3 & 2 - i \\ 2 + i & -1 \end{pmatrix}$

7. Justify the second through fifth equalities in (17), citing relevent equation numbers or theorems.

8. Verify that if $\mathbf{U}$ is a normalized modal matrix of $\mathbf{A}$, then F does reduce to the canonical form (20), as claimed.

9. Verify that the normalized modal matrix $\mathbf{U}$ satisfies (21).

***10.** Is the Lorentz transformation matrix, in (9), unitary? Orthogonal?

11. If $\mathbf{x} \cdot (\mathbf{Ax}) = \mathbf{x} \cdot (\mathbf{Bx})$ for all $\mathbf{x}$, where $\mathbf{A}$ and $\mathbf{B}$ are Hermitian, does it follow that $\mathbf{A} = \mathbf{B}$? Explain.

12. (*Necessary and sufficient condition for existence of solutions of* $\mathbf{Ax} = \mathbf{c}$) A necessary and sufficient condition for the *existence* of solution(s) to $\mathbf{Ax} = \mathbf{c}$ (where $\mathbf{A}$ is $m \times n$, $\mathbf{x}$ is $n \times 1$, and $\mathbf{c}$ is $m \times 1$) is that $\mathbf{c}$ be orthogonal to every solution $\mathbf{z}$ of the associated homogeneous equation $\mathbf{A}^*\mathbf{z} = \mathbf{0}$. Prove that this condition is *necessary*. (You need *not* prove it is also sufficient.) *Hint:* Dot both sides of $\mathbf{Ax} = \mathbf{c}$ with $\mathbf{z}$, and then use (7).

13. Use the result stated in Exercise 12 to determine conditions, if any, on the components of $\mathbf{c}$, for the given system to be consistent. Compare your results with those obtained by direct application of Gauss elimination to the given system.

*(a) $\begin{pmatrix} 2 & 1 \\ 2 & 1 \end{pmatrix}\begin{pmatrix} x_1 \\ x_2 \end{pmatrix} = \begin{pmatrix} c_1 \\ c_2 \end{pmatrix}$

*(b) $\begin{pmatrix} 2 & 1 \\ 4 & 1 \end{pmatrix}\begin{pmatrix} x_1 \\ x_2 \end{pmatrix} = \begin{pmatrix} c_1 \\ c_2 \end{pmatrix}$

(c) $\begin{pmatrix} 2 & 1 \\ 4 & 2 \\ i & 1 \end{pmatrix}\begin{pmatrix} x_1 \\ x_2 \end{pmatrix} = \begin{pmatrix} c_1 \\ c_2 \\ c_3 \end{pmatrix}$

(d) $\begin{pmatrix} 1 & 3 & 2 & 1 \\ 2 & -1 & 1 & 0 \\ 3 & 2 & 3 & 1 \end{pmatrix}\begin{pmatrix} x_1 \\ x_2 \\ x_3 \\ x_4 \end{pmatrix} = \begin{pmatrix} c_1 \\ c_2 \\ c_3 \end{pmatrix}$

(e) $\begin{pmatrix} 1 & 3 & 2 & i \\ 2 & -1 & 1 & 0 \\ 3 & 2 & 3 & i \end{pmatrix}\begin{pmatrix} x_1 \\ x_2 \\ x_3 \\ x_4 \end{pmatrix} = \begin{pmatrix} c_1 \\ c_2 \\ c_3 \end{pmatrix}$

(f) $\begin{pmatrix} 2 & 1 & 1 \\ i & 1 & 2i-3 \\ 1 & 2 & -4 \\ -1 & 1 & -5 \end{pmatrix}\begin{pmatrix} x_1 \\ x_2 \\ x_3 \end{pmatrix} = \begin{pmatrix} c_1 \\ c_2 \\ c_3 \\ c_4 \end{pmatrix}$

14. Given any $m \times n$ matrix $\mathbf{A}$, self-adjoint or not, show that $\mathbf{A}$ can be split as $\mathbf{A} = \mathbf{B} + i\mathbf{C}$, where $\mathbf{B}$ and $\mathbf{C}$ are each self-adjoint. Show that $\mathbf{B} = (\mathbf{A}^* + \mathbf{A})/2$ and $\mathbf{C} = i(\mathbf{A}^* - \mathbf{A})/2$.

15. (a) If $\mathbf{A}$ is self-adjoint, is $i\mathbf{A}$ self-adjoint? Explain.
(b) If $\mathbf{A}$ is self-adjoint, is $\mathbf{A}^2$ self-adjoint? Explain.

ADDITIONAL REFERENCES FOR PART I

B. CARNAHAN, H. LUTHER, and J. WILKES, *Applied Numerical Methods*. New York: Wiley, 1969.

Chapter 4 provides a compact (59-page) treatment of "Matrices and Related Topics," which includes numerical and algorithmic aspects of the subject.

D. FADDEEV and V. FADDEEVA, *Computational Methods of Linear Algebra*. San Francisco: W. H. Freeman, 1963.

The first chapter includes basic linear algebra theory, and subsequent chapters deal with computational methods and algorithms.

T. J. FLETCHER, *Linear Algebra through Its Applications*. New York: Van Nostrand Reinhold, 1972.

Includes interesting applications to magic squares, curve fitting, the vibration of mechanical and electrical systems, chemical systems, beetles, buns and cakes, and other diverse systems.

ERNST A. GUILLEMIN, *The Mathematics of Circuit Analysis*. New York; Wiley, 1949, Chaps. I–IV.

Essentially a text on applied mathematics, with electrical circuit applications as a unifying theme.

GEORGE HADLEY, *Linear Algebra*. Reading, Mass.: Addison-Wesley, 1961.

An introductory text, about the same level as this book. Emphasis on geometrical approach (e.g., Chapter 6 on "Convex Sets and *n*-Dimensional Geometry").

F. B. HILDEBRAND, *Methods of Applied Mathematics*. Englewood Cliffs, N.J.:Prentice-Hall, 1952, Chap. 1.

See, in particular, Section 1.22 on "Functions of Symmetric Matrices," including Sylvester's formula and infinite series of matrices, and Section 1.28 on "Function Spaces."

MICHAEL O'NAN, *Linear Algebra*. 2nd ed. New York: Harcourt Brace Jovanovich, 1976.

Chapters 4, 5, and 7 on "Vector Spaces," "Linear Transformations," and "Eigenvalues and Canonical Forms," respectively, are recommended as collateral reading. The approach and level are about the same as in Anton's *Elementary Linear Algebra*.

GILBERT STRANG, *Linear Algebra and Its Applications*. New York: Academic Press, 1976.

Includes numerous examples, illustrations, and geometrical interpretation. See, in particular, the introduction to *linear programming*.

A. MARY TROPPER, *Matrix Theory for Electrical Engineers*. Reading, Mass.: Addison-Wesley, 1962.

Introductory linear algebra.

S. YAKOWITZ and F. SZIDAROVSZKY, *An Introduction to Numerical Computations*. New York: Macmillan, 1986.

Chapter 4 contains an up-to-date discussion of the numerical solution of simultaneous linear equations, including the use of pivoting in Gauss elimination, and ill-conditioned systems.

Differential Calculus of Functions of Several Variables 6

INTRODUCTION 6.1

The heart of Part II is the final chapter, Chapter 9, on scalar and vector field theory. The three preceding chapters pave the way for that material by providing an introduction to a number of topics from the subject area generally known as "advanced calculus."

In *Chapter 6* we consider (real-valued) functions of more than one (real) variable, and lay some of the groundwork for our subsequent development of field theory and partial differential equations. Much of the development parallels that in the calculus of functions of a single variable: derivatives, chain differentiation, Taylor's formula, mean value theorem, and maxima and minima.

Chapter 7 is not a continuation of the development begun in Chapter 6. Rather, it covers the fundamentals of vectors and their manipulation: the dot and cross product, base vectors, differentiation of vectors, both Cartesian and non-Cartesian reference systems, and the representation of curves in space. *Chapter 8* returns to the calculus of functions of several variables, begun in Chapter 6, with introductory material on double and triple integrals, and surfaces and volumes. Finally, in *Chapter 9* we consider both scalar and vector fields; we introduce the divergence, gradient, and curl, and consider the divergence theorem (for transforming certain volume integrals to surface integrals), and a number of physical applications from the subject of heat conduction, fluid flow, and electrostatics.

Discussion of non-Cartesian coordinates (polar, cylindrical, and spherical) is confined to OPTIONAL sections and may be omitted in a shorter course.

6.2 PRELIMINARY NOTIONS

Here we introduce concepts from elementary point set theory, concepts that will be needed in subsequent sections. We plan to consider functions of any (finite) number of real variables, say $f(x_1, \ldots, x_n)$. The physical nature of the independent variables $x_1, \ldots, x_n$ will not be germane in this discussion; $x_1, \ldots, x_n$ may be electrical currents in a circuit, pressures, temperatures, distances, or whatever. It will be helpful to regard $x_1, \ldots, x_n$ as the coordinates of a point in an n-dimensional space; we denote such a point as $P = (x_1, \ldots, x_n)$. Further, we define the **distance** $d(P, P')$ between two points, $P = (x_1, \ldots, x_n)$ and $P' = (x_1', \ldots, x_n')$, as

$$d(P, P') \equiv \sqrt{(x_1 - x_1')^2 + (x_2 - x_2')^2 + \cdots + (x_n - x_n')^2}. \tag{1}$$

If $n = 1$, then P and P' are two points x_1 and x_1' on an x axis, and (1) becomes

$$d(P, P') = |x_1 - x_1'|. \tag{2a}$$

For $n = 2$ we have

$$d(P, P') = \sqrt{(x_1 - x_1')^2 + (x_2 - x_2')^2}, \tag{2b}$$

and for $n = 3$,

$$d(P, P') = \sqrt{(x_1 - x_1')^2 + (x_2 - x_2')^2 + (x_3 - x_3')^2}. \tag{2c}$$

These formulas are familiar to us; in particular, (2b) and (2c) are the Pythagorean formulas for the distance between points in two- and three-dimensional Euclidean space. For $n > 3$, then, (1) amounts to an n-dimensional generalization of these Pythagorean formulas.*

Next, we define a **neighborhood** $N(P_0; r)$ of a point P_0 as the set of all points P closer to P_0 than r, i.e., such that

$$d(P_0, P) < r \qquad (r > 0). \tag{3}$$

In one dimension (3) becomes $|x_0 - x| < r$, which corresponds to the *interval* shown in Fig. 6.1a (not including the endpoints $x_0 + r$ and $x_0 - r$); in two dimen-

Fig. 6.1 One- and two-dimensional neighborhoods.

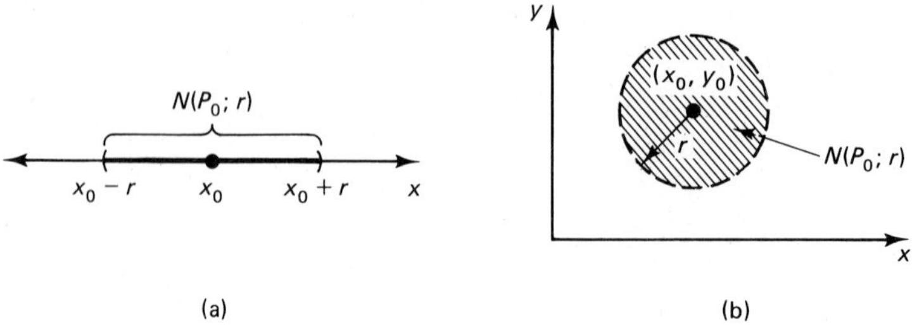

* If you have studied Part I of this book, you may recall that the right-hand side of (1) is the Euclidean norm of the vector from P to P' in n-space. We might add that (1) is not the *only* definition of distance that is used in analysis, although it is no doubt the most common one. For example, the definition $d(P, P') \equiv |x_1 - x_1'| + |x_2 - x_2'| + \cdots + |x_n - x_n'|$ is also acceptable, and is sometimes favored over (1) because it is algebraically simpler.

sions N is the circular *disk* shown in Fig. 6.1b (not including the points on its edge); in three dimensions N is a *sphere* (not including the points on its surface); and if $n > 3$, we speak of N as an n-dimensional *hypersphere*.

Next, we say that a point set S is **connected** if each pair of points in S can be joined by an unbroken line consisting of a finite number of straight segments, each contained entirely within S.*

EXAMPLE 1 Each of the point sets S_1 and S_2 in the two-dimensional plane, shown in Fig. 6.2, is connected. The points A, B, for example, may be joined as shown. In contrast, the set S_3 is not connected since not *all* pairs of points in S_3 can be joined by linear segments lying entirely within S_3. The points A, B, for example, cannot be so joined. ◀

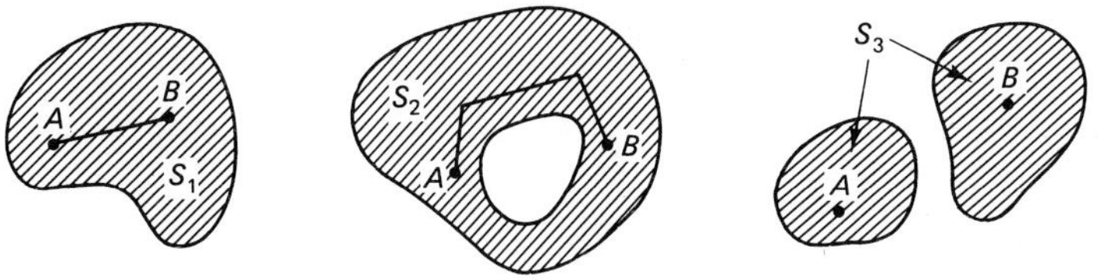

Fig. 6.2 Connectedness.

A point P is said to be a **boundary point** of a point set S if *every* neighborhood $N(P; r)$ (i.e., no matter how small we take r to be) contains points in S *as well as* points not in S. Thus a boundary point is just what it sounds like. To illustrate, the point P in the two-dimensional point set S shown in Fig. 6.3 is *not* a boundary point since the disk $N(P; r)$ contains no points outside S if we choose r to be smaller than ϵ. The point Q, on the other hand, *is* a boundary point since $N(Q; r)$ evidently contains points in S *and* points not in S, no matter what value we choose for r. (Recall, from the definition of neighborhood, that $r > 0$; i.e., r cannot be zero.)

A point P of a set S is said to be an **interior point** of S if there exists some neighborhood of P lying entirely within S.

Fig. 6.3 Boundary points.

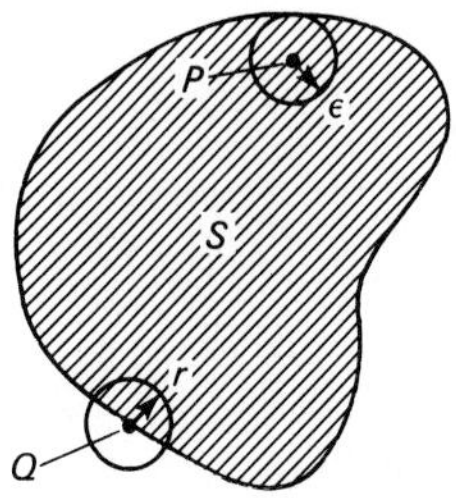

*A straight line may be defined in n-dimensional space, even if $n > 3$, by parametric equations $x_1 = a_1 + b_1 t$, $x_2 = a_2 + b_2 t$, . . . , $x_n = a_n + b_n t$, where $a_1, \ldots, a_n$ and $b_1, \ldots, b_n$ are constants, and where t is the parameter.

Finally, we call a connected set S a **region:** an **open region** or **domain** if it contains *none* of its boundary points, and a **closed region** if it contains *all* of its boundary points.

EXAMPLE 2 Let S_1 be the set of points (x, y), in Cartesian 2-space, such that $x^2 + y^2 < 1$, as shown in Fig. 6.4a. We write $S_1 = \{(x, y) \mid x^2 + y^2 < 1\}$. Evidently, S_1 is connected. Its boundary points are the points on the unit circle $x^2 + y^2 = 1$; none of these points belong to S_1 (as conveyed in the figure by the use of dashed lines), so S_1 is an open domain. One calls this domain the *open unit disk*. Every point in S_1 is an interior point.

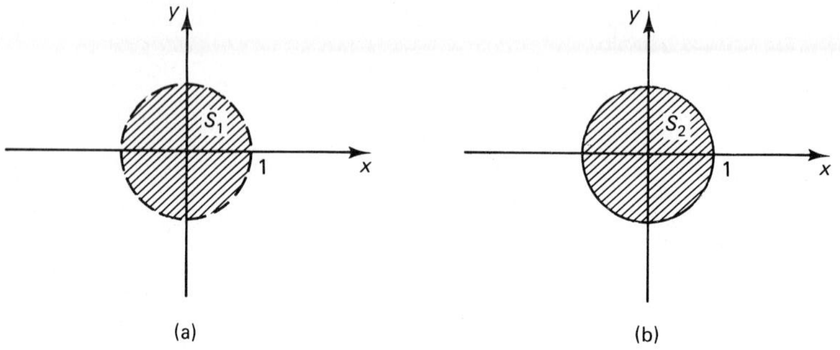

Fig. 6.4 Open and closed regions.

Next, let $S_2 = \{(x, y) \mid x^2 + y^2 \leq 1\}$, as shown in Fig. 6.4b. This time all the boundary points (those on the circle $x^2 + y^2 = 1$) are contained in S_2, as emphasized by the solid boundary line in the figure, so S_2 is a closed region, the *closed unit disk*. All points (x, y) such that $x^2 + y^2 < 1$ are interior points of S_2. ◀

Of course, if S contains some, but not all, of its boundary points, it is neither an open region *nor* a closed region. However, the regions that we shall work with will generally be either open or closed. Further, it should be noted that the terms "open" and "closed" are not mutually exclusive. For example, the connected set $S = \{x \mid -\infty < x < \infty\}$, namely the entire real axis, has no boundary points. Thus it is at once open (since it contains none of its boundary points) and closed (since it contains all of its boundary points).

6.2 EXERCISES

1. Determine the distance $d(P, P')$ in each case.

*(a) $P = (3, 1, 0)$, $P' = (-1, 2, 2)$

(b) $P = (1, -1, 5, 0)$, $P' = (0, 4, 3, 2)$

(c) $P = (1, -4)$, $P' = (6, 5)$

*(d) $P = (0, 4, 3, 0)$, $P' = (0, 0, 0, 5)$

(e) $P = (-6)$, $P' = (-2)$

(f) $P = (8, 0, 1, 0)$, $P' = (0, 2, -6, 7)$

***2.** Is $P = (3.2, 3.9)$ in $N(P_0; r)$ if $P_0 = (3, 4)$ and $r = 0.2$?

3. Is $P = (4.3, 1.1)$ in $N(P_0; r)$ if $P_0 = (4.2, 1)$ and $r = 0.2$?

4. Is $P = (2, 5, 7)$ in $N(P_0; r)$ if $P_0 = (3, 4, 5)$ and $r = 3$?

5. Is $P = (0.99, 1.96, -0.95, 0.03)$ in $N(P_0; r)$ if $P_0 = (1, 2, -1, 0)$ and $r = 0.01$?

6. In each case identify the boundary points, and indicate whether the set is connected, an open region, a closed region, or neither.

*(a) $\{x \mid 0 < x \leq 1\}$
(b) $\{x \mid -3 \leq x < 5\}$
(c) $\{x \mid 0 < x < \infty\}$
(d) $\{x \mid 0 \leq x < \infty\}$
(e) $\{x \mid 0 < \sin x \leq 1\}$
*(f) $\{x \mid \sin x = 0\}$
(g) $\{(x_1, x_2) \mid 2 < x_1 < 3, 1 < x_2 < 5\}$
(h) $\{(x_1, x_2) \mid -\infty < x_1 < \infty, 0 < x_2 < 1\}$
(i) $\{(x_1, x_2) \mid 6 < x_1 < 8, x_2 = 0\}$
(j) $\{(x_1, x_2) \mid 1 < x_1^2 + x_2^2 \leq 4\}$
*(k) $\{(x_1, x_2) \mid 0 < x_1^2 + x_2^2 < 1\}$
(l) $\{(x_1, x_2) \mid -2 < x_1 x_2 < 2\}$
(m) $\{(x_1, x_2, x_3) \mid 1 < x_1^2 + x_3^2 < 2, x_2 = 0\}$
*(n) $\{(x_1, x_2, x_3, x_4) \mid 3 < x_1^2 + x_2^2 + x_3^2 + x_4^2 < \infty\}$
(o) $\{(x_1, x_2, x_3, x_4) \mid 0 < x_1 < 1, 0 < x_2 < 1, 0 < x_3 < 1, 0 < x_4 < 1\}$

PARTIAL DERIVATIVES 6.3

While it is assumed that the reader has already met partial derivatives in elementary calculus, it may be worthwhile to review a few ideas before proceeding. First will be the notion of "continuity."

Recall that "$f(x)$ being continuous at x_0" means that $\lim_{x \to x_0} f(x)$ exists and is equal to $f(x_0)$. Similarly, for functions of several variables we say that $f(x_1, \ldots, x_n) \equiv f(P)$ is **continuous** at P_0 if $\lim_{P \to P_0} f(P) = f(P_0)$. In "$\epsilon$, δ language," $f(P)$ being continuous at P_0 means that to each $\epsilon > 0$ (no matter how small) there corresponds a $\delta(\epsilon)$ such that $|f(P) - f(P_0)| < \epsilon$ for all points P such that $d(P, P_0) < \epsilon$, where $d(P, P_0)$ was defined in the preceding section. If f is not continuous, it is **discontinuous.**

Turning to partial differentiation, it should suffice to consider a function f of two variables x, y (or x_1, x_2 if you prefer). Suppose $f(x, y)$ is defined throughout some neighborhood of a point $P_0 = (x_0, y_0)$. Let us hold y fixed at y_0, so that $f(x, y) = f(x, y_0)$ is then a function of x alone. If the x-derivative of this function exists at x_0, it is called the **partial derivative** of f with respect to x, at (x_0, y_0), and is usually denoted either as $\partial f/\partial x$, or as f_x. Thus

$$f_x = \frac{\partial f}{\partial x} = \lim_{\Delta x \to 0} \frac{f(x_0 + \Delta x, y_0) - f(x_0, y_0)}{\Delta x} \tag{1a}$$

at (x_0, y_0). Similarly,

$$f_y = \frac{\partial f}{\partial y} = \lim_{\Delta y \to 0} \frac{f(x_0, y_0 + \Delta y) - f(x_0, y_0)}{\Delta y} \tag{1b}$$

at (x_0, y_0). For example, if $f(x, y) = x^2 y^3$, then $f_x = 2xy^3$, and $f_y = 3x^2 y^2$, at any given point (x, y).

In geometrical terms, (1a) is the slope of the tangent line A, and (1b) is the slope of the tangent line B in Fig. 6.5. For the illustrative case shown in Fig. 6.5, $f_x > 0$ and $f_y < 0$ at P_0.

If the partial derivatives f_x and f_y exist not only at P_0, but throughout some neighborhood of P_0, they are functions of x and y which may, in turn, admit further derivatives, namely the *second partial derivatives*

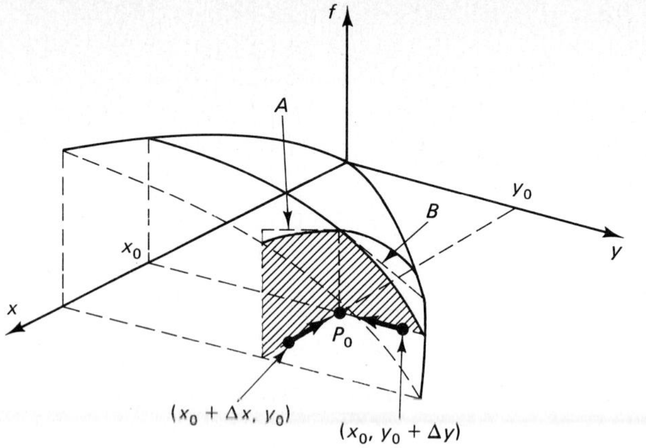

Fig. 6.5 f_x and f_y at P_0.

$$\frac{\partial}{\partial x}\left(\frac{\partial f}{\partial x}\right) = \frac{\partial^2 f}{\partial x^2} = f_{xx}, \qquad \frac{\partial}{\partial x}\left(\frac{\partial f}{\partial y}\right) = \frac{\partial^2 f}{\partial x \partial y} = f_{yx},$$
$$\frac{\partial}{\partial y}\left(\frac{\partial f}{\partial x}\right) = \frac{\partial^2 f}{\partial y \partial x} = f_{xy}, \qquad \frac{\partial}{\partial y}\left(\frac{\partial f}{\partial y}\right) = \frac{\partial^2 f}{\partial y^2} = f_{yy}. \tag{2}$$

Similarly, f may admit *third partial derivatives,* such as

$$\frac{\partial}{\partial x}\left(\frac{\partial^2 f}{\partial y^2}\right) = \frac{\partial^3 f}{\partial x\, \partial y^2} = f_{yyx},$$

and so on.

Note the order of the subscripts. For example, f_{yx} means $(f_y)_x$, i.e.,

$$\frac{\partial}{\partial x}\left(\frac{\partial f}{\partial y}\right); \qquad f_{xyy} = ((f_x)_y)_y = \frac{\partial}{\partial y}\left(\frac{\partial}{\partial y}\left(\frac{\partial f}{\partial x}\right)\right),$$

and so on. Does the order really matter? That is, for a "mixed" derivative such as f_{xy}, is it true that $f_{xy} = f_{yx}$ always? Sometimes? Never? Consider two examples.

EXAMPLE 1 Let $f(x, y) = x \sin(xy^2)$. Then

$$f_x = \sin(xy^2) + xy^2 \cos(xy^2),$$
$$f_{xy} = 2xy\cos(xy^2) + 2xy\cos(xy^2) - 2x^2y^3 \sin(xy^2),$$
$$f_y = 2x^2 y \cos(xy^2),$$
$$f_{yx} = 4xy\cos(xy^2) - 2x^2y^3 \sin(xy^2),$$

so that $f_{xy} = f_{yx}$, in this case, for all values of x and y. ◀

EXAMPLE 2 Let

$$f(x, y) = \begin{cases} \dfrac{xy(x^2 - y^2)}{x^2 + y^2} & \text{if } (x, y) \neq (0, 0) \quad \text{(3a)} \\ 0 & \text{if } (x, y) = (0, 0). \quad \text{(3b)} \end{cases}$$

[The separate specification (3b) is needed because at the origin (3a) gives 0/0, which is not defined; (3b) was *not* obtained from (3a) by letting x and y tend to zero, it was stated as the author's choice, as part of the *definition* of $f(x, y)$.] If we stay away from the origin, and work only with (3a), we would find, as in Example 1, that $f_{xy} = f_{yx}$ at each point (x, y) in the plane. We plan to demonstrate that $f_{xy} = f_{yx}$ does *not* hold, however, at the origin (0, 0).

First, take $\partial/\partial x$ of f. This step gives

$$f_x(x, y) = \begin{cases} \dfrac{y(x^4 + 4x^2y^2 - y^4)}{(x^2 + y^2)^2} & \text{if } (x, y) \neq (0, 0) \quad \text{(4a)} \\ 0 & \text{if } (x, y) = (0, 0). \quad \text{(4b)} \end{cases}$$

Obtaining (4a) from (3a) was straightforward, but where did we get (4b)? We obtained (4b) directly from (1a), as follows:

$$f_x(0, 0) = \lim_{\Delta x \to 0} \frac{f(\Delta x, 0) - f(0, 0)}{\Delta x}$$

$$= \lim_{\Delta x \to 0} \frac{0 - 0}{\Delta x} = \lim_{\Delta x \to 0} 0 = 0,$$

where $f(\Delta x, 0) = 0$ followed from (3a), and $f(0, 0) = 0$ from (3b). Thus

$$f_{xy}(0, 0) = \lim_{\Delta y \to 0} \frac{f_x(0, \Delta y) - f_x(0, 0)}{\Delta y}$$

$$= \lim_{\Delta y \to 0} \frac{-\Delta y - 0}{\Delta y} \quad \text{from (4a) and (4b)} \qquad (5)$$

$$= -1.$$

Similarly, we find that

$$f_y(x, y) = \begin{cases} \dfrac{x(x^4 - 4x^2y^2 - y^4)}{(x^2 + y^2)^2} & \text{if } (x, y) \neq (0, 0) \quad \text{(6a)} \\ 0 & \text{if } (x, y) = (0, 0) \quad \text{(6b)} \end{cases}$$

and

$$f_{yx}(0, 0) = \lim_{\Delta x \to 0} \frac{f_y(\Delta x, 0) - f_y(0, 0)}{\Delta x}$$

$$= \lim_{\Delta x \to 0} \frac{\Delta x - 0}{\Delta x} \quad \text{from (6a) and (6b)} \qquad (7)$$

$$= 1.$$

Comparing (5) and (7), we see that $f_{xy}(0, 0) \neq f_{yx}(0, 0)$ in this example. ◀

In general, then, the order of differentiation does matter. Theorem 1, below, gives conditions which guarantee that mixed "partials" (i.e., partial derivatives) f_{xy} and f_{yx} of a given function $f(x, y)$ will be equal.

Theorem 1 *Equality of Mixed Partials*

If f_x, f_y, f_{xy}, and f_{yx} are continuous in some neighborhood of (x_0, y_0), then $f_{yx} = f_{xy}$ at (x_0, y_0).*

Evidently, then, the function $f(x, y)$ in Example 2 must not have met all of the conditions of Theorem 1 (Exercise 6).

Statements similar to Theorem 1 can be proved for higher-order mixed partials as well, but we choose not to go into these details since the vast majority of the functions that we are likely to meet in applications are sufficiently well behaved to ensure that the order of differentiation is immaterial. That being the case, why all the fuss? Because the issue is not limited to the equality or inequality of the mixed partials f_{xy} and f_{yx}. More basically, it involves the effect of interchanging the order of application of two or more limit processes. In the present case the limit processes are the limits of the x and y difference quotients. Analogously, there is the question of the effect of the order of integration in multiple integration (to be discussed in Chapter 8); e.g., is

$$\int_{y_1}^{y_2}\left\{\int_{x_1(y)}^{x_2(y)} f(x, y)\, dx\right\} dy = \int_{x_1}^{x_2}\left\{\int_{y_1(x)}^{y_2(x)} f(x, y)\, dy\right\} dx?$$

In this case the two limit processes are the limits of the x and y Riemann sums. In fact, the calculus is *built on* the limit concept, so the question of the order of application of the various limits in a multiple-limit process is rather fundamental. At the same time, as mentioned above for the case of mixed partials, it turns out that the order of successive limits *can* be reversed without changing the result—provided that the functions involved are sufficiently well behaved, and happily, in most engineering applications the functions are indeed well enough behaved. Thus, we will try, as these specific questions of limit interchange arise, neither to "beat them to death" nor to let them go unmentioned.

6.3 EXERCISES

1. In each case evaluate f_x, f_y, f_{xy}, f_{yx}, f_{xx}, and f_{yy}. Is $f_{xy} = f_{yx}$ for all (x, y) in the (finite) plane?

*(a) $f = x^3y^5$
(b) $f = y \sin(3xy + 2)$
(c) $f = 1/(x^2 + y^2 + 1)$
(d) $f = \tan^{-1}(y/x)$ for $(x, y) \neq (0, 0)$
(e) $f = x^3 + y^5$
(f) $f = (x^2 + y^2)^{1/2}$

2. Verify that $f_{xxy} = f_{xyx} = f_{yxx}$ in each case.

(a) $f = x^4y^3$
(b) $f = \cos(x^2y)$
(c) $f = e^{x^2+y^2}$
(d) $f = e^{-x/y}$ for $(x, y) \neq (0, 0)$

3. Show that if

(a) $f = \ln(x^2 + y^2)$, then $f_{xx} + f_{yy} = 0$ for all $(x, y) \neq (0, 0)$ *Note:* ln ( ) is the natural logarithm.
(b) $f = \ln[(x - x_1)^2 + (y - y_1)^2]$, then $f_{xx} + f_{yy} = 0$ for all $(x, y) \neq (x_1, y_1)$
(c) $f = \tan^{-1}(y/x)$, then $f_{xx} + f_{yy} = 0$ for all $(x, y) \neq (0, 0)$
(d) $f = r^3 \sin 3\theta$, then $r^2f_{rr} + rf_r + f_{\theta\theta} = 0$
(e) $f = r^3 \cos 3\theta$, then $r^2f_{rr} + rf_r + f_{\theta\theta} = 0$
(f) $f = 1/(x^2 + y^2 + z^2)^{1/2}$, then $f_{xx} + f_{yy} + f_{zz} = 0$ for all $(x, y, z) \neq (0, 0, 0)$
(g) $f = 1/[(x - x_1)^2 + (y - y_1)^2 + (z - z_1)^2]$, then $f_{xx} + f_{yy} + f_{zz} = 0$ for all $(x, y, z) \neq (x_1, y_1, z_1)$

*For proof, see MARSDEN AND TROMBA, p. 120. Actually, they ask a bit more in their theorem, namely, that f_{xx} and f_{yy} be continuous, too. Nevertheless, these conditions are not used in their proof, so that proof holds for our Theorem 1 as well.

(h) $f = 1/[(x - x_1)^2 + (y - y_1)^2 + (z - z_1)^2]^{1/2} + 1/[(x - x_2)^2 + (y - y_2)^2 + (z - z_2)^2]^{1/2}$, then $f_{xx} + f_{yy} + f_{zz} = 0$ for all $(x, y, z) \neq (x_1, y_1, z_1), (x_2, y_2, z_2)$
(i) $f = \sin(x - ct)$, then $c^2 f_{xx} = f_{tt}$
(j) $f = \sin(x + ct)$, then $c^2 f_{xx} = f_{tt}$

4. Determine the allowable value(s) of the constant α such that $f = (x_1^2 + x_2^2 + \cdots + x_N^2)^\alpha$ is a solution of the *Laplace equation* $f_{x_1x_1} + f_{x_2x_2} + \cdots + f_{x_Nx_N} = 0$.

5. Let $f(x, y) = \begin{cases} x, & y = 0 \\ 0, & y \neq 0 \end{cases}$. Evaluate each of the following; if they do not exist, state that.

*(a) $f_x(0, 0)$	(b) $f_x(0, 2)$
(c) $f_x(2, 0)$	(d) $f_x(3, 4)$
*(e) $f_y(6, 0)$	(f) $f_y(0, 2)$
(g) $f_y(0, 0)$	(h) $f_{yx}(0, 0)$
*(i) $f_{xy}(0, 0)$	(j) $f_{xy}(3, 0)$
(k) $f_{yxx}(3, 0)$	(l) $f_{xxy}(3, 0)$

6. In Example 2 we found that $f_{xy}(0, 0) \neq f_{yx}(0, 0)$. Evidently, then, the function $f(x, y)$ defined by (3) does not meet all the requirements stated in Theorem 1.

(a) Specifically, show that f_{xy} is discontinuous at $(0, 0)$. *Hint:* Evaluate $f_{xy}(x, y)$ for $(x, y) \neq (0, 0)$. Setting $y = \alpha x$ in that result, show that

$$f_{xy}(x, y) = \frac{1 + 9\alpha^2 - 9\alpha^4 - \alpha^6}{(1 + \alpha^2)^3}$$

on each ray $y = \alpha x$, so that the limit of $f_{xy}(x, y)$, as we approach the origin, depends on the direction of approach. Thus, conclude that $\lim_{(x, y)\to(0, 0)} f_{xy}(x, y)$ does not exist, so that $\lim_{(x, y)\to(0, 0)} f_{xy}(x, y) = f_{xy}(0, 0)$ cannot possibly hold.
(b) Proceeding as in part (a), show that $f_{yx}(x, y)$ is discontinuous at $(0, 0)$.
(c) Show that $f_x(x, y)$, given by (4), *is* continuous at $(0, 0)$.
(d) Show that $f_y(x, y)$, given by (6), *is* continuous at $(0, 0)$.

7. If $f_x(x, y)$ and $f_y(x, y)$ exist at (x_0, y_0), does that imply that f is continuous at (x_0, y_0)? *Hint:* Consider the function

$$f(x, y) = \begin{cases} 1, & x = 0 \text{ or } y = 0 \\ 0, & x \neq 0 \text{ and } y \neq 0. \end{cases}$$

COMPOSITE FUNCTIONS; CHAIN DIFFERENTIATION 6.4

Let $f(x)$ be differentiable over some interval $X = \{x \mid a < x < b\}$. If $x = x(t)$ is, in turn a differentiable function of the variable t over some interval $T = \{t \mid \alpha < t < \beta\}$, such that the value $x(t)$ is in X whenever t is in T, then we speak of $f(x) = f(x(t)) \equiv F(t)$ as a **composite function** of t. As noted in a first course in calculus, we can compute dF/dt by the **chain rule,**

$$\frac{dF}{dt} = \frac{df}{dx}\frac{dx}{dt}. \tag{1}$$

EXAMPLE 1 If $f(x) = \sin x$ and $x = t^2$ (over $-\infty < t < \infty$, say), then

$$f(x(t)) = \sin(t^2) \equiv F(t)^* \quad \text{and} \quad \frac{dF}{dt} = \frac{df}{dx}\frac{dx}{dt} = (\cos x)(2t) = 2t\cos(t^2).$$ ◀

Just as the chain rule was indispensable in the calculus of functions of a single variable, its extension to functions of several variables will be indispensable here. For the case $f(x(t), y(t))$, we have the following basic theorem.

* It is tempting to avoid introducing the additional letter F, and to say that "$f(t) = \sin(t^2)$." This notation would be incorrect since f and F are different functions. For example, observe that $f(3) = \sin 3$, whereas $F(3) = \sin(3^2) = \sin(9)$. Nevertheless, the incorrect notation is sometimes used, in the literature, perhaps to minimize the nomenclature.

Theorem 1 *Chain Rule*

Let $f(x, y)$, $f_x(x, y)$, and $f_y(x, y)$ be continuous at each point of an open region $\mathscr{R}$ in the x, y plane. And let $x = x(t)$, $y = y(t)$ be differentiable functions of t over some open interval T on the t axis, such that the point $(x(t), y(t))$ is in $\mathscr{R}$ whenever t is in T. Then the composite function $f(x(t), y(t)) \equiv F(t)$ is a differentiable function of t for all t in T, and

$$\frac{dF}{dt} = \frac{\partial f}{\partial x}\frac{dx}{dt} + \frac{\partial f}{\partial y}\frac{dy}{dt}. \tag{2}$$

Proof Let t be in T, and let Δt be small enough so that $t + \Delta t$ is in T as well. Define

$$\Delta x \equiv x(t + \Delta t) - x(t) \quad \text{and} \quad \Delta y \equiv y(t + \Delta t) - y(t). \tag{3}$$

Then

$$\begin{aligned} \Delta F &= F(t + \Delta t) - F(t) \\ &= f(x(t + \Delta t), y(t + \Delta t)) - f(x(t), y(t)) \\ &= f(x + \Delta x, y + \Delta y) - f(x, y) \qquad (4) \\ &= [f(x, y + \Delta y) - f(x, y)] + [f(x + \Delta x, y + \Delta y) - f(x, y + \Delta y)] \\ &= f\big|_P^Q + f\big|_Q^R, \end{aligned}$$

where P, Q, R are the points shown in Fig. 6.6.* That is, instead of passing directly from P to R, we break the trip into two parts, from P to Q and then from Q to R, in order to follow constant-coordinate lines.

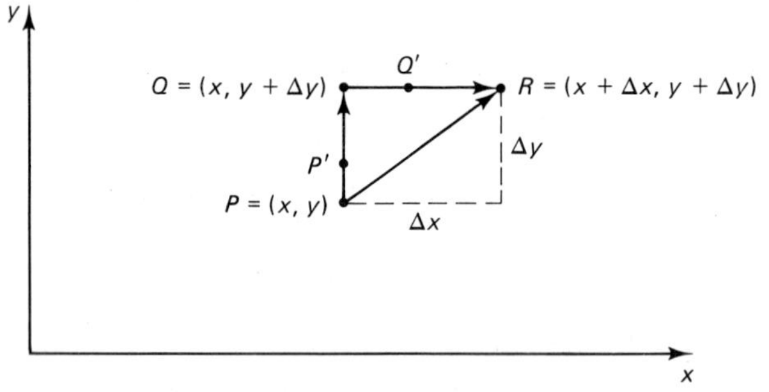

Fig. 6.6 Following constant-coordinate lines.

Next, we apply the mean-value theorem of the differential calculus,† to each of the terms $f\big|_P^Q$ and $f\big|_Q^R$ in (4):

* We use the symbol $(\ \ )\big|_P$ to denote $(\ \ )$ evaluated at P, and $(\ \ )\big|_P^Q$ to denote $(\ \ )\big|_Q - (\ \ )\big|_P$. Incidentally, observe that in the fourth line of (4) we have added and subtracted the quantity $f(x, y + \Delta y)$. This simple idea, the adding and subtracting of a certain quantity, is often useful in analysis.

† The *mean value theorem:* If $f(x)$ is continuous over $a \le x \le b$, and $f'(x)$ exists over $a < x < b$, then there is at least one point x_1 between a and b such that $f(b) - f(a) = f'(x_1)(b - a)$.

$$\Delta F = \left.\frac{\partial f}{\partial y}\right|_{P'} \Delta y + \left.\frac{\partial f}{\partial x}\right|_{Q'} \Delta x, \tag{5}$$

where Q' is some point between Q and R, and P' is some point between P and Q, as shown in Fig. 6.6. (This step is justified since it was assumed that f is continuous and that f_x and f_y exist within $\mathcal{R}$.)

Finally, divide (5) by Δt and let $\Delta t \to 0$. As $\Delta t \to 0$, we see from (3) that $\Delta x \to 0$ and $\Delta y \to 0$; hence $Q' \to P$ and $P' \to P$. Thus

$$\lim_{\Delta t \to 0} \frac{\Delta F}{\Delta t} = \lim_{\Delta t \to 0} \left(\left.\frac{\partial f}{\partial x}\right|_{Q'} \frac{\Delta x}{\Delta t} + \left.\frac{\partial f}{\partial y}\right|_{P'} \frac{\Delta y}{\Delta t} \right)$$

becomes*

$$\frac{dF}{dt} = \left(\lim_{Q' \to P} \frac{\partial f}{\partial x} \right) \frac{dx}{dt} + \left(\lim_{P' \to P} \frac{\partial f}{\partial y} \right) \frac{dy}{dt}. \tag{6}$$

And if the partials f_x and f_y are continuous, as assumed, then the limit of f_x as $Q' \to P$ is equal to f_x *at P*, and similarly for f_y. Thus (6) yields

$$\frac{dF}{dt} = f_x(x, y)\frac{dx}{dt} + f_y(x, y)\frac{dy}{dt},$$

as was to be shown. ■

Note carefully how the assumed continuity of the partials f_x, f_y is finally called upon in the last step of the preceding proof. Our need for continuity of the partials, at the point in question, is really quite reasonable since (2) is essentially an *interpolation* formula, wherein the change in F is computed as a linear combination of the rates of change in the perpendicular x and y directions.

EXAMPLE 2 Let $r(x, y) = \sqrt{x^2 + y^2}$, where

$$x = 3t^2, \qquad y = \sin t \qquad (1 < t < 4).$$

Then $r = r(x(t), y(t)) \equiv R(t)$, and

$$\frac{dR}{dt} = \frac{\partial r}{\partial x}\frac{dx}{dt} + \frac{\partial r}{\partial y}\frac{dy}{dt} = \frac{x}{\sqrt{x^2 + y^2}}\,6t + \frac{y}{\sqrt{x^2 + y^2}}\cos t$$

$$= \frac{18t^3 + \sin t \cos t}{\sqrt{9t^4 + \sin^2 t}}$$

for $1 < t < 4$. ◀

EXAMPLE 3 Suppose that $f(u, v) = \sin(uv^2)$, where

$$u = 5x + 3y, \qquad v = x^2 - y.$$

* Recall from the calculus that $\lim(A + B) = \lim A + \lim B$ and $\lim(AB) = (\lim A)(\lim B)$ if $\lim A$ and $\lim B$ both exist. Thus $\lim(AB + CD) = \lim(AB) + \lim(CD) = (\lim A)(\lim B) + (\lim C)(\lim D)$ if the four limits exist.

Then $f(u, v) = f(u(x, y), v(x, y)) \equiv F(x, y)$. To compute $\partial F/\partial x$, say, we use the chain rule (2):

$$\frac{\partial F}{\partial x} = \frac{\partial f}{\partial u}\frac{\partial u}{\partial x} + \frac{\partial f}{\partial v}\frac{\partial v}{\partial x}$$

$$= v^2 \cos (uv^2)(5) + 2uv \cos (uv^2)(2x) \tag{7}$$

$$= [5(x^2 - y)^2 + 4x(5x + 3y)(x^2 - y)] \cos [(5x + 3y)(x^2 - y)^2].$$

The point to appreciate in this example is that even though u and v are functions of *two* variables (x and y), the chain rule (2) still applies because y is held fixed when we compute $\partial F/\partial x$, so that u and v are considered, for the moment, as functions of x alone. ◀

A bit of ambiguity enters in Example 3. Namely, what do the notations $\partial/\partial u$, $\partial/\partial v$, $\partial/\partial x$, and $\partial/\partial y$ mean? For example, is $\partial v/\partial x$ the derivative of v with respect to x with y held fixed, or is it with u held fixed:

$$\left.\frac{\partial v}{\partial x}\right|_{y \text{ fixed}} = \left.\frac{\partial}{\partial x}(x^2 - y)\right|_{y \text{ fixed}} = 2x,$$

$$\left.\frac{\partial v}{\partial x}\right|_{u \text{ fixed}} = \left.\frac{\partial}{\partial x}\left[x^2 - \left(\frac{u - 5x}{3}\right)\right]\right|_{u \text{ fixed}} = 2x + \frac{5}{3}?$$

Let us agree to the following standard *convention*: If $u = u(x, y)$, $v = v(x, y)$, say, as in Example 3, then we have two sets of variables, $\{x, y\}$ and $\{u, v\}$. We will understand $\partial/\partial x$ to mean the derivative with respect to x with all other variables in the x set (namely, y) held fixed; similarly, $\partial/\partial u$ will imply that all other variables in the u set (namely, v) are held fixed, and so on. If we *do* wish to take $\partial/\partial x$ with u fixed, instead, we will simply have to spell out that intention by writing $\left.\dfrac{\partial(\ )}{\partial x}\right|_{u \text{ fixed}}$. Such vertical braces are not used in (7), so it is, according to this convention, understood that $\partial F/\partial x$ is with y fixed, $\partial F/\partial u$ is with v fixed, and so on.

Extension of these ideas to more than two variables should be evident. Namely, if $f[x_1(t), \ldots, x_n(t)] \equiv F(t)$, then the chain rule (2) becomes

$$\frac{dF}{dt} = \frac{\partial f}{\partial x_1}\frac{dx_1}{dt} + \frac{\partial f}{\partial x_2}\frac{dx_2}{dt} + \cdots + \frac{\partial f}{\partial x_n}\frac{dx_n}{dt}, \tag{8}$$

subject to conditions analogous to those stated in Theorem 1.

EXAMPLE 4 Let $f(x, y, z) = (x^2 + y^2 + z^2)^{3/2}$, where

$$x = 2u + v - w + t^2$$

$$y = v^2 + w$$

$$z = u \sin t + vw.$$

With $f(x, y, z) = f(x(t, u, v, w), y(v, w), z(t, u, v, w)) \equiv F(t, u, v, w)$, let us compute $\partial F/\partial t$, say:

$$\frac{\partial F}{\partial t} = \frac{\partial f}{\partial x}\frac{\partial x}{\partial t} + \frac{\partial f}{\partial y}\frac{\partial y}{\partial t} + \frac{\partial f}{\partial z}\frac{\partial z}{\partial t}$$

$$= \frac{3}{2}(2x)(x^2 + y^2 + z^2)^{1/2}(2t) + \frac{3}{2}(2y)(x^2 + y^2 + z^2)^{1/2}(0)$$

$$+ \frac{3}{2}(2z)(x^2 + y^2 + z^2)^{1/2}(u \cos t)$$

$$= 3(x^2 + y^2 + z^2)^{1/2}(2xt + zu \cos t). \blacktriangleleft$$

In this section we have extended the chain rule (1) to the multivariable form (8). Fundamental to the chain rule (8) is the assumed continuity of the partials $\partial f/\partial x_1, \ldots, \partial f/\partial x_n$ that appear.

6.4 EXERCISES

***1.** Let $f(x, y) = \sin(x^4 + 3y)$, where $x = 5t$ and $y = t^2 + 1$, and denote $f(x(t), y(t)) = F(t)$. Evaluate dF/dt using the chain rule,

$$\frac{dF}{dt} = \frac{\partial f}{\partial x}\frac{dx}{dt} + \frac{\partial f}{\partial y}\frac{dy}{dt}. \qquad \text{(a)}$$

Note: Actually, (a) is not the end of the "chain differentiation story," for in computing $\partial f/\partial x$ we set $x^4 + 3y = u$, so that, again applying chain differentiation,

$$\frac{\partial f}{\partial x} = \frac{d}{du}(\sin u)\frac{\partial u}{\partial x} = \text{etc.},$$

and similarly for $\partial f/\partial y$.

2. Let $f(x, y) = e^{xy}$, and denote $f(x(t), y(t)) = F(t)$. Evaluate dF/dt in each case, using the chain rule.

(a) $x = t^2 - 1$, $y = \sin 3t$
(b) $x = \sqrt{t + 1}$, $y = \cos t$
(c) $x = t^2$, $y = 1/(t^2 + 1)$
(d) $x = \ln t$, $y = t$ $(t > 0)$

Note: ln will be understood to be the *natural logarithm,* i.e., with base $e \approx 2.7183$.

3. Let $g(u, v) = \sqrt{u^2 + v}$, and denote $g(u(s), v(s)) = G(s)$. Evaluate dG/ds in each case, using the chain rule. Next, evaluate dG/ds directly; i.e., put $u(s)$ and $v(s)$ into $g(u, v)$, to obtain $G(s)$, and then take d/ds. Show that your two answers agree.

*(a) $u = \sin s$, $v = \cos 6s$ (b) $u = 4s^2$, $v = e^{-3s}$
(c) $u = s + 1$, $v = s^3$ (d) $u = \sin 5s$, $v = 4$

4. If $r = \sqrt{x^2(t) + y^2(t) + z^2(t)} = R(t)$ is the distance of a particle from the origin of a Cartesian x,y,z coordinate system, and t is the time, determine the speed dR/dt in each case.

*(a) $x = t$, $y = t \sin t$, $z = 4$
(b) $x = 2t$, $y = t^2$, $z = t^3 + 1$
(c) $x = \cos 2t$, $y = 3$, $z = \sin 2t$
(d) $x = e^t$, $y = 4t$, $z = e^{-t}$

5. *(a) Let the Cartesian coordinates of a tiny fish be x, y, z. If the fish swims so that $x = 6t$, $y = t + 2$, $z = e^{-t}$, where t is the time, and the temperature distribution in the water is given by

$$T(x, y, z) = \left(5 + \frac{1}{x^2 + y^2 + 1}\right)e^{-z},$$

determine the time rate of change of temperature experienced by the fish when $t = 0$.
(b) Repeat part (a), with

$$T(x, y, z, t) = \frac{60e^z(1 + 0.1 \sin t)}{x^2 + y^2 + 2}.$$

6. $f(x_1, \ldots, x_n)$ is said to be **homogeneous of degree k** if

$$f(\lambda x_1, \ldots, \lambda x_n) = \lambda^k f(x_1, \ldots, x_n). \qquad \text{(a)}$$

(a) In each case, show whether the function is homogeneous, and if it is, indicate its degree: $f = x^2 + 3xy$, $g = \ln(x^2 + y^2)$, $h = (x^2 - xy)/(2x + y)$, and $p = x^3e^{x/2y}$. (Assume that $x^2 + y^2 \neq 0$ in g, that $2x + y \neq 0$ in h, and that $y \neq 0$ in p.)

(b) If $f = f(u_1, \ldots, u_m)$ is a homogeneous function of $u_1, \ldots, u_m$, of degree p, and $u_1 = u_1(x_1, \ldots, x_n), \ldots, u_m = u_m(x_1, \ldots, x_n)$ are homogeneous functions of $x_1, \ldots, x_n$ of degree q, show whether or not f is necessarily a homogeneous function of $x_1, \ldots, x_n$. If so, of what degree?
(c) Show that if $f(x, y, z)$ is homogeneous of degree k, and has partials $\partial f/\partial x$, $\partial f/\partial y$, $\partial f/\partial z$, then these partials are homogeneous of degree $k - 1$.
(d) (*Euler's theorem on homogeneous functions*) Prove **Euler's theorem**—that if $f(x_1, \ldots, x_n)$ is homogeneous of degree k, and has continuous first-order partials, then

$$x_1\frac{\partial f}{\partial x_1} + x_2\frac{\partial f}{\partial x_2} + \cdots + x_n\frac{\partial f}{\partial x_n} = kf. \qquad \text{(b)}$$

Hint: Differentiate equation (a) with respect to λ, then set $\lambda = 1$, and recall part (c).

7. Verify Euler's theorem [(b) in Exercise 8] for these cases.

(a) $f(x, y) = \sqrt{x^4 + 2y^4}\sin(3x/y) \quad (y \neq 0)$
(b) $f(x, y) = (x^3 - 2x^2y + 5y^3)/(x^2 + y^2) \quad (x^2 + y^2 \neq 0)$
(c) $f(x, y, z) = (x - y)\exp[(x + 2y + z)/(3x - z)] \quad (3x - z \neq 0)$
(d) $f(p, q, r, s) = (p^2 + q^2 + s^2)/(p^2 + r^2 + s^2) \quad (p^2 + r^2 + s^2 \neq 0)$

8. Show that $u = f(x + ct) + g(x - ct)$ satisfies the "partial differential equation" $c^2u_{xx} - u_{tt} = 0$ (the *wave equation*), where c is a constant and f and g are arbitrary twice-differentiable functions.

9. The differential equation $xy'' + y' + xy = 0$, known as *Bessel's equation of order zero*, has the general solution $y = AJ_0(x) + BY_0(x)$, where J_0 is the *Bessel function of the first kind and order zero*, and Y_0 is the *Bessel function of the second kind and order zero*.

*(a) Solve $xy'' + y' + k^2xy = 0$ in terms of Bessel functions. *Hint:* Set $x = \alpha t$ [and $y(x) = y(\alpha t) \equiv u(t)$], and choose α so that the new differential equation is the Bessel equation.
(b) Solve $xy'' + y' + k^2y = 0$ in terms of Bessel functions. *Hint:* Set $x = \alpha t^\beta$ [and $y(x) \equiv u(t)$], and choose α, β so that the new differential equation is the Bessel equation.

6.5 TAYLOR'S FORMULA; MEAN VALUE THEOREM

Before developing Taylor's formula for functions of more than one variable, it may be helpful to summarize the results (as introduced in elementary calculus) for functions of a single variable.

SINGLE-VARIABLE CASE

Given some (sufficiently differentiable) function $f(x)$, let us define a sequence of polynomials $p_0(x), p_1(x), \ldots$, as follows:

$$\begin{aligned} p_0(x) &\equiv f(a), \\ p_1(x) &\equiv f(a) + f'(a)(x - a), \\ p_2(x) &\equiv f(a) + f'(a)(x - a) + \frac{f''(a)}{2!}(x - a)^2, \end{aligned} \qquad (1)$$

and so on. That is,

$$p_n(x) \equiv f(a) + f'(a)(x - a) + \cdots + \frac{f^{(n)}(a)}{n!}(x - a)^n. \qquad (2)$$

Differentiating these expressions and setting $x = a$, we see that

$$
\begin{aligned}
p_0(a) &= f(a), \qquad & p_1(a) &= f(a) \qquad & p_2(a) &= f(a) \\
& & p_1'(a) &= f'(a), & p_2'(a) &= f'(a) \\
& & & & p_2''(a) &= f''(a),
\end{aligned} \tag{3}
$$

and so on; i.e., $p_n(x)$ agrees with $f(x)$, at the point $x = a$, through the nth derivative. That being the case, it seems reasonable to expect that $p_n(x)$ may provide a useful approximation to $f(x)$ throughout some neighborhood of the point a, useful in the sense of being sufficiently accurate, yet analytically more tractable in that f may be a rather complicated function while p_n is merely a polynomial.

EXAMPLE 1 Consider $f(x) = e^{-x}$, say, with $a = 1$. Then $f(1) = e^{-1}$, $f'(1) = -e^{-1}$, $f''(1) = e^{-1}, \ldots$, so

$$
\begin{aligned}
p_0(x) &= e^{-1}, \\
p_1(x) &= e^{-1} - e^{-1}(x-1), \\
p_2(x) &= e^{-1} - e^{-1}(x-1) + \tfrac{1}{2}e^{-1}(x-1)^2,
\end{aligned} \tag{4}
$$

and so on, as depicted in Fig. 6.7. Observe, from the figure, that $p_0(x)$ is in exact agreement with $f(x)$ at $x = 1$, but provides only a crude approximation to $f(x)$ in the neighborhood of $x = 1$; $p_1(x)$ is a *tangent-line* fit to $f(x)$ at $x = 1$, and provides a better approximation to $f(x)$ in the neighborhood of $x = 1$; $p_2(x)$ is a *parabolic* fit to $f(x)$, and provides a still better approximation. We have gone only as far as $p_2(x)$, but if we were to examine $p_3(x), p_4(x), \ldots$, we would find that each, in turn, provides a better approximation to the given function e^{-x} in the neighborhood of $x = 1$.

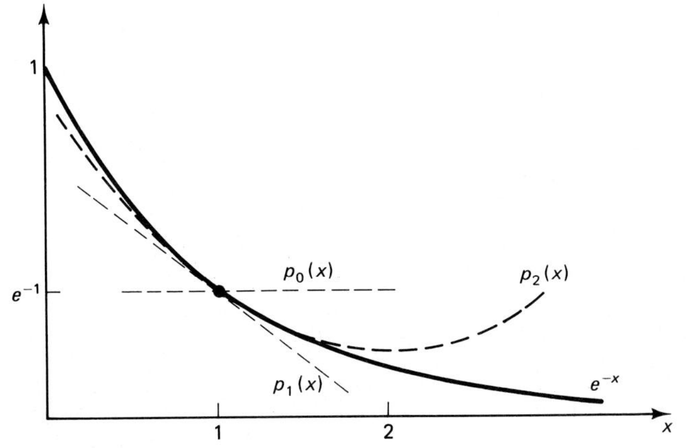

Fig. 6.7 Example 1.

Just as a rodeo rider endeavors to stay on the horse, we may imagine the polynomials $p_0(x), p_1(x), \ldots$ endeavoring to "stay on the function": $p_1(x)$ does a better job than $p_0(x)$, $p_2(x)$ does a better job than $p_1(x)$, and so on, although they all eventually bite the dust. ◀

In general, then, it is natural to wonder what can be said about the magnitude of the discrepancy between $f(x)$ and $p_n(x)$. In fact, we have the following fundamental theorem from the calculus.*

Theorem 1 *Taylor's Formula with Lagrange Remainder*
Let f be defined in a neighborhood $N(a)$ of the point a, and suppose that f's first $n + 1$ derivatives are continuous in $N(a)$. Let n be a nonnegative integer. Then there exists a number μ_n between a and x such that†

$$f(x) = f(a) + \frac{f'(a)}{1!}(x - a) + \cdots + \frac{f^{(n)}(a)}{n!}(x - a)^n + R_{n+1}(x) \tag{5}$$

where

$$R_{n+1}(x) = \frac{f^{(n+1)}(\mu_n)}{(n + 1)!}(x - a)^{n+1}. \tag{6}$$

Here the *remainder term* $R_{n+1}(x)$ is expressed in the so-called *Lagrange form*; an alternative *integral form* is also commonly used (Exercise 5).

Comparing (2) and (5), we see that $f(x) = p_n(x) + R_{n+1}(x)$, so that the error incurred in the approximation $f(x) \approx p_n(x)$ is precisely the remainder term $R_{n+1}(x)$. Unfortunately, we cannot use (6) to *compute* the error since we do not know the value of μ_n; all we know is that μ_n lies somewhere between a and x. Nevertheless, (6) can be useful in establishing a *bound* on the error, as we shall illustrate in the example to follow.

EXAMPLE 2 Returning to Example 1, suppose that we wish to use $p_2(x)$, given in (4), to approximate e^{-x} over the interval $0.7 \le x \le 1.3$. It is important, then, to have a bound on the error, namely, on $R_3(x)$. From (6) we have

$$R_3(x) = \frac{(x - 1)^3}{3!} \frac{d^3}{dx^3} e^{-x} \bigg|_{\mu_2} = -\frac{e^{-\mu_2}}{6}(x - 1)^3. \tag{7}$$

Now μ_2 is some point between 1 and x. Since we desire an error bound for the entire interval $0.7 \le x \le 1.3$, we must be prepared for μ_2 to lie anywhere between 0.7 and 1.3. And since the negative exponential function is monotone decreasing, it must be true that $e^{-\mu_2} < e^{-0.7}$. Furthermore, $|x - 1|^3$ is *at most* $(0.3)^3$ on the interval $0.7 \le x \le 1.3$, so we can say, with certainty, that

* Theorem 1 and its proof can be found in most introductory texts on the calculus. See, for example, R. C. Fisher and A. D. Ziebur, *Calculus and Analytic Geometry*, 3rd ed. (Englewood Cliffs, N.J.: Prentice-Hall, 1975).

† By "μ_n lying between a and x," we mean $a < \mu_n < x$ if $x > a$, and $x < \mu_n < a$ if $x < a$.

$$|e^{-x} - p_2(x)| = |R_3(x)| = \left| -\frac{e^{-\mu_2}}{6}(x-1)^3 \right|$$

$$< \frac{e^{-0.7}}{6}(0.3)^3 \approx 0.002235.$$

Thus the approximation

$$e^{-x} \approx e^{-1}[1 - (x-1) + \tfrac{1}{2}(x-1)^2]$$

is quantified by the error bound

$$|e^{-x} - e^{-1}[1 - (x-1) + \tfrac{1}{2}(x-1)^2]| < 0.00224 \qquad (0.7 \le x \le 1.3). \quad ◀$$

By the way, we have chosen to emphasize the notion of polynomial approximation, in introducing Taylor's formula, because it lends a readily understandable geometrical (and pictorial) basis to the subject. We certainly do not mean to imply that $p_n(x)$, defined by (2), is the only, or best, polynomial approximation of a given function $f(x)$ over a given x interval.

It seems reasonable, next, to pose the *question:* Does

$$\lim_{n\to\infty} \left[f(a) + f'(a)(x-a) + \frac{f''(a)}{2!}(x-a)^2 + \cdots + \frac{f^{(n)}(a)}{n!}(x-a)^n \right] \tag{8}$$

actually *equal* $f(x)$, over some x interval? That is, does the polynomial approximation $p_n(x)$ become exact in the limit as $n \to \infty$? We call (8) **the Taylor series of f,** about the point a, and denote it as TSf. Thus

$$\boxed{\mathrm{TS}f \equiv \sum_{j=0}^{\infty} \frac{f^{(j)}(a)}{j!}(x-a)^j,} \tag{9}$$

where $(x-a)^0 \equiv 1$ and $0! \equiv 1$ in order that the leading term will be $f(a)$, as in (8). [In contrast, note that the right-hand side of (5), *Taylor's formula with remainder,* was *not* an infinite series; it was the sum of a finite number of terms!]

To answer the foregoing *question,* observe from (5) that

$$\lim_{n\to\infty} \left\{ f(x) - \left[f(a) + \cdots + \frac{f^{(n)}(a)}{n!}(x-a)^n \right] \right\} = \lim_{n\to\infty} R_{n+1}(x),$$

so

$$f(x) - \sum_{j=0}^{\infty} \frac{f^{(j)}(a)}{j!}(x-a)^j = \lim_{n\to\infty} R_{n+1}(x). \tag{10}$$

It follows from (10) that *a necessary and sufficient condition for the Taylor series of f to converge to $f(x)$ over some interval $|x-a| < r$ is that*

$$\lim_{n\to\infty} R_{n+1}(x) = 0 \tag{11}$$

[or, equivalently, $\lim_{n\to\infty} R_n(x) = 0$*] over that interval,* for then, and only then, does (10) yield the desired equality*

$$f(x) = \sum_{j=0}^{\infty} \frac{f^{(j)}(a)}{j!}(x - a)^j. \tag{12}$$

We wish not to fall into a detailed review of the calculus, since it is presumed that the reader has already studied that subject. Rather, the foregoing discussion is intended as a frame of reference for our extension to functions of more than one variable.

Two final points: First, observe that both Taylor's formula and Taylor series may be viewed in terms of *extrapolation*. That is, given information about f at some point a, namely the values $f(a), f'(a), f''(a), \ldots$, can we determine the value $f(x)$ at some other point x? Second, observe that for the special case $n = 0$, Taylor's formula (5), with Lagrange remainder (6), reduces to the fundamental and important **mean value theorem**.

Theorem 2 *Mean Value Theorem*

Let f be continuous on the closed interval $[a, x]$ and differentiable on the open interval (a, x).† Then there exists a number ξ in (a, x) such that

$$\boxed{f(x) = f(a) + f'(\xi)(x - a).} \tag{13}$$

For this reason, Taylor's formula (5) is sometimes referred to as the "extended mean value theorem." The formula (13) may look strange in that the right-hand side appears to be a linear function of x, whereas $f(x)$ on the left certainly need not be linear. The catch is that the innocent-looking ξ is not really a constant; in general, it varies with x.

EXTENSION TO MORE THAN ONE VARIABLE

We now proceed to extend Taylor's formula to functions of two or more independent variables. The results obtained here will be needed in subsequent sections.

Consider the extrapolation problem in *two* variables. That is, let $f(x, y)$ be

* The function

$$f(x) = \begin{cases} e^{-1/x^2}, & x \neq 0 \\ 0, & x = 0 \end{cases}$$

is often called upon to illustrate an important point, namely, that the Taylor series of a given function f, about a given point $x = a$, may converge throughout some interval $|x - a| < r$, *yet not to the given function*. For suppose that we expand the function f, defined above, about $x = 0$. It turns out that $f(0) = f'(0) = f''(0) = \cdots = 0$, so that

$$\mathrm{TS}f = 0 + 0x + 0x^2 + \cdots,$$

which surely converges, for *all* x in fact, to zero. Yet $f(x)$ is zero only at the origin (sketch f), and so while TSf converges, it does not converge to f! The reason is that the remainder term $R_{n+1}(x)$, in Taylor's formula, does *not* tend to zero, in this case, as $n \to \infty$. In principle, then, merely showing that a Taylor series converges does not prove that its sume *equals* the given function. In fact, for a proper understanding of Taylor series one really must enter into *complex variable theory,* and this is the subject of Part V.

† By a "*closed interval* $[x_1, x_2]$" we mean the point set $\{x \mid x_1 \leq x \leq x_2\}$. By an "*open interval* (x_1, x_2)" we mean the point set $\{x \mid x_1 < x < x_2\}$. But be careful; we also use the notation (a, b) to denote a point $x = a$, $y = b$ in the x,y plane. We ask the reader to rely on the context in distinguishing between these two meanings.

defined, and sufficiently differentiable, in an open region $\mathcal{R}$ in the x, y plane, and suppose that the values $f, f_x, f_y, f_{xx}, f_{xy}, f_{yy}, \ldots$, up to nth order are all known at a point (a, b) in $\mathcal{R}$. Can we, using these data, extrapolate away from the point (a, b) and determine the value of f at some other point (x, y) in $\mathcal{R}$?

The basic idea is this: To a large extent, "new things" in mathematics are developed as limits or extensions of "old ones." Thus the approach here will be to try to reduce the present problem to one involving a single independent variable, since that case is already in hand. Toward that end, draw a straight line from the given point (a, b) to a fixed point (x_0, y_0), as in Fig. 6.8, and regard (x, y) as a variable point along that line. [We are supposing that the points (a, b) and (x_0, y_0), and the shape of the region $\mathcal{R}$, are such that the straight line connecting (a, b) and (x_0, y_0) lies entirely inside $\mathcal{R}$.] The straight line may be parametrized by

$$\begin{aligned} x &= a + (x_0 - a)t \\ y &= b + (y_0 - b)t, \end{aligned} \tag{14}$$

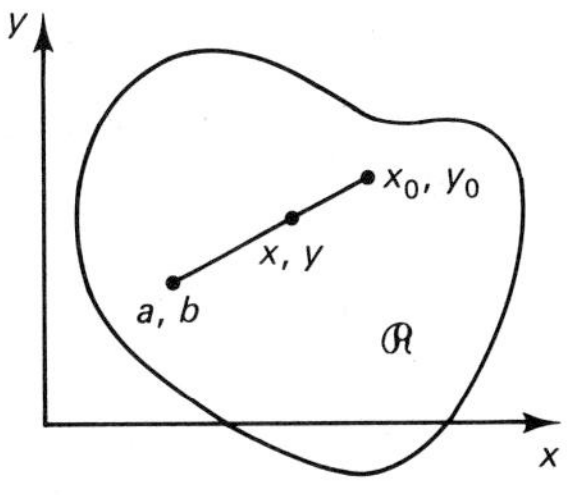

Fig. 6.8 Points of interest.

where t is the parameter; for $t = 0$ the point (x, y) coincides with (a, b), and for $t = 1$ it coincides with (x_0, y_0). Then, and this is the point,

$$f(x, y) = f(a + (x_0 - a)t, b + (y_0 - b)t) \equiv F(t) \tag{15}$$

is a function of the *single variable t*, for $0 \leq t \leq 1$. And if F is sufficiently differentiable we can write down Taylor's formula with Lagrange remainder,

$$F(t) = F(0) + F'(0)t + \frac{F''(0)}{2!}t^2 + \cdots + \frac{F^{(n)}(0)}{n!}t^n + \frac{F^{(n+1)}(\tau)}{(n+1)!}t^{n+1} \tag{16}$$

for some τ such that $0 < \tau < 1$. Here we have expanded about $t = 0$ because $t = 0$ corresponds to $x = a$, $y = b$, which is the "known" point.

We need to evaluate the coefficients $F(0), F'(0), \ldots$, in (16). By chain differentiation,

$$\frac{d}{dt} = \frac{\partial}{\partial x}\frac{dx}{dt} + \frac{\partial}{\partial y}\frac{dy}{dt} = (x_0 - a)\frac{\partial}{\partial x} + (y_0 - b)\frac{\partial}{\partial y} \equiv D, \tag{17}$$

so that

$$F'(0) = \frac{d}{dt}F(t)\bigg|_{t=0} = Df(x, y)\bigg|_{x=a,\, y=b}, \tag{18}$$

$$F''(0) = \frac{d}{dt}\frac{d}{dt}F(t)\bigg|_{t=0} = D^2 f(x, y)\bigg|_{x=a,\, y=b}, \tag{19}$$

and so on. Finally, we put these expressions into (16) and set $t = 1$. Since $F(1) = f(x_0, y_0)$, this step gives

$$f(x_0, y_0) = f(a, b) + \frac{1}{1!}Df\Big|_{a,b} + \cdots + \frac{1}{n!}D^n f\Big|_{a,b} + \frac{1}{(n+1)!}D^{n+1}f\Big|_{\xi,\eta}, \tag{20}$$

where ξ, η are given by (14) when $t = \tau$; i.e., $\xi = a + (x_0 - a)\tau$, $\eta = b + (y_0 - b)\tau$, as shown in Fig. 6.9.

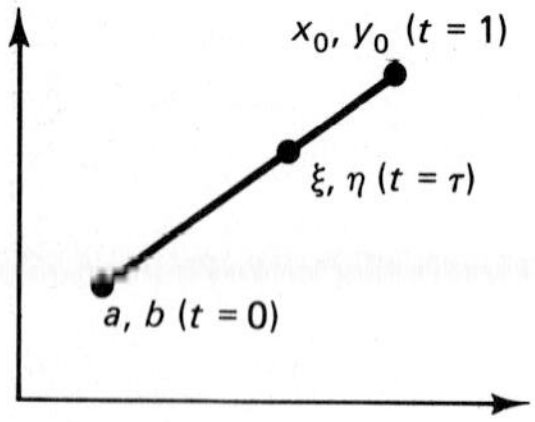

Fig. 6.9 The point (ξ, η).

Equation (20) is **Taylor's formula** in *two* variables, with Lagrange remainder. It holds if $f(x, y)$ has continuous partials, through $(n + 1)$st order, in $\mathcal{R}$, and if the straight line from (a, b) to (x_0, y_0) lies entirely within $\mathcal{R}$.

We could, at this point, let $n \to \infty$ in (20), and thus consider Taylor *series* for functions of two variables, as we did for functions of a single variable. However, for our purposes in this book, it will suffice to limit our attention to the cases $n = 0$ and $n = 1$. Thus, let us write out (20) for these two cases. First, setting $n = 0$ and recalling the definition (17) of D, (20) becomes

$$\begin{aligned} f(x_0, y_0) &= f(a, b) + \left[(x_0 - a)\frac{\partial}{\partial x} + (y_0 - b)\frac{\partial}{\partial y}\right] f\Big|_{\xi,\eta} \\ &= f(a, b) + f_x(\xi, \eta)(x_0 - a) + f_y(\xi, \eta)(y_0 - b). \end{aligned} \tag{21}$$

And if $n = 1$, then (20) becomes

$$\begin{aligned} f(x_0, y_0) &= f(a, b) + \left[(x_0 - a)\frac{\partial}{\partial x} + (y_0 - b)\frac{\partial}{\partial y}\right] f\Big|_{a,b} \\ &\quad + \frac{1}{2!}\left[(x_0 - a)\frac{\partial}{\partial x} + (y_0 - b)\frac{\partial}{\partial y}\right]^2 f\Big|_{\xi,\eta} \\ &= f(a, b) + [f_x(a, b)(x_0 - a) + f_y(a, b)(y_0 - b)] \\ &\quad + \frac{1}{2!}\left[(x_0 - a)^2\frac{\partial^2}{\partial x^2} + 2(x_0 - a)(y_0 - b)\frac{\partial^2}{\partial x\,\partial y} + (y_0 - b)^2\frac{\partial^2}{\partial y^2}\right] f\Big|_{\xi,\eta} \\ &= f(a, b) + [f_x(a, b)(x_0 - a) + f_y(a, b)(y_0 - b)] \\ &\quad + \frac{1}{2!}[f_{xx}(\xi, \eta)(x_0 - a)^2 + 2f_{xy}(\xi, \eta)(x_0 - a)(y_0 - b) + f_{yy}(\xi, \eta)(y_0 - b)^2]. \end{aligned} \tag{22}$$

Notice that x, y were "transition" variables that carried us from (a, b) to (x_0, y_0). In the final formula [such as (21) or (22)] it is only the initial point (a, b) and the final point (x_0, y_0) that appear. Since we no longer need to distinguish between x, y

and x_0, y_0, we can, for notational simplicity, drop the subscripted zeros, and reexpress (21) and (22) as

$$\boxed{f(x, y) = f(a, b) + f_x(\xi, \eta)(x - a) + f_y(\xi, \eta)(y - b)} \tag{23}$$

and

$$\boxed{\begin{aligned} f(x, y) &= f(a, b) + [f_x(a, b)(x - a) + f_y(a, b)(y - b)] \\ &\quad + \frac{1}{2!}[f_{xx}(\xi, \eta)(x - a)^2 + 2f_{xy}(\xi, \eta)(x - a)(y - b) \\ &\quad + f_{yy}(\xi, \eta)(y - b)^2], \end{aligned}} \tag{24}$$

respectively.

In fact, (23) is the two-variable version of the **mean value theorem,** which we state now for future reference:

Theorem 3 *Mean Value Theorem*

Let $f(x, y)$ and its first partials be continuous in an open region $\mathcal{R}$, and let (a, b) and (x, y) be points in $\mathcal{R}$ such that the straight line joining these points lies entirely within $\mathcal{R}$. Then there exists a point (ξ, η) on that line, between the endpoints, such that

$$f(x, y) = f(a, b) + f_x(\xi, \eta)(x - a) + f_y(\xi, \eta)(y - b). \tag{25}$$

Extension to functions of more than two variables should be reasonably evident. To illustrate, the mean value theorem, for a function $f(w, x, y, z)$ of four variables, would be

$$\begin{aligned} f(w, x, y, z) = f(a, b, c, d) &+ f_w(\omega, \xi, \eta, \zeta)(w - a) + f_x(\omega, \xi, \eta, \zeta)(x - b) \\ &+ f_y(\omega, \xi, \eta, \zeta)(y - c) + f_z(\omega, \xi, \eta, \zeta)(z - d), \end{aligned}$$

where $(\omega, \xi, \eta, \zeta)$ is some point on the straight-line segment connecting the initial point (a, b, c, d) and the final point (w, x, y, z) in four-dimensional space, provided that f and its first partials are continuous in an open region $\mathcal{R}$ containing that line segment.*

In closing this section, let us introduce some notation that will prove useful in what follows. Specifically, if all of the partials of f, through nth order, are continuous in a region $\mathcal{R}$, then f is said to be **of class C^n** in $\mathcal{R}$. For example, $f(x, y)$ is of class C^1 in $\mathcal{R}$ if f_x and f_y are continuous in $\mathcal{R}$, and it is of class C^2 in $\mathcal{R}$ if f_x, f_y, f_{xx}, f_{xy}, and f_{yy} are continuous in $\mathcal{R}$. Generally, one omits the words "of class" and simply says that f is C^1 in $\mathcal{R}$, C^2 in $\mathcal{R}$, or whatever. Further, we state without proof that

* By a "straight line" in 4-space, we mean the set of points (w', x', y', z') defined by

$$w' = a + (w - a)t, \qquad x' = b + (x - b)t, \qquad y' = c + (y - c)t, \qquad z' = d + (z - d)t,$$

for $0 \leq t \leq 1$.

*the continuity of all of the first partials of f, throughout some neighborhood point, implies the continuity of f at that point.** Thus, having asked f_x and f_y to be continuous, in Theorem 3, we do not need to ask f to be continuous, and the theorem can be restated, equivalently, as: Let $f(x, y)$ be C^1 in an open region $\mathcal{R}$, ...

Let us now complete our extension from two variables to n variables. Specifically, we are interested in the n-variable versions of (23) and (24). Having discussed the one- and two-variable cases in some detail, the following results will be stated without proof.

First, the n-variable version of the **mean value theorem** (23):† Let $f(x_1, \ldots, x_n)$ be C^1 in an open region $\mathcal{R}$ in $(x_1, \ldots, x_n)$ space, and let $(x_{1_0}, \ldots, x_{n_0})$ and $(x_1, \ldots, x_n)$ be points in $\mathcal{R}$ such that the straight line joining these points lies entirely within $\mathcal{R}$. Then there exists a point $(\xi_1, \ldots, \xi_n)$ on that line, between the endpoints, such that

$$f(x_1, \ldots, x_n) = f(x_{1_0}, \ldots, x_{n_0}) + \sum_{j=1}^{n} f_{x_j}(\xi_1, \ldots, \xi_n)(x_j - x_{j_0}). \tag{26}$$

Finally, the n-variable version of the **Taylor's formula** (24): Let $f(x_1, \ldots, x_n)$ be C^2 in an open region $\mathcal{R}$ in $(x_1, \ldots, x_n)$ space, and let $(x_{1_0}, \ldots, x_{n_0})$ and $(x_1, \ldots, x_n)$ be points in $\mathcal{R}$ such that the straight line joining these points lies entirely within $\mathcal{R}$. Then there exists a point $(\xi_1, \ldots, \xi_n)$ on that line, between the endpoints, such that

$$\begin{aligned} f(x_1, \ldots, x_n) = f(x_{1_0}, \ldots, x_{n_0}) &+ \sum_{j=1}^{n} f_{x_j}(x_{1_0}, \ldots, x_{n_0})(x_j - x_{j_0}) \\ &+ \frac{1}{2} \sum_{i=1}^{n} \sum_{j=1}^{n} f_{x_i x_j}(\xi_1, \ldots, \xi_n)(x_i - x_{i_0})(x_j - x_{j_0}). \end{aligned} \tag{27}$$

(Note that $f_{x_i x_j} = f_{x_j x_i}$ since f is C^2.)

These results, (26) and (27), will be drawn on at various points in the remainder of Part II.

Finally, we mention that just as we passed from Taylor's formula (5) to Taylor's *series* (9) we can do the same for functions of more than one variable. We choose not to do so, however, because the convergence question is more difficult to handle than in the one-variable case, and because the Taylor's *formula* (20) [or (23), (24)] is all that we shall need in this book.

6.5 EXERCISES

1. Expand each of the following functions in Taylor series about the indicated point, through third-order terms. *Note:* $(x - a)^n$ is said to be of nth *order*, or *degree*.

* See Th. 8 and 9 on p. 98 of MARSDEN AND TROMBA.

† Strictly speaking, (23) is a formula, not a theorem; it is the formula contained within the mean value theorem. Thus (23) might better be referred to as the "mean value formula," but that name is not standard, and might cause more confusion than clarification.

*(a) e^{-2x} about $x = 0$
(b) e^{-2x} about $x = 5$
(c) e^{-2x} about $x = -3$
(d) $\ln x$ about $x = 2$
(e) $1/(1 + x^2)$ about $x = 0$
*(f) $1/(1 + x^2)$ about $x = -1$
(g) $\sin x$ about $x = \pi$
(h) $\sin 2x$ about $x = \pi/2$
(i) $\sin x$ about $x = 2$
(j) $\sin (x^3)$ about $x = 0$

2. Expand $f(x) = \ln x$ about $x = 1$, through third-order terms. Plot $\ln x$ versus x, on graph paper, over $0 < x < 4$. On the same graph, plot the first partial sum [namely, $p_0(x)$ given by (1)], the second, the third, and the fourth (as we did in Fig. 6.7).

3. *(a) Expanding $\sin x$ about $x = 0$, through second-order terms, use (6) and (7) to show that

$$\sin x = x + R_3(x); \qquad R_3(x) = -\frac{\cos \mu}{3!} x^3,$$

where μ is some number between 0 and x. Supposing that the interval of interest is $0 \le x \le 0.5$, show that

$$|\sin x - x| < 0.021 \text{ over } 0 \le x \le 0.5.$$

(b) Expanding through fourth-order terms, show that

$$\left| \sin x - \left(x - \frac{x^3}{3!} \right) \right| < 0.000261$$

over $0 \le x \le 0.5$.

(c) Expanding through fifth-order terms, show that

$$\left| \sin x - \left(x - \frac{x^3}{3!} + \frac{x^5}{5!} \right) \right| < 0.000011$$

over $0 \le x \le 0.5$.

4. Expanding $\sin x$ about $x = 2$, through second-order terms, use (5) and (6) to show that

$$\sin x = \sin 2 + (\cos 2)(x - 2) - \left(\frac{\sin 2}{2} \right)(x - 2)^2 + R_3(x),$$

where $R_3(x) = -(\cos \mu/3!)(x - 2)^3$, and μ is some number between 2 and x. Supposing that the interval of interest is $1.5 \le x \le 2.5$, show that

$$\left| \sin x - \left[\sin 2 + (\cos 2)(x - 2) - \left(\frac{\sin 2}{2} \right)(x - 2)^2 \right] \right| < 0.0167$$

over $1.5 \le x \le 2.5$.

5. The right-hand side of (6) is called the *Lagrange form* of the remainder $R_{n+1}(x)$. Alternatively, the *integral form*

$$R_{n+1}(x) = \frac{1}{n!} \int_a^x (x - t)^n f^{(n+1)}(t)\, dt \tag{a}$$

is also used. Derive Taylor's formula (5), with the remainder given by (a), by induction. *Hint:* First, show that (5) holds for $n = 0$, namely that $R_1(x) = f(x) - f(a)$, by evaluating the integral in (a) for $n = 0$. Next, integrate the right-hand side of (a) by parts and show that

$$R_{n+1}(x) = R_n(x) - \frac{1}{n!} f^{(n)}(a)(x - a)^n,$$

so that the truth of

$$f(x) = f(a) + f'(a)(x - a) + \cdots + \frac{f^{(n-1)}(a)}{(n - 1)!}(x - a)^{n-1} + R_n(x)$$

implies the truth of

$$f(x) = f(a) + f'(a)(x - a) + \cdots + \frac{f^{(n)}(a)}{n!}(x - a)^n + R_{n+1}(x).$$

6. Define

$$p_0(x, y) \equiv f(a, b),$$

$$p_1(x, y) \equiv f(a, b) + f_x(a, b)(x - a) + f_y(a, b)(y - b),$$

$$p_2(x, y) \equiv f(a, b) + f_x(a, b)(x - a) + f_y(a, b)(y - b) + \frac{1}{2!} f_{xx}(a, b)(x - a)^2 + \frac{2}{2!} f_{xy}(a, b)(x - a)(y - b) + \frac{1}{2!} f_{yy}(a, b)(y - b)^2,$$

and so on; these are the partial sums in Taylor's formula (20). To determine the utility of these partial sums in *approximating* $f(x, y)$, take $(a, b) = (1, 1)$, say, and compare p_0, p_1, and p_2 with the exact value of f at each of the points $(1, 1)$, $(1.1, 1)$, $(1, 1.1)$, and $(2, 2)$.

(a) $f = 3 - 2y + xy$
(b) $f = x - y + 5y^2$
(c) $f = x^3 y^2$
(d) $f = 1/(x^2 + y^2)$
(e) $f = \ln (x + y^2)$
(f) $f = x^2/y$
(g) $f = \sin (x - 2y^3)$
(h) $f = \cos (xy)$
(i) $f = y^x$

7. If x is close to a, and y is close to b, then the second-order terms $(x-a)^2$, $(x-a)(y-b,)$ $(y-b)^2$ are small compared with the first-order terms $(x-a)$, $(y-b)$, and (24) can be approximated as

$$f(x, y) \approx f(a, b) + f_x(a, b)(x-a) + f_y(a, b)(y-b). \qquad \text{(a)}$$

[In graphical terms analogous to those in Example 1, the right-hand side of (a) describes the *tangent plane* to the f surface, at the point $x = a$, $y = b$. The "tangent plane" will be discussed in a later chapter.] Use (a) to derive the approximate equations (48) on page 170 from the original equations (42) on page 169.

8. Recall that we elected to drop the subscripted zeros in (21) and (22), for notational simplicity, and this step yielded the final versions (23) and (24), respectively. Why not drop the subscripted zeros back in (20)? To see what would happen, let $n = 1$. Then

$$\begin{aligned} f(x, y) &= f(a, b) + \left[(x-a)\frac{\partial}{\partial x} + (y-b)\frac{\partial}{\partial y}\right] f\Big|_{a,b} \\ &\quad + \frac{1}{2!}\left[(x-a)\frac{\partial}{\partial x} + (y-b)\frac{\partial}{\partial y}\right] \\ &\quad \times \left[(x-a)\frac{\partial}{\partial x} + (y-b)\frac{\partial}{\partial y}\right] f\Big|_{\xi,\eta} \\ &= f(a, b) + [f_x(a, b)(x-a) + f_y(a, b)(y-b)] \\ &\quad + \frac{1}{2!}\left[(x-a)^2\frac{\partial^2}{\partial x^2} + (x-a)\frac{\partial}{\partial x} + 2(x-a)\right. \\ &\quad \times (y-b)\frac{\partial^2}{\partial x\,\partial y} + (y-b)^2\frac{\partial^2}{\partial y^2} \\ &\quad \left. + (y-b)\frac{\partial}{\partial y}\right] f\Big|_{\xi,\eta} \\ &= f(a, b) + f_x(a, b)(x-a) + f_y(a, b)(y-b) \\ &\quad + \frac{1}{2!}[(x-a)^2 f_{xx}(\xi, \eta) \\ &\quad + 2(x-a)(y-b)f_{xy}(\xi, \eta) \\ &\quad + (y-b)^2 f_{yy}(\xi, \eta) \\ &\quad + (x-a)f_x(\xi, \eta) + (y-b)f_y(\xi, \eta)], \qquad \text{(a)} \end{aligned}$$

which is not the same as (24), and is incorrect. Identify the error incurred in deriving (a).

9. (a) Write out (26) for $n = 1$, 2, and 3.
(b) Write out (27) for $n = 1$, 2, and 3.

6.6 IMPLICIT FUNCTIONS; JACOBIANS

An equation

$$f(x, y) = 0 \qquad (1)$$

is said to constitute a *relation*, i.e., the set of pairs (x, y) that satisfy the equation. An example is the equation

$$x^2 + 4y^2 - 4 = 0 \qquad (2)$$

of the ellipse shown in Fig. 6.10.

Depending on the problem at hand, it may be desirable to take (1) as an indirect, or implicit, definition of a *function* $y(x)$ [or perhaps of a function $x(y)$]. For example, (2) can be solved for y as

$$y = \pm\sqrt{1 - \left(\frac{x}{2}\right)^2}. \qquad (3)$$

If we are interested in the interval $0 \le x \le 1$, say, there are two such differentiable functions—namely, the positive square root, corresponding to the upper branch AB in Fig. 6.10, and the negative square root, corresponding to the lower branch CD*;

* We cannot count *both* branches as a single function because functions are required to be single valued.

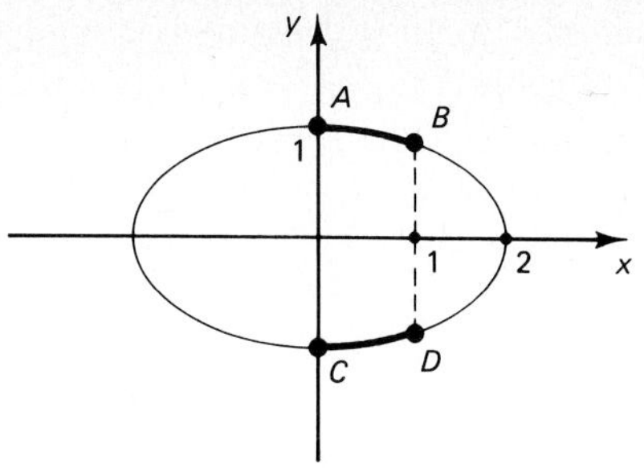

Fig. 6.10 The ellipse $x^2 + 4y^2 - 4 = 0$.

if, instead we consider the interval $3 \le x \le 8$, say, then there are *no* such (real-valued) functions.

If, for a given x neighborhood, a differentiable function $y = y(x)$ is implied by (1), we speak of $y(x)$ as an **implicit function.** A fundamental question presents itself: Under what conditions on $f(x, y)$ will (1) imply an implicit function $y(x)$? The **implicit function theorem,** stated below, deals with this question *locally,* i.e., in the neighborhood of a point (x_0, y_0) that satisfies (1).

Theorem 1 *Implicit Function Theorem*

Let $f(x, y) = 0$ be satisfied by a pair of real numbers x_0, y_0, so that $f(x_0, y_0) = 0$. And suppose that $f(x, y)$ is C^1 in some neighborhood N of (x_0, y_0), with

$$\boxed{\frac{\partial f}{\partial y}(x_0, y_0) \neq 0.} \tag{4}$$

Then $f(x, y) = 0$ uniquely implies a function $y(x)$ such that $y(x_0) = y_0$, where $y(x)$ is differentiable in some neighborhood of the point x_0.*

Proof of Theorem 1 is beyond our present scope and is normally included in a course on advanced calculus.†

Again, note that the argument is a local one. There is no mention, in the theorem, of the *size* of the neighborhoods.

EXAMPLE 1 Consider, again, the simple case of the ellipse (2), namely,

$$x^2 + 4y^2 - 4 = 0. \tag{5}$$

Observe that the pair $(1, -\sqrt{3}/2)$, for example, satisfies (5). Let us take that as our point (x_0, y_0). Clearly,

$$f(x, y) = x^2 + 4y^2 - 4, \qquad f_x(x, y) = 2x, \qquad f_y(x, y) = 8y$$

are continuous in some neighborhood of $(1, -\sqrt{3}/2)$, since they are continuous in the entire plane! Further, $f_y(1, -\sqrt{3}/2) = -4\sqrt{3} \neq 0$, so it follows from Theo-

* The neighborhood of x_0 is an open *interval* (Fig. 6.1a, page 214), whereas the neighborhood of (x_0, y_0) is an open *disk* (Fig. 6.1b, page 214).

† See, for example, I. S. Sokolnikoff, *Advanced Calculus,* (New York: McGraw-Hill, 1939), Chap. 12.

rem 1 that (5) does imply a unique function $y(x)$ through the point $(1, -\sqrt{3}/2)$. Graphically, that function is the entire lower half of the ellipse (Fig. 6.11).

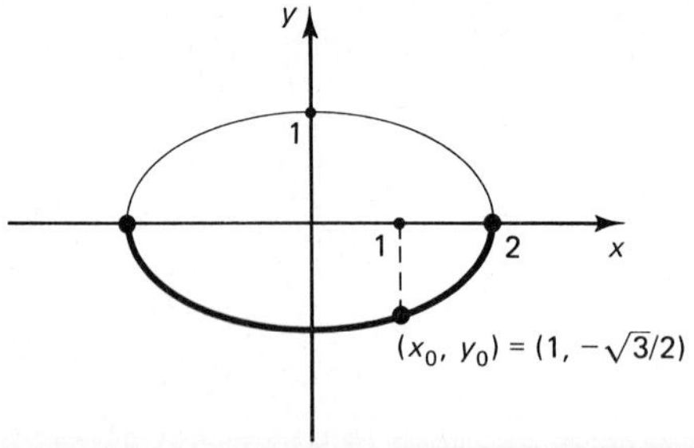

Fig. 6.11 Implicit function $y(x)$ through $(1, -\sqrt{3}/2)$.

COMMENT 1 Recall that the neighborhood N, in this case, is the entire x, y plane, while the domain of the function $y(x)$ is at most the segment $-2 \le x \le 2$.

COMMENT 2 If we select (x_0, y_0) to be at one of the two ends, say (2, 0), the theorem would furnish *no information,* since $f_y(2, 0) = (8)(0) = 0$, so that condition (4) is not satisfied. ◀

We used the ellipse (2) to illustrate because its graph was simple and familiar, so the situation was quite transparent. The power of Theorem 1, however, is that it can be applied to cases that are by no means transparent, or even translucent.

EXAMPLE 2 We see, by inspection, that one solution of the equation

$$(y - 2x)e^y - \sqrt{x} + 1 = 0 \tag{6}$$

is the pair (1, 2), or equivalently, the point (1, 2) in the x, y plane. Does there exist a function $y(x)$, implied by (6), through the point $(x_0, y_0) = (1, 2)$? Well,

$$f(x, y) = (y - 2x)e^y - \sqrt{x} + 1, \qquad f_x(x, y) = -2e^y - \tfrac{1}{2}x^{-1/2},$$

$$f_y(x, y) = (y - 2x + 1)e^y.$$

These functions are continuous in the neighborhood of (1, 2). Furthermore,

$$f_y(1, 2) = e^2 \neq 0,$$

so that, according to Theorem 1, there does exist such a function $y(x)$. ◀

How to obtain the implicit function $y(x)$ is another matter. For the ellipse, we passed from (2) to (3) by simple algebra; for equation (6), however, simple algebra does not suffice. If we are willing to assume that $f(x, y)$ is sufficiently well behaved in the vicinity of the point (x_0, y_0), we can at least develop $y(x)$ in a *Taylor series* about the point x_0,

$$y(x) = y(x_0) + y'(x_0)(x - x_0) + \frac{y''(x_0)}{2!}(x - x_0)^2 + \cdots. \tag{7}$$

Here $y(x_0)$ is known—it is y_0, but it remains to evaluate the other coefficients $y'(x_0)$, $y''(x_0)$, ... We begin by taking d/dx of

$$f[x, y(x)] = 0. \tag{8}$$

[Notice the change in viewpoint here: in (1), x and y were of the same status, i.e., they were both independent variables, whereas now it is convenient to consider y to be a function of x.] Using the chain rule, we have

$$\frac{df}{dx} = f_x + f_y y' = 0, \tag{9}$$

so that

$$y' = -\frac{f_x}{f_y}. \tag{10}$$

Continuing, differentiate (10):

$$y'' = -\frac{f_{xx} + f_{xy}y'}{f_y} + \frac{f_x(f_{yx} + f_{yy}y')}{f_y^2}. \tag{11}$$

Recalling (10), and assuming that $f_{xy} = f_{yx}$, (11) becomes

$$y'' = \frac{2f_x f_y f_{xy} - f_x^2 f_{yy} - f_y^2 f_{xx}}{f_y^3}; \tag{12}$$

similarly for y''', and so on. It remains merely to evaluate these expressions at (x_0, y_0).

Observe that powers of f_y build up in the denominators of y', y'', . . . , so that we need f_y to be nonzero at (x_0, y_0) if these derivatives are to exist. But $f_y(x_0, y_0) \neq 0$ is none other than condition (4) in Theorem 1.

EXAMPLE 3 Let us return to Example 2 and obtain the Taylor series of $y(x)$ about $x_0 = 1$. Rather than merely "plug" numbers into (10) and (12), it may be more instructive to carry out steps (8) to (12) for the given equation

$$(y - 2x)e^y - \sqrt{x} + 1 = 0.$$

Thus, taking d/dx of this equation,

$$(y' - 2)e^y + (y - 2x)y'e^y - \tfrac{1}{2}x^{-1/2} = 0,$$

so that

$$y' = \frac{4\sqrt{x} + e^{-y}}{2\sqrt{x}(1 + y - 2x)}. \tag{13}$$

Next,

$$y'' = \frac{2x^{-1/2} - y'e^{-y}}{2\sqrt{x}(1 + y - 2x)} - \frac{(4\sqrt{x} + e^{-y})[x^{-1/2}(1 + y - 2x) + 2\sqrt{x}(y' - 2)]}{[2\sqrt{x}(1 + y - 2x)]^2}, \tag{14}$$

and similarly for y''', ...

Evaluating (13) and (14) at (1, 2), we have

$$y'(x_0) = y'(1) = 2 + \tfrac{1}{2}e^{-2}, \tag{15}$$

$$y''(x_0) = y''(1) = -\tfrac{9}{4}e^{-2} - \tfrac{1}{2}e^{-4}, \tag{16}$$

so that (7) becomes

$$y(x) = 2 + \left(2 + \frac{1}{2}e^{-2}\right)(x - 1) + \frac{1}{2!}\left(-\frac{9}{4}e^{-2} - \frac{1}{2}e^{-4}\right)(x - 1)^2 + \cdots$$

$$\approx 2 + 2.068(x - 1) - 0.157(x - 1)^2 + \cdots. \tag{17}$$

Of course, the values (15) and (16) could also have been obtained from formulas (10) and (12), as mentioned above. ◀

Notice that the *inverse function* story, introduced in calculus, is but a special case of the implicit function theorem discussed in this section. For suppose that we have got a function $y = y(x)$, the graph of which passes through the point x_0, y_0 [i.e., $y(x_0) = y_0$], where $y(x)$ is C^1 in some neighborhood of x_0. Then the question *"Is there a unique inverse function, say $x = x(y)$, such that $x(y_0) = x_0$, where $x(y)$ is differentiable in some neighborhood of y_0?"* can be dealt with by Theorem 1; all we need to do is to recast $y = y(x)$ in the form of a relation $f = 0$, as in the theorem, and this is done easily by taking $f = y - y(x)$. Let us illustrate with a simple example.

EXAMPLE 4 Consider the case $y = x^2$, with $x_0 = 2$ and $y_0 = 4$; see Fig. 6.12a. First, we reexpress this equation in the form $y - x^2 = 0$, and take $f = y - x^2$. Surely, f is C^1 in some neighborhood of (x_0, y_0) since $f_y = 1$ and $f_x = -2x$ are continuous for *all* x, y. Furthermore, $f_x = -2x = -4 \neq 0$ at (x_0, y_0), in accordance with (4). [Note that since we seek $x(y)$, not $y(x)$, we need to interchange the roles of x and y in Theorem 1. Thus (4) involves f_x rather than f_y.] Then, according to Theorem 1, $f = y - x^2 = 0$ uniquely implies a function $x(y)$ such that $x(4) = 2$, where $x(y)$ is differentiable in some neighborhood of the point $x_0 = 2$. This function is, of course, $x = +\sqrt{y}$, as graphed in Fig. 6.12b.

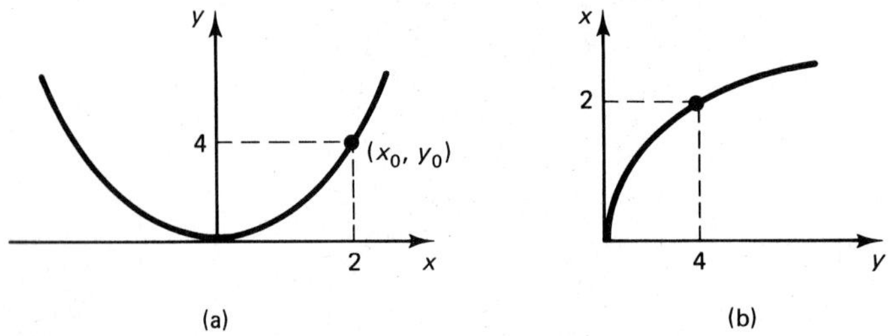

Fig. 6.12 Graph of the function.

COMMENT The only "singular point" on the parabola in Fig. 6.12a is the origin (0, 0), for $f_x = -2x = 0$ there, so that (4) is not satisfied. In fact, a differentiable inverse function $x(y)$ does *not* exist at the singular point, since, as seen from Fig. 6.12b, the slope of $x(y)$ is infinite at the origin. But note carefully that this result was not predictable from Theorem 1. Theorem 1 says, essentially, that if the stated conditions are met, there does exist a unique, differentiable inverse; it does *not* say, further, that if the conditions are *not* met, there does *not* exist a unique, differentiable inverse. That is, the theorem does not include a "converse." If it *did,* it would read somewhat as follows: A unique, differentiable inverse exists *if and only if* the stated conditions are met. (Apologies for beating this point to death, but reading converses into theorems where they do not exist is a common error.) ◀

Thus far we have addressed the question, "Given

$$f(x, y) = 0, \tag{18}$$

and a point (x_0, y_0) such that $f(x_0, y_0) = 0$, does (18) imply the existence of a differentiable function $y(x)$ through the point (x_0, y_0)?" Similarly, we may be confronted with more questions, and more variables. For example, given

$$f(x, y, u, v) = 0 \tag{19a}$$

$$g(x, y, u, v) = 0, \tag{19b}$$

and a point (x_0, y_0, u_0, v_0) such that $f(x_0, y_0, u_0, v_0) = 0$ and $g(x_0, y_0, u_0, v_0) = 0$, does (19) imply the existence of functions $u = u(x, y)$, $v = v(x, y)$ through the point (x_0, y_0, u_0, v_0)? We state, again without proof, the following theorem.

Theorem 2 *Implicit Function Theorem*

Let

$$f(x, y, u, v) = 0 \tag{20a}$$

$$g(x, y, u, v) = 0 \tag{20b}$$

be satisfied by real numbers x_0, y_0, u_0, v_0, so that $f(x_0, y_0, u_0, v_0) = 0$ and $g(x_0, y_0, u_0, v_0) = 0$. Suppose, further, that f and g are C^1 in some neighborhood of the point (x_0, y_0, u_0, v_0) and that the determinant*

$$\boxed{\begin{vmatrix} f_u & f_v \\ g_u & g_v \end{vmatrix} \neq 0} \tag{21}$$

at (x_0, y_0, u_0, v_0). Then (20) uniquely implies functions $u(x, y)$, $v(x, y)$ in some neighborhood N of the point (x_0, y_0), such that $u(x_0, y_0) = u_0$, $v(x_0, y_0) = v_0$, where u and v are C^1 in N.

* Determinants are introduced in Chapter 3. In case you have not yet studied that material, it should suffice, here, to define the *second-order determinant*

$$\begin{vmatrix} a & b \\ c & d \end{vmatrix} \equiv ad - bc,$$

and the *third-order determinant*

$$\begin{vmatrix} a & b & c \\ d & e & f \\ g & h & i \end{vmatrix} \equiv a(ei - fh) - b(di - fg) + c(dh - eg).$$

The determinant in (21) is known as the **Jacobian** of f and g with respect to u and v, and is denoted either as $J(u, v)$ or as $\partial(f, g)/\partial(u, v)$:

$$\begin{vmatrix} \dfrac{\partial f}{\partial u} & \dfrac{\partial f}{\partial v} \\[2ex] \dfrac{\partial g}{\partial u} & \dfrac{\partial g}{\partial v} \end{vmatrix} \equiv J(u, v) \quad \text{or} \quad \frac{\partial(f, g)}{\partial(u, v)}. \tag{22}$$

Similarly, one defines higher-order Jacobians. If, for example, f, g, and h are functions of u, v, w, then

$$\begin{vmatrix} \dfrac{\partial f}{\partial u} & \dfrac{\partial f}{\partial v} & \dfrac{\partial f}{\partial w} \\[2ex] \dfrac{\partial g}{\partial u} & \dfrac{\partial g}{\partial v} & \dfrac{\partial g}{\partial w} \\[2ex] \dfrac{\partial h}{\partial u} & \dfrac{\partial h}{\partial v} & \dfrac{\partial h}{\partial w} \end{vmatrix} \equiv J(u, v, w) \quad \text{or} \quad \frac{\partial(f, g, h)}{\partial(u, v, w)}. \tag{23}$$

Theorems 1 and 2 are special cases of a more general implicit function theorem that holds for any number of equations in any number of unknowns.* For our purposes, however, Theorems 1 and 2 will suffice. A key point in these theorems, to be noted carefully, is the *nonvanishing of the Jacobian* at the point of interest, namely, condition (21) in Theorem 2, and condition (4) in Theorem 1 (where $\partial f/\partial y$ is merely a *first*-order Jacobian determinant.) Some of the "algebra" of second- and third-order Jacobians is considered in Exercises 7, 8, and 11.

In this section we introduced the subject of implicit functions. Beginning with the relation $f(x, y) = 0$ in two variables, and a point (x_0, y_0) such that $f(x_0, y_0) = 0$, we gave conditions on f (in Theorem 1) such that $f(x, y) = 0$ uniquely implies an "implicit function" $y(x)$ over some neighborhood N of x_0. The argument was a local one inasmuch as no information was provided as to the size of the neighborhood N. Then we extended the idea to the case of more than one equation and more than two variables. As representative, we considered the relations $f(x, y, u, v) = 0$, $g(x, y, u, v) = 0$ and considered the possible existence of implicit functions $u(x, y)$, $v(x, y)$ in some neighborhood of the point in question.

The thread that weaves through these implicit function theorems is the condition on the nonvanishing of the relevant Jacobian determinant. These Jacobian determinants will be found to arise in other contexts as well—for example, when we discuss surface and volume integrals in Chapter 8.

6.6 EXERCISES

1. Given $f(x, y) = 0$ and a point (x_0, y_0) such that $f(x_0, y_0) = 0$, see if the conditions of Theorem 1 are met. If so, develop the implicit function $y(x)$ in a Taylor series about x_0, through second-order terms, as we did in Example 3.

*(a) $(x - 2)^2 + (y - 1)^2 = 0$; $(2, 1)$
(b) $x^2 + 4y^2 - 4 = 0$; $(0, 1)$
(c) $x^2 + 4y^2 - 4 = 0$; $(0, -1)$
*(d) $x(\cos \pi y + 1) + x^3 y + 8 = 0$; $(-2, 1)$
(e) $x(\cos \pi y + 1) + (x^3 + 8)y = 0$; $(-2, 1)$

* See I. S. Sokolnikoff and R. M. Redheffer, *Mathematics of Physics and Modern Engineering*, 2nd ed. (New York: McGraw-Hill, 1966), p. 335.

(f) $x - y - \sin y = 0$; $(0, 0)$
(g) $x - y + \sin y = 0$; $(0, 0)$
*(h) $(y - 1)e^y - x^2 + 1 = 0$; $(1, 1)$

2. In each case, find $y'(x)$ and $y''(x)$.

*(a) $xy - y^3 = 1$ (b) $xe^y + y = 3$
(c) $y + y^2 + y^3 = x$ (d) $xye^y = 1$

3. Given that $xy + \sin(x + z) - z^2 = 5$, find

(a) z_x (b) z_y

4. Given that $xe^y - y^2 - z^2 \sin z = 0$, find

*(a) y_x (b) z_x (c) z_y

5. Apply Theorem 2, in each case, to see if implicit functions $u(x, y)$, $v(x, y)$ exist corresponding to the given point (x_0, y_0, u_0, v_0). (You need not attempt to *find* u and v.) *Note:* The conditions of the theorem are not stated to be necessary and sufficient. Thus, if the conditions are met, u and v exist; if they are not met, *no* conclusion may be drawn.

*(a) $x - u \cos v = 0$,
$y - u \sin v = 0$; $(0, 0, 0, 0)$
(b) $x - u \cos v = 0$,
$y - u \sin v = 0$; $(0, 2, 2, \pi/2)$
(c) $x \sin u + y^2 - v^2 = 0$,
$(x + v)^2 - \sin(uy) = 0$; $(1, 1, 0, -1)$
(d) $x \cos u + y + v^2 = 0$,
$x - y + \sin(u^2 v) = 0$; $(1, 1, \pi, 0)$
(e) $y \cos u + x - v^3 = 0$,
$v^2 + \sin(x - y) = 0$; $(1, 1, \pi, 0)$
(f) $xe^y - 2u^2 + v + 7 = 0$,
$\sin y - x^2 \sin v = 0$; $(1, 0, 2, 0)$

6. Evaluate the indicated Jacobian.

*(a) $f(u, v) = u^2 + 3v^2$, $g(u, v) = u^2 - v^2$; $J(u, v) = ?$
(b) $f(u, v, w) = uv^2 + 5$, $g(u, v, w) = u^2 + v - \sin w$, $h(u, v, w) = u + v + w$; $J(u, v, w) = ?$
(c) $F(p, q) = p^2 + 2$, $G(p, q) = p \sin q - q^3$; $\dfrac{\partial(F, G)}{\partial(p, q)} = ?$
(d) $P(x, y) = y^3 + 4y$, $Q(x, y) = x^2 + y^3$; $J(x, y) = ?$
(e) $F(x, y, z) = x + y + z$, $G(x, y, z) = x^2 + y^2 + z^2$, $H(x, y, z) = x^3 + y^3 + z^3$; $\dfrac{\partial(F, G, H)}{\partial(x, y, z)} = ?$

7. Show that

(a) $J(u, v) = -J(v, u)$
(b) $J(u, v, w) = -J(v, u, w) = J(v, w, u) = -J(u, w, v)$

8. Recall that if $x = x(u(s))$, then

$$\frac{dx}{du}\frac{du}{ds} = \frac{dx}{ds}.$$

Prove that the following analogous results.

(a)
$$\boxed{\frac{\partial(x, y)}{\partial(u, v)}\frac{\partial(u, v)}{\partial(r, s)} = \frac{\partial(x, y)}{\partial(r, s)}}$$

(b)
$$\boxed{\frac{\partial(x, y, z)}{\partial(u, v, w)}\frac{\partial(u, v, w)}{\partial(r, s, t)} = \frac{\partial(x, y, z)}{\partial(r, s, t)}}$$

Hint: Simply write out the Jacobians on the left and multiply them out.

9. Verify Exercise 8(a) for these cases.

(a) $x = u \cos v$, $y = u \sin v$ and $u = r + s$, $v = r^2 + s^2$
(b) $x = u + v$, $y = u - v$ and $u = r^2 + 2s$, $v = r \cos s$
(c) $x = u$, $y = u + v$ and $u = r \cos s$, $v = r \sin s$

10. Verify Exercise 8(b) for these cases.

(a) $x = u \cos v$, $y = u \sin v$, $z = w$ and $u = r + s + t$, $v = r^2 + s^2 + t^2$, $w = r^3 + s^3 + t^3$
(b) $x = u + v + w$, $y = u + v - w$, $z = u - v - w$ and $u = r$, $v = 4s$, $w = t$
(c) $x = u$, $y = u + v$, $z = u + v + w^2$ and $u = r^3$, $v = re^{-s} + t$, $w = rt^2$

11. Recall from the calculus that if $x = x(u)$ admits an inverse $u = u(x)$, then dx/du and du/dx are numerical inverses, i.e.,

$$\frac{dx}{du} = \left(\frac{du}{dx}\right)^{-1}. \tag{a}$$

In general, this result does *not* carry over to partial derivatives. For example, if $x = x(u, v)$ and $y = y(u, v)$, then

$$\frac{\partial x}{\partial u} \neq \left(\frac{\partial u}{\partial x}\right)^{-1}, \quad \frac{\partial x}{\partial v} \neq \left(\frac{\partial v}{\partial x}\right)^{-1},$$
$$\frac{\partial y}{\partial u} \neq \left(\frac{\partial u}{\partial y}\right)^{-1}, \quad \frac{\partial y}{\partial v} \neq \left(\frac{\partial v}{\partial y}\right)^{-1}.$$

Nevertheless, show that the following analogs of (a) *do* hold.

(a) If $x = x(u, v)$, $y = y(u, v)$ and $u = u(x, y)$, $v = v(x, y)$, then

$$\boxed{\frac{\partial(x, y)}{\partial(u, v)} = \left[\frac{\partial(u, v)}{\partial(x, y)}\right]^{-1}.} \tag{b}$$

(b) If $x = x(u, v, w)$, $y = y(u, v, w)$, $z = z(u, v, w)$ and $u = u(x, y, z)$, $v = v(x, y, z)$, $w = w(x, y, z)$, then

$$\boxed{\frac{\partial(x, y, z)}{\partial(u, v, w)} = \left[\frac{\partial(u, v, w)}{\partial(x, y, z)}\right]^{-1}.} \tag{c}$$

Note: You may either work "from scratch" or you may use the equations in Exercise 8.

12. (a)–(c) Verify equation (b) in Exercise 11 for each of the cases in Exercise 9.

13. (a)–(c) Verify equation (c) in Exercise 11 for each of the cases in Exercise 10.

14. If $f(x, y) = 0$ determines $y = y(x)$ implicitly, then $y' = -f_x/f_y$, as given by (10). Analogously, suppose that $f(x, y, z) = 0$ determines $z = z(x, y)$. Then show that

$$z_x = -\frac{f_x}{f_z}, \qquad z_y = -\frac{f_y}{f_z} \quad \text{if } f_z \neq 0. \tag{a}$$

15. One speaks of a relation $f(p, T, v) = 0$, among the pressure p in a gas, the absolute temperature T, and the specific volume v, as an *equation of state*. One such well-known relation, known as *van der Waals equation*, is

$$\left(p + \frac{a}{v^2}\right)(v - b) = R'T,$$

where a, b, R' are constants.

(a) Regarding $v = v(p, T)$, use equation (a) in Exercise 14 to compute v_p and v_T.

(b) Alternatively, compute v_p and v_T from

$$v_p = \frac{1}{p_v} \quad \text{where} \quad p = \frac{R'T}{v - a} - \frac{a}{v^2},$$

$$v_T = \frac{1}{T_v} \quad \text{where} \quad T = \frac{1}{R'}\left(p + \frac{a}{v^2}\right)(v - b),$$

and show why the formulas $v_p = 1/p_v$ and $v_T = 1/T_v$ are valid. (Recall the first two sentences in Exercise 11.)

6.7 APPLICATION TO CHANGE OF VARIABLES

It sometimes happens that it is convenient, in a given problem, to change from one set of independent variables to another. Our plan in this section is to illustrate the main ideas by considering a specific example, and then to generalize the method and indicate its connection to the material in Section 6.6.

EXAMPLE 1 *A Boundary Value Problem.* Suppose that we wish to know the temperature distribution $T(x, y)$ in a semicircular plate (half of a coin, say), with the temperature maintained at 100° along the circular edge, and at 0° along the straight edge. We state, without derivation, that $T(x, y)$ can be found as the solution to the "boundary value problem" shown in Fig. 6.13a, namely, the differential equation

$$T_{xx} + T_{yy} = 0 \tag{1}$$

in the semicircular region $\mathscr{R}$, of radius c, together with the "boundary conditions" $T = 100$ on the circular edge and $T = 0$ on the straight edge. The differential equation (1) is called a *partial differential equation* because partial derivatives appear; it will be derived in Section 9.9. We will not be concerned with the *solution* of the stated boundary value problem; that is the subject of Part IV. Here all we wish to indicate is the first step, namely, the reexpressing of the problem in terms of the *polar coordinates* r, θ, shown in Fig. 6.13b. These coordinates seem more

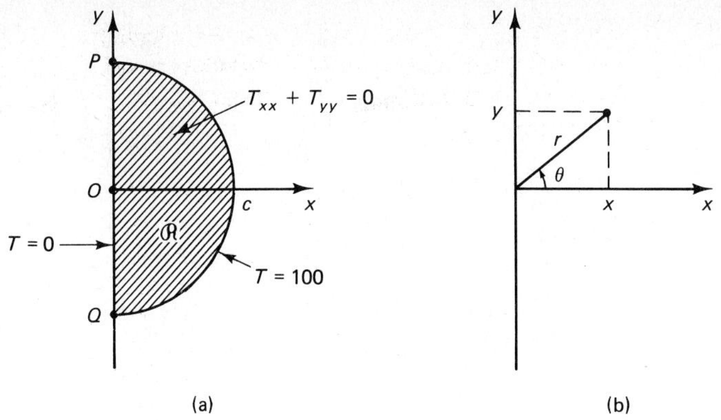

Fig. 6.13 Boundary value problem on *T*.

natural here since the boundary of $\mathcal{R}$ will then consist of constant-coordinate curves: $r = c$ on the semicircle, $\theta = \pi/2$ on OP, and $\theta = -\pi/2$ on OQ. (If $\mathcal{R}$ were, instead, the rectangular region $0 < x < a$, $0 < y < b$, say, we would be quite content to stick with the Cartesian coordinates x, y, since then the boundary would consist of the constant-coordinate curves $x = 0$, $x = a$, $y = 0$, and $y = b$.)

To begin, we record the connection

$$x = r \cos \theta \tag{2a}$$

$$y = r \sin \theta \tag{2b}$$

between x, y and r, θ. Now, consider first the T_{xx} term in (1). Writing $T_{xx} = \dfrac{\partial}{\partial x}\dfrac{\partial}{\partial x} T$, we see that our job is to express the differential operator $\dfrac{\partial}{\partial x}$ in terms of r, θ. Using chain differentiation,

$$\frac{\partial(\ )}{\partial x} = \frac{\partial(\ )}{\partial r}\frac{\partial r}{\partial x} + \frac{\partial(\ )}{\partial \theta}\frac{\partial \theta}{\partial x}, \tag{3}$$

so we need the partial derivatives r_x and θ_x. This is a bit embarassing since (2) gives us x and y as functions of r and θ, not the other way around. In other words, the "forward" derivatives x_r, x_θ, y_r, y_θ are easily obtained, from (2), as

$$x_r = \cos \theta, \qquad x_\theta = -r \sin \theta, \qquad y_r = \sin \theta, \qquad y_\theta = r \cos \theta, \tag{4}$$

but how do we obtain the "reverse" derivatives r_x, θ_x, r_y, θ_y? Well, if we take $\partial/\partial x$ of (2a) and (2b), we can generate two linear algebraic equations in the two unknowns r_x, θ_x. Doing so, and noting that $\partial x/\partial x = 1$ and $\partial y/\partial x = 0$ (since $\partial/\partial x$ implies that y is held fixed), we have

$$\begin{aligned} 1 &= (\cos \theta) r_x + (-r \sin \theta)\theta_x \\ 0 &= (\sin \theta) r_x + (r \cos \theta)\theta_x. \end{aligned} \tag{5}$$

Solving (5) for r_x and θ_x, we obtain the desired partials

$$r_x = \cos \theta, \qquad \theta_x = -\frac{\sin \theta}{r}. \tag{6}$$

Thus we may now express*

$$T_{xx} = \left(\frac{\partial}{\partial x}\right)\left(\frac{\partial}{\partial x}\right)T$$

$$= \left(r_x \frac{\partial}{\partial r} + \theta_x \frac{\partial}{\partial \theta}\right)\left(r_x \frac{\partial}{\partial r} + \theta_x \frac{\partial}{\partial \theta}\right)T$$

$$= \left(\cos\theta \frac{\partial}{\partial r} - \frac{\sin\theta}{r}\frac{\partial}{\partial \theta}\right)\left(\cos\theta\, T_r - \frac{\sin\theta}{r} T_\theta\right)$$

$$T_{xx} = \cos^2\theta\, T_{rr} + \frac{\cos\theta\sin\theta}{r^2} T_\theta - \frac{\cos\theta\sin\theta}{r} T_{\theta r} + \frac{\sin^2\theta}{r} T_r - \frac{\sin\theta\cos\theta}{r} T_{r\theta}$$

$$+ \frac{\sin\theta\cos\theta}{r^2} T_\theta + \frac{\sin^2\theta}{r^2} T_{\theta\theta},$$

or, with c and s as shorthand for $\cos\theta$ and $\sin\theta$, respectively,

$$T_{xx} = c^2 T_{rr} + \frac{cs}{r^2} T_\theta - \frac{cs}{r} T_{\theta r} + \frac{s^2}{r} T_r - \frac{sc}{r} T_{r\theta} + \frac{sc}{r^2} T_\theta + \frac{s^2}{r^2} T_{\theta\theta}. \tag{7}$$

Turning to the $T_{yy} = \dfrac{\partial}{\partial y}\dfrac{\partial}{\partial y} T$ term in (1), we write

$$\frac{\partial(\ )}{\partial y} = \frac{\partial(\ )}{\partial r}\frac{\partial r}{\partial y} + \frac{\partial(\ )}{\partial \theta}\frac{\partial \theta}{\partial y}. \tag{8}$$

This time we take $\partial/\partial y$ of (2a) and (2b) to obtain two equations in r_y and θ_y. Doing so, and solving the resulting two equations for r_y and θ_y, we find [Exercise 2(a)] that

$$r_y = \sin\theta, \qquad \theta_y = \frac{\cos\theta}{r}, \tag{9}$$

and that

$$T_{yy} = s^2 T_{rr} - \frac{cs}{r^2} T_\theta + \frac{cs}{r} T_{\theta r} + \frac{c^2}{r} T_r + \frac{sc}{r} T_{r\theta} - \frac{sc}{r^2} T_\theta + \frac{c^2}{r^2} T_{\theta\theta}. \tag{10}$$

Finally, adding (7) and (10) (and assuming that $T_{r\theta} = T_{\theta r}$),

$$T_{xx} + T_{yy} = T_{rr} + \frac{1}{r} T_r + \frac{1}{r^2} T_{\theta\theta}, \tag{11}$$

so that, expressed now in terms of r and θ, the boundary value problem in Fig. 6.13a becomes

$$T_{rr} + \frac{1}{r} T_r + \frac{1}{r^2} T_{\theta\theta} = 0 \qquad \text{in } \mathcal{R}; \tag{12a}$$

* In what follows we use the same letter, T, for the temperature, independent of whether it is regarded as a function of x, y or as a function of r, θ. Strictly speaking, however, we should use different letters; e.g. $T(x, y) = T(x(r, \theta), y(r, \theta)) = U(r, \theta)$, say.

$$T(c, \theta) = 100 \qquad \left(-\frac{\pi}{2} < \theta < \frac{\pi}{2}\right) \tag{12b}$$

$$T\left(r, \frac{\pi}{2}\right) = 0 \qquad (0 \le r < c) \tag{12c}$$

$$T\left(r, -\frac{\pi}{2}\right) = 0 \qquad (0 \le r < c). \tag{12d}$$

We ask the reader to accept, on faith, that the polar coordinate version (12) will indeed prove more convenient (when it is time to *solve* for T, in Part IV) than the Cartesian version. Here we deal only with the transition from one form to the other.

COMMENT 1 Why all the fuss about computing the "reverse" derivatives $r_x, r_y, \theta_x, \theta_y$? Could we not merely have computed the "forward" derivatives (4), directly from (2), and then turned them "upside down"? For example, (2a) gives $x_r = \cos\theta$, so can we not say that

$$\frac{\partial r}{\partial x} = \frac{1}{\partial x/\partial r} = \frac{1}{\cos\theta}? \tag{13}$$

No! This sort of manipulation is valid for *ordinary* derivatives but not, in general, for partials. (Recall Exercise 11 on page 243.) In fact, we see from (6) that $r_x = \cos\theta$, not $1/\cos\theta$. Note that the derivatives $\partial x/\partial r$ and $\partial r/\partial x$ have the geometrical significance shown in Fig. 6.14. When we hold θ fixed, that sets up a *different elemental triangle* than when we hold y fixed, so there is no reason why the ratio $\partial x/\partial r$ with θ fixed should be the numerical inverse of the ratio $\partial r/\partial x$ with y fixed.

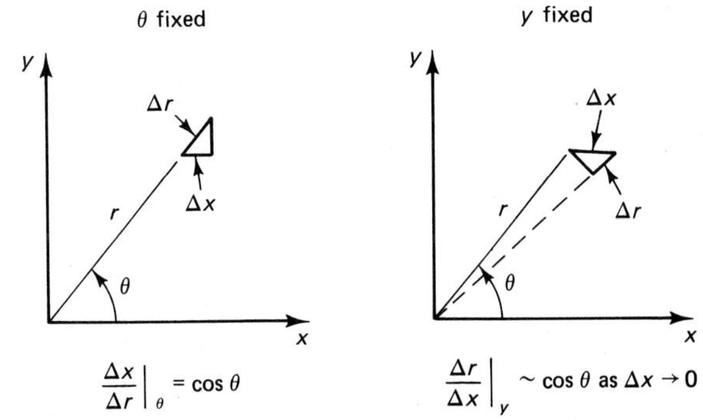

Fig. 6.14 Geometrical significance of $\partial x/\partial r$ and $\partial r/\partial x$.

COMMENT 2 Still seeking a more direct method for computing the "reverse" derivatives, one may wonder if we can obtain them merely by solving (2) for r and θ in terms of x and y and then computing the desired partials. For if we square (2a) and (2b) and add, we have $x^2 + y^2 = r^2$, or

$$r = \sqrt{x^2 + y^2}. \tag{14a}$$

And, dividing (2b) by (2a) gives $\tan\theta = y/x$, or

$$\theta = \tan^{-1}\left(\frac{y}{x}\right) \tag{14b}$$

[where we elect to take the *principal value* of $\tan^{-1}(\ )$, namely, such that $-\pi/2 \le \tan^{-1}(\ ) \le \pi/2$]. From (14a), then, $r_x = (\frac{1}{2})(2x)(x^2 + y^2)^{-1/2} = x/r = (r\cos\theta)/r = \cos\theta$, as before, and similarly for r_y, θ_x, θ_y. The reason we avoided this approach, which is of course correct, is that it depends on our being able to invert (2) to obtain explicit expressions for $r(x, y)$ and $\theta(x, y)$. In the present example that inversion is simple, but in other examples it may, practically speaking, be difficult or impossible. The method contained between (3) and (6), however, sidesteps these difficulties; it is generalized following this example. ◀

More generally than (2), consider any change of variables of the form

$$x = X(u, v) \tag{15a}$$

$$y = Y(u, v). \tag{15b}$$

As in Example 1, we are interested in computing the "reverse" derivatives u_x, u_y, v_x, v_y. Before beginning, let us reflect on whether such calculation will be *possible*, even in principle. We will use the implicit function theorem on page 241. First, we recast (15) in the form

$$\begin{aligned} f(x, y, u, v) &= x - X(u, v) = 0 \\ g(x, y, u, v) &= y - Y(u, v) = 0. \end{aligned} \tag{16}$$

Considering a particular "solution point" (x_0, y_0, u_0, v_0) of (16), we ask first, according to the theorem, that f and g be C^1 in some neighborhood N of that point. That means that $f_x = 1$, $f_y = 0$, $f_u = -X_u$, $f_v = -X_v$, $g_x = 0$, $g_y = 1$, $g_u = -Y_u$, $g_v = -Y_v$ are continuous in N, or, equivalently, that X, Y are C^1 in some neighborhood of (u_0, v_0). Second, we ask, according to condition (21) in the theorem, that we have

$$\begin{vmatrix} f_u & f_v \\ g_u & g_v \end{vmatrix} = \begin{vmatrix} -X_u & -X_v \\ -Y_u & -Y_v \end{vmatrix} = \begin{vmatrix} X_u & X_v \\ Y_u & Y_v \end{vmatrix} \neq 0 \tag{17}$$

in some neighborhood of (u_0, v_0). Observe that the determinant in (17) is the *Jacobian*

$$\begin{vmatrix} X_u & X_v \\ Y_u & Y_v \end{vmatrix} = \frac{\partial(X, Y)}{\partial(u, v)}. \tag{18}$$

According to the implicit function theorem, cited above, these two conditions will guarantee that (15) uniquely implies inverse functions $u(x, y)$, $v(x, y)$ with first-order partials u_x, u_y, v_x, v_y which are continuous in some neighborhood of (x_0, y_0).

Assuming that these conditions are met, we turn to the actual calculation of u_x, u_y, v_x, v_y. Mimicking the method used in Example 1, first we take $\partial/\partial x$ of (15a) and (15b):

$$\begin{aligned} 1 &= X_u u_x + X_v v_x \\ 0 &= Y_u u_x + Y_v v_x. \end{aligned} \tag{19}$$

[For the case considered in Example 1, (19) corresponds to (5).] Solving (19) for u_x and v_x* yields

$$u_x = \frac{\begin{vmatrix} 1 & X_v \\ 0 & Y_v \end{vmatrix}}{\begin{vmatrix} X_u & X_v \\ Y_u & Y_v \end{vmatrix}} = \frac{Y_v}{\dfrac{\partial(X, Y)}{\partial(u, v)}} \tag{20a}$$

and

$$v_x = \frac{\begin{vmatrix} X_u & 1 \\ Y_u & 0 \end{vmatrix}}{\begin{vmatrix} X_u & X_v \\ Y_u & Y_v \end{vmatrix}} = -\frac{Y_u}{\dfrac{\partial(X, Y)}{\partial(u, v)}} \tag{20b}$$

where the right-hand sides are all directly computable quantities.

* In solving (19) we have used *Cramer's rule*, from Chapter 3. In case you have not studied that material, let us note, briefly, that the unique solution of

$$ax + by = p$$
$$cx + dy = q$$

is given by

$$x = \frac{\begin{vmatrix} p & b \\ q & d \end{vmatrix}}{D}, \qquad y = \frac{\begin{vmatrix} a & p \\ c & q \end{vmatrix}}{D},$$

where

$$D = \begin{vmatrix} a & b \\ c & d \end{vmatrix},$$

provided that $D \neq 0$. And the unique solution of

$$ax + by + cz = p$$
$$dx + ey + fz = q$$
$$gx + hy + iz = r$$

is

$$x = \frac{\begin{vmatrix} p & b & c \\ q & e & f \\ r & h & i \end{vmatrix}}{D}, \qquad y = \frac{\begin{vmatrix} a & p & c \\ d & q & f \\ g & r & i \end{vmatrix}}{D}, \qquad z = \frac{\begin{vmatrix} a & b & p \\ d & e & q \\ g & h & r \end{vmatrix}}{D},$$

where

$$D = \begin{vmatrix} a & b & c \\ d & e & f \\ g & h & i \end{vmatrix},$$

provided, again, that $D \neq 0$.

Similarly, $\partial/\partial y$ of (15a) and (15b) gives

$$\begin{aligned} 0 &= X_u u_y + X_v v_y \\ 1 &= Y_u u_y + Y_v v_y, \end{aligned} \tag{21}$$

so that

$$u_y = \frac{\begin{vmatrix} 0 & X_v \\ 1 & Y_v \end{vmatrix}}{\begin{vmatrix} X_u & X_v \\ Y_u & Y_v \end{vmatrix}} = -\frac{X_v}{\dfrac{\partial(X, Y)}{\partial(u, v)}} \tag{22a}$$

and

$$v_y = \frac{\begin{vmatrix} X_u & 0 \\ Y_u & 1 \end{vmatrix}}{\begin{vmatrix} X_u & X_v \\ Y_u & Y_v \end{vmatrix}} = \frac{X_u}{\dfrac{\partial(X, Y)}{\partial(u, v)}}. \tag{22b}$$

Notice that all four denominators in (20) and (22) are the same, namely, the *Jacobian of the transformation*. We have assumed, in (17), that the Jacobian is nonzero, so that the foregoing expressions for u_x, v_x, u_y, v_y are all well defined.

Of course, the expressions (20) and (22) should reproduce our earlier results (6) and (9) for the special case where $u = r$, $v = \theta$, $X(u, v) = r\cos\theta$, and $Y(u, v) = r\sin\theta$, and we leave it for the reader to verify that that is the case.

The result is that under the change of variables (15), where X, Y are assumed to be C^1 and $\partial(X, Y)/\partial(u, v) \neq 0$ in the region under consideration, the "reverse" partials u_x, u_y, v_x, v_y are given by (20) and (22). These partials will be needed in various calculations, such as the one discussed in Example 1.

6.7 EXERCISES

1. In each case, evaluate the partials x_u, x_v, y_u, y_v, u_x, u_y, v_x, and v_y.

*(a) $x = u + v$, $y = 2uv$
(b) $x = u^2 + v$, $y = ue^v$
(c) $x = u^2 - v^2$, $y = 2uv$
(d) $x = u + \sin v$, $y = uv$
*(e) $x = u + v$, $y = u^3 - v^3$
(f) $x = u^3 - 3uv^2$, $y = 3u^2v - v^3$
(g) $x = u + \sin v$, $y = v$
(h) $x = \dfrac{u}{u^2 + v^2}$, $y = -\dfrac{v}{u^2 + v^2}$
(i) $x = \sin u \cosh v$, $y = \cos u \sinh v$

2. (*The Laplacian*) If f is a function of x and y, the quantity $f_{xx} + f_{yy}$ is called the **Laplacian** of f and is denoted as $\nabla^2 f$, read as "del square f." Thus

$$\nabla^2 f = f_{xx} + f_{yy}. \tag{a}$$

This quantity will be of great importance to us later in Parts III to V, and was met in Example 1. In this exercise, as in Example 1, we are after the form of $\nabla^2 f$ following a change of variables, from x, y to new variables, say u, v.

(a) (*Polar coordinates*) Under the change of variables

$$x = r\cos\theta, \qquad y = r\sin\theta \tag{b}$$

we found, in Example 1, that

$$\nabla^2 f = f_{rr} + \frac{1}{r} f_r + \frac{1}{r^2} f_{\theta\theta}, \tag{c}$$

but the detailed derivations of (9) and (10) were omitted. Here we ask you to provide the missing steps.

(b) (*Rotated Cartesian coordinates*) Let

$$\begin{aligned} x &= (\cos\alpha)x' - (\sin\alpha)y' \\ y &= (\sin\alpha)x' + (\cos\alpha)y'. \end{aligned} \tag{d}$$

This is a linear change of variables which (as discussed in Section 3.7) corresponds to a counterclockwise rotation of the Cartesian x, y axes through an angle α, as shown below. Following the procedure outlined in this section, show that under the change of variables (d) the Laplacian becomes

$$\nabla^2 f = f_{x'x'} + f_{y'y'}. \tag{e}$$

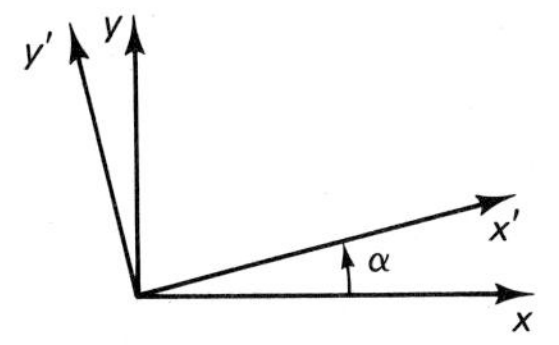

[Comparing equations (a) and (e), we say that $\nabla^2 f$ is *invariant* under rotation of axes.]

(c) Following the procedure outlined in this section, determine $\nabla^2 f$ in terms of u and v, if $x = 2u + v$, $y = u - v$.

*(d) Repeat part (c), for $x = u$, $y = u + v$.

(e) Repeat part (c), for $x = u^2 - v^2$, $y = 2uv$.

(f) Repeat part (c), for $x = e^u \cos v$, $v = e^u \sin v$.

3. (*Extension to three variables*)

(a) If

$$x = X(u, v, w), \qquad y = Y(u, v, w), \qquad z = Z(u, v, w),$$

show that

$$u_x = \frac{Y_v Z_w - Y_w Z_v}{\dfrac{\partial(X, Y, Z)}{\partial(u, v, w)}} \tag{a}$$

provided, of course, that the Jacobian in the denominator is nonzero.

(b) Obtain analogous expressions for v_x and w_x.

(c) Obtain analogous expressions for u_y, v_y, w_y.

(d) Obtain analogous expressions for u_z, v_z, w_z.

4. Apply equation (a) in Exercise 3 in each case, to evaluate u_x.

*(a) $x = u + v + w$
$y = u^2 + v^2 + w^2$
$z = u^3 + v^3 + w^3$

(b) $x = u + 2v$
$y = v - w$
$z = uvw$

(c) $x = u + v$
$y = u - v$
$z = w$

5. (*Spherical coordinates*) The coordinates ρ, ϕ, θ, shown below, are known as **spherical coordinates**,

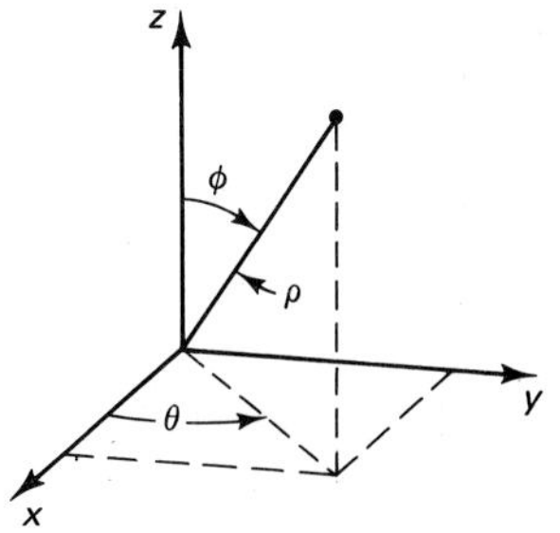

and are related to the Cartesian x, y, z coordinates according to

$$x = \rho\sin\phi\cos\theta, \qquad y = \rho\sin\phi\sin\theta, \qquad z = \rho\cos\phi. \tag{a}$$

(a) Show that the Jacobian of the transformation is

$$\frac{\partial(x, y, z)}{\partial(\rho, \phi, \theta)} = \rho^2 \sin\phi. \tag{b}$$

*(b) Evaluate ρ_x, ϕ_x, θ_x.

(c) Evaluate ρ_y, ϕ_y, θ_y.

(d) Evaluate ρ_z, ϕ_z, θ_z.

6. For the change of variables $x = r\cos\theta$, $y = r\sin\theta$ evaluate $\left.\dfrac{\partial r}{\partial x}\right|_{\theta\text{ fixed}}$, $\left.\dfrac{\partial r}{\partial y}\right|_{\theta\text{ fixed}}$, $\left.\dfrac{\partial r}{\partial x}\right|_{r\text{ fixed}}$, and $\left.\dfrac{\partial r}{\partial y}\right|_{r\text{ fixed}}$. Show that

$$\left.\frac{\partial r}{\partial x}\right|_{\theta\text{ fixed}} = \frac{1}{\left.\dfrac{\partial x}{\partial r}\right|_{\theta\text{ fixed}}} \quad\text{and}\quad \left.\frac{\partial r}{\partial y}\right|_{\theta\text{ fixed}} = \frac{1}{\left.\dfrac{\partial y}{\partial r}\right|_{\theta\text{ fixed}}}.$$

Do these equalities hold only by coincidence? Explain.

7. For the change of variables $x = r\cos\theta$, $y = r\sin\theta$, evaluate $\left.\dfrac{\partial\theta}{\partial x}\right|_{\theta\text{ fixed}}$, $\left.\dfrac{\partial\theta}{\partial y}\right|_{\theta\text{ fixed}}$, $\left.\dfrac{\partial\theta}{\partial x}\right|_{r\text{ fixed}}$, and $\left.\dfrac{\partial\theta}{\partial y}\right|_{r\text{ fixed}}$. Show that

$$\left.\frac{\partial\theta}{\partial x}\right|_{r\text{ fixed}} = \frac{1}{\left.\dfrac{\partial x}{\partial\theta}\right|_{r\text{ fixed}}} \quad\text{and}\quad \left.\frac{\partial\theta}{\partial y}\right|_{r\text{ fixed}} = \frac{1}{\left.\dfrac{\partial y}{\partial\theta}\right|_{r\text{ fixed}}}.$$

Do these two equalities hold only be coincidence? Explain.

8. If the system $f(x, y, u, v) = 0$, $g(x, y, u, v) = 0$ determines $u = u(x, y)$, $v = v(x, y)$ implicitly, show that

$$u_x = -\frac{\dfrac{\partial(f, g)}{\partial(x, v)}}{\dfrac{\partial(f, g)}{\partial(u, v)}}, \qquad v_x = -\frac{\dfrac{\partial(f, g)}{\partial(u, x)}}{\dfrac{\partial(f, g)}{\partial(u, v)}},$$

$$u_y = -\frac{\dfrac{\partial(f, g)}{\partial(y, v)}}{\dfrac{\partial(f, g)}{\partial(u, v)}}, \qquad v_y = -\frac{\dfrac{\partial(f, g)}{\partial(u, y)}}{\dfrac{\partial(f, g)}{\partial(u, v)}},$$

if $\dfrac{\partial(f, g)}{\partial(u, v)} \neq 0$. For the *special case* where $f(x, y, u, v) = x - X(u, v)$, $g(x, y, u, v) = y - Y(u, v)$, show that the expressions above reduce to those given in (20) and (22).

6.8 MAXIMA AND MINIMA

PREREQUISITE: Section 4.7 is recommended, although not essential.

Before examining the case of functions of more than one variable, let us review the situation for functions of a single variable.

We say that $f(x)$ has an **absolute maximum** at x_0, over an x-interval I, if

$$f(x) \leq f(x_0) \tag{1}$$

for all x in I. [Similarly, it has an **absolute minimum** at x_0 if $f(x) \geq f(x_0)$ for all x in I.] In this section, however, we limit our attention to "local" maxima and minima: $f(x)$ has a **local maximum** at an interior point x_0 of I if there is some neighborhood $N(x_0)$ of x_0 such that (1) holds in $N(x_0)$. [Similarly, $f(x)$ has a **local minimum** at an interior point x_0 if there is some neighborhood $N(x_0)$ of x_0 such that $f(x) \geq f(x_0)$ holds for all x in $N(x_0)$]. Observe that a local **extremum** (i.e., a local maximum or a local minimum) *may* also be an absolute extremum, whereas an absolute extremum is necessarily also a local extremum.*

To illustrate, the function f sketched in Fig. 6.15 has a local maximum at R, and local minima at P and S. Observe that the derivative f' does not exist at P due to the "kink."

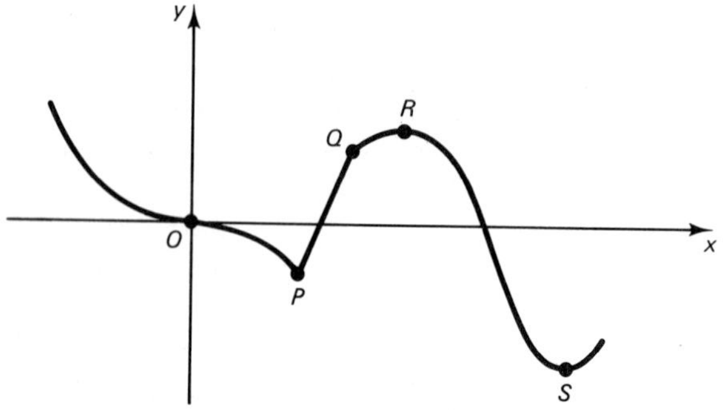

Fig. 6.15 Relative maxima and minima.

* A local extremum is also known as a *relative* extremum.

Theorem 1

For $f(x)$, defined on an interval I, to have a local extremum at an interior point x_0 of I, it is necessary that $f'(x_0)$ either vanish or fail to exist.

That these conditions are not also sufficient is apparent from Fig. 6.15: f' vanishes at the origin and fails to exist at Q, yet these points are neither local maxima nor local minima. One of these two points, the origin, is said to be a **horizontal inflection point**; i.e., $f' = 0$ there, and f increases to one side of the point and decreases to the other. Put another way, x_0 is a horizontal inflection point if $f'(x_0) = 0$ and if every neighborhood of x_0 (no matter how small) contains points x such that $f(x) > f(x_0)$ as well as points x such that $f(x) < f(x_0)$.

Evidently, if $f'(x_0) = 0$, then x_0 may be a local maximum, a local minimum, or a horizontal inflection point,* and it is important to have a test that distinguishes among these cases without having to plot the graph of the function. Along these lines, we have the following theorem.

Theorem 2 *Maximum/Minimum/Horizontal Inflection Point*

Suppose that

$$f'(x_0) = f''(x_0) = \cdots = f^{(n-1)}(x_0) = 0 \quad \text{but} \quad f^{(n)}(x_0) \neq 0,$$

and that $f^{(n)}(x)$ is continuous in some neighborhood of x_0, where $n \geq 2$. If n is even, then x_0 is a local minimum if $f^{(n)}(x_0) > 0$, and is a local maximum if $f^{(n)}(x_0) < 0$. If n is odd, then x_0 is a horizontal inflection point.

Proof Since, by assumption, $f^{(n)}(x)$ is continuous in some neighborhood of x_0, it follows that there is some neighborhood $N(x_0)$ throughout which $f^{(n)}(x)$ has the same sign as $f^{(n)}(x_0)$.† By Taylor's theorem with Lagrange remainder, we may express

$$f(x) = f(x_0) + \frac{f^{(n)}(x_1)}{n!}(x - x_0)^n, \qquad x_1 \text{ in } N(x_0) \tag{2}$$

[since $f'(x_0) = \cdots = f^{(n-1)}(x_0) = 0$] for every x in $N(x_0)$. Or,

$$f(x) - f(x_0) = \frac{f^{(n)}(x_1)}{n!}(x - x_0)^n. \tag{3}$$

Recalling that $f^{(n)}(x_1)$ is of the same sign as $f^{(n)}(x_0)$, for every x in $N(x_0)$, it follows from the form of (3) that the different possibilities are as indicated in Fig. 6.16, as was to be proved. ■

* When we say that "a point is a maximum" (or minimum, or horizontal inflection point) what we mean is that the *function* has a maximum at that point.

† If $F(x)$ is continuous at x_0, then, according to the definition of continuity, to each number $\epsilon > 0$ there corresponds another number $\delta > 0$ such that $|F(x) - F(x_0)| < \epsilon$ whenever $|x - x_0| < \delta$. If we choose ϵ to be $|F(x_0)|$ (or smaller), it follows that there exists a $\delta > 0$ such that $F(x)$ has the same sign as $F(x_0)$ for all x in the neighborhood $|x - x_0| < \delta$.

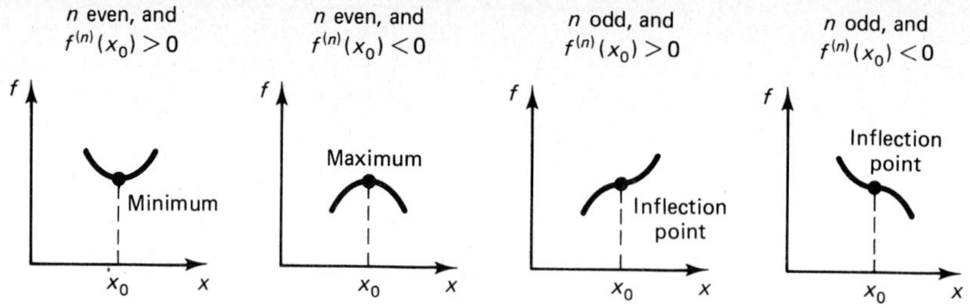

Fig. 6.16 Maximum, minimum, or inflection point?

EXAMPLE 1 Let $f(x) = -(2\sqrt{x} - x - 1)^2$ over $0 < x < \infty$. Then

$$f' = -2\left(\frac{1}{\sqrt{x}} - 1\right)(2\sqrt{x} - x - 1) = \frac{2}{\sqrt{x}}(1 - \sqrt{x})^3, \tag{4}$$

which vanishes at $x = 1$. Differentiating further, at $x = 1$, until we come to a nonvanishing derivative, we find that

$$f'(1) = 0, \qquad f''(1) = 0, \qquad f'''(1) = 0, \qquad f''''(1) = -3/2.$$

Thus $n = 4$ is even, $f''''(1) < 0$, so Theorem 2 tells us that $x = 1$ must be a local maximum. ◀

EXAMPLE 2 Let $f(x) = (x - 1)^2 \ln x$ over $0 < x < \infty$. Again $f'(1) = 0$, but this time $f''(1) = 0$, $f'''(1) = 6$. Thus $n = 3$ is odd, and $x = 1$ must be a horizontal inflection point. ◀

Next we wish to extend these ideas to functions of *two* variables, say $f(x, y)$. While local maxima and minima can occur at points where the $f(x, y)$ surface is "kinky," in the same way that $f(x)$ has a local minimum at the point P in Fig. 6.15, we restrict our attention, in the rest of this section, to the consideration of functions f that are better behaved than that; specifically, we *suppose that f is C^2 throughout some neighborhood of the point in question.*

Evidently, if f is to be a local extremum at a point (x_0, y_0), it must be true that f is *stationary* there, i.e.,

$$df = 0 \tag{5}$$

there. Then, by chain differentiation (which holds due to the assumed continuity of f and its first-order partial derivatives),*

$$df = f_x dx + f_y dy = 0 \tag{6}$$

Now x and y are independent variables, so the increments dx and dy are independent as well. Thus we can ask dx to be zero, and dy to be nonzero, for example; it then

* Expressing the chain rule in *differential* form involves some explaining. Let us merely state that if f and its first-order partials are continuous, the chain rule may be expressed in differential form. Further discussion of this point is contained in the optional material at the end of this section.

follows from (6) that f_y must vanish at (x_0, y_0). Similarly, we can ask dy to be zero and dx to be nonzero, and it then follows from (6) that f_x must vanish at (x_0, y_0). Conversely, if f_x and f_y both vanish at (x_0, y_0), then $df = 0$ there.

Thus f is stationary at (x_0, y_0) if and only if

$$f_x(x_o, y_0) = 0 \tag{7a}$$

$$f_y(x_0, y_0) = 0, \tag{7b}$$

and such a point is said to be a **critical point** of f.

Assuming that we have found a critical point (x_0, y_0), we ask: Is it a local maximum, a local minimum, or whatever? As with functions of one variable, there are precisely three possibilities:

1. $f(x, y)$ has a local **maximum** at (x_0, y_0) if there is some neighborhood N of (x_0, y_0) such that $f(x, y) \leq f(x_0, y_0)$ throughout N.
2. $f(x, y)$ has a local **minimum** at (x_0, y_0) if there is some neighborhood N of (x_0, y_0) such that $f(x, y) \geq f(x_0, y_0)$ throughout N.
3. $f(x, y)$ has a **saddle** at (x_0, y_0) if within each neighborhood N of (x_0, y_0) (no matter how small) there exist (x, y) points such that $f(x, y) > f(x_0, y_0)$, as well as (x, y) points such that $f(x, y) < f(x_0, y_0)$.

In simple examples we can distinguish among these cases by inspection. For example, $f(x, y) = x^2 + y^2$ evidently has a minimum at $(0, 0)$, $g(x, y) = -(x^2 + y^2)$ evidently has a maximum at $(0, 0)$, and $h(x, y) = x^2 - y^2$ evidently has a saddle at $(0, 0)$, as sketched in Fig. 6.17. The saddle is the two-variable analog of the horizontal inflection point. Observe the appropriateness of the name, since the h surface is indeed in the general shape of an equestrian saddle.

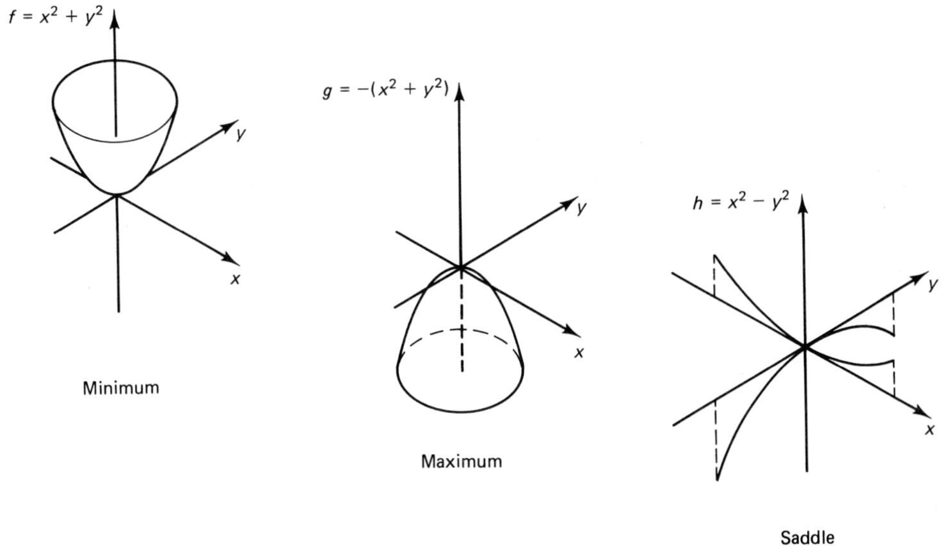

Fig. 6.17 Minimum, maximum, and saddle.

As in the one-variable case, we would like a *test*, such as Theorem 2, that can be applied in a straightforward way, even if the function is unwieldy. We have the following:

Theorem 3 *Maximum/Minimum/Saddle*
Suppose that

$$f_x(x_0, y_0) = f_y(x_0, y_0) = 0, \tag{8}$$

and that f is C^2 throughout some neighborhood of (x_0, y_0). Define

$$D \equiv \begin{vmatrix} f_{xx}(x_0, y_0) & f_{xy}(x_0, y_0) \\ f_{xy}(x_0, y_0) & f_{yy}(x_0, y_0) \end{vmatrix}. \tag{9}$$

(i) If $f_{xx}(x_0, y_0) > 0$ and $D > 0$, then f has a local minimum at (x_0, y_0).
(ii) If $f_{xx}(x_0, y_0) < 0$ and $D > 0$, then f has a local maximum at (x_0, y_0).
(iii) If $D < 0$, then f has a saddle at (x_0, y_0).

Proof Using Taylor's formula (24) on page 233, we have

$$f(x, y) - f(x_0, y_0) = \tfrac{1}{2} f_{xx}(\xi, \eta)(x - x_0)^2 + \tfrac{1}{2} f_{yy}(\xi, \eta)(y - y_0)^2 + f_{xy}(\xi, \eta)(x - x_0)(y - y_0), \tag{10}$$

for some point (ξ, η) on the straight line from (x_0, y_0) to (x, y). Defining

$a_{11} = \frac{1}{2} f_{xx}(\xi, \eta)$, $a_{22} = \frac{1}{2} f_{yy}(\xi, \eta)$, $a_{12} = \frac{1}{2} f_{xy}(\xi, \eta)$, $\bar{x} = x - x_0$, $\bar{y} = y - y_0$,

(10) becomes

$$f(x, y) - f(x_0, y_0) = a_{11}\bar{x}^2 + a_{22}\bar{y}^2 + 2a_{12}\bar{x}\bar{y}. \tag{11}$$

(Note that the a_{ij}'s are not constants, since ξ and η vary with x and y.) The right-hand side of (11) is a *quadratic form* (Section 4.7), so we can reexpress (11) in the canonical form

$$f(x, y) - f(x_0, y_0) = \lambda_1\bar{x}'^2 + \lambda_2\bar{y}'^2, \tag{12}$$

where λ_1, λ_2 are the eigenvalues of the matrix $\mathbf{A} = \begin{pmatrix} a_{11} & a_{12} \\ a_{12} & a_{22} \end{pmatrix}$, both real since $\mathbf{A}$ is symmetric. From the form of (12) we see that if both λ's are positive [for (x, y) in some neighborhood of (x_0, y_0)], then f has a local *minimum* at (x_0, y_0); that if both λ's are negative [for (x, y) in some neighborhood of (x_0, y_0)], then f has a local *maximum* at (x_0, y_0); and that if the λ's are of opposite sign [for (x, y) in some neighborhood of (x_0, y_0)], then f has a *saddle* at (x_0, y_0). We find, easily, that

$$\lambda_{1,2} = \frac{a_{11} + a_{22} \pm \sqrt{(a_{11} + a_{22})^2 - 4(a_{11}a_{22} - a_{12}^2)}}{2}. \tag{13}$$

From (13), it can be seen that both λ's will be positive if $a_{11}a_{22} - a_{12}^2 > 0$ and $a_{11} + a_{22} > 0$ or, equivalently, if $a_{11}a_{22} - a_{12}^2 > 0$, $a_{11} > 0$, and $a_{22} > 0$. (Actually, if $a_{11}a_{22} - a_{12}^2 > 0$ and $a_{11} > 0$, it *follows* that $a_{22} > 0$, so we can omit the "$a_{22} > 0$" part.) In this manner, we find that both λ's will be positive [so that f has a local *minimum* at (x_0, y_0)] if

$$a_{11}a_{22} - a_{12}^2 > 0 \quad \text{and} \quad a_{11} > 0, \tag{14a}$$

that both λ's will be negative [so that f has a local *maximum* at (x_0, y_0)] if

$$a_{11}a_{22} - a_{12}^2 > 0 \quad \text{and} \quad a_{11} < 0, \tag{14b}$$

and that the λ's will be of opposite sign [so that f has a *saddle* at (x_0, y_0)] if

$$a_{11}a_{22} - a_{12}^2 < 0. \tag{14c}$$

Now, since f is C^2, it follows that there is some neighborhood N of (x_0, y_0) throughout which f_{xx}, $f_{xx}f_{yy} - f_{xy}^2$ have the same signs as $f_{xx}(x_0, y_0)$, $f_{xx}(x_0, y_0)f_{yy}(x_0, y_0) - f_{xy}(x_0, y_0)^2$, respectively.* If we restrict (x, y) to be in N, we see from (14), and the definitions of D and of the a_{ij}'s, that if $D > 0$ and $f_{xx}(x_0, y_0) > 0$, then f has a local minimum at (x_0, y_0); that if $D > 0$ and $f_{xx}(x_0, y_0) < 0$, then f has a local maximum at (x_0, y_0); and that if $D < 0$, then f has a saddle at (x_0, y_0), as was to be proved.

In reviewing this proof, note the elegant assistance provided by the theory of quadratic forms. ■

EXAMPLE 3 Let us apply Theorem 3 to the function $f = x^2 + y^2$ shown in Fig. 6.17. Setting

$$f_x = 2x = 0, \qquad f_y = 2y = 0, \tag{15a,b}$$

we see that (15a) is satisfied at all points on the y axis, and that (15b) is satisfied at all points on the x axis. The only point at which both (15a) *and* (15b) are satisfied is the intersection of these two lines, namely, the origin $(0, 0)$. Thus $(x_0, y_0) = (0, 0)$. We find that $f_{xx}(0, 0) = 2$, $f_{yy}(0, 0) = 2$, and $f_{xy}(0, 0) = 0$, so that $D = (2)(2) - 0 > 0$ and $f_{xx}(0, 0) > 0$. Further, f is C^2 in a neighborhood of $(0, 0)$, so that, according to Theorem 3, $(0, 0)$ is a local minimum. This result is in agreement with our earlier conclusion, which was based on inspection. ◀

EXAMPLE 4 As a less obvious example, classify the critical point $(0, 1)$ of the function

$$f(x, y) = \ln [2x(y - 1) + 1]. \tag{16}$$

Differentiating, we find that f is C^2 in a neighborhood of $(0, 1)$, and that $f_{xx}(0, 1) = 0$, $f_{yy}(0, 1) = 0$, and $f_{xy}(0, 1) = 2$, so that $D = (0)(0) - 4 < 0$. Hence $(0, 1)$ is a saddle. ◀

EXAMPLE 5 Consider

$$f(x, y) = x^3y - xy^3. \tag{17}$$

Then

$$f_x = 3x^2y - y^3 = 0, \qquad f_y = x^3 - 3xy^2 = 0,$$

*Verification of this claim follows essentially the same lines as the footnote on page 253 (for the *one*-dimensional case).

and the only x, y pair that satisfies both of these equations is (0, 0). (Why?) Thus we consider the critical point (0, 0). At that point, $f_{xx} = f_{yy} = f_{xy} = 0$. Hence $D = 0$ so Theorem 3 *does not apply*. We speak of (0, 0), in this example, as a *higher-order* critical point.

Of course, higher-order critical points occur for functions of a single variable as well, as in Example 2, where we had both $f'(1) = 0$ and $f''(1) = 0$, and had to look to $f'''(1)$ for clarification. But whereas Theorem 2 covered such extension to higher-order critical points, Theorem 3 does not.

In the present case, inspection happens to suffice. For if we factor f as $xy(x - y)(x + y)$, we can see that f is alternately positive and negative in 45° wedges, as shown in Fig. 6.18. Hence the critical point at the origin must be a saddle. ◀

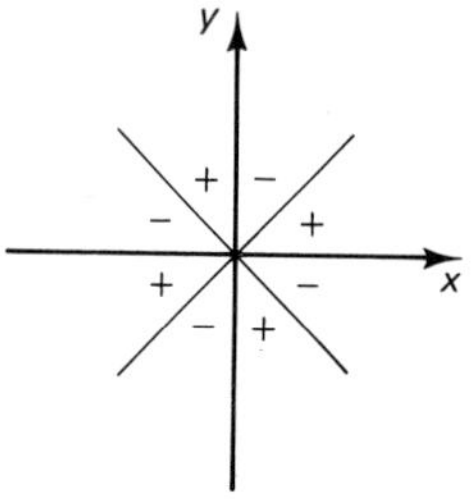

Fig. 6.18 Sign of $f(x, y) = x^3y - xy^3$.

Finally, we extend some of these ideas to the case of functions of two *or more* independent variables. First, we say that $f(x_1, \ldots, x_n)$, or $f(P)$ for brevity, has a local *maximum* at $(x_{1_0}, \ldots, x_{n_0}) \equiv P_0$ if there is some neighborhood $N(P_0)$ such that $f(P) \leq f(P_0)$ throughout $N(P_0)$, and that it has a local *minimum* at P_0 if there is some neighborhood $N(P_0)$ such that $f(P) \geq f(P_0)$ throughout $N(P_0)$. If $f(P)$ is C^1, the condition $df = 0$, to locate points at which f is stationary, yields the necessary and sufficient conditions

$$\boxed{f_{x_1}(P) = 0, \; \ldots, \; f_{x_n}(P) = 0,} \tag{18}$$

as the n-variable version of (7). If $x_{1_0}, \ldots, x_{n_0}$ is a solution of (18), P_0 is called a **critical point** of f. Somewhat in the vein of Theorem 3, for the case $n = 2$, we have the following result.

> ***Theorem 4*** *Maximum/Minimum*
> Suppose that
>
> $$f_{x_1}(P_0) = \cdots = f_{x_n}(P_0) = 0, \tag{19}$$
>
> and that f is C^2 throughout some neighborhood of P_0. Let $\mathbf{A}$ be an $n \times n$ matrix, the i, j element of which is $f_{x_ix_j}(P_0)$. If all the eigenvalues of $\mathbf{A}$ are positive (i.e., if $\mathbf{A}$ is positive definite), then f has a local minimum at P_0; if all of them are negative (i.e., if $\mathbf{A}$ is negative definite), then f has a local maximum at P_0.

Proof Using the n-variable version of Taylor's formula, (27) on page 234, we have

$$f(P) - f(P_0) = \frac{1}{2} \sum_{i=1}^{n} \sum_{j=1}^{n} f_{x_i x_j}(\xi_1, \ldots, \xi_n)(x_i - x_{i_0})(x_j - x_{j_0}), \tag{20}$$

for some point $(\xi_1, \ldots, \xi_n)$ on the straight line from P_0 to P. (Note that $f_{x_i x_j} = f_{x_j x_i}$ since f is C^2.) Since f is C^2, there is some neighborhood $N(P_0)$ throughout which the quadratic form on the right-hand side of (20) has the same sign as the quadratic form

$$\phi = \frac{1}{2} \sum_{i=1}^{n} \sum_{j=1}^{n} f_{x_i x_j}(P_0)(x_i - x_{i_0})(x_j - x_{j_0}). \tag{21}$$

Thus, if ϕ (and hence the matrix $\mathbf{A}$) is positive definite, then $f(P) - f(P_0) \geq 0$ in $N(P_0)$ and f has a local minimum at P_0. Similarly, if ϕ is negative definite, then f has a local maximum there. ■

EXAMPLE 6 Consider

$$f(x, y, z) = \sin(x^2 + y^2 + z^2) + xy + xz + yz. \tag{22}$$

Writing out (18), it is easily found that (0, 0, 0) is a critical point of f (although not the only one; see Exercise 7). Let us apply Theorem 4. Computing, and examining, the various first- and second-order partials of f, we find that f is indeed C^2 in a neighborhood of (0, 0, 0). Further, $f_{xx} = f_{yy} = f_{zz} = 2$ and $f_{xy} = f_{xz} = f_{yz} = 1$ at (0, 0, 0), so that

$$\mathbf{A} = \begin{pmatrix} 2 & 1 & 1 \\ 1 & 2 & 1 \\ 1 & 1 & 2 \end{pmatrix}. \tag{23}$$

The eigenvalues of $\mathbf{A}$ are (from Example 2 on page 140) $\lambda = 1, 1, 4$. Thus $\mathbf{A}$ is positive definite, so f has a local minimum at (0, 0, 0). ◀

One particularly important physical application of the concepts presented in this section involves *equilibrium states and their stability*. Many important force fields (such as gravitational fields) have associated with them a potential energy, i.e., a scalar function $V(x, y, z)$, such that the partials $V_x(x, y, z)$, $V_y(x, y, z)$, $V_z(x, y, z)$ are the x, y, z force components, respectively, experienced at (x, y, z). Thus the critical points of the function V (i.e., points at which $V_x = V_y = V_z = 0$) are the *equilibrium points* of the force field, i.e., points at which there is no force. Further, if V has a local minimum (maximum) at an equilibrium point, the equilibrium at that point is classified as *stable* (*unstable*). Force fields and their potentials are investigated in Chapter 9.

DIFFERENTIALS [Optional]

Our *differential* form of the chain rule, given by the first equality in (6), needs some explanation. To motivate that explanation, consider first the simpler case of a function of a single variable. Remember that $f(x)$ being *differentiable* at x_0 means that

$$f'(x_0) = \lim_{x \to x_0} \frac{f(x) - f(x_0)}{x - x_0} \tag{24}$$

exists or, equivalently, that

$$\lim_{x \to x_0} \frac{f(x) - [f(x_0) + f'(x_0)(x - x_0)]}{x - x_0} = \lim_{x \to x_0} \frac{[f(x) - f(x_0)] - f'(x_0)\, dx}{x - x_0} = 0, \tag{25}$$

where $x - x_0 \equiv dx$. If we write

$$\begin{aligned} f(x) - f(x_0) &\equiv df, \\ f'(x_0)\, dx &\equiv \Delta f \end{aligned} \tag{26}$$

(Fig. 6.19), then (25) states that the tangent line to f at x_0 is a good approximation to f in the neighborhood of x_0—"good" in the sense that the "error" $df - \Delta f$ not only tends to zero as $dx \to 0$, but tends to zero faster than dx [since dx appears in the denominator in (25)]. Thus $df \approx \Delta f = f'\, dx$, so the usual differential statement

$$\boxed{df = f'dx} \tag{27}$$

is a good approximation, good in the sense that the difference between the left- and right-hand sides tends to zero faster than dx.

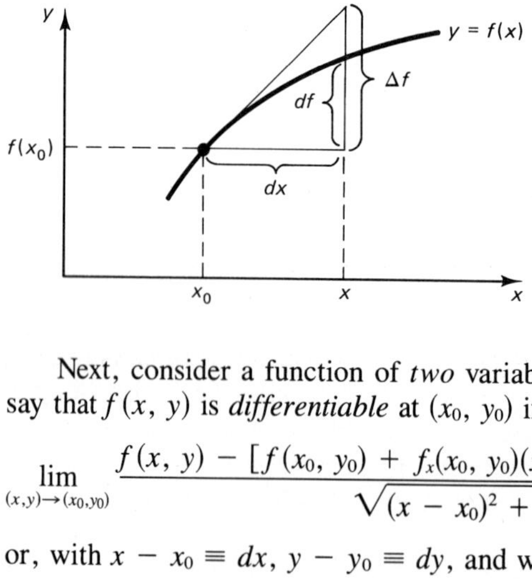

Fig. 6.19 Interpretation of (25).

Next, consider a function of *two* variables, say $f(x, y)$. Analogous to (25), we say that $f(x, y)$ is *differentiable* at (x_0, y_0) if f_x and f_y exist at (x_0, y_0), and

$$\lim_{(x,y) \to (x_0,y_0)} \frac{f(x, y) - [f(x_0, y_0) + f_x(x_0, y_0)(x - x_0) + f_y(x_0, y_0)(y - y_0)]}{\sqrt{(x - x_0)^2 + (y - y_0)^2}} = 0 \tag{28}$$

or, with $x - x_0 \equiv dx$, $y - y_0 \equiv dy$, and with some rearranging,

$$\lim_{(x,y) \to (x_0,y_0)} \frac{[f(x, y) - f(x_0, y_0)] - [f_x(x_0, y_0)\, dx + f_y(x_0, y_0)\, dy]}{\sqrt{(dx)^2 + (dy)^2}} = 0. \tag{29}$$

If we write

$$\begin{aligned} f(x, y) - f(x_0, y_0) &\equiv df, \\ f_x(x_0, y_0)\, dx + f_y(x_0, y_0)\, dy &\equiv \Delta f, \end{aligned} \tag{30}$$

then (29) states that the "error" $df - \Delta f$ not only tends to zero as the distance $\sqrt{(dx)^2 + (dy)^2} \equiv d(P, P_0)$ tends to zero, but tends to zero faster than $d(P, P_0)$. Thus $df \approx \Delta f = f_x\, dx + f_y\, dy$, so

$$\boxed{df = f_x\,dx + f_y\,dy} \tag{31}$$

is a *good approximation*—good in the sense that the difference between the left- and right-hand sides tends to zero faster than $d(P, P_0)$.

We have defined "differentiability" for a function $f(x, y)$, but have not, thus far, given any conditions on $f(x, y)$ that will guarantee its differentiability. In this connection, observe that the existence of f_x and f_y at (x_0, y_0) does *not*, in itself, imply that f is differentiable there! For example, let

$$f(x, y) = \begin{cases} x & \text{for } y = 0 \\ 0 & \text{for } y \neq 0, \end{cases} \tag{32}$$

and take $(x_0, y_0) = (0, 0)$. Then $f_x(0, 0) = 1$, $f_y(0, 0) = 0$ (Do you agree? Sketch f.). So the left-hand side of (28) becomes

$$\text{LHS} = \lim_{(x,y)\to(0,0)} \frac{f(x, y) - (0 + x + 0)}{\sqrt{x^2 + y^2}}. \tag{33}$$

If we approach (0, 0) along the ray $y = x$, say, then the fraction in (33) is $(0 - x)/\sqrt{2}x = -1/\sqrt{2} \neq 0$. Thus (28) fails to hold, so f is not differentiable at (0, 0).

We state, without proof, that if f_x and f_y are *continuous* in some neighborhood of (x_0, y_0), then f will be differentiable there,from which the truth of (31) then follows.* The importance of the continuity of the partials should be no surprise, since, after all, (31) is essentially the chain rule, and continuity of the partials is called for in the chain rule (Theorem 1, page 222). Looking back at (32)—sure enough—f_x and f_y are *not* both continuous in some neighborhood of (0, 0); for example, $f_x = 1$ all along the x axis, and $f_x = 0$ everywhere else in the plane.

Extension to functions of more than two variables should be evident and, in any case, can be found in MARSDEN AND TROMBA.

6.8 EXERCISES

1. Find all critical points of these functions, i.e., points x_0 such that $f'(x_0) = 0$, and classify them as local maxima, local minima, or horizontal inflection points, by applying Theorem 2.

*(a) e^{-x^3}, $-\infty < x < \infty$

(b) $\dfrac{1}{x^2 - 4x + 5}$, $-\infty < x < \infty$

(c) $e^{4x - x^3}$, $-\infty < x < \infty$

(d) $-(\ln x)^3$, $0 < x < \infty$

*(e) $(\ln x)^2$, $0 < x < \infty$

(f) $e^{-\sin x}$, $-1 < x < 5$

(g) $x^2 e^{-x}$, $-\infty < x < \infty$

(h) $4\sqrt{x} - x^2$, $0 < x < \infty$

2. Find all critical points of the following functions $f(x, y)$ defined over the whole x, y plane, and determine whether they are maxima, minima, or saddles. If possible, use Theorem 3.

*(a) $4xy$
(b) $x(2x - y)$
(c) $e^{-(x^2 + y^2 + 1)}$
(d) $y \cos x$
(e) $e^{x^2 - y^2}$
*(f) $\dfrac{1}{x^2 - 2x + y^2 + 4y + 6}$
(g) $x^3 y$
(h) $x^3 - xy + x^5$
(i) $\ln(x^2 + y^2 + 1)$
(j) $x \sin y$
(k) $e^{x^4 - 2y^4}$
(l) $x^2 + 2x + 2xy - 2y - 3$
*(m) $x^2 y^2$
(n) $y^2 \cos x$
(o) $2xy + x^8$

* For proof, and a more complete discussion, see MARSDEN AND TROMBA, Th. 9, p. 98.

3. Determine all critical points of f, and apply Theorem 4. If Theorem 4 does not apply, or yields no information, state that.

*(a) $f(x, y, z) = x^2 + 3xy + z^2$
(b) $f(x, y, z) = e^{-[x^2 + y^2 + (z-1)^2]}$
(c) $f(x, y, z) = x^2 + y^2 + z^2 + xy + xz + yz$
*(d) $f(x, y, z) = \ln(x^2 + y^2 + z^2 + 1)$
(e) $f(w, x, y, z) = e^{w^2 + 2x^2 - y^2 + z^2}$
(f) $f(w, x, y, z) = 7 - 4(w^2 + x^2 + y^2 + z^2) + 4wx + 2wz$

4. Show that $f(x, y, z) = 1 + x^2 + 5y^2 + 2(z-1)^2 + 2\sin[x(z-1)]$ has a local minimum at $(0, 0, 1)$.

5. Let $f(x, y, z) = (1 + x^2 + y^2)^5 + \alpha \sin(xy) + 6z^2(1 - z)$. For what values of α, if any, will f have a local minimum at $(0, 0, 0)$?

6. (*Use of Routh–Hurwitz criterion*) In applying Theorem 4 we need to know if all the eigenvalues of $\mathbf{A}$ are positive, or if all the eigenvalues of $\mathbf{A}$ are negative. (If neither case is obtained, the theorem gives no information.) Since only the *signs* of the λ's are of interest, we may avoid the unnecessary labor of actually determining the λ's by applying the Routh–Hurwitz criterion given on page 91. Application of that criterion tells us whether or not all of the λ's are negative. (Recall that they must be real since $\mathbf{A}$ is symmetric.) If they are not all negative, check to see if they are all positive. That may be done, using the Routh–Hurwitz criterion, by setting $\lambda = -\Lambda$ in the characteristic equation and asking if all of the Λ's are negative. We now state the problem: Each of the following functions is rigged so as to have a critical point at the origin. Applying Theorem 4 and the Routh–Hurwitz criterion, determine if the origin is a local minimum or a local maximum. If the theorem gives no information, state that.

*(a) $f(x, y, z) = 4x^2 + 3y^2 + 5z^2 - 20xy + xz$
*(b) $f(x, y, z) = 4x^2 + 3y^2 + 5z^2 - xy + xz$
(c) $f(w, x, y, z) = 7 - 2(w^2 + x^2 + y^2 + z^2) + w(2x + y - z) + yz$
(d) $f(x, y, z) = \dfrac{(1 - x^2 - y^2 - z^2)^6 + 3\sin(xy)}{1 + 2(xy + xz - yz)}$
(e) $f(x, y, z) = \dfrac{10 + 4x(y + z) + 2yz}{x^2 + y^2 + z^2 + 2}$
(f) $f(x, y, z) = [3 + xy + yz - \sin(xz)]e^{-(x^2 + y^2 + 4z^2)}$

7. In Example 6 we considered the critical point at $(0, 0, 0)$. Show that f has infinitely many other critical points as well. Find them, and show that they comprise an infinite set of circles in 3-space. *Hint:* In seeking nontrivial solutions to

$$2cx + y + z = 0$$

$$x + 2cy + z = 0$$

$$x + y + 2cz = 0$$

where c is short for $\cos(x^2 + y^2 + z^2)$, set the determinant

$$\begin{vmatrix} 2c & 1 & 1 \\ 1 & 2c & 1 \\ 1 & 1 & 2c \end{vmatrix}$$

equal to zero.

*8. Recalling that $f(P)$ has a local minimum at P_0 if $f(P)$ is greater than *or equal to* $f(P_0)$ in some neighborhood of P_0, one might expect Theorem 4 to read ". . . eigenvalues of $\mathbf{A}$ are nonnegative" for a local minimum, and ". . . nonpositive" for a local maximum. Can you explain why such rewording would be incorrect? (A counterexample will suffice.)

9. (*Linear least-squares fit*) Suppose that the values $f(x_1) = f_1, f(x_2) = f_2, \ldots, f(x_N) = f_N$ are known; e.g., they may be experimental datum points. And suppose that we wish to find the best linear fit $f(x) \approx ax + b \equiv F(x)$ to these data—best in the sense that the total squared error E is minimized:

$$E(a, b) = \sum_{j=1}^{N} [F(x_j) - f_j]^2 = \text{minimum}. \qquad \text{(a)}$$

It may be assumed that $x_1, \ldots, x_N$ are distinct points.

(a) Derive the results

$$a = \frac{N \Sigma x_j f_j - (\Sigma f_j)(\Sigma x_j)}{N \Sigma x_j^2 - (\Sigma x_j)^2}, \qquad \text{(b)}$$

$$b = \frac{(\Sigma x_j^2)(\Sigma f_j) - (\Sigma x_j)(\Sigma x_j f_j)}{N \Sigma x_j^2 - (\Sigma x_j)^2}, \qquad \text{(c)}$$

where Σ denotes $\Sigma_{j=1}^{N}$.
(b) Verify that (b) and (c) give a local *minimum* of $E(a, b)$ and, also, that the denominators in (b) and (c) cannot vanish. *Hint:* The Schwarz inequality $|\mathbf{u} \cdot \mathbf{v}| \le \|\mathbf{u}\| \, \|\mathbf{v}\|$, where $\mathbf{u} = (u_1, \ldots, u_N)$, $\mathbf{v} = (v_1, \ldots, v_N)$ should be useful if $\mathbf{u}$ and $\mathbf{v}$ are suitably chosen.
(c) Show that the local minimum of $E(a, b)$ is, in fact, an *absolute* minimum.

Optional Section

The focus of Section 6.8 was the consideration of points $(x_1, \ldots, x_n)$ such that

$$f(x_1, \ldots, x_n) = \text{max} \quad \text{or} \quad f(x_1, \ldots, x_n) = \text{min}, \tag{1}$$

where "max" and "min" are short for local maximum and local minimum. Such points were called critical points and were found as solutions of the equations

$$\frac{\partial f}{\partial x_1} = 0, \quad \frac{\partial f}{\partial x_2} = 0, \quad \ldots, \quad \frac{\partial f}{\partial x_n} = 0. \tag{2}$$

For the cases of one or two variables ($n = 1$ or 2), Theorems 2 and 3 provided information as to whether a given critical point was a maximum, a minimum, or neither—namely, a horizontal inflection point (for $n = 1$) or a saddle (for $n = 2$).

In this section, however, we consider problems of **constrained** maxima and minima, such as

$$f(x_1, \ldots, x_n) = \text{extremum (maximum or minimum)} \tag{3a}$$

$$g(x_1, \ldots, x_n) = c; \tag{3b}$$

i.e., where a given function f is to be extremized (maximized or minimized) *subject to the constraint* that some other function g is to be held fixed. [In some cases there may be more than one constraint, say, $g_1(x_1, \ldots, x_n) = c_1$ and $g_2(x_1, \ldots, x_n) = c_2$.]

We assume that f and g are C^1 in the $x_1, \ldots, x_n$ region under consideration. Further, we assume that the constraint equation $g(x_1, \ldots, x_n) = c$ can be solved for one of the variables, say x_j, in terms of the others, throughout some neighborhood of the desired extremum; this will be true if

$$\frac{\partial g}{\partial x_j} \neq 0 \tag{4}$$

at the extremum. (Recall the implicit function theorem on page 237.)

For definiteness, let there be three variables ($n = 3$), and consider the case

$$f(x, y, z) = \text{extremum}, \tag{5a}$$

$$g(x, y, z) = c. \tag{5b}$$

Suppose that $\partial g/\partial z \neq 0$ at the extremum, so that (5b) can (at least in principle) be solved for z as a function of x and y, to yield

$$z = Z(x, y). \tag{6}$$

If we substitute (6) into (5a), we have

$$f(x, y, Z(x, y)) \equiv F(x, y) = \text{extremum}. \tag{7}$$

(Thus, for reference purposes, we will refer to this method as the *method of elimination*.)

Now, although it is true that x, y, z are *not* independent variables, for they are related through (5b), the variables x and y, by themselves, *are* independent.* Consequently, (7) is an *unconstrained*, or *free extremum* problem, so equation (2) applies:

$$\frac{\partial F}{\partial x} = 0, \qquad \frac{\partial F}{\partial y} = 0. \tag{8a,b}$$

Then (8a), (8b), and (5b) are three equations in the three unknowns x, y, z.

What if $\partial g/\partial z$ *does* vanish at the extremum? If $\partial g/\partial y \neq 0$, instead, we can solve (5b) for $y = Y(x, z)$, and proceed essentially as before. Similarly, if $\partial g/\partial z$ and $\partial g/\partial y$ *both* vanish at the extremum but $\partial g/\partial x$ does *not*, we can solve (5b) for $x = X(y, z)$, and proceed as before. The method fails only in the event that $\partial g/\partial x$, $\partial g/\partial y$, and $\partial g/\partial z$ *all* vanish at the extremum.

EXAMPLE 1 Suppose that we wish to construct a tin can in the shape of a rectangular prism. Let the base be x by y, and let the height be z, such that the volume xyz is a prescribed value V. The base is to be twice as thick as the other five sides, so its cost per unit area is 2α, where α is the cost per unit area of the other sides. Seeking to minimize the material cost, we have the problem

$$\text{Material cost: } f(x, y, z) = \alpha(3xy + 2xz + 2yz) = \min, \tag{9a}$$

subject to the constraint

$$\text{Volume: } xyz = V. \tag{9b}$$

Solving the constraint (9b) for z, $z = V/xy$ [provided that xy is nonzero at the minimum, but that is certainly the case since (9b) cannot be satisfied if $xy = 0$]. Putting the expression $z = V/xy$ into (9a), there follows

$$f(x, y, z) = \alpha(3xy + 2xz + 2yz) = \alpha\left(3xy + \frac{2V}{y} + \frac{2V}{x}\right) \equiv F(x, y) = \min, \tag{10}$$

so we set

$$\frac{\partial F}{\partial x} = \alpha\left(3y - \frac{2V}{x^2}\right) = 0, \qquad \frac{\partial F}{\partial y} = \alpha\left(3x - \frac{2V}{y^2}\right). \tag{11a,b}$$

Solving (11) for x and y, then solving (9b) for z, we obtain

$$x = y = (\tfrac{2}{3}V)^{1/3}, \qquad z = \tfrac{3}{2}(\tfrac{2}{3}V)^{1/3}. \tag{12}$$

Presumably, (12) does provide a minimum, as desired—not a maximum or a saddle. To be certain, apply Theorem 3 on page 256 to $F(x, y)$:

$$D = F_{xy}^2 - F_{xx}F_{yy} = -27\alpha^2 < 0, \qquad F_{xx} = 6\alpha > 0,$$

at $x = y = (2V/3)^{1/3}$, so that, according to Theorem 3, (12) does correspond to a minimum, as desired.

COMMENT Does (12) *look* right? Surely, if the bottom of the prism were of the same thickness as the other sides, the optimum shape would be a cube. But since the bottom is twice as thick, and hence twice as costly, it seems reasonable to ex-

* That is, we can assign values to x and y independently; z, however, must then follow suit according to the constraint (5b).

pect that the base dimensions should be diminished and the height z increased. Sure enough, (12) says that z is somewhat greater than the base dimensions. ◀

In Example 1, solving the constraint equation for one of the variables in terms of the others was simple. In other problems, this step may not be simple; for example, try solving the equation $(y - 2x)e^y - \sin x = 1$ for y in terms of x or, for that matter, for x in terms of y. Thus it would be nice if we could alter our procedure so as to avoid the necessity of solving the constraint equation for one of the variables. In fact, we can do that.

To illustrate, consider again the problem

$$f(x, y, z) = \text{extremum}, \tag{13a}$$

$$g(x, y, z) = c, \tag{13b}$$

where we assume that $\partial g/\partial z \neq 0$ at the extremum so that (13b) is solvable, in *principle,* for z as a function of x and y, in the neighborhood of the extremum.* Taking differentials of f and g yields

$$df = f_x\, dx + f_y\, dy + f_z\, dz = 0, \tag{14a}$$

$$dg = g_x\, dx + g_y\, dy + g_z\, dz = 0; \tag{14b}$$

$df = 0$ because f is stationary at an extremum, and $dg = 0$ because g equals a constant. Now, since $g_z \neq 0$ at the extremum, we can divide (14b) by g_z and solve for dz:

$$dz = -\frac{g_x}{g_z}\, dx - \frac{g_y}{g_z}\, dy. \tag{15}$$

Putting (15) into (14a), the latter becomes

$$\left(f_x - f_z \frac{g_x}{g_z}\right) dx + \left(f_y - f_z \frac{g_y}{g_z}\right) dy = 0. \tag{16}$$

And since dx and dy are independent increments (because x and y, by themselves, are independent variables) it follows from (16) that

$$f_x - f_z \frac{g_x}{g_z} = 0, \qquad f_y - f_z \frac{g_y}{g_z} = 0; \tag{17a,b}$$

for if we choose $dx \neq 0$ and $dy = 0$, then (16) yields (17a), and if we choose $dx = 0$ and $dy \neq 0$, then (16) yields (17b). Finally, the equations (17a), (17b), and (13b) constitute three equations in the three unknowns x, y, z. The key point is that (14b) is *easily* solved for dz, even though it might have been unfeasible to solve (13b) for z.

EXAMPLE 2 Let us apply this method to the problem contained in Example 1. We have

$$df = \alpha(3y + 2z)\, dx + \alpha(3x + 2z)\, dy + \alpha(2x + 2y)\, dz = 0, \tag{18a}$$

$$dg = yz\, dx + xz\, dy + xy\, dz = 0. \tag{18b}$$

* If $\partial g/\partial z$ does vanish there, we can still get by if either $\partial g/\partial y \neq 0$ there, or if $\partial g/\partial x \neq 0$ there, as discussed above.

Then (18b) gives

$$dz = -\frac{z}{x}\,dx - \frac{z}{y}\,dy,$$

and putting this expression into (18*a*), we obtain

$$df = \left[\alpha(3y + 2z) - \frac{z}{x}\right] dx + \left[\alpha(3x + 2z) - \frac{z}{y}\right] dy = 0.$$

Thus we have the equations

$$\alpha(3y + 2z) - \frac{z}{x} = 0, \qquad \alpha(3x + 2z) - \frac{z}{y} = 0, \qquad xyz = V. \qquad \text{(19a,b,c)}$$

Solving,we obtain $x = y = (2V/3)^{1/3}$, $z = \frac{3}{2}(2V/3)^{1/3}$, as before.

COMMENT Admittedly, it can be argued that to solve (19) we *still* need to face up to the constraint equation (19c). But now this facing up occurs in the *final* step, and (19) can, if necessary, be solved on a computer, by Newton's method, or by some other iterative scheme. ◀

There exists an elegant variation of the foregoing method of solving extremum problems such as (13). Due to Lagrange, it is known as the method of **Lagrange multipliers.** To explain the method we again consider the problem (13), for definiteness.

At an extremum, $df = 0$ since f is necessarily stationary there. Similarly, $dg = 0$, because g is a constant. Thus (if f and g satisfy the conditions assumed in this section),

$$df = f_x\,dx + f_y\,dy + f_z\,dz = 0 \qquad \text{(20a)}$$

$$dg = g_x\,dx + g_y\,dy + g_z\,dz = 0, \qquad \text{(20b)}$$

from which it follows that

$$df - \lambda\,dg = (f_x - \lambda g_x)\,dx + (f_y - \lambda g_y)\,dy + (f_z - \lambda g_z)\,dz = 0, \qquad \text{(21)}$$

where λ is a yet-to-be-determined constant, the so-called *Lagrange multiplier*. It is to be appreciated that (21) holds *at* the extremum, so that the coefficients of dx, dy, and dz are *numbers*. If $g_z \neq 0$ at the extremum we may choose λ such that $f_z - \lambda g_z = 0$ in (21). Now, dx and dy, by themselves, are independent increments, so the resulting equation,

$$(f_x - \lambda g_x)\,dx + (f_y - \lambda g_y)\,dy = 0, \qquad \text{(22)}$$

implies that $f_x - \lambda g_x = 0$ and $f_y - \lambda g_y = 0$, too. Consequently, we have the four equations

$$f_x - \lambda g_x = 0, \qquad f_y - \lambda g_y = 0, \qquad f_z - \lambda g_z = 0, \qquad \text{(23a)}$$

and

$$g = c, \qquad \text{(23b)}$$

in the four unknowns x, y, z, λ. In other words, the Lagrange procedure is as follows: *Given (13), form a new function*

$$f^* = f - \lambda g \tag{24}$$

*(or $f + \lambda g$; it will not matter) and extremize f^* subject to **no** constraints*. Thus set $f_x^* = 0$, $f_y^* = 0$, $f_z^* = 0$; that step amounts to (23a). To these three equations in the four unknowns x, y, z, λ we must adjoin the constraint equation $g(x, y, z) = c$ to complete our system of four equations in the four unknowns.

EXAMPLE 3 Consider, once more, the problem in Example 1, namely,

$$f(x, y, z) = \alpha(3xy + 2xz + 2yz) = \text{min}, \tag{25a}$$

$$g(x, y, z) = xyz = V. \tag{25b}$$

Defining $f^* = f - \lambda g$, we set

$$f_x^* = f_x - \lambda g_x = \alpha(3y + 2z) - \lambda yz = 0, \tag{26a}$$

$$f_y^* = f_y - \lambda g_y = \alpha(3x + 2z) - \lambda xz = 0, \tag{26b}$$

$$f_z^* = f_z - \lambda g_z = \alpha(2x + 2y) - \lambda xy = 0. \tag{26c}$$

Solving the four equations (25b) and (26a) to (26c) yields $x = y = (2V/3)^{1/3}$, $z = \frac{3}{2}(2V/3)^{1/3}$, as before. ◀

Naturally, the number of independent variables need not be three. Furthermore, there may be more than one constraint imposed. More generally than (13), then, consider the extremization problem

$$\begin{aligned} f(x_1, \dots, x_n) &= \text{extremum}, \\ g_1(x_1, \dots, x_n) &= c_1, \\ &\vdots \\ g_m(x_1, \dots, x_n) &= c_m. \end{aligned} \tag{27}$$

According to Lagrange's method, we define

$$f^* = f - \lambda_1 g_1 - \cdots - \lambda_m g_m; \tag{28}$$

i.e., there are m Lagrange multipliers (namely, $\lambda_1, \dots, \lambda_m$). Setting $f_{x_1}^* = \cdots = f_{x_n}^* = 0$ gives n equations in the $n + m$ unknowns $x_1, \dots, x_n, \lambda_1, \dots, \lambda_m$. Appending the constraint equations $g_1 = c_1, \dots, g_m = c_m$, brings the total to $m + n$ equations in the $m + n$ unknowns.

6.9 EXERCISES

1. *(a) Find the point(s) on the line $x + 2y = 2$ that is closest to the origin, by the method of elimination, and also by the Lagrange method. Verify, analytically, that your result is indeed a minimum. *Hint:* Minimize $f(x, y) = x^2 + y^2$ subject to the constraint $g(x, y) = x + 2y = 2$.

(b) Repeat part (a), but for the curve $x = y^2 - 2$.

2. (a) Suppose that we wish to design a cylindrical soup can, out of sheet metal having a cost of α cents per unit area, with a prescribed volume V, so as to minimize the material cost. Letting x be the radius and

y be the height, we have the optimization problem

$$\text{material cost: } f(x, y) = \alpha(2\pi x^2 + 2\pi xy) = \min, \quad \text{(a)}$$

subject to the constraint

$$\text{volume: } \pi x^2 y = V. \quad \text{(b)}$$

Solve (a) by the method of elimination and also by the Lagrange method, and show that $x = (V/2\pi)^{1/3}$, $y = 2(V/2\pi)^{1/3}$. Verify that this solution does indeed give a minimum.
(b) Notice, from the solution to part (a), that the resulting soup can has a height that is equal to its diameter, whereas actual soup cans are a bit taller than that. Perhaps the catch is that our Soup King would not only minimize the cost, for a given volume, but would also like a height-to-diameter ratio that makes the can *look* as large as possible. Suppose the proportions that make the can look as large as possible are defined by $y = kx$, where the constant k can be considered to be known, say, empirically. Then the optimization problem (a) and (b) may be restated as

$$a[\alpha(2\pi x^2 + 2\pi xy)] + (1 - a)(y - kx)^2 = \min, \quad \text{(c)}$$

$$\pi x^2 y = V, \quad \text{(d)}$$

where $0 \le a \le 1$. For example, if we care only about minimizing the cost, we set $a = 1$; if we care only about making the volume look as large as possible, we set $a = 0$; if we care equally about these considerations, we set $a = 0.5$; and so on. [You need not solve (c) and (d).] Why was it important to square the $y - kx$ term in (c)? Why did we *not* need to square the square-bracketed material cost term in (c)?

3. Find the point(s) on the following curves that are closest to the origin, and those that are farthest from the origin.

(a) $x^2 + 2y^2 + xy = 1$ (b) $x^2 + y^2 + x = 1$
*(c) $x^2 + y^2 - 4x + 2y = 2$

4. Find the point (x, y), on the given line, which is closest to the point $(1, -2)$.

*(a) $2x + y = 4$ (b) $x + y = -5$
(c) $x - 3y = 2$

5. Find the point (x, y, z), on the given plane, which is closest to the point $(2, 0, -1)$.

*(a) $x + y + z = 4$ (b) $x - y + 2z = 4$
(c) $2x - y + z = 3$

6. Find the point on the curve $y = x^{3/2}$ which is closest to the point $(1, 0)$.

7. Find the points at which $f = x + z$ is maximized and minimized, respectively, subject to the constraint $x^2 + y^2 + z^2 = 1$. Interpret the situation geometrically.

8. (*Fermat's principle*) (a) Let there be a light source at a given point A (shown in the figure) in a medium in which the speed of light is v_1. Of the rays emitted from A, we are interested in the one that arrives at a given point B in a second medium, in which the speed of light is v_2, the interface between the two media being the plane P. Fermat's fundamental principle of optics* states that of all possible paths (such as those shown as dashed lines), the one actually followed (shown as the solid line) is the one which is such that the travel time T, from A to B, is a minimum. Thus show that

$$T(\alpha\ \beta) = \frac{a}{v_1 \cos\alpha} + \frac{b}{v_2 \cos\beta} = \min \quad \text{(a)}$$

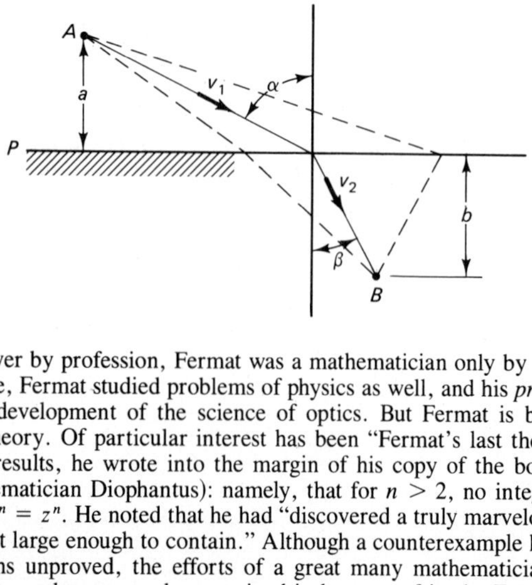

* PIERRE DE FERMAT (1601–1665). A lawyer by profession, Fermat was a mathematician only by avocation. Like most mathematicians of his time, Fermat studied problems of physics as well, and his *principle of least time* was fundamental in the development of the science of optics. But Fermat is best known for his pioneering work in number theory. Of particular interest has been "Fermat's last theorem" (which, along with most of his other results, he wrote into the margin of his copy of the book *Arithmetica*, by the great Alexandrian mathematician Diophantus): namely, that for $n > 2$, no integer solutions x, y, z exist for the equation $x^n + y^n = z^n$. He noted that he had "discovered a truly marvelous proof of this, which however the margin is not large enough to contain." Although a counterexample has never been put forward, the theorem remains unproved, the efforts of a great many mathematicians notwithstanding. Besides these marginal notes, and some results contained in letters to friends, Fermat published but little; thus it was, in 1665, that he perished.

subject to the constraint that

$$a \tan \alpha + b \tan \beta = \text{constant}, \qquad \text{(b)}$$

and hence derive the *law of refraction*

$$\frac{\sin \alpha}{\sin \beta} = \frac{v_1}{v_2}, \qquad \text{(c)}$$

where α is the angle of incidence and β is the angle of refraction.

(b) Besides the incident and transmitted (refracted) rays considered in part (a), there will also be a reflected ray, as shown below. Using the same ideas as in part (a), derive the law of *reflection*

$$\alpha = \gamma,$$

where γ is the angle of reflection.

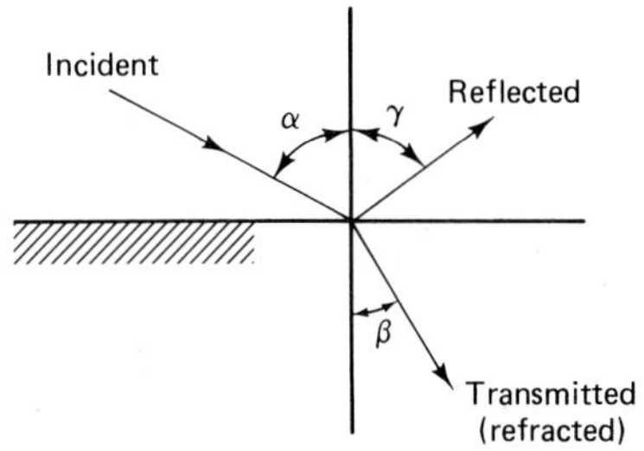

Note: We have tacitly assumed that the paths within each medium are straight. The truth of this assumption can, itself, be deduced from Fermat's principle. We might add that the principle of least time is but one of a number of such fundamental physical principles, such as the principles of *least action* and *least work* in mechanics. These discoveries were even held, by some, to prove the existence of God, inasmuch as they revealed nature to be consistently as economical and simple as possible.

9. Show that the application of the Lagrange method to the problem

$$f = x_1^2 + x_2^2 = \text{extremum}, \qquad \text{(a)}$$

$$g = a_{11}x_1^2 + a_{22}x_2^2 + 2a_{12}x_1x_2 = c \qquad \text{(b)}$$

produces the eigenvalue problem

$$\begin{pmatrix} a_{11} & a_{12} \\ a_{12} & a_{22} \end{pmatrix}\begin{pmatrix} x_1 \\ x_2 \end{pmatrix} = \frac{1}{\lambda}\begin{pmatrix} x_1 \\ x_2 \end{pmatrix}. \qquad \text{(c)}$$

[Thus, observe the correspondence between a given eigenvalue problem (c) and the finding of maximum and minimum distances from the origin of an x_1, x_2 plane to quadric curves $a_{11}x_1^2 + a_{22}x_2^2 + 2a_{12}x_1x_2 =$ constant. As discussed in Section 4.7, $a_{11}x_1^2 + a_{22}x_2^2 + 2a_{12}x_1x_2$ is the quadratic form associated with the **A** matrix in (c).]

10. Solve by the Lagrange method.

(a) $f = x^2 + y^2 + z^2 = \text{extremum}$
$g = x^2 + 4y^2 + 4z^2 = 4$
$h = x + y + z = 0$

(b) $f = x + 2z = \text{extremum}$
$g = x^2 + y^2 + z^2 = 1$
$h = y - z = 0$

11. Show that the coordinates of the point on the plane

$$ax + by + cz = d \qquad \text{(a)}$$

which is closest to the origin are $x = ad$, $y = bd$, $z = cd$, where (a) is scaled so that $a^2 + b^2 + c^2 = 1$, for definiteness. Thus show that the shortest distance from the origin to the plane is the constant d in (a).

12. The constrained extremum problem

$$z = \text{maximum}$$

$$x + y + z = 1$$

$$\frac{z^2}{xy^3} = 3$$

occurs in seeking to maximize the yield in an ammonia reactor [as discussed in B. Noble, *Applications of Undergraduate Mathematics in Engineering* (New York: Macmillan, 1967), p. 75]. Show that the desired maximum of z is $(17 + 4\sqrt{13})/9$.

7 Vectors in 3-Space*

7.1 INTRODUCTION

Having introduced vectors in 3-space, and the dot product $\mathbf{u} \cdot \mathbf{v}$ in Sections 2.2 and 2.3, we continue here with the cross product $\mathbf{u} \times \mathbf{v}$, and the multiple products $\mathbf{u} \cdot (\mathbf{v} \times \mathbf{w})$ and $\mathbf{u} \times (\mathbf{v} \times \mathbf{w})$, both from an intrinsic point of view (i.e., without reference to a coordinate system) and also with respect to a Cartesian reference frame x, y, z with base vectors $\hat{\mathbf{i}}, \hat{\mathbf{j}}, \hat{\mathbf{k}}$. We follow these topics with some vector differential calculus and the fundamentals of curves in 3-space. The vector *integral* calculus is taken up in Chapter 8.

7.2 GEOMETRICAL REPRESENTATION; DOT AND CROSS PRODUCT

It will be assumed here that you have studied Sections 2.2 and 2.3. By way of a brief review, recall that in Section 2.2 we introduced the notion of a vector in terms of a directed magnitude; we defined the magnitude or *norm* $\|\mathbf{u}\|$ of a vector $\mathbf{u}$, the *addition* of vectors $\mathbf{u} + \mathbf{v}$, the *scalar multiplication* $\alpha\mathbf{u}$, the *negative inverse* $-\mathbf{u}$, and the zero vector $\mathbf{0}$. And in Section 2.3 we defined the *dot product* $\mathbf{u} \cdot \mathbf{v}$ between any two vectors $\mathbf{u}$ and $\mathbf{v}$ as

$$\mathbf{u} \cdot \mathbf{v} \equiv \begin{cases} \|\mathbf{u}\|\|\mathbf{v}\| \cos\theta & \text{if } \mathbf{u}, \mathbf{v} \neq \mathbf{0} \quad (1a) \\ 0 & \text{if } \mathbf{u} = \mathbf{0} \text{ or } \mathbf{v} = \mathbf{0}, \quad (1b) \end{cases}$$

* PREREQUISITES: Sections 2.2, 2.3

where θ is the interior angle $(0 \le \theta \le \pi)$ between $\mathbf{u}$ and $\mathbf{v}$ (Fig. 7.1). If $\mathbf{v} = \mathbf{u} \ne \mathbf{0}$, then $\theta = 0$, and (1a) gives $\mathbf{u} \cdot \mathbf{u} = \|\mathbf{u}\|^2$, which result holds even if $\mathbf{u} = \mathbf{v} = \mathbf{0}$. Solving for $\|\mathbf{u}\|$, we obtain the relationship

$$\|\mathbf{u}\| = \sqrt{\mathbf{u} \cdot \mathbf{u}}, \tag{2}$$

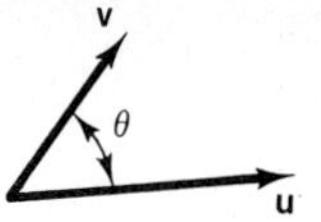

Fig. 7.1 The angle θ in (1).

noted in Section 2.3, between the norm and the dot product. The dot product, defined by (1), admits the following properties:

$$\mathbf{u} \cdot \mathbf{v} = \mathbf{v} \cdot \mathbf{u} \qquad \text{(commutativity)} \tag{3a}$$

$$(\alpha \mathbf{u}) \cdot \mathbf{v} = \alpha (\mathbf{u} \cdot \mathbf{v}) \qquad \text{(associativity)} \tag{3b}$$

$$(\mathbf{u} + \mathbf{v}) \cdot \mathbf{w} = \mathbf{u} \cdot \mathbf{w} + \mathbf{v} \cdot \mathbf{w}, \qquad \text{(distributivity)} \tag{3c}$$

for any vectors $\mathbf{u}$, $\mathbf{v}$, $\mathbf{w}$ and any scalar α.* Of these properties, (3b) and (3c) are equivalent to the single statement that

$$(\alpha \mathbf{u} + \beta \mathbf{v}) \cdot \mathbf{w} = \alpha (\mathbf{u} \cdot \mathbf{w}) + \beta (\mathbf{v} \cdot \mathbf{w}) \qquad \text{(linearity)} \tag{4}$$

for any vectors $\mathbf{u}$, $\mathbf{v}$, $\mathbf{w}$ and any scalars α, β; the property (4) is known as *linearity*.

These properties permit us to manipulate dot products as if by ordinary scalar algebra. For example, just as

$$(2a + b)(4a - 3b) = 8a^2 - 2ab - 3b^2,$$

where a, b are scalars, it is equally true that

$$\begin{aligned}(2\mathbf{u} + \mathbf{v}) \cdot (4\mathbf{u} - 3\mathbf{v}) &= 8\mathbf{u} \cdot \mathbf{u} - 2\mathbf{u} \cdot \mathbf{v} - 3\mathbf{v} \cdot \mathbf{v} \\ &= 8\|\mathbf{u}\|^2 - 2\mathbf{u} \cdot \mathbf{v} - 3\|\mathbf{v}\|^2,\end{aligned}$$

since

$$\begin{aligned}(2\mathbf{u} + \mathbf{v}) \cdot (4\mathbf{u} - 3\mathbf{v}) &= 2\mathbf{u} \cdot (4\mathbf{u} - 3\mathbf{v}) + \mathbf{v} \cdot (4\mathbf{u} - 3\mathbf{v}) && \text{by (4)} \\ &= 2(4\mathbf{u} - 3\mathbf{v}) \cdot \mathbf{u} + (4\mathbf{u} - 3\mathbf{v}) \cdot \mathbf{v} && \text{by (3a)} \\ &= 2(4\mathbf{u} \cdot \mathbf{u} - 3\mathbf{v} \cdot \mathbf{u}) + 4\mathbf{u} \cdot \mathbf{v} - 3\mathbf{v} \cdot \mathbf{v} && \text{by (4)} \\ &= 8\mathbf{u} \cdot \mathbf{u} - 6\mathbf{u} \cdot \mathbf{v} + 4\mathbf{u} \cdot \mathbf{v} - 3\mathbf{v} \cdot \mathbf{v} && \text{by (3a)} \\ &= 8\|\mathbf{u}\|^2 - 2\mathbf{u} \cdot \mathbf{v} - 3\|\mathbf{v}\|^2.\end{aligned}$$

Before leaving the dot product, observe from (1) that if $\mathbf{u}$ and $\mathbf{v}$ are nonzero, and $\theta = \pi/2$, then $\mathbf{u}$ and $\mathbf{v}$ are **perpendicular** to each other, and $\mathbf{u} \cdot \mathbf{v} = 0$. The converse, however, is not true, for if $\mathbf{u} \cdot \mathbf{v} = 0$, then either $\mathbf{u}$ and $\mathbf{v}$ are perpendicular, *or* at least one of $\mathbf{u}$ and $\mathbf{v}$ is zero. Thus we introduce a separate term, "orthogonal": $\mathbf{u}$ and $\mathbf{v}$ are **orthogonal** if $\mathbf{u} \cdot \mathbf{v} = 0$. Perpendicularity implies orthogonality, but only if $\mathbf{u}$ and $\mathbf{v}$ are both nonzero does orthogonality imply perpendicularity.

Further, we say that a *set* of vectors $\{\mathbf{v}_1, \ldots, \mathbf{v}_k\}$ is an **orthogonal set** if every vector in the set is orthogonal to every other vector in the set:

$$\mathbf{v}_i \cdot \mathbf{v}_j = 0 \quad \text{if} \quad i \ne j. \tag{5}$$

* In Part II, all scalars will be *real* numbers.

If, in addition, each $\mathbf{v}_j$ is scaled or "normalized" so as to have unit length, then

$$\mathbf{v}_i \cdot \mathbf{v}_j = \begin{cases} 1, & i = j \\ 0, & i \neq j \end{cases} = \delta_{ij}, \tag{6}$$

since $\mathbf{v}_j \cdot \mathbf{v}_j = \| \mathbf{v}_j \|^2 = 1$, and we say that $\{\mathbf{v}_1, \ldots, \mathbf{v}_k\}$ is an **orthonormal set,** i.e., both orthogonal and normalized. Such sets will be used extensively in subsequent sections.

Besides the dot product, we now introduce another kind of product between two vectors, the **cross product** of **u** and **v**, denoted as $\mathbf{u} \times \mathbf{v}$, and defined as*

$$\mathbf{u} \times \mathbf{v} \equiv \begin{cases} \| \mathbf{u} \| \| \mathbf{v} \| \sin \theta \, \hat{\mathbf{e}} & \text{if } \mathbf{u}, \mathbf{v} \neq \mathbf{0},\ \theta \neq 0, \text{ and } \theta \neq \pi \quad (7a) \\ \mathbf{0} & \text{if } \mathbf{u} = \mathbf{0}, \text{ or } \mathbf{v} = \mathbf{0}, \text{ or } \theta = 0, \text{ or } \theta = \pi, \quad (7b) \end{cases}$$

where θ is again the interior angle between **u** and **v**, and $\hat{\mathbf{e}}$ is a unit vector normal to the plane of **u** and **v**, directed such that the vectors **u**, **v**, $\hat{\mathbf{e}}$ form a *right-handed system;* i.e., curling the other four fingers of our right hand from **u** (the first vector in $\mathbf{u} \times \mathbf{v}$) into **v** (the second vector in $\mathbf{u} \times \mathbf{v}$), our thumb points in the $\hat{\mathbf{e}}$ direction (Fig. 7.2).

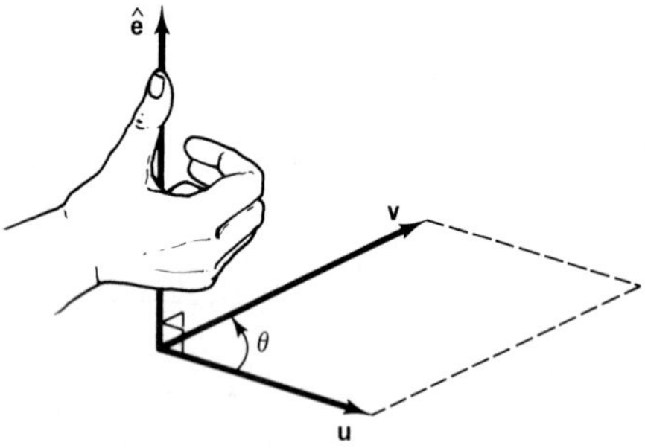

Fig. 7.2 Cross product.

Observe, first, that while the dot product $\mathbf{u} \cdot \mathbf{v}$ is a scalar, the cross product $\mathbf{u} \times \mathbf{v}$ is a vector; for that reason, $\mathbf{u} \cdot \mathbf{v}$ is also called the **scalar product** of **u** and **v**, and $\mathbf{u} \times \mathbf{v}$ is also called the **vector product** of **u** and **v**. (Some authors use the notation "**uv**" in place of our $\mathbf{u} \cdot \mathbf{v}$, and "$\mathbf{u} \wedge \mathbf{v}$" in place of our $\mathbf{u} \times \mathbf{v}$.)

EXAMPLE 1 Let **u**, **v** be as shown in Fig. 7.3: $\| \mathbf{u} \| = 5$, $\| \mathbf{v} \| = 4$, and $\theta = 60°$. Then $\mathbf{u} \times \mathbf{v} = (5)(4)(\sin 60°)\hat{\mathbf{e}} = (10\sqrt{3})\hat{\mathbf{e}}$, as sketched in the figure; $\mathbf{v} \times \mathbf{u}$ is of the same magnitude as $\mathbf{u} \times \mathbf{v}$, but points in the opposite direction. ◀

* You may wonder why we need to spell out, in (7b), that $\mathbf{u} \times \mathbf{v} = \mathbf{0}$ if $\theta = 0$ or $\theta = \pi$ since, after all, (7a) *already* seems to say that $\mathbf{u} \times \mathbf{v} = \| \mathbf{u} \| \| \mathbf{v} \| \sin \theta \, \hat{\mathbf{e}} = 0\hat{\mathbf{e}} = \mathbf{0}$ (since $\sin 0 = 0$ and $\sin \pi = 0$). The catch is that $\hat{\mathbf{e}}$ is *undefined* if $\theta = 0$ or $\theta = \pi$ since then the **u**, **v** vectors fail to define a plane uniquely.

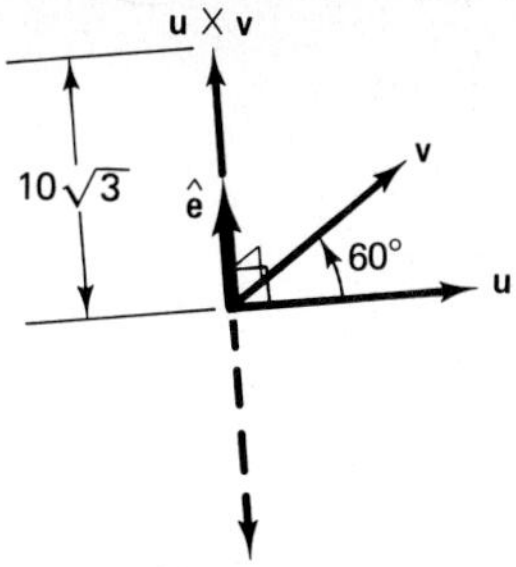

Fig. 7.3 u × v and v × u.

In contrast with the commutativity property of the dot product, namely $\mathbf{u} \cdot \mathbf{v} = \mathbf{v} \cdot \mathbf{u}$, we have $\mathbf{u} \times \mathbf{v} = -(\mathbf{v} \times \mathbf{u})$ for the cross product, since

$$\mathbf{u} \times \mathbf{v} = \| \mathbf{u} \| \| \mathbf{v} \| \sin \theta \hat{\mathbf{e}}_1, \qquad \mathbf{v} \times \mathbf{u} = \| \mathbf{v} \| \| \mathbf{u} \| \sin \theta \hat{\mathbf{e}}_2,$$

where, according to the right-hand rule, $\hat{\mathbf{e}}_2 = -\hat{\mathbf{e}}_1$. The property $\mathbf{u} \times \mathbf{v} = -(\mathbf{v} \times \mathbf{u})$ is known as *anticommutativity* and was illustrated in Fig. 7.3. While commutativity fails to hold, associative and distributive properties do hold:

$$\mathbf{u} \times \mathbf{v} = -(\mathbf{v} \times \mathbf{u}) \qquad (\textit{anti}\text{commutativity}) \tag{8a}$$

$$(\alpha \mathbf{u}) \times \mathbf{v} = \alpha (\mathbf{u} \times \mathbf{v}) \qquad (\text{associativity}) \tag{8b}$$

$$(\mathbf{u} + \mathbf{v}) \times \mathbf{w} = (\mathbf{u} \times \mathbf{w}) + (\mathbf{v} \times \mathbf{w}). \qquad (\text{distributivity}) \tag{8c}$$

[Compare these properties with those given by (3) for the dot product.] Proof of (8b) and (8c) is left for the exercises.

Besides these properties, there is a geometrical significance to be noted. Specifically, the *magnitude* of $\mathbf{u} \times \mathbf{v}$ is equal to the area of the "$\mathbf{u}$, $\mathbf{v}$ parallelogram," as shown in Fig. 7.4 (in which $\mathbf{u}$ and $\mathbf{v}$ lie in the plane of the paper). For the area (shaded) is the altitude $\| \mathbf{v} \| \sin \theta$ times the base $\| \mathbf{u} \|$, as labeled in Fig. 7.4a, or, equivalently, the altitude $\| \mathbf{u} \| \sin \theta$ times the base $\| \mathbf{v} \|$, as labeled in Fig. 7.4b. Let us state this result as an equation, for reference:

$$\boxed{\| \mathbf{u} \times \mathbf{v} \| = \text{area of } \mathbf{u},\, \mathbf{v} \text{ parallelogram.}} \tag{9}$$

We close with a physical application of the cross product.

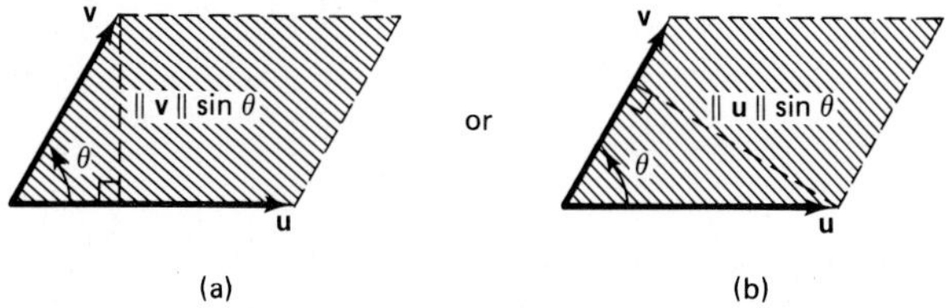

Fig. 7.4 Area significance of ‖ u × v ‖.

EXAMPLE 2 *Moment of a Force*. In mechanics, one defines the *moment* M of a force $\mathbf{F}$, about a point P, as the product $\| \mathbf{F} \| d$, where d is the perpendicular distance from P to the line of action L of $\mathbf{F}$, as shown in Fig. 7.5. Further, the *vector moment* $\mathbf{M}$, of $\mathbf{F}$ about P, is defined as

$$\mathbf{M} \equiv \mathbf{r} \times \mathbf{F}, \tag{10}$$

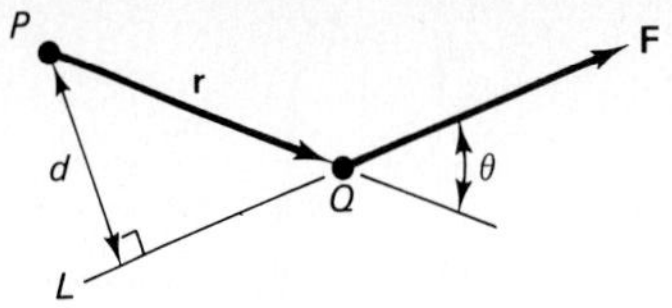

Fig. 7.5 Moment of **F** about P.

where $\mathbf{r} = \mathbf{PQ}$ is a vector from P to the tail of $\mathbf{F}$ (Fig. 7.5). Observe, first, that $\mathbf{M}$ is independent of the position of the point Q on the line of action L. For suppose that Q_1 and Q_2 are any two points on L (Fig. 7.6). Then

$$\begin{aligned} \mathbf{PQ}_1 \times \mathbf{F} - \mathbf{PQ}_2 \times \mathbf{F} &= (\mathbf{PQ}_1 - \mathbf{PQ}_2) \times \mathbf{F} && \text{by (6c),} \\ &= \mathbf{Q}_2\mathbf{Q}_1 \times \mathbf{F} && \text{by Fig. 7.6b,} \\ &= \mathbf{0}, \end{aligned}$$

since the angle between $\mathbf{Q}_2\mathbf{Q}_1$ and $\mathbf{F}$ is either 0 or π. Thus $\mathbf{PQ}_1 \times \mathbf{F} = \mathbf{PQ}_2 \times \mathbf{F}$, as claimed.

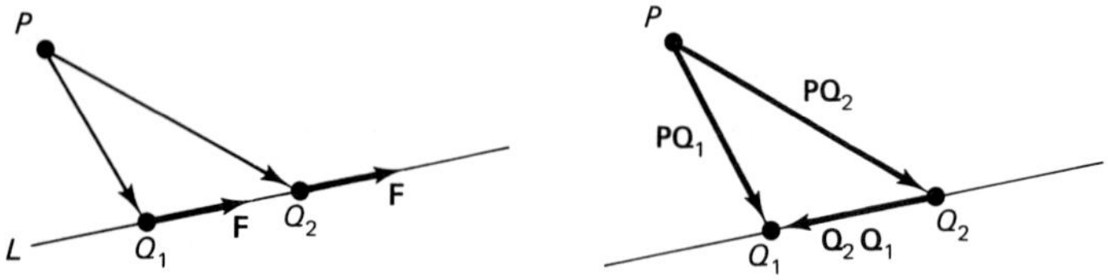

(a) (b) **Fig. 7.6** Location of Q.

Second, observe that the magnitude $\|\mathbf{M}\|$ of $\mathbf{M}$ is the "moment M" defined above, since

$$\mathbf{M} = \mathbf{r} \times \mathbf{F} = \|\mathbf{r}\|\|\mathbf{F}\| \sin\theta\, \hat{\mathbf{e}} = \|\mathbf{F}\|(\|\mathbf{r}\| \sin\theta)\hat{\mathbf{e}} = \|\mathbf{F}\|d\hat{\mathbf{e}},$$

so that $\|\mathbf{M}\| = \|\mathbf{F}\|d = M$. ◀

More about the cross product in subsequent sections.

7.2 EXERCISES

1. If $\mathbf{u} \times \mathbf{v} = 2\mathbf{u}$, what can one conclude about $\mathbf{u}$? Explain.

2. If $\mathbf{u} \times \mathbf{v} = \mathbf{0}$ and $\mathbf{u} \cdot \mathbf{v} = 0$, must $\mathbf{u} = \mathbf{0}$ and/or $\mathbf{v} = \mathbf{0}$? Explain.

3. Use the dot product to derive the *law of cosines*,

$$c^2 = a^2 + b^2 - 2ab \cos\theta, \qquad \text{(a)}$$

where c, a, b, θ are shown in the figure. *Hint:* Regard the sides of the triangle as vectors, oriented such that $\mathbf{c} = \mathbf{a} - \mathbf{b}$, and note that $\mathbf{c} \cdot \mathbf{c} = (\mathbf{a} - \mathbf{b}) \cdot (\mathbf{a} - \mathbf{b})$.

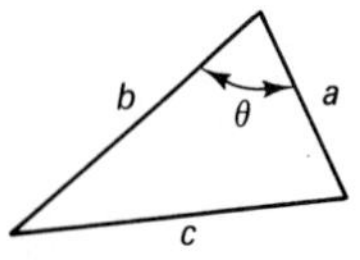

4. Use the cross product to derive the *law of sines*,

$$\frac{a}{\sin\alpha} = \frac{b}{\sin\beta}, \qquad \text{(a)}$$

where a, b, α, β are as shown in part (a) of the accompanying figure. *Hint:* Regard the sides of the tri-

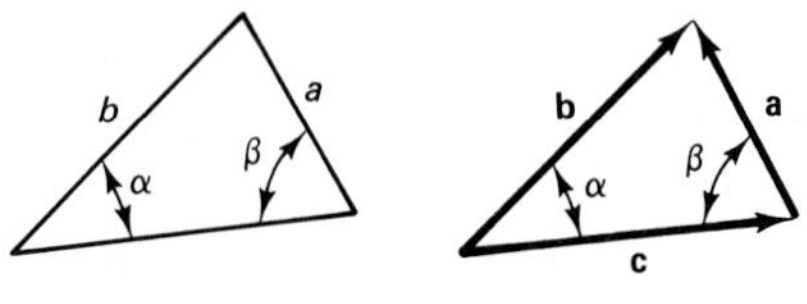

(a) (b)

angle as vectors, as in part (b), and cross a suitable vector into both sides of the equation $\mathbf{b} - \mathbf{c} = \mathbf{a}$.

5. Derive the **Lagrange identity**

$$\|\mathbf{u} \times \mathbf{v}\|^2 = \|\mathbf{u}\|^2\|\mathbf{v}\|^2 - (\mathbf{u} \cdot \mathbf{v})^2. \tag{a}$$

6. Why did we bother to include the parentheses in the right-hand side of (8c) but not in the analogous equation (3c)?

7. If $\mathbf{u} \cdot \mathbf{v} = 0$ and $\mathbf{u} \times \mathbf{v} \equiv \mathbf{w}$, is $\{\mathbf{u}, \mathbf{v}, \mathbf{w}\}$ necessarily an orthogonal set? Explain.

***8.** Is $\mathbf{u} \times (\mathbf{v} \times \mathbf{w})$ necessarily equal to $(\mathbf{u} \times \mathbf{v}) \times \mathbf{w}$? Explain.

9. Prove the associative law (8b). [Proof of the distributive law (8c) is left for the exercises in Section 7.3.]

10. (a) Prove that

$$(\alpha_1\mathbf{u}_1 + \alpha_2\mathbf{u}_2 + \cdots + \alpha_n\mathbf{u}_n) \cdot \mathbf{v} = \alpha_1(\mathbf{u}_1 \cdot \mathbf{v}) + \alpha_2(\mathbf{u}_2 \cdot \mathbf{v}) + \cdots + \alpha_n(\mathbf{u}_n \cdot \mathbf{v}), \tag{a}$$

namely, that (4) holds even if $n > 2$.
(b) Prove that

$$(\alpha_1\mathbf{u}_1 + \alpha_2\mathbf{u}_2 + \cdots + \alpha_n\mathbf{u}_n) \times \mathbf{v} = \alpha_1(\mathbf{u}_1 \times \mathbf{v}) + \alpha_2(\mathbf{u}_2 \times \mathbf{v}) + \cdots + \alpha_n(\mathbf{u}_n \times \mathbf{v}). \tag{b}$$

11. (*Linear dependence*) Prove that vectors $\mathbf{u}$, $\mathbf{v}$ are linearly dependent if and only if $\mathbf{u} \times \mathbf{v} = \mathbf{0}$.

12. Prove that if $\mathbf{u}$ and $\mathbf{v}$ are nonzero vectors, and $\mathbf{u} \times \mathbf{v} = \mathbf{0}$, then $\mathbf{u} = \alpha\mathbf{v}$ for some nonzero constant α.

CARTESIAN COORDINATES 7.3

In Sections 2.2, 2.3, and 7.2 we introduced vectors in 3-space, and defined the norm of a vector, the multiplication of a vector by a scalar, addition and subtraction of vectors, and the dot and cross products of two vectors. These definitions were *intrinsic* inasmuch as they contained no reference whatsoever to any coordinate system.

In applications, however, our computations may often be carried out more conveniently if we introduce a reference coordinate system and a corresponding set of base vectors. (Note the words "we introduce"; coordinate systems are not supplied by nature.) It is to be stressed that our "answers" should be the same whether we select one coordinate system or another, due to the above-mentioned intrinsic nature of the operations involved. Thus the choice of the coordinate system is a matter of convenience.

Although there are many coordinate systems from which to choose, we limit our attention here to those that we regard as the most important: *Cartesian, cylindrical,* and *spherical*. In the present section we consider the Cartesian case.

Beginning with 2-space, for simplicity, we adopt the rectangular Cartesian x, y coordinate system shown in Fig. 7.7, together with the reference vectors $\hat{\mathbf{i}}$, $\hat{\mathbf{j}}$, where

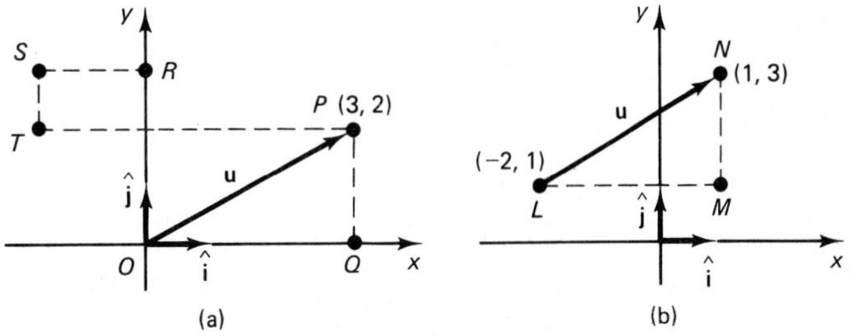

Fig. 7.7 Cartesian x, y system.

$\hat{\mathbf{i}}$ is a unit vector in the positive x direction, and $\hat{\mathbf{j}}$ is a unit vector in the positive y direction. We have placed $\hat{\mathbf{i}}$ and $\hat{\mathbf{j}}$ with their tails at the origin, but one can place them wherever one wishes, as long as their magnitudes and directions are preserved. Observe that $\{\hat{\mathbf{i}}, \hat{\mathbf{j}}\}$ constitutes an orthonormal set, since

$$\hat{\mathbf{i}} \cdot \hat{\mathbf{i}} = \hat{\mathbf{j}} \cdot \hat{\mathbf{j}} = (1)(1) \cos 0 = 1 \quad \text{and} \quad \hat{\mathbf{i}} \cdot \hat{\mathbf{j}} = (1)(1) \cos 90^\circ = 0. \tag{1}$$

Now, consider the vector $\mathbf{u}$ in Fig. 7.7a; whether $\mathbf{u}$ is being used as a *position vector* to locate the point P, namely the point (3, 2) in the x, y plane, or to designate a certain force vector,* or a velocity vector, or whatever, is not important here. We can express $\mathbf{u}$ as a linear combination of $\hat{\mathbf{i}}$ and $\hat{\mathbf{j}}$ as follows:

$$\mathbf{u} = \mathbf{OQ} + \mathbf{QP} = 3\hat{\mathbf{i}} + 2\hat{\mathbf{j}}.$$

The end result, $\mathbf{u} = 3\hat{\mathbf{i}} + 2\hat{\mathbf{j}}$, is independent of the fact that the $\mathbf{u}$ vector happens to spring from the origin; if we move its tail to $(-2, 1)$, say, as in Fig. 7.7b, then

$$\mathbf{u} = \mathbf{LM} + \mathbf{MN} = 3\hat{\mathbf{i}} + 2\hat{\mathbf{j}},$$

which result is the same as above.

More generally, let $\mathbf{u}$ be a vector from the origin to *any* point (a, b) [or, equivalently, from (x_0, y_0) to $(x_0 + a, y_0 + b)$]. By the same reasoning as above, we can express $\mathbf{u}$ in terms of $\hat{\mathbf{i}}$, $\hat{\mathbf{j}}$ as

$$\mathbf{u} = a\hat{\mathbf{i}} + b\hat{\mathbf{j}}. \tag{2}$$

Is (2) unique? For example, breaking OP (in Fig. 7.7a) into OQP gave $\mathbf{u} = 3\hat{\mathbf{i}} + 2\hat{\mathbf{j}}$; but if we had broken it into $ORSTP$, instead, might we have obtained a different result, such as $\mathbf{u} = 4\hat{\mathbf{i}} + 2\hat{\mathbf{j}}$? No. To prove that the expression (2) of a given vector $\mathbf{u}$, as a linear combination of $\hat{\mathbf{i}}$ and $\hat{\mathbf{j}}$, is indeed unique, suppose that $\mathbf{u}$ also admits an expansion

$$\mathbf{u} = a'\hat{\mathbf{i}} + b'\hat{\mathbf{j}}. \tag{3}$$

Subtracting equals from equals, namely (3) from (2), yields

$$(a - a')\hat{\mathbf{i}} + (\mathrm{b} - \mathrm{b}')\hat{\mathbf{j}} = \mathbf{0}. \tag{4}$$

Dotting both sides of (4) with $\hat{\mathbf{i}}$, then with $\hat{\mathbf{j}}$, and using (1), we find that $a - a' = 0$ and $b - b' = 0$, so that $a' = a$ and $b' = b$. Consequently, (3) is necessarily identical to (2), so (2) is unique, as claimed.

Similarly for 3-space: Suppose that we adopt a Cartesian x, y, z coordinate system, with reference vectors $\hat{\mathbf{i}}$, $\hat{\mathbf{j}}$, $\hat{\mathbf{k}}$ (Fig. 7.8), where

$$\hat{\mathbf{i}} \cdot \hat{\mathbf{i}} = \hat{\mathbf{j}} \cdot \hat{\mathbf{j}} = \hat{\mathbf{k}} \cdot \hat{\mathbf{k}} = 1, \tag{5a}$$

$$\hat{\mathbf{i}} \cdot \hat{\mathbf{j}} = \hat{\mathbf{i}} \cdot \hat{\mathbf{k}} = \hat{\mathbf{j}} \cdot \hat{\mathbf{k}} = 0. \tag{5b}$$

It follows from (5) that $\{\hat{\mathbf{i}}, \hat{\mathbf{j}}, \hat{\mathbf{k}}\}$ is an orthonormal set. Furthermore,

$$\hat{\mathbf{i}} \times \hat{\mathbf{j}} = \|\hat{\mathbf{i}}\| \, \|\hat{\mathbf{j}}\| \sin 90^\circ \, \hat{\mathbf{k}} = \hat{\mathbf{k}}. \tag{6}$$

Working out all of the various cross products in this manner, we find that

* For example, if we choose a scale of 1 newton per unit length, then $\mathbf{u}$, in Fig. 7.7a, would represent a force of $\sqrt{13}$ newtons, in the direction OP.

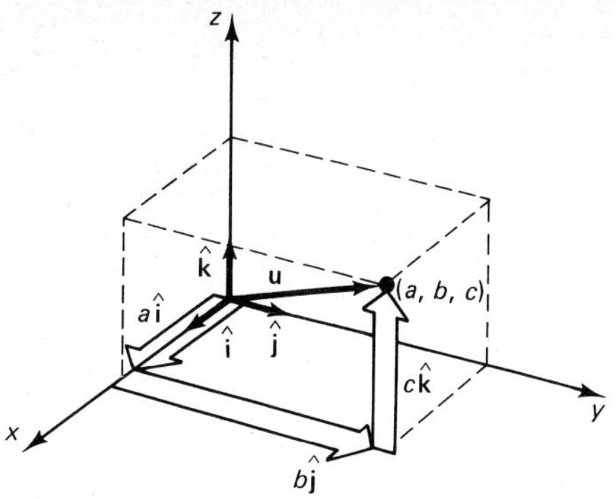

Fig. 7.8 Cartesian coordinates; $\{\hat{\mathbf{i}}, \hat{\mathbf{j}}, \hat{\mathbf{k}}\}$ vectors.

$$\hat{\mathbf{i}} \times \hat{\mathbf{i}} = \hat{\mathbf{j}} \times \hat{\mathbf{j}} = \hat{\mathbf{k}} \times \hat{\mathbf{k}} = \mathbf{0}, \tag{7a}$$

$$\hat{\mathbf{i}} \times \hat{\mathbf{j}} = \hat{\mathbf{k}}, \qquad \hat{\mathbf{j}} \times \hat{\mathbf{k}} = \hat{\mathbf{i}}, \qquad \hat{\mathbf{k}} \times \hat{\mathbf{i}} = \hat{\mathbf{j}}, \tag{7b}$$

$$\hat{\mathbf{j}} \times \hat{\mathbf{i}} = -\hat{\mathbf{k}}, \qquad \hat{\mathbf{k}} \times \hat{\mathbf{j}} = -\hat{\mathbf{i}}, \qquad \hat{\mathbf{i}} \times \hat{\mathbf{k}} = -\hat{\mathbf{j}}. \tag{7c}$$

Of these formulas, (7b) and (7c) can be remembered easily if one keeps in mind the mnemonic device shown in Fig. 7.9. Note carefully, however, that the signs in (7b), (7c), and Fig. 7.9, are correct only if our x, y, z coordinate system is *righthanded,* as in Fig. 7.8; i.e., "curling x into y gives z," as shown in Fig. 7.10a. If we were to choose a *left-handed system,* as in Fig. 7.10b, the signs in (7b), (7c), and Fig. 7.9 would all be reversed; for example, we would have $\hat{\mathbf{i}} \times \hat{\mathbf{j}} = -\hat{\mathbf{k}}$, and $\hat{\mathbf{j}} \times \hat{\mathbf{k}} = -\hat{\mathbf{i}}$. *As long as we are consistent* it will not matter whether we choose a right-handed system or a left-handed one. But to minimize confusion, we shall always adopt *right*-handed systems, as is standard mathematical practice.

$\longrightarrow$ (+)

$\cdots\ i\ j\ k\ i\ j\ k\ i\ j\ k\ \cdots$

$\longleftarrow$ (−)

Fig. 7.9 Mnemonic device for (7b) and (7c).

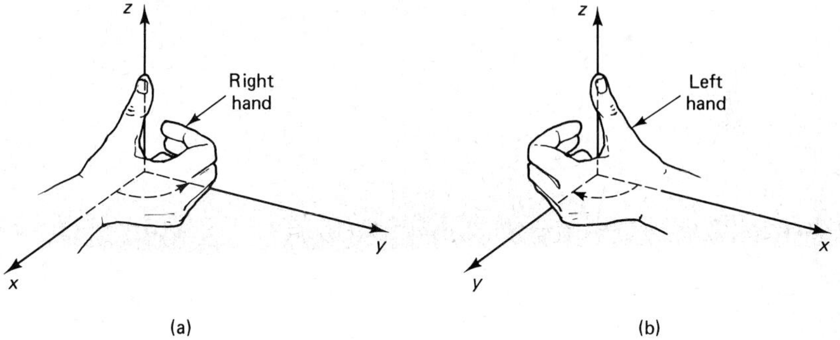

Fig. 7.10 Right- and left-handed systems.

Analogous to the expression (2) for 2-space, any given vector $\mathbf{u}$ in 3-space, say from (0, 0, 0) to (a, b, c) [or, equivalently, from (x_0, y_0, z_0) to $(x_0 + a, y_0 + b, z_0 + c)$], may be expressed as a unique linear combination of $\hat{\mathbf{i}}$, $\hat{\mathbf{j}}$, $\hat{\mathbf{k}}$, namely,

$$\mathbf{u} = a\hat{\mathbf{i}} + b\hat{\mathbf{j}} + c\hat{\mathbf{k}}, \tag{8}$$

as illustrated in Fig. 7.8. Here a, b, c are called the x, y, z *components* of $\mathbf{u}$, respectively. Instead of the letters a, b, c, it is more common to use the letters u_1, u_2, u_3 for the components of $\mathbf{u}$, so that

$$\mathbf{u} = u_1\hat{\mathbf{i}} + u_2\hat{\mathbf{j}} + u_3\hat{\mathbf{k}}. \tag{9}$$

Since each vector in 3-space can be expressed, or *expanded,* as a unique linear combination of $\hat{\mathbf{i}}$, $\hat{\mathbf{j}}$, $\hat{\mathbf{k}}$, we say that the set $\{\hat{\mathbf{i}}, \hat{\mathbf{j}}, \hat{\mathbf{k}}\}$ is a **basis** for 3-space, an orthonormal basis, in fact. (In much the same spirit, some red, blue, and yellow pigments form a "basis" for a painter.)

The form (9) is especially convenient for calculations. For example, if

$$\mathbf{u} = u_1\hat{\mathbf{i}} + u_2\hat{\mathbf{j}} + u_3\hat{\mathbf{k}} \quad \text{and} \quad \mathbf{v} = v_1\hat{\mathbf{i}} + v_2\hat{\mathbf{j}} + v_3\hat{\mathbf{k}}, \tag{10}$$

then

$$\mathbf{u} + \mathbf{v} = (u_1 + v_1)\hat{\mathbf{i}} + (u_2 + v_2)\hat{\mathbf{j}} + (u_3 + v_3)\hat{\mathbf{k}}, \tag{11a}$$

$$\mathbf{u} - \mathbf{v} = (u_1 - v_1)\hat{\mathbf{i}} + (u_2 - v_2)\hat{\mathbf{j}} + (u_3 - v_3)\hat{\mathbf{k}}, \tag{11b}$$

$$\alpha\mathbf{u} = (\alpha u_1)\hat{\mathbf{i}} + (\alpha u_2)\hat{\mathbf{j}} + (\alpha u_3)\hat{\mathbf{k}}, \tag{11c}$$

$$\begin{aligned} \mathbf{u} \cdot \mathbf{v} &= (u_1\hat{\mathbf{i}} + u_2\hat{\mathbf{j}} + u_3\hat{\mathbf{k}}) \cdot (v_1\hat{\mathbf{i}} + v_2\hat{\mathbf{j}} + v_3\hat{\mathbf{k}}) \\ &= u_1v_1\hat{\mathbf{i}} \cdot \hat{\mathbf{i}} + u_1v_2\hat{\mathbf{i}} \cdot \hat{\mathbf{j}} + \cdots + u_3v_2\hat{\mathbf{k}} \cdot \hat{\mathbf{j}} + u_3v_3\hat{\mathbf{k}} \cdot \hat{\mathbf{k}} \\ &= u_1v_1 + u_2v_2 + u_3v_3, \end{aligned} \tag{11d}$$

and

$$\begin{aligned} \mathbf{u} \times \mathbf{v} &= (u_1\hat{\mathbf{i}} + u_2\hat{\mathbf{j}} + u_3\hat{\mathbf{k}}) \times (v_1\hat{\mathbf{i}} + v_2\hat{\mathbf{j}} + v_3\hat{\mathbf{k}}) \\ &= u_1v_1\hat{\mathbf{i}} \times \hat{\mathbf{i}} + u_1v_2\hat{\mathbf{i}} \times \hat{\mathbf{j}} + \cdots + u_3v_2\hat{\mathbf{k}} \times \hat{\mathbf{j}} + u_3v_3\hat{\mathbf{k}} \times \hat{\mathbf{k}} \\ &= (u_2v_3 - u_3v_2)\hat{\mathbf{i}} - (u_1v_3 - u_3v_1)\hat{\mathbf{j}} + (u_1v_2 - u_2v_1)\hat{\mathbf{k}}. \end{aligned} \tag{11e}$$

The right-hand side of (11e) happens to be expressible as a third-order determinant, so that

$$\mathbf{u} \times \mathbf{v} = \begin{vmatrix} \hat{\mathbf{i}} & \hat{\mathbf{j}} & \hat{\mathbf{k}} \\ u_1 & u_2 & u_3 \\ v_1 & v_2 & v_3 \end{vmatrix}, \tag{12}$$

this form being easier to remember than (11e).

EXAMPLE 1 Given

$$\mathbf{u} = \hat{\mathbf{i}} - 2\hat{\mathbf{k}}, \qquad \mathbf{v} = 3\hat{\mathbf{i}} + \hat{\mathbf{j}} + \hat{\mathbf{k}}, \qquad \mathbf{w} = \hat{\mathbf{j}} - \hat{\mathbf{k}},$$

compute $(\mathbf{u} + 2\mathbf{v}) \times \mathbf{w}$ and $\mathbf{u} \cdot \mathbf{w}$.

$$\begin{aligned} (\mathbf{u} + 2\mathbf{v}) \times \mathbf{w} &= [(1 + 6)\hat{\mathbf{i}} + (0 + 2)\hat{\mathbf{j}} + (-2 + 2)\hat{\mathbf{k}}] \times (\hat{\mathbf{j}} - \hat{\mathbf{k}}) \\ &= (7\hat{\mathbf{i}} + 2\hat{\mathbf{j}}) \times (\hat{\mathbf{j}} - \hat{\mathbf{k}}) = \begin{vmatrix} \hat{\mathbf{i}} & \hat{\mathbf{j}} & \hat{\mathbf{k}} \\ 7 & 2 & 0 \\ 0 & 1 & -1 \end{vmatrix} = -2\hat{\mathbf{i}} + 7\hat{\mathbf{j}} + 7\hat{\mathbf{k}} \end{aligned}$$

and $\mathbf{u} \cdot \mathbf{w} = (1)(0) + (0)(1) + (-2)(-1) = 2.$ ◀

In Section 7.6 we consider three more systems: polar, cylindrical, and spherical.

1. Let $\mathbf{u} = 2\hat{\mathbf{i}} - \hat{\mathbf{j}} - 3\hat{\mathbf{k}}$, $\mathbf{v} = \hat{\mathbf{i}} + \hat{\mathbf{j}} - \hat{\mathbf{k}}$, $\mathbf{w} = 3\hat{\mathbf{i}} + 2\hat{\mathbf{k}}$, $\mathbf{x} = 8\hat{\mathbf{i}} - \hat{\mathbf{j}} - 11\hat{\mathbf{k}}$.

(a) Compute $2\mathbf{u} - \mathbf{v}$, $\mathbf{u} \cdot \mathbf{v}$, $\mathbf{v} \cdot \mathbf{u}$, $\mathbf{u} \times \mathbf{v}$, $\mathbf{v} \times \mathbf{u}$, and $\|\mathbf{u} \times \mathbf{v}\|$.
(b) Compute $(\mathbf{u} + 3\mathbf{w}) \times \mathbf{v}$, $\|(\mathbf{u} + 3\mathbf{w}) \times \mathbf{v}\|$, $\mathbf{u} \cdot \mathbf{w}$, and $|\mathbf{u} \cdot \mathbf{w}|$.
(c) Compute $(\mathbf{u} \cdot 2\mathbf{w})\mathbf{v}$, $\mathbf{x} \times (-2\mathbf{u}) + 3\mathbf{v}$, $(\mathbf{u} + \mathbf{w}) \times \mathbf{v}$, and $\|\mathbf{x}\|$.
(d) Compute $\mathbf{u} + 2\mathbf{v} - \mathbf{w} + 3\mathbf{x}$, $(2\mathbf{u} + \mathbf{w}) \cdot (\mathbf{v} - \mathbf{x})$, and $\mathbf{w} \times (\mathbf{v} - \mathbf{x})$.
(e) Compute $(3\mathbf{v} + \mathbf{w} - \mathbf{x}) \cdot \mathbf{v}$, $(\mathbf{w} - \mathbf{x}) \times (2\mathbf{v})$, and $\|\mathbf{u} \times (\mathbf{v} \times \mathbf{w})\|$.
(f) With **u**, **v**, **x** tail to tail, show that the three vectors lie in a plane. Do this two ways: first, by taking suitable cross and dot products, and then by showing that one of the vectors can be expressed as a linear combination of the others.
(g) With **u**, **v**, **w** tail to tail, show—by taking suitable cross and dot products—that the three vectors do *not* lie in the same plane.
*(h) Find a vector perpendicular to **u** and **v**. Verify your answer.
(i) Find a vector perpendicular to **u** and **w**. Verify your answer.
(j) Find a vector perpendicular to **v** and **w**. Verify your answer.
*(k) With **u**, **v**, **w** tail to tail, find the area of the triangle formed by their heads, and find a vector perpendicular to that triangle.
(l) Repeat part (k), for **u**, **v**, **x**.
(m) Repeat part (k), for **u**, **w**, **x**.
(n) With **u**, **v**, **w**, **x** tail to tail, show whether or not their heads lie in a common plane.

2. Consider three forces: $\mathbf{F}_1 = 2\hat{\mathbf{i}} + \hat{\mathbf{k}}$ with its tail at $(2, 1, -1)$, $\mathbf{F}_2 = \hat{\mathbf{i}} - \hat{\mathbf{j}} + \hat{\mathbf{k}}$ with its tail at $(0, 0, 0)$, and $\mathbf{F}_3 = \hat{\mathbf{i}} + 4\hat{\mathbf{j}}$ with its tail at $(1, 1, 1)$.

*(a) Find the total vector moment **M** about $(0, 0, 0)$.
(b) Find the total vector moment **M** about $(1, 1, 0)$.
(c) Find the total vector moment **M** about $(8, 6, -10)$.
(d) Determine (if possible) an additional force $\mathbf{F}_4$ with its tail at $(2, -1, -1)$, such that the total vector moment **M** about $(1, 0, 0)$ is zero.
(e) Repeat part (d), with $(2, -1, -1)$ changed to $(1, -1, -1)$.

3. Use a suitable cross product to determine whether or not the following points lie on a straight line.

*(a) $(2, 3, 1)$, $(1, -1, 4)$, $(2, 2, 1)$
(b) $(1, 3, 0)$, $(2, -1, 1)$, $(3, -5, 2)$
(c) $(5, 1, -1)$, $(1, 3, 2)$, $(-3, -5, 5)$
(d) $(1, 0, 2)$, $(-4, 3, 0)$, $(12, -6, 6)$

4. Use a suitable property of the cross product to find the area of the triangles with the following vertices.

*(a) $(1, 4, 3)$, $(2, 0, -1)$, $(0, 0, 5)$
(b) $(2, -2, 1)$, $(4, 0, 3)$, $(2, 3, 5)$
(c) $(0, 0, 2)$, $(0, 4, 0)$, $(3, 1, 1)$
(d) $(8, 7, 4)$, $(2, -5, 0)$, $(1, 6, 8)$
(e) $(1, 1, 1)$, $(1, 1, 2)$, $(3, 2, 1)$
(f) $(5, 4, 1)$, $(3, 2, 3)$, $(-4, 0, 6)$
(g) $(2, -1, 1)$, $(0, 2, 3)$, $(9, 6, 1)$
(h) $(14, 1, -6)$, $(2, 2, 1)$, $(0, 4, 9)$

5. *(a) Determine a unit normal vector to the plane $x + 2y - z = 5$ by finding three distinct (noncollinear) points A, B, C in the plane, crossing **AB** with **AC**, and normalizing.
(b) Repeat part (a), for the plane $2x + y - z = 0$.
(c) Repeat part (a), for the plane $x - 3y + 4z = -2$.
(d) Repeat part (a), for the plane $ax + by + cz = d$.

6. *(Equation of a line)* (a) Let $\mathbf{R}_0$ be a given point in 3-space; i.e., the point at the head of the position vector $\mathbf{R}_0$ issuing from the origin. And let **v** be a given (nonzero) vector (see the figure). Show that the locus of points **R** which constitute a straight line L through $\mathbf{R}_0$, parallel to **v**, is determined by either of the equations

$$(\mathbf{R} - \mathbf{R}_0) \times \mathbf{v} = \mathbf{0}, \quad \text{or} \tag{a}$$

$$\mathbf{R} = \mathbf{R}_0 + \mathbf{v}t \qquad (-\infty < t < \infty). \tag{b}$$

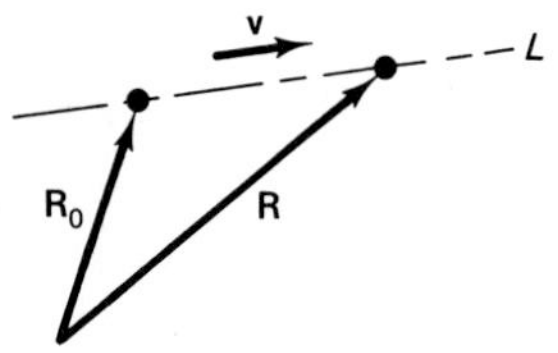

(b) Using equation (b), show that the straight line through $(2, 5, -1)$, parallel to the vector $4\hat{\mathbf{i}} - \hat{\mathbf{k}}$, may be defined by the parametric equations

$$x = 2 + 4t, \quad y = 5, \quad z = -1 - t$$

$$(-\infty < t < \infty).$$

(c) Determine parametric equations for the straight line through (1, 0, 5) which is parallel to the vector $-3\hat{\mathbf{i}} + \hat{\mathbf{j}} + 2\hat{\mathbf{k}}$.

7. (*Equation of a plane*) (a) To obtain the equation of a given plane, suppose that $\mathbf{R}_0$ is a position vector, from the origin to the plane, which is normal to the plane, and let $\hat{\mathbf{n}}$ be a unit vector normal to the plane. If $\mathbf{R}$ is a position vector to any point in the plane, then surely $(\mathbf{R} - \mathbf{R}_0) \cdot \hat{\mathbf{n}} = 0$, so that $\mathbf{R} \cdot \hat{\mathbf{n}} = \mathbf{R}_0 \cdot \hat{\mathbf{n}}$, which is of the form

$$\mathbf{R} \cdot \hat{\mathbf{n}} = d. \tag{a}$$

Show that the constant d in (a) happens to be the shortest distance from the origin to the plane, and that that shortest distance occurs when $\mathbf{R}$ is normal to the plane (except in the case when the plane passes right through the origin). *Hint:* you may use the results given in Exercise 11 on page 269.

*(b) Find the shortest distance from the origin to the plane, and a unit vector normal to the plane, for the plane defined by the equation $2x + y - 3z = 4$.

(c) Repeat part (b), for $x - y - z = 5$.

(d) Repeat part (b), for $3x + y - z = 0$.

(e) Repeat part (b), for $x + 2y + 3z = 8$.

(f) Repeat part (b), for $ax + by + cz = d$.

7.4 MULTIPLE PRODUCTS

We have discussed the dot and cross products of two vectors, $\mathbf{u} \cdot \mathbf{v}$ and $\mathbf{u} \times \mathbf{v}$, respectively. Products of *more* than two vectors are also encountered and are the subject of this section.

What products of *three* vectors $\mathbf{u}$, $\mathbf{v}$, $\mathbf{w}$ are possible? Writing down all such combinations, we have

$$\mathbf{u} \cdot (\mathbf{v} \cdot \mathbf{w}), \qquad \mathbf{u} \times (\mathbf{v} \cdot \mathbf{w}), \qquad \mathbf{u} \cdot (\mathbf{v} \times \mathbf{w}), \qquad \mathbf{u} \times (\mathbf{v} \times \mathbf{w}) \tag{1}$$

to consider. [You may feel that some possibilities, such as $(\mathbf{u} \times \mathbf{v}) \times \mathbf{w}$, have been left out. But $(\mathbf{u} \times \mathbf{v}) \times \mathbf{w} = -\mathbf{w} \times (\mathbf{u} \times \mathbf{v})$, and this form, give or take a minus sign, is the same as the last one in (1).] Now, $\mathbf{v} \cdot \mathbf{w}$ is a scalar, so the first two members of (1) amount to a vector dotted with a scalar, and a vector crossed with a scalar, respectively. Such quantities are *not defined,* so they can be discarded. It remains to consider

$$\mathbf{u} \cdot (\mathbf{v} \times \mathbf{w}), \tag{2}$$

called the **scalar triple product** because the result is a scalar, and

$$\mathbf{u} \times (\mathbf{v} \times \mathbf{w}), \tag{3}$$

called the **vector triple product** because the result is a vector.

First, the scalar triple product $\mathbf{u} \cdot (\mathbf{v} \times \mathbf{w})$.* We can, for notational simplicity, drop the parentheses and write $\mathbf{u} \cdot \mathbf{v} \times \mathbf{w}$, since $\mathbf{u} \cdot \mathbf{v} \times \mathbf{w}$ can only mean $(\mathbf{u} \cdot \mathbf{v}) \times \mathbf{w}$ or $\mathbf{u} \cdot (\mathbf{v} \times \mathbf{w})$, and of these two the former is not defined and is not a viable candidate.

To observe an important fact about $\mathbf{u} \cdot \mathbf{v} \times \mathbf{w}$, let us sketch the "$\mathbf{u}$, $\mathbf{v}$, $\mathbf{w}$ parallelepiped," as shown in Fig. 7.11 (for the case where $\mathbf{u}$, $\mathbf{v}$, $\mathbf{w}$ do not lie in the same plane). Now $\mathbf{v} \times \mathbf{w}$ is the magnitude (norm) of $\mathbf{v} \times \mathbf{w}$ times the unit vector $\hat{\mathbf{e}}$ shown

* The triple product $\mathbf{u} \cdot (\mathbf{v} \times \mathbf{w})$ is sometimes denoted as "(**uvw**)." That notation will not be used in this book.

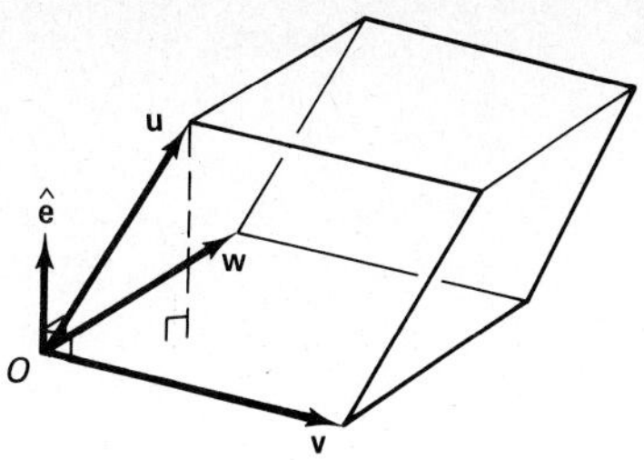

Fig. 7.11 u, v, w parallelepiped.

in Fig. 7.11. Thus

$$\mathbf{u}\cdot\mathbf{v}\times\mathbf{w} = \mathbf{u}\cdot\|\mathbf{v}\times\mathbf{w}\|\hat{\mathbf{e}} = \|\mathbf{v}\times\mathbf{w}\|(\mathbf{u}\cdot\hat{\mathbf{e}}). \tag{4}$$

But $\|\mathbf{v}\times\mathbf{w}\|$ is, according to (9) on page 273, the area of the $\mathbf{v}$, $\mathbf{w}$, parallelogram, i.e., the *base area* of the $\mathbf{u}$, $\mathbf{v}$, $\mathbf{w}$ parallelepiped. And $\mathbf{u}\cdot\hat{\mathbf{e}}$ is equal to the *altitude* (dashed line). Hence it follows from (4) that $\mathbf{u}\cdot\mathbf{v}\times\mathbf{w}$ is the volume of the $\mathbf{u}$, $\mathbf{v}$, $\mathbf{w}$ parallelepiped. However, if $\mathbf{u}$ were directed such that $\mathbf{u}\cdot\hat{\mathbf{e}}$ were negative, then $\mathbf{u}\cdot\mathbf{v}\times\mathbf{w}$ would be the *negative* of the volume. In any case, if we introduce absolute values, then

$$\boxed{|\mathbf{u}\cdot\mathbf{v}\times\mathbf{w}| = \text{volume of } \mathbf{u}, \mathbf{v}, \mathbf{w} \text{ parallelepiped.}} \tag{5}$$

Finally, if we recall from Section 7.3 that

$$\mathbf{v}\times\mathbf{w} = \begin{vmatrix} \hat{\mathbf{i}} & \hat{\mathbf{j}} & \hat{\mathbf{k}} \\ v_1 & v_2 & v_3 \\ w_1 & w_2 & w_3 \end{vmatrix},$$

where $\mathbf{v} = v_1\hat{\mathbf{i}} + v_2\hat{\mathbf{j}} + v_3\hat{\mathbf{k}}$ and $\mathbf{w} = w_1\hat{\mathbf{i}} + w_2\hat{\mathbf{j}} + w_3\hat{\mathbf{k}}$, it should not be hard to see that $\mathbf{u}\cdot\mathbf{v}\times\mathbf{w}$ can be expressed neatly as

$$\mathbf{u}\cdot\mathbf{v}\times\mathbf{w} = \begin{vmatrix} u_1 & u_2 & u_3 \\ v_1 & v_2 & v_3 \\ w_1 & w_2 & w_3 \end{vmatrix}. \tag{6}$$

Now, interchanging two rows of a determinant changes the sign of the determinant. If, in (6), we interchange the first row with the second, and then the third with the first, the new determinant can be identified [according to the pattern in (6)] as $\mathbf{w}\cdot\mathbf{u}\times\mathbf{v}$. Since there were two sign changes, we see that $\mathbf{u}\cdot\mathbf{v}\times\mathbf{w} = \mathbf{w}\cdot\mathbf{u}\times\mathbf{v}$, or

$$\boxed{\mathbf{u}\cdot\mathbf{v}\times\mathbf{w} = \mathbf{u}\times\mathbf{v}\cdot\mathbf{w},} \tag{7}$$

i.e., interchanging the dot and the cross leaves the scalar triple product unchanged.

Next, consider the vector triple product $\mathbf{u}\times(\mathbf{v}\times\mathbf{w})$. Here we *do* need to retain the parentheses since $\mathbf{u}\times\mathbf{v}\times\mathbf{w}$ could mean either $(\mathbf{u}\times\mathbf{v})\times\mathbf{w}$ *or* $\mathbf{u}\times(\mathbf{v}\times\mathbf{w})$. Both of these quantities are indeed defined, and they are not necessarily equal to each other; for example, $\hat{\mathbf{i}}\times(\hat{\mathbf{i}}\times\hat{\mathbf{j}}) = \hat{\mathbf{i}}\times\hat{\mathbf{k}} = -\hat{\mathbf{j}}$, whereas $(\hat{\mathbf{i}}\times\hat{\mathbf{i}})\times\hat{\mathbf{j}} = \mathbf{0}\times\hat{\mathbf{j}} = \mathbf{0}$.

Thus, let us state, for reference, that (in general)

$$(\mathbf{u} \times \mathbf{v}) \times \mathbf{w} \neq \mathbf{u} \times (\mathbf{v} \times \mathbf{w}). \tag{8}$$

Recall that $\mathbf{v} \times \mathbf{w}$ is perpendicular to the $\mathbf{v} \times \mathbf{w}$ plane. Thus (Fig. 7.11) it must be some multiple of $\hat{\mathbf{e}}$. Similarly, $\mathbf{u} \times (\mathbf{v} \times \mathbf{w})$ is perpendicular to both $\mathbf{u}$ and $\mathbf{v} \times \mathbf{w}$, and hence to both $\mathbf{u}$ and $\hat{\mathbf{e}}$. Since it is perpendicular to $\hat{\mathbf{e}}$, it must lie in the $\mathbf{v} \times \mathbf{w}$ plane, so it must be expressible in the form $\alpha\mathbf{v} + \beta\mathbf{w}$. To determine α and β, let us introduce a convenient reference coordinate system and set of base vectors. Specifically, let the point O in Fig. 7.11 be the origin of a Cartesian coordinate system with the usual base vectors $\hat{\mathbf{i}}, \hat{\mathbf{j}}, \hat{\mathbf{k}}$. And let the system be oriented so that $\hat{\mathbf{i}}$ is aligned with $\mathbf{v}$, and $\hat{\mathbf{k}}$ coincides with the $\hat{\mathbf{e}}$ shown in Fig. 7.11. Then $\hat{\mathbf{j}}$ must lie in the $\mathbf{v}$, $\mathbf{w}$ plane, so we can express

$$\mathbf{v} = v_1\hat{\mathbf{i}}, \qquad \mathbf{w} = w_1\hat{\mathbf{i}} + w_2\hat{\mathbf{j}}, \qquad \mathbf{u} = u_1\hat{\mathbf{i}} + u_2\hat{\mathbf{j}} + u_3\hat{\mathbf{k}}.$$

Hence $\mathbf{v} \times \mathbf{w} = v_1 w_2 \hat{\mathbf{k}}$, and

$$\begin{aligned}
\mathbf{u} \times (\mathbf{v} \times \mathbf{w}) &= (u_1\hat{\mathbf{i}} + u_2\hat{\mathbf{j}} + u_3\hat{\mathbf{k}}) \times (v_1 w_2 \hat{\mathbf{k}}) \\
&= -u_1 v_1 w_2 \hat{\mathbf{j}} + u_2 v_1 w_2 \hat{\mathbf{i}} \\
&= (u_1 w_1 + u_2 w_2) v_1 \hat{\mathbf{i}} - u_1 v_1 (w_1 \hat{\mathbf{i}} + w_2 \hat{\mathbf{j}}) \\
&= (u_1 w_1 + u_2 w_2)\mathbf{v} - u_1 v_1 \mathbf{w}.
\end{aligned}$$

But $u_1 w_1 + u_2 w_2 = \mathbf{u} \cdot \mathbf{w}$ and $u_1 v_1 = \mathbf{u} \cdot \mathbf{v}$, so that we have the useful formula

$$\boxed{\mathbf{u} \times (\mathbf{v} \times \mathbf{w}) = (\mathbf{u} \cdot \mathbf{w})\mathbf{v} - (\mathbf{u} \cdot \mathbf{v})\mathbf{w}.} \tag{9}$$

We could consider quadruple products, such as $\mathbf{u} \times (\mathbf{v} \times (\mathbf{w} \times \mathbf{x}))$ and $(\mathbf{u} \times \mathbf{v}) \cdot (\mathbf{w} \times \mathbf{x})$, quintuple products, and so on, but the triple products discussed here should suffice for our purposes. The formulas and properties to note are (5) to (9).

7.4 EXERCISES

1. If $\mathbf{u} = \hat{\mathbf{i}} - \hat{\mathbf{j}}$, $\mathbf{v} = 2\hat{\mathbf{i}} + \hat{\mathbf{j}} + 3\hat{\mathbf{k}}$, $\mathbf{w} = \hat{\mathbf{j}} - \hat{\mathbf{k}}$, evaluate

*(a) $\mathbf{u} \cdot \mathbf{v} \times \mathbf{w}$ and $\mathbf{u} \times \mathbf{v} \cdot \mathbf{w}$
(b) $\mathbf{u} \times (\mathbf{v} \times \mathbf{w})$ and $(\mathbf{u} \times \mathbf{v}) \times \mathbf{w}$

2. If $\mathbf{A} = \hat{\mathbf{i}} + \hat{\mathbf{j}} - \hat{\mathbf{k}}$, $\mathbf{B} = 3\hat{\mathbf{j}} - \hat{\mathbf{k}}$, $\mathbf{C} = \hat{\mathbf{i}} + 2\hat{\mathbf{k}}$, evaluate

(a) $\mathbf{A} \cdot \mathbf{B} \times \mathbf{C}$ and $\mathbf{A} \times \mathbf{B} \cdot \mathbf{C}$ (b) $\mathbf{A} \times (\mathbf{B} \times \mathbf{C})$ and $(\mathbf{A} \times \mathbf{B}) \times \mathbf{C}$

3. Check the identity (9) by working out the left- and right-hand sides separately, for each case.

(a) $\mathbf{u} = \hat{\mathbf{i}}$, $\mathbf{v} = \hat{\mathbf{j}}$, $\mathbf{w} = \hat{\mathbf{k}}$
(b) $\mathbf{u} = \hat{\mathbf{i}}$, $\mathbf{v} = \hat{\mathbf{i}}$, $\mathbf{w} = \hat{\mathbf{j}}$
(c) $\mathbf{u} = \hat{\mathbf{j}} - \hat{\mathbf{k}}$, $\mathbf{v} = \hat{\mathbf{i}} + 3\hat{\mathbf{j}}$, $\mathbf{w} = \hat{\mathbf{i}} + 2\hat{\mathbf{k}}$
(d) $\mathbf{u} = 8\hat{\mathbf{i}} + 6\hat{\mathbf{j}}$, $\mathbf{v} = \hat{\mathbf{i}} - 4\hat{\mathbf{k}}$, $\mathbf{w} = 2\hat{\mathbf{j}}$

4. Find the volume of the parallelepiped having the following vectors as adjacent edges.

(a) $\hat{\mathbf{i}}, 2\hat{\mathbf{j}}, -5\hat{\mathbf{k}}$
(b) $\hat{\mathbf{i}}, \hat{\mathbf{j}}, \hat{\mathbf{i}} + \hat{\mathbf{j}} + \hat{\mathbf{k}}$
(c) $\hat{\mathbf{i}} + 2\hat{\mathbf{j}}, 3\hat{\mathbf{i}}, \hat{\mathbf{j}} + \hat{\mathbf{k}}$
*(d) $3\hat{\mathbf{j}}, 2\hat{\mathbf{i}} - \hat{\mathbf{j}}, \hat{\mathbf{i}} + 5\hat{\mathbf{k}}$
(e) $\hat{\mathbf{i}}, \hat{\mathbf{i}} + \hat{\mathbf{j}}, \hat{\mathbf{i}} + \hat{\mathbf{j}} + \hat{\mathbf{k}}$
(f) $\hat{\mathbf{i}} + \hat{\mathbf{j}}, \hat{\mathbf{i}}, \hat{\mathbf{i}} + \hat{\mathbf{j}} + \hat{\mathbf{k}}$

5. Show that $(\mathbf{u} \times \mathbf{v}) \times \mathbf{w} = (\mathbf{w} \cdot \mathbf{u})\mathbf{v} - (\mathbf{w} \cdot \mathbf{v})\mathbf{u}$. You may use (9).

6. Show that $\mathbf{u} \times (\mathbf{v} \times \mathbf{w}) + \mathbf{w} \times (\mathbf{u} \times \mathbf{v}) + \mathbf{v} \times (\mathbf{w} \times \mathbf{u}) = \mathbf{0}$.

7. If $\mathbf{A}$, $\mathbf{B}$, $\mathbf{C}$ are distinct vectors issuing from a common point, show that the vector $(\mathbf{A} \times \mathbf{B}) + (\mathbf{B} \times \mathbf{C}) + (\mathbf{C} \times \mathbf{A})$ is perpendicular to the plane containing their heads.

8. (*Orthogonal separation*) Let a given (nonzero) vector $\mathbf{u}$ be separated into the sum of two orthogonal vectors, one parallel to a given (nonzero) vector $\mathbf{v}$, and the other perpendicular to $\mathbf{v}$, i.e., $\mathbf{u} = \mathbf{u}_{\text{par}} + \mathbf{u}_{\text{perp}}$. Show that

$$\mathbf{u}_{\text{par}} = (\mathbf{u} \cdot \hat{\mathbf{v}})\hat{\mathbf{v}}, \qquad \mathbf{u}_{\text{perp}} = \hat{\mathbf{v}} \times (\mathbf{u} \times \hat{\mathbf{v}}), \tag{a}$$

where $\hat{\mathbf{v}} = \mathbf{v}/\|\mathbf{v}\|$.

9. Prove the following identities involving "quadruple products." *Hint:* Use (7) and (9).

(a) $(\mathbf{A} \times \mathbf{B}) \cdot (\mathbf{C} \times \mathbf{D}) = (\mathbf{A} \cdot \mathbf{C})(\mathbf{B} \cdot \mathbf{D}) - (\mathbf{A} \cdot \mathbf{D})(\mathbf{B} \cdot \mathbf{C})$ (a)

This is **Lagrange's identity,** of which equation (a) of Exercise 5 on page 275 is a special case.

(b) $(\mathbf{A} \times \mathbf{B}) \times (\mathbf{C} \times \mathbf{D}) = (\mathbf{A} \cdot \mathbf{B} \times \mathbf{D})\mathbf{C} - (\mathbf{A} \cdot \mathbf{B} \times \mathbf{C})\mathbf{D}.$ (b)

10. In deriving (9), we introduced the orthonormal basis $\{\hat{\mathbf{i}}, \hat{\mathbf{j}}, \hat{\mathbf{k}}\}$, oriented in such a way that $\mathbf{v} = v_1\hat{\mathbf{i}}$, $\mathbf{w} = w_1\hat{\mathbf{i}} + w_2\hat{\mathbf{j}}$, and $\mathbf{u} = u_1\hat{\mathbf{i}} + u_2\hat{\mathbf{j}} + u_3\hat{\mathbf{k}}$. Although this orientation was *convenient* (since then $\mathbf{v}$ had only one component, and $\mathbf{w}$ had only two, so that the calculations were rendered as short as possible), we claim that it was not essential. Verify this claim by rederiving (9) using the expansions $\mathbf{u} = u_1\hat{\mathbf{i}} + u_2\hat{\mathbf{j}} + u_3\hat{\mathbf{k}}$, $\mathbf{v} = v_1\hat{\mathbf{i}} + v_2\hat{\mathbf{j}} + v_3\hat{\mathbf{k}}$, $\mathbf{w} = w_1\hat{\mathbf{i}} + w_2\hat{\mathbf{j}} + w_3\hat{\mathbf{k}}$, which, of course, hold for *any* orientation.

11. *(Linear dependence of* $\mathbf{u}$, $\mathbf{v}$, $\mathbf{w}$*)* Prove that vectors $\mathbf{u}$, $\mathbf{v}$, $\mathbf{w}$ are linearly dependent if and only if $\mathbf{u} \cdot \mathbf{v} \times \mathbf{w} = 0$.

12. Do the following sets of four points lie in a plane? *Hint:* You may use the result stated in Exercise 11, without proving it, if you wish.

*(a) (1, 3, 0), (2, 1, −1), (0, 0, 4), (5, 0, 8)
(b) (2, 1, −1), (1, 3, 0), (5, 0, 9), (0, 0, 4)
(c) (4, 0, 0), (0, 1, 0), (1, 2, −4), (0, 0, 1)
(d) (0, 0, 0), (2, 6, −1), (1, 0, 1), (1, 2, 0)

13. Give an example of three vectors $\mathbf{u}$, $\mathbf{v}$, $\mathbf{w}$ (*not* the example in the text) such that $(\mathbf{u} \times \mathbf{v}) \times \mathbf{w} \neq \mathbf{u} \times (\mathbf{v} \times \mathbf{w})$, and an example of three vectors $\mathbf{u}$, $\mathbf{v}$, $\mathbf{w}$ such that $(\mathbf{u} \times \mathbf{v}) \times \mathbf{w} = \mathbf{u} \times (\mathbf{v} \times \mathbf{w})$. (The latter part of the exercise is simple if we let at least one of the three vectors be $\mathbf{0}$. To make the problem more interesting, let us insist that $\mathbf{u}$, $\mathbf{v}$, $\mathbf{w}$ all be nonzero.)

DIFFERENTIATION OF VECTOR FUNCTIONS OF A SINGLE VARIABLE 7.5

Suppose that a vector $\mathbf{u}(\tau)$ is defined for each value of a real variable τ in some τ-interval. Then we say that $\mathbf{u}$ is a vector function of τ over that interval. In a given application τ may correspond to the time t, to the arc length s along a certain curve, or it may be a purely mathematical parameter.

EXAMPLE 1 To illustrate, suppose that

$$\mathbf{u} = \mathbf{A} + \tau^3(\mathbf{B} - \mathbf{A}); \qquad 0 \le \tau \le 1, \tag{1}$$

where $\mathbf{A}$ and $\mathbf{B}$ are given vectors (which do not vary with τ). If the tail of $\mathbf{u}$ is fixed at P, then $\mathbf{u}(\tau)$ varies, with τ, as shown in Fig. 7.12. ◀

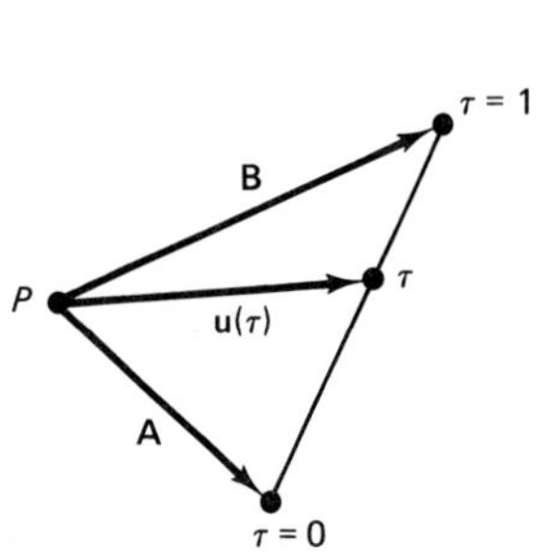

Fig. 7.12 u(τ) given by (1).

Whereas there is no coordinate system present in Example 1, it is often useful to introduce some reference Cartesian system x, y, z, with the usual base vectors $\hat{\mathbf{i}}$, $\hat{\mathbf{j}}$, $\hat{\mathbf{k}}$. In that case one can express any given vector $\mathbf{u}(\tau)$ in component form, as

$$\mathbf{u}(\tau) = u_1(\tau)\hat{\mathbf{i}} + u_2(\tau)\hat{\mathbf{j}} + u_3(\tau)\hat{\mathbf{k}}, \tag{2}$$

where we assume that the $\hat{\mathbf{i}}$, $\hat{\mathbf{j}}$, $\hat{\mathbf{k}}$ base vectors are constant; i.e., they do not vary with τ. (Cases in which the base vectors do vary will be encountered in subsequent sections.)

We now define the derivative $d\mathbf{u}/d\tau$, or $\mathbf{u}'(\tau)$. In doing so, we stay as close as possible to the classical derivative of scalar functions, and define

$$\frac{d\mathbf{u}}{d\tau} = \mathbf{u}'(\tau) \equiv \lim_{\Delta\tau\to 0} \frac{\mathbf{u}(\tau + \Delta\tau) - \mathbf{u}(\tau)}{\Delta\tau}. \tag{3}$$

If the limit on the right-hand side exists, for a given value of τ, we say that $\mathbf{u}(\tau)$ is **differentiable** at that τ, and that $\mathbf{u}'(\tau)$ is its **derivative.***

EXAMPLE 2 Let us compute $\mathbf{u}'(\tau)$ for the $\mathbf{u}$ given by (1). Applying (3) yields

$$\begin{aligned} \mathbf{u}'(\tau) &= \lim_{\Delta\tau\to 0} \frac{\mathbf{A} + (\tau + \Delta\tau)^3(\mathbf{B} - \mathbf{A}) - \mathbf{A} - \tau^3(\mathbf{B} - \mathbf{A})}{\Delta\tau} \\ &= \lim_{\Delta\tau\to 0} \frac{3\tau^2\Delta\tau + 3\tau(\Delta\tau)^2 + (\Delta\tau)^3}{\Delta\tau}(\mathbf{B} - \mathbf{A}) \\ &= \lim_{\Delta\tau\to 0} [3\tau^2 + 3\tau\Delta\tau + (\Delta\tau)^2](\mathbf{B} - \mathbf{A}) = 3\tau^2(\mathbf{B} - \mathbf{A}). \end{aligned}$$

To illustrate, we have shown $\mathbf{u}'(\tau)$ at $\tau = 0.5$ in Fig. 7.13. ◀

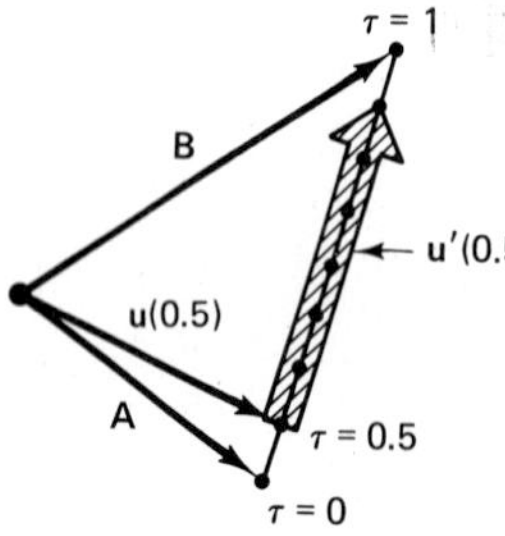

Fig. 7.13 $\mathbf{u}'(\tau)$ at $\tau = 0.5$.

The definition (3) admits a graphical interpretation. Suppose that the tail of the $\mathbf{u}(\tau)$ vector is "bound" at a fixed point P, and that the head of the vector traces a space curve $\mathscr{C}$ as τ varies continuously over some interval $\tau_1 \le \tau \le \tau_2$, for example as sketched in Fig. 7.14. The difference $\mathbf{u}(\tau + \Delta\tau) - \mathbf{u}(\tau)$, in (3), is the vector

* Observe that the right-hand side of (3) is of the general form

$$\lim_{\tau\to\tau_0} \mathbf{F}(\tau). \tag{a}$$

Thus our definition (3) is meaningful only if we also define the *limit of a vector sequence*. Well, by

$$\lim_{\tau\to\tau_0} \mathbf{F}(\tau) = \mathbf{L} \tag{b}$$

[i.e., $\mathbf{F}(\tau)$ tends to $\mathbf{L}$ as τ tends to τ_0] we shall mean that

$$\lim_{\tau\to\tau_0} \| \mathbf{F}(\tau) - \mathbf{L} \| = 0, \tag{c}$$

where the limit in (c) is the ordinary limit met in calculus since the norm $\| \mathbf{F}(\tau) - \mathbf{L} \|$ is a *scalar* function of τ. Further, we say that a vector function $\mathbf{F}(\tau)$ is *continuous* at τ_0 if $\lim_{\tau\to\tau_0} \mathbf{F}(\tau) = \mathbf{F}(\tau_0)$.

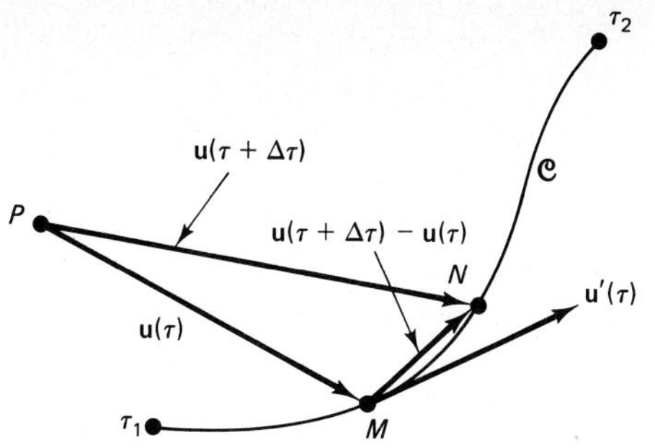

Fig. 7.14 Graphical interpretation of $\mathbf{u}'(\tau)$.

MN. The endpoint M is fixed, for a given value of τ, and the other endpoint N moves along $\mathscr{C}$, and tends to M as $\Delta\tau \to 0$. The limiting direction of $[\mathbf{u}(\tau + \Delta\tau) - \mathbf{u}(\tau)]/\Delta\tau$ as $\Delta\tau \to 0$, i.e., the direction of $\mathbf{u}'(\tau)$, defines a straight line called the **tangent line** to $\mathscr{C}$ at τ [provided that $\mathbf{u}(\tau)$ is indeed differentiable there, and that $\mathbf{u}'(\tau) \neq \mathbf{0}$, for the zero vector would not imply any particular direction], and $\mathbf{u}'(\tau)$ is called a **tangent vector.**

In Example 2, $\mathscr{C}$ was simply a straight line, and $\mathbf{u}'(\tau)$ was indeed found to be tangent to that line (Fig. 7.13). If $\mathbf{u}(\tau)$ is expressed in the Cartesian form (2), then $\mathbf{u}'$, $\mathbf{u}''$ (i.e., $d\mathbf{u}'/d\tau$), . . . , are computed easily (Exercise 3) as

$$\mathbf{u}'(\tau) = u_1'(\tau)\hat{\mathbf{i}} + u_2'(\tau)\hat{\mathbf{j}} + u_3'(\tau)\hat{\mathbf{k}}, \tag{4a}$$

$$\mathbf{u}''(\tau) = u_1''(\tau)\hat{\mathbf{i}} + u_2''(\tau)\hat{\mathbf{j}} + u_3''(\tau)\hat{\mathbf{k}}, \tag{4b}$$

and so on.

EXAMPLE 3 Suppose that a particle is located, with respect to a plane Cartesian coordinate system, by the "position vector"

$$\mathbf{R}(t) = x(t)\hat{\mathbf{i}} + y(t)\hat{\mathbf{j}} = t\hat{\mathbf{i}} + t^2\hat{\mathbf{j}}, \tag{5}$$

where t is the time. By a **position vector** we mean a vector from the origin to the particle. Then $\mathbf{R}'(t) = \mathbf{v}(t)$ is called the **velocity** of the particle, and $\mathbf{R}''(t) = \mathbf{v}'(t) = \mathbf{a}(t)$ is called its **acceleration:**

$$\mathbf{v} = \mathbf{R}'(t) = \hat{\mathbf{i}} + 2t\hat{\mathbf{j}}, \tag{6a}$$

$$\mathbf{a} = \mathbf{v}'(t) = 2\hat{\mathbf{j}}. \tag{6b}$$

Here the acceleration happens to be a constant. The vectors $\mathbf{R}$, $\mathbf{v}$, and $\mathbf{a}$ are shown in Fig. 7.15 for the instant $t = 1$, namely $\mathbf{R}(1) = \hat{\mathbf{i}} + \hat{\mathbf{j}}$, $\mathbf{v}(1) = \hat{\mathbf{i}} + 2\hat{\mathbf{j}}$, and

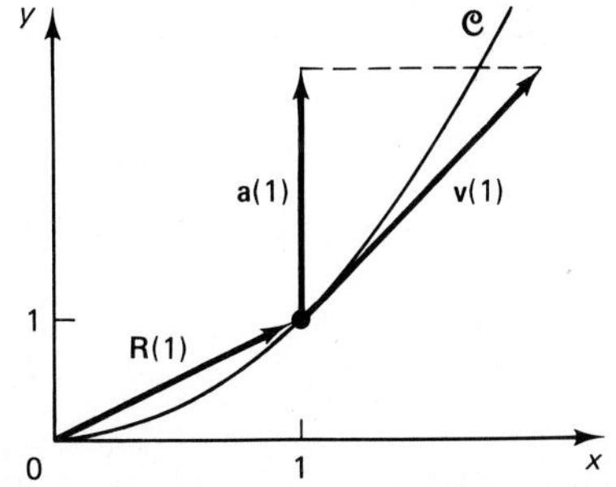

Fig. 7.15 The motion (5).

$\mathbf{a}(1) = 2\hat{\mathbf{j}}$. Do you see, if only approximately, how $\mathbf{a}(1) = 2\hat{\mathbf{j}}$ results as the limit of $[\mathbf{v}(1 + \Delta t) - \mathbf{v}(1)]/\Delta t$ as $\Delta t \to 0$?

In this example the curve $\mathscr{C}$, i.e., the path of motion, is a plane curve, since it lies in the x, y plane. It is given parametrically by

$$x(t) = t, \qquad y(t) = t^2,$$

or, eliminating t, it is the parabola $y = x^2$. ◀

Just as we have rules such as $(uv)' = u'v + uv'$ for the differentiation of scalar functions, we have a number of such rules, which we now list, for the differentiation of vector functions:

$$(f\mathbf{u})' = f'\mathbf{u} + f\mathbf{u}', \qquad \text{where } f = f(\tau) \tag{7a}$$

$$(\alpha\mathbf{u} + \beta\mathbf{v})' = \alpha\mathbf{u}' + \beta\mathbf{v}', \qquad \alpha, \beta \text{ constants} \tag{7b}$$

$$(\mathbf{u} \cdot \mathbf{v})' = \mathbf{u}' \cdot \mathbf{v} + \mathbf{u} \cdot \mathbf{v}', \tag{7c}$$

$$(\mathbf{u} \times \mathbf{v})' = \mathbf{u}' \times \mathbf{v} + \mathbf{u} \times \mathbf{v}', \tag{7d}$$

$$(\mathbf{u} \cdot \mathbf{v} \times \mathbf{w})' = \mathbf{u}' \cdot \mathbf{v} \times \mathbf{w} + \mathbf{u} \cdot \mathbf{v}' \times \mathbf{w} + \mathbf{u} \cdot \mathbf{v} \times \mathbf{w}', \tag{7e}$$

$$[\mathbf{u} \times (\mathbf{v} \times \mathbf{w})]' = \mathbf{u}' \times (\mathbf{v} \times \mathbf{w}) + \mathbf{u} \times (\mathbf{v}' \times \mathbf{w}) + \mathbf{u} \times (\mathbf{v} \times \mathbf{w}'), \tag{7f}$$

$$\frac{d}{d\tau}\mathbf{u}(f(\tau)) = \frac{d\mathbf{u}}{df} f'(\tau), \qquad \text{(chain rule)} \tag{7g}$$

provided, of course, that the needed derivatives do exist.

As representative, let us prove (7c). Remembering the definition (3), we find that

$$\begin{aligned}
(\mathbf{u} \cdot \mathbf{v})' &= \lim_{\Delta\tau \to 0} \frac{\mathbf{u}(\tau + \Delta\tau) \cdot \mathbf{v}(\tau + \Delta\tau) - \mathbf{u}(\tau) \cdot \mathbf{v}(\tau)}{\Delta\tau} \\
&= \lim_{\Delta\tau \to 0} \left[\frac{\mathbf{u}(\tau + \Delta\tau) \cdot \{\mathbf{v}(\tau) + [\mathbf{v}(\tau + \Delta\tau) - \mathbf{v}(\tau)]\} - \mathbf{u}(\tau) \cdot \mathbf{v}(\tau)}{\Delta\tau}\right] \\
&= \lim_{\Delta\tau \to 0} \frac{[\mathbf{u}(\tau + \Delta\tau) - \mathbf{u}(\tau)] \cdot \mathbf{v}(\tau) + \mathbf{u}(\tau + \Delta\tau) \cdot [\mathbf{v}(\tau + \Delta\tau) - \mathbf{v}(\tau)]}{\Delta\tau} \\
&= \lim_{\Delta\tau \to 0} \left[\frac{\mathbf{u}(\tau + \Delta\tau) - \mathbf{u}(\tau)}{\Delta\tau}\right] \cdot \mathbf{v}(\tau) + \lim_{\Delta\tau \to 0} \mathbf{u}(\tau + \Delta\tau) \cdot \left[\frac{\mathbf{v}(\tau + \Delta\tau) - \mathbf{v}(\tau)}{\Delta\tau}\right] \\
&= \mathbf{u}'(\tau) \cdot \mathbf{v}(\tau) + \mathbf{u}(\tau) \cdot \mathbf{v}'(\tau).
\end{aligned}$$

Proofs of the other formulas are left for the exercises.

Vector functions of *more* than one independent variable are also of great importance, but discussion of this case is deferred to Chapter 9.

7.5 EXERCISES

1. For each of the following $\mathbf{u}(\tau)$ vectors, determine $\mathbf{u}'$, $\mathbf{u}''$, and $\|\mathbf{u}'\|$.

*(a) $\mathbf{A} + \tau^2\mathbf{B}$ ($\mathbf{A}$, $\mathbf{B}$ constants)

(b) $6\hat{\mathbf{i}} - e^{\tau}\hat{\mathbf{j}}$

(c) $\tau^2\hat{\mathbf{i}} - 4\hat{\mathbf{j}} + 3\cos 2\tau\hat{\mathbf{k}}$

*(d) $\cos\tau\hat{\mathbf{i}} + \sin\tau\hat{\mathbf{j}} + 2\hat{\mathbf{k}}$

(e) $e^{-\tau}(\cos 2\tau\hat{\mathbf{i}} + \sin 2\tau\hat{\mathbf{j}})$
(f) $e^{\tau}(\cos 2\tau\hat{\mathbf{i}} + \sin 2\tau\hat{\mathbf{j}})$
(g) $\cos 3\tau\hat{\mathbf{i}} - 4\hat{\mathbf{j}} - \sin 3\tau\hat{\mathbf{k}}$
(h) $3\tau\hat{\mathbf{i}} - \hat{\mathbf{j}} + 2\tau^3\hat{\mathbf{k}}$

2. (a) Letting $\mathbf{u} = \hat{\mathbf{i}} - \tau^2\hat{\mathbf{j}}$, $\mathbf{v} = 2\cos\tau\hat{\mathbf{i}} - \tau\hat{\mathbf{k}}$, and $\mathbf{w} = \sin\tau\hat{\mathbf{j}}$, verify (7c) by working out the left- and right-hand sides.
(b) Repeat part (a), for (7d).
(c) Repeat part (a), for (7e).
(d) Repeat part (a), for (7f).

3. Use the definition (3) to derive (4a). Then show how (4b) follows from (4a).

4. Use the definition (3) to

(a) prove (7a) (b) prove (7d)

5. (a) Show that (7e) follows from (7c) and (7d).
(b) Show that (7f) follows from (7d).

6. Derive (7g). *Hint:* Express $\mathbf{u}(f(\tau)) = u_1(f(\tau))\hat{\mathbf{i}} + u_2(f(\tau))\hat{\mathbf{j}} + u_3(f(\tau))\hat{\mathbf{k}}$, and use (4a).

7. *(a) Obtain an expression for $(\mathbf{u} \cdot \mathbf{v})''$ analogous to the expression for $(\mathbf{u} \cdot \mathbf{v})'$ given by (7c).
(b) Obtain an expression for $(\mathbf{u} \times \mathbf{v})''$ analogous to the expression for $(\mathbf{u} \times \mathbf{v})'$ given by (7d).

8. (a) Derive the formula

$$\|\mathbf{u}\|' = \frac{\mathbf{u} \cdot \mathbf{u}'}{\|\mathbf{u}\|}. \quad \text{(a)}$$

(b) Show, from (a), that *if* $\|\mathbf{u}(\tau)\| = $ *constant* $\neq 0$, *then* $\mathbf{u}'(\tau)$ *is necessarily either perpendicular to* $\mathbf{u}(\tau)$, *or* $\mathbf{0}$.

POLAR, CYLINDRICAL, AND SPHERICAL COORDINATES 7.6

Optional Section

In preceding sections we worked either with no reference coordinate system at all, or with a Cartesian system. Often, it is most convenient to work with a coordinate system other than Cartesian—with a "non-Cartesian" system. Our purpose, in the present section, is to introduce three extremely important non-Cartesian systems: polar, cylindrical, and spherical. We choose to do this within the context of a single important physical application, the kinematics of a point (or particle). Specifically, we will develop expressions for the position vector $\mathbf{R}$, the velocity vector $\mathbf{v}$, and the acceleration $\mathbf{a}$ of a point, as it moves about in space, in terms of these three coordinate systems.

For reference, let us first note the corresponding results in a Cartesian system x, y, z, with base vectors $\hat{\mathbf{i}}, \hat{\mathbf{j}}, \hat{\mathbf{k}}$. If

$$\mathbf{R}(t) = x(t)\hat{\mathbf{i}} + y(t)\hat{\mathbf{j}} + z(t)\hat{\mathbf{k}} \quad (1)$$

denotes the *position vector* from the origin of a (stationary) Cartesian coordinate system to the point $(x(t), y(t), z(t))$, where t is the time, then the *velocity* $\mathbf{v}$ and *acceleration* $\mathbf{a}$ of the point are

$$\mathbf{v} = \dot{\mathbf{R}} = \dot{x}\hat{\mathbf{i}} + \dot{y}\hat{\mathbf{j}} + \dot{z}\hat{\mathbf{k}}, \quad (2)$$

$$\mathbf{a} = \dot{\mathbf{v}} = \ddot{\mathbf{R}} = \ddot{x}\hat{\mathbf{i}} + \ddot{y}\hat{\mathbf{j}} + \ddot{z}\hat{\mathbf{k}}, \quad (3)$$

respectively, where dots will be used (instead of primes) to denote differentiation with respect to the time.

POLAR COORDINATES

The coordinates r, θ and their respective unit base vectors $\hat{\mathbf{e}}_r$, $\hat{\mathbf{e}}_\theta$ are shown in Fig. 7.16; r, θ are related to the reference x, y coordinates according to

$$x = r\cos\theta, \qquad y = r\sin\theta; \qquad r = \sqrt{x^2 + y^2}, \qquad \theta = \tan^{-1}\frac{y}{x}, \quad (4)$$

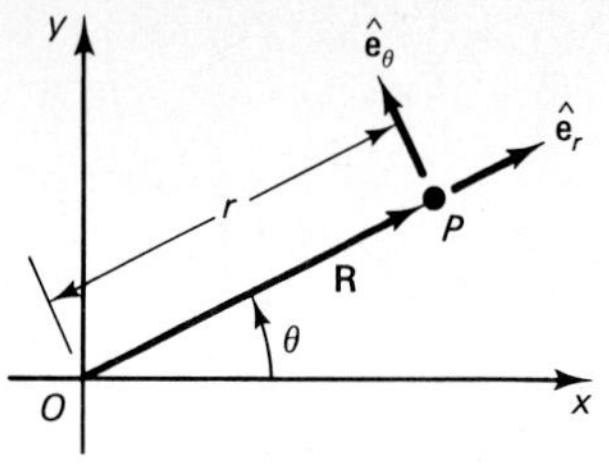

Fig. 7.16 Polar coordinates.

with θ undefined if $x = y = 0$. It will be understood that θ is measured in radians unless we specify that it is measured in degrees.

In general, both r and θ may be positive, negative, or zero, but we choose, in this book, always to have $r \geq 0$, so that r is the *distance* from the origin 0 to the point in question, say P. In addition, if we limit θ according to $0 \leq \theta < 2\pi$, each point in the x, y plane (except for the origin) corresponds to a unique value of θ.

Unfortunately, the relation $\theta = \tan^{-1} y/x$, given in (4), does not completely suffice to determine the unique value of θ at a given point without taking into account the signs of x and y. For example, if $x = y = 1$, then surely $\theta = \pi/4$, whereas $\theta = \tan^{-1}1$ gives both (the correct value) $\theta = \pi/4$ and the (incorrect value) $\theta = 5\pi/4$. Such ambiguity can always be resolved by the original relations $x = r \cos \theta$, $y = r \sin \theta$. For example, for the case $x = y = 1$ mentioned above, $\theta = \pi/4$ satisfies the relations $1 = \sqrt{2} \cos \theta$, $1 = \sqrt{2} \sin \theta$, whereas $\theta = 5\pi/4$ does not and is to be discarded.

The base vectors $\hat{\mathbf{e}}_r$, $\hat{\mathbf{e}}_\theta$ at any point P (other than the origin) are in the positive r, θ directions, respectively, as in Fig. 7.16. Observe that while $\hat{\mathbf{i}}$, $\hat{\mathbf{j}}$ are *constant* vectors,* $\hat{\mathbf{e}}_r$, $\hat{\mathbf{e}}_\theta$ are not! Specifically, $\hat{\mathbf{e}}_r$ and $\hat{\mathbf{e}}_\theta$ vary with θ, although not with r. For example, if we imagine sliding $\hat{\mathbf{e}}_r$, $\hat{\mathbf{e}}_\theta$ to a new r location, say $r + \Delta r$, with θ held fixed, we see that both vectors remain unchanged because both their magnitude (unity) and their direction remain unchanged, even though their location is different. But if we vary θ, with r fixed, $\hat{\mathbf{e}}_r$ and $\hat{\mathbf{e}}_\theta$ both rotate. The upshot is that

$$\hat{\mathbf{e}}_r = \hat{\mathbf{e}}_r(\theta), \qquad \hat{\mathbf{e}}_\theta = \hat{\mathbf{e}}_\theta(\theta). \tag{5}$$

Now, to obtain expressions for the velocity $\mathbf{v}$ and acceleration $\mathbf{a}$ of a point P moving in the x, y plane, we begin with the position vector from O to P (Fig. 7.16), namely,

$$\boxed{\mathbf{R} = r\hat{\mathbf{e}}_r.} \tag{6}$$

Before proceeding, two points should be made in connection with (6). First, students sometimes write "$\mathbf{R} = r\hat{\mathbf{e}}_r + \theta\hat{\mathbf{e}}_\theta$," in place of (6), in an effort to follow the pattern in the Cartesian formula $\mathbf{R} = x\hat{\mathbf{i}} + y\hat{\mathbf{j}}$. However, the quoted expression is *incorrect*; the correct version is given by (6), since (from Fig. 7.16) the magnitude of $\mathbf{R}$ is r and its direction is $\hat{\mathbf{e}}_r$. Second, is it not strange that θ does not appear in (6)? The answer is that θ *does* appear in (6) since, according to (5), $\hat{\mathbf{e}}_r$ is a function of θ; i.e., (6) is really $\mathbf{R} = r\hat{\mathbf{e}}_r(\theta)$.

* We should qualify that statement: Cartesian base vectors $\hat{\mathbf{i}}$, $\hat{\mathbf{j}}$, $\hat{\mathbf{k}}$ do not vary with the *space* coordinates x, y, z. They may, however, vary with *time* if the coordinate system itself is rotating with respect to the observer.

Now, if the point P moves about according to $r = r(t)$, $\theta = \theta(t)$, then

$$\mathbf{R}(t) = r(t)\hat{\mathbf{e}}_r[\theta(t)], \tag{7}$$

so its velocity is [recall (7a) on page 286]

$$\mathbf{v}(t) = \dot{\mathbf{R}}(t) = \dot{r}\hat{\mathbf{e}}_r + r\dot{\hat{\mathbf{e}}}_r, \tag{8}$$

the dots denoting time derivatives, as usual. But $\hat{\mathbf{e}}_r = \hat{\mathbf{e}}_r[\theta(t)]$, so, by chain differentiation, we can express*

$$\dot{\hat{\mathbf{e}}}_r = \frac{d}{dt}\hat{\mathbf{e}}_r[\theta(t)] = \frac{d\hat{\mathbf{e}}_r}{d\theta}\frac{d\theta}{dt} = \dot{\theta}\frac{d\hat{\mathbf{e}}_r}{d\theta}. \tag{9}$$

Fine, but what is $d\hat{\mathbf{e}}_r/d\theta$? The point to note here is that *all* vectors are ultimately to be expressed as linear combinations of the chosen base vectors—in this case $\hat{\mathbf{e}}_r$, $\hat{\mathbf{e}}_\theta$; after all, that is what base vectors are for. Thus it remains to express $d\hat{\mathbf{e}}_r/d\theta$ in the form $d\hat{\mathbf{e}}_r/d\theta = (\ )\hat{\mathbf{e}}_r + (\ )\hat{\mathbf{e}}_\theta$. To accomplish this, note that $\hat{\mathbf{e}}_r(\theta)$ is a vector function of a single variable, as discussed in Section 7.5, so we may fall back on the definition of the derivative,

$$\frac{d\hat{\mathbf{e}}_r}{d\theta} = \lim_{\Delta\theta\to 0}\frac{\hat{\mathbf{e}}_r(\theta + \Delta\theta) - \hat{\mathbf{e}}_r(\theta)}{\Delta\theta}. \tag{10}$$

The vector difference in the numerator is easily evaluated if we slide the two vectors back to O (Fig. 7.17) so that they are tail to tail. Then $\hat{\mathbf{e}}_r(\theta + \Delta\theta) - \hat{\mathbf{e}}_r(\theta)$ is the little vector from a to b; its length is $1\ \Delta\theta$ and its direction is $\hat{\mathbf{e}}_\theta$—at least, in the limit as $\Delta\theta \to 0$. Thus

$$\frac{d\hat{\mathbf{e}}_r}{d\theta} = \lim_{\Delta\theta\to 0}\frac{(1\ \Delta\theta)\hat{\mathbf{e}}_\theta}{\Delta\theta} = \hat{\mathbf{e}}_\theta, \tag{11}$$

so (9) is $\dot{\hat{\mathbf{e}}}_r = \dot{\theta}\hat{\mathbf{e}}_\theta$, and (8) becomes

$$\boxed{\mathbf{v}(t) = \dot{r}\hat{\mathbf{e}}_r + r\dot{\theta}\hat{\mathbf{e}}_\theta.} \tag{12}$$

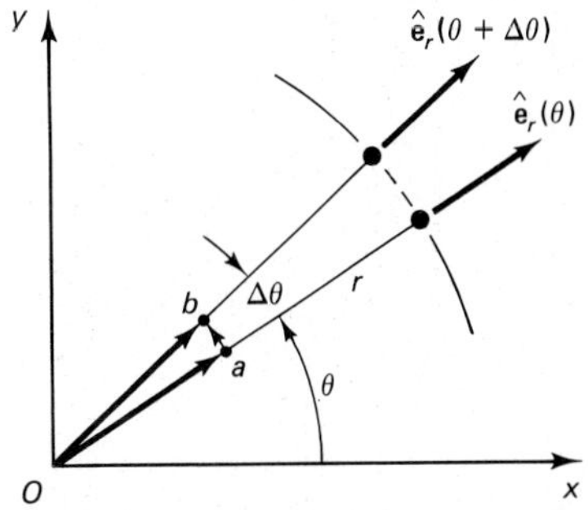

Fig. 7.17 Calculation of $d\hat{\mathbf{e}}_r/d\theta$.

* From a pedagogical point of view, observe that the simple act of writing out the functional dependence, in the second member of (9), goes a long way toward suggesting the subsequent steps. A trivial point, perhaps, but one worth keeping in mind in terms of "technique."

The forms $\dot{r}$, $r\dot{\theta}$ for the r, θ velocity components, respectively, may well be familiar to the reader from a course in introductory physics.

Continuing, we differentiate once more to obtain the acceleration,

$$\mathbf{a}(t) = \dot{\mathbf{v}}(t) = \ddot{r}\hat{\mathbf{e}}_r + \dot{r}\dot{\hat{\mathbf{e}}}_r + \dot{r}\dot{\theta}\hat{\mathbf{e}}_\theta + r\ddot{\theta}\hat{\mathbf{e}}_\theta + r\dot{\theta}\dot{\hat{\mathbf{e}}}_\theta. \tag{13}$$

We have already seen that $\dot{\hat{\mathbf{e}}}_r = \dot{\theta}\hat{\mathbf{e}}_\theta$, but we still need to evaluate the $\dot{\hat{\mathbf{e}}}_\theta$ in (13). We have

$$\dot{\hat{\mathbf{e}}}_\theta = \frac{d}{dt}\hat{\mathbf{e}}_\theta[\theta(t)] = \frac{d\hat{\mathbf{e}}_\theta}{d\theta}\frac{d\theta}{dt} = \dot{\theta}\frac{d\hat{\mathbf{e}}_\theta}{d\theta}, \tag{14}$$

where

$$\frac{d\hat{\mathbf{e}}_\theta}{d\theta} = \lim_{\Delta\theta\to 0}\frac{\hat{\mathbf{e}}_\theta(\theta + \Delta\theta) - \hat{\mathbf{e}}_\theta(\theta)}{\Delta\theta}. \tag{15}$$

To evaluate the difference $\hat{\mathbf{e}}_\theta(\theta + \Delta\theta) - \hat{\mathbf{e}}_\theta(\theta)$, where these two vectors are shown in Fig. 7.18a, we pick them up and place them tail to tail (without altering their orientation), as shown in Fig. 7.18b. Their difference is the little vector from a to b, namely $(1\ \Delta\theta)(-\hat{\mathbf{e}}_r)$, so that

$$\frac{d\hat{\mathbf{e}}_\theta}{d\theta} = \lim_{\Delta\theta\to 0}\frac{(1\ \Delta\theta)(-\hat{\mathbf{e}}_r)}{\Delta\theta} = -\hat{\mathbf{e}}_r. \tag{16}$$

Then (14) becomes $\dot{\hat{\mathbf{e}}}_\theta = -\dot{\theta}\hat{\mathbf{e}}_r$, and (13) gives

$$\mathbf{a}(t) = \ddot{r}\hat{\mathbf{e}}_r + \dot{r}\dot{\theta}\hat{\mathbf{e}}_\theta + \dot{r}\dot{\theta}\hat{\mathbf{e}}_\theta + r\ddot{\theta}\hat{\mathbf{e}}_\theta - r\dot{\theta}^2\hat{\mathbf{e}}_r$$

or

$$\boxed{\mathbf{a}(t) = (\ddot{r} - r\dot{\theta}^2)\hat{\mathbf{e}}_r + (r\ddot{\theta} + 2\dot{r}\dot{\theta})\hat{\mathbf{e}}_\theta.} \tag{17}$$

Of the four terms constituting $\mathbf{a}$, two with well-known names are the *centripetal acceleration* $-r\dot{\theta}^2\hat{\mathbf{e}}_r$, and the *Coriolis acceleration* $2\dot{r}\dot{\theta}\hat{\mathbf{e}}_\theta$. The latter is named after the French engineer *G. Coriolis* (1792–1843), but it might be mentioned that the expressions $a_r = \ddot{r} - r\dot{\theta}^2$ and $a_\theta = r\ddot{\theta} + 2\dot{r}\dot{\theta}$ were derived by Euler in his book *Theoria Motus Corporum Solidorum seu Rigidorum,* published in 1765.

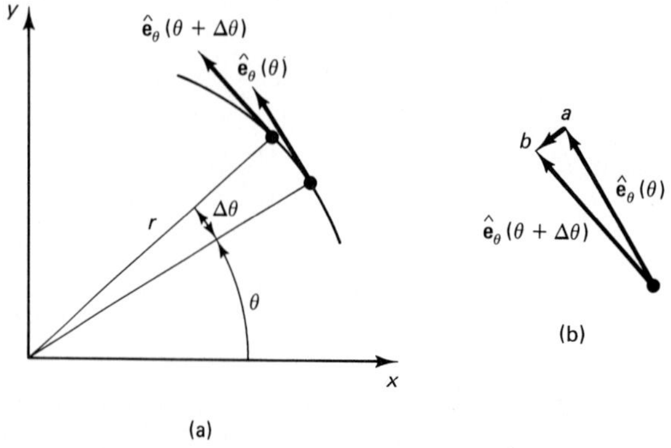

Fig. 7.18 Calculation of $d\hat{\mathbf{e}}_\theta/d\theta$.

Although the formulas (12) and (17) are of great importance and fully deserve to be "framed," as they are, let us stress that for our purposes the heart of the discussion above lies, instead, in our coping with the differentiation of the base vectors. For in non-Cartesian systems our base vectors generally depend on one or more of the space variables. [The space variables may, in turn, depend on the time, but that dependence presents no additional difficulty since we can always go from time derivatives to space derivatives via chain differentiation, as in (9) and (14).] In particular, we found that for the polar coordinate base vectors, $\hat{\mathbf{e}}_r$ and $\hat{\mathbf{e}}_\theta$,

$$\boxed{\frac{d\hat{\mathbf{e}}_r}{d\theta} = \hat{\mathbf{e}}_\theta \quad \text{and} \quad \frac{d\hat{\mathbf{e}}_\theta}{d\theta} = -\hat{\mathbf{e}}_r,} \tag{18a, b}$$

the r derivatives being zero since, as mentioned above, $\hat{\mathbf{e}}_r$ and $\hat{\mathbf{e}}_\theta$ do not vary with r.

Our difference-quotient type of derivation of (18a) and (18b) was, we believe, informative through the geometry and pictures that were involved. As you may have noticed, however, we were guilty of "hand waving" at one or two points, so that the derivation can only be regarded as heuristic.* Furthermore, the difference quotient method is found to be quite unwieldy in other cases, such as spherical coordinates. Thus we now indicate a rather different line of approach, which is rigorous, and of general and straightforward applicability. The idea is to express $\hat{\mathbf{e}}_r$ and $\hat{\mathbf{e}}_\theta$ (temporarily) in terms of the alternative Cartesian basis $\hat{\mathbf{i}}$, $\hat{\mathbf{j}}$, the point being that $\hat{\mathbf{i}}$ and $\hat{\mathbf{j}}$ are constant vectors, and hence easier to work with. Specifically,

$$\hat{\mathbf{e}}_r = \cos\theta\hat{\mathbf{i}} + \sin\theta\hat{\mathbf{j}}, \tag{19a}$$

$$\hat{\mathbf{e}}_\theta = -\sin\theta\hat{\mathbf{i}} + \cos\theta\hat{\mathbf{j}}, \tag{19b}$$

[The fact that $\hat{\mathbf{e}}_r$ and $\hat{\mathbf{e}}_\theta$ depend only on θ, as stated in (5), is seen to follow from the absence of any r dependence in the right-hand sides of (19).] Taking $d/d\theta$, we have

$$\frac{d\hat{\mathbf{e}}_r}{d\theta} = -\sin\theta\hat{\mathbf{i}} + \cos\theta\hat{\mathbf{j}}, \tag{20a}$$

$$\frac{d\hat{\mathbf{e}}_\theta}{d\theta} = -\cos\theta\hat{\mathbf{i}} - \sin\theta\hat{\mathbf{j}}. \tag{20b}$$

Again, we emphasize that this step was simple because $\hat{\mathbf{i}}$ and $\hat{\mathbf{j}}$ are constant vectors. With the differentiation completed, we now return to the polar base vectors by the "inverse" relations

$$\hat{\mathbf{i}} = \cos\theta\hat{\mathbf{e}}_r - \sin\theta\hat{\mathbf{e}}_\theta, \tag{21a}$$

$$\hat{\mathbf{j}} = \sin\theta\hat{\mathbf{e}}_r + \cos\theta\hat{\mathbf{e}}_\theta. \tag{21b}$$

That is, putting (21) into (20),

$$\frac{d\hat{\mathbf{e}}_r}{d\theta} = -\sin\theta(\cos\theta\hat{\mathbf{e}}_r - \sin\theta\hat{\mathbf{e}}_\theta) + \cos\theta(\sin\theta\hat{\mathbf{e}}_r + \cos\theta\hat{\mathbf{e}}_\theta)$$

$$= (\sin^2\theta + \cos^2\theta)\hat{\mathbf{e}}_\theta = \hat{\mathbf{e}}_\theta,$$

* It can, however, be made rigorous.

and

$$\frac{d\hat{\mathbf{e}}_\theta}{d\theta} = -\cos\theta(\cos\theta\hat{\mathbf{e}}_r - \sin\theta\hat{\mathbf{e}}_\theta) - \sin\theta(\sin\theta\hat{\mathbf{e}}_r + \cos\theta\hat{\mathbf{e}}_\theta)$$

$$= -(\cos^2\theta + \sin^2\theta)\hat{\mathbf{e}}_r = -\hat{\mathbf{e}}_r,$$

as before.

In case the source of the relations (19) and (21) was not clear, let us elaborate. According to the general expansion formula (21) on page 53, we have $\hat{\mathbf{e}}_r = (\hat{\mathbf{e}}_r \cdot \hat{\mathbf{i}})\hat{\mathbf{i}} + (\hat{\mathbf{e}}_r \cdot \hat{\mathbf{j}})\hat{\mathbf{j}}$ and $\hat{\mathbf{e}}_\theta = (\hat{\mathbf{e}}_\theta \cdot \hat{\mathbf{i}})\hat{\mathbf{i}} + (\hat{\mathbf{e}}_\theta \cdot \hat{\mathbf{j}})\hat{\mathbf{j}}$. Turning to the coefficients, $\hat{\mathbf{e}}_r \cdot \hat{\mathbf{i}} = \|\hat{\mathbf{e}}_r\| \|\hat{\mathbf{i}}\| \cos$ (angle between $\hat{\mathbf{e}}_r$ and $\hat{\mathbf{i}}$) $= (1)(1)\cos\theta$ (Fig. 7.19), $\hat{\mathbf{e}}_r \cdot \hat{\mathbf{j}} = (1)(1)\cos(\pi/2 - \theta) = \sin\theta$, $\hat{\mathbf{e}}_\theta \cdot \hat{\mathbf{i}} = (1)(1)\cos(\pi/2 + \theta) = -\sin\theta$, and $\hat{\mathbf{e}}_\theta \cdot \hat{\mathbf{j}} = (1)(1)\cos\theta = \cos\theta$. Similarly for the inverse relations, $\hat{\mathbf{i}} = (\hat{\mathbf{i}} \cdot \hat{\mathbf{e}}_r)\hat{\mathbf{e}}_r + (\hat{\mathbf{i}} \cdot \hat{\mathbf{e}}_\theta)\hat{\mathbf{e}}_\theta$, and so on.

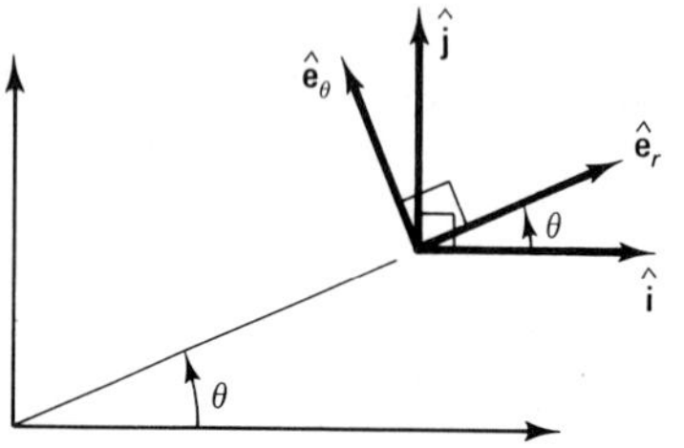

Fig. 7.19 Angles between $\hat{\mathbf{e}}_r$, $\hat{\mathbf{e}}_\theta$, $\hat{\mathbf{i}}$, and $\hat{\mathbf{j}}$.

It may be helpful to consider a rough analogy that exists between the latter method of base vector differentiation and the method of integral transforms.* For example, Laplace transforming the equation $\ddot{x} + x = F(t)$, one obtains the equation $s^2\bar{x} - sx(0) - \dot{x}(0) + \bar{x} = \bar{F}$. Thus in place of a differential equation on $x(t)$, we have merely an algebraic equation on $\bar{x}(s)$. Solving this simple equation for $\bar{x}(s)$, we then recover the desired solution $x(t)$ by applying the inverse transform to $\bar{x}$. With this procedure in mind, notice that we may regard (19) as a "transform" from $\hat{\mathbf{e}}_r$, $\hat{\mathbf{e}}_\theta$ to $\hat{\mathbf{i}}$, $\hat{\mathbf{j}}$. In (20) we carried out the desired calculation, a simple calculation by virtue of $\hat{\mathbf{i}}$ and $\hat{\mathbf{j}}$ being constant vectors, and then we employed the "inverse transformation" (21) to return to $\hat{\mathbf{e}}_r$, $\hat{\mathbf{e}}_\theta$.

CYLINDRICAL COORDINATES

The cylindrical coordinate system r, θ, z (with unit base vectors $\hat{\mathbf{e}}_r$, $\hat{\mathbf{e}}_\theta$, $\hat{\mathbf{e}}_z$) shown in Fig. 7.20a is essentially the plane polar coordinate system that we have just discussed, but with z (and $\hat{\mathbf{e}}_z$) tossed in. Such a coordinate system might well be employed in studying the electric field within a coaxial cable, for example. These coordinates are related to the reference x, y, z coordinates according to

$$x = r\cos\theta, \qquad y = r\sin\theta, \qquad z = z; \tag{22a}$$

$$r = \sqrt{x^2 + y^2}, \qquad \theta = \tan^{-1}\frac{y}{x}, \qquad z = z. \tag{22b}$$

* Laplace and Fourier transforms are not presented in this book until Part III, but most readers will have met the Laplace transform, if only briefly, in a course in ordinary differential equations.

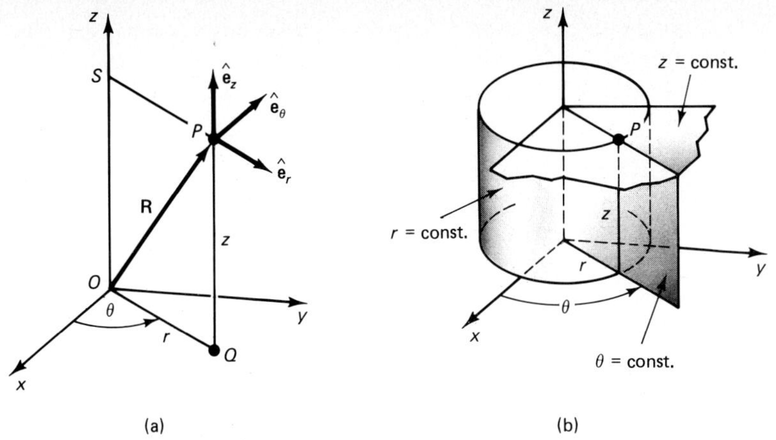

Fig. 7.20 Cylindrical coordinates.

Notice that the z in r, θ, z is the same as the Cartesian z variable. Similarly, $\hat{\mathbf{e}}_z$ is identical to $\hat{\mathbf{k}}$, and we would write $\hat{\mathbf{e}}_r$, $\hat{\mathbf{e}}_\theta$, $\hat{\mathbf{k}}$, except that $\hat{\mathbf{e}}_r$, $\hat{\mathbf{e}}_\theta$, $\hat{\mathbf{e}}_z$ looks better, in the author's opinion, from an aesthetic point of view.

Observe, from Fig. 7.20b, that the r = constant surface through P is a *circular cylinder* of radius r, about the z axis; the θ = constant surface through P is a plane, called a *meridional plane;* and the z = constant surface through P is a *plane* parallel to the x, y plane.

The position vector is $\mathbf{R} = \mathbf{OQ} + \mathbf{QP}$, where $\mathbf{OQ} = r\hat{\mathbf{e}}_r$ and $\mathbf{QP} = z\hat{\mathbf{e}}_z$. Thus

$$\boxed{\mathbf{R} = r\hat{\mathbf{e}}_r + z\hat{\mathbf{e}}_z,} \tag{23}$$

which is the same as (6), with $z\hat{\mathbf{e}}_z$ added on. Here it is important to see that whereas $\hat{\mathbf{e}}_r$ and $\hat{\mathbf{e}}_\theta$ are functions of θ, $\hat{\mathbf{e}}_z$ is a *constant vector;* at every point P, $\hat{\mathbf{e}}_z$ has the same magnitude and the same direction. Thus if $r = r(t)$, $\theta = \theta(t)$, and $z = z(t)$, where t is the time, the velocity $\mathbf{v} = \dot{\mathbf{R}}$ and the acceleration $\mathbf{a} = \ddot{\mathbf{R}}$ are given by the formulas

$$\boxed{\mathbf{v}(t) = \dot{\mathbf{R}}(t) = \dot{r}\hat{\mathbf{e}}_r + r\dot{\theta}\hat{\mathbf{e}}_\theta + \dot{z}\hat{\mathbf{e}}_z} \tag{24}$$

and

$$\boxed{\mathbf{a}(t) = \ddot{\mathbf{R}}(t) = (\ddot{r} - r\dot{\theta}^2)\hat{\mathbf{e}}_r + (r\ddot{\theta} + 2\dot{r}\dot{\theta})\hat{\mathbf{e}}_\theta + \ddot{z}\hat{\mathbf{e}}_z;} \tag{25}$$

i.e., we merely append $\dot{z}\hat{\mathbf{e}}_z$ to (12) and $\ddot{z}\hat{\mathbf{e}}_z$ to (17).

EXAMPLE 1 Let a particle move according to

$$r = \text{constant}, \qquad \theta = \omega t, \qquad z = vt,$$

where ω and v are constants, and $0 \le t < \infty$. Evidently, the path of motion is helical. From (24) and (25),

$$\mathbf{v}(t) = r\omega\hat{\mathbf{e}}_\theta + v\hat{\mathbf{e}}_z, \tag{26a}$$

$$\mathbf{a}(t) = -r\omega^2\hat{\mathbf{e}}_r. \tag{26b}$$

Observe that $\mathbf{v}(t)$ is *not* a constant, even though its components $r\omega$ and v are constant, because $\hat{\mathbf{e}}_\theta = \hat{\mathbf{e}}_\theta(\theta(t))$ varies with t. [Indeed, if $\mathbf{v}(t)$ *were* constant, then $\mathbf{a}(t) = \dot{\mathbf{v}}(t)$ would be zero, not $-r\omega^2\hat{\mathbf{e}}_r$.] ◀

SPHERICAL COORDINATES

Finally, we present the spherical coordinates ρ, ϕ, θ, with their respective unit base vectors $\hat{\mathbf{e}}_\rho$, $\hat{\mathbf{e}}_\phi$, $\hat{\mathbf{e}}_\theta$, as shown in Fig. 7.21a. Some authors use the notation r, ϕ, θ, but we prefer to emphasize the difference between the spherical coordinate ρ and the cylindrical coordinate r by using different letters. What difference? Well, $\rho = \sqrt{x^2 + y^2 + z^2}$ is the distance from the origin to P, whereas $r = \sqrt{x^2 + y^2}$ is not (unless $z = 0$); it is the perpendicular distance from P to the z axis. The angle θ, however *is* the same in the two coordinate systems—cylindrical and spherical.

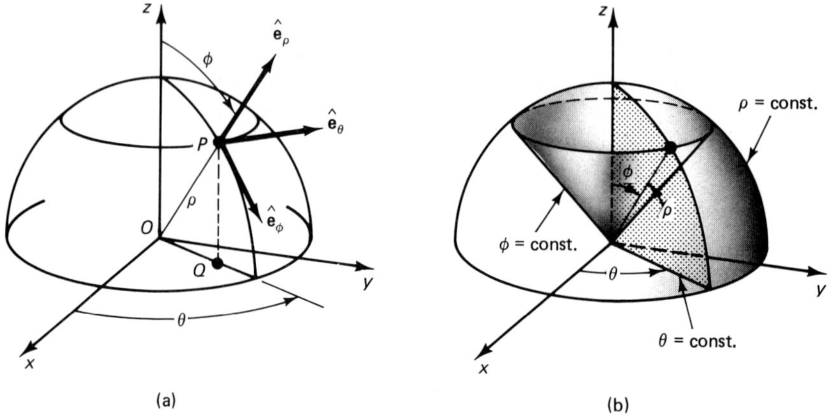

Fig. 7.21 Spherical coordinates.

In general, ρ, ϕ, and θ may be positive, negative, or zero; however, in this book we choose always to have $\rho \geq 0$, so that ρ is the *distance* from the origin to P.

It may be seen from Fig. 7.21(a) that ρ, ϕ, θ are related to x, y, z according to*

$$x = \rho \sin \phi \cos \theta, \qquad y = \rho \sin \phi \sin \theta, \qquad z = \rho \cos \phi; \tag{27a}$$

$$\rho = \sqrt{x^2 + y^2 + z^2}, \qquad \phi = \cos^{-1} \frac{z}{\rho}, \qquad \theta = \tan^{-1} \frac{y}{x}, \tag{27b}$$

where θ is undefined if $x = y = 0$ and ϕ is undefined if $x = y = z = 0$. The ρ = constant surface through P is the *spherical* surface of radius ρ centered at the origin (Fig. 7.21b), since $x^2 + y^2 + z^2 = \rho^2$; the ϕ = constant surface through P is *conical*; and the θ = constant surface through P is a *meridional plane*.

EXAMPLE 2 Given that P is the point $x = 2$, $y = -1$, $z = 3$, find ρ, ϕ, θ such that $0 \leq \phi \leq \pi$, $0 \leq \theta < 2\pi$ (and $\rho \geq 0$, as noted above). From (27b), $\rho = \sqrt{2^2 + (-1)^2 + 3^3} = \sqrt{14}$, $\phi = \cos^{-1}(3/\sqrt{14}) \approx 36.70°$, and $\theta = \tan^{-1}(-1/2) \approx 153.4°$ and $333.4°$. Proceeding as suggested on page 288 we consider the equations $x = \rho \sin \phi \cos \theta$, $y = \rho \sin \phi \sin \theta$, which become 2 =

* For example, $x = \| \mathbf{OQ} \| \cos \theta$, where $\| \mathbf{OQ} \| = \rho \sin \phi$, so $x = \rho \sin \phi \cos \theta$.

$\sqrt{14}(\sin 36.7°) \cos \theta$ and $-1 = \sqrt{14}(\sin 36.7°) \sin \theta$. These equations are satisfied by $\theta \approx 333.4°$, and not by $\theta \approx 153.4°$. Thus the former is correct and the latter is incorrect. ◀

As emphasized earlier in this section, it will be essential, in working with this coordinate system, to know the "space derivatives" of the base vectors, i.e., $\partial/\partial\rho$, $\partial/\partial\phi$, $\partial/\partial\theta$ of each of the three base vectors. From Fig. 7.21a we see that if we hold ϕ and θ fixed and vary ρ, the $\hat{\mathbf{e}}_\rho$, $\hat{\mathbf{e}}_\phi$, $\hat{\mathbf{e}}_\theta$, triad translates parallel to itself as P moves along the radial line. Thus $\hat{\mathbf{e}}_\rho$, $\hat{\mathbf{e}}_\phi$, $\hat{\mathbf{e}}_\theta$, do not vary with ρ, so $\partial\hat{\mathbf{e}}_\rho/\partial\rho = \partial\hat{\mathbf{e}}_\phi/\partial\rho = \partial\hat{\mathbf{e}}_\theta/\partial\rho = \mathbf{0}$. Next, imagine varying ϕ, with ρ and θ fixed. Then (Fig. 7.21a) $\hat{\mathbf{e}}_\theta$ moves parallel to itself, and hence does not change, whereas $\hat{\mathbf{e}}_\rho$ and $\hat{\mathbf{e}}_\phi$ both rotate. Finally, if we vary θ, with ρ and ϕ fixed, we see that all three base vectors rotate. The upshot is that the dependence of the base vectors on the coordinates is as follows:

$$\hat{\mathbf{e}}_\rho = \hat{\mathbf{e}}_\rho(\phi, \theta), \qquad \hat{\mathbf{e}}_\phi = \hat{\mathbf{e}}_\phi(\phi, \theta), \qquad \hat{\mathbf{e}}_\theta = \hat{\mathbf{e}}_\theta(\theta). \tag{28}$$

And the space derivatives are found to be

$$\boxed{\begin{aligned} &\frac{\partial\hat{\mathbf{e}}_\rho}{\partial\rho} = \mathbf{0}, \quad &&\frac{\partial\hat{\mathbf{e}}_\rho}{\partial\phi} = \hat{\mathbf{e}}_\phi, \quad &&\frac{\partial\hat{\mathbf{e}}_\rho}{\partial\theta} = \sin\phi\,\hat{\mathbf{e}}_\theta, \\ &\frac{\partial\hat{\mathbf{e}}_\phi}{\partial\rho} = \mathbf{0}, &&\frac{\partial\hat{\mathbf{e}}_\phi}{\partial\phi} = -\hat{\mathbf{e}}_\rho, &&\frac{\partial\hat{\mathbf{e}}_\phi}{\partial\theta} = \cos\phi\,\hat{\mathbf{e}}_\theta, \\ &\frac{\partial\hat{\mathbf{e}}_\theta}{\partial\rho} = \mathbf{0}, &&\frac{\partial\hat{\mathbf{e}}_\theta}{\partial\phi} = \mathbf{0}, &&\frac{\partial\hat{\mathbf{e}}_\theta}{\partial\theta} = -\sin\phi\,\hat{\mathbf{e}}_\rho - \cos\phi\,\hat{\mathbf{e}}_\phi. \end{aligned}} \tag{29}$$

Derivation of equations (29) is left for the exercises.

Let us illustrate the use of (29) by deriving spherical-coordinate expressions for the velocity and acceleration, expressions analogous to those obtained for polar and cylindrical coordinates. We begin with the position vector $\mathbf{R} = \mathbf{OP} = \|\mathbf{OP}\|\hat{\mathbf{e}}_\rho$, i.e.,

$$\boxed{\mathbf{R} = \rho\hat{\mathbf{e}}_\rho.} \tag{30}$$

Since $\hat{\mathbf{e}}_\rho = \hat{\mathbf{e}}_\rho[\phi(t), \theta(t)]$, differentiation with respect to t gives

$$\begin{aligned} \mathbf{v} = \dot{\mathbf{R}} &= \dot{\rho}\hat{\mathbf{e}}_\rho + \rho\left(\frac{\partial\hat{\mathbf{e}}_\rho}{\partial\phi}\frac{d\phi}{dt} + \frac{\partial\hat{\mathbf{e}}_\rho}{\partial\theta}\frac{d\theta}{dt}\right) \\ &= \dot{\rho}\hat{\mathbf{e}}_\rho + \rho(\dot{\phi}\hat{\mathbf{e}}_\phi + \dot{\theta}\sin\phi\,\hat{\mathbf{e}}_\theta) \end{aligned}$$

or

$$\boxed{\mathbf{v}(t) = \dot{\rho}\hat{\mathbf{e}}_\rho + \rho\dot{\phi}\hat{\mathbf{e}}_\phi + \rho\dot{\theta}\sin\phi\,\hat{\mathbf{e}}_\theta.} \tag{31}$$

One more differentiation (Exercise 7) gives

$$\boxed{\begin{aligned} \mathbf{a}(t) = {} &(\ddot{\rho} - \rho\dot{\phi}^2 - \rho\dot{\theta}^2\sin^2\phi)\hat{\mathbf{e}}_\rho + (\rho\ddot{\phi} + 2\dot{\rho}\,\dot{\phi} - \rho\dot{\theta}^2\sin\phi\cos\phi)\hat{\mathbf{e}}_\phi \\ &+ (\rho\ddot{\theta}\sin\phi + 2\dot{\rho}\dot{\theta}\sin\phi + 2\rho\dot{\theta}\dot{\phi}\cos\phi)\hat{\mathbf{e}}_\theta \end{aligned}} \tag{32}$$

for the acceleration.

In this section we have introduced three non-Cartesian coordinate systems—polar, cylindrical, and spherical—and their base vectors. As an important application, we considered the kinematics of a point, in each of these systems, and obtained expressions for the position vector **R**, the velocity **v**, and the acceleration **a**. This discussion forced us to deal with time derivatives of the various base vectors. Applying chain differentiation, we managed to trade in the time derivatives for space derivatives. And to evaluate these space derivatives we put forward two methods: (1) the difference quotient method, and (2) expressing the base vector in terms of $\hat{\mathbf{i}}$, $\hat{\mathbf{j}}$, $\hat{\mathbf{k}}$, differentiating, and then reexpressing in terms of the non-Cartesian base vectors. A third method, for evaluating time *or* space derivatives of base vectors, is described on pages 139–141 (especially Example 8.2) of the book by M. Greenberg [*Foundations of Applied Mathematics*, (Englewood Cliffs, N.J.: Prentice-Hall, 1978)].

Finally, let us add emphasis to an important feature of cylindrical and spherical coordinates. Any given point in 3-space corresponds uniquely to a set of x, y, z coordinate values. The same is *not true,* however, for cylindrical and spherical coordinates because the inverse functions $r(x, y)$, $\theta(x, y)$, z implied by the relations $x = r \cos\theta$, $y = r\sin\theta$, $z = z$, and the inverse functions $\rho(x, y, z)$, $\phi(x, y, z)$, $\theta(x, y)$ implied by the relations $x = \rho\sin\phi\cos\theta$, $y = \rho\sin\phi\sin\theta$, $z = \rho\cos\phi$, are not single valued. For example, $x = y = z = 2$ corresponds to $r = \sqrt{2}$, $\theta = \pi/4$, $z = 2$, to $r = -\sqrt{2}$, $\theta = 5\pi/4$, $z = 2$, to $r = \sqrt{2}$, $\theta = -7\pi/4$, $z = 2$, and so on, and similarly for spherical coordinates. We did choose to restrict $r \geq 0$ and $\rho \geq 0$ throughout this book, and this restriction reduces, but does not completely eliminate, the noted absence of single valuedness. The lack of single valuedness even carries over to the base vectors and the vector fields. For example, $\mathbf{v} = 6\hat{\mathbf{e}}_\rho - 2\hat{\mathbf{e}}_\phi + 5\hat{\mathbf{e}}_\theta$ at the point $P = (x, y, z) = (0, -1, 0)$ is the vector $\mathbf{v} = 6(-\hat{\mathbf{j}}) - 2(-\hat{\mathbf{k}}) + 5(\hat{\mathbf{i}}) = 5\hat{\mathbf{i}} - 6\hat{\mathbf{j}} + 2\hat{\mathbf{k}}$ if P is regarded as $(\rho, \phi, \theta) = (1, \pi/2, 3\pi/2)$, and is the (different!) vector $\mathbf{v} = 6(-\hat{\mathbf{j}}) - 2(\hat{\mathbf{k}}) + 5(-\hat{\mathbf{i}}) = -5\hat{\mathbf{i}} - 6\hat{\mathbf{j}} - 2\hat{\mathbf{k}}$ if P is regarded as $(\rho, \phi, \theta) = (1, 3\pi/2, \pi/2)$, The important conclusion, then, is that one must be clear, in a given discussion or application, on the restrictions placed on the coordinate variables. For example, in working with all of 3-space one may choose the restriction $\rho \geq 0$, $0 \leq \phi \leq \pi$, $0 \leq \theta < 2\pi$, the restriction $\rho \geq 0$, $0 \leq \phi < 2\pi$, $0 \leq \theta \leq \pi$, or some other restriction.

7.6 EXERCISES

1. Determine r, θ, z corresponding to each given point $P = (x, y, z)$. Give θ both in radians $(0 \leq \theta < 2\pi)$ and in degrees $(0° \leq \theta < 360°)$.

*(a) (2, 2, 0) (b) (2, −1, 0)
(c) (−3, 0, 0) *(d) (0, 5, 2)
(e) (6, −1, 3) (f) (−1, −2, 6)
(g) (−1, −5, 1) (h) (6, 0, −4)

2. Determine ρ, ϕ, θ corresponding to each given point $P = (x, y, z)$, such that $\rho \geq 0$, $0 \leq \phi \leq \pi$, $0 \leq \theta < 2\pi$. Give ϕ and θ both in radians and in degrees.

*(a) (2, 0, 0) (b) (0, 3, 0)
(c) (0, 5, 0) (d) (−2, 0, 0)
*(e) (6, −3, 1) (f) (0, −5, 0)
(g) (2, 3, 5) (h) (2, 3, −5)
(i) (−2, 3, 5) (j) (2, −3, 5)
(k) (−1, −2, 1) (l) (4, −2, −3)

3. Compute $d\mathbf{A}/dt$ in each case.

*(a) $\mathbf{A} = \sin\theta\,\hat{\mathbf{e}}_r - r\theta^2\hat{\mathbf{e}}_\theta + r\hat{\mathbf{e}}_z$; $r = t^2$, $\theta = 3t$
(b) $\mathbf{A} = t\hat{\mathbf{e}}_r$; $r = 4$, $\theta = 2t$
(c) $\mathbf{A} = r\hat{\mathbf{e}}_r$; $r = 6 + \sin t$, $\theta = \cos t$
(d) $\mathbf{A} = \rho^2\hat{\mathbf{e}}_\rho$; $\rho = t$, $\phi = 2t$, $\theta = 3t$

(e) $\mathbf{A} = \hat{\mathbf{e}}_\phi$; $\rho = 1 + t$, $\phi = t^2$, $\theta = \sin 2t$
(f) $\mathbf{A} = \hat{\mathbf{e}}_\rho + t\hat{\mathbf{e}}_\theta$; $\rho = 1$, $\phi = t$, $\theta = t^2$.

4. A particle moves in the x,y plane according to $x = t^2$, $y = 2$. Compute its velocity and acceleration in terms of $\hat{\mathbf{e}}_r$ and $\hat{\mathbf{e}}_\theta$.

5. (*Derivation of space derivatives of* $\hat{\mathbf{e}}_\rho$, $\hat{\mathbf{e}}_\phi$, $\hat{\mathbf{e}}_\theta$) If one sketches in the cylindrical base vectors $\hat{\mathbf{e}}_z$ and $\hat{\mathbf{e}}_r$ at P, in Fig. 7.21, it can be seen that $\hat{\mathbf{e}}_\rho = \sin\phi\hat{\mathbf{e}}_r + \cos\phi\hat{\mathbf{e}}_z$. Furthermore, $\hat{\mathbf{e}}_r = \cos\theta\hat{\mathbf{i}} + \sin\theta\hat{\mathbf{j}}$ per (19a), and $\hat{\mathbf{e}}_z = \hat{\mathbf{k}}$, so that

$$\hat{\mathbf{e}}_\rho = \sin\phi(\cos\theta\hat{\mathbf{i}} + \sin\theta\hat{\mathbf{j}}) + \cos\phi\hat{\mathbf{k}}. \qquad \text{(a)}$$

Next, we see from Fig. 7.21 that $\hat{\mathbf{e}}_\phi$ can be obtained from $\hat{\mathbf{e}}_\rho$ by adding $\pi/2$ to ϕ. Thus

$$\hat{\mathbf{e}}_\phi = \sin\left(\phi + \frac{\pi}{2}\right)(\cos\theta\hat{\mathbf{i}} + \sin\theta\hat{\mathbf{j}}) + \cos\left(\phi + \frac{\pi}{2}\right)\hat{\mathbf{k}},$$

so

$$\hat{\mathbf{e}}_\phi = \cos\phi(\cos\theta\hat{\mathbf{i}} + \sin\theta\hat{\mathbf{j}}) - \sin\phi\hat{\mathbf{k}}. \qquad \text{(b)}$$

Finally,

$$\hat{\mathbf{e}}_\theta = -\sin\theta\hat{\mathbf{i}} + \cos\theta\hat{\mathbf{j}}, \qquad \text{(c)}$$

since the spherical coordinate base vector $\hat{\mathbf{e}}_\theta$ is the same as for cylindrical coordinates; hence (19b) applies. Expressing (a), (b), and (c) in matrix form, we have

$$\begin{pmatrix} \hat{\mathbf{e}}_\rho \\ \hat{\mathbf{e}}_\phi \\ \hat{\mathbf{e}}_\theta \end{pmatrix} = \begin{pmatrix} \sin\phi\cos\theta & \sin\phi\sin\theta & \cos\phi \\ \cos\phi\cos\theta & \cos\phi\sin\theta & -\sin\phi \\ -\sin\theta & \cos\theta & 0 \end{pmatrix} \begin{pmatrix} \hat{\mathbf{i}} \\ \hat{\mathbf{j}} \\ \hat{\mathbf{k}} \end{pmatrix}. \qquad \text{(d)}$$

(a) Solving (d) for $\hat{\mathbf{i}}$, $\hat{\mathbf{j}}$, $\hat{\mathbf{k}}$, show that

$$\hat{\mathbf{i}} = \sin\phi\cos\theta\hat{\mathbf{e}}_\rho + \cos\phi\cos\theta\hat{\mathbf{e}}_\phi - \sin\theta\hat{\mathbf{e}}_\theta \qquad \text{(e)}$$

$$\hat{\mathbf{j}} = \sin\phi\sin\theta\hat{\mathbf{e}}_\rho + \cos\phi\sin\theta\hat{\mathbf{e}}_\phi + \cos\theta\hat{\mathbf{e}}_\theta \qquad \text{(f)}$$

$$\hat{\mathbf{k}} = \cos\phi\hat{\mathbf{e}}_\rho - \sin\phi\hat{\mathbf{e}}_\phi. \qquad \text{(g)}$$

Hint: If you can verify that the coefficient matrix in (d) is orthogonal (Section 3.7), then its inverse is merely its transpose.
(b) Use (a), (b), (c), (e), (f), and (g) to derive $\partial\hat{\mathbf{e}}_\rho/\partial\rho$, $\partial\hat{\mathbf{e}}_\rho/\partial\phi$, and $\partial\hat{\mathbf{e}}_\rho/\partial\theta$. Your results should agree with those given in (29).
(c) Repeat part (b), for $\partial\hat{\mathbf{e}}_\phi/\partial\rho$, $\partial\hat{\mathbf{e}}_\phi/\partial\phi$, and $\partial\hat{\mathbf{e}}_\phi/\partial\theta$.
(d) Repeat part (b), for $\partial\hat{\mathbf{e}}_\theta/\partial\rho$, $\partial\hat{\mathbf{e}}_\theta/\partial\phi$, and $\partial\hat{\mathbf{e}}_\theta/\partial\theta$.

6. Evaluate each of the following by the difference quotient method, and show that your result agrees with that given in (29).

(a) $\partial\hat{\mathbf{e}}_\rho/\partial\phi$
(b) $\partial\hat{\mathbf{e}}_\rho/\partial\theta$
(c) $\partial\hat{\mathbf{e}}_\phi/\partial\phi$
(d) $\partial\hat{\mathbf{e}}_\phi/\partial\theta$
(e) $\partial\hat{\mathbf{e}}_\theta/\partial\theta$

7. Derive (32) from (31), using (29).

8. Beginning at O at time $t = 0$, a bead moves at a constant speed V through a straight hollow tube, which rotates at constant angular velocity Ω about the z axis, so as to sweep out a cone of half angle $\pi/4$, as shown. Compute the velocity $\mathbf{v}$, and the acceleration $\mathbf{a}$ of the particle, in terms of s, V, and Ω, using

(a) Cartesian coordinates
(b) cylindrical coordinates
*(c) spherical coordinates

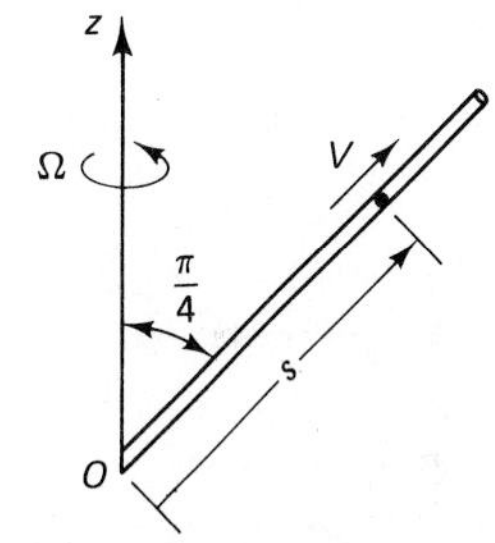

Note: Let us orient the x, y, z coordinate frame so that the tube lies in the x, z plane at $t = 0$.

***9.** Beginning at the "north pole" ($\phi = 0$), a particle spirals down the surface of a sphere of radius ρ such that the spherical coordinates ϕ and θ vary as $\phi = \Omega_1 t$, $\theta = \Omega_2 t$. Find the magnitude of the velocity and acceleration vectors at the instant when the particle crosses the "equator."

10. Observe, in (29), that none of the derivatives of $\hat{\mathbf{e}}_\rho$ contain an $\hat{\mathbf{e}}_\rho$ component, that none of the derivatives of $\hat{\mathbf{e}}_\phi$ contain an $\hat{\mathbf{e}}_\phi$ component, and that none of the derivatives of $\hat{\mathbf{e}}_\theta$ contain an $\hat{\mathbf{e}}_\theta$ component. The same pattern holds in (18). Explain why this pattern is more than coincidence.

7.7 SPACE CURVES; SERRET–FRENET FORMULAS

SPACE CURVES

It should be evident that curves in space are of great importance. In mechanics, for example, the relationship between the forces acting on a point mass and the trajectory of the mass (i.e., the space curve developed by the motion) is of critical interest.

We met curves, indirectly, in the preceding section, when we considered the variation of $\mathbf{u}(\tau)$ with τ. For, in general, if the tail of $\mathbf{u}(\tau)$ is fixed, then the head of $\mathbf{u}(\tau)$ generates a space curve as the parameter τ is varied. In the present section, however, we shift our focus from the vector $\mathbf{u}(\tau)$ to the space curve itself.

First, some basic terminology. Let a Cartesian x, y, z coordinate system be specified, and let

$$x = x(\tau), \qquad y = y(\tau), \qquad z = z(\tau) \tag{1}$$

be continuous functions of a real parameter τ over a closed interval $[\tau_1, \tau_2]$ (i.e., $\tau_1 \leq \tau \leq \tau_2$). The points $(x(\tau), y(\tau), z(\tau)) \equiv P(\tau)$ for $\tau_1 \leq \tau \leq \tau_2$ are said to constitute a **curve** joining the endpoints $P(\tau_1)$ and $P(\tau_2)$, and we call (1) a *parametrization* of the curve.* If the endpoints coincide, the curve is called a **closed curve**; if not, it is called an **arc**. If the tail of the position vector

$$\mathbf{R}(\tau) = x(\tau)\hat{\mathbf{i}} + y(\tau)\hat{\mathbf{j}} + z(\tau)\hat{\mathbf{k}} \tag{2}$$

is fixed at the origin, then the head of $\mathbf{R}(\tau)$ generates the curve as τ varies from τ_1 to τ_2.

EXAMPLE 1 Suppose that

$$x = a\tau + \cos\tau, \qquad y = \sin\tau, \qquad z = 0 \qquad (a = \text{constant}), \tag{3}$$

so that $\mathbf{R}(\tau) = (a\tau + \cos\tau)\hat{\mathbf{i}} + \sin\tau\hat{\mathbf{j}}$. Since $z = 0$, the curve lies in a plane (the x, y plane in this case) and is thus called a *plane curve*. Choosing different values of a and different τ intervals, we obtain different curves. Four such cases are illustrated in Fig. 7.22. ◀

Observe that different parametrizations may produce the same curve. For example, $P(\tau) = (\tau, \tau, 0)$ and $P(\tau) = (\tau^3 + 6, \tau^3 + 6, 0)$, $-\infty < \tau < \infty$, are parametrizations of the same straight line, namely, the straight line $y = x$ in the x, y plane.

Next, we consider the "arc length" $s(\tau)$ of a curve $\mathscr{C}$, say, from some point $P(\tau_0)$ to any point $P(\tau)$ on the curve. We know what we mean by the length of a *straight*-line segment, but what is the "length" of a curved arc? As we do so often in mathematics, we define this new quantity as the limit of a sequence of old quanti-

* If each of $x(\tau)$, $y(\tau)$, and $z(\tau)$ is constant, the point set $P(\tau)$ is a single point and is called a *point curve*. By the way, although we limit ourselves, in this section, to curves in 3-space, the definitions given here may be extended to n-space.

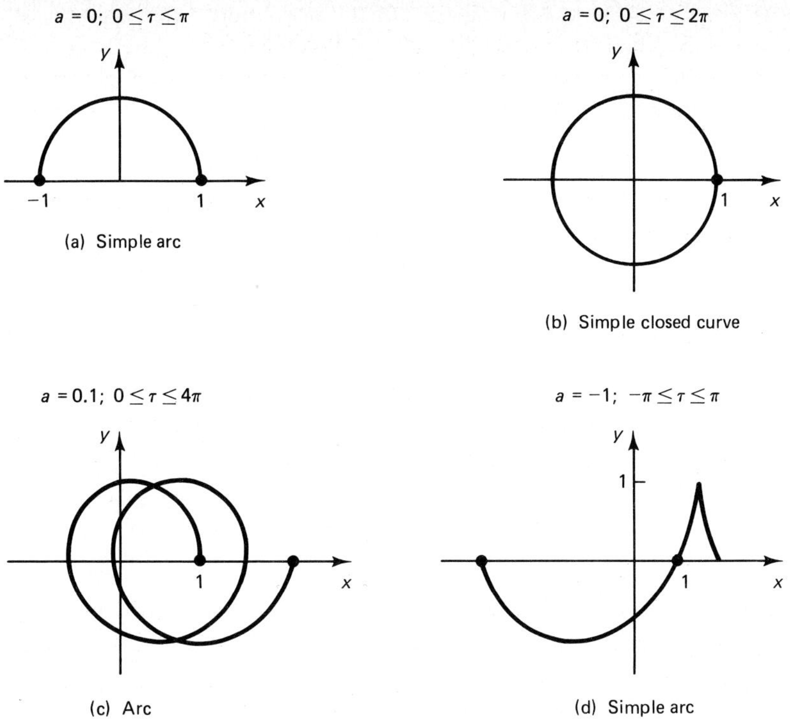

Fig. 7.22 Several cases of the curve (3).

ties. Thus we approximate the curve by a system of linear segments, as in Fig. 7.23, and sum the lengths of those segments. Then we repeat the process using a "finer" system of linear segments, and so on. If the endpoints of any single linear segment (such as AB in Fig. 7.23) are located with respect to the origin of some coordinate system by position vectors $\mathbf{R}_A$ and $\mathbf{R}_B$, then the length of the segment is

$$\| \mathbf{R}_B - \mathbf{R}_A \| = \| \Delta \mathbf{R} \| = \sqrt{\Delta \mathbf{R} \cdot \Delta \mathbf{R}} = \sqrt{\frac{\Delta \mathbf{R}}{\Delta \tau} \cdot \frac{\Delta \mathbf{R}}{\Delta \tau}}\, \Delta \tau,$$

so that the limiting process of summation, described above, evidently leads to the Riemann integral

$$\boxed{s(\tau) = \int_{\tau_0}^{\tau} \sqrt{\mathbf{R}'(t) \cdot \mathbf{R}'(t)}\, dt,} \tag{4}$$

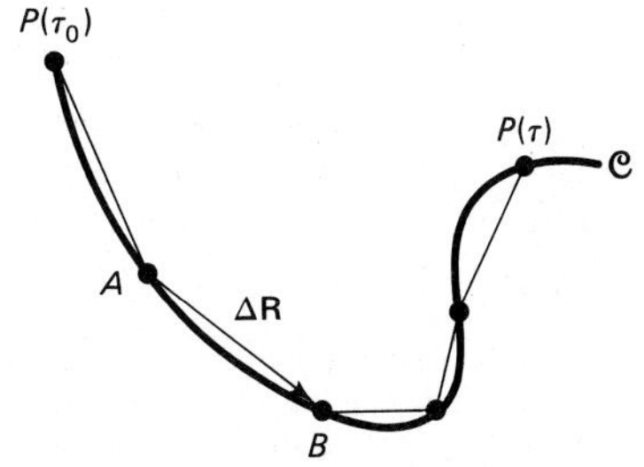

Fig. 7.23 Approximation of $\mathscr{C}$ by linear segments.

which we hereby adopt as our *definition* of the **arc length** of $\mathscr{C}$, from τ_0 to τ, provided, of course, that the integral exists. It can be shown that the length of a given arc is independent of the location and orientation of the reference Cartesian coordinate system, and is also independent of the particular choice of parametrization $x(\tau)$, $y(\tau)$, $z(\tau)$.

EXAMPLE 2 As an (admittedly simple) illustration of the arc length formula (4), let us use (4) to compute the arc length of the curve shown in Fig. 7.22a. Then

$$\mathbf{R}(\tau) = x(\tau)\hat{\mathbf{i}} + y(\tau)\hat{\mathbf{j}} = \cos\tau\hat{\mathbf{i}} + \sin\tau\hat{\mathbf{j}},$$

$$\mathbf{R}'(\tau) = -\sin\tau\hat{\mathbf{i}} + \cos\tau\hat{\mathbf{j}},$$

$$\mathbf{R}'(\tau)\cdot\mathbf{R}'(\tau) = \sin^2\tau + \cos^2\tau = 1,$$

so (4) is simply

$$s = \int_0^{\pi} \sqrt{1}\,dt = \pi. \qquad ◀$$

CAUTION $s(\tau)$, as given by (4), is the arc length only if $\tau \geq \tau_0$; if $\tau < \tau_0$, then the integral is negative and the arc length is $-s(\tau)$. Thus we often refer to $s(\tau)$, as defined by (4), as the "directed" arc length.

The arc length variable s is itself a convenient parameter for the representation of space curves. Thus let the parameter τ, in (2), be s, so that

$$\mathbf{R}(s) = x(s)\hat{\mathbf{i}} + y(s)\hat{\mathbf{j}} + z(s)\hat{\mathbf{k}}. \tag{5}$$

In the remainder of this section we assume that $x(s)$, $y(s)$, $z(s)$ [and hence $\mathbf{R}(s)$ as well] are three times continuously differentiable over the length of the curve, and that $x'(s)$, $y'(s)$, $z'(s)$ [and hence $\mathbf{R}'(s)$] do not vanish simultaneously anywhere on the curve.* A curve satisfying these requirements is said to be **regular.**

According to our definition of the tangent to a curve, on page 285, $d\mathbf{R}/ds$ will be a tangent vector. It will necessarily be of unit length since if we choose $\tau = s$, then (4) becomes $s = \int_{s_0}^{s} \sqrt{\mathbf{R}'(t)\cdot\mathbf{R}'(t)}\,dt$, d/ds of which gives $1 = \sqrt{\mathbf{R}'(s)\cdot\mathbf{R}'(s)} = \|\mathbf{R}'(s)\|$.† Consequently, $d\mathbf{R}/ds$ is a unit **tangent vector**, denoted as $\hat{\mathbf{T}}$:

$$\frac{d\mathbf{R}}{ds} = \hat{\mathbf{T}}. \tag{6}$$

SERRET-FRENET FORMULAS [optional]

How does $\hat{\mathbf{T}}(s)$ vary along the curve? Well, since $\hat{\mathbf{T}}$ is a unit vector we have $\hat{\mathbf{T}}\cdot\hat{\mathbf{T}} = 1$, and if we take d/ds of this equation, we obtain $\hat{\mathbf{T}}'\cdot\hat{\mathbf{T}} + \hat{\mathbf{T}}\cdot\hat{\mathbf{T}}' = 0$, or $2\hat{\mathbf{T}}\cdot\hat{\mathbf{T}}' = 0$. Hence $\hat{\mathbf{T}}'$ is either perpendicular to $\hat{\mathbf{T}}$, or else it is $\mathbf{0}$, so we may ex-

* A function is **continuously differentiable** if its derivative exists and is continuous.

† In differentiating the integral we use the fundamental theorem of the integral calculus (page 344), which is applicable since $\mathbf{R}(s)$ has been assumed to be continuously differentiable, so that the integrand in (4) is continuous.

press*

$$\frac{d\hat{\mathbf{T}}}{ds} = \kappa\hat{\mathbf{N}} \qquad (\kappa \geq 0) \tag{7}$$

where $\hat{\mathbf{N}}$ is a unit vector perpendicular to $\hat{\mathbf{T}}$ and κ is a scalar multiplier; $\hat{\mathbf{N}}$ is called the **principal normal**, and κ is called the **curvature**. If the curve happens to be straight (in some neighborhood of the point in question), then $\hat{\mathbf{T}}(s)$ is a constant vector and $d\hat{\mathbf{T}}/ds = \mathbf{0}$, so that $\kappa = 0$, as seems reasonable, since surely a straight line should have no curvature. In that case $\hat{\mathbf{N}} = (1/\kappa)\hat{\mathbf{T}}'(s)$ is undefined. The plane containing $\hat{\mathbf{T}}$ and $\hat{\mathbf{N}}$ is called the **osculating plane.**

Finally, we introduce a third unit vector $\hat{\mathbf{B}}$, called the **binormal,** according to the definition

$$\hat{\mathbf{B}} = \hat{\mathbf{T}} \times \hat{\mathbf{N}} \tag{8}$$

Then $\{\hat{\mathbf{T}}, \hat{\mathbf{N}}, \hat{\mathbf{B}}\}$ constitutes a right-handed orthonormal set, as displayed in Fig. 7.24. Now, a vector comprises both a magnitude and a direction, and while the $\hat{\mathbf{T}}$, $\hat{\mathbf{N}}$, $\hat{\mathbf{B}}$ vectors are constant in magnitude, their directions evidently vary with s since the spatial orientation of the $\hat{\mathbf{T}}$, $\hat{\mathbf{N}}$, $\hat{\mathbf{B}}$ triad varies, in general, as the representative point [at the tip of $\mathbf{R}(s)$] moves along the curve $\mathscr{C}$. In general, then, $\hat{\mathbf{T}}(s)$, $\hat{\mathbf{N}}(s)$, $\hat{\mathbf{B}}(s)$ will all be functions of s. Indeed, the variation of $\hat{\mathbf{T}}$ with s has already been noted in (7). Let us now obtain analogous expressions for $d\hat{\mathbf{N}}/ds$ and $d\hat{\mathbf{B}}/ds$.

First $d\hat{\mathbf{B}}/ds$. Differentiating the defining equation (8) yields

$$\frac{d\hat{\mathbf{B}}}{ds} = \frac{d\hat{\mathbf{T}}}{ds} \times \hat{\mathbf{N}} + \hat{\mathbf{T}} \times \frac{d\hat{\mathbf{N}}}{ds} = \kappa\hat{\mathbf{N}} \times \hat{\mathbf{N}} + \hat{\mathbf{T}} \times \frac{d\hat{\mathbf{N}}}{ds} = \hat{\mathbf{T}} \times \frac{d\hat{\mathbf{N}}}{ds}, \tag{9}$$

since $\hat{\mathbf{N}} \times \hat{\mathbf{N}} = \mathbf{0}$. It follows from (9) that $\hat{\mathbf{B}}'$ is perpendicular to $\hat{\mathbf{T}}$ (also to $\hat{\mathbf{N}}'$, but that fact will not be of use here). But $\hat{\mathbf{B}}$ is a unit vector, so $\hat{\mathbf{B}}'$ must also be either perpendicular to $\hat{\mathbf{B}}$ or else $\mathbf{0}$. Thus $\hat{\mathbf{B}}'$ is perpendicular to the $\hat{\mathbf{B}}$, $\hat{\mathbf{T}}$ plane, or else it is

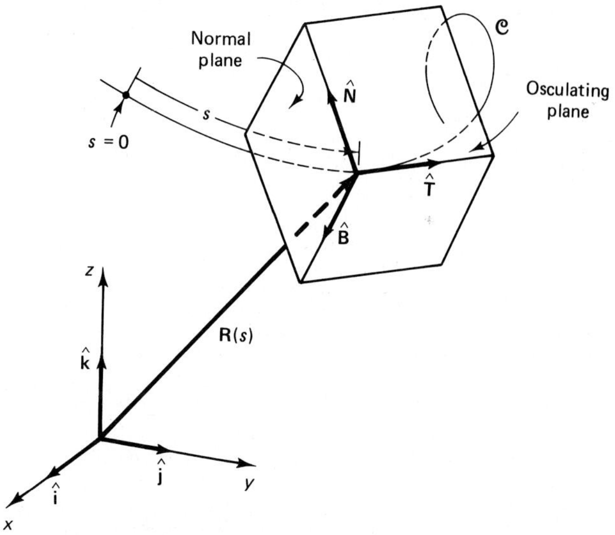

Fig. 7.24 $\hat{\mathbf{T}}$, $\hat{\mathbf{N}}$, $\hat{\mathbf{B}}$ triad.

* Our conclusion that $\hat{\mathbf{T}}'$ is perpendicular to $\hat{\mathbf{T}}$ is in agreement with the content of Exercise 8 on page 308.

0, so it must (see Fig. 7.24) be expressible in the form

$$\frac{d\hat{\mathbf{B}}}{ds} = \nu\hat{\mathbf{N}}, \tag{10}$$

where the scalar multiple ν in (10) is called the **torsion** because it is a measure of the rate at which the curve twists out of its osculating plane; if the curve is straight, we define $\nu = 0$. *Warning:* The torsion is generally denoted as τ, not ν, in the literature, but we have already used τ extensively, as a parameter, and prefer to use a different letter for the torsion.

Finally turning to $d\hat{\mathbf{N}}/ds$, we proceed by taking d/ds of $\hat{\mathbf{N}} = \hat{\mathbf{B}} \times \hat{\mathbf{T}}$:

$$\frac{d\hat{\mathbf{N}}}{ds} = \frac{d\hat{\mathbf{B}}}{ds} \times \hat{\mathbf{T}} + \hat{\mathbf{B}} \times \frac{d\hat{\mathbf{T}}}{ds} = \nu\hat{\mathbf{N}} \times \hat{\mathbf{T}} + \hat{\mathbf{B}} \times \kappa\hat{\mathbf{N}} = -\nu\hat{\mathbf{B}} - \kappa\hat{\mathbf{T}}. \tag{11}$$

Formulas (7), (10), and (11), namely

$$\frac{d\hat{\mathbf{T}}}{ds} = \kappa\hat{\mathbf{N}}, \tag{12a}$$

$$\frac{d\hat{\mathbf{N}}}{ds} = -\kappa\hat{\mathbf{T}} - \nu\hat{\mathbf{B}}, \tag{12b}$$

$$\frac{d\hat{\mathbf{B}}}{ds} = \nu\hat{\mathbf{N}}, \tag{12c}$$

are the important **Serret–Frenet formulas.***

It can be shown that if one specifies (continuous functions) $\kappa(s)$ and $\nu(s)$, these two quantities completely determine a regular curve which, except for its position and orientation in space, can be found by integrating equations (12) and (6).†

Let us see why κ is called the "curvature." Consider the osculating plane, i.e., the $\hat{\mathbf{T}}$, $\hat{\mathbf{N}}$ plane through a given point P on C, as sketched in Fig. 7.25a. Locally, i.e., in the immediate neighborhood of P, the curve lies in that plane. From (12a),

$$\Delta\hat{\mathbf{T}} \sim \kappa\hat{\mathbf{N}}\,\Delta s. \tag{13}$$

Alternatively, let us pick up the $\hat{\mathbf{T}} + \Delta\hat{\mathbf{T}}$ vector in Fig. 7.25a and move its tail to the point P, as in Fig. 7.25b. Then we can see that

$$\Delta\hat{\mathbf{T}} \sim (\|\hat{\mathbf{T}}\|\Delta\theta)\hat{\mathbf{N}} = \hat{\mathbf{N}}\,\Delta\theta. \tag{14}$$

*These formulas were obtained by *Frederic-Jean Frenet* (1816–1900) in his dissertation (1847) and were published by him in 1852. They were also obtained, independently, by *Joseph Alfred Serret* (1819–1885) and published by him in 1851. Their work built on that of *Alexis-Claude Clairaut* (1713–1765), *Leonhard Euler* (1707–1783), and *Michel-Ange Lancret* (1774–1807).

†Briefly, the idea is as follows. If $\hat{\mathbf{T}}$, $\hat{\mathbf{N}}$, $\hat{\mathbf{B}}$ are expressed in terms of their scalar components, then (12) amounts to a system of nine linear, first-order differential equations. Since the prescribed coefficients $\kappa(s)$ and $\nu(s)$ are to be continuous, this system of differential equation does, according to the results contained in Appendix A, admit a solution, which is unique to within the specification of $\hat{\mathbf{T}}(0)$, $\hat{\mathbf{N}}(0)$, $\hat{\mathbf{B}}(0)$. With $\hat{\mathbf{T}}(s)$ thus available from (12), $\mathbf{R}(s)$ can be obtained by integrating (6). It remains, then, to verify that the resulting $\mathbf{R}$ is indeed regular, and that the curve that it defines is unique to within "rigid motions." For details, we refer the interested reader to J. J. Stoker, *Differential Geometry* (New York: Wiley–Interscience, 1969), Chap. III, Secs. 13 and 14. For shorter but more restricted proofs, see Chap. II, Sec. 12 of Stoker, or D. J. Struik, *Differential Geometry*, 2nd ed., (Reading, Mass.: Addison-Wesley, 1961), p 29.

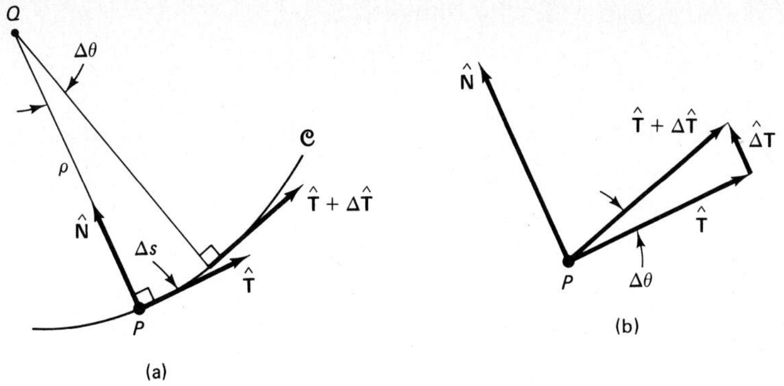

Fig. 7.25 Getting at the significance of κ.

Comparing (13) and (14), it follows that $\kappa\,\Delta s \sim \Delta\theta$. But from Fig, 7.25a, $\Delta s \sim \rho\Delta\theta$, where ρ is the local radius of curvature (and Q is the local center of curvature). Thus

$$\boxed{\kappa = \frac{1}{\rho}.} \tag{15}$$

That is, κ is the inverse of the local **radius of curvature** ρ: *large κ means small radius of curvature, small κ means large radius of curvature. Hence the name "curvature" for κ.*

As already mentioned, the significance of the torsion ν is that it is a measure of the rate at which the curve twists out of its osculating plane; for example, if $\mathscr{C}$ is a *plane* curve, then $\nu = 0$ all along its length.

Before working some examples, let us show how to determine $\hat{\mathbf{T}}$, $\hat{\mathbf{N}}$, $\hat{\mathbf{B}}$, κ, and ν when the curve is specified in the form

$$\mathbf{R}(s) = x(s)\hat{\mathbf{i}} + y(s)\hat{\mathbf{j}} + z(s)\hat{\mathbf{k}}. \tag{16}$$

First, $\hat{\mathbf{T}}$ may be computed from (6) as $\hat{\mathbf{T}} = \mathbf{R}'$. (Here, primes denote d/ds.) Then (12a) becomes $\hat{\mathbf{N}} = (1/\kappa)\hat{\mathbf{T}}' = (1/\kappa)\mathbf{R}''$ (if $\kappa \neq 0$), and since $\hat{\mathbf{N}}$ is to be a unit vector, there follows

$$\kappa = \|\mathbf{R}''\|, \tag{17}$$

$$\hat{\mathbf{N}} = \frac{\mathbf{R}''}{\|\mathbf{R}''\|}. \tag{18}$$

With $\hat{\mathbf{T}}$ and $\hat{\mathbf{N}}$ known, $\hat{\mathbf{B}}$ follows easily as

$$\hat{\mathbf{B}} = \hat{\mathbf{T}} \times \hat{\mathbf{N}} = \frac{\mathbf{R}' \times \mathbf{R}''}{\|\mathbf{R}' \times \mathbf{R}''\|}. \tag{19}$$

Finally, to compute ν we begin by taking d/ds of (12a):

$$\hat{\mathbf{T}}'' = \kappa\hat{\mathbf{N}}' + \kappa'\hat{\mathbf{N}} = -\kappa^2\hat{\mathbf{T}} - \kappa\nu\hat{\mathbf{B}} + \kappa'\hat{\mathbf{N}}, \qquad \text{by (12b).}$$

To isolate the ν on the right-hand side we need to eliminate the $\hat{\mathbf{T}}$ and $\hat{\mathbf{N}}$ terms. First, we eliminate $\hat{\mathbf{T}}$ by crossing both sides with $\hat{\mathbf{T}}$,

$$\hat{\mathbf{T}} \times \hat{\mathbf{T}}'' = \mathbf{0} - \kappa\nu\hat{\mathbf{T}} \times \hat{\mathbf{B}} + \kappa'\hat{\mathbf{T}} \times \hat{\mathbf{N}} = \kappa\nu\hat{\mathbf{N}} + \kappa'\hat{\mathbf{B}}.$$

Then we dot both sides with $\hat{\mathbf{N}}$ to eliminate $\hat{\mathbf{B}}$,

$$\hat{\mathbf{N}} \cdot \hat{\mathbf{T}} \times \hat{\mathbf{T}}'' = \kappa\nu. \tag{20}$$

Putting $\hat{\mathbf{T}} = \mathbf{R}'$, $\hat{\mathbf{T}}'' = \mathbf{R}'''$, and $\hat{\mathbf{N}} = \frac{1}{\kappa}\hat{\mathbf{T}}' = \frac{1}{\kappa}\mathbf{R}''$ (for $\kappa \neq 0$) into (20), and recalling that $\kappa^2 = \|\mathbf{R}''\|^2 = \mathbf{R}'' \cdot \mathbf{R}''$, we have

$$\nu = \frac{\mathbf{R}'' \cdot \mathbf{R}' \times \mathbf{R}'''}{\mathbf{R}'' \cdot \mathbf{R}''}. \tag{21}$$

Collecting these results, for reference,

$$\hat{\mathbf{T}} = \mathbf{R}', \qquad \hat{\mathbf{N}} = \frac{\mathbf{R}''}{\|\mathbf{R}''\|}, \qquad \hat{\mathbf{B}} = \hat{\mathbf{T}} \times \hat{\mathbf{N}} = \frac{\mathbf{R}' \times \mathbf{R}''}{\|\mathbf{R}' \times \mathbf{R}''\|}, \tag{22a,b,c}$$

$$\kappa = \frac{1}{\rho} = \|\mathbf{R}''\|, \qquad \nu = \frac{\mathbf{R}'' \cdot \mathbf{R}' \times \mathbf{R}'''}{\mathbf{R}'' \cdot \mathbf{R}''} = \frac{\mathbf{R}'' \cdot \mathbf{R}' \times \mathbf{R}'''}{\kappa^2}, \tag{22d,e}$$

where $(\ )' = d(\ )/ds$. *Given the position vector* $\mathbf{R}(s)$, *the quantities of interest* ($\hat{\mathbf{T}}$, $\hat{\mathbf{N}}$, $\hat{\mathbf{B}}$, κ, ν) *may be computed, in any order, from (22). For points at which* $\kappa(s) = 0$, *the quantities* $\hat{\mathbf{N}}$, $\hat{\mathbf{B}}$, *and* $\nu(s)$ *are undefined.*

EXAMPLE 3 *Velocity and Acceleration of a Particle.* Let the position of a moving particle be given by a position vector $\mathbf{R} = \mathbf{R}(t)$, where t is the time. We wish to obtain expressions for the velocity $\mathbf{v} = d\mathbf{R}/dt$ and the acceleration $\mathbf{a} = d\mathbf{v}/dt = d^2\mathbf{R}/dt^2$, in terms of the quantities $\hat{\mathbf{T}}$, $\hat{\mathbf{N}}$, $\hat{\mathbf{B}}$, κ, and ν. Well,

$$\mathbf{v} = \frac{d\mathbf{R}}{dt} = \frac{d\mathbf{R}}{ds}\frac{ds}{dt} = v\hat{\mathbf{T}}, \tag{23}$$

where $v = ds/dt = \|\mathbf{v}\|$ is the *speed*. Differentiating again,

$$\mathbf{a} = \frac{d\mathbf{v}}{dt} = \frac{dv}{dt}\hat{\mathbf{T}} + v\frac{d\hat{\mathbf{T}}}{dt} = \frac{dv}{dt}\hat{\mathbf{T}} + v\frac{d\hat{\mathbf{T}}}{ds}\frac{ds}{dt},$$

or

$$\mathbf{a} = \frac{dv}{dt}\hat{\mathbf{T}} + \kappa v^2\hat{\mathbf{N}} \qquad \text{by (12a).} \tag{24}$$

Equation (24) is simple and informative. First, we see that the acceleration $\mathbf{a}$ is a linear combination of $\hat{\mathbf{T}}$ and $\hat{\mathbf{N}}$, and hence that it lies in the osculating plane. The first term on the right is simply the linear acceleration, i.e., the acceleration that would occur if the particle moved in a straight line with a variable speed $v(t)$. The second term is directed toward the instantaneous center of curvature (the point Q in Fig. 7.25a) and its magnitude is κv^2, or v^2/ρ. This is the familiar *centripetal* acceleration that we meet in physics when studying circular motion. ◀

Looking back at Example 3, observe that we expressed the vectors $\mathbf{v}$ and $\mathbf{a}$ not in terms of $\hat{\mathbf{i}}$, $\hat{\mathbf{j}}$, $\hat{\mathbf{k}}$, but rather in terms of the natural, or intrinsic, base vectors $\hat{\mathbf{T}}$, $\hat{\mathbf{N}}$,

$\hat{\mathbf{B}}$, which are provided by the curve itself. In this connection, let us draw attention to an important point. Let $\mathbf{u}$ be any vector (such as $\mathbf{v}$ or $\mathbf{a}$ in Example 3) defined along a space curve. Expressing

$$\mathbf{u} = a\hat{\mathbf{T}} + b\hat{\mathbf{N}} + c\hat{\mathbf{B}}, \tag{25}$$

we often wish to compute derivatives, such as $d\mathbf{u}/dt$, $d^2\mathbf{u}/dt^2$, . . . , $d\mathbf{u}/ds$, $d^2\mathbf{u}/ds^2$, . . . , etc. It must be understood that the calculation

$$\frac{d\mathbf{u}}{dt} = \frac{da}{dt}\hat{\mathbf{T}} + \frac{db}{dt}\hat{\mathbf{N}} + \frac{dc}{dt}\hat{\mathbf{B}}$$

is *incorrect* since $\hat{\mathbf{T}}$, $\hat{\mathbf{N}}$, $\hat{\mathbf{B}}$ are functions of s, and s is a function of t. Instead, we have

$$\frac{d\mathbf{u}}{dt} = \frac{da}{dt}\hat{\mathbf{T}} + a\frac{d\hat{\mathbf{T}}}{ds}\frac{ds}{dt} + \frac{db}{dt}\hat{\mathbf{N}} + b\frac{d\hat{\mathbf{N}}}{ds}\frac{ds}{dt} + \frac{dc}{dt}\hat{\mathbf{B}} + c\frac{d\hat{\mathbf{B}}}{ds}\frac{ds}{dt}.$$

In order to proceed, we need to know the derivatives $d\hat{\mathbf{T}}/ds$, $d\hat{\mathbf{N}}/ds$, and $d\hat{\mathbf{B}}/ds$ as linear combinations of the base vectors $\hat{\mathbf{T}}$, $\hat{\mathbf{N}}$, $\hat{\mathbf{B}}$. These expressions are, in fact, provided by the important Serret–Frenet formulas (12).

We close with one more example.

EXAMPLE 4 *Circular Helix*. The parametric equations

$$x = a\cos\theta, \qquad y = a\sin\theta, \qquad z = b\theta \qquad (a, b > 0) \tag{26}$$

describe a circular helix about the z axis, as shown in Fig. 7.26. Observe that in one turn of the helix, i.e., as θ increases by 2π, z increases by $2\pi b$; this quantity is known as the *pitch* of the helix. As b is diminished, the helix becomes more and more compressed, collapsing to a circle of radius a in the x, y plane as $b \to 0$; conversely, it becomes more and more stretched out as b is increased.

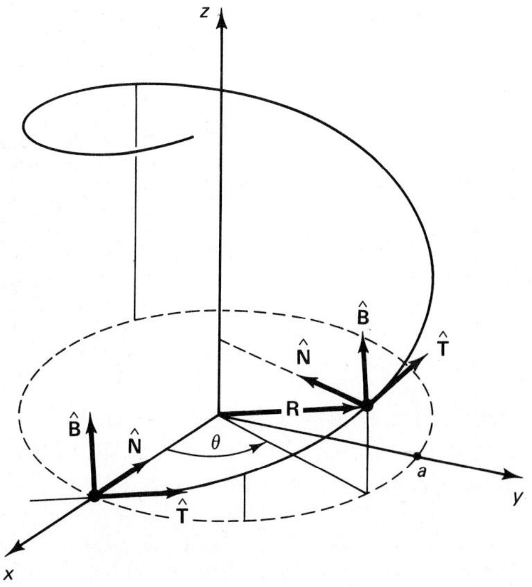

Fig. 7.26 Circular helix.

To compute $\hat{\mathbf{T}}$, $\hat{\mathbf{N}}$, $\hat{\mathbf{B}}$, κ, and ν we apply (22), being careful to remember that the primes in (22) are (d/ds)'s, whereas here $\mathbf{R}$ is given as a function of θ rather than s, namely,

$$\mathbf{R} = a \cos \theta \hat{\mathbf{i}} + a \sin \theta \hat{\mathbf{j}} + b\theta \hat{\mathbf{k}}. \tag{27}$$

Then

$$\begin{aligned} d\mathbf{R} &= (-a \sin \theta \hat{\mathbf{i}} + a \cos \theta \hat{\mathbf{j}} + b\hat{\mathbf{k}})\, d\theta, \\ (ds)^2 &= d\mathbf{R} \cdot d\mathbf{R} = (a^2 \sin^2 \theta + a^2 \cos^2 \theta + b^2)(d\theta)^2 \\ &= (a^2 + b^2)(d\theta)^2, \end{aligned}$$

so $d\theta/ds = 1/\sqrt{a^2 + b^2} \equiv c$, say, for short. Next,

$$\hat{\mathbf{T}} = \frac{d\mathbf{R}}{ds} = \frac{d\mathbf{R}}{d\theta}\frac{d\theta}{ds} = (-a \sin \theta \hat{\mathbf{i}} + a \cos \theta \hat{\mathbf{j}} + b\hat{\mathbf{k}})c, \tag{28}$$

$$\frac{d^2\mathbf{R}}{ds^2} = \frac{d}{d\theta}\left(\frac{d\mathbf{R}}{ds}\right)\frac{d\theta}{ds} = (-a \cos \theta \hat{\mathbf{i}} - a \sin \theta \hat{\mathbf{j}})c^2,$$

$$\kappa = \frac{1}{\rho} = \left\| \frac{d^2\mathbf{R}}{ds^2} \right\| = \sqrt{a^2 \cos^2 \theta + a^2 \sin^2 \theta}\, c^2 = ac^2 = \frac{a}{a^2 + b^2}, \tag{29}$$

$$\hat{\mathbf{N}} = -\cos \theta \hat{\mathbf{i}} - \sin \theta \hat{\mathbf{j}} \qquad \text{by (22b).} \tag{30}$$

Rather than use (22c) to compute $\hat{\mathbf{B}}$, it is a bit easier to use

$$\begin{aligned} \hat{\mathbf{B}} = \hat{\mathbf{T}} \times \hat{\mathbf{N}} &= \begin{vmatrix} \hat{\mathbf{i}} & \hat{\mathbf{j}} & \hat{\mathbf{k}} \\ -ac \sin \theta & ac \cos \theta & bc \\ -\cos \theta & -\sin \theta & 0 \end{vmatrix} \\ &= c(b \sin \theta \hat{\mathbf{i}} + b \cos \theta \hat{\mathbf{j}} + a\hat{\mathbf{k}}). \end{aligned} \tag{31}$$

Finally,

$$\frac{d^3\mathbf{R}}{ds^3} = \frac{d}{d\theta}\left(\frac{d^2\mathbf{R}}{ds^2}\right)\frac{d\theta}{ds} = (a \sin \theta \hat{\mathbf{i}} - a \cos \theta \hat{\mathbf{j}})c^3,$$

so that (22e) [and (6) on page 281] gives

$$\nu = \frac{1}{a^2c^4} \begin{vmatrix} -ac^2 \cos \theta & -ac^2 \sin \theta & 0 \\ -ac \sin \theta & ac \cos \theta & bc \\ ac^3 \sin \theta & -ac^3 \cos \theta & 0 \end{vmatrix} = -bc^2 = -\frac{b}{a^2 + b^2}. \tag{32}$$

Thus the desired quantities $\hat{\mathbf{T}}$, $\hat{\mathbf{N}}$, $\hat{\mathbf{B}}$, κ, ν are given by (28) to (32).

COMMENT 1 As a partial check, let $b \to 0$. Then (29) gives $\kappa \to 1/a$, and (32) gives $\nu \to 0$. This is as it should be since when $b \to 0$ the helix flattens into a circle in the x, y plane; this circle has constant radius of curvature $\rho = a$, so $\kappa = 1/\rho = 1/a$. Further, the circle is a plane curve, so the torsion ν should be zero. We leave the other obvious check case, namely $b \to \infty$, for the reader.

COMMENT 2 Observe that the helix has constant curvature and torsion, i.e., κ and ν are independent of θ. Thus the situation is the same from one θ to the next; for example, $\hat{\mathbf{N}}$ is always parallel to the x, y plane and always points toward the z axis. ◀

To place the subject of space curves in historical perspective, briefly, let us note first that the first major contributions were those of the prodigy *Alexis-Claude Clairaut* (1713–1765), who took up the subject before the age of 12. Clairaut's work was built on by the remarkable *Euler* (1707–1783), and by *Michel-Ange Lancret* (1774–1807), who focused attention on the three principal directions at any point of a curve. Yet the fundamental Serret–Frenet formulas were not published until the 1850s.

The theory of curves is part of a larger subject, **differential geometry,** the study of curves and surfaces by means of the calculus. We do not have the space to include much on the theory of surfaces (some is contained in Chapter 8), but we wish to mention, in passing, that a principal force in the development of that theory was an interest in the surface of the earth, an interest stimulated by the desire to carry out commerce between points on the earth's surface.

The first question, of course, was "What *is* the shape of the earth?", since it was known that the sphere is only an approximate idealization. This question was studied in the eighteenth century by measuring the period of a pendulum, given approximately as $T = 2\pi\sqrt{l/g}$, where l is the length and g is the acceleration of gravity, at various points on the earth. Relating g back to the local radius of the earth, Newton was able to discover the slight bulge in the globe at the equator. Even given the shape of the earth, what is the shortest arc (on the earth's surface) connecting two given points—a problem of obvious interest in terms of trade routes? More generally, what is the shortest arc connecting two given points on *any* given surface? Such a path is known as a *geodesic*. Further, there arose, in connection with mapmaking, the problem of *developable* surfaces, namely, surfaces that may be flattened without distortion. Spherical surfaces happen not to be developable, and the problem, then, was to find surfaces *close* to spherical that *are* developable. These few words hardly suffice, and we encourage the interested reader to pursue the historical part of the story in the book by Kline.*

7.7 EXERCISES

1. Determine a parametrization for each of the following curves: the intersection of

*(a) the planes $x - 2y + z = 4$, $2x + y - z = 0$

(b) the planes $4x - 3y + 5z = 1$, $x + y - 2z = 6$

(c) the planes $2x + y + z = 3$, $x + 4z = 5$

(d) the planes $x - y + z = 0$, $5x - y + z = 2$

(e) the planes $2x + y - z = 1$, $2y + z = 4$

*(f) the plane $x + y + 2z = 5$ and the circular cylinder $x^2 + y^2 = 4$

(g) the plane $4x - y + z = 3$ and the circular cylinder $x^2 + z^2 = 1$

(h) the plane $x - y + 2z = 1$ and the elliptic cylinder $x^2 + 4y^2 = 4$

* Morris Kline, *Mathematical Thought from Ancient to Modern Times* (New York: Oxford University Press, 1972).

(i) surfaces $2x - y - 3z = 5$ and $z = x^2 + y + 1$, between $(0, -2, -1)$ and $(2, -4, 1)$
(j) surfaces $x - y^2 + z = 0$ and $x - y + 2z = 0$, between $(6, 2, -2)$ and $(1, 1, 0)$
(k) surfaces $x = y^2 + z^2$ and $z = xy$, between $(0, 0, 0)$ and $(1, -1/\sqrt{2}, -1/\sqrt{2})$

2. (*Parametrization of straight line*) Verify that a parametrization of the straight line with endpoints (x_1, y_1, z_1), (x_2, y_2, z_2) is $x = x_1 + (x_2 - x_1)\tau$, $y = y_1 + (y_2 - y_1)\tau$, $z = z_1 + (z_2 - z_1)\tau$ $\quad (0 \le \tau \le 1)$.

3. Let each of the following $\mathbf{R}(\tau)$'s, for $0 \le \tau < \infty$, define a space curve. In each case, find the arc length s as a function of the parameter τ, namely $s(\tau)$, if $\tau = 0$ is taken to correspond to $s = 0$. Further, determine $\hat{\mathbf{T}}(\tau)$, $\hat{\mathbf{N}}(\tau)$, $\hat{\mathbf{B}}(\tau)$, $\kappa(\tau)$, $\rho(\tau)$, and $\nu(\tau)$.

*(a) $\hat{\mathbf{i}} + \tau\hat{\mathbf{j}} + \tau^2\hat{\mathbf{k}}$ (b) $\tau^2\hat{\mathbf{i}} - \tau^3\hat{\mathbf{j}} - \tau^2\hat{\mathbf{k}}$
(c) $e^\tau(\cos\tau\hat{\mathbf{i}} + \sin\tau\hat{\mathbf{j}})$ (d) $e^{-\tau}(\cos\tau\hat{\mathbf{i}} - \sin\tau\hat{\mathbf{k}})$
(e) $e^\tau(\cos\tau\hat{\mathbf{i}} - \sin\tau\hat{\mathbf{j}} + 2\hat{\mathbf{k}})$
(f) $\cos\tau(\hat{\mathbf{i}} + \hat{\mathbf{j}}) - \sqrt{2}\sin\tau\hat{\mathbf{k}}$

***4.** For the circular helix of Example 4, determine the arc length s between the points corresponding to $\theta = 0$ and $\theta = 2\pi$. Verify that your answer reduces to the correct values for the two simple limiting cases: $b \to 0$ and $b \to \infty$.

5. Compute the normal $\hat{\mathbf{N}}(x)$ for the plane curve $y = x^3$. Sketch the curve over $-2 \le x \le 2$, and show $\hat{\mathbf{N}}$ at a number of points, say, $x = \pm 0.01$ and $x = \pm 1.0$.

6. Let a particle move with $x = x(t)$, $y = y(t)$, $z = z(t)$ as prescribed below, where t is the time. Compute its tangential and normal acceleration components, dv/dt and κv^2, respectively, in (24).

*(a) $x = t$, $y = t^2$, $z = 0$
(b) $x = t^2$, $y = -2t$, $z = t^3$
(c) $x = 6t$, $y = \sin t$, $z = 0$
(d) $x = \cos t$, $y = \sin t$, $z = t^2$
(e) $x = t$, $y = e^{-t}\cos t$, $z = 0$
(f) $x = a\cos\omega t$, $y = a\sin\omega t$, $z = 0$
(a, ω constants)

7. Let a curve in the x, y plane be defined by $y = y(x)$. Show that

$$\boxed{\kappa = \frac{1}{\rho} = \frac{|y''|}{(1 + y'^2)^{3/2}},} \tag{a}$$

provided, of course, that $y(x)$ is twice differentiable.

8. (*Integration of Serret–Frenet formulas*) The Serret–Frenet formulas (12) are three linear, coupled, differential equations in $\hat{\mathbf{T}}(s)$, $\hat{\mathbf{N}}(s)$, and $\hat{\mathbf{B}}(s)$. In general, the coefficients κ and ν are functions of s. Show that if κ and ν are both *constants*, not both zero, then (12) can be integrated (show steps) to yield

$$\hat{\mathbf{N}} = \mathbf{C}_1 \sin\omega s + \mathbf{C}_2 \cos\omega s \tag{a}$$

$$\hat{\mathbf{T}} = \frac{\kappa}{\omega}\mathbf{C}_2 \sin\omega s - \frac{\kappa}{\omega}\mathbf{C}_1 \cos\omega s + \nu\mathbf{C}_3 \tag{b}$$

$$\hat{\mathbf{B}} = \frac{\nu}{\omega}\mathbf{C}_2 \sin\omega s - \frac{\nu}{\omega}\mathbf{C}_1 \cos\omega s - \kappa\mathbf{C}_3 \tag{c}$$

where $\omega \equiv \sqrt{\kappa^2 + \nu^2}$, and $\mathbf{C}_1$, $\mathbf{C}_2$, $\mathbf{C}_3$ are the (vector) constants of integration. Then show, from (6), that

$$\mathbf{R} = \mathbf{C}_4 \cos\omega s + \mathbf{C}_5 \sin\omega s + \mathbf{C}_6 s + \mathbf{C}_7. \tag{d}$$

Finally, verify that (27), for the circular helix (for which we found that both κ and ν were constant), is indeed of the form (d).

9. Prove that $P(\tau) = (x(\tau), y(\tau), z(\tau))$ is a plane curve if and only if

$$\begin{vmatrix} x' & y' & z' \\ x'' & y'' & z'' \\ x''' & y''' & z''' \end{vmatrix} = 0. \tag{a}$$

Hint: Recall the general equation of a plane, $ax + by + cz = d$, where a, b, c, d are constants and a, b, c are not all zero. If $P(\tau)$ lies in a plane, then $ax(\tau) + by(\tau) + cz(\tau) = d$.

10. (a)–(f) Use the results in Exercise 9 to show whether or not the curves in Exercise 3(a)–3(f) are plane curves.

Double and Triple Integrals; Surfaces and Volumes 8

INTRODUCTION 8.1

Recall that the subject of Chapter 6 was the differential calculus of functions of several variables. In the present chapter we begin our consideration of the *integral* calculus of functions of several variables, in Sections 8.2 and 8.3, with an elementary look at multiple integration. Sections 8.4 to 8.6, on the representation of surfaces and volumes, are OPTIONAL.

DOUBLE INTEGRALS 8.2

In calculus, one studies "single integrals"

$$I = \int_L f(x)\, dx, \tag{1}$$

where L is some segment of an x axis. A generalization of this case is the so-called "line integral," which we meet in Section 9.10, in which L is a segment of a space curve. Analogously, one encounters *double integrals*

$$I = \iint_{\mathscr{R}} f(x, y)\, dA, \tag{2}$$

where the region $\mathscr{R}$ lies in the x, y plane, as well as double integrals, in which $\mathscr{R}$ is some portion of a curved surface. In this section we consider only the case where $\mathscr{R}$ lies in the x, y plane.

Before continuing, we need to define several terms. Let a curve $\mathscr{C}$ be defined parametrically by

$$x = x(\tau), \qquad y = y(\tau), \qquad z = z(\tau); \qquad \tau_1 \le \tau \le \tau_2. \tag{3}$$

If $\mathscr{C}$ has a continuously turning tangent, it is said to be **smooth.** By having a continuously turning tangent we mean that the first derivatives $x'(\tau)$, $y'(\tau)$, $z'(\tau)$ are continuous over $\tau_1 \le \tau \le \tau_2$, so that $\mathscr{C}$ has no "kinks".* Further, if a curve consists of at most a finite number of smooth curves, strung end to end, it is said to be **piecewise smooth.** (Naturally, any curve that is smooth is also piecewise smooth. Furthermore, it can be shown that a piecewise smooth curve is necessarily *rectifiable*—i.e., has finite length.) To illustrate, a piecewise smooth plane curve is shown in Fig. 8.1. Evidently, each of the segments AB, BC, and CD is smooth, so AD is piecewise smooth.

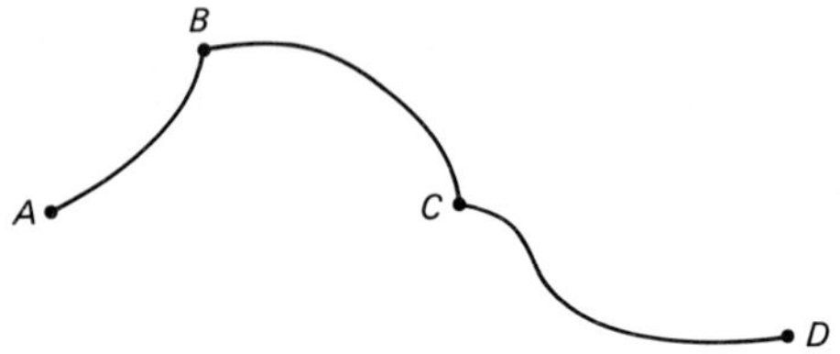

Fig. 8.1 Piecewise smooth curve.

Returning to (2), we will assume that $\mathscr{R}$ is a closed, bounded region in the x, y plane,† that its boundary $\mathscr{C}$ is a closed, piecewise smooth curve, and that $f(x, y)$ is defined on $\mathscr{R}$.

Let us lay down a rectangular grid on $\mathscr{R}$ consisting of a finite number of lines parallel to the coordinate axes, for example, as shown in Fig. 8.2. The N rectangles lying entirely within $\mathscr{R}$ (the shaded ones in Fig. 8.2) constitute a *partition* of $\mathscr{R}$, and the greatest of the dimensions Δx_j, Δy_j for $j = 1, \ldots, N$ will be called the *norm* of the partition and will be denoted as $|p|$. Let (x_j, y_j) be an arbitrarily selected point in the jth partition rectangle, for each $j = 1, 2, \ldots, N$. Then, denoting the area

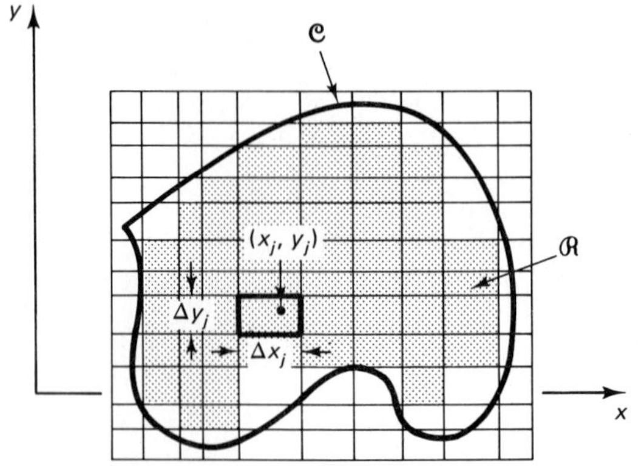

Fig. 8.2 Partition of $\mathscr{R}$.

* If you studied Section 6.7, you will see that $\mathscr{C}$ is smooth if its tangent vector $\hat{\mathbf{T}}(s)$ is a continuous function of s.

†The term "closed region" was defined on page 216. $\mathscr{R}$ being bounded means that it can be enclosed within a sufficiently large circle.

$\Delta x_j\, \Delta y_j$ as ΔA_j,

$$\sum_{j=1}^{N} f(x_j, y_j)\, \Delta A_j \tag{4}$$

is called the **Riemann sum** corresponding to the chosen partition and (x_j, y_j) points. The idea, in principle at least, is to compute the Riemann sum (4), then to introduce a finer partition (i.e., one with a smaller norm) and compute the new Riemann sum, and so on, such that the norm of the partitions tends to zero. Two things happen: The partitioning rectangles become arbitrarily small, and the unshaded area within $\mathcal{R}$ (Fig. 8.2) evidently tends to zero.

If the sequence of values of the Riemann sum, thus generated, converges to a unique limit, independent of the choice of the partition sequence and (x_j, y_j) points, that limit is, by definition, the **double integral** (2); that is,

$$\iint_{\mathcal{R}} f(x, y)\, dA \equiv \lim_{|p| \to 0} \sum f(x_j, y_j)\, \Delta A_j. \tag{5}$$

It can be shown that the limit will indeed exist if f is continuous in the closed region $\mathcal{R}$; that condition is sufficient, not necessary. If the limit does exist, we say that the integral *converges,* or *exists,* and that f is *integrable* on $\mathcal{R}$, Riemann-integrable to be more specific, since the Riemann definition (5) is not the only definition of the double integral.

Double integrals admit the following properties, each of which corresponds to a similar property for single integrals:

$$\iint_{\mathcal{R}} \alpha f(x, y)\, dA = \alpha \iint_{\mathcal{R}} f(x, y)\, dA, \tag{6a}$$

$$\iint_{\mathcal{R}} [f(x, y) + g(x, y)]\, dA = \iint_{\mathcal{R}} f(x, y)\, dA + \iint_{\mathcal{R}} g(x, y)\, dA, \tag{6b}$$

$$\iint_{\mathcal{R}} f(x, y)\, dA = \iint_{\mathcal{R}_1} f(x, y)\, dA + \iint_{\mathcal{R}_2} f(x, y)\, dA, \tag{6c}$$

where α is a constant and all integrals are assumed to exist. In (6c) $\mathcal{R}$ is divided (by a piecewise smooth curve) into two subregions, $\mathcal{R}_1$ and $\mathcal{R}_2$, as illustrated in Fig. 8.3. In addition to (6a) to (6c), we call attention to the **mean value theorem** for double integrals: If $f(x, y)$ is continuous throughout the closed region $\mathcal{R}$, there exists at least one point (x_0, y_0) in $\mathcal{R}$ such that

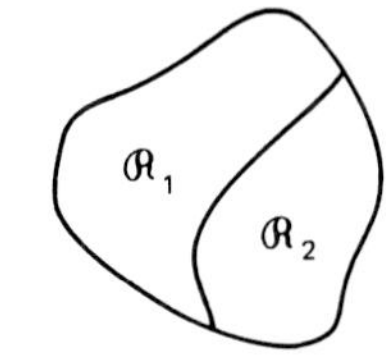

Fig. 8.3 Subdivision of $\mathcal{R}$.

$$\boxed{\iint_{\mathcal{R}} f(x, y)\, dA = f(x_0, y_0) A,} \tag{6d}$$

where

$$A = \iint_{\mathcal{R}} dA \tag{7}$$

is the **area** of $\mathcal{R}$.

Besides serving to define the double integral on the left, (5) is useful from a computational standpoint since the Riemann sum (4), for a given partition, will provide an accurate approximation to the integral if the partition is sufficiently fine. [In practice, however, one normally uses approximations which are more efficient and more sophisticated than the simplest approximation provided by (4).]

Of course, we resort to numerical integration only when necessary, i.e., only when we are unable to carry out the evaluation analytically. How do we evaluate a double integral analytically? By dealing with it as an *iterated integral,* i.e., by integrating on one variable at a time. The procedure is similar to that employed in differentiation. For example, in computing $u_{xy} = \dfrac{\partial}{\partial y}\left(\dfrac{\partial}{\partial x}u\right)$, first we differentiate u with respect to x, holding y fixed, and then we differentiate the resulting function $\partial u/\partial x$ with respect to y. Analogously, if we recall that $\Delta A_j = \Delta x_j \Delta y_j$ in (4), this fact suggests that we write $\iint_{\mathcal{R}} f(x, y)\, dA$ as $\iint_{\mathcal{R}} f(x, y)\, dx\, dy$, and that we contemplate two *successive* integrations, first one on x, and then one on y. Thus if $\mathcal{R}$ is the region shown in Fig. 8.4a, let us tentatively express

$$\iint_{\mathcal{R}} f(x, y)\, dA = \int_{y_1}^{y_2} \left\{ \int_{x_1(y)}^{x_2(y)} f(x, y)\, dx \right\} dy$$

or, omitting the parentheses for brevity,

$$\iint_{\mathcal{R}} f(x, y)\, dA = \int_{y_1}^{y_2} \int_{x_1(y)}^{x_2(y)} f(x, y)\, dx\, dy. \tag{8}$$

In words, we integrate across the (shaded) horizontal sliver in Fig. 8.4a, from $x_1(y)$ on the left to $x_2(y)$ on the right, and then we sweep the sliver from bottom ($y = y_1$) to top ($y = y_2$).

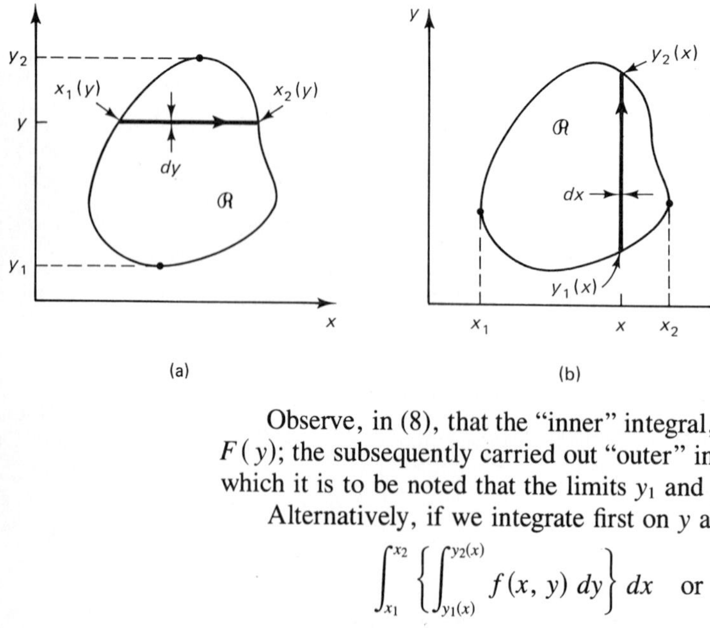

Fig. 8.4 Iterated integrals.

Observe, in (8), that the "inner" integral, $\int_{x_1(y)}^{x_2(y)} f(x, y)\, dx$, is a function of y, say $F(y)$; the subsequently carried out "outer" integration is of the form $\int_{y_1}^{y_2} F(y)\, dy$, in which it is to be noted that the limits y_1 and y_2 are constants.

Alternatively, if we integrate first on y and then on x, as in Fig. 8.4b, we have

$$\int_{x_1}^{x_2} \left\{ \int_{y_1(x)}^{y_2(x)} f(x, y)\, dy \right\} dx \quad \text{or} \quad \int_{x_1}^{x_2} \int_{y_1(x)}^{y_2(x)} f(x, y)\, dy\, dx. \tag{9}$$

Are the iterated integrals in (8) and (9) necessarily equal? This question is analogous to the one regarding *differentiation*: e.g., are the mixed partials f_{xy} and f_{yx} equal? Before continuing, we suggest that you review the discussion, about interchanging the order of two or more limit processes, following Theorem 1 on page 220.

Returning to the question at hand, we state, without proof, that *if* $f(x, y)$ *is continuous over* $\mathcal{R}$*, then all three quantities are equal: the double integral (2), the iterated integral (8), and the "inverted" iterated integral (9),* *

$$\iint_{\mathcal{R}} f(x, y)\, dA = \int_{y_1}^{y_2} \int_{x_1(y)}^{x_2(y)} f(x, y)\, dx\, dy = \int_{x_1}^{x_2} \int_{y_1(x)}^{y_2(x)} f(x, y)\, dy\, dx. \tag{10}$$

EXAMPLE 1 As a simple first example, consider

$$I = \iint_{\mathcal{R}} xy^2\, dA, \tag{11}$$

where $\mathcal{R}$ is the triangular region depicted in Fig. 8.5. First, observe that $f(x, y) = xy^2$ is indeed continuous over $\mathcal{R}$. If we integrate first on x, as in (8), then $x_1(y) = y/2$, $x_2(y) = 1$, $y_1 = 0$, and $y_2 = 2$, so

$$\begin{aligned} I &= \int_0^2 \left\{ \int_{y/2}^1 xy^2\, dx \right\} dy = \int_0^2 \left\{ \frac{x^2 y^2}{2}\bigg|_{y/2}^{1} \right\} dy \\ &= \int_0^2 \left(\frac{y^2}{2} - \frac{y^4}{8} \right) dy = \frac{8}{6} - \frac{32}{40} = \frac{8}{15}. \end{aligned} \tag{12}$$

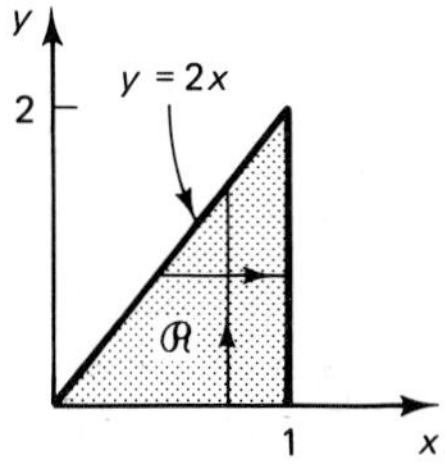

Fig. 8.5 The region $\mathcal{R}$ in (11).

Alternatively, integrating first on y, as in (9), we have

$$I = \int_0^1 \left\{ \int_0^{2x} xy^2\, dy \right\} dx = \int_0^1 \left\{ \frac{xy^3}{3}\bigg|_0^{2x} \right\} dx = \frac{8}{15}, \tag{13}$$

which does agree with (12), in accordance with (10). ◀

EXAMPLE 2 In Example 1 we were given a picture of $\mathcal{R}$, and from that picture we deduced the integration limits $x_1(y) = y/2$, $x_2(y) = 1$, $y_1 = 0$, $y_2 = 2$ in (12). In the present example, in which we seek to evaluate the iterated integral

$$I = \int_2^4 \int_{y/2}^{\sqrt{y}} e^{y/x}\, dx\, dy, \tag{14}$$

* See MARSDEN AND TROMBA, Chap. 5, especially *Fubini's theorem* for rectangular regions, on p. 224, and the "rectangularization" idea on p. 230. By the way, note that we have stated (italicized type) that all *three* integrals are equal if f is continuous over $\mathcal{R}$. If f is *not* continuous, it is not only possible for the iterated integrals in (8) and (9) to be unequal (or for one or both to fail to exist), it is even possible that they *are* equal, but not equal to the double integral $\iint_{\mathcal{R}} f(x, y)\, dA$. For such an example, see T. M. Apostol, *Mathematical Analysis* (Reading, Mass.: Addison-Wesley, 1957). Exer. 10–9.

we are given the *limits,* rather than a picture of $\mathcal{R}$, and merely asked to carry out the integrations. Fine, but the catch is that $\exp(y/x)$ is a formidable function of x to integrate. It would seem much more promising to integrate first on y, since $\exp(y/x)$ is a simple function of y. Thus let us *invert the order of integration,* in (14), and consider

$$I = \int_?^? \int_?^? e^{y/x}\, dy\, dx \tag{15}$$

instead. But what are the new limits of integration? [They are *not* merely $\int_{y/2}^{\sqrt{y}} \int_2^4$, i.e., the reverse of the limits in (14).] It is essential to work from a *picture* of the region $\mathcal{R}$, as can be inferred from the limits given in (14). From those limits it follows that $\mathcal{R}$ is the shaded region in Fig. 8.6. Integrating on y first, we break $\mathcal{R}$ into two subregions, $\mathcal{R}_1$ and $\mathcal{R}_2$, and express

$$\begin{aligned} I &= \iint_{\mathcal{R}_1} e^{y/x}\, dy\, dx + \iint_{\mathcal{R}_2} e^{y/x}\, dy\, dx \\ &= \int_1^{\sqrt{2}} \int_2^{2x} e^{y/x}\, dy\, dx + \int_{\sqrt{2}}^2 \int_{x^2}^{2x} e^{y/x}\, dy\, dx \\ &= \int_1^{\sqrt{2}} \left\{ xe^{y/x}\Big|_2^{2x} \right\} dx + \int_{\sqrt{2}}^2 \left\{ xe^{y/x}\Big|_{x^2}^{2x} \right\} dx. \end{aligned}$$

Thus

$$I = \frac{e^2}{2} + (\sqrt{2} - 1)e^{\sqrt{2}} - \int_1^{\sqrt{2}} xe^{2/x}\, dx. \tag{16}$$

Whether or not the last integral in (16) can be evaluated analytically remains to be seen; we will not attempt that evaluation. Even if we cannot evaluate that integral it should be appreciated that we have at least succeeded in reducing I from a double integral to a single integral. If, ultimately, we need to resort to numerical integration [of the remaining integral in (16)], it will be substantially simpler to deal with that single integral than with a double integral.

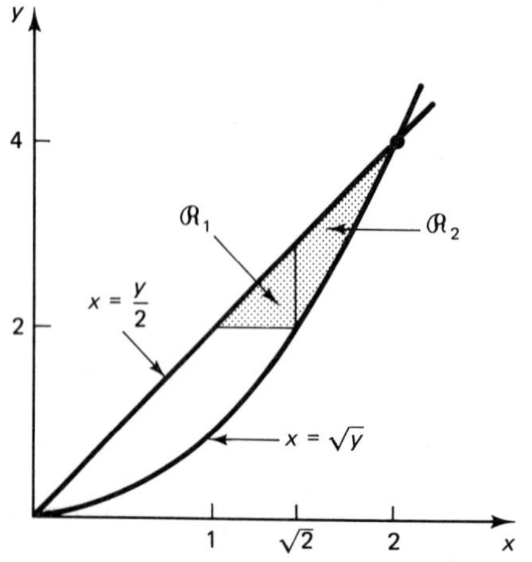

Fig. 8.6 Region of integration.

COMMENT Be sure to see that the functional nature of the integrand was not relevant in our search for the new limits needed in (15). Rather, the original limits [in (14)] implied the region $\mathcal{R}$ (shaded in Fig. 8.6), and the region $\mathcal{R}$, in turn, implied the new limits. ◀

8.2 EXERCISES

1. Evaluate each of the following iterated integrals. Then integrate again, with the order of integration reversed, and show that the same result is obtained.

*(a) $\int_0^1 \int_0^y y^2\,dx\,dy$ (b) $\int_0^1 \int_x^{2x} x^3 y\,dy\,dx$
(c) $\int_0^2 \int_y^2 x e^{x+y}\,dx\,dy$ *(d) $\int_1^2 \int_0^y \sin(x-y)\,dx\,dy$
(e) $\int_0^1 \int_y^{(2y+1)/4} (x+y)^8\,dx\,dy$ (f) $\int_0^1 \int_{-y}^{2-y} x\,dx\,dy$
(g) $\int_{-1}^3 \int_{-x}^x x^2\,dy\,dx$ (h) $\int_1^4 \int_2^{\sqrt{x}} x^2\,dy\,dx$

2. Show that $\int_0^T \int_0^t x(\tau)\,d\tau\,dt$ can be reduced to the single integral $\int_0^T (T-\tau)x(\tau)\,d\tau$ (T = constant). *Hint:* See the Comment at the end of Example 2.

3. Show that

(a) $\int_0^6 \int_{y/2}^3 \frac{1}{x} e^{y/x}\,dx\,dy = 3(e^2-1)$

(b) $\int_4^{16} \int_{y/2}^{\sqrt{y}} \frac{1}{x} e^{y/x}\,dx\,dy = 7e^2 - e^4 - \int_4^8 e^{16/x}\,dx$

(c) $\int_0^1 \int_{y/2}^y \sin(x^2 y)\,dx\,dy = \int_0^{1/2} \frac{\cos(x^3) - \cos(2x^3)}{x^2}\,dx + \int_{1/2}^1 \frac{\cos(x^3)-\cos(x^2)}{x^2}\,dx$

(d) $\int_0^{\pi/2} \int_x^{\pi/2} \frac{\sin y}{y}\,dy\,dx = 1$

4. (*Mass and center of gravity*) Let $\sigma(x, y)$ be the density of a distribution of mass over a region $\mathcal{R}$ in the x, y plane; i.e., $\sigma(x, y)$ is the mass per unit area at (x, y). Then the x, y coordinates of the **center of gravity** are defined as

$$x_c = \frac{1}{M}\iint_{\mathcal{R}} x\sigma(x,y)\,dA,$$
$$y_c = \frac{1}{M}\iint_{\mathcal{R}} y\sigma(x,y)\,dA, \quad \text{(a)}$$

where

$$M = \iint_{\mathcal{R}} \sigma(x,y)\,dA \quad \text{(b)}$$

is the total mass. Evaluate x_c and y_c in each case. In parts (a) to (d), $\sigma(x, y)$ is a constant, say σ.

*(a)

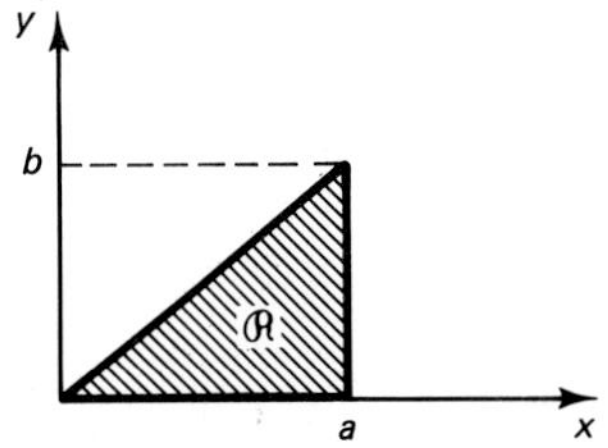

(b)

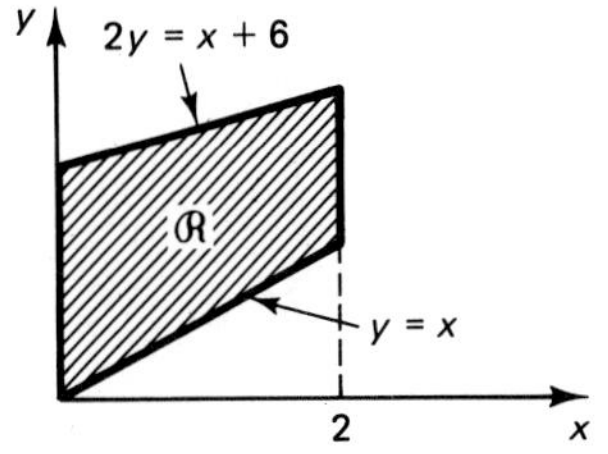

(c)

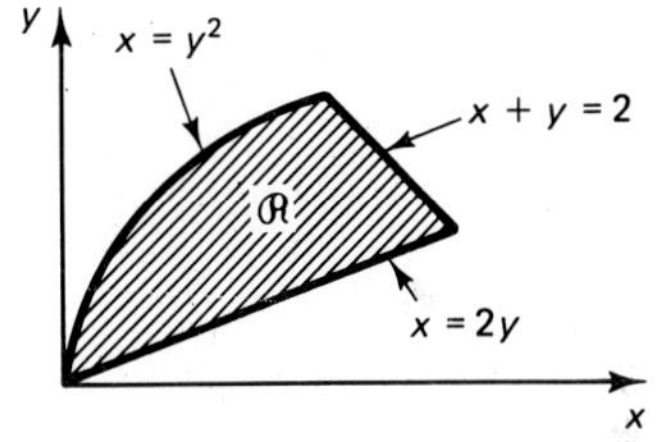

*(d)

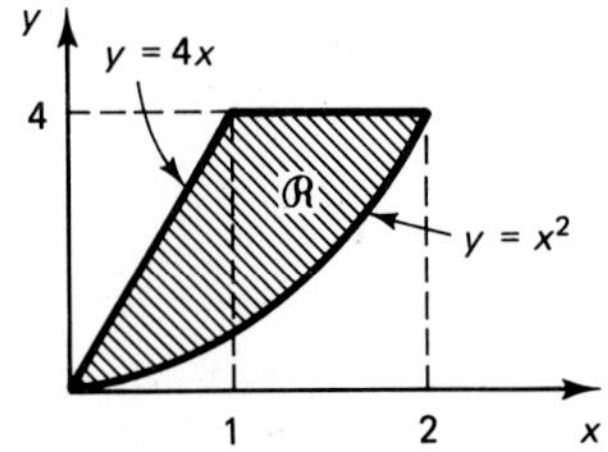

(e) Same $\mathcal{R}$ as in part (a), but $\sigma(x, y) = 1 + x$
(f) Same $\mathcal{R}$ as in part (a), but $\sigma(x, y) = y$
(g) Same $\mathcal{R}$ as in part (c), but $\sigma(x, y) = x$
(h) Same $\mathcal{R}$ as in part (c), but $\sigma(x, y) = y$

5. (*Moments of inertia*) Let $\sigma(x, y)$ be the density of a distribution of mass over a region $\mathcal{R}$ in the x, y plane; i.e., $\sigma(x, y)$ is the mass per unit area at (x, y). Then the **moments of inertia** I_x and I_y, about the x, y

axes, respectively, are defined as

$$I_x = \iint_{\mathcal{R}} y^2 \sigma(x, y)\, dA, \quad I_y = \iint_{\mathcal{R}} x^2 \sigma(x, y)\, dA \qquad \text{(a)}$$

Evaluate I_x and I_y in each case. In parts (a) and (b), $\sigma(x, y)$ is a constant, say σ.

*(a)

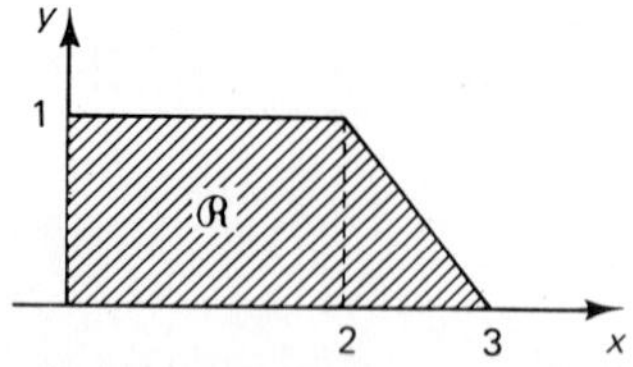

(b)

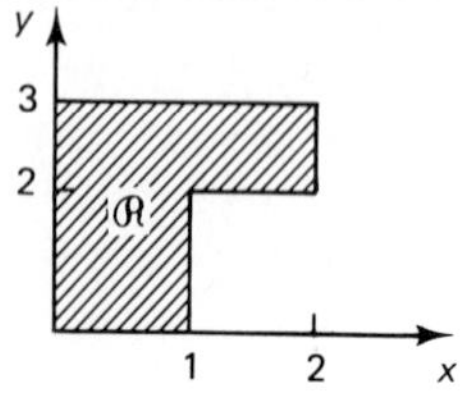

(c) $\mathcal{R}$, σ as in Exercise 4(a)
(d) $\mathcal{R}$, σ as in Exercise 4(b)
(e) $\mathcal{R}$, σ as in Exercise 4(c)
(f) $\mathcal{R}$, σ as in Exercise 4(d)
(g) $\mathcal{R}$, σ as in Exercise 4(e)
(h) $\mathcal{R}$, σ as in Exercise 4(f)

6. The **exponential integral** function $Ei(t)$ is defined by the formula

$$Ei(t) = \int_t^\infty \frac{e^{-\tau}}{\tau}\, d\tau, \qquad \text{(a)}$$

and is tabulated in the literature, just as are $\sin t$, e^t, and so on. Evaluate the integral $\int_0^x Ei(t)\, dt$, and show that it equals $1 - e^{-x} + xEi(x)$.

7. If

$$f(x, y) = \begin{cases} 1, & 0 \le y \le 2x, \quad 0 \le x \le 1 \\ 0, & \text{elsewhere,} \end{cases}$$

show that

$$\int_{-\infty}^{\infty} \int_{-\infty}^{u} f(x, y)\, dx\, dy = \begin{cases} 0, & u \le 0 \\ u^2, & 0 < u < 1 \\ 1, & u \ge 1. \end{cases}$$

8.3 TRIPLE INTEGRALS

Our discussion of triple integrals, i.e., integrals of the form

$$I = \iiint_{\mathcal{R}} f(x, y, z)\, dV, \qquad (1)$$

will closely parallel our discussion in the preceding sections on double integrals, so that we will be able to streamline it a bit.

Recall that for double integrals we asked that the boundary curve $\mathcal{C}$ of the region $\mathcal{R}$ be piecewise smooth—i.e., consisting of at most a finite number of smooth curves strung end to end, where a smooth curve is one that has a continuously turning tangent. Turning to the triple integral (1), we assume that $\mathcal{R}$ is a closed, bounded region* in 3-space, that $f(x, y, z)$ is defined in $\mathcal{R}$, and that the boundary $\mathcal{S}$ of $\mathcal{R}$ is a piecewise smooth surface. By a **smooth surface** we mean one that has a continuously turning normal†, and by a **piecewise smooth surface** we mean one that consists of at most a finite number of smooth surfaces arranged edge to edge.

To define the triple integral (1), we partition $\mathcal{R}$ into a cellular structure analogous to that shown in Fig. 8.2 on page 310 for the double integral. This time, however, the cells are rectangular prisms rather than rectangles. Corresponding to

* "Closed region" was defined on page 216 $\mathcal{R}$ being "bounded" means that it can be enclosed within a sufficiently large sphere.

† For present purposes, one's intuitive notion of the "normal to a surface" should suffice; a definition is provided in Section 8.4.

this N-cell partition we form the Riemann sum [see (4) on page 311]

$$\sum_{J=1}^{N} f(x_j, y_j, z_j)\, \Delta V_j, \tag{2}$$

where $\Delta V_j = \Delta x_j\, \Delta y_j\, \Delta z_j$ is the volume of the jth cell. Then we define a *finer* partition, compute its Riemann sum, and repeat the procedure over and over (in principle, that is; one does not actually carry out this procedure in practice). If the sequence of values of the Riemann sum thus generated converges to a limit, that limit is, by definition, the **triple integral** (1). That is,

$$\iiint_{\mathcal{R}} f(x, y, z)\, dV \equiv \lim_{|p|\to 0} \sum f(x_j, y_j, z_j)\, \Delta V_j \tag{3}$$

if the limit on the right exists, where $|p|$ is the *norm* of the partition, namely, the greatest of the dimensions $\Delta x_j, \Delta y_j, \Delta z_j$ for $j = 1, \ldots, N$. It can be shown that the limit (3) will indeed exist if f is continuous in the closed region $\mathcal{R}$, that condition being sufficient, but not necessary.

We state, without actually writing them out, that properties (6a) to (6c), and the mean value theorem (6d), on page 311, carry over in the obvious way to the case of triple integrals. For example, the **mean value theorem** for triple integrals states: If $f(x, y, z)$ is continuous throughout the closed region $\mathcal{R}$, there exists at least one point (x_0, y_0, z_0) in $\mathcal{R}$ such that

$$\boxed{\iiint_{\mathcal{R}} f(x, y, z)\, dV = f(x_0, y_0, z_0)V,} \tag{4}$$

where

$$V = \iiint_{\mathcal{R}} dV \tag{5}$$

is the **volume** of $\mathcal{R}$.

And to integrate *analytically*, we deal with (1) as an *iterated integral*. The idea is the same as for double integrals, so let us proceed directly to some examples.

EXAMPLE 1 Consider

$$I = \iiint_{\mathcal{R}} yz^2\, dV, \tag{6}$$

where $\mathcal{R}$ is the closed region bounded by the planes $x = 0$, $y = 0$, $z = 0$, and $x + y + z = 1$, as depicted in Fig. 8.7. Expressing (6) as an iterated integral, in which we integrate first on x, then on y, and then on z, say, we have

$$\begin{aligned} I &= \int_0^1 \int_0^{1-z} \int_0^{1-y-z} yz^2\, dx\, dy\, dz \\ &= \int_0^1 \int_0^{1-z} yz^2 x \Big|_{x=0}^{x=1-y-z} dy\, dz \\ &= \int_0^1 \int_0^{1-z} yz^2 (1 - y - z)\, dy\, dz \end{aligned} \tag{7}$$

$$= \int_0^1 z^2\left(\frac{y^2}{2} - \frac{y^3}{3} - \frac{y^2 z}{2}\right)\Bigg|_{y=0}^{y=1-z} dz$$

$$= \int_0^1 z^2\left[\frac{(1-z)^2}{2} - \frac{(1-z)^3}{3} - \frac{z(1-z)^2}{2}\right]dz = \frac{1}{360}.$$

In other words, first we integrate on x from a to b (Fig. 8.7), i.e., from $x = 0$ to $x = 1 - y - z$; then we sweep the ab sliver from cd to e, i.e., from $y = 0$ to $y = 1 - z$ (since e is on the line $y + z = 1$ in the y, z plane); finally, we sweep the plane cde from $z = 0$ to $z = 1$. Observe that merely drawing the triangle cde is half the battle; try obtaining the integration limits in (7) *without* doing that.

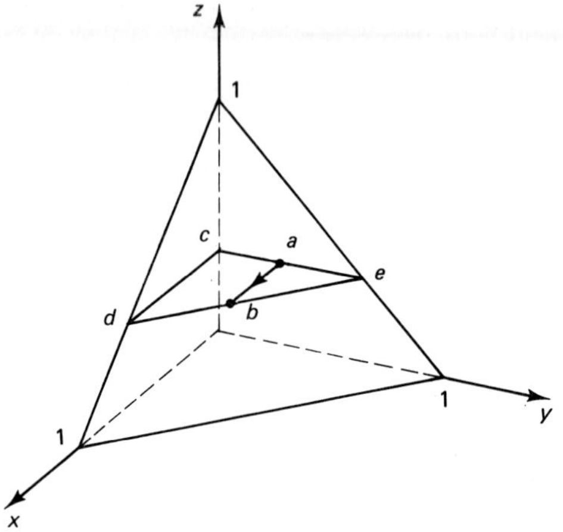

Fig. 8.7 The region $\mathcal{R}$.

COMMENT The order of integration is a matter of choice, but it is to be appreciated that if we were to adopt a different order of integration, the integration limits would be different, too. For example, if we integrate on z, then x, then y, then we would express

$$I = \int_0^1 \int_0^{1-y} \int_0^{1-x-y} yz^2 \, dz \, dx \, dy. \tag{8}$$

Or, integrating on y, then x, then z,

$$I = \int_0^1 \int_0^{1-z} \int_0^{1-x-z} yz^2 \, dy \, dx \, dz. \tag{9}$$

[The reader should verify the integration limits in (8) and (9) by drawing pictures similar to Fig. 8.7.] Working out (8) and (9), one should obtain $I = 1/360$ in each case, as in (7). ◀

EXAMPLE 2. Consider the integral

$$I = \int_0^4 \int_{z/2}^{2} \int_{z-y}^{z} f(x, y, z) \, dx \, dy \, dz. \tag{10}$$

Rather than integrate in the order x, y, z, as specified in (10), suppose that for one reason or another we wish to integrate in the order z, x, y. The problem that we pose, for this example, is the determination of the new limits in

$$I = \int_?^? \int_?^? \int_?^? f(x, y, z)\, dz\, dx\, dy. \tag{11}$$

(We assume that f is continuous over the region of integration, so that such interchange in the order of integration is permissible.) In principle, we can use the original limits, in (10), to determine the region of integration, say $\mathcal{R}$. If we can come up with a picture of $\mathcal{R}$ (analogous to the one in Fig. 8.7), we should be able to see the new integration limits. In practice, however, the necessary three-dimensional graphics may be more than we can handle. [Try it, for the limits given in (10).]

The point of this example is that *in carrying out a change in the order of integration we can simplify the graphics by replacing a three-dimensional problem by a sequence of two-dimensional ones*. That is, we can interchange the order of *two* variables at a time. In the present case, the interchange sequence may be expressed symbolically as

$$xyz \longrightarrow xzy \qquad \text{then} \qquad xzy \longrightarrow zxy. \tag{12}$$

To carry out the first step in (12) we write

$$I = \int_0^4 \int_{z/2}^2 \left\{ \int_{z-y}^{z} f(x, y, z)\, dx \right\} dy\, dz, \tag{13}$$

where the braces are not essential, but help to emphasize that we are focusing on the y, z integrations and regarding the quantity in braces as the integrand. The y, z limits in (13) enable us to infer the two-dimensional region of integration (in the y, z plane) shown in Fig. 8.8. From this figure it is easy to invert the y and z integrations, and to obtain

$$I = \int_0^2 \int_0^{2y} \left\{ \int_{z-y}^{z} f(x, y, z)\, dx \right\} dz\, dy. \tag{14}$$

Regrouping (14) as

$$I = \int_0^2 \left\{ \int_0^{2y} \int_{z-y}^{z} f(x, y, z)\, dx\, dz \right\} dy, \tag{15}$$

we now focus on the x, z inversion. From the x, z limits in (15) we infer the region shown in Fig. 8.9. (Note that y is regarded as fixed in the x, z integrations, and hence in Fig. 8.9.) Inverting the order so that we integrate on z first, we see from the figure that we must break the region into the sum of the three parts: A, B, and

Fig. 8.8 y, z interchange.

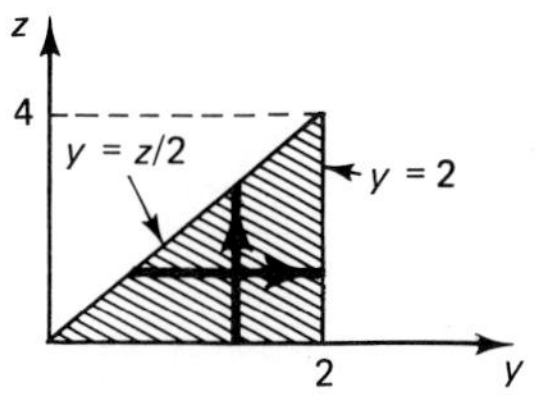

Fig. 8.9 x, y interchange.

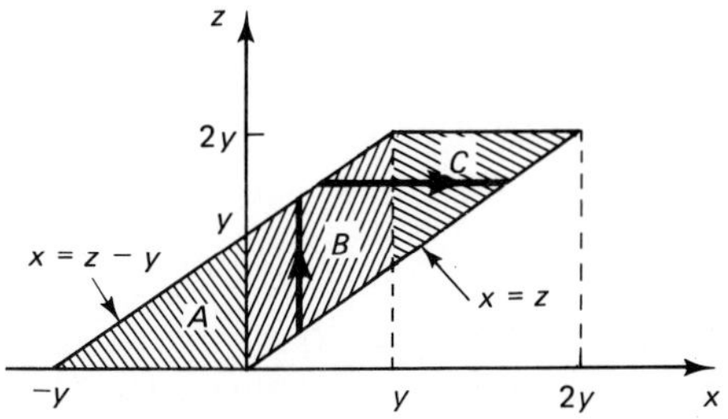

C. Thus we obtain

$$I = \int_0^2 \left\{ \iint_A f\,dz\,dx \right\} dy + \int_0^2 \left\{ \iint_B f\,dz\,dx \right\} dy + \int_0^2 \left\{ \iint_C f\,dz\,dx \right\} dy$$

$$= \int_0^2 \int_{-y}^0 \int_0^{x+y} f\,dz\,dx\,dy + \int_0^2 \int_0^y \int_x^{x+y} f\,dz\,dx\,dy + \int_0^2 \int_y^{2y} \int_x^{2y} f\,dz\,dx\,dy \tag{16}$$

which is the desired form, even if it is expressed as the sum of three integrals.

COMMENT 1 We have used "$f(x, y, z)$" as the integrand, rather than selecting some specific function, to emphasize that in deducing the new limits of integration, the functional form of the integrand is irrelevant. Nowhere, in this example, did we need to know the function $f(x, y, z)$.

COMMENT 2 In this book we deal with single, double, and triple integrals. Quadruple, quintuple, . . . , integrals also occur, however, and it should be noted that the idea developed in this example, namely, working with a sequence of two-dimensional problems, can be applied in those cases as well. ◀

8.3 EXERCISES

1. Evaluate each of the following iterated integrals.

*(a) $\int_1^2 \int_0^{3x} \int_{2y}^{x} dz\,dy\,dx$

(b) $\int_{-1}^1 \int_0^z \int_2^3 z^2 \sin(yz)\,dx\,dy\,dz$

(c) $\int_0^\pi \int_0^{2y} \int_0^{y+z} \cos(x+y)\,dx\,dz\,dy$

*(d) $\int_{-1}^3 \int_0^{z^2} \int_{\pi y}^0 \sin\dfrac{x}{y}\,dx\,dy\,dz$

(e) $\int_0^2 \int_0^{4z} \int_0^{2-z} -ze^{x+y}\,dx\,dy\,dz$

(f) $\int_0^1 \int_0^1 \int_0^y z^3y^2e^{xyz}\,dx\,dy\,dz$

2. Evaluate

$$I = \int_0^1 \int_0^{\pi z} \int_{y/\pi}^{z} \sin\frac{y}{x}\,dx\,dy\,dz. \tag{a}$$

Hint: The x integration looks quite difficult, so try inverting the order of integration to the form

$$I = \int_0^1 \int_?^? \int_?^? \sin\frac{y}{x}\,dy\,dx\,dz. \tag{b}$$

To determine the "?" integration limits we do *not* need to draw the full three-dimensional region of integration. Rather, a look at the x, y plane (with z regarded as a *fixed* value, somewhere between its limits of 0 and 1) will suffice since it is only the x and y integrations that we are interchanging.

3. Evaluate the following integrals. The idea, in each case, is the same as discussed in Exercise 2.

(a) $\int_0^\pi \int_0^{z^2} \int_{\sqrt{y}}^{z} \dfrac{1}{x} \sin\dfrac{y}{x}\,dx\,dy\,dz$

(b) $\int_0^2 \int_0^{z^3} \int_{\sqrt{y/z}}^{z} \dfrac{e^{y/x^2}}{x^2 z}\,dx\,dy\,dz$

4. (*Mass and center of gravity*) Let $\sigma(x, y, z)$ be the density of a distribution of mass over a region $\mathcal{R}$ in x, y, z space; i.e., $\sigma(x, y, z)$ is the mass per unit volume at (x, y, z). Then the x, y, z coordinates of the **center of gravity** are defined as

$$x_c = \frac{1}{M} \iiint_{\mathcal{R}} x\sigma(x, y, z)\,dV$$

$$y_c = \frac{1}{M} \iiint_{\mathcal{R}} y\sigma(x, y, z)\,dV \tag{a}$$

$$z_c = \frac{1}{M} \iiint_{\mathcal{R}} z\sigma(x, y, z)\,dV,$$

where

$$M = \iiint_{\mathcal{R}} \sigma(x, y, z)\,dV \tag{b}$$

is the total mass.

*(a) $\mathcal{R}$: the tetrahedron with vertices at $(1, 0, 0)$, $(0, 2, 0)$, $(0, 0, 1)$, $(0, 0, 0)$; σ = constant. Evaluate x_c.

(b) $\mathcal{R}$: the tetrahedron with vertices at (1, 0, 1), (0, 0, 1), (0, 1, 1), (0, 0, 0); $\sigma = x$. Evaluate z_c.

(c) $\mathcal{R}$: the finite region bounded by $z = 4 - x^2 - y^2$ and the x, y plane; σ = constant. Evaluate z_c.

(d) $\mathcal{R}$: the finite region bounded by $z = 1 - x^2 - y^2$, the x, z plane, and the x, y plane; σ = constant. Evaluate z_c.

(e) Repeat part (d), but with $\sigma = z$.

5. (*Moments of inertia*) Let $\sigma(x, y, z)$ be the density of a distribution of mass over a region $\mathcal{R}$ in x, y, z space [i.e., $\sigma(x, y, z)$ is the mass per unit volume at (x, y, z)]. Then the **moments of inertia** I_x, I_y, and I_z, about the x, y, z axes, respectively, are defined as

$$\begin{aligned} I_x &= \iiint_{\mathcal{R}} (y^2 + z^2)\sigma(x, y, z)\,dV \\ I_y &= \iiint_{\mathcal{R}} (x^2 + z^2)\sigma(x, y, z)\,dV \\ I_z &= \iiint_{\mathcal{R}} (x^2 + y^2)\sigma(x, y, z)\,dV. \end{aligned} \qquad \text{(a)}$$

In each case evaluate I_x.

*(a) $\mathcal{R}$, σ as given in Exercise 4(a).

(b) $\mathcal{R}$ the rectangular prism $0 < x < a$, $0 < y < b$, $0 < z < c$; σ = constant. Show that $I_x = \sigma abc(b^2 + c^2)/3$.

(c) $\mathcal{R}$ the rectangular prism $0 < x < a$, $0 < y < b$, $0 < z < c$, but with the corner $0 < x < a/2$, $0 < y < b/2$, $0 < z < c/2$ cut out, as shown in the figure; σ = constant. *Hint:* You may use the result given in part (b).

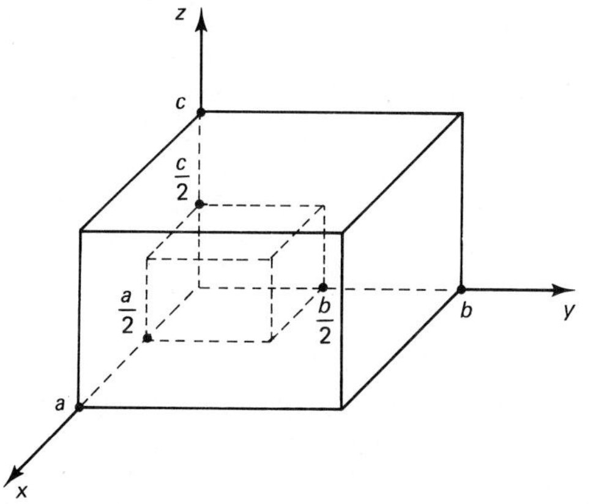

6. Determine the "?" integration limits. *Note:* More than one integral may be needed, as occurred in (16).

*(a) $\displaystyle\int_0^1\int_0^z\int_0^z f(x, y, z)\,dx\,dy\,dz = \int_?^?\int_?^?\int_?^? f(x, y, z)\,dx\,dz\,dy$

(b) $\displaystyle\int_0^1\int_0^z\int_0^{2z} f(x, y, z)\,dx\,dy\,dz = \int_?^?\int_?^?\int_?^? f(x, y, z)\,dy\,dz\,dx$

(c) $\displaystyle\int_0^1\int_0^z\int_0^z f(x, y, z)\,dx\,dy\,dz = \int_?^?\int_?^?\int_?^? f(x, y, z)\,dz\,dy\,dx$

*(d) $\displaystyle\int_0^2\int_0^z\int_z^2 f(x, y, z)\,dx\,dy\,dz = \int_?^?\int_?^?\int_?^? f(x, y, z)\,dy\,dz\,dx$

(e) $\displaystyle\int_0^4\int_{z/2}^{\sqrt{z}}\int_0^{y+z} f(x, y, z)\,dx\,dy\,dz = \int_?^?\int_?^?\int_?^? f(x, y, z)\,dx\,dz\,dy$

(f) $\displaystyle\int_4^6\int_1^3\int_0^2 f(x, y, z)\,dx\,dy\,dz = \int_?^?\int_?^?\int_?^? f(x, y, z)\,dz\,dy\,dx$

(g) $\displaystyle\int_0^2\int_0^{z/2}\int_y^z f(x, y, z)\,dx\,dy\,dz = \int_?^?\int_?^?\int_?^? f(x, y, z)\,dy\,dz\,dx$

SURFACES 8.4

[Optional Section]

The major theorems in Chapter 9 involve integrations over curves, surfaces, and volumes. We have been building up to those theorems by discussing curves (in Section 7.7) and double and triple integrals (in Sections 8.2 and 8.3). At the bare minimum there is one more important result, regarding the "area element" on a curved surface, that requires our attention before we are prepared to continue. Besides deriving it in Section 8.5, that result will be given when needed, in Chapter 9, so that the material in these remaining sections of Chapter 8 can be treated as OPTIONAL for a shorter course.

In the present section we discuss the parametric representation of surfaces, and introduce the "tangent plane" and "normal." To begin, recall from Section 7.7 that a space curve may be represented parametrically by the equations*

$$x = x(u), \qquad y = y(u), \qquad z = z(u) \tag{1a}$$

over some interval of the parameter u. Or, in vector form, we expressed the position vector $\mathbf{R}(u)$, from the origin of the reference x, y, z coordinate system to a point on the curve, as

$$\mathbf{R}(u) = x(u)\hat{\mathbf{i}} + y(u)\hat{\mathbf{j}} + z(u)\hat{\mathbf{k}}. \tag{1b}$$

Similarly, it is natural to expect a *two*-parameter system

$$x = x(u, v), \qquad y = y(u, v), \qquad z = z(u, v) \tag{2a}$$

or

$$\mathbf{R}(u, v) = x(u, v)\hat{\mathbf{i}} + y(u, v)\hat{\mathbf{j}} + z(u, v)\hat{\mathbf{k}}, \tag{2b}$$

where u and v are real, to define a *surface*. For if we imagine v to be fixed, these expressions will, in general, define a curve. As we vary v, we produce a family of curves which, in general, will generate a surface.

EXAMPLE 1 Let

$$x = a \sin v \cos u, \qquad y = a \sin v \sin u, \qquad z = a \cos v, \tag{3}$$

where $0 \le u \le \pi/2$, $0 \le v \le \pi/2$, and a is a positive constant. Observe that squaring and adding these three equations gives $x^2 + y^2 + z^2 = a^2$, which represents a spherical surface of radius a centered at the origin. In fact, a comparison of (3) with equation (27) on page 294 reveals that a, v, u are actually the spherical coordinates ρ, ϕ, θ, respectively, in disguise. Since $\rho = a =$ constant, the surface is spherical. More precisely, it is one-eighth of a spherical surface, as shown in Fig. 8.10b, where it is shaded and denoted as $\mathcal{S}$. Thus in the present example the parameters u and v have quite a definite geometric significance; they are the angles shown in Fig. 8.10b. In other cases, u and v in (2) may bear no such obvious significance.

If v is fixed and u is varied over the line AB in Fig. 8.10a, then (3) generates the curve $A'B'$ shown in Fig. 8.10b. Similarly, if u is fixed and v is varied over CD, then (3) generates the curve $C'D'$. If we think of $\mathcal{S}$ as part of the earth's globe, with the positive z direction as north, the $v =$ constant curves are lines of latitude and the $u =$ constant curves are lines of longitude. ◀

It is common to refer to u, v as **curvilinear coordinates** of the generated surface $\mathcal{S}$. In Example 1, for instance, the network of lines of latitude (the $v =$ constant curves) and longitude (the $u =$ constant curves) forms a coordinate system on the

* In Section 7.7 we used τ as our parameter; here we prefer the letter u.

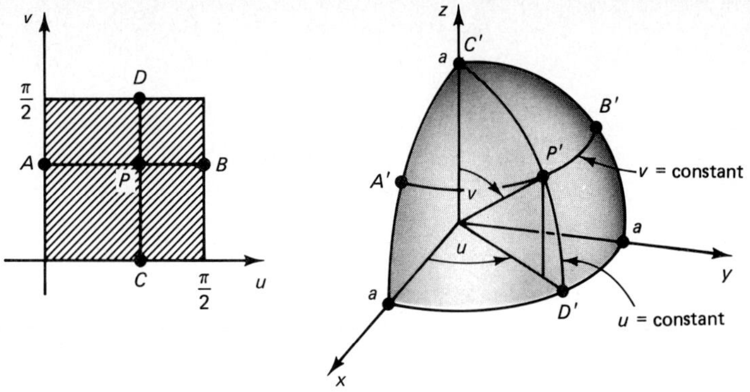

Fig. 8.10 The surface $\mathscr{S}$ generated by (3). (a) (b)

surface of the sphere just as surely as a rectilinear network of $x =$ constant and $y =$ constant lines forms a coordinate system in the x, y plane. We call the $u =$ constant and $v =$ constant curves on $\mathscr{S}$ the **coordinate curves.**

Now, suppose that with u, v confined to some region $\mathscr{R}$ of the u, v plane (e.g., the shaded rectangle in Fig. 8.10a) the system (2) generates a surface $\mathscr{S}$ in the x, y, z space (e.g., $\mathscr{S}$ in Fig. 8.10b). In turn, curves on $\mathscr{S}$ (not necessarily coordinate curves) may be parametrized in the form

$$u = u(\tau), \qquad v = v(\tau), \tag{4}$$

where τ is a real parameter. *We will assume, of the curves under consideration, that $u(\tau)$, $v(\tau)$ have continuous first derivatives $u'(\tau)$, $v'(\tau)$, and that at each τ under consideration at least one of these two derivatives is nonzero. Furthermore, we will assume two properties of the surface $\mathscr{S}$*: (1) *that $\mathbf{R}(u, v)$ has continuous first-order partials [i.e., $\mathbf{R}(u, v)$ is C^1]*, and (2) *that*

$$\mathbf{R}_u \times \mathbf{R}_v \neq \mathbf{0}, \tag{5}$$

where properties 1 and 2 hold over that part of $\mathscr{R}$ which is of interest. Observe that (5) implies that $\mathbf{R}_u = \partial\mathbf{R}/\partial u$ and $\mathbf{R}_v = \partial\mathbf{R}/\partial v$ are linearly independent. For if they were linearly *de*pendent, we could express one as a nonzero scalar multiple of the other, say $\mathbf{R}_v = \alpha\mathbf{R}_u(\alpha \neq 0)$. But then we would have $\mathbf{R}_u \times \mathbf{R}_v = \mathbf{R}_u \times \alpha\mathbf{R}_u = \alpha\mathbf{R}_u \times \mathbf{R}_u = \mathbf{0}$, in violation of (5).

Since $\mathbf{R}(u, v)$ is C^1, and $u(\tau)$, $v(\tau)$ are differentiable, we may use chain differentiation to compute

$$\mathbf{R}' = \frac{d}{d\tau}\mathbf{R}(u(\tau), v(\tau)) = \mathbf{R}_u u' + \mathbf{R}_v v'. \tag{6}$$

The vector $\mathbf{R}'$ is nonzero, for it is a linear combination of linearly independent vectors $\mathbf{R}_u$ and $\mathbf{R}_v$; thus it will be zero if and only if the coefficients u', v' are both zero. But in the preceding paragraph we assumed that u', v' do not both vanish at any point on the curve. Thus $\mathbf{R}' \neq \mathbf{0}$, and it follows from our definition on page 285 that $\mathbf{R}'$ is a tangent vector to the curve.

Considering any point P on $\mathscr{S}$ observe that the linearly independent vectors $\mathbf{R}_u$, $\mathbf{R}_v$, at P, determine a plane through P. From (6) we see that that plane contains the tangent to every curve (4) on $\mathscr{S}$ through P, so we call that plane the **tangent plane** to $\mathscr{S}$ at P and denote it as $T(P)$ (see Fig. 8.11).

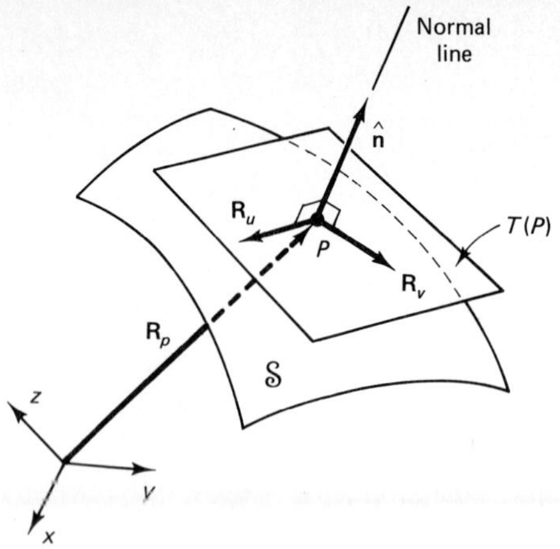

Fig. 8.11 Tangent plane and normal $\mathcal{S}$ at P.

The straight line through P which is perpendicular to $T(P)$ is called the **normal line** to $\mathcal{S}$ at P. Evidently, the vector $\mathbf{R}_u \times \mathbf{R}_v$ is perpendicular to $T(P)$ and hence lies along the normal line. Dividing this vector by its length produces a **unit normal** to $\mathcal{S}$ at P,

$$\hat{\mathbf{n}} = \frac{\mathbf{R}_u \times \mathbf{R}_v}{\|\mathbf{R}_u \times \mathbf{R}_v\|}, \tag{7}$$

as depicted in Fig. 8.11. The right-hand member of (7) fails to exist if $\mathbf{R}_u \times \mathbf{R}_v = \mathbf{0}$, but this possibility has been ruled out by (5). Thus (7) does define a unit normal at P, and this definition is unique to within a factor of ± 1; i.e., the negative of the right-hand member of (7) would also be a unit normal vector.

Next, let us obtain an equation for the tangent plane $T(P)$. If we denote the position vector to any point (x, y, z) on $T(P)$ as $\mathbf{R} = x\hat{\mathbf{i}} + y\hat{\mathbf{j}} + z\hat{\mathbf{k}}$, and the position vector to P as $\mathbf{R}_p = x_p\hat{\mathbf{i}} + y_p\hat{\mathbf{j}} + z_p\hat{\mathbf{k}}$, then the statement that (x, y, z) is on $T(P)$ is equivalent to the statement

$$(\mathbf{R} - \mathbf{R}_p) \cdot \hat{\mathbf{n}} = 0, \tag{8}$$

where $\hat{\mathbf{n}}$ may be computed from (7) and is considered as known in (8). If we express $\hat{\mathbf{n}}$ as $\hat{\mathbf{n}} = a\hat{\mathbf{i}} + b\hat{\mathbf{j}} + c\hat{\mathbf{k}}$, for simplicity, and use the foregoing expressions for $\mathbf{R}$ and $\mathbf{R}_p$, then (8) becomes

$$a(x - x_p) + b(y - y_p) + c(z - z_p) = 0 \tag{9a}$$

or

$$ax + by + cz = d, \tag{9b}$$

where

$$d = \text{constant} = ax_p + by_p + cz_p.$$

Equations (8) and (9) are the desired equations of the tangent plane; (9) may well look familiar from a course in calculus.

EXAMPLE 2 Obtain $\hat{\mathbf{n}}$ and the equation of the tangent plane to the spherical surface in Example 1 at the point P corresponding to $u = v = \pi/4$. We have

$$\mathbf{R} = a \sin v \cos u\hat{\mathbf{i}} + a \sin v \sin u\hat{\mathbf{j}} + a \cos v\hat{\mathbf{k}},$$

$$\mathbf{R}_u = -a \sin v \sin u\hat{\mathbf{i}} + a \sin v \cos u\hat{\mathbf{j}},$$

$$\mathbf{R}_v = a \cos v \cos u\hat{\mathbf{i}} + a \cos v \sin u\hat{\mathbf{j}} - a \sin v\hat{\mathbf{k}},$$

$$\mathbf{R}_u\big|_{u=v=\pi/4} = \frac{a}{2}(-\hat{\mathbf{i}} + \hat{\mathbf{j}}),$$

$$\mathbf{R}_v\big|_{u=v=\pi/4} = \frac{a}{2}(\hat{\mathbf{i}} + \hat{\mathbf{j}} - \sqrt{2}\,\hat{\mathbf{k}}),$$

so that (7) gives

$$\hat{\mathbf{n}} = -\frac{\hat{\mathbf{i}} + \hat{\mathbf{j}} + \sqrt{2}\,\hat{\mathbf{k}}}{2}.$$

Next, $x_p = a \sin(\pi/4) \cos(\pi/4) = a/2$, $y_p = a \sin(\pi/4) \sin(\pi/4) = a/2$, $z_p = a \cos(\pi/4) = a/\sqrt{2}$, so that (9a) becomes

$$-\frac{1}{2}\left(x - \frac{a}{2}\right) - \frac{1}{2}\left(y - \frac{a}{2}\right) - \frac{1}{\sqrt{2}}\left(z - \frac{a}{\sqrt{2}}\right) = 0,$$

or

$$x + y + \sqrt{2}z = 2a. \qquad ◀$$

Before closing, notice that in this section we have encountered both parametric and nonparametric representations of surfaces. For example, the spherical surface $\mathcal{S}$ in Fig. 8.10b is represented parametrically by (3), and nonparametrically by the (perhaps more familiar) form

$$x^2 + y^2 + z^2 = a^2. \tag{10}$$

In the case of (10) the nonparametric representation occurs in the *implicit* form $f(x, y, z) = 0$; in other cases it may occur in one of the *explicit* forms $z = z(x, y)$, $y = y(x, z)$, or $x = x(y, z)$. For example, (10) may be solved for z as $z = \sqrt{a^2 - x^2 - y^2}$, or for y, or for x. Thus it is natural to wonder: "How do we get from the parametric representation to the nonparametric one, and vice versa?" and "Does a given parametric representation uniquely determine a nonparametric representation, and vice versa?" Although we will not attempt a complete discussion of these questions, we *are* anxious to make two important points.

First, we note that the parametrization of a given surface $\mathcal{S}$ is not unique.

EXAMPLE 3 To illustrate that claim, we observe that in place of the parametrization (3) of the spherical surface shown in Fig. 8.10b, we can use the parametrization

$$x = u, \qquad y = v, \qquad z = \sqrt{a^2 - u^2 - v^2}, \tag{11}$$

where u, v are in the shaded region shown in Fig. 8.12a. In a given example, of course, one tries to adopt the most *convenient* parametrization for the problem at hand. ◀

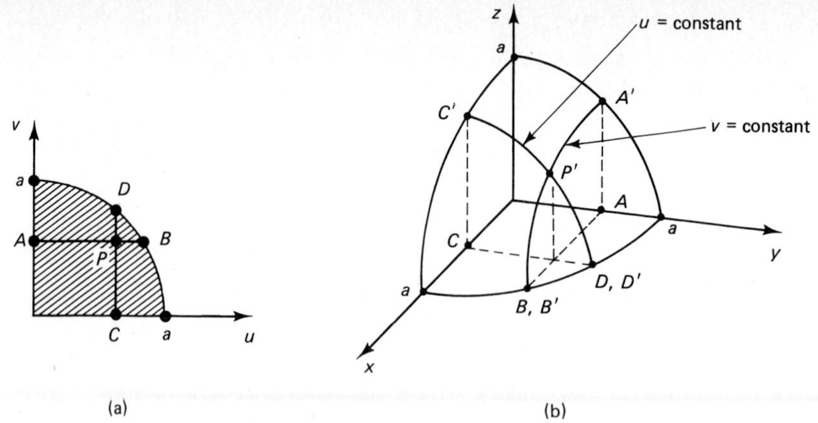

Fig. 8.12 Alternative parametrization of $\mathscr{S}$.

Second, consider the prospects for being able to deduce a nonparametric representation from a given parametric representation (2). (In Example 1 we accomplished that deduction by simple algebra.) Writing out (5) yields

$$\mathbf{R}_u \times \mathbf{R}_v = \begin{vmatrix} \hat{\mathbf{i}} & \hat{\mathbf{j}} & \hat{\mathbf{k}} \\ x_u & y_u & z_u \\ x_v & y_v & z_v \end{vmatrix} = \begin{vmatrix} y_u & z_u \\ y_v & z_v \end{vmatrix} \hat{\mathbf{i}} - \begin{vmatrix} x_u & z_u \\ x_v & z_v \end{vmatrix} \hat{\mathbf{j}} + \begin{vmatrix} x_u & y_u \\ x_v & y_v \end{vmatrix} \hat{\mathbf{k}}$$

$$= \frac{\partial(y, z)}{\partial(u, v)}\hat{\mathbf{i}} - \frac{\partial(x, z)}{\partial(u, v)}\hat{\mathbf{j}} + \frac{\partial(x, y)}{\partial(u, v)}\hat{\mathbf{k}} \neq \mathbf{0}. \tag{12}$$

Thus the three Jacobians in (12) do not *all* vanish, at any given u, v point. Suppose, for example, that $\partial(y, z)/\partial(u, v) \neq 0$ in some neighborhood in the relevant u, v region. Then, according to the Implicit Function Theorem 2 on page 241, we can solve (not necessarily in closed form) the equations

$$y = y(u, v), \qquad z = z(u, v),$$

in (2), for u and v, i.e., for $u = u(y, z)$ and $v = v(y, z)$. Putting these expressions into the third equation in (2), we have the result $x = x(u(y, z), v(y, z)) = f(y, z)$, say. Or if $\partial(x, z)/\partial(u, v) \neq 0$, we can obtain $y = g(x, z)$, if $\partial(x, y)/\partial(u, v) \neq 0$, we can obtain $z = h(x, y)$. The essential idea, which we do not claim to have proved in this paragraph, is that the "regularity" conditions that we have required of $\mathbf{R}(u, v)$ suffice to ensure that it is possible to pass from a parametric representation to a nonparametric one. For a detailed discussion of these points, we refer the interested reader to Chapter IV of J. J. Stoker's *Differential Geometry* (New York: Wiley, 1969).

Summarizing the main points in this section, we introduced the two-parameter representation of a surface in the form

$$\mathbf{R}(u, v) = x(u, v)\hat{\mathbf{i}} + y(u, v)\hat{\mathbf{j}} + z(u, v)\hat{\mathbf{k}},$$

as an extension of the idea of a one-parameter representation of a space curve. It was noted that the network of u = constant and v = constant curves provides a curvilinear coordinate system on the surface.

In addition, we obtained the expression (7) for a unit normal at any point on the surface (under the assumption that $\mathbf{R}_u \times \mathbf{R}_v \neq \mathbf{0}$), and an equation for the tangent plane $T(P)$ at any point P on the surface, namely, any of the equations (8), (9a), or (9b).

8.4 EXERCISES

1. In Fig. 8.10 we showed the curves on $\mathscr{S}$ which are the images of the lines AB and CD in the u, v plane, namely, $A'P'B'$ and $C'P'D'$, respectively. Sketch, or trace, or photocopy the surface $\mathscr{S}$, in Fig. 8.10b, and show the curve on $\mathscr{S}$ which is the image of the following line in the u, v plane (see the accompanying figure).

(a) OE (b) EF (c) FG (d) OG
(e) the line $v = u$, from O to F
(f) the line $v = \pi/2 - u$, from E to G

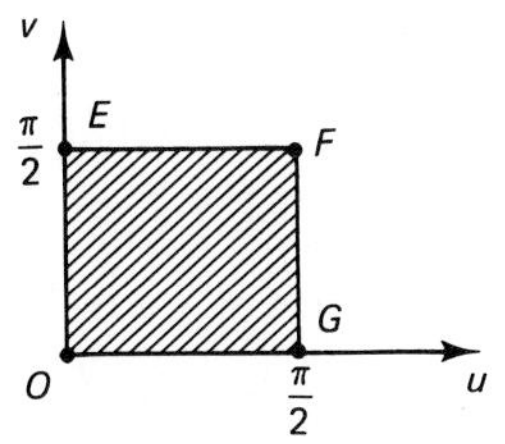

2. Consider the parametrization

$$x = u, \qquad y = u + v, \qquad z = 0$$

over $0 < u < 4$, $0 < v < 4$.
(a) Show $\mathscr{S}$ in a labeled sketch.
(b) Show the $u = 1, 2, 3$ and $v = 1, 2, 3$ coordinate curves on $\mathscr{S}$.
(c) Evaluate $\hat{\mathbf{n}}$ using (7). Are there any points on $\mathscr{S}$ at which (5) is not satisfied?

3. Consider the parametrization

$$x = u, \qquad y = u - v, \qquad z = 4 - 2u + v \tag{a}$$

over the open region shown (shaded) below.

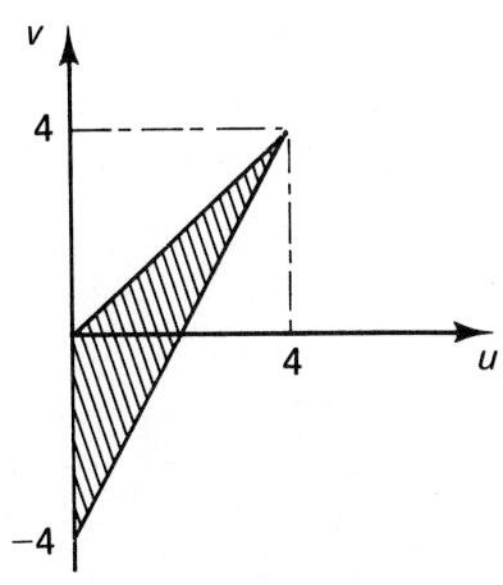

(a) Eliminating u and v from (a), obtain a nonparametric representation of the surface $\mathscr{S}$, and show $\mathscr{S}$ in a neat, labeled sketch.
(b) Show the $u = 1, 2, 3$ and $v = -2, 0, 2$ coordinate curves on $\mathscr{S}$.
*(c) Evaluate $\hat{\mathbf{n}}$ using (7).

4. Consider the parametrization

$$x = u \cos v, \qquad y = u \sin v, \qquad z = 0$$

over $0 \le u < 3$, $0 \le v < 2\pi$.
(a) Show $\mathscr{S}$ in a labeled sketch.
(b) Show the $u = 1, 2$ and $v = 0, \pi/4, \pi/2, 3\pi/4, \pi, 5\pi/4, 3\pi/2, 7\pi/4$ coordinate curves on $\mathscr{S}$.
*(c) Evaluate $\hat{\mathbf{n}}$ using (7). Show that (5) is *not* satisfied at the origin, but that a unit normal $\hat{\mathbf{n}}$ does, nevertheless, exist there.

5. Consider the parametrization

$$x = au \cos v, \qquad y = bu \sin v, \qquad z = 0$$

over $0 \le u < 1$, $0 \le v < 2\pi$.
(a) Show $\mathscr{S}$ in a labeled sketch.
(b) Show the $u = \frac{1}{2}$ and $v = \pi/4, 3\pi/4, 5\pi/4, 7\pi/4$ coordinate curves on $\mathscr{S}$.
(c) Evaluate $\hat{\mathbf{n}}$ using (7). Show that (5) is *not* satisfied at the origin, but that a unit normal $\hat{\mathbf{n}}$ does, nevertheless, exist there.

6. Consider the parametrization

$$x = (1 - u) \cos v, \qquad y = (1 - u) \sin v, \qquad z = u \tag{a}$$

over $0 < u \le 1$, $0 \le v < 2\pi$.
(a) Eliminating u and v from (a), obtain a nonparametric representation of the surface $\mathscr{S}$, and show $\mathscr{S}$ in a neat, labeled sketch. Identify $\mathscr{S}$. (Is it a plane? Is it a bird? A cone? . . .)
(b) Show the $u = \frac{1}{4}, \frac{1}{2}, \frac{3}{4}$, and $v = 0, \pi/4$ coordinate curves on $\mathscr{S}$.
*(c) Evaluate $\hat{\mathbf{n}}$ using (7). Show that there is one point on $\mathscr{S}$ at which (5) is not satisfied. Does $\mathscr{S}$ admit a unique normal line at that point?

*(d) Find the equation of the tangent plane T, in the form (9b), at $u = \frac{1}{2}$, $v = 0$. Sketch T and $\mathcal{S}$.
(e) Repeat part (d), for $u = \frac{1}{4}$, $v = 0$.
(f) Repeat part (d), for $u = \frac{1}{2}$, $v = \pi/4$.
(g) Repeat part (d), for $u = \frac{1}{2}$, $v = \pi/2$.

7. Consider the parametrization

$$x = a \sin v \cos u, \qquad y = b \sin v \sin u,$$
$$z = c \cos v \tag{a}$$

(which is similar to the one in Example 1) over $0 \le u < 2\pi$, $0 \le v \le \pi$.
(a) Eliminating u and v from (a) obtain a nonparametric representation of the surface $\mathcal{S}$, and show $\mathcal{S}$ in a labeled sketch.
(b) Show the $u = 0, \pi/4$ and $v = \pi/4, \pi/2$ coordinate curves on $\mathcal{S}$.
(c) Evaluate $\hat{\mathbf{n}}$ using (7). Find the two points on $\mathcal{S}$ at which (5) is not satisfied. Does a unique normal line (and hence an $\hat{\mathbf{n}}$) nevertheless exist at those points? If so, give $\hat{\mathbf{n}}$ there.
*(d) Find the equation of the tangent plane T, in the form (9b), at $u = 0$, $v = \pi/4$.
(e) Repeat part (d), for $u = 0$, $v = \pi/2$.
(f) Repeat part (d), for $u = \pi/4$, $v = \pi/4$.
(g) Repeat part (d), for $u = \pi/2$, $v = \pi/4$.

8. Consider the parametrization

$$x = a \cos u, \qquad y = b \sin u, \qquad z = v^2 \tag{a}$$

over $0 \le u < 2\pi$, $0 < v < 3$.
(a) Sketch $\mathcal{S}$, and verify that it is an elliptic cylinder.
(b) Show the $u = 0, \pi/4$, and $v = 2, 4$ coordinate curves on $\mathcal{S}$.

9. Find two different parametrizations of each surface.
*(a) the x, y plane
(b) the x, z plane
(c) the y, z plane
(d) the plane $ax + by + cz = d$
*(e) the hyperboloid $x^2 + y^2 - z^2 = 1$ over $0 \le z < \infty$
(f) the elliptic paraboloid $x^2 + y^2 = z$
(g) the quadric cone $x^2 + y^2 = z^2$

10. Let $\mathcal{S}$ be given in the form $z = f(x, y)$, where f is C^1 in the x, y region of interest. Show that

$$\hat{\mathbf{n}} = \frac{f_x\hat{\mathbf{i}} + f_y\hat{\mathbf{j}} - \hat{\mathbf{k}}}{\sqrt{f_x^2 + f_y^2 + 1}} \tag{a}$$

is a unit normal to $\mathcal{S}$. *Hint:* Let $x = u$, $y = v$, and use (7).

11. Find the tangent plane (if it exists), in the form (9b), to the given surface $\mathcal{S}$ at the given point P. If it does *not* exist, state that.
*(a) $\mathcal{S}$: $z = x^2 + y^2$, $P = (2, 1, 5)$ (see Exercise 10)
(b) $\mathcal{S}$: $z = x^2 + y^2$, $P = (0, 0, 0)$ (see Exercise 10)
(c) $\mathcal{S}$: $z = xy$, $P = (3, -1, -3)$ (see Exercise 10)
*(d) $\mathcal{S}$: $z = x^2 - 2y + 4$, $P = (1, 1, 3)$ (see Exercise 10)
(e) $\mathcal{S}$: $z = 1 - \sqrt{x^2 + y^2}$, $P = (0, 0, 1)$ (see Exercise 10)
(f) $\mathcal{S}$: $x = u$, $y = u + v^2$, $z = v + 1$, P: $u = 0$, $v = 0$
(g) $\mathcal{S}$: $x = u \cos v$, $y = u \sin v$, $z = u^2$, P: $u = 2$, $v = \pi/6$
(h) $\mathcal{S}$: $x = u - v$, $y = u + v$, $z = uv$, P: $u = 2$, $v = 1$
(i) $\mathcal{S}$: $x = u$, $y = u^2 + v$, $z = u - v$, P: $u = 0$, $v = 1$

8.5 SURFACE AREA

[Optional Section]

In Section 8.2 we dealt with the "area element" $dA = dx\,dy$, in the x, y plane, and with integrals of the form $\iint_{\mathcal{R}} f\,dA$, where $\mathcal{R}$ was some part of the x, y plane. In the present section we generalize these notions in two ways: We switch from Cartesian x, y coordinates to general curvilinear coordinates, and we allow $\mathcal{R}$ to be a curved surface in 3-space, not just a flat portion of the x, y plane. Thus we will have integrals over curved surfaces in space. The physical applications of such integrals occur in Chapter 9. For example, suppose that we have a distribution of electric charge over a surface, and we wish to know the total charge, or the electric field induced by that distribution. Such quantities are expressible as integrals of the sort that we are about to consider.

We consider a surface $\mathcal{S}$ given by $\mathbf{R}(u, v) = x(u, v)\hat{\mathbf{i}} + y(u, v)\hat{\mathbf{j}} + z(u, v)\hat{\mathbf{k}}$, where (as assumed on page 323) $\mathbf{R}(u, v)$ is C^1 and where $\mathbf{R}_u \times \mathbf{R}_v \neq \mathbf{0}$. These conditions ensure that $\mathcal{S}$ is "nice"; specifically, they ensure that there exists a normal $\hat{\mathbf{n}}$ on $\mathcal{S}$ which is unique (to within a factor of ± 1) and which varies continuously on $\mathcal{S}$ (i.e., is a continuous function of u, v). Such a surface is said to be **smooth.**

Since the position vector from the origin (of our reference x, y, z frame) to any point on $\mathcal{S}$ is $\mathbf{R} = \mathbf{R}(u, v)$, we may express

$$d\mathbf{R} = \mathbf{R}_u \, du + \mathbf{R}_v \, dv, \tag{1}$$

so that along the u = constant and v = constant curves through any point P on $\mathcal{S}$ we have $d\mathbf{R} = \mathbf{R}_v \, dv$ (since u = constant, so that $du = 0$) and $d\mathbf{R} = \mathbf{R}_u \, du$, respectively, as shown in Fig. 8.13. These vectors define a parallelogram (Fig. 8.13) lying in the tangent plane to $\mathcal{S}$ at P. The area of this parallelogram is [recall (9) on page 273]

$$dA = \|\mathbf{R}_u \, du \times \mathbf{R}_v \, dv\| = \|\mathbf{R}_u \times \mathbf{R}_v\| du \, dv. \tag{2}$$

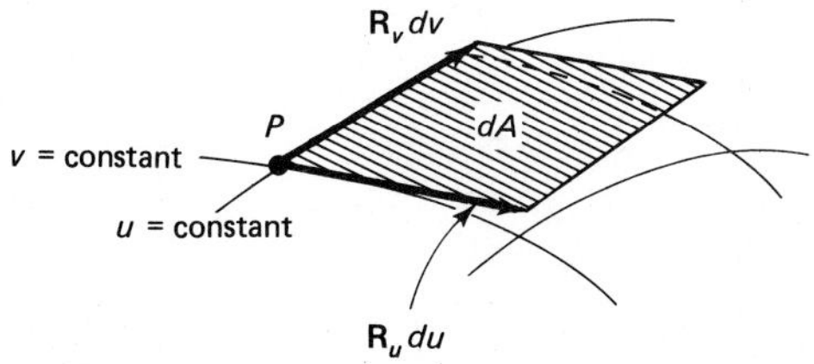

Fig. 8.13 Area element.

As du and dv tend to zero this plane area element lies closer and closer to $\mathcal{S}$, so that it seems reasonable to define the **area** of the curved surface $\mathcal{S}$ by the double integral

$$\boxed{A = \iint_{\mathcal{S}} dA = \iint_{\mathcal{R}} \|\mathbf{R}_u \times \mathbf{R}_v\| du \, dv,} \tag{3}$$

where $\mathcal{R}$ is the region in the u, v plane that corresponds to the surface $\mathcal{S}$ in 3-space. Notice that we have not proved (3); it is a *definition.** Further, we call

$$\boxed{dA = \|\mathbf{R}_u \times \mathbf{R}_v\| du \, dv} \tag{4}$$

the **area element** on $\mathcal{S}$.

To obtain a computational version of (4), cross $\mathbf{R}_u = x_u\hat{\mathbf{i}} + y_u\hat{\mathbf{j}} + z_u\hat{\mathbf{k}}$ with $\mathbf{R}_v = x_v\hat{\mathbf{i}} + y_v\hat{\mathbf{j}} + z_v\hat{\mathbf{k}}$. The norm of the resulting vector is the square root of the sum of the squares of its components. Carrying out these steps, we obtain

$$dA = \sqrt{EG - F^2} \, du \, dv, \tag{5a}$$

where

$$\begin{aligned} E &= x_u^2 + y_u^2 + z_u^2 \\ F &= x_u x_v + y_u y_v + z_u z_v \\ G &= x_v^2 + y_v^2 + z_v^2. \end{aligned} \tag{5b}$$

* The merits of this particular definition are mentioned on p. 82 of J. J. Stoker, *Differential Geometry* (New York: Wiley, 1969).

Notice that we may attach a special significance to F for, by inspection, we see that $F = \mathbf{R}_u \cdot \mathbf{R}_v$. Thus if $\mathbf{R}(u, v)$ is such that F is identically zero, then that condition implies that $\mathbf{R}_u$ and $\mathbf{R}_v$ are perpendicular to each other at each point on $\mathcal{S}$. In that event, we say that the curvilinear coordinates u and v are **orthogonal;** i.e., they form an "orthogonal net" on $\mathcal{S}$.

EXAMPLE 1 *Surface Area of a Sphere.* To illustrate the use of (5), let us compute the surface area of the spherical surface $\mathcal{S}$ defined by

$$x = a \sin v \cos u, \qquad y = a \sin v \sin u, \qquad z = a \cos v, \tag{6}$$

over $0 \le u \le \pi/2$ and $0 \le v \le \pi/2$ (which was the subject of Example 1 on page 322). $\mathcal{S}$ constitutes one-eighth of a complete spherical surface and is shown in Fig. 8.14. Putting (6) into (5b) gives

$$E = a^2 \sin^2 v, \qquad F = 0, \qquad G = a^2. \tag{7}$$

Thus

$$dA = a^2 \,|\sin v|\, du\, dv = a^2 \sin v\, du\, dv \tag{8}$$

since $\sin v \ge 0$ over $0 \le v \le \pi/2$, so

$$A = a^2 \int_0^{\pi/2} \int_0^{\pi/2} \sin v\, du\, dv = \frac{\pi a^2}{2}. \tag{9}$$

Of course, (9) is correct since we all know that the surface area of the sphere is $4\pi a^2$, and $\mathcal{S}$ is only one-eighth of that.

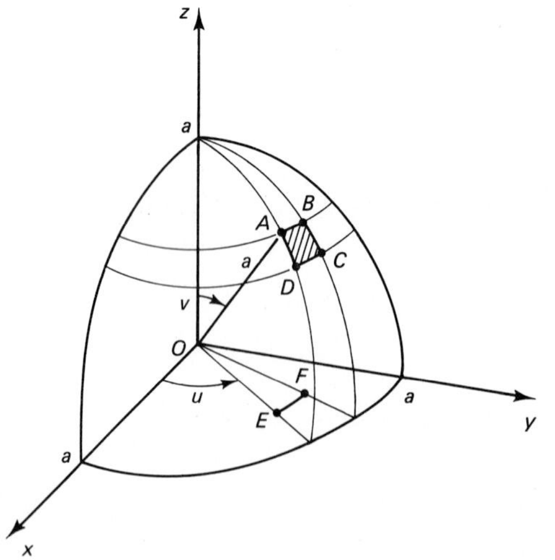

Fig. 8.14 The surface $\mathcal{S}$.

COMMENT 1 The expression (8) could, in this case, have been obtained directly from Fig. 8.14, without recourse to (5). For dA is the shaded area $ABCD$, so

$$\begin{aligned} dA &\sim (AB)(AD) = (EF)(AD) = (OE\, du)(a\, dv) \\ &= (a \sin v\, du)(a\, dv) = a^2 \sin v\, du\, dv. \end{aligned} \tag{10}$$

Here "AB," for example, denotes the length of the arc connecting the points A and

B, du is the angle FOE, and dv is the angle DOA. But while the connection between (8) and the geometry contained in Fig. 8.14 is interesting and supportive, we should emphasize that the "method of pictures," used in (10), may not be feasible in other cases, whereas (5) is quite simple and automatic.

COMMENT 2 In this case $F = 0$ everywhere on $\mathcal{S}$, so the u, v coordinate curves must be *orthogonal*. This result is no great surprise, since it should be evident that the curves of longitude and latitude intersect, at each point on $\mathcal{S}$, at right angles.

COMMENT 3 A striking feature of this example is the beautiful simplicity of the calculation in (9). This simplicity emphasizes that the u, v curvilinear coordinates defined in (6) are rather "natural" for the representation of this particular surface. ◀

There are two special cases of (5) that should be singled out:

Case 1: $z = 0$. If $z = 0$, so that $\mathcal{S}$ is flat and lies in the x, y plane, then $x = x(u, v)$, $y = y(u, v)$, $z = 0$, and (5b) simplifies to

$$E = x_u^2 + y_u^2, \qquad F = x_u x_v + y_u y_v, \qquad G = x_v^2 + y_v^2. \tag{11}$$

It follows from (11) that

$$\begin{aligned} EG - F^2 &= x_u^2 y_v^2 - 2x_u y_u x_v y_v + x_v^2 y_u^2 \\ &= (x_u y_v - x_v y_u)^2, \end{aligned} \tag{12}$$

which is none other than the *Jacobian* $\partial(x, y)/\partial(u, v)$ squared! Thus, for the case where $z = 0$, (5) simplifies to the form

$$\boxed{dA = \left|\frac{\partial(x, y)}{\partial(u, v)}\right| du\, dv,} \tag{13}$$

the absolute value signs being included to ensure that we have the *positive* square root in (5a), since dA must surely be positive.

EXAMPLE 2 As an illustration of case 1, note that the choice

$$x = u \cos v, \qquad y = u \sin v, \qquad z = 0 \tag{14}$$

amounts to the familiar case of *plane polar coordinates*; i.e., u is r and v is θ. Then the Jacobian is

$$\frac{\partial(x, y)}{\partial(u, v)} = \begin{vmatrix} x_u & x_v \\ y_u & y_v \end{vmatrix} = \begin{vmatrix} \cos v & -u \sin v \\ \sin v & u \cos v \end{vmatrix} = u,$$

so (13) gives

$$dA = |u|\, du\, dv$$

or, in terms of the more familiar letters r and θ,

$$\boxed{dA = r\, dr\, d\theta,} \tag{15}$$

where we omit the absolute values since the polar variable r is understood (in this book) to be nonnegative.*

Again seeking a geometrical interpretation, note that the length of AB, in Fig. 8.15, is dr, while the length of AD is $r\,d\theta$, so that $dA \sim (dr)(r\,d\theta) = r\,dr\,d\theta$, as in (15). ◀

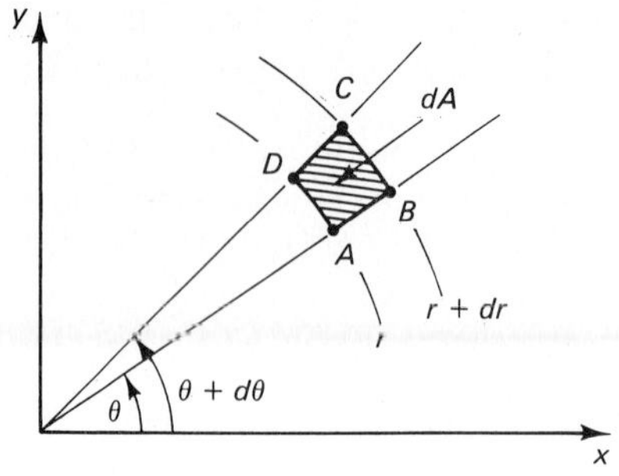

Fig. 8.15 dA in polar coordinates.

Case 2: $z = f(x, y)$. If $\mathcal{S}$ is given in the form $z = f(x, y)$, over some region $\mathcal{R}$ in the x, y plane, we may parametrize it conveniently as

$$x = x(u, v) = u, \qquad y = y(u, v) = v, \qquad z = z(u, v) = f(u, v). \tag{16}$$

Putting (16) into (5) yields $E = 1 + f_u^2$, $F = f_u f_v$, $G = 1 + f_v^2$, and hence the form

$$dA = \sqrt{1 + f_u^2 + f_v^2}\,du\,dv. \tag{17}$$

But since $x = u$ and $y = v$ it seems silly to retain the new variables u and v. Thus, let us write, in place of (17),

$$\boxed{dA = \sqrt{1 + f_x^2 + f_y^2}\,dx\,dy.} \tag{18}$$

Correspondingly,

$$\boxed{A = \iint_{\mathcal{R}} \sqrt{1 + f_x^2 + f_y^2}\,dx\,dy} \tag{19}$$

is the area of $\mathcal{S}$, where $\mathcal{R}$ is the region in the x, y plane lying directly beneath $\mathcal{S}$.

EXAMPLE 3 *Surface Area of a Sphere, Revisited.* Here we once again compute the surface area of the surface $\mathcal{S}$ shown in Fig. 8.14 (Example 1), but this time we use the parametrization

$$x = u, \qquad y = v, \qquad z = \sqrt{a^2 - u^2 - v^2}. \tag{20}$$

Since $x = u$ and $y = v$, the coordinate curves on $\mathcal{S}$ are simply the projections onto $\mathcal{S}$ of the $x =$ constant and $y =$ constant lines in the x, y plane. To illustrate, the coordinate curves through a given point P on $\mathcal{S}$ are sketched in Fig. 8.16. To visualize the coordinate curves more easily, imagine the $x =$ constant and

* In Cartesian coordinates $dA = dx\,dy$, and in polar coordinates $dA = r\,dr\,d\theta$, but it is incorrect to write $dx\,dy = r\,dr\,d\theta$.

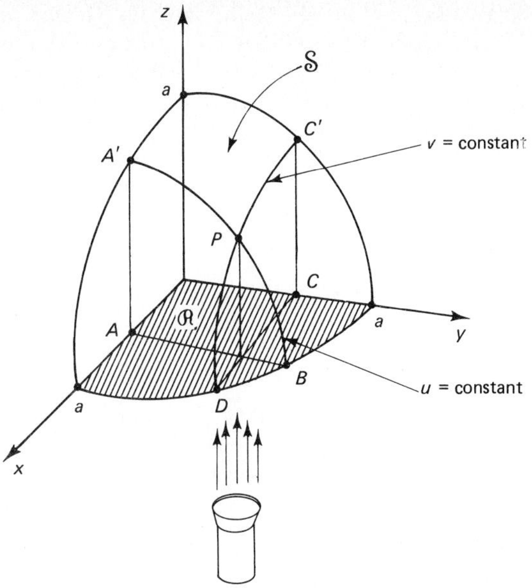

Fig. 8.16 Visualizing the coordinate curves.

$y =$ constant lines in the x, y plane (such as AB and CD, respectively) as thin wires, and imagine shining a flashlight upward, as shown in the figure. Then the shadow on $\mathcal{S}$ of the $x =$ constant lines will be the $u =$ constant curves (e.g., $A'PB$), and the shadow on $\mathcal{S}$ of the $y =$ constant lines will be the $v =$ constant curves, (e.g., $C'PD$). Observe that the u, v curves are *not* orthogonal, in this case, since $F = f_u f_v$ is not zero; nor do they *look* orthogonal in Fig. 8.16.

Returning to our calculation of the surface area of $\mathcal{S}$, we use (19), where $\mathcal{R}$ is the shaded quarter disk in the x, y plane (Fig. 8.16). Or, since $f_x = (\frac{1}{2})(-2x)(a^2 - x^2 - y^2)^{-1/2}$ and $f_y = (\frac{1}{2})(-2y)(a^2 - x^2 - y^2)^{-1/2}$, we have

$$A = \int_0^a \int_0^{\sqrt{a^2 - y^2}} \frac{a}{\sqrt{a^2 - x^2 - y^2}} \, dx \, dy. \tag{21}$$

Evaluation of the iterated integral in (21) is left for the exercises; the answer, of course, is $\pi a^2/2$, as before. ◀

Summarizing this section, the key notion was the definition, by (4), of the area element dA of a smooth surface $\mathcal{S}$ which is defined parametrically in terms of u, v. Working out $\|\mathbf{R}_u \times \mathbf{R}_v\|$ in terms of $x(u, v)$, $y(u, v)$, $z(u, v)$ then led to the less elegant but computationally useful version (5). In addition, two special cases were spelled out. In the first, $\mathcal{S}$ is flat and lies in the x, y plane and dA reduces to the absolute magnitude of the Jacobian times $du\, dv$; in the second, the shape of $\mathcal{S}$ is known in the form $z = f(x, y)$, and dA then simplifies to the form given in (18).

8.5 EXERCISES

1. In each case evaluate the surface area A of the surface $\mathcal{S}$ using (5).

*(a) Let $\mathcal{S}$ be the *circular cylinder* $x^2 + y^2 = 1$, between $z = 0$ and $z = h$. Use $x = \cos v$, $y = \sin v$, $z = u$. Would $x = \sin v$, $y = \cos v$, $z = u$ work? How about $x = \sin u$, $y = \cos u$, $z = v$?

(b) Let $\mathcal{S}$ be the *circular cylinder* $x^2 + y^2 = 1$, between $z = 0$ and $z = 1 + y$. *Hint:* Use $x = \cos v$, $y = \sin v$, $z = u$.
(c) Let $\mathcal{S}$ be the *circular cylinder* $x^2 + y^2 = 1$, between $z = 0$ and $z = 1 - y^2$. *Hint:* Same hint as in part (b).
*(d) Let $\mathcal{S}$ be the *quadric cone* $x^2 + y^2 = z^2$, between $z = 0$ and $z = h$. Show that $A = \sqrt{2}\pi h^2$. *Hint:* Use $x = u \cos v$, $y = u \sin v$, $z = u$.

2. Let $\mathcal{S}$ be the *elliptic paraboloid* $x^2 + y^2 = z$, between $z = 0$ and $z = h$.

(a) Using (5), show that $A = \left(\frac{\pi}{6}\right)[(1 + 4h)^{3/2} - 1]$.
(b) Applying Taylor's series to the answer in part (a), show that $A \sim \pi h$ as $h \to 0$. Explain why this result looks correct [and hence provides us with a partial check on our answer to part (a)].

3. Let $\mathcal{S}$ be the one-sheeted *hyperboloid* $x^2 + y^2 - z^2 = 1$ between $z = 0$ and $z = h(>1)$.
(a) Show that

$$A = \pi\left[h\sqrt{1 + 2h^2} + \frac{1}{\sqrt{2}} \ln |\sqrt{2}h + \sqrt{1 + 2h^2}|\right]. \quad \text{(a)}$$

Hint: The integral

$$\int \sqrt{\frac{a + bx}{c + dx}}\, dx = \frac{1}{d}\sqrt{(a + bx)(c + dx)} + \frac{ad - bc}{d\sqrt{bd}} \ln |\sqrt{bd(c + dx)} + d\sqrt{a + bx}|,$$

if $bd > 0$, should be useful.
(b) Applying Taylor's series to (a), show that $A \sim 2\pi h$ as $h \to 0$. Explain why this result looks correct [and hence provides us with a partial check on (a)].

4. Let $\mathcal{S}$ be the *hyperboloid* $z^2 - x^2 - y^2 = 1$, between $z = 1$ and $z = h$.

(a) Using (5), with $x = u \cos v$, $y = u \sin v$, $z = \sqrt{u^2 + 1}$, show that

$$A = \pi\left[h\sqrt{2h^2 - 1} - \frac{1}{\sqrt{2}} \ln |\sqrt{2}h + \sqrt{2h^2 - 1}| - 1 + \frac{1}{\sqrt{2}} \ln |1 + \sqrt{2}|\right]. \quad \text{(a)}$$

Hint: Same hint as in Exercise 3(a).
(b) To examine the case where $\mathcal{S}$ is very "shallow," set $h = 1 + \epsilon$ in (a), and consider the behavior of A as $\epsilon \to 0$. Explain why the result looks correct [and hence provides us with a partial check on (a)].
(c) In the same spirit as part (b), show that $A \sim \sqrt{2}\pi h^2$ as $h \to \infty$. Explain why this result looks correct [and hence provides us with another partial check on (a)]. *Hint:* Recall the result of Exercise 1(d).

5. Parametrizing the circular cylinder $x^2 + y^2 = a^2$ by $x = a \cos v$, $y = a \sin v$, $z = u$, show that the area element is $dA = a\, du\, dv$. Interpret this result geometrically.

6. Find the area A of the following regions in the x, y plane.
*(a) the region enclosed by $r = \sin \theta$ $(0 \le \theta < \pi)$
(b) the region enclosed by the limaçon $r = 2 + \cos \theta$ $(0 \le \theta < 2\pi)$
(c) the region enclosed by one leaf of the "daisy" $r = 2 \sin 3\theta$
(d) the region (in the second quadrant) between the circle $r = \sin \theta$ $(0 \le \theta < \pi)$ and the cardioid $r = 1 + \cos \theta$ $(0 \le \theta < 2\pi)$

7. Consider a portion $\mathcal{S}$ of a plane $ax + by + cz = d$ with a "shadow" on the x, y plane designated as the region $\mathcal{R}$. We assume that the plane is not perpendicular to the x, y plane, so that $c \neq 0$ and $z = (d - ax - by)/c$. Using (19), show that the area of $\mathcal{S}$ is

$$A = (\sec \alpha)(\text{area of } \mathcal{R}), \quad \text{(a)}$$

where α is the acute angle between the z axis and the normal line to $\mathcal{S}$. *Hint:* Recall Exercise 10, Section 8.4.

8. Use (19) to show that the surface area of the paraboloid $z = h(1 - x^2 - y^2)$, between $z = 0$ and $z = h$, is

$$A = \iint_{\mathcal{R}} \sqrt{1 + 4h^2(x^2 + y^2)}\, dx\, dy, \quad \text{(a)}$$

where $\mathcal{R}$ is the unit disk $0 \le x^2 + y^2 \le 1$. To integrate (a), change over to polar coordinates r, θ, and show that

$$A = \frac{\pi}{6h^2}[(1 + 4h^2)^{3/2} - 1]. \quad \text{(b)}$$

As a partial check on (b), show that the right-hand side of (b) tends to π (namely, the area of the unit disk) as $h \to 0$.

9. Sketch the surface $\mathcal{S}$ defined by $z = \epsilon(1 - x^2)(1 - y^2)$ over the square $0 \le x \le 1$,

$0 \le y \le 1$, where $0 \le \epsilon \ll 1$. Show that (19) gives the area of $\mathcal{S}$ as

$$A = \int_0^1 \int_0^1 \sqrt{1 + 4\epsilon^2[x^2(1-y^2)^2 + (1-x^2)^2y^2]}\, dx\, dy. \qquad \text{(a)}$$

Evidently, this integral is difficult to evaluate. However, recalling that ϵ is small, suppose that we set $4\epsilon^2[x^2(1-y^2)^2 + (1-x^2)^2y^2] \equiv t$ and expand the integrand as a Maclaurin series in t:

$$\begin{aligned}
&\sqrt{1 + 4\epsilon^2[x^2(1-y^2)^2 + (1-x^2)^2y^2]} \\
&\quad = (1+t)^{1/2} \\
&\quad = 1 + \frac{1}{2}t - \frac{1}{8}t^2 + \cdots \qquad (|t| < 1) \qquad \text{(b)} \\
&\quad = 1 + 2\epsilon^2[x^2(1-y^2)^2 + (1-x^2)^2y^2] \\
&\qquad -2\epsilon^4[x^2(1-y^2)^2 + (1-x^2)^2y^2]^2 + \cdots.
\end{aligned}$$

Replacing the integrand in (a) by the infinite series on the right-hand side of (b), we succeed in trading in one function that is very difficult to integrate for many that are quite simple to integrate (since they are of the form $x^m y^n$). In fact, we do not even need many terms, for good accuracy, if ϵ is sufficiently small, for then $t \ll 1$, so that $(1+t)^{1/2} \approx 1 + \frac{1}{2}t$ or $1 + \frac{1}{2}t - \frac{1}{8}t^2$, say, may suffice. Using $(1+t)^{1/2} \approx 1 + \frac{1}{2}t$, show that $A \approx 1 + \frac{32}{45}\epsilon^2$. *Note:* The preceding discussion does not pretend to be any more than heuristic. Rigorous basis for integrating the infinite series in a term-by-term manner is provided by the following *theorem*: If $|a_n(x, y)| < M_n$ over the closed region $\mathcal{R}$, where the M_n's are constants and $\sum^{\infty} M_n$ is convergent, then

$$\iint_{\mathcal{R}} \sum^{\infty} a_n(x, y)\, dx\, dy = \sum^{\infty} \iint_{\mathcal{R}} a_n(x, y)\, dx\, dy; \qquad \text{(c)}$$

i.e., we may integrate term by term.

SURFACE INTEGRALS 8.6

[Optional Section]

In Section 8.2 we studied double integrals of the form $\iint_{\mathcal{R}} f(x, y)\, dx\, dy$, where $\mathcal{R}$ was a region in the x, y plane, and in Section 8.5 we discussed the area element dA of a parametrized curved surface $\mathcal{S}$. In the present section we combine these ingredients and consider the *surface integral* $\iint_{\mathcal{S}} f\, dA$, i.e., a double integral over a curved surface. Such integrals arise in many ways, for example, in connection with surface distributions of mass or electric charge. For example, the total mass, centroid, and components of inertia of a twisted sheet of paper or metal foil are all expressed as surface integrals (if the thickness is negligible compared to the other dimensions).

With only some minor changes, our definition of the surface integral $\iint_{\mathcal{S}} f\, dA$ will be essentially the same as that given on page 311 for the double integral $\iint_{\mathcal{R}} f\, dA$. That is, we partition $\mathcal{S}$ into N parts $\mathcal{S}_1, \mathcal{S}_2, \ldots, \mathcal{S}_N$, and define the *norm* of the partition $|p|$ as the "size" of the largest one of these parts. (As a measure of the "size" of an element $\mathcal{S}_j$, we can, for example, use the least upper bound of the linear distances between all possible pairs of points on $\mathcal{S}_j$.) Next, let (x_j, y_j, z_j) be an arbitrarily selected point on $\mathcal{S}_j$, for each $j = 1, 2, \ldots, N$. Then, denoting the area of $\mathcal{S}_j$ as ΔA_j,

$$\sum_{j=1}^{N} f(x_j, y_j, z_j)\, \Delta A_j \qquad (1)$$

is called the **Riemann sum** corresponding to the chosen partition and (x_j, y_j, z_j) points. The idea, in principle at least, is to compute the Riemann sum (1), then to introduce a finer partition (i.e., one with a smaller norm) and compute the new Riemann sum, and so on, such that the norm of the partitions tends to zero. If the sequence of values of the Riemann sum thus generated converges to a unique limit, independent of the choice of the partition sequence and (x_j, y_j, z_j) points, that limit is, by definition, the **surface integral** $\iint_{\mathcal{S}} f\, dA$; that is,

$$\iint_{\mathcal{S}} f(x, y, z) dA \equiv \lim_{|p| \to 0} \sum f(x_j, y_j, z_j)\, \Delta A_j. \tag{2}$$

To *evaluate* a surface integral we do *not* use the definition (2) (although we *could* carry out that exercise in simple enough cases). Rather, we convert the integral to a double integral by parametrizing $\mathcal{S}$ in the form $\mathbf{R}(u, v)$ and using the expression $dA = \|\mathbf{R}_u \times \mathbf{R}_v\|\, du\, dv = \sqrt{EG - F^2}\, du\, dv$ from Section 8.5. Thus

$$\iint_{\mathcal{S}} f\, dA = \iint_{\mathcal{R}} f(x(u, v), y(u, v), z(u, v)) \|\mathbf{R}_u \times \mathbf{R}_v\|\, du\, dv \tag{3a}$$

or

$$\iint_{\mathcal{S}} f\, dA = \iint_{\mathcal{R}} f(x(u, v), y(u, v), z(u, v)) \sqrt{EG - F^2}\, du\, dv, \tag{3b}$$

where $\mathcal{R}$ is the region in the u, v plane that corresponds to the surface $\mathcal{S}$ in 3-space. Or if $\mathcal{S}$ is given in the form $z = z(x, y)$, then

$$\iint_{\mathcal{S}} f\, dA = \iint_{\mathcal{R}} f(x, y, z\,(x, y)) \sqrt{1 + z_x^2 + z_y^2}\, dx\, dy, \tag{3c}$$

where $\mathcal{R}$ is the "shadow" of $\mathcal{S}$ on the x, y plane.

EXAMPLE 1 *Mass of a Conical Shell.* Consider a thin shell in the shape of a right circular cone $\mathcal{S}$ of height h, as shown in Fig. 8.17a. Assuming that the mass density distribution σ (mass per unit surface area) is known, we wish to compute the total mass, which may be expressed as the surface integral

$$M = \iint_{\mathcal{S}} \sigma\, dA. \tag{4}$$

First, let us parametrize $\mathcal{S}$. (Before reading on, you should try to make up a suitable parametrization, recalling that the parametrization of a given surface is not unique, and that the rule of thumb is to construct a parametrization which is as sim-

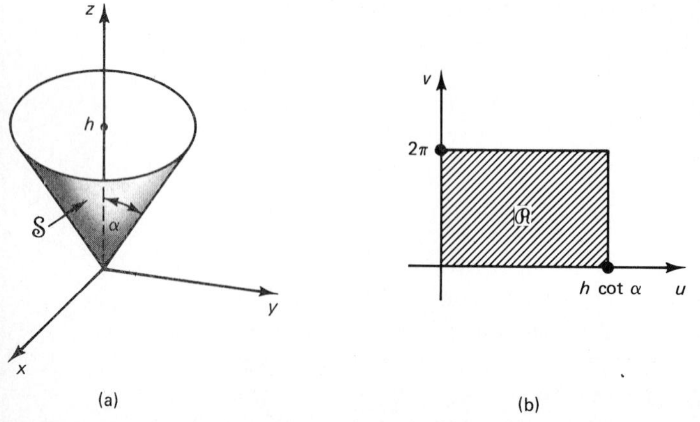

Fig. 8.17 Conical shell.

ple and natural as possible.) Adopting

$$x = u \cos v, \qquad y = u \sin v, \qquad z = u \tan \alpha \tag{5}$$

over the region $\mathcal{R}$ shown in Fig. 8.17b, we compute $E = x_u^2 + y_u^2 + z_u^2 = 1 + \tan^2 \alpha = 1/\cos^2 \alpha$, $F = x_u x_v + y_u y_v + z_u z_v = 0$, and $G = x_v^2 + y_v^2 + z_v^2 = u^2$, so that the form (3b) gives

$$M = \iint_{\mathcal{R}} \sigma(u, v) \frac{u}{\cos \alpha} \, du \, dv = \sec \alpha \int_0^{2\pi} \int_0^{h \cot \alpha} \sigma(u, v) u \, du \, dv. \tag{6}$$

For example, if $\sigma(u, v) = \text{constant} = \sigma_0$, in which case we say that the shell is homogeneous, then

$$M = \sigma_0 \sec \alpha \int_0^{2\pi} \int_0^{h \cot \alpha} u \, du \, dv = \pi \sigma_0 h^2 \sec \alpha \cot^2 \alpha. \tag{7}$$

COMMENT It should be realized that u, v in (5) are really our old friends r, θ expressed in our standard "u, v" notation. We suggest that you understand the parametrization (5) and corresponding region $\mathcal{R}$ (Fig. 8.17b) completely before leaving this example. ◀

EXAMPLE 2 *Surface Charge.* Let a charge distribution $\sigma(x, y) = \sigma_0 e^{-(x^2 + y^2)}$ coulombs/meter² be distributed over the upper half of the circular disk of radius c, shown in Fig. 8.18a. We wish to compute the total charge, namely,

$$Q = \iint_{\mathcal{S}} \sigma \, dA. \tag{8}$$

In this case $\mathcal{S}$ happens to be flat. Naturally, equations (3a) to (3c) for the evaluation of surface integrals still apply, since a flat surface is but a special case of a curved surface. We can use (3b) as it stands, or we can recall, from page 331 that for the special case where $\mathcal{S}$ is the surface $z = 0$, the quantity $\sqrt{EG - F^2}$ reduces to the absolute value of the Jacobian, $|\partial(x, y)/\partial(u, v)|$. In fact, if we use the obvious (polar coordinate) parametrization

$$x = u \cos v, \qquad y = u \sin v, \qquad z = 0 \tag{9}$$

over the region $\mathcal{R}$ shown in Fig. 8.18b, we need merely recall the important polar coordinate formula $dA = r \, dr \, d\theta$ or, in u, v notation, $dA = u \, du \, dv$. Noting further that $x^2 + y^2 = u^2$, (8) becomes

$$Q = \int_0^{\pi} \int_0^{c} \sigma_0 e^{-u^2} u \, du \, dv = \frac{\pi}{2} \sigma_0 (1 - e^{-c^2}). \tag{10}$$

◀

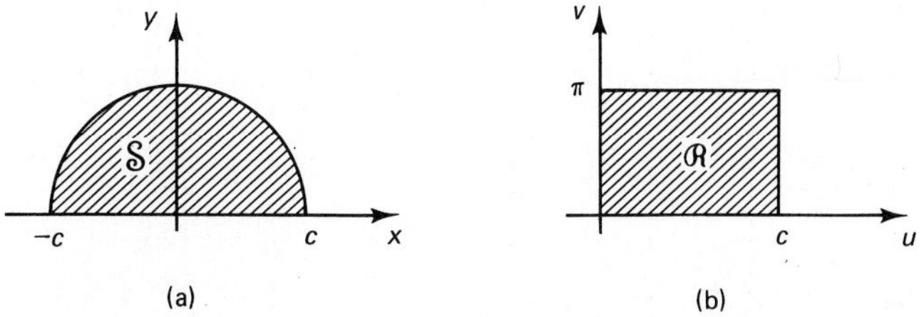

Fig. 8.18 The surface $\mathcal{S}$.

8.6 EXERCISES

1. Evaluate $\iint_{\mathcal{S}} (1 + x)\, dA$, where $\mathcal{S}$ is the

*(a) plane surface $z = 1 + y$ with vertices at $(0, 0, 1)$, $(1, 0, 1)$, $(1, 1, 2)$, and $(0, 1, 2)$

(b) plane surface $z = x + y$ with vertices at $(0, 0, 0)$, $(1, 0, 1)$, $(0, 1, 1)$

(c) cylindrical surface $x^2 + y^2 = 1$, between $z = 0$ and $z = h$

*(d) cylindrical surface $x^2 + y^2 = 1$, between $z = 0$ and $z = 1 + y$

(e) spherical surface $x^2 + y^2 + z^2 = 9$, between $z = 0$ and $z = 3$

(f) spherical surface $x^2 + y^2 + z^2 = 4$

(g) quadric cone $x^2 + y^2 = z^2$, between $z = 0$ and $z = h$ *Hint:* Use $x = u \cos v$, $y = u \sin v$, $z = u$.

(h) elliptic paraboloid $x^2 + y^2 = z$, between $z = 0$ and $z = h$ *Hint:* Part of the integral gives zero by cancellation.

2. (*Mass and center of gravity*) Let σ be the mass density of a (negligibly thick) distribution of mass over a surface $\mathcal{S}$. That is, σ is the mass per unit area at each point on $\mathcal{S}$; it may be a constant or it may vary over $\mathcal{S}$. Then the x, y, z coordinates of the **center of gravity** are defined as

$$x_c = \frac{1}{M}\iint_{\mathcal{S}} x\sigma\, dA,$$
$$y_c = \frac{1}{M}\iint_{\mathcal{S}} y\sigma\, dA, \qquad \text{(a)}$$
$$z_c = \frac{1}{M}\iint_{\mathcal{S}} z\sigma\, dA,$$

where

$$M = \iint_{\mathcal{S}} \sigma\, dA \qquad \text{(b)}$$

is the total mass. Evaluate x_c in each case. (You need not evaluate y_c, z_c.)

*(a) $\mathcal{S}$ is the plane surface $z = x + 2y$ with vertices at $(0, 0, 0)$, $(1, 0, 1)$, $(0, 1, 2)$; σ = constant = σ_0.

(b) $\mathcal{S}$ is the plane surface $z = x + y$ with vertices at $(0, 0, 0)$, $(1, 0, 1)$, $(0, 1, 1)$; $\sigma = 1 + y$.

(c) $\mathcal{S}$ is the plane surface $z = 2 - x$ with vertices at $(0, 0, 2)$, $(0, 1, 2)$, $(2, 0, 0)$, $(2, 1, 0)$; $\sigma = 4 - x$.

*(d) $\mathcal{S}$ is the plane surface $z = 2 - x$ with vertices at $(0, 0, 2)$, $(0, 1, 2)$, $(2, 0, 0)$; $\sigma = 1 + x$.

(e) $\mathcal{S}$ is the cylindrical surface $x^2 + y^2 = 4$ between $z = 0$ and $z = h$; $\sigma = 1 + x$.

(f) $\mathcal{S}$ is the cylindrical surface $x^2 + y^2 = 4$ between $z = 0$ and $z = 2 + x$; σ = constant = σ_0.

(g) $\mathcal{S}$ is the hemispherical surface $x^2 + y^2 + z^2 = 1$ between $x = 0$ and $x = 1$; σ = constant = σ_0.

(h) $\mathcal{S}$ is the spherical surface $x^2 + y^2 + z^2 = 9$; $\sigma = 4 + x$.

3. (*Moments of inertia*) Let σ be the mass density of a (negligibly thick) distribution of mass over a surface $\mathcal{S}$, as in Exercise 2. Then the **moments of inertia** I_x, I_y, I_z, about the x, y, z axes, respectively, are defined as

$$I_x = \iint_{\mathcal{S}} (y^2 + z^2)\sigma\, dA,$$
$$I_y = \iint_{\mathcal{S}} (x^2 + z^2)\sigma\, dA, \qquad \text{(a)}$$
$$I_z = \iint_{\mathcal{S}} (x^2 + y^2)\sigma\, dA.$$

Evaluate I_x in each case.

*(a) Same as in Exercise 2(a)

(b) Same as in Exercise 2(b)

(c) Same as in Exercise 2(c)

*(d) $\mathcal{S}$ is the spherical surface $x^2 + y^2 + z^2 = c^2$; σ = constant = σ_0.

(e) $\mathcal{S}$ is the cylindrical surface $y^2 + z^2 = 4$ between $x = 0$ and $x = 3$; σ = constant = σ_0.

(f) $\mathcal{S}$ is a flat disk of radius c, lying in the y, z plane, with its center at the origin; σ = constant = σ_0.

(g) $\mathcal{S}$ is a flat disk of radius c, lying in the x, z plane, with its center at the origin; σ = constant = σ_0.

4. In each case $\mathcal{S}$ is flat and lies in the x, y plane. Evaluate each integral by introducing polar coordinates r, θ.

*(a) $\iint_{\mathcal{S}} \frac{y}{x}\, dx\, dy$, $\mathcal{S}$: $1 \le r \le 2$, $0 \le \theta \le \pi/4$

(b) $\iint_{\mathcal{S}} \sin(x^2 + y^2)\, dx\, dy$, $\mathcal{S}$: $0 \le r \le 2$, $0 \le \theta \le \pi/3$

(c) $\iint_{\mathcal{S}} \frac{y(x^2 + y^2)^2}{x}\, dx\, dy$, $\mathcal{S}$: $1 \le r \le 2$, $-\pi/3 \le \theta \le \pi/3$

(d) $\iint_{\mathcal{S}} (x^2 + y^2)^{-1/2}\, dx\, dy$, $\mathcal{S}$: $1 \le r \le 2$, $0 \le \theta \le \pi/2$

(e) $\iint_{\mathcal{S}} x^2(x^2 + y^2)^{-3/2}\, dx\, dy$, $\mathcal{S}$: triangle with vertices at $(0, 0)$, $(1, 0)$, and $(1, 1)$

[Optional Section]

Having discussed the generation of curves (in 3-space) by one-parameter families of the form $x = x(u)$, $y = y(u)$, $z = z(u)$, and the generation of surfaces by two-parameter families of the form $x = x(u, v)$, $y = y(u, v)$, $z = z(u, v)$, it should be no great surprise that we now consider the generation of *volumes* by three-parameter families of the form

$$x = x(u, v, w), \qquad y = y(u, v, w), \qquad z = z(u, v, w), \tag{1}$$

or in terms of the position vector $\mathbf{R}$,

$$\mathbf{R}(u, v, w) = x(u, v, w)\hat{\mathbf{i}} + y(u, v, w)\hat{\mathbf{j}} + z(u, v, w)\hat{\mathbf{k}}. \tag{2}$$

We assume that $\mathbf{R}(u, v, w)$ is C^1, and that $\mathbf{R}_u,\mathbf{R}_v,\mathbf{R}_w$ are linearly independent—or, equivalently, that $\mathbf{R}_u \cdot \mathbf{R}_v \times \mathbf{R}_w \neq 0$. Mimicking our discussion of surface area in Section 8.5, consider the u = constant, v = constant, and w = constant surfaces through a given point P, as sketched in Fig. 8.19. If the curve PQ is the intersection of the w = constant and v = constant surfaces through P, then only u varies along PQ, so PQ is the u coordinate curve through P. Similarly, PR is the v coordinate curve through P, and PS is the w coordinate curve through P.

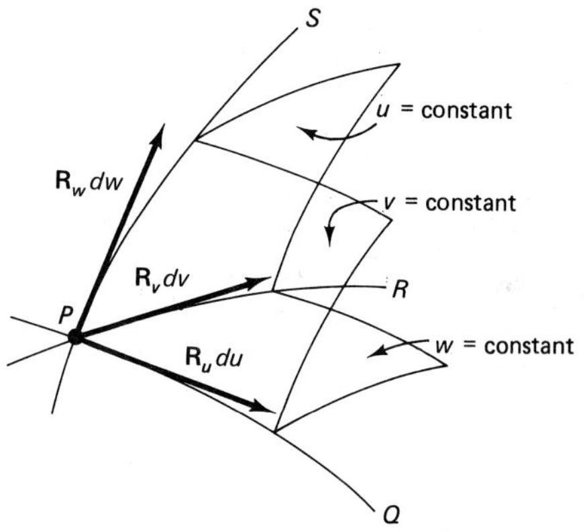

Fig. 8.19 Parallelepiped for dV.

Since $\mathbf{R}_u$, $\mathbf{R}_v$, $\mathbf{R}_w$ are linearly independent, by assumption, the vectors $\mathbf{R}_u\, du$, $\mathbf{R}_v\, dv$, $\mathbf{R}_w\, dw$ determine a parallelepiped of nonzero volume dV. According to (5) and (6) on page 281,

$$\begin{aligned} dV &= |\mathbf{R}_u\, du \cdot \mathbf{R}_v\, dv \times \mathbf{R}_w\, dw| = |\mathbf{R}_u \cdot \mathbf{R}_v \times \mathbf{R}_w|\, du\, dv\, dw \\ &= \left\| \begin{matrix} x_u & y_u & z_u \\ x_v & y_v & z_v \\ x_w & y_w & z_w \end{matrix} \right\| du\, dv\, dw, \end{aligned} \tag{3}$$

where the inner vertical rules on the right-hand side of (3) denote determinant, and the outer vertical rules denote absolute value. But the determinant in (3) is none other than the Jacobian $\partial(x, y, z)/\partial(u, v, w)$,* so that

$$\boxed{dV = \left|\frac{\partial(x, y, z)}{\partial(u, v, w)}\right| du\, dv\, dw,} \tag{4}$$

and this quantity is hereby *defined* to be the **volume element** at P. Then the volume V of a given region $\mathcal{V}$ in x, y, z space may be expressed as

$$\boxed{V = \iiint_{\mathcal{V}} dV = \iiint_{\mathcal{R}} \left|\frac{\partial(x, y, z)}{\partial(u, v, w)}\right| du\, dv\, dw,} \tag{5}$$

where $\mathcal{R}$ is the region in u, v, w space corresponding to the region $\mathcal{V}$ in x, y, z space.

Analogous to the surface integral $\iint_{\mathcal{S}} f\, dA$ considered in Section 8.6, we meet the **volume integral**

$$\boxed{\iiint_{\mathcal{V}} f\, dV = \iiint_{\mathcal{R}} f(x(u, v, w), y(u, v, w), z(u, v, w)) \left|\frac{\partial(x, y, z)}{\partial(u, v, w)}\right| du\, dv\, dw,} \tag{6}$$

Let us specialize the foregoing results to the extremely important cases of cylindrical and spherical coordinates.

CYLINDRICAL COORDINATES

In this case the quantities u, v, w correspond to the cylindrical coordinates r, θ, z, where

$$x = r\cos\theta, \qquad y = r\sin\theta, \qquad z = z. \tag{7}$$

Designating $u = r, v = \theta, w = z$, say,

$$\frac{\partial(x, y, z)}{\partial(u, v, w)} = \frac{\partial(x, y, z)}{\partial(r, \theta, z)} = \begin{vmatrix} x_r & x_\theta & x_z \\ y_r & y_\theta & y_z \\ z_r & z_\theta & z_z \end{vmatrix} = \begin{vmatrix} \cos\theta & -r\sin\theta & 0 \\ \sin\theta & r\cos\theta & 0 \\ 0 & 0 & 1 \end{vmatrix} = r,$$

* Recall that the determinants

$$\begin{vmatrix} a & b & c \\ d & e & f \\ g & h & i \end{vmatrix} \quad \text{and} \quad \begin{vmatrix} a & d & g \\ b & e & h \\ c & f & i \end{vmatrix}$$

are equal, so that $\partial(x, y, z)/\partial(u, v, w)$ may be expressed either as

$$\begin{vmatrix} x_u & x_v & x_w \\ y_u & y_v & y_w \\ z_u & z_v & z_w \end{vmatrix} \quad \text{or as} \quad \begin{vmatrix} x_u & y_u & z_u \\ x_v & y_v & z_v \\ x_w & y_w & z_w \end{vmatrix}.$$

and (4) becomes

$$\boxed{dV = r\,dr\,d\theta\,dz.} \tag{8}$$

Here the absolute value signs are omitted since we consider r to be nonnegative in this book (as noted on page 288).

In geometric terms, (8) is not very surprising since dV is the area $dA = r\,dr\,d\theta$ times the height dz (Fig. 8.20).

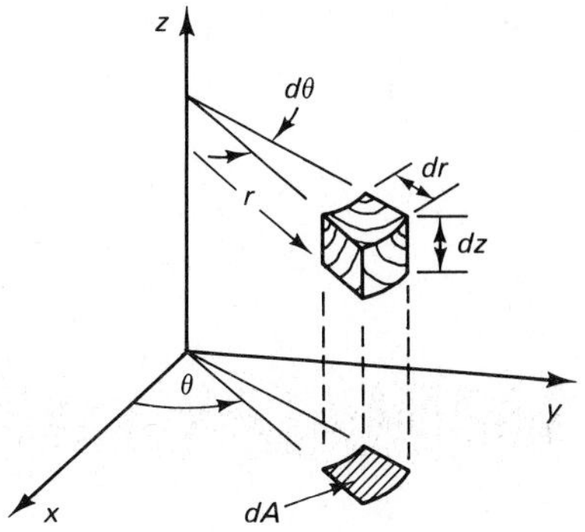

Fig. 8.20 Volume element in cylindrical coordinates.

EXAMPLE 1 *Gravitational Attraction of a Cone.* **Newton's law of gravitation** states that the force of attraction **F** exerted by any one point mass M on any other point mass m is given by*

$$\mathbf{F} = G\frac{Mm}{d^2}\hat{\mathbf{e}}, \tag{9}$$

where (Fig. 8.21) d is the distance of separation, $\hat{\mathbf{e}}$ is a unit vector directed from m toward M, and G ($= 6.67 \times 10^{-8}$ cm^3/g sec^2) is the "universal gravitational constant"; (9) is said to be an *inverse-square law* since the force varies as the inverse square of the distance. (By M and m being *point masses,* we mean that their sizes are negligible compared with d.) If M is at (x, y, z) and m is at (x_0, y_0, z_0), we may

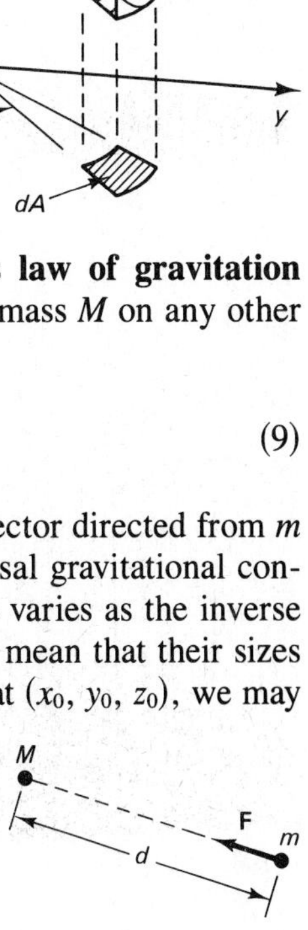

Fig. 8.21 Gravitational force **F** exerted by M on m.

* Newton derived (9) from Kepler's laws of planetary motion, which, in turn, were inferred empirically from the voluminous measurements recorded by the Danish astronomer Tycho Brahe (1546–1601). Usually, in applications (not to mention homework assignments in mechanics), we are given the force exerted on a mass and seek to determine the motion $\mathbf{R}(t)$ by twice integrating Newton's law of motion $\mathbf{F} = m\ddot{\mathbf{R}}$. In deriving (9), however, Newton worked "backward": The motion of the planets was supplied by Kepler's laws and what Newton did was to infer the force that was needed to sustain that motion. That force turned out to be an inverse-square force directed toward the most massive object around, namely, the sun. Being aware of other such forces between masses—for example, the force that kept his shoes on the floor—Newton then supplied the final bold generalization, namely, that (9) holds not just between planets and the sun, but between *any* two bodies in the universe; hence the name *universal* law of gravitation. This story, from the ancients through Copernicus, Brahe, Kepler, and Newton, to Einstein, is quite beautiful. We recommend R. Feynman, R. Leighton, and M. Sands, *The Feynman Lectures on Physics,* Vol. 1 (Reading, Mass.: Addison-Wesley, (1963), as but one of many excellent sources for further reading on this subject.

express $\hat{\mathbf{e}}$ as

$$\hat{\mathbf{e}} = \frac{(x - x_0)\hat{\mathbf{i}} + (y - y_0)\hat{\mathbf{j}} + (z - z_0)\hat{\mathbf{k}}}{\sqrt{(x - x_0)^2 + (y - y_0)^2 + (z - z_0)^2}}. \tag{10}$$

The problem that we pose here is to calculate the force of attraction exerted at the origin, per unit mass at the origin (i.e., $m = 1$), by the right circular cone of uniform mass density σ (g/cm³) shown in Fig. 8.22. Since the cone is not a point mass, we need to find the forces induced by the individual mass elements that constitute the cone, and to sum them by integration. With M changed to $\sigma\, dV$, and $x_0 = y_0 = z_0 = 0$, (9) and (10) give

$$\mathbf{F} = G \iiint_{\mathcal{V}} \frac{x\hat{\mathbf{i}} + y\hat{\mathbf{j}} + z\hat{\mathbf{k}}}{(x^2 + y^2 + z^2)^{3/2}} \sigma\, dV. \tag{11}$$

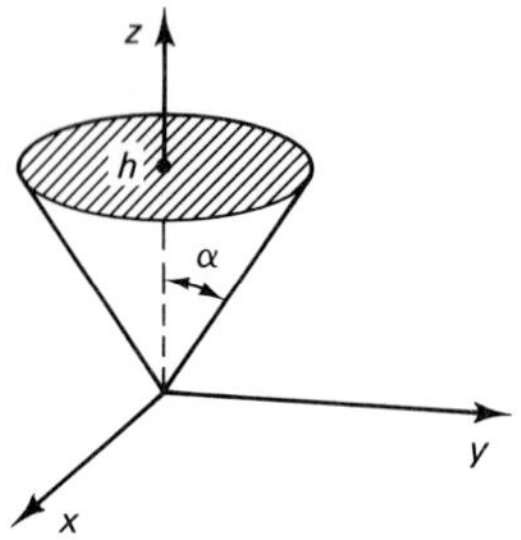

Fig. 8.22 The cone $\mathcal{V}$.

Surely, the symmetry revealed in Fig. 8.22 implies that the $\hat{\mathbf{i}}$ and $\hat{\mathbf{j}}$ components of $\mathbf{F}$ will turn out to be zero, so that (11) may be reduced, immediately, to the volume integral

$$\mathbf{F} = \sigma G\hat{\mathbf{k}} \iiint_{\mathcal{V}} \frac{z}{(x^2 + y^2 + z^2)^{3/2}} dV. \tag{12}$$

The shape of $\mathcal{V}$ implies that cylindrical coordinates will be more convenient than Cartesian. Thus, if we introduce the cylindrical coordinates r, θ, z and, at the same time, express the volume integral as an iterated integral, (12) becomes

$$\begin{aligned}
\mathbf{F} &= \sigma G\hat{\mathbf{k}} \int_0^h \int_0^{2\pi} \int_0^{z\tan\alpha} \frac{zr\, dr\, d\theta\, dz}{(r^2 + z^2)^{3/2}} \\
&= 2\pi\sigma G\hat{\mathbf{k}} \int_0^h \int_{u=z^2}^{u=z^2(1+\tan^2\alpha)} \frac{z\, du\, dz}{u^{3/2}} \qquad (u = r^2 + z^2) \\
&= 2\pi\sigma G\hat{\mathbf{k}} \int_0^h z\left(-\frac{1}{\sqrt{u}}\right)\Bigg|_{z^2}^{z^2/\cos^2\alpha} dz \\
&= 2\pi\sigma G\hat{\mathbf{k}} \int_0^h z\left(-\frac{\cos\alpha}{z} + \frac{1}{z}\right) dz
\end{aligned} \tag{13}$$

so that

$$\mathbf{F} = 2\pi\sigma Gh\,(1 - \cos\alpha)\,\hat{\mathbf{k}}. \blacktriangleleft \tag{14}$$

SPHERICAL COORDINATES

Here, u, v, w correspond to the spherical coordinates ρ, ϕ, θ, where

$$x = \rho \sin \phi \cos \theta, \qquad y = \rho \sin \phi \sin \theta, \qquad z = \rho \cos \phi. \tag{15}$$

Designating $u = \rho$, $v = \phi$, $w = \theta$, say, the Jacobian is

$$\frac{\partial(x, y, z)}{\partial(u, v, w)} = \begin{vmatrix} x_\rho & x_\phi & x_\theta \\ y_\rho & y_\phi & y_\theta \\ z_\rho & z_\phi & z_\theta \end{vmatrix}$$
$$= \begin{vmatrix} \sin\phi\cos\theta & \rho\cos\phi\cos\theta & -\rho\sin\phi\sin\theta \\ \sin\phi\sin\theta & \rho\cos\phi\sin\theta & \rho\sin\phi\cos\theta \\ \cos\phi & -\rho\sin\phi & 0 \end{vmatrix} = \rho^2 \sin\phi, \tag{16}$$

so that (4) becomes

$$\boxed{dV = \rho^2 \,|\sin\phi|\, d\rho\, d\phi\, d\theta.} \tag{17}$$

Geometrically, (17) should be evident from Fig. 8.23, since $dV = (d\rho)(\rho\, d\phi)(\rho\,|\sin\phi|\, d\theta) = \rho^2\,|\sin\phi|\, d\rho\, d\phi\, d\theta$.

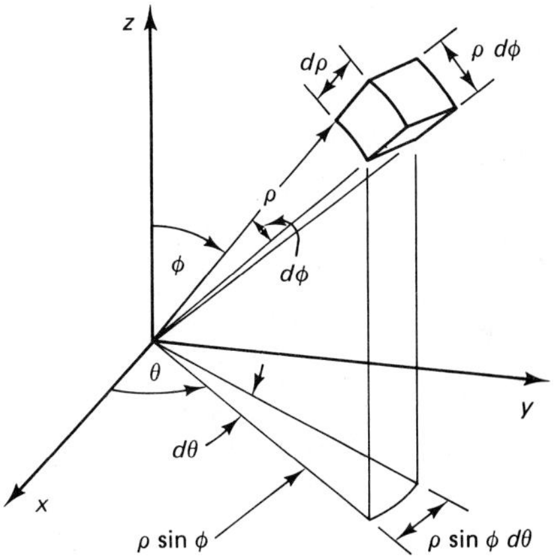

Fig. 8.23 Volume element in spherical coordinates.

EXAMPLE 2 In Example 1 we evaluated the volume integral (12) by using cylindrical coordinates. It turns out that spherical coordinates are just as convenient, for the conical part of the surface of V is a $\phi =$ constant surface, namely $\phi = \alpha$. Proceeding, (12) becomes

$$\begin{aligned} \mathbf{F} &= \sigma G \hat{\mathbf{k}} \int_0^{2\pi} \int_0^{\alpha} \int_0^{h/\cos\phi} \frac{\rho \cos\phi}{(\rho^2)^{3/2}} \rho^2 \sin\phi\, d\rho\, d\phi\, d\theta \\ &= 2\pi\sigma G \hat{\mathbf{k}} \int_0^{\alpha} \cos\phi \sin\phi \frac{h}{\cos\phi}\, d\phi = 2\pi\sigma G h(1 - \cos\alpha)\hat{\mathbf{k}}, \end{aligned} \tag{18}$$

which agrees with the expression obtained in Example 1. ◀

8.7 EXERCISES

1. Compute the volume of a sphere of radius R by triple integration

(a) using cylindrical coordinates
(b) using spherical coordinates

2. Show, by triple integration, that the volume of the right circular cone shown in Fig. 8.22 is $V = (\pi h^3/3)\tan^2\alpha$

(a) using cylindrical coordinates
(b) using spherical coordinates

3. Evaluate the gravitational force $\mathbf{F}$ given by (11), this time letting $\mathcal{V}$ be the hemisphere $x^2 + y^2 + z^2 \le R^2$, for $0 \le z \le R$

*(a) using cylindrical coordinates
(b) using spherical coordinates

4. (*Mass and center of gravity*) First, read Exercise 4 on page 320. In each of the following, take the density σ to be a constant.

*(a) Let $\mathcal{R}$ be the cone considered in Example 1. Compute z_c.
(b) Let $\mathcal{R}$ be one-eighth of the sphere $x^2 + y^2 + z^2 \le R^2$, namely, that part which lies within $x \ge 0$, $y \ge 0$, $z \ge 0$. Compute x_c, y_c, z_c.
*(c) Let $\mathcal{R}$ be that part of the sphere $x^2 + y^2 + z^2 \le R^2$ which lies between $z = a$ and $z = R$ (where $0 < a < R$). Compute z_c.
(d) Let $\mathcal{R}$ be the spherical sector $0 \le \rho \le R$, $0 \le \phi \le \alpha$, $0 \le \theta < 2\pi$. Compute z_c.

5. (*Moments of inertia*) First, read Exercise 5 on page 321. In each of the following, take the density σ to be a constant. Let M be the total mass.

(a) Consider a hollow sphere $a^2 \le x^2 + y^2 + z^2 \le b^2$. Show that

$$I_x = \frac{2}{5}M\frac{b^5 - a^5}{b^3 - a^3}.$$

(b) In the limit $a \to b$, the hollow sphere in part (a) is called a "thin shell." For a thin shell of radius b, show that the answer to part (a) reduces to the form $I_x = \frac{2}{3}Mb^2$.
(c) Consider a hollow right circular cylinder $a^2 \le x^2 + y^2 \le b^2$, $0 \le z \le h$. Show that $I_x = (M/12)(3b^2 + 3a^2 + 4h^2)$.
(d) For the cylinder in part (c), show that $I_z = (M/2)(a^2 + b^2)$.
(e) For the right circular cone shown in Fig. 8.22, show that $I_z = (3M/10)(h\tan\alpha)^2$.
(f) For the right circular cone shown in Fig. 8.22, show that $I_x = (3Mh^2/20)(\tan^2\alpha + 4)$.

6. In the case of cylindrical coordinates, we set $u = r$, $v = \theta$, $w = z$. Show that the result (8) would obtain if, instead, we set $u = \theta$, $v = r$, $w = z$, say.

7. (*Gravitational force induced by hollow sphere*) Consider a hollow sphere, $a^2 \le x^2 + y^2 + z^2 \le b^2$, of uniform mass density σ.

(a) Show that the gravitational force of attraction induced by the hollow sphere, per unit mass at $(0, 0, z_0)$, is

$$\mathbf{F}(0, 0, z_0) = \sigma G\hat{\mathbf{k}} \iiint_{\mathcal{V}} \frac{(z - z_0)\,dV}{[x^2 + y^2 + (z - z_0)^2]^{3/2}}. \tag{a}$$

(b) Carrying out the integration in (a) show that

$$\mathbf{F}(0, 0, z_0) = \begin{cases} -\dfrac{MG}{z_0^2}\hat{\mathbf{k}} & \text{if } z_0 > b \\ \mathbf{0} & \text{if } z_0 < a. \end{cases} \tag{b}$$

Note: The result (b) is remarkable, for it says that the force induced by the hollow sphere at any point outside the sphere is the same as if the entire mass of the sphere were compressed into a *point* mass M at the origin, and that there is *no* force within the cavity.

8. Using the results obtained in Example 1:

*(a) What is the gravitational force induced by an infinite slab $(-\infty < x < \infty,\ -\infty < y < \infty,\ 0 < z < h)$ of uniform mass density σ, per unit mass, at any point on either face of the slab ($z = 0$ or $z = h$)?
(b) What is the gravitational force induced by an infinite halfspace $(-\infty < x < \infty,\ -\infty < y < \infty,\ 0 \le z < \infty)$ of uniform mass density σ, per unit mass, at any point on the face $z = 0$?

8.8 LEIBNIZ RULE

Optional Section

Recall, from your study of the calculus, the **fundamental theorem of the integral calculus**: *If f is a continuous function on the closed interval $[a, b]$, then*

$$\frac{d}{dt}\int_a^t f(x)\,dx = f(t) \tag{1}$$

for $a \le t \le b$. We will see, in this section and in Chapter 9, that it is also useful to be able to differentiate integrals of the more general form

$$I(t) = \int_{A(t)}^{B(t)} f(x, t)\,dx. \tag{2}$$

This form is more general than the integral $\int_a^t f(x)\,dx$ in (1) in as much as it allows for an arbitrary t dependence in both integration limits as well as in the integrand itself.

To differentiate $I(t)$ it is convenient to put the three sources of t dependence (namely, A, B, and f) in evidence by expressing $I(t)$ as

$$I(t) = F(A(t), B(t), t). \tag{3}$$

That is, I is surely a function of the lower limit A (which, in turn, is a function of t), and of the upper limit B (which, in turn, is a function of t). The third argument in F reflects the fact that even if A and B are regarded as fixed, I is still a function of t through the t dependence in the integrand f. The form of (3) suggests chain differentiation, which gives

$$I'(t) = \frac{\partial F}{\partial A}A'(t) + \frac{\partial F}{\partial B}B'(t) + \frac{\partial}{\partial t}\int_A^B f(x, t)\,dx, \tag{4}$$

where A, B are regarded as constants in the last term in (4). To evaluate $\partial F/\partial A$ and $\partial F/\partial B$ we apply (1):

$$\frac{\partial F}{\partial B} = \frac{\partial}{\partial B}\int_A^B f(x, t)\,dx = f(B, t), \tag{5}$$

and

$$\frac{\partial F}{\partial A} = \frac{\partial}{\partial A}\int_A^B f(x, t)\,dx = -\frac{\partial}{\partial A}\int_B^A f(x, t)\,dx = -f(A, t). \tag{6}$$

Finally, it is reasonable to expect that

$$\frac{\partial}{\partial t}\int_A^B f(x, t)\,dx = \int_A^B \frac{\partial}{\partial t}f(x, t)\,dx, \tag{7}$$

in which case we have the desired formula

$$\boxed{\frac{d}{dt}\int_{A(t)}^{B(t)} f(x, t)\,dx = \int_{A(t)}^{B(t)} \frac{\partial}{\partial t}f(x, t)\,dx + B'(t)f(B(t), t) - A'(t)f(A(t), t).} \tag{8}$$

This result is generally known as the **Leibniz rule.**

Under what conditions is the Leibniz rule valid? According to the fundamental theorem (1), (5) is valid if $f(B, t)$ is a continuous function of B i.e., if f is a continuous function of its first argument. Similarly, (6) is valid if f is a continuous function of its first argument. For the chain differentiation (4) to be valid, we ask that $\partial F/\partial A$

and $\partial F/\partial B$ be continuous. Finally, it can be shown that (7) holds if f and $\partial f/\partial t$ are continuous functions of x and t.* Putting these results together, we state the following theorem.†

> ***Theorem 1*** *Leibniz Rule*
> Let $A(t)$ and $B(t)$ be differentiable for $a \le t \le b$, and let c and d be finite constants such that $c \le A(t) \le d$ and $c \le B(t) \le d$ for each t in $a \le t \le b$. If $f(x, t)$ and $\partial f(x, t)/\partial t$ are continuous in the rectangle $a \le t \le b$, $c \le x \le d$, then the Leibniz rule (8) holds for each t in $a < t < b$.

First, an example to illustrate the "mechanics" of (8).

EXAMPLE 1 If

$$I(t) = \int_{-t}^{t^2} \cos(tx^2)\, dx, \tag{9}$$

then, according to the Leibniz rule (8),

$$\begin{aligned} I'(t) &= -\int_{-t}^{t^2} x^2 \sin(tx^2)\, dx + (2t)\cos[t(t^2)^2] - (-1)\cos[t(-t)^2] \\ &= -\int_{-t}^{t^2} x^2 \sin(tx^2)\, dx + 2t\cos(t^5) + \cos(t^3) \end{aligned} \tag{10}$$

for all finite t, since $A(t) = -t$ and $B(t) = t^2$ are differentiable over $-\infty < t < \infty$, and $f(x, t) = \cos(tx^2)$ and $\partial f/\partial t = -x^2 \sin(tx^2)$ are continuous at each point in the x, t plane. ◀

Having considered the "mechanics" of the Leibniz rule in the foregoing example, we offer, next, an illustration of a useful application. A number of other applications are included in the exercises.

EXAMPLE 2 The boundary value problem

$$y'' = f(x); \qquad y(0) = 0, \qquad y(1) = 0 \tag{11}$$

governs (in an approximate way) the static deflection $y(x)$ of a string that is stretched under unit tension between fixed endpoints and subjected to a lateral force distribution $f(x)$ newtons per unit length, as sketched in Fig. 8.24.

* In the last paragraph of Section 6.3 on page 220, we mentioned the pitfalls of limit interchanges. Limit interchange is precisely the issue in (7), for the integrals are limits of Riemann sums, and the derivatives are limits of difference quotients. For the interchange in (7) (which is often called *differentiating under the integral sign*) to be guaranteed, we need f to be sufficiently well behaved. Specifically, we state without proof that it suffices for $\partial f(x, t)/\partial t$ to be a continuous function of x and t.

† While the foregoing remarks outline the main ideas, they do not constitute a complete proof of the theorem. For a detailed proof, we refer the interested reader to T. M. Apostol, *Mathematical Analysis* (Reading, Mass.: Addison-Wesley, 1957); see Theorem 9-38 on p. 220.

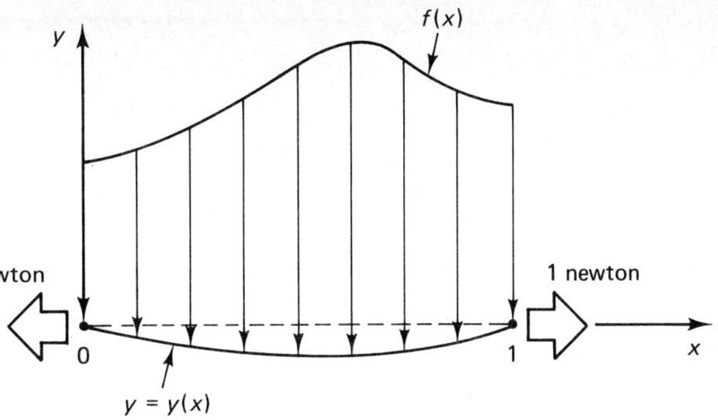

Fig. 8.24 Loaded string.

Integrating twice, and then applying the boundary conditions, we find (Exercise 11) that

$$y(x) = (x - 1)\int_0^x \xi f(\xi)\,d\xi + x\int_x^1 (\xi - 1)f(\xi)\,d\xi. \tag{12}$$

The problem that we pose here is to verify that (12) does indeed satisfy (11). Considering the boundary conditions first, we have

$$y(0) = (-1)\int_0^0 \xi f(\xi)\,d\xi + (0)\int_0^1 (\xi - 1)f(\xi)\,d\xi = 0 + 0 = 0 \tag{13a}$$

and

$$y(1) = (0)\int_0^1 \xi f(\xi)\,d\xi + (1)\int_1^1 (\xi - 1)f(\xi)\,d\xi = 0 + 0 = 0, \tag{13b}$$

as required.

Next, differentiation of (12), using the Leibniz rule (8), gives

$$\begin{aligned} y'(x) &= (1)\int_0^x \xi f(\xi)\,d\xi + (x - 1)xf(x) + (1)\int_x^1 (\xi - 1)f(\xi)\,d\xi \\ &\quad + x(-1)(x - 1)f(x), \\ y''(x) &= xf(x) + (-1)(x - 1)f(x) = f(x), \end{aligned} \tag{14}$$

which completes the verification.

Of course, the names of the variables here happen to be different from those in (8) (to protect the innocent): Here x is the parameter and ξ is the dummy variable of integration; in (8) t was the parameter and x was the dummy variable of integration. Surely, the names of the variables is of no consequence. ◀

The Leibniz rule (8) may be extended to multiple integrals as well. For our purposes it will suffice to limit that extension to the case of double and triple integrals over regions that are independent of the parameter in question (t, say). In the one-dimensional version (8), that corresponds to the case where $A(t)$ and $B(t)$ are constants; then (8) reads

$$\frac{d}{dt}\int_A^B f(x, t)\,dx = \int_A^B \frac{\partial}{\partial t} f(x, t)\,dx, \tag{15}$$

i.e., *the derivative of the integral is equal to the integral of the derivative*. In two and three dimensions, the analogs of (15) are

$$\boxed{\frac{d}{dt}\iint_{\mathscr{R}} f(x, y, t)\, dA = \iint_{\mathscr{R}} \frac{\partial}{\partial t} f(x, y, t)\, dA} \tag{16}$$

and

$$\boxed{\frac{d}{dt}\iiint_{\mathscr{V}} f(x, y, z, t)\, dV = \iiint_{\mathscr{V}} \frac{\partial}{\partial t} f(x, y, z, t)\, dV,} \tag{17}$$

respectively, where $\mathscr{R}$ and $\mathscr{V}$ are independent of t; i.e., if the multiple integrals in (16) and (17) were expressed as iterated integrals, there would be no t dependence present in the limits of integration. *Sufficient conditions for (16) to hold are that f and $\partial f/\partial t$ be continuous over the relevant x, y, t space. Similarly, (17) will hold if f and $\partial f/\partial t$ are continuous over the relevant x, y, z, t space.*

EXAMPLE 3 *Gravitational Potential.* According to Newton's law of gravitation (Example 1 on page 341), the gravitational force of attraction $\mathbf{F}$ induced per unit mass at a field point (x, y, z) by a point mass M at (x', y', z') is

$$\mathbf{F} = GM\frac{(x' - x)\hat{\mathbf{i}} + (y' - y)\hat{\mathbf{j}} + (z' - z)\hat{\mathbf{k}}}{[(x' - x)^2 + (y' - y)^2 + (z' - z)^2]^{3/2}}, \tag{18}$$

where G is the universal gravitational constant. In place of the force $\mathbf{F}$, it is often preferable to work with the so-called *gravitational potential* Φ induced by M, namely,

$$\Phi = -\frac{GM}{\sqrt{(x' - x)^2 + (y' - y)^2 + (z' - z)^2}}. \tag{19}$$

As is easily verified, the connection between Φ and $\mathbf{F}$ is that

$$\mathbf{F} = -\left(\frac{\partial \Phi}{\partial x}\hat{\mathbf{i}} + \frac{\partial \Phi}{\partial y}\hat{\mathbf{j}} + \frac{\partial \Phi}{\partial z}\hat{\mathbf{k}}\right). \tag{20}$$

Thus we say that $\mathbf{F}$ is "derivable" from Φ, according to (20). The point is that it is simpler to work with Φ than with $\mathbf{F}$ since Φ is a scalar and $\mathbf{F}$ is a vector; $\mathbf{F}$ can always be recovered from Φ by means of (20), if we wish. Furthermore, Φ itself has an important physical significance, involving work and energy, as we will see in Section 9.12.

Now, if we have mass distributed over a region $\mathscr{V}$ in 3-space with a density distribution σ, instead of a single point mass M, then the total induced gravitational potential at (x, y, z) may be built up, from (19), by superposition, as

$$\Phi(x, y, z) = -G\iiint_{\mathscr{V}} \frac{\sigma(x', y', z')\, dV}{\sqrt{(x' - x)^2 + (y' - y)^2 + (z' - z)^2}}. \tag{21}$$

As noted above, the force components F_x, F_y, F_z are derivable from (21) as $F_x = -\partial\Phi/\partial x$, $F_y = -\partial\Phi/\partial y$, $F_z = -\partial\Phi/\partial z$, respectively. For example,

$$F_x = -\frac{\partial\Phi}{\partial x} = \frac{\partial}{\partial x}\left\{G \iiint_{\mathcal{V}} \frac{\sigma(x', y', z')\, dV}{\sqrt{(x'-x)^2 + (y'-y)^2 + (z'-z)^2}}\right\}$$
$$= G \iiint_{\mathcal{V}} \frac{\partial}{\partial x}\left\{\frac{\sigma(x', y', z')}{\sqrt{(x'-x)^2 + (y'-y)^2 + (z'-z)^2}}\right\} dV \tag{22}$$
$$= G \iiint_{\mathcal{V}} \frac{(x'-x)\sigma(x', y', z')}{[(x'-x)^2 + (y'-y)^2 + (z'-z)^2]^{3/2}}\, dV.$$

The mathematical point of interest in this example is the third equality in (22), namely, that the derivative of the integral is equal to the integral of the derivative. This step is an application of the extended Leibniz rule (17).

COMMENT 1 Do not be thrown by the notation. In (17) the dummy variables of integration were x, y, z, and the parameter was t; in (22) the dummy variables of integration happen to be called x', y', z', and the parameter with respect to which we are differentiating is x.

COMMENT 2 Recall that sufficient conditions, for the validity of (17), are the continuity of the two integrands. Assuming that σ is continuous, those conditions are indeed satisfied in (22) if the point (x, y, z) is *outside* $\mathcal{V}$. If it is *inside* $\mathcal{V}$, the two integrands are *not* continuous since they "blow up" (i.e., they tend to infinity) as $(x', y', z') \to (x, y, z)$. Thus, for all (x, y, z) points outside $\mathcal{V}$ the italicized sufficient conditions given on page 348 guarantee that (22) is correct; for (x, y, z) points inside $\mathcal{V}$ those sufficient conditions are not met, and hence they provide no information as to the correctness or incorrectness of (22). ◀

In summary, it is often useful to be able to differentiate a given integral with respect to a parameter without having to first carry out the integration. For the case of a single integral, with parametric dependence in the integration limits and/or in the integrand, the formula for carrying out that differentiation was given as the Leibniz rule (8), subject to the conditions stated in Theorem 1. Extension to double and triple integrals was indicated, briefly, for the case where the parametric dependence occurs only in the integrand, not in the limits of integration.

8.8 EXERCISES

1. Apply the Leibniz rule (8) in each case.

*(a) $d/dt \int_0^{t^2} \sin(tx^2)\, dx$

(b) $d/dt \int_3^t x^t \sin x\, dx$

(c) $d/d\alpha \int_\alpha^2 e^{x^2}\, dx$

*(d) $d/d\alpha \int_{-2}^{-\alpha} e^{\alpha x^3}\, dx$

(e) $d^2/dx^2 \int_x^{2x} \ln(u^2 + x^2)\, du$

(f) $d/dx \int_{x+1}^{x+2} e^{-t^2}\, dt$

(g) $d/dy \int_{y^2}^1 x\,dx/(x^3 + y^3)$

(h) $d^2/da^2 \int_{5a}^{a^2} \cos(v^2 + a^2)\, dv$

2. Derive the Taylor series of $f(x)$, about $x = 0$, through third order (i.e., through the x^3 term).

*(a) $f(x) = \int_0^x e^{-t^2}\, dt$

(b) $f(x) = \int_{-x}^x dt/(t^3 + 1)$

(c) $f(x) = \int_0^{2x} \ln(t^2 + 1)\, dt$

(d) $f(x) = \int_{-x}^0 e^{xt^2}\, dt$

3. Observe that Theorem 1 does not apply if one or both of the integration limits are infinite. That case is more complicated, and relevant theorems, analogous to our Theorem 1, are to be found in most books on advanced calculus [e.g., F. B. Hildebrand, *Advanced*

Calculus for Applications, 2nd ed. (Englewood Cliffs, N.J.: Prentice-Hall, 1976), Sec. 7.9]. *In this exercise you may simply proceed under the (verifiable) assumption that differentiation under the integral sign is legitimate*.

(a) By repeated differentiation of the formula

$$\int_0^\infty e^{-ax}\,dx = \frac{1}{a},$$

show that $\int_0^\infty x^n e^{-x}\,dx = n!$ for $n = 0, 1, \ldots$.
(b) Evaluate $\int_0^\infty x^4 e^{-x^2}\,dx$. *Hint:* Use the known integral $\int_0^\infty e^{-x^2}\,dx = \sqrt{\pi}/2$ to show (by making the change of variables $x = \sqrt{a}y$) that

$$\int_0^\infty e^{-ay^2}\,dy = \frac{1}{2}\sqrt{\frac{\pi}{a}}. \qquad \text{(a)}$$

Then differentiate (a) a suitable number of times.
(c) Wishing to evaluate

$$I = \int_0^\infty \frac{(\ln x)^2}{1 + x^3}\,dx, \qquad \text{(b)}$$

we look in an integral table and although we do not find the integral (b), we do find the formula

$$\int_0^\infty \frac{x^a}{1 + x^3}\,dx = \frac{\pi}{3\sin\left(\dfrac{a+1}{3}\pi\right)}. \qquad \text{(c)}$$

Differentiating (c) a suitable number of times, show that $I = 10\pi^3/(81\sqrt{3})$.
(d) Use equation (c) to evaluate the integral

$$I = \int_0^\infty \frac{x \ln x}{1 + x^3}\,dx. \qquad \text{(d)}$$

4. Show that

(a) $y(x) = \frac{1}{6}\int_a^x (x - t)^3 f(t)\,dt$ satisfies the initial-value problem $y''''(x) = f(x)$; $y(a) = y'(a) = y''(a) = y'''(a) = 0$
(b) $y(x) = \frac{1}{x}\int_a^x (x - t) f(t)\,dt$ satisfies the initial-value problem $(xy)'' = f(x)$; $y(a) = y'(a) = 0$
(c) $y(x) = e^x + \int_0^x t^2\cosh(x - t)\,dt$ satisfies the initial-value problem $y'' - y = 2x$; $y(0) = y'(0) = 1$
(d) $x(t) = \frac{1}{k}\int_0^t \sin k(t - \tau) f(\tau)\,d\tau$ satisfies the driven harmonic oscillator initial value problem $\ddot{x} + k^2 x = f(t)$; $x(0) = \dot{x}(0) = 0$

5. Evaluate $\int_0^1 x^{0.7}\ln x\,dx$ by differentiating the known formula

$$\int_0^1 x^a\,dx = \frac{1}{a+1} \qquad (a > -1).$$

6. Show that

$$\int_0^1 \frac{x^3 - 1}{\ln x}\,dx = \ln 4.$$

Hint: Considering

$$I(a) = \int_0^1 \frac{x^a - 1}{\ln x}\,dx \qquad (a \geq 0),$$

show that $I'(a) = 1/(a + 1)$ with the "initial condition" $I(0) = 0$. Solve for $I(a)$ and set $a = 3$.

7. The conditions in Theorem 1 are sufficient, not necessary. To illustrate this point, show that Leibniz differentiation of the integral

$$I(t) = \int_0^t \frac{e^{\sqrt{x}}}{\sqrt{x}}\,dx \qquad (t > 0)$$

does give the correct result even though the integrand $f(x, t) = e^{\sqrt{x}}/\sqrt{x}$ is not continuous (since $f \to \infty$ as $x \to 0$).

8. Consider a one-dimensional fluid flow, say flow in a channel of cross-sectional area A, with velocity $v(x, t)$ meters/second and mass density $\sigma(x, t)$ grams/meter³; x is measured positive downstream, and t is the time. Consider a "control volume" $a(t) \leq x \leq b(t)$ which drifts with the fluid; i.e., $da/dt = v[a(t), t]$ and $db/dt = v[b(t), t]$. Then show that the principle of conservation of mass (i.e., that the amount of mass within the control volume remains constant) may be expressed as

$$\frac{d}{dt}\int_{a(t)}^{b(t)} \sigma(x, t)\,A\,dx = A\int_{a(t)}^{b(t)} \left[\frac{\partial\sigma}{\partial t} + \frac{\partial}{\partial x}(v\sigma)\right] dx = 0. \qquad \text{(a)}$$

9. Show that

(a) $u(x, t) = \int_0^1 f(\xi)\,\dfrac{e^{-(\xi - x)^2/4\alpha^2 t}}{2\alpha\sqrt{\pi t}}\,d\xi$
($-\infty < x < \infty$, $t > 0$) satisfies the "partial differential equation" $\alpha^2 u_{xx} = u_t$ (which is known as the *heat equation*, or the *diffusion equation*, and which will be studied in Part IV); f is prescribed.

(b) $y(x, t) = \dfrac{F(x + ct) + F(x - ct)}{2} + \dfrac{1}{2c}\int_{x-ct}^{x+ct} G(\alpha)\,d\alpha$

($-\infty < x < \infty$, $t \geq 0$) satisfies the "partial differential equation" $c^2 y_{xx} = y_{tt}$ (known as the *wave equation*) and the initial conditions $y(x, 0) = F(x)$, $y_t(x, 0) = G(x)$.

(c) $u(x, y) = \frac{y}{\pi} \int_{-1}^{1} \frac{f(\xi)}{(\xi - x)^2 + y^2} \, d\xi$
$(-\infty < x < \infty, y > 0)$ satisfies the *Laplace equation* $u_{xx} + u_{yy} = 0$. f is prescribed.

(d) $u(x, y) =$
$$\int_0^1 \int_0^1 \ln [(x - \xi)^2 + (y - \eta)^2] f(\xi, \eta) \, d\xi \, d\eta$$
satisfies the *Laplace equation* $u_{xx} + u_{yy} = 0$ at all points (x,y) outside the square $0 \le x \le 1$, $0 \le y \le 1$; f is prescribed.

(e) $u(x, y, z) =$
$$\int_0^1 \int_0^1 \int_0^1 \frac{f(\xi, \eta, \zeta) \, d\xi \, d\eta \, d\zeta}{\sqrt{(x - \xi)^2 + (y - \eta)^2 + (z - \zeta)^2}}$$ satisfies the *Laplace equation* $u_{xx} + u_{yy} + u_{zz} = 0$ at all points (x, y, z) outside the cube $0 \le x \le 1$, $0 \le y \le 1$, $0 \le z \le 1$; f is prescribed.

10. Apply (16) or (17) in each case.

*(a) $\frac{d}{dt} \int_0^2 \int_1^4 \sin (tx^2 + y^3) \, dx \, dy = ?$

(b) $\frac{d}{dt} \int_0^1 \int_0^z \int_y^1 \frac{dx \, dy \, dz}{x^2 + y^2 + z^2 + t^2} = ?$

(c) $\frac{d}{da} \int_0^3 \int_{y^2}^9 \cos (ax) e^{-a(x^2+y^2)} \, dx \, dy = ?$

11. Derive (12) by integrating $y'' = f(x)$ twice and applying the boundary conditions.

9 Scalar and Vector Field Theory

9.1 INTRODUCTION

In a sense, the role of Chapters 6 to 8 was to lay the groundwork for the present chapter, which we believe to be the heart of Part II. Here we consider scalar and vector fields in Euclidean 3-space, we introduce several scalar and vector differential operators, and we consider volume, surface, and line integrals over those fields. The chief results, such as the Gauss divergence theorem and Stokes' theorem, evolved over the course of the nineteenth century. They had a profound impact on pure and applied mathematics, and on the study of such important physical phenomena as the diffusion of heat and matter, fluid flow, electrostatics, electrodynamics, gravitational attraction, waves in solids, liquids, and gases, and electromagnetic waves. Understanding these phenomena is of great importance in the design of such diverse systems as waveguides, airfoils, and thermal energy storage devices.

9.2 THE CURVES, SURFACES, AND VOLUMES UNDER CONSIDERATION

Throughout this chapter we ask that the curves, surfaces, and volumes under consideration be "suitably decent." Specifically, we ask our curves to be *piecewise smooth* (page 310). We ask our surfaces to be *piecewise smooth,* too (page 316), but, in addition, we ask that they be "orientable." Since nonorientable surfaces are rarely encountered in applications, and since a rigorous definition would turn into a long story, we will define the term only in an intuitive way. Namely, we say that a surface is **orientable** if it is two-sided, i.e., if we can paint one side green and the other side blue. The classic example of a *non*orientable surface is the *Möbius band,* which can be constructed by taking a rectangular strip of paper, twisting one end through 180°, and then taping that end to the other (Fig. 9.1). If an insect starts at any point P on one side of the band and follow the arrows, it eventually visits the entire surface, so that the Möbius band has only one side. Our objection to such a surface is that we are going to wish to "orient" a given surface $\mathcal{S}$ by defining a normal vector $\hat{\mathbf{n}}$ at some point on $\mathcal{S}$ and then extending the field of normals continuously over the rest of $\mathcal{S}$. But when we do that with the Möbius band, say, we end up with *two* vectors, $\hat{\mathbf{n}}$ and $-\hat{\mathbf{n}}$, at each point on $\mathcal{S}$.

Finally, we ask that our volumes be *regions (page 216) which are bounded by piecewise-smooth orientable surfaces;* we do *not* ask that the bounding surface be connected, but if it is not connected, we ask that it consist of a finite number of parts such that each part is piecewise smooth and orientable. For example, let $\mathcal{V}$ be a prism with two spherical cavities, as shown in Fig. 9.2. Then $\mathcal{S} = \mathcal{S}_1 + \mathcal{S}_2 + \mathcal{S}_3$, where $\mathcal{S}_1$ is piecewise smooth, $\mathcal{S}_2$ and $\mathcal{S}_3$ are smooth, and $\mathcal{S}_1$, $\mathcal{S}_2$, and $\mathcal{S}_3$ are all orientable. Thus $\mathcal{S}$ is suitable. Further, it makes sense—because $\mathcal{S}$ is orientable—to speak of a field of "outward unit normals" to $\mathcal{S}$, as indicated by the $\hat{\mathbf{n}}$'s in Fig. 9.2.

Fig. 9.1 Möbius band.

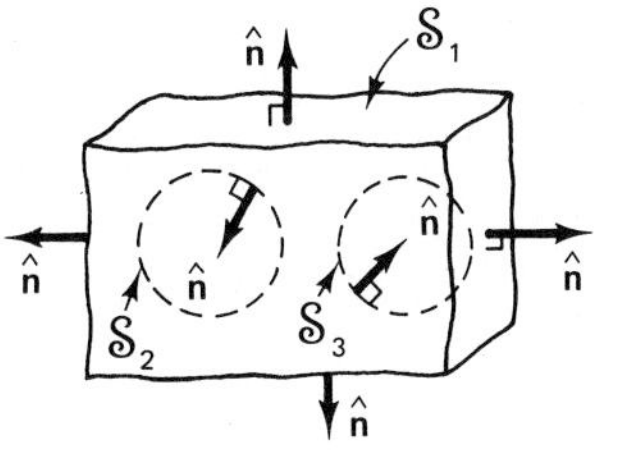

Fig. 9.2 The volume $\mathcal{V}$.

SCALAR AND VECTOR FIELDS 9.3

The objects of interest in this chapter are scalar fields and vector fields. By a **scalar field** we shall mean a scalar-valued function, say f, defined over a region $\mathcal{R}$, which is a one-, two-, or three-dimensional connected subset of 3-space. Besides the space variables, f may depend on the time t as well. Normally, f will be real valued.

EXAMPLE 1 *Temperature Field.* Let $T(x, y)$ denote the temperature (in degrees Celsius, say) at any given point (x, y) in a square plate, of negligible thickness, which extends over $0 \le x \le 1$, $0 \le y \le 1$, and let

$$T(x, y) = 100xy. \tag{1}$$

For example, the temperature at the center of the plate is $T(0.5, 0.5) = 100(0.5)(0.5) = 25°$. In this case the region $\mathcal{R}$ is the two-dimensional set $0 \le x \le 1$, $0 \le y \le 1$, and the scalar function is $T(x, y) = 100xy$. By way of graphical display, one can plot the surface $T(x, y)$ above the x, y plane, as in Fig. 9.3a, but such a display is normally quite difficult to carry out without resorting to computer graphics. It is much simpler, in portraying a two-dimensional field such

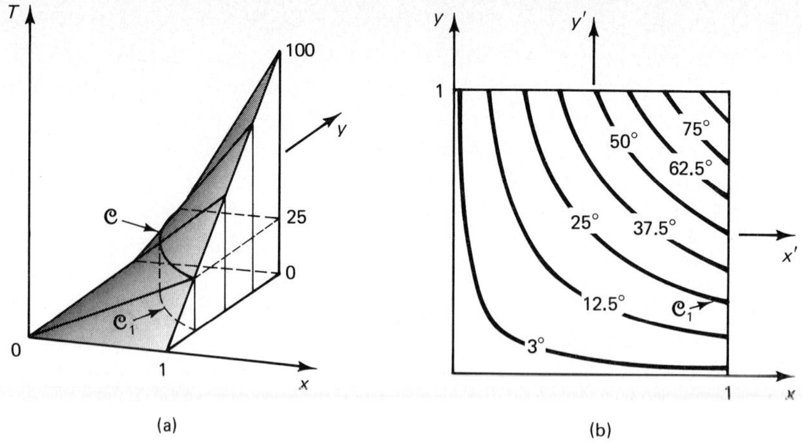

Fig. 9.3 The scalar field $T(x, y) = 100xy$.

as $T(x, y)$, to plot a number of representative $T(x, y) =$ constant curves over the region $\mathcal{R}$, say $T(x, y) = 3°, 12.5°, 25°, 37.5°, 50°, 62.5°, 75°$, and $87.5°$, as we have done in Fig. 9.3b. These curves are called *isotherms* (i.e., curves of constant temperature). For example, the 25° isotherm is the curve $T(x, y) = 100xy = 25$, i.e., the hyperbola $xy = \frac{1}{4}$.

Such curves, in the x, y plane, are also called **level curves,** for if we imagine constructing a level road around the $T = T(x, y)$ mountain shown in Fig. 9.3a, say, at the height $T = 25$, that road would lie along the curve $\mathscr{C}$. Thus the "shadow" of $\mathscr{C}$ onto the x, y plane, $\mathscr{C}_1$, is called the $T = 25$ level curve, and is the same as the $\mathscr{C}_1$ curve in Fig. 9.3b.

COMMENT 1 It is to be emphasized that the field is independent of the coordinate system that is adopted. For example, if we had used the x', y' coordinates shown in Fig. 9.3b, with their origin at the center of the plate, instead of the x, y coordinates, then (since $x = x' + \frac{1}{2}$ and $y = y' + \frac{1}{2}$) we would have had

$$T = 100(x' + \tfrac{1}{2})(y' + \tfrac{1}{2}) \tag{2}$$

in place of (1). That is, (1) and (2) are merely different representations of the same field. To illustrate, observe that at the center of the plate (1) gives $T = 100(\frac{1}{2})(\frac{1}{2}) = 25$, and (2) gives $T = 100(0 + \frac{1}{2})(0 + \frac{1}{2}) = 25$, too.

COMMENT 2 The field (1) happens not to depend on the time t, so it is said to be a *steady* field.

COMMENT 3 We spoke of the field T as *two-dimensional* not because the region was a two-dimensional set ($0 \le x \le 1$, $0 \le y \le 1$), but because $T(x, y)$ was a function of two space variables. Thus if instead, $T = 100xy$ were the temperature field in the *three*-dimensional set $0 \le x \le 1$, $0 \le y \le 1$, $0 \le z \le L$, (i.e., in a plate of finite thickness L), say, we would still refer to T as two-dimensional since it varies only with respect to x and y; it does not vary with z. ◀

In Example 1 we encountered level curves. More generally, we say that the **level set** of value c, of a function $f(x_1, \ldots, x_n)$, is the set of points $(x_1, \ldots, x_n)$, for which $f(x_1, \ldots, x_n) = c$. If $n = 2$, the level set may be a level *curve*, and if

$n = 3$, the level set may be a level *surface*. To illustrate some of the possibilities, consider a few examples (for $n = 2$, say). Let

$$f(x, y) = \ln(x^2 + y^2), \qquad g(x, y) = \sin(x + 3y), \qquad h(x, y) = 6,$$

each defined over the whole plane. It is not hard to see that the level sets of f are concentric circles centered at the origin; specifically, for any given value c $(-\infty < c < \infty)$ the level set of $f(x, y)$ is the circle $x^2 + y^2 = e^c$. Turning to g, the level set of value $\frac{1}{2}$, say, is the set of straight lines $x + 3y = \pi/6 + 2n\pi$ $(n = 0, \pm 1, \pm 2, \ldots)$, and the level set of value 4, say, is empty. Finally, turning to h, the level set of value 2, say, is empty, whereas the level set of value 6 is the whole plane (i.e., it is not merely a curve).

In contrast with a scalar field, a *vector-valued function* defined over a given region is called a **vector field.***

EXAMPLE 2 *Fluid Velocity Field.* Imagine a steady, uniform flow of fluid (such as air or water), at a speed U meters/second, parallel to a wall, as shown in Fig. 9.4. That is, at every instant, and at every point (x, y) in the region (namely, $-\infty < x < \infty$, $0 < y < \infty$), the fluid velocity $\mathbf{q}$ is equal to $U\hat{\mathbf{i}}$, where U is a constant. Then the vector function

$$\mathbf{q} = U\hat{\mathbf{i}}, \tag{3}$$

in the stated region, constitutes a vector field—a rather simple one, but a vector field nonetheless.

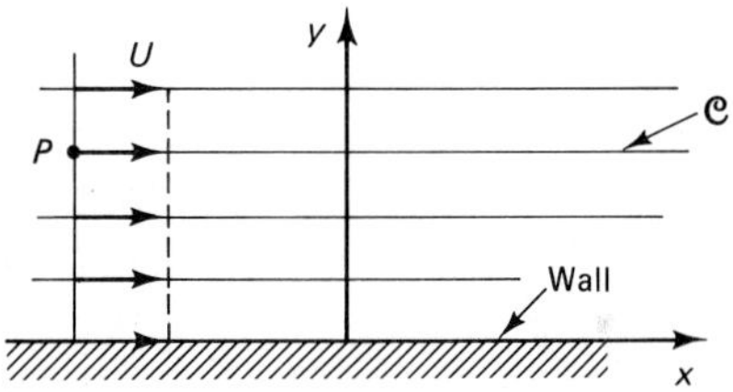

Fig. 9.4 Steady, uniform flow field.

Since the flow is steady, every fluid particle that passes through the point P (Fig. 9.4), at one time or another, must follow the same path, namely, the curve $\mathscr{C}$. Fluid mechanicists call such curves *streamlines*. (In general, streamlines do not exist if the flow is *un*steady.) Thus we speak of the family of horizontal lines in Fig. 9.4 as the *streamline pattern*.

As a more complicated case, let the wall have a semicircular bump of radius a, centered at the origin, and let the fluid velocity field be

$$\mathbf{q} = U\hat{\mathbf{i}} + \frac{Ua^2}{(x^2 + y^2)^2}[(y^2 - x^2)\hat{\mathbf{i}} - 2xy\hat{\mathbf{j}}] \qquad (x^2 + a^2 > 0 \text{ and } y > 0) \tag{4}$$

as depicted in Fig. 9.5. At the top of the bump, for example, where $x = 0$ and $y = a$,

$$\mathbf{q}(0, a) = U\hat{\mathbf{i}} + \frac{Ua^2}{a^4}(a^2\hat{\mathbf{i}} - 0\hat{\mathbf{j}}) = 2U\hat{\mathbf{i}}.$$

* That is, a *vector field* $\mathbf{v}$ on a region $\mathscr{R}$, which is a subset of $\mathbb{R}^n$, is a transformation or mapping $\mathbf{v}$: $\mathscr{R} \subset \mathbb{R}^n \to \mathbb{R}^n$. In this chapter n will be 2 or 3; the general case is considered in MARSDEN AND TROMBA. Similarly, a *scalar field* f on a region $\mathscr{R}$, is a mapping f: $\mathscr{R} \subset \mathbb{R}^n \to \mathbb{R}$.

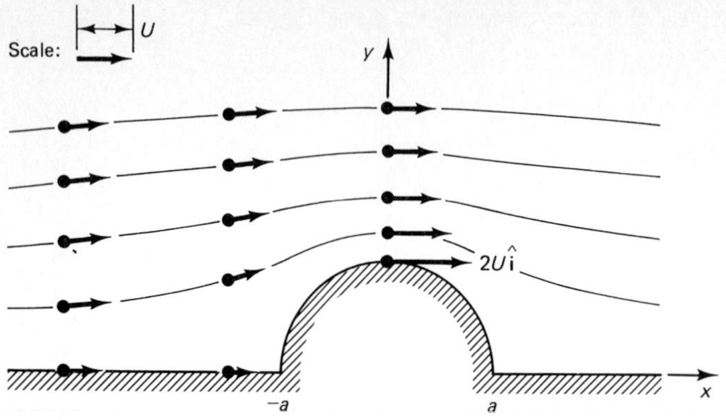

Fig. 9.5 The flow field (4).

Note that, by convention, we place the *tail* (not the head) of the arrow at the point at which the vector is defined. ◀

Both examples illustrated two-dimensional fields. Some examples of three-dimensional fields are

$$u(x, y, z, t) = (x^2 + 2yz) \sin t \qquad (x^2 + y^2 < 1, 0 < z < 2)$$

is a three-dimensional (unsteady) scalar field, and

$$\mathbf{v}(x, y, z) = xz\hat{\mathbf{i}} + 4(x^2 + y^2 + z^2)\hat{\mathbf{k}} \qquad (|x| < 1, y > 0, z > 0)$$

is a three-dimensional (steady) vector field.

Where these fields "come from" is another question. In some cases they may be measured experimentally, and in some cases they may be computed analytically. In the present chapter this point will be of no concern.

9.3 EXERCISES

1. Let $T(x, y)$ be a temperature field in $|x| \le 10$, $0 \le y \le 10$. Determine, and graph, the $T = 0, 20, 40, 60$ level sets. If the level set is empty, state that.

(a) $T = x^2 + y^2$ (b) $T = 10(x - y)$
(c) $T = 10(x + y)$ (d) $T = x^2 - y^2$
(e) $T = 2x^2$
(f) $T = 100/(x^2 + y^2 + 1)$
(g) $T = x + 20y$ (h) $T = x^2y^2/20$
(i) $T = 60 \sin \dfrac{\pi xy}{128}$ (j) $T = 53$
(k) $T = \sin \dfrac{x^2 + y^2}{24}$ (l) $T = 20$

2. Let $p(x, y, z, t)$ be a pressure field in $|x| < 1$, $|y| < 1$, $0 \le z < \infty$. Determine, and draw a careful sketch of, the $p = 4$ level set, at the instant $t = 2$.

(a) $p = t(z - 1) - y + 1$
(b) $p = t^2(x - 1) - 8y - 4z + 12$
(c) $p = 100[z - x^2 + (t^2 - 4)y^3]$
(d) $p = (\cos \pi t)(x^2 + y^2) + z^2 + z + 3$

3. The position vector $\mathbf{R} = x\hat{\mathbf{i}} + y\hat{\mathbf{j}}$, to any point (x, y) in the x, y plane, constitutes a vector field. Draw the $\mathbf{R}$ vector (to scale) at eight points that are equally spaced around the circle $r = 1$, and at eight points that are equally spaced around the circle $r = 3$.

4. Consider the vector field $\mathbf{v} = x\hat{\mathbf{i}} - y\hat{\mathbf{j}}$ in $0 \le x < \infty$, $0 \le y < \infty$.

(a) On a single graph, sketch the $\mathbf{v}$ vectors at the 16 points (m, n), where m and n are integers such that $0 \le m \le 3$ and $0 \le n \le 3$. (Here it will help to assign a convenient scale, as we have done in Fig. 9.5, so that the arrow representations of the vectors will not lie on top of each other.)

*(b) Determine the curves along which **v** has constant magnitude, and those along which **v** has constant direction. Are these results in agreement with your sketch of the field in part (a)?

5. Given the vector field $\mathbf{w}(x, y, z)$, determine parametric equations $x = x(\tau)$, $y = y(\tau)$, $z = z(\tau)$ for the curve(s) through the point $(2, 3, -1)$ along which **w** has constant direction.

*(a) $\mathbf{w} = y\hat{\mathbf{i}} - x\hat{\mathbf{j}} + z\hat{\mathbf{k}}$
(b) $\mathbf{w} = (y + 2z)\hat{\mathbf{i}} - x\hat{\mathbf{j}} + (x + y)\hat{\mathbf{k}}$
(c) $\mathbf{w} = x^2\hat{\mathbf{i}} + y\hat{\mathbf{j}} + z\hat{\mathbf{k}}$
(d) $\mathbf{w} = 2x\hat{\mathbf{i}} + (x + z)\hat{\mathbf{j}} - y\hat{\mathbf{k}}$
*(e) $\mathbf{w} = yz\hat{\mathbf{i}} - \hat{\mathbf{j}} - (x + 2)\hat{\mathbf{k}}$
(f) $\mathbf{w} = x\hat{\mathbf{i}} + y\hat{\mathbf{j}} + z\hat{\mathbf{k}}$

6. Refer to Example 2—specifically, to the flow field given by (4).
(a) Determine the speed $\|\mathbf{q}\|$, as a function of x, along the wall (namely, $y = 0$ for $|x| \geq a$, and $x^2 + y^2 = a^2$ for $|x| \leq a$). Show that $\|\mathbf{q}\| = 2U$ at $(0, a)$ and that $\|\mathbf{q}\| = 0$ at $(\pm a, 0)$.
(b) A point at which $\mathbf{q} = \mathbf{0}$ is called a *stagnation point*. Show that the only stagnation points in the field are $(\pm a, 0)$.
(c) Show that as $r = \sqrt{x^2 + y^2} \to \infty$ along any "ray," $y = mx$, the velocity **q** tends to $U\hat{\mathbf{i}}$. (Thus, far away from the semicircular bump the flow tends to the uniform flow $U\hat{\mathbf{i}}$ shown in Fig. 9.3; this flow is called the *free stream*.)

7. If a charge q (coulombs) moves with velocity **v** (meters/second) in the presence of both an *electric field* **E** (newtons/coulomb) and a *magnetic flux density field* **B** (webers/meter²), the force **F** (newtons) exerted on q is known to be given by the *Lorentz force equation*

$$\mathbf{F} = q(\mathbf{E} + \mathbf{v} \times \mathbf{B}). \tag{a}$$

Is **F** a vector field? Explain.

8. Recall the polar coordinate base vectors $\hat{\mathbf{e}}_r(\theta)$ and $\hat{\mathbf{e}}_\theta(\theta)$, introduced on page 288. Each of these is a vector field.
(a) Sketch the field $\hat{\mathbf{e}}_r(\theta)$.
(b) Sketch the field $\hat{\mathbf{e}}_\theta(\theta)$.

DIVERGENCE 9.4

In this section and in the next two, we introduce the divergence, the gradient, and the curl, concepts that are closely related and are of importance in field theory. We begin with the divergence.

Let **v** be a C^1 vector field defined in a region $\mathscr{R}$.* The physical nature of **v** is immaterial here, but for definiteness it may help to think of **v** as a fluid velocity field, as introduced in Section 9.3.

Focusing our attention on a particular point $P = (x, y, z)$ in the flow, let us introduce a "control volume" around P, as shown in Fig. 9.6, namely, a region $\mathscr{B}$ with piecewise smooth orientable surface $\mathscr{S}$, P being an interior point in $\mathscr{B}$; for example, $\mathscr{B}$ may be a prism, a sphere, or a "potato" shape, as in the figure. The control volume is only a mathematical entity; it is completely permeable, and its presence in no way affects the flow field **v**.

Consider the integral†

$$\int_{\mathscr{S}} \hat{\mathbf{n}} \cdot \mathbf{v}\, dA, \tag{1}$$

* Let $\mathbf{v} = v_x(x, y, z, t)\hat{\mathbf{i}} + v_y(x, y, z, t)\hat{\mathbf{j}} + v_z(x, y, z, t)\hat{\mathbf{k}}$, where t is the time. By **v** being C^1 in $\mathscr{R}$, we mean that v_x, v_y and v_z are all C^1 in $\mathscr{R}$; i.e., $\partial/\partial x$, $\partial/\partial y$, and $\partial/\partial z$ of v_x, v_y, and v_z all exist and are continuous in $\mathscr{R}$.

† In Chapter 8 we denoted double and triple integrals by $\int\int$ and $\int\int\int$, respectively. In this section we switch to the more compact $\int$ notation used in (1), unless, of course, integration limits are to be spelled out. Another point of notation is that some authors prefer to combine $\hat{\mathbf{n}}$ and dA in (1) as $\hat{\mathbf{n}}\, dA = d\mathbf{A}$; then (1) becomes $\int_{\mathscr{S}} \mathbf{v} \cdot d\mathbf{A}$, which is a bit more compact than (1). We will not adopt this notation.

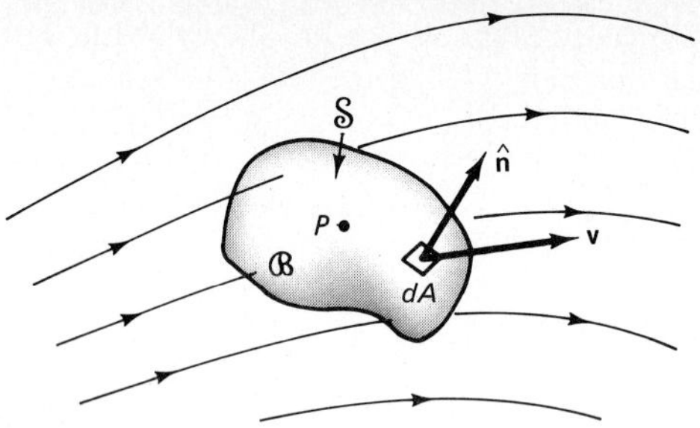

Fig. 9.6 Control volume.

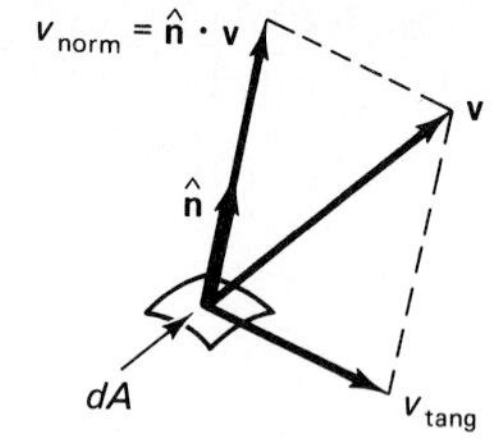

Fig. 9.7 Flux across dA.

where $\hat{\mathbf{n}}$ is the unit outward normal vector on the surface $\mathcal{S}$, as shown in the figure. What is the physical significance of (1)? If, at a given point on the surface $\mathcal{S}$, we break $\mathbf{v}$ into normal and tangential components (Fig. 9.7), the flux across dA is due entirely to the normal component $\hat{\mathbf{n}} \cdot \mathbf{v}$; the tangential flow is *along* the surface and does not cross it. Then the outflow through the surface element dA is the normal velocity component $\hat{\mathbf{n}} \cdot \mathbf{v}$ (meters per second, say) times dA (square meters)—i.e., $\hat{\mathbf{n}} \cdot \mathbf{v}\, dA$ m^3/sec. Thus, integrating over the entire surface $\mathcal{S}$, (1) is the *net outflow*, in m^3/sec, say, across $\mathcal{S}$—*out*flow because we took $\hat{\mathbf{n}}$ to be the *out*ward unit normal. This outflow can be positive, zero, or negative. For example, if heat is extracted from the fluid and the fluid contracts, one can imagine a net *in*flow into the control volume, so that the outflow will be negative.

Next, we divide (1) by the volume V of $\mathcal{B}$ to obtain the outflow *per unit volume* of $\mathcal{B}$. Finally, we shrink $\mathcal{B}$ down to point P and obtain the outflow per unit volume *at P*. This result is called the **divergence of v** at P and is defined as

$$\boxed{\operatorname{div} \mathbf{v}(P) \equiv \lim_{\mathcal{B}\to 0} \left\{ \frac{\int_{\mathcal{S}} \hat{\mathbf{n}} \cdot \mathbf{v}\, dA}{V} \right\},} \tag{2}$$

where $\mathcal{B} \to 0$ means that $\mathcal{B}$ shrinks to the point P in such a way that the maximum linear dimension (the "diameter") of $\mathcal{B}$ tends to zero; hence $\mathcal{B} \to 0$ implies that the volume V tends to zero. Having assumed that $\mathbf{v}$ is continuously differentiable, it can be shown that the limit in (2) does indeed exist at each point P in the field.

Observe, first, that div $\mathbf{v}(P)$ is a scalar, not a vector, since $\hat{\mathbf{n}} \cdot \mathbf{v}$, dA, and V, in (2), are all scalars. Thus div $\mathbf{v}$ is a *scalar field* associated with the given vector field $\mathbf{v}$.

Second, notice that (2) provides an "intrinsic" definition of div $\mathbf{v}$. That is, it contains no reference to any particular coordinate system; *whether we introduce one coordinate system or another, the value of div v(P) is uniquely determined at any point P*. (This fact is important and is stressed in Exercise 5.)

The price that we pay for this elegant generality is that (2) is of little use computationally. To obtain a computationally convenient expression, we need to introduce a reference coordinate system. Introducing a Cartesian system, let us carry out the limit indicated in (2). The rectangular nature of the Cartesian system suggests that we choose $\mathcal{B}$ to be a prism, aligned with the coordinate axes, as in Fig. 9.8. Let P be the point (x_0, y_0, z_0) at the "center" of the prism.

Consider first the contribution from the front and back faces, on which the outward unit normal is $\hat{\mathbf{n}} = +\hat{\mathbf{i}}$ and $\hat{\mathbf{n}} = -\hat{\mathbf{i}}$, respectively. Expressing $\mathbf{v} =$

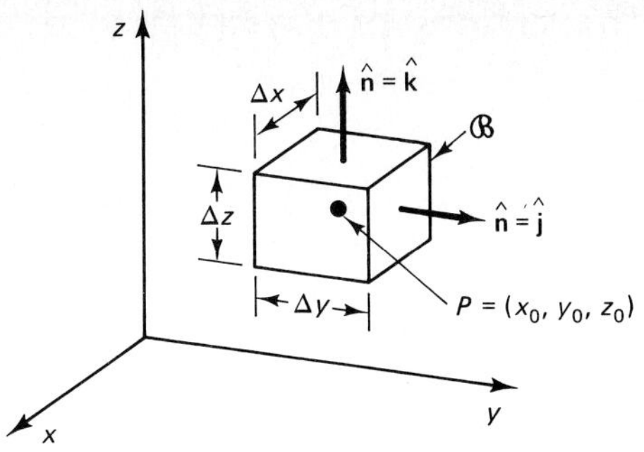

Fig. 9.8 Cartesian coordinates.

$v_x(x, y, z)\hat{\mathbf{i}} + v_y(x, y, z)\hat{\mathbf{j}} + v_z(x, y, z)\hat{\mathbf{k}}$,* we have

$$\begin{aligned}\int_{\text{front face}} \hat{\mathbf{n}} \cdot \mathbf{v}\, dA &= \int_{\text{front face}} \hat{\mathbf{i}} \cdot (v_x\hat{\mathbf{i}} + v_y\hat{\mathbf{j}} + v_z\hat{\mathbf{k}})\, dA \\ &= \int_{\text{front face}} v_x\left(x_0 + \frac{\Delta x}{2}, y, z\right) dy\, dz \\ &= v_x\left(x_0 + \frac{\Delta x}{2}, y_1, z_1\right) \Delta y\, \Delta z,\end{aligned} \tag{3}$$

for some point $(x_0 + \Delta x/2, y_1, z_1)$ on the front face, where the last equality in (3) follows from the mean value theorem (6d) on page 311. Similarly,

$$\begin{aligned}\int_{\text{back face}} \hat{\mathbf{n}} \cdot \mathbf{v}\, dA &= \int_{\text{back face}} -\hat{\mathbf{i}} \cdot (v_x\hat{\mathbf{i}} + v_y\hat{\mathbf{j}} + v_z\hat{\mathbf{k}}) dA \\ &= -v_x\left(x_0 - \frac{\Delta x}{2}, y_2, z_2\right)\Delta y\, \Delta z,\end{aligned} \tag{4}$$

for some point $(x_0 - \Delta x/2, y_2, z_2)$ on the back face. Since the volume of $\mathcal{B}$ is $V = \Delta x\, \Delta y\, \Delta z$, it follows that

$$\begin{aligned}&\lim_{\mathcal{B}\to 0} \left\{\frac{\int_{\text{front+back faces}} \hat{\mathbf{n}} \cdot \mathbf{v}\, dA}{V}\right\} \\ &= \lim_{\Delta x, \Delta y, \Delta z \to 0} \left\{\frac{[v_x(x_0 - \Delta x/2, y_1, z_1) - v_x(x_0 - \Delta x/2, y_2, z_2)]\Delta y\, \Delta z}{\Delta x\, \Delta y\, \Delta z}\right\} \\ &= \lim_{\Delta x \to 0} \frac{v_x(x_0 + \Delta x/2, y_0, z_0) - v_x(x_0 - \Delta x/2, y_0, z_0)}{\Delta x} = \frac{\partial v_x}{\partial x}.\end{aligned} \tag{5}$$

Similarly, the top and bottom faces contribute $\partial v_z/\partial z$, and the right and left faces contribute $\partial v_y/\partial y$, so that†

$$\boxed{\operatorname{div} \mathbf{v} = \frac{\partial v_x}{\partial x} + \frac{\partial v_y}{\partial y} + \frac{\partial v_z}{\partial z}.} \tag{6}$$

* Inclusion of a time dependence in **v** would be of no consequence in the present discussion.

† Having elected to use subscripted x, y, z to denote the particular component of **v**, it would be masochistic also to denote partials by subscripts. Thus we express the partial of v_x with respect to x as $\partial v_x/\partial x$, not as $(v_x)_x$ or v_{xx}.

Analogous expressions for cylindrical and spherical coordinates will be given in Section 9.8.

EXAMPLE 1 If $\mathbf{v} = x^2z\hat{\mathbf{i}} - 3\hat{\mathbf{j}} + 4xy\hat{\mathbf{k}}$, then

$$\text{div } \mathbf{v} = \frac{\partial}{\partial x}(x^2z) + \frac{\partial}{\partial y}(-3) + \frac{\partial}{\partial z}(4xy) = 2xz.$$

At (2, 3, −1), for example, div **v** is −4. ◀

EXAMPLE 2 If $\mathbf{v} = y^2zt\hat{\mathbf{j}}$, where t is the time, then

$$\text{div } \mathbf{v} = \frac{\partial}{\partial x}(0) + \frac{\partial}{\partial y}(y^2zt) + \frac{\partial}{\partial z}(0) = 2yzt;$$

i.e., t is treated as a constant. ◀

Rewriting (6) as

$$\text{div } \mathbf{v} = \left(\hat{\mathbf{i}}\frac{\partial}{\partial x} + \hat{\mathbf{j}}\frac{\partial}{\partial y} + \hat{\mathbf{k}}\frac{\partial}{\partial z}\right) \cdot (v_x\hat{\mathbf{i}} + v_y\hat{\mathbf{j}} + v_z\hat{\mathbf{k}}) \tag{7}$$

suggests that we define a vector differential operator

$$\boxed{\nabla \equiv \hat{\mathbf{i}}\frac{\partial}{\partial x} + \hat{\mathbf{j}}\frac{\partial}{\partial y} + \hat{\mathbf{k}}\frac{\partial}{\partial z},} \tag{8}$$

in which case we can write

$$\boxed{\text{div } \mathbf{v} = \nabla \cdot \mathbf{v}.} \tag{9}$$

We will have more to say about the $\nabla \cdot \mathbf{v}$ operation in subsequent sections, but one point that must be mentioned immediately is that $\nabla \cdot \mathbf{v}$ is not a dot product in the usual sense. Specifically, it is *not* true that $\nabla \cdot \mathbf{v}$ equals $\|\nabla\|$ times $\|\mathbf{v}\|$ times the cosine of the angle between ∇ and $\mathbf{v}$, because $\nabla = \hat{\mathbf{i}}(\partial/\partial x) + \hat{\mathbf{j}}(\partial/\partial y) + \hat{\mathbf{k}}(\partial/\partial z)$ is a vector *differential operator*, not a vector with a certain length and a certain direction. Thus $\|\nabla\|$ is not defined, nor is the "angle between ∇ and $\mathbf{v}$." Furthermore, $\nabla \cdot \mathbf{v}$ is *not* the same as $\mathbf{v} \cdot \nabla$, since

$$\begin{aligned} \nabla \cdot \mathbf{v} &= \left(\hat{\mathbf{i}}\frac{\partial}{\partial x} + \hat{\mathbf{j}}\frac{\partial}{\partial y} + \hat{\mathbf{k}}\frac{\partial}{\partial z}\right) \cdot (v_x\hat{\mathbf{i}} + v_y\hat{\mathbf{j}} + v_z\hat{\mathbf{k}}) \\ &= \frac{\partial v_x}{\partial x} + \frac{\partial v_y}{\partial y} + \frac{\partial v_z}{\partial z}, \end{aligned} \tag{10}$$

whereas

$$\begin{aligned} \mathbf{v} \cdot \nabla &= (v_x\hat{\mathbf{i}} + v_y\hat{\mathbf{j}} + v_z\hat{\mathbf{k}}) \cdot \left(\hat{\mathbf{i}}\frac{\partial}{\partial x} + \hat{\mathbf{j}}\frac{\partial}{\partial y} + \hat{\mathbf{k}}\frac{\partial}{\partial z}\right) \\ &= v_x\frac{\partial}{\partial x} + v_y\frac{\partial}{\partial y} + v_z\frac{\partial}{\partial z}. \end{aligned} \tag{11}$$

The symbol ∇, introduced by Hamilton,* is read as *del*—sometimes as *nabla* because it looks like an ancient Hebrew instrument of that name; in the two sections to follow, ∇ will be our link to the gradient and the curl.

9.4 EXERCISES

1. Work out div **v** for the following vector fields, each of which is defined over all of 3-space, say. Further, evaluate div **v** at (3, −1, 4). (t is the time.)

*(a) $\mathbf{v} = a\hat{\mathbf{i}} + b\hat{\mathbf{j}} + c\hat{\mathbf{k}}$ (a, b, c constants)
(b) $\mathbf{v} = x\hat{\mathbf{i}} + y\hat{\mathbf{j}} + z\hat{\mathbf{k}} = \mathbf{R}$
(c) $\mathbf{v} = x\hat{\mathbf{i}} - y\hat{\mathbf{j}} + z^2t\hat{\mathbf{k}}$
(d) $\mathbf{v} = xyz(\hat{\mathbf{i}} + \hat{\mathbf{j}} - 3\hat{\mathbf{k}})$
*(e) $\mathbf{v} = xy\hat{\mathbf{i}} - 2(x^2 + z^2)\hat{\mathbf{k}}$
(f) $\mathbf{v} = \hat{\mathbf{i}} + \hat{\mathbf{j}} + z\hat{\mathbf{k}}$
(g) $\mathbf{v} = z\hat{\mathbf{i}} + x^2t^2\hat{\mathbf{j}}$
(h) $\mathbf{v} = \sin(x^2 + y^2 + z^2)\hat{\mathbf{j}}$

2. Determine the divergence div **q** of the fluid flow field **q** given by (4) on page 355.

3. Make up a vector field $\mathbf{v}(x, y, z)$ such that

*(a) $\nabla\cdot\mathbf{v} = 0$ everywhere
(b) $\nabla\cdot\mathbf{v} > 0$ everywhere
(c) $\nabla\cdot\mathbf{v} < 0$ everywhere
(d) $\nabla\cdot\mathbf{v} > 0$ in $x^2 + y^2 + z^2 > 1$ and $\nabla\cdot\mathbf{v} < 0$ in $x^2 + y^2 + z^2 < 1$
*(e) $\nabla\cdot\mathbf{v} > 0$ in $|x| > 1$ and $\nabla\cdot\mathbf{v} < 0$ in $|x| < 1$

4. Evaluate div **v** at $P = (0, 0, 0)$, say, by actually evaluating $1/V \int_{\mathcal{S}} \hat{\mathbf{n}}\cdot\mathbf{v}\, dA$ and taking the limit as $\mathcal{B} \to 0$, as in the definition (2); take $\mathcal{B}$ to be the cube $|x| \le \epsilon$, $|y| \le \epsilon$, $|z| \le \epsilon$. Show that your result is the same as that obtained (more easily) from (6).

(a) $\mathbf{v} = 2\hat{\mathbf{i}} - \hat{\mathbf{j}} + 4\hat{\mathbf{k}}$
(b) $\mathbf{v} = x\hat{\mathbf{i}} + 2y\hat{\mathbf{j}} - 4z^3\hat{\mathbf{k}}$
(c) $\mathbf{v} = x(y^2 - 5)(z + 1)\hat{\mathbf{i}} - 3\hat{\mathbf{j}}$
(d) $\mathbf{v} = (x + 2)(y - y^2z^2)\hat{\mathbf{j}}$
(e) $\mathbf{v} = (2y + \sin x)\hat{\mathbf{i}} - z\cos x\hat{\mathbf{k}}$

Note: In studying the calculus, one first learns how to compute the derivative df/dx, of simple functions such as $f(x) = x^2$, sin x, . . . , by working directly with the limit definition

$$\frac{df}{dx} \equiv \lim_{\Delta x\to 0} \frac{f(x + \Delta x) - f(x)}{\Delta x},$$

before developing more efficient lines of approach. That is the idea in this exercise: We are trying to encourage a better fundamental understanding of the important limit definition (2). We suggest that you do *not* proceed by mimicking steps (3) to (5). Rather, it will be more instructive (and easier) simply to compute $\int \hat{\mathbf{n}}\cdot\mathbf{v}\, dA$ on each of the six faces, add up the results, divide by $V = (2\epsilon)^3 = 8\epsilon^3$, and then take the limit as $\epsilon \to 0$.

5. (*Invariance property of div v*) Let a C^1 vector field **v** be represented in terms of some particular Cartesian x, y frame as $\mathbf{v} = v_x(x, y)\hat{\mathbf{i}} + v_y(x, y)\hat{\mathbf{j}}$. (We limit ourselves to the two-dimensional case merely to reduce the algebra; the story is essentially identical for three-dimensional fields.) Then, as derived in this section,

$$\text{div}\ \mathbf{v} = \frac{\partial v_x}{\partial x} + \frac{\partial v_y}{\partial y}. \tag{a}$$

As emphasized in the text, this number will be the same, at a given point $P = (x, y)$, independent of the choice of the location and orientation of the reference coordinate system. In other words, it should be equally true that

$$\text{div}\ \mathbf{v} = \frac{\partial v_{x'}}{\partial x'} + \frac{\partial v_{y'}}{\partial y'} \tag{b}$$

for any values of a, b and α (see the accompanying figure). Here we ask you to *show* that this is true,

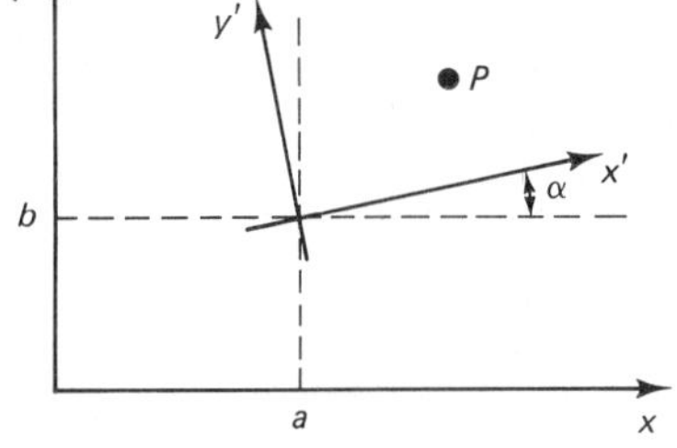

* *William R. Hamilton* (1805–1865) was both a great mathematician and a great physicist. While still an undergraduate, he was named Professor of Astronomy at Trinity College, and Royal Astronomer of Ireland.

namely, that

$$\frac{\partial v_x}{\partial x} + \frac{\partial v_y}{\partial y} = \frac{\partial v_{x'}}{\partial x'} + \frac{\partial v_{y'}}{\partial y'}. \qquad \text{(c)}$$

Hint: First, show (either by referring back to Section 3.7, or from a suitable sketch and some trigonometry) that

$$v_x = (\cos\alpha)v_{x'} - (\sin\alpha)v_{y'},$$
$$v_y = (\text{etc.})v_{x'} + (\text{etc.})v_{y'},$$
$$x' = (\cos\alpha)(x-a) + (\sin\alpha)(y-b),$$
$$y' = -(\sin\alpha)(x-a) + (\cos\alpha)(y-b).$$

(We leave the etceteras for you to determine.) Then use chain differentiation to express $\partial/\partial x$ and $\partial/\partial y$ as linear combinations of $\partial/\partial x'$ and $\partial/\partial y'$.

9.5 GRADIENT

We found in Section 9.4 that the divergence of a vector field **v** can be expressed in the form div **v** = $\nabla \cdot \mathbf{v}$, where ∇ is a vector differential operator which, in Cartesian coordinates, is given by

$$\nabla = \hat{\mathbf{i}}\frac{\partial}{\partial x} + \hat{\mathbf{j}}\frac{\partial}{\partial y} + \hat{\mathbf{k}}\frac{\partial}{\partial z}. \qquad (1)$$

Thus, dotting ∇ into a vector field **v** produces a scalar field associated with **v**, namely, the divergence of **v**. With ∇ in hand, we wonder if it might not be profitable to consider other possible actions of ∇, specifically, ∇u (where u is a scalar field) and $\nabla \times \mathbf{v}$ (where **v** is a vector field). In fact, these combinations will be of great importance. Just as $\nabla \cdot \mathbf{v}$ has a name ("the divergence of **v**," or div **v**, for short) which suggests its physical significance, we call ∇u the **gradient** of u, or grad u, and we call $\nabla \times \mathbf{v}$ the **curl** of **v**, or curl **v**.

The pattern is as follows:*

	Input		*Output*
div **v** = $\nabla \cdot \mathbf{v}$:	vector field	⟶	scalar field
grad u = ∇u:	scalar field	⟶	vector field
curl **v** = $\nabla \times \mathbf{v}$:	vector field	⟶	vector field

In this section we consider the gradient; in the next we turn to the curl.

As stated, we define

$$\boxed{\text{grad } u \equiv \nabla u,} \qquad (2)$$

where u is a C^1 scalar field. In Cartesian coordinates,

$$\text{grad } u = \left(\hat{\mathbf{i}}\frac{\partial}{\partial x} + \hat{\mathbf{j}}\frac{\partial}{\partial y} + \hat{\mathbf{k}}\frac{\partial}{\partial z}\right)u$$

* A fourth combination, $\nabla \mathbf{v}$, is possible, but will not be discussed in this book. For if we write out $\nabla \mathbf{v}$, in Cartesian coordinates, we have

$$\nabla \mathbf{v} = \left(\hat{\mathbf{i}}\frac{\partial}{\partial x} + \hat{\mathbf{j}}\frac{\partial}{\partial y}\right)(v_x\hat{\mathbf{i}} + v_y\hat{\mathbf{j}}) = \frac{\partial v_x}{\partial x}\hat{\mathbf{i}}\hat{\mathbf{i}} + \frac{\partial v_y}{\partial y}\hat{\mathbf{j}}\hat{\mathbf{j}} + \frac{\partial v_y}{\partial x}\hat{\mathbf{i}}\hat{\mathbf{j}} + \frac{\partial v_x}{\partial y}\hat{\mathbf{j}}\hat{\mathbf{i}} \qquad \text{(a)}$$

(in two dimensions, for brevity). The objects $\hat{\mathbf{i}}\hat{\mathbf{i}}, \hat{\mathbf{j}}\hat{\mathbf{j}}, \hat{\mathbf{i}}\hat{\mathbf{j}}, \hat{\mathbf{j}}\hat{\mathbf{i}}$ are neither scalars nor vectors; they are called *dyads*, and the linear combination of dyads (a) is called a second-order tensor. Tensors are indeed important in such applications as continuum mechanics, differential geometry, and the theory of relativity, but will not be dealt with in this more introductory development.

or

$$\boxed{\operatorname{grad} u = \frac{\partial u}{\partial x}\hat{\mathbf{i}} + \frac{\partial u}{\partial y}\hat{\mathbf{j}} + \frac{\partial u}{\partial z}\hat{\mathbf{k}}.} \tag{3}$$

EXAMPLE 1 If $u(x, y, z) = x^2y + 2z$, then $\nabla u = 2xy\hat{\mathbf{i}} + x^2\hat{\mathbf{j}} + 2\hat{\mathbf{k}}$.

COMMENT If the time t is present, it is inactive in the gradient operation, which involves only space derivatives. Thus, if $u(x, y, z, t) = x^2zt$, then $\nabla u = 2xzt\,\hat{\mathbf{i}} + x^2t\hat{\mathbf{k}}$. ◀

We stressed in Section 9.4 that the number $\nabla \cdot \mathbf{v}$, at a given point in the region, is independent of the choice of the reference coordinate system. Similarly for the gradient: Whether we use one Cartesian coordinate system or another, the vector given by the right-hand side of (3) is the same. Let us verify this—in two dimensions, for simplicity. We wish to show that

$$\frac{\partial u}{\partial x}\hat{\mathbf{i}} + \frac{\partial u}{\partial y}\hat{\mathbf{j}} = \frac{\partial u}{\partial x'}\hat{\mathbf{i}}' + \frac{\partial u}{\partial y'}\hat{\mathbf{j}}', \tag{4}$$

where the x, y and x', y' systems differ by an arbitrary displacement and an arbitrary rotation, as drawn in Fig. 9.9. We have (with $\cos\alpha \equiv c$ and $\sin\alpha \equiv s$, for short)

$$\begin{aligned} \hat{\mathbf{i}} &= c\hat{\mathbf{i}}' - s\hat{\mathbf{j}}', \\ \hat{\mathbf{j}} &= s\hat{\mathbf{i}}' + c\hat{\mathbf{j}}', \end{aligned} \tag{5}$$

and considering the coordinates of any given point P,*

$$\begin{aligned} x &= a + cx' - sy' \\ y &= b + sx' + cy' \end{aligned} \tag{6}$$

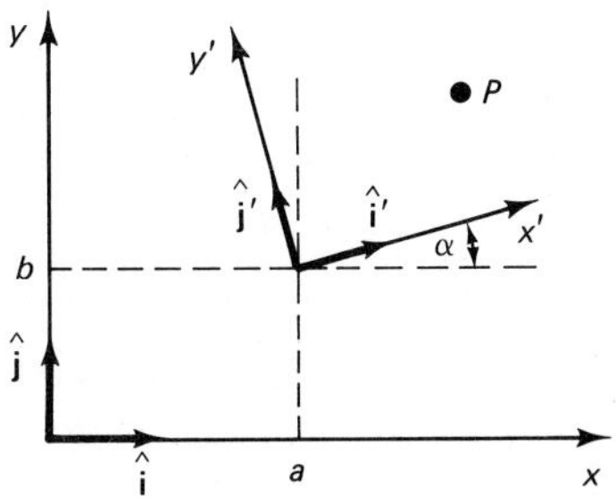

Fig. 9.9 Different reference frames.

*Equations (6) can be obtained from Fig. 9.9 through some trigonometry. Alternatively, observe that if $a = b = 0$, we have a pure rotation, so, as in (17) on page 122,

$$\begin{pmatrix} x \\ y \end{pmatrix} = \begin{pmatrix} c & -s \\ s & c \end{pmatrix}\begin{pmatrix} x' \\ y' \end{pmatrix}.$$

If a and b are *not* both zero, we have an additional translation, so that

$$\begin{pmatrix} x \\ y \end{pmatrix} = \begin{pmatrix} c & -s \\ s & c \end{pmatrix}\begin{pmatrix} x' \\ y' \end{pmatrix} + \begin{pmatrix} a \\ b \end{pmatrix},$$

as in (6).

or solving for x' and y',

$$x' = c(x - a) + s(y - b)$$
$$y' = -s(x - a) + c(y - b). \tag{7}$$

Thus

$$\begin{aligned}\frac{\partial u}{\partial x}\hat{\mathbf{i}} + \frac{\partial u}{\partial y}\hat{\mathbf{j}} &= \left(\frac{\partial u}{\partial x'}\frac{\partial x'}{\partial x} + \frac{\partial u}{\partial y'}\frac{\partial y'}{\partial x}\right)(c\hat{\mathbf{i}}' - s\hat{\mathbf{j}}') \\ &\quad + \left(\frac{\partial u}{\partial x'}\frac{\partial x'}{\partial y} + \frac{\partial u}{\partial y'}\frac{\partial y'}{\partial y}\right)(s\hat{\mathbf{i}}' + c\hat{\mathbf{j}}') \\ &= \left(c\frac{\partial u}{\partial x'} - s\frac{\partial u}{\partial y'}\right)(c\hat{\mathbf{i}}' - s\hat{\mathbf{j}}') + \left(s\frac{\partial u}{\partial x'} + c\frac{\partial u}{\partial y'}\right)(s\hat{\mathbf{i}}' + c\hat{\mathbf{j}}') \\ &= \frac{\partial u}{\partial x'}\hat{\mathbf{i}}' + \frac{\partial u}{\partial y'}\hat{\mathbf{j}}'.\end{aligned} \tag{8}$$

At this point, we introduce another entity, the so-called "directional derivative," which is closely related to the gradient. Basically, the idea is this. Given a scalar field $u(x, y, z)$,the partials $\partial u/\partial x$, $\partial u/\partial y$, $\partial u/\partial z$, are the rates of change of u in the directions of $\hat{\mathbf{i}}$, $\hat{\mathbf{j}}$, $\hat{\mathbf{k}}$, respectively. One can imagine that it would also be useful to be able to compute the rate of change of u in *any* direction, not necessarily one that coincides with $\hat{\mathbf{i}}$, $\hat{\mathbf{j}}$, or $\hat{\mathbf{k}}$. Such a derivative is the directional derivative, which we now define.

Consider a scalar field u, a given point P, and a direction at P defined by a unit vector $\hat{\mathbf{s}}$. Further, let $\mathscr{C}$ be the straight line that passes through P and is collinear with $\hat{\mathbf{s}}$. Locating any given point in the field by a position vector from a fixed reference point O, let the position vector to P be denoted as $\mathbf{R}$. If $P = (x, y, z)$, then u at P is, of course, written as $u(x, y, z)$. In some situations, however, we prefer not to commit ourselves to any coordinate system in particular, and find it more convenient to denote u at (any) point P as either

$$u(P) \quad \text{or} \quad u(\mathbf{R}),$$

where $\mathbf{R}$ is the position vector from a fixed reference point to P. With this notation, we define the **directional derivative** of u, at P, in the direction of $\hat{\mathbf{s}}$, as (see Fig. 9.10)

$$\boxed{\frac{du}{ds} \equiv \lim_{h\to 0}\frac{u(\mathbf{R} + h\hat{\mathbf{s}}) - u(\mathbf{R})}{h},} \tag{9}$$

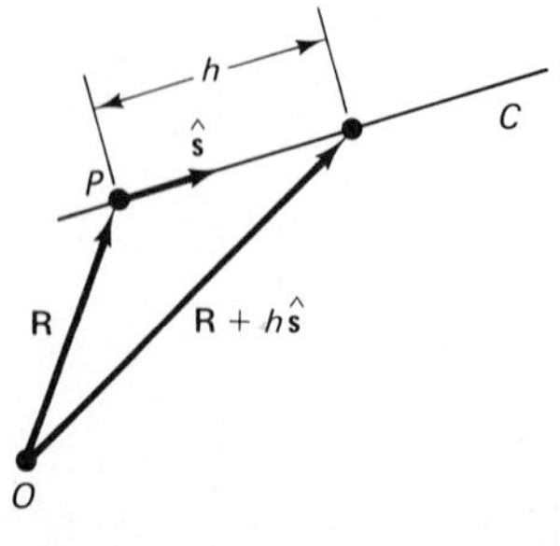

Fig. 9.10 Directional derivative.

provided that the limit exists. (Other common notations for this quantity are $\partial u/\partial s$ and $D_{\hat{\mathbf{s}}}u$.) Evidently, du/ds is the *rate of change of u in the direction* $\hat{\mathbf{s}}$.

As in the case of our limit definition of the divergence, (9) is an intrinsic definition in that it contains no mention of any particular coordinate system. Its limit-of-a-difference-quotient form renders it inconvenient for purposes of calculation, so we now seek a more convenient form. Toward that end, introduce a Cartesian coordinate system x, y, z with its origin at any point, say at O (Fig. 9.10), and oriented in any way. Then $\mathbf{R} = x\hat{\mathbf{i}} + y\hat{\mathbf{j}} + z\hat{\mathbf{k}}$ and $\hat{\mathbf{s}} = s_x\hat{\mathbf{i}} + s_y\hat{\mathbf{j}} + s_z\hat{\mathbf{k}}$, say. Observing that the right-hand side of (9) is also expressible as $\frac{d}{dh}u(\mathbf{R} + h\hat{\mathbf{s}})|_{h=0}$, we have

$$
\begin{aligned}
\frac{du}{ds} &= \frac{d}{dh}u(\mathbf{R} + h\hat{\mathbf{s}})\bigg|_{h=0} = \frac{d}{dh}u(x + hs_x, y + hs_y, z + hs_z)\bigg|_{h=0} \\
&= \bigg[\frac{\partial u}{\partial x}(x + hs_x, y + hs_y, z + hs_z)s_x + \frac{\partial u}{\partial y}(x + hs_x, y + hs_y, z + hs_z)s_y \\
&\quad + \frac{\partial u}{\partial z}(x + hs_x, y + hs_y, z + hs_z)s_z\bigg]\bigg|_{h=0} \\
&= \frac{\partial u}{\partial x}(x, y, z)s_x + \frac{\partial u}{\partial y}(x, y, z)s_y + \frac{\partial u}{\partial z}(x, y, z)s_z,
\end{aligned}
\tag{10}
$$

if $u(x, y, z)$ is C^1 [so that the use of the chain differentiation, in (10), is justified]. Finally, we observe that the expression derived in (10) is equivalent to

$$
\boxed{\frac{du}{ds} = \nabla u \cdot \hat{\mathbf{s}}.} \tag{11}
$$

In (11) we again have an intrinsic expression of du/ds, but one that is computationally more convenient than (9). To evaluate $\nabla u \cdot \hat{\mathbf{s}}$ we express ∇u and $\hat{\mathbf{s}}$ in terms of a coordinate system of our choice. Note that if $\hat{\mathbf{s}} = \hat{\mathbf{i}}$, then (11) gives $du/ds = (u_x\hat{\mathbf{i}} + u_y\hat{\mathbf{j}} + u_z\hat{\mathbf{k}}) \cdot \hat{\mathbf{i}} = \partial u/\partial x$. Similarly, if $\hat{\mathbf{s}} = \hat{\mathbf{j}}$, then $du/ds = \partial u/\partial y$, and if $\hat{\mathbf{s}} = \hat{\mathbf{k}}$, then $du/ds = \partial u/\partial z$. More generally, however, (11) gives the rate of change of u in *any* $\hat{\mathbf{s}}$ direction.

Note carefully the way (11) amounts to an *interpolation* of the rates of change u_x, u_y, u_z in the three coordinate directions. This fact can be seen most easily from the right-hand side of (10), in which u_x, u_y, u_z are weighted by the direction cosines of $\hat{\mathbf{s}}$: $s_x = \hat{\mathbf{s}} \cdot \hat{\mathbf{i}} = \cos\theta(\hat{\mathbf{s}}, \hat{\mathbf{i}})$, $s_y = \hat{\mathbf{s}} \cdot \hat{\mathbf{j}} = \cos\theta(\hat{\mathbf{s}}, \hat{\mathbf{j}})$, and $s_z = \hat{\mathbf{s}} \cdot \hat{\mathbf{k}} = \cos\theta(\hat{\mathbf{s}}, \hat{\mathbf{k}})$, where $\theta(\mathbf{A},\mathbf{B})$ here denotes the angle θ between $\mathbf{A}$ and $\mathbf{B}$. Of course, such interpolation can only be expected to be correct if the quantities involved are continuous. Sure enough, recall that we asked u to be C^1, so that we could apply chain differentiation in (10).

Finally, notice that if we rewrite (11) as $du/ds = (\hat{\mathbf{s}} \cdot \nabla)u$, we see that d/ds can be identified as the differential operator $d/ds = \hat{\mathbf{s}} \cdot \nabla$.

EXAMPLE 2 Determine the directional derivative of the scalar field $u = x^2(y + 3z)$ in the direction of $\mathbf{s} = \hat{\mathbf{i}} - 5\hat{\mathbf{j}} + 2\hat{\mathbf{k}}$, at the point $P = (-2, 4, 1)$.

First, we normalize $\mathbf{s}$: $\hat{\mathbf{s}} = (\hat{\mathbf{i}} - 5\hat{\mathbf{j}} + 2\hat{\mathbf{k}})/\sqrt{30}$. Then (11) gives

$$\frac{du}{ds}(-2, 4, 1) = [2x(y + 3z)\hat{\mathbf{i}} + x^2\hat{\mathbf{j}} + 3x^2\hat{\mathbf{k}}]\Big|_{(-2,4,1)} \cdot \left(\frac{\hat{\mathbf{i}} - 5\hat{\mathbf{j}} + 2\hat{\mathbf{k}}}{\sqrt{30}}\right)$$
$$= \frac{-28 - 20 + 24}{\sqrt{30}} = -\frac{24}{\sqrt{30}}. \tag{12}$$

COMMENT Remember that the gradient of u is a vector, but the directional derivative of u is a scalar. ◀

Having thus introduced the directional derivative, we return to our discussion of the gradient. In particular, we plan to use (11) to explore the geometrical significance of the gradient. Consider any point P in a region throughout which a C^1 scalar field u is defined, and suppose that $\nabla u \neq \mathbf{0}$ at P. According to (11) and the definition of the dot product, the derivative du/ds in any chosen $\hat{\mathbf{s}}$ direction, at P is

$$\frac{du}{ds} = \|\nabla u\|\|\hat{\mathbf{s}}\| \cos\theta(\nabla u, \hat{\mathbf{s}}) = \|\nabla u\| \cos\theta(\nabla u, \hat{\mathbf{s}}). \tag{13}$$

What direction $\hat{\mathbf{s}}$ produces the *maximum* rate of change du/ds? Well, $\|\nabla u\|$ is independent of $\hat{\mathbf{s}}$; it depends only on the u field. Thus the only $\hat{\mathbf{s}}$ dependence in the right-hand side of (13) is in the cosine. The cosine will attain its maximum value (unity) when $\theta(\nabla u, \hat{\mathbf{s}}) = 0$, i.e., when $\hat{\mathbf{s}}$ points in the same direction as ∇u. Furthermore, in that event (13) becomes $du/ds = \|\nabla u\|$. We conclude that *if* $\nabla u \neq \mathbf{0}$ *at* P*, then* ∇u *points in the direction of the greatest rate of increase of* u*, at* P*, and its magnitude* $\|\nabla u\|$ *is equal to that greatest rate of increase of* u.

The latter statement begs the question "What *is* the direction of the greatest rate of increase of u?" Suppose that there is a unique level surface $\mathcal{S}$, of the field u, passing through the point P. Let $\mathbf{R}(\tau) = x(\tau)\hat{\mathbf{i}} + y(\tau)\hat{\mathbf{j}} + z(\tau)\hat{\mathbf{k}}$ be a vector function of a parameter τ such that with the tail of $\mathbf{R}$ fixed at the origin (Fig. 9.11), the head of $\mathbf{R}$ traces out a curve $\mathscr{C}_1$ on the surface $\mathcal{S}$ as τ is varied. Suppose that $\mathscr{C}_1$ passes through P and has a tangent vector $\mathbf{T} = d\mathbf{R}/d\tau$ at that point. (Tangent vectors were introduced on page 285). Since $\mathscr{C}_1$ lies in a u = constant surface, the rate of change

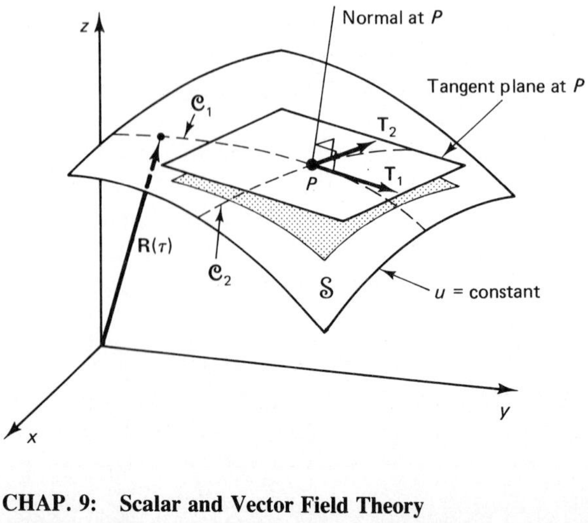

Fig. 9.11 Direction of ∇u at P.

of u along $\mathscr{C}_1$, with respect to τ, must surely be zero. Thus

$$\frac{d}{d\tau}u(x(\tau), y(\tau), z(\tau)) = \frac{\partial u}{\partial x}\frac{dx}{d\tau} + \frac{\partial u}{\partial y}\frac{dy}{d\tau} + \frac{\partial u}{\partial z}\frac{dz}{d\tau} \tag{14}$$
$$= \nabla u \cdot \mathbf{T}_1$$

must be zero. But $\nabla u \neq \mathbf{0}$, by assumption, and $\mathbf{T}_1$ cannot be zero because it is, by assumption, a tangent vector. It follows, then, that ∇u is perpendicular to $\mathbf{T}_1$. Since this perpendicularity holds for *all* such $\mathbf{T}$'s (e.g., $\mathbf{T}_1$ and $\mathbf{T}_2$ in Fig. 9.11), we see that ∇u is perpendicular, or normal, to $\mathscr{S}$ at P. Thus *if there is a unique level surface* $\mathscr{S}$, *of* u, *passing through* P, *and* $\nabla u \neq \mathbf{0}$ *at* P, *then* ∇u *at* P *is normal to* $\mathscr{S}$.

Finally, we define the plane containing all such $\mathbf{T}$ vectors (and they must indeed lie in a common plane if they are all to be perpendicular to the same vector ∇u) as the **tangent plane** to $\mathscr{S}$ at P. Thus if $\nabla u \neq \mathbf{0}$ at $P = (x_0, y_0, z_0)$, the tangent plane to the u = constant surface through P is defined by the equation

$$\nabla u(x_0, y_0, z_0) \cdot [(x - x_0)\hat{\mathbf{i}} + (y - y_0)\hat{\mathbf{j}} + (z - z_0)\hat{\mathbf{k}}] = 0$$

or

$$u_x(x_0, y_0, z_0)(x - x_0) + u_y(x_0, y_0, z_0)(y - y_0) + u_z(x_0, y_0, z_0)(z - z_0) = 0. \tag{15}$$

For example, if $u(x, y, z) = x(y^2 + 3z)$, the tangent plane to the u = constant surface through $(2, -1, 5)$ is given by

$$16(x - 2) - 4(y + 1) + 6(z - 5) = 0 \quad \text{or} \quad 8x - 2y + 3z = 33.$$

In the foregoing discussion we have considered three-dimensional fields $u(x, y, z)$. Modification for the two-dimensional case $u(x, y)$ is simple, and should be evident. The only change needed in the two italicized conclusions above is that the word "surface" in the second conclusion needs to be changed to *curve*. Also, in place of the equation (15) of the tangent plane, we have the equation

$$u_x(x_0, y_0)(x - x_0) + u_y(x_0, y_0)(y - y_0) = 0 \tag{16}$$

of the tangent *line*.

EXAMPLE 3 Let our scalar field be a two-dimensional temperature field $T(x, y)$, defined over the closed region $0 \leq x \leq 2$, $0 \leq y \leq 2$. Instead of writing down a functional form for $T(x, y)$, let us suppose that T is measured experimentally, and that when the data are organized into isotherms (T = constant curves) the result is as shown in Fig. 9.12. We ask: What is ∇T at $P = (1, 0.4)$? Writing

$$\nabla T = \frac{\partial T}{\partial x}\hat{\mathbf{i}} + \frac{\partial T}{\partial y}\hat{\mathbf{j}}, \tag{17}$$

we compute (Fig. 9.12)

$$\frac{\partial T}{\partial x} \approx \frac{T(B) - T(P)}{\|\mathbf{PB}\|} \approx \frac{60 - 40}{0.51} \approx 39 \tag{18}$$

and

$$\frac{\partial T}{\partial y} \approx \frac{T(A) - T(P)}{\|\mathbf{PA}\|} \approx \frac{60 - 40}{0.2} = 100 \tag{19}$$

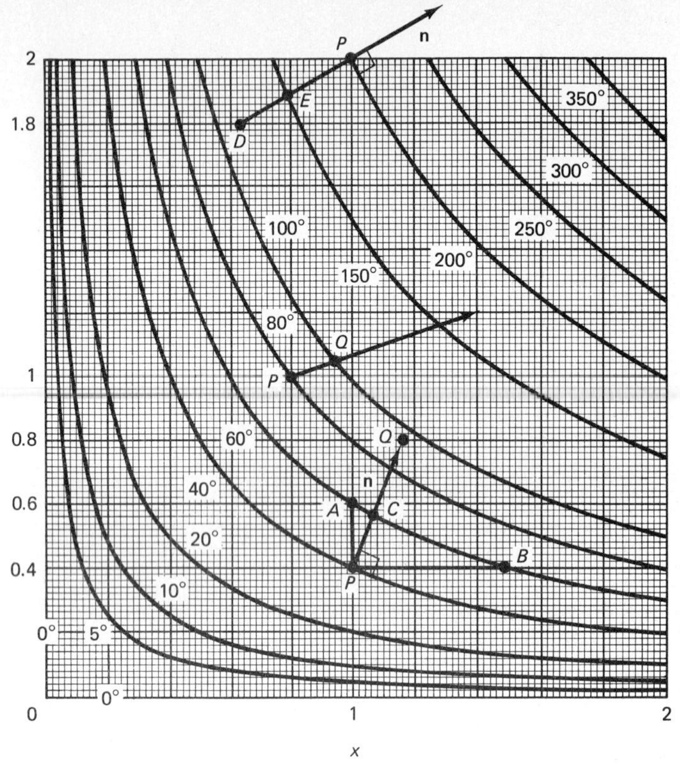

Fig. 9.12 Level curves of $T(x, y)$.

at (1, 0.4), so that

$$\nabla T(1, 0.4) \approx 39\hat{\mathbf{i}} + 100\hat{\mathbf{j}}. \tag{20}$$

Observe that in (18) [similarly for (19)] we appealed to the definition

$$\frac{\partial T}{\partial x} = \lim_{\Delta x \to 0} \frac{T(x + \Delta x, y) - T(x, y)}{\Delta x} \tag{21}$$

but were unable to pass to the limit because of the discrete spacing of the level curves. Thus we took the smallest possible increment, $\|\mathbf{PB}\|$, and lived with the approximation (18).

In place of (17), we can compute ∇T from the formula

$$\nabla T = \frac{\partial T}{\partial n}\hat{\mathbf{n}}, \tag{22}$$

which is implied by the foregoing italicized conclusions. Here $\hat{\mathbf{n}}$ is the unit normal to the T = constant curve, in the direction of increasing T, and $\partial T/\partial n$ is the directional derivative of T in the direction $\hat{\mathbf{n}}$. (Recall that dT/dn and $\partial T/\partial n$ are alternative notations for the directional derivative.) Drawing the normal to the $T = 40$ curve, from P to some other point, say Q, we have

$$\hat{\mathbf{n}} = \frac{\mathbf{PQ}}{\|\mathbf{PQ}\|} \approx \frac{0.16\hat{\mathbf{i}} + 0.4\hat{\mathbf{j}}}{\sqrt{(0.16)^2 + (0.4)^2}} \approx 0.37\hat{\mathbf{i}} + 0.93\hat{\mathbf{j}}, \tag{23}$$

and

$$\frac{\partial T}{\partial n} \approx \frac{T(C) - T(P)}{\|\mathbf{PC}\|} \approx \frac{60 - 40}{0.18} \approx 111, \tag{24}$$

so (22) gives

$$\nabla T \approx (111)(0.37\hat{\mathbf{i}} + 0.93\hat{\mathbf{j}}) \approx 41\hat{\mathbf{i}} + 103\hat{\mathbf{j}}, \tag{25}$$

which is reasonably close to our previous result (20).

In fact, the temperature field that we have plotted in Fig. 9.12 is $T(x, y) = 100xy$. Thus the *exact* value of ∇T at (1, 0.4) is

$$\nabla T = \frac{\partial T}{\partial x}\hat{\mathbf{i}} + \frac{\partial T}{\partial y}\hat{\mathbf{j}} = 100y\hat{\mathbf{i}} + 100x\hat{\mathbf{j}} = 40\hat{\mathbf{i}} + 100\hat{\mathbf{j}}, \tag{26}$$

in the light of which our estimates (20) and (25) are seen to be respectable, considering that our increments Δx, Δy, and Δn were not especially small.

It should be mentioned that more sophisticated difference quotients could have been used, to squeeze out more accuracy, but the thrust of this example is to illustrate concepts, not to maximize numerical accuracy.

Finally, we ask: What is ∇T at $P = (1, 2)$? Let us use (22). The catch, here, is that if we step away from P in the $\hat{\mathbf{n}}$ direction, we leave the region in which T is defined. Looking back at definition (9), note that the limit needs to exist as $h \to 0$ in any manner, for example, through positive values *or* through negative values—if P is an interior point. If P is a *boundary* point of the region, the sign of h must be chosen, in (9), so that the points $\mathbf{R} + h\hat{\mathbf{s}}$ fall within the region. In the present case, that amounts to taking h to be negative, so that

$$\frac{\partial T}{\partial n} \approx \frac{T(E) - T(P)}{-\|\mathbf{PE}\|} = \frac{T(P) - T(E)}{\|\mathbf{PE}\|} \approx \frac{200 - 150}{0.23} \approx 217. \tag{27}$$

Also,

$$\hat{\mathbf{n}} = \frac{\mathbf{DP}}{\|\mathbf{DP}\|} \approx \frac{0.36\hat{\mathbf{i}} + 0.2\hat{\mathbf{j}}}{\sqrt{(0.36)^2 + (0.2)^2}} \approx 0.87\hat{\mathbf{i}} + 0.49\hat{\mathbf{j}}, \tag{28}$$

so

$$\nabla T \approx (217)(0.87\hat{\mathbf{i}} + 0.49\hat{\mathbf{j}}) \approx 189\hat{\mathbf{i}} + 106\hat{\mathbf{j}}, \tag{29}$$

compared with the exact value $\nabla T = 100y\hat{\mathbf{i}} + 100x\hat{\mathbf{j}} = 200\hat{\mathbf{i}} + 100\hat{\mathbf{j}}$. ◀

EXAMPLE 4 *Fourier Law of Heat Conduction.* The **Fourier law of heat conduction*** states that the heat flux q (calories per second, say) across a plane area element A (square meters) is proportional to the temperature gradient $\partial T/\partial n$ normal to A, and to the area A itself. Specifically,

$$q = -kA\frac{\partial T}{\partial n}, \tag{30}$$

* *Joseph B. J. Fourier* (1768–1830). Although Fourier's original paper on the conduction of heat was rejected by the Academy of Sciences of Paris in 1807, his subsequent treatise *Théorie analytique de la chaleur*, published in 1822, now stands as a classic in the history of mathematics.

where the constant of proportionality k depends on the conducting material, and is called the *thermal conductivity*; for example, the conductivity of copper is about 20 times that of steel, which, in turn, is about 30 times that of water, which, in turn, is about 20 times that of air. In fact, k is not really a constant for a given material, but varies with the temperature T, so that $k = k(T)$. However, in most applications the variation in k over the relevant temperature range is small enough so that it suffices to regard k as a constant*; that assumption is adopted here.

The normal $\hat{\mathbf{n}}$ serves to establish the sign convention for q: Heat flux across A in the $\hat{\mathbf{n}}$ direction is taken to be positive, while heat flux in the opposite direction is taken to be negative. To understand the minus sign in (30), consider the two cases illustrated in Fig. 9.13, bearing in mind that k and A are positive and that heat flows from "hot to cold." In Fig. 9.13a the flow (from hot to cold) will be from right to left. This is opposite to the assigned $\hat{\mathbf{n}}$ direction, so that q, in (30), will be negative. However, k, A, and $\partial T/\partial n$ are all positive, and hence the minus sign in (30) is needed. In Fig. 9.13b, on the other hand, q is positive, $\partial T/\partial n$ is negative, and again the minus sign is needed.

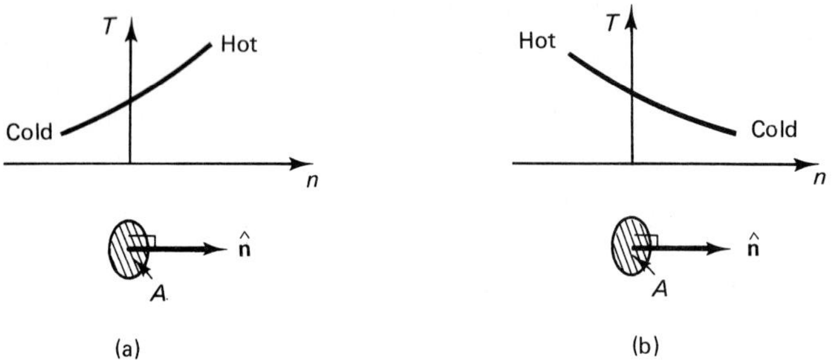

Fig. 9.13 Sorting out the signs.

It is to be understood that the area element A is merely a mathematical "control surface," i.e., a surface across which we keep track of certain traffic—in this case, the traffic of heat; A may be on the boundary of the given region, or it may be situated in the interior.

To illustrate, suppose that the temperature in a metal bar, of conductivity k and occupying the region $0 \leq x \leq 2$, $0 \leq y \leq 2$, $0 \leq z \leq 10$, is given by

$$T(x, y, z) = 50(x^2 + y^2). \tag{31}$$

What is the heat flux q in the $\hat{\mathbf{n}}$ direction across an arbitrarily small area A at any given point (x, y, z) in the bar (Fig. 9.14), where the plane of A is perpendicular to

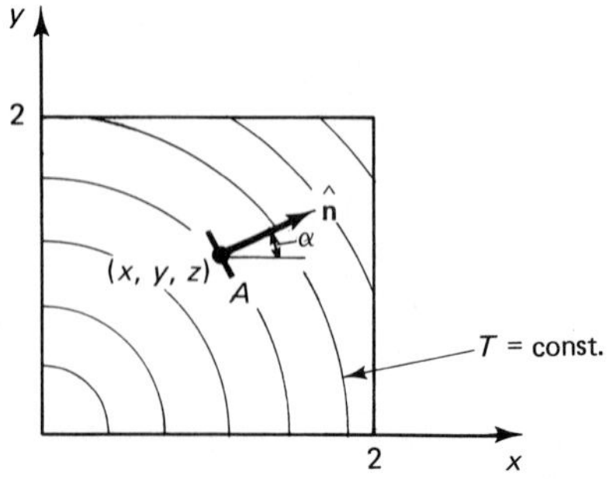

Fig. 9.14 Heat flux across A.

* Thus one says that k is only "weakly" dependent on T.

the x, y plane? Well,

$$q = -kA\frac{\partial T}{\partial n} = -kA\nabla T \cdot \hat{\mathbf{n}} \tag{32}$$

or

$$\begin{aligned} q &= -kA(100x\hat{\mathbf{i}} + 100y\hat{\mathbf{j}}) \cdot (\cos\alpha\hat{\mathbf{i}} + \sin\alpha\hat{\mathbf{j}}) \\ &= -100kA(x\cos\alpha + y\sin\alpha). \end{aligned} \tag{33}$$

At $x = y = 1$, for instance, this gives $q = -100kA\,(\cos\,\alpha + \sin\,\alpha) = -100\sqrt{2}kA\,\sin\,(\alpha + \pi/4)$, which varies continuously with α (i.e., with the orientation of A), from zero when $\alpha = -\pi/4$, to its maximum magnitude at $\alpha = \pi/4$ and $-3\pi/4$. Note how the flux through the "window" A varies with the spatial orientiation of A.

COMMENT Physically, the process of heat conduction, described by the Fourier law (32), is one of **diffusion**. Observe, from the form of (32), that the diffusion of heat is attributable to the presence of a temperature gradient in the field. It is to be noted, further, that diffusion can also be a *mass* transport mechanism. For example, if dye is concentrated in a liquid, it will spread—by diffusion. The relevant law is **Fick's first law,**

$$J = -DA\frac{\partial c}{\partial n} = -DA\nabla c \cdot \hat{\mathbf{n}}, \tag{34}$$

where J is the mass flux (mass per unit time), D is the mass diffusivity, A is the control surface area, and c is the concentration of the diffusing species (mass per unit volume). We see that the Fick and Fourier laws are identical in form. ◀

EXAMPLE 5 *Normals to Surfaces.* Sometimes we require an expression for the unit normal vector to a given surface (or, in two dimensions, to a given curve). For example, to compute the efflux $\int_{\mathcal{S}} \hat{\mathbf{n}} \cdot \mathbf{v}\, dA$, of a velocity field $\mathbf{v}$ through a closed surface $\mathcal{S}$, we need an expression for $\hat{\mathbf{n}}$, the outward unit normal to $\mathcal{S}$. It is simple: If $\mathcal{S}$ is given in the form $f(x, y, z) = 0$, we may regard $f(x, y, z)$ as a scalar field, with the level surfaces given by $f(x, y, z) = c$. Then $\mathcal{S}$ is one of these surfaces, the one corresponding to $c = 0$, and we know that the normal to that surface (if it exists) can be found as ∇f.

To illustrate, let us find the outward unit normal $\hat{\mathbf{n}}$ to the surface of the cone shown in Fig. 9.15. Consider the conical surface $\mathcal{S}_1$ and the flat base $\mathcal{S}_2$ separately. On $\mathcal{S}_1$, $x^2 + y^2 = (1 - z)^2$, so

$$f_1(x, y, z) = x^2 + y^2 - (1 - z)^2.$$

Thus

$$\nabla f_1 = 2x\hat{\mathbf{i}} + 2y\hat{\mathbf{j}} + 2(1 - z)\hat{\mathbf{k}}$$

and

$$\hat{\mathbf{n}}_1 = \frac{\nabla f_1}{\|\nabla f_1\|} = \frac{x\hat{\mathbf{i}} + y\hat{\mathbf{j}} + (1 - z)\hat{\mathbf{k}}}{\sqrt{x^2 + y^2 + (1 - z)^2}} \tag{35}$$

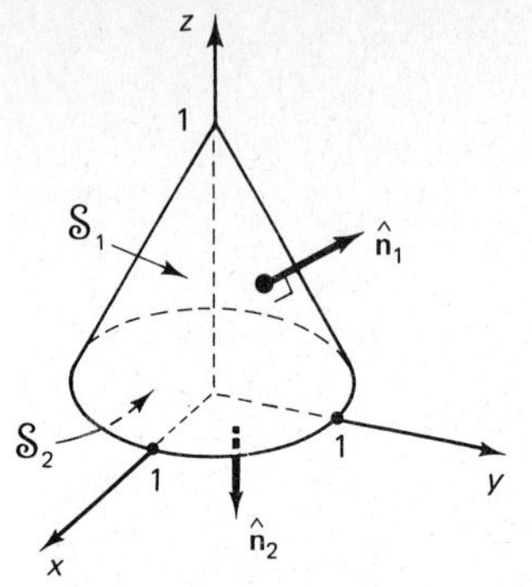

Fig. 9.15 Normal to cone.

on $\mathcal{S}_1$. We do need to examine (35) to be sure that it is the desired *out*ward normal, not the inward normal. To do so, it will suffice to check at a single point. For example, at (0, 1, 0) (35) gives $\hat{\mathbf{n}}_1 = (\hat{\mathbf{j}} + \hat{\mathbf{k}})/\sqrt{2}$, which, evidently, is indeed directed outward.

Turning to the base $\mathcal{S}_2$, we have $z = 0$ or $f_2(x, y, z) = z = 0$. Thus

$$f_2 = z$$

$$\nabla f_2 = \hat{\mathbf{k}},$$

$$\hat{\mathbf{n}}_2 = \frac{\nabla f_2}{\|\nabla f_2\|} = \hat{\mathbf{k}}.$$

Clearly, however, this is the *in*ward normal. To convert it to the outward normal, we merely multiply it by -1. Thus $\hat{\mathbf{n}}_2 = -\hat{\mathbf{k}}$ on $\mathcal{S}_2$. Of course, this result was obvious by inspection, but we have included it as a further illustration of the method.

Similarly for obtaining the normal to a plane curve $\mathscr{C}$, given in the form $f(x, y) = 0$. This story is left for the exercises. ◀

In this section we discussed the gradient of a scalar field u: grad $u = \nabla u = (\partial u/\partial x)\hat{\mathbf{i}} + (\partial u/\partial y)\hat{\mathbf{j}} + (\partial u/\partial z)\hat{\mathbf{k}}$. We also introduced the directional derivative du/ds because that quantity is important in its own right, and also because of its close relationship with the gradient through the formula $du/ds = \nabla u \cdot \hat{\mathbf{s}}$. In fact, from that formula we learned that if $\nabla u \neq \mathbf{0}$ at P, then ∇u points in the direction of the greatest rate of increase of u at P (namely, normal to the level surface at P), and its magnitude $\|\nabla u\|$ is equal to that greatest rate of increase of u.

9.5 EXERCISES

1. Work out grad u for the following scalar fields, each of which is defined over all of 3-space. Further, evaluate grad u at $(9, 4, -1)$.

*(a) $u = 6x$
(b) $u = x^2$
(c) $u = z \sin(x^2 + y^2)$
(d) $u = x^3$
(e) $u = xyz$
(f) $u = x^2 + y^2 + z^2$
(g) $u = x^2 + z^2$
(h) $u = x - y$
(i) $u = x + y + z$

2. Evaluate the directional derivative du/ds, at the designated point P, in the direction of the given vector $\mathbf{v}$. (t is the time.)

*(a) $u = x^2 + y^2 + z^2$, $P = (2, 1, 5)$, $\mathbf{v} = \hat{\mathbf{i}}$
(b) $u = x + y + z$, $P = (4, 0, 1)$, $\mathbf{v} = 2\hat{\mathbf{i}} + \hat{\mathbf{j}} - \hat{\mathbf{k}}$
(c) $u = xyzt$, $P = (1, -1, 2)$, $\mathbf{v} = 3\hat{\mathbf{i}} + 2\hat{\mathbf{j}} - t\hat{\mathbf{k}}$
(d) $u = xyz$, $P = (0, 0, 0)$, $\mathbf{v} = \hat{\mathbf{i}} - \hat{\mathbf{j}}$

*(e) $u = 2x + z^2 - 4t^2$, $P = (8, -1, 2)$, $\mathbf{v} = 2\hat{\mathbf{j}} + \hat{\mathbf{k}}$
(f) $u = 50xy \sin t$, $P = (2, 3, 5)$, $\mathbf{v} = \hat{\mathbf{i}} + 4\hat{\mathbf{j}}$
(g) $u = 3x$, $P = (2, 6, -1)$, $\mathbf{v} = \hat{\mathbf{i}} + 2\hat{\mathbf{j}}$
(h) $u = 3x^2$, $P = (2, 6, -1)$, $\mathbf{v} = 2\hat{\mathbf{j}} + 5\hat{\mathbf{k}}$

3. For the temperature field $T(x, y)$ given in Fig. 9.12, evaluate the following quantities directly from the figure (or from a photocopy of it), with the help of suitable difference quotients, and compare your results with the exact values obtained from the expression $T = 100xy$.

(a) ∇T at $(0.6, 0)$ *(b) ∇T at $(1.4, 1.8)$
(c) ∇T at $(2, 0.4)$ (d) ∇T at $(2, 1)$
(e) ∇T at $(1.5, 2)$ (f) ∇T at $(1.6, 0.5)$
(g) dT/ds at $(0, 1)$ in the direction of $2\hat{\mathbf{i}} + \hat{\mathbf{j}}$
(h) dT/ds at $(1, 0)$ in the direction of $-2\hat{\mathbf{i}} + 3\hat{\mathbf{j}}$
(i) dT/ds at $(2, 1)$ in the direction of $-\hat{\mathbf{i}}$
(j) dT/ds at $(2, 1)$ in the direction of $\hat{\mathbf{j}}$
(k) dT/ds at $(1, 1)$ in the direction of $-\hat{\mathbf{i}} - 2\hat{\mathbf{j}}$
(l) dT/ds at $(0.5, 0.4)$ in the direction of $\hat{\mathbf{i}} - 2\hat{\mathbf{j}}$
(m) dT/ds at $(0.2, 1)$ in the direction of $\hat{\mathbf{i}}$

4. For the metal bar whose cross section is shown in Fig. 9.14, and whose temperature is given by (31), evaluate the heat flux Q, per unit depth in the z direction.

*(a) out of the upper surface, namely,

$$Q = -k \int \nabla T \cdot \hat{\mathbf{n}} dA = -k \int_0^2 (\nabla T \cdot \hat{\mathbf{j}})\Big|_{y=2} dx$$

*(b) out of the right-hand surface
(c) out of the bottom surface
(d) out of the left-hand surface
(e) across the cylindrical control surface $x^2 + y^2 = 4$, taking a radially outward flow as positive

5. Determine an expression [analogous to (35)] for the outward unit normal $\hat{\mathbf{n}}$ to each of the following closed surfaces $\mathscr{S}$. Evaluate $\hat{\mathbf{n}}$ at any one particular point of your choice on $\mathscr{S}$.

(a) $\mathscr{S}: x^2 + y^2 + z^2 = 1$
(b) $\mathscr{S}: x^2 + y^2 + 3z^2 = 6$
*(c) $\mathscr{S}: x^2 - x + 2y^2 + z^2 = 5$
(d) $\mathscr{S}: x^2 + y^2 + z^4 = 3$
(e) $\mathscr{S}: x^4 + y^4 + z^4 = 1$
(f) $\mathscr{S}: x^8 + y^8 + z^8 = 1$

6. Determine an expression for the outward unit normal $\hat{\mathbf{n}}$ to each of the following closed curves $\mathscr{C}$. Evaluate $\hat{\mathbf{n}}$ at any one point of your choice on $\mathscr{C}$.

*(a) $\mathscr{C}: x^2 + y^2 = 8$
(b) $\mathscr{C}: x^2 + 2y^2 + x - y = 3$
(c) $\mathscr{C}: x^4 + y^4 = 1$
(d) $\mathscr{C}: 3x^2 + 3y^2 + 2xy - 2x + 2y = 8$
(e) $\mathscr{C}: x^8 + y^8 = 1$
(f) $\mathscr{C}: x^6 + (y-1)^2 = 0$

7. Determine the equation of the tangent plane, and a unit normal vector $\hat{\mathbf{n}}$, to $\mathscr{S}$ at the given point P. If these quantities are not defined at P, state that.

*(a) $\mathscr{S}: x^2 + y^2 - z^2 = 1$, $P = (1, 1, 1)$
(b) $\mathscr{S}: x^2 + y^2 + z^2 = 1$, $P = (\frac{1}{2}, -\frac{1}{2}, -1/\sqrt{2})$
(c) $\mathscr{S}: x^4 + y^4 + z^4 = 18$, $P = (-1, 1, -2)$
(d) $\mathscr{S}: xyz^2 = 3$, $P = (3, 1, -1)$
(e) $\mathscr{S}: xyz^2 = 3$, $P = (1, 3, 1)$
(f) $\mathscr{S}: xyz^2 = 8$, $P = (4, 2, 1)$

8. Determine the equation of the tangent line, and a unit normal vector $\hat{\mathbf{n}}$, to $\mathscr{C}$ at the given point P. If these quantities are not defined at P, state that.

(a) $\mathscr{C}: x^2 - y^2 = 4$, $P = (-2, 0)$
(b) $\mathscr{C}: x^2 - y^2 = 4$, $P = (3, -\sqrt{5})$
*(c) $\mathscr{C}: xy^2 = 4$, $P = (1, -2)$
(d) $\mathscr{C}: xy^2 = 4$, $P = (4, 1)$

9. Let the electric potential (voltage) be given, in some region of space, by $V(x, y, z) = 3x^2y - xz$. If a positive charge is placed at a point $P = (x, y, z)$, in what direction will it begin to move? *Note:* It is known, from electric field theory, that such a charge will begin to move in the direction of maximum rate of voltage drop.

*(a) $P = (2, 3, -1)$ (b) $P = (5, 0, 2)$
(c) $P = (-1, 2, 4)$ (d) $P = (7, 2, 4)$

10. (*Convective derivative*) Let $\mathbf{q}(x, y, z, t) = u\hat{\mathbf{i}} + v\hat{\mathbf{j}} + w\hat{\mathbf{k}}$ be a fluid velocity field, and consider some scalar property of the flow, such as the temperature field $T(x, y, z, t)$. If we swim along any desired path according to $x = x(t)$, $y = y(t)$, $z = z(t)$, then the timewise rate of change of T that we observe is

$$\frac{d}{dt}T(x(t), y(t), z(t), t) = \frac{\partial T}{\partial t} + \frac{\partial T}{\partial x}\frac{dx}{dt} + \frac{\partial T}{\partial y}\frac{dy}{dt} + \frac{\partial T}{\partial z}\frac{dz}{dt}. \qquad \text{(a)}$$

(a) If we simply choose to *drift* with the fluid, then $dx/dt = u$, $dy/dt = v$, and $dz/dt = w$. In this case, show that (a) becomes

$$\frac{dT}{dt} = \frac{\partial T}{\partial t} + (\mathbf{q} \cdot \nabla)T. \qquad \text{(b)}$$

This is often called the **convective derivative** because it is the derivative obtained when we drift, or convect, with the fluid. The special notation D/Dt, suggested by *Sir G. G. Stokes* (1819–1903), is often used:

$$\boxed{\frac{D(\,)}{Dt} = \frac{\partial(\,)}{\partial t} + (\mathbf{q}\cdot\nabla)(\,).} \tag{c}$$

(b) To understand the nature of the contributions of each of the two terms on the right-hand side of (b) apply (b) to the three simple cases: $T = 2t$, $\mathbf{q} = \mathbf{0}$; $T = 3x$, $\mathbf{q} = U\hat{\mathbf{i}}$; $T = 2t + 3x$, $\mathbf{q} = U\hat{\mathbf{i}}$. Include whatever words of explanation (and sketches) seem appropriate.

(c) Does it matter if we rewrite $\mathbf{q}\cdot\nabla$ in equation (c) as $\nabla\cdot\mathbf{q}$? That is, is it true that

$$\frac{D}{Dt}(\,) = \frac{\partial}{\partial t}(\,) + (\operatorname{div}\mathbf{q})(\,)?$$

Explain.

11. Evaluate the rate of change of temperature, dT/dt, measured by a thermometer that drifts along with the fluid velocity $\mathbf{q}$. Evaluate dT/dt at $x = 2$, $y = -1$, $z = 3$, and $t = 4$. *Hint:* See Exercise 10.

*(a) $T = 100 + 2(x^2 + y^2)$, $\mathbf{q} = 20x\hat{\mathbf{i}} - 10y\hat{\mathbf{j}}$
(b) $T = 25xt^2 - 2xyz$, $\mathbf{q} = 20\hat{\mathbf{i}} + xy\hat{\mathbf{j}} - xzt\hat{\mathbf{k}}$
(c) $T = 35 - 3\sin x\cos 2y\sin 2t$, $\mathbf{q} = 8y(1 + t^2)\hat{\mathbf{i}} - 5xz\hat{\mathbf{j}}$

12. (*Integral definition of gradient*) Reviewing the last two sections, note that we began with the definition

$$\operatorname{div}\mathbf{v} = \lim_{\mathcal{B}\to 0}\left\{\frac{\int_{\mathcal{S}}\hat{\mathbf{n}}\cdot\mathbf{v}\,dA}{V}\right\} \tag{a}$$

on page 358, showed that this can be expressed as

$$\operatorname{div}\mathbf{v} = \left(\hat{\mathbf{i}}\frac{\partial}{\partial x} + \hat{\mathbf{j}}\frac{\partial}{\partial y} + \hat{\mathbf{k}}\frac{\partial}{\partial z}\right)\cdot\mathbf{v} = \nabla\cdot\mathbf{v},$$

and then used the ∇ operator to introduce

$$\operatorname{grad} u \equiv \nabla u.$$

Alternatively, one can define the gradient in an integral form that is analogous to (a)

$$\operatorname{grad} u \equiv \lim_{\mathcal{B}\to 0}\left\{\frac{\int_{\mathcal{S}}\hat{\mathbf{n}}u\,dA}{V}\right\}. \tag{b}$$

Following the general lines of (3) to (6) on page 359, derive the result

$$\operatorname{grad} u = \frac{\partial u}{\partial x}\hat{\mathbf{i}} + \frac{\partial u}{\partial y}\hat{\mathbf{j}} + \frac{\partial u}{\partial z}\hat{\mathbf{k}} = \nabla u$$

directly from (a).

13. Define $u(x, y)$ to be 1 along the curve $y = x^2$ except for the origin $x = y = 0$, and define it to be zero at all other points in the plane, including the origin. Show that du/ds exists, and equals 0, at the origin, for *all* directions $\hat{\mathbf{s}}$, but that $u(x, y)$ is, nevertheless, discontinuous at the origin. [Recall from the calculus that if $y'(x)$ exists at x_0, then $y(x)$ is necessarily continuous at x_0. For functions of more than one variable, we see, from this example, that the existence of directional derivatives in *every direction,* at a given point, does *not* suffice to imply that the function is continuous at that point.]

14. For the field $T = 100xy$ in Example 3, let us consider the situation at the origin. Through the origin there pass *two* isotherms; the lines $x = 0$ and $y = 0$, as shown in the accompanying figure. In that case a (unique) normal direction [recall (22)] is, evidently, not defined. Does this mean that ∇T is not defined (does not exist) at the origin? Explain.

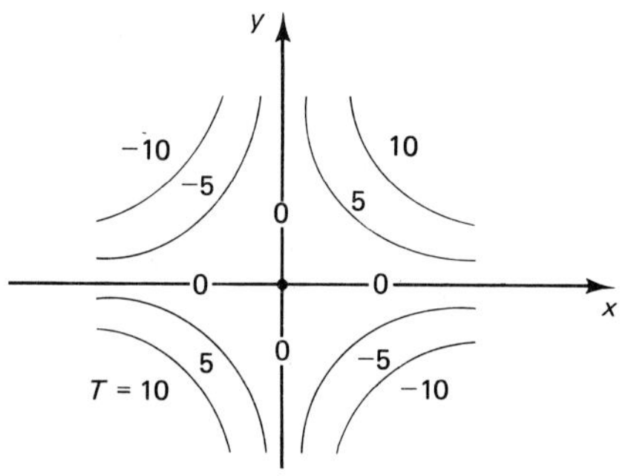

15. Some level curves of a scalar field $u(x, y)$ are sketched below. Trace (or photocopy) that sketch, and indicate the approximate location of the point(s) at which $\nabla u = \mathbf{0}$, as well as the point(s) at which ∇u takes on its greatest magnitude.

(a)

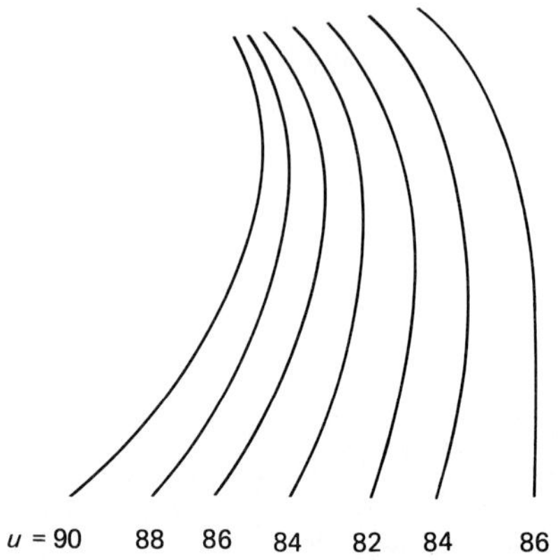

(b)

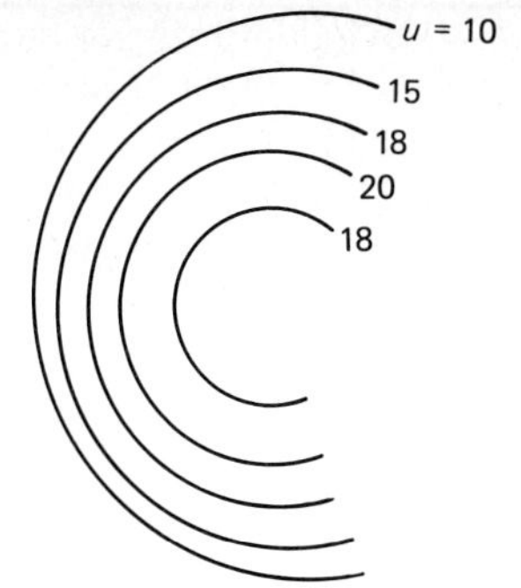

CURL 9.6

Having considered the divergence and gradient, div $\mathbf{v} = \nabla \cdot \mathbf{v}$ and grad $u = \nabla u$, we now turn to the **curl of v**, defined here as

$$\boxed{\text{curl } \mathbf{v} \equiv \nabla \times \mathbf{v},} \tag{1}$$

where $\mathbf{v}$ is a C^1 vector field. Working out the right-hand side of (1) in Cartesian coordinates yields

$$\begin{aligned} \text{curl } \mathbf{v} &= \left(\hat{\mathbf{i}}\frac{\partial}{\partial x} + \hat{\mathbf{j}}\frac{\partial}{\partial y} + \hat{\mathbf{k}}\frac{\partial}{\partial z}\right) \times (v_x\hat{\mathbf{i}} + v_y\hat{\mathbf{j}} + v_z\hat{\mathbf{k}}) \\ &= \begin{vmatrix} \hat{\mathbf{i}} & \hat{\mathbf{j}} & \hat{\mathbf{k}} \\ \frac{\partial}{\partial x} & \frac{\partial}{\partial y} & \frac{\partial}{\partial z} \\ v_x & v_y & v_z \end{vmatrix} \end{aligned} \tag{2}$$

or*

$$\boxed{\text{curl } \mathbf{v} = \left(\frac{\partial v_z}{\partial y} - \frac{\partial v_y}{\partial z}\right)\hat{\mathbf{i}} - \left(\frac{\partial v_z}{\partial x} - \frac{\partial v_x}{\partial z}\right)\hat{\mathbf{j}} + \left(\frac{\partial v_y}{\partial x} - \frac{\partial v_x}{\partial y}\right)\hat{\mathbf{k}}.} \tag{3}$$

EXAMPLE 1 If $\mathbf{v}(x, y, z, t) = xyz\hat{\mathbf{i}} - 2y^2t\hat{\mathbf{k}}$, then

$$\begin{aligned} \text{curl } \mathbf{v} &= (-4yt - 0)\hat{\mathbf{i}} - (0 - xy)\hat{\mathbf{j}} + (0 - xz)\hat{\mathbf{k}} \\ &= -4yt\hat{\mathbf{i}} + xy\hat{\mathbf{j}} - xz\hat{\mathbf{k}}. \quad \blacktriangleleft \end{aligned}$$

* Evidently, if we expand the determinant about the *first row,* we do obtain the terms on the right-hand side of (3). Yet if we expand about the third row, say, we obtain

$$v_x = \left(\hat{\mathbf{j}}\frac{\partial}{\partial z} - \frac{\partial}{\partial y}\hat{\mathbf{k}}\right) - v_y\left(\hat{\mathbf{i}}\frac{\partial}{\partial z} - \frac{\partial}{\partial x}\hat{\mathbf{k}}\right) + v_z\left(\hat{\mathbf{i}}\frac{\partial}{\partial y} - \frac{\partial}{\partial x}\hat{\mathbf{j}}\right), \tag{a}$$

which is not the same. The point to bear in mind is that ∇ is located to the left of $\mathbf{v}$ in (1), so that $\partial/\partial x$, $\partial/\partial y$, and $\partial/\partial z$ act on v_x, v_y, and v_z. Thus the terms in (a) need to be rearranged: The first term, $v_x\hat{\mathbf{j}}\partial/\partial z$, should be rearranged as $(\partial v_x/\partial z)\hat{\mathbf{j}}$, and so on, for each of the other terms. If we remember to do that, the correct expression is obtained no matter which row or column is expanded about.

To interpret curl **v** physically, consider the case of fluid flow, where "**v**" is the fluid velocity vector

$$\mathbf{q} = u\hat{\mathbf{i}} + v\hat{\mathbf{j}} + w\hat{\mathbf{k}}. \tag{4}$$

Here $u(x, y, z)$, $v(x, y, z)$, $w(x, y, z)$ are the x, y, z velocity components, respectively. [The $\mathbf{q}$, u, v, w notation in (4) is widely used in fluid mechanics.] Let us examine curl $\mathbf{q}$, which is called the **vorticity** vector. For simplicity, let $\mathbf{q}$ be a *plane flow,* where $w = 0$ and u, v do not vary with z. Thus $\mathbf{q} = u(x, y)\hat{\mathbf{i}} + v(x, y)\hat{\mathbf{j}}$ and (3) reduces to

$$\text{curl }\mathbf{q} = \left(\frac{\partial v}{\partial x} - \frac{\partial u}{\partial y}\right)\hat{\mathbf{k}}. \tag{5}$$

Consider, heuristically, the motion of the little rectangular element of fluid shown in Fig. 9.16. At time t it is in position 1. If the element were *rigid*, its motion would consist of a translation plus a rotation; if so, then at time $t + \Delta t$ it might be in configuration 2, say, due to a translation OO' plus a rotation $\Delta\alpha$, and its angular velocity (taken as positive counterclockwise, with the right-hand rule used to assign a direction) would be $\boldsymbol{\omega} \sim (\Delta\alpha/\Delta t)\hat{\mathbf{k}}$. However, a fluid element is *deformable*, not rigid, so it may also suffer a "shear" deformation, as indicated in the configuration 3. What, then, is the fluid's "angular velocity" to mean? It is *defined,* in fluid mechanics, as the average angular velocity of initially perpendicular edges such as OA and OB. Then*

$$\text{angular velocity of } OA = \frac{v(A) - v(O)}{\Delta x}\hat{\mathbf{k}} \to \frac{\partial v}{\partial x}\hat{\mathbf{k}} \text{ as } \Delta x \to 0$$

$$\text{angular velocity of } OB = \frac{u(O) - u(B)}{\Delta y}\hat{\mathbf{k}} \to -\frac{\partial u}{\partial y}\hat{\mathbf{k}} \text{ as } \Delta y \to 0,$$

so that the

$$\text{average of the two} \equiv \boldsymbol{\omega} = \frac{1}{2}\left(\frac{\partial v}{\partial x} - \frac{\partial u}{\partial y}\right)\hat{\mathbf{k}}. \tag{6}$$

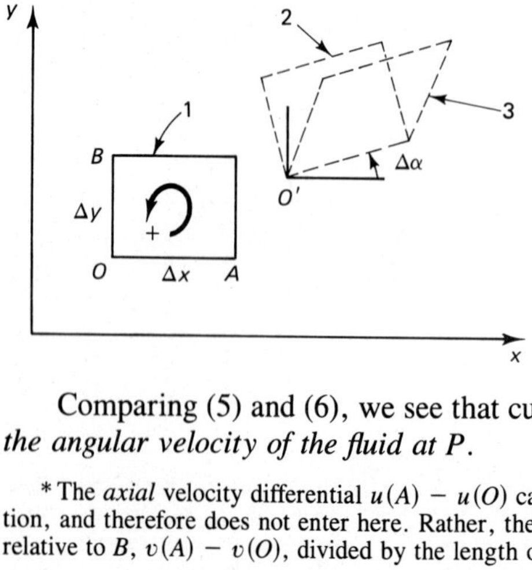

Fig. 9.16 Plane motion of fluid element.

Comparing (5) and (6), we see that curl $\mathbf{q} = 2\boldsymbol{\omega}$: *The vorticity curl $\mathbf{q}(P)$ is twice the angular velocity of the fluid at P.*

* The *axial* velocity differential $u(A) - u(O)$ causes an extension or contraction of OA, but no rotation, and therefore does not enter here. Rather, the angular velocity of OA is the *vertical* velocity of A relative to B, $v(A) - v(O)$, divided by the length of OA.

Although our discussion was for plane flows, it is not hard to show that the foregoing italicized result holds for nonplanar flows as well. We repeat that out discussion was intended only as heuristic, and is not claimed to be rigorous.

EXAMPLE 2 As a simple illustration of the angular velocity interpretation of the curl, consider a flow that is a counterclockwise "solid-body rotation" about the z axis, with angular velocity $\boldsymbol{\omega} = \omega\hat{\mathbf{k}}$, as sketched in Fig. 9.17. That is, the fluid might just as well be frozen solid, and spun like a phonograph record. Introducing polar coordinates r, θ, the position vector $\mathbf{R}$ is

$$\mathbf{R} = x\hat{\mathbf{i}} + y\hat{\mathbf{j}} = r\cos\theta\hat{\mathbf{i}} + r\sin\theta\hat{\mathbf{j}} \tag{7}$$

and since $\dot{r} = 0$ and $\dot{\theta} = \omega$, we have*

$$\begin{aligned}\mathbf{q} = \dot{\mathbf{R}} &= r(-\dot{\theta}\sin\theta\hat{\mathbf{i}} + \dot{\theta}\cos\theta\hat{\mathbf{j}}) \\ &= \omega(-r\sin\theta\hat{\mathbf{i}} + r\cos\theta\hat{\mathbf{j}}) = \omega(-y\hat{\mathbf{i}} + x\hat{\mathbf{j}}).\end{aligned} \tag{8}$$

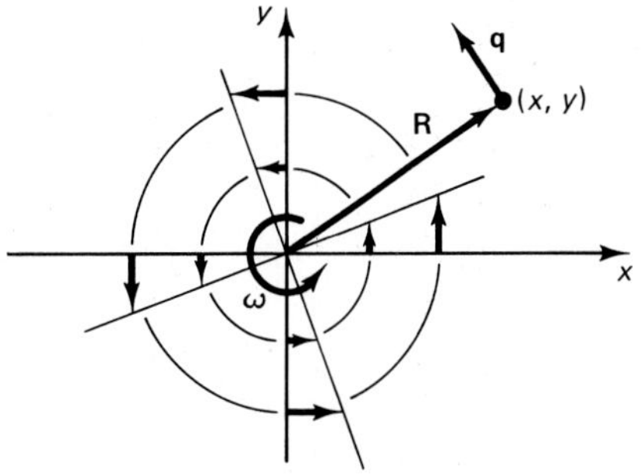

Fig. 9.17 Solid-body rotation.

Then, applying (3) to the field "$\mathbf{v}$" $= \mathbf{q} = \omega(-y\hat{\mathbf{i}} + x\hat{\mathbf{j}})$, we obtain

$$\operatorname{curl}\mathbf{q} = (0-0)\hat{\mathbf{i}} - (0-0)\hat{\mathbf{j}} + (\omega+\omega)\hat{\mathbf{k}} = 2\omega\hat{\mathbf{k}} = 2\boldsymbol{\omega},$$

which is in accordance with the results of the foregoing discussion, namely, that curl $\mathbf{q}$ is twice the "spin" of the fluid particles. In the present example, *all* the fluid particles happen to have the same spin, $\boldsymbol{\omega}$, since the flow is a solid-body rotation. ◀

EXAMPLE 3 *Maxwell's Equations*. To emphasize the prominent role of the curl ($\nabla\times$) in physical applications, let us merely state, without elaboration, that the equations

$$\nabla\times\mathbf{E} = \mathbf{0}, \tag{9a}$$

$$\nabla\times\mathbf{H} = \mathbf{J}, \tag{9b}$$

* If you have studied mechanics, you may recall that if a vector $\mathbf{A}$ of *fixed length* (i.e., $|\mathbf{A}|$ does not vary with t) is bound to a body experiencing an angular velocity $\boldsymbol{\omega}$, then $\dot{\mathbf{A}} = \boldsymbol{\omega}\times\mathbf{A}$. In the present case $\mathbf{R}$ is of fixed length, so we may compute $\dot{\mathbf{R}} = \boldsymbol{\omega}\times\mathbf{R} = \omega\hat{\mathbf{k}}\times(x\hat{\mathbf{i}} + y\hat{\mathbf{j}}) = \omega(-y\hat{\mathbf{i}} + x\hat{\mathbf{j}})$, the same as obtained in (8).

are two of the four classical **Maxwell's equations*** governing steady (i.e., not varying with time) electromagnetic fields; **E**, **H**, **J** are the *electric field intensity* (newtons/coulomb), the *magnetic field intensity* (amperes/meter), and the *current density* (amperes/meter^2), respectively. ◀

In this section we introduced a new quantity, the curl of any C^1 vector field $\mathbf{v}$, as curl $\mathbf{v} \equiv \nabla \times \mathbf{v}$, and obtained the alternative expressions (2) and (3) for its calculation in Cartesian coordinates. In addition, we provided a useful physical interpretation: If $\mathbf{v}$ is a fluid velocity field (or, in any case, if it is *regarded* as one), then, at each point in the field, curl $\mathbf{v}$ is twice the *angular velocity* of the fluid at that point.

9.6 EXERCISES

1. Work out curl $\mathbf{v}$ for the following vector fields, each of which is defined over all of 3-space, say. Further, evaluate curl $\mathbf{v}$ at $(3, 4, -1)$. (t is the time.)

*(a) $\mathbf{v} = a\hat{\mathbf{i}} + b\hat{\mathbf{j}} + c\hat{\mathbf{k}}$ (a, b, c constants)
(b) $\mathbf{v} = x\hat{\mathbf{i}} + y\hat{\mathbf{j}} + z\hat{\mathbf{k}} = \mathbf{R}$
(c) $\mathbf{v} = x\hat{\mathbf{i}} - y\hat{\mathbf{j}} + z^2t\hat{\mathbf{k}}$
(d) $\mathbf{v} = xyz(\hat{\mathbf{i}} + \hat{\mathbf{j}} - 3\hat{\mathbf{k}})$
*(e) $\mathbf{v} = xy\hat{\mathbf{i}} - 2(x^2 + z^2)\hat{\mathbf{k}}$
(f) $\mathbf{v} = \hat{\mathbf{i}} + \hat{\mathbf{j}} + z\hat{\mathbf{k}}$
(g) $\mathbf{v} = z\hat{\mathbf{i}} + x^2t^2\hat{\mathbf{j}}$
(h) $\mathbf{v} = \sin(x + y + z)\hat{\mathbf{j}}$
(i) $\mathbf{v} = f(x)\hat{\mathbf{i}} + g(y)\hat{\mathbf{j}} + h(z)\hat{\mathbf{k}}$
(j) $\mathbf{v} = f(y)\hat{\mathbf{i}} + g(x)\hat{\mathbf{j}}$

2. The flow $\mathbf{q} = \kappa y\hat{\mathbf{i}}$ in $y > 0$, sketched in the figure, is known as a linear shear flow. Examining a typical fluid particle, say P, observe that the top of the particle is translating faster than the bottom, so the particle should be undergoing a clockwise angular velocity as it translates to the right. Furthermore, it appears that *all* particles may have the same angular velocity since (for a given particle size) the velocity differential from top to bottom of the particle is the same for each particle. Compute the angular velocity $\boldsymbol{\omega} = \frac{1}{2}\text{curl } \mathbf{q}$, and see if the foregoing conjectures are correct.

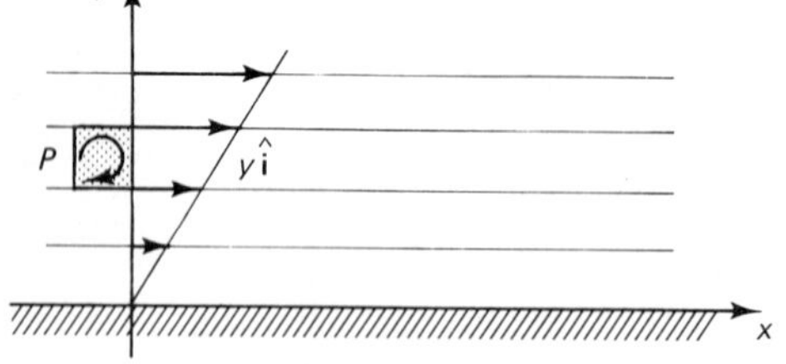

3. (*Vortex flow*) The fluid velocity field

$$\mathbf{q} = \frac{\Gamma}{2\pi r}\hat{\mathbf{e}}_\theta \qquad (\Gamma = \text{constant}) \tag{a}$$

is purely tangential, i.e., there is no radial ($\hat{\mathbf{e}}_r$) component, so that the streamlines are concentric circles centered at the origin, as sketched in the accompanying figure. Furthermore, the magnitude of the tangential velocity tends to zero as $r \to \infty$, and to ∞ as $r \to 0$. [Equation (a) is said to give the flow induced by a *vortex* of strength Γ located at the origin.]

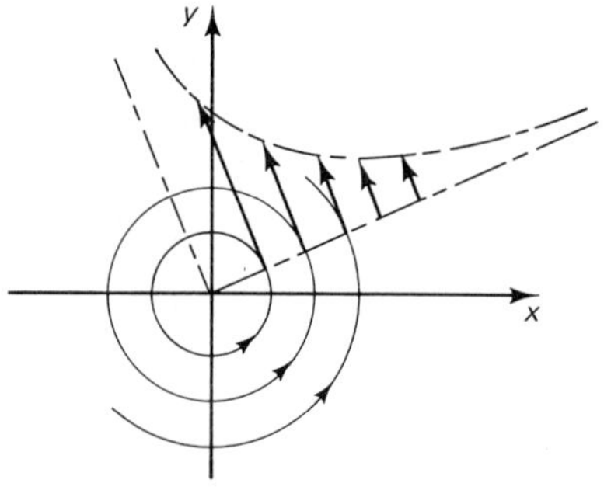

(a)

* Building on the work of Faraday and others, *James Clerk Maxwell* derived the governing equations of the electromagnetic field theory in 1864. With these equations, Maxwell predicted the existence of electromagnetic waves which travel at the speed of light. Thus were electromagnetics and optics united in one of the major steps in the history of science.

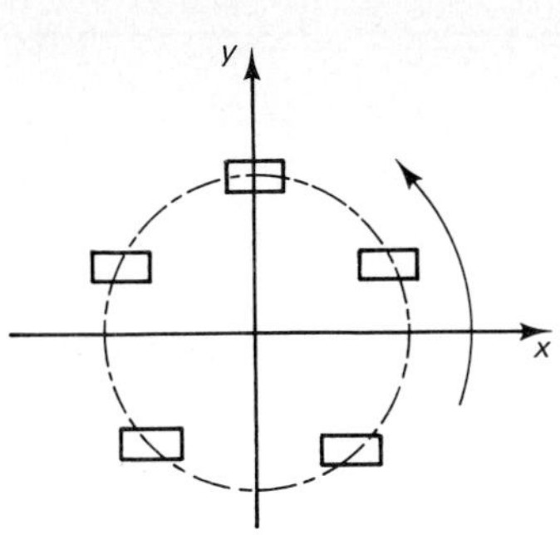

(b)

(a) Reexpress (a) in terms of x, y, $\hat{\mathbf{i}}$, $\hat{\mathbf{j}}$ and show that $\nabla \times \mathbf{q} = \mathbf{0}$ everywhere in the field (except at the origin, where $\nabla \times \mathbf{q}$ is not defined), so that every fluid particle (not at the origin) has *no spin*. [This result may seem strange in view of the fact that the particles are in circular motion! Evidently, the particles must maintain their spatial orientation (much as the seats on a Ferris wheel do), as in the figure, as they carry out their circular motion.]
(b) In Example 2 we considered a flow that was different from the one in part (a) but which had *the same streamline pattern*, namely, concentric circles centered at the origin, and in that case we found that $\nabla \times \mathbf{q} = 2\boldsymbol{\omega} \neq \mathbf{0}$. Sketch the orientation of a typical fluid particle, as the particle carries out its circular motion, as we have done in the accompanying figure for the flow given by equation (a).
(c) Observe, from parts (a) and (b), that if two flow fields, say $\mathbf{q}_1$ and $\mathbf{q}_2$, have the same streamline patterns, it does *not* follow that curl $\mathbf{q}_1$ = curl $\mathbf{q}_2$. Similarly, it does not follow that div $\mathbf{q}_1$ = div $\mathbf{q}_2$. For example, show that $\mathbf{q}_1 = e^x\hat{\mathbf{i}}$ and $\mathbf{q}_2 = e^{2x}\hat{\mathbf{i}}$ have the same streamline pattern, but that div $\mathbf{q}_1 \neq$ div $\mathbf{q}_2$.

4. (*Invariance property of curl* **v**) Let a C^1 vector field **v** be represented in terms of some particular x, y frame as $\mathbf{v} = v_x(x, y)\,\hat{\mathbf{i}} + v_y(x, y)\,\hat{\mathbf{j}}$. (We limit ourselves to the two-dimensional case merely to reduce the algebra.) Then, according to (3),

$$\text{curl } \mathbf{v} = \left(\frac{\partial v_y}{\partial x} - \frac{\partial v_x}{\partial y}\right)\hat{\mathbf{k}}. \tag{a}$$

Show that this vector is the same even if a different coordinate system is used, say, the x', y' system shown in the figure. That is, show that

$$\left(\frac{\partial v_y}{\partial x} - \frac{\partial v_x}{\partial y}\right)\hat{\mathbf{k}} = \left(\frac{\partial v_{y'}}{\partial x'} - \frac{\partial v_{x'}}{\partial y'}\right)\hat{\mathbf{k}}'$$

or, since $\hat{\mathbf{k}}' = \hat{\mathbf{k}}$, that

$$\frac{\partial v_y}{\partial x} - \frac{\partial v_x}{\partial y} = \frac{\partial v_{y'}}{\partial x'} - \frac{\partial v_{x'}}{\partial y'} \tag{b}$$

for any values of a, b and α (see the figure). *Hint:* Same hint as in Exercise 5 on page 361.

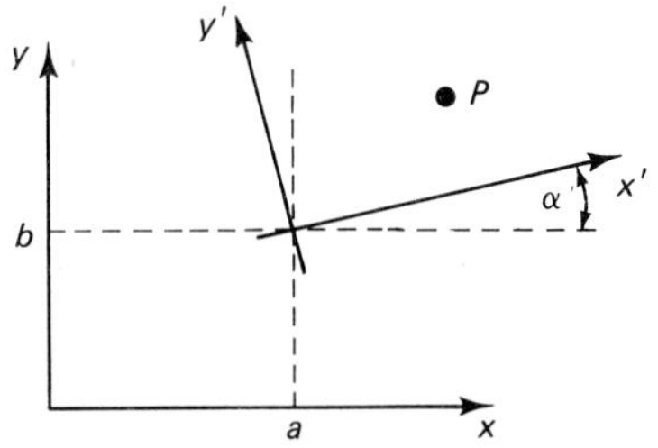

5. (*Integral definition of curl*) Instead of defining curl $\mathbf{v} \equiv \nabla \times \mathbf{v}$, as we have done, one can, equivalently, define

$$\text{curl } \mathbf{v} \equiv \lim_{\mathcal{B}\to\theta} \left\{\frac{\int_{\mathcal{S}} \hat{\mathbf{n}} \times \mathbf{v}\,dA}{V}\right\}, \tag{a}$$

analogous to the definition (2) of the divergence on page 358. Following the general lines of (3) to (6) on page 359, derive the result

$$\begin{aligned}\text{curl } \mathbf{v} &= \left(\frac{\partial v_z}{\partial y} - \frac{\partial v_y}{\partial z}\right)\hat{\mathbf{i}} - \left(\frac{\partial v_z}{\partial x} - \frac{\partial v_x}{\partial z}\right)\hat{\mathbf{j}} \\ &\quad + \left(\frac{\partial v_y}{\partial x} - \frac{\partial v_x}{\partial y}\right)\hat{\mathbf{k}} \\ &= \nabla \times \mathbf{v}\end{aligned} \tag{b}$$

directly from (a).

6. Show whether or not $\nabla \times \mathbf{v}$ is necessarily orthogonal to **v**. *Hint:* That is, is $\mathbf{v} \cdot \nabla \times \mathbf{v}$ necessarily zero? Write

$$\mathbf{v} \cdot \nabla \times \mathbf{v} = \begin{vmatrix} v_x & v_y & v_z \\ \dfrac{\partial}{\partial x} & \dfrac{\partial}{\partial y} & \dfrac{\partial}{\partial z} \\ v_x & v_y & v_z \end{vmatrix}$$

and see if the determinant is necessarily zero. It is true that two rows are identical, which seems to imply that the determinant must be zero, but be careful; and recall the footnote on page 375.

9.7 COMBINATIONS; LAPLACIAN

We have introduced the div, grad, and curl operators, and found that all three can be expressed in terms of ∇; specifically, div $= \nabla\cdot$, grad $= \nabla$, curl $= \nabla\times$.

In this section we consider combinations: one of the above operators acting on a combination of fields, such as $\nabla(\alpha u + \beta v)$ and $\nabla\cdot(u\mathbf{v})$, or a combination of the operators above acting on a single field, such as $\nabla\cdot\nabla u$ and $\nabla\times(\nabla u)$. Beginning with the former, i.e., the action of one such operator on a combination of fields, we note the following results:

If α, β are scalars, then

$$\text{div}\,(\alpha\mathbf{u} + \beta\mathbf{v}) = \nabla\cdot(\alpha\mathbf{u} + \beta\mathbf{v}) = \alpha\nabla\cdot\mathbf{u} + \beta\nabla\cdot\mathbf{v}, \tag{1}$$

$$\text{grad}\,(\alpha u + \beta v) = \nabla(\alpha u + \beta v) = \alpha\nabla u + \beta\nabla v, \tag{2}$$

$$\text{curl}\,(\alpha\mathbf{u} + \beta\mathbf{v}) = \nabla\times(\alpha\mathbf{u} + \beta\mathbf{v}) = \alpha\nabla\times\mathbf{u} + \beta\nabla\times\mathbf{v}, \tag{3}$$

so that div, grad, and curl are *linear* operators. Furthermore,

$$\text{div}\,(u\mathbf{v}) = \nabla\cdot(u\mathbf{v}) = \nabla u\cdot\mathbf{v} + u\nabla\cdot\mathbf{v}, \tag{4}$$

$$\text{curl}\,(u\mathbf{v}) = \nabla\times(u\mathbf{v}) = \nabla u\times\mathbf{v} + u\nabla\times\mathbf{v}, \tag{5}$$

$$\text{div}\,(\mathbf{u}\times\mathbf{v}) = \nabla\cdot(\mathbf{u}\times\mathbf{v}) = \mathbf{v}\cdot\nabla\times\mathbf{u} - \mathbf{u}\cdot\nabla\times\mathbf{v}, \tag{6}$$

$$\text{curl}\,(\mathbf{u}\times\mathbf{v}) = \nabla\times(\mathbf{u}\times\mathbf{v}) = \mathbf{u}\nabla\cdot\mathbf{v} - \mathbf{v}\nabla\cdot\mathbf{u} + (\mathbf{v}\cdot\nabla)\mathbf{u} - (\mathbf{u}\cdot\nabla)\mathbf{v}, \tag{7}$$

$$\begin{aligned}\text{grad}\,(\mathbf{v}\cdot\mathbf{w}) &= \nabla(\mathbf{v}\cdot\mathbf{w})\\ &= (\mathbf{v}\cdot\nabla)\mathbf{w} + (\mathbf{w}\cdot\nabla)\mathbf{v} + \mathbf{v}\times(\nabla\times\mathbf{w}) + \mathbf{w}\times(\nabla\times\mathbf{v}),\end{aligned} \tag{8}$$

where $(\mathbf{u}\cdot\nabla)\mathbf{v}$ in (7) and (8) means

$$\begin{aligned}(\mathbf{u}\cdot\nabla)\mathbf{v} &= (\mathbf{u}\cdot\nabla)(v_x\hat{\mathbf{i}} + v_y\hat{\mathbf{j}} + v_z\hat{\mathbf{k}})\\ &= (\mathbf{u}\cdot\nabla v_x)\hat{\mathbf{i}} + (\mathbf{u}\cdot\nabla v_y)\hat{\mathbf{j}} + (\mathbf{u}\cdot\nabla v_z)\hat{\mathbf{k}}\\ &= \left(u_x\frac{\partial v_x}{\partial x} + u_y\frac{\partial v_x}{\partial y} + u_z\frac{\partial v_x}{\partial z}\right)\hat{\mathbf{i}} + (\text{etc.})\hat{\mathbf{j}} + (\text{etc.})\hat{\mathbf{k}},\end{aligned}$$

and similarly for $(\mathbf{v}\cdot\nabla)\mathbf{u}$.

Derivation of these results is simple, and we will limit our discussion to the verification of one representative case, (4):

$$\begin{aligned}\nabla\cdot(u\mathbf{v}) &= \left(\hat{\mathbf{i}}\frac{\partial}{\partial x} + \hat{\mathbf{j}}\frac{\partial}{\partial y} + \hat{\mathbf{k}}\frac{\partial}{\partial z}\right)\cdot(uv_x\hat{\mathbf{i}} + uv_y\hat{\mathbf{j}} + uv_z\hat{\mathbf{k}})\\ &= \frac{\partial}{\partial x}(uv_x) + \frac{\partial}{\partial y}(uv_y) + \frac{\partial}{\partial z}(uv_z)\\ &= \frac{\partial u}{\partial x}v_x + \frac{\partial u}{\partial y}v_y + \frac{\partial u}{\partial z}v_z + u\left(\frac{\partial v_x}{\partial x} + \frac{\partial v_y}{\partial y} + \frac{\partial v_z}{\partial z}\right)\\ &= \nabla u\cdot\mathbf{v} + u\nabla\cdot\mathbf{v}.\end{aligned}$$

The form of this result is not surprising, and is reminiscent of the (scalar) statement $(d/dx)(uv) = (du/dx)v + u(dv/dx)$ from the calculus. That is, ∇ is a differential operator, and $u\mathbf{v}$ is a product, so we get two terms: one in which ∇ acts on u, and one in which it acts on $\mathbf{v}$.

Next, look at the action of a combination of div, grad, and curl operators on a single field. One such case that will be of great importance to us is the operator $\nabla \cdot \nabla$, i.e., div grad. This operator is called the **Laplacian** operator,* or just the Laplacian, and is denoted by the symbol ∇^2; i.e.,†

$$\nabla^2 \equiv \nabla \cdot \nabla = \left(\hat{\mathbf{i}}\frac{\partial}{\partial x} + \hat{\mathbf{j}}\frac{\partial}{\partial y} + \hat{\mathbf{k}}\frac{\partial}{\partial z}\right) \cdot \left(\hat{\mathbf{i}}\frac{\partial}{\partial x} + \hat{\mathbf{j}}\frac{\partial}{\partial y} + \hat{\mathbf{k}}\frac{\partial}{\partial z}\right)$$

or

$$\boxed{\nabla^2 = \frac{\partial^2}{\partial x^2} + \frac{\partial^2}{\partial y^2} + \frac{\partial^2}{\partial z^2}.} \tag{9}$$

Read as *del square,* we emphasize that ∇^2 is not ∇ times ∇, but rather, ∇ *dot* ∇. It can act on scalar fields *or* on vector fields:

$$\nabla^2 u = \frac{\partial^2 u}{\partial x^2} + \frac{\partial^2 u}{\partial y^2} + \frac{\partial^2 u}{\partial z^2}, \tag{10}$$

$$\begin{aligned} \nabla^2 \mathbf{v} &= \nabla^2(v_x\hat{\mathbf{i}} + v_y\hat{\mathbf{j}} + v_z\hat{\mathbf{k}}) \\ &= \hat{\mathbf{i}}\nabla^2 v_x + \hat{\mathbf{j}}\nabla^2 v_y + \hat{\mathbf{k}}\nabla^2 v_z \\ &= \left(\frac{\partial^2 v_x}{\partial x^2} + \frac{\partial^2 v_x}{\partial y^2} + \frac{\partial^2 v_x}{\partial z^2}\right)\hat{\mathbf{i}} + (\text{etc.})\hat{\mathbf{j}} + (\text{etc.})\hat{\mathbf{k}}. \end{aligned} \tag{11}$$

Besides the div grad combination, just mentioned, some others to be noted are

$$\boxed{\text{div curl } \mathbf{v} = \nabla \cdot \nabla \times \mathbf{v} = 0,} \tag{12}$$

$$\boxed{\text{curl grad } u = \nabla \times \nabla u = \mathbf{0},} \tag{13}$$

$$\text{curl curl } \mathbf{v} = \text{curl}^2\mathbf{v} = \nabla \times (\nabla \times \mathbf{v}) = \nabla(\nabla \cdot \mathbf{v}) - \nabla^2\mathbf{v}, \tag{14}$$

which hold if $\mathbf{v}$ and u are C^2.

We have drawn attention to (12) and (13), by placing them in a box, because they will be important to us later, and also because they are striking results, striking in the sense that the divergence of the curl of *every* C^2 vector field is found to be zero, and the curl of the gradient of *every* C^2 scalar field is found to be zero.

MNEMONIC DEVICE A nice way to remember (12) and (13) is to think of the letters d, g, and c (for divergence, gradient, and curl). The only combinations that come readily to mind (for me, at least) are dc (for *direct current*), and cg (for *center of gravity*); that is, the divergence of a curl is zero, and the curl of a gradient is zero.

* After *Pierre Simon de Laplace* (1749–1827).

† Some authors use the notation Δ in place of our ∇^2; i.e., they define $\Delta \equiv \nabla \cdot \nabla$, following Robert Murphy (1833).

EXAMPLE 1 If $u = x^2y$ and $\mathbf{v} = x^2y\hat{\mathbf{i}} - z^3\hat{\mathbf{j}} + 2\hat{\mathbf{k}}$, then

$$\nabla^2 u = 2y \qquad \text{by (10)},$$

$$\nabla^2 \mathbf{v} = (2y + 0 + 0)\hat{\mathbf{i}} + (0 + 0 - 6z)\hat{\mathbf{j}} + (0 + 0 + 0)\hat{\mathbf{k}} \qquad \text{by (11)}$$
$$= 2y\hat{\mathbf{i}} - 6z\hat{\mathbf{j}},$$

$$\nabla \cdot \nabla \times \mathbf{v} = 0 \qquad \text{by (12)},$$

$$\nabla \times \nabla u = \mathbf{0} \qquad \text{by (13)},$$

$$\nabla \times (\nabla \times \mathbf{v}) = \nabla(2xy) - (2y\hat{\mathbf{i}} - 6z\hat{\mathbf{j}}) \qquad \text{by (14)},$$
$$= (2x + 6z)\hat{\mathbf{j}}. \blacktriangleleft$$

9.7 EXERCISES

1. Evaluate $\nabla^2 u$ and $\nabla \times \nabla u$ in each case.

(a) $u = x$
(b) $u = x^2 + y^2$
(c) $u = x^2 + y^2 + z^2$
(d) $u = x \sin y$
(e) $u = xe^y$
(f) $u = \cos(x - 2y)$
(g) $u = xyz$
(h) $u = \sin(xyz)$
(i) $u = ax + by + cz + d$ (a, b, c, d constants).

2. Evaluate $\nabla \cdot \nabla \times \mathbf{v}$ and $\nabla \times (\nabla \times \mathbf{v})$ in each case.

*(a) $\mathbf{v} = x\hat{\mathbf{i}} + y\hat{\mathbf{j}} + z\hat{\mathbf{k}}$
(b) $\mathbf{v} = xe^y\hat{\mathbf{i}} - 2\hat{\mathbf{j}} + z^2\hat{\mathbf{k}}$
(c) $\mathbf{v} = z^3\hat{\mathbf{i}}$
(d) $\mathbf{v} = yz\hat{\mathbf{i}} - x^2\hat{\mathbf{j}}$
(e) $\mathbf{v} = x^2y\hat{\mathbf{j}}$
(f) $\mathbf{v} = f(y)\hat{\mathbf{i}} + g(x)\hat{\mathbf{j}}$

3. Are the parentheses needed in (14), i.e., in $\nabla \times (\nabla \times \mathbf{v})$? Explain.

4. $\nabla^2 u = 0$ is called **Laplace's equation.** Show that the following are solutions of Laplace's equation.

(a) xy
(b) $x^2 - y^2$
(c) $x^3 - 3xy^2$
(d) $y^3 - 3x^2y$
(e) $\ln(x^2 + y^2)$ for $x^2 + y^2 \neq 0$
(f) $\dfrac{1}{x^2 + y^2 + z^2}$ for $x^2 + y^2 + z^2 \neq 0$

5. If $\mathbf{v}$ is any vector, and $\mathbf{R} = x\hat{\mathbf{i}} + y\hat{\mathbf{j}} + z\hat{\mathbf{k}}$, show that $(\mathbf{v} \cdot \nabla)\mathbf{R} = \mathbf{v}$.

6. Derive the following equations [as we have done in the text for (4)].

(a) equation (5)
(b) equation (6)
(c) equation (7)
(d) equation (12)
(e) equation (13)
(f) equation (14)

7. The following scalar equations occur in fluid mechanics, solid mechanics, and electromagnetics, respectively. Reexpress them more concisely in terms of vector and vector differential operator notation. Here x, y, z subscripts denote the respective components of a given vector, *not* partial derivatives. [For example, the scalar equations $\partial u/\partial x = F_x$, $\partial u/\partial y = F_y$, $\partial u/\partial z = F_z$ can be expressed more concisely as $\nabla u = \mathbf{F}$. To see that, multiply the first by $\hat{\mathbf{i}}$, the second by $\hat{\mathbf{j}}$, the third by $\hat{\mathbf{k}}$, and add.]

(a) $$\frac{\partial \sigma}{\partial t} + \frac{\partial}{\partial x}(\sigma v_x) + \frac{\partial}{\partial y}(\sigma v_y) + \frac{\partial}{\partial z}(\sigma v_z) = 0$$

(b) $$\sigma \frac{\partial^2 u_x}{\partial t^2} = \mu\left(\frac{\partial^2 u_x}{\partial x^2} + \frac{\partial^2 u_x}{\partial y^2} + \frac{\partial^2 u_x}{\partial z^2}\right) + (\lambda + \mu)\frac{\partial \Theta}{\partial x} + F_x$$

$$\sigma \frac{\partial^2 u_y}{\partial t^2} = \mu\left(\frac{\partial^2 u_y}{\partial x^2} + \frac{\partial^2 u_y}{\partial y^2} + \frac{\partial^2 u_y}{\partial z^2}\right) + (\lambda + \mu)\frac{\partial \Theta}{\partial y} + F_y$$

$$\sigma \frac{\partial^2 u_z}{\partial t^2} = \mu\left(\frac{\partial^2 u_z}{\partial x^2} + \frac{\partial^2 u_z}{\partial y^2} + \frac{\partial^2 u_z}{\partial z^2}\right) + (\lambda + \mu)\frac{\partial \Theta}{\partial z} + F_z$$

(σ, μ, λ are constants)

(c) $$\frac{\partial E_z}{\partial y} - \frac{\partial E_y}{\partial z} + \frac{\partial B_x}{\partial t} = 0$$

$$\frac{\partial E_x}{\partial z} - \frac{\partial E_z}{\partial x} + \frac{\partial B_y}{\partial t} = 0$$

$$\frac{\partial E_y}{\partial x} - \frac{\partial E_x}{\partial y} + \frac{\partial B_z}{\partial t} = 0$$

8. The differential operator $\nabla^4 \equiv \nabla^2\nabla^2$ is known as the **biharmonic** (or **bi-Laplacian**) **operator,** and the partial differential equation $\nabla^4 u = 0$ is known as the **biharmonic equation.**

(a) If $u = u(x, y)$, show that

$$\nabla^4 u = u_{xxxx} + 2u_{xxyy} + u_{yyyy}.$$

(b) Write out $\nabla^4 u$, in Cartesian coordinates, for the case $u = u(x, y, z)$.

9. *Caution:* Familiar properties such as $\mathbf{A}\cdot\mathbf{B} = \mathbf{B}\cdot\mathbf{A}$, $\mathbf{B}\times\mathbf{A} = -\mathbf{A}\times\mathbf{B}$, and $\mathbf{A}\cdot(\mathbf{B}\times\mathbf{C}) = (\mathbf{A}\times\mathbf{B})\cdot\mathbf{C}$ (page 281) are, in general, *not* true if one or more of the vectors is the vector differential operator ∇. Specifically, show that

$$\nabla\cdot\mathbf{v} \neq \mathbf{v}\cdot\nabla, \qquad \nabla\times\mathbf{v} \neq -\mathbf{v}\times\nabla, \quad \text{and} \quad \nabla\cdot(\mathbf{v}\times\mathbf{w}) \neq (\nabla\times\mathbf{v})\cdot\mathbf{w}.$$

10. Given that

$$\nabla\cdot\mathbf{v} = 0 \tag{a}$$

$$\nabla\cdot\mathbf{w} = 0 \tag{b}$$

$$\nabla\times\mathbf{v} = -\frac{1}{c}\frac{\partial\mathbf{w}}{\partial t} \tag{c}$$

$$\nabla\times\mathbf{w} = \frac{1}{c}\frac{\partial\mathbf{v}}{\partial t}, \tag{d}$$

show that

$$c^2\nabla^2\mathbf{v} = \frac{\partial^2\mathbf{v}}{\partial t^2} \tag{e}$$

and

$$c^2\nabla^2\mathbf{w} = \frac{\partial^2\mathbf{w}}{\partial t^2} \tag{f}$$

Equations (e) and (f) are known as *wave equations*. *Hint:* One of the formulas (1) to (14) will be useful.

11. Show whether or not the following formulas are correct.

(a) $\dfrac{\partial}{\partial t}\nabla\cdot\mathbf{v}(x, y, z, t) = \nabla\cdot\dfrac{\partial\mathbf{v}}{\partial t}$

(b) $\dfrac{\partial}{\partial t}\nabla\times\mathbf{v}(x, y, z, t) = \nabla\times\dfrac{\partial\mathbf{v}}{\partial t}$

NONCARTESIAN SYSTEMS; DIV, GRAD, CURL, AND LAPLACIAN 9.8

[Optional Section]

Recall the pattern of the last several sections. Our starting point was the definition

$$\operatorname{div}\mathbf{v} \equiv \lim_{\mathscr{B}\to 0}\left\{\frac{\int_{\mathscr{S}} \hat{\mathbf{n}}\cdot\mathbf{v}\, dA}{V}\right\}. \tag{1}$$

To obtain a more tractable form, we introduced a reference Cartesian coordinate system and, accordingly, specified $\mathscr{B}$ to be a prism, of dimension Δx by Δy by Δz, the faces of $\mathscr{B}$ being made up of constant-coordinate surfaces; i.e., $x =$ constant, $y =$ constant, $z =$ constant. Simplification of the right-hand side of (1) then led to the form

$$\operatorname{div}\mathbf{v} = \frac{\partial v_x}{\partial x} + \frac{\partial v_y}{\partial y} + \frac{\partial v_z}{\partial z}, \tag{2}$$

which we proceeded to express as

$$\left(\hat{\mathbf{i}}\frac{\partial}{\partial x} + \hat{\mathbf{j}}\frac{\partial}{\partial y} + \hat{\mathbf{k}}\frac{\partial}{\partial z}\right)\cdot(v_x\hat{\mathbf{i}} + v_y\hat{\mathbf{j}} + v_z\hat{\mathbf{k}}),$$

or $\nabla\cdot\mathbf{v}$, where

$$\nabla = \hat{\mathbf{i}}\frac{\partial}{\partial x} + \hat{\mathbf{j}}\frac{\partial}{\partial y} + \hat{\mathbf{k}}\frac{\partial}{\partial z}. \tag{3}$$

With ∇ in hand we then introduced the gradient and curl as grad $u \equiv \nabla u$ and curl $\mathbf{v} \equiv \nabla \times \mathbf{v}$.

But Cartesian coordinates are not necessarily the most convenient ones. For example, in studying the temperature field in a spherical domain, one would certainly be better advised to use spherical coordinates. Rather than throw the discussion wide open and consider arbitrary curvilinear coordinate systems,* we intend merely to pick up the thread of Section 7.6 and extend our results to include the extremely important cases of polar, cylindrical, and spherical coordinates. Or, since the polar system is really a special case of the cylindrical, in which there is no z dependence, it will suffice to consider cylindrical and spherical coordinates.

CYLINDRICAL COORDINATES

In cylindrical coordinates it is most appropriate to take $\mathscr{B}$ to be of the type shown in Fig. 9.18, i.e., bounded by constant-coordinate surfaces; the θ = constant and z = constant surfaces are flat, and the r = constant surfaces are curved. Pursuing steps analogous to (3) to (8) on pages 359 to 360, we would obtain the expression

$$\boxed{\nabla = \hat{\mathbf{e}}_r \frac{\partial}{\partial r} + \hat{\mathbf{e}}_\theta \frac{1}{r}\frac{\partial}{\partial \theta} + \hat{\mathbf{e}}_z \frac{\partial}{\partial z}} \tag{4}$$

for the del operator in cylindrical coordinates. For pedagogical reasons, however, we prefer to leave those steps for the exercises and to use this space to present a different line of approach. Specifically, instead of passing from (1) to (4) via Fig. 9.18 we will obtain (4) from (3) using the known relationships

$$\hat{\mathbf{i}} = c\hat{\mathbf{e}}_r - s\hat{\mathbf{e}}_\theta \qquad (c \equiv \cos\theta,\ s \equiv \sin\theta, \text{ for brevity})$$

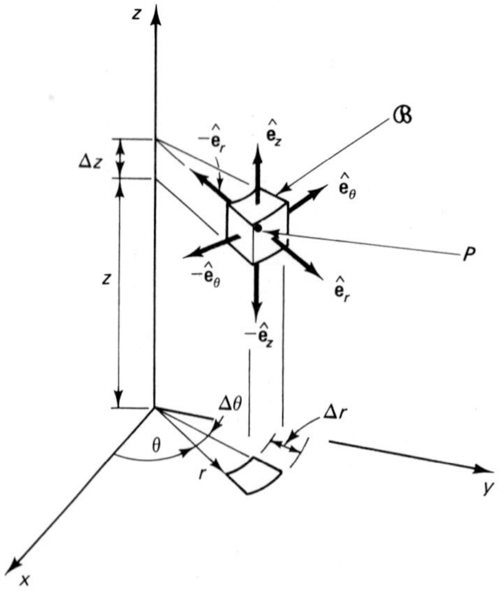

Fig. 9.18 Cylindrical coordinates.

*The general case is considered in numerous texts, e.g., P. Moon and D. E. Spencer, *Field Theory for Engineers* (Princeton, N.J.:D. Van Nostrand, 1961), Chap. 3.

$$\hat{\mathbf{j}} = s\hat{\mathbf{e}}_r + c\hat{\mathbf{e}}_\theta$$
$$\hat{\mathbf{k}} = \hat{\mathbf{e}}_z \tag{5}$$
$$x = r\cos\theta, \qquad y = r\sin\theta, \qquad z = z,$$

together with some chain differentiation. Thus*

$$\begin{aligned}\nabla &= \hat{\mathbf{i}}\frac{\partial}{\partial x} + \hat{\mathbf{j}}\frac{\partial}{\partial y} + \hat{\mathbf{k}}\frac{\partial}{\partial z} = (c\hat{\mathbf{e}}_r - s\hat{\mathbf{e}}_\theta)\left(c\frac{\partial}{\partial r} - \frac{s}{r}\frac{\partial}{\partial \theta}\right)\\ &\quad + (s\hat{\mathbf{e}}_r + c\hat{\mathbf{e}}_\theta)\left(s\frac{\partial}{\partial r} + \frac{c}{r}\frac{\partial}{\partial \theta}\right) + \hat{\mathbf{e}}_z\frac{\partial}{\partial z}\\ &= \hat{\mathbf{e}}_r\frac{\partial}{\partial r} + \hat{\mathbf{e}}_\theta\frac{1}{r}\frac{\partial}{\partial \theta} + \hat{\mathbf{e}}_z\frac{\partial}{\partial z},\end{aligned} \tag{6}$$

as claimed in (4). *Caution:* Students sometimes write "$\nabla = \hat{\mathbf{e}}_r(\partial/\partial r) + \hat{\mathbf{e}}_\theta(\partial/\partial\theta) + \hat{\mathbf{e}}_z(\partial/\partial z)$." This is *wrong*. The middle term should be $\hat{\mathbf{e}}_\theta(1/r)(\partial/\partial\theta)$, as may be remembered by noting the necessary dimensional consistency: each term $(\partial/\partial r,\ 1/r\ \partial/\partial\theta,\ \partial/\partial z)$ has the same dimensions, namely 1/length.

Obtaining expressions for $\nabla\cdot$, $\nabla\times$, and ∇^2 from (4) is straightforward, but it is crucial to remember, from Section 7.6, that *the base vectors are not constants;* specifically,

$$\hat{\mathbf{e}}_r = \hat{\mathbf{e}}_r(\theta), \qquad \frac{d\hat{\mathbf{e}}_r}{d\theta} = \hat{\mathbf{e}}_\theta \quad \text{and} \quad \hat{\mathbf{e}}_\theta = \hat{\mathbf{e}}_\theta(\theta), \qquad \frac{d\hat{\mathbf{e}}_\theta}{d\theta} = -\hat{\mathbf{e}}_r.$$

For example, given the vector field $\mathbf{v} = v_r\hat{\mathbf{e}}_r + v_\theta\hat{\mathbf{e}}_\theta + v_z\hat{\mathbf{e}}_z$, consider its divergence

$$\nabla\cdot\mathbf{v} = \left(\hat{\mathbf{e}}_r\frac{\partial}{\partial r} + \hat{\mathbf{e}}_\theta\frac{1}{r}\frac{\partial}{\partial \theta} + \hat{\mathbf{e}}_z\frac{\partial}{\partial z}\right)\cdot(v_r\hat{\mathbf{e}}_r + v_\theta\hat{\mathbf{e}}_\theta + v_z\hat{\mathbf{e}}_z).$$

Carrying out the dot product on the right-hand side yields nine terms: the first term in ∇ dotted with the first term in $\mathbf{v}$, the first with the second, the first with the third, the second with the first, and so on. Moreover, each of these terms involves the derivative of a product, and hence produces two terms. To illustrate, consider the first term dotted with the first:

$$\begin{aligned}\left(\hat{\mathbf{e}}_r\frac{\partial}{\partial r}\right)\cdot(v_r\hat{\mathbf{e}}_r) &= \hat{\mathbf{e}}_r\cdot\frac{\partial}{\partial r}(v_r\hat{\mathbf{e}}_r) = \hat{\mathbf{e}}_r\cdot\left(\frac{\partial \mathbf{v}_r}{\partial r}\hat{\mathbf{e}}_r + v_r\overset{\mathbf{0}}{\cancel{\frac{\partial\hat{\mathbf{e}}_r}{\partial r}}}\right)\\ &= \frac{\partial v_r}{\partial r}\hat{\mathbf{e}}_r\cdot\hat{\mathbf{e}}_r + v_r\hat{\mathbf{e}}_r\cdot\mathbf{0} = \frac{\partial v_r}{\partial r}.\end{aligned}$$

Now $\partial/\partial r$ and $\partial/\partial z$ of $\hat{\mathbf{e}}_r$, $\hat{\mathbf{e}}_\theta$, $\hat{\mathbf{e}}_z$ are all zero, as is $\partial/\partial\theta$ of $\hat{\mathbf{e}}_z$. These zeros reduce the 18 terms to 11, namely:

$$\begin{aligned}\nabla\cdot\mathbf{v} &= \left(\hat{\mathbf{e}}_r\cdot\frac{\partial v_r}{\partial r}\hat{\mathbf{e}}_r\right) + \left(\hat{\mathbf{e}}_r\cdot\frac{\partial v_\theta}{\partial r}\hat{\mathbf{e}}_\theta\right) + \left(\hat{\mathbf{e}}_r\cdot\frac{\partial v_z}{\partial r}\hat{\mathbf{e}}_z\right) + \left(\hat{\mathbf{e}}_\theta\cdot\frac{1}{r}\frac{\partial v_r}{\partial \theta}\hat{\mathbf{e}}_r\right)\\ &\quad + \left(\hat{\mathbf{e}}_\theta\cdot\frac{1}{r}v_r\frac{\partial\hat{\mathbf{e}}_r}{\partial\theta}\right) + \left(\hat{\mathbf{e}}_\theta\cdot\frac{1}{r}\frac{\partial v_\theta}{\partial \theta}\hat{\mathbf{e}}_\theta\right) + \left(\hat{\mathbf{e}}_\theta\cdot\frac{1}{r}v_\theta\frac{\partial\hat{\mathbf{e}}_\theta}{\partial\theta}\right) + \left(\hat{\mathbf{e}}_\theta\cdot\frac{1}{r}\frac{\partial v_z}{\partial \theta}\hat{\mathbf{e}}_z\right)\end{aligned} \tag{7}$$

* Here we recall, from Section 6.7, that $\partial r/\partial x = \cos\theta$, $\partial\theta/\partial x = -(\sin\theta)/r$, $\partial r/\partial y = \sin\theta$, and $\partial\theta/\partial y = (\cos\theta)/r$.

$$+\left(\hat{\mathbf{e}}_z \cdot \frac{\partial v_r}{\partial z}\hat{\mathbf{e}}_r\right) + \left(\hat{\mathbf{e}}_z \cdot \frac{\partial v_\theta}{\partial z}\hat{\mathbf{e}}_\theta\right) + \left(\hat{\mathbf{e}}_z \cdot \frac{\partial v_z}{\partial z}\hat{\mathbf{e}}_z\right)$$

$$= \frac{\partial v_r}{\partial r} + 0 + 0 + 0 + \frac{1}{r}v_r + \frac{1}{r}\frac{\partial v_\theta}{\partial \theta} + 0 + 0 + 0 + 0 + \frac{\partial v_z}{\partial z} \tag{7}$$

or

$$\boxed{\nabla \cdot \mathbf{v} = \frac{1}{r}\frac{\partial}{\partial r}(rv_r) + \frac{1}{r}\frac{\partial}{\partial \theta}v_\theta + \frac{\partial}{\partial z}v_z.} \tag{8}$$

Having completed the derivation of (8), let us go back in order to bring up and clarify an important point. Reconsidering the dot product of the second term in ∇ with the first term in $\mathbf{v}$,

$$\left(\hat{\mathbf{e}}_\theta \frac{1}{r}\frac{\partial}{\partial \theta}\right) \cdot (v_r\hat{\mathbf{e}}_r),$$

for example, observe that there are two operations to carry out, the dot product and the $\partial/\partial\theta$. The order of carrying out these operations *does* matter because if we first do the $\partial/\partial\theta$ and then the dot product, we obtain

$$\left(\hat{\mathbf{e}}_\theta \frac{1}{r}\frac{\partial}{\partial \theta}\right) \cdot (v_r\hat{\mathbf{e}}_r) = \hat{\mathbf{e}}_\theta\frac{1}{r} \cdot \frac{\partial}{\partial \theta}(v_r\hat{\mathbf{e}}_r) = \frac{1}{r}\hat{\mathbf{e}}_\theta \cdot \left(\frac{\partial v_r}{\partial \theta}\hat{\mathbf{e}}_r + v_r\frac{\partial \hat{\mathbf{e}}_r}{\partial \theta}\right)$$

$$= \frac{1}{r}\hat{\mathbf{e}}_\theta \cdot \left(\frac{\partial v_r}{\partial \theta}\hat{\mathbf{e}}_r + v_r\hat{\mathbf{e}}_\theta\right) = 0 + \frac{1}{r}v_r = \frac{1}{r}v_r,$$

whereas if we first do the dot product and then the $\partial/\partial\theta$, we obtain zero since $\hat{\mathbf{e}}_\theta \cdot \hat{\mathbf{e}}_r = 0$. *The correct procedure in working out* $\nabla \cdot \mathbf{v}$ *(and* $\nabla \times \mathbf{v}$*) will always be to do the differentiation first and then the dot (or cross) product.** This issue did not arise when we used Cartesian coordinates. In that case the base vectors $\hat{\mathbf{i}}, \hat{\mathbf{j}}, \hat{\mathbf{k}}$ were constant so that the order of carrying out the differentiations and the dot (or cross) products turns out to be inconsequential.

Proceeding in similar fashion, one obtains

$$\boxed{\nabla \times \mathbf{v} = \left(\frac{1}{r}\frac{\partial v_z}{\partial \theta} - \frac{\partial v_\theta}{\partial z}\right)\hat{\mathbf{e}}_r + \left(\frac{\partial v_r}{\partial z} - \frac{\partial v_z}{\partial r}\right)\hat{\mathbf{e}}_\theta + \frac{1}{r}\left(\frac{\partial (rv_\theta)}{\partial r} - \frac{\partial v_r}{\partial \theta}\right)\hat{\mathbf{e}}_z} \tag{9}$$

and

$$\boxed{\nabla^2 u = \frac{\partial^2 u}{\partial r^2} + \frac{1}{r}\frac{\partial u}{\partial r} + \frac{1}{r^2}\frac{\partial^2 u}{\partial \theta^2} + \frac{\partial^2 u}{\partial z^2}.} \tag{10}$$

Of these formulas, may we suggest that (4) and (10) be memorized. Along these lines, it is helpful to note the dimensional homogeneity: in (4) each term is 1/(length), and in (10) each term is $1/(\text{length})^2$.

* This rule can be substantiated by working out $\nabla \cdot \mathbf{v}$ (and $\nabla \times \mathbf{v}$) by other means and comparing results. For example, if we begin with the known formula $\nabla \cdot \mathbf{v} = \partial v_x/\partial x + \partial v_y/\partial y + \partial v_z/\partial z$ and enter the change of variables $x = r\cos\theta$, $y = r\sin\theta$, $z = z$, we do obtain the same result as that given in (8).

EXAMPLE 1 If $u = r^3 z^4 \sin 2\theta$ and $\mathbf{v} = z^2\hat{\mathbf{e}}_r + 2\hat{\mathbf{e}}_\theta + r\hat{\mathbf{e}}_z$, then

$$\nabla u = 3r^2z^4 \sin 2\theta\hat{\mathbf{e}}_r + 2r^2z^4 \cos 2\theta\hat{\mathbf{e}}_\theta + 4r^3z^3 \sin 2\theta\hat{\mathbf{e}}_z, \tag{11a}$$

$$\nabla^2 u = 6rz^4 \sin 2\theta + 3rz^4 \sin 2\theta - 4rz^4 \sin 2\theta + 12r^3z^2 \sin 2\theta, \tag{11b}$$

and since $v_r = z^2$, $v_\theta = 2$, $v_z = r$,

$$\nabla \cdot \mathbf{v} = \frac{z^2}{r} + 0 + 0, \tag{11c}$$

$$\nabla \times \mathbf{v} = (0 - 0)\hat{\mathbf{e}}_r + (2z - 1)\hat{\mathbf{e}}_\theta + \frac{1}{r}(2 - 0)\hat{\mathbf{e}}_z. \tag{11d}$$

COMMENT It is essential, when working with non-Cartesian systems, to bear in mind that the base vectors themselves may be nonconstant. In the present case, the $2\hat{\mathbf{e}}_\theta$ in $\mathbf{v}$ is not an innocent constant vector; rather, it varies with θ, and this variation leads to the $(2/r)\hat{\mathbf{e}}_z$ term in (11d). ◀

POLAR COORDINATES

As mentioned above, two-dimensional polar coordinates fall out as a special case of the foregoing results, for if

$$u = u(r, \theta), \qquad \mathbf{v} = v_r(r, \theta)\hat{\mathbf{e}}_r + v_\theta(r, \theta)\hat{\mathbf{e}}_\theta, \tag{12}$$

the foregoing results reduce to

$$\nabla u = \frac{\partial u}{\partial r}\hat{\mathbf{e}}_r + \frac{1}{r}\frac{\partial u}{\partial \theta}\hat{\mathbf{e}}_\theta, \tag{13}$$

$$\nabla^2 u = \frac{\partial^2 u}{\partial r^2} + \frac{1}{r}\frac{\partial u}{\partial r} + \frac{1}{r^2}\frac{\partial^2 u}{\partial \theta^2}, \tag{14}$$

$$\nabla \cdot \mathbf{v} = \frac{1}{r}\frac{\partial}{\partial r}(rv_r) + \frac{1}{r}\frac{\partial}{\partial \theta}v_\theta, \tag{15}$$

$$\nabla \times \mathbf{v} = \frac{1}{r}\left[\frac{\partial(rv_\theta)}{\partial r} - \frac{\partial v_r}{\partial \theta}\right]\hat{\mathbf{e}}_z. \tag{16}$$

SPHERICAL COORDINATES

Here we consider

$$u = u(\rho, \phi, \theta), \qquad \mathbf{v} = v_\rho(\rho, \phi, \theta)\hat{\mathbf{e}}_\rho + v_\phi(\rho, \phi, \theta)\hat{\mathbf{e}}_\phi + v_\theta(\rho, \phi, \theta)\hat{\mathbf{e}}_\theta, \tag{17}$$

where ρ, ϕ, θ are the spherical coordinates introduced on page 294. We state the following useful results without derivation.

$$\boxed{\nabla = \hat{\mathbf{e}}_\rho\frac{\partial}{\partial \rho} + \hat{\mathbf{e}}_\phi\frac{1}{\rho}\frac{\partial}{\partial \phi} + \hat{\mathbf{e}}_\theta\frac{1}{\rho \sin \phi}\frac{\partial}{\partial \theta},} \tag{18}$$

$$\boxed{\nabla u = \frac{\partial u}{\partial \rho}\hat{\mathbf{e}}_\rho + \frac{1}{\rho}\frac{\partial u}{\partial \phi}\hat{\mathbf{e}}_\phi + \frac{1}{\rho \sin \phi}\frac{\partial u}{\partial \theta}\hat{\mathbf{e}}_\theta,} \tag{19}$$

$$\nabla^2 u = \frac{1}{\rho^2}\left[\frac{\partial}{\partial \rho}\left(\rho^2 \frac{\partial u}{\partial \rho}\right) + \frac{1}{\sin\phi}\frac{\partial}{\partial \phi}\left(\sin\phi \frac{\partial u}{\partial \phi}\right) + \frac{1}{\sin^2\phi}\frac{\partial^2 u}{\partial \theta^2}\right], \tag{20}$$

$$\nabla \cdot \mathbf{v} = \frac{1}{\rho^2}\frac{\partial}{\partial \rho}(\rho^2 v_\rho) + \frac{1}{\rho \sin\phi}\frac{\partial}{\partial \phi}(v_\phi \sin\phi) + \frac{1}{\rho\sin\phi}\frac{\partial v_\theta}{\partial \theta}, \tag{21}$$

$$\begin{aligned}\nabla \times \mathbf{v} = &\frac{1}{\rho\sin\phi}\left[\frac{\partial}{\partial \phi}(v_\theta \sin\phi) - \frac{\partial v_\phi}{\partial \theta}\right]\hat{\mathbf{e}}_\rho \\ &+ \frac{1}{\rho}\left[\frac{1}{\sin\phi}\frac{\partial v_\rho}{\partial \theta} - \frac{\partial(\rho v_\theta)}{\partial \rho}\right]\hat{\mathbf{e}}_\phi + \frac{1}{\rho}\left[\frac{\partial(\rho v_\phi)}{\partial \rho} - \frac{\partial v_\rho}{\partial \phi}\right]\hat{\mathbf{e}}_\theta.\end{aligned} \tag{22}$$

We close this section with a word of caution regarding the use of determinants for the representation of $\nabla \times \mathbf{v}$ in non-Cartesian coordinate systems. Recall that the cross product $\mathbf{u} \times \mathbf{v}$ of two vectors $\mathbf{u} = u_x\hat{\mathbf{i}} + u_y\hat{\mathbf{j}} + u_z\hat{\mathbf{k}}$ and $\mathbf{v} = v_x\hat{\mathbf{i}} + v_y\hat{\mathbf{j}} + v_z\hat{\mathbf{k}}$ can be expressed as the determinant

$$\mathbf{u} \times \mathbf{v} = \begin{vmatrix} \hat{\mathbf{i}} & \hat{\mathbf{j}} & \hat{\mathbf{k}} \\ u_x & u_y & u_z \\ v_x & v_y & v_z \end{vmatrix}, \tag{23}$$

as can be verified by working out $(u_x\hat{\mathbf{i}} + u_y\hat{\mathbf{j}} + u_z\hat{\mathbf{k}}) \times (v_x\hat{\mathbf{i}} + v_y\hat{\mathbf{j}} + v_z\hat{\mathbf{k}})$ term by term, expanding the determinant in (23), and verifying that the two results are identical.

Similarly for cylindrical and spherical polar coordinates: If $\mathbf{u} = u_r\hat{\mathbf{e}}_r + u_\theta\hat{\mathbf{e}}_\theta + u_z\hat{\mathbf{e}}_z$ and $\mathbf{v} = v_r\hat{\mathbf{e}}_r + v_\theta\hat{\mathbf{e}}_\theta + v_z\hat{\mathbf{e}}_z$, it is easily verified that

$$\mathbf{u} \times \mathbf{v} = \begin{vmatrix} \hat{\mathbf{e}}_r & \hat{\mathbf{e}}_\theta & \hat{\mathbf{e}}_z \\ u_r & u_\theta & u_z \\ v_r & v_\theta & v_z \end{vmatrix}; \tag{24}$$

if $\mathbf{u} = u_\rho\hat{\mathbf{e}}_\rho + u_\phi\hat{\mathbf{e}}_\phi + u_\theta\hat{\mathbf{e}}_\theta$ and $\mathbf{v} = v_\rho\hat{\mathbf{e}}_\rho + v_\phi\hat{\mathbf{e}}_\phi + v_\theta\hat{\mathbf{e}}_\theta$, then

$$\mathbf{u} \times \mathbf{v} = \begin{vmatrix} \hat{\mathbf{e}}_\rho & \hat{\mathbf{e}}_\phi & \hat{\mathbf{e}}_\theta \\ u_\rho & u_\phi & u_\theta \\ v_\rho & v_\phi & v_\theta \end{vmatrix}. \tag{25}$$

Now consider the curl of a vector field $\mathbf{v}$, namely, $\nabla \times \mathbf{v}$. Are the determinants in (23) to (25) still correct representations of $\nabla \times \mathbf{v}$ if we merely write the middle rows as $\partial/\partial x$, $\partial/\partial y$, $\partial/\partial z$, and $\partial/\partial r$, $(1/r)(\partial/\partial\theta)$, $\partial/\partial z$, and $\partial/\partial\rho$, $(1/\rho)(\partial/\partial\phi)$, $(1/\rho \sin\phi)$ $(\partial/\partial\theta)$, respectively? The answer is "yes" for the Cartesian case; i.e.,

$$\nabla \times \mathbf{v} = \begin{vmatrix} \hat{\mathbf{i}} & \hat{\mathbf{j}} & \hat{\mathbf{k}} \\ \dfrac{\partial}{\partial x} & \dfrac{\partial}{\partial y} & \dfrac{\partial}{\partial z} \\ v_x & v_y & v_z \end{vmatrix}. \tag{26}$$

In cylindrical and spherical polar coordinates, however, the answer is *no*. Thus, in cylindrical coordinates, for example,

$$\nabla \times \mathbf{v} = \begin{vmatrix} \hat{\mathbf{e}}_r & \hat{\mathbf{e}}_\theta & \hat{\mathbf{e}}_z \\ \dfrac{\partial}{\partial r} & \dfrac{1}{r}\dfrac{\partial}{\partial \theta} & \dfrac{\partial}{\partial z} \\ v_r & v_\theta & v_z \end{vmatrix} \tag{27}$$

is *NOT* correct, for if we expand the determinant [Exercise 13(a)] the result is not in agreement with (9). [You may wish to cross out the incorrect formula (27) as a precaution against using it accidentally.] Determinant representations of $\nabla \times \mathbf{v}$ are in fact available for cylindrical and spherical coordinates (Exercises 13 and 18), but they are not quite of the same form as (24) and (25).

9.8 EXERCISES

Cylindrical coordinates:

1. Evaluate ∇u, $\nabla^2 u$, $\nabla \cdot \mathbf{v}$, and $\nabla \times \mathbf{v}$, using the relevant formulas (4), (8), (9), and (10).

*(a) $u = r$, $\mathbf{v} = r\hat{\mathbf{e}}_r + z\hat{\mathbf{e}}_z$
(b) $u = r^2 \sin 2\theta$, $\mathbf{v} = \cos\theta\, \hat{\mathbf{e}}_r - \sin\theta\, \hat{\mathbf{e}}_\theta$
(c) $u = r^2 \sin\theta$, $\mathbf{v} = z^2\hat{\mathbf{e}}_r$
(d) $u = z^3 r$, $\mathbf{v} = \hat{\mathbf{e}}_\theta$
(e) $u = 1/r$, $\mathbf{v} = r\sin\theta\hat{\mathbf{e}}_z$
(f) $u = 6$, $\mathbf{v} = z^2\hat{\mathbf{e}}_r + (r^2 z + \cos^2\theta)\hat{\mathbf{e}}_z$

2. Evaluate $\nabla \cdot \mathbf{v}$ three different ways, and show that the results are in agreement with each other: first, use (8); second, work it out term by term, as we have done in (7); third, re-express $\mathbf{v}$ in terms of $x, y, z, \hat{\mathbf{i}}, \hat{\mathbf{j}}, \hat{\mathbf{k}}$ and use the formula $\nabla \cdot \mathbf{v} = \partial v_x/\partial x + \partial v_y/\partial y + \partial v_z/\partial z$.

(a) $\mathbf{v} = \hat{\mathbf{e}}_r$
(b) $\mathbf{v} = \hat{\mathbf{e}}_\theta$
(c) $\mathbf{v} = r\hat{\mathbf{e}}_r + z\hat{\mathbf{e}}_z$
(d) $\mathbf{v} = \cos^2\theta\hat{\mathbf{e}}_\theta$
(e) $\mathbf{v} = r^2 z \sin\theta\, \hat{\mathbf{e}}_z$
(f) $\mathbf{v} = \cos\theta\, \hat{\mathbf{e}}_r - \sin\theta\, \hat{\mathbf{e}}_\theta$
(g) $\mathbf{v} = r\hat{\mathbf{e}}_\theta$
(h) $\mathbf{v} = r^3\hat{\mathbf{e}}_r$
(i) $\mathbf{v} = \cos\theta\, \hat{\mathbf{e}}_z$

3. Derive formula (9), by following an approach similar to that employed in (7).

4. Show that the following are solutions of *Laplace's equation* $\nabla^2 u = 0$.
(a) $u = r^n \sin n\theta$ for any integer n (for $r \neq 0$ if n is negative)
(b) $u = r^n \cos n\theta$ for any integer n (for $r \neq 0$ if n is negative)
(c) $u = \ln r$ $(r \neq 0)$
(d) $u = \dfrac{1}{\sqrt{r^2 + z^2}}$ $(r^2 + z^2 \neq 0)$

5. Evaluate $\nabla^2 \mathbf{v}$.

(a) $\mathbf{v} = r\hat{\mathbf{e}}_r + z\hat{\mathbf{e}}_z$
(b) $\mathbf{v} = \cos\theta\hat{\mathbf{e}}_r - \sin\theta\, \hat{\mathbf{e}}_\theta$
*(c) $\mathbf{v} = \hat{\mathbf{e}}_\theta$
(d) $\mathbf{v} = z^2\hat{\mathbf{e}}_r - 2\hat{\mathbf{e}}_\theta + \hat{\mathbf{e}}_z$

6. Following the general lines of (3) to (6) on page 359, use definition (1) and Fig. 9.18 in this section to derive formula (8) for the divergence.

7. Derive formula (10) for the Laplacian,
(a) by a term-by-term working out of

$$\nabla \cdot \nabla u = \left(\hat{\mathbf{e}}_r \frac{\partial}{\partial r} + \hat{\mathbf{e}}_\theta \frac{1}{r}\frac{\partial}{\partial \theta} + \hat{\mathbf{e}}_z \frac{\partial}{\partial z}\right) \cdot \left(\hat{\mathbf{e}}_r \frac{\partial u}{\partial r} + \hat{\mathbf{e}}_\theta \frac{1}{r}\frac{\partial u}{\partial \theta} + \hat{\mathbf{e}}_z \frac{\partial u}{\partial z}\right)$$

(b) by beginning with the Cartesian expression

$$\nabla^2 u = \frac{\partial^2 u}{\partial x^2} + \frac{\partial^2 u}{\partial y^2} + \frac{\partial^2 u}{\partial z^2},$$

introducing the relations $x = r\cos\theta$, $y = r\sin\theta$, $z = z$, and using chain differentiation. *Hint:* $\partial^2/\partial x^2$, for example, is a double application of the operator

$$\frac{\partial}{\partial x} = \frac{\partial}{\partial r}\frac{\partial r}{\partial x} + \frac{\partial}{\partial \theta}\frac{\partial \theta}{\partial x} + \frac{\partial}{\partial z}\frac{\partial z}{\partial x} = \cos\theta \frac{\partial}{\partial r} - \frac{\sin\theta}{r}\frac{\partial}{\partial \theta}.$$

Similarly,

$$\frac{\partial}{\partial y} = \sin\theta\frac{\partial}{\partial r} + \frac{\cos\theta}{r}\frac{\partial}{\partial\theta} \quad\text{and}\quad \frac{\partial}{\partial z} = \frac{\partial}{\partial z}.$$

***8.** Recall the formula $du/ds = \nabla u \cdot \hat{\mathbf{s}}$. Does it follow that $\partial u/\partial\theta = \nabla u \cdot \hat{\mathbf{e}}_\theta$? Explain.

9. Is $\nabla^2\mathbf{v} = \nabla^2(v_r\hat{\mathbf{e}}_r + v_\theta\hat{\mathbf{e}}_\theta + v_z\hat{\mathbf{e}}_z)$ equal to $(\nabla^2 v_r)\hat{\mathbf{e}}_r + (\nabla^2 v_\theta)\hat{\mathbf{e}}_\theta + (\nabla^2 v_z)\hat{\mathbf{e}}_z$? Explain.

10. Grade the following claim from an examination paper:

$$\nabla\cdot(y\hat{\mathbf{i}}) = \left(\hat{\mathbf{i}}\frac{\partial}{\partial x} + \hat{\mathbf{j}}\frac{\partial}{\partial y} + \hat{\mathbf{k}}\frac{\partial}{\partial z}\right)\cdot(x\tan\theta\,\hat{\mathbf{i}})$$

$$= \tan\theta.$$

11. Write out the *biharmonic equation* $\nabla^4 u = 0$, where $\nabla^4 \equiv \nabla^2\nabla^2$, in both Cartesian coordinates and cylindrical coordinates.

12. Sketch the isotherms (i.e., level curves) $T = 0°$, $25°$, $50°$, $75°$, $100°$ for the temperature field $T(r, \theta) = 200\theta/\pi$, over $0 \le r < \infty$, $0 \le \theta \le \pi/2$. Show that ∇T becomes infinite as $r \to 0$, and interpret this result physically, graphically, . . . , in any way you can.

13. (a) Show that (27) is incorrect unless v_θ happens to be zero.
(b) Expanding the determinant and comparing with (9), verify that

$$\nabla\times\mathbf{v} = \frac{1}{r}\begin{vmatrix} \hat{\mathbf{e}}_r & r\hat{\mathbf{e}}_\theta & \hat{\mathbf{e}}_z \\ \frac{\partial}{\partial r} & \frac{\partial}{\partial\theta} & \frac{\partial}{\partial z} \\ v_r & rv_\theta & v_z \end{vmatrix} \qquad \text{(a)}$$

is correct.

Spherical coordinates:

14. Evaluate ∇u, $\nabla^2 u$, $\nabla\cdot\mathbf{v}$, and $\nabla\times\mathbf{v}$, using the relevant formulas (19) to (22).

*(a) $u = \rho$, $\mathbf{v} = \rho\hat{\mathbf{e}}_\rho$ (b) $u = \rho^2$, $\mathbf{v} = 3\hat{\mathbf{e}}_\phi$
(c) $u = \sin\phi$, $\mathbf{v} = \rho\hat{\mathbf{e}}_\phi$
(d) $u = \rho^2\sin\theta$, $\mathbf{v} = \hat{\mathbf{e}}_\rho + \hat{\mathbf{e}}_\phi + \hat{\mathbf{e}}_\theta$
(e) $u = \rho\cos\theta$, $\mathbf{v} = \rho^3\hat{\mathbf{e}}_\theta$ (f) $u = \cos\phi$, $\mathbf{v} = 6\hat{\mathbf{e}}_\theta$

15. Evaluate $\nabla\cdot\mathbf{v}$ three different ways, and show that the results are in agreement with each other: first, use (21); second, work it out term by term [as we did in (7) for the case of cylindrical coordinates]; third, reexpress $\mathbf{v}$ in terms of x, y, z, $\hat{\mathbf{i}}$, $\hat{\mathbf{j}}$, $\hat{\mathbf{k}}$ and use the formula $\nabla\cdot\mathbf{v} = \partial v_x/\partial x + \partial v_y/\partial y + \partial v_z/\partial z$.

(a) $\mathbf{v} = \hat{\mathbf{e}}_\rho$ (b) $\mathbf{v} = \hat{\mathbf{e}}_\phi$
(c) $\mathbf{v} = \hat{\mathbf{e}}_\theta$
(d) $\mathbf{v} = \rho\hat{\mathbf{e}}_\rho$ (e) $\mathbf{v} = \rho\hat{\mathbf{e}}_\phi$
(f) $\mathbf{v} = \sin\phi\hat{\mathbf{e}}_\rho$ (g) $\mathbf{v} = \cos\theta\hat{\mathbf{e}}_\phi$

16. Find α, if possible, so that $u = \rho^\alpha$ is a solution of the *Laplace equation* $\nabla^2 u = 0$.

17. Using the expression

$$\nabla = \hat{\mathbf{e}}_\rho\frac{\partial}{\partial\rho} + \hat{\mathbf{e}}_\phi\frac{1}{\rho}\frac{\partial}{\partial\phi} + \hat{\mathbf{e}}_\theta\frac{1}{\rho\sin\phi}\frac{\partial}{\partial\theta},$$

and, as needed, the expressions for the space derivatives of $\hat{\mathbf{e}}_\rho$, $\hat{\mathbf{e}}_\phi$, $\hat{\mathbf{e}}_\theta$ given on page 295, derive

(a) formula (20) for $\nabla^2 u$
(b) formula (21) for $\nabla\cdot\mathbf{v}$
(c) formula (22) for $\nabla\times\mathbf{v}$

18. Expanding the determinant and comparing with (22), verify that

$$\nabla\times\mathbf{v} = \frac{1}{\rho^2\sin\phi}\begin{vmatrix} \hat{\mathbf{e}}_\rho & \rho\hat{\mathbf{e}}_\phi & \rho\sin\phi\hat{\mathbf{e}}_\theta \\ \frac{\partial}{\partial\rho} & \frac{\partial}{\partial\phi} & \frac{\partial}{\partial\theta} \\ v_\rho & \rho v_\phi & \rho\sin\phi v_\theta \end{vmatrix} \qquad \text{(a)}$$

9.9 DIVERGENCE THEOREM

We now arrive at a most important result, the divergence theorem. Generally attributed to *Gauss,* the divergence theorem was obtained independently by the Russian mathematician *Michel Ostrogradsky* (1801–1861), and was published in the mémoires of the St. Petersburg Academy of Sciences in 1831.

Theorem 1 *Divergence Theorem*
Let $\mathcal{V}$ be a closed region, in 3-space, the boundary of which is a piecewise smooth orientable surface $\mathcal{S}$, and let $\mathbf{v}$ be a vector field that is defined and C^1 in $\mathcal{V}$. If $\hat{\mathbf{n}}$ denotes the outward unit normal on $\mathcal{S}$, then

$$\boxed{\int_{\mathcal{V}} \operatorname{div} \mathbf{v}\, dV = \int_{\mathcal{S}} \hat{\mathbf{n}} \cdot \mathbf{v}\, dA.} \tag{1}$$

Outline of Proof Detailed proof of this sophisticated theorem would be out of place in the present development, and we choose to limit ourselves here to an outline of the major steps of such a proof.* First, we partition $\mathcal{V}$ into a number of abutting rectangular prisms, say $\mathcal{V}_j$ for $j = 1, 2, \ldots, N$, in essentially the same way that we partitioned the *two*-dimensional region $\mathcal{R}$ into rectangles (in Fig. 8.2 on page 310). Let P_j be the center of the jth prism. One such prism is shown in Fig. 9.19a. Recalling that

$$\operatorname{div} \mathbf{v}(P_j) \equiv \lim_{\mathcal{V}_j \to 0} \left\{ \frac{\int_{\mathcal{S}_j} \hat{\mathbf{n}} \cdot \mathbf{v}\, dA}{\Delta V_j} \right\}, \tag{2}$$

it follows that we should be able to express

$$\operatorname{div} \mathbf{v}(P_j) - \frac{1}{\Delta V_j} \int_{\mathcal{S}_j} \hat{\mathbf{n}} \cdot \mathbf{v}\, dA = \epsilon_j$$

or

$$\operatorname{div} \mathbf{v}(P_j)\, \Delta V_j - \int_{\mathcal{S}j} \hat{\mathbf{n}} \cdot \mathbf{v}\, dA = \epsilon_j\, \Delta V_j, \tag{3}$$

where $\epsilon_j \to 0$ as $\mathcal{V}_j \to 0$. Now, (3) holds for each prism, and if we sum over all the

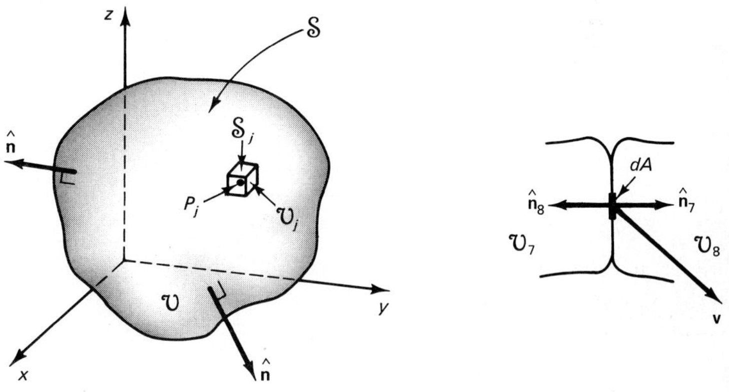

Fig. 9.19 Partition of $\mathcal{V}$. (a) (b)

* See the comments on the bottom half of p. 47 in SCHEY.

prisms, we obtain

$$\sum_{j=1}^{N} \operatorname{div} \mathbf{v}(P_j)\, \Delta V_j - \sum_{j=1}^{N} \int_{\mathscr{S}_j} \hat{\mathbf{n}} \cdot \mathbf{v}\, dA = \sum_{j=1}^{N} \epsilon_j\, \Delta V_j. \tag{4}$$

Consider the fate of each of the three terms in (4), as the partition is made finer and finer (i.e., as the "norm of the partition"→0). The first term on the left tends to the integral $\int_{\mathscr{V}} \operatorname{div} \mathbf{v}\, dV$. The second term tends to $\int_{\mathscr{S}} \hat{\mathbf{n}} \cdot \mathbf{v}\, dA$, but only by virtue of a process of "internal cancellation." For consider two abutting prisms, say $\mathscr{V}_7$ and $\mathscr{V}_8$ (Fig. 9.19b) for definiteness. The contributions $\hat{\mathbf{n}}_7 \cdot \mathbf{v}\, dA$ to $\int_{\mathscr{S}_7} \hat{\mathbf{n}} \cdot \mathbf{v}\, dA$ and $\hat{\mathbf{n}}_8 \cdot \mathbf{v}\, dA$ to $\int_{\mathscr{S}_8} \hat{\mathbf{n}} \cdot \mathbf{v}\, dA$ exactly cancel because $\hat{\mathbf{n}}_8 = -\hat{\mathbf{n}}_7$. Such cancellation occurs along all of the internal boundaries. Only the contributions from the outermost faces survive, since these faces have no neighbors and hence suffer no such cancellation. In the limit, then, as the partition is made finer and finer, the second term tends to $\int_{\mathscr{S}} \hat{\mathbf{n}} \cdot \mathbf{v}\, dA$. Finally, for ϵ an arbitrarily small positive number, we should be able to have $|\epsilon_j| \le \epsilon$ for all $j = 1, 2, \ldots, N$ by making the partition sufficiently fine. Then

$$\left| \sum_{j=1}^{N} \epsilon_j\, \Delta V_j \right| \le \sum_{j=1}^{N} |\epsilon_j|\, \Delta V_j \le \epsilon \sum_{j=1}^{N} \Delta V_j \le \epsilon V,$$

where V is the volume of the region $\mathscr{V}$, and since ϵ is arbitrarily small, it follows that (1) must hold. ■

Before showing off the power and elegance of this theorem in connection with some important applications, let us illustrate the "mechanics."

EXAMPLE 1 Let $\mathbf{v} = x(y+1)z^3\hat{\mathbf{j}}$, and let $\mathscr{V}$ be the pentahedron shown in Fig. 9.20, with faces given by the planes $x = 0$, $x = 2$, $y = 0$, $z = 0$, and $y + z = 1$. The problem that we pose is merely to evaluate the two sides of (1) and to verify that they are equal. Proceeding, we have

$$\int_{\mathscr{V}} \operatorname{div} \mathbf{v}\, dV = \int_{\mathscr{V}} \left\{ \frac{\partial}{\partial x}(0) + \frac{\partial}{\partial y}[x(y+1)z^3] + \frac{\partial}{\partial z}(0) \right\} dV$$

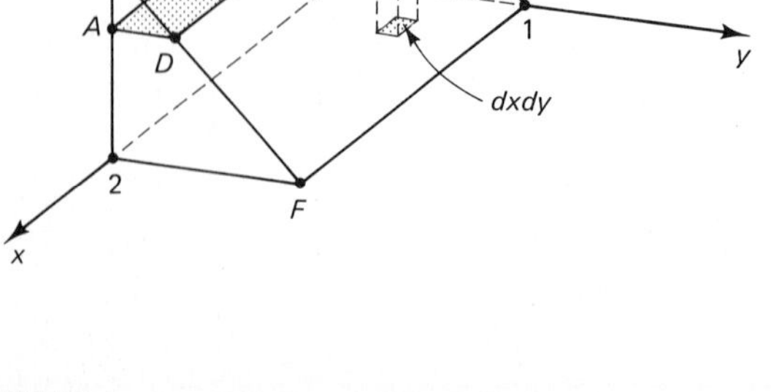

Fig. 9.20 The pentahedron $\mathscr{V}$.

$$= \underbrace{\int_0^1 \int_0^{1-z} \int_0^2}_{\text{shaded rectangle } ABCD} xz^3 \, dx \, dy \, dz = \int_0^1 \int_0^{1-z} 2z^3 \, dy \, dz \tag{5}$$

$$= 2 \int_0^1 z^3(1 - z) \, dz = \tfrac{1}{10}.$$

Turning to the surface integral in (1), we consider the five faces separately. Since those faces are planes, $\hat{\mathbf{n}}$ is simply a constant over each one. On the $x = 0$ face $\hat{\mathbf{n}} = -\hat{\mathbf{i}}$, so $\int \hat{\mathbf{n}} \cdot \mathbf{v} \, dA = \int 0 \, dA = 0$ over that face. Similarly, $\hat{\mathbf{n}} = +\hat{\mathbf{i}}$ on the $x = 2$ face, so $\int \hat{\mathbf{n}} \cdot \mathbf{v} \, dA = \int 0 \, dA = 0$ for that face, too. Similarly, for the $z = 0$ face, since $\hat{\mathbf{n}} \cdot \mathbf{v} = x(y + 1)z^3\hat{\mathbf{j}} \cdot (-\hat{\mathbf{k}}) = 0$ there. On $y = 0$,

$$\int_{y=0 \text{ face}} \hat{\mathbf{n}} \cdot \mathbf{v} \, dA = \int_{y=0 \text{ face}} -\hat{\mathbf{j}} \cdot [x(y + 1)z^3\hat{\mathbf{j}}]\Big|_{y=0} dA = -\int_0^1 \int_0^2 xz^3 \, dx \, dz$$
$$= -\tfrac{1}{2}. \tag{6}$$

Finally, consider the slanted face. There, $\hat{\mathbf{n}} = (\hat{\mathbf{j}} + \hat{\mathbf{k}})/\sqrt{2}$. In case this expression for $\hat{\mathbf{n}}$ is not evident by inspection of Fig. 9.20, observe that it can be obtained by taking the gradient of $f = y + z - 1$ (as in Example 5 on page 371) and normalizing the result. Or one may recall the well-known result that the normal to a plane $ax + by + cz = d$ is $a\hat{\mathbf{i}} + b\hat{\mathbf{j}} + c\hat{\mathbf{k}}$. Comparing $ax + by + cz = d$ with the given equation $y + z = 1$, we see that $a = 0$, $b = c = 1$, so that $\mathbf{n} = \hat{\mathbf{j}} + \hat{\mathbf{k}}$, and $\hat{\mathbf{n}} = (\hat{\mathbf{j}} + \hat{\mathbf{k}})/\sqrt{2}$. Still a third method for obtaining $\hat{\mathbf{n}}$ would be to cross two noncollinear vectors in that plane. For example (Fig. 9.20), $\mathbf{n} = \mathbf{EF} \times \mathbf{EG} = (\hat{\mathbf{j}} - \hat{\mathbf{k}}) \times (-2\hat{\mathbf{i}}) = 2(\hat{\mathbf{j}} + \hat{\mathbf{k}})$, so $\hat{\mathbf{n}} = (\hat{\mathbf{j}} + \hat{\mathbf{k}})/\sqrt{2}$ once again.

Next, we need an expression for dA on the slanted face. From Fig. 9.20 we see that dA is $\sqrt{2}$ times its projected area $dx\,dy$, since dA is inclined at 45° relative to the x, y plane. Thus

$$\int_{y+z=1 \text{ face}} \hat{\mathbf{n}} \cdot \mathbf{v} \, dA = \int_0^1 \int_0^2 \left(\frac{\hat{\mathbf{j}} + \hat{\mathbf{k}}}{\sqrt{2}}\right) \cdot [x(y + 1)z^3\hat{\mathbf{j}}]\Big|_{z=1-y} (\sqrt{2} \, dx \, dy)$$
$$= \int_0^1 \int_0^2 x(y + 1)(1 - y)^3 \, dx \, dy = \tfrac{3}{5}. \tag{7}$$

Combining these results yields

$$\int_{\mathcal{S}} \hat{\mathbf{n}} \cdot \mathbf{v} \, dA = 0 + 0 + 0 - \tfrac{1}{2} + \tfrac{3}{5} = \tfrac{1}{10},$$

which does agree with (5). ◀

In Example 1 it was easy to relate the area element dA on the slanted face to the projected area $dx\,dy$ in the x, y plane (Fig. 9.20) as $dA = \sqrt{2}\, dx\, dy$. More generally, let us note the relationship

$$\boxed{dA = \sqrt{1 + f_x^2 + f_y^2} \, dx \, dy} \tag{8}$$

between the area element dA on a surface $z = f(x, y)$ and its projection $dx\,dy$ down on the x, y plane. In the present case $z = 1 - y$, so $f_x = 0$ and $f_y = -1$; thus (8) becomes $dA = \sqrt{1 + 0^2 + (-1)^2}\,dx\,dy = \sqrt{2}\,dx\,dy$, as noted in Example 1.

The expression (8) was derived on page 332, but that section was OPTIONAL. Thus in case you have not studied that material, we have stated the useful result (8) here, without derivation, for your use.

Next, some important, and interesting, physical applications.

EXAMPLE 2 *The Continuity Equation of Fluid Mechanics.* Let us try "making up" a fluid flow. For example, let the vector velocity field be $\mathbf{q} = -x\hat{\mathbf{i}}$, and let the scalar mass density field σ (i.e., the mass per unit volume at any given point) be $\sigma =$ constant.* Is such a flow *possible*? Consider a control volume bounded by the planes $x = -1$, $x = +1$, $y = 0$, $y = 1$, $z = 0$, and $z = 1$, say (Fig. 9.21). We have $\mathbf{q} = -\hat{\mathbf{i}}$ at $x = 1$, and $\mathbf{q} = +\hat{\mathbf{i}}$ at $x = -1$. Thus fluid flows in through both the left- and right-hand faces. Since the amount of fluid in the control volume is ever increasing, due to this sustained influx, it follows from the principle of conservation of mass that the average mass density therein must be increasing with time. Yet we have prescribed that $\sigma =$ constant, so the prescribed flow is impossible. Evidently, then, fluid velocity and density fields are not independent; they must satisfy some relationship that is implied by the fundamental physical requirement of conservation of mass. Let us find that relationship.

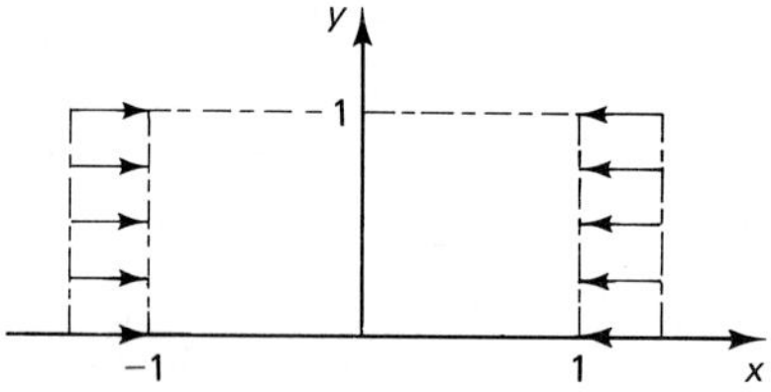

Fig. 9.21 Control volume.

Generalizing the preceding illustration, consider a flow throughout some region $\mathcal{R}$ in 3-space, and let $\mathcal{V}$ be a stationary control volume of arbitrary shape (although we ask that its surface be piecewise smooth and orientable), located within $\mathcal{R}$. The mass within $\mathcal{V}$ at any time t is $M = \int_{\mathcal{V}} \sigma\,dV$, where $\sigma(x, y, z, t)$ is the mass density, so the rate of increase of M is†

$$\frac{dM}{dt} = \frac{d}{dt}\int_{\mathcal{V}} \sigma\,dV = \int_{\mathcal{V}} \frac{\partial \sigma}{\partial t}\,dV. \tag{9}$$

Next, we observe that the rate at which mass enters $\mathcal{V}$ through its boundary $\mathcal{S}$ is

$$-\int_{\mathcal{S}} \sigma\hat{\mathbf{n}}\cdot\mathbf{q}\,dA; \tag{10}$$

where $\hat{\mathbf{n}}$ is the unit outward normal to $\mathcal{S}$. The story behind (10) is essentially the same as that on page 348, except that here we are talking about *mass* per unit time,

* The letter ρ is usually used for the mass density, but we will reserve ρ for the ρ in ρ, ϕ, θ spherical coordinate systems.

† Recall (17) on page 348.

whereas on page 358 we were talking about *volume* per unit time: (mass per unit time) = (volume per unit time) × (mass per unit volume), hence the presence of σ in (10). Also, we need the minus sign because we are after the rate at which mass *enters* $\mathcal{V}$, whereas $\hat{\mathbf{n}}$ is the *out*ward normal to $\mathcal{V}$.

Finally, suppose that—somehow—mass is being created within the field at the rate $f(x, y, z, t)$ mass per unit volume per unit time. Then the creation within $\mathcal{V}$ is

$$\int_{\mathcal{V}} f\, dV \tag{11}$$

mass per unit time.

The rate of increase of mass within $\mathcal{V}$ is certainly equal to the rate at which mass enters through $\mathcal{S}$, plus the rate at which mass is created within $\mathcal{V}$; i.e.,

$$\int_{\mathcal{V}} \frac{\partial \sigma}{\partial t}\, dV = -\int_{\mathcal{S}} \sigma \hat{\mathbf{n}} \cdot \mathbf{q}\, dA + \int_{\mathcal{V}} f\, dV. \tag{12}$$

To combine these integrals, we convert the surface integral to a volume integral using the divergence theorem (1), with "$\mathbf{v}$" = $\sigma\mathbf{q}$:

$$\int_{\mathcal{S}} \sigma \hat{\mathbf{n}} \cdot \mathbf{q}\, dA = \int_{\mathcal{S}} \hat{\mathbf{n}} \cdot (\sigma \mathbf{q})\, dA = \int_{\mathcal{V}} \nabla \cdot (\sigma \mathbf{q})\, dV. \tag{13}$$

Thus (12) becomes

$$\int_{\mathcal{V}} \left[\frac{\partial \sigma}{\partial t} + \nabla \cdot (\sigma \mathbf{q}) - f \right] dV = 0. \tag{14}$$

We could accept (14) as the desired relationship, but its integral form leaves something to be desired. To achieve the final simplification, observe that the control volume $\mathcal{V}$ is arbitrary. If $\int_{\mathcal{V}} [\ ]\, dV = 0$ for *arbitrary* $\mathcal{V}$, and we are willing to assume that the [ ] integrand is continuous throughout the field $\mathcal{R}$, it can be concluded that $[\ ] = 0$ throughout $\mathcal{R}$.* This step yields the relation $\partial\sigma/\partial t + \nabla \cdot (\sigma \mathbf{q}) - f = 0$, or

$$\frac{\partial \sigma}{\partial t} + \nabla \cdot (\sigma \mathbf{q}) = f. \tag{15}$$

Thus far, (15) involves nothing more than logic and bookkeeping. Finally, enters the *physics*: If matter can be neither created nor destroyed, as suggested in the beginning of this example, then $f = 0$ and (15) reduces to the more usual form

$$\frac{\partial \sigma}{\partial t} + \nabla \cdot (\sigma \mathbf{q}) = 0, \tag{16}$$

*For suppose the [ ] integrand were *non*zero, say positive, at some point P in the flow region $\mathcal{R}$. Then, by the assumed continuity of [ ], there must be some spherical neighborhood N of P such that $[\ ] > 0$ throughout N. Since $\mathcal{V}$ is arbitrary, we can let $\mathcal{V}$ be N. Then $\int_{\mathcal{V}} [\ ]\, dV = \int_N [\ ]\, dV > 0$, which contradicts (14). In case this still is not clear, try a simpler *one*-dimensional analog of (14): Suppose that

$$\int_a^x F(\xi)\, d\xi = 0$$

for arbitrary x. Taking d/dx of both sides gives $F(x) = 0$ according to the fundamental theorem of the integral calculus, provided that F is continuous.

which is the well-known **continuity equation** of fluid mechanics and is a statement of the physical principle of conservation of mass. It is a *partial differential equation* on σ and $\mathbf{q}$, which needs to be satisfied throughout the flow field. If we express

$$\mathbf{q} = u\hat{\mathbf{i}} + v\hat{\mathbf{j}} + w\hat{\mathbf{k}},$$

i.e., if we denote the x, y, z velocity components as u, v, w, then (16) may be written out as

$$\frac{\partial \sigma}{\partial t} + \frac{\partial}{\partial x}(\sigma u) + \frac{\partial}{\partial y}(\sigma v) + \frac{\partial}{\partial z}(\sigma w) = 0. \tag{17}$$

(We are not claiming that this is the *only* equation that needs to be satisfied; for example, we have not yet brought in Newton's second law of motion.)

In particular, if $\sigma =$ constant (i.e., if the fluid is *incompressible* *), then (16) and (17) reduce to

$$\nabla \cdot \mathbf{q} = 0; \qquad \frac{\partial u}{\partial x} + \frac{\partial v}{\partial y} + \frac{\partial w}{\partial z} = 0. \tag{18}$$

COMMENT Here $\sigma(x, y, z, t)$ has been the fluid mass density (mass per unit volume). Now suppose that the fluid carries an electric charge, and that the *charge density* (charge per unit volume) is designated as $\sigma(x, y, z, t)$. Observe that the entire story in this example still applies. That is, if we change the word "mass" to the word "charge" everywhere in this example, we obtain the continuity equation $\partial\sigma/\partial t + \nabla \cdot (\sigma \mathbf{q}) = f$ relating the scalar charge density field σ, the fluid velocity field $\mathbf{q}$, and the charge generation f per unit volume per unit time. ◀

EXAMPLE 3 *Unsteady Heat Conduction.* Consider the unsteady conduction of heat within some region $\mathscr{R}$ in 3-space. Our derivation of a partial differential equation governing the temperature field $T(x, y, z, t)$ will closely parallel our derivation of the continuity equation in the preceding example.

First, we choose a fixed arbitrary control volume $\mathscr{V}$ within $\mathscr{R}$. Instead of a mass balance, this time we carry out a heat balance; i.e., we equate the rate at which heat accumulates in $\mathscr{V}$ to the rate at which it enters through the surface $\mathscr{S}$ of $\mathscr{V}$ plus the rate at which it is generated within $\mathscr{V}$.

Since the heat (in calories, say) contained in a mass m at (absolute) temperature T is mcT, where c is the *specific heat* of the material, the rate of accumulation of heat within $\mathscr{V}$ is

$$\frac{d}{dt}\int_{\mathscr{V}} cT\sigma \, dV \quad \text{or} \quad \int_{\mathscr{V}} c\sigma \frac{\partial T}{\partial t} \, dV. \tag{19}$$

As in Example 2, σ is the mass density (mass per unit volume) of the material and dV is an infinitesimal volume element. Thus, $\sigma \, dV$ in (19) is d(mass).

* For the reader with an interest in fluid mechanics: Just as the *Reynolds number* turns out to be a measure of the effects of *viscosity*, the nondimensional parameter that provides a measure of the effects of *compressibility* is the so-called *Mach number* M, defined as the ratio of the fluid velocity to the local speed of sound. If $M \ll 1$, we can, with good accuracy, make the simplifying assumption that $\sigma =$ constant, i.e., that the fluid is *incompressible*. For example, the speed of sound in air at 20°C and sea level is 344 m/sec, so that if $|\mathbf{q}| < 30$ m/sec, say, the fluid may be considered as incompressible. Do you think that we could take $\sigma =$ constant in the theory of water waves on the ocean?

Next, the heat flux into $\mathscr{V}$ through $\mathscr{S}$ is, according to the Fourier law of heat conduction [(30) on page 369],

$$\int_{\mathscr{S}} k \frac{\partial T}{\partial n}\, dA, \tag{20}$$

where k is the conductivity of the material and $\hat{\mathbf{n}}$ is the outward unit normal. (The plus sign is correct because a positive $\partial T/\partial n$ causes a flux *into* $\mathscr{V}$ as assumed.) If heat is being generated at the rate $f(x, y, z, t)$ calories per unit volume per unit time, the rate of generation within $\mathscr{V}$ is

$$\int_{\mathscr{V}} f\, dV. \tag{21}$$

Hence

$$\int_{\mathscr{V}} c\sigma \frac{\partial T}{\partial t}\, dV = \int_{\mathscr{S}} k \frac{\partial T}{\partial n}\, dA + \int_{\mathscr{V}} f\, dV. \tag{22}$$

To convert the surface integral to a volume integral, we need to identify a vector "$\mathbf{v}$" such that $k(\partial T/\partial n) = \hat{\mathbf{n}} \cdot \mathbf{v}$. But $\partial T/\partial n = \nabla T \cdot \hat{\mathbf{n}}$, so "$\mathbf{v}$" $= k\nabla T$. Applying the divergence theorem, then, $\int_{\mathscr{S}} k(\partial T/\partial n)\, dA = \int_{\mathscr{S}} \hat{\mathbf{n}} \cdot (k\nabla T)\, dA = \int_{\mathscr{V}} \nabla \cdot (k\nabla T)\, dV$, so (22) becomes

$$\int_{\mathscr{V}} \left[c\sigma \frac{\partial T}{\partial t} - \nabla \cdot (k\nabla T) - f\right] dV = 0. \tag{23}$$

From the arbitrariness of $\mathscr{V}$, there follows the governing partial differential equation

$$c\sigma \frac{\partial T}{\partial t} - \nabla \cdot (k\nabla T) - f = 0 \tag{24}$$

on T. If k is independent of x, y, z, then $\nabla \cdot (k\nabla T) = k\nabla \cdot \nabla T = k\nabla^2 T$, and (24) may be written as

$$\alpha^2 \nabla^2 T = \frac{\partial T}{\partial t} - F, \tag{25}$$

where $F(x, y, z, t) = f/c\sigma$ is the source term and $\alpha^2 = k/c\sigma$ is the *diffusivity* of the material. The version

$$\boxed{\alpha^2 \nabla^2 T = \frac{\partial T}{\partial t},} \tag{26}$$

for $F = 0$, is called the **heat equation**, but is also known as the **diffusion equation** because it applies not only to the diffusion of heat but to diffusion processes in general.

Of special importance is the case of *steady-state* conduction, i.e., where $\partial T/\partial t = 0$. Then (26) gives way to the **Laplace equation**

$$\boxed{\nabla^2 T = 0.} \tag{27}$$

It may well be argued that the diffusion and Laplace equations are two of the three most important equations of mathematical physics, the third being the **wave equation**, which we meet in Part IV.

COMMENT In applications, F may be nonzero. For example, there may be taking place throughout the region a chemical reaction—which either releases heat (exothermic) or absorbs heat (endothermic). Or, to mention one more example, a mechanical member subjected to a cyclic loading may be heated by mechanical hysteresis losses, which will vary from point to point within the member proportional to the local cyclic stress level. ◀

As by-products of these applications of the divergence theorem, we have started to meet some (important) *partial differential equations*. Thus these examples help set the stage for Part IV, where we turn our attention to such equations and their solution.

EXAMPLE 4 *Green's Identities*. If u and v are scalar fields, the combination $u\nabla v$ is a vector field. Applying the divergence theorem to that vector field gives

$$\int_{\mathcal{V}} \nabla \cdot (u\nabla v)\, dV = \int_{\mathcal{S}} \hat{\mathbf{n}} \cdot (u\nabla v)\, dA.$$

But [recall (4) on page 380 with ∇v as "$\mathbf{v}$"] $\nabla \cdot (u\nabla v) = \nabla u \cdot \nabla v + u\nabla \cdot \nabla v = \nabla u \cdot \nabla v + u\nabla^2 v$, and $\hat{\mathbf{n}} \cdot (u\nabla v) = u\hat{\mathbf{n}} \cdot \nabla v = u\,\partial v/\partial n$, so

$$\boxed{\int_{\mathcal{V}} (\nabla u \cdot \nabla v + u\nabla^2 v)\, dV = \int_{\mathcal{S}} u \frac{\partial v}{\partial n}\, dA.} \tag{28}$$

This formula, known as **Green's first identity**,* is quite useful, especially in the study of partial differential equations.

In some cases, evaluation of the $\partial v/\partial n$ term in (28) is simple. For example, if V is the cube $|x| < 1$, $|y| < 1$, $|z| < 1$, then $\partial v/\partial n$ on the $x = +1$ face is merely $\partial v/\partial x$, and on the $x = -1$ face it is $-\partial v/\partial x$. For more complicated surface shapes we suggest that you use the expression $\partial v/\partial n = \nabla v \cdot \hat{\mathbf{n}}$ for the calculation of $\partial v/\partial n$ on $\mathcal{S}$.

Now, interchanging the letters u and v in (28), it should be equally true that

$$\int_{\mathcal{V}} (\nabla v \cdot \nabla u + v\nabla^2 u)\, dV = \int_{\mathcal{S}} v \frac{\partial u}{\partial n}\, dA,$$

and substracting these last two equations yields **Green's second identity,**

$$\boxed{\int_{\mathcal{V}} (u\nabla^2 v - v\nabla^2 u)\, dV = \int_{\mathcal{S}} \left(u \frac{\partial v}{\partial n} - v \frac{\partial u}{\partial n}\right) dA.} \tag{29}$$

* *George Green* (1793–1841) was a self-taught English mathematical physicist. His work on electricity and magnetism helped to place field theory on a firm mathematical foundation. His "Green's identities," "Green's theorem," and "Green's functions" are important tools in the study of field theory and partial differential equations.

What conditions on u, v assure the validity of (29)? Recall that the three components of $\mathbf{v}$ in the divergence theorem (1) were to have continuous first-order partials with respect to x, y, z. Since in deriving (28) and (29) we first set "$\mathbf{v}$" $= u\nabla v = uv_x\hat{\mathbf{i}} + uv_y\hat{\mathbf{j}} + uv_z\hat{\mathbf{k}}$, and then "$\mathbf{v}$" $= v\nabla u = vu_x\hat{\mathbf{i}} + vu_y\hat{\mathbf{j}} + vu_z\hat{\mathbf{k}}$, we must ask uv_x, uv_y, uv_z, vu_x, vu_y, and vu_z to have continuous first-order partials in the closed region $\mathscr{V}$; equivalently, we ask u and v to be C^2 in the closed region $\mathscr{V}$. Similarly, $\mathscr{S}$ is to be a piecewise smooth orientable surface, as in the divergence theorem (page 391). ◀

TWO-DIMENSIONAL CASE

Suppose that $\mathbf{v}$ is but a *two*-dimensional field, say $\mathbf{v} = v_x(x, y)\hat{\mathbf{i}} + v_y(x, y)\hat{\mathbf{j}}$, defined over a closed region $\mathscr{R}$ in the x, y plane (Fig. 9.22a). Then let us consider a slab-like volume $\mathscr{V}$ with $\mathscr{R}$ as its base, and of unit thickness, say, in the z direction, as in Fig. 9.22b. Applying the divergence theorem to $\mathbf{v}$ in $\mathscr{V}$ gives us

$$\int_{\mathscr{V}} \operatorname{div} \mathbf{v}\, dV = \int_{\mathscr{S}} \hat{\mathbf{n}} \cdot \mathbf{v}\, dA$$

or

$$\int_{\mathscr{V}} \operatorname{div} \mathbf{v}\, dV = \int_{\text{top}} \cancelto{0}{\hat{\mathbf{k}} \cdot \mathbf{v}}\, dA + \int_{\text{bottom}} (-\cancelto{0}{\hat{\mathbf{k}} \cdot \mathbf{v}})\, dA + \int_{\text{side}} \hat{\mathbf{n}} \cdot \mathbf{v}\, dA.$$

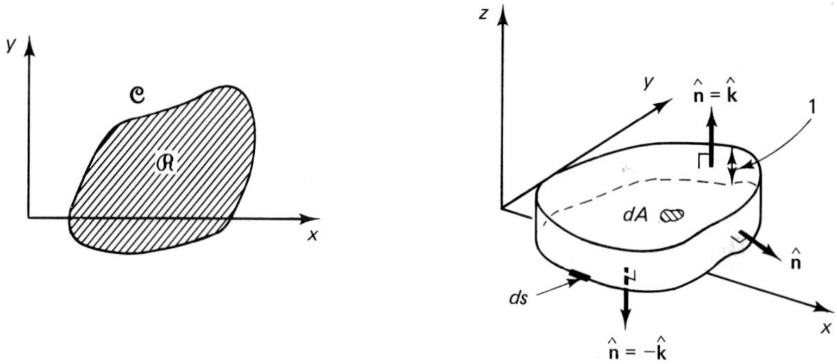

Fig. 9.22 Plane case. (a) (b)

Since div $\mathbf{v}$ and $\hat{\mathbf{n}} \cdot \mathbf{v}$ do not vary with z, this equation simplifies to

$$\int_{\mathscr{R}} \operatorname{div} \mathbf{v}\, (1)(dA) = \int_{\mathscr{C}} \hat{\mathbf{n}} \cdot \mathbf{v}\, (1)(ds)$$

or

$$\int_{\mathscr{R}} \operatorname{div} \mathbf{v}\, dA = \int_{\mathscr{C}} \hat{\mathbf{n}} \cdot \mathbf{v}\, ds, \tag{30}$$

where dA and ds are the increments shown in Fig. 9.22b. Thus (30) is the two-dimensional version of the divergence theorem. We simply drop back by one dimension: $\mathscr{V} \to \mathscr{R}$, $dV \to dA$, $\mathscr{S} \to \mathscr{C}$, and $dA \to ds$.

Observe that a new quantity has appeared, in (30), an integral around a *curve* $\mathscr{C}$. Such integrals—*line integrals*—are the subject of the next section, but let us not be intimidated out of illustrating (30) with a simple example. At worst, you will be hopelessly confused.

EXAMPLE 5 Verify (30) for the case where $\mathbf{v} = x^2y\hat{\mathbf{i}} - 3\hat{\mathbf{j}}$ and $\mathscr{R}$ is the rectangle shown in Fig. 9.23. Then

$$\int_{\mathscr{R}} \nabla \cdot \mathbf{v} \, dA = \int_0^2 \int_0^3 2xy \, dx \, dy = 18,$$

and

$$\int_{\mathscr{C}} \hat{\mathbf{n}} \cdot \mathbf{v} \, ds = \int_0^3 (-\hat{\mathbf{j}}) \cdot \mathbf{v}\Big|_{y=0} dx + \int_0^2 \hat{\mathbf{i}} \cdot \mathbf{v}\Big|_{x=3} dy$$

$$+ \int_0^3 \hat{\mathbf{j}} \cdot \mathbf{v}\Big|_{y=2} dx + \int_0^2 (-\hat{\mathbf{i}}) \cdot \mathbf{v}\Big|_{x=0} dy$$

$$= \int_0^3 3 \, dx + \int_0^2 9y \, dy - \int_0^3 3 \, dx + \int_0^2 0 \, dy = 18.$$

COMMENT In the integral $\int_0^2 (-\hat{\mathbf{i}}) \cdot \mathbf{v} \,|_{x=0} \, dy$, say, how do we know that the limits are 0 to 2, not 2 to 0? The idea is that the ds in (30) came from "(1)(ds)," namely, the area element dA, and since area elements are necessarily positive, we need to choose integration limits so that the ds increments are all positive. Hence we let y go from 0 to 2, not from 2 to 0. ◀

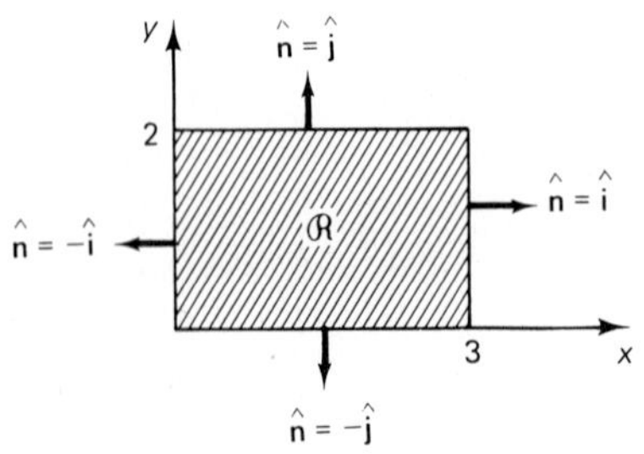

Fig. 9.23 The region $\mathscr{R}$.

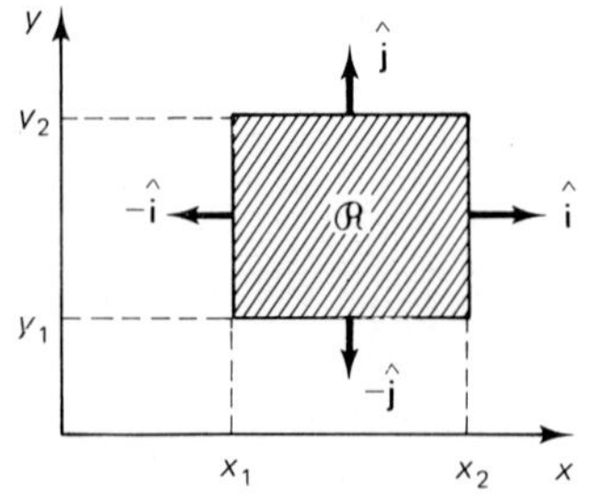

Fig. 9.24 The region $\mathscr{R}$.

Having obtained (30) as the two-dimensional version of the divergence theorem (1), it will be instructive to drop back one more dimension to the one-dimensional case. To do so, let $\mathbf{v} = v(x)\hat{\mathbf{i}}$ in (30), and let $\mathscr{R}$ be as shown in Fig. 9.24. Then (30) becomes

$$\int_{y_1}^{y_2} \int_{x_1}^{x_2} v'(x) \, dx \, dy = (y_2 - y_1)[v(x_2) - v(x_1)].$$

Carrying out the y integration, we obtain

$$(y_2 - y_1) \int_{x_1}^{x_2} v'(x) \, dx = (y_2 - y_1)[v(x_2) - v(x_1)],$$

which can be reexpressed as

$$\int_{x_1}^{x_2} v'(x)\, dx = v(x)\Big|_{x_1}^{x_2}. \tag{31}$$

In other words, an integral $\int_{x_1}^{x_2} f(x)\, dx$ on a region of integration consisting of the line segment $x_1 \le x \le x_2$ can be reduced to a certain evaluation on the *boundary* of the region of integration (namely, at the endpoints x_1 and x_2 of the line segment) if the integrand $f(x)$ happens to be a derivative, i.e., if there exists a function v such that $f(x) = v'(x)$.

In *two dimensions*, the analogous statement is that $\int_{\mathcal{R}} f(x, y)\, dA$ can be reduced to a certain evaluation on the boundary of $\mathcal{R}$ if f happens to be a divergence, i.e., if there exists a field $\mathbf{v}$ such that $f(x, y) = \nabla \cdot \mathbf{v}$. That reduction, from an integral over $\mathcal{R}$ to one over the boundary of $\mathcal{R}$, is given by (30).

Finally, in *three dimensions*, $\int_{\mathcal{V}} f(x, y, z)\, dV$ can be reduced to an evaluation on the boundary $\mathcal{S}$ of $\mathcal{V}$ if f happens to be a divergence, and that reduction is none other than the divergence theorem (1).

In reviewing this section, we suggest that you keep this idea in mind, namely, that the divergence theorem (30) and (1) are, in effect, the two- and three-dimensional generalizations, respectively, of the familiar formula (31).

9.9 EXERCISES

1. In each case, verify the divergence theorem by working out $\int_{\mathcal{V}} \nabla \cdot \mathbf{v}\, dV$ and $\int_{\mathcal{S}} \hat{\mathbf{n}} \cdot \mathbf{v}\, dA$ and showing that the results are equal.

(a) $\mathbf{v} = 2\hat{\mathbf{i}} - \hat{\mathbf{j}} + 4\hat{\mathbf{k}}$, $\mathcal{V}$: the rectangular prism $0 \le x \le 1, 0 \le y \le 3, 0 \le z \le 2$

(b) $\mathbf{v} = x\hat{\mathbf{i}} + 2y\hat{\mathbf{j}}$, $\mathcal{V}$: the cube $|x| \le 1$, $|y| \le 1$, $|z| \le 1$

(c) $\mathbf{v} = y\hat{\mathbf{i}} - 2\hat{\mathbf{j}} + x\hat{\mathbf{k}}$, $\mathcal{V}$: the rectangular prism $|x| \le 2, 0 \le y \le 1, 0 \le z \le 1$

*(d) $\mathbf{v} = \hat{\mathbf{j}} + x^2 z\hat{\mathbf{k}}$, $\mathcal{V}$: the cube $0 \le x \le 1$, $0 \le y \le 1, 0 \le z \le 1$

(e) $\mathbf{v} = 3xy^2\hat{\mathbf{j}}$, $\mathcal{V}$: the rectangular prism $0 \le x \le 1$, $0 \le y \le 1, 0 \le z \le 1$

(f) $\mathbf{v} = x^2\hat{\mathbf{i}} - 2z\hat{\mathbf{j}}$, $\mathcal{V}$: the rectangular prism $|x| \le 2$, $|y| \le 2$, $|z| \le 3$, with the cubical cavity $0 < x < 1, 0 < y < 1, 0 < z < 1$

*(g) $\mathbf{v} = xy\hat{\mathbf{j}}$, $\mathcal{V}$: the pentahedron with vertices at (0, 0, 0), (1, 0, 0), (0, 2, 0), (0, 0, 1), (1, 0, 1), (1, 2, 0)

(h) $\mathbf{v} = y^2 z\hat{\mathbf{k}}$, $\mathcal{V}$: the pentahedron with vertices at (0, 0, 0), (2, 0, 0), (0, 0, 3), (2, 0, 3), (0, 4, 3), (2, 4, 3)

(i) $\mathbf{v} = x^2 y \sin z\, \hat{\mathbf{i}}$, $\mathcal{V}$: same as in part (h)

(j) $\mathbf{v} = (3x^2 - 2yz)\hat{\mathbf{j}}$, $\mathcal{V}$: same as in part (h)

(k) $\mathbf{v} = 6\hat{\mathbf{i}} + 2x\hat{\mathbf{j}} + x^2 yz\hat{\mathbf{k}}$, $\mathcal{V}$: the pentahedron with vertices at (0, 0, 0), (1, 0, 0), (0, 2, 0), (1, 2, 0), (0, 0, 5), (0, 2, 5)

(l) $\mathbf{v} = z^2\hat{\mathbf{k}}$, $\mathcal{V}$: the tetrahedron bounded by the planes $x = 0$, $y = 0$, $z = 0$, $2x + y + 2z = 2$

(m) $\mathbf{v} = x^2 z\hat{\mathbf{i}}$, $\mathcal{V}$: same as in part (l)

(n) $\mathbf{v} = x^2 z\hat{\mathbf{i}} - 2z(x^2 + 1)\hat{\mathbf{j}} + z\hat{\mathbf{k}}$, $\mathcal{V}$: same as in part (l)

(o) $\mathbf{v} = z^2\hat{\mathbf{k}}$, $\mathcal{V}$: the tetrahedron bounded by the planes $x = 0$, $y = 0$, $z = 1$, $z = x + y$

2. Let $\mathcal{S}$ be a piecewise-smooth orientable closed surface enclosing a region of volume V. Show that

(a) $\int_{\mathcal{S}} \hat{\mathbf{n}}\, dA = \mathbf{0}$ *Hint:* Show that $\int_{\mathcal{S}} \hat{\mathbf{n}} \cdot \mathbf{a}\, dA = 0$ for every constant vector $\mathbf{a}$.

(b) $\int_{\mathcal{S}} \hat{\mathbf{n}} \cdot (x\hat{\mathbf{i}})\, dA = V$

(c) $\int_{\mathcal{S}} \hat{\mathbf{n}} \cdot (x\hat{\mathbf{i}} + y\hat{\mathbf{j}})\, dA = 2V$

(d) $\int_{\mathcal{S}} \hat{\mathbf{n}} \cdot (x\hat{\mathbf{i}} + y\hat{\mathbf{j}} + z\hat{\mathbf{k}})\, dA = 3V$

3. Verify Green's first identity (28) in each case.

*(a) $u = 2x^3$, $v = xy^2$, $\mathcal{V}$: the rectangular prism $0 \le x \le 2, 0 \le y \le 3, 0 \le z \le 1$

(b) $u = 1$, $v = x^2 + y^2 + z^2$, $\mathcal{V}$: the cube $0 \le x \le 1, 0 \le y \le 1, 0 \le z \le 1$

(c) $u = 1$, $v = x^2 + y^2 + z^2$, $\mathcal{V}$: the pentahedron with vertices at (0, 0, 0), (1, 0, 0), (0, 1, 0), (0, 0, 1), (1, 0, 1), (1, 1, 0)

4. Verify the two-dimensional divergence theorem (30) in each case.

*(a) $\mathbf{v} = x\hat{\mathbf{i}} + y\hat{\mathbf{j}}$, $\mathscr{R}$: the rectangle $0 \le x \le a$, $0 \le y \le b$
(b) $\mathbf{v} = x^2 y\hat{\mathbf{i}}$, $\mathscr{R}$: the rectangle $0 \le x \le 2$, $0 \le y \le 1$
(c) $\mathbf{v} = xy^2\hat{\mathbf{i}}$, $\mathscr{R}$: the triangle with vertices at (0, 0), (2, 0), (2, 1)
(d) $\mathbf{v} = xy\hat{\mathbf{j}}$, $\mathscr{R}$: the triangle with vertices at (0, 0), (2, 0), (0, 1)

5. In each case evaluate $I = \int_0^1 \int_0^1 \int_0^1 f\, dx\, dy\, dz$ directly. Then determine a vector field $\mathbf{v}$ such that $\nabla \cdot \mathbf{v} = f$, convert I to a surface integral by using the divergence theorem, and evaluate the surface integral.
(a) $f = x^2yz$ (b) $f = xz^2 - 2y$
(c) $f = 4$ (d) $f = x + y^2z$

6. Derive the following results from (28) and (29).

(a) $\int_{\mathscr{V}} \nabla^2 u\, dV = \int_{\mathscr{S}} \frac{\partial u}{\partial n}\, dA$

(b) $\int_{\mathscr{V}} [\|\nabla u\|^2 + u\nabla^2 u] dV = \int_{\mathscr{S}} u \frac{\partial u}{\partial n}\, dA$

Watch out: Most authors write $(\nabla u)^2$ for $\nabla u \cdot \nabla u$, in place of our $\|\nabla u\|^2$, within the same spirit as the Laplacian notation $\nabla \cdot \nabla \equiv$ "∇^2."

7. Just as (30) is the two-dimensional version of (1), work out the two-dimensional versions of Green's
(a) first identity (b) second identity

8. (*Alternative proof of divergence theorem*) An alternative approach to the proof of the divergence theorem (1) is to express the volume integral as an iterated integral, and to carry out one integration. To illustrate the procedure, consider the simpler *two*-dimensional case (30), and suppose that $\mathscr{R}$ is *convex* in the x direction, i.e., each crosshatched sliver running from $x_L(y)$ *to* $x_R(y)$ (see sketch) lies entirely within $\mathscr{R}$. Now

$$\int_{\mathscr{R}} \nabla \cdot \mathbf{v}\, dA = \int_{\mathscr{R}} \left(\frac{\partial v_x}{\partial x} + \frac{\partial v_y}{\partial y}\right) dx\, dy$$
$$= \int_{\mathscr{R}} \frac{\partial v_x}{\partial x}\, dx\, dy + \int_{\mathscr{R}} \frac{\partial v_y}{\partial y}\, dx\, dy.$$

The first term becomes

$$\int_{\mathscr{R}} \frac{\partial v_x}{\partial x}\, dx\, dy$$
$$= \int_{y_1}^{y_2} \int_{x_L(y)}^{x_R(y)} \frac{\partial v_x}{\partial x}\, dx\, dy$$
$$= \int_{\text{right}} v_x(ds \cos \alpha) - \int_{\text{left}} v_x(ds \cos \beta)$$
$$= \int_{\text{right}} v_x(\hat{\mathbf{i}} \cdot \hat{\mathbf{n}}) ds - \int_{\text{left}} v_x(-\hat{\mathbf{i}} \cdot \hat{\mathbf{n}})\, ds \quad \text{(a)}$$
$$= \int_{\text{right}} (v_x\hat{\mathbf{i}}) \cdot \hat{\mathbf{n}}\, ds + \int_{\text{left}} (v_x\hat{\mathbf{i}}) \cdot \hat{\mathbf{n}}\, ds$$
$$= \int_{\mathscr{C}} (v_x\hat{\mathbf{i}}) \cdot \hat{\mathbf{n}}\, ds.$$

We now state the problem: Assuming that $\mathscr{R}$ is convex in the y direction as well, show that

$$\int_{\mathscr{R}} \frac{\partial v_y}{\partial y}\, dx\, dy = \int_{\mathscr{C}} (v_y\hat{\mathbf{j}}) \cdot \hat{\mathbf{n}}\, ds, \quad \text{(b)}$$

and hence infer (30) from (a) and (b). *Note:* Extension to nonconvex regions would not be difficult, but it need not be considered here.

9. Besides the divergence theorem, $\int_{\mathscr{S}} \hat{\mathbf{n}} \cdot \mathbf{v}\, dA = \int_{\mathscr{V}} \nabla \cdot \mathbf{v}\, dV$, one may derive the "companion" results

$$\boxed{\int_{\mathscr{S}} \hat{\mathbf{n}} u\, dA = \int_{\mathscr{V}} \nabla u\, dV} \quad \text{(a)}$$

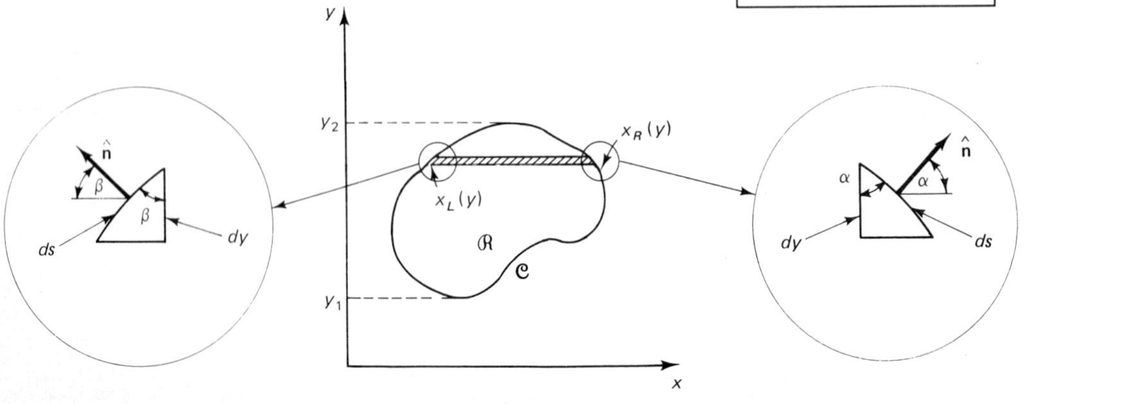

and

$$\boxed{\int_{\mathscr{S}} \hat{\mathbf{n}} \times \mathbf{v}\, dA = \int_{\mathscr{V}} \nabla \times \mathbf{v}\, dV.} \tag{b}$$

(a) Derive (a). *Hint:* Write

$$\begin{aligned}
\int_{\mathscr{S}} \hat{\mathbf{n}} u\, dA &= \int_{\mathscr{S}} [(\hat{\mathbf{n}}\cdot\hat{\mathbf{i}})\hat{\mathbf{i}} + (\hat{\mathbf{n}}\cdot\hat{\mathbf{j}})\hat{\mathbf{j}} + (\hat{\mathbf{n}}\cdot\hat{\mathbf{k}})\hat{\mathbf{k}}]u\, dA \\
&= \hat{\mathbf{i}}\int_{\mathscr{S}} (\hat{\mathbf{n}}\cdot\hat{\mathbf{i}})u\, dA + \hat{\mathbf{j}}\int_{\mathscr{S}} (\hat{\mathbf{n}}\cdot\hat{\mathbf{j}})u\, dA \\
&\quad + \hat{\mathbf{k}}\int_{\mathscr{S}} (\hat{\mathbf{n}}\cdot\hat{\mathbf{k}})u\, dA \\
&= \hat{\mathbf{i}}\int_{\mathscr{S}} \hat{\mathbf{n}}\cdot(u\hat{\mathbf{i}})\, dA + \hat{\mathbf{j}}\int_{\mathscr{S}} \hat{\mathbf{n}}\cdot(u\hat{\mathbf{j}})\, dA \\
&\quad + \hat{\mathbf{k}}\int_{\mathscr{S}} \hat{\mathbf{n}}\cdot(u\hat{\mathbf{k}})\, dA,
\end{aligned}$$

apply the divergence theorem to each integral, and combine the results into one integral.
(b) Derive (b). *Hint:* Essentially the same hint as in part (a). Write

$$\begin{aligned}
\int_{\mathscr{S}} \hat{\mathbf{n}} \times \mathbf{v}\, dA &= \int_{\mathscr{S}} \begin{vmatrix} \hat{\mathbf{i}} & \hat{\mathbf{j}} & \hat{\mathbf{k}} \\ \hat{\mathbf{n}}\cdot\hat{\mathbf{i}} & \hat{\mathbf{n}}\cdot\hat{\mathbf{j}} & \hat{\mathbf{n}}\cdot\hat{\mathbf{k}} \\ v_x & v_y & v_z \end{vmatrix} dA \\
&= \hat{\mathbf{i}}\int_{\mathscr{S}} \hat{\mathbf{n}}\cdot(v_z\hat{\mathbf{j}} - v_y\hat{\mathbf{k}})\, dA + \text{etc.},
\end{aligned}$$

apply the divergence theorem to each integral, and so on.
(c) Deduce, from equation (a), that $\int_{\mathscr{S}} \hat{\mathbf{n}}\, dA = \mathbf{0}$ for every $\mathscr{S}$. Verify this result, by direct integration, for the case where $\mathscr{S}$ is the surface of the rectangular prism $0 \le x \le a$, $0 \le y \le b$, $0 \le z \le c$.
Note: Just as the "global" statement $\int_{\mathscr{S}} \hat{\mathbf{n}}\cdot\mathbf{v}\, dA = \int_{\mathscr{V}} \nabla\cdot\mathbf{v}\, dV$ corresponds to the "local" statement

$$\nabla\cdot\mathbf{v} = \lim_{\mathscr{V}\to 0} \frac{\int_{\mathscr{S}} \hat{\mathbf{n}}\cdot\mathbf{v}\, dA}{V}$$

(V = the volume enclosed by $\mathscr{S}$), (a) and (b) correspond to the local statements

$$\nabla u = \lim_{\mathscr{V}\to 0} \frac{\int_{\mathscr{S}} \hat{\mathbf{n}} u\, dA}{V} \tag{c}$$

and

$$\nabla \times \mathbf{v} = \lim_{\mathscr{V}\to 0} \frac{\int_{\mathscr{S}} \hat{\mathbf{n}} \times \mathbf{v}\, dA}{V}, \tag{d}$$

respectively.

10. (*Continuity equation*) Let S_1 be a completely permeable plane surface within a steady fluid flow field. Let the velocity field be $\mathbf{q}(x, y, z)$, and let the mass density field be $\sigma(x, y, z)$. Then the set of streamlines that pass through the set of points on the edge of S_1 form a "streamtube," as sketched in the accompanying figure. Let S_2 be another plane cross section of the streamtube an arbitrary distance downstream of S_1, and let the areas of S_1, S_2 be A_1, A_2, respectively. Recalling the continuity equation (16), namely $\nabla\cdot(\sigma\mathbf{q}) = 0$ (since the field is steady, so that $\partial\sigma/\partial t = 0$), integrate this equation over a control volume V which is bounded by S_1, S_2, and the streamtube surface S_3 between S_1 and S_2, apply the divergence theorem, and thus show that

$$\int_{S_1} \hat{\mathbf{n}}\cdot(\sigma\mathbf{q})\, dA + \int_{S_2} \hat{\mathbf{n}}\cdot(\sigma\mathbf{q})\, dA = 0. \tag{a}$$

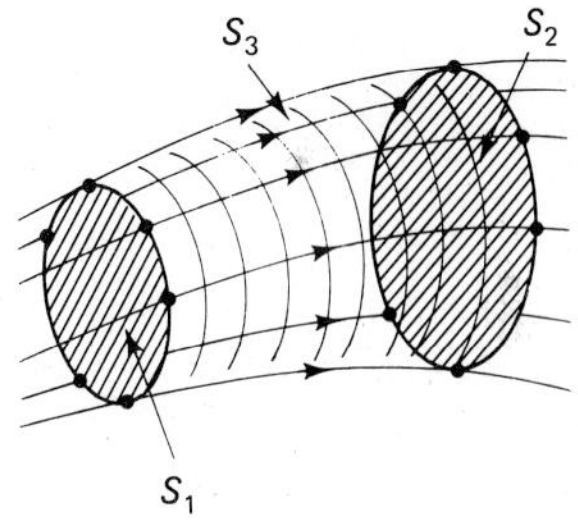

If σ and $\mathbf{q}$ are constant over S_1 and S_2, and S_1, S_2 are normal to the flow, show that (a) reduces to the simpler form

$$\sigma_1 A_1 V_1 = \sigma_2 A_2 V_2, \tag{b}$$

often given in fluid mechanics texts, where $\|\mathbf{q}\| = V_1$ on S_1 and $\|\mathbf{q}\| = V_2$ on S_2.

9.10 LINE INTEGRALS

Having considered volume and surface integrals, we finally turn to "line integrals" or "curve integrals," i.e., integrals along space curves. This sequence may seem pedagogically backward, but the fact is that we will need to draw on some of the machinery developed in connection with volume and surface integrals in carrying out our discussion of line integrals in these final sections.

Consider a space curve $\mathscr{C}$ and suppose that $\mathscr{C}$ may be parametrized, with respect to some x, y, z Cartesian coordinate system, by

$$x = x(\tau), \qquad y = y(\tau), \qquad z = z(\tau) \qquad (a \le \tau \le b). \tag{1}$$

For brevity, denote the point $(x(\tau), y(\tau), z(\tau))$ as $P(\tau)$. If $P(a) = P(b)$, the curve $\mathscr{C}$ is called a **closed curve;** otherwise, it is called an **arc.** We say that $\mathscr{C}$ is **simple** if it does not intersect itself: If $\mathscr{C}$ is an arc, it will be a *simple arc* if $\tau_1 \neq \tau_2$ implies that $P(\tau_1) \neq P(\tau_2)$ whenever τ_1 and τ_2 are in $[a, b]$; if $\mathscr{C}$ is a closed curve, it will be a *simple closed curve* if $\tau_1 \neq \tau_2$ implies that $P(\tau_1) \neq P(\tau_2)$ whenever τ_1 and τ_2 are in $[a, b]$, except when $\tau_1 = a$ and $\tau_2 = b$, for then $P(a) = P(b)$. For example, a script el (ℓ) is an arc but not a simple one, a roman es (s) is a simple arc, a figure eight is a closed curve but not a simple one, and a roman oh (o) is a simple closed curve.

Further, we say that $\mathscr{C}$ is **smooth** if it possesses a tangent that varies continuously along the length of $\mathscr{C}$. If $\mathscr{C}$ is a simple arc, it will be smooth if $x'(\tau)$, $y'(\tau)$, $z'(\tau)$ exist at each point on $\mathscr{C}$ and do not vanish simultaneously [so that $x'(\tau)\hat{\mathbf{i}} + y'(\tau)\hat{\mathbf{j}} + z'(\tau)\hat{\mathbf{k}}$ does indeed define a tangent]. If $\mathscr{C}$ is a simple closed curve it will be smooth if $x'(\tau)$, $y'(\tau)$, $z'(\tau)$ exist at each point on $\mathscr{C}$ and do not vanish simultaneously, and if $x'(a) = x'(b)$, $y'(a) = y'(b)$, $z'(a) = z'(b)$.

Finally, $\mathscr{C}$ is **piecewise smooth** if it can be broken into finitely many smooth curves. *Henceforth, we assume that all of our curves are both piecewise smooth and simple.*

Now, consider a given curve $\mathscr{C}$, and a function of $f(x, y, z)$ defined along $\mathscr{C}$ (perhaps off of $\mathscr{C}$ as well). Measuring arc length s from one endpoint, say A (Fig. 9.25), divide $\mathscr{C}$ into n arcs by specifying points P_0 $(= A)$, P_1, P_2, . . . , P_{n-1}, P_n $(=B)$ along $\mathscr{C}$. Let the division be chosen arbitrarily, provided that the P_j points are spaced and numbered so that the arc length from A to P_j is less than arc length from A to P_k if $j < k$. Denote the arcs as $\mathscr{C}_1, \mathscr{C}_2, \ldots, \mathscr{C}_n$, where the endpoints of $\mathscr{C}_j$ are P_{j-1} and P_j. On each arc $\mathscr{C}_j$ choose, arbitrarily, some point Q_j that is anywhere between the endpoints of $\mathscr{C}_j$, or *at* one of the endpoints, and form the sum

$$J_n = \sum_{j=1}^{n} f(Q_j)\Delta s_j, \tag{2}$$

where Δs_j is the arc length of $\mathscr{C}_j$. The choice of the P_j's and Q_j's defines a *partition* of $\mathscr{C}$, and we call the largest Δs_j the *norm* of the partition. Actually, we introduce not just one partition, but a sequence of them such that the norm of the nth partition tends to zero as $n \to \infty$. If the corresponding sequence of sums $J_1, J_2, \ldots$ converges

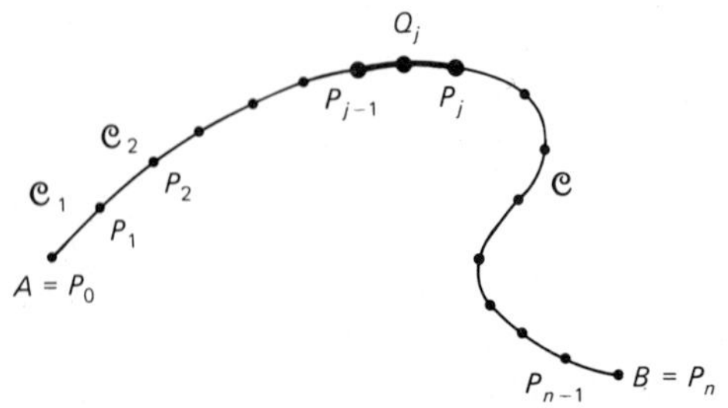

Fig. 9.25 Partition of $\mathscr{C}$.

to a limit, we call that limit the **line integral** of f over $\mathscr{C}$, and write it as

$$\int_{\mathscr{C}} f\, ds. \tag{3}$$

The limit will indeed exist if f is continuous along $\mathscr{C}$ and (as assumed above) if $\mathscr{C}$ is piecewise smooth and simple.*

From this definition of the line integral it can be shown that the following two important properties follow:

$$\int_{\mathscr{C}} (\alpha f + \beta g)\, ds = \alpha \int_{\mathscr{C}} f\, ds + \beta \int_{\mathscr{C}} g\, ds \qquad \text{(linearity)} \tag{4a}$$

and

$$\int_{\mathscr{C}} f\, ds = \int_{\mathscr{C}_1} f\, ds + \int_{\mathscr{C}_2} f\, ds, \tag{4b}$$

where α, β are any scalars, f, g are any two functions (continuous along $\mathscr{C}$), and where "$\mathscr{C} = \mathscr{C}_1 + \mathscr{C}_2$," i.e., where $\mathscr{C}$ is divided into two parts, $\mathscr{C}_1$ and $\mathscr{C}_2$ (just as $\mathscr{C}$ was divided into n parts in Fig. 9.25).

In practice, however, we do not evaluate line integrals by seeking the limit of the sequence $J_1, J_2, \ldots$. Rather, we introduce a coordinate system and proceed as follows. If $\mathscr{C}$ is parametrized with respect to some parameter τ by

$$x = x(\tau), \qquad y = y(\tau), \qquad z = z(\tau), \qquad (a \leq \tau \leq b), \tag{5}$$

then

$$\int_{\mathscr{C}} f(x, y, z)\, ds = \int_a^b f(x(\tau), y(\tau), z(\tau)) \frac{ds}{d\tau}\, d\tau. \tag{6}$$

Now from Section 7.7 we know that

$$\frac{ds}{d\tau} = \|\mathbf{R}'(\tau)\| = \sqrt{\mathbf{R}'(\tau)\cdot\mathbf{R}'(\tau)}, \tag{7}$$

so that

$$\boxed{\int_{\mathscr{C}} f(x, y, z)\, ds = \int_a^b f(x(\tau), y(\tau), z(\tau)) \sqrt{\mathbf{R}'(\tau)\cdot\mathbf{R}'(\tau)}\, d\tau} \tag{8}$$

where

$$\mathbf{R}(\tau) = x(\tau)\hat{\mathbf{i}} + y(\tau)\hat{\mathbf{j}} + z(\tau)\hat{\mathbf{k}}$$

and

$$\mathbf{R}'(\tau) = x'(\tau)\hat{\mathbf{i}} + y'(\tau)\hat{\mathbf{j}} + z'(\tau)\hat{\mathbf{k}}.$$

The point is that the right-hand side of (8) is in the familiar form "$\int_a^b F(x)\, dx$" met in the elementary integral calculus.

* Actually, it will suffice if f is *piecewise* continuous along $\mathscr{C}$, i.e., if $\mathscr{C}$ can be divided into a finite number of arcs on each of which f is a continuous function of arc length.

EXAMPLE 1 Evaluate $\int_{\mathscr{C}} f\, ds$, where $f = x^2 y$ and $\mathscr{C}$ is given by $x = a \cos \tau$, $y = a \sin \tau$, for $0 \le \tau \le \pi$. Then

$$\mathbf{R} = a \cos \tau \hat{\mathbf{i}} + a \sin \tau \hat{\mathbf{j}},$$

$$\mathbf{R}' = -a \sin \tau \hat{\mathbf{i}} + a \cos \tau \hat{\mathbf{j}},$$

$$\sqrt{\mathbf{R}'(\tau) \cdot \mathbf{R}'(\tau)} = \sqrt{a^2 \sin^2 \tau + a^2 \cos^2 \tau} = a,$$

so (8) gives

$$\int_{\mathscr{C}} f\, ds = \int_0^{\pi} (a \cos \tau)^2 (a \sin \tau)(a)\, d\tau$$

$$= -a^4 \int_{\tau=0}^{\tau=\pi} \cos^2 \tau\, d(\cos \tau) = -\frac{a^4}{3} \cos^3 \tau \Big|_0^{\pi} = \frac{2a^4}{3}. \tag{9}$$

COMMENT In this case we can see, from the form of $x(\tau)$ and $y(\tau)$, that $\mathscr{C}$ is a semicircular arc of radius a, as shown in Fig. 9.26. It is natural to wonder whether $\int_{\mathscr{C}} f\, ds$ really depends on the detailed shape of $\mathscr{C}$, or whether it depends only on the location of the two endpoints of $\mathscr{C}$. Thus suppose that we change $\mathscr{C}$, in the present example, to a straight line, say, connecting the given endpoints A and B (Fig. 9.26). That line may be parametrized by

$$x = \tau, \qquad y = 0 \qquad (-a \le \tau \le a)$$

so $\mathbf{R} = \tau \hat{\mathbf{i}} + 0 \hat{\mathbf{j}}$, $\mathbf{R}' = \hat{\mathbf{i}}$, and $\sqrt{\mathbf{R}'(\tau) \cdot \mathbf{R}'(\tau)} = 1$. Thus

$$\int_{\text{modified } \mathscr{C}} f\, ds = \int_{-a}^{a} (\tau^2)(0)(1)\, d\tau = 0,$$

which is not the same as the value $2a^4/3$ obtained in (9). *In general,* then, it follows that the value of a line integral $\int_{\mathscr{C}} f\, ds$ depends not only on the endpoints of $\mathscr{C}$, but on the shape of $\mathscr{C}$ as well. ◀

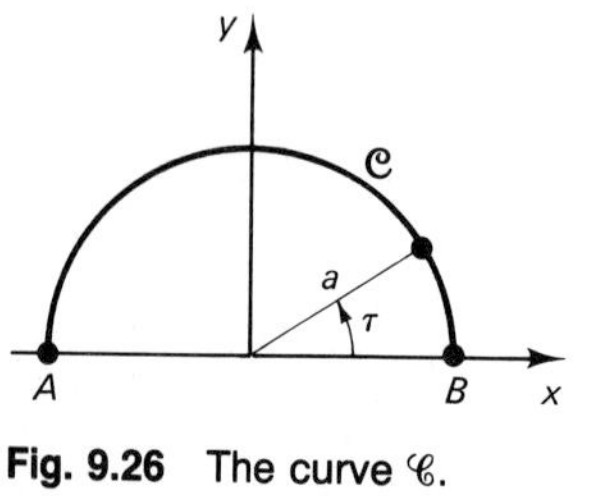

Fig. 9.26 The curve $\mathscr{C}$.

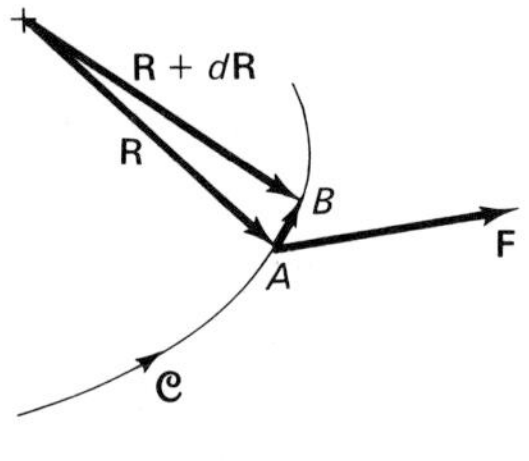

Fig. 9.27 Work.

Besides the form $\int_{\mathscr{C}} f\, ds$, we also meet line integrals in the form

$$\int_{\mathscr{C}} \mathbf{F} \cdot d\mathbf{R}, \tag{10}$$

where $\mathbf{R}$ is the position vector from some reference point, or origin, to points on the curve $\mathscr{C}$. For example, if a particle is subjected to a force $\mathbf{F}$ as the particle moves along a curve $\mathscr{C}$, then the work done by $\mathbf{F}$, as the particle moves an infinitesimal distance along $\mathscr{C}$, say from A to B (Fig. 9.27), is (according to Example 1, page 24)

$$dW = \mathbf{F} \cdot \mathbf{AB} = \mathbf{F} \cdot d\mathbf{R}. \tag{11}$$

Evidently, then, the net work done in traversing the entire curve $\mathscr{C}$ is

$$W = \int_{\mathscr{C}} \mathbf{F} \cdot d\mathbf{R}. \tag{12}$$

In this case the curve $\mathscr{C}$ is actually traversed by the particle, so we sometimes refer to it as a *path*. By the way, if $\mathbf{F} = P(x, y, z)\hat{\mathbf{i}} + Q(x, y, z)\hat{\mathbf{j}} + R(x, y, z)\hat{\mathbf{k}}$, and we express $\mathbf{R} = x\hat{\mathbf{i}} + y\hat{\mathbf{j}} + z\hat{\mathbf{k}}$, then $\int_{\mathscr{C}} \mathbf{F} \cdot d\mathbf{R}$ may be "spread out" as

$$\begin{aligned} \int_{\mathscr{C}} \mathbf{F} \cdot d\mathbf{R} &= \int_{\mathscr{C}} (P\hat{\mathbf{i}} + Q\hat{\mathbf{j}} + R\hat{\mathbf{k}}) \cdot (dx\, \hat{\mathbf{i}} + dy\, \hat{\mathbf{j}} + dz\, \hat{\mathbf{k}}) \\ &= \int_{\mathscr{C}} (P\, dx + Q\, dy + R\, dz). \end{aligned} \tag{13}$$

If desired, the integral in (12) may be reexpressed in the standard line integral form $\int_{\mathscr{C}} f\, ds$ since

$$\int_{\mathscr{C}} \mathbf{F} \cdot d\mathbf{R} = \int_{\mathscr{C}} \left(\mathbf{F} \cdot \frac{d\mathbf{R}}{ds}\right) ds = \int_{\mathscr{C}} f\, ds \qquad \left(f \equiv \mathbf{F} \cdot \frac{d\mathbf{R}}{ds}\right). \tag{14}$$

Alternatively, if $\mathscr{C}$ is parametrized as $\mathbf{R} = \mathbf{R}(\tau)$, where τ is a parameter and $a \le \tau \le b$ on $\mathscr{C}$, we may reexpress the integral in the "ordinary integral" form $\int_a^b f(\tau)\, d\tau$ since

$$\int_{\mathscr{C}} \mathbf{F} \cdot d\mathbf{R} = \int_a^b \left(\mathbf{F} \cdot \frac{d\mathbf{R}}{d\tau}\right) d\tau = \int_a^b f(\tau)\, d\tau \qquad \left(f \equiv \mathbf{F} \cdot \frac{d\mathbf{R}}{d\tau}\right). \tag{15}$$

But there is a difference between $\int_{\mathscr{C}} f\, ds$ and $\int_{\mathscr{C}} \mathbf{F} \cdot d\mathbf{R}$ that should be understood. Namely, the curve $\mathscr{C}$ in $\int_{\mathscr{C}} \mathbf{F} \cdot d\mathbf{R}$ is *oriented* (as indicated by the arrow in Fig. 9.27) by virtue of the presence of the "$d\mathbf{R}$." For example, if the particle moves along $\mathscr{C}$ (Fig. 9.27) in the direction of the arrow, then $d\mathbf{R}$ between $\mathbf{A}$ and $\mathbf{B}$ is $d\mathbf{R} = \mathbf{AB}$, whereas if the motion is in the opposite direction, then $d\mathbf{R} = \mathbf{BA} = -\mathbf{AB}$. Thus if we denote by $-\mathscr{C}$ the same curve as $\mathscr{C}$, but traversed in the opposite direction, we have

$$\int_{-\mathscr{C}} \mathbf{F} \cdot d\mathbf{R} = -\int_{\mathscr{C}} \mathbf{F} \cdot d\mathbf{R}. \tag{16}$$

In contrast, the ds's in $\int_{\mathscr{C}} f\, ds$ are incremental *lengths,* and are always positive, so that $\int_{\mathscr{C}} f\, ds$ is insensitive to the orientation of $\mathscr{C}$; the orientation of $\mathscr{C}$ simply *is not relevant* in $\int_{\mathscr{C}} f\, ds$.* This point could, if you wish, be emphasized by writing the integral as $\int_{\mathscr{C}} f\,|ds|$ instead.

EXAMPLE 2 Let $\mathbf{F} = 2xz\hat{\mathbf{i}} + x^3\hat{\mathbf{j}} - z\hat{\mathbf{k}}$, and let $\mathscr{C}$ be the path from (1, 0, 0) to (0, 2, 0) shown in Fig. 9.28. According to (12), the work done is

$$W = \int_{\mathscr{C}} \mathbf{F} \cdot d\mathbf{R} = \int_{\mathscr{C}} (2xz\hat{\mathbf{i}} + x^3\hat{\mathbf{j}} - z\hat{\mathbf{k}}) \cdot (dx\hat{\mathbf{i}} + dy\hat{\mathbf{j}} + dz\hat{\mathbf{k}})$$

* Looking back at (14), an interesting puzzle arises: If we reverse the orientation of $\mathscr{C}$, it appears that the integral $\int_{\mathscr{C}} \mathbf{F} \cdot d\mathbf{R}$ (on the left-hand side) changes sign, whereas the integral $\int_{\mathscr{C}} f\, ds$ (on the right) does not. However, notice that the integrand $f = \mathbf{F} \cdot d\mathbf{R}/ds$ contains $d\mathbf{R}$, so that f itself changes sign if the orientation of $\mathscr{C}$ is reversed.

$$= \int_{\mathscr{C}} (2xz\,dx + x^3\,dy - z\,dz) \tag{17}$$

$$= \int_{\mathscr{C}_1} (2xz\,dx + x^3\,dy - z\,dz) + \int_{\mathscr{C}_2} (2xz\,dx + x^3\,dy - z\,dz).$$

In this case **R** is not handed to us in parametric form (as it was in Example 1), so we need to develop such a parametrization. From Fig. 9.28 we see that $\mathscr{C}_1$ and $\mathscr{C}_2$ may be parametrized (independently) as

$$\mathscr{C}_1: \quad x = 1 - \tau,\ y = 0,\ z = \tau, \quad \text{as } \tau \text{ increases from 0 to 1,} \tag{18a}$$

$$\mathscr{C}_2: \quad x = 0,\ y = 2 - 2\tau,\ z = \tau, \quad \text{as } \tau \text{ decreases from 1 to 0,} \tag{18b}$$

Then (17) may, as noted in (15), be expressed as

$$W = \int_{\mathscr{C}_1} \left(2xz\frac{dx}{d\tau} + x^3\frac{dy}{d\tau} - z\frac{dz}{d\tau}\right) d\tau + \int_{\mathscr{C}_2} \left(2xz\frac{dx}{d\tau} + x^3\frac{dy}{d\tau} - z\frac{dz}{d\tau}\right) d\tau$$

$$= \int_0^1 [2(1-\tau)\tau(-1) + 0 - \tau]\,d\tau + \int_1^0 (0 + 0 - \tau)\,d\tau \tag{19}$$

$$= -\frac{5}{6} + \frac{1}{2} = -\frac{1}{3}.$$

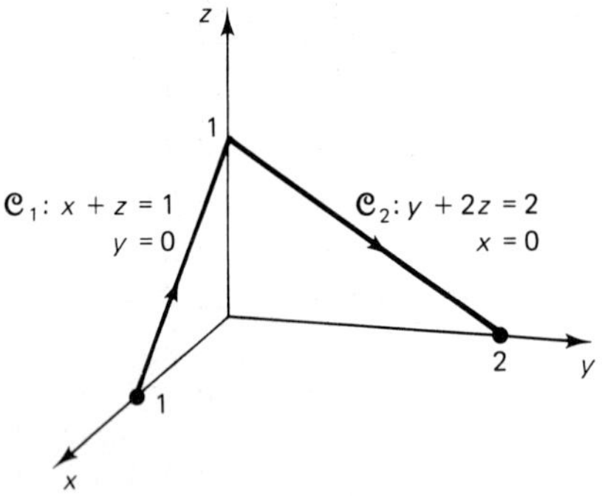

Fig. 9.28 The path $\mathscr{C} = \mathscr{C}_1 + \mathscr{C}_2$.

COMMENT 1 Where did we get the parametrizations (18)? Would other parametrizations have led to the same final result? Consider $\mathscr{C}_2$, say. $\mathscr{C}_2$ is the intersection of the planes $y + 2z = 2$ and $x = 0$. Solving these two equations in the three unknowns x, y, z, say by Gauss elimination, we obtain the one-parameter family of solutions $z = \tau$, $y = 2 - 2\tau$, $x = 0$. These results, which are of the form $x = x(\tau)$, $y = y(\tau)$, $z = z(\tau)$, are in fact the desired parametric equations of $\mathscr{C}_2$. The parametrizations given in (18) are by no means the only possible ones, and other parametrizations would serve as well, and would lead to the same final result. To illustrate, consider just the $\mathscr{C}_2$ part of the integral, and use the (different) parametrization $x = 0$, $y = 2\tau^2$, $z = 1 - \tau^2$ as τ increases from 0 to 1. Then

$$\int_{\mathscr{C}_2} \left(2xz\frac{dx}{d\tau} + x^3\frac{dy}{d\tau} - z\frac{dz}{d\tau}\right) d\tau = \int_0^1 [0 + 0 - (1-\tau^2)(-2\tau)]\,d\tau = \frac{1}{2},$$

as was obtained in (19).

COMMENT 2 In this case $W = -\frac{1}{3}$ is negative: line integrals may be positive, negative, or zero.

COMMENT 3 Suppose that we close the contour $\mathscr{C}$ by adding a straight segment $\mathscr{C}_3$ from (0, 2, 0) to (1, 0, 0). Since $z = 0$ and $2x + y = 2$ on $\mathscr{C}_3$, we may parametrize $\mathscr{C}_3$ by $x = \tau$, $y = 2 - 2\tau$, $z = 0$, say, as τ increases from 0 to 1. The integral $\int \mathbf{F} \cdot d\mathbf{R}$ over $\mathscr{C}_1 + \mathscr{C}_2$ is the same as before, so that the integral around the *closed path* $\mathscr{C} = \mathscr{C}_1 + \mathscr{C}_2 + \mathscr{C}_3$ is

$$\begin{aligned}\int_{\mathscr{C}} \mathbf{F} \cdot d\mathbf{R} &= \int_{\mathscr{C}_1} \mathbf{F} \cdot d\mathbf{R} + \int_{\mathscr{C}_2} \mathbf{F} \cdot d\mathbf{R} + \int_{\mathscr{C}_3} \mathbf{F} \cdot d\mathbf{R} \\ &= -\frac{5}{6} + \frac{1}{2} + \int_0^1 [0 + \tau^3(-2) - 0]\, d\tau \qquad (20) \\ &= -\frac{5}{6} + \frac{1}{2} - \frac{1}{2} = -\frac{5}{6}.\end{aligned}$$

Notice that the result happens not to be zero. That is, even though $\mathscr{C}$ is a closed path and "we end up right back where we started," that does *not* imply that $\int_{\mathscr{C}} \mathbf{F} \cdot d\mathbf{R}$ is necessarily zero (although it *may* be). ◀

If $\mathscr{C}$ is a closed curve, as in Comment 3, we often call attention to that fact by putting a circle through the integral sign, so that the line integral is then denoted as

$$\oint_{\mathscr{C}} \mathbf{F} \cdot d\mathbf{R}. \qquad (21)$$

An example of this form that might be mentioned here is the integral on the left-hand side of the equation

$$\oint_{\mathscr{C}} \mathbf{H} \cdot d\mathbf{R} = I \qquad (22)$$

encountered in electromagnetics.* Known as *Ampère's law,* (22) states that the line integral of the *magnetic field intensity* $\mathbf{H}$ (amperes/meter) around a closed curve $\mathscr{C}$ equals the *current* I (amperes) enclosed by $\mathscr{C}$.

The fluid mechanics analog of (22) is the statement

$$\oint_{\mathscr{C}} \mathbf{q} \cdot d\mathbf{R} = \Gamma, \qquad (23)$$

where $\mathbf{q}$ is the fluid velocity field (meters/second) and Γ is known as the *circulation* (meters^2/second) around $\mathscr{C}$. Γ is of great importance in aerodynamics because of its place in the *Kutta–Joukowsky formula* for the lift force on an airfoil (i.e., a wing),

$$L = \sigma U \Gamma, \qquad (24)$$

where L is the lift force per unit spanwise length of the airfoil (i.e., per unit length

* The formula holds for steady fields. For time-varying fields an additional term is needed in (22), as noted on p. 345 of W. H. Hayt, Jr., *Engineering Electromagnetics,* 3rd ed. (New York: McGraw Hill, 1974).

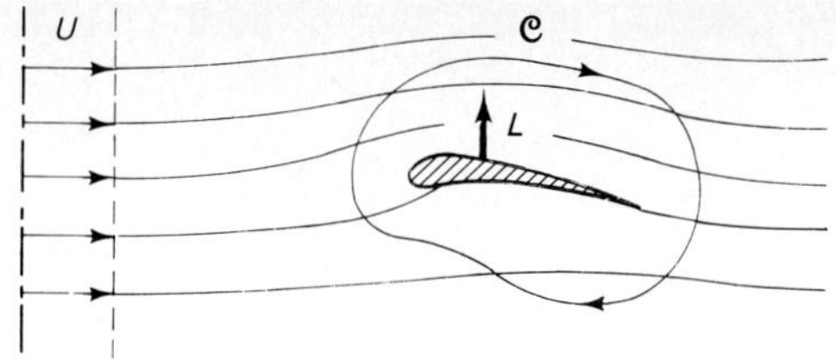

Fig. 9.29 Generation of lift on stationary airfoil.

normal to the paper in Fig. 9.29), σ is the mass density of the air (or other fluid), U is the air velocity,* and Γ is the circulation around any closed clockwise contour $\mathscr{C}$ which encloses the airfoil, as in Fig. 9.29. Formula (24) begs an observation. If we choose different contours $\mathscr{C}$, and hence obtain different values of the line integral, we obtain different values for the lift. Yet surely the lift must be uniquely determined. The resolution of this "paradox" lies in the fact that the flow field $\mathbf{q}$ around airfoils happens to be such that $\nabla \times \mathbf{q} = \mathbf{0}$, and this condition—as we shall see in the sections to follow—ensures that the line integral in (23) is uniquely determined, independent of the shape of $\mathscr{C}$. The point of this comment is that whereas we have defined line integrals and illustrated their calculation in this section, there do remain some important issues to be explored.

EXAMPLE 3 Evaluate $\int_{\mathscr{C}} (y^2\,dx - xy\,dy)$, where $\mathscr{C}$ is the parabolic path shown in Fig. 9.30. An obvious parametrization of $\mathscr{C}$ is

$$x = \tau, \qquad y = 3\tau - \tau^2 \tag{25}$$

as τ increases from 0 to 3, so that

$$\int_{\mathscr{C}} (y^2\,dx - xy\,dy) = \int_0^3 [(3\tau - \tau^2)^2 - \tau(3\tau - \tau^2)(3 - 2\tau)]\,d\tau = \frac{243}{20}. \tag{26}$$

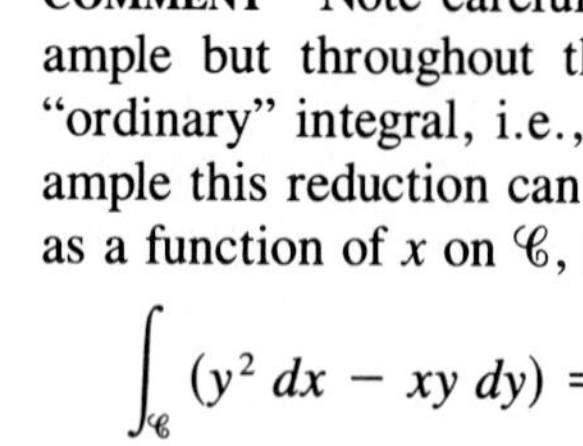

Fig. 9.30 The path $\mathscr{C}$.

COMMENT Note carefully that the reason we parametrize $\mathscr{C}$, not only in this example but throughout this section, is to reduce the given line integral to an "ordinary" integral, i.e., to an integral of the form $\int_a^b F(x)\,dx$. In the present example this reduction can be accomplished easily by noting that y may be regarded as a function of x on $\mathscr{C}$, namely, $y = 3x - x^2$.† Thus

$$\int_{\mathscr{C}} (y^2\,dx - xy\,dy) = \int_0^3 [y^2(x) - xy(x)y'(x)]\,dx \tag{27}$$

* Whether the airfoil is stationary and the fluid is moving (as in a wind tunnel), or the reverse is true (as in actual flight), the lift is the same.

† But x is *not* a function of y on $\mathscr{C}$ since it is double valued; if we *insist* on regarding x as a function of y on $\mathscr{C}$ we would have to break $\mathscr{C}$ into two parts, OP and PQ. On OP we have $x = (3 - \sqrt{9 - 4y})/2$, and on PQ we have $x = (3 + \sqrt{9 - 4y})/2$.

$$= \int_0^3 [(3x - x^2)^2 - x(3x - x^2)(3 - 2x)]\, dx = \frac{243}{20}.$$

The calculation in (27) is virtually the same as in (26) since, after all, we merely had $x = \tau$ in (25). That is, it was a bit of overkill to introduce the parametrization (25) since x itself is a suitable parameter for the given curve $\mathscr{C}$. ◀

EXAMPLE 4 Evaluate $\int_{\mathscr{C}} y^2\, dx$, where $\mathscr{C}$ is as shown in Fig. 9.31. Since x is a constant all along $\mathscr{C}$, all of the dx increments are zero, so $\int_{\mathscr{C}} y^2\, dx = 0$. In case this statement is not convincing, let us parametrize $\mathscr{C}$ *by* $x = 2$, $y = \tau$. Then

$$\int_{\mathscr{C}} y^2\, dx = \int_0^3 (\tau^2)\left(\frac{dx}{d\tau}\, d\tau\right) = \int_0^3 (\tau^2)(0)\, d\tau = 0. \quad ◀$$

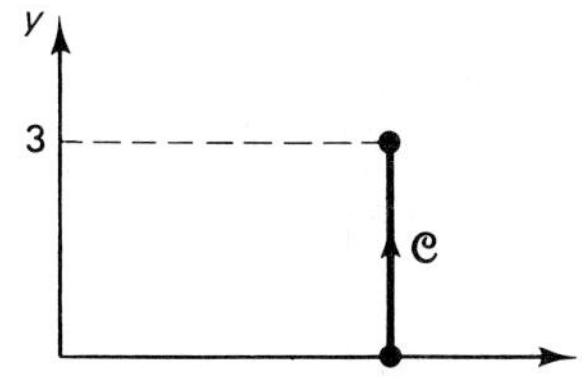

Fig. 9.31 The path $\mathscr{C}$.

In summary, we have introduced the line integral $\int_{\mathscr{C}} f\, ds$, where $\mathscr{C}$ is either an arc or a closed curve, and have shown how to evaluate it by parametrizing $\mathscr{C}$ so as to obtain an "ordinary" integral on the parameter τ. We noted that line integrals also occur in the form $\int_{\mathscr{C}} \mathbf{F} \cdot d\mathbf{R}$, and only in this form is the orientation of $\mathscr{C}$ relevant, owing to the directed nature of the $d\mathbf{R}$ increments. Such integrals arise frequently in applications in such subjects as dynamics, electromagnetics, fluid mechanics, and thermodynamics.

9.10 EXERCISES

1. Evaluate $\int_{\mathscr{C}} f\, ds$ in each case.

*(a) $f = xy^2 + 2xy$, $\mathscr{C}$: $x = \tau$, $y = 3$, $z = 0$ $(-1 \le \tau \le 2)$

(b) $f = 2x^3y$, $\mathscr{C}$: $x = \tau$, $y = 4$, $z = 0$ $(0 \le \tau \le 2)$

(c) $f = x^2 + y^2$, $\mathscr{C}$: $x = 2\tau - 1$, $y = 3$, $z = \tau$ $(0 \le \tau \le 1)$

(d) $f = \sqrt{x - yz}$, $\mathscr{C}$: $x = 2$, $y = -4\tau$, $z = 3$ $(0 \le \tau \le 5)$

*(e) $f = \sqrt{1 + 30x^2 + 10y}$, $\mathscr{C}$: $x = \tau$, $y = \tau^2$, $z = 3\tau^2$ $(0 \le \tau \le 2)$

(f) $f = x$, $\mathscr{C}$: $x = \tau$, $y = \tau^2$, $z = \tau^2$ $(1 \le \tau \le 3)$

(g) $f = xy - 3z^2$, $\mathscr{C}$ $x = 2\cos\tau$, $y = 2\sin\tau$, $z = 3\tau$ $(\pi \le \tau \le 4\pi)$

(h) $f = x$, $\mathscr{C}$: $x = \tau$, $y = 2\tau^2 + 1$, $z = \tau - \tau^2$ $(0 \le \tau \le 1)$

2. Define these points in Cartesian 3-space: $P = (1, 0, 0)$, $Q = (1, 0, 2)$, $R = (0, 0, 2)$, $S = (0, 0, 0)$, $T = (0, 4, 0)$, $U = (0, 4, 3)$. By $\mathscr{C} = PQR$, say, we will mean the curve consisting of a straight line from P to Q and then a straight line from Q to R. Evaluate $\int_{\mathscr{C}} \mathbf{F} \cdot d\mathbf{R}$ in each case. *Hint:* A straight-line path from (x_1, y_1, z_1) to (x_2, y_2, z_2) may be parametrized according to $x = x_1 + (x_2 - x_1)\tau$, $y = y_1 + (y_2 - y_1)\tau$, $z = z_1 + (z_2 - z_1)\tau$ $(0 \le \tau \le 1)$.

*(a) $\mathbf{F} = 3x^2z\hat{\mathbf{j}}$, $\mathscr{C} = PQ$

(b) $\mathbf{F} = 6\hat{\mathbf{j}} - x^3z\hat{\mathbf{k}}$, $\mathscr{C} = PQ$

(c) $\mathbf{F} = 6\hat{\mathbf{i}} - 2\hat{\mathbf{k}}$, $\mathscr{C} = PQR$

(d) $\mathbf{F} = 2\hat{\mathbf{i}} + \hat{\mathbf{j}} + 4\hat{\mathbf{k}}$, $\mathscr{C} = PT$

*(e) $\mathbf{F} = z\hat{\mathbf{j}} - \hat{\mathbf{k}}$, $\mathscr{C} = PUQP$

(f) $\mathbf{F} = xz\hat{\mathbf{i}} + y^2\hat{\mathbf{k}}$, $\mathscr{C} = PU$

(g) $\mathbf{F} = y\hat{\mathbf{i}} - xyj - \hat{\mathbf{k}}$, $\mathscr{C} = PRUP$

(h) $\mathbf{F} = y \sin x\hat{\mathbf{i}} + x^3 \cos^2 y\hat{\mathbf{k}}$, $\mathscr{C} = STP$
(i) $\mathbf{F} = e^x\hat{\mathbf{i}} + xz\hat{\mathbf{k}}$, $\mathscr{C} = QRTQ$
(j) $\mathbf{F} = \hat{\mathbf{i}} + 4 \sin x\hat{\mathbf{j}}$, $\mathscr{C} = PTU$
(k) $\mathbf{F} = xyz\hat{\mathbf{j}}$, $\mathscr{C} = PSRQT$
(l) $\mathbf{F} = y \sin^2 z\hat{\mathbf{i}} - x^3 z\hat{\mathbf{k}}$, $\mathscr{C} = PRQ$
(m) $\mathbf{F} = (x^3 - y \sin z)\hat{\mathbf{j}}$, $\mathscr{C} = PQTP$
(n) $\mathbf{F} = (x^2 - z^2)\hat{\mathbf{i}} - 6\hat{\mathbf{k}}$, $\mathscr{C} = QS$
(o) $\mathbf{F} = x^3 z^2\hat{\mathbf{i}}$, $\mathscr{C} = QU$
(p) $\mathbf{F} = xe^{\sin z}\hat{\mathbf{k}}$, $\mathscr{C} = QRS$
(q) $\mathbf{F} = y\hat{\mathbf{i}} + x\hat{\mathbf{j}}$, $\mathscr{C} = UQU$
(r) $\mathbf{F} = xy\hat{\mathbf{i}} + yz\hat{\mathbf{k}}$, $\mathscr{C} = UT$

3. Evaluate $\int_{\mathscr{C}} \mathbf{v} \cdot d\mathbf{R}$ in each case, given the path $\mathscr{C}$ in the x, y plane, and the field $\mathbf{v}(x, y)$.
*(a) $\mathbf{v} = \sin y\, \mathbf{i}$, $\mathscr{C}: y = \sqrt{x}$, from (9, 3) to (1, 1)
(b) $\mathbf{v} = x\hat{\mathbf{i}} - xy\hat{\mathbf{j}}$, $\mathscr{C}: y = x^3 - 2x$, from (−1, 1) to (2, 4)
(c) $\mathbf{v} = 2\hat{\mathbf{i}} - 5\hat{\mathbf{j}}$, $\mathscr{C}: y = x^4 \sin [\pi(\sqrt{x} + \frac{1}{2})]$, from (0, 0) to (1, −1)
(d) $\mathbf{v} = e^x\hat{\mathbf{i}} - 3y^2\hat{\mathbf{j}}$, $\mathscr{C}: y = x^2 \sin [(\pi/2)(x^2 + 2)]$, from (0, 0) to (1, −1)
*(e) $\mathbf{v} = (x^2 + y^2)\hat{\mathbf{j}}$, $\mathscr{C}: y = x^3$, from (2, 8) to (1, 1)
(f) $\mathbf{v} = (x^3 - 5y)\hat{\mathbf{j}}$, $\mathscr{C}: y + x^2 = 1$, from (1, 0) to (−1, 0)
(g) $\mathbf{v} = y^2\hat{\mathbf{i}} - \hat{\mathbf{j}}$, $\mathscr{C}: y^4 - x = 1$, from (0, −1) to (0, 1)
(h) $\mathbf{v} = e^{-x} \sin^2 x\hat{\mathbf{i}} + xy^2\hat{\mathbf{j}}$, $\mathscr{C}: y^6 - x = 1$, from (0, −1) to (0, 1)
(i) $\mathbf{v} = y\hat{\mathbf{i}} - x\hat{\mathbf{j}}$, $\mathscr{C}: y^6 - x = 1$, from (0, 1) to (0, −1)

4. Evaluate $\oint_{\mathscr{C}} (P\, dx + Q\, dy)$, where $\mathscr{C}$ is the triangle with vertices at (0, 0), (1, 0), (1, 2) in the x, y plane, traversed counterclockwise.
*(a) $P = x^3$, $Q = 0$ (b) $P = 0$, $Q = y^2$
*(c) $P = x^3 \sin x$, $Q = x$ (d) $P = xy$, $Q = y^4 e^y$

5. Evaluate the following line integrals, where $\mathscr{C}$ is the closed ellipse $(x/a)^2 + (y/b)^2 = 1$, traversed clockwise. *Hint:* You may wish to use the parametrization $x = a \cos \tau$, $y = b \sin \tau$.
(a) $\oint_{\mathscr{C}} (y\, dx + x\, dy)$ *(b) $\oint_{\mathscr{C}} (y\, dx - x\, dy)$
(c) $\oint_{\mathscr{C}} (x^6 \sin x\, dx + dy)$ (d) $\oint_{\mathscr{C}} x^3 y\, dy$
(e) $\oint_{\mathscr{C}} x^7\, dx$ (f) $\oint_{\mathscr{C}} (x + y)\, dy$

6. Show that $\oint_{\mathscr{C}} \mathbf{F} \cdot d\mathbf{R} = 0$ for every closed path $\mathscr{C}$ if $\mathbf{F}$ is a constant vector.

7. Evaluate $\int_{\mathscr{C}} (x^4\, dx + xy\, dy)$, where $\mathscr{C}$ is
(a) the upper half of the unit circle, taken clockwise
(b) the lower half of the unit circle, taken clockwise

8. If a charge q (coulombs) moves with velocity $\mathbf{v}$ (meters/second) in the presence of both an *electric field* $\mathbf{E}$ (newtons/coulomb) and a *magnetic flux density field* $\mathbf{B}$ (webers/meter^2), the force $\mathbf{F}$ (newtons) exerted on q is known to be given by the *Lorentz force equation*

$$\mathbf{F} = q(\mathbf{E} + \mathbf{v} \times \mathbf{B}). \qquad \text{(a)}$$

Show that the $\mathbf{B}$ field does no work, i.e., $\int_{\mathscr{C}} q\mathbf{v} \times \mathbf{B} \cdot d\mathbf{R} = 0$, so that the work done is $W = \int_{\mathscr{C}} \mathbf{F} \cdot d\mathbf{R} = q \int_{\mathscr{C}} \mathbf{E} \cdot d\mathbf{R}$. *Hint*: The material in Section 7.4 is relevant here. *Note:* To place the physics in perspective, let us note that the magnetic field intensity $\mathbf{H}$ in (22), and the magnetic flux density $\mathbf{B}$ are closely related: $\mathbf{B} = \mu_0\mathbf{H}$ in free space (i.e., vacuum), where μ_0 is a constant known as the permeability of free space. If the space is *not* free of matter and there is a magnetic dipole moment per unit volume present, called the *magnetization* $\mathbf{M}$ (amperes/meter), then $\mathbf{B} = \mu_0(\mathbf{H} + \mathbf{M})$.

9.11 STOKES' THEOREM; GREEN'S THEOREM

Following Newton's death in 1727 the mathematical scene in the British Isles was relatively quiet for almost 100 years. There then appeared a number of exceptional mathematical physicists, beginning with *George Green* (1793–1841) and *William R. Hamilton* (1805–1865), and followed by the "Cambridge school," which included the likes of *Sir G. Gabriel Stokes* (1819–1903), *Lord Kelvin* (Sir William Thomson; 1824–1907), *James Clerk Maxwell* (1831–1879), and *Lord Rayleigh* (John William Strutt; 1842–1919).

In this section we examine two important and closely related theorems, one due to Stokes and one due to Green. We begin with Stokes' theorem, which expresses an integral over a surface in terms of an integral along the edge of that surface.

STOKES' THEOREM

Recall the two-dimensional divergence theorem [(30) on page 399],

$$\int_{\mathcal{S}} \operatorname{div} \mathbf{V}\, dA = \int_{\mathcal{C}} \hat{\mathbf{N}} \cdot \mathbf{V}\, ds, \tag{1}$$

where $\mathcal{S}$ (denoted as $\mathcal{R}$ on page 399) is a plane closed region, and $\hat{\mathbf{N}}$ is the outward unit normal to the boundary curve $\mathcal{C}$ of $\mathcal{S}$, as in Fig. 9.32. Writing out the integrands in (1) gives us

$$\int_{\mathcal{S}} \left(\frac{\partial V_x}{\partial x} + \frac{\partial V_y}{\partial y} \right) dA = \int_{\mathcal{C}} (N_x V_x + N_y V_y)\, ds, \tag{2}$$

where $\mathbf{V} = V_x\hat{\mathbf{i}} + V_y\hat{\mathbf{j}}$ and $\hat{\mathbf{N}} = N_x\hat{\mathbf{i}} + N_y\hat{\mathbf{j}}$. If we define a new vector $\mathbf{v} = v_x\hat{\mathbf{i}} + v_y\hat{\mathbf{j}} \equiv -V_y\hat{\mathbf{i}} + V_x\hat{\mathbf{j}}$, then (2) becomes

$$\begin{aligned} \int_{\mathcal{S}} \left(\frac{\partial v_y}{\partial x} - \frac{\partial v_x}{\partial y} \right) dA &= \int_{\mathcal{C}} (N_x v_y - N_y v_x)\, ds, \\ &= \int_{\mathcal{C}} (v_x\hat{\mathbf{i}} + v_y\hat{\mathbf{j}}) \cdot (-N_y\hat{\mathbf{i}} + N_x\hat{\mathbf{j}})\, ds \\ &= \int_{\mathcal{C}} \mathbf{v} \cdot \hat{\mathbf{T}}\, ds, \end{aligned} \tag{3}$$

where (Fig. 9.32) $\hat{\mathbf{T}} = -N_y\hat{\mathbf{i}} + N_x\hat{\mathbf{j}}$ is the unit (counterclockwise) tangent vector to $\mathcal{C}$. Noting that the integrand on the left is the z component of curl $\mathbf{v}$ and that $\hat{\mathbf{T}}\, ds = d\mathbf{R}$, (3) becomes

$$\int_{\mathcal{S}} \hat{\mathbf{k}} \cdot \operatorname{curl} \mathbf{v}\, dA = \oint_{\mathcal{C}} \mathbf{v} \cdot d\mathbf{R}, \tag{4}$$

where $\hat{\mathbf{k}}$ is the Cartesian base vector in the z direction, and $\mathcal{C}$ is oriented counterclockwise. Here $\mathcal{S}$ is a *flat* surface, but it turns out that (4) can be shown to hold for curved surfaces as well (see Exercise 9), and the full result is known as **Stokes' theorem.**

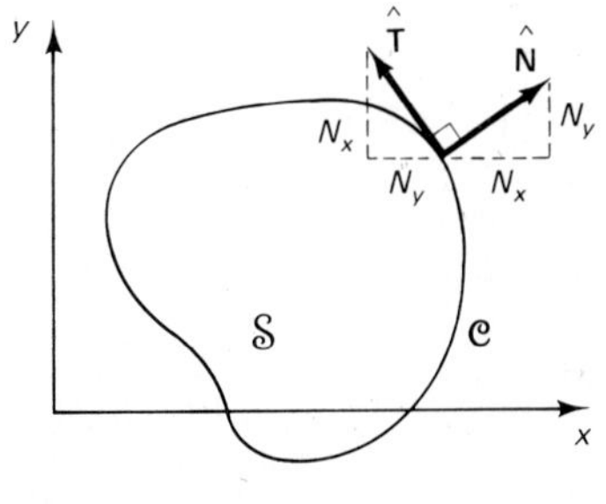

Fig. 9.32 $\mathcal{S}$, $\mathcal{C}$, and $\hat{\mathbf{N}}$ in (1).

> ***Theorem 1*** *Stokes' Theorem*
>
> Let a C^1 vector field $\mathbf{v}$ be defined in a region $\mathscr{R}$ in 3-space. Let $\mathscr{S}$ be a piecewise-smooth orientable surface within $\mathscr{R}$,* and let the edge of $\mathscr{S}$ be a piecewise-smooth simple closed curve $\mathscr{C}$. Then
>
> $$\boxed{\int_{\mathscr{S}} \hat{\mathbf{n}} \cdot \operatorname{curl} \mathbf{v} \, dA = \oint_{\mathscr{C}} \mathbf{v} \cdot d\mathbf{R},} \tag{5}$$
>
> where $\hat{\mathbf{n}}$ is a unit normal to $\mathscr{S}$, the orientation of $\mathscr{C}$ and the direction of $\hat{\mathbf{n}}$ being in accordance with the right-hand rule.†

We need to explain our statement in the theorem about the right-hand rule. First, observe that we refrain from calling $\hat{\mathbf{n}}$ the "outward" or "inward" normal to $\mathscr{S}$. If $\mathscr{S}$ were a *closed* surface, such as the surface of a sphere or cube, it would make sense to speak of an outward (or inward) normal to $\mathscr{S}$, since $\mathscr{S}$ would "inherit" an orientation from the volume $\mathscr{V}$ that it enclosed: normal vectors on $\mathscr{S}$ directed into $\mathscr{V}$ would be called inward, and those directed out of $\mathscr{V}$ would be called outward. But in Stokes' theorem $\mathscr{S}$ is *not* a closed surface, and it would not be meaningful to designate $\hat{\mathbf{n}}$ as the outward (or inward) normal because the terms "outward" and "inward" do not apply here.

The idea, then, is that $\hat{\mathbf{n}}$, in (5), can be *either* of the two (oppositely directed) fields of normals on $\mathscr{S}$. Similarly, $\mathscr{C}$ can be oriented in *either* of two possible directions. Selecting one of those two orientations for $\mathscr{C}$, arbitrarily, we then choose between the two possible normals so that $\hat{\mathbf{n}}$ and $\mathscr{C}$ are in accordance with the right-hand rule. That is, if we consider a small contour c, part of which coincides with (and is oriented in the same way as) the boundary curve $\mathscr{C}$, then applying the right-hand rule to c yields a normal $\hat{\mathbf{n}}$ (Fig. 9.33). We then continue this normal over the rest of $\mathscr{S}$. For example, if the surface $\mathscr{S}$ is a flat surface in the x, y plane, as in (4), we can have $\hat{\mathbf{n}} = +\hat{\mathbf{k}}$ and $\mathscr{C}$ counterclockwise [as in (4)], *or* $\hat{\mathbf{n}} = -\hat{\mathbf{k}}$ and $\mathscr{C}$ clockwise.

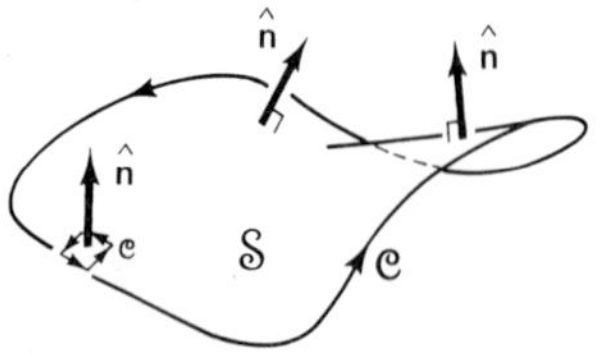

Fig. 9.33 $\mathscr{S}$, $\mathscr{C}$, and $\hat{\mathbf{n}}$ in Stokes' theorem.

EXAMPLE 1 Suppose that $\mathscr{S}$ is that part of the parabolic surface $z = 1 - x^2 - y^2$ that lies in the region $x \geq 0$, $y \geq 0$, $z \geq 0$, as depicted in Fig. 9.34. Let the edge curve $\mathscr{C}$ be oriented as $ABCA$, and let $\mathbf{v} = yz\hat{\mathbf{k}}$. Our object in this example is to il-

* "Piecewise-smooth surface" was defined on page 316; "orientable surface" was defined on page 352.

† For a concise proof of Stokes' theorem, see, for example, I. S. Sokolnikoff and R. M. Redheffer, *Mathematics of Physics and Modern Engineering*, 2nd ed. (New York: McGraw-Hill, 1966), p. 404. For a more detailed discussion, see MARSDEN AND TROMBA, Sec. 7.2.

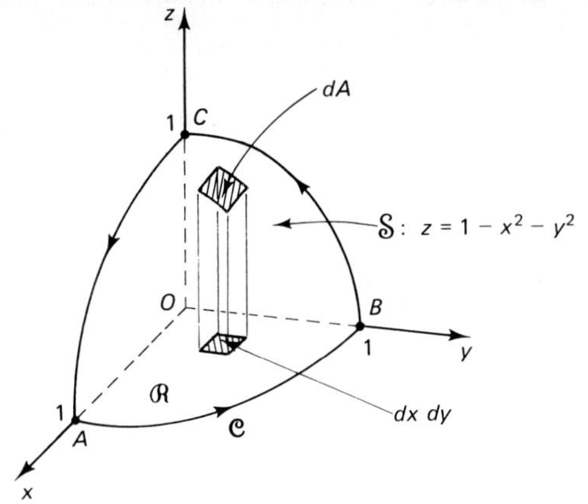

Fig. 9.34 $\mathcal{S}$ and $\mathcal{C}$ for Example 1.

lustrate the calculations involved in (5) by working out both integrals and verifying the equality.

First,

$$\operatorname{curl} \mathbf{v} = \begin{vmatrix} \hat{\mathbf{i}} & \hat{\mathbf{j}} & \hat{\mathbf{k}} \\ \dfrac{\partial}{\partial x} & \dfrac{\partial}{\partial y} & \dfrac{\partial}{\partial z} \\ 0 & 0 & yz \end{vmatrix} = z\hat{\mathbf{i}}.$$

Next, we obtain $\hat{\mathbf{n}}$ on $\mathcal{S}$ by taking the gradient of $f(x, y, z) = z + x^2 + y^2 - 1$ and normalizing the result. Thus

$$\mathbf{n} = \nabla(z + x^2 + y^2 - 1) = 2x\hat{\mathbf{i}} + 2y\hat{\mathbf{j}} + \hat{\mathbf{k}}$$

and

$$\hat{\mathbf{n}} = \frac{2x\hat{\mathbf{i}} + 2y\hat{\mathbf{j}} + \hat{\mathbf{k}}}{\sqrt{1 + 4(x^2 + y^2)}}. \tag{6}$$

[If $\mathcal{C}$ were oriented the other way, as *ACBA*, then $\hat{\mathbf{n}}$ would be the negative of the expression given in (6).] Finally, observe that $\mathcal{S}$ is given in the form $z = f(x, y) = 1 - x^2 - y^2$, so that we can use (8) on page 393 to give

$$dA = \sqrt{1 + f_x^2 + f_y^2}\, dx\, dy = \sqrt{1 + (-2x)^2 + (-2y)^2}\, dx\, dy. \tag{7}$$

Thus

$$\begin{aligned} \int_{\mathcal{S}} \hat{\mathbf{n}} \cdot \operatorname{curl} \mathbf{v}\, dA &= \int_{\mathcal{R}} \frac{2xz}{\sqrt{1 + 4(x^2 + y^2)}} \sqrt{1 + 4(x^2 + y^2)}\Big|_{z=1-x^2-y^2} dx\, dy \\ &= 2\int_0^1 \int_0^{\sqrt{1-y^2}} x(1 - x^2 - y^2)\, dx\, dy = \frac{4}{15}, \end{aligned} \tag{8}$$

where $\mathcal{R}$ is the quarter-circle region *OABO*, i.e., the projection of $\mathcal{S}$ down onto the x, y plane. [But be sure to understand that we are indeed integrating on $\mathcal{S}$; for example, note that the integrand in (8) is evaluated on $z = 1 - x^2 - y^2$. It is just that the area element dA on $\mathcal{S}$ has been related, by means of (7), to the projected area element $dx\, dy$ in the x, y plane; as $dx\, dy$ moves about on $\mathcal{R}$, dA moves about on $\mathcal{S}$.]

Turning to the line integral, we have

$$\oint_{\mathscr{C}} \mathbf{v} \cdot d\mathbf{R} = \oint_{\mathscr{C}} yz\, dz = \int_{CA} yz\, dz + \int_{AB} yz\, dz + \int_{BC} yz\, dz. \tag{9}$$

Observe that $y = 0$ on CA and that $z = 0$ on AB. On BC we have $z = 1 - y^2$, so

$$\oint_{\mathscr{C}} \mathbf{v} \cdot d\mathbf{R} = 0 + 0 + \int_1^0 y(1 - y^2)(-2y\, dy) = \tfrac{4}{15}, \tag{10}$$

which result does agree with (8). ◀

Before turning to Green's theorem, let us indicate a modest extension of Stokes' theorem to the case where $\mathscr{S}$ has one or more "holes" in it. It should suffice to consider the surface $\mathscr{S}$ shown in Fig. 9.35, which has one hole in it and which, for simplicity, lies in the plane of the paper. The point to appreciate is that the boundary $\mathscr{C}$ of $\mathscr{S}$ is not a simple closed curve, as is required in Stokes' theorem. To remedy that difficulty, slit $\mathscr{S}$ as shown in the middle of Fig. 9.35. The slit surface $\mathscr{S}'$ *is* bounded by a simple closed curve $\mathscr{C}$, so we *can* apply Stokes' theorem to $\mathscr{S}'$. Orienting $\mathscr{C}$ one way or the other, for example as in the middle of the figure (in which case $\hat{\mathbf{n}}$ would be directed toward the reader), we have

$$\int_{\mathscr{S}'} \hat{\mathbf{n}} \cdot \operatorname{curl} \mathbf{v}\, dA = \oint_{\mathscr{C}} \mathbf{v} \cdot d\mathbf{R}. \tag{11}$$

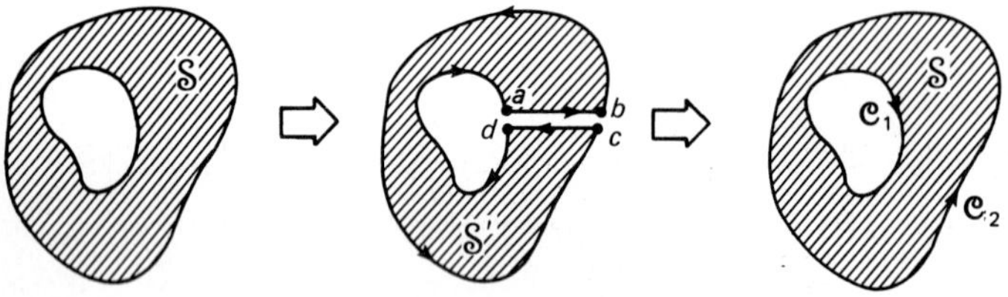

Fig. 9.35 The surface $\mathscr{S}$ with a hole.

We have exaggerated the gap between the edges *ab* and *cd* of the slit in Fig. 9.35 for graphical clarity; actually *ab* and *cd* abut. Surely, then, $\int_{\mathscr{S}'} = \int_{\mathscr{S}}$, since the only difference between $\mathscr{S}$ and $\mathscr{S}'$ is a slit of zero width; thus the prime may be dropped in (11). Further, the contributions to $\oint_{\mathscr{C}}$ from *ab* and *cd* are equal and opposite. Hence they cancel, and we are left with $\oint_{\mathscr{C}} = \oint_{\mathscr{C}_1} + \oint_{\mathscr{C}_2}$, where $\mathscr{C}_1$ and $\mathscr{C}_2$ are as shown in the right-hand part of the figure. (Note that $\mathscr{C}_1$ and $\mathscr{C}_2$ are oppositely oriented.) The result is that Stokes' theorem now takes on the modified form

$$\int_{\mathscr{S}} \hat{\mathbf{n}} \cdot \operatorname{curl} \mathbf{v}\, dA = \oint_{\mathscr{C}_1} \mathbf{v} \cdot d\mathbf{R} + \oint_{\mathscr{C}_2} \mathbf{v} \cdot d\mathbf{R}. \tag{12}$$

Observe that the slit procedure was only an artifice that permitted us to apply Stokes' theorem; no trace of the slit remains in the final equation (12).

GREEN'S THEOREM

Let us apply Stokes' theorem (Theorem 1) to the plane case where $\mathbf{v} = P(x, y)\hat{\mathbf{i}} + Q(x, y)\hat{\mathbf{j}}$ and where $\mathscr{S}$ is a flat surface in the x, y plane, and let $\mathscr{C}$ be

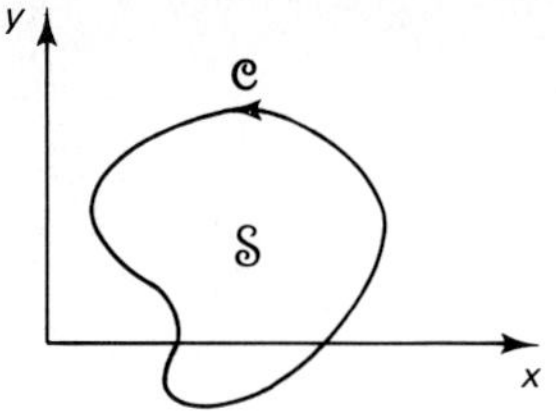

Fig. 9.36 Stokes' theorem for the plane case.

counterclockwise, say, as in Fig. 9.36. Then $\hat{\mathbf{n}} = +\hat{\mathbf{k}}$ and curl $\mathbf{v} = \left(\frac{\partial Q}{\partial x} - \frac{\partial P}{\partial y}\right)\hat{\mathbf{k}}$, so that (5) becomes

$$\int_{\mathcal{S}} \left(\frac{\partial Q}{\partial x} - \frac{\partial P}{\partial y}\right) dA = \oint_{\mathcal{C}} (P\,dx + Q\,dy).$$

Thus we have:

***Theorem 2** Green's Theorem*

Let a C^1 vector field $\mathbf{v} = P(x, y)\hat{\mathbf{i}} + Q(x, y)\hat{\mathbf{j}}$ be defined in a region $\mathcal{R}$ in 2-space. Let $\mathcal{S}$ be a region within $\mathcal{R}$, and let the edge of $\mathcal{S}$ be a piecewise-smooth simple closed curve $\mathcal{C}$, oriented counterclockwise. Then

$$\boxed{\int_{\mathcal{S}} \left(\frac{\partial Q}{\partial x} - \frac{\partial P}{\partial y}\right) dA = \oint_{\mathcal{C}} (P\,dx + Q\,dy).} \tag{13}$$

Green's theorem is really a special case of Stokes' theorem [and is also essentially the same as the two-dimensional divergence theorem (2)]. Besides the derivation of (13) from Stokes' theorem, given above, let us take a moment to offer a different, and in a sense more "fundamental," derivation.

Let us assume that $\mathcal{S}$ can be described by each of the statements

$$y_1(x) \le y \le y_2(x) \qquad \text{for } x_1 \le x \le x_2 \tag{14a}$$

and

$$x_1(y) \le x \le x_2(y) \qquad \text{for } y_1 \le y \le y_2 \tag{14b}$$

as depicted in Fig. 9.37a and b, respectively.* Considering $\int_{\mathcal{S}} \partial Q/\partial x \, dA$ and $\int_{\mathcal{S}} \partial P/\partial y \, dA$ in (13) separately, we have

$$\begin{aligned} \int_{\mathcal{S}} \frac{\partial Q}{\partial x}\, dA &= \int_{y_1}^{y_2} \int_{x_1(y)}^{x_2(y)} \frac{\partial Q}{\partial x}\, dx\, dy \qquad \text{[using (14b)]} \\ &= \int_{y_1}^{y_2} \left\{ Q(x, y) \Big|_{x=x_1(y)}^{x=x_2(y)} \right\} dy \end{aligned} \tag{15}$$

* If (14a) holds, we say that $\mathcal{S}$ is *convex in the y direction,* and if (14b) holds, we say that $\mathcal{S}$ is *convex in the x direction.*

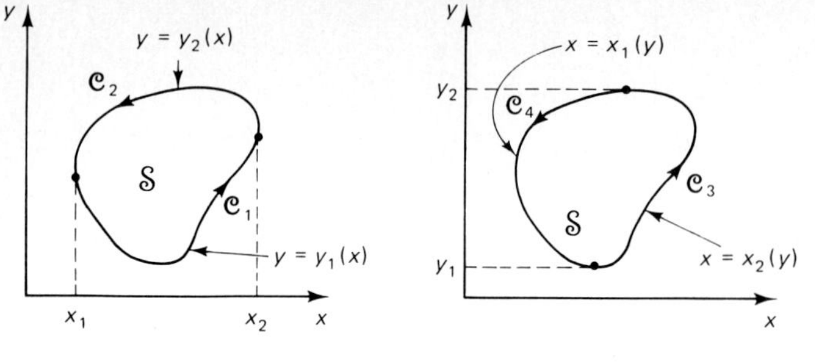

Fig. 9.37 The region $\mathcal{S}$.

$$= \int_{y_1}^{y_2} Q(x_2(y), y)\, dy - \int_{y_1}^{y_2} Q(x_1(y), y)\, dy$$

$$= \int_{y_1}^{y_2} Q(x_2(y), y)\, dy + \int_{y_2}^{y_1} Q(x_1(y), y)\, dy$$

$$= \int_{\mathscr{C}_3} Q\, dy + \int_{\mathscr{C}_4} Q\, dy = \oint_{\mathscr{C}} Q\, dy.$$

Similarly,

$$\int_{\mathcal{S}} \frac{\partial P}{\partial y}\, dA = \int_{x_1}^{x_2} \int_{y_1(x)}^{y_2(x)} \frac{\partial P}{\partial y}\, dy\, dx \qquad \text{[using (14a)]}$$

$$= \int_{x_1}^{x_2} \left\{ P(x, y) \Big|_{y=y_1(x)}^{y=y_2(x)} \right\} dx$$

$$= \int_{x_1}^{x_2} P(x, y_2(x))\, dx - \int_{x_1}^{x_2} P(x, y_1(x))\, dx \tag{16}$$

$$= -\int_{x_2}^{x_1} P(x, y_2(x))\, dx - \int_{x_1}^{x_2} P(x, y_1(x))\, dx$$

$$= -\int_{\mathscr{C}_2} P\, dx - \int_{\mathscr{C}_1} P\, dx = -\oint_{\mathscr{C}} P\, dx,$$

so

$$\int_{\mathcal{S}} \left(\frac{\partial Q}{\partial x} - \frac{\partial P}{\partial y} \right) dA = \oint_{\mathscr{C}} (P\, dx + Q\, dy).$$

We might note that the first equalities in (15) and (16) amount to the application of (10) on page 313, and are legitimate steps since $\partial Q/\partial x$ and $\partial P/\partial y$ have been assumed to be continuous in $\mathcal{S}$.

Not all regions $\mathcal{S}$ admit the representations (14a) and (14b). The region $\mathcal{S}$ shown in Fig. 9.38a, for example, admits a representation (14a) but not (14b); i.e., $\mathcal{S}$ is convex in the y direction but not in the x direction. Nevertheless, $\mathcal{S}$ and $\mathscr{C}$ may be broken up as shown in Fig. 9.38b. Then each of the regions $\mathcal{S}_1$, $\mathcal{S}_2$, $\mathcal{S}_3$ *is* convex in both the x and y directions, so that (as shown above)

$$\int_{\mathcal{S}_1} \left(\frac{\partial Q}{\partial x} - \frac{\partial P}{\partial y} \right) dA = \oint_{\mathscr{C}_1} (P\, dx + Q\, dy),$$

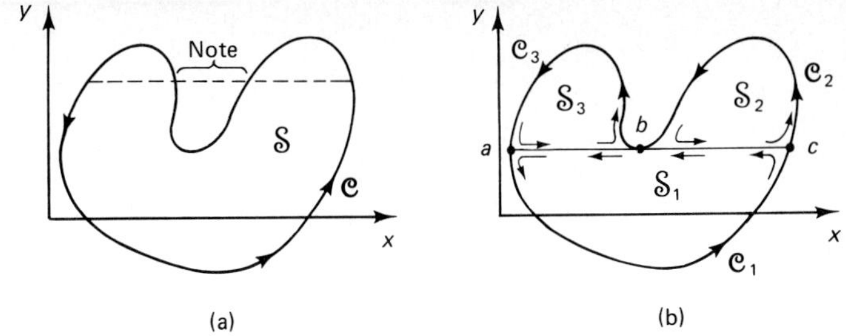

Fig. 9.38 Nonconvex $\mathscr{S}$.

$$\int_{\mathscr{S}_2}\left(\frac{\partial Q}{\partial x}-\frac{\partial P}{\partial y}\right)dA=\oint_{\mathscr{C}_2}(P\,dx+Q\,dy),$$
$$\int_{\mathscr{S}_3}\left(\frac{\partial Q}{\partial x}-\frac{\partial P}{\partial y}\right)dA=\oint_{\mathscr{C}_3}(P\,dx+Q\,dy).$$

Adding these results and noting that the *bc* portions of $\oint_{\mathscr{C}_1}$ and $\oint_{\mathscr{C}_2}$ cancel, as do the *ab* portions of $\oint_{\mathscr{C}_1}$ and $\oint_{\mathscr{C}_3}$, we again obtain (13).

Finally, we note that if $\mathscr{S}$ has holes in it, (13) may be modified just as we modified Stokes' theorem for that case. For example, if $\mathscr{S}$ is the region shown in Fig. 9.35, we obtain

$$\int_{\mathscr{S}}\left(\frac{\partial Q}{\partial x}-\frac{\partial P}{\partial y}\right)dA=\oint_{\mathscr{C}_1}(P\,dx+Q\,dy)+\oint_{\mathscr{C}_2}(P\,dx+Q\,dy) \tag{17}$$

in place of (13).

EXAMPLE 2 Let us illustrate (13) by working out both sides of the equation, and verifying the equality, for the case where $P(x,y)=xy^3$, $Q(x,y)=x^2-y^2$, and where $\mathscr{S}$ is as shown in Fig. 9.39. Then

$$\begin{aligned}\int_{\mathscr{S}}\left(\frac{\partial Q}{\partial x}-\frac{\partial P}{\partial y}\right)dA&=\int_0^2\int_{y/2}^1(2x-3xy^2)\,dx\,dy\\&=\int_0^2\left(x^2-\frac{3}{2}x^2y^2\right)\Big|_{x=y/2}^{x=1}dy\\&=\int_0^2\left(1-\frac{3}{2}y^2-\frac{y^2}{4}+\frac{3}{2}\frac{y^2}{4}y^2\right)dy\\&=\left(y-\frac{1}{2}y^3-\frac{1}{12}y^3+\frac{3}{40}y^5\right)\Big|_0^2=-\frac{4}{15}.\end{aligned} \tag{18}$$

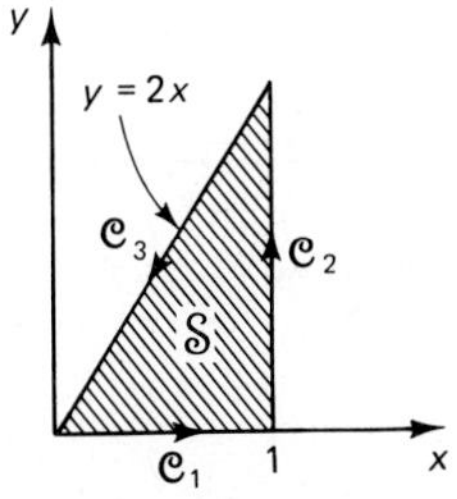

Fig. 9.39 The region $\mathscr{S}$ in Example 2.

Breaking $\mathscr{C}$ into $\mathscr{C} = \mathscr{C}_1 + \mathscr{C}_2 + \mathscr{C}_3$, we have

$$\begin{aligned}
\oint_{\mathscr{C}} (P\,dx + Q\,dy) &= \int_{\mathscr{C}_1} [x\underbrace{y}_{0 \text{ on } \mathscr{C}_1}{}^3\,dx + (x^2 - y^2)\underbrace{dy}_{0 \text{ on } \mathscr{C}_1}] \\
&\quad + \int_{\mathscr{C}_2} [xy^3\underbrace{dx}_{0 \text{ on } \mathscr{C}_2} + (x^2 - y^2)\,dy] \\
&\quad + \int_{\mathscr{C}_3} [xy^3\,dx + (x^2 - y^2)\,dy] \\
&= \int_{\mathscr{C}_2} (x^2 - y^2)\,dy + \int_{\mathscr{C}_3} [xy^3\,dx + (x^2 - y^2)\,dy].
\end{aligned} \tag{19}$$

Since $x = 1$ on $\mathscr{C}_2$ and $y = 2x$ on $\mathscr{C}_3$, we have

$$\begin{aligned}
\int_{\mathscr{C}} (P\,dx + Q\,dy) &= \int_0^2 (1 - y^2)\,dy + \int_1^0 [8x^4 + (x^2 - 4x^2)(2)]\,dx \\
&= -\frac{4}{15},
\end{aligned}$$

as in (18). ◀

Stokes' theorem, which was the principal subject of this section, might well be ranked with the Gauss divergence theorem in terms of its significance in theory and applications alike. Whereas our examples in this section did not involve physical applications, we note that important applications to Faraday's law and Ampère's law are contained in the exercises and that Stokes' theorem will be used in Section 9.12 when we discuss an important class of fields known as "irrotational fields."

9.11 EXERCISES

1. Evaluate the surface and line integrals in Stokes' theorem, and show that they are equal. $\mathscr{S}$ is a plane surface with straight edges. The vertices and orientation of $\mathscr{C}$ are given below.

(*a*) $\mathbf{v} = xy\hat{\mathbf{i}} - (2x - y)\hat{\mathbf{k}}$, $\mathscr{C}$: (0, 0, 0) to (2, 0, 0) to (2, 1, 0) to (0, 1, 0) to (0, 0, 0)

(b) $\mathbf{v} = x^2z\hat{\mathbf{j}} - y\hat{\mathbf{k}}$, $\mathscr{C}$: (0, 0, 0) to (0, 3, 0) to (3, 0, 0) to (0, 0, 0)

(c) $\mathbf{v} = z\hat{\mathbf{i}} + y\hat{\mathbf{j}} + x\hat{\mathbf{k}}$, $\mathscr{C}$: (1, 1, 0) to (4, 4, 0) to (2, 1, 0) to (1, 1, 0)

*(d) $\mathbf{v} = x^2yz\hat{\mathbf{j}}$, $\mathscr{C}$: (0, 1, 0) to (1, 1, 0) to (1, 0, 1) to (0, 0, 1) to (0, 1, 0)

(e) $\mathbf{v} = (x + 2y - z)\hat{\mathbf{i}}$, $\mathscr{C}$: (1, 1, 0) to (0, 0, 1) to (0, 1, 0) to (1, 1, 0)

(f) $\mathbf{v} = y^2\hat{\mathbf{i}} - x^2\hat{\mathbf{k}}$, $\mathscr{C}$: (1, −1, 0) to (0, 0, 1) to (0, 1, 0) to (1, −1, 0)

2. Verify Stokes' theorem, in each case, by working out the surface and line integrals and showing that the results are equal.

*(a) $\mathscr{S}$: the surface of the unit cube with corners at (0, 0, 0), (1, 0, 0), (0, 1, 0), (0, 0, 1), (1, 0, 1), (1, 1, 0), (0, 1, 1), (1, 1, 1), *excluding* the face $x = 1$; take $\hat{\mathbf{n}} = \hat{\mathbf{k}}$ on the $z = 1$ face; $\mathbf{v} = y^2\hat{\mathbf{j}} - xy^2z\hat{\mathbf{k}}$

(b) $\mathscr{S}$: same as in part (a), but excluding the face $y = 1$; $\hat{\mathbf{n}} = -\hat{\mathbf{k}}$ on the $z = 1$ face; $\mathbf{v} = x^2y^2z^3\hat{\mathbf{k}}$

(c) $\mathscr{S}$: same as in part (a), but excluding the face

$z = 1$; $\hat{\mathbf{n}} = -\hat{\mathbf{j}}$ on the $y = 1$ face; $\mathbf{v} = 3\hat{\mathbf{i}} + x^2y^2\hat{\mathbf{j}} - 2yz\hat{\mathbf{k}}$

(d) $\mathcal{S}$: same as in part (a), but excluding the face $z = 0$; $\hat{\mathbf{n}} = -\hat{\mathbf{k}}$ on the $z = 1$ face; $\mathbf{v} = \hat{\mathbf{i}} - 6\hat{\mathbf{j}} + 8\hat{\mathbf{k}}$

(e) $\mathcal{S}$: same as in part (a), but excluding the faces $x = 0$, $x = 1$, $y = 1$ and $z = 1$; $\hat{\mathbf{n}} = \hat{\mathbf{j}}$ on the $y = 0$ face; $\mathbf{v} = xz^3\hat{\mathbf{j}} - \hat{\mathbf{k}}$

(f) $\mathcal{S}$: same as in part (a), but excluding the faces $x = 1$ and $y = 1$; $\hat{\mathbf{n}} = \hat{\mathbf{k}}$ on the face $z = 0$; $\mathbf{v} = 3\hat{\mathbf{i}} - \hat{\mathbf{j}} + 5\hat{\mathbf{k}}$

(g) $\mathcal{S}$: same as in part (a), but excluding the faces $x = 1$, $y = 0$, and $y = 1$; $\hat{\mathbf{n}} = \hat{\mathbf{i}}$ on the face $x = 0$; $\mathbf{v} = e^xy\hat{\mathbf{i}} - e^{-y}\hat{\mathbf{j}} + z^6e^z\hat{\mathbf{k}}$

3. Evaluate the surface and line integrals in Stokes' theorem, and show that the results are equal.

*(a) $\mathcal{S}$: the bent-plane surface shown in the figure; $\mathscr{C}$ is the curve $ABDEFGA$, oriented as shown; $\mathbf{v} = y^3z\hat{\mathbf{k}}$.

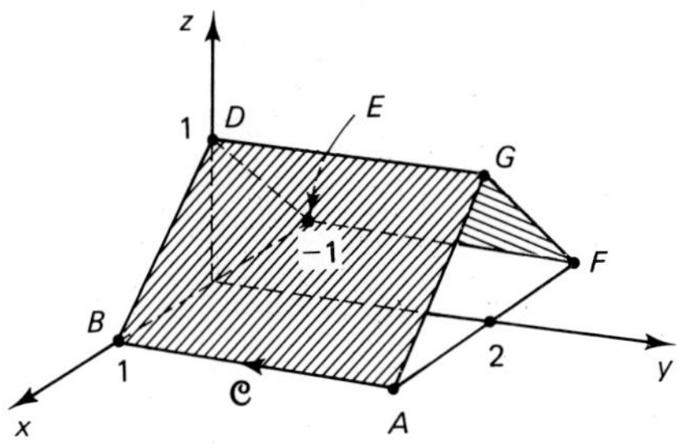

(b) Referring to the figure, let $\mathcal{S}$ be the bent-plane surface defined by the boundary curve $C = ABEDGFA$; $\mathbf{v} = y\hat{\mathbf{i}} - x\hat{\mathbf{j}}$.

(c) $\mathcal{S}$: the surface $z = 1 - x^2$ for $-1 \le x \le 1$, $0 \le y \le 3$; $\mathbf{v} = x^2z\hat{\mathbf{i}} - 3xy\hat{\mathbf{k}}$. To fix the orientation of $\mathscr{C}$, let y be increasing between the points (1, 0, 0) and (1, 3, 0) on $\mathscr{C}$.

(d) Repeat part (c), but let $\mathcal{S}$ also include the two "end faces" $0 \le z \le 1 - x^2$, $-1 \le x \le 1$, at $y = 0$ and at $y = 3$.

(e) $\mathcal{S}$: same as in part (c); $\hat{\mathbf{n}} = \hat{\mathbf{k}}$ along $x = 0$; $\mathbf{v} = z^2\hat{\mathbf{j}} + 3x^2\hat{\mathbf{k}}$.

4. Evaluate $\int_{\mathcal{S}} \hat{\mathbf{n}} \cdot \nabla \times \{[y^2 + x^3 \sin (yz)]\hat{\mathbf{i}} - x^2\hat{\mathbf{k}}\}\, dA$ any way you can, where $\mathcal{S}$ is the surface $z = 1 - x^4 - y^4$ for $z \ge 0$, and $\hat{\mathbf{n}} = \hat{\mathbf{k}}$ at (0, 0, 1).

5. (*Surfaces with holes*) Evaluate $\int_{\mathcal{S}} \hat{\mathbf{n}} \cdot \nabla \times \mathbf{v}\, dA$, both directly and as a suitable combination of line integrals, and verify that the results are the same.

*(a) $\mathcal{S}$: the plane surface $\mathcal{S}_1$ shown; $\hat{\mathbf{n}} = \hat{\mathbf{k}}$; $\mathbf{v} = y^3\hat{\mathbf{i}}$

(b) $\mathcal{S}$: the plane surface $\mathcal{S}_2$ shown; $\hat{\mathbf{n}} = -\hat{\mathbf{k}}$; $\mathbf{v} = xy\hat{\mathbf{i}}$

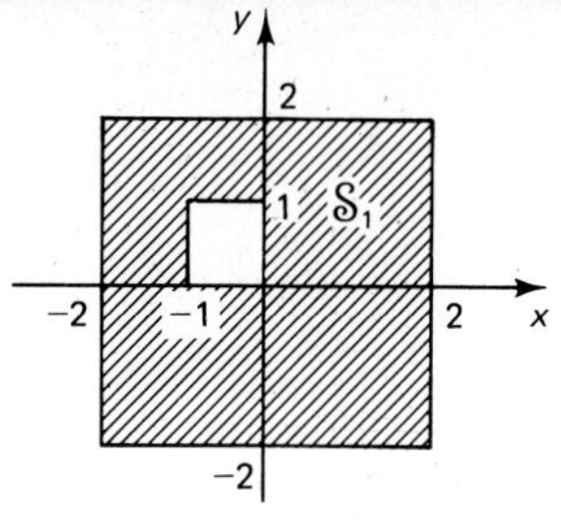

(a)

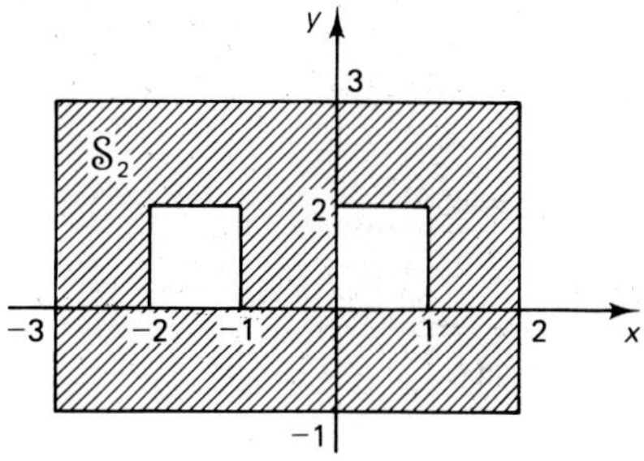

(b)

(c) $\mathcal{S}$: the four-sided surface shown, open at the top and bottom; $\mathbf{v} = x^3y(1 + z)\hat{\mathbf{i}} + 3 \cos (x^2 + z^2)\hat{\mathbf{k}}$

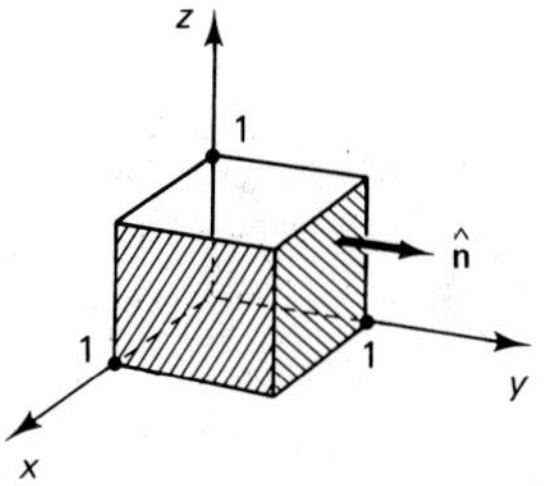

6. Given the field $\mathbf{F} = y^2\hat{\mathbf{i}}$ and the contour shown, the following conflicting calculations were put forward in an exam paper:

$$\oint_{\mathscr{C}} \mathbf{F} \cdot d\mathbf{R} = \oint_{\mathscr{C}} y^2\, dx = \int_0^4 [4 - (x - 2)^2]\, dx + \int_4^0 0\, dx = \tfrac{32}{3},$$

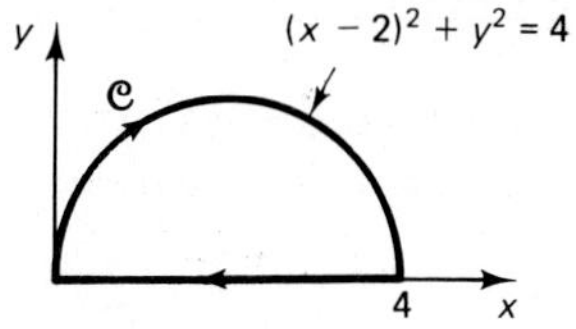

but

$$\oint_{\mathscr{C}} \mathbf{F}\cdot d\mathbf{R} = \int_{\mathscr{S}} \hat{\mathbf{n}}\cdot\nabla\times\mathbf{F}\,dA$$
$$= \int_{\mathscr{S}} 2y\,dA = 2\int_0^4 y(y\,dx)$$
$$= 2\int_0^4 [4-(x-2)^2]\,dx = \tfrac{64}{3}.$$

Find, and correct, the error.

7. (*Faraday's law*) **Faraday's law** (that the emf around a closed curve equals the negative of the time rate of change of the magnetic flux through the curve) may be expressed as

$$\oint_{\mathscr{C}} \mathbf{E}\cdot d\mathbf{R} = -\frac{d}{dt}\int_{\mathscr{S}} \mathbf{B}\cdot\hat{\mathbf{n}}\,dA$$
$$= -\int_{\mathscr{S}} \frac{\partial\mathbf{B}}{\partial t}\cdot\hat{\mathbf{n}}\,dA \tag{a}$$

for every (fixed) surface $\mathscr{S}$ (with closed boundary curve $\mathscr{C}$) in the field, where $\mathbf{E}$ is the electric field intensity, $\mathbf{B}$ is the magnetic flux density, t is the time, and where the relative orientations of $\mathscr{C}$ and $\hat{\mathbf{n}}$ are the same as in Stokes' theorem. Applying Stokes' theorem to the line integral, use the arbitrariness of $\mathscr{S}$ and $\mathscr{C}$ to deduce (heuristically) that the relation

$$\nabla\times\mathbf{E} = -\frac{\partial\mathbf{B}}{\partial t} \tag{b}$$

holds at all points in the field. Equation (b) is one of the celebrated *Maxwell's equations*, for time-varying fields; for steady fields (b) reduces to $\nabla\times\mathbf{E} = \mathbf{0}$.

8. (*Ampère's law*) **Ampère's law** states that

$$\oint_{\mathscr{C}} \mathbf{H}\cdot d\mathbf{R} = I, \tag{a}$$

i.e., the line integral of the magnetic field intensity $\mathbf{H}$ (amperes/meter) around a closed curve $\mathscr{C}$ equals the current I (amperes) passing through any surface $\mathscr{S}$ having $\mathscr{C}$ as its boundary. (Recall that our curves and surfaces were restricted in Section 9.2, to be "suitably decent.") Evidently, we can express I as

$$I = \int_{\mathscr{S}} \sigma\hat{\mathbf{n}}\cdot\mathbf{q}\,dA \quad\text{or}\quad \int_{\mathscr{S}} \hat{\mathbf{n}}\cdot(\sigma\mathbf{q})\,dA, \tag{b}$$

where σ is the charge density (coulombs/meter^3) and $\mathbf{q}$ is the velocity field (meters/second). One defines $\mathbf{J} = \sigma\mathbf{q}$ as the *current density*. We now state the problem: Show that

$$\int_{\mathscr{S}} \hat{\mathbf{n}}\cdot(\nabla\times\mathbf{H} - \mathbf{J})\,dA = 0$$

and use the arbitrariness of $\mathscr{S}$ to deduce (heuristically) that

$$\nabla\times\mathbf{H} = \mathbf{J}. \tag{c}$$

Note: Equation (c) is another one (recall Exercise 7) of Maxwell's equations (for steady fields). It is a "first-order partial differential equation" that relates $\mathbf{H}$ and $\mathbf{J}$ at each point in the field, and is sometimes said to be the "point" form of Ampère's law (a).

9. (*Outline of heuristic proof of Stokes' theorem for not-necessarily-flat surfaces*) Beginning with the expression

$$\operatorname{curl}\mathbf{v}(P) = \lim_{\mathscr{B}\to 0}\left\{\frac{\int_{\mathscr{S}} \hat{\mathbf{n}}\times\mathbf{v}\,dA}{V}\right\}, \tag{a}$$

given on page 379, let $\mathscr{B}$ be a right cylinder of a small height h, and let the base of $\mathscr{B}$ be a plane region, of area A, bounded by a simple closed curve $\mathscr{C}_j$, oriented so that the unit normal $\hat{\boldsymbol{\nu}}$ to the base, and $\mathscr{C}_j$, are in accordance with the right-hand rule, as shown. Dotting (b) with $\hat{\boldsymbol{\nu}}$, and recalling that $\mathbf{A}\cdot\mathbf{B}\times\mathbf{C} = \mathbf{A}\times\mathbf{B}\cdot\mathbf{C}$, show that

$$\hat{\boldsymbol{\nu}}\cdot\operatorname{curl}\mathbf{v} = \lim_{A\to 0}\left\{\frac{\oint_{\mathscr{C}_j} \mathbf{v}\cdot d\mathbf{R}}{A}\right\} \tag{b}$$

or, in differential form,

$$\hat{\boldsymbol{\nu}}\cdot\operatorname{curl}\mathbf{v}\,dA \sim \oint_{\mathscr{C}_j} \mathbf{v}\cdot d\mathbf{R}. \tag{c}$$

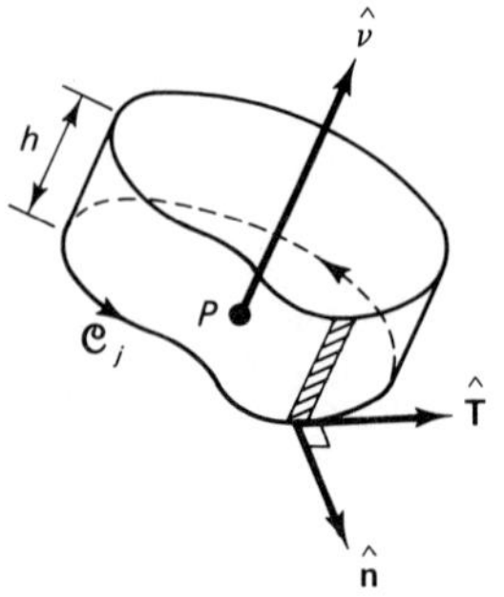

Thus far we have engaged in a "local" argument. Now take the surface $\mathscr{S}$ in Stokes' theorem, partition it with a large number of such curves as $\mathscr{C}_j$ (as shown); write down (c) for each such curve, realizing that $\hat{\boldsymbol{\nu}}$ is really the normal $\hat{\mathbf{n}}$ to $\mathscr{S}$; add all these equations and,

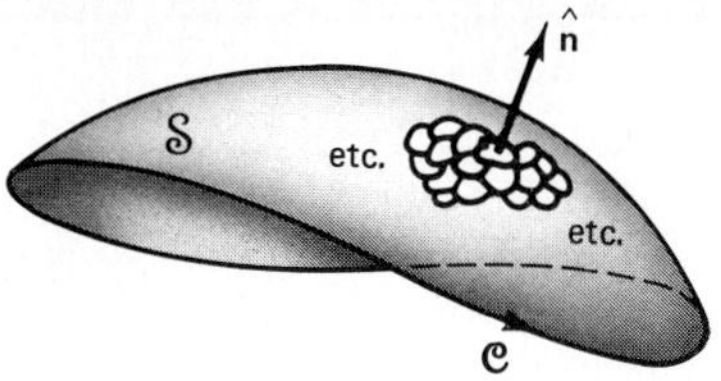

noting "internal cancellation" analogous to that which occurred in our proof of the divergence theorem, show that Stokes' theorem follows. [Note that the $\mathcal{S}$ in (a) is merely the surface of the tiny right cylinder $\mathcal{B}$; $\mathcal{S}$ in the second figure is the cap-like surface in Stokes' theorem.]

10. Evaluate $\oint_{\mathscr{C}} (P\,dx + Q dy)$ both directly and, using Green's theorem (13), as an integral over the region $\mathcal{S}$ enclosed by $\mathscr{C}$. $\mathscr{C}$ is counterclockwise.

*(a) $P = y$, $Q = 3x$; $\mathscr{C}$ is the boundary of the rectangle $-1 \le x \le 4$, $0 \le y \le 2$

(b) $P = x^2y$, $Q = 0$; $\mathscr{C}$ the same as in part (a)

(c) $P = 2$, $Q = ye^x$; $\mathscr{C}$ the same as in part (a)

(d) $P = x^2 + 2y$, $Q = 3x - \cos y$; $\mathscr{C}$ the same as in part (a)

*(e) $P = e^x - 3y$, $Q = e^y + 5x$; $\mathscr{C}$ is the unit circle

(f) $P = y$, $Q = y^3e^y$; $\mathscr{C}$ is the unit circle

(g) $P = 0$, $Q = \sin y - 2x$; $\mathscr{C}$ is the unit circle

(h) $P = 5$, $Q = x^2y^3$; $\mathscr{C}$ is the boundary of the triangle with vertices at (0, 0), (4, 0), and (4, 3)

(i) $P = y\cos x$, $Q = \frac{1}{2}x^2y^2 + \sin x$; $\mathscr{C}$ is the boundary of the triangle with vertices at (0, 0), (0, 1), and (2, 0)

(j) $P = \cos y$, $Q = 0$; $\mathscr{C}$ is the boundary of the quadrangle with vertices at (0, 0), $(\pi, 0)$, (π, π), and $(0, 2\pi)$

(k) $P = xy$, $Q = 2$; $\mathscr{C}$ is the boundary of the quadrangle with vertices at (1, 0), (0, 2), (−2, 0), and (0, −3)

11. Evaluate $\oint_{\mathscr{C}} (P\,dx + Q\,dy)$ any way you can.

*(a) $P = \ln y$, $Q = (x/y) + \frac{1}{3}x^3y$; $\mathscr{C}$ is the boundary of the region $x^3 + 2 \le y \le 4x + 2$, $0 \le x \le 1$, clockwise

(b) $P = \sin(x^2 + 1) + y\ln x$, $Q = x\ln x - x + y^2e^x$; $\mathscr{C}$ is the boundary of the quadrangle with vertices at (1, 1) (2, 2), (2, 3), and (1, 3), clockwise

(c) $P = y\sinh x$, $Q = x + \cosh x$; $\mathscr{C}$ is the unit circle, clockwise

12. If $\mathscr{C}$ is a piecewise-smooth simple closed curve in the x, y plane, oriented counterclockwise, show that the area A enclosed by $\mathscr{C}$ is given by the line integral

$$A = \frac{1}{2}\oint_{\mathscr{C}} (x\,dy - y\,dx). \tag{a}$$

13. Use (a) in Exercise 12 to compute A if $\mathscr{C}$ is the boundary of the

(a) rectangle with vertices at (0, 0), $(a, 0)$, (a, b), $(0, b)$

(b) triangle with vertices at $(a, 0)$, (a, b), $(0, b)$

(c) circle $x^2 + y^2 = 9$

14. Show that equation (13) does *not* hold for the case where $P = -y/(x^2 + y^2)$, $Q = x/(x^2 + y^2)$, and $\mathcal{S}$ is the unit disk $x^2 + y^2 \le 1$. Explain why this failure does not violate Green's theorem (Theorem 2).

15. (a) If $\mathcal{S}$ is the plane region shown below, show that Green's theorem (13) needs to be modified to the form

$$\int_{\mathcal{S}} \left(\frac{\partial Q}{\partial x} - \frac{\partial P}{\partial y}\right) dx\,dy = \oint_{\mathscr{C}_1} (P\,dx + Q\,dy) + \oint_{\mathscr{C}_2} (P\,dx + Q\,dy). \tag{a}$$

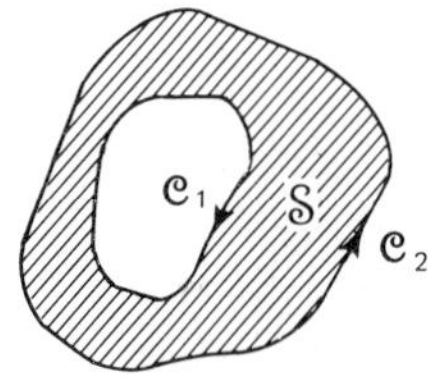

(b) Verify (a), by evaluating both sides of the equation, for the case where $P = x^2y$, $Q = 2xy$, and where $\mathcal{S}$ is the region $\mathcal{S}_1$ shown in Exercise 5.

(c) Repeat part (b), where $Q = x$, $P = -y$, and where $\mathcal{S}$ is the annulus between $x^2 + y^2 = 1$ and $x^2 + y^2 = 9$.

16. (*An observation about Stokes' theorem*) Notice that the value of the line integral in Stokes' theorem (5) is independent of the shape of the surface $\mathcal{S}$. Thus the surface integral in (5) must, similarly, be independent of the shape of $\mathcal{S}$. That is, it must be true that $\int_{\mathcal{S}_1} \hat{\mathbf{n}} \cdot \nabla \times \mathbf{v}\,dA = \int_{\mathcal{S}_2} \hat{\mathbf{n}} \cdot \nabla \times \mathbf{v}\,dA$ for any two surfaces $\mathcal{S}_1$ and $\mathcal{S}_2$ that share the same edge curve $\mathscr{C}$. Provide an alternative argument as to why the two integrals (in preceding sentence) must be equal. *Hint:* Note that $\mathcal{S}_1 + \mathcal{S}_2$ is a closed surface. Apply the divergence theorem to the surface integral of $\hat{\mathbf{n}} \cdot \nabla \times \mathbf{v}$ over that closed surface.

9.12 IRROTATIONAL FIELDS

Let $\mathbf{v}$ be a C^1 vector field defined in a region $\mathscr{R}$. If $\nabla \times \mathbf{v} = \mathbf{0}$ at each point in $\mathscr{R}$, then $\mathbf{v}$ is said to be **irrotational** in $\mathscr{R}$. Recall from Section 9.6 that if $\mathbf{v}$ is a fluid velocity field, then $\nabla \times \mathbf{v}$ may be interpreted physically as twice the fluid particle angular velocity at the point in question. Thus $\nabla \times \mathbf{v} = \mathbf{0}$ means that there is no angular velocity, or rotation, at that point—hence the term "irrotational."

Further, we say that the line integral $\int_{\mathscr{C}} \mathbf{v} \cdot d\mathbf{R}$, between endpoints P and Q, is **independent of path** if the value of the integral is the same for *every* piecewise smooth path $\mathscr{C}$, from P to Q, lying entirely within $\mathscr{R}$. Finally, if $\int_{\mathscr{C}} \mathbf{v} \cdot d\mathbf{R}$ is independent of path for *every* pair of endpoints P and Q in $\mathscr{R}$, we say that the integral is independent of path *in* $\mathscr{R}$.

We have the following major theorem.

> ***Theorem 1*** *Irrotational Field*
>
> If $\mathbf{v}$ is C^1 in a simply connected region $\mathscr{R}$, then the following statements are equivalent (i.e., if one holds then the other three do, too):
>
> (i) There exists a C^2 scalar function Φ in $\mathscr{R}$ such that $\mathbf{v} = \nabla\Phi$ throughout $\mathscr{R}$.
> (ii) $\nabla \times \mathbf{v} = \mathbf{0}$ throughout $\mathscr{R}$.
> (iii) $\oint_{\mathscr{C}} \mathbf{v} \cdot d\mathbf{R} = 0$ for every piecewise-smooth simple closed path $\mathscr{C}$ in $\mathscr{R}$.
> (iv) $\int_{\mathscr{C}} \mathbf{v} \cdot d\mathbf{R}$ is independent of path in $\mathscr{R}$.

Proof It will suffice to show that (i) → (ii) → (iii) → (iv) → (i), where "→" means implies.

(i) → (ii): If $\mathbf{v} = \nabla\Phi = \Phi_x\hat{\mathbf{i}} + \Phi_y\hat{\mathbf{j}} + \Phi_z\hat{\mathbf{k}}$, then $\nabla \times \mathbf{v} = (\Phi_{zy} - \Phi_{yz})\hat{\mathbf{i}} - (\Phi_{zx} - \Phi_{xz})\hat{\mathbf{j}} + (\Phi_{yx} - \Phi_{xy})\hat{\mathbf{k}} = \mathbf{0}$ since (recall Theorem 1, page 220) $\Phi_{zy} = \Phi_{yz}$, $\Phi_{zx} = \Phi_{xz}$, and $\Phi_{yx} = \Phi_{xy}$.

(ii) → (iii): Let $\mathscr{C}$ be any piecewise-smooth simple closed path within $\mathscr{R}$. Suppose that we can introduce a piecewise-smooth surface $\mathscr{S}$ with $\mathscr{C}$ as its boundary. (Note that if $\mathscr{R}$ were not simply connected, $\mathscr{S}$ might have one or more holes in it, and then $\mathscr{C}$ would be only part of the boundary of $\mathscr{S}$.) Then, by Stokes' theorem,

$$\oint_{\mathscr{C}} \mathbf{v} \cdot d\mathbf{R} = \int_{\mathscr{S}} \hat{\mathbf{n}} \cdot \nabla \times \mathbf{v}\, dA = \int_{\mathscr{S}} \hat{\mathbf{n}} \cdot \mathbf{0}\, dA = 0, \tag{1}$$

as claimed. Now, given a piecewise-smooth simple closed path $\mathscr{C}$, *can* we necessarily find a piecewise-smooth surface $\mathscr{S}$ having $\mathscr{C}$ as its boundary, as assumed above? For the $\mathscr{C}$ shown in Fig. 9.40a for example, such an $\mathscr{S}$ is easily constructed, as

Fig. 9.40 Is there an $\mathscr{S}$?

sketched in the figure. But what about more complicated $\mathscr{C}$'s—for example, the overhand knot shown in Fig. 9.41. In that case the idea is to add cancelling line segments, shown as dashed lines in Fig. 9.41 so that the curve $\mathscr{C}$ can be split into two noninterlocking curves ($\mathscr{C} = \mathscr{C}_1 + \mathscr{C}_2$) which *do* admit suitable surfaces $\mathscr{S}_1$ and $\mathscr{S}_2$, respectively. Analogous to (1), then, we have

$$\oint_{\mathscr{C}} \mathbf{v}\cdot d\mathbf{R} = \oint_{\mathscr{C}_1} \mathbf{v}\cdot d\mathbf{R} + \oint_{\mathscr{C}_2} \mathbf{v}\cdot d\mathbf{R} = \int_{\mathscr{S}_1} \hat{\mathbf{n}}\cdot\nabla\times\mathbf{v}\, dA + \int_{\mathscr{S}_2} \hat{\mathbf{n}}\cdot\nabla\times\mathbf{v}\, dA$$
$$= \int_{\mathscr{S}_1} \hat{\mathbf{n}}\cdot\mathbf{0}\, dA + \int_{\mathscr{S}_2} \hat{\mathbf{n}}\cdot\mathbf{0}\, dA = 0 + 0 = 0.$$

Rigorous proof that we can handle *any* piecewise-smooth simple closed path $\mathscr{C}$, however, is beyond our present scope.

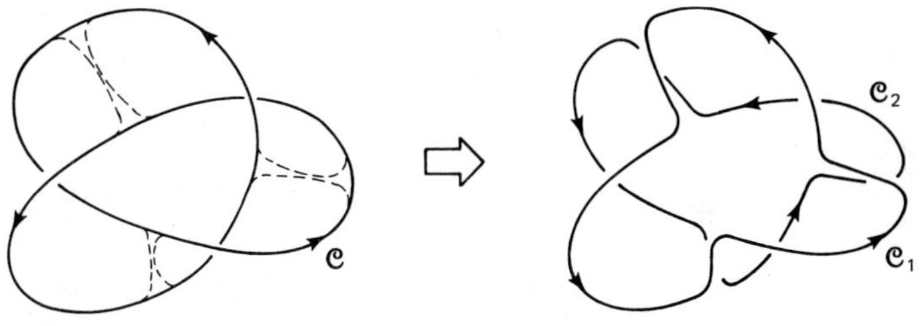

Fig. 9.41 Undoing the knot.

(iii) → (iv): Let $\mathscr{C}_1$ and $\mathscr{C}_2$ be any two piecewise-smooth paths from any point $P_0 = (x_0, y_0, z_0)$ in $\mathscr{R}$ to any point $P = (x, y, z)$ in $\mathscr{R}$ (Fig. 9.42a). Suppose that $\mathscr{C}_1$ and $\mathscr{C}_2$ are both simple curves and that they intersect each other only at the endpoints P_0 and P. (The argument needed for the case where additional intersections occur will be omitted here.) Then $\mathscr{C}_1 + (-\mathscr{C}_2)$ is a piecewise-smooth simple closed path (Fig. 9.42b) and, according to statement (iii),

$$\oint_{\mathscr{C}_1+(-\mathscr{C}_2)} \mathbf{v}\cdot d\mathbf{R} = 0. \tag{2}$$

But

$$\begin{aligned}\oint_{\mathscr{C}_1+(-\mathscr{C}_2)} \mathbf{v}\cdot d\mathbf{R} &= \int_{\mathscr{C}_1} \mathbf{v}\cdot d\mathbf{R} + \int_{-\mathscr{C}_2} \mathbf{v}\cdot d\mathbf{R} \\ &= \int_{\mathscr{C}_1} \mathbf{v}\cdot d\mathbf{R} - \int_{\mathscr{C}_2} \mathbf{v}\cdot d\mathbf{R},\end{aligned} \tag{3}$$

and it follows from (2) and (3) that

$$\int_{\mathscr{C}_1} \mathbf{v}\cdot d\mathbf{R} = \int_{\mathscr{C}_2} \mathbf{v}\cdot d\mathbf{R}, \tag{4}$$

as claimed.

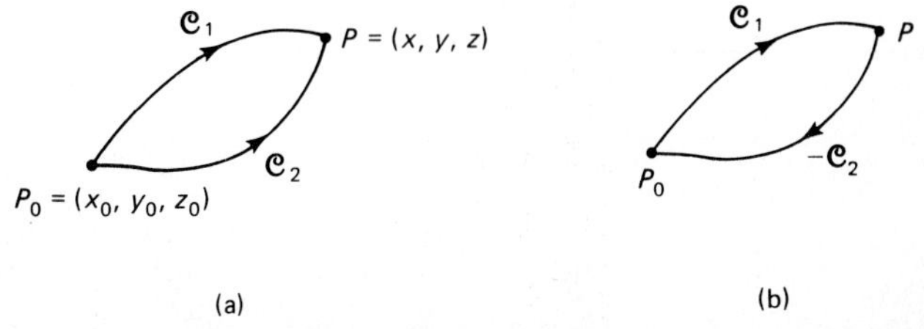

Fig. 9.42 You take the high road, I'll take the low.

(iv) → (i): Regarding $P_0 = (x_0, y_0, z_0)$ as fixed, and $P = (x, y, z)$ as a variable endpoint, it follows from the path independence (4) that

$$f(x, y, z) \equiv \int_{(x_0, y_0, z_0)}^{(x, y, z)} \mathbf{v} \cdot d\mathbf{R} \tag{5}$$

is indeed a *function* of x, y, z.* Let us deal with the dependence on x, y, and z one at a time. First the x dependence. Regarding y and z as fixed, let us take the path from (x_0, y_0, z_0) to (x, y, z) in (5) to be the one shown in Fig. 9.43. That is, the end point P moves parallel to the x axis as x is varied (with y and z fixed). Then (5) becomes

$$\begin{aligned} f(x, y, z) &= \int_{(x_0,y_0,z_0)}^{(x_0,y,z)} \mathbf{v} \cdot d\mathbf{R} + \int_{(x_0,y,z)}^{(x,y,z)} \mathbf{v} \cdot d\mathbf{R} \\ &= \text{constant} + \int_{(x_0,y,z)}^{(x,y,z)} (v_x\, dx + v_y\, dy + v_z\, dz) \\ &= \text{constant} + \int_{x_0}^{x} v_x(x, y, z)\, dx, \end{aligned} \tag{6}$$

where $\mathbf{v} = v_x\hat{\mathbf{i}} + v_y\hat{\mathbf{j}} + v_z\hat{\mathbf{k}}$, and where the last step follows from the fact that y and z are constant along the path from (x_0, y, z) to (x, y, z). Or, introducing a dummy variable of integration to avoid confusion, we have

$$f(x, y, z) = \text{constant} + \int_{x_0}^{x} v_x(\xi, y, z)\, d\xi, \tag{7}$$

and since v_x is assumed to be continuous it follows from the fundamental theorem of the integral calculus that $\partial f/\partial x = v_x(x, y, z)$. In the same manner, we may show that $\partial f/\partial y = v_y(x, y, z)$, and that $\partial f/\partial z = v_z(x, y, z)$. Thus $\mathbf{v} = \nabla f$, and f is the scalar function that we've been looking for. This completes the proof. ■

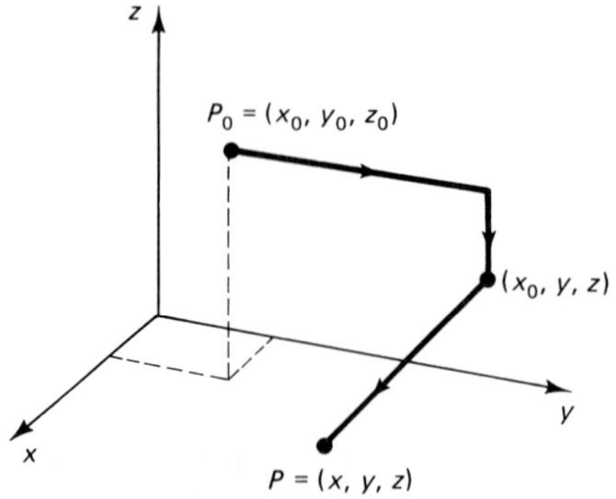

Fig. 9.43 Getting ready for the fundamental theorem of the intergral calculus.

Theorem 1 is quite helpful. For suppose that we wish to evaluate a given line integral

$$I = \int_{\mathscr{C}} \mathbf{v} \cdot d\mathbf{R}. \tag{8}$$

As our first step, we should check to see if $\mathbf{v}$ is irrotational, i.e., if $\nabla \times \mathbf{v} = \mathbf{0}$, for

* If different paths to (x, y, z) were to give *different* values of the integral, the integral would not be uniquely determined by x, y, z; i.e., it would not be a single-valued function of x, y, z, and (5) would not hold.

if that is the case, and $\mathscr{C}$ is a *closed* contour, it follows immediately from statement (iii) that $I = 0$. If $\nabla \times \mathbf{v} = \mathbf{0}$ but $\mathscr{C}$ is *not* closed, Theorem 1 at least provides two alternative simplifications. First, we can use statement (iv) to justify changing the path to a simpler one, keeping the endpoints fixed. Or, we can use statement (i), which guarantees the existence of a scalar field Φ such that $\nabla\Phi = \mathbf{v}$. For if we can solve the relation $\nabla\Phi = \mathbf{v}$ for Φ, which is referred to as the scalar **potential** corresponding to the field $\mathbf{v}$, then we have

$$\begin{aligned} I &= \int_P^Q \mathbf{v}\cdot d\mathbf{R} = \int_P^Q \nabla\Phi\cdot d\mathbf{R} = \int_P^Q \left(\frac{\partial\Phi}{\partial x}\hat{\mathbf{i}} + \frac{\partial\Phi}{\partial y}\hat{\mathbf{j}} + \frac{\partial\Phi}{\partial z}\hat{\mathbf{k}}\right)\cdot(dx\hat{\mathbf{i}} + dy\hat{\mathbf{j}} + dz\hat{\mathbf{k}}) \\ &= \int_P^Q \left(\frac{\partial\Phi}{\partial x}dx + \frac{\partial\Phi}{\partial y}dy + \frac{\partial\Phi}{\partial z}dz\right) = \int_P^Q d\Phi = \Phi\Big|_P^Q. \end{aligned} \tag{9}$$

Both of these lines of approach are illustrated in the example to follow.

EXAMPLE 1 Evaluate $I = \int_{\mathscr{C}} \mathbf{v}\cdot d\mathbf{R}$, where $\mathbf{v} = 2x^2\hat{\mathbf{i}} - 2yz\hat{\mathbf{j}} - (y^2 + 3)\hat{\mathbf{k}}$ and where $\mathscr{C}$ is some rather complicated path from (0, 0, 0) to (0, 0, 4), as sketched in Fig. 9.44. Working out $\nabla \times \mathbf{v}$, we find that $\nabla \times \mathbf{v} = \mathbf{0}$. Hence the integral $\int_{(0,0,0)}^{(0,0,4)} \mathbf{v}\cdot d\mathbf{R}$ is independent of path, so we might as well replace the complicated path $\mathscr{C}$ that is given by one that is simpler. The simplest path that we can think of is the straight line from (0, 0, 0) to (0, 0, 4), i.e., along the z axis. Calling this path $\mathscr{C}'$, we have, quite easily,

$$\begin{aligned} I &= \int_{\mathscr{C}'} \mathbf{v}\cdot d\mathbf{R} = \int_{\mathscr{C}'} [2x^2\,dx - 2yz\,dy - (y^2+3)\,dz] \\ &= 0 + 0 - \int_0^4 (0+3)\,dz = -12. \end{aligned} \tag{10}$$

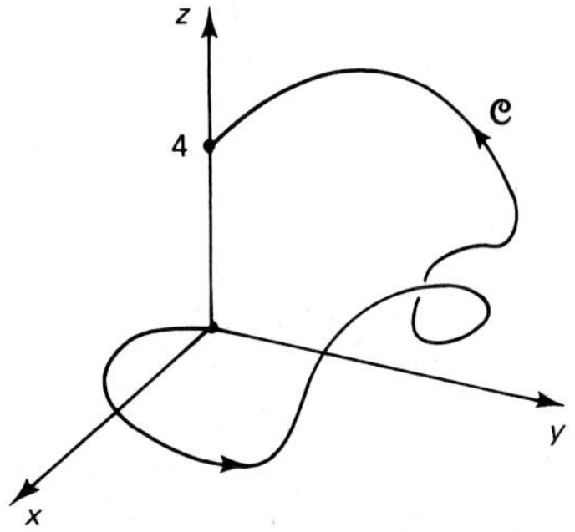

Fig. 9.44 The path $\mathscr{C}$.

Alternatively, let us evaluate I using the potential Φ, the existence of Φ being assured by the fact that $\nabla \times \mathbf{v} = \mathbf{0}$. To find Φ we use the connection $\nabla\Phi = \mathbf{v}$ between $\mathbf{v}$ and Φ:

$$\frac{\partial\Phi}{\partial x} = v_x = 2x^2, \tag{11a}$$

$$\frac{\partial\Phi}{\partial y} = v_y = -2yz, \tag{11b}$$

$$\frac{\partial\Phi}{\partial z} = v_z = -y^2 - 3. \tag{11c}$$

These are partial derivatives, and to undo them (to get at Φ) we carry out "partial integrals." First, integrate (11a) with respect to x, regarding y and z as fixed. Thus

$$\Phi(x, y, z) = \int 2x^2 \, \partial x = \frac{2}{3}x^3 + A(y, z), \tag{12}$$

where the "∂x" is to remind us that the other variables (y and z) are being held fixed in the integration, and where the constant of integration A must be allowed to depend on y and z. [If unconvinced that $A = A(y, z)$, observe that $\partial/\partial x$ of (12) does yield (11a).] Next, put (12) into (11b):

$$\frac{\partial \Phi}{\partial y} = \frac{\partial}{\partial y}\left[\frac{2}{3}x^3 + A(y, z)\right] = \frac{\partial A}{\partial y} = -2yz,$$

so

$$A(y, z) = -\int 2yz \, \partial y = -y^2 z + B(z). \tag{13}$$

Then put (12) and (13) into (11c):

$$\frac{\partial \Phi}{\partial z} = \frac{\partial}{\partial z}\left[\frac{2}{3}x^3 - y^2 z + B(z)\right] = -y^2 + B'(z) = -y^2 - 3, \tag{14}$$

$$B'(z) = -3, \qquad B = -3z + C, \tag{15}$$

where C is an arbitrary constant. Combining (12), (13), and (15) yields

$$\Phi = \tfrac{2}{3}x^3 - y^2 z - 3z + C, \tag{16}$$

so (9) gives

$$I = \Phi\Big|_{\text{initial}}^{\text{final}} = \left(\frac{2}{3}x^3 - y^2 z - 3z + C\right)\Big|_{(0,0,0)}^{(0,0,4)} = -12, \tag{17}$$

in agreement with (10).

COMMENT 1 Looking back at the calculation of Φ, notice that $\Phi(x, y, z)$ was an unknown function of three variables; after integrating (11a), our unknown was reduced to $A(y, z)$, after integrating (11b) it was reduced to $B(z)$, and after integrating (11c) the remaining unknown was merely the constant C. By the way, a potential Φ will *always* include an arbitrary additive constant since if $\nabla\Phi$ equals $\mathbf{v}$, so does $\nabla(\Phi + \text{constant}) = \mathbf{v}$. But the constant necessarily cancels, as in (17), when we evaluate the *change* in Φ between the initial and final points; thus one can set the constant equal to zero without affecting the computed value of I.

COMMENT 2 Obviously, the simplification-of-path procedure (10) was much shorter than the potential procedure (11) to (17). However, it is to be emphasized that beyond the answer (17), the latter procedure also yielded the potential $\Phi(x, y, z)$, as given by (16). With Φ in hand, one can then easily compute the line integral $\int_P^Q \mathbf{v} \cdot d\mathbf{R}$ between *any* two points P and Q, from (9), as $\Phi|_P^Q$.

COMMENT 3 One may wonder how the procedure (11) to (17) can possibly *fail* to work. Well, suppose that we change $\mathbf{v}$ to $\mathbf{v} = 2x^2\hat{\mathbf{i}} - 2yz\hat{\mathbf{j}} + y^3\hat{\mathbf{k}}$. Then $\nabla \times \mathbf{v} = (3y^2 + 2z)\hat{\mathbf{i}} \neq \mathbf{0}$, so we have no right to expect a scalar potential Φ to exist. Nevertheless, let us follow the same steps and see what happens. Setting

$$\frac{\partial \Phi}{\partial x} = v_x = 2x^2, \qquad \frac{\partial \Phi}{\partial y} = v_y = -2yz, \qquad \frac{\partial \Phi}{\partial z} = v_z = y^3, \tag{18a,b,c}$$

the steps are the same as before, down to (14), which now takes the form

$$-y^2 + B'(z) = y^3 \tag{19}$$

instead. It would *not* be correct to deduce, by integration of (19), that $B(z) = (y^3 + y^2)z + C$, and that

$$\Phi = \tfrac{2}{3}x^3 - y^2 z + B(z) = \tfrac{2}{3}x^3 - y^2 z + (y^3 + y^2)z + C, \tag{20}$$

because $B(z)$ was (as its argument indicates) to be a function of z alone, not a function of z and y! If not completely convinced, work out the gradient of the right-hand side of (20), and see that the result does *not* equal the given vector field $\mathbf{v} = 2x^2\hat{\mathbf{i}} - 2yz\hat{\mathbf{j}} + y^3\hat{\mathbf{k}}$. In short, (19) is impossible, and we must conclude that no scalar potential Φ exists for this field. That result was inevitable in view of the equivalence of statements (i) and (ii) in Theorem 1, and the fact that $\boldsymbol{\nabla} \times \mathbf{v} \neq \mathbf{0}$ in the present case. ◀

EXAMPLE 2 *Conservative Force Fields.* A force field $\mathbf{F}$ defined in a region $\mathcal{R}$ is said to be **conservative** *if the work*

$$W = \oint_{\mathscr{C}} \mathbf{F} \cdot d\mathbf{R} \tag{21}$$

is zero for every piecewise-smooth simple closed path $\mathscr{C}$ *in* $\mathcal{R}$. If $\mathbf{F}$ is C^1 throughout $\mathcal{R}$, it follows from Theorem 1 that $\mathbf{F}$ is conservative if and only if it is irrotational. If so, there exists a scalar potential Φ such that

$$\mathbf{F} = -\boldsymbol{\nabla}\Phi, \tag{22}$$

where the minus sign is customary, in the case of force fields, but not essential.

To illustrate, consider the uniform gravitational field $\mathbf{F} = -g\hat{\mathbf{k}}$ per unit mass, where g is the acceleration due to gravity.* Surely $\boldsymbol{\nabla} \times \mathbf{F} = \mathbf{0}$, since $\mathbf{F}$ is a constant. Then $\mathbf{F} = -g\hat{\mathbf{k}} = -\boldsymbol{\nabla}\Phi$, so that

$$\frac{\partial \Phi}{\partial x} = 0, \qquad \frac{\partial \Phi}{\partial y} = 0, \qquad \frac{\partial \Phi}{\partial z} = g.$$

Integrating gives us

$$\Phi = gz + C,$$

which is the familiar "gravitational potential energy" from elementary physics.

Returning to the general case, suppose that $\mathbf{F}$ is conservative, and consider the work $\int \mathbf{F} \cdot d\mathbf{R}$ over any path from an initial point P_0 to a final point P. With $\mathbf{F} = m\ddot{\mathbf{R}}$ from Newton's second law, where m is the mass (assumed constant), we

* Actually, the earth's gravitational force field is a "central force field," to be discussed in the next section. But in the neighborhood of the earth's surface we may approximate this force by $\mathbf{F} \approx -g\hat{\mathbf{k}}$, where g is a "local" constant.

have

$$\int_{P_0}^{P} \mathbf{F}\cdot d\mathbf{R} = \int_{P_0}^{P} m\ddot{\mathbf{R}}\cdot d\mathbf{R} = m\int \ddot{\mathbf{R}}\cdot\dot{\mathbf{R}}\,dt$$

$$= \frac{1}{2}m\int \frac{d}{dt}(\dot{\mathbf{R}}\cdot\dot{\mathbf{R}})\,dt = \frac{1}{2}m\,(\dot{\mathbf{R}}\cdot\dot{\mathbf{R}})\Big|_{P_0}^{P} = \frac{1}{2}m\,\|\dot{\mathbf{R}}\|^2\Big|_{P_0}^{P}. \tag{23}$$

But since **F** is conservative, we may also express

$$\int_{P_0}^{P} \mathbf{F}\cdot d\mathbf{R} = \int_{P_0}^{P} -\nabla\Phi\cdot d\mathbf{R} = -\int_{P_0}^{P} d\Phi = -\Phi\Big|_{P_0}^{P}. \tag{24}$$

Comparing (23) with (24), we see that $\frac{1}{2}m\,\|\dot{\mathbf{R}}\|^2\,|_{P_0}^{P} = -\Phi\,|_{P_0}^{P}$, or $(\frac{1}{2}m\,\|\dot{\mathbf{R}}\|^2 + \Phi)\,|_{P_0}^{P} = 0$. That is, there is no change in $\frac{1}{2}m\,\|\dot{\mathbf{R}}\|^2 + \Phi$:

$$\tfrac{1}{2}m\,\|\dot{\mathbf{R}}\|^2 + \Phi = \text{constant} \tag{25}$$

or

$$\text{kinetic energy} + \text{“potential energy”} = \text{constant}, \tag{26}$$

and (26) explains why such a force field is called *conservative*—because the total energy (kinetic plus potential) is conserved. ◀

EXAMPLE 3 *Irrotational Fluid Flow*. Some fluid flow fields **q** are irrotational (i.e., $\nabla \times \mathbf{q} = \mathbf{0}$) and some are not; here we consider only those flows that *are* irrotational. As an aid in determining whether a given flow is irrotational or not, we state the following basic result, which goes back to Kelvin and Helmholtz:* *If the fluid is barotropic and inviscid,*† *the vorticity vector* $\nabla \times \mathbf{q}$ *of any fluid particle (which, we saw in Section 9.6, is actually twice the particle's angular velocity) is constant in time.*

It follows from the Kelvin–Helmholtz statement that if for such a fluid, a particle once has zero vorticity, it will *always* have zero vorticity. Physically, this situation is plausible because the way to impart spin (and hence vorticity) to the particle is by applying a torque through the action of shear stresses at its surface. But an inviscid fluid, by its nature, cannot support shear stresses, so there is no way to impart a torque.

If we do have $\nabla \times \mathbf{q} = \mathbf{0}$ throughout the flow, it follows from Theorem 1 that there exists a **velocity potential** Φ such that

$$\mathbf{q} = \nabla\Phi \tag{27}$$

(although English writers often write $\mathbf{q} = -\nabla\Phi$, instead). If, in addition, the fluid is incompressible, the continuity equation [(18) on page 396] states that

$$\nabla\cdot\mathbf{q} = 0. \tag{28}$$

* *Herman Ludwig Ferdinand von Helmholtz* (1821–1894), German physiologist and physicist; *Lord Kelvin* (Sir William Thomson; 1824–1907), English physicist and mathematician.

† By *inviscid* we mean that the fluid has no viscosity; i.e., it cannot support shear stresses. By *barotropic* we mean that the fluid mass density h depends on the pressure p alone; i.e., $h = h(p)$. For example if the fluid is a perfect gas (i.e., $p = hRT$, where R is a constant and T is the absolute temperature) and heat is transferred such that $T =$ constant, then RT is constant, and h depends only on p; specifically, it is proportional to p. Or if the fluid can be considered as incompressible (recall the footnote on page 396) then, of course, $h(p) =$ constant.

Inserting (27) into (28) yields $\nabla \cdot \nabla\Phi = 0$, or the **Laplace equation**

$$\nabla^2\Phi = 0 \tag{29}$$

governing Φ.

To illustrate, consider the steady two-dimensional flow of an inviscid, incompressible fluid over a rigid impermeable wall with a "bump," as sketched in Fig. 9.45. The flow is the uniform "free stream" $U\hat{\mathbf{i}}$, plus whatever disturbance is induced by the presence of the bump. Now $\mathbf{q} \sim U\hat{\mathbf{i}}$ as $x \to -\infty$, so $\nabla \times \mathbf{q} \sim \nabla \times U\hat{\mathbf{i}} = \mathbf{0}$ as $x \to -\infty$. Thus, initially (i.e., far upstream), the particles have no spin. Since the flow is inviscid and incompressible, by assumption, it follows from the discussion above that $\nabla \times \mathbf{q} = \mathbf{0}$ *throughout* the flow, that $\mathbf{q} = \nabla\Phi$, and that Φ is governed by the *partial differential equation* (29).

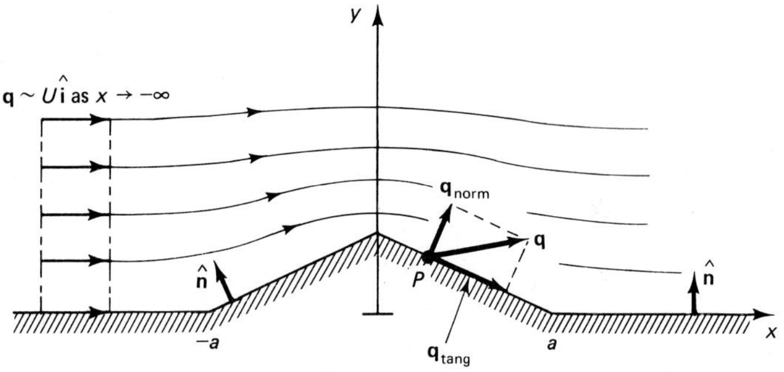

Fig. 9.45 Flow over a bump.

Besides the differential equation, there are *boundary conditions* that need to be imposed in completing the problem statement. If we imagine the boundary of the region $\mathcal{R}$ to be as shown in Fig. 9.46 as $R \to \infty$, it seems reasonable that we will need conditions both on the large semicircle (i.e., "at infinity") and along the wall. At infinity (i.e., far from the bump) we have

$$\mathbf{q} \sim U\hat{\mathbf{i}} \quad \text{as} \quad x^2 + y^2 \to \infty. \tag{30}$$

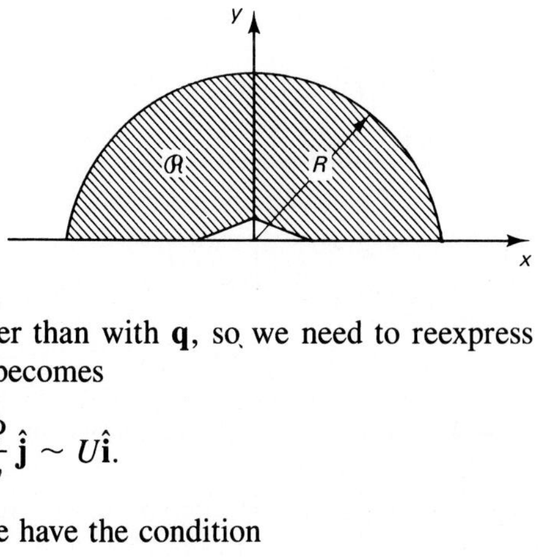

Fig. 9.46 Boundary of $\mathcal{R}$.

But we have elected to work with Φ rather than with $\mathbf{q}$, so we need to reexpress (30) in terms of Φ. Since $\mathbf{q} = \nabla\Phi$, (30) becomes

$$\frac{\partial\Phi}{\partial x}\hat{\mathbf{i}} + \frac{\partial\Phi}{\partial y}\hat{\mathbf{j}} \sim U\hat{\mathbf{i}}.$$

Thus $\partial\Phi/\partial x \sim U$ and $\partial\Phi/\partial y \to 0$, so we have the condition

$$\Phi \sim Ux \quad \text{as} \quad x^2 + y^2 \to \infty. \tag{31}$$

On the wall, we decompose $\mathbf{q}$ into normal and tangential components, as at P in Fig. 9.45. Since the wall has been assumed to be rigid and impermeable, it follows that we must set $\|\mathbf{q}_{\text{norm}}\| = 0$ all along the wall. Thus the flow is entirely tangential at the wall; hence this condition is often called the *tangent-flow condition*. Expressed in terms of Φ,

$$\|\mathbf{q}_{\text{norm}}\| = \hat{\mathbf{n}} \cdot \mathbf{q} = \hat{\mathbf{n}} \cdot \nabla \Phi = \frac{\partial \Phi}{\partial n} = 0 \tag{32}$$

on the wall.

Summarizing, the boundary value problem on Φ is:

$$\nabla^2 \Phi = \frac{\partial^2 \Phi}{\partial x^2} + \frac{\partial^2 \Phi}{\partial y^2} = 0 \quad \text{in } \mathcal{R}, \tag{33a}$$

$$\Phi \sim Ux \qquad \text{as} \quad x^2 + y^2 \to \infty, \tag{33b}$$

$$\frac{\partial \Phi}{\partial n} = 0 \quad \text{on the wall.} \tag{33c}$$

If we were to solve (33) for $\Phi(x, y)$ (e. g., by methods to be discussed in Part IV), the fluid velocity field $\mathbf{q}(x, y)$ could, according to (27), be recovered from $\mathbf{q} = \nabla \Phi$.

COMMENT 1 An advantage of working with the potential Φ, instead of the vector field $\mathbf{q}$, is that whereas $\mathbf{q}$ is comprised of two or three components (two in the present problem), the scalar field Φ is comprised of but one. Consequently, we can expect the analysis to be somewhat more compact when expressed in terms of the scalar potential Φ.

COMMENT 2 It is reasonable to wonder if the velocity potential Φ admits a simple physical significance. In fact, such significance *can* be attached to Φ, in terms of so-called "impulsive pressures." Discussion of this point can be found in the book by Wilson.* ◀

Two closing remarks are in order regarding the material that has been presented in Part II. First, notice the pattern, in evaluating integrals, of passing from n dimensions to $n - 1$: In the divergence theorem we pass from a volume integral to a surface integral (if the integrand of the volume integral is a divergence $\nabla \cdot \mathbf{v}$), in Stokes' theorem we pass from a surface integral to a line integral (if the integrand of the surface integral is essentially a curl, i.e., $\hat{\mathbf{n}} \cdot \nabla \times \mathbf{v}$), and in the case of line integrals we pass to the evaluation (of the potential) at the two endpoints (if the integrand of the line integral is a gradient $\nabla \Phi$). In fact, there exists an elegant mathematical theory of *differential forms* and *wedge products,* which brings these results together as a single theorem. For an introduction to this material, we refer the interested reader to MARSDEN AND TROMBA, pp. 397–409.

Second, observe the way the content of Part II sets the stage for our study of PDEs (partial differential equations) in Part IV. Specifically, we have seen how two of the most important PDEs, the diffusion equation and the Laplace equation, "fall right out" through application of the principles developed in the past several sec-

* D. H. WILSON, *Hydrodynamics* (London: Edward Arnold, 1959), Sec. 10.

tions. In addition, formulas such as Green's identities will prove useful in studying the question of the uniqueness of solutions of such equations.

9.12 EXERCISES

1. Show whether or not $\mathbf{v}$ is irrotational; if it is, find its potential Φ such that $\mathbf{v} = \nabla\Phi$.

*(a) $\mathbf{v} = \hat{\mathbf{i}} - 2\hat{\mathbf{j}} - 8\hat{\mathbf{k}}$
(b) $\mathbf{v} = x^3\hat{\mathbf{i}} - y\hat{\mathbf{j}} + \sin z\hat{\mathbf{k}}$
(c) $\mathbf{v} = z\hat{\mathbf{i}} + y^3\hat{\mathbf{j}} + x\hat{\mathbf{k}}$
(d) $\mathbf{v} = x(2z + y)\hat{\mathbf{i}} + \dfrac{x^2}{2}\hat{\mathbf{j}} + x^2\hat{\mathbf{k}}$
*(e) $\mathbf{v} = 2xz\hat{\mathbf{i}} + 3y\hat{\mathbf{j}} + x^2\hat{\mathbf{k}}$
(f) $\mathbf{v} = z\hat{\mathbf{i}} + z^2\hat{\mathbf{j}} + (x + 2yz)\hat{\mathbf{k}}$
(g) $\mathbf{v} = 2ze^{2y}\hat{\mathbf{j}} + e^{2y}\hat{\mathbf{k}}$
(h) $\mathbf{v} = 2xy\hat{\mathbf{i}} + (2ze^{2y} + x^2)\hat{\mathbf{j}} + e^{2y}\hat{\mathbf{k}}$
(i) $\mathbf{v} = xy\hat{\mathbf{i}} - y\hat{\mathbf{k}}$
(j) $\mathbf{v} = 6\hat{\mathbf{i}} - 2\hat{\mathbf{j}} + xyz\hat{\mathbf{k}}$
(k) $\mathbf{v} = 2xz\hat{\mathbf{i}} + x^2\hat{\mathbf{k}}$
(l) $\mathbf{v} = xz\hat{\mathbf{i}} + 2(y + 1)z\hat{\mathbf{j}} + \left(\dfrac{x^2}{2} + y^2 + 2y\right)\hat{\mathbf{k}}$
(m) $\mathbf{v} = z\hat{\mathbf{i}} + y\hat{\mathbf{j}} + x\hat{\mathbf{k}}$
(n) $\mathbf{v} = yz\hat{\mathbf{i}} + xz\hat{\mathbf{j}} + xy\hat{\mathbf{k}}$

2. Can functions $f(x, y, z)$, $g(x, y, z)$ be found such that $\mathbf{v}$ is irrotational? If so, find one such f and g. If not, why not?

*(a) $\mathbf{v} = xy\hat{\mathbf{i}} - z\hat{\mathbf{j}} + f\hat{\mathbf{k}}$
(b) $\mathbf{v} = 2xy\hat{\mathbf{i}} + x^2\hat{\mathbf{j}} + f\hat{\mathbf{k}}$
(c) $\mathbf{v} = f\hat{\mathbf{i}} + 2xyz\hat{\mathbf{j}} + g\hat{\mathbf{k}}$
(d) $\mathbf{v} = z^2\hat{\mathbf{i}} + f\hat{\mathbf{j}} + g\hat{\mathbf{k}}$

3. Show that if $\mathbf{v}$ is irrotational then

$$\int_{(x_0,y_0,z_0)}^{(x_1,y_1,z_1)} \mathbf{v}\cdot d\mathbf{R} = \int_{x_0}^{x_1} v_x(x, y_0, z_0)\,dx + \int_{y_0}^{y_1} v_y(x_1, y, z_0)\,dy + \int_{z_0}^{z_1} v_z(x_1, y_1, z)\,dz. \quad \text{(a)}$$

Hint: Use a path consisting of three straight-line segments parallel to the x, y, z coordinate axes, respectively.

4. Consider $\int_{\mathscr{C}} \mathbf{v}\cdot d\mathbf{R}$, where $\mathscr{C}$ is the path $x = \sin\tau$, $y = \cos 3\tau$, $z = 2\tau$, from $\tau = 0$ to $\tau = \pi$. Show that $\mathbf{v}$ is irrotational, and use this fact to evaluate the integral two ways: by path simplification and by the potential method. Sketch the simplified path.

(a) $\mathbf{v} = y\hat{\mathbf{i}} + x\hat{\mathbf{j}}$
(b) $\mathbf{v} = 3x^2\cos 2y\hat{\mathbf{i}} - 2x^3\sin 2y\hat{\mathbf{j}}$
*(c) $\mathbf{v} = 5x^{3/2}e^{2y}\hat{\mathbf{i}} + (4x^{5/2}e^{2y} + 5y^2)\hat{\mathbf{j}}$
(d) $\mathbf{v} = 3\hat{\mathbf{i}} + 6y^2z^{5/2}\hat{\mathbf{j}} + (5y^3z^{3/2} + 2)\hat{\mathbf{k}}$
(e) $\mathbf{v} = (y^3 - \cos z)\hat{\mathbf{j}} + (y\sin z + 2)\hat{\mathbf{k}}$
(f) $\mathbf{v} = 2x^2\hat{\mathbf{i}} - 2yz\hat{\mathbf{j}} - (y^2 + 3)\hat{\mathbf{k}}$

5. Repeat Exercise 4, but where $\mathscr{C}$ is the path $x = \cos^3\tau$, $y = \tau^2$, $z = 3\tau$, from $\tau = 0$ to $\tau = \pi$.

*(a) $\mathbf{v} = x\hat{\mathbf{i}} + y\hat{\mathbf{j}} + z\hat{\mathbf{k}}$
(b) $\mathbf{v} = 8\hat{\mathbf{i}} + (z^2 - 3y)\hat{\mathbf{j}} + (2zy - \sqrt{z})\hat{\mathbf{k}}$
(c) $\mathbf{v} = (x^2 - 2y^{3/2})\hat{\mathbf{i}} - 3x\sqrt{y}\,\hat{\mathbf{j}} + e^z\hat{\mathbf{k}}$
(d) $\mathbf{v} = y^2z^2\hat{\mathbf{i}} + 2xyz^2\hat{\mathbf{j}} + 2xy^2z\hat{\mathbf{k}}$

6. (*Exact differentials*) An expression $P\,dx + Q\,dy + R\,dz$, where P, Q, and R are functions of x, y, z defined in some region $\mathscr{R}$, is called a *first-order differential form* in three variables. If there exists a function f in $\mathscr{R}$, such that $P\,dx + Q\,dy + R\,dz = df$ in $\mathscr{R}$, the form is said to be an **exact differential.** Assuming that P, Q, R are C^1 in $\mathscr{R}$, show that for $P\,dx + Q\,dy + R\,dz$ to be an exact differential it is necessary and sufficient that $\nabla \times (P\hat{\mathbf{i}} + Q\hat{\mathbf{j}} + R\hat{\mathbf{k}}) = \mathbf{0}$ in $\mathscr{R}$. Further, show that f is the scalar potential of $P\hat{\mathbf{i}} + Q\hat{\mathbf{j}} + R\hat{\mathbf{k}}$.

7. (*Stream function*) Consider the plane flow $\mathbf{q} = u(x, y)\hat{\mathbf{i}} + v(x, y)\hat{\mathbf{j}}$ of an incompressible fluid, where $\mathbf{q}$ is C^1. The volume flow rate per unit depth (in cubic meters per second, say) crossing the curve OP (shown below) from left to right is

$$Q = \int_{\mathscr{C}} (u\,dy - v\,dx) \equiv \int_{\mathscr{C}} \mathbf{f}\cdot d\mathbf{R}, \qquad \text{(a)}$$

where $\mathbf{f} = -v\hat{\mathbf{i}} + u\hat{\mathbf{j}}$. Since $\nabla \times \mathbf{f} = (\partial u/\partial x + \partial v/\partial y)\hat{\mathbf{k}}$ is zero by virtue of the continuity equation [see (18) on page 396 and note that $w = 0$ in this ex-

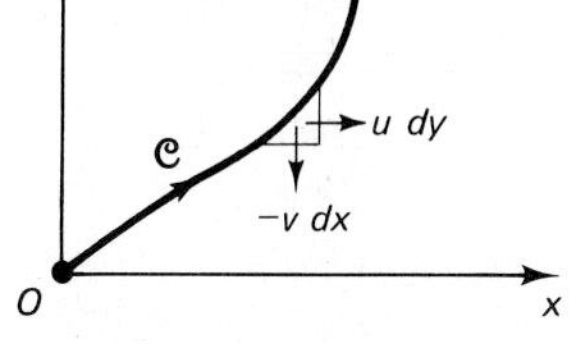

ercise], it follows that

$$Q = \int_{(0,0)}^{(x,y)} (u\,dy - v\,dx)$$

is a (single-valued) function of x and y, say $\Psi(x, y)$, where

$$\frac{\partial \Psi}{\partial x} = -v, \qquad \frac{\partial \Psi}{\partial y} = u. \tag{b}$$

Ψ is called the **stream function.**

(a) Show that the $\Psi(x, y) =$ constant curves are the *streamlines* (as introduced on page 355).
(b) If $\mathbf{q} = 2y\hat{\mathbf{i}}$, verify that $\nabla \cdot \mathbf{q} = 0$ (so that Ψ exists), and determine $\Psi(x, y)$ (to within an arbitrary additive constant).
(c) Repeat part (b), for $\mathbf{q} = 2xe^{2y}\hat{\mathbf{i}} - e^{2y}\hat{\mathbf{j}}$. Sketch the streamline through $(1, 0)$.
(d) If $\nabla \times \mathbf{q} \equiv \Omega(x, y)\hat{\mathbf{k}}$, show that

$$\nabla^2 \Psi = -\Omega(x, y). \tag{c}$$

Note: If the flow is incompressible *and* irrotational (so that $\Omega = 0$), there exist both a velocity potential Φ, satisfying $\nabla^2 \Phi = 0$, *and* a stream function Ψ, satisfying $\nabla^2 \Psi = 0$. If the flow is incompressible but *not* irrotational, Φ does not exist—yet the stream function does exist and satisfies (c).
(e) If the flow is incompressible and irrotational, so that both Ψ and Φ exist, show that the $\Psi =$ constant curves and the $\Phi =$ constant curves are everywhere *orthogonal*; i.e., at each point $P = (x, y)$ the $\Psi =$ constant curve through P, and the $\Phi =$ constant curve through P intersect at right angles. *Hint:* Consider $\nabla \Psi \cdot \nabla \Phi$.

8. (*Entropy of an ideal gas*) Any gas satisfying the equation of state $pv = RT$, where p is the pressure, v is the volume per mole, T is the absolute temperature, and R is the universal gas constant, is said to be an *ideal gas*. The first law of thermodynamics for one mole of an ideal gas can be expressed as

$$\delta q = p\,dv + c_v\,dT, \tag{a}$$

where δq is the heat input and $c_v = c_v(T)$ is the specific heat at constant volume. Show that the right-hand side of (a) is *not* an exact differential (see Exercise 6), but that if we multiply through by $1/T$, then

$$\frac{\delta q}{T} = \frac{p}{T}\,dv + \frac{c_v}{T}\,dT \tag{b}$$

is an exact differential, say $\delta q/T \equiv ds$, where $s(v, T)$ is called the *entropy* of the (one mole of) gas. [Since ds is an exact differential, s is indeed a *function* of v, T. That is, it is uniquely determined, for the given gas, by the point (v, T) in the v, T plane (i.e., by the "state"), independent of the path history.]

9. (*Solenoidal fields*) Let $\mathbf{v}$ be a vector field defined in a region $\mathcal{R}$. If $\nabla \cdot \mathbf{v} = 0$ at each point in $\mathcal{R}$, then $\mathbf{v}$ is said to be **solenoidal** in $\mathcal{R}$. We have the following theorem:

> ***Theorem*** *Vector Potential of Solenoidal Field*
>
> If $\mathbf{v}$ is C^1 and solenoidal in a simply connected region $\mathcal{R}$, then there exists a vector field $\mathbf{w}$ in $\mathcal{R}$ such that $\mathbf{v} = \nabla \times \mathbf{w}$.

Prove this theorem, say for the case where $\mathcal{R}$ is the rectangular prism $x_1 \le x \le x_2$, $y_1 \le y \le y_2$, $z_1 \le z \le z_2$. *Hint:* We need to show that the equation $\mathbf{v} = \nabla \times \mathbf{w}$ does indeed admit a solution $\mathbf{w}$. To do this, show that $\mathbf{v} = \nabla \times \mathbf{w}$ is equivalent to the three scalar equations

$$\frac{\partial w_z}{\partial y} - \frac{\partial w_y}{\partial z} = v_x, \qquad \frac{\partial w_x}{\partial z} - \frac{\partial w_z}{\partial x} = v_y,$$
$$\frac{\partial w_y}{\partial x} - \frac{\partial w_x}{\partial y} = v_z, \tag{a}$$

and that these equations are satisfied by the choice

$$\mathbf{w} = 0\hat{\mathbf{i}} + \left[\int_{x_0}^{x} v_z(\xi, y, z)\,\partial\xi\right]\hat{\mathbf{j}} + \left[\int_{y_0}^{y} v_x(x_0, \eta, z)\partial\eta - \int_{x_0}^{x} v_y(\xi, y, z)\,\partial\xi\right]\hat{\mathbf{k}} + \nabla f, \tag{b}$$

where x_0, y_0 are any constants such that $x_1 \le x_0 \le x_2$ and $y_1 \le y_0 \le y_2$, and where f is an arbitrary scalar function which is C^2 in $\mathcal{R}$. *Note:* Note the pattern that emerges: If $\mathbf{v}$ is irrotational ($\nabla \times \mathbf{v} = \mathbf{0}$), $\mathbf{v}$ is expressible as the gradient of a scalar potential Φ ($\mathbf{v} = \nabla\Phi$). Analogously, if $\mathbf{v}$ is solenoidal ($\nabla \cdot \mathbf{v} = 0$), $\mathbf{v}$ is expressible as the curl of a vector potential $\mathbf{w}$ ($\mathbf{v} = \nabla \times \mathbf{w}$). The notions of irrotational and solenoidal fields are complementary in the sense that *every* C^1 *vector field* $\mathbf{v}$*, defined in a bounded simply connected region* $\mathcal{R}$*, can be split as* $\mathbf{v} = \mathbf{v}_1 + \mathbf{v}_2$*, where* $\mathbf{v}_1$ *is irrotational in* $\mathcal{R}$*, and* $\mathbf{v}_2$ *is solenoidal in* $\mathcal{R}$, a useful fact that we state without proof.

10. (First, read Exercise 9.) In each case, verify that $\mathbf{v}$ is solenoidal, and use equation (b) in Exercise 9 to determine a vector potential $\mathbf{w}$, feeling free to choose any convenient x_0, y_0, and f.

*(a) $\mathbf{v} = a\hat{\mathbf{i}} + b\hat{\mathbf{j}} + c\hat{\mathbf{k}}$ (a, b, c constants)
(b) $\mathbf{v} = y\hat{\mathbf{i}} + x\hat{\mathbf{j}}$
(c) $\mathbf{v} = 3\hat{\mathbf{i}} + x^2\hat{\mathbf{j}} + 4y\hat{\mathbf{k}}$
*(d) $\mathbf{v} = xy\hat{\mathbf{i}} - yz\hat{\mathbf{k}}$
(e) $\mathbf{v} = 2y\hat{\mathbf{i}} + x^2y^2\hat{\mathbf{j}} - 2x^2yz\hat{\mathbf{k}}$
(f) $\mathbf{v} = x^3y\hat{\mathbf{i}} - z\hat{\mathbf{j}} - 3x^2y(z+1)\hat{\mathbf{k}}$
(g) $\mathbf{v} = x \sin y\hat{\mathbf{i}} + (\cos y + 2z)\hat{\mathbf{j}} + x^2y\hat{\mathbf{k}}$

11. *(Integrating equations of motion)* In Example 2 we considered a single particle. Here we consider a *continuum* of particles. Consider the motion of a fluid, assumed irrotational and incompressible, in a region $\mathcal{R}$, under the action of a uniform gravitational force field $-g\hat{\mathbf{k}}$ (per unit mass). If σ is the mass density, $\mathbf{q}$ is the velocity field, and p is the pressure field, then we state, without derivation, that Newton's second law leads to the *Euler equation*

$$\sigma \frac{D\mathbf{q}}{Dt} = -\nabla p - g\hat{\mathbf{k}}$$

or

$$\frac{\partial \mathbf{q}}{\partial t} + (\mathbf{q}\cdot\nabla)\mathbf{q} + \nabla\left(\frac{p}{\sigma}\right) + \frac{g}{\sigma}\hat{\mathbf{k}} = \mathbf{0}, \qquad \text{(a)}$$

where D/Dt is the "convective derivative" defined on page 373. Use (8) on page 380 to show that $(\mathbf{q}\cdot\nabla)\mathbf{q} = \nabla(\frac{1}{2}v^2)$, where $\|\mathbf{q}\| \equiv v$, and show that (a) may be expressed as

$$\frac{\partial \Phi}{\partial t} + \frac{1}{2}v^2 + \frac{p}{\sigma} + \frac{g}{\sigma}z = \text{"constant"} = F(t) \quad \text{(b)}$$

everywhere in $\mathcal{R}$, for arbitrary $F(t)$. Equation (b) is one form of the well-known *Bernoulli equation*.

12. (a) Show that if Φ is a scalar potential of $\mathbf{v}$ (i.e., $\nabla\Phi = \mathbf{v}$), so is $\Phi + C$, where C is an arbitrary constant.
(b) Show that if Φ_1 and Φ_2 are scalar potentials of $\mathbf{v}$ (i.e., $\nabla\Phi_1 = \mathbf{v}$ and $\nabla\Phi_2 = \mathbf{v}$), they differ by *at most* a constant; i.e., Φ_2 equals Φ_1 plus an arbitrary constant.

NONCARTESIAN SYSTEMS; THE INTEGRAL THEOREMS 9.13

Optional Section

Let us reiterate our strategy: we have separated most of the development for non-Cartesian coordinate systems into "optional" sections so that that material could be bypassed in a shorter course, or in a first reading. Thus in this final section we introduce no new concepts of theorems; we merely illustrate line integrals and the divergence theorem in terms of cylindrical and spherical coordinates.

We will need expressions for $d\mathbf{R}$, dA, and dV, so let us derive these expressions before turning to examples. You may wish to review Section 7.6 before continuing.

CYLINDRICAL COORDINATES

Beginning with the position vector

$$\mathbf{R} = r\hat{\mathbf{e}}_r(\theta) + z\hat{\mathbf{e}}_z \tag{1}$$

(Fig. 9.47a), we have

$$d\mathbf{R} = dr\,\hat{\mathbf{e}}_r + r\,d\hat{\mathbf{e}}_r + dz\,\hat{\mathbf{e}}_z = dr\,\hat{\mathbf{e}}_r + r\frac{d\hat{\mathbf{e}}_r}{d\theta}d\theta + dz\,\hat{\mathbf{e}}_z.$$

Since $d\hat{\mathbf{e}}_r/d\theta = \hat{\mathbf{e}}_\theta$, this expression for $d\mathbf{R}$ becomes

$$\boxed{d\mathbf{R} = dr\,\hat{\mathbf{e}}_r + r\,d\theta\,\hat{\mathbf{e}}_\theta + dz\,\hat{\mathbf{e}}_z.} \tag{2}$$

The right-hand side of (2) contains all the information that we need in order to obtain the desired expressions for dA and dV. Naturally, our expression of dA will

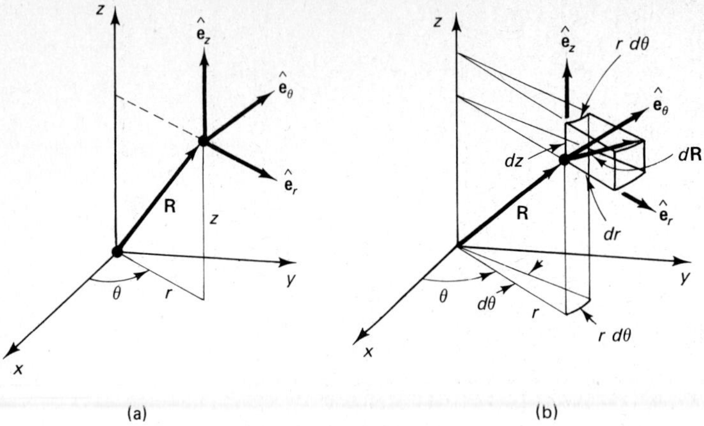

Fig. 9.47 Cylindrical coordinates.

depend on the nature of the specific surface under consideration. Often, although not always, our surfaces are comprised of constant-coordinate portions. Thus in cylindrical coordinates we are especially interested in constant r, constant θ, and constant z surfaces. The area element dA for such surfaces can be seen immediately from Fig. 9.47b to be

$$\text{Constant } r \text{ surface:} \quad dA = r\,d\theta\,dz \tag{3a}$$

$$\text{Constant } \theta \text{ surface:} \quad dA = dr\,dz \tag{3b}$$

$$\text{Constant } z \text{ surface:} \quad dA = r\,dr\,d\theta \tag{3c}$$

As mentioned above, these expressions could also have been obtained directly from (2). For example, if r is constant, (2) becomes $d\mathbf{R} = r\,d\theta\,\hat{\mathbf{e}}_\theta + dz\,\hat{\mathbf{e}}_z$; the components $r\,d\theta$ and dz are the dimensions of the dA rectangle, so $dA = (r\,d\theta)(dz) = r\,d\theta\,dz$, as in (3a); similarly for (3b) and (3c). More general surfaces are considered in the exercises.

Turning to dV, the components dr, $r\,d\theta$, and dz are the dimensions of the dV parallelipiped (at least, dV *approaches* a parallelipiped as dr, $d\theta$, and dz tend to zero), so $dV = (dr)(r\,d\theta)(dz) = r\,dr\,d\theta\,dz$, in agreement with the result derived in Section 8.7. We state this result here for reference:

$$dV = r\,dr\,d\theta\,dz. \tag{4}$$

Notice that there are *unique* expressions for $d\mathbf{R}$ and dV, namely, (2) and (4), whereas the expression of dA depends on the particular surface under consideration.

SPHERICAL COORDINATES

Here the position vector is

$$\mathbf{R} = \rho\hat{\mathbf{e}}_\rho(\phi, \theta) \tag{5}$$

(Fig. 9.48), so

$$d\mathbf{R} = d\rho\,\hat{\mathbf{e}}_\rho + \rho\,d\hat{\mathbf{e}}_\rho = d\rho\,\hat{\mathbf{e}}_\rho + \rho\frac{\partial\hat{\mathbf{e}}_\rho}{\partial\phi}\,d\phi + \rho\frac{\partial\hat{\mathbf{e}}_\rho}{\partial\theta}\,d\theta.$$

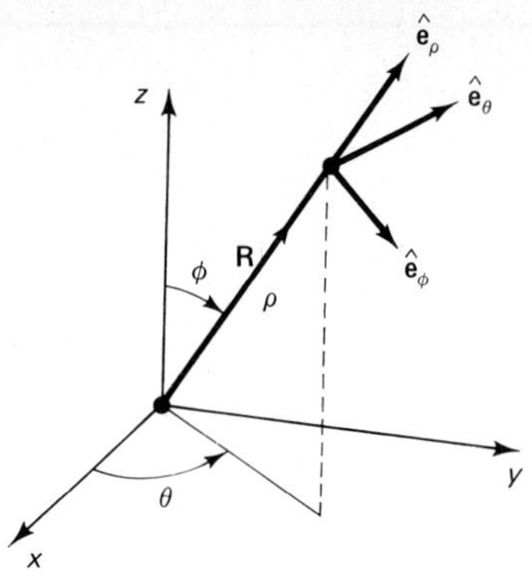

Fig. 9.48 Spherical coordinates.

Since $\partial\hat{\mathbf{e}}_\rho/\partial\phi = \hat{\mathbf{e}}_\phi$ and $\partial\hat{\mathbf{e}}_\rho/\partial\theta = \sin\phi\,\hat{\mathbf{e}}_\theta$, this expression becomes

$$d\mathbf{R} = d\rho\,\hat{\mathbf{e}}_\rho + \rho\,d\phi\,\hat{\mathbf{e}}_\phi + \rho\sin\phi\,d\theta\,\hat{\mathbf{e}}_\theta, \tag{6}$$

graphical interpretation of which is left for the reader.

As for cylindrical coordinates, we will limit our attention to constant-coordinate surfaces. On a constant ρ surface, for example, we can infer from (6) that $dA = (\rho\,d\phi)(\rho\sin\phi\,d\theta)$. Actually, we should write $dA = \rho^2\,|\sin\phi|\,d\phi\,d\theta$ to ensure that dA is positive. Similarly for constant ϕ and constant θ surfaces, so that we have these results:

$$\text{Constant } \rho \text{ surface:} \quad dA = \rho^2\,|\sin\phi|\,d\phi\,d\theta \tag{7a}$$

$$\text{Constant } \phi \text{ surface:} \quad dA = \rho\,|\sin\phi|\,d\rho\,d\theta \tag{7b}$$

$$\text{Constant } \theta \text{ surface:} \quad dA = \rho\,d\rho\,d\phi. \tag{7c}$$

As for the volume element, the product of the (absolute magnitude of the) coefficients in (6) gives

$$dV = \rho^2\,|\sin\phi|\,d\rho\,d\phi\,d\theta. \tag{8}$$

In what follows we will routinely restrict ϕ to $0 \le \phi \le \pi$. In that case $\sin\phi \ge 0$, so the absolute value signs in (7) and (8) can be dropped.

With these preliminaries out of the way, let us spend the remainder of this section looking at some examples.

EXAMPLE 1 *Line Integral; Cylindrical Coordinates.* Evaluate $\int_{\mathscr{C}} r^3 ds$, where $\mathscr{C}$ is given by the parametrization $r = \tau$, $\theta = 2\tau$, $z = \tau + 5$ over $0 \le \tau \le 2$. Well,

$$\begin{aligned} d\mathbf{R} = dr\hat{\mathbf{e}}_r + r\,d\theta\hat{\mathbf{e}}_\theta + dz\hat{\mathbf{e}}_z &= (d\tau)\hat{\mathbf{e}}_r + (\tau)(2d\tau)\hat{\mathbf{e}}_\theta + (d\tau)\hat{\mathbf{e}}_z \\ &= (\hat{\mathbf{e}}_r + 2\tau\hat{\mathbf{e}}_\theta + \hat{\mathbf{e}}_z)\,d\tau, \end{aligned}$$

so

$$ds = \|d\mathbf{R}\| = \sqrt{d\mathbf{R}\cdot d\mathbf{R}} = \sqrt{1 + 4\tau^2 + 1}\,d\tau = \sqrt{2 + 4\tau^2}\,d\tau.$$

Thus

$$\int_{\mathscr{C}} r^3\, ds = \int_0^2 \tau^3 \sqrt{2 + 4\tau^2}\, d\tau = \frac{149}{15}\sqrt{2}. \quad \blacktriangleleft$$

EXAMPLE 2 *Line Integral; Polar Coordinates*. Evaluate the work $W = \int_{\mathscr{C}} \mathbf{F}\cdot d\mathbf{R}$, where

$$\mathbf{F} = r\cos^2\theta\, \hat{\mathbf{e}}_r - \frac{\cos\theta}{r^2}\hat{\mathbf{e}}_\theta, \tag{9}$$

and where $\mathscr{C}$ is the closed path shown in Fig. 9.49, the curved portion of which is a circular arc, centered at the origin, and lying in the x, y plane. Noting that $\mathscr{C}$ is a closed path, W will be zero if $\mathbf{F}$ is irrotational, so let us first check to see if that is the case. Using (16) on page 387,

$$\nabla \times \mathbf{F} = \frac{1}{r}\left(\frac{\cos\theta}{r^2} + 2r\sin\theta\cos\theta\right)\hat{\mathbf{e}}_z \neq \mathbf{0}.$$

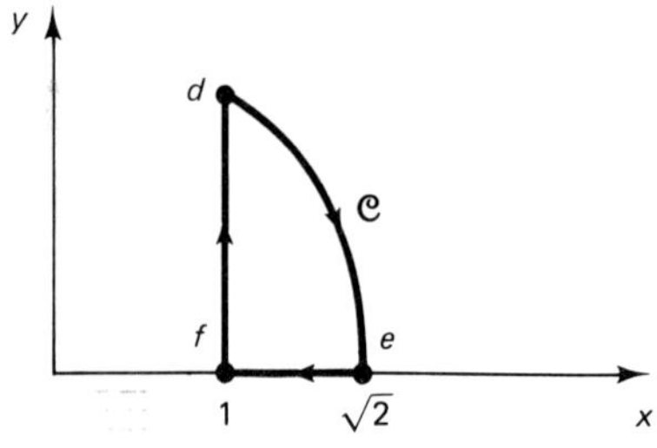

Fig. 9.49 The path $\mathscr{C}$.

Thus F is *rotational* (i.e., not irrotational), so we cannot merely state at the outset that $W = 0$; we need to face up to the integration.

Using (2), we have

$$\begin{aligned} W = \int_{\mathscr{C}} \mathbf{F}\cdot d\mathbf{R} &= \int_{\mathscr{C}} \left(r\cos^2\theta\,\hat{\mathbf{e}}_r - \frac{\cos\theta}{r^2}\hat{\mathbf{e}}_\theta\right)\cdot(dr\,\hat{\mathbf{e}}_r + r\,d\theta\,\hat{\mathbf{e}}_\theta) \\ &= \int_{\mathscr{C}} \left(r\cos^2\theta\, dr - \frac{\cos\theta}{r}\, d\theta\right). \end{aligned} \tag{10}$$

Breaking $\mathscr{C}$ into $de + ef + fd$, we have $r = \sqrt{2}$ on de, $\theta = 0$ on ef, and $x = 1$ on fd. Since $x = r\cos\theta$, the relation $x = 1$, on fd, may be expressed in terms of r, θ as $r\cos\theta = 1$; thus we have $r = 1/\cos\theta$ or $\cos\theta = 1/r$, whichever is more convenient. Noting that $\int_{de} r\cos^2\theta\, dr = 0$ because $r =$ constant on de, and that $\int_{ef} (\cos\theta/r)\, d\theta = 0$ because $\theta =$ constant on ef, we have

$$\begin{aligned} W &= \int_{de} + \int_{ef} + \int_{fd} \\ &= \left\{0 - \int_{\pi/4}^{0} \frac{\cos\theta}{\sqrt{2}}\, d\theta\right\} + \left\{\int_{\sqrt{2}}^{1} r\, dr - 0\right\} + \left\{\int_1^{\sqrt{2}} \frac{dr}{r} - \int_0^{\pi/4} \cos^2\theta\, d\theta\right\} \end{aligned}$$

$$= -\frac{\sin\theta}{\sqrt{2}}\Bigg|_{\pi/4}^{0} + \frac{r^2}{2}\Bigg|_{\sqrt{2}}^{1} + \ln r\Bigg|_{1}^{\sqrt{2}} - \left(\frac{\theta}{2} + \frac{\sin 2\theta}{4}\right)\Bigg|_{0}^{\pi/4} \tag{11}$$

$$= \ln\sqrt{2} - \frac{\pi}{8} - \frac{1}{4}. \quad ◀$$

EXAMPLE 3 *Irrotational Field; Cylindrical Coordinates.* Show that the field

$$\mathbf{v} = z \sin\theta\hat{\mathbf{e}}_r + z\cos\theta\hat{\mathbf{e}}_\theta + (r\sin\theta - 3z^2)\hat{\mathbf{e}}_z \tag{12}$$

is irrotational, and determine its scalar potential Φ such that $\mathbf{v} = \nabla\Phi$. Using (9) on page 386, we find that $\nabla \times \mathbf{v} = \mathbf{0}$, so $\mathbf{v}$ is indeed irrotational. To compute Φ, we write out the components of the equation $\nabla\Phi = \mathbf{v}$:

$$\frac{\partial\Phi}{\partial r} = z\sin\theta, \tag{13a}$$

$$\frac{1}{r}\frac{\partial\Phi}{\partial\theta} = z\cos\theta, \tag{13b}$$

$$\frac{\partial\Phi}{\partial z} = r\sin\theta - 3z^2. \tag{13c}$$

Integrating (13a), we have

$$\Phi(r, \theta, z) = \int z\sin\theta\,\partial r = rz\sin\theta + A(\theta, z), \tag{14}$$

and putting (14) into (13b) yields

$$\frac{1}{r}\left(rz\cos\theta + \frac{\partial A}{\partial\theta}\right) = z\cos\theta,$$

so that $\partial A(\theta, z)/\partial\theta = 0$. Thus $A(\theta, z)$ does not depend on θ, so it can be reexpressed as a function of z only, say $B(z)$. Then (14) becomes $\Phi = rz\sin\theta + B(z)$, and putting this expression into (13c) gives $r\sin\theta + B'(z) = r\sin\theta - 3z^2$, so that $B(z) = -z^3 + C$, where C is an arbitrary constant. Hence

$$\Phi = rz\sin\theta - z^3 + C. \quad ◀ \tag{15}$$

EXAMPLE 4 *Line Integral; Spherical Coordinates.* Evaluate $\int_{\mathscr{C}} \mathbf{v}\cdot d\mathbf{R}$, where

$$\mathbf{v} = \rho\cos^2\phi\hat{\mathbf{e}}_\rho - \rho\cos\phi\sin\phi\,\hat{\mathbf{e}}_\phi, \tag{16}$$

and where $\mathscr{C}$ is the straight-line path from P to Q (Fig. 9.50). Recalling (6) gives us

$$\begin{aligned}\int_{\mathscr{C}} \mathbf{v}\cdot d\mathbf{R} &= \int_{\mathscr{C}} (\rho\cos^2\phi\hat{\mathbf{e}}_\rho - \rho\cos\phi\sin\phi\hat{\mathbf{e}}_\phi)\cdot(d\rho\hat{\mathbf{e}}_\rho + \rho\, d\phi\hat{\mathbf{e}}_\phi + \rho\sin\phi\, d\theta\hat{\mathbf{e}}_\theta) \\ &= \int_{\mathscr{C}} (\rho\cos^2\phi\, d\rho - \rho^2\cos\phi\sin\phi\, d\phi).\end{aligned} \tag{17}$$

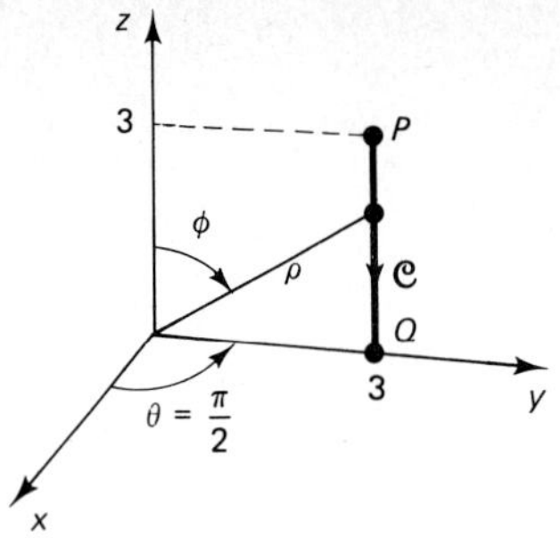

Fig. 9.50 The given path $\mathscr{C}$.

Now, on $\mathscr{C}$ we have $\rho \sin \phi = 3$ [and $\theta = \pi/2$, although θ happens not to be present in (17)], so that (17) may be expressed as

$$\begin{aligned}\int_{\mathscr{C}} \mathbf{v} \cdot d\mathbf{R} &= \int_{\mathscr{C}} \rho(1 - \sin^2 \phi)\, d\rho - \int_{\mathscr{C}} \rho^2 \sin \phi \cos \phi \, d\phi \\ &= \int_{3\sqrt{2}}^{3} \rho\left(1 - \frac{9}{\rho^2}\right) d\rho - \int_{\pi/4}^{\pi/2} \frac{9}{\sin^2 \phi} \sin \phi \cos \phi \, d\phi \\ &= \left(\frac{\rho^2}{2} - 9 \ln \rho\right)\bigg|_{3\sqrt{2}}^{3} - 9 \int_{\phi=\pi/4}^{\phi=\pi/2} \frac{1}{\sin \phi} d(\sin \phi) \\ &= \frac{9}{2}(\ln 2 - 1) - 9 \ln (\sin \phi)\bigg|_{\pi/4}^{\pi/2} = -\frac{9}{2}.\end{aligned} \tag{18}$$

Alternatively, if we use the formula (22) on page 388, we find that $\nabla \times \mathbf{v} = \mathbf{0}$, so that $\mathbf{v}$ is irrotational and admits a scalar potential Φ such that $\mathbf{v} = \nabla\Phi$. Writing out the components of $\nabla\Phi = \mathbf{v}$, where $\nabla\Phi$ is given by (19) on page 387,

$$\frac{\partial \Phi}{\partial \rho} = \rho \cos^2 \phi, \tag{19a}$$

$$\frac{1}{\rho} \frac{\partial \Phi}{\partial \phi} = -\rho \cos \phi \sin \phi, \tag{19b}$$

$$\frac{1}{\rho \sin \phi} \frac{\partial \Phi}{\partial \theta} = 0. \tag{19c}$$

Integrating (19a) yields

$$\Phi = \int \rho \cos^2 \phi \, \partial\rho = \frac{\rho^2}{2} \cos^2 \phi + A(\phi, \theta). \tag{20}$$

Putting (20) into (19b), we have

$$-\rho \sin \phi \cos \phi + \frac{1}{\rho} \frac{\partial A}{\partial \phi} = -\rho \cos \phi \sin \phi,$$

so $\partial A/\partial \phi = 0$ and $A(\phi, \theta) =$ function of θ only $= B(\theta)$. Thus far

$$\Phi = \frac{\rho^2}{2} \cos^2 \phi + B(\theta). \tag{21}$$

Putting (21) into (19c) tells us that $B'(\theta) = 0$, so that $B(\theta)$ is a constant, say C. Thus

$$\Phi = \frac{\rho^2}{2}\cos^2\phi + C$$

and

$$\begin{aligned}\int_{\mathscr{C}} \mathbf{v}\cdot d\mathbf{R} &= \int_{\mathscr{C}} \nabla\Phi\cdot d\mathbf{R} = \int_{\mathscr{C}} d\Phi = \Phi\Big|_P^Q \\ &= \left(\frac{\rho^2}{2}\cos^2\phi + C\right)\Bigg|_{\rho=3\sqrt{2},\phi=\pi/4}^{\rho=3,\phi=\pi/2},\ \phi = \pi/4 = -\frac{9}{2},\end{aligned} \tag{22}$$

as found by "direct integration" in (18).

Finally, observe that instead of using the scalar potential method we could (since $\mathbf{v}$ is irrotational) have used the method of path simplification to simplify the evaluation of $\int_{\mathscr{C}} \mathbf{v}\cdot d\mathbf{R}$. That observation begs the question "*What **is** a simple (i.e., computationally convenient) path?*" The answer is that *the recommended curves are the coordinate curves*. (By a coordinate curve we mean a curve along which only one coordinate varies.) To illustrate this idea, consider the case of Cartesian coordinates. A recommended path connecting an initial point (x_1, y_1, z_1) to a final point (x_2, y_2, z_2) is shown in Fig. 9.51 and consists of segments $\mathscr{C}_1$ (along which only x varies), $\mathscr{C}_2$ (along which only y varies), and $\mathscr{C}_3$ (along which only z varies). Then

$$\begin{aligned}\int_{\mathscr{C}} \mathbf{v}\cdot d\mathbf{R} &= \int_{\mathscr{C}_1} (v_x\,dx + v_y\,\overset{0}{\cancel{dy}} + v_z\,\overset{0}{\cancel{dz}}) + \int_{\mathscr{C}_2} (v_x\,\overset{0}{\cancel{dx}} + v_y\,dy + v_z\,\overset{0}{\cancel{dz}}) \\ &\quad + \int_{\mathscr{C}_3} (v_x\,\overset{0}{\cancel{dx}} + v_y\,\overset{0}{\cancel{dy}} + v_z\,dz) \\ &= \int_{x_1}^{x_2} v_x(x, y_1, z_1)\,dx + \int_{y_1}^{y_2} v_y(x_2, y, z_1)\,dy \\ &\quad + \int_{z_1}^{z_2} v_z(x_2, y_2, z)\,dz,\end{aligned} \tag{23}$$

where we notice, with gratitude, that y and z are held fixed in the first integral, x and z in the second, and x and y in the third. Similarly for cylindrical and spherical coordinates, we recommend paths that are coordinate curves. Returning to the example at hand, note that the given path $\mathscr{C}$ (Fig. 9.50) is not a coordinate curve

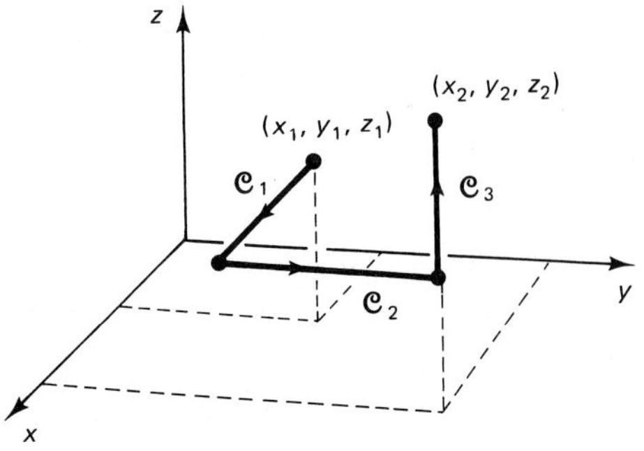

Fig. 9.51 Simplest path.

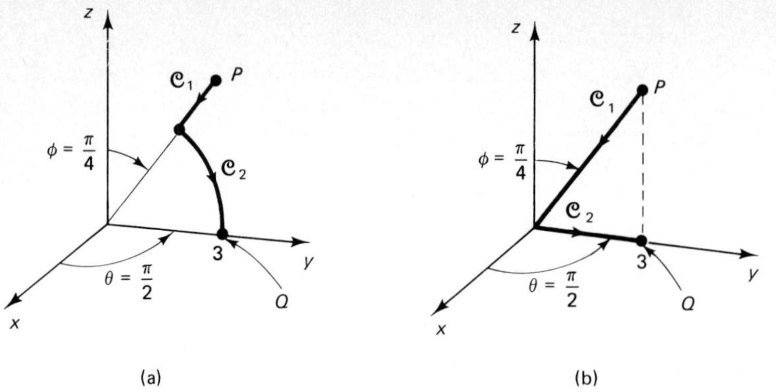

Fig. 9.52 Path simplification.

since both ρ and ϕ vary along its length. Two simpler paths that come to mind are shown in Fig. 9.52. Let us use the one in Fig. 9.52a. Along $\mathscr{C}_1$ only ρ varies, and along $\mathscr{C}_2$ only ϕ varies. Thus (17) becomes

$$\begin{aligned}\int_{\mathscr{C}} \mathbf{v}\cdot d\mathbf{R} &= \int_{\mathscr{C}_1} (\rho \cos^2 \phi \, d\rho - \rho^2 \cos \phi \sin \phi \, \overset{0}{\cancel{d\phi}}) \\ &\quad + \int_{\mathscr{C}_2} (\rho \cos^2 \phi \, \overset{0}{\cancel{d\rho}} - \rho^2 \cos \phi \sin \phi \, d\phi) \\ &= \int_{3\sqrt{2}}^{3} (\rho \cos^2 \phi)\Big|_{\phi=\pi/4,\theta=\pi/2} d\rho \\ &\quad - \int_{\pi/4}^{\pi/2} (\rho^2 \cos \phi \sin \phi)\Big|_{\rho=3,\theta=\pi/2} d\phi \\ &= \int_{3\sqrt{2}}^{3} \frac{\rho}{2} d\rho - \int_{\pi/4}^{\pi/2} 9 \cos \phi \sin \phi \, d\phi = -\frac{9}{2},\end{aligned} \tag{24}$$

in agreement with the results obtained in (18) and (22). We suggest that you repeat the calculation, but this time using the path simplification shown in Fig. 9.52b. ◀

EXAMPLE 5 *Divergence Theorem; Cylindrical Coordinates*. Let $\mathbf{v} = rz\hat{\mathbf{e}}_r - 3\hat{\mathbf{e}}_\theta + rz^2\hat{\mathbf{e}}_z$, and let $\mathscr{V}$ be the cylinder $0 \le r \le 2$, $0 \le z \le 6$ shown in Fig. 9.53.

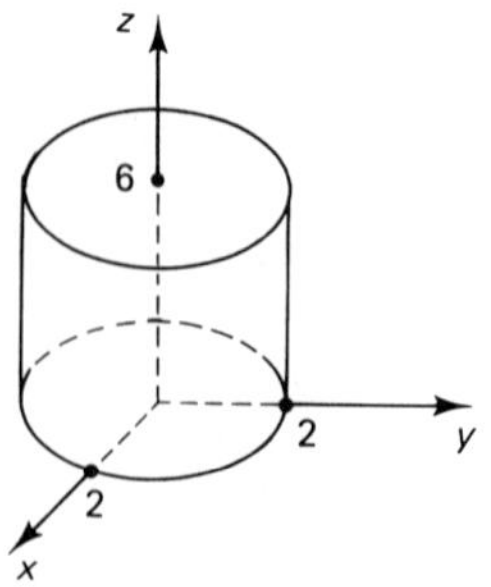

Fig. 9.53 The cylinder $\mathscr{V}$.

We wish to illustrate the computational mechanics, so the problem that we set is merely to evaluate the two sides of the divergence theorem equation and to verify that they are indeed equal. First, the volume integral. Using (4) for the volume element and (8) on page 386 for the divergence in cylindrical coordinates, we have

$$\begin{aligned}\int_{\mathcal{V}} \operatorname{div} \mathbf{v}\, dV &= \int_V \left[\frac{1}{r}\frac{\partial}{\partial r}(r^2 z) + \frac{1}{r}\frac{\partial}{\partial \theta}(-3) + \frac{\partial}{\partial z}(rz^2)\right] r\, dr\, d\theta\, dz \\ &= \int_0^6 \int_0^{2\pi} \int_0^2 2r(r+1)z\, dr\, d\theta\, dz = 336\pi.\end{aligned} \tag{25}$$

To evaluate the surface integral $\int_{\mathcal{S}} \hat{\mathbf{n}} \cdot \mathbf{v}\, dA$, we consider the top, bottom, and side separately. On the top, $\hat{\mathbf{n}} = \hat{\mathbf{e}}_z$ and $dA = r\, dr\, d\theta$ from (3c), so that

$$\begin{aligned}\int_{\text{top}} \hat{\mathbf{n}} \cdot \mathbf{v}\, dA &= \int_0^{2\pi} \int_0^2 [\hat{\mathbf{e}}_z \cdot (rz\hat{\mathbf{e}}_r - 3\hat{\mathbf{e}}_\theta + rz^2\hat{\mathbf{e}}_z)]\Big|_{z=6} r\, dr\, d\theta \\ &= \int_0^{2\pi} \int_0^2 36r^2\, dr\, d\theta = 192\pi.\end{aligned} \tag{26}$$

On the bottom, $\hat{\mathbf{n}} = -\hat{\mathbf{e}}_z$, so

$$\begin{aligned}\int_{\text{bottom}} \hat{\mathbf{n}} \cdot \mathbf{v}\, dA &= \int_0^{2\pi} \int_0^2 [-\hat{\mathbf{e}}_z \cdot (rz\hat{\mathbf{e}}_r - 3\hat{\mathbf{e}}_\theta + rz^2\hat{\mathbf{e}}_z)]\Big|_{z=0} r\, dr\, d\theta \\ &= \int_0^{2\pi} \int_0^2 0\, dr\, d\theta = 0.\end{aligned} \tag{27}$$

On the side $\hat{\mathbf{n}} = \hat{\mathbf{e}}_r$ and $dA = r\, d\theta\, dz$ from (3a), so that

$$\begin{aligned}\int_{\text{side}} \hat{\mathbf{n}} \cdot \mathbf{v}\, dA &= \int_0^6 \int_0^{2\pi} [\hat{\mathbf{e}}_r \cdot (rz\hat{\mathbf{e}}_r - 3\hat{\mathbf{e}}_\theta + rz^2\hat{\mathbf{e}}_z)]r\Big|_{r=2} d\theta\, dz \\ &= \int_0^6 \int_0^{2\pi} 4z\, d\theta\, dz = 144\pi.\end{aligned} \tag{28}$$

Combining (26) to (28), $\int_{\mathcal{S}} \hat{\mathbf{n}} \cdot \mathbf{v}\, dA = 336\pi$, which does agree with (25). ◀

EXAMPLE 6 *Divergence Theorem; Spherical Coordinates.* Let us verify the divergence theorem equation for the case where $\mathbf{v} = \rho^2\hat{\mathbf{e}}_\rho - 2\hat{\mathbf{e}}_\phi + \rho\hat{\mathbf{e}}_\theta$, and where $\mathcal{V}$ is the hemisphere of radius 3, with one quarter of it cut away and discarded, as shown in Fig. 9.54. Using (7) for the volume element dV, and (21) on page 388 for the divergence, we have

$$\begin{aligned}\int_{\mathcal{V}} \operatorname{div} \mathbf{v}\, dV &= \int_{\mathcal{V}} \left[\frac{1}{\rho^2}\frac{\partial}{\partial \rho}(\rho^4) + \frac{1}{\rho \sin\phi}\frac{\partial}{\partial \phi}(-2\sin\phi) + \frac{1}{\rho\sin\phi}\frac{\partial}{\partial \theta}(\rho)\right] \\ &\quad \times \rho^2 \sin\phi\, d\rho\, d\phi\, d\theta \\ &= \int_{\pi/2}^{2\pi} \int_0^{\pi/2} \int_0^3 (4\rho^3 \sin\phi - 2\rho\cos\phi) d\rho\, d\phi\, d\theta = 108\pi.\end{aligned} \tag{29}$$

In evaluating the surface integral $\int_{\mathcal{S}} \hat{\mathbf{n}} \cdot \mathbf{v}\, dA$, we treat the four parts separately.

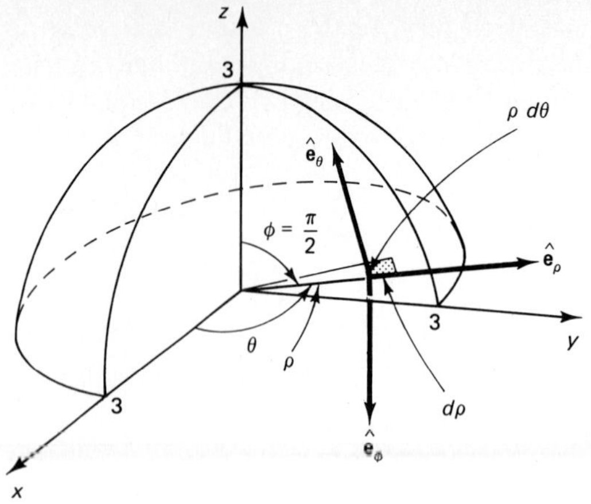

Fig. 9.54 The region $\mathcal{V}$.

On the hemispherical surface, dA is given by (7a), and $\hat{\mathbf{n}} = \hat{\mathbf{e}}_\rho$, so that

$$\int_{\substack{\text{hemispherical}\\\text{surface}}} \hat{\mathbf{n}} \cdot \mathbf{v}\, dA = \int_{\pi/2}^{2\pi} \int_0^{\pi/2} \hat{\mathbf{e}}_\rho \cdot (\rho^2 \hat{\mathbf{e}}_\rho - 2\hat{\mathbf{e}}_\phi + \rho \hat{\mathbf{e}}_\theta)(\rho^2 \sin\phi\, d\phi\, d\theta) \Big|_{\rho=3}$$
$$= \int_{\pi/2}^{2\pi} \int_0^{\pi/2} (\rho^4 \sin\phi) \Big|_{\rho=3} d\phi\, d\theta = \frac{243\pi}{2}. \qquad (30)$$

On the flat base, dA is given by (7b) (with $\phi = \pi/2$), and $\hat{\mathbf{n}} = \hat{\mathbf{e}}_\phi$ (Fig. 9.54), so

$$\int_{\text{base}} \hat{\mathbf{n}} \cdot \mathbf{v}\, dA = \int_{\pi/2}^{2\pi} \int_0^{3} \hat{\mathbf{e}}_\phi \cdot (\rho^2 \hat{\mathbf{e}}_\rho - 2\hat{\mathbf{e}}_\phi + \rho \hat{\mathbf{e}}_\theta)(\rho\, d\rho\, d\theta) \Big|_{\phi=\pi/2}$$
$$= \int_{\pi/2}^{2\pi} \int_0^{3} -2\rho\, d\rho\, d\theta = -\frac{27\pi}{2}. \qquad (31)$$

On the $\theta = \pi/2$ face, dA is given by (7c), and $\hat{\mathbf{n}} = -\hat{\mathbf{e}}_\theta$, so

$$\int_{\theta=\pi/2\text{ face}} \hat{\mathbf{n}} \cdot \mathbf{v}\, dA = \int_0^{\pi/2} \int_0^{3} -\hat{\mathbf{e}}_\theta \cdot (\rho^2 \hat{\mathbf{e}}_\rho - 2\hat{\mathbf{e}}_\phi + \rho \hat{\mathbf{e}}_\theta)(\rho\, d\rho\, d\phi) \Big|_{\theta=\pi/2}$$
$$= -\int_0^{\pi/2} \int_0^{3} \rho^2\, d\rho\, d\phi = -\frac{9\pi}{2}. \qquad (32)$$

Finally, on the $\theta = 2\pi$ face $\hat{\mathbf{n}} = \hat{\mathbf{e}}_\theta$, and

$$\int_{\theta=2\pi\text{ face}} \hat{\mathbf{n}} \cdot \mathbf{v}\, dA = \int_0^{\pi/2} \int_0^{3} \hat{\mathbf{e}}_\theta \cdot (\rho^2 \hat{\mathbf{e}}_\rho - 2\hat{\mathbf{e}}_\phi + \rho \hat{\mathbf{e}}_\theta)(\rho\, d\rho\, d\phi) \Big|_{\theta=2\pi}$$
$$= \int_0^{\pi/2} \int_0^{3} \rho^2\, d\rho\, d\phi = \frac{9\pi}{2}. \qquad (33)$$

Combining (30) to (33) gives us

$$\int_{\mathcal{S}} \hat{\mathbf{n}} \cdot \mathbf{v}\, dA = \frac{243\pi}{2} - \frac{27\pi}{2} - \frac{9\pi}{2} + \frac{9\pi}{2} = 108\pi,$$

which agrees with (29).

COMMENT We stated that $\theta = \pi/2$ on the flat face in the y, z plane and that $\theta = 2\pi$ on the flat face in the x, z plane. Other equivalent choices could have been used. For example, we could have had $\theta = 0$ on the x, z face and $\theta = -3\pi/2$ on the y, z face. Notice carefully that if we did choose $\theta = 0$ on the x, z face, then θ would *have* to be $-3\pi/2$ on the y, z face because if we start at any point on the x, z face with $\theta = 0$ and make a trip to the y, z face *without leaving* $\mathscr{V}$, θ inevitably attains the value $-3\pi/2$ when we reach the y, z face. ◀

We choose *not* to work representative examples of Stokes' theorem here because such examples would illustrate no new computational points. That is, Stokes' theorem involves a surface integral and a line integral; surface integrals were illustrated in Examples 5 and 6 (in connection with the divergence theorem), and line integrals were illustrated in Examples 1, 2, and 4.

In closing, note that we have tended to classify vector fields as irrotational everywhere in 3-space, or not. Yet there is an important class of fields that are irrotational everywhere except at one or more points or curves or surfaces. We say that the field is "singular" at these points, or on these curves or surfaces, and the presence of such singularities has important consequences. This case is covered in Exercise 14, and we suggest careful attention, in particular, to parts (b), (c), and (d).

9.13 EXERCISES

1. (*Divergence theorem*) Verify the divergence theorem, in each case, by working out $\int_{\mathscr{V}} \nabla \cdot \mathbf{v}\, dV$ and $\int_{\mathscr{S}} \hat{\mathbf{n}} \cdot \mathbf{v}\, dA$ and showing that the results are equal.

*(a) $\mathbf{v} = 3\hat{\mathbf{e}}_r + \hat{\mathbf{e}}_\theta + 2\hat{\mathbf{e}}_z$; $\mathscr{V}$: the cylinder $r \le 4$, $0 \le \theta < 2\pi$, $0 \le z \le 5$

(b) $\mathbf{v} = z\hat{\mathbf{e}}_z$; $\mathscr{V}$: the cylinder $r \le 2$, $0 \le \theta < 2\pi$, $-3 \le z \le 6$

(c) $\mathbf{v} = 3\hat{\mathbf{e}}_\rho - 2\hat{\mathbf{e}}_\phi - \hat{\mathbf{e}}_\theta$; $\mathscr{V}$: the sphere $\rho \le a$

*(d) $\mathbf{v} = \rho\hat{\mathbf{e}}_\rho + \sin\phi\hat{\mathbf{e}}_\theta$; $\mathscr{V}$: the cone $0 \le \phi \le \pi/6$, $0 \le z \le 2$

(e) $\mathbf{v} = z^2 \sin\theta\hat{\mathbf{e}}_\theta$; $\mathscr{V}$: the half-cylinder $r \le 4$, $\pi/2 \le \theta \le 3\pi/2$, $0 \le z \le 3$

(f) $\mathbf{v} = z\hat{\mathbf{e}}_r - \sin\theta\hat{e}_\theta + 2\hat{\mathbf{e}}_z$; $\mathscr{V}$: $r \le 2$, $\pi/2 \le \theta \le 2\pi$, $0 \le z \le 5$

(g) $\mathbf{v} = r^3 z\hat{\mathbf{e}}_r + z\hat{\mathbf{e}}_\theta$; $\mathscr{V}$: the cylinder $r \le 1$, $0 \le \theta < 2\pi$, $0 \le z \le 2$

(h) $\mathbf{v} = z^2\hat{\mathbf{e}}_r$; $\mathscr{V}$: the hollow cylinder $2 \le r \le 3$, $0 \le \theta < 2\pi$, $1 \le z \le 5$

(i) $\mathbf{v} = z^2\hat{\mathbf{e}}_z$; $\mathscr{V}$: the cone $r \le 2z$, $0 \le \theta < 2\pi$, $0 \le z \le 3$

(j) $\mathbf{v} = \rho^2\hat{\mathbf{e}}_\rho$; $\mathscr{V}$: the sphere $\rho \le a$

(k) $\mathbf{v} = \rho^3\hat{\mathbf{e}}_\rho$; $\mathscr{V}$: the hemisphere $\rho \le a$, $0 \le \phi \le \pi/2$, $0 \le \theta < 2\pi$

(l) $\mathbf{v} = \rho^2\hat{\mathbf{e}}_\rho$; $\mathscr{V}$: the hollow sphere $a \le \rho \le b$

(m) $\mathbf{v} = 2\hat{\mathbf{e}}_\rho - \hat{\mathbf{e}}_\theta + \hat{\mathbf{e}}_\phi$; $\mathscr{V}$: the hollow sphere $a \le \rho \le b$

(n) $\mathbf{v} = \hat{\mathbf{e}}_\rho + 2\rho\hat{\mathbf{e}}_\phi + 4\sin\theta\hat{\mathbf{e}}_\theta$; $\mathscr{V}$: $\rho \le 3$, $0 \le \phi \le \pi/2$, $\pi/2 \le \theta \le 2\pi$

*(o) $\mathbf{v} = \rho^2 \cos 3\theta\hat{\mathbf{e}}_\theta$; $\mathscr{V}$: $\rho \le 2$, $0 \le \phi \le \pi/2$, $0 \le \theta \le \pi/2$

2. Reduce each line integral to an ordinary integral (which you need not evaluate), i.e., one of the form $\int_a^b F(\tau)\, d\tau$.

*(a) $\int_{\mathscr{C}} ds$, $\mathscr{C}$: $r = 4$, $\theta = \tau$, $z = 3$ $(0 \le \tau \le \pi)$

*(b) $\int_{\mathscr{C}} z^3 \sin 2\theta\, ds$, $\mathscr{C}$: $r = 3\tau$, $\theta = \tau$, $z = e^{-\tau}$ $(0 \le \tau \le 1)$

(c) $\int_{\mathscr{C}} (r^2 + 3rz) \cos\theta\, ds$, $\mathscr{C}$: $r = \tau^2$, $\theta = \tau - 2$, $z = \sin\tau$ $(0 \le \tau \le 2)$

(d) $\int_{\mathscr{C}} ds$, $\mathscr{C}$: $\rho = 3$, $\phi = \pi/4$, $\theta = 2\tau$ $(0 \le \tau \le \pi)$

(e) $\int_{\mathscr{C}} ds$, $\mathscr{C}$: $\rho = e^{-\tau}$, $\phi = \tau$, $\theta = \pi/4$ $(0 \le \tau < \infty)$

(f) $\int_{\mathscr{C}} \rho^2 \sin 6\phi\, ds$, $\mathscr{C}$: $\rho = \tau$, $\phi = \tau - \pi/2$, $\theta = \tau^2 + \tau$ $(\pi/2 \le \tau \le \pi)$

3. Evaluate each line integral. OP, PQ, RO, and OQ are straight lines (see the figure), and QR and PS are circular arcs.

*(a) $\int_{OPQ} r\, ds$

(b) $\int_{PQR} r^2 \sin 3\theta\, ds$

(c) $\int_{ROQ} r^2 e^z \cos\theta\, ds$

(d) $\int_{OPS} \rho^2\, ds$

(e) $\int_{QR} \rho \sin 5\theta\, ds$

(f) $\int_{PS} \rho \cos 3\theta\, ds$

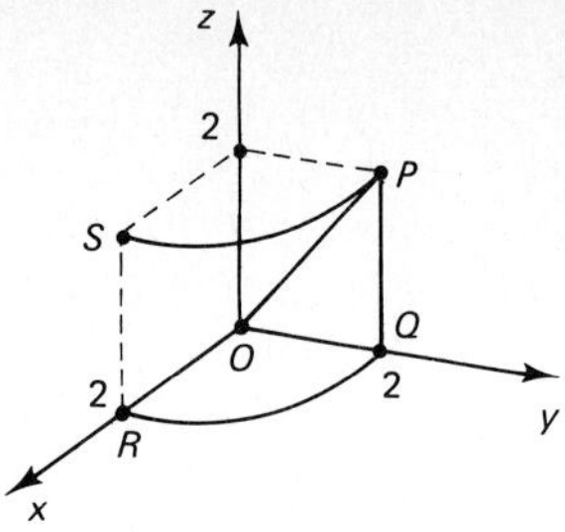

4. Determine the field $\mathbf{F}$ such that the given line integral is in the form $\int_{\mathscr{C}} \mathbf{F} \cdot d\mathbf{R}$. (You need *not* evaluate the integral; merely give $\mathbf{F}$.)

*(a) $\int_{\mathscr{C}} (2 \sin \theta \, dr - r^2 z \, d\theta + 5 dz)$
(b) $\int_{\mathscr{C}} (r^3 \, dr + z^2 \, d\theta)$
(c) $\int_{\mathscr{C}} (\cos^4 \theta \, d\theta + 3r^2 z \, dz)$
(d) $\int_{\mathscr{C}} (r \sin \theta + 2) \, d\theta$
*(e) $\int_{\mathscr{C}} (\rho^2 \, d\rho + \sin \theta \, d\phi - d\theta)$
(f) $\int_{\mathscr{C}} (\rho^3 \, d\phi + \cos \theta \, d\theta)$
(g) $\int_{\mathscr{C}} (d\rho + \rho \, d\phi + \rho \sin \phi \, d\theta)$
(h) $\int_{\mathscr{C}} \rho^2 \sin^2 \phi \, d\theta$

5. Evaluate $\int_{\mathscr{C}} r \cos^2 \theta \, d\theta$ for each given path $\mathscr{C}$.

(a)

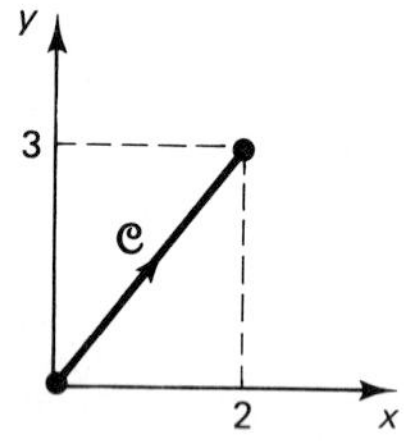

(b)

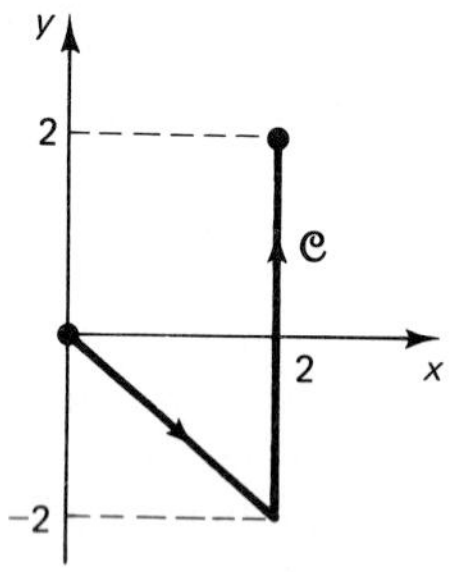

(c)

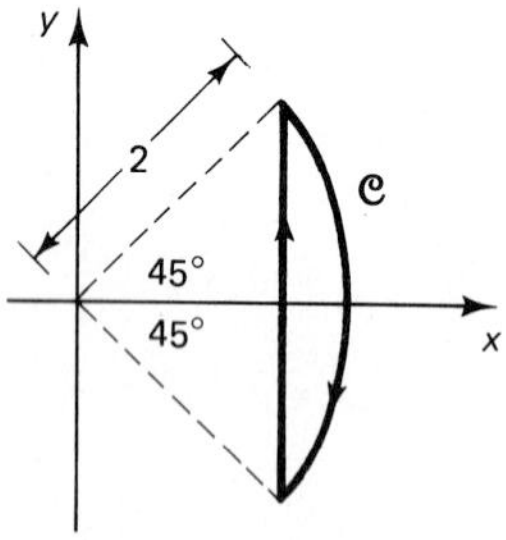

6. Evaluate $\oint_{\mathscr{C}} \mathbf{F} \cdot d\mathbf{R}$, where $\mathscr{C}$ is the cardioid $r = a(1 + \cos \theta)$ from $\theta = 0$ to $\theta = 2\pi$.

*(a) $\mathbf{F} = y\hat{\mathbf{i}}$
(b) $\mathbf{F} = 4\hat{\mathbf{e}}_r - r\hat{\mathbf{e}}_\theta$
(c) $\mathbf{F} = 5 \sin \theta \hat{\mathbf{e}}_r + 2\hat{\mathbf{e}}_\theta$

7. (*Stokes' theorem*) Verify Stokes' theorem, in each case, by working out $\int_{\mathscr{S}} \hat{\mathbf{n}} \cdot \nabla \times \mathbf{v} \, dA$ and $\oint_{\mathscr{C}} \mathbf{v} \cdot d\mathbf{R}$ and showing that the results are equal.

*(a) $\mathscr{S}$: the "waterglass" surface consisting of the cylinder $r = a$ over $0 \leq z \leq h$, and the flat base $z = 0$; $\hat{\mathbf{n}} = \hat{\mathbf{e}}_z$ on the base; $\mathbf{v} = \omega r \hat{\mathbf{e}}_\theta$, where a, h, ω are constants.

(b) $\mathscr{S}$: the "upside-down waterglass" surface consisting of the cylinder $r = a$ over $0 \leq z \leq h$, and the flat face $z = h$; $\hat{\mathbf{n}} = \hat{\mathbf{k}}$ on the face $z = h$; $\mathbf{v} = 3r\hat{\mathbf{e}}_r - rz^2\hat{\mathbf{e}}_\theta + 5r^2\hat{\mathbf{e}}_z$.

(c) $\mathscr{S}$: the flat circular disk $r \leq 1$, $z = 0$; $\hat{\mathbf{n}} = \hat{\mathbf{e}}_z$; $\mathbf{v} = (50 - 2y)\hat{\mathbf{i}}$.

(d) $\mathscr{S}$: the conical surface, shown below, open at the top; $\mathscr{C}$ oriented as shown; $\mathbf{v} = \omega r \hat{\mathbf{e}}_\theta$ (ω = constant). *Hint:* Show, with the help of a careful sketch, that $dA = r \, d\theta \, dz / \cos \alpha$ on $\mathscr{S}$.

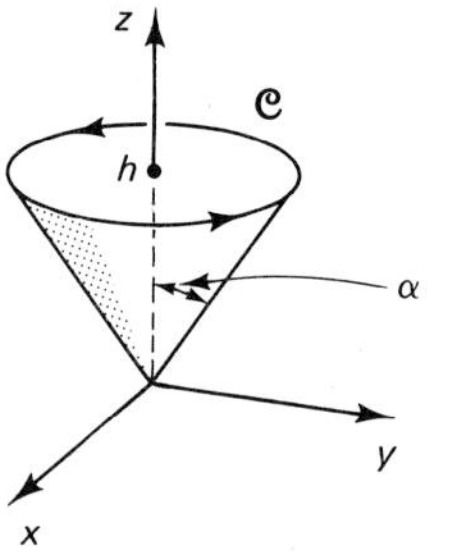

(e) Repeat part (d), but with $\mathbf{v} = 3\hat{\mathbf{e}}_r - r \sin^2 \theta \hat{\mathbf{e}}_\theta$.

(f) $\mathscr{S}$: the conical surface $\phi = \alpha$ (in spherical coordinates) shown in (d); $\mathscr{C}$ oriented as shown; $\mathbf{v} = \rho \sin \phi \hat{\mathbf{e}}_\theta$. *Hint:* $\hat{\mathbf{n}}$ may be computed either by inspection or by taking the gradient of f in the equation $f = \phi - \alpha = 0$ of the surface $\mathscr{S}$.

(g) Repeat part (f), but for $\mathbf{v} = \rho^4 \hat{\mathbf{e}}_\rho$.

8. Show whether or not $\mathbf{v}$ is irrotational; if it is, find its potential Φ such that $\mathbf{v} = \nabla\Phi$.

*(a) $\mathbf{v} = \hat{\mathbf{e}}_r + \hat{\mathbf{e}}_\theta + \hat{\mathbf{e}}_z$
(b) $\mathbf{v} = z\hat{\mathbf{e}}_r + r\hat{\mathbf{e}}_z$
*(c) $\mathbf{v} = \rho^5 \hat{\mathbf{e}}_\rho$
(d) $\mathbf{v} = \cos 5\theta \, \hat{\mathbf{e}}_r - 5 \sin 5\theta \, \hat{\mathbf{e}}_\theta + z^2 \hat{\mathbf{e}}_z$
(e) $\mathbf{v} = \hat{\mathbf{e}}_\rho + \hat{\mathbf{e}}_\phi + \hat{\mathbf{e}}_\theta$
(f) $\mathbf{v} = z \sin \theta \, \hat{\mathbf{e}}_r + z \cos \theta \, \hat{\mathbf{e}}_\theta + r \sin \theta \, \hat{\mathbf{e}}_z$
(g) $\mathbf{v} = \cos 5\phi \, \hat{\mathbf{e}}_\rho - 5 \sin 5\phi \, \hat{\mathbf{e}}_\phi$
(h) $\mathbf{v} = \rho \sin \theta \, (2 \sin \phi \, \hat{\mathbf{e}}_\rho + \cos \phi \, \hat{\mathbf{e}}_\phi) + \rho \cos \theta \, \hat{\mathbf{e}}_\theta$

9. Show that $\mathbf{v}$ is irrotational, and use this fact to evaluate $\int_{\mathscr{C}} \mathbf{v} \cdot d\mathbf{R}$ by two different methods: by path simplification and by the potential method. In each case, $\mathscr{C}$ is the path $x = \sin t$, $y = \cos t$, $z = 2t$, from $t = 0$ to $t = \pi$.

*(a) $\mathbf{v} = 3\hat{\mathbf{e}}_r - 6\hat{\mathbf{e}}_z$
(b) $\mathbf{v} = rz^2\hat{\mathbf{e}}_r + r^2z\hat{\mathbf{e}}_z$
(c) $\mathbf{v} = (2rz + 5r^4)\sin\theta\,\hat{\mathbf{e}}_r + (rz + r^4)\cos\theta\,\hat{\mathbf{e}}_\theta + r^2\sin\theta\,\hat{\mathbf{e}}_z$
(d) $\mathbf{v} = (\sin\theta + z)\hat{\mathbf{e}}_r + \cos\theta\,\hat{\mathbf{e}}_\theta + r\hat{\mathbf{e}}_z$
*(e) $\mathbf{v} = \rho^2\hat{\mathbf{e}}_\rho$
(f) $\mathbf{v} = \sin\phi\,\hat{\mathbf{e}}_\rho + \cos\phi\,\hat{\mathbf{e}}_\phi$
(g) $\mathbf{v} = (3\rho^2 - \cos\theta)\sin\phi\,\hat{\mathbf{e}}_\rho + (\rho^2 - \cos\theta)\cos\phi\,\hat{\mathbf{e}}_\phi + \sin\theta\,\hat{\mathbf{e}}_\theta$

10. Consider the following claims: The field $\mathbf{v} = \theta\hat{\mathbf{e}}_r + \hat{\mathbf{e}}_\theta$ is irrotational, and $\Phi = r\theta$ is its potential. Now if $\mathscr{C}$ is the counterclockwise unit circle in the x, y plane, then

$$\int_{\mathscr{C}} \mathbf{v}\cdot d\mathbf{R} = \int_{\mathscr{C}} d\Phi = \Phi\Bigg|_{\text{initial}}^{\text{final}} = (r\theta)\Bigg|_{r=1,\,\theta=0}^{r=1,\,\theta=2\pi} = 2\pi.$$

Yet, it is claimed, the integral should be zero, by Stokes' theorem, since $\nabla\times\mathbf{v} = \mathbf{0}$. Can you explain this apparent contradiction?

11. We got by, in this section, with the expressions (3) and (7) for dA. More generally, we can always fall back on the expression (5) in Section 8.5, namely,

$$dA = \sqrt{EG - F^2}\,du\,dv, \tag{a}$$

where

$$E = x_u^2 + y_u^2 + z_u^2$$
$$F = x_u x_v + y_u y_v + z_u z_v \tag{b}$$
$$G = x_v^2 + y_v^2 + z_v^2.$$

Use (a) and (b) to obtain the expression

(a) of dA given in (3a) *Hint:* Let $x = x(u, v)$, $y = y(u, v)$, $z = z(u, v)$ be given by $x = r\cos u$, $y = r\sin u$, $z = v$; i.e., let θ be u and let z be v.
(b) of dA given in (3b) *Hint:* Let $x = x(u, v)$, $y = y(u, v)$, $z = z(u, v)$ be given by $x = u\cos\theta$, $y = u\sin\theta$, $z = v$; i.e., let r be u and let z be v.
(c) of dA given in (3c) *Hint:* Let $r = u$ and let $\theta = v$ in $x = r\cos\theta$, $y = r\sin\theta$, $z = z$.
(d) of dA given in (7a)
(e) of dA given in (7b)
(f) of dA given in (7c)
(g) $dA = (\tan\alpha/\cos\alpha)z\,dz\,d\theta$ for the conical surface $r = z\tan\alpha$ ($z \geq 0$, say)
(h) $dA = (z^2\sin\phi/\cos^2\phi)\,d\phi\,d\theta$ for the surface $z =$ constant (≥ 0, say)
(i) $dA = |x|/(\cos^2\theta)\,d\theta\,dz$ for the surface $x =$ constant
(j) $dA = x^2/(\sin^2\phi\,|\cos\theta|\,\sin^2\theta)\,d\phi\,d\theta$ for the surface $x =$ constant

12. Show that the work $W = \int_{\mathscr{C}} q\mathbf{E}\cdot d\mathbf{R}$ (read Exercise 8 on page 412) done on a charge q in moving it from one point ρ_1, ϕ_1, θ_1 to another point ρ_2, ϕ_2, θ_2 under the action of an electric field $\mathbf{E} = (1/\rho^2)\hat{\mathbf{e}}_\rho$ (induced by a point charge at the origin) is

$$W = q\left(\frac{1}{\rho_1} - \frac{1}{\rho_2}\right),$$

independent of the path, and independent of the initial and final angular positions $\phi_1, \theta_1, \phi_2, \theta_2$.

13. (*Central force fields*) Consider the motion of a particle of mass m under the action of a central force field $\mathbf{F} = f(\rho)\hat{\mathbf{e}}_\rho$ in a region $\mathscr{R}$; i.e., at each point in $\mathscr{R}$, $\mathbf{F}$ is directed toward (or away from) some fixed point O, which we choose as the origin of a spherical coordinate system. [For example, the gravitational force field induced by a point mass is of this form, where $f(\rho)$ is proportional to $1/\rho^2$; thus we speak of an "inverse-square central force field."]

(a) Show that the moment $\mathbf{R}\times\mathbf{F}$ about O is zero and, recalling Newton's law $\mathbf{F} = m\ddot{\mathbf{R}}$, show that the *moment of momentum* $\mathbf{R}\times m\dot{\mathbf{R}}$ is a constant vector. Show, heuristically, that the constancy of $\mathbf{R}\times\dot{\mathbf{R}}$ implies that *the motion must lie in a plane* and that *the areal velocity dA/dt* (the rate at which area is swept out by the $\mathbf{R}$ vector; see the accompanying figure) *is a constant*. [The latter two results are among *Kepler's laws* (published by Johannes Kepler in 1609–1619) governing the motion of the planets about the sun. Newton inferred from these laws that the sun exerts an inverse-square force of attraction on the planets. In a bold stroke, he then reasoned that such a force field must be set up by *every* mass, and arrived at his *universal law of gravitation*.]

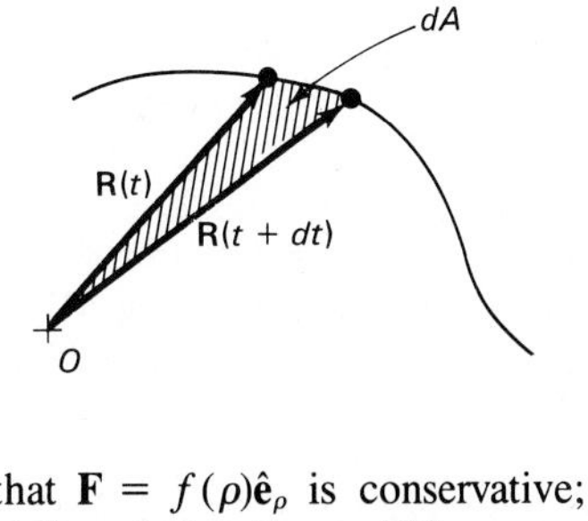

(b) Show that $\mathbf{F} = f(\rho)\hat{\mathbf{e}}_\rho$ is conservative; and find the potential Φ such that $\mathbf{F} = -\nabla\Phi$.

14. (*Biot–Savart law*) According to the **Biot–Savart law** of electrodynamics, the *magnetic field intensity* $\mathbf{H}$ induced at a point P by a current I following through a wire that forms a curve $\mathscr{C}$ is given by the line integral

$$\mathbf{H}(P) = -\frac{I}{4\pi}\int_{\mathscr{C}} \frac{\mathbf{QP} \times d\mathbf{R}}{\|\mathbf{QP}\|^3}, \tag{a}$$

where $\mathscr{C}$ is oriented in the direction of the current and **QP** is the vector from $d\mathbf{R}$ to the point P, as sketched.

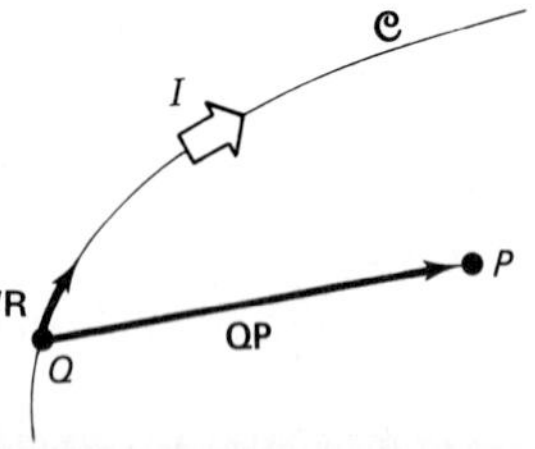

(a) Let the wire be straight, and let it coincide with the z axis, over $-\infty < z < \infty$, with I flowing in the positive z direction, as noted in the accompanying sketch. Integrating (a), obtain

$$\mathbf{H}(x_0, y_0, z_0) = \frac{I}{2\pi}\left(\frac{x_0\hat{\mathbf{j}} - y_0\hat{\mathbf{i}}}{x_0^2 + y_0^2}\right), \tag{b}$$

and show that this result simplifies, in cylindrical coordinates, to

$$\mathbf{H}(r, \theta, z) = \frac{I}{2\pi r}\hat{\mathbf{e}}_\theta. \tag{c}$$

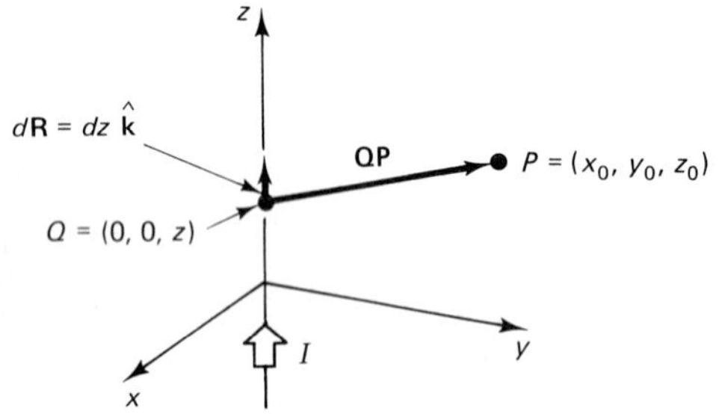

(b) Show that $\nabla \times \mathbf{H} = \mathbf{0}$ everywhere *except* at $r = 0$ (i.e., all along the wire itself).
(c) Verify that $\oint_{\mathscr{C}} \mathbf{H} \cdot d\mathbf{R} = I$, as stated on page 409, for any closed curve $\mathscr{C}$ around the wire, where the orientation of $\mathscr{C}$ and the direction of the current I are in accordance with the right-hand rule. (By the way, the fluid mechanics analog of the **H** field induced by a straight infinite wire carrying a current I is the fluid velocity field induced by a straight infinite vortex filament of strength Γ.)
(d) Evaluate $\oint_{\mathscr{C}} \mathbf{H} \cdot d\mathbf{R}$ if $\mathscr{C}$ does *not* surround the wire.
(e) Derive (c) from (a) again, but this time use cylindrical coordinates from the start.
(f) Let the wire be shaped in a circle of radius a in x, y plane, as shown. Integrating (a), show that the value of **H** at any point z_0 on the z axis is

$$\mathbf{H}(0, 0, z_0) = \frac{Ia^2}{2(z_0^2 + a^2)^{3/2}}\hat{\mathbf{e}}_z. \tag{d}$$

Hint: An integral of the form $\int_0^{2\pi} \hat{\mathbf{e}}_r d\theta$ should arise. This integral is *not* equal to $\hat{\mathbf{e}}_r \int_0^{2\pi} d\theta$ since $\hat{\mathbf{e}}_r = \hat{\mathbf{e}}_r(\theta)$ is a function of θ and must remain under the integral sign. The clue will be to express $\int_0^{2\pi} \hat{\mathbf{e}}_r\, d\theta = \int_0^{2\pi} (\cos\theta\, \hat{\mathbf{i}} + \sin\theta\, \hat{\mathbf{j}})\, d\theta = \hat{\mathbf{i}} \int_0^{2\pi} \cos\theta\, d\theta + \hat{\mathbf{j}} \int_0^{2\pi} \sin\theta\, d\theta$, since $\hat{\mathbf{i}}$ and $\hat{\mathbf{j}}$ are constant vectors which can therefore be brought outside the integrals.

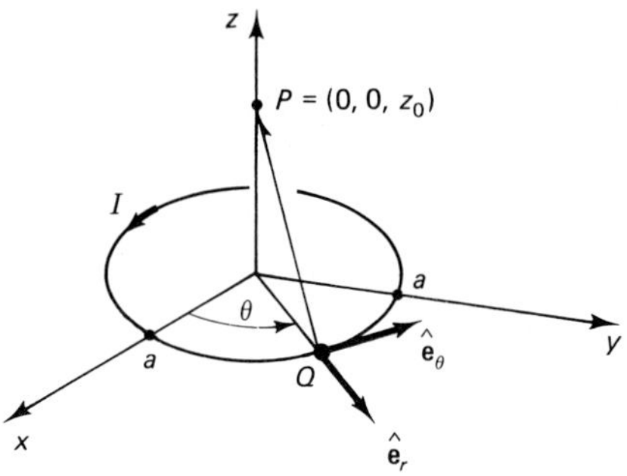

15. (*Coulomb's law*) **Coulomb's law** states, essentially, that a point charge induces an inverse-square central force field. Specifically, given two charges, Q_1 and Q_2, each induces a force on the other; the force $\mathbf{F}_2$ exerted on Q_2 by Q_1 is, according to Coulomb's law,

$$\mathbf{F}_2 = \frac{1}{4\pi\epsilon_0}\frac{Q_1 Q_2}{d^2}\hat{\mathbf{e}}, \tag{a}$$

where ϵ_0 is a constant called the permittivity of free space, d is the distance between Q_1 and Q_2, and $\hat{\mathbf{e}}$ is a unit vector directed from Q_1 toward Q_2 (so the force is repulsive if Q_1 and Q_2 are of the same sign, and attractive if they are of opposite sign). Thus given the charge Q_1, there is a force per unit charge

$$\frac{\mathbf{F}_2}{Q_2} = \frac{1}{4\pi\epsilon_0}\frac{Q_1}{d^2}\hat{\mathbf{e}} \tag{b}$$

induced at every other point in space. The quantity given in (b) is a vector field and is called the *electric field intensity* **E**. If we reexpress Q_1 as Q, for simplicity, and introduce a spherical polar coordinate system with its origin at Q, then

$$\mathbf{E} = \frac{1}{4\pi\epsilon_0}\frac{Q}{\rho^2}\hat{\mathbf{e}}_\rho. \tag{c}$$

[Observe that **E**, given by (c) is a central force field (recall Exercise 13), more specifically an inverse-square central force field, of exactly the same form as the gravitational force field induced by a point mass, as was discussed in Example 1 on page 341.] *While (c) holds only for a single point charge, the field induced by several point charges or by a continuous distribution of charge can be built up by superposition.*

(a) Determine the **E** field induced by charges Q_1 at (x_1, y_1, z_1), Q_2 at (x_2, y_2, z_2), and Q_3 at (x_3, y_3, z_3).
(b) Consider a "line charge distribution," along the z axis, over $-\infty < z < \infty$, of strength σ (coulombs/meter), where σ is a constant. Show that the induced **E** field is

$$\mathbf{E}(x_0, y_0, z_0) = \frac{\sigma}{4\pi\epsilon_0}\int_{-\infty}^{\infty}\frac{x_0\hat{\mathbf{i}} + y_0\hat{\mathbf{j}} + (z_0 - z)\hat{\mathbf{k}}}{[x_0^2 + y_0^2 + (z - z_0)^2]^{3/2}}\,dz. \tag{d}$$

Evaluating the integral, with the help of an integral table, show that

$$\mathbf{E}(x_0, y_0, z_0) = \frac{\sigma}{2\pi\epsilon_0}\frac{x_0\hat{\mathbf{i}} + y_0\hat{\mathbf{j}}}{x_0^2 + y_0^2}. \tag{e}$$

Finally, expressing (e) more naturally, in cylindrical coordinates, show that

$$\mathbf{E}(r, \theta, z) = \frac{\sigma}{2\pi\epsilon_0 r}\hat{\mathbf{e}}_r. \tag{f}$$

(c) Consider a uniform distribution of charge over the x, y plane ($-\infty < x < \infty$, $-\infty < y < \infty$), of strength σ (coulombs/meter^2), where σ is a constant. Following the general ideas in part (b) and integrating over the plane, show that

$$\mathbf{E}(x, y, z) = \begin{cases} \dfrac{\sigma}{2\epsilon_0}\hat{\mathbf{k}}, & z > 0 \\ -\dfrac{\sigma}{2\epsilon_0}\hat{\mathbf{k}}, & z < 0. \end{cases} \tag{g}$$

(d) Using the result in part (c), what is the **E** field induced by *two* planar charge distributions, one of strength $+\sigma$ over the plane $z = 0$, and one of strength $-\sigma$ over the plane $z = a$? *Hint:* Consider $z > a$, $0 < z < a$, and $z < 0$ separately.

16. (*Gauss' law*) First, read Exercise 15.

(a) Considering the **E** field of a point charge Q, given by (c) in Exercise 15, show that $\nabla\cdot\mathbf{E} = 0$ for all $\rho \neq 0$.

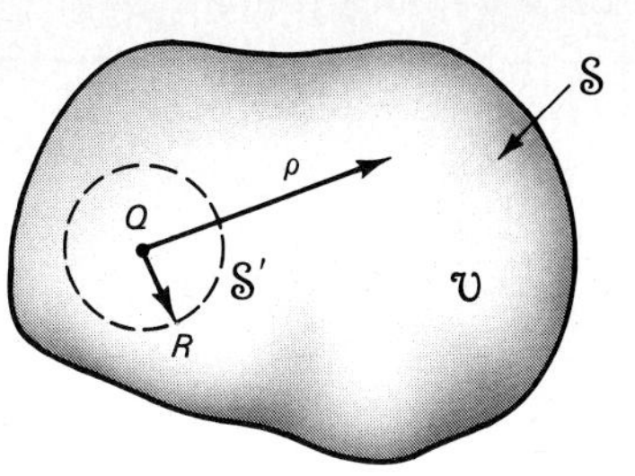

(b) Show that

$$\int_{\mathcal{S}}\mathbf{E}\cdot\hat{\mathbf{n}}\,dA = \begin{cases} \dfrac{Q}{\epsilon_0} & \text{if } Q \text{ is inside } \mathcal{S} \\ 0 & \text{if } Q \text{ is outside } \mathcal{S}. \end{cases} \tag{a}$$

Hint: For the case where Q is inside $\mathcal{S}$, apply the divergence theorem to the region $\mathcal{V}$ lying between $\mathcal{S}$ and some spherical surface $\mathcal{S}'$ centered at Q and small enough to be contained entirely within $\mathcal{S}$, as shown in the figure; let its radius be R, say. Since $\nabla\cdot\mathbf{E} = 0$ in $\mathcal{V}$, you should obtain

$$\int_{\mathcal{S}}\mathbf{E}\cdot\hat{\mathbf{n}}\,dA = \int_{\mathcal{S}'}\mathbf{E}\cdot\hat{\mathbf{n}}\,dA,$$

whereupon the integral on the right-hand side can be evaluated as Q/ϵ_0. For Q *outside* $\mathcal{S}$, (a) follows easily from the divergence theorem. *Note:* Equation (a) is virtually indispensible in the study of inverse-square central force fields (e.g., electrostatic fields and gravitational fields) and is the simplest version of "Gauss' law"—simplest in that it is for a single point charge. More generally, we may have several point charges, or line, surface, or volume distributions of charge. All of these possibilities are accounted for in the full statement of **Gauss' law:**

$$\boxed{\int_{\mathcal{S}}\mathbf{E}\cdot\hat{\mathbf{n}}\,dA = \frac{1}{\epsilon_0}\begin{array}{l}\text{times the net charge}\\ \text{enclosed by } \mathcal{S}.\end{array}} \tag{b}$$

Depending on the type of charge distribution, the right-hand side may be one or more discrete terms, a line integral, a surface integral, or a volume integral. For sufficiently simple distributions, we can use (b) to determine the **E** field, thus avoiding the line, surface, or volume integrals that would otherwise arise (as they did in Exercise 15).
(c) Use Gauss' law (b) to derive the **E** field (f) in Exercise 15 induced by a line charge of density σ (coulombs/meter). *Hint:* Argue, by symmetry, that **E** should be independent of θ and z, and that the θ and z components of **E** should be zero, so that **E** is of the

form $f(r)\hat{\mathbf{e}}_r$. Using this expression for **E**, apply (b) to a cylindrical region $\mathcal{V}$ of arbitrary radius r_0 and arbitrary length L, as shown; (f) of Exercise 15 should follow in one short step.

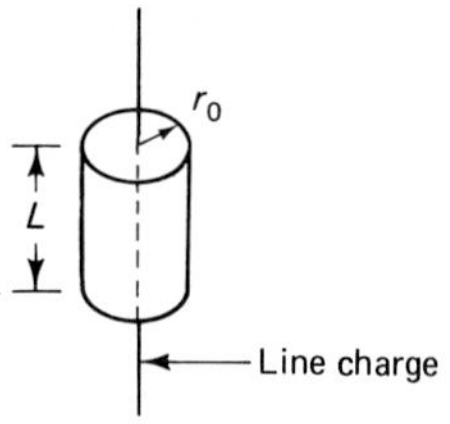

(d) Use Gauss' law (b) to derive the **E** field (g) of Exercise 15. *Hint:* Argue that **E** should be of the form $\mathbf{E} = f(z)\hat{\mathbf{k}}$ for $z > 0$, and $-f(-z)\hat{\mathbf{k}}$ for $z < 0$, and then apply equation (b) to a rectangular prism $x_1 \le x \le x_2$, $y_1 \le y \le y_2$, $-z_1 \le z \le z_1$, where x_1, x_2, y_1, y_2 are arbitrary and z_1 is an arbitrary positive number.

(e) Consider a uniform surface charge distribution of strength σ (coulombs/meter^2) over the circular cylinder $r = R$, $-\infty < z < \infty$. Using (e) of Exercise 15, show that the induced field is

$$\mathbf{E} = \begin{cases} \mathbf{0}, & r < R \\ \dfrac{\sigma R}{\epsilon_0 r}\hat{\mathbf{e}}_r, & r > R. \end{cases} \tag{c}$$

This result is quite striking: Inside the cylinder ($r < R$) the effects of all the little incremental charges that constitute the cylinder somehow cancel. This result is obvious, by symmetry, for points on the axis ($r = 0$), but it is *not* especially obvious for points that are inside the cylinder but *off* the axis. Furthermore, for $r > R$ (c) says that the field is the same as if the cylindrical distribution were squeezed down to a line distribution along the z axis. Verify this last claim. *Hint:* Recall (f) of Exercise 15. *Note:* This exercise is impressive inasmuch as the use of (b) is much simpler than the calculation of **E** by a direct superposition-type integration over the surface, as proposed in Exercise 15.

ADDITIONAL REFERENCES FOR PART II

A. I. BORISENKO and I. E. TARAPOV, *Vector and Tensor Analysis with Applications*. Englewood Cliffs, N.J.: Prentice-Hall, 1968.

A clear introduction to tensor analysis.

MICHAEL J. CROWE, *A History of Vector Analysis*. Notre Dame, Ind.: Notre Dame Press, 1967.

Beginning with the introduction of velocity and force parallelograms by the Greeks, Crowe traces the work of Hamilton, Gibbs, Heaviside, and the development by around 1910 of the modern system of vector analysis.

J. CUNNINGHAM, *Vectors*. London: Heinemann, 1969.

Contains a discussion of finite rotations and quaternions.

KRISHNAMURTY KARAMCHETI, *Vector Analysis and Cartesian Tensors*. San Francisco: Holden-Day, 1967.

A bit more advanced treatment than ours. Includes Cartesian tensors and applications to dynamics, solid mechanics, fluid mechanics, and heat conduction.

B. W. LINDGREN, *Vector Calculus*. New York: Macmillan, 1964.

Covers the same material as in Chapters 13 to 15 of this book, and includes a final chapter on curvilinear coordinates (whereas we have limited our discussion to the cylindrical and spherical curvilinear systems).

HOMER E. NEWELL, JR., *Vector Analysis*. New York: McGraw-Hill, 1955.

Chapter 11 presents a useful 43-page introduction to the application of vector analysis to electromagnetic theory.

Fourier Series 10

INTRODUCTION 10.1

To an extent, Part III is a bridge between Parts II and IV. In Part II we began to meet some of the important partial differential equations of mathematical physics, such as the Laplace equation and the diffusion equation, and in Part IV we will take a systematic look at the solution of such equations. In between, here in Part III, we develop the additional mathematical tools that we will need in Part IV.

We begin, in *Chapter 10*, with a discussion of the "classical" Fourier series representation of periodic functions, i.e., as infinite series of sine and cosine harmonics. In the (OPTIONAL) Section 10.5 we reconsider Fourier series from the point of view of approximation theory, within the context of function space, i.e., vector space wherein the vectors are functions. And in the final (OPTIONAL) Section 10.6 we present the Sturm–Liouville theory, which in a sense, shows where the classical Fourier series "comes from". At the same time, the Sturm–Liouville theory provides a powerful generalization such that the classical Fourier series is revealed as but one special case out of a whole class of such expansions.

Letting the "period" of the periodic functions tend to infinity, in *Chapter 11*, the Fourier series gives way to the Fourier integral, and a slight restatement of the Fourier integral yields the so-called Fourier transform.

Finally, in *Chapter 12* we develop the Laplace transform. Use of the integral inversion formula is postponed until Part V because it requires complex variable theory to implement. Both the Fourier and Laplace transforms are applied, in Part III, to the solution of ordinary differential equations. Important applications to partial differential equations are presented subsequently in Part IV.

Although Fourier series are named after Joseph Fourier (1768–1830), who argued in 1807, in connection with his work on the conduction of heat, that *every* function defined on $(-\pi, \pi)$ could be represented in the form $\Sigma_{n=0}^{\infty} (a_n \cos nx + b_n \sin nx)$, the fact is that the subject enjoyed a long and turbulent history, and that many individuals made important contributions, beginning around 1750. At that time "Fourier series" were employed by Leonhard Euler (1707–1783), Jean Le Rond d'Alembert (1717–1783), Daniel Bernoulli (1700–1782), Alexis-Claude Clairaut (1713–1765), and others, in seeking expressions for the paths of the planets by the interpolation of a number of observed positions, and also in connection with the problem of the vibrating string (discussed in Part IV). A considerable controversy developed, having mostly to do with whether or not *every* function defined on $(-\pi, \pi)$ could be represented by such a series. To appreciate the chaotic state of affairs that existed, one must realize that even the fundamental notion of what comprises a "function" was not yet clearly established, with some workers disallowing all but analytic functions, others allowing their functions to be discontinuous, and so on.

In fact, Fourier's claim that *every* function could be so represented turned out to be not quite true; certain conditions do need to be satisfied by a given function if its Fourier series representation is to be assured. Such a set of sufficient conditions was first established by Peter Gustav Lejeune Dirichlet (1805–1859) in 1829.

All told, the subject of Fourier series has been one of the most fertile in the development of modern mathematics, and important results and extensions continue to be obtained. For an interesting historical (and mathematical) account, we suggest the little book by R. L. Jeffery [*Trigonometric Series* (Toronto: University of Toronto Press, (1956)], as well as the historical treatise by Morris Kline [*Mathematical Thought from Ancient to Modern Times* (New York: Oxford, 1972)].*

10.2 EVEN, ODD, AND PERIODIC FUNCTIONS

Our discussion of Fourier series, which begins in Section 10.3, will proceed more smoothly if we take care of some preliminaries first, namely, "even," "odd," and "periodic" functions.

We say that f is an **even** function of x if

$$f(-x) = f(x) \tag{1}$$

for all x (i.e., for all x in the domain of f, which domain is some interval—open or closed—centered at $x = 0$) or, equivalently, if its graph is *symmetric* about $x = 0$. And f is an **odd** function of x if

$$f(-x) = -f(x) \tag{2}$$

for all x or, equivalently, if its graph is *antisymmetric* about $x = 0$. Some examples are sketched in Fig. 10.1.

For example, 6, x^2, $3x^4$, $\cos x$, $\sin (x^2)$, $\sin |x|$, e^{-x^2} are even, and x, x^3, $\sin x$, $x \cos x$ are odd. It is easy to deduce a number of properties regarding even and odd

*Other standard sources include H. S. Carslaw, *Introduction to the Theory of Fourier's Series and Integrals*, 3rd ed. (New York: Dover, 1930); and I. Grattan-Guinness, *Joseph Fourier, 1768–1830* (Cambridge, Mass.: MIT Press, 1972).

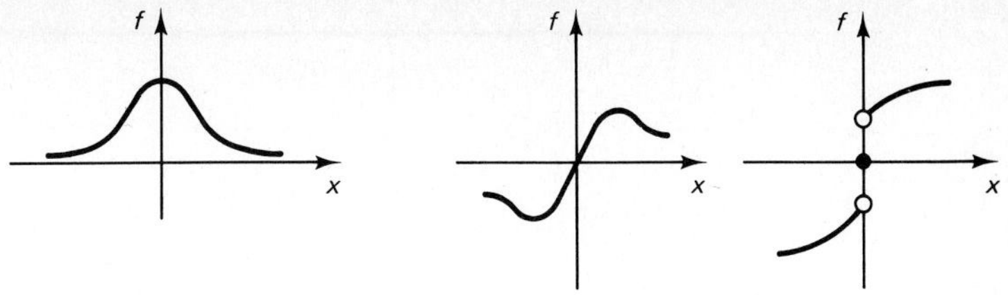

Fig. 10.1 Some even and odd functions. (a) Even (b) Odd

functions, such as the following:

$$\text{even} + \text{even} = \text{even}, \tag{3a}$$

$$\text{even} \times \text{even} = \text{even}, \tag{3b}$$

$$\text{odd} + \text{odd} = \text{odd}, \tag{3c}$$

$$\text{odd} \times \text{odd} = \text{even}, \tag{3d}$$

$$\text{even} \times \text{odd} = \text{odd}. \tag{3e}$$

To derive (3e), for example, let $F(x)$ be even and let $G(x)$ be odd. Then $F(-x)G(-x) = F(x)[-G(x)] = -F(x)G(x)$, so that "even × odd = odd." For example, x^2 is even and x is odd, and their product $(x^2)(x) = x^3$ is odd.

In addition, two useful integral properties are as follows:

1. *If f is even, then*

$$\int_{-A}^{A} f(x)\,dx = 2\int_{0}^{A} f(x)\,dx, \tag{4a}$$

for if we interpret the integrals as areas (positive above the x-axis, negative below it), then the area $\int_{-A}^{0} f(x)\,dx$ is equal to the area $\int_0^A f(x)\,dx$ due to the symmetry of the graph of f.

2. *If f is odd, then*

$$\int_{-A}^{A} f(x)\,dx = 0, \tag{4b}$$

for then the areas $\int_{-A}^{0} f(x)\,dx$ and $\int_0^A f(x)\,dx$ are negatives of each other, due to the antisymmetry of the graph of f, and hence cancel.

Alternatively, (4a) and (4b) follow directly from (1) and (2), respectively. For example, if f is odd, then

$$\begin{aligned}
\int_{-A}^{A} f(x)\,dx &= \int_{-A}^{0} f(x)\,dx + \int_{0}^{A} f(x)\,dx. \\
&= \int_{A}^{0} f(-t)(-dt) + \int_{0}^{A} f(x)\,dx \qquad (x = -t \text{ in first integral}) \\
&= \int_{0}^{A} f(-t)(dt) + \int_{0}^{A} f(x)\,dx \qquad\qquad (5) \\
&= \int_{0}^{A} -f(t)\,dt + \int_{0}^{A} f(x)\,dx \qquad (\text{oddness of } f)
\end{aligned}$$

$$= -\int_0^A f(x)\,dx + \int_0^A f(x)\,dx \qquad (t = x \text{ in first integral})$$

$$= 0,$$

as stated in (4b).

Note carefully that a given function is not necessarily even or odd: It may be *both* even and odd, or it may be *neither* even nor odd. It is easy to show (Exercise 3) that the only function which is both even and odd is the zero function, where $f(x)$ is identically zero. Excluding this special case, it turns out that *every function f can be uniquely decomposed into the sum of an even function, say f_e, and an odd function, say f_o,* as demonstrated by the simple identity (see Exercise 4)

$$f(x) = \underbrace{\frac{f(x) + f(-x)}{2}}_{f_e(x)} + \underbrace{\frac{f(x) - f(-x)}{2}}_{f_o(x)}. \tag{6}$$

For observe that

$$f_o(-x) = \frac{f(-x) - f(x)}{2} = -\frac{f(x) - f(-x)}{2} = -f_o(x)$$

and similarly, that $f_e(-x) = f_e(x)$.

EXAMPLE 1 If $f(x) = e^x$, then

$$f_e(x) = \frac{e^x + e^{-x}}{2} \quad \text{and} \quad f_o(x) = \frac{e^x - e^{-x}}{2}, \tag{7}$$

which are the well-known functions $\cosh x$ and $\sinh x$, respectively. Thus $\cosh x$ and $\sinh x$ happen to be the even and odd parts, respectively, of e^x. ◀

Turning to "periodic functions," suppose that there exists a positive constant T such that

$$f(x + T) = f(x) \tag{8}$$

for every x in the domain of f. Then we say that f is **periodic** with **period** T.

EXAMPLE 2 For example, $\sin x$ is periodic with period 2π since $\sin(x + 2\pi) = \sin x \cos 2\pi + \sin 2\pi \cos x = \sin x$. For brevity, we sometimes say that $\sin x$ is "2π periodic." ◀

In graphical terms, it may be helpful to imagine the graph of any periodic function f as generated by stamping it out one period at a time, as with an inked woodblock.

EXAMPLE 3 The function f shown in Fig. 10.2 is, by inspection, seen to be periodic with period $T = 4$, for if the segment BCD, for example, is "stamped out"

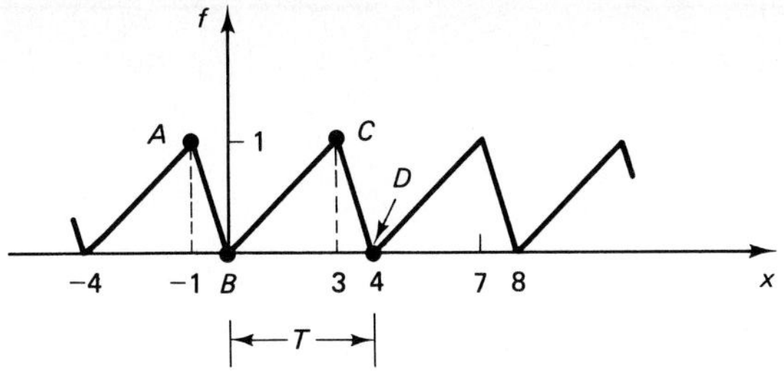

Fig. 10.2 Periodic function f.

indefinitely to the right and left we generate the graph of f. There is nothing special about choosing the segment BCD for this purpose; ABC, or any other segment of length 4, would do as well. ◀

Notice that if f is periodic with period T, it is necessarily periodic with period $2T$, $3T$, $4T$, . . . , as well. For example, $f(x + 2T) = f((x + T) + T) = f(x + T) = f(x)$, so that f is periodic with period $2T$. Of all these possible periods, if there exists a *smallest* one, that period is called the **fundamental period**. Thus sin x (in Example 2) is periodic with period 2π, 4π, 6π, . . . , and its fundamental period is 2π; f in Example 3 is periodic with period 4, 8, 12, . . . , and its fundamental period is 4.

In constrast, observe that if $f(x)$ = constant, then f is periodic and *every* $T > 0$ is a period. Thus there exists no smallest period, so f does not have a fundamental period. Another example of a function that is periodic but does not admit a fundamental period is given in Exercise 16.

10.2 EXERCISES

1. (a) Derive property (3a).
(b) Derive property (3b).
(c) Derive property (3c).
(d) Derive property (3d).

2. Provide a derivation of (4a) analogous to the one in (5).

3. Show that

(a) f is both even and odd if and only if it is identically zero
(b) if f is even (and integrable), then $F(x) = \int_0^x f(t)\,dt$ is odd
(c) if f is odd (and integrable), then $F(x) = \int_0^x f(t)\,dt$ is even
(d) if f is even (and differentiable), then $F(x) = df/dx$ is odd
(e) if f is odd (and differentiable), then $F(x) = df/dx$ is even

4. Derive the decomposition formula (6). *Hint:* Start with $f(x) = f_e(x) + f_o(x)$ and change x to $-x$.

5. Determine $f_e(x)$ and $f_o(x)$. Is f even? Odd? Neither?

*(a) $2 - 5x$
(b) $\sin(x + 2)$
(c) $x/(x^2 + x + 3)$
(d) xe^{-x}
*(e) $x/(x^4 + 2)$
(f) $x^2 \cos(x^3) - 8$
(g) $x^4 + x^3 + x^2 + x + 1$
(h) $\ln(1 + x^2)$
(i) $e^{-2 \sin x}$
(j) $\sin(\sin x)$
(k) $\cos(\sin x)$
(l) $e^{-x}/(x^2 + 1)$

6. If F is even and G is odd (on $-\infty < x < \infty$, say), show that

(a) $1/F(x)$ is even
(b) $1/G(x)$ is odd
(c) $F(G(x))$ is even
(d) $G(F(x))$ is even

7. Show that if f is odd, then it is necessarily true that $f(0) = 0$.

8. Let f be even (and not identically zero), and let g be odd (and not identically zero). If f and g are defined on a common interval, show that f and g are necessarily linearly independent on that interval.

9. Show that if $f(x) = g(x)$ (over a common x interval), we can equate even and odd parts: $f_e(x) = g_e(x)$, and $f_o(x) = g_o(x)$.

10. Show that if f is even and g is odd, and $f + g = 0$ (over a common x interval), then $f(x) = 0$ and $g(x) = 0$.

11. Determine the fundamental period in each case. Also, draw the graphs of f_e and f_o.

(a)

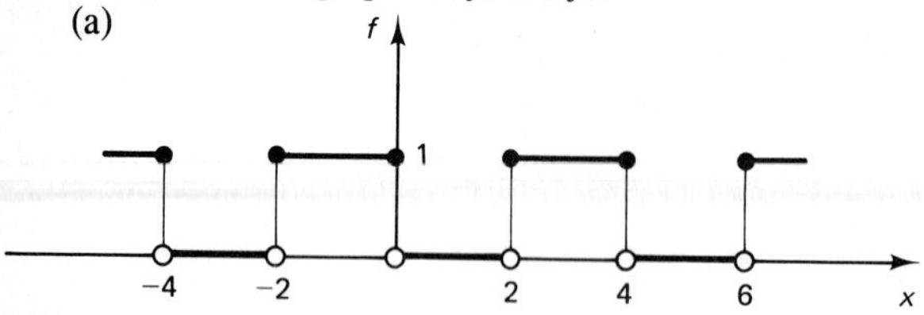

(b)

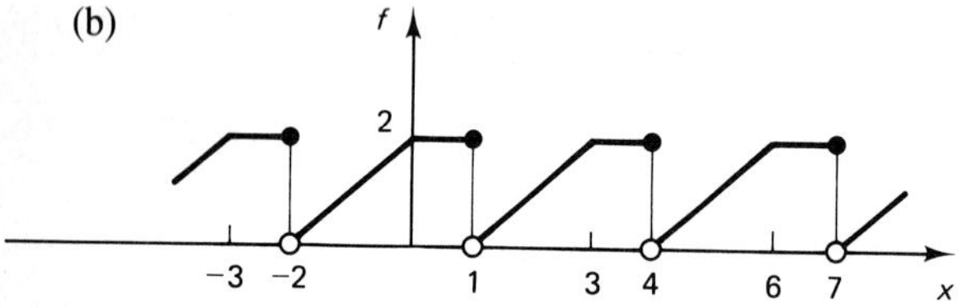

(c)

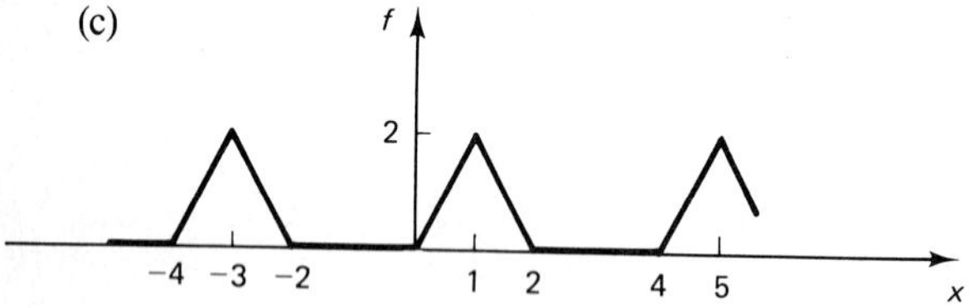

(d)

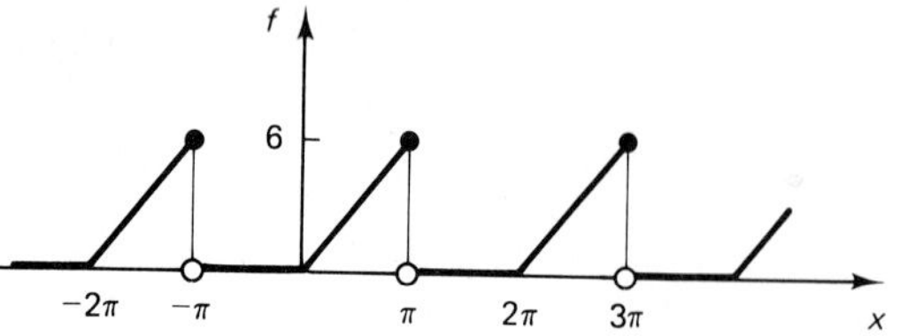

(e)

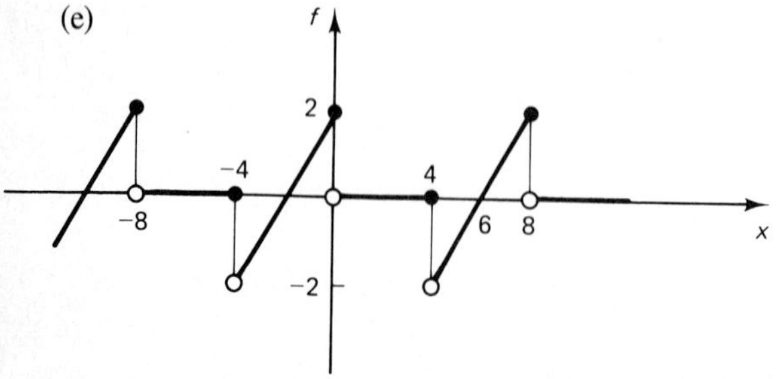

12. Determine whether or not the given function (defined on $-\infty < x < \infty$) is periodic. If it is, find its fundamental period (if indeed it has one).

*(a) x^4	(b) e^x
(c) e^{-x}	(d) $\sin(\omega x + \phi)$
(e) $\cos 6x$	(f) $\sin 2x$
*(g) $\tan x$	(h) $\sinh x$
(i) $\cosh x$	(j) $\cos^2 x$
(k) $\sin^2 x$	(l) $\sin x \cos 2x$
*(m) $e^{\sin 2x}$	(n) $\sinh(\cos 2x)$
(o) $\sin(\sin x)$	(p) $\cos(\sin x)$
(q) $\sin(8\pi \cos x)$	(r) $\sin(\sin 4x)$

13. The following functions are periodic. Determine the fundamental period in each case. (The a_n's and b_n's are nonzero constants.)

*(a) $a_0 + a_1 \cos x$

(b) $a_0 + a_1 \cos x + a_2 \cos 2x$

(c) $6 \cos x - 4 \sin 3x$

(d) $\cos 5x + \sin 5x$

*(e) $a_0 + a_1 \cos x + b_1 \sin x + a_2 \cos 2x + b_2 \sin 2x$

(f) $a_0 + \sum_{n=1}^{\infty} (a_n \cos nx + b_n \sin nx)$

(g) $a_0 + \sum_{n=1}^{\infty} \left(a_n \cos \frac{n\pi x}{\ell} + b_n \sin \frac{n\pi x}{\ell}\right)$

14. Show that if f is periodic with period T, then

$$\int_0^T f(x)\,dx = \int_A^{A+T} f(x)\,dx \tag{a}$$

for any finite value of A.

15. Show that if $f(x)$ is periodic with period T, then

(a) so is its derivative $f'(x)$

(b) so is its integral $\int_0^x f(t)\,dt$, if and only if $\int_0^T f(t)\,dt = 0$

16. Let $f(x) = 1$ whenever x is rational, and let $f(x) = 0$ whenever x is irrational. Show that f is periodic with period T where T is any (positive) rational number. (Thus there exists no smallest period, so that f does not have a fundamental period.) Is it also true that f is periodic with period T, where T is any (positive) *ir*rational number? Explain.

17. Show that if f is periodic with period T, then $g(f(x))$ is, too. Give two examples.

Recall that if $f(x)$ is infinitely differentiable at $x = a$, then *the Taylor series of f* is defined (page 229) as

$$\sum_{n=0}^{\infty} \frac{f^{(n)}(a)}{n!}(x - a)^n, \tag{1}$$

and there exist three possibilities: The series may (1) diverge for all $x \neq a$; (2) converge over some interval, centered at a, but not to $f(x)$ for all x in the interval; (3) converge over some interval, centered at a, to $f(x)$. Note that whereas the Taylor series of f is defined [by (1)] in any event, it is only in the event of case (3) that it is useful to us, for then we have the equality

$$f(x) = \sum_{n=0}^{\infty} \frac{f^{(n)}(a)}{n!}(x - a)^n, \tag{2}$$

i.e., we have a "representation" of the function f. We know from experience that Taylor series representations are useful in many ways.

Similarly, there exist other types of representations which are of great utility. In this chapter we are concerned, specifically, with the representation of periodic functions by trigonometric series of the form

$$a_0 + \sum_{n=1}^{\infty} \left(a_n \cos \frac{n\pi x}{\ell} + b_n \sin \frac{n\pi x}{\ell} \right). \tag{3}$$

First, observe that *(3) is a periodic function with fundamental period 2ℓ*. To see this, note that (3) is a linear combination of the functions 1, $\cos(\pi x/\ell)$, $\sin(\pi x/\ell)$, $\cos(2\pi x/\ell)$, $\sin(2\pi x/\ell)$, and so on, and that these functions are periodic with the following periods:

	Periods				
1	arbitrary period				
$\cos\frac{\pi x}{\ell}$ and $\sin\frac{\pi x}{\ell}$	2ℓ	4ℓ	6ℓ	8ℓ	...
$\cos\frac{2\pi x}{\ell}$ and $\sin\frac{2\pi x}{\ell}$	ℓ	2ℓ	3ℓ	4ℓ	...
$\cos\frac{3\pi x}{\ell}$ and $\sin\frac{3\pi x}{\ell}$	$\frac{2\ell}{3}$	$\frac{4\ell}{3}$	2ℓ	$\frac{8\ell}{3}$	...
⋮	⋮	⋮	⋮	⋮	

We see that the smallest period shared by all the terms is 2ℓ; hence 2ℓ is the fundamental period of (3).*

* Actually, the fundamental period of the function (3) *may* be less than 2ℓ. For example, if all the coefficients except for a_3 are zero, then the fundamental period is $2\ell/3$. Thus we should say that (3) is always periodic with period 2ℓ; its fundamental period is at most 2ℓ, but may be less.

Now, consider the possibility of representing a given function f, which is periodic with fundamental period 2ℓ, in the form (3), i.e., as*

$$f(x) = a_0 + \sum_{n=1}^{\infty} \left(a_n \cos \frac{n\pi x}{\ell} + b_n \sin \frac{n\pi x}{\ell} \right). \tag{4}$$

Tentatively supposing that such a representation is possible, let us see how the coefficients ($a_0, a_1, \ldots, b_1, \ldots$) are to be computed from f. We will need the following key integral formulas, which are generally known as **orthogonality relations**:[†]

$$\int_{-\ell}^{\ell} \cos \frac{m\pi x}{\ell} \cos \frac{n\pi x}{\ell}\, dx = \begin{cases} 0 & m \neq n \\ \ell & m = n \neq 0 \\ 2\ell, & m = n = 0 \end{cases} \tag{5a}$$

$$\int_{-\ell}^{\ell} \sin \frac{m\pi x}{\ell} \sin \frac{n\pi x}{\ell}\, dx = \begin{cases} 0, & m \neq n, \\ \ell, & m = n \neq 0 \end{cases} \tag{5b}$$

$$\int_{-\ell}^{\ell} \cos \frac{m\pi x}{\ell} \sin \frac{n\pi x}{\ell}\, dx = 0 \qquad \text{for all } m, n, \tag{5c}$$

where m and n are integers. Of these, (5c) follows immediately from (4b) on page 453, and (5a) and (5b) are left for the exercises. Proceeding, we multiply both sides of (4) by $\cos (m\pi x/\ell)$, where m is any nonnegative integer, and integrate over $(-\ell, \ell)$, i.e., over one fundamental period:

$$\begin{aligned} \int_{-\ell}^{\ell} f(x) \cos \frac{m\pi x}{\ell}\, dx &= \int_{-\ell}^{\ell} \left[a_0 + \sum_{n=1}^{\infty} \left(a_n \cos \frac{n\pi x}{\ell} + b_n \sin \frac{n\pi x}{\ell} \right) \right] \cos \frac{m\pi x}{\ell}\, dx \\ &= a_0 \int_{-\ell}^{\ell} \cos \frac{m\pi x}{\ell}\, dx + \sum_{n=1}^{\infty} \int_{-\ell}^{\ell} \left(a_n \cos \frac{n\pi x}{\ell} + b_n \sin \frac{n\pi x}{\ell} \right) \cos \frac{m\pi x}{\ell}\, dx \\ &= a_0 \int_{-\ell}^{\ell} \cos \frac{m\pi x}{\ell} \cos \frac{0\pi x}{\ell}\, dx + \sum_{n=1}^{\infty} \left[a_n \int_{-\ell}^{\ell} \cos \frac{n\pi x}{\ell} \cos \frac{m\pi x}{\ell}\, dx \right. \\ &\qquad \left. + b_n \int_{-\ell}^{\ell} \sin \frac{n\pi x}{\ell} \cos \frac{m\pi x}{\ell}\, dx \right], \end{aligned} \tag{6}$$

where we tentatively assume, in writing the second equality in (6), that the order of summation and integration can be interchanged, i.e., that the series can be integrated termwise. (We will see, in Section 11.4, that termwise integration is permissible for Fourier series.) Now, if $m = 0$, then we see, from (5a) and (5c), that (6) becomes

$$\int_{-\ell}^{\ell} f(x)\, dx = (a_0)(2\ell) + 0 + 0 + 0 + \cdots, \tag{7}$$

* For example, the representation (4) will appear in Part IV when we consider the unsteady conduction of heat in a rod of length ℓ.

[†] This name will make more sense when we take another look at Fourier series, in Section 10.5, from a vector space point of view.

so that

$$a_0 = \frac{1}{2\ell}\int_{-\ell}^{\ell} f(x)\,dx. \tag{8}$$

Similarly, if m is any positive integer, then the only term in (6) that survives, according to (5a) and (5c), is the $\cos(n\pi x/\ell)\cos(m\pi x/\ell)$ integral when n hits the value m. (Note that m is being regarded as fixed, for the moment, while n is the summation index and hence takes on the values 1, 2, 3, ...) Thus

$$\int_{-\ell}^{\ell} f(x)\cos\frac{m\pi x}{\ell}\,dx = 0 + 0 + \cdots + 0 + (a_m)(\ell) + 0 + 0 + \cdots. \tag{9}$$

Surely, (9) is equally true if we use any other letter in place of the two m's. Thus, changing these m's to n's and solving for a_n, we have

$$a_n = \frac{1}{\ell}\int_{-\ell}^{\ell} f(x)\cos\frac{n\pi x}{\ell}\,dx \tag{10}$$

for $n = 1, 2, \ldots$.

If, instead, we multiply both sides of (4) by $\sin(m\pi x/\ell)$, integrate over $(-\ell, \ell)$, and use (5b) and (5c), we obtain the expression

$$b_n = \frac{1}{\ell}\int_{-\ell}^{\ell} f(x)\sin\frac{n\pi x}{\ell}\,dx \tag{11}$$

for the b_n's. Pulling (8), (10), and (11) together, for reference, we have

$$a_0 = \frac{1}{2\ell}\int_{-\ell}^{\ell} f(x)\,dx, \tag{12a}$$

$$a_n = \frac{1}{\ell}\int_{-\ell}^{\ell} f(x)\cos\frac{n\pi x}{\ell}\,dx, \qquad n = 1, 2, \ldots \tag{12b}$$

$$b_n = \frac{1}{\ell}\int_{-\ell}^{\ell} f(x)\sin\frac{n\pi x}{\ell}\,dx, \qquad n = 1, 2, \ldots . \tag{12c}$$

Although the integration interval, in (12), is from $-\ell$ to ℓ, it is to be emphasized that *any interval of length* 2ℓ *may be used,* as follows from Exercise 13 of Section 10.2. For example, the limits 0 to 2ℓ are equally appropriate and may, in some examples, be slightly more convenient.

Historically, the discovery of equations (12) represented a major step. Obtained by Euler in 1777, using the orthogonality relations method described above, they are known as **Euler's formulas** (or as the Fourier-Euler formulas), although it is true that others, including Clairaut, d'Alembert, and Euler himself, had obtained them earlier by other methods.

It should be mentioned that some authors write (4) as

$$f(x) = \frac{a_0}{2} + \sum_{n=1}^{\infty}\left(a_n\cos\frac{n\pi x}{\ell} + b_n\sin\frac{n\pi x}{\ell}\right), \tag{13}$$

i.e., with $a_0/2$ instead of a_0, since then one has, in place of the two formulas (12a) and (12b), the single formula

$$a_n = \frac{1}{\ell}\int_{-\ell}^{\ell} f(x)\cos\frac{n\pi x}{\ell}\,dx, \qquad n = 0, 1, 2, \ldots . \tag{14}$$

However, in this book we will consistently use the notation adopted in (4).

Speaking of a_0, notice from (12a) that a_0 admits a simple graphical interpretation as *the average value of f over the interval* $(-\ell, \ell)$.

Now, with the coefficients computed according to (12), the right-hand side of (4) is called the **Fourier series** of f; the coefficients $a_0, a_1, b_1, a_2, b_2, \ldots$ are called the **Fourier coefficients** of f, and the individual terms in (4) are generally referred to as *harmonics*. It must be clearly understood that we have in no way established the truth of the equality in (4). All we have done is to show that *if* (4) holds, then the coefficients are to be computed from the Euler formulas (12). In fact, whether or not the Fourier series of a given function f, periodic with period 2ℓ, necessarily converges to f was the central question in the controversy surrounding Fourier series, and it was nearly 100 years before solid answers began to appear. Those answers were in the form of convergence theorems, theorems that gave conditions on f sufficient to guarantee that the Fourier series of f converges to f. We will give one such theorem in a moment, as soon as we introduce the necessary terminology.

First, we say that a function f, defined on an inverval from $x = a$ to $x = b$ is **piecewise continuous** on that interval if there exist at most a finite number of points $x_1, x_2, \ldots, x_N$ such that f is continuous on each of the open intervals $a < x < x_1$, $x_1 < x < x_2, \ldots, x_N < x < b$, and has a finite limit as x approaches each endpoint from the interior (i.e., as x approaches a from the right, x_1 from the left, x_1 from the right, x_2 from the left, . . . , and b from the left). Observe that the values of f *at* the endpoints a, b are not at all relevant to the piecewise continuity (or lack of piecewise continuity) of f on that interval. Thus piecewise continuity on $[a, b]$ means the same as piecewise continuity on (a, b), or on $[a, b)$, or on $(a, b]$.

Further, we define the **left-hand limit** of f at any point x_0 as the limit of $f(x)$ as $x \to x_0$ from the left, and we denote it as $f(x_0-)$. Thus $f(x_0-) \equiv \lim_{h\to 0} f(x_0 - h)$ as $h \to 0$ through positive values. Analogously, the **right-hand limit** of f at x_0 is the limit of $f(x)$ as $x \to x_0$ from the right, and we denote it as $f(x_0+)$. Thus $f(x_0+) \equiv \lim_{h\to 0} f(x_0 + h)$ as $h \to 0$ through positive values.

Finally, the **left-** and **right-hand derivatives** of f at x_0 are defined as the limits of

$$\frac{f(x_0-) - f(x_0 - h)}{h} \quad \text{and} \quad \frac{f(x_0 + h) - f(x_0+)}{h},$$

respectively, as $h \to 0$ through positive values.

EXAMPLE 1 If

$$f(x) = \begin{cases} x^2, & 0 \le x < 2 \\ 7, & x = 2 \\ 8 - x, & 2 < x < 5 \\ 0, & x = 5, \end{cases} \tag{15}$$

as sketched in Fig. 10.3, then f is continuous on $(0, 2)$ and $(2, 5)$ and admits the

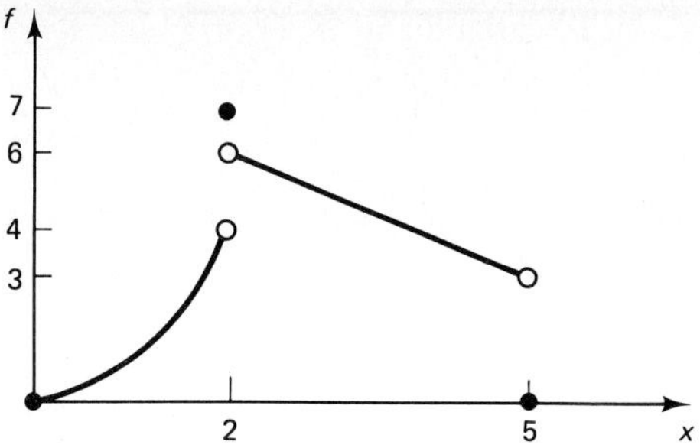

Fig. 10.3 f defined by (15).

finite limits $f(0+) = 0$, $f(2-) = 4$, $f(2+) = 6$, $f(5-) = 3$; thus f is piecewise continuous on $[0, 5]$. Furthermore, the left- hand derivatives of f at $x = 1, 2, 5$, say, are $2, 4, -1$, respectively, and the right-hand derivatives of f at $x = 1, 2$, say, are $2, -1$, respectively. ◀

> ***Theorem 1*** *A Fourier Convergence Theorem*
> If a periodic function f, with period 2ℓ, is piecewise continuous on $[-\ell, \ell]$, then the Fourier series of f converges to the mean value $[f(x+) + f(x-)]/2$ at each point x $(-\infty < x < \infty)$ at which left- and right-hand derivatives of f both exist.

A proof of this theorem is given in Sec. 41 of CHURCHILL AND BROWN. It is to be emphasized that the conditions are stated as *sufficient*, not necessary, for convergence to $[f(x+) + f(x-)]/2$. There exist numerous examples for which the stated conditions are not met, yet such convergence is obtained. Furthermore, there are Fourier convergence theorems other than our Theorem 1, which give various other sets of sufficient conditions. However, Theorem 1 is powerful and will easily suffice for our purposes. Before turning to an example, be sure to see that if f is continuous at x, then $f(x+) = f(x-) = f(x)$, so that $[f(x+) + f(x-)]/2 = f(x)$. Thus Theorem 1 says that under the stated conditions the Fourier series of f converges to $f(x)$ everywhere that f is continuous, but if f has a jump discontinuity at x, the Fourier series converges to the *average* value at the jump, namely, $[f(x+) + f(x-)]/2$.

EXAMPLE 2 *Square Wave*. Consider the periodic function f shown in Fig. 10.4; by virtue of the shape of its graph, f is called a *square wave*. In this example we plan to work out the Fourier series of f, and to examine its convergence, with reference to Theorem 1.

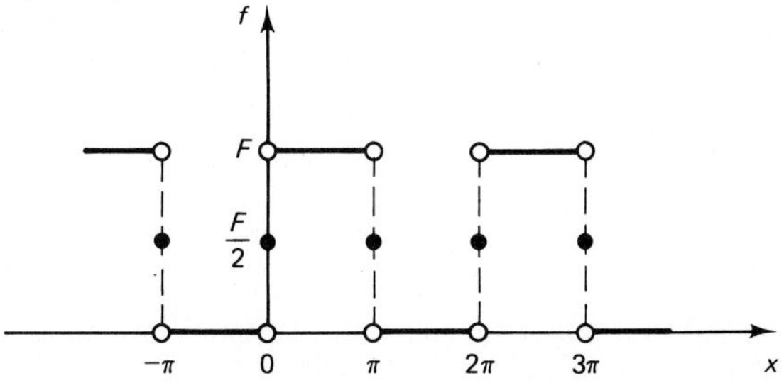

Fig. 10.4 Square wave f.

To expand f in its Fourier series we first need to know ℓ in (4) and (12). Well, the fundamental period is evidently 2π, and since ℓ is defined as half of the fundamental period, we have $\ell = \pi$. Next, we compute the Fourier coefficients. Since a_0 is always the average value of f over the interval $(-\ell, \ell)$ (or, equivalently, over *any* interval of length 2ℓ) we can see, by inspection of Fig. 10.4, that $a_0 = F/2$ in this case. In other cases, the average value of f may not be obtainable by inspection, so let us illustrate the calculation of a_0 using (12a).

$$\begin{aligned} a_0 &= \frac{1}{2\ell}\int_{-\ell}^{\ell} f\,dx = \frac{1}{2\pi}\int_{-\pi}^{\pi} f\,dx \\ &= \frac{1}{2\pi}\left[\int_{-\pi}^{0} 0\,dx + \int_{0}^{\pi} F\,dx\right] = \frac{1}{2\pi}(0 + \pi F) = \frac{F}{2}, \end{aligned} \tag{16}$$

as noted above.

Next,

$$\begin{aligned} a_n &= \frac{1}{\ell}\int_{-\ell}^{\ell} f \cos\frac{n\pi x}{\ell}\,dx = \frac{1}{\pi}\left[\int_{-\pi}^{0} 0\,dx + \int_{0}^{\pi} F\cos nx\,dx\right] \\ &= \frac{1}{\pi}\left[0 + \frac{F\sin nx}{n}\bigg|_0^{\pi}\right] = 0, \qquad (n = 1, 2, \ldots). \end{aligned} \tag{17}$$

since $\sin n\pi = 0$ and $\sin 0 = 0$. Finally,

$$\begin{aligned} b_n &= \frac{1}{\ell}\int_{-\ell}^{\ell} f \sin\frac{n\pi x}{\ell}\,dx = \frac{1}{\pi}\left[\int_{-\pi}^{0} 0\,dx + \int_{0}^{\pi} F\sin nx\,dx\right] \\ &= \frac{1}{\pi}\left[0 - \frac{F\cos nx}{n}\bigg|_0^{\pi}\right] = \frac{F}{n\pi}(1 - \cos n\pi) \qquad (n = 1, 2, \ldots). \end{aligned} \tag{18}$$

We can leave (18) as it stands, but since we generally simplify results as much as possible let us reexpress b_n as

$$b_n = \frac{F}{n\pi}[1 - (-1)^n] = \begin{cases} \dfrac{2F}{n\pi}, & n = 1, 3, \ldots \\ 0, & n = 2, 4, \ldots. \end{cases} \tag{19}$$

Thus the Fourier series representation of f is

$$\begin{aligned} f(x) &= \frac{F}{2} + \sum_{n=1,3,\ldots}^{\infty} \frac{2F}{n\pi}\sin nx \\ &= \frac{F}{2} + \frac{2F}{\pi}\sum_{n=1,3,\ldots}^{\infty} \frac{\sin nx}{n}, \end{aligned} \tag{20}$$

where the "n = 1, 3, . . ." tells us to skip over the terms corresponding to $n = 2, 4, \ldots$. If this notation is unappealing, one can express the result (20), equivalently, as

$$f(x) = \frac{F}{2} + \frac{2F}{\pi}\sum_{n=1}^{\infty} \frac{\sin(2n-1)x}{2n-1}, \tag{21}$$

with $\Sigma_{n=1}^{\infty}$ denoting the usual summation over $n = 1, 2, 3, \ldots$.

Does the Fourier series of f [i.e., the right-hand side of (20)] actually converge to $f(x)$? That is, are the left- and right-hand sides of (20) actually equal? To answer this question we appeal to Theorem 1. Observe that f is periodic with period 2π, that it is piecewise continuous on $[-\pi, \pi]$, and that it admits both right- and left-hand derivatives at every point x. (We do not actually need to evaluate these derivatives in order to apply the theorem; all we need to know is that they exist. Nevertheless, for pedagogical reasons let us note that both the left- and right-hand derivatives happen to equal zero, for *all* x, in the present example.) According to Theorem 1, then, the Fourier series of f does converge to $f(x)$ wherever f is continuous (i.e., for all $x \neq 0, \pm\pi, \pm 2\pi, \ldots$). At the jump discontinuities (i.e., at $x = 0, \pm\pi, \pm 2\pi, \ldots$) the Fourier series must converge to the average value $F/2$. That value is, in fact, the defined value of f at those points (Fig. 10.4), so, in this example, we conclude that the Fourier series (20) converges to $f(x)$ for all x; i.e., the equality (20) holds for all x.

It is really quite remarkable that a collection of sines and cosines is capable of representing functions as poorly behaved as the square wave f, since each sine and cosine is beautifully smooth (infinitely differentiable), whereas f is not even continuous! (Little wonder that there was so much controversy surrounding the development of Fourier series.) To obtain some insight as to how (20) "works," it will be valuable to sketch some of the partial sums of the series on the right-hand side to see how they compare with the square wave f. Toward this end, let us write out (20) as

$$f(x) = \frac{F}{2} + \frac{2F}{\pi}\sin x + \frac{2F}{3\pi}\sin 3x + \frac{2F}{5\pi}\sin 5x + \cdots \tag{22}$$

and define the *partial sums* of the series as

$$\begin{aligned} s_1(x) &= \frac{F}{2}, \\ s_2(x) &= \frac{F}{2} + \frac{2F}{\pi}\sin x, \\ s_3(x) &= \frac{F}{2} + \frac{2F}{\pi}\sin x + \frac{2F}{3\pi}\sin 3x, \end{aligned} \tag{23}$$

and so on; i.e., $s_N(x)$ is the sum of the first N terms on the right-hand side of (22). The first four of these partial sums are plotted in Fig. 10.5. Interpreting the results rather intuitively, notice that $s_1(x) = a_0/2 = F/2$ is a constant equal to the average value of f. To move $s_1(x)$ toward the square wave f we need a negative correction on the left and an equal positive correction on the right, as called for by the $\Downarrow$ and $\Uparrow$ arrows, respectively, in the figure. Such an antisymmetric correction calls for a sin x harmonic; evidently, the (symmetric) cos x term in the Fourier series $a_0 + \Sigma_{n=1}^{\infty} (a_n \cos nx + b_n \sin nx)$ is not needed. Sure enough, the second term in (22) provides such a correction, and $s_2(x)$ begins to conform to the square wave. Next, we need corrections as indicated by the $\uparrow, \downarrow$ arrows, namely, a third sine harmonic, and sure enough, the third term in (22) provides such a correction.

It would be interesting to plot $s_N(x)$ for an appreciably larger N, and we have done that in Fig. 10.6 for $N = 20$. Observe that as x increases from zero, each

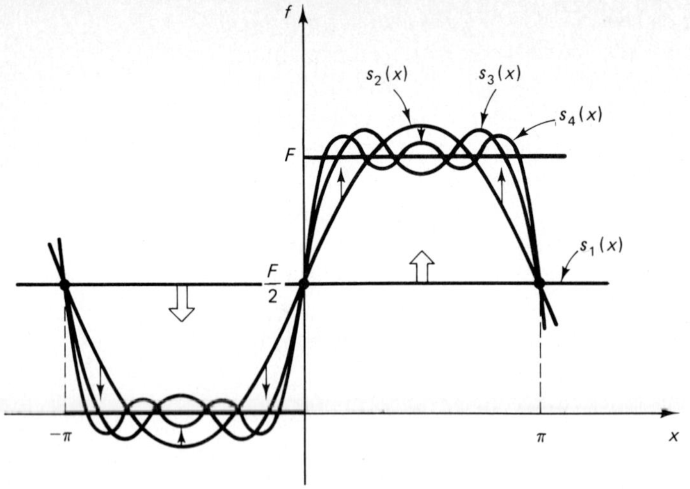

Fig. 10.5 Partial sums, through $s_4(x)$.

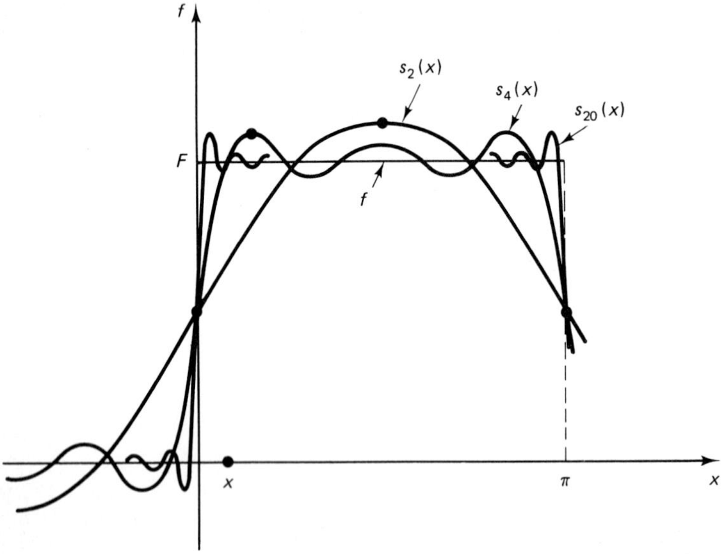

Fig. 10.6 Gibbs phenomenon.

$s_N(x)$ rises from $F/2$ and overshoots the horizontal F line. It turns out that *the overshoot does not tend to zero as N increases*; rather, it tends to a fixed percentage of the jump. [The "jump" is $f(0+) - f(0-) = F - 0 = F$.] For example, the peak values of $s_2(x)$, $s_4(x)$, and $s_{20}(x)$ (at the heavy dots) are $1.137F$, $1.094F$, and $1.090F$, respectively, and as $N \to \infty$ the overshoot approaches a limiting value of around 9% of the jump. This persistent 9% overshoot, which occurs not only in this example but in the Fourier series representation of any function with a jump discontinuity, is known as the **Gibbs phenomenon**.*

In view of this overshoot one may well wonder how convergence to the square wave in Fig. 10.4 is attained, for there are no overshoots in Fig. 10.4. The key

* *Josiah Willard Gibbs* (1839–1903) was one of the first important American mathematical physicists, and is especially well known for his work on vector analysis. The Gibbs phenomenon was noted by Gibbs in 1899 (*Nature,* Vol. 59, p. 606) and explained in 1906 by Maxime Bôcher (*Annals of Mathematics,* Vol. 2, No. 7, p. 81).

point is that when we say that $\lim_{N\to\infty} s_N(x) = f(x)$, it is N that is increasing; x is regarded as *fixed*. Picking any fixed point x (Fig. 10.6) as close to the origin as we wish, observe that as we increase N the overshoot "spike" eventually moves to the left of x, and subsequent values of $s_N(x)$ do "settle down" and approach $f(x)$. The Gibbs phenomenon is of practical importance since it implies that the convergence of Fourier series may be painfully slow (and expensive) in the neighborhood of a jump discontinuity.* ◀

One point, before working more examples: Suppose that the functions f and g, both defined on $a \le x \le b$, have identical values [i.e., $f(x) = g(x)$] on that interval, except at a finite set of points $x_1, \ldots, x_k$—for example, as illustrated in Fig. 10.7 with $k = 2$. According to the integral calculus, the integrals $\int_a^b f\,dx$ and $\int_a^b g\,dx$ are *equal*; i.e., the areas under the graphs of f and g are the same.

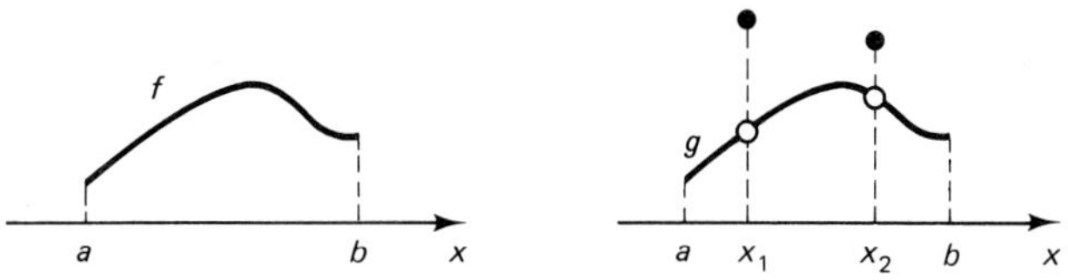

Fig. 10.7 Pointwise discrepancies.

EXAMPLE 3 *Another Square Wave.* Now consider the Fourier series expansion of the square wave g shown in Fig. 10.8. Comparing g with the square wave f in Example 2 (Fig. 10.4), we see that $g(x) = f(x)$ over $[-\pi, \pi]$, say, except at the four points $x = -\pi, 0, \pi/2, \pi$. It follows that $g(x) \cos nx = f(x) \cos nx$ and $g(x) \sin nx = f(x) \sin nx$ over $[-\pi, \pi]$, except at a finite number of points, so that (according to the comment immediately preceding this example)

$$\frac{1}{2\pi}\int_{-\pi}^{\pi} g(x)\,dx = \frac{1}{2\pi}\int_{-\pi}^{\pi} f(x)\,dx, \quad \frac{1}{\pi}\int_{-\pi}^{\pi} g(x)\cos nx\,dx$$
$$= \frac{1}{\pi}\int_{-\pi}^{\pi} f(x)\cos nx\,dx, \quad \text{and} \quad \frac{1}{\pi}\int_{-\pi}^{\pi} g(x)\sin nx\,dx = \frac{1}{\pi}\int_{-\pi}^{\pi} f(x)\sin nx\,dx; \tag{24}$$

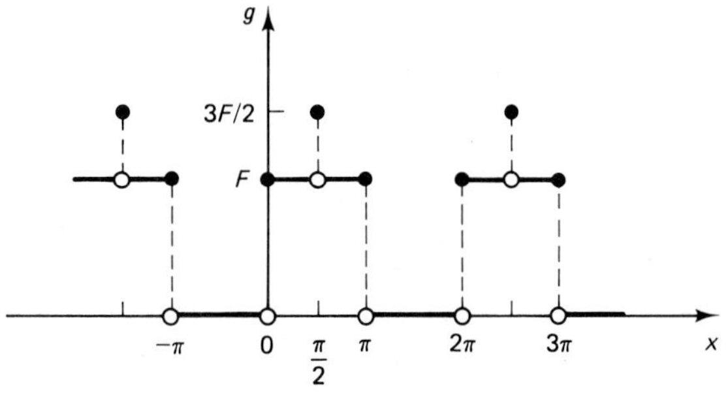

Fig. 10.8 Square wave g.

* We might remark that in studying infinite series in the elementary calculus one merely learns to classify series as convergent or divergent, with the tacit implication that convergent series are "good" and divergent series are "bad." Practically speaking, however, a series may converge—but so slowly as to be almost worthless. Thus interest exists in developing *acceleration* techniques, i.e., techniques that permit us to transform a given slowly convergent series into a more rapidly convergent one. See, for example, D. Shanks, "Non-linear Transformations of Divergent and Slowly Convergent Sequences," *Journal of Mathematics and Physics,* Vol. XXXIV, 1955, pp. 1–42.

i.e., the Fourier coefficients of g are the same as those of f. Thus the Fourier series of g is the same as that of f, and we write

$$g(x) \overset{ae}{=} \frac{F}{2} + \frac{2F}{\pi} \sum_{n=1,3,\ldots}^{\infty} \frac{\sin nx}{n}, \tag{25}$$

where the "ae" means *almost everywhere*, for the Fourier series of g, on the right-hand side of (25), converges to $g(x)$ everywhere except at $x = 0, \pi/2, -\pi, \pi, -3\pi/2, 2\pi, \ldots$. For example, at $x = 0$ the series converges to F/2, whereas $g(0) = F$, and at $x = \pi/2$ it converges to F, whereas $g(\pi/2) = 3F/2$.

COMMENT 1 For notational simplicity we generally omit the "*ae*" above the equal sign, with the understanding that *we mean equality in the sense of Theorem 1.*

COMMENT 2 It would be natural to feel uneasy upon learning that such pointwise failures of Fourier series can occur. However, such discrepancies should not be an issue in applications for our physical systems are generally described by differential equations, and the solution of such equations involves—in one way or another—integration. And as noted just above this example, pointwise differences have no effect at all on the results of the integration. Indeed, this insensitivity to pointwise details might well be a source of *comfort* to engineers and scientists since we cannot measure or carry out physical processes with such resolution anyhow. *Thus in subsequent sections we will not fuss so much with the pointwise details of our graphs. For example, if the square wave shown in Fig. 10.4 is needed later this book, its graph will be shown more simply, as in Fig. 10.9.* ◀

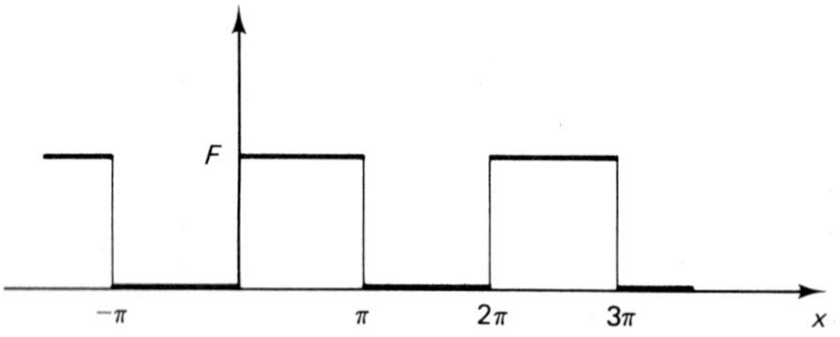

Fig. 10.9 Simplified graph of square wave.

Thus far, the notions of even and odd functions, introduced in Section 10.2, have not come up in our discussion of Fourier series. Suppose now that f is an *even* periodic function of period 2ℓ. Then $f(x) \cos(n\pi x/\ell)$ is even and $f(x) \sin(n\pi x/\ell)$ is odd, and, by virtue of (4a) and (4b) on page 453, the Euler formulas simplify to

$$a_0 = \frac{1}{2\ell}\int_{-\ell}^{\ell} f(x)\,dx = \frac{1}{\ell}\int_0^{\ell} f(x)\,dx,$$

$$a_n = \frac{1}{\ell}\int_{-\ell}^{\ell} f(x)\cos\frac{n\pi x}{\ell}\,dx = \frac{2}{\ell}\int_0^{\ell} f(x)\cos\frac{n\pi x}{\ell}\,dx, \qquad n = 1, 2, \ldots \tag{26}$$

$$b_n = \frac{1}{\ell}\int_{-\ell}^{\ell} f(x)\sin\frac{n\pi x}{\ell}\,dx = 0. \qquad n = 1, 2, \ldots.$$

Similarly, if f is an *odd* periodic function of period 2ℓ, then

$$a_0 = \frac{1}{2\ell}\int_{-\ell}^{\ell} f(x)\,dx = 0,$$

$$a_n = \frac{1}{\ell}\int_{-\ell}^{\ell} f(x)\cos\frac{n\pi x}{\ell}\,dx = 0, \qquad n = 1, 2, \ldots \tag{27}$$

$$b_n = \frac{1}{\ell}\int_{-\ell}^{\ell} f(x)\sin\frac{n\pi x}{\ell}\,dx = \frac{2}{\ell}\int_{0}^{\ell} f(x)\sin\frac{n\pi x}{\ell}\,dx, \qquad n = 1, 2, \ldots .$$

EXAMPLE 4 The periodic function f drawn in Fig. 10.10 evidently has a fundamental period of 16, so that $\ell = 8$, and has an average height of $-\frac{1}{4}$, so that $a_0 = -\frac{1}{4}$. Furthermore, we see that f is even so that, according to (26), we can set $b_n = 0$ $(n = 1, 2, \ldots)$ without further ado, and compute the a_n's as

$$\begin{aligned} a_n &= \frac{2}{\ell}\int_0^{\ell} f(x)\cos\frac{n\pi x}{\ell}\,dx = \frac{2}{8}\int_0^{8} f(x)\cos\frac{n\pi x}{8}\,dx \\ &= \frac{1}{4}\left[\int_0^4 (2-x)\cos\frac{n\pi x}{8}\,dx + \int_4^6 (x-6)\cos\frac{n\pi x}{8}\,dx + \int_6^8 0\cos\frac{n\pi x}{8}\,dx\right] \\ &= \frac{1}{4}\left[2\frac{\sin(n\pi x/8)}{n\pi/8} - \frac{1}{(n\pi/8)^2}\left(\cos\frac{n\pi x}{8} + \frac{n\pi x}{8}\sin\frac{n\pi x}{8}\right)\right]\Bigg|_0^4 \\ &\quad + \frac{1}{4}\left[\frac{1}{(n\pi/8)^2}\left(\cos\frac{n\pi x}{8} + \frac{n\pi x}{8}\sin\frac{n\pi x}{8}\right) - 6\frac{\sin(n\pi x/8)}{n\pi/8}\right]\Bigg|_4^6 \\ &= \frac{16}{n^2\pi^2}\left(1 - 2\cos\frac{n\pi}{2} + \cos\frac{3n\pi}{4}\right). \end{aligned} \tag{28}$$

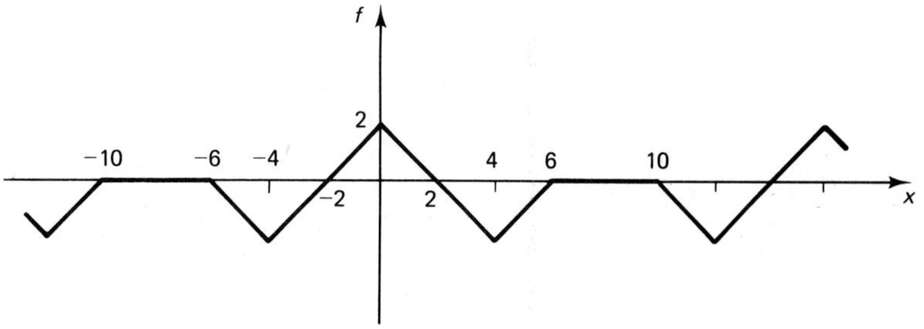

Fig. 10.10 *f* in Example 4.

Thus,

$$f(x) = -\frac{1}{4} + \frac{16}{\pi^2}\sum_{n=1}^{\infty}\frac{1 - 2\cos(n\pi/2) + \cos(3n\pi/4)}{n^2}\cos\frac{n\pi x}{8}, \tag{29}$$

with the equality holding for all x, without exception, since f is continuous everywhere, i.e., since $[f(x+) + f(x-)]/2 = [f(x) + f(x)]/2 = f(x)$ for all x.

COMMENT 1 Recall that we compute a_0 and a_n $(n = 1, 2, \ldots)$ separately: a_0 from (12a), and $a_n (n = 1, 2, \ldots)$ from (12b). Yet a comparison of (12a) and (12b) reveals that we can also obtain a_0 from our expression for a_n if we set $n = 0$ and multiply by $\frac{1}{2}$. More precisely,*

* The legitimacy of the interchange in the order of carrying out the limit $n \to 0$ and the integration, i.e., the third equality in (30), follows from the fact that $f(x)\cos(n\pi x/\ell)$ converges to $f(x)$ *uniformly* over the interval $-\ell \le x \le \ell$. See, for example, M. D. Greenberg, *Foundations of Applied Mathematics* (Englewood Cliffs, N.J.: Prentice-Hall, 1978), p. 67.

$$
\begin{aligned}
a_0 &= \frac{1}{2\ell}\int_{-\ell}^{\ell} f(x)\,dx = \frac{1}{2\ell}\int_{-\ell}^{\ell} \lim_{n\to 0}\left[f(x)\cos\frac{n\pi x}{\ell}\right]dx \\
&= \frac{1}{2}\lim_{n\to 0}\left[\frac{1}{\ell}\int_{-\ell}^{\ell} f(x)\cos\frac{n\pi x}{\ell}\,dx\right] = \frac{1}{2}\lim_{n\to 0} a_n.
\end{aligned} \tag{30}
$$

In the present example we have, from (30) and (28),

$$
\begin{aligned}
a_0 &= \frac{1}{2}\lim_{n\to 0} a_n = \frac{1}{2}\lim_{n\to 0}\frac{16}{n^2\pi^2}\left(1 - 2\cos\frac{n\pi}{2} + \cos\frac{3n\pi}{4}\right) \\
&= \frac{1}{2}\lim_{n\to 0}\frac{16}{2n\pi^2}\left(\pi\sin\frac{n\pi}{2} - \frac{3\pi}{4}\sin\frac{3n\pi}{4}\right) \\
&= \frac{1}{2}\lim_{n\to 0}\frac{16}{2\pi^2}\left(\frac{\pi^2}{2}\cos\frac{n\pi}{2} - \frac{9\pi^2}{16}\cos\frac{3n\pi}{4}\right) = -\frac{1}{4},
\end{aligned} \tag{31}
$$

where the second and third equalities follow from l'Hospital's rule.* The result obtained in (31), namely, $a_0 = -\frac{1}{4}$, agrees with the value obtained earlier by inspection, so the calculation (31) provides a welcome partial check on our expression for a_n derived in (28).

COMMENT 2 Observe that in this example the Fourier coefficients diminish as $1/n^2$ as $n \to \infty$, whereas in Example 2 they diminished as $1/n$. Thus the Fourier series in (29) is more rapidly convergent than the one in (20); i.e., to achieve a given accuracy we can expect that fewer terms need to be summed in (29) than in (20). This situation reflects the fact that the periodic function being represented in this example is better behaved than the one in Example 2. For, in Example 2, f was discontinuous, and it is asking a lot of beautifully smooth sines and cosines when we ask them to represent a function that suffers jump discontinuities. Thus we needed considerable help from the higher harmonics, in squaring off the corners at the jumps, so the Fourier coefficients died off quite slowly as $n \to \infty$. In the present example f is continuous [although it does have "kinks"—discontinuities in $f'(x)$], so the sines and cosines have an easier time of it and the convergence is faster. ◀

EXAMPLE 5 *Infinite Beam on Elastic Foundation.* As a physical application of Fourier series, consider an infinitely long beam on an elastic foundation, as sketched in Fig. 10.11, where the constant k is the "foundation modulus" (i.e., the spring stiffness per unit x length) and the square wave $w(x)$ is a prescribed periodic loading (force per unit x length).† Physically, the beam might be a train track, with the elastic foundation used to model the track bed.

According to classical *Euler beam theory*‡ the vertical deflection $u(x)$ resulting

* Actually, the well-known theorem for obtaining the limit of a fraction whose numerator and denominator both tend to zero was derived by *John Bernoulli* (1667–1748). The theorem was included in a book on the calculus by *Guillaume l'Hospital* (1661–1704) and is now generally known as "l'Hospital's rule."

† That is, the downward load between any points x_1 and x_2 ($x_2 > x_1$) is $\int_{x_1}^{x_2} w(x)\,dx$.

‡ See, for example, S. Timoshenko, *Strength of Materials,* Part I (Princeton, N.J.: D. Van Nostrand, 1955).

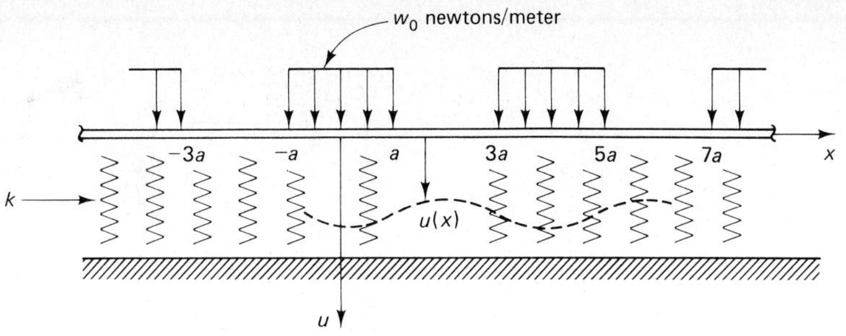

Fig. 10.11 Infinite beam on elastic foundation.

from a load distribution $p(x)$ newtons per unit length satisfies the fourth-order differential equation

$$EIu'''' = p(x), \tag{32}$$

where E and I are physical constants of the beam; EI is called the "flexural rigidity" of the beam (and is considered here as a known constant) since u'''', and hence the deflection u, is inversely proportional to EI. Now $p(x)$ is the *net* loading and consists of the applied periodic loading $w(x)$ downward and the spring force $ku(x)$ upward. (We neglect the weight of the beam, for simplicity.) Thus $p(x) = w(x) - ku(x)$, and (32) becomes

$$EIu'''' + ku = w(x). \tag{33}$$

To solve for $u(x)$ we expand w in a Fourier series (Exercise 14),

$$w(x) = \frac{w_0}{2} + \frac{2w_0}{\pi} \sum_{n=1}^{\infty} \frac{\sin(n\pi/2)}{n} \cos\frac{n\pi x}{2a}, \tag{34}$$

and seek $u(x)$ in the form

$$u(x) = a_0 + \sum_{n=1}^{\infty} a_n \cos\frac{n\pi x}{2a}, \tag{35}$$

where sines are omitted (if only tentatively) since $u(x)$ is evidently symmetric about $x = 0$. Formally differentiating (35) termwise four times, putting this result and (34) and (35) into (33), and formally equating coefficients of each cosine harmonic, we obtain

$$ka_0 = \frac{w_0}{2}$$

and

$$\left(EI\frac{n^4\pi^4}{16a^4} + k\right)a_n = \frac{2w_0}{\pi}\frac{\sin(n\pi/2)}{n} \qquad \text{for } n \geq 1$$

or

$$a_0 = \frac{w_0}{2k}, \qquad a_n = \frac{2w_0}{\pi}\frac{\sin(n\pi/2)}{n[EI(n^4\pi^4/16a^4) + k]} \qquad \text{for } n \geq 1, \tag{36}$$

so that (35) becomes

$$u(x) = \frac{w_0}{2k} + \frac{2w_0}{\pi} \sum_{n=1}^{\infty} \frac{\sin(n\pi/2)}{n[EI(n^4\pi^4/16a^4) + k]} \cos\frac{n\pi x}{2a}$$

$$= \frac{w_0}{2k} + \frac{2w_0}{\pi} \frac{1}{[EI(\pi^4/16a^4) + k]} \cos\frac{\pi x}{2a} \tag{37}$$

$$- \frac{2w_0}{3\pi} \frac{1}{[81EI(\pi^4/16a^4) + k]} \cos\frac{3\pi x}{2a} + \cdots .$$

COMMENT 1 Rigorous verification that (37) does satisfy (33) will be postponed until the following section, when we discuss the differentiation of Fourier series.

COMMENT 2 Observe that the coefficients in (37) diminish as $1/n^5$; hence they die out extremely rapidly as $n \to \infty$. Thus even the first couple of terms in (37) may provide a sufficiently accurate solution. We might well wonder how the "output" $u(x)$ manages to be so smooth (three times continuously differentiable) when the "input" loading $w(x)$ is discontinuous. Physically, this result is due to the stiffness of the beam. [Indeed, if the stiffness $EI \to 0$, then (33) gives $u(x) = w(x)/k$, which is just as discontinuous as w.] Mathematically, the general idea is that we (in effect) obtain u from (33) through four integrations, and these integrations are smoothing operations (Exercise 15).

COMMENT 3 Actually, (37) is a *particular* solution of (33). To obtain the *general* solution we need to add the complementary solution

$$e^{\beta x}(A \sin \beta x + B \cos \beta x) + e^{-\beta x}(C \sin \beta x + D \cos \beta x), \tag{38}$$

where $\beta \equiv \sqrt[4]{EI}/\sqrt{2}$. To determine A, B, C, D we need some sort of boundary conditions at the "ends" of the interval, i.e., at $x \to \pm\infty$. By way of such conditions let us simply ask that $u(x)$ be *bounded* as $x \to \infty$, as is surely a reasonable requirement. Then the fact that $e^{\beta x} \to \infty$ as $x \to +\infty$ requires that we set $A = B = 0$, and the fact that $e^{-\beta x} \to \infty$ as $x \to -\infty$ requires that we set $C = D = 0$. Thus (38) is knocked out entirely, and we are left with (37). ◀

EXAMPLE 6 *Finite Interval; Half-Range Expansions.* Consider the function f shown in Fig. 10.12. *In this case f happens to be defined only on the finite interval $(0, L)$, so it is not a periodic function.* Thus, it may appear that we cannot represent f by a Fourier series. However, suppose that we create a new function, say f_{ext}, which is a *periodic extension* of f and which is identical to f over $(0, L)$. Two such extensions are the even and odd extensions shown in Fig. 10.13a and 13b, respec-

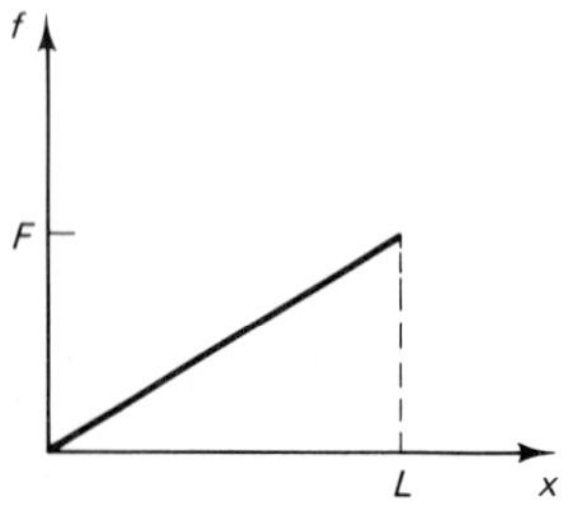

Fig. 10.12 f in Example 6.

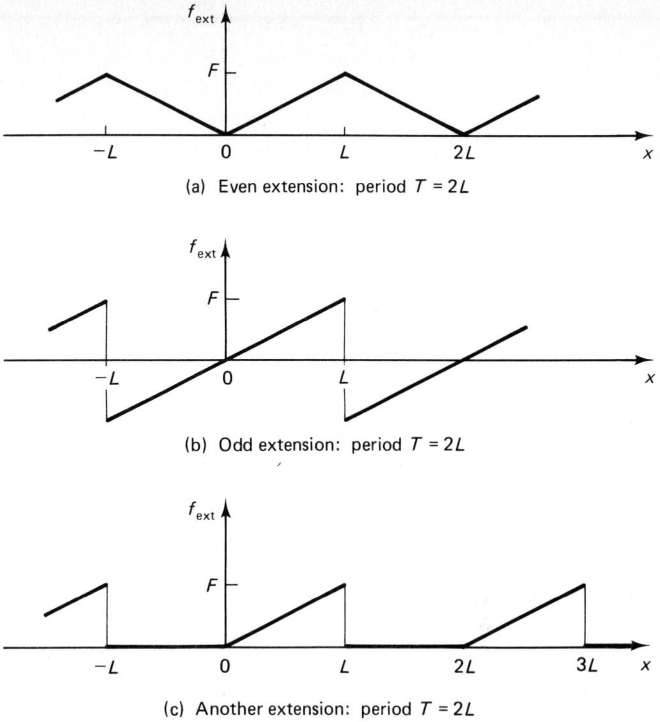

Fig. 10.13 Some periodic extensions of f.

tively. In fact, there are always an infinity of such extensions, and one more is shown in Fig. 10.13c. The point is that each of these periodic extensions of f admits a Fourier series representation which converges to the original function f (in the sense of Theorem 1) over the original interval $(0, L)$.

For example, the even extension in Fig. 10.13a has a period $T = 2L$ so that $\ell = L$, and we find from (26) that

$$f_{\text{ext}}(x) = \frac{F}{2} - \frac{4F}{\pi^2} \sum_{n=1,3,\ldots}^{\infty} \frac{1}{n^2} \cos \frac{n\pi x}{L} \tag{39}$$

over $(-\infty, \infty)$. Hence we have the representation

$$f(x) = \frac{F}{2} - \frac{4F}{\pi^2} \sum_{n=1,3,\ldots}^{\infty} \frac{1}{n^2} \cos \frac{n\pi x}{L} \tag{40}$$

of $f(x)$ over $(0, L)$. Alternatively, if we use the odd extension in Fig. 10.13b, we obtain the Fourier series

$$f_{\text{ext}}(x) = \frac{2F}{\pi} \sum_{n=1}^{\infty} \frac{(-1)^{n+1}}{n} \sin \frac{n\pi x}{L} \tag{41}$$

over $(-\infty, \infty)$, and

$$f(x) = \frac{2F}{\pi} \sum_{n=1}^{\infty} \frac{(-1)^{n+1}}{n} \sin \frac{n\pi x}{L} \tag{42}$$

over $(0, L)$.

The expansion (40) is called a **half-range cosine expansion** of f because the original interval length L is *half* the period of the periodic extension and only *cosine* terms are present. Similarly, (42) is a **half-range sine expansion** because L is half the period and only sine terms are present. Observe that in the half-range cosine case (Fig. 10.13a) the extension is symmetric about both endpoints, $x = 0$ and $x = L$; in the half-range sine case (Fig. 10.13b) the extension is *anti*symmetric about both endpoints. Also important are periodic extensions that are symmetric about one endpoint and antisymmetric about the other. These extensions give the so-called **quarter-range cosine** and **quarter-range sine expansions**, as discussed in Exercise 27.

In summary, if we are given f over a finite interval $(0, L)$, then an infinite variety of periodic extensions are possible. Out of all of these possible extensions, *four* will be important to us when we use Fourier series to help us solve partial differential equations in Part IV: the half- and quarter-range cosine and sine expansions. ◀

In Section 10.4 we indicate some useful theorems regarding the *properties* of Fourier series.

10.3 EXERCISES

1. (a) Derive the orthogonality relation (5a) using the identity $\cos A \cos B = \frac{1}{2}[\cos(A + B) + \cos(A - B)]$.
(b) Derive the orthogonality relation (5b) using the identity $\sin A \sin B = \frac{1}{2}[\cos(A - B) - \cos(A + B)]$.

2. If both left- and right-hand derivatives of f exist at x_0 and are equal, does that imply that f is differentiable at x_0? Explain.

3. Are these functions piecewise continuous over $[0, \pi]$? Explain.

*(a) $f(x) = \sin^2 x$
(b) $f(x) = \tan x$
(c) $f(x) = \sin(1/x)$
*(d) $f(x) = \cos(1/x)$
(e) $f(x) = e^{-x}$
(f) $f(x) = 1/(x - 1)$
(g) $f(x) = 1/(x - \pi)$
(h) $f(x) = \begin{cases} 100, & x = 0 \\ 0 & 0 < x \le \pi \end{cases}$

4. Sketch several periods of the given periodic function f. Compute the Fourier series of f and (if that is called for) sketch the designated partial sums of the series. Give the values of x, if any, at which the Fourier series of f fails to converge to $f(x)$; to what values does it converge at those points?

*(a) $f(x) = x$ on $(-\pi, \pi]$; $f(x + 2\pi) = f(x)$ Sketch $s_1(x)$, $s_2(x)$, $s_3(x)$.
(b) $f(x) = 100$ on $(-\infty, \infty)$
(c) $f(x) = |x|$ on $[-\pi, \pi)$; $f(x + 2\pi) = f(x)$ Sketch $s_1(x)$, $s_2(x)$, $s_3(x)$.
*(d) $f(x) = |x|$ on $[-2\pi, 2\pi)$; $f(x + 4\pi) = f(x)$ Sketch $s_1(x)$, $s_2(x)$, $s_3(x)$.
(e) $f(x) = \begin{cases} 100, & x = \pi/2 \\ 0, & x \ne \pi/2 \end{cases}$ on $[0, \pi]$; $f(x + \pi) = f(x)$
(f) $f(x) = \begin{cases} 50, & -4 < x < -2 \\ 0, & -2 \le x \le 4 \end{cases}$; $f(x + 8) = f(x)$
*(g) $f(x) = |\sin x|$ Sketch $s_1(x)$, $s_2(x)$, $s_3(x)$.
(h) $f(x) = |\cos x|$ Sketch $s_1(x)$, $s_2(x)$, $s_3(x)$.
(i) $f(x) = \begin{cases} \sin x, & 0 \le x < \pi \\ 0, & \pi \le x < 2\pi \end{cases}$; $f(x + 2\pi) = f(x)$
(j) $f(x) = \begin{cases} 20, & -2 < x < -1 \\ 0, & -1 \le x < 0 \\ 5, & x = 0 \\ 10, & 0 < x \le 2 \end{cases}$; $f(x + 4) = f(x)$
(k) $f(x) = \begin{cases} -50, & -4 \le x < 0 \\ 50, & x = 0 \\ 0, & 0 < x < 4 \\ 50, & 4 \le x < 8 \end{cases}$; $f(x + 12) = f(x)$
(l) $f(x) = 2 \sin 6\pi x$
(m) $f(x) = \cos^2 x$ *Hint:* $\cos^2 x = (1 + \cos 2x)/2$.
(n) $f(x) = \sin^2 x$

(o) $f(x) = \cos^3 x$ *Hint:* $\cos^3 x = (\cos 3x + 3\cos x)/4$.

(p) $f(x) = \cos^5 x$

(q) $f(x) = x^2$ on $-2 \le x < 2$; $f(x+4) = f(x)$

***5.** If the Fourier coefficients of a periodic function $f(x)$ are a_n $(n = 0, 1, 2, \ldots)$ and b_n $(n = 1, 2, \ldots)$, what are the Fourier coefficients, say A_n, B_n, of the periodic function $f(x - a)$?

6. Derive the Fourier series of g, shown below, in three different ways:

(a) by using (12) to compute the Fourier coefficients

(b) by observing that $g(x) + (50/F)f(x) = 50$, where $f(x)$ is shown in Fig. 10.4 and has the known Fourier series (20)

(c) by observing that $g(x) = (50/F)f(x + \pi)$, where $f(x)$ is shown in Fig. 10.4 and has the known Fourier series (20)

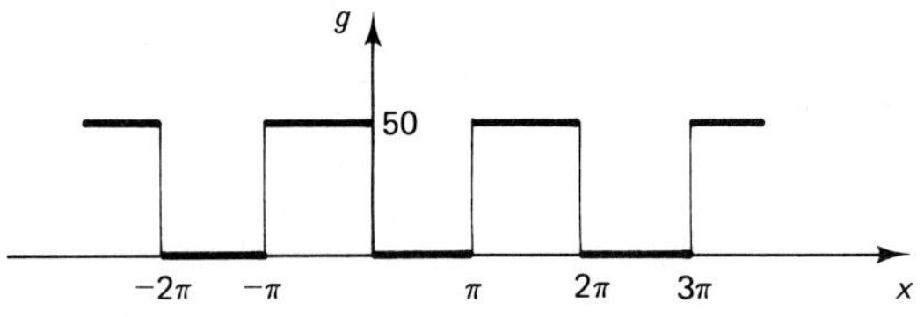

7. Derive the Fourier series of g, shown below, in two different ways.

(a) by using (12) to compute the Fourier coefficients

(b) from the Fourier series (20) of the function f shown in Fig. 10.4, by introducing a suitable scaling of x and f.

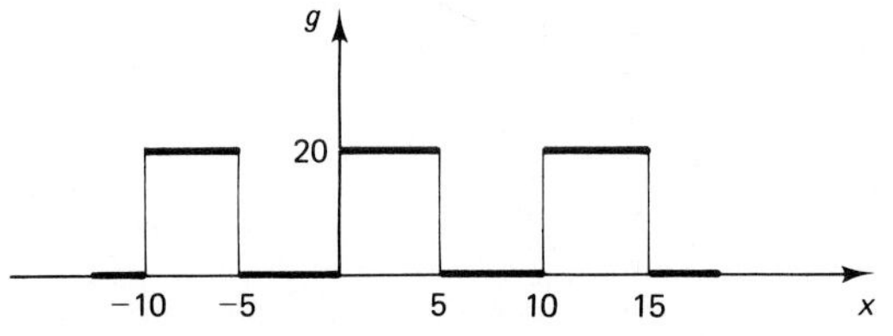

8. If $f(x) = a_0 + \Sigma_{n=1}^{\infty} [a_n \cos(n\pi x/\ell) + b_n \sin(n\pi x/\ell)]$, give expressions for the even and odd parts of f, $f_e(x)$ and $f_o(x)$, respectively. Next, decompose the function f shown in Fig. 10.4 into its even and odd parts; i.e., sketch the graphs of f_e and f_o. Then, explain why $a_1, a_2, \ldots$ are all equal to zero in Example 2.

9. From (21) show that

$$\frac{\pi}{4} = \sum_{n=1}^{\infty} \frac{(-1)^{n+1}}{2n-1} = 1 - \frac{1}{3} + \frac{1}{5} - \frac{1}{7} + \cdots. \tag{a}$$

Equation (a) provides an expansion that can be used to compute π and was given by Leibniz in 1673.

10. From (40) show that

$$\frac{\pi^2}{8} = \sum_{n=1,3,\ldots}^{\infty} \frac{1}{n^2}, \tag{a}$$

which can be used to evaluate π (or π^2).

11. Derive the Fourier series representation

$$x^2 = \frac{\pi^2}{3} + 4\sum_{n=1}^{\infty} \frac{(-1)^n}{n^2} \cos nx, \qquad -\pi \le x \le \pi. \tag{a}$$

12. The **Riemann zeta function** is defined by

$$\zeta(p) = \sum_{n=1}^{\infty} \frac{1}{n^p}, \qquad p > 1. \tag{a}$$

Show, from (a) in Exercise 11 that $\zeta(2) = \pi^2/6$.

13. In Example 2 we observed from the graph of f that f's fundamental period is 2π, so we set $\ell = \pi$. Is it critical that ℓ, in (12), be half of the *fundamental* period? No, it is not; the resulting Fourier series will be the same as long as ℓ is half of a period, *any* period, of f. The purpose of this exercise is not to prove that claim but merely to illustrate its truth. Specifically, observe that f, in Example 2, is also periodic with period 4π (and $6\pi, \ldots$). Thus, take ℓ to be half of 4π, in (12) and show that the resulting Fourier series is identical to (20) anyhow.

14. Derive the Fourier series (34) in Example 5.

15. It was noted, in Comment 2 on page 470 that integration is a smoothing process. To illustrate the truth of this claim, sketch the graphs of f, "$\int f$" $= \int_{-\infty}^{x} f(t)\,dt$, and "$\int\int f$" $= \int_{-\infty}^{x}\int_{-\infty}^{u} f(t)\,dt\,du$ if

$$f(x) = \begin{cases} 0, & -\infty < x < 0 \\ 1, & 0 \le x < \infty. \end{cases}$$

Whereas f is discontinuous, you should find that $\int f$ is continuous—although with a kink, and that $\int\int f$ is smooth.

16. (*Trigonometric approximation*) In applications, we may truncate a Fourier series and work with an approximation

$$f(x) \approx a_0 + \sum_{n=1}^{N} \left(a_n \cos\frac{n\pi x}{\ell} + b_n \sin\frac{n\pi x}{\ell} \right). \tag{a}$$

This raises an interesting question. If we *are* going to work with only a finite number of harmonics, what is the optimal choice for $a_0, a_1, \ldots, a_N, b_1, \ldots, b_N$? Specifically, are the Fourier coefficients, given by (12), still the best choice? The answer to that question will depend on the criterion that we choose in measuring the goodness of the approximation. Thus let us consider an approximation of the form

$$f(x) \approx A_0 + \sum_{n=1}^{N} \left(A_n \cos \frac{n\pi x}{\ell} + B_n \sin \frac{n\pi x}{\ell} \right), \qquad \text{(b)}$$

where we use capital letters for the A's and B's to emphasize that they may not turn out to be the same as the Fourier coefficients, which we continue to denote by lowercase letters. And let us choose, as a measure of the error between the left- and right-hand sides of (b), the so-called *mean square error*

$$E = \int_{-\ell}^{\ell} \left[f(x) - A_0 - \sum_{n=1}^{N} \left(A_n \cos \frac{n\pi x}{\ell} + B_n \sin \frac{n\pi x}{\ell} \right) \right]^2 dx. \qquad \text{(c)}$$

(a) Observe that E is a quadratic function of $A_0, A_1, \ldots, A_N, B_1, \ldots, B_N$. To minimize E, set $\partial E/\partial A_0 = 0$, $\partial E/\partial A_1 = 0, \ldots, \partial E/\partial B_N = 0$. Solving these equations for $A_0, A_1, \ldots, B_N$, show that $A_0 = a_0$, $A_1 = a_1, \ldots, B_N = b_N$; i.e., the Fourier coefficients do the best job, after all, in the sense of the definition (c) of the error. (You need not attempt to verify that the extremum thus obtained is indeed a minimum.)
(b) Since the integrand in (c) is squared, it is surely true that $E \geq 0$. Using this fact and letting $A_0 = a_0$, $A_1 = a_1, \ldots, B_N = b_N$, deduce the **Bessel inequality**

$$2a_0^2 + \sum_{n=1}^{N} (a_n^2 + b_n^2) \leq \frac{1}{\ell} \int_{-\ell}^{\ell} [f(x)]^2 \, dx. \qquad \text{(d)}$$

[Since (d) holds for every N, no matter how large, it also holds with the upper summation limit changed to ∞.]

17. (*Complex form of Fourier series*) Recalling (see Section A.5 in Appendix A) that

$$\cos \frac{n\pi x}{\ell} = \frac{e^{in\pi x/\ell} + e^{-in\pi x/\ell}}{2} \quad \text{and}$$
$$\sin \frac{n\pi x}{\ell} = \frac{e^{in\pi x/\ell} - e^{-in\pi x/\ell}}{2i}, \qquad \text{(a)}$$

show that (4) and (12) are equivalent to

$$f(x) = \sum_{n=-\infty}^{\infty} c_n e^{in\pi x/\ell}, \qquad \text{(b)}$$

where

$$c_n = \frac{1}{2\ell} \int_{-\ell}^{\ell} f(x) e^{-in\pi x/\ell} \, dx, \qquad \text{(c)}$$

for $n = 0, \pm 1, \pm 2, \ldots$, and where $\sum_{n=-\infty}^{\infty}$ is understood to mean $\lim_{N\to\infty} \sum_{n=-N}^{N}$.

18. Computing the c_n's according to (c) in Exercise 17, obtain the complex Fourier series (b) in Exercise 17 for the given function.

*(a) the square wave f in Example 2
(b) $f(x) = e^x$ on $0 \leq x < 2$; $f(x+2) = f(x)$
(c) $f(x) = e^{-x}$ on $-4 \leq x < 4$; $f(x+8) = f(x)$
(d) $f(x) = \sin x$
(e) $f(x) = 4 - 5 \cos 2x$

19. (*Polynomials*) It is a useful fact that if $p(x)$ is an even polynomial (i.e., containing only even-integer powers of x) on $[-\ell, \ell]$, the Fourier cosine coefficients are

$$a_n = \frac{2\ell}{n^2\pi^2}(-1)^n \left[p'(\ell) - \frac{\ell^2}{n^2\pi^2} p'''(\ell) + \frac{\ell^4}{n^4\pi^4} p^{(v)}(\ell) - \cdots \right] \qquad \text{(a)}$$

for $n \geq 1$; and if $p(x)$ is an odd polynomial on $[-\ell, \ell]$, then the Fourier sine coefficients are

$$b_n = -\frac{2}{n\pi}(-1)^n \left[p(\ell) - \frac{\ell^2}{n^2\pi^2} p''(\ell) + \frac{\ell^4}{n^4\pi^4} p^{(iv)}(\ell) - \cdots \right] \qquad \text{(b)}$$

for $n \geq 1$.

(a) Derive (a) through the p''' term.
(b) Derive (b) through the p'' term.

20. Use (a) and/or (b) of Exercise 19 to obtain the Fourier series in each case. *Note:* Equation (a) does not hold for $n = 0$, so you need to compute a_0 separately, in the usual way.

*(a) $f(x) = x$ on $[-\ell, \ell]$
(b) $f(x) = x^2$ on $[-\ell, \ell]$
(c) $f(x) = 6 + 2x - x^3$ on $[-2, 2]$
*(d) $f(x) = x^2(x^2 - 8)$ on $[-2, 2]$
(e) $f(x) = x(x^2 - 3)$ on $[-1, 1]$

(f) $f(x) = 2 + x - x^2$ on $[-3, 3]$
(g) $f(x) = x + x^2$ on $[-1, 1]$

21. The voltage V is maintained at $V = 100$ along the top half of the disk (shown in the figure), and at $V = 20$ along the bottom half. Expand $V(\theta)$ in a Fourier series.

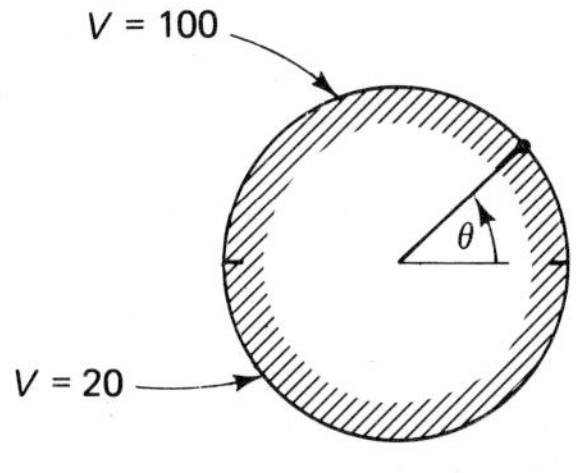

22. The temperature $T(x)$ in a rod that extends from $x = 0$ to $x = \ell$ is given by $T(x) = 100(\ell - x)/\ell$.

(a) Derive the half-range cosine expansion of T.
(b) Derive the half-range sine expansion of T.

23. (*Rms current*) If a steady electric current I flows through a resistor of resistance R, the power delivered (i.e., the rate of doing work) is equal to I^2R. In many applications I is not a constant, but a periodic function of the time t. In such cases one defines the *average power* as

$$\text{average power} = \frac{1}{T}\int_{-T/2}^{T/2} I^2(t)R\,dt \tag{a}$$

where T is the fundamental period of $I(t)$. Expressing $I(t)$ as a Fourier series,

$$I(t) = a_0 + \sum_{n=1}^{\infty}\left(a_n \cos\frac{2n\pi t}{T} + b_n \sin\frac{2n\pi t}{T}\right), \tag{b}$$

show that the

$$\text{average power} = \left[a_0^2 + \frac{1}{2}\sum_{n=1}^{\infty}(a_n^2 + b_n^2)\right]R, \tag{c}$$

and that the steady current which is equivalent to $I(t)$, in that it will deliver the same power, is

$$I_{\text{rms}} = \sqrt{a_0^2 + \frac{1}{2}\sum_{n=1}^{\infty}(a_n^2 + b_n^2)}. \tag{d}$$

I_{rms} is known as the *root-mean-square (rms) current*.

24. (*Relaxation oscillator*) There exist a great many periodic occurrences, called **relaxation oscillations**, which are characterized by a slow buildup and a rapid discharge. Examples include epidemics, economic crises, the sound generated by the bowing of a violin

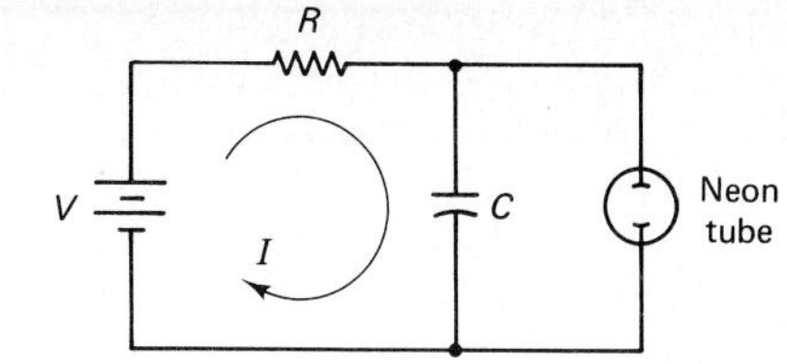

string, shivering from the cold, menstruation, the beating of the heart, and the discharge of a capacitor through a neon tube. Here we consider the latter (see the accompanying figure). The resistance R, capacitance C, and voltage V are constants. If $q(t)$ is the charge on the capacitor then $I(t) = dq/dt$ is the current in the V, R, C loop, and Kirchhoff's voltage law gives

$$R\frac{dq}{dt} + \frac{1}{C}q = V. \tag{a}$$

(a) Solve (a) subject to the initial condition $q(0) = 0$.
(b) When the voltage q/C on the capacitor, and hence on the neon tube, reaches a certain level, say $V/2$, the neon tube fires, and the charge q on the capacitor drops to zero. The firing is so rapid compared to the "buildup time" that we may assume it to be instantaneous. From your solution to part (a), show that the neon tube fires at $t = RC \ln 2$.

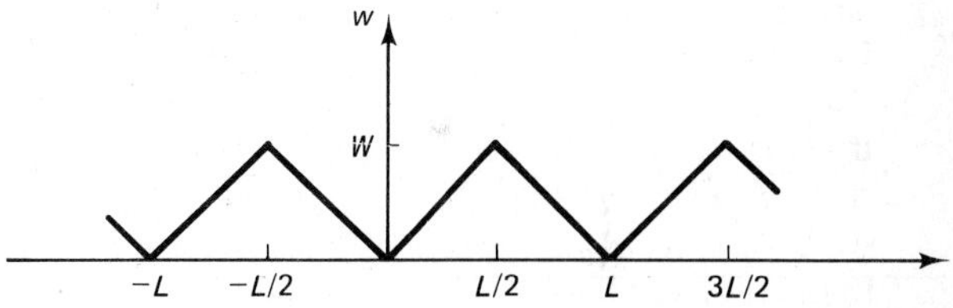

*(c) The cycle then repeats indefinitely. Sketch, and label, the graph of the periodic function $q(t)$, and work out its Fourier series.

25. Suppose, in Example 5, that $w(x)$ is as shown, and that $L = 5$ meters and $EI/k = 50$ meter^4. Obtain the Fourier series representation of the deflection $u(x)$ and compute $u(x)$ at $x = 0$. *Hint:* You may use the expansion (39) (with suitable change in notation) since the periodic function in Fig. 10.13a is of the same form as the one shown here for w.

26. (*Forced mechanical oscillator*) Suppose that a mechanical oscillator can be modeled by the differential equation

$$m\ddot{x} + c\dot{x} + kx = f(t), \tag{a}$$

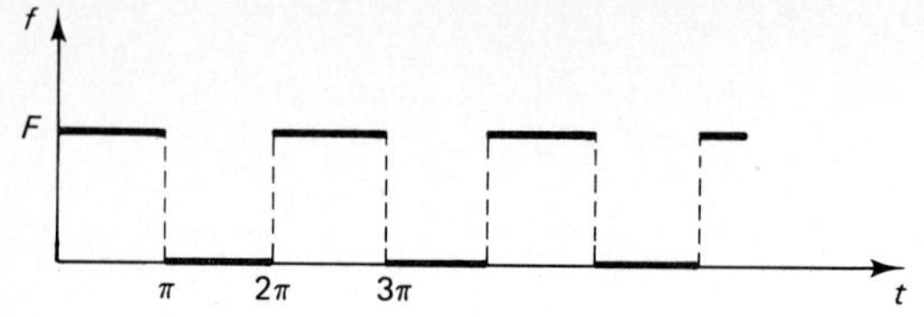

where the constants m, c, k are the mass, damping constant, and spring stiffness, respectively, and where $x(t)$ is the linear displacement of the mass and $f(t)$ is the applied force. Let $f(t)$ be the square wave shown in the figure.

(a) Proceeding formally, derive the general solution

$$x(t) = e^{-(c/2m)t}\left[A \cos \sqrt{\frac{k}{m} - \left(\frac{c}{2m}\right)^2}\, t + B \sin \sqrt{\frac{k}{m} - \left(\frac{c}{2m}\right)^2}\, t\right]$$

$$+ \frac{F}{2k} + \frac{2F}{\pi} \sum_{n=1,3,\ldots}^{\infty} \frac{cn \cos nt - (k - mn^2) \sin nt}{n[(k - mn^2)^2 + c^2n^2]}. \quad \text{(b)}$$

(b) Letting $m = 1$ kilogram, $c = 0.1$ kilogram/second, and $k = 9$ newtons/meter, show that as t increases $x(t)$ approaches the "steady-state" oscillation

$$\begin{aligned} x(t) \approx F[&0.056 + (0.001 \cos t - 0.080 \sin t) \\ &+ (0.707 \cos 3t) \\ &+ (0.000 \cos 5t + 0.008 \sin 5t) \\ &+ (0.000 \cos 7t + 0.002 \sin 7t) + \cdots]. \end{aligned} \quad \text{(c)}$$

Superimpose careful labeled sketches of $f(t)$ and $x(t)$ over one period, say from $t = 80\pi$ to $t = 82\pi$; for this purpose it will suffice to simplify (c) as $x(t) \approx F(0.06 - 0.08 \sin t + 0.71 \cos 3t)$. Explain, briefly, why the third harmonic turns out to be predominant.

27. (*Half- and quarter-range formulas*) In this exercise we generalize the discussion begun in Example 6, and obtain four expansion formulas that will be used extensively in Part IV when we solve partial differential equations. Let f be given and piecewise continuous on $(0, \ell)$.

(a) (*Half-range sine expansion*) Extend f periodically, over $(-\infty, \infty)$, so that the extended function, f_{ext}, is *antisymmetric* about $x = 0$ *and* about $x = \ell$. Expanding f_{ext} in a Fourier series, and then refocusing on the interval $(0, \ell)$, show that f admits the representation

$$f(x) = \sum_{n=1}^{\infty} b_n \sin \frac{n\pi x}{\ell} \quad \text{(a)}$$

on $(0, \ell)$, where

$$b_n = \frac{2}{\ell}\int_0^{\ell} f(x) \sin \frac{n\pi x}{\ell}\, dx; \quad \text{(b)}$$

Equation (a) is called the **half-range sine expansion** of f. (To illustrate the extension idea, we have sketched f_{ext}, in the accompanying figure, for the case where $f(x) = Fx/\ell$. The two A's denote the antisymmetry of f_{ext} about $x = 0$ and $x = \ell$.)

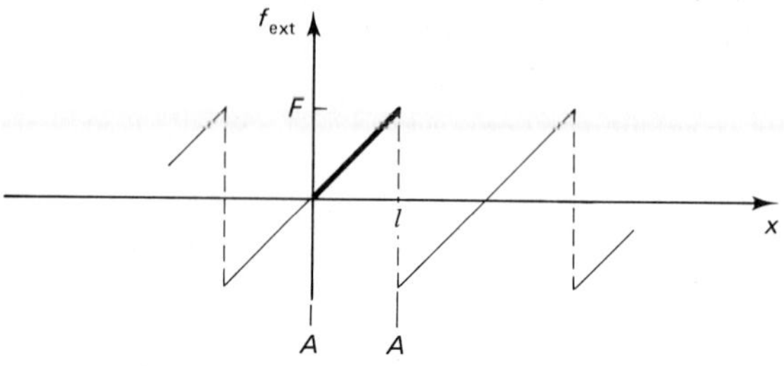

(b) (*Half-range cosine expansion*) Extend f periodically, over $(-\infty, \infty)$, so that the extended function, f_{ext}, is *symmetric* about $x = 0$ *and* about $x = \ell$. Expanding f_{ext} in a Fourier series, and then refocusing on the interval $(0, \ell)$, show that f admits the representation

$$f(x) = a_0 + \sum_{n=1}^{\infty} a_n \cos \frac{n\pi x}{\ell} \quad \text{(c)}$$

on $(0, \ell)$, where

$$a_0 = \frac{1}{\ell}\int_0^{\ell} f(x)\, dx, \quad a_n = \frac{2}{\ell}\int_0^{\ell} f(x) \cos \frac{n\pi x}{\ell}\, dx. \quad \text{(d)}$$

Equation (c) is called the **half-range cosine expansion of f**. (To illustrate the extension, we have sketched f_{ext}, in the accompanying figure, for the case where $f(x) = Fx/\ell$. The two S's denote the symmetry of f_{ext} about $x = 0$ and $x = \ell$.)

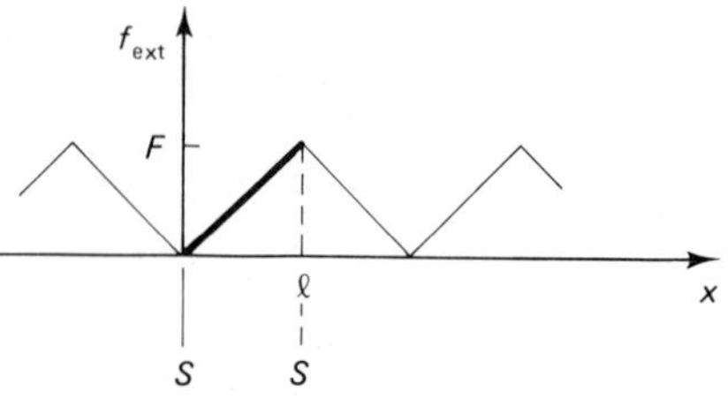

(c) (*Quarter-range sine expansion*). Extend f periodically, over $(-\infty, \infty)$, so that the extended function, f_{ext}, is *antisymmetric* about $x = 0$ and *symmetric* about $x = \ell$. Expanding f_{ext} in a Fourier series, and then refocusing upon the interval $(0, \ell)$, show that f admits the representation

$$f(x) = \sum_{n=1,3,\ldots}^{\infty} b_n \sin \frac{n\pi x}{2\ell} \qquad \text{(e)}$$

on $(0, \ell)$, where

$$b_n = \frac{2}{\ell} \int_0^{\ell} f(x) \sin \frac{n\pi x}{2\ell}\, dx \quad (n \text{ odd}). \qquad \text{(f)}$$

Equation (e) will be called the **quarter-range sine expansion** *of f*, "quarter-range" because the given interval length ℓ is only a quarter of the period of f_{ext}. [To illustrate the extension, we have sketched f_{ext}, in the accompanying figure, for the case where $f(x) = Fx/\ell$]. *Hint:* The Fourier coefficients of f_{ext} are expressed as integrals over one period, such as -2ℓ to $+2\ell$. Using the antisymmetry of f_{ext} about $x = 0$, show that $a_0 = 0$ and $a_n = 0$ $(n = 1, 2, \ldots)$, and reduce b_n to an integral over 0 to 2ℓ. Then use the symmetry of f_{ext} about $x = \ell$, namely, the property $f_{\text{ext}}(x) = f_{\text{ext}}(2\ell - x)$, to reduce b_n to an integral over 0 to ℓ.

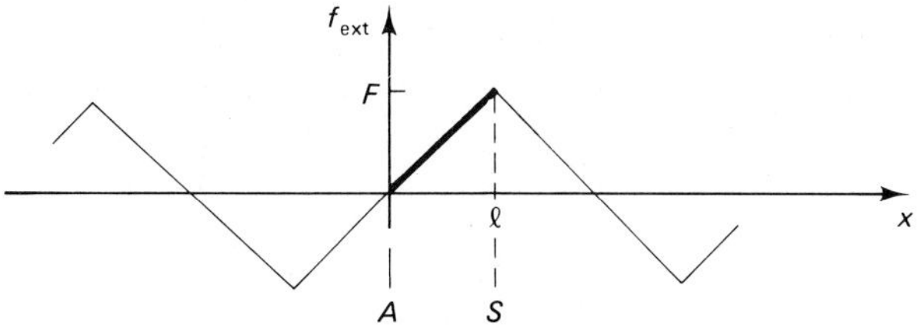

(d) (*Quarter-range cosine expansion*). Extend f periodically, over $(-\infty, \infty)$, so that the extended function, f_{ext}, is *symmetric* about $x = 0$ and *antisymmetric* about $x = \ell$. Expanding f_{ext} in a Fourier series, and then refocusing on the interval $(0, \ell)$, show that f admits the representation

$$f(x) = \sum_{n=1,3,\ldots}^{\infty} a_n \cos \frac{n\pi x}{2\ell} \qquad \text{(g)}$$

on $(0, \ell)$, where

$$a_n = \frac{2}{\ell} \int_0^{\ell} f(x) \cos \frac{n\pi x}{2\ell}\, dx \quad (n \text{ odd}). \qquad (h)$$

Equation (g) will be called the **quarter-range cosine expansion of f**. [To illustrate the extension, we have sketched f_{ext}, in the accompanying figure, for the case where $f(x) = Fx/\ell$]. *Hint:* Antisymmetry of f_{ext} about $x = \ell$ means that $f_{\text{ext}}(x) = -f_{\text{ext}}(2\ell - x)$.

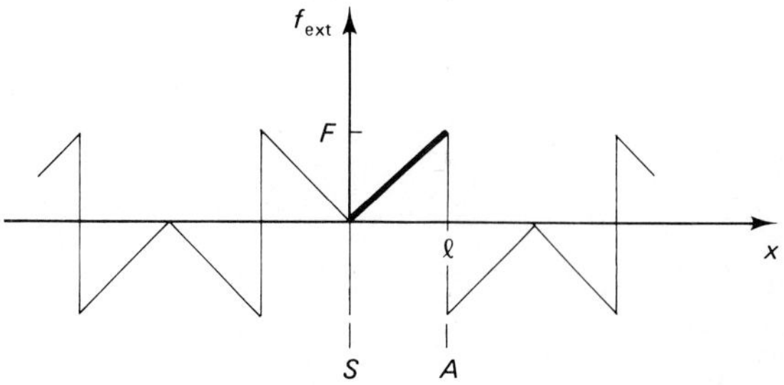

28. Given f, defined on $[0, \ell]$, derive its half-range sine, half-range cosine, quarter-range sine, and quarter-range cosine expansions, and sketch the respective periodic extensions (see Exercise 27).

*(a) $f(x) = 100$ (b) $f(x) = x$

(c) $f(x) = \begin{cases} 100, & 0 \le x < \dfrac{3\ell}{4} \\ 0, & \dfrac{3\ell}{4} \le x \le \ell \end{cases}$

(d) $f(x) = \begin{cases} 100, & 0 \le x < \dfrac{\ell}{2} \\ 50, & \dfrac{\ell}{2} \le x \le \ell \end{cases}$

(e) $f(x) = \sin \dfrac{\pi x}{\ell}$ (f) $f(x) = \cos \dfrac{\pi x}{2\ell}$

MANIPULATION OF FOURIER SERIES 10.4

[Optional Section]

Commonly, in working with Fourier series, we manipulate the series in various ways. Such manipulations were carried out, for example, in Example 5 on page 468, even though we were not yet in a position to justify them rigorously. First, we differentiated the Fourier series of u termwise (four times, in fact). That is, we wrote, in effect,

$$\begin{aligned} u' &= \frac{d}{dx}\left(a_0 + \sum_{n=1}^{\infty} a_n \cos \frac{n\pi x}{2a}\right) = \frac{d}{dx} \sum_{n=1}^{\infty} a_n \cos \frac{n\pi x}{2a} \\ &= \sum_{n=1}^{\infty} \frac{d}{dx}\left(a_n \cos \frac{n\pi x}{2a}\right) = -\frac{\pi}{2a} \sum_{n=1}^{\infty} n a_n \sin \frac{n\pi x}{2a}. \end{aligned} \qquad (1)$$

Admittedly, these steps look quite reasonable, yet the third equality in (1) is subject to question: Is the derivative of the sum function necessarily equal to the sum of the derivatives of the individual terms? That is, is it really legitimate to differentiate the series "termwise"? Second, we deduced from the equality

$$ka_0 + \sum_{n=1}^{\infty}\left(EI\frac{n^4\pi^4}{16a^4} + k\right)a_n \cos\frac{n\pi x}{2a} = \frac{w_0}{2} + \sum_{n=1}^{\infty}\frac{2w_0}{\pi}\frac{\sin(n\pi/2)}{n}\cos\frac{n\pi x}{2a} \tag{2}$$

that

$$ka_0 = \frac{w_0}{2} \quad \text{and} \quad \left(EI\frac{n^4\pi^4}{16a^4} + k\right)a_n = \frac{2w_0}{\pi}\frac{\sin(n\pi/2)}{n}, \qquad n = 1, 2, \ldots. \tag{3}$$

That is, we merely equated coefficients of like harmonics on both sides of (2). Again, this step looks quite reasonable, yet is it really obvious that we need to have the individual harmonics balance in order to have their sums balance?

Our purpose in this section is to provide a number of theorems that will put such manipulations on solid ground.

Theorem 1 *Uniqueness*

If two trigonometric series, each of the form

$$a_0 + \sum_{n=1}^{\infty}\left(a_n \cos\frac{n\pi x}{\ell} + b_n \sin\frac{n\pi x}{\ell}\right), \tag{4}$$

converge to the same sum for all x, then the corresponding coefficients are equal.*

Let us illustrate Theorem 1.

EXAMPLE 1 Given that (2) holds for all x, notice that we have a trigonometric series on each side of the equality. It follows immediately from Theorem 1, then, that corresponding coefficients are equal, as expressed in (3). ◀

* Proof of this theorem is rather sophisticated and can be found in the book by E. C. Titchmarsh [*The Theory of Functions*, 2nd ed. (London: Oxford University Press, 1939), pp. 427–432]. Note the wording "trigonometric series" in the theorem. A *trigonometric series* is, by definition, a series of the form (4). Is it not true that every trigonometric series is a Fourier series? No. For example,

$$\sum_{n=1}^{\infty}\frac{1}{\ln(1+n)}\sin nx$$

is surely a trigonometric series (and it can be shown that it converges for all x), yet it is *not* a Fourier series [see I. S. Sokolnikoff and R. M. Redheffer, *Mathematics of Physics and Modern Engineering*, 2nd ed. (New York: McGraw Hill, 1966), p. 86, Exer. 3]; i.e., there happens to be no function f such that

$$\int_{-\pi}^{\pi} f(x)\cos nx\,dx = 0, \qquad n = 0, 1, 2, \ldots$$

$$\frac{1}{\pi}\int_{-\pi}^{\pi} f(x)\sin nx\,dx = \frac{1}{\ln(1+n)}, \qquad n = 1, 2, \ldots.$$

Thus every Fourier series is a trigonometric series, but not every trigonometric series is a Fourier series.

Turning to the termwise differentiation and integration of Fourier series, we consider first the latter.

Theorem 2 *Termwise Integration of Fourier Series*
Let $f(x)$ be periodic with period 2ℓ, piecewise continuous on $[-\ell, \ell]$, let its average height over $[-\ell, \ell]$ be zero, and let its Fourier series be

$$\sum_{n=1}^{\infty}\left(a_n \cos\frac{n\pi x}{\ell} + b_n \sin\frac{n\pi x}{\ell}\right). \tag{5}$$

Then the Fourier series of the integral function $F(x) \equiv \int_{-\ell}^{x} f(t)\,dt$ can be obtained by termwise integration of (5), and converges to $F(x)$ for all x.*

Proof First, we note that it follows from the piecewise continuity of f that F is continuous and admits both left- and right-hand derivatives at each point x. We will leave the proof of this statement as an exercise, and will be content, for the moment, merely to illustrate its truth for a single example. Specifically, note that if f is the piecewise-continuous square wave in Fig. 10.14a, then $F(x)$ is the triangular wave shown in Fig. 10.14b. If this is not clear, recall the graphical significance of $F(x)$, namely, the area under f between $-\ell$ and x (if $x > -\ell$, and the negative of that area if $x < -\ell$), where area above the x axis is counted positive, and area below it is counted negative. Notice that whereas f has jump discontinuities, F is continuous (as claimed), and admits right- and left-hand derivatives at each x (as claimed).

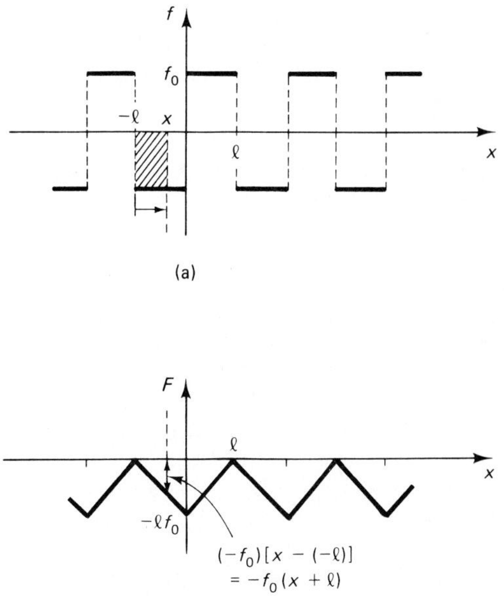

Fig. 10.14 An example of f and F.

* This theorem can be strengthened by dropping the condition that f be piecewise continous, and requiring, instead, the integrability of f and $|f|$. See Sokolnikoff and Redheffer, op. cit., p. 83.

Returning to our proof, note further that F is periodic of period 2ℓ since

$$
\begin{aligned}
F(x+2\ell) &= \int_{-\ell}^{x+2\ell} f(t)\,dt = \int_{-\ell}^{x} f(t)\,dt + \int_{x}^{x+2\ell} f(t)\,dt \\
&= F(x) + (2\ell)(\text{average height of } f) \\
&= F(x) + (2\ell)(0) = F(x).
\end{aligned} \tag{6}
$$

In view of these properties of F, we can conclude (Theorem 1, page 461) that the Fourier series of F converges to $F(x)$ for all x. Denoting F's Fourier coefficients as $A_0, A_1, B_1, \ldots$, we write

$$
F(x) = A_0 + \sum_{n=1}^{\infty} \left(A_n \cos \frac{n\pi x}{\ell} + B_n \sin \frac{n\pi x}{\ell} \right). \tag{7}
$$

Computing the coefficients, we begin with A_0. Integrating by parts, and noting that $F(\ell) = F(-\ell) = 0$ and that (Exercise 9) $F'(x) = f(x)$, we have

$$
\begin{aligned}
A_0 &= \frac{1}{2\ell} \int_{-\ell}^{\ell} F(x)\,dx = \frac{1}{2\ell} \left[F(x)x \Big|_{-\ell}^{\ell} - \int_{-\ell}^{\ell} xF'(x)\,dx \right] \\
&= -\frac{1}{2\ell} \int_{-\ell}^{\ell} xf(x)\,dx.
\end{aligned} \tag{8}
$$

Alternatively, we could regard A_0 as an iterated integral and invert the order of integration, so that (Exercise 10)

$$
\begin{aligned}
A_0 &= \frac{1}{2\ell} \int_{-\ell}^{\ell} \left(\int_{-\ell}^{x} f(t)\,dt \right) dx = \frac{1}{2\ell} \int_{-\ell}^{\ell} dx \int_{-\ell}^{x} f(t)\,dt \\
&= \frac{1}{2\ell} \int_{-\ell}^{\ell} f(t)\,dt \int_{t}^{\ell} dx = \frac{1}{2\ell} \int_{-\ell}^{\ell} f(t)(\ell - t)\,dt \\
&= \frac{\ell}{2\ell} \int_{-\ell}^{\ell} f(t)\,dt - \frac{1}{2\ell} \int_{-\ell}^{\ell} tf(t)\,dt = -\frac{1}{2\ell} \int_{-\ell}^{\ell} tf(t)\,dt.
\end{aligned} \tag{9}
$$

Similarly, we find (Exercise 11) that

$$
A_n = -\frac{\ell}{n\pi} \frac{1}{\ell} \int_{-\ell}^{\ell} f(x) \sin \frac{n\pi x}{\ell}\,dx = -\frac{\ell}{n\pi} b_n, \tag{10a}
$$

$$
B_n = \frac{\ell}{n\pi} \frac{1}{\ell} \int_{-\ell}^{\ell} f(x) \cos \frac{n\pi x}{\ell}\,dx = \frac{\ell}{n\pi} a_n, \tag{10b}
$$

for $n \geq 1$. Putting (9) and (10) into (7), we have, as the Fourier series representation of F,

$$
F(x) = -\frac{1}{2\ell} \int_{-\ell}^{\ell} tf(t)\,dt + \sum_{n=1}^{\infty} \left(-\frac{\ell}{n\pi} b_n \cos \frac{n\pi x}{\ell} + \frac{\ell}{n\pi} a_n \sin \frac{n\pi x}{\ell} \right). \tag{11}
$$

Finally, we need to show that the right-hand side of (11) obtains from the termwise integration of (5). Well,

$$\sum_{n=1}^{\infty}\left(a_n\int_{-\ell}^{x}\cos\frac{n\pi t}{\ell}\,dt + b_n\int_{-\ell}^{x}\sin\frac{n\pi t}{\ell}\,dt\right)$$
$$= \sum_{n=1}^{\infty}\frac{\ell}{n\pi}(-1)^n b_n + \sum_{n=1}^{\infty}\left(-\frac{\ell}{n\pi}b_n\cos\frac{n\pi x}{\ell} + \frac{\ell}{n\pi}a_n\sin\frac{n\pi x}{\ell}\right). \tag{12}$$

Comparing (11) and (12), we see that it remains to show that

$$-\frac{1}{2\ell}\int_{-\ell}^{\ell} tf(t)\,dt = \sum_{n=1}^{\infty}\frac{\ell}{n\pi}(-1)^n b_n. \tag{13}$$

The truth of (13) can be seen by setting $x = -\ell$ (or $+\ell$) in (11) and noting that $F(-\ell) = 0$. This step completes the proof. ■

Two comments regarding Theorem 2 and its application:

COMMENT 1 In fact, we can integrate the Fourier series of f between *any* limits, say α and β, for

$$\int_{\alpha}^{\beta} f(t)\,dt = \int_{-\ell}^{\beta} f(t)\,dt - \int_{-\ell}^{\alpha} f(t)\,dt$$
$$= F(\beta) - F(\alpha). \tag{14}$$

COMMENT 2 The condition that the average height of f be zero is not at all restrictive, for if f has a nonzero average height a_0, one can apply the theorem to the function $f(x) - a_0$, which function *does* have zero average height.

Next, termwise *differentiation* of Fourier series.

***Theorem 3** Termwise Differentiation of Fourier Series*

Let $f(x)$ be periodic with period 2ℓ, and continuous on $(-\infty, \infty)$, and let $f'(x)$ be piecewise continuous on $[-\ell, \ell]$. Then the Fourier series for $f'(x)$ can be obtained by the termwise differentiation of the Fourier series for $f(x)$.

Proof The idea is to apply Theorem 2 to $f'(x)$. To do so we must first verify that f' satisfies the conditions of Theorem 2. Well the average height of f' is

$$\frac{1}{2\ell}\int_{-\ell}^{\ell} f'(t)\,dt = \frac{1}{2\ell}f(t)\Big|_{-\ell}^{\ell} = \frac{1}{2\ell}[f(\ell) - f(-\ell)] = 0 \tag{15}$$

since f is periodic with period 2ℓ. Furthermore, f' is piecewise continuous by assumption, and is 2ℓ periodic because f is 2ℓ periodic (Exercise 12). Thus if the Fourier series of f' is

$$f'(x) = \sum_{n=1}^{\infty}\left(A_n\cos\frac{n\pi x}{\ell} + B_n\sin\frac{n\pi x}{\ell}\right), \tag{16}$$

then according to Theorem 2 we may integrate (16) termwise, to give

$$\int_{-\ell}^{x} f'(t)\,dt = \sum_{n=1}^{\infty}\left(A_n\int_{-\ell}^{x}\cos\frac{n\pi t}{\ell}\,dt + B_n\int_{-\ell}^{x}\sin\frac{n\pi t}{\ell}\,dt\right)$$

or

$$f(x) = \left[f(-\ell) + \sum_{n=1}^{\infty} \frac{\ell}{n\pi}(-1)^n B_n\right] + \sum_{n=1}^{\infty}\left[-\frac{\ell}{n\pi}B_n \cos\frac{n\pi x}{\ell} + \frac{\ell}{n\pi}A_n \sin\frac{n\pi x}{\ell}\right]. \tag{17}$$

And if the Fourier series of f is

$$f(x) = a_0 + \sum_{n=1}^{\infty}\left(a_n \cos\frac{n\pi x}{\ell} + b_n \sin\frac{n\pi x}{\ell}\right), \tag{18}$$

then a comparison of (17) and (18) reveals (with the help of Theorem 1) that

$$a_n = -\frac{\ell}{n\pi}B_n, \qquad b_n = \frac{\ell}{n\pi}A_n$$

or

$$B_n = -\frac{n\pi}{\ell}a_n, \qquad A_n = \frac{n\pi}{\ell}b_n. \tag{19}$$

Thus (16) becomes

$$f'(x) = \sum_{n=1}^{\infty}\left(-\frac{n\pi}{\ell}a_n \sin\frac{n\pi x}{\ell} + \frac{n\pi}{\ell}b_n \cos\frac{n\pi x}{\ell}\right), \tag{20}$$

which is the same as one obtains by termwise differentiation of (18). This step concludes the proof. ■

Looking back at Theorems 2 and 3, observe that the conditions on f in Theorem 3 are more stringent than those in Theorem 2. Roughly put, the idea is that when we termwise differentiate the Fourier series (18), we pull out a factor of $n\pi/\ell$ under the summation. Thus we must ask f to be well-enough behaved so that its a_n, b_n Fourier coefficients die out fast enough (as $n \to \infty$) to withstand the adverse effect of this factor n. Conversely, termwise integration pulls out a factor of $\ell/n\pi$ which *aids* the convergence, so f need not be as well behaved.

10.4 EXERCISES

1. In Fig. 10.14b we have sketched the graph of the integral function $F(x) = \int_{-\ell}^{x} f(t)\,dt$, where f is as shown in Fig. 10.14a. Sketch instead

(a) $F(x) = \int_0^x f(t)\,dt$ (b) $F(x) = \int_\ell^x f(t)\,dt$
(c) $F(x) = \int_{-\ell/2}^x f(t)\,dt$ (d) $F(x) = \int_{\ell/2}^x f(t)\,dt$

2. Sketch the graph of the function f which equals x on $(-\pi, \pi]$ and is 2π periodic, and also the graph of the integral function:

(a) $F(x) = \int_{-\pi}^x f(t)\,dt$ (b) $F(x) = \int_0^x f(t)\,dt$

3. Show that the Fourier series of the function f in Exercise 2 is

$$x = 2\sum_{n=1}^{\infty}\frac{(-1)^{n-1}}{n}\sin nx \qquad (-\pi, \pi). \tag{a}$$

First verifying that Theorem 2 applies, integrate (a) termwise from $-\pi$ to x, and show that

$$x^2 = C + 4\sum_{n=1}^{\infty}\frac{(-1)^n}{n^2}\cos nx, \qquad (-\pi, \pi) \tag{b}$$

where C is a constant. Noting that C is the average value of x^2 over $(-\pi, \pi)$, show that $C = \pi^2/3$.

4. First verifying that Theorem 2 applies, integrate the Fourier series

$$x^2 = \frac{\pi^2}{3} + 4 \sum_{n=1}^{\infty} \frac{(-1)^n}{n^2} \cos nx \qquad (-\pi, \pi) \quad \text{(a)}$$

(from Exercise 3) from $-\pi$ to x, and thus show that

$$x^3 - \pi^2 x = 12 \sum_{n=1}^{\infty} \frac{(-1)^n}{n^3} \sin nx \qquad (-\pi, \pi). \quad \text{(b)}$$

5. Show that the conditions of Theorem 3 are satisfied, so that (b) of Exercise 4 can be differentiated termwise. (You need not *do* the differentiation.)

***6.** Can termwise differentiation of (a) of Exercise 4 be justified by Theorem 3? Explain.

7. Can termwise differentiation of (a) of Exercise 3 be justified by Theorem 3? Explain.

8. Can termwise differentiation of the Fourier series

$$x^3 = 2 \sum_{n=1}^{\infty} (-1)^{n+1} \frac{n^2\pi^2 - 6}{n^3} \sin nx \qquad (-\pi, \pi) \quad \text{(a)}$$

be justified by Theorem 3? Explain.

9. In (10) we used the fact that $F'(x) = f(x)$, which result is surely correct—by the fundamental theorem of the integral calculus on page 344—if f is continuous, but in the present case f is merely assumed to be piecewise continuous. Show that (10) is, nevertheless, correct.

10. Recall the interchange in the order of integration,

$$\int_{-\ell}^{\ell} dx \int_{-\ell}^{x} f(t)\, dt = \int_{-\ell}^{\ell} f(t)\, dt \int_{t}^{\ell} dx, \qquad \text{(a)}$$

in (10). Verify the integration limits in the right-hand side of (a) by sketching the region of integration (in the x, t plane) corresponding to the integration limits on the left-hand side of (a).

11. (a) Derive the first equality in (10a) two different ways: by integration by parts and by double integration (as we did for A_0).
(b) Derive the first equality in (10b) two different ways: by integration by parts and by double integration (as we did for A_0).

12. It is stated, below (15), that the 2ℓ periodicity of f implies the 2ℓ periodicity of f'. Prove this statement. *Hint:* Express $f'(x)$ as the limit of a difference quotient.

VECTOR SPACE APPROACH 10.5

[Optional Section]

A different, informative, and elegant approach to Fourier series is available within the *vector space* context, and involves the so-called *best approximation* problem. In this discussion our vector space is going to be a *function space,* i.e., a vector space in which the vectors are functions. Our plan is first to examine the best approximation problem for *any* vector space, and then to specialize the results to function space.

BEST APPROXIMATION

Suppose that we have a real vector space $\mathcal{S}$ (i.e., *all* quantities are to be real) with a dot product defined [and possessing the properties (12) on page 31], and that we have a finite set of ON (i.e., orthonormal) vectors $\{\hat{\mathbf{e}}_1, \ldots, \hat{\mathbf{e}}_N\}$ within $\mathcal{S}$. Then span $\{\hat{\mathbf{e}}_1, \ldots, \hat{\mathbf{e}}_N\}$ is a subspace of $\mathcal{S}$, which we denote as $\mathcal{T}$. The **best approximation problem,** which we address, is this: Given a vector $\mathbf{u}$ in $\mathcal{S}$, what is the best approximation

$$\mathbf{u} \approx c_1\hat{\mathbf{e}}_1 + c_2\hat{\mathbf{e}}_2 + \cdots + c_N\hat{\mathbf{e}}_N = \sum_{n=1}^{N} c_n\hat{\mathbf{e}}_n; \qquad (1)$$

i.e., how do we compute the c_n coefficients so as to render the error vector $\mathbf{E} = \mathbf{u} - \sum_{n=1}^{N} c_n\hat{\mathbf{e}}_n$ as small as possible? In other words, how do we compute the

c_n's so as to minimize the norm of the error vector $\|\mathbf{E}\|$? Equivalently, let us minimize $\|\mathbf{E}\|^2$, where

$$\begin{aligned}\|\mathbf{E}\|^2 = \mathbf{E}\cdot\mathbf{E} &= \left(\mathbf{u} - \sum_{n=1}^{N} c_n\hat{\mathbf{e}}_n\right)\cdot\left(\mathbf{u} - \sum_{n=1}^{N} c_n\hat{\mathbf{e}}_n\right) \\ &= \mathbf{u}\cdot\mathbf{u} - 2\sum_{n=1}^{N} c_n(\mathbf{u}\cdot\hat{\mathbf{e}}_n) + \sum_{n=1}^{N} c_n^2.\end{aligned} \tag{2}$$

In (2) we have used the fact that $(\sum_{n=1}^{N} c_n\hat{\mathbf{e}}_n)\cdot(\sum_{n=1}^{N} c_n\hat{\mathbf{e}}_n) = \sum_{n=1}^{N} c_n^2$, which follows from the orthogonality of the $\hat{\mathbf{e}}_n$'s. To see this, one can either work out $(c_1\hat{\mathbf{e}}_1 + \cdots + c_N\hat{\mathbf{e}}_N)\cdot(c_1\hat{\mathbf{e}}_1 + \cdots + c_N\hat{\mathbf{e}}_N)$ term by term, or, using the Kronecker delta notation introduced on page 59, one can write

$$\begin{aligned}\left(\sum_{n=1}^{N} c_n\hat{\mathbf{e}}_n\right)\cdot\left(\sum_{n=1}^{N} c_n\hat{\mathbf{e}}_n\right) &= \left(\sum_{n=1}^{N} c_n\hat{\mathbf{e}}_n\right)\cdot\left(\sum_{m=1}^{N} c_m\hat{\mathbf{e}}_m\right) \\ &= \sum_{n=1}^{N}\sum_{m=1}^{N} c_nc_m\hat{\mathbf{e}}_n\cdot\hat{\mathbf{e}}_m = \sum_{n=1}^{N}\sum_{m=1}^{N} c_nc_m\delta_{nm} \\ &= \sum_{n=1}^{N}\left(\sum_{m=1}^{N} c_m\delta_{nm}\right)c_n = \sum_{n=1}^{N}(c_n)c_n = \sum_{n=1}^{N} c_n^2.\end{aligned} \tag{3}$$

Defining $\mathbf{u}\cdot\hat{\mathbf{e}}_n \equiv \alpha_n$ and noting that $\mathbf{u}\cdot\mathbf{u} = \|\mathbf{u}\|^2$, we may express (2) as

$$\|\mathbf{E}\|^2 = \sum_{n=1}^{N} c_n^2 - 2\sum_{n=1}^{N} \alpha_nc_n + \|\mathbf{u}\|^2,$$

or, completing the square, as

$$\|\mathbf{E}\|^2 = \sum_{n=1}^{N} (c_n - \alpha_n)^2 + \|\mathbf{u}\|^2 - \sum_{n=1}^{N} \alpha_n^2. \tag{4}$$

Observe that $\mathbf{u}$ and the ON set $\{\hat{\mathbf{e}}_1, \ldots, \hat{\mathbf{e}}_N\}$ are given, so that $\|\mathbf{u}\|$ and the α_n's in (4) are fixed quantities: $\|\mathbf{u}\| = \sqrt{\mathbf{u}\cdot\mathbf{u}}$ and $\alpha_n = \mathbf{u}\cdot\hat{\mathbf{e}}_n$ for $n = 1, 2, \ldots, N$. Thus, in seeking to minimize the right-hand side of (4), the only control we can exercise is in our choice of the c_n's. Well, the right-hand side of (4) is greater than or equal to zero,* and so is the $\sum_{n=1}^{N} (c_n - \alpha_n)^2$ term containing the c_n's. Thus the best that we can do is to set $c_n = \alpha_n$ $(n = 1, 2, \ldots, N)$. With that choice, our best approximation (1) becomes

$$\mathbf{u} \approx \sum_{n=1}^{N} (\mathbf{u}\cdot\hat{\mathbf{e}}_n)\hat{\mathbf{e}}_n. \tag{5}$$

Let us summarize these results.

> ***Theorem 1** Best Approximation*
> Let $\mathbf{u}$ be any given vector in a vector space $\mathcal{S}$ with a dot product defined, and let an ON set $\{\hat{\mathbf{e}}_1, \ldots, \hat{\mathbf{e}}_N\}$ be given so that the span of that set is a subspace $\mathcal{T}$ of $\mathcal{S}$. Then the best approximation to $\mathbf{u}$ within $\mathcal{T}$ i.e., of the form $\mathbf{u} \approx c_1\hat{\mathbf{e}}_1 + c_2\hat{\mathbf{e}}_2 + \cdots + c_N\hat{\mathbf{e}}_N$, is obtained when the c_n's are given by $c_n = \mathbf{u}\cdot\hat{\mathbf{e}}_n$.

* This fact may not be obvious due to the minus sign in front of the last summation. But remember that the right-hand side of (4) is equal to $\|\mathbf{E}\|^2$, and it is surely true that $\|\mathbf{E}\|^2 \geq 0$.

Furthermore, with the choice $c_n = \mathbf{u} \cdot \hat{\mathbf{e}}_n$ (4) becomes

$$\|\mathbf{E}\|^2 = \|\mathbf{u}\|^2 - \sum_{n=1}^{N} (\mathbf{u} \cdot \hat{\mathbf{e}}_n)^2 \geq 0, \tag{6}$$

which yields the well-known **Bessel inequality**

$$\boxed{\sum_{n=1}^{N} (\mathbf{u} \cdot \hat{\mathbf{e}}_n)^2 \leq \|\mathbf{u}\|^2.} \tag{7}$$

Understand that if $\mathcal{S}$ is N-dimensional, then $\{\hat{\mathbf{e}}_1, \ldots, \hat{\mathbf{e}}_N\}$ is a *basis* for $\mathcal{S}$, and (5) is then an *equality*—the same, in fact, as our expansion formula (21) on page 53. However, our main interest, in this section, is in the case where the dimension of $\mathcal{S}$ is greater than N, so that $\{\hat{\mathbf{e}}_1, \ldots, \hat{\mathbf{e}}_N\}$ is somewhat short of being a basis for $\mathcal{S}$. Of course, even in that case (5) will be an equality if $\mathbf{u}$ happens to be in span $\{\hat{\mathbf{e}}_1, \ldots, \hat{\mathbf{e}}_N\}$, but in general (5) can only be expected to hold as an approximation.

EXAMPLE 1 Let $\mathcal{S}$ be $\mathbb{R}^3$, let $N = 2$ with $\hat{\mathbf{e}}_1 = (1, 0, 0)$ and $\hat{\mathbf{e}}_2 = (0, 1, 0)$, and let $\mathbf{u} = (a, b, c)$, as shown in Fig. 10.15. Then the subspace $\mathcal{T}$ of $\mathcal{S}$ is the (shaded) plane containing axis 1 and axis 2.

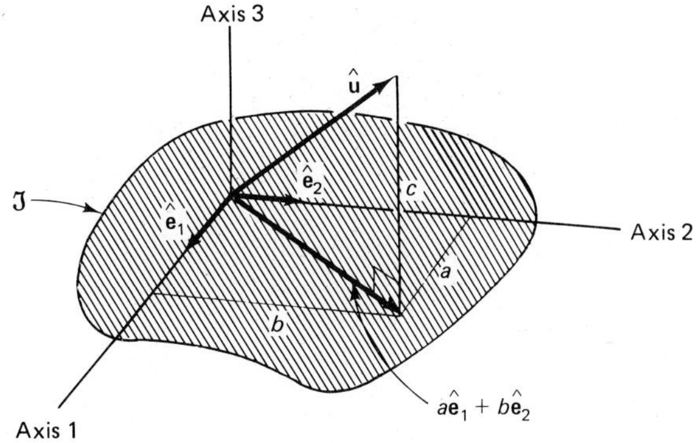

Fig. 10.15 Example 1.

Computing the coefficients in (5), $\mathbf{u} \cdot \hat{\mathbf{e}}_1 = a$ and $\mathbf{u} \cdot \hat{\mathbf{e}}_2 = b$, so that (5) becomes

$$\mathbf{u} \approx a\hat{\mathbf{e}}_1 + b\hat{\mathbf{e}}_2, \tag{8}$$

which, of course, is an equality if c happens to be 0, i.e., if $\mathbf{u}$ happens to lie in $\mathcal{T}$. If c is *not* 0, observe from the figure that the best approximation $a\hat{\mathbf{e}}_1 + b\hat{\mathbf{e}}_2$ is the *orthogonal projection of* $\mathbf{u}$ onto $\mathcal{T}$. This result makes a lot of sense, since if we are to choose c_1, c_2 so that $c_1\hat{\mathbf{e}}_1 + c_2\hat{\mathbf{e}}_2$ is the best possible approximation to $\mathbf{u}$, then the distance from the tip of $\mathbf{u}$ to the tip of $c_1\hat{\mathbf{e}}_1 + c_2\hat{\mathbf{e}}_2$ should be as small as possible; that shortest distance is the perpendicular distance from the tip of $\mathbf{u}$ to the $\mathcal{T}$ plane, so the best possible approximation $c_1\hat{\mathbf{e}}_1 + c_2\hat{\mathbf{e}}_2$ must be the orthogonal projection of $\mathbf{u}$ onto $\mathcal{T}$. ◀

In Example 1 $\mathcal{S}$ was "merely" $\mathbb{R}^3$, so that we were able to draw a picture which lent considerable clarity to the situation. In particular, we discovered that the best approximation to $\mathbf{u}$ in $\mathcal{T}$ was the orthogonal projection of $\mathbf{u}$ onto $\mathcal{T}$. It is reasonable to wonder whether or not that result is true in *all* cases. Well, from (5) the error vector $\mathbf{E}$ is

$$\mathbf{E} = \mathbf{u} - \sum_{n=1}^{N} (\mathbf{u} \cdot \hat{\mathbf{e}}_n)\hat{\mathbf{e}}_n, \tag{9}$$

and from the orthogonality of the $\hat{\mathbf{e}}_n$'s it follows that

$$\begin{aligned} \mathbf{E} \cdot \hat{\mathbf{e}}_j &= \left[\mathbf{u} - \sum_{n=1}^{N} (\mathbf{u} \cdot \hat{\mathbf{e}}_n)\hat{\mathbf{e}}_n\right] \cdot \hat{\mathbf{e}}_j = \mathbf{u} \cdot \hat{\mathbf{e}}_j - \sum_{n=1}^{N} (\mathbf{u} \cdot \hat{\mathbf{e}}_n)(\hat{\mathbf{e}}_n \cdot \hat{\mathbf{e}}_j) \\ &= \mathbf{u} \cdot \hat{\mathbf{e}}_j - \mathbf{u} \cdot \hat{\mathbf{e}}_j = 0 \end{aligned} \tag{10}$$

for each $j = 1, 2, \ldots, N$. Since $\mathbf{E}$ is orthogonal to every one of the $\hat{\mathbf{e}}_j$'s it is therefore orthogonal to every vector in $\mathcal{T}$, and in that sense we may say that the right-hand side of (5) is the **orthogonal projection of u onto** $\mathcal{T}$, which we denote as $\text{proj}_{\mathcal{T}}\, \mathbf{u}$:

$$\text{proj}_{\mathcal{T}}\, \mathbf{u} \equiv \sum_{n=1}^{N} (\mathbf{u} \cdot \hat{\mathbf{e}}_n)\mathbf{e}_n. \tag{11}$$

This result lends a welcome geometrical interpretation to the problem of best approximation. Let us rephrase Theorem 1 in terms of orthogonal projection.

> ***Theorem 1′*** *Best Approximation by Orthogonal Projection*
> Let $\mathbf{u}$ by any given vector in a vector space $\mathcal{S}$, and let an ON set $\{\hat{\mathbf{e}}_1, \ldots, \hat{\mathbf{e}}_N\}$ be given so that the span of that set is a subspace $\mathcal{T}$ of $\mathcal{S}$. Then the best approximation to $\mathbf{u}$ within $\mathcal{T}$, i.e., of the form $\mathbf{u} \approx c_1\hat{\mathbf{e}}_1 + c_2\hat{\mathbf{e}}_2 + \cdots + c_N\hat{\mathbf{e}}_N$, is given by the orthogonal projection of $\mathbf{u}$ onto $\mathcal{T}$, i.e., by $\mathbf{u} \approx \text{proj}_{\mathcal{T}}\, \mathbf{u}$.

EXAMPLE 2 Let $\mathcal{S}$ be $\mathbb{R}^6$, let $N = 4$ with

$$\begin{aligned} \hat{\mathbf{e}}_1 &= \frac{1}{\sqrt{2}}(1, -1, 0, 0, 0, 0), \\ \hat{\mathbf{e}}_2 &= \frac{1}{\sqrt{3}}(1, 1, 1, 0, 0, 0), \\ \hat{\mathbf{e}}_3 &= \frac{1}{\sqrt{7}}(1, 1, -2, 1, 0, 0), \\ \hat{\mathbf{e}}_4 &= (0, 0, 0, 0, 0, 1), \end{aligned} \tag{12}$$

and let $\mathbf{u} = (3, 0, 1, -2, 6, 4)$. Then $\mathbf{u} \cdot \hat{\mathbf{e}}_1 = 3/\sqrt{2}$, $\mathbf{u} \cdot \hat{\mathbf{e}}_2 = 4/\sqrt{3}$, $\mathbf{u} \cdot \hat{\mathbf{e}}_3 = -1/\sqrt{7}$, $\mathbf{u} \cdot \hat{\mathbf{e}}_4 = 4$, so the best approximation to $\mathbf{u}$ within the four-dimensional subspace spanned by $\hat{\mathbf{e}}_1, \hat{\mathbf{e}}_2, \hat{\mathbf{e}}_3, \hat{\mathbf{e}}_4$ is

$$\mathbf{u} \approx \text{proj}_{\mathcal{T}}\, \mathbf{u} = \frac{3}{\sqrt{2}}\hat{\mathbf{e}}_1 + \frac{4}{\sqrt{3}}\hat{\mathbf{e}}_2 - \frac{1}{\sqrt{7}}\hat{\mathbf{e}}_3 + 4\hat{\mathbf{e}}_4. \tag{13}$$

We cannot draw a picture like Fig. 10.15 in this case (except schematically), because dim $\mathcal{S} = 6 > 3$ and dim $\mathcal{T} = 4 > 3$, but we can still retain the underlying geometrical notion of orthogonal projection. ◀

FUNCTION SPACE

Next we introduce function space and establish the desired connection with Fourier series. Specifically, we choose to consider the **function space** $C_p[a, b]$ of all (real-valued) piecewise-continuous functions defined on $[a, b]$, i.e., on $a \leq x \leq b$. First, let us verify that $C_p[a, b]$ is indeed a vector space. Let $\mathbf{f} = f(x)$ and $\mathbf{g} = g(x)$ be any two functions* in $C_p[a, b]$, and let α be any (real) scalar. We define the sum $\mathbf{f} + \mathbf{g}$ and scalar multiple $\alpha\mathbf{f}$ by

$$\mathbf{f} + \mathbf{g} \equiv f(x) + g(x), \qquad \alpha\mathbf{f} \equiv \alpha f(x), \tag{14}$$

respectively. Observe that if f and g are piecewise continuous on $[a, b]$, so is $f + g$, so that $C_p[a, b]$ is closed under vector addition. Similarly, if f is piecewise continuous on $[a, b]$, so is αf, so that $C_p[a, b]$ is closed under scalar multiplication. Furthermore, we define the zero vector $\mathbf{0}$ as the function which is identically zero, so that $\mathbf{f} + \mathbf{0} = f(x) + 0 = f(x) = \mathbf{f}$. And we define the negative inverse of $\mathbf{f} = f(x)$ as $-\mathbf{f} \equiv -f(x)$, in which case we have $\mathbf{f} + (-\mathbf{f}) = f(x) + [-f(x)] = 0 = \mathbf{0}$.

With these definitions of vector addition, scalar multiplication, the zero vector, and the negative inverse, we can see that all of the requirements listed in Definition 1 on page 37 are satisfied, so that $C_p[a, b]$ is indeed a vector space.

Next, we wish to define a dot product for $C_p[a, b]$. Actually, when working with function spaces one normally uses the term **inner product** in place of the term "dot product," and the notation $\langle \mathbf{f}, \mathbf{g} \rangle$ in place of the notation $\mathbf{f} \cdot \mathbf{g}$. How shall we define $\langle \mathbf{f}, \mathbf{g} \rangle$ for $C_p[a, b]$? Looking back at the form of the "Euclidean" dot product

$$\mathbf{f} \cdot \mathbf{g} = \sum_{j=1}^{n} f_j g_j \tag{15}$$

adopted in $\mathbb{R}^n$ space, it seems reasonable to define $\langle \mathbf{f}, \mathbf{g} \rangle$ somewhat analogously as†

$$\boxed{\langle \mathbf{f}, \mathbf{g} \rangle \equiv \int_a^b f(x) g(x)\, dx.} \tag{16}$$

This is not the only possible definition of $\langle \mathbf{f}, \mathbf{g} \rangle$, nor is it the only one that is used in practice, but it is quite commonly used, it does possess the commutativity, nonnegativeness, and linearity properties listed on page 31, and it is the definition that we hereby choose to adopt.

As within the dot product terminology, we say that $\mathbf{f}$ and $\mathbf{g}$ are *orthogonal* if $\langle \mathbf{f}, \mathbf{g} \rangle = 0$, we define the *norm* $\|\mathbf{f}\|$ of $\mathbf{f}$, by means of the inner product, as

$$\boxed{\|\mathbf{f}\| = \sqrt{\langle \mathbf{f}, \mathbf{f} \rangle},} \tag{17}$$

and we say that $\mathbf{f}$ is *normalized* if $\|\mathbf{f}\| = 1$.

* By "$\mathbf{f} = f(x)$" we mean that the vector $\mathbf{f}$ is the function whose values are $f(x)$. Notation becomes a bit sticky here since there are now three quantities to be distinguished: the function f considered as a mapping, the values $f(x)$ of that function, and the vector $\mathbf{f}$.

† Recall from Section 5.2 that in the *complex* n-space $\mathbb{C}^n$ we used. $\mathbf{f} \cdot \mathbf{g} = \sum_{j=1}^{n} f_j \bar{g}_j$ in place of (15). Thus if we had not restricted ourselves to *real* vector spaces in the present section, we would have adopted $\langle \mathbf{f}, \mathbf{g} \rangle \equiv \int_a^b f(x) \bar{g}(x)\, dx$ in place of (16).

BEST APPROXIMATION IN FUNCTION SPACE

Having introduced the problem of best approximation and the function space $C_p[a, b]$, we now combine these ideas and consider the problem of best approximation within the function space $C_p[a, b]$.

Let $\mathscr{S}$ be $C_p[a, b]$, let $\{\hat{\mathbf{e}}_1, \ldots, \hat{\mathbf{e}}_N\}$ be an ON set in $\mathscr{S}$, and let $\mathbf{f} = f(x)$ be any vector in $\mathscr{S}$. Then the best approximation of $\mathbf{f}$ of the form $c_1\hat{\mathbf{e}}_1 + \cdots + c_N\hat{\mathbf{e}}_N$ is given, as we have seen, by

$$\mathbf{f} \approx \operatorname{proj}_{\mathscr{T}} \mathbf{f} \equiv \sum_{n=1}^{N} \langle \mathbf{f}, \hat{\mathbf{e}}_n \rangle \hat{\mathbf{e}}_n, \tag{18}$$

i.e., by the orthogonal projection of $\mathbf{f}$ onto the subspace $\mathscr{T} = \operatorname{span}\{\hat{\mathbf{e}}_1, \ldots, \hat{\mathbf{e}}_N\}$ of $\mathscr{S}$. Let $a = -\ell$ and $b = \ell$, and consider the vectors

$$\mathbf{e}_1 = 1, \quad \mathbf{e}_2 = \cos\frac{\pi x}{\ell}, \quad \mathbf{e}_3 = \sin\frac{\pi x}{\ell}, \quad \ldots, \quad \mathbf{e}_{2k} = \cos\frac{k\pi x}{\ell}, \quad \mathbf{e}_{2k+1} = \sin\frac{k\pi x}{\ell} \tag{19}$$

in $\mathscr{S}$. The set $\{\hat{\mathbf{e}}_1, \ldots, \hat{\mathbf{e}}_{2k+1}\}$ is orthogonal by virtue of the inner product definition (16) and the orthogonality relations (5) on page 458; for example,

$$\langle \mathbf{e}_2, \mathbf{e}_3 \rangle = \int_{-\ell}^{\ell} \cos\frac{2\pi x}{\ell} \cos\frac{3\pi x}{\ell}\, dx = 0. \tag{20}$$

Furthermore,

$$\begin{aligned}
\langle \mathbf{e}_1, \mathbf{e}_1 \rangle &= \int_{-\ell}^{\ell} (1)(1)\, dx = 2\ell, \\
\langle \mathbf{e}_2, \mathbf{e}_2 \rangle &= \int_{-\ell}^{\ell} \cos^2\frac{\pi x}{\ell}\, dx = \ell, \\
&\vdots \\
\langle \mathbf{e}_{2k+1}, \mathbf{e}_{2k+1} \rangle &= \int_{-\ell}^{\ell} \sin^2\frac{(2k+1)\pi x}{\ell}\, dx = \ell,
\end{aligned} \tag{21}$$

so that the normalized $\mathbf{e}_n$'s are

$$\begin{aligned}
\hat{\mathbf{e}}_1 &= \frac{1}{\|\mathbf{e}_1\|}\mathbf{e}_1 = \frac{1}{\sqrt{\langle \mathbf{e}_1, \mathbf{e}_1 \rangle}}\mathbf{e}_1 = \frac{1}{\sqrt{2\ell}}, \\
\hat{\mathbf{e}}_2 &= \frac{1}{\|\mathbf{e}_2\|}\mathbf{e}_2 = \frac{1}{\sqrt{\langle \mathbf{e}_2, \mathbf{e}_2 \rangle}}\mathbf{e}_2 = \frac{1}{\sqrt{\ell}}\cos\frac{\pi x}{\ell}, \\
&\vdots \\
\hat{\mathbf{e}}_{2k+1} &= \frac{1}{\sqrt{\ell}}\sin\frac{(2k+1)\pi x}{\ell}.
\end{aligned} \tag{22}$$

Now, since the set $\{\hat{\mathbf{e}}_1, \ldots, \hat{\mathbf{e}}_{2k+1}\}$ is ON it is certainly LI, and since k (and hence $2k + 1$) is arbitrarily large, it follows that we have an arbitrarily large number of LI vectors in $C_p[-\ell, \ell]$, so that $C_p[-\ell, \ell]$ is *infinite dimensional*. This is our first encounter, in this book, with an infinite-dimensional vector space.

Returning to (18), we are approximating a given $\mathbf{f} = f(x)$, in $C_p[-\ell, \ell]$, in the form

$$\begin{aligned} f(x) \approx c_1 \frac{1}{\sqrt{2\ell}} + c_2 \frac{1}{\sqrt{\ell}} \cos \frac{\pi x}{\ell} + c_3 \frac{1}{\sqrt{\ell}} \sin \frac{\pi x}{\ell} + \cdots \\ + c_{2k} \frac{1}{\sqrt{\ell}} \cos \frac{k\pi x}{\ell} + c_{2k+1} \frac{1}{\sqrt{\ell}} \sin \frac{k\pi x}{\ell}, \end{aligned} \tag{23a}$$

where

$$\begin{aligned} c_1 &= \langle \mathbf{f}, \hat{\mathbf{e}}_1 \rangle = \int_{-\ell}^{\ell} f(x) \frac{1}{\sqrt{2\ell}}\, dx = \frac{1}{\sqrt{2\ell}} \int_{-\ell}^{\ell} f(x)\, dx \\ c_2 &= \langle \mathbf{f}, \hat{\mathbf{e}}_2 \rangle = \int_{-\ell}^{\ell} f(x) \frac{1}{\sqrt{\ell}} \cos \frac{\pi x}{\ell}\, dx = \frac{1}{\sqrt{\ell}} \int_{-\ell}^{\ell} f(x) \cos \frac{\pi x}{\ell}\, dx \\ &\ \ \vdots \\ c_{2k+1} &= \langle \mathbf{f}, \hat{\mathbf{e}}_{2k+1} \rangle = \frac{1}{\sqrt{\ell}} \int_{-\ell}^{\ell} f(x) \sin \frac{k\pi x}{\ell}\, dx. \end{aligned} \tag{23b}$$

Equivalently,

$$\begin{aligned} f(x) &\approx a_0 + a_1 \cos \frac{\pi x}{\ell} + b_1 \sin \frac{\pi x}{\ell} + \cdots + a_k \cos \frac{k\pi x}{\ell} + b_k \sin \frac{k\pi x}{\ell} \\ &= a_0 + \sum_{n=1}^{k} \left(a_n \cos \frac{n\pi x}{\ell} + b_n \sin \frac{n\pi x}{\ell} \right), \end{aligned} \tag{24a}$$

where

$$\begin{aligned} a_0 &= \frac{1}{2\ell} \int_{-\ell}^{\ell} f(x)\, dx \\ a_n &= \frac{1}{\ell} \int_{-\ell}^{\ell} f(x) \cos \frac{n\pi x}{\ell}\, dx, \qquad n = 1, 2, \ldots, \\ b_n &= \frac{1}{\ell} \int_{-\ell}^{\ell} f(x) \sin \frac{n\pi x}{\ell}\, dx, \qquad n = 1, 2, \ldots . \end{aligned} \tag{24b}$$

Let us review the situation. The right-hand side of (24a) is the orthogonal projection of $\mathbf{f}$ on the (2k + 1)-dimensional subspace $\mathcal{T}$ of $C_p[-\ell, \ell]$, where $\mathcal{T}$ is the span of the ON vectors

$$\frac{1}{\sqrt{2\ell}}, \quad \frac{1}{\sqrt{\ell}} \cos \frac{\pi x}{\ell}, \quad \frac{1}{\sqrt{\ell}} \sin \frac{\pi x}{\ell}, \ldots, \frac{1}{\sqrt{\ell}} \cos \frac{k\pi x}{\ell}, \quad \frac{1}{\sqrt{\ell}} \sin \frac{k\pi x}{\ell}. \tag{25}$$

With the coefficients in (24a) equal to the familiar *Fourier coefficients*, as given in (24b), (24a) is the *best possible approximation* to $f(x)$ of the form (23a). That is, it is the "best" possible approximation *in the vector sense of minimizing the norm of the error vector*, or, equivalently, the square of the norm of the error vector

$$\left\| \mathbf{f} - \left(c_1 \frac{1}{\sqrt{2\ell}} + c_2 \frac{1}{\sqrt{\ell}} \cos \frac{\pi x}{\ell} + \cdots + c_{2k+1} \frac{1}{\sqrt{\ell}} \sin \frac{k\pi x}{\ell} \right) \right\|^2$$
$$= \int_{-\ell}^{\ell} \left[f(x) - \left(c_1 \frac{1}{\sqrt{2\ell}} + c_2 \frac{1}{\sqrt{\ell}} \cos \frac{\pi x}{\ell} + \cdots + c_{2k+1} \frac{1}{\sqrt{\ell}} \sin \frac{k\pi x}{\ell} \right) \right]^2 dx. \tag{26}$$

The integral in (26) is known as the **mean square error.*** Thus (24a) is the best possible approximation in the sense of minimizing the mean square error (26), and is said to be the **mean square approximation** (or **least squares approximation**) of $f(x)$ with respect to the ON set (25).

We can well expect the mean square error in (24a) to decrease as we increase k, but does it tend to zero as $k \to \infty$? It does.

Theorem 2 *Mean Square Convergence*

If $f(x)$ is piecewise continuous on $[-\ell, \ell]$ and $a_0, a_1, b_1, a_2, b_2, \ldots$ are the Fourier coefficients defined by (24b), then

$$f(x) = a_0 + \sum_{n=1}^{\infty} \left(a_n \cos \frac{n\pi x}{\ell} + b_n \sin \frac{n\pi x}{\ell} \right) \tag{27}$$

holds in the sense of mean square convergence, i.e.,

$$\lim_{k\to\infty} \int_{-\ell}^{\ell} \left[f(x) - a_0 - \sum_{n=1}^{k} \left(a_n \cos \frac{n\pi x}{\ell} + b_n \sin \frac{n\pi x}{\ell} \right) \right]^2 dx = 0. \tag{28}$$

Proof of this sophisticated theorem is well beyond our present scope.

It is absolutely crucial to be aware that the equality in (27) has quite a different meaning from the equality in preceding sections—for example, in (4) on page 458. For (27) holds in the mean square, or "vector" sense, as spelled out in (28), whereas (4) on page 458 holds in the **pointwise** sense, namely, that at a specific fixed value of x (at which f is continuous) we have

$$\lim_{k\to\infty} \left[a_0 + \sum_{n=1}^{k} \left(a_n \cos \frac{n\pi x}{\ell} + b_n \sin \frac{n\pi x}{\ell} \right) \right] = f(x)$$

or, getting as close to the form of (28) as possible,

$$\lim_{k\to\infty} \left[f(x) - a_0 - \sum_{n=1}^{k} \left(a_n \cos \frac{n\pi x}{\ell} + b_n \sin \frac{n\pi x}{\ell} \right) \right]^2 = 0. \tag{29}$$

In contrast with pointwise convergence, mean square convergence is a sort of "global" convergence since it involves the squared error *integrated over the whole interval*. Pointwise convergence does not imply mean square convergence, nor does mean square convergence imply pointwise convergence (see Exercise 9)! In no way do we wish to imply that one form of convergence is "better" or "more correct" than the other; they are simply different, so when we speak of convergence it is important for us to be clear as to what sort of convergence we have in mind.

* Actually, it *would* be the mean square error if it were multiplied by $1/2\ell$, but we call it the mean square error anyway.

In closing this section, we note that even though our discussion has focused on *trigonometric* mean square approximation over $[-\ell, \ell]$, the method used in general and is not limited to this case. For the sake of brevity, however, we have saved our discussion of other cases for the exercises.

10.5 EXERCISES

1. We concluded from (4) that the best choice for the c_j's is $c_j = \alpha_j = \mathbf{u} \cdot \hat{\mathbf{e}}_j$. Show that this same result is obtained by setting $\partial\|\mathbf{E}\|^2/\partial c_j = 0$ in (2). (You need not attempt to verify that the extremum thus obtained is a minimum.)

***2.** Compute the norm of the error vector, $\|\mathbf{E}\|$, corresponding to the best approximation (13).

3. Let $\mathcal{S}$ be $\mathbb{R}^5$, and let $N = 3$ with $\hat{\mathbf{e}}_1 = (1/\sqrt{5})(1, 0, 2, 0, 0)$, $\hat{\mathbf{e}}_2 = (1/\sqrt{6})(2, 0, -1, 0, 1)$, $\hat{\mathbf{e}}_3 = (0, 0, 0, 1, 0)$. Find the best approximation to $\mathbf{u}$ within span $\{\hat{\mathbf{e}}_1, \hat{\mathbf{e}}_2, \hat{\mathbf{e}}_3\}$, and the norm $\|\mathbf{E}\|$ of the error vector.

*(a) $\mathbf{u} = (3, -2, 0, 0, 5)$ (b) $\mathbf{u} = (0, 0, 0, 2, 1)$
(c) $\mathbf{u} = (3, 0, 1, 4, 1)$ (d) $\mathbf{u} = (1, 1, 0, 1, 1)$
(e) $\mathbf{u} = (0, 2, 0, 0, 0)$ (f) $\mathbf{u} = (1, 0, -3, 3, 1)$

4. Let $\mathcal{S}$ be $\mathbb{R}^4$, and let

$\hat{\mathbf{e}}_1 = (1/\sqrt{3})(1, 1, 0, -1)$,
$\hat{\mathbf{e}}_2 = (1/\sqrt{3})(1, -1, -1, 0)$,
$\hat{\mathbf{e}}_3 = (1/\sqrt{3})(1, 0, 1, 1)$, and
$\hat{\mathbf{e}}_4 = (1/\sqrt{3})(0, 1, -1, 1)$.

Find the best approximations to $\mathbf{u} = (4, -2, 1, 6)$ within span $\{\hat{\mathbf{e}}_1\}$, span $\{\hat{\mathbf{e}}_1, \hat{\mathbf{e}}_2\}$, span $\{\hat{\mathbf{e}}_1, \hat{\mathbf{e}}_2, \hat{\mathbf{e}}_3\}$, and span $\{\hat{\mathbf{e}}_1, \hat{\mathbf{e}}_2, \hat{\mathbf{e}}_3, \hat{\mathbf{e}}_4\}$, and in each case, compute the norm $\|\mathbf{E}\|$ of the error vector.

5. Repeat Exercise 4, but for

*(a) $\mathbf{u} = (4, 1, 0, -1)$ (b) $\mathbf{u} = (3, -1, 1, 2)$
(c) $\mathbf{u} = (0, 0, 2, 5)$ (d) $\mathbf{u} = (1, 2, 4, 4)$
(e) $\mathbf{u} = (0, 5, 3, -1)$ (f) $\mathbf{u} = (2, 0, -1, -1)$

6. Let $f(x)$ be piecewise continuous on $[-\ell, \ell]$, and let $a_0, a_1, b_1, a_2, b_2, \ldots$ be the Fourier coefficients of f defined by (24b). Then show that for the approximation

$$f(x) \approx a_0 + \sum_{n=1}^{k} \left(a_n \cos\frac{n\pi x}{\ell} + b_n \sin\frac{n\pi x}{\ell}\right) \quad \text{(a)}$$

(6) becomes

$$\|\mathbf{E}\|^2 = \int_{-\ell}^{\ell} [f(x)]^2\,dx - \ell\left[2a_0^2 + \sum_{n=1}^{k}(a_n^2 + b_n^2)\right] \ge 0, \quad \text{(b)}$$

so that **Bessel's inequality** (7) assumes the more specific form

$$2a_0^2 + \sum_{n=1}^{k}(a_n^2 + b_n^2) \le \frac{1}{\ell}\int_{-\ell}^{\ell}[f(x)]^2\,dx, \quad \text{(c)}$$

which holds for each $k = 1, 2, \ldots$. Noting, from Theorem 2, that $\|\mathbf{E}\| \to 0$ as $k \to \infty$, show that (c) becomes

$$2a_0^2 + \sum_{n=1}^{\infty}(a_n^2 + b_n^2 = \frac{1}{\ell}\int_{-\ell}^{\ell}[f(x)]^2\,dx, \quad \text{(d)}$$

which is known as the **Parseval equality,** and which is a sort of infinite-dimensional function space version of the familiar Pythagorean theorem.

7. Recalling from Exercise 6 that

$$\|\mathbf{E}\|^2 = \int_{-\ell}^{\ell}[f(x)]^2\,dx - \ell\left[2a_0^2 + \sum_{n=1}^{k}(a_n^2 + b_n^2)\right], \quad \text{(a)}$$

compute $\|\mathbf{E}\|$ for $k = 1, 2, 3, 4, 5, 6$, where

*(a) $f(x) = |x|$
(b) $f(x) = x$
(c) $f(x) = \cos^2 x$
(d) $f(x) = \begin{cases} 1, & 0 \le x \le \ell \\ 0, & -\ell \le x < 0 \end{cases}$
(e) $f(x) = \begin{cases} x, & 0 < x \le \ell \\ 0, & -\ell \le x \le 0 \end{cases}$
(f) $f(x) = \begin{cases} 100, & -\ell \le x \le \ell/2 \\ 50, & \ell/2 < x \le \ell \end{cases}$
(g) $f(x) = x^2$ (h) $f(x) = |\sin x|$

8. Let f and g both be members of $C_p[-\ell, \ell]$, and let $f(x) = g(x)$ on $[-\ell, \ell]$ except at a finite number of points, at which $f(x) \ne g(x)$. Show that $\mathbf{f} = \mathbf{g}$ in spite of these pointwise differences; i.e., show that $\|\mathbf{f} - \mathbf{g}\| = 0$, so that within the vector space framework $\mathbf{f}$ and $\mathbf{g}$ are indistinguishable.

9. (*Mean square convergence; pointwise convergence*) Just below (29) we stated that mean square convergence and pointwise convergence are independent: The truth of (29) does not imply the truth of (28) or vice versa. To illustrate this idea simply, let us consider, in place of the messy $[\ ]^2$ quantity in (28) and (29), the sequence $F_k(x)$ defined below.

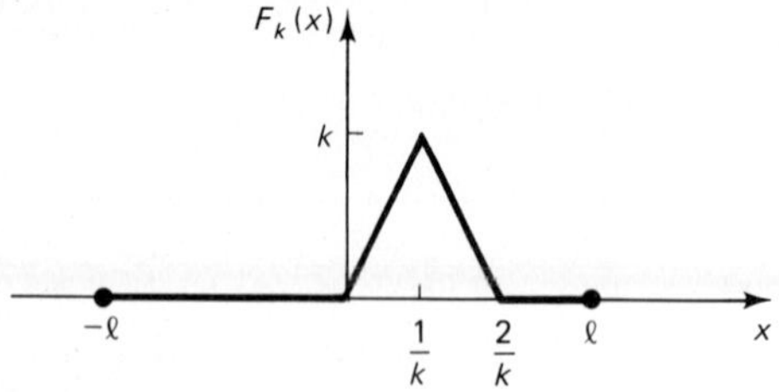

(a) Let $F_k(x)$ be as shown below. Observe that as k increases the "mountain" becomes taller and narrower. Show that

$$\lim_{k\to\infty} F_k(x) = 0 \quad \text{on} \quad [-\ell, \ell],$$

whereas

$$\lim_{k\to\infty} \int_{-\ell}^{\ell} F_k(x)\, dx = 1 \neq 0.$$

(b) With $F_k(x)$ as shown below, show that

$$\lim_{k\to\infty} \int_{-\ell}^{\ell} F_k(x)\, dx = 0,$$

whereas

$$\lim_{k\to\infty} F_k(x) = \begin{cases} 0, & x \neq 0 \\ 1, & x = 0 \end{cases} \neq 0.$$

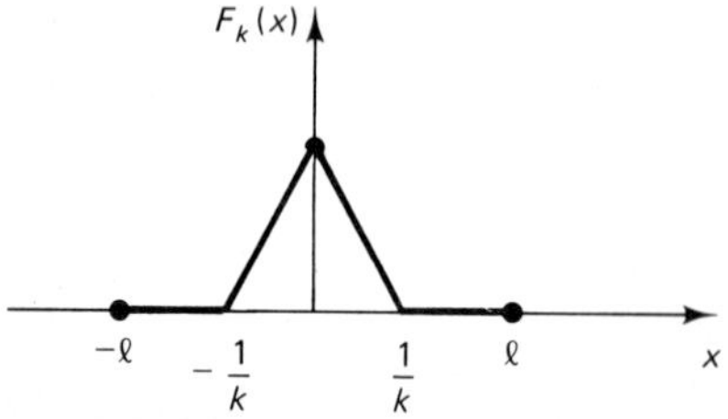

(c) Let $F_k(x)$ be the same as in part (b), except that the height of the "mountain" is $1/k$ instead of 1. Show that in this case *both* limits are zero.

Moral: The statements $\lim_{k\to\infty} \int_{-\ell}^{\ell} F_k(x)\, dx = 0$ and $\lim_{k\to\infty} F_k(x) = 0$ on $[-\ell, \ell]$ are *independent;* the truth of one does not imply the truth of the other.

In the text we considered the function space $C_p[-\ell, \ell]$ and the ON vectors given in (25). In the exercises to follow we apply the technique of mean square approximation to some other cases. The Gram–Schmidt process, which is required in some of the exercises, was given in Exercise 11 on page 56.

10. Here we consider $C_p[0, \ell]$.

(a) Show that the set $\{\sqrt{2/\ell} \sin(\pi x/\ell), \ldots, \sqrt{2/\ell} \sin(k\pi x/\ell)\}$ is ON. *Note:* In (16), $a = 0$ and $b = \ell$.

(b) Using the ON set in part (a), show that the mean square approximation (18) becomes

$$f(x) \approx b_1 \sin\frac{\pi x}{\ell} + b_2 \sin\frac{2\pi x}{\ell} + \cdots + b_k \sin\frac{k\pi x}{\ell}, \tag{a}$$

where

$$b_n = \frac{2}{\ell}\int_0^{\ell} f(x) \sin\frac{n\pi x}{\ell}\, dx, \quad n = 1, 2, \ldots, k. \tag{b}$$

11. Here we consider $C_p[0, \ell]$.

(a) Show that the set $\{1/\sqrt{\ell}, \sqrt{2/\ell} \cos(\pi x/\ell), \ldots, \sqrt{2/\ell} \cos(k\pi x/\ell)\}$ is ON. *Note:* In (16), $a = 0$ and $b = \ell$.

(b) Using the ON set in part (a), show that the mean square approximation (18) becomes

$$f(x) \approx a_0 + a_1 \cos\frac{\pi x}{\ell} + a_2 \cos\frac{2\pi x}{\ell} + \cdots + a_k \cos\frac{k\pi x}{\ell}, \tag{a}$$

where

$$a_0 = \frac{1}{\ell}\int_0^{\ell} f(x)\, dx$$

$$a_n = \frac{2}{\ell}\int_0^{\ell} f(x) \cos\frac{n\pi x}{\ell}\, dx, \quad n = 1, 2, \ldots, k. \tag{b}$$

12. (*Polynomial approximation*) We consider $C_p[-1, 1]$ and mean square approximations of the form $f(x) \approx c_0 + c_1 x + c_2 x^2 + \cdots c_k x^k$. For simplicity, we will choose $k = 2$. *Note:* In (16), $a = -1$ and $b = 1$.

(a) Use the Gram–Schmidt process (Exercise 12, Section 2.9) to obtain from the LI set $\{1, x, x^2\}$ the ON set

$$\hat{\mathbf{e}}_1 = \frac{1}{\sqrt{2}}, \qquad \hat{\mathbf{e}}_2 = \sqrt{\frac{3}{2}}x, \qquad \hat{\mathbf{e}}_3 = \sqrt{\frac{5}{8}}(3x^2 - 1). \tag{a}$$

Note: If, instead of normalizing these vectors, we scaled them so as to equal unity at $x = 1$, we would have obtained the first three **Legendre polynomials** $P_0(x) = 1$, $P_1(x) = x$, $P_2(x) = \frac{3}{2}x^2 - \frac{1}{2}$.

(b) Using the ON set (a) show that the mean square approximation (18) becomes

$$f(x) \approx a_1 + a_2 x + a_3(3x^2 - 1), \tag{b}$$

where

$$a_1 = \frac{1}{2}\int_{-1}^{1} f(x)\,dx, \qquad a_2 = \frac{3}{2}\int_{-1}^{1} xf(x)\,dx, \qquad a_3 = \frac{5}{8}\int_{-1}^{1} (3x^2 - 1)f(x)\,dx. \tag{c}$$

*(c) Evaluate a_1, a_2, a_3 for the case where $f(x) = |x|$, and plot the left- and right-hand sides of equation (b) over $[-1, 1]$.

(d) Repeat part (c), for $f(x) = e^x$.

(e) Repeat part (c), for $f(x) = e^{-x}$.

(f) Repeat part (c), for $f(x) = \sin x$.

(g) Repeat part (c), for $f(x) = \cos x$.

(h) Repeat part (c), for $f(x) = x^3$.

THE STURM–LIOUVILLE THEORY 10.6

Optional Section

Recall from Section 10.3 that every (sufficiently well behaved) function $f(x)$ that is periodic with period 2ℓ can be expanded in a Fourier series, i.e., as a linear combination of the functions (or "vectors," depending on one's viewpoint) 1, $\cos(\pi x/\ell)$, $\sin(\pi x/\ell)$, $\cos(2\pi x/\ell)$, $\sin(2\pi x/\ell)$, ... Similarly for functions defined only on finite intervals such as $[-\ell, \ell]$ or $(0, \ell)$. It is natural to wonder where the remarkable set $\{1, \cos(\pi x/\ell), \sin(\pi x/\ell), \ldots\}$ "comes from" and whether there are other such sets that can be used to expand a given function over a given interval. It is with these questions in mind that we now consider the "Sturm–Liouville theory," our principal application of which will be in the *solution of partial differential equations by the method of separation of variables,* as discussed in Part IV. In that connection we will find that the classical sine and cosine Fourier series *often* suffices, but not always. As collateral reading for this section we recommend Chap. 11 of BOYCE AND DIPRIMA.

We assume here a general familiarity with the eigenvalue problem of matrix theory, as discussed in Part I, as well as a knowledge of the simple arithmetic properties of complex numbers.

Here, too, we are concerned with eigenvalue problems, but this time the operators are differential operators rather than matrix operators. To ease our way into the Sturm–Liouville theory, we begin with a simple introductory example.

EXAMPLE 1 Consider the problem

$$y'' + \lambda y = 0, \qquad (0 < x < \ell) \tag{1a}$$

$$y(0) = 0, \qquad y(\ell) = 0, \tag{1b}$$

where λ is a constant that is not known in advance. Certainly, $y(x) = 0$ is a solution of (1), but our interest will lie in the *nontrivial* solutions (if any) of (1). We call (1) an *eigenvalue problem;* the values of λ that permit nontrivial solutions of

(1) are called *eigenvalues,* or characteristic values, and the corresponding nontrivial solutions are called *eigenfunctions,* or characteristic functions.

If we note that $y(x) = 0$ is a solution of (1), and recall notions of uniqueness (Section A. 3 of Appendix A), we may wonder how (1) can possibly admit *non*trivial solutions, i.e., solutions other than $y(x) = 0$. The point is that the uniqueness theorem in Section A.3 is for *initial-value problems,* i.e., problems in which all of the data are at one endpoint of the interval, such as the problem

$$y'' + \lambda y = 0, \qquad (0 < x < \ell) \tag{2a}$$

$$y(0) = 0, \qquad y'(0) = 0. \tag{2b}$$

Our problem (1), however, is not an initial-value problem because the conditions (1b) are prescribed at *different points;* thus we call it a *boundary value problem.*

To see if (1) admits nontrivial solutions, let us not be intimidated by the fact that (1) is a mysterious "eigenvalue problem." After all, (1a) is a simple differential equation. Its general solution is*

$$y(x) = \begin{cases} A \cos \sqrt{\lambda}\, x + B \sin \sqrt{\lambda}\, x & \text{if } \lambda \neq 0 \quad (3a) \\ C + Dx & \text{if } \lambda = 0. \quad (3b) \end{cases}$$

Treating the cases $\lambda = 0$ and $\lambda \neq 0$ separately, let us first consider the case $\lambda = 0$. Applying the boundary conditions (1b) to $y(x) = C + Dx$ gives

$$\begin{aligned} y(0) &= 0 = C \\ y(\ell) &= 0 = C + D\ell. \end{aligned} \tag{4}$$

Thus $C = D = 0$ so the *only* solution corresponding to $\lambda = 0$ is the trivial solution $y(x) = 0$; i.e., $\lambda = 0$ is not an eigenvalue of (1). Turning to the case $\lambda \neq 0$, application of (1b) to (3a) gives

$$y(0) = 0 = A \tag{5a}$$

$$y(\ell) = 0 = A \cos \sqrt{\lambda}\, \ell + B \sin \sqrt{\lambda}\, \ell. \tag{5b}$$

Since $A = 0$, (5*b*) tells us that $B \sin \sqrt{\lambda}\, \ell = 0$ so that either $B = 0$, or $\sin \sqrt{\lambda}\, \ell = 0$ and B is arbitrary. We rule out the choice $B = 0$ since then we would have $A = B = 0$ and hence the trivial solution $y(x) = 0$. Thus B is arbitrary and

$$\sin \sqrt{\lambda}\, \ell = 0. \tag{6}$$

Solving (6), we have $\sqrt{\lambda}\, \ell = n\pi$ for $n = 0, \pm 1, \pm 2, \ldots$. Of these values, $n = 0$ can be discarded because it gives $\lambda = 0$, whereas we are now considering

* Surely, (3a) is the general solution of (2a) if $\lambda < 0$, but is it the general solution if $\lambda < 0$? Should we not have a cosh and a sinh in that case? Well, if $\lambda < 0$, then (3a) becomes $y(x) = A \cos (i \sqrt{|\lambda|}\, x) + B \sin (i \sqrt{|\lambda|}\, x) = A \cosh (\sqrt{|\lambda|}\, x) + iB \sinh (\sqrt{|\lambda|}\, x)$, where the last equality follows from equations (10a) and (10b) of Section A.5. Thus we do have an arbitrary linear combination of $\cosh (\sqrt{|\lambda|}\, x)$ and $\sinh (\sqrt{|\lambda|}\, x)$, as we should, so there is no need to break the case $\lambda \neq 0$ into the two separate cases $\lambda < 0$ and $\lambda > 0$ (although some authors choose to do that). In fact, (3a) holds even if λ is allowed to be complex, but we will soon see that within the Sturm–Liouville theory, λ is always real.

the case (3a), where $\lambda \neq 0$. Thus we have the eigenfunctions

$$y(x) = B \sin \frac{n\pi x}{\ell} \tag{7}$$

where B is arbitrary and $n = \pm 1, \pm 2, \ldots$. We now see that the negative values of n can be discarded as well, since the positive and negative values of n do not lead to distinct (i.e., linearly independent) eigenfunctions. For example, $n = +2$ gives $\sin(2\pi x/\ell)$, whereas $n = -2$ gives $\sin(-2\pi x/\ell) = -\sin(2\pi x/\ell)$, and since the scale factor B is arbitrary it can absorb the difference in sign. Let us set $B = 1$, for definiteness.

Thus we have an infinite set of eigenvalues and eigenfunctions:

$$\lambda_n = \frac{n^2\pi^2}{\ell^2}, \tag{8a}$$

$$\phi_n(x) = \sin \frac{n\pi x}{\ell}, \tag{8b}$$

for $n = 1, 2, \ldots$, where we use the symbol ϕ_n for the nth eigenfunction.

We will see that (1) is an example of a "Sturm–Liouville problem." Certain features found in this example will be seen to be common to *all* Sturm–Liouville problems. For example, there are an infinite number of eigenvalues and eigenfunctions; the eigenvalues and eigenfunctions are all real; the set $\{\phi_n(x)\}$ is orthogonal (as will be explained below); the eigenvalues are *simple,* i.e., to each eigenvalue there corresponds only *one* linearly independent eigenfunction. And most important, an essentially arbitrary function f, defined on the interval $(0, \ell)$, can be represented in the form

$$f(x) = \sum_{n=1}^{\infty} c_n\phi_n(x) = \sum_{n=1}^{\infty} c_n \sin \frac{n\pi x}{\ell}, \tag{9}$$

i.e., as a linear combination of the eigenfunctions. We call (9) an *eigenfunction expansion.* In this example our eigenfunction expansion is "old hat"; it is a Fourier sine series, as discussed in Example 5 on page 468. In other Sturm–Liouville problems the eigenfunction expansions may *not* be old hat.

COMMENT Although the solution of (5) was quite simple, it may be helpful to recast it in a form that renders the connection with the *matrix* case ($\mathbf{Ax} = \lambda\mathbf{x}$) more apparent. Reexpressing (5) as

$$\begin{pmatrix} 1 & 0 \\ \cos\sqrt{\lambda}\,\ell & \sin\sqrt{\lambda}\,\ell \end{pmatrix}\begin{pmatrix} A \\ B \end{pmatrix} = \begin{pmatrix} 0 \\ 0 \end{pmatrix}, \tag{10}$$

we see that we have a nontrivial solution of (10) [and hence of (1)] if and only if the determinant of the coefficient matrix is zero:

$$\begin{vmatrix} 1 & 0 \\ \cos\sqrt{\lambda}\,\ell & \sin\sqrt{\lambda}\,\ell \end{vmatrix} = \sin\sqrt{\lambda}\,\ell = 0. \tag{11}$$

[Of course, (11) is the same as (6).] As in the matrix case, (11) is called the *characteristic equation* corresponding to the eigenvalue problem (1). Whereas in the matrix case the characteristic equation is always algebraic (i.e., a polynomial in λ equal to zero), with a finite number of roots, in the Sturm–Liouville case it will always be *transcendental,* with an infinite number of roots. In the present example the transcendental equation (11) was solved by inspection; in other cases that may be impossible, and we may need to resort to numerical or graphical methods of solution. ◀

We stated Example 1 in purely mathematical terms. In applications, the eigenvalues and eigenfunctions will often be of considerable physical interest, as we now illustrate.

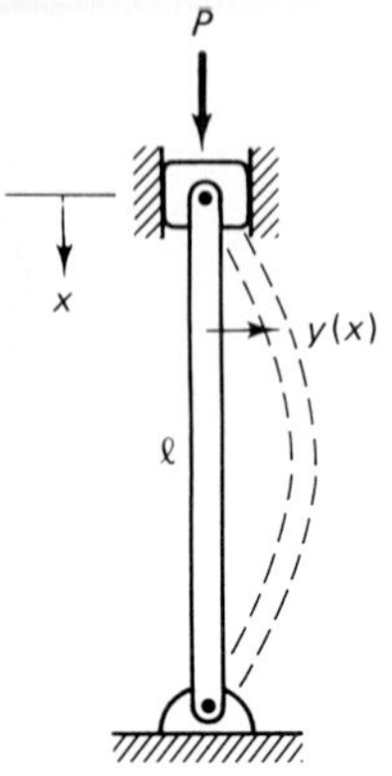

Fig. 10.16 Column buckling.

EXAMPLE 2 *Buckling of a Column.* A classical problem in structural mechanics is the determination of the *buckling load* of a given structure. For example, consider the column shown in Fig. 10.16, which is of length ℓ, which is pinned at both ends and which is subjected to a load P. Experience tells us that as we increase P nothing happens, i.e., the column remains essentially straight, until a certain value of P is reached, which we call the critical load or the *buckling load* and which we denote as P_{cr}. Under the application of that load, the column "bows" out (dashed curve in Fig. 10.16) and may collapse. Clearly, it is important to be able to predict the critical load P_{cr}. To do so, we note (without derivation) that it follows from *Euler beam theory** that the lateral deflection $y(x)$ is governed by the boundary value problem

$$EIy'' + Py = 0, \qquad (0 < x < \ell) \tag{12a}$$

$$y(0) = 0, \qquad y(\ell) = 0, \tag{12b}$$

where E and I are physical constants of the column; E is Young's modulus of the material and I is a cross-sectional inertia. In fact, (12) is identical to (1), where $\lambda = P/EI$. Now, surely $y(x) = 0$ satisfies (12), but that solution is of no interest since we are interested in the buckling of the column. From Example 1 we recall that *non*trivial solutions occur for $\lambda = P/EI = \pi^2/\ell^2, 4\pi^2/\ell^2, 9\pi^2/\ell^2, \ldots$. The smallest of these, $P/EI = \pi^2/\ell^2$, gives the **critical buckling load**

$$P_{cr} = \frac{\pi^2 EI}{\ell^2},$$

and the corresponding eigenfunction, $\sin(\pi x/\ell)$, gives (to within an arbitrary scale factor) the shape of the corresponding *buckling mode;* the formula $P_{cr} = \pi^2 EI/\ell^2$ was published by Euler in 1757.

COMMENT 1 The Euler beam theory holds only for small deflections, but that is no drawback here since we are looking for the inception of buckling, not its entire history.

COMMENT 2 In this example only the first eigenvalue and eigenfunction are of interest because as we increase P from zero, the column buckles when we reach the first eigenvalue, $\lambda = P/EI = \pi^2/\ell^2$; the higher buckling modes, corresponding to

* See, for example, S. Timoshenko, *Strength of Materials,* Part I (Princeton, N.J.: D. Van Nostrand, 1955).

$\lambda = P/EI = 4\pi^2/\ell^2, 9\pi^2/\ell^2, \ldots$, are not observed in practice. In other examples, however, *all* of the eigenvalues and eigenfunctions may be of interest. For example, we will see in Part IV that in general the vibration of a plucked violin string includes an infinity of frequencies (eigenvalues) and mode shapes (eigenfunctions).

COMMENT 3 Observe that the buckling load P_{cr} decreases very rapidly with ℓ, namely, as $1/\ell^2$. If you have had any practice at breaking rulers and yardsticks, this result will seem quite reasonable. ◀

The Sturm-Liouville theory, to which we now turn, amounts to a generalization of Example 1. Specifically, *the linear second-order boundary value problem*

$$[p(x)y']' + q(x)y + \lambda r(x)y = 0, \qquad (a < x < b) \tag{13a}$$

$$\alpha y(a) + \beta y'(a) = 0, \qquad \gamma y(b) + \delta y'(b) = 0, \tag{13b}$$

where a, b are finite, where p, p', q, r are continuous on [a, b], where p(x) > 0 and r(x) > 0 on [a, b], where α, β are not both zero, where γ, δ are not both zero, and where a, b, p(x), q(x), r(x) α, β, γ, δ are all real, is known as a ***Sturm–Liouville problem***.*

Such eigenvalue problems arise in a great many applications, sometimes, directly, as in Example 2, and sometimes less directly, as generally occurs in solving the various partial differential equations of mathematical physics by the method of "separation of variables," as we shall see in Part IV. We should emphasize that eigenvalue problems do arise which are *not* of Sturm–Liouville type—for example, problems involving higher-order differential equations, nonlinear differential equations, and so on. In many of those cases there is no well-developed theory, like the Sturm–Liouville theory, to guide us. Fortunately, though, a great many of the eigenvalue problems that we encounter are indeed of Sturm–Liouville type.

Our presentation of the theory will involve several important theorems, and to prepare for those theorems we define an "**inner product**" $\langle u, v\rangle$ of two functions u and v defined on the interval $[a, b]$ as

$$\langle u, v\rangle \equiv \int_a^b u(x)\bar{v}(x)r(x)\,dx, \tag{14}$$

where r is the same r as in (13a), and the overhead bar denotes the complex conjugate. (Actually, the functions with which we deal will turn out to be real-valued, but we are not yet in a position to know that; see Exercise 12.) We call r the *weight function,* so that (14) defines the inner product of u and v "with respect to the weight function r." If the weight function $r(x)$ is unity, then (14) is the function space analog of the dot product

*The theory presented in this section was discovered by *Charles Sturm* (1803–1855) and *Joseph Liouville* (1809–1882), and published in 1836–1837. Sturm, a professor of mechanics at the Sorbonne, became involved in this work as an outgrowth of his studies of the partial differential equation governing the flow of heat in a bar of nonuniform density. He was soon joined in this work by his friend Liouville, who was a professor of mathematics at the Collège de France and who is also well known for his work on complex variable theory and on transcendental numbers. Note the spelling Liouville (not Louisville), and the pronunciation lē-oo͞'vil (not lo͞o'ē-vil).

$$\mathbf{u}\cdot\mathbf{v} \equiv \sum_{j=1}^{n} u_n\overline{v}_n \tag{15}$$

defined (on page 201) for complex n-space, and if, in addition, all quantities are real (in which case the overhead bar can be dropped), then (14) is the analog of the dot product

$$\mathbf{u}\cdot\mathbf{v} \equiv \sum_{j=1}^{n} u_n v_n \tag{16}$$

defined (on page 29) for real n-space.

It is easy to show (Exercise 10), from definition (14), that if α is any scalar, then

$$\langle \alpha u, v\rangle = \alpha\langle u, v\rangle \tag{17a}$$

and

$$\langle u, \alpha v\rangle = \overline{\alpha}\langle u, v\rangle. \tag{17b}$$

Finally, extending our n-space terminology to the present case, we say that u and v are **orthogonal** if $\langle u, v\rangle = 0$, and we define the **norm** of u as $\|u\| = \sqrt{\langle u, u\rangle}$. If u is scaled so that $\|u\| = 1$, then u is said to be **normalized.**

As an additional bit of useful terminology, let us define L as the differential operator

$$L = -\frac{1}{r}\left[\frac{d}{dx}\left(p\frac{d}{dx}\right) + q\right] \tag{18}$$

on the set of twice-differentiable functions defined on $a < x < b$ and satisfying the boundary conditions (13b). With this notation, (13a) is simply $Ly = \lambda y$, analogous to the matrix eigenvalue problem, $\mathbf{Ax} = \lambda\mathbf{x}$, studied in Chapter 4.

To derive an important identity due to Lagrange, we consider the inner product

$$\begin{aligned}\langle Lu, v\rangle &= \int_a^b -\frac{1}{r}[(pu')' + qu]\,\overline{v}r\,dx \\ &= \int_a^b -[(pu')' + qu]\,\overline{v}\,dx,\end{aligned} \tag{19}$$

where u, v are any two twice-differentiable functions defined on $[a, b]$ and satisfying the boundary conditions (13b). The idea will be to integrate the $(pu')'\overline{v}$ term by parts twice so as to get the primes "off of u's back" and onto $\overline{v}$, and to leave the undifferentiated term $qu\overline{v}$ alone. Thus

$$\begin{aligned}\langle Lu, v\rangle &= \int_a^b -[(pu')' + qu]\,\overline{v}\,dx \\ &= -(pu'\overline{v})\Big|_a^b + \int_a^b [(p\overline{v}')u' - qu\overline{v}]\,dx \\ &= [p(u\overline{v}' - u'\overline{v})]\Big|_a^b - \int_a^b [(p\overline{v}')' + q\overline{v}]u\,dx.\end{aligned} \tag{20}$$

We will now show that $u\overline{v}' - u'\overline{v}$ vanishes at the endpoints a, b, so that the boundary term in (20) drops out. Consider the endpoint $x = b$. Since u, v have been assumed to satisfy the boundary conditions (13b), we have $\gamma u(b) + \delta u'(b) = 0$ and $\gamma v(b) + \delta v'(b) = 0$. If $\gamma \neq 0$, these equations can be expressed as

$$u(b) = -\frac{\delta}{\gamma}u'(b), \tag{21a}$$

$$v(b) = -\frac{\delta}{\gamma}v'(b), \tag{21b}$$

or, taking the complex conjugate of both sides of (21b) and recalling that δ, γ are real, (21b) becomes

$$\overline{v}(b) = -\frac{\delta}{\gamma}\overline{v}'(b). \tag{21c}$$

Using (21a) and (21c) gives us

$$u(b)\overline{v}'(b) - u'(b)\overline{v}(b) = -\frac{\delta}{\gamma}u'(b)\overline{v}'(b) - u'(b)\left[-\frac{\delta}{\gamma}\overline{v}'(b)\right] = 0. \tag{22}$$

In deriving (22) we supposed that $\gamma \neq 0$, so that we could divide by γ. If γ *does* equal zero, the second member of (13b) becomes $y'(b) = 0$. Since u and v are to satisfy this condition, we have $u'(b) = 0$, $v'(b) = 0$, and hence $\overline{v}'(b) = 0$, so that

$$u(b)\overline{v}'(b) - u'(b)\overline{v}(b) = 0 - 0 = 0 \tag{23}$$

once again. Similarly, we find that $u(a)\overline{v}'(a) - u'(a)\overline{v}(a) = 0$, so that the boundary term in (20) does drop out, as claimed, and (20) becomes

$$\begin{aligned}\langle Lu, v\rangle &= 0 - \int_a^b [(p\overline{v}')' + q\overline{v}]u\,dx \\ &= \int_a^b -\frac{1}{r}[(p\overline{v}')' + q\overline{v}]ur\,dx \\ &= \int_a^b u\,\overline{Lv}\,r\,dx = \langle u, Lv\rangle.\end{aligned} \tag{24}$$

Thus we have established **Lagrange's identity,**

$$\boxed{\langle Lu, v\rangle = \langle u, Lv\rangle,} \tag{25}$$

which will be used in proving the Sturm–Liouville theorems to follow.

> ***Theorem 1*** *Real Eigenvalues*
> All of the eigenvalues of the Sturm–Liouville problem (13) are real.

Proof Let λ be any eigenvalue of (13), and let ϕ be its corresponding eigenfunction. Thus

$$L\phi = \lambda\phi. \tag{26}$$

It follows from (26) and (17) that

$$\langle L\phi, \phi\rangle = \langle \lambda\phi, \phi\rangle = \lambda\langle \phi, \phi\rangle = \lambda\|\phi\|^2, \tag{27a}$$

and that

$$\langle \phi, L\phi\rangle = \langle \phi, \lambda\phi\rangle = \bar{\lambda}\langle \phi, \phi\rangle = \bar{\lambda}\|\phi\|^2. \tag{27b}$$

Subtracting (27b) from (27a), we have $\langle L\phi, \phi\rangle - \langle \phi, L\phi\rangle = (\lambda - \bar{\lambda})\|\phi\|^2$. But $\langle L\phi, \phi\rangle - \langle \phi, L\phi\rangle = 0$ according to (25), so that

$$0 = (\lambda - \bar{\lambda})\|\phi\|^2. \tag{28}$$

Finally, $\|\phi\| \neq 0$ since ϕ is an eigenfunction, so $0 = \lambda - \bar{\lambda}$ and hence $\bar{\lambda} = \lambda$. Thus λ is necessarily real, as was to be shown. ■

> ***Theorem 2*** *Orthogonality of Eigenfunctions*
>
> Eigenfunctions corresponding to distinct eigenvalues of the Sturm–Liouville problem (13) are orthogonal.

Proof Let ϕ_j and ϕ_k be eigenfunctions corresponding to distinct eigenvalues λ_j and λ_k, respectively. Thus

$$L\phi_j = \lambda_j\phi_j \tag{29a}$$

and

$$L\phi_k = \lambda_k\phi_k. \tag{29b}$$

Taking the inner product of ϕ_k with both sides of (29a),

$$\langle \phi_k, L\phi_j\rangle = \langle \phi_k, \lambda_j\phi_j\rangle = \bar{\lambda}_j\langle \phi_k, \phi_j\rangle, \tag{30a}$$

and taking the inner product of both sides of (29b) with ϕ_j,

$$\langle L\phi_k, \phi_j\rangle = \langle \lambda_k\phi_k, \phi_j\rangle = \lambda_k\langle \phi_k, \phi_j\rangle. \tag{30b}$$

Subtracting (30b) from (30a) yields

$$\langle L\phi_k, \phi_j\rangle - \langle \phi_k, L\phi_j\rangle = (\lambda_k - \bar{\lambda}_j)\langle \phi_k, \phi_j\rangle. \tag{31}$$

The left-hand side of (31) is zero by virtue of (25), and $\bar{\lambda}_j = \lambda_j$ virtue of Theorem 1, so (31) becomes

$$0 = (\lambda_k - \lambda_j)\langle \phi_k, \phi_j\rangle. \tag{32}$$

Finally, $\lambda_k - \lambda_j \neq 0$ since λ_k and λ_j have been assumed to be distinct eigenvalues, so (32) gives $\langle \phi_k, \phi_j\rangle = 0$; i.e., the eigenfunctions corresponding to distinct eigenvalues are orthogonal, as was to be proved. ■

> ***Theorem 3*** *Simple Eigenvalues*
>
> All of the eigenvalues of the Sturm–Liouville problem (13) are simple; i.e., there is only one linearly independent eigenfunction corresponding to each eigenvalue.

Proof Suppose that ϕ_1 and ϕ_2 are two eigenfunctions corresponding to an eigenvalue λ of (13), and suppose that $\alpha \neq 0$ in (13b). Then the Wronskian $W(x)$ of ϕ_1 and ϕ_2, evaluated at $x = a$, is

$$W(a) = \begin{vmatrix} \phi_1(a) & \phi_2(a) \\ \phi_1'(a) & \phi_2'(a) \end{vmatrix} = \begin{vmatrix} -\frac{\beta}{\alpha}\phi_1'(a) & -\frac{\beta}{\alpha}\phi_2'(a) \\ \phi_1'(a) & \phi_2'(a) \end{vmatrix} = 0. \tag{33}$$

On the other hand, if α does equal zero in (13b), then (13b) becomes $y'(0) = 0$, so

$$W(a) = \begin{vmatrix} \phi_1(a) & \phi_2(a) \\ \phi_1'(a) & \phi_2'(a) \end{vmatrix} = \begin{vmatrix} \phi_1(a) & \phi_2(a) \\ 0 & 0 \end{vmatrix} = 0$$

once again.

Now, from Abel's formula [equation (5) on page 885],

$$W(x) = W(a)e^{-\int_a^x (p'/p)dx} = W(a)\frac{p(a)}{p(x)}, \tag{34}$$

and since $p(a)/p(x)$ is finite on $[a, b]$ it follows from (33) and (34) that $W(x) \equiv 0$ on $[a, b]$. Then, from Theorem 3 on page 882 it follows that ϕ_1 and ϕ_2 must be linearly dependent on $[a, b]$. And surely, if we cannot find *two* linearly independent eigenfunctions corresponding to λ, we cannot possibly find *more* than two. But we can certainly find *one* because otherwise λ would not be an eigenvalue as assumed. Thus to each eigenvalue λ of (13) there corresponds only one linearly independent eigenfunction, as was to be proved. ■

Notice that we have tacitly assumed that the Sturm–Liouville problem does indeed *have* eigenvalues. (See Exercise 4 for an example of an eigenvalue problem that does *not* have any eigenvalues.) In fact, it can be shown that *every Sturm–Liouville problem has an infinite number of eigenvalues which are discrete* and can be ordered as $\lambda_1 < \lambda_2 < \lambda_3 < \dots$.* The heart of the Sturm–Liouville theory lies in the fact that the infinite set of eigenfunctions constitutes an orthogonal *basis,* in the sense of the next theorem, and can therefore be used to expand any (suitably decent) function defined on that interval. Proof of this statement can be found in more advanced and specialized texts.

Theorem 4 *Pointwise Convergence of Eigenfunction Expansion*

Let $\phi_1, \phi_2, \dots$ be the eigenfunctions of the Sturm–Liouville problem (13), and let f and f' be piecewise continuous on $[a, b]$. Then the series

$$\sum_{n=1}^{\infty} \frac{\langle f, \phi_n \rangle}{\langle \phi_n, \phi_n \rangle} \phi_n(x)$$

converges to $[f(x+) + f(x-)]/2$ at each point x in the open interval (a, b).

We write

$$f(x) = \sum_{n=1}^{\infty} \frac{\langle f, \phi_n \rangle}{\langle \phi_n, \phi_n \rangle} \phi_n(x), \tag{35}$$

* See H. Sagan, *Boundary and Eigenvalue Problems in Mathematical Physics* (New York: Wiley, 1961), Chap. 5; or G. Birkhoff and G.-C. Rota, *Ordinary Differential Equations,* 2nd ed. (New York: Blaisdell, 1969), Chap. 10.

where, as in our discussion of Fourier series, the equality is understood in the sense of Theorem 4, namely, the series converges to $f(x)$ where f is continuous, and to the average value $[f(x+) + f(x-)]/2$ where f has jump discontinuities. In case you do not see where the coefficients $\langle f, \phi_n\rangle/\langle\phi_n, \phi_n\rangle$ (which are, of course, *numbers*) in (35) come from, let us provide a brief heuristic derivation. If

$$f(x) = \sum_{n=1}^{\infty} c_n \phi_n(x), \tag{36}$$

then taking the inner product of each side with ϕ_m (for any fixed m), and using the fact that the set $\{\phi_n\}$ is orthogonal gives

$$\begin{aligned}\langle f, \phi_m\rangle &= \sum_{n=1}^{\infty} \langle c_n\phi_n, \phi_m\rangle = \sum_{n=1}^{\infty} c_n\langle\phi_n, \phi_m\rangle \\ &= c_1\langle\phi_1, \phi_m\rangle + \cdots + c_{m-1}\langle\phi_{m-1}, \phi_m\rangle + c_m\langle\phi_m, \phi_m\rangle \\ &\quad + c_{m+1}\langle\phi_{m+1}, \phi_m\rangle + \cdots \\ &= (c_1)(0) + \cdots + (c_{m-1})(0) + (c_m)\langle\phi_m, \phi_m\rangle + (c_{m+1})(0) + \cdots \\ &= c_m\langle\phi_m, \phi_m\rangle,\end{aligned} \tag{37}$$

so $c_m = \langle f, \phi_m\rangle/\langle\phi_m, \phi_m\rangle$ or, equivalently, $c_n = \langle f, \phi_n\rangle/\langle\phi_n, \phi_n\rangle$, as claimed.

As for the Fourier series of Section 10.3, one can also make positive statements about the *mean square* convergence of (35), and about the termwise differentiation and integration of the series. We choose to omit such further discussion for the sake of brevity.

One last theorem, and then some examples.

Theorem 5 *Nonnegative Eigenvalues*

If, for the Sturm–Liouville problem (13), $q(x) \le 0$ on $[a, b]$, and $(py'\bar{y})|_a^b \le 0$, then all of the eigenvalues are nonnegative.

Proof of Theorem 5 is outlined in Exercise 11.

EXAMPLE 3 Let us reconsider the results of Example 1 in the light of Theorems 1 to 5. In that example we found that the eigenvalue problem

$$y'' + \lambda y = 0 \qquad (0 < x < \ell) \tag{38a}$$

$$y(0) = 0, \quad y(\ell) = 0 \tag{38b}$$

admitted the eigenvalues and eigenfunctions

$$\lambda_n = \frac{n^2\pi^2}{\ell^2}, \qquad \phi_n(x) = \sin\frac{n\pi x}{\ell} \tag{39}$$

for $n = 1, 2, \ldots$. First, comparison of (38) with (13) reveals that (38) *is* a Sturm–Liouville problem, where $p(x) = 1$, $q(x) = 0$, $r(x) = 1$, $a = 0$, $b = \ell$, $\alpha = \gamma = 1$, and $\beta = \delta = 0$. Sure enough, the eigenvalues are real (in accordance with Theorem 1) and simple (in accordance with Theorem 3), and the eigenfunctions are orthogonal (in accordance with Theorem 2) since

$$\begin{aligned}\langle \phi_m, \phi_n \rangle &= \int_a^b \phi_m(x)\overline{\phi}_n(x) r(x)\, dx = \int_0^\ell \sin\frac{m\pi x}{\ell} \sin\frac{n\pi x}{\ell}\, dx \\ &= \frac{1}{2}\int_{-\ell}^{\ell} \sin\frac{m\pi x}{\ell} \sin\frac{n\pi x}{\ell}\, dx.\end{aligned} \tag{40}$$

Recalling (5b) on page 458, it follows that $\langle \phi_m, \phi_n \rangle = 0$ for $m \neq n$, as claimed. Furthermore, (5b) gives $\langle \phi_n, \phi_n \rangle = \ell/2$.

To illustrate the eigenfunction expansion (35), consider the case where $f(x) = x$. Then $f'(x) = 1$, so f and f' are piecewise continuous on $[0, \ell]$ (in fact, they are *continuous* there), as called for in Theorem 4. We compute

$$\langle f, \phi_n \rangle = \int_0^\ell (x)\left(\sin\frac{n\pi x}{\ell}\right) dx = \frac{\ell^2}{n\pi}(-1)^{n+1}, \tag{41}$$

so that (35) becomes

$$x = \sum_{n=1}^{\infty} \left(\frac{(\ell^2/n\pi)(-1)^{n+1}}{\ell/2}\right) \sin\frac{n\pi x}{\ell} \tag{42}$$

or,

$$x = \frac{2\ell}{\pi}\sum_{n=1}^{\infty} \frac{(-1)^{n+1}}{n} \sin\frac{n\pi x}{\ell}. \tag{43}$$

COMMENT 1 In this case the series is merely a Fourier sine series, as was studied in Example 5 on page 468. Thus the Sturm–Liouville apparatus was not really needed, to derive (43), although it does tell us, finally, where the $\sin(n\pi x/\ell)$ expansion functions "come from": they are the eigenfunctions of a particular Sturm–Liouville problem, the problem (38).

COMMENT 2 *Note carefully* that f, in Theorem 4, is *not* required to satisfy the boundary conditions (13b); only the eigenfunctions need satisfy those conditions. In the present example $f(x) = x$ happens to satisfy the left boundary condition $y(0) = 0$ but not the right boundary condition $y(\ell) = 0$. No matter; we still obtain the convergence, over $(0, \ell)$, guaranteed by Theorem 4. To elaborate this comment a bit we have sketched both $f(x) = x$ and the fifth partial sum,

$$s_5(x) = \frac{2\ell}{\pi}\left(\sin\frac{\pi x}{\ell} - \frac{1}{2}\sin\frac{2\pi x}{\ell} + \frac{1}{3}\sin\frac{3\pi x}{\ell} - \frac{1}{4}\sin\frac{4\pi x}{\ell} + \frac{1}{5}\sin\frac{5\pi x}{\ell}\right), \tag{44}$$

of the series, in Fig. 10.17. Since each $\phi_n(x)$ satisfies the boundary condition $\phi_n(\ell) = 0$, each partial sum of the series inevitably drops down to zero at $x = \ell$. Nevertheless, $s_N(x)$ *does* converge to $f(x) = x$, as $N \to \infty$, for each x in $0 \leq x < \ell$.

COMMENT 3 There is one small gap in our logic. Recall that the solutions $\sqrt{\lambda}\,\ell = n\pi$ of (6) gave us the eigenvalues $\lambda_n = n^2\pi^2/\ell^2$. But in obtaining those solutions we looked only on the real axis. Is it possible that there are additional roots of (6) that are *complex*? Well, we know from Theorem 1 that the λ's

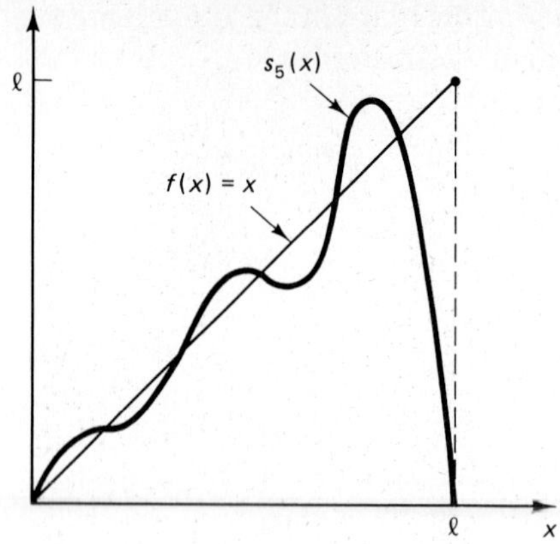

Fig. 10.17 Fifth partial sum in (43).

are necessarily real. Furthermore, $q(x) = 0$ and $(py'\bar{y})|_a^b = (y'\bar{y})|_0^\ell = y'(\ell)0 - y'(0)0 = 0$, so Theorem 5 tells us that the λ's are nonnegative. Thus $\sqrt{\lambda}\,\ell$, in (6), *is* necessarily real, so it suffices to look for the roots only on the real axis. ◀

EXAMPLE 4 Consider the eigenvalue problem

$$y'' + \lambda y = 0, \qquad (0 < x < \ell) \tag{45a}$$

$$y(0) = 0, \qquad y(\ell) + 2y'(\ell) = 0, \tag{45b}$$

which *is* seen to be of Sturm–Liouville type. To find the eigenvalues and eigenfunctions we begin by writing down the general solution of (45a),

$$y(x) = \begin{cases} A\cos\sqrt{\lambda}\,x + B\sin\sqrt{\lambda}\,x & \text{if } \lambda \neq 0 \quad (46a) \\ A + Bx & \text{if } \lambda = 0. \quad (46b) \end{cases}$$

Considering the possibility that $\lambda = 0$, we apply the boundary conditions (45b) to the solution (46b):

$$y(0) = 0 = A, \tag{47a}$$

$$y(\ell) + 2y'(\ell) = 0 = A + (\ell + 2)B, \tag{47b}$$

which admits only the trivial solution $A = B = 0$. Hence $\lambda = 0$ gives $y(x) = 0$, so $\lambda = 0$ is *not* an eigenvalue. Turning to (46a), we have

$$\begin{aligned} y(0) &= 0 = A, \\ y(\ell) + 2y'(\ell) &= 0 \\ &= (\cos\sqrt{\lambda}\,\ell - 2\sqrt{\lambda}\sin\sqrt{\lambda}\,\ell)A \\ &\quad + (\sin\sqrt{\lambda}\,\ell + 2\sqrt{\lambda}\cos\sqrt{\lambda}\,\ell)B, \end{aligned}$$

which admits the nontrivial solution

$$A = 0, \qquad B = \text{arbitrary} = 1, \text{ say}, \tag{49}$$

provided that $\sin\sqrt{\lambda}\,\ell + 2\sqrt{\lambda}\cos\sqrt{\lambda}\,\ell = 0$, or

$$\tan\sqrt{\lambda}\,\ell + 2\sqrt{\lambda} = 0. \tag{50}$$

The characteristic equation (50) cannot be solved analytically [unlike the characteristic equation (6), which was solved easily by inspection], so we resort to numerical and/or graphical methods. First, observe that $q(x) = 0$ and that $(py'\bar{y})|_a^b = (y'\bar{y})|_0^\ell = y'(\ell)\bar{y}(\ell) - y'(0)\bar{y}(0) = y'(\ell)[-2\bar{y}'(\ell)] - y'(0)0 = -2|y'(\ell)|^2 \le 0$,* so that Theorem 5 applies. It follows from Theorems 1 and 5 that the λ's are real and nonnegative. Thus $\sqrt{\lambda}$ is *real,* and if, for convenience, we regard $\sqrt{\lambda}$ as the unknown in (50), then it suffices to look for solutions of (50) along the real $\sqrt{\lambda}$ axis. In graphical terms, we seek the crossings of the graphs of $\tan\sqrt{\lambda}\,\ell$ and $-2\sqrt{\lambda}$, plotted as functions of $\sqrt{\lambda}$, as in Fig. 10.18. We have excluded the crossing at $\sqrt{\lambda} = 0$ since we have already established that $\lambda = 0$ is not an eigenvalue, and also the crossings at negative values of $\sqrt{\lambda}$ since they would be found to lead to the same eigenvalues and eigenfunctions as the positive crossings—which we have designated as $z_1, z_2, \ldots$. Supposing that the z_n's are now known,† we have the eigenvalues and eigenfunctions

$$\lambda_n = z_n^2, \tag{51a}$$

$$\phi_n = \sin z_n x, \tag{51b}$$

for $n = 1, 2, \ldots$. Computing

$$\langle \phi_n, \phi_n \rangle = \int_0^\ell \sin^2 z_n x\, dx = \frac{1}{4z_n}[2z_n\ell - \sin(2z_n\ell)], \tag{52}$$

the expansion of a given function f, over $(0, \ell)$, is of the form

$$f(x) = \sum_{n=1}^{\infty} \langle f, \phi_n \rangle \frac{4z_n}{2z_n\ell - \sin(2z_n\ell)} \sin z_n x, \tag{53}$$

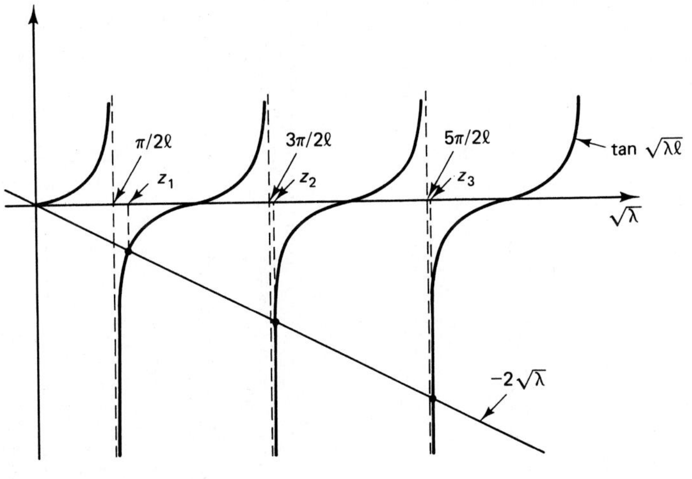

Fig. 10.18 Solutions of (50).

* If $z = a + ib$, then $z\bar{z} = (a + ib)(a - ib) = a^2 + b^2 = |z|^2$.

† From the figure it is evident that $z_n \sim (2n - 1)\pi/2$ as $n \to \infty$. We should be able to compute z_n (for $n = 1, 2, \ldots$, in turn) quite accurately by Newton's method, for example, using "initial guesses" near $(2n - 1)\pi/2$. Or, depending on the accuracy desired, it may be that the graphically determined values of the z_n's will suffice.

where

$$\langle f, \phi_n \rangle = \int_0^\ell f(x) \sin z_n x \, dx. \tag{54}$$

COMMENT 1 Observe that (53) is *not* a Fourier series since the frequencies z_n, in $\sin z_n x$, are not of the form "$n\pi/\ell$."

COMMENT 2 Observe that there are *many* (an infinite number, in fact) possible eigenfunction expansions of a given function f on any given finite interval. For example, Example 3 and the present example involve two different Sturm–Liouville problems on the interval $(0, \ell)$; each of the two provides us with an orthogonal set of eigenfunctions that can be used in eigenfunction expansions of given functions. How, then, in applications, do we know which eigenfunction expansion to use? Is one better, or more convenient, than another? These questions will be answered in Part IV, wherein we work numerous applications. For now, let us merely state that the choice of the eigenfunction expansion will be clear in each application and will be dictated by the context. ◀

In summary, the Sturm–Liouville problem is a particular class of eigenvalue problems of frequent occurrence in applications. Fortunately, there is a well-developed theory that provides information about the eigenvalues and eigenfunctions. Much of this theory is embodied in our Theorems 1 to 5. Especially important to us in solving the various partial differential equations of mathematical physics in Part IV will be the process of eigenfunction expansion of a given function, which process is put on firm ground by Theorem 4.

In closing this section we wish to point out the close connection between the matrix eigenvalue problem $\mathbf{Ax} = \lambda\mathbf{x}$, for the case where $\mathbf{A}$ is self-adjoint, and the Sturm–Liouville eigenvalue problem. For example, if $\mathbf{A}$ is self-adjoint, then $\mathbf{A}^* = \mathbf{A}$, so that (7) on page 206 becomes $(\mathbf{Ax}) \cdot \mathbf{y} = \mathbf{x} \cdot (\mathbf{Ay})$, which is the analog of the Lagrange identity (25) in the present section. See also Theorems 1, 3, and 4 on pages 207 to 208, and compare them with the analogous Sturm–Liouville theorems.

10.6 EXERCISES

1. Find the eigenvalues and eigenfunctions, and work out the eigenfunction expansion (35) of the given function f. If the characteristic equation is too difficult to solve analytically, merely note that and proceed with the rest of the problem as though the λ_n's were known.

*(a) $y'' + \lambda y = 0, \quad (0 < x < \ell)$
$y(0) = 0, \quad y'(\ell) = 0, \quad f(x) = 100$

(b) $y'' + \lambda y = 0, \quad (0 < x < \ell)$
$y'(0) = 0, \quad y(\ell) = 0, \quad f(x) = 1$

(c) $y'' + \lambda y = 0, \quad (0 < x < \ell)$
$y'(0) = 0, \quad y'(\ell) = 0,$
$f(x) = \begin{cases} 1, & 0 \le x < \ell/2 \\ 0, & \ell/2 \le x \le \ell \end{cases}$

*(d) $y'' + \lambda y = 0, \quad (0 < x < \ell)$
$y'(0) = 0, \quad y(\ell) + y'(\ell) = 0, \quad f(x) = 50$

(e) $y'' + \lambda y = 0, \quad (0 < x < \pi)$
$y(0) + y'(0) = 0, \quad y(\pi) = 0, \quad f(x) = 10$

(f) $y'' + \lambda y = 0, \quad (-\pi < x < \pi)$
$y'(-\pi) = 0, \quad y'(\pi) = 0,$
$f(x) = \begin{cases} 0, & -\pi \le x \le 0 \\ 50, & 0 < x \le \pi \end{cases}$

(g) $y'' + \lambda y = 0, \quad (0 < x < 2)$
$y(0) - 2y'(0) = 0, \quad y'(2) = 0,$
$f(x) = 100$

2. Show that the smallest eigenvalue of the eigenvalue problem

$$y'' + \lambda y = 0, \qquad (0 < x < \ell)$$
$$y'(0) = 0, \quad y(\ell) - y'(\ell) = 0$$

lies between $(\pi/2\ell)^2$ and $(\pi/\ell)^2$ and that $\lambda_n \sim n^2\pi^2/\ell^2$ as $n \to \infty$.

3. (*Periodic boundary conditions*) The eigenvalue problem

$$y'' + \lambda y = 0, \qquad (-\ell < x < \ell) \qquad \text{(a)}$$
$$y(-\ell) - y(\ell) = 0, \quad y'(-\ell) - y'(\ell) = 0 \quad \text{(b)}$$

is *not* of Sturm–Liouville type because the boundary conditions (b) are not of the *separated* form (13b); rather, (b) are known as **periodicity conditions** because they state that $y(-\ell) = y(\ell)$ and $y'(-\ell) = y'(\ell)$. Show that $\lambda = 0$ is a simple eigenvalue, with eigenfunction $\phi(x) = 1$, and that $\lambda = n^2\pi^2/\ell^2$ is a nonsimple eigenvalue (for $n = 1, 2, \ldots$), with eigenfunctions $\phi(x) = \cos(n\pi x/\ell)$ and $\sin(n\pi x/\ell)$. (Observe that the eigenfunction expansion is precisely the classical *Fourier series* studied in Section 10.3.)

4. Recall that the characteristic equation of an $n \times n$ matrix is necessarily an nth-degree algebraic equation in λ. According to the *fundamental theorem of algebra,* such an equation *must* have at least one solution. Thus *every $n \times n$ matrix has at least one eigenvalue.* Differential operators, however, do not necessarily have any eigenvalues. To verify the foregoing statement it suffices to find one such example. Thus show that the eigenvalue problem

$$y'' + \lambda y = 0, \qquad (0 < x < 1)$$
$$2y(0) - y(1) + 4y'(1) = 0, \quad y(0) + 2y'(1) = 0 \qquad \text{(a)}$$

has *no* eigenvalues. Since we know that Sturm–Liouville problems always have an infinite number of eigenvalues, (a) must not be a Sturm–Liouville problem. Show that that is the case.

5. Show that for

$$y'' + \lambda y = 0 \qquad (0 < x < 1)$$
$$y(0) - y(1) = 0, \quad y'(0) + y'(1) = 0 \qquad \text{(a)}$$

every λ (real or complex) is an eigenvalue! Is (a) a Sturm–Liouville system? Explain.

6. (*Obtaining Sturm–Liouville form*) Observe that the equation

$$a(x)y'' + b(x)y' + c(x)y + \lambda d(x)y = 0 \qquad \text{(a)}$$

is in the Sturm–Liouville form (13a) only if $b(x) = a'(x)$, for if we write out (13a) we have

$$p(x)y'' + p'(x)y' + q(x)y + \lambda r(x)y = 0 \qquad \text{(b)}$$

But even if $b \neq a'$, in (a), we can always throw (a) into the Sturm–Liouville form by multiplying through by a suitable function $\sigma(x)$. For the resulting equation, $\sigma ay'' + \sigma by' + \sigma cy + \lambda\sigma dy = 0$, to be of the form (b) we need σb to be the derivative of σa: $\sigma b = (\sigma a)'$. Solving for σ, show that

$$\sigma(x) = e^{\int[(b-a')/a]\,dx}. \qquad \text{(c)}$$

7. Use the results of Exercise 6 to recast each of the following differential equations in the Sturm–Liouville form (13a). Identify $p(x)$, $q(x)$, and $r(x)$.

*(a) $xy'' + 5y' + \lambda xy = 0$
(b) $y'' + 2y' + xy + \lambda x^2 y = 0$
(c) $y'' + y' + \lambda y = 0$
(d) $y'' - y' + \lambda xy = 0$
(e) $x^2y'' + xy' + \lambda x^2 y = 0$
(f) $y'' + (\cot x)y' + \lambda y = 0$

8. Consider the eigenvalue problem

$$x^2y'' + xy' + \lambda y = 0, \qquad (1 < x < a) \qquad \text{(a)}$$
$$y(1) = 0, \quad y(a) = 0. \qquad \text{(b)}$$

(a) Show that the eigenvalues and eigenfunctions are

$$\lambda_n = \frac{n^2\pi^2}{(\ln a)^2}, \qquad \phi_n(x) = \sin\left(n\pi\frac{\ln x}{\ln a}\right) \qquad \text{(c)}$$
$$(n = 1, 2, \ldots).$$

(b) Show that the eigenfunction expansion of a given function f is of the form

$$f(x) = \sum_{n=1}^{\infty} c_n \sin\left(n\pi\frac{\ln x}{\ln a}\right), \qquad \text{(d)}$$

where

$$c_n = \frac{\int_1^a f(x)\sin\left(n\pi\frac{\ln x}{\ln a}\right)\frac{dx}{x}}{\int_1^a \sin^2\left(n\pi\frac{\ln x}{\ln a}\right)\frac{dx}{x}}. \qquad \text{(e)}$$

Hint: You will need to get (a) into Sturm–Liouville form, as discussed in Exercise 6, before you can identify the weight function $r(x)$ for the inner product.

(c) Work out the c_n's for the case where $f(x) = 100$ over $[1, a]$.

***9.** Expand $f(x) = \begin{cases} 60, & 0 \le x < 2 \\ 0, & 2 \le x \le 3 \end{cases}$ in terms of the eigenfunctions of the eigenvalue problem $y'' - 2y' + \lambda y = 0$; $y(0) = 0$, $y(3) = 0$. *Hint:* See Exercise 6.

10. (a) Derive (17a).
(b) Derive (17b).

11. Prove Theorem 5. *Hint:* Multiply each term in $(py')' + qy + \lambda ry = 0$ by $\bar{y}$ and integrate over (a, b). Thus show that

$$\lambda \| y \|^2 = -(py'\bar{y})\Big|_a^b + \int_a^b p|y'|^2\,dx - \int_a^b q|y|^2\,dx,$$

and examine the signs of the individual terms.

12. (*Real eigenfunctions*) Show that if $\phi(x)$ is an eigenfunction of a Sturm–Liouville problem, then $\phi(x)$ is either a real-valued function, or else it is a complex constant times a real-valued function. *Hint:* Show that if $\phi(x)$ is an eigenfunction corresponding to an eigenvalue λ, then so is $\bar{\phi}(x)$. Then use Theorem 3 and show that $\phi(x) = c\bar{\phi}(x)$, where c is a constant. Expressing the latter equation in the (polar) form $A(x)e^{iB(x)} = Ce^{iD}A(x)e^{-iB(x)}$, show that $B(x)$ is at most a constant.

13. (*Column buckling with lateral restraint*) Consider the buckling of the column of length ℓ and stiffness EI shown below. It is fixed into the floor such that $y(0) = y'(0) = 0$, and it is restrained laterally, at the free end, by a spring of stiffness k. Then it turns out that the lateral deflection $y(x)$ is governed by the eigenvalue problem

$$\begin{aligned} y'''' + \lambda y'' &= 0, \qquad (0 < x < \ell) \\ y(0) = y'(0) &= y''(\ell) = 0, \\ y'''(\ell) &= -\lambda y'(\ell) + \kappa y(\ell), \end{aligned} \tag{a}$$

where $\lambda \equiv P/EI$ and $\kappa \equiv k/EI$.

(a) Show that the characteristic equation of (a) is

$$(\Lambda^2 - \kappa\ell)\Lambda \cos \Lambda\ell + \kappa \sin \Lambda\ell = 0, \tag{b}$$

where $\Lambda = \sqrt{\lambda}$, and that the corresponding eigenfunctions (buckling modes) are (to within an arbitrary scale factor)

$$y = \sin \Lambda x - \tan \Lambda\ell \cos \Lambda x - \Lambda x + \tan \Lambda\ell. \tag{c}$$

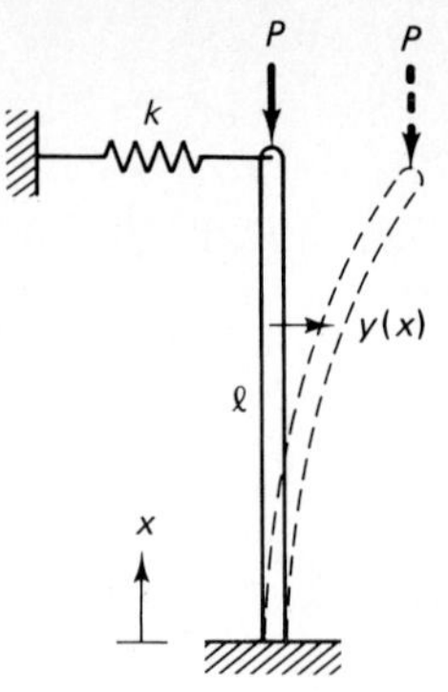

*(b) Solve (b) for the critical buckling load, P_{cr}, for the case where $\kappa = 0$.

(c) Is (a) a Sturm–Liouville problem? Explain.

14. (*Buckling of linearly tapered column*) Consider a column of circular cross section, the radius of which varies linearly with x. It extends over $a < x < b$, as shown in the figure, is pinned at both ends, and is loaded axially by a force P. Then the cross-sectional moment of inertia I is not a constant; it is given by $I(x) = I_0(x/b)^4$, where I_0 is its value at $x = b$, so the eigenvalue problem governing buckling is found to be

$$x^4 y'' + \lambda y = 0, \qquad (a < x < b) \tag{a}$$

$$y(a) = 0, \quad y(b) = 0, \tag{b}$$

where $\lambda \equiv b^4 P/EI_0$.

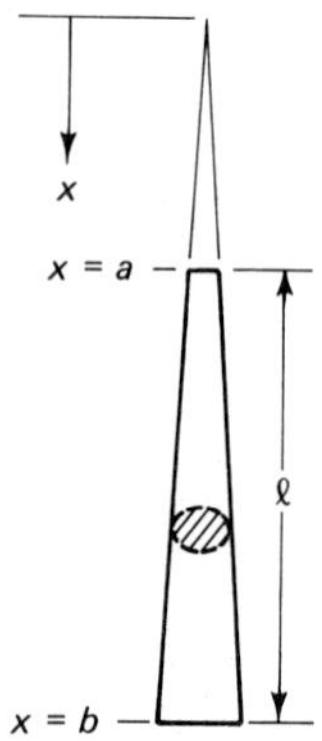

(a) Verify that the general solution of (a) can be expressed as

$$y(x) = x\left[A \sin\left(\frac{\sqrt{\lambda}}{x}\right) + B \cos\left(\frac{\sqrt{\lambda}}{x}\right)\right]. \tag{c}$$

(b) Applying the boundary conditions (b), show that the eigenvalues and eigenfunctions are

$$\lambda_n = \left(\frac{n\pi ab}{\ell}\right)^2,$$

$$\phi_n(x) = x \sin\left[n\pi\frac{b}{\ell}\left(1 - \frac{a}{x}\right)\right] \qquad \text{(d)}$$

for $n = 1, 2, \ldots$, and that the buckling load is $P_{cr} = \pi^2 EI_0 a^2/b^2\ell^2$, where $\ell = b - a$.

15. (*Buckling of nonlinearly tapered column*) Although not wishing to give undue prominence to the subject of the buckling of columns, we cannot restrain ourselves from including this one additional exercise, which we regard as especially interesting, and a bit more challenging than the others. If in the problem of Exercise 14, the column radius is proportional to $\sqrt{x}$ rather than to x, then $I(x) = I_0(x/b)^2$, and we have

$$\begin{aligned} &x^2y'' + \lambda y = 0, \qquad (a < x < b) \\ &y(a) = 0, \quad y(b) = 0, \end{aligned} \qquad \text{(a)}$$

where $\lambda \equiv b^2P/EI_0$. Show that the buckling load is

$$P_{\text{cr}} = \frac{EI_0}{b^2}\left\{\frac{1}{4} + \frac{\pi^2}{[\ln(b/a)]^2}\right\}. \qquad \text{(b)}$$

11 Fourier Integral, Fourier Transform

11.1 INTRODUCTION

We begin this chapter with a brief section on two functions that are of general utility in applications and which are used later in this chapter and in Part IV: the Heaviside step function and the Dirac delta function. The former is quite simple, but the latter is more subtle and will require the reader's careful attention.

In Section 11.3 we come to the principal subject of this chapter, the Fourier integral. This integral is a limiting form of the Fourier series as the period of the function tends to infinity. Thus it finds numerous applications to problems in which one or more of the independent variables varies over an infinite domain. Such problems often occur in the form of ordinary or partial differential equations.

Following our discussion of the Fourier integral, we introduce the Fourier transform. The latter is not really an independent statement. Rather, it amounts to a restatement of the Fourier integral formula as an equivalent pair of formulas: the *Fourier transform* and its *inverse*. This step, presented in Section 11.4, permits the development of a systematic *integral transform* methodology. Finally, in Section 11.5, we show how to derive the *Laplace transform* from the Fourier transform, and this step completes our passage from the Fourier series to the Fourier integral to the Fourier transform to the Laplace transform. The Laplace transform is then developed in detail in Chapter 12.

11.2 HEAVISIDE AND DIRAC FUNCTIONS

Functions encountered in practice are not always continuously varying. They sometimes vary in stepwise fashion, and are sometimes impulsive, i.e., sharply focused in space or time. These situations will be encountered in Parts III and IV, so it will be useful to take a brief "time out," before continuing, to introduce the relevant mathematical notation, specifically, the Heaviside step function and the Dirac delta function.

We begin by defining the **Heaviside step function***

$$\boxed{H(t) = \begin{cases} 1, & t \geq 0 \\ 0, & t < 0, \end{cases}} \tag{1}$$

shown in Fig. 11.1a. The main point about the step function (so called because its graph resembles a step) is that its value is unity when its argument is positive, and zero when its argument is negative. [Its value *at* $t = 0$ will not be consequential for us, and we have defined $H(0) = 1$ somewhat arbitrarily; other authors may define $H(0)$ as $1/2$ or 0, or not at all.]

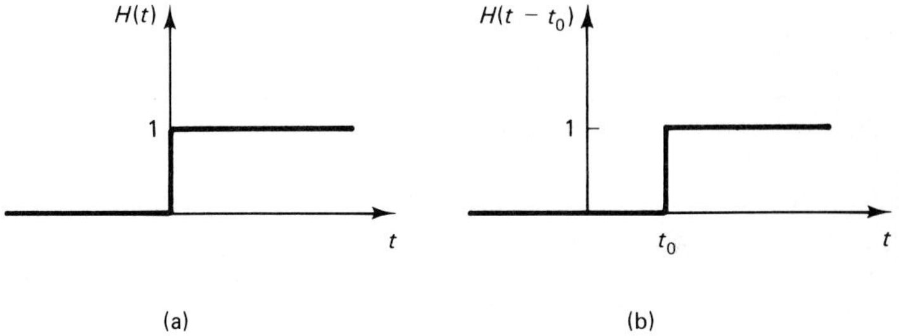

Fig. 11.1 Heaviside step function.

It follows from (1) that $H(t - t_0)$ is a "shifted step," as displayed in Fig. 11.1b, and that the example functions shown in Fig. 11.2 can be expressed, with the help of Heaviside notation, as

$$f_1(t) = 50[H(t-2) - H(t-6)], \tag{2}$$

$$f_2(t) = 2tH(t), \tag{3}$$

and

$$f_3(t) = (5 + 3t)[H(t+1) - H(t)] - 4H(t), \tag{4}$$

respectively. For example, $f_1(t)$ might be an applied voltage which jumps up to 50 volts at the time $t = 2$, when a switch is closed, and which drops back to zero at the time $t = 6$, when the switch is opened again.

Observe that the Heaviside notation is attractively compact. For example, compare (4) with the alternative "three-tier" statement

$$f_3(t) = \begin{cases} 0, & t < -1 \\ 5 + 3t, & -1 < t < 0 \\ -4, & t > 0. \end{cases} \tag{5}$$

To motivate our definition of the delta function, to which we now turn, let $F(t)$ be a force applied to some physical system, where t is the time. Besides forces that are rather distributed in time, as in Fig. 11.3a, one sometimes deals with

* *Oliver Heaviside* (1850–1925) was an electrical engineer who contributed to the development of electromagnetic theory, modern vector analysis, and Laplace transform methods. In connection with the latter, he is especially well known for his "Heaviside expansion theorem," which is discussed in Chapter 12. Note the spelling: Heaviside, not Heavyside.

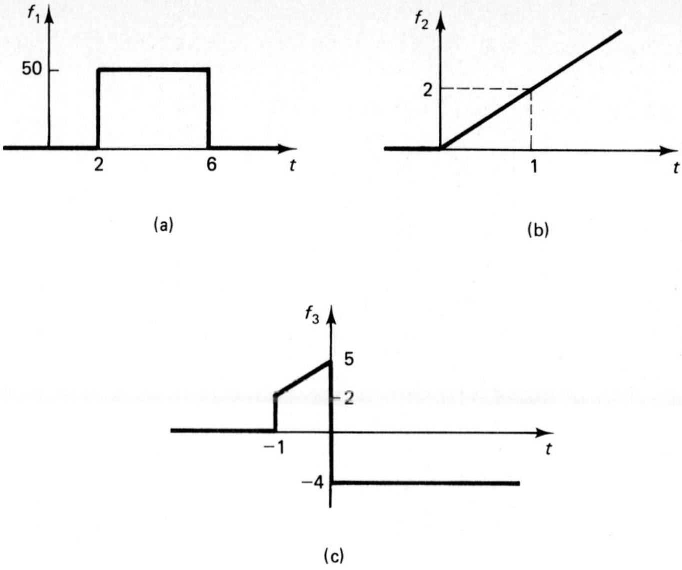

Fig. 11.2 Example functions.

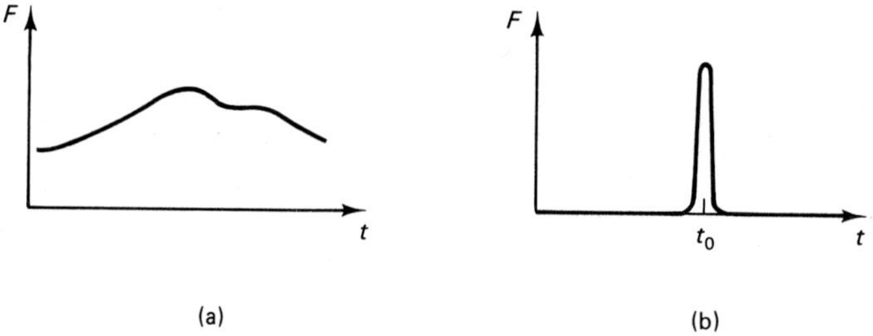

Fig. 11.3 Force distributions.

"impulsive" forces, such as hammer blows, that are sharply focused, as in Fig. 11.3b.

To see how to work with impulsive forces, consider the simple representative problem

$$\dot{x} + x = F(t), \qquad (-\infty < t < \infty) \tag{6a}$$

$$x(-\infty) = 0, \tag{6b}$$

where F is an impulsive force acting at $t = 0$, as shown by the solid curve in Fig. 11.4a, and $x(t)$ is the resulting response, such as the displacement of a mass.

Suppose that the impulse delivered by F is I; i.e., suppose that the area under F's graph is I. [In mechanics, the "impulse" I delivered by a force $F(t)$ between times t_1 and t_2 is $I = \int_{t_1}^{t_2} F(t)\, dt$.] In practice, we may not even know the function F in (6a); all we know is that it is sharply focused at $t = 0$ and that it has an impulse I.

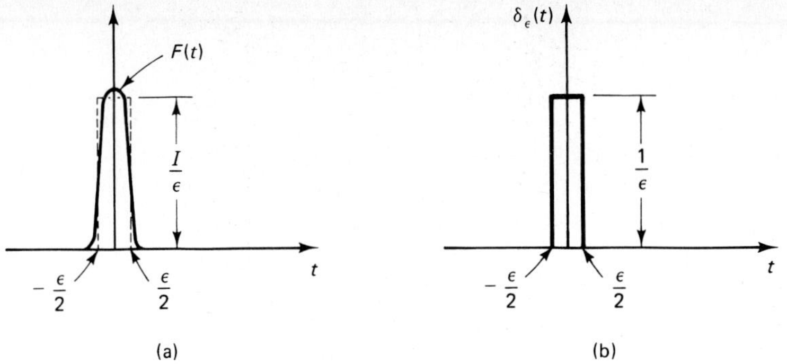

Fig. 11.4 Impulsive force at $t = 0$.

Thus, to render (6) tractable, one can adopt the following reasonable approximate procedure.

First, approximate F by a simple rectangular pulse, as indicated by the dashed lines in Fig. 11.4a; the width ϵ is to be arbitrarily small so that the pulse is sharply focused, and the height is chosen to be I/ϵ so that the impulse of the rectangular pulse is identical to the impulse of $F(t)$. Thus, we have the approximate representation $F(t) = I\delta_\epsilon(t)$, where $\delta_\epsilon(t)$ is the *unit* impulse function shown in Fig. 11.4b. Then (6) becomes

$$\dot{x} + x = I\delta_\epsilon(t), \qquad (-\infty < t < \infty) \tag{7a}$$

$$x(-\infty) = 0. \tag{7b}$$

Next, we solve (7) for $x(t)$, and finally, in the resulting solution for $x(t)$, we let $\epsilon \to 0$. In effect, then, our final result is the response $x(t)$ due to an idealized impulsive force, i.e., one that acts over an infinitesimally short time.

To carry out these steps, observe first that the solution to (7) is*

$$x(t) = Ie^{-t} \int_{-\infty}^{t} e^{\tau}\delta_\epsilon(\tau)\, d\tau. \tag{8}$$

Then letting $\epsilon \to 0$ in this result gives

$$\begin{aligned} x(t) &= \lim_{\epsilon \to 0} \left[Ie^{-t} \int_{-\infty}^{t} e^{\tau}\delta_\epsilon(\tau)\, d\tau \right] \\ &= \lim_{\epsilon \to 0} \begin{cases} Ie^{-t} \displaystyle\int_{-\epsilon/2}^{\epsilon/2} e^{\tau} \frac{1}{\epsilon}\, d\tau, & \text{if } t > 0 \\ 0, & \text{if } t < 0 \end{cases} \\ &= \lim_{\epsilon \to 0} \begin{cases} Ie^{-t} \dfrac{e^{\epsilon/2} - e^{-\epsilon/2}}{\epsilon}, & t > 0 \\ 0, & t < 0 \end{cases} \end{aligned} \tag{9}$$

* Recall equation (29) in Section A.8.

$$= \begin{cases} Ie^{-t}, & t > 0 \\ 0, & t < 0 \end{cases}$$

$$= Ie^{-t}H(t),$$

where the fourth equality in (9) follows from l'Hospital's rule.

Although the preceding was a specific example, the procedure was fairly general. We represented an impulsive input by a rectangular pulse $\delta_\epsilon(t)$, solved for $x(t)$, and then let $\epsilon \to 0$ in the resulting response. The Dirac delta function, to be introduced in a moment, will enable us to reduce this procedure to its essentials, while omitting the tedious part of the limit process. Specifically, we will eventually need, as in (9), to evaluate the limit of an integral of the form

$$\int_{t_1}^{t_2} f(t)\delta_\epsilon(t)\,dt$$

as $\epsilon \to 0$. Well, that step can be carried out *once and for all* as follows. Assuming that $f(t)$ is continuous at $t = 0$, we have

$$\begin{aligned} \lim_{\epsilon \to 0} \int_{t_1}^{t_2} f(t)\delta_\epsilon(t)\,dt &= \lim_{\epsilon \to 0} \int_{-\epsilon/2}^{\epsilon/2} f(t)\frac{1}{\epsilon}\,dt \\ &= \lim_{\epsilon \to 0} \left[f(\tau)\frac{1}{\epsilon}\epsilon \right] = \lim_{\epsilon \to 0} f(\tau) = f(0) \end{aligned} \tag{10}$$

if $t = 0$ is inside the interval (i.e., if $t_1 < 0 < t_2$), and 0 if $t = 0$ is outside the interval (i.e., if $t_2 < 0$ or $t_1 > 0$); the case where $t = 0$ is at an endpoint ($t_1 = 0$ or $t_2 = 0$) will not be considered here. The second equality in (10) followed from the *mean value theorem of the integral calculus,** where τ is *some* point in the closed interval $[-\epsilon/2, \epsilon/2]$; thus, as $\epsilon \to 0$, it follows that τ is forced to 0. In summary, we have found that

$$\lim_{\epsilon \to 0} \int_{t_1}^{t_2} f(t)\delta_\epsilon(t)\,dt = \begin{cases} f(0), & t_1 < 0 < t_2 \\ 0, & \text{otherwise.} \end{cases} \tag{11}$$

Going one step further, it is customary to dispense with calling attention to the ϵ limit, and to simply write the foregoing result as

$$\boxed{\int_{t_1}^{t_2} f(t)\,\delta(t)\,dt = \begin{cases} f(0), & t_1 < 0 < t_2 \\ 0, & \text{otherwise;} \end{cases}} \tag{12}$$

$\delta(t)$ is known as the **Dirac delta function**† and corresponds to an idealized point

*The delta function was introduced by the British physicist *P. A. M. Dirac* (1902–) in the paper "The Physical Interpretation of the Quantum Mechanics," Proceedings of the Royal Society of London,

$$\int_a^b f(x)\,dx = f(\xi)(b - a).$$

† The delta function was introduced by the British physicist *P. A. M. Dirac* (1902–) in the paper "The Physical Interpretation of the Quantum Mechanics," Proceedings of the Royal Society of London, Series A113, 1926–1927, pp. 621–641. For a historical account, see G. Temple, *Journal of the London Mathematical Society*, Vol. 28, 1953, pp. 134–148. Dirac and Erwin Schrödinger won a Nobel prize in 1933 for their work in quantum mechanics. For a different approach to the delta function, using the *theory of distributions*, see E. F. Beckenbach (ed.), *Modern Mathematics for the Engineer*, (New York: McGraw-Hill, 1961).

unit impulse. We must remember that what we mean by (12) is the limit statement (11).

The formula (12) is said to express the "sifting property" of the delta function, for one can imagine $\delta(t)$ as sifting through the values of f and picking out the value $f(0)$ at the point of action $t = 0$ of $\delta(t)$.

To see what we have accomplished by introducing the delta function, observe carefully that with (12) available to us, our solution of (6) can be streamlined, for with $F(t) = I\delta(t)$, we have, very simply,

$$\begin{aligned} x(t) &= e^{-t}\int_0^t e^{\tau}\delta(\tau)\,d\tau \\ &= \begin{cases} Ie^{-t}, & t > 0 \\ 0, & t < 0 \end{cases} \qquad (13) \\ &= Ie^{-t}H(t). \end{aligned}$$

Heuristically, it is helpful to regard the delta function $\delta(t)$ as the limit of the *delta sequence* $\delta_\epsilon(t)$, as $\epsilon \to 0$. Thus (Fig. 11.5) we can think of $\delta(t)$ as a spike-like pulse at $t = 0$, having zero width and infinite height, so as to have unit area. Strictly speaking, of course, a function cannot have an infinite value, but we reiterate, this conceptualization of the delta function is merely heuristic. *The key point to bear in mind is that the defining property (12) of $\delta(t)$ is merely a shorthand statement of the rigorous limit statement (10).*

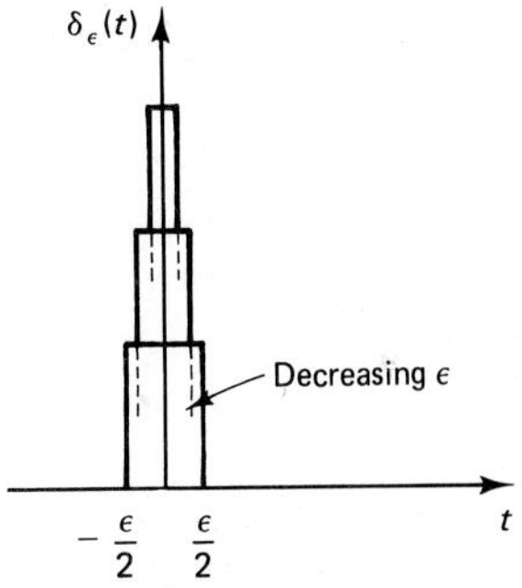

Fig. 11.5 Delta sequence.

In the preceding discussion, we had the delta function $\delta(t)$ act (i.e., be focused) at $t = 0$ for pedagogical simplicity. More generally, $\delta(t - t_0)$ is focused at $t = t_0$, and (12) then becomes

$$\int_{t_1}^{t_2} f(t)\delta(t - t_0)\,dt = \begin{cases} f(t_0) & \text{if } t_0 \text{ is in } (t_1, t_2) \\ 0 & \text{otherwise.} \end{cases} \qquad (14)$$

Some additional properties of the delta function will be explored in the exercises.

By the way, in the foregoing discussion we introduced the delta function in connection with impulsive forces, but delta functions can be used in a variety of other contexts as well, to model focused actions or events. Let us offer one more example, and at the same time include some words of caution.

Specifically, suppose that we press a circular coin against the edge of a metal plate, of the same thickness, which extends over $-\infty < x < \infty$ and $y > 0$, as sketched in Fig. 11.6a. We press with a force P and are interested in the resulting stress field induced in the plate. To set up the governing boundary value problem we

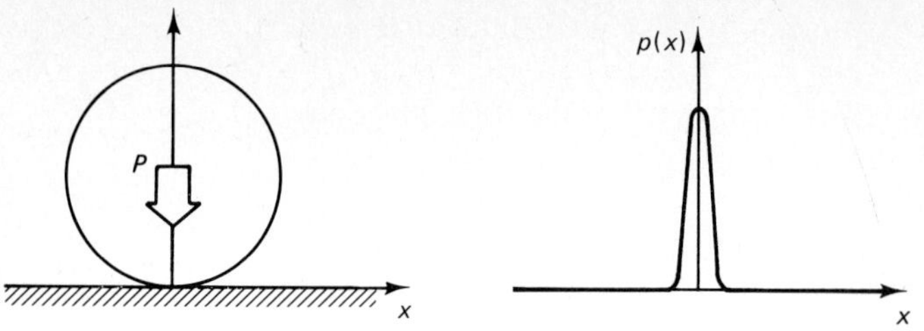

(a) (b) **Fig. 11.6** Force applied to edge of plate.

would need to know the force distribution, say $p(x)$, applied to the edge of the plate. However, the function p, which is probably of the general form shown in Fig. 11.6b, is not known a priori. We do know that it will be quite concentrated, and that

$$\int_{-\infty}^{\infty} p(x)\,dx = P, \tag{15}$$

so that its net force is P, but its exact shape must be computed, together with the stress field, as part of the overall problem. (In the theory of elasticity, this is called a "contact problem.") Now, *if* our interest is in the "far" stress field (i.e., not near the origin), we would be well advised to argue that the stresses should be rather insensitive to the detailed shape of p* and to simplify the problem by assuming, a priori, that $p(x) = P\delta(x)$, i.e., an idealized point force of strength P acting at the origin. However, if our interest is in the "near" stress field (as it would be, say, for a ball-bearing manufacturer, who is especially interested in the contact stresses), we can expect the point force idealization to lead to serious error.

In this section we have tried to present the delta function as simply as possible, yet carefully from a mathematical point of view. The essential idea is contained in our discussion of the representative probiem (6), and the key property of the delta function is the sifting property (12).

11.2 EXERCISES

1. Express the functions sketched in terms of Heaviside notation, as we have done in (2) to (4).

(a)

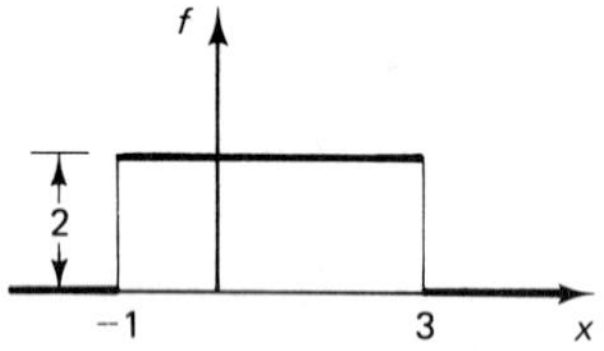

(b)

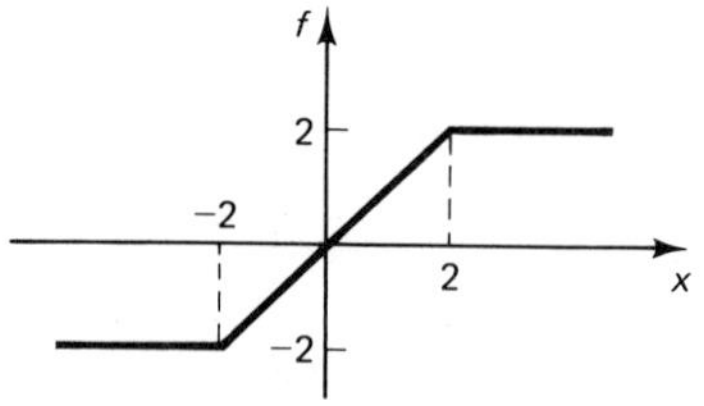

(c)

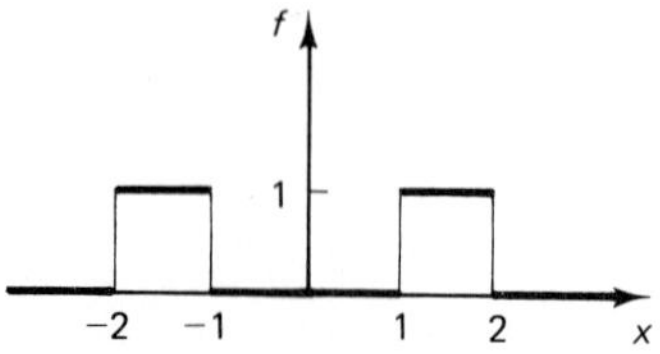

(d)

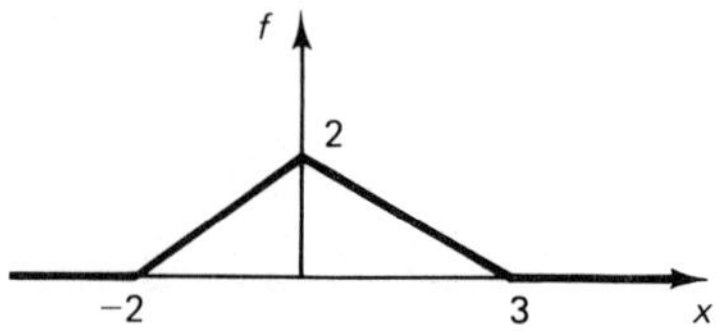

* Such an argument would be supported by the so-called *Saint-Venant's principle* from the theory of elasticity.

2. (*Delta sequences*) The sequence of rectangular pulses $\delta_\epsilon(t)$, shown in Fig. 11.4b, is known as a **delta sequence.** We took δ_ϵ to be rectangular and symmetric about $t = 0$ for simplicity, but any other shape could have been used, provided that the key property,

$$\lim_{\epsilon \to 0} \int_{-\infty}^{\infty} f(t)\delta_\epsilon(t)\, dt = f(0), \qquad \text{(a)}$$

is satisfied. By verifying (a), show that the following are equally legitimate as delta sequences.

(a)

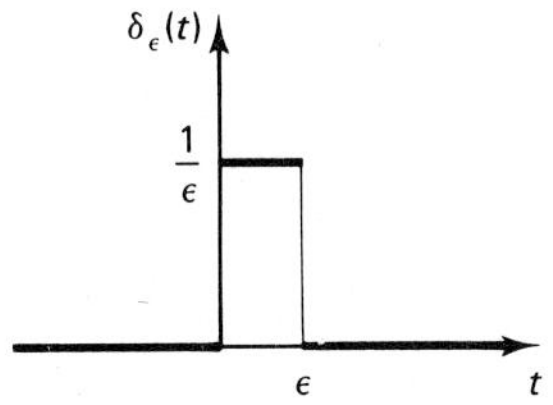

(b)

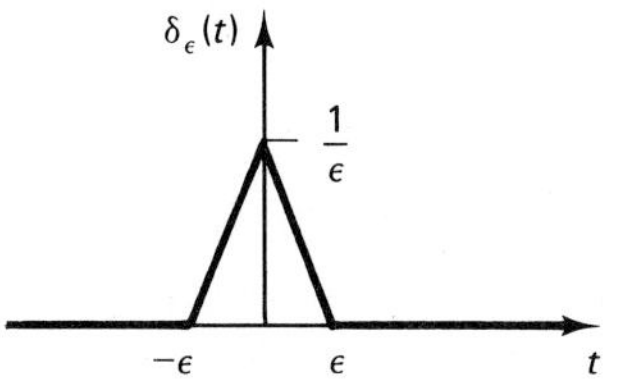

(c)

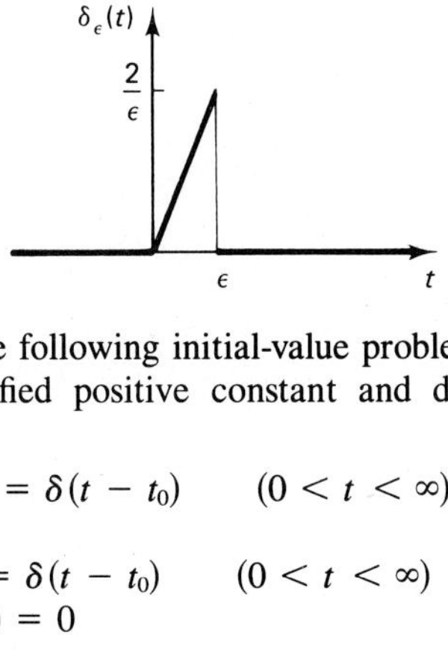

3. Solve the following initial-value problems, where t_0 is a specified positive constant and dots denote d/dt.

*(a) $\dot{x} + 2x = \delta(t - t_0) \qquad (0 < t < \infty)$
$x(0) = 3$
(b) $\ddot{x} + x = \delta(t - t_0) \qquad (0 < t < \infty)$
$x(0) = \dot{x}(0) = 0$

Hint for part (b): Use the method of variation of parameters to obtain a particular solution.

4. (*Additional properties of the delta function*) Show that

(a) $\delta(-t) = \delta(t)$
(b) $g(t)\delta(t) = g(0)\delta(t)$, where the right-hand side is 0 if $g(0) = 0$
(c) $\delta(at) = \dfrac{1}{|a|}\delta(t) \quad (a \neq 0)$

Hint: The key point is that the delta function is defined in terms of its "integral action" on other functions, specifically,

$$\int_{-\infty}^{\infty} f(t)\delta(t)\, dt = f(0).$$

[With no loss, we have set $t_1 = -\infty$, $t_2 = \infty$, and $t_0 = 0$ in (10).] In part (a), for example, we say that $\delta(-t)$ and $\delta(t)$ are equal if their integral actions are identical. Thus, to prove that $\delta(-t) = \delta(t)$, one needs to show that

$$\int_{-\infty}^{\infty} f(t)\delta(-t)\, dt = \int_{-\infty}^{\infty} f(t)\delta(t)\, dt$$

for all possible functions f that are continuous at $t = 0$.

5. Show that

(a) $\displaystyle\int_{-\infty}^{x} \delta(\xi)\, d\xi = H(x)$

(b) $\displaystyle\int_{0}^{x} H(\xi - 1)e^{\xi} d\xi = (e^x - e)H(x - 1)$

(c) $\displaystyle\int_{0}^{\infty} H(\xi - x)e^{-\xi} d\xi = e^{-x}$

(d) $\displaystyle\int_{0}^{x} [H(\xi - 1) - H(\xi - 2)]d\xi$
$= H(x - 2) + (x - 1)[H(x - 1) - H(x - 2)]$

FOURIER INTEGRAL 11.3

Can the function $f(x) = e^{-x^2}$ shown in Fig. 11.7 be expanded in a Fourier series? Evidently not, since it is not periodic. Yet one might argue that it *is* periodic, but with an infinite period. Thus let us consider the limiting form of the classical Fourier series representation

$$f(x) = \sum_{n=0}^{\infty} \left(a_n \cos \frac{n\pi x}{\ell} + b_n \sin \frac{n\pi x}{\ell} \right), \qquad \text{(1a)}$$

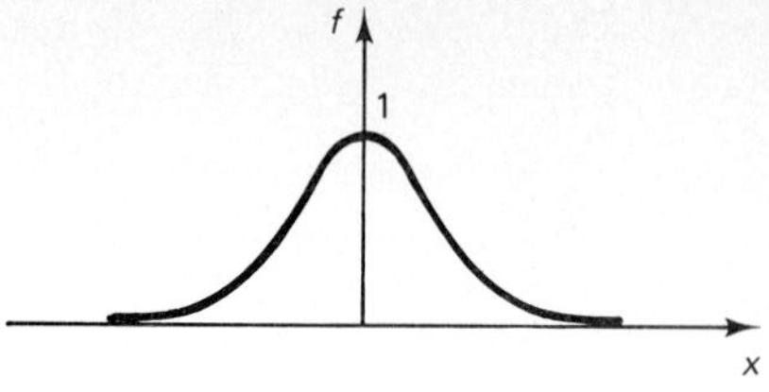

Fig. 11.7 Graph of $f(x) = e^{-x^2}$.

where

$$a_0 = \frac{1}{2\ell}\int_{-\ell}^{\ell} f(x)\,dx, \qquad a_n = \frac{1}{\ell}\int_{-\ell}^{\ell} f(x)\cos\frac{n\pi x}{\ell}\,dx, \qquad n = 1,2,\ldots$$
$$b_n = \frac{1}{\ell}\int_{-\ell}^{\ell} f(x)\sin\frac{n\pi x}{\ell}\,dx, \qquad n = 1, 2, \ldots \tag{1b}$$

as $\ell \to \infty$. We cannot simply *set* $\ell = \infty$ in (1), as that would yield nonsense. Rather, one needs to carry out a careful limit process, as ℓ *tends* to ∞.

First, note that the $n\pi/\ell$'s in (1a) are the *frequencies*—spatial , temporal, or whatever, depending on whether x is a space variable, time, or whatever. The set of all of the frequencies,

$$0, \frac{\pi}{\ell}, \frac{2\pi}{\ell}, \frac{3\pi}{\ell}, \ldots$$

is called the *frequency spectrum*. To illustrate, the frequency spectra corresponding to $\ell = \pi, 2\pi, 10\pi$ are as follows:

ℓ	*Frequencies*					
π	0	1	2	3	4	...
2π	0	0.5	1.0	1.5	2.0	...
10π	0	0.1	0.2	0.3	0.4	...

Observe carefully that as ℓ increases the spectrum becomes finer and finer, and evidently approaches a *continuous* spectrum (from 0 to ∞) as $\ell \to \infty$. It is therefore reasonable to expect that as $\ell \to \infty$ the (discrete) summation in (1a) will give way to a (continuous) integration from 0 to ∞. In fact, if f is sufficiently well behaved (as spelled out in Theorem 1 below), one can show that

$$\boxed{f(x) = \int_0^\infty [a(\omega)\cos\omega x + b(\omega)\sin\omega x]\,d\omega,} \tag{2a}$$

where

$$\boxed{\begin{aligned} a(\omega) &= \frac{1}{\pi}\int_{-\infty}^{\infty} f(x)\cos\omega x\,dx, \\ b(\omega) &= \frac{1}{\pi}\int_{-\infty}^{\infty} f(x)\sin\omega x\,dx. \end{aligned}} \tag{2b}$$

The right-hand side of (2a) is called the **Fourier integral** of f, and (2a) is called the Fourier integral representation of f.

Naturally, if f is even, then

$$a(\omega) = \frac{2}{\pi}\int_0^\infty f(x)\cos\omega x\,dx, \qquad b(\omega) = 0, \tag{3}$$

and if f is odd, then

$$a(\omega) = 0, \qquad b(\omega) = \frac{2}{\pi}\int_0^\infty f(x)\sin\omega x\,dx. \tag{4}$$

Alternatively, a single formula can be obtained by putting (2b) into (2a). In doing so, it is important to change the dummy variable of integration, x, in (2b), to some other letter, say ξ, to avoid confusion with the x's in (2a). Thus

$$\begin{aligned} f(x) &= \frac{1}{\pi}\int_0^\infty\int_{-\infty}^\infty (\cos\omega x\cos\omega\xi + \sin\omega x\sin\omega\xi) f(\xi)d\xi\,d\omega \\ &= \frac{1}{\pi}\int_0^\infty\int_{-\infty}^\infty f(\xi)\cos\omega(\xi - x)\,d\xi\,d\omega \end{aligned} \tag{5}$$

or, equivalently,

$$f(x) = \frac{1}{\pi}\int_0^\infty d\omega\int_{-\infty}^\infty f(\xi)\cos\omega(\xi - x)\,d\xi. \tag{6}$$

Whereas (2) has the advantage of looking "reasonable" and familiar, since it is so similar to the Fourier series (1), the equivalent forms (5) and (6) are more compact and are used more often than (2) in the scientific and mathematical literature. Rather than looking reasonable and familiar, however, (5) and (6) may very well appear confusing and redundant. For if we put f in on the right and get it out on the left, how can that possibly be useful? Yet notice that this same "redundancy" is exhibited by Fourier *series,* since if we put (1b) into (1a), we obtain the form

$$f(x) = \frac{1}{2\ell}\int_{-\ell}^{\ell} f(\xi)\,d\xi + \frac{1}{\ell}\sum_{n=1}^\infty \int_{-\ell}^{\ell} f(\xi)\cos\frac{n\pi}{\ell}(\xi - x)\,d\xi. \tag{7}$$

Thus we assert that just as Fourier series are important in theory and applications, so is the Fourier integral.

Theorem 1 *Fourier Integral Theorem*

If a function f is piecewise continuous on every bounded interval of the x axis, and if it is such that the integral

$$\int_{-\infty}^\infty |f(x)|\,dx$$

converges, then the Fourier integral of f,

$$\frac{1}{\pi}\int_0^\infty\int_{-\infty}^\infty f(\xi)\cos\omega(\xi - x)\,d\xi\,d\omega,$$

converges to the mean value $[f(x+) + f(x-)]/2$ at each point x $(-\infty < x < \infty)$ at which both left- and right-hand derivatives of f exist.*

* Our consideration of vector space and mean-square convergence in Section 10.5 is *not* being carried forward into the present chapter. Our point of view in Theorem 1, as elsewhere in this chapter, is that of *pointwise* convergence.

Proof of this theorem is given in Sec. 63 of CHURCHILL AND BROWN. It is instructive to compare this theorem with the analogous one for Fourier *series* on page 461.

Next, we examine two examples. The first illustrates the mathematical "mechanics" of Fourier integral representation, and the second involves a physical application.

EXAMPLE 1 *Rectangular Pulse.* Let us obtain the Fourier integral representation of the rectangular pulse f shown in Fig. 11.8. Since f is even, (3) applies and gives

$$\begin{aligned} a(\omega) &= \frac{2}{\pi}\int_0^\infty f(x)\cos\omega x\,dx = \frac{2F}{\pi}\int_0^L \cos\omega x\,dx \\ &= \frac{2F}{\pi}\frac{\sin\omega L}{\omega}, \end{aligned} \tag{8a}$$

$$b(\omega) = 0. \tag{8b}$$

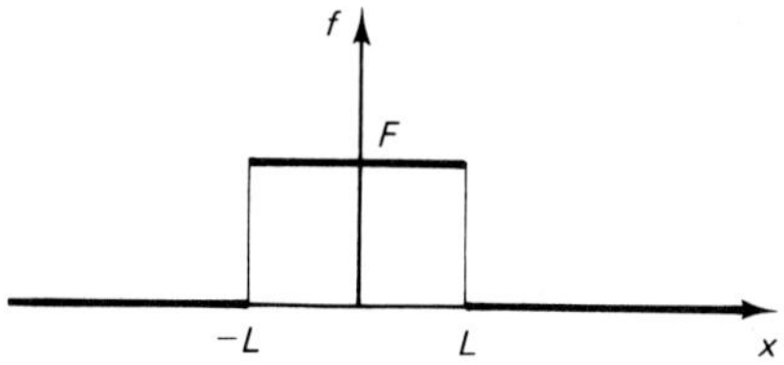

Fig. 11.8 Rectangular pulse.

According to (2a), then,

$$f(x) = \frac{2F}{\pi}\int_0^\infty \frac{\sin\omega L}{\omega}\cos\omega x\,d\omega. \tag{9}$$

Since f satisfies the conditions of Theorem 1, the Fourier integral of f, on the right-hand side of (9), must converge to $f(x)$ at each point x where f is continuous, and to the average value $F/2$ at the points $x = \pm L$ where f has jump discontinuities.

In our study of Fourier series we found it informative to plot some partial sums of the series, $s_N(x)$, in order to see just how the series goes about converging to the given function. Analogously, it should be instructive here to plot the "partial integral"

$$I_\Omega(x) \equiv \frac{2F}{\pi}\int_0^\Omega \frac{\sin\omega L}{\omega}\cos\omega x\,d\omega \tag{10}$$

for several values of Ω, so that we can see how the integral approaches the rectangular pulse as $\Omega \to \infty$. Fortunately, the integral in (10) can be evaluated (so that we need not resort to numerical integration) in terms of the function

$$\boxed{Si(x) = \int_0^x \frac{\sin t}{t}\,dt,} \tag{11}$$

which is known as the **sine integral,** and which is a tabulated function of x.* For if we recall the identity $2 \sin A \cos B = \sin (A + B) + \sin (A - B)$, we can express

$$
\begin{aligned}
I_\Omega(x) &= \frac{F}{\pi}\int_0^\Omega \frac{\sin \omega(L + x)}{\omega}\,d\omega + \frac{F}{\pi}\int_0^\Omega \frac{\sin \omega(L - x)}{\omega}\,d\omega \\
&= \frac{F}{\pi}\int_0^{\Omega(L+x)} \frac{\sin t}{t}\,dt + \frac{F}{\pi}\int_0^{\Omega(L-x)} \frac{\sin t}{t}\,dt \qquad (12)\\
&= \frac{F}{\pi}\{\mathrm{Si}[\Omega(L + x)] + \mathrm{Si}[\Omega(L - x)]\},
\end{aligned}
$$

which we have plotted in Fig. 11.9 for $\Omega = 4$, 16, and 128. Note the presence of the Gibbs phenomenon at the jump discontinuities.

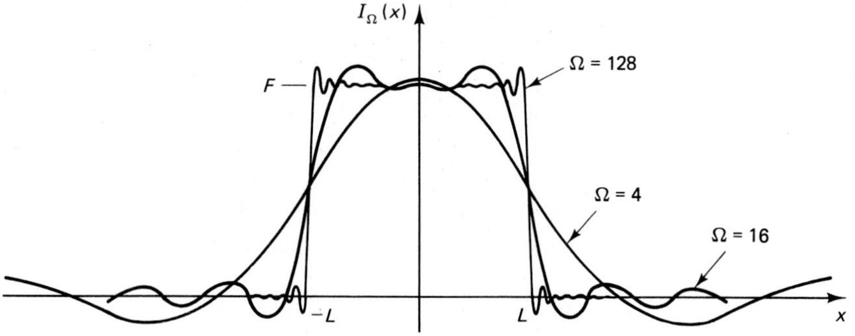

Fig. 11.9 Partial integral $I_\Omega(x)$.

It might also be helpful to sketch the Fourier coefficient $a(\omega)$, as we have in Fig. 11.10. Note from (2a) that $a(\omega)$ tells us the "harmonic content" of f, i.e., the amplitude of each $\cos \omega x$ harmonic present. ◀

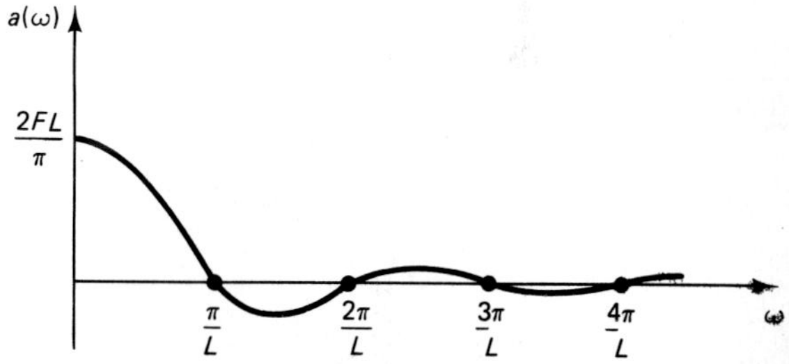

Fig. 11.10 Fourier coefficient $a(\omega)$.

EXAMPLE 2 *Infinite Beam on Elastic Foundation.* Here we consider the same problem as contained in Example 5 on page 468, except that instead of having a periodic (square wave) loading we have the nonperiodic (rectangular pulse) loading shown in Fig. 11.11. Recall that the beam's deflection $u(x)$ is governed by the dif-

* M. Abramowitz and I. Stegun (eds.), National Bureau of Standards Applied Mathematics Series, 1964. See also Y. L. Luke, *Mathematical Functions and their Approximation* (New York: Academic Press, 1975).

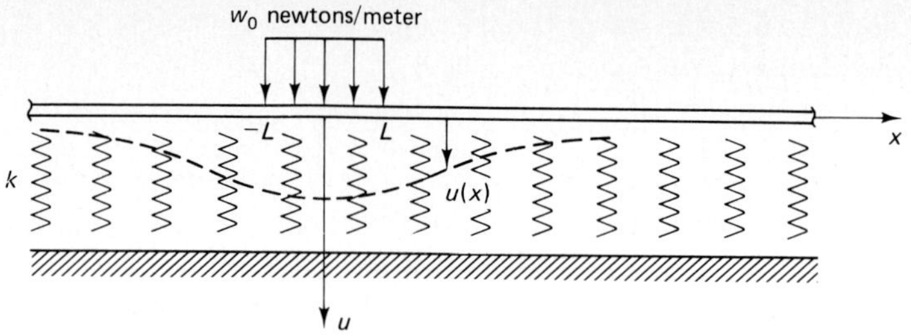

Fig. 11.11 Infinite beam on elastic foundation.

ferential equation

$$EIu'''' + ku = w(x), \tag{13}$$

where E, I, k are physical constants, and

$$w(x) = \begin{cases} w_0, & |x| < L \\ 0, & |x| > L \end{cases} \tag{14}$$

is the rectangular-pulse applied load distribution. Proceeding essentially as in Example 6 (which you may wish to review before continuing), we first express $w(x)$ in (13) in Fourier integral form. Observing that $w(x)$ in this example is the same as $f(x)$ in Example 1 (with F changed to w_0), we have, from (9),

$$w(x) = \frac{2w_0}{\pi} \int_0^\infty \frac{\sin \omega L}{\omega} \cos \omega x \, d\omega. \tag{15}$$

Next, we seek $u(x)$ in the Fourier integral form

$$u(x) = \int_0^\infty a(\omega) \cos \omega x \, d\omega, \tag{16}$$

where the $\sin \omega x$ part is omitted since $u(x)$ is evidently symmetric about $x = 0$, and where $a(\omega)$ remains to be determined. Formally differentiating (16) under the integral sign four times, and putting this result and (15) and (16) into (13), we have

$$\int_0^\infty (EI\omega^4 + k)a(\omega) \cos \omega x \, d\omega = \frac{2w_0}{\pi} \int_0^\infty \frac{\sin \omega L}{\omega} \cos \omega x \, d\omega. \tag{17}$$

Then, formally equating the coefficients of each cosine harmonic gives

$$(EI\omega^4 + k)a(\omega) = \frac{2w_0}{\pi} \frac{\sin \omega L}{\omega} \tag{18}$$

or

$$a(\omega) = \frac{2w_0}{\pi} \frac{\sin \omega L}{\omega} \frac{1}{EI\omega^4 + k}, \tag{19}$$

so that (16) becomes

$$u(x) = \frac{2w_0}{\pi} \int_0^\infty \frac{\sin \omega L}{\omega} \frac{\cos \omega x}{EI\omega^4 + k} \, d\omega. \tag{20}$$

This integral can be evaluated analytically by means of the "residue theorem" (given in Part V), but for our present purposes it will suffice to let (20) stand as it is.

COMMENT Recall that our derivation of (20) was only formal. If we wish to rigorously establish the correctness of (20), we need to verify that it does satisfy (13). To do that we need to justify differentiating the right-hand side of (20) under the integral sign four times. Unfortunately, our Theorem 1 on page 346 (the Leibniz rule) does not apply because of the infinite upper limit in (20). In view of this fact, and the fact that sufficiently powerful theorems are a bit more sophisticated, we elect to close this discussion by referring the interested reader to the book by Carslaw.* ◀

Here we have introduced the Fourier integral representation of functions as an outgrowth of the Fourier series concept. Our two brief examples have been intended to support the mathematical concept rather than to develop an easy fluency with a wide range of applications, because the Fourier *transform* will be a bit more "user friendly" for applications. Thus we turn to the Fourier transform in the next section, and then devote a full chapter to the Laplace transform.

11.3 EXERCISES

1. Derive the Fourier integral representations of the following functions. At which points, if any, does the Fourier integral fail to converge to $f(x)$? To what value does the integral converge at those points?

*(a) $f(x) = \begin{cases} 100, & 0 \le x \le 2 \\ 0, & x < 0, x > 2 \end{cases}$

(b) $f(x) = \begin{cases} x, & 0 \le x < L \\ 0, & x < 0, x \ge L \end{cases}$

(c) $f(x) = \begin{cases} x, & |x| \le L \\ 0, & |x| > L \end{cases}$

(d) $f(x) = \begin{cases} -x, & -5 < x \le 0 \\ 0, & x \le -5, x > 0 \end{cases}$

(e) $f(x) = \begin{cases} |x|, & -1 < x < 2 \\ 0, & x \le -1, x \ge 2 \end{cases}$

(f) $f(x) = \begin{cases} 10, & 0 \le x \le 3 \\ 5, & 6 \le x \le 9 \\ 0, & x < 0, 3 < x < 6, x > 9 \end{cases}$

*(g) $f(x) = \begin{cases} e^{-x}, & x \ge 0 \\ 0, & x < 0 \end{cases}$ Evaluate the Fourier integral of f at $x = 0$, and compare its value with $f(0)$.

(h) $f(x) = \begin{cases} e^{x}, & x \le 0 \\ 0, & x > 0 \end{cases}$ Evaluate the Fourier integral of f at $x = 0$, and compare its value with $f(0)$.

(i) $f(x) = e^{-|x|}$ (j) $f(x) = e^{-|x|} \sin x$

2. (a) Show that $Si(x)$ is an odd function of x.
(b) Using the known integral

$$Si(\infty) = \int_0^\infty \frac{\sin t}{t}\, dt = \frac{\pi}{2} \tag{a}$$

and recalling (12), show that

$$\lim_{\Omega \to \infty} f_\Omega(x) = \begin{cases} F, & |x| < L \\ F/2, & |x| = L \\ 0, & |x| > L \end{cases} \tag{b}$$

so that the Fourier integral (9) *does* converge to the rectangular pulse and (in accordance with Theorem 1) to the average values at the two jump discontinuities.

3. Comparing (2a) with the classical Fourier *series,* it may appear that $a(0)$ is analogous to the $a_0/2$ term in the Fourier series and represents the average value

*H. S. Carslaw, *Theory of Fourier Series and Integrals,* 2nd ed. (London: Macmillan, 1921), Sec. 86.

of f. Is it true that $a(0)$ is the average value of f, where, by the "average value of f" we mean $\lim_{A\to\infty} [(1/2A) \int_{-A}^{A} f(x)\, dx]$? Explain.

***4.** Rework Example 2 for the case where $w(x) = \delta(x)$, i.e., for the case of a point unit load at the origin. Leave the answer in integral form, as we have in (20). *Note:* Working with the delta function will require a rather formal approach. For example, you may notice that the Fourier integral representation of $\delta(x)$ is, strictly speaking, a divergent integral. Accept it, and proceed nonetheless.

5. (*Deflection of loaded string*) Related to the problem of a beam on an elastic foundation is the analogous problem for a flexible string. Imagine a string (of negligible mass per unit length) stretched along the x axis, over $-\infty < x < \infty$, by a tension of T newtons, and let $w(x)$ be an applied load distribution (newtons/meter), as sketched in the figure. If the displacement $u(x)$ of the string, away from the x axis, is resisted by a distributed spring of stiffness k (newtons per meter per meter), and the slope $u'(x)$ is sufficiently small over $-\infty < x < \infty$, then $u(x)$ is accurately governed by the differential equation $Tu''(x) - ku(x) = w(x)$, or

$$u'' - \alpha^2 u = f(x) \qquad (-\infty < x < \infty), \tag{a}$$

where $\alpha^2 \equiv k/T$ and $f(x) \equiv w(x)/T$. (Here we consider the *static* deflection. In our discussion of the *wave equation* in Chapter 16, we will derive this differential equation for the not-necessarily-static case.) Suppose that the loading $w(x)$ is sufficiently localized so that it makes sense to assume that $u(x)$ satisfies the boundary conditions

$$u \to 0, \qquad u' \to 0 \quad \text{as} \quad x \to \pm\infty \tag{b}$$

as well.

(a) Assume, for simplicity, that f is an even function of x. Proceeding essentially as in Example 2, derive the solution

$$u(x) = -\frac{1}{\pi}\int_0^\infty \frac{\cos \omega x}{\omega^2 + \alpha^2}\, d\omega \int_{-\infty}^{\infty} f(\xi) \cos \omega\xi \, d\xi. \tag{c}$$

Using the known integral

$$\int_0^\infty \frac{\cos at}{t^2 + 1}\, dt = \frac{\pi}{2} e^{-|a|}, \tag{d}$$

show that (c) can be reduced to the form

$$u(x) = -\frac{1}{2\alpha}\int_{-\infty}^{\infty} f(\xi) e^{-\alpha|x-\xi|}\, d\xi. \tag{e}$$

(b) Verify directly from (e) that if f is even, as assumed, then so is u.
(c) Use (e) to determine $u(x)$ for the case where $w(x) = \delta(x)$ [i.e., $f(x) = \delta(x)/T$]. Sketch the graph of u.
(d) Use (e) to determine $u(x)$ for the case where $w(x) = \begin{cases} 1, & |x| < L \\ 0, & |x| > L \end{cases}$. Sketch the graph of u.
(e) Show that the solution (e) holds whether or not f is an even function: f can be even, odd, or neither.
(f) Use (e) to obtain the solution for the case where the string is *finite*, namely, where it extends over $0 \le x \le \ell$, with $u(0) = u(\ell) = 0$. *Hint:* In this case, $w(x) = 0$ for $x < 0$ and for $x > \ell$, and we need to allow for point "reaction" forces F_1 and F_2 at the ends of the string, as shown in the accompanying sketch.

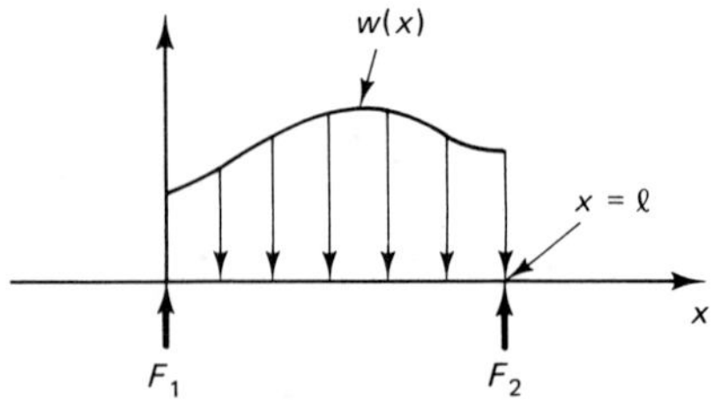

Thus (e) becomes

$$u(x) = -\frac{1}{2\alpha T}\left\{\int_0^\ell w(\xi) e^{-\alpha|x-\xi|}\, d\xi + \int_{-\infty}^{\infty} [-F_1\delta(\xi) - F_2\delta(\xi - \ell)] e^{-\alpha|x-\xi|}\, d\xi\right\},$$

and F_1, F_2 are found so that $u(0) = u(\ell) = 0$.

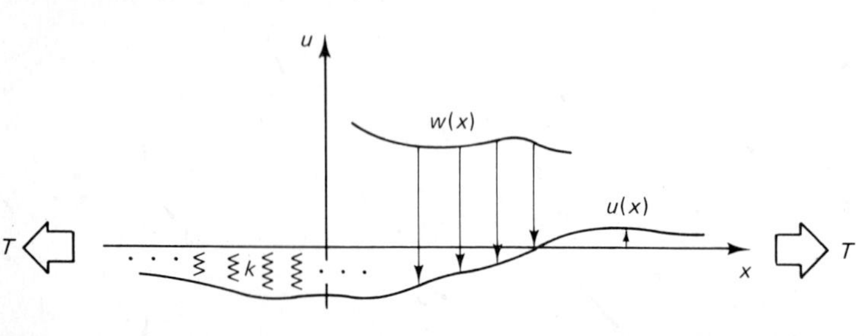

As noted in the introduction to this chapter, the Fourier transform amounts to a restatement of the Fourier integral formula

$$f(x) = \frac{1}{\pi}\int_0^\infty d\omega \int_{-\infty}^\infty f(\xi) \cos \omega (\xi - x)\, d\xi. \tag{1}$$

To accomplish that restatement we first reexpress (1) in an equivalent complex exponential form as follows:*

$$\begin{aligned} f(x) &= \frac{1}{\pi}\int_0^\infty d\omega \int_{-\infty}^\infty f(\xi) \left[\frac{e^{i\omega(\xi-x)} + e^{-i\omega(\xi-x)}}{2}\right] d\xi \\ &= \frac{1}{2\pi}\int_0^\infty e^{-i\omega x}\, d\omega \int_{-\infty}^\infty f(\xi)\, e^{i\omega\xi}\, d\xi \\ &\quad + \frac{1}{2\pi}\int_0^\infty e^{i\omega x}\, d\omega \int_{-\infty}^\infty f(\xi)\, e^{-i\omega\xi}\, d\xi. \end{aligned} \tag{2}$$

To combine the two terms on the right-hand side of (2), let us change the dummy integration variable from ω to "$-\omega$" in the first term. Thus

$$\begin{aligned} f(x) &= \frac{1}{2\pi}\int_0^{-\infty} e^{i\omega x}\, (-d\omega) \int_{-\infty}^\infty f(\xi)\, e^{-i\omega\xi}\, d\xi \\ &\quad + \frac{1}{2\pi}\int_0^\infty e^{i\omega x}\, d\omega \int_{-\infty}^\infty f(\xi)\, e^{-i\omega\xi}\, d\xi \\ &= \frac{1}{2\pi}\int_{-\infty}^{0} e^{i\omega x}\, d\omega \int_{-\infty}^\infty f(\xi)\, e^{-i\omega\xi}\, d\xi \\ &\quad + \frac{1}{2\pi}\int_0^\infty e^{i\omega x}\, d\omega \int_{-\infty}^\infty f(\xi)\, e^{-i\omega\xi}\, d\xi, \end{aligned} \tag{3}$$

so we have the desired form

$$f(x) = \frac{1}{2\pi}\int_{-\infty}^\infty e^{i\omega x}\, d\omega \int_{-\infty}^\infty f(\xi)\, e^{-i\omega\xi}\, d\xi. \tag{4}$$

We are now ready to introduce the so-called Fourier transform. Noting that $\int_{-\infty}^\infty f(\xi)e^{-i\omega\xi}\, d\xi$, in (4), is a function of ω, let us denote that function as $\hat{f}(\omega)$. That step splits (4) into the *pair* of equations

$$\hat{f}(\omega) = \int_{-\infty}^\infty f(\xi)e^{-i\omega\xi}\, d\xi \tag{5a}$$

and

$$f(x) = \frac{1}{2\pi}\int_{-\infty}^\infty \hat{f}(\omega)e^{i\omega x}\, d\omega. \tag{5b}$$

* Recall the formula $\cos x = (e^{ix} + e^{-ix})/2$, discussed in Section A.5.

Now, in (4) it was important to distinguish between the dummy integration variable ξ and the quantity x which, in (4), was regarded as fixed. But having split (4) into (5a) and (5b), we see that there are no x's in (5a), so we can change the dummy variable ξ, in (5a), to a new dummy variable x in order to minimize to nomenclature. Thus we have*

$$\hat{f}(\omega) = \int_{-\infty}^{\infty} f(x)e^{-i\omega x}\,dx, \tag{6a}$$

$$f(x) = \frac{1}{2\pi}\int_{-\infty}^{\infty} \hat{f}(\omega)e^{i\omega x}\,d\omega. \tag{6b}$$

In transform terminology, we call $\hat{f}(\omega)$ the **Fourier transform** of f and denote it, alternatively, as $\mathbf{F}\{f\}$. Then (6b) is the *inversion formula* since it gives us back f as the inverse of $\hat{\mathbf{f}}$, i.e., as $\mathbf{F}^{-1}\{\hat{f}\}$.

EXAMPLE 1 Given

$$f(x) = \begin{cases} e^{-ax}, & x > 0 \\ 0, & x < 0 \end{cases} = H(x)e^{-ax}, \qquad (a > 0) \tag{7}$$

determine its Fourier transform, $\hat{f}(\omega)$. From (6a),

$$\begin{aligned} \hat{f}(\omega) &= \int_{-\infty}^{\infty} H(x)e^{-ax}e^{-i\omega x}\,dx = \int_0^{\infty} e^{-(a+i\omega)x}\,dx \\ &= -\frac{e^{-(a+i\omega)x}}{a+i\omega}\bigg|_0^{\infty} = \frac{1}{a+i\omega} - \frac{1}{a+i\omega}\lim_{x\to\infty}(e^{-ax}e^{-i\omega x}) \\ &= \frac{1}{a+i\omega}. \end{aligned} \tag{8}$$

In fact, it is found that $\mathbf{F}\{H(x)e^{-ax}\} = 1/(a+i\omega)$ even if a is allowed to be complex, as long as Re $a > 0$ [Exercise 1(a)].† ◀

In principle, then, one can evaluate $\hat{f}(\omega)$ for a number of selected functions $f(x)$, and can tabulate them, as we have in Appendix B.‡ Such tables are useful, when we apply the Fourier transform method, in much the same way that integral tables are useful when we study, or apply, the elementary integral calculus.

* More generally, the pair

$$\hat{f}(\omega) = a\int_{-\infty}^{\infty} f(x)e^{-i\omega x}\,dx, \qquad f(x) = b\int_{-\infty}^{\infty} \hat{f}(\omega)e^{i\omega x}\,d\omega$$

is equivalent to (4) provided that $ab = 1/2\pi$. Whereas we have chosen $a = 1$, $b = 1/2\pi$, we wish to note that some authors, perhaps out of a greater sense of fair play, use $a = b = 1/\sqrt{2\pi}$.

† In case the last equality in (8) is unclear, observe that $|e^{-ax}e^{-i\omega x}| = |e^{-ax}|\,|e^{-i\omega x}| = e^{-ax}|\cos\omega x - i\sin\omega x| = e^{-ax}\sqrt{\cos^2\omega x + \sin^2\omega x} = e^{-ax} \to 0$ as $x \to \infty$. Also, the real and imaginary parts of a complex number $z = x + iy$ are defined as Re $z \equiv x$ and Im $z \equiv y$, respectively.

‡ The table provided in Appendix B is short but will suffice for our present purposes. A number of extensive tables of Fourier transforms are also available. See, for example, A. Erdèlyi (ed.), *Tables of Integral Transforms*, Vols. 1 and 2 (New York: McGraw-Hill, 1954). Volume 1 contains Fourier, Laplace, and Mellin transforms, and Volume 2 contains Hankel and various other transforms.

In addition to having a transform table at our disposal, it is important to be aware of various operational properties of the Fourier transform. In the discussion to follow, we limit our attention to three of the most important properties. We shall assume, sometimes without reiteration, that *each of the functions being transformed satisfies the conditions contained in the Fourier integral theorem on page 519.*

F1 *Linearity of the transform and its inverse.* For any scalars α, β and functions f, g,

$$\boxed{\mathbf{F}\{\alpha f + \beta g\} = \alpha \mathbf{F}\{f\} + \beta \mathbf{F}\{g\}} \tag{9}$$

and

$$\boxed{\mathbf{F}^{-1}\{\alpha \hat{f} + \beta \hat{g}\} = \alpha \mathbf{F}^{-1}\{\hat{f}\} + \beta \mathbf{F}^{-1}\{\hat{g}\}.} \tag{10}$$

These *linearity* properties follow immediately from the integral definitions of the transform and its inverse, because of the known (from the calculus) linearity of the Riemann integral. Of course, the right-hand sides of (9) and (10) may be expressed as $\alpha\hat{f}(\omega) + \beta\hat{g}(\omega)$ and $\alpha f(x) + \beta g(x)$, respectively.

F2 *Transform of the nth derivative.* If $f(x), f'(x), \ldots, f^{(n-1)}(x)$ all tend to zero as $x \to \pm\infty$, and $\int_{-\infty}^{\infty} |f^{(j)}(x)|\, dx$ converges for each $j = 0, 1, \ldots, n$, then

$$\boxed{\mathbf{F}\{f^{(n)}(x)\} = (i\omega)^n \hat{f}(\omega) \qquad (n = 0, 1, 2, \ldots).} \tag{11}$$

Proof Let us prove (11) by induction. First, observe that (11) holds, by definition, for $n = 0$. What we need to establish is that if it holds for $n = k$, it must also hold for $n = k + 1$. To do so, we integrate by parts:

$$\begin{aligned}
\mathbf{F}\{f^{(k+1)}(x)\} &= \int_{-\infty}^{\infty} f^{(k+1)}(x)e^{-i\omega x}\, dx \\
&= [f^{(k)}(x)e^{-i\omega x}]\Big|_{-\infty}^{\infty} + i\omega \int_{-\infty}^{\infty} f^{(k)}(x)e^{-i\omega x}\, dx \\
&= [f^{(k)}(x)e^{-i\omega x}]\Big|_{-\infty}^{\infty} + i\omega[(i\omega)^k \hat{f}(\omega)] \\
&= [f^{(k)}(x)e^{-i\omega x}]\Big|_{-\infty}^{\infty} + (i\omega)^{k+1}\hat{f}(\omega).
\end{aligned} \tag{12}$$

Now,*

$$|e^{-i\omega x}| = |\cos \omega x - i \sin \omega x| = \sqrt{\cos^2 \omega x + \sin^2 \omega x} = 1, \tag{13}$$

so that $|f^{(k)}(x)e^{-i\omega x}| = |f^{(k)}(x)|\,|e^{-i\omega x}| = |f^{(k)}(x)|$. Since $f^{(k)}(x) \to 0$ as $x \to \pm\infty$, by assumption, the boundary term in (12) drops out. Thus $\mathbf{F}\{f^{(k+1)}(x)\} = (i\omega)^{k+1}\hat{f}(\omega)$, so that (11) does hold for $n = k + 1$. This completes our proof by induction. ■

F3 *Fourier convolution.* We denote the **Fourier convolution** of f and g as $f * g$; it, too, is a function of x, defined as

$$(f * g)(x) \equiv \int_{-\infty}^{\infty} f(x - \xi)g(\xi)\, d\xi. \tag{14}$$

*The absolute value, or "modulus," of a complex number $a + ib$ is defined as $|a + ib| \equiv \sqrt{a^2 + b^2}$.

Then the **Fourier convolution theorem** states that

$$\boxed{\mathbf{F}\{f * g\} = \hat{f}(\omega)\hat{g}(\omega)} \tag{15}$$

or, equivalently, that

$$\boxed{\mathbf{F}^{-1}\{\hat{f}\hat{g}\} = f * g.} \tag{16}$$

Proof It suffices to prove (15) *or* (16). We will prove (15). We have

$$\begin{aligned}
\mathbf{F}\{f * g\} &= \int_{-\infty}^{\infty} \left\{ \int_{-\infty}^{\infty} f(x - \xi) g(\xi)\, d\xi \right\} e^{-i\omega x}\, dx \\
&= \int_{-\infty}^{\infty} g(\xi)\, d\xi \int_{-\infty}^{\infty} f(x - \xi) e^{-i\omega x}\, dx \\
&= \int_{-\infty}^{\infty} g(\xi)\, d\xi \int_{-\infty}^{\infty} f(\eta) e^{-i\omega(\xi + \eta)}\, d\eta \qquad (17) \\
&= \left(\int_{-\infty}^{\infty} g(\xi) e^{-i\omega\xi}\, d\xi \right) \left(\int_{-\infty}^{\infty} f(\eta) e^{-i\omega\eta}\, d\eta \right) \\
&= \hat{g}(\omega)\hat{f}(\omega),
\end{aligned}$$

as was to be shown; in the second equality we reversed the order of integration,* and in obtaining the third equality we entered the change of variables $x - \xi = \eta$. ■

Before leaving the Fourier convolution, let us us call attention to the commutative property of $f * g$, namely, that

$$f * g = g * f. \tag{18}$$

Proof of (18) is simple and is left for the exercises.

EXAMPLE 2 Find the inverse of $e^{-2|\omega|}$. Well, item 4 in Appendix B states that

$$\mathbf{F}^{-1}\left\{ \frac{\pi}{a} e^{-a|\omega|} \right\} = \frac{1}{x^2 + a^2}. \tag{19}$$

Further, it follows from the linearity property F1 that

$$\mathbf{F}^{-1}\left\{ \frac{\pi}{a} e^{-a|\omega|} \right\} = \frac{\pi}{a} \mathbf{F}^{-1}\{e^{-a|\omega|}\}. \tag{20}$$

Finally, comparing (19) and (20), and setting $a = 2$ gives

$$\mathbf{F}^{-1}\{e^{-2|\omega|}\} = \frac{2}{\pi} \frac{1}{x^2 + 4}. \quad ◀ \tag{21}$$

* Sufficient conditions for the validity of this reversal are that f and g both be *absolutely integrable*, i.e., that $\int_{-\infty}^{\infty} |f(x)|\, dx$ and $\int_{-\infty}^{\infty} |g(x)|\, dx$ both converge. But these conditions have already been assumed (in the italicized statement immediately preceding property F1). For a detailed discussion, see T. M. Apostol, *Mathematical Analysis* (Reading, Mass.: Addison-Wesley, 1957), p. 491.

EXAMPLE 3 Derive item 3, in Appendix B, from items 1 and 2. First, notice that

$$\frac{1}{\omega^2 + a^2} = \frac{1}{a + i\omega}\frac{1}{a - i\omega}, \tag{22}$$

and that the inverse of each of the two factors on the right-hand side is known. Specifically,

$$\mathbf{F}^{-1}\left\{\frac{1}{a + i\omega}\right\} = H(x)e^{-ax} \tag{23}$$

from item 1, and

$$\mathbf{F}^{-1}\left\{\frac{1}{a - i\omega}\right\} = (1 - H(x))e^{ax} \tag{24}$$

from item 2. Then, according to the convolution property,

$$\begin{aligned}\mathbf{F}^{-1}\left\{\frac{1}{\omega^2 + a^2}\right\} &= [H(x)e^{-ax}] * [(1 - H(x))e^{ax}] \\ &= \int_{-\infty}^{\infty} H(x - \xi)e^{-a(x-\xi)}(1 - H(\xi))e^{a\xi}\, d\xi \\ &= e^{-ax}\int_{-\infty}^{0} H(x - \xi)e^{2a\xi}\, d\xi.\end{aligned} \tag{25}$$

To evaluate the last integral, it is convenient to treat the cases $x > 0$ and $x < 0$ separately. For $x > 0$,

$$\mathbf{F}^{-1}\left\{\frac{1}{\omega^2 + a^2}\right\} = e^{-ax}\int_{-\infty}^{0} e^{2a\xi}\, d\xi = \frac{e^{-ax}}{2a}, \tag{26}$$

and for $x < 0$,

$$\mathbf{F}^{-1}\left\{\frac{1}{\omega^2 + a^2}\right\} = e^{-ax}\int_{-\infty}^{x} e^{2a\xi}\, d\xi = \frac{e^{ax}}{2a}, \tag{27}$$

so

$$\mathbf{F}^{-1}\left\{\frac{1}{\omega^2 + a^2}\right\} = \frac{e^{-a|x|}}{2a} \qquad (-\infty < x < \infty). \tag{28}$$

Finally, linearity gives

$$\mathbf{F}^{-1}\left\{\frac{2a}{\omega^2 + a^2}\right\} = 2a\mathbf{F}^{-1}\left\{\frac{1}{\omega^2 + a^2}\right\} = 2a\frac{e^{-a|x|}}{2a} = e^{-a|x|}, \tag{29}$$

which is the desired result.

COMMENT Another line of approach that comes to mind is the following. Instead of factoring $1/(\omega^2 + a^2)$ as we have in (22), we can express

$$\frac{1}{\omega^2 + a^2} = \frac{1}{2a}\frac{1}{a + i\omega} + \frac{1}{2a}\frac{1}{a - i\omega} \tag{30}$$

and use linearity together with items 1 and 2. We leave this calculation for the reader. ◀

We close this section with a physical application.

EXAMPLE 4 *Infinite Beam on Elastic Foundation.* We begin by apologizing for considering this problem now for the third time—first for a periodic loading using Fourier series, then for a rectangular pulse loading using the Fourier integral, and now again using the Fourier transform. Our intention, in keeping the physics essentially the same from one case to the next is to permit us to focus instead on the slight shifting of the mathematics in passing from the Fourier series to the Fourier integral to the Fourier transform.

Recall that we wish to solve

$$EIu'''' + ku = w(x) \tag{31}$$

for the deflection $u(x)$, where E, I, k are physical constants, and where $w(x)$ is a prescribed load distribution. Taking the Fourier transform of (31) (i.e., multiplying each term by $e^{-i\omega x}\,dx$ and integrating from $x = -\infty$ to $x = +\infty$), we have

$$\mathbf{F}\{EIu'''' + ku\} = \mathbf{F}\{w(x)\}. \tag{32}$$

Then

$$EI\mathbf{F}\{u''''\} + k\mathbf{F}\{u\} = \mathbf{F}\{w\} \tag{33}$$

by (9), and

$$EI\,(i\omega)^4\hat{u} + k\hat{u} = \hat{w} \tag{34}$$

by (11) (if u, u', u'', u''' all tend to zero as $x \to \pm\infty$, and if $\int_{-\infty}^{\infty} |u^{(j)}(x)|\,dx$ converges for $j = 0, 1, 2, 3$), so

$$\hat{u} = \frac{\hat{w}}{EI\omega^4 + k}. \tag{35}$$

To invert (35), let us first rewrite it in the more suggestive form

$$\hat{u} = \left(\frac{1}{EI\omega^4 + k}\right)(\hat{w}). \tag{36}$$

Note carefully that the inverse of the product on the right-hand side is *not* the product of the two inverses, but rather, the Fourier *convolution* of the two inverses:

$$u(x) = \mathbf{F}^{-1}\left\{\frac{1}{EI\omega^4 + k}\right\} * \mathbf{F}^{-1}\{\hat{w}\} = \mathbf{F}^{-1}\left\{\frac{1}{EI\omega^4 + k}\right\} * w(x). \tag{37}$$

Now, from item 5 in Appendix B,

$$\mathbf{F}^{-1}\left\{\frac{1}{EI\omega^4 + k}\right\} = \frac{\alpha}{2k}e^{-\alpha|x|/\sqrt{2}} \sin\left(\frac{\alpha\,|x|}{\sqrt{2}} + \frac{\pi}{4}\right) \tag{38}$$

where $\alpha = (k/EI)^{1/4}$, so that (37) gives, as the solution,

$$u(x) = \frac{\alpha}{2k}\int_{-\infty}^{\infty} w(\xi)e^{-\alpha|x-\xi|/\sqrt{2}} \sin\left(\frac{\alpha\,|x-\xi|}{\sqrt{2}} + \frac{\pi}{4}\right) d\xi. \tag{39}$$

COMMENT 1 Notice that we came "full cycle" on $w(x)$: *Transforming the* $w(x)$ term in (31) we obtained $\hat{w}$, but then in inverting (36) by the convolution theorem we inverted $\hat{w}$ to obtain $w(x)$ once again. Thus, given any particular $w(x)$, it would have been wasteful to have actually *worked out* its Fourier transform $\hat{w}$.

COMMENT 2 It is always important to check our results in various ways. In this example a simple special case comes to mind, which can be used as a partial check on our solution (39). Specifically, if $w(x) = \text{constant} = W$, say, then it seems clear that the beam should be displaced uniformly; i.e., we should have $u(x) =$ constant, too. Well, if $w(x) = W$ and $u(x)$ is a constant, then (31) becomes $0 + ku = W$, so $u(x) = W/k$. Is this result the same as

$$u(x) = \frac{\alpha W}{2k} \int_{-\infty}^{\infty} e^{-\alpha|x-\xi|/\sqrt{2}} \sin\left(\frac{\alpha|x-\xi|}{\sqrt{2}} + \frac{\pi}{4}\right) d\xi \tag{40}$$

given by (39)? Although we leave the evaluation of the integral in (40) for the exercises, we note that the result is indeed the same, $u(x) = W/k$, and this partial check serves to inspire some confidence in (39).

In fact, observe that the correctness of (39) for the case $w(x) = \text{constant} = W$ is a pleasant surprise since a number of assumptions, built into our solution, break down in that case. For example, $\int_{-\infty}^{\infty} |w(x)|\,dx = \int_{-\infty}^{\infty} W\,dx$ does *not* converge, and u does *not* tend to zero as $x \to \pm\infty$. Without belaboring the point, we mention that this "bonus" can be traced, at least in part, to the interchange in the order of integration in the second equality in (17). In any case, the moral is that it is often best to proceed formally until the answer is in hand. *If it can be verified that the answer thus obtained does indeed satisfy all of the specified requirements* (such as a differential equation, boundary conditions, etc.) *one need not worry about the rigor of intermediate steps.* ◀

Additional applications of the Fourier transform, to the solution of ordinary differential equations, are contained in the exercises. Its application to the solution of *partial* differential equations is covered in Part IV.

11.4 EXERCISES

1. Given $f(x)$ determine $\hat{f}(\omega)$ by actually evaluating the integral in (6a). If possible, compare your result with a corresponding item in Appendix B.

(a) $H(x)e^{-ax}$ (Re $a > 0$)
(b) $[1 - H(x)]e^{ax}$ (Re $a > 0$)
(c) $e^{-a|x|}$ $(a > 0)$ *Hint*: Show that $\hat{f}(\omega) = 2\int_0^\infty e^{-ax}\cos\omega x\,dx$, and then integrate by parts twice.
(d) $H(x + a) - H(x - a)$ $(a > 0)$
*(e) $[H(x) - H(x - 1)]x$
(f) $[H(x + 1) - H(x - 1)]|x|$ (g) $\delta(x - a)$.

2. Given $\hat{f}(\omega)$, determine $f(x)$ by actually evaluating the integral in (6b). If possible, compare your result with a corresponding item in Appendix B.

(a) $e^{-a|\omega|}$ $(a > 0)$
*(b) $H(\omega + a) - H(\omega - a)$ $(a > 0)$
(c) $[H(\omega) - H(\omega - 1)]\omega$
(d) $H(\omega)e^{-a\omega}$ (Re $a > 0$)
(e) $[H(\omega + 1) - H(\omega - 1)]|\omega|$
(f) $\delta(\omega - a)$

3. Prove (18).

4. (*Preservation of evenness and oddness*)
(a) Show that *f(x) is an even function of x if and only if $\hat{f}(\omega)$ is an even function of ω.*
(b) Show that *f(x) is an odd function of x if and only if $\hat{f}(\omega)$ is an odd function of ω.*

5. (*Extension of transform tables*) It follows from the results in Exercise 4 that the transform of the even and odd parts of $f(x)$ are the even and odd parts of $\hat{f}(\omega)$, respectively. This result can be used to wring out more information from a given transform table. For example, consider item 1 in Appendix B. Breaking f and $\hat{f}$ into even and odd parts, show that

$$\mathbf{F}\{e^{-a|x|}\} = \frac{2a}{\omega^2 + a^2} \tag{a}$$

and

$$\mathbf{F}\{(\operatorname{sgn} x)e^{-a|x|}\} = -\frac{i\omega}{\omega^2 + a^2}, \tag{b}$$

where $\operatorname{sign} x \equiv \begin{cases} +1, & x > 0 \\ -1, & x < 0 \end{cases}$ (and may be read as "sign of x"). Of these two results, observe that (a) is identical to item 3, but that (b) is not contained in, and therefore "extends," the table.

6. (*Reciprocity relations*) Derive the reciprocity relations

$$\boxed{\mathbf{F}\{\hat{f}(x)\} = 2\pi f(-\omega)} \tag{a}$$

and

$$\boxed{\mathbf{F}^{-1}\{f(-\omega)\} = \frac{\hat{f}(x)}{2\pi}.} \tag{b}$$

7. (*Extension of transform tables*) The reciprocity relations (a) and (b) in Exercise 6 can be used to extend a given transform table. For example,

(a) Use (a) and item 3 in Appendix B to show that

$$\mathbf{F}\left\{\frac{2a}{x^2 + a^2}\right\} = 2\pi e^{-a|\omega|} \qquad (a > 0),$$

or, equivalently,

$$\mathbf{F}\left\{\frac{1}{x^2 + a^2}\right\} = \frac{\pi}{a}e^{-a|\omega|} \qquad (a > 0).$$

(In this case the result does not extend our table since it is already contained as item 4.)

(b) Use (a) and item 6 in Appendix B to show that

$$\mathbf{F}\left\{\frac{\sin ax}{x}\right\} = \begin{cases} \pi, & |\omega| < a \\ 0, & |\omega| > a \end{cases} \qquad (a > 0).$$

(c) Use (a) and item 2 in Appendix B to show that

$$\mathbf{F}\left\{\frac{1}{a - ix}\right\} = \begin{cases} 2\pi e^{-a\omega}, & \omega > 0 \\ 0, & \omega < 0 \end{cases} \qquad (\operatorname{Re} a < 0).$$

8. Evaluate the integral in (40) and thus verify that $u(x) = W/k$, as we claimed in the text. *Hint:* Break the integral into two parts, one from $-\infty$ to x and one form x to ∞, and then set $\alpha(\xi - x)/\sqrt{2} = t$.

9. Derive entry 10 in Appendix B.

10. Derive entry 11 in Appendix B from entry 10.

11. Derive entry 12 in Appendix B from entry 10.

12. Derive entry 16 in Appendix B by formally differentiating both sides of

$$\hat{f}(\omega) = \int_{-\infty}^{\infty} f(x)e^{-i\omega x}\,dx.$$

13. Derive entry 19 in Appendix B. *Hint:* Integrate by parts.

14. Derive the *translation formulas*

$$\boxed{\begin{aligned} &\mathbf{F}\{g(x + a)\} = e^{ia\omega}\hat{g}(\omega), \\ &\mathbf{F}^{-1}\{\hat{g}(\omega + a)\} = e^{-iax}g(x) \end{aligned}} \tag{a}$$

from the items given in Appendix B.

15. Evaluate the following using Appendix B. You may need to use one or more of the entries 10 to 20 in conjunction with one or more of the entries 1 to 9. Identify, by number, the entries that you use.

*(a) $\mathbf{F}\{4x^2e^{-3|x|}\}$

*(b) $\mathbf{F}\{xe^{-x^2}\}$

(c) $\mathbf{F}\left\{\dfrac{\cos 3x}{x^2 + 2}\right\}$

(d) $\mathbf{F}\left\{\dfrac{\sin 2x}{4x^2 + 3}\right\}$

(e) $\mathbf{F}\left\{\dfrac{3}{2x^2 + 1} - 5e^{-|x|}\right\}$

(f) $\mathbf{F}\{e^{-|x|} + e^{-3|x+2|}\}$

*(g) $\mathbf{F}^{-1}\left\{\dfrac{4\sin\omega}{\omega} - \dfrac{1}{\sqrt{|\omega|}}\right\}$

*(h) $\mathbf{F}^{-1}\{e^{-2|\omega - 3|}\}$

(i) $\mathbf{F}^{-1}\left\{\dfrac{9}{2\omega + i}\right\}$

(j) $\mathbf{F}^{-1}\{e^{-\omega^2+4\omega}\}$

(k) $\mathbf{F}^{-1}\{e^{-|\omega|}\cos\omega\}$

(l) $\mathbf{F}^{-1}\{\omega e^{-3\omega^2}\}$

(m) $\mathbf{F}^{-1}\left\{\dfrac{1}{\omega^2 + i\omega + 2}\right\}$

(n) $\mathbf{F}^{-1}\left\{\dfrac{\omega}{\omega^2 + 1}\right\}$

16. Applying the Fourier transform to the problem

$$u'' - \alpha^2 u = f(x), \qquad u(x) \to 0,$$
$$u'(x) \to 0 \quad \text{as} \quad x \to \pm\infty \tag{a}$$

show that

$$\hat{u}(\omega) = -\frac{\hat{f}(\omega)}{\omega^2 + \alpha^2}, \tag{b}$$

and derive from this result the solution

$$u(x) = -\frac{1}{2\alpha}\int_{-\infty}^{\infty} e^{-\alpha|x-\xi|} f(\xi)\, d\xi. \tag{c}$$

(This is the "loaded string problem," which was solved in Exercise 5 of Section 11.3 by the Fourier integral method.)

17. (*Pollution in a river*) Suppose that a chemical plant discharges a certain pollutant, dibolic, into an initially clear river at the rate of Q (grams/second). We wish to determine the resulting steady-state distribution of pollutant in the river, i.e., its concentration c (grams/meter^3). Measure x along the river, positive downstream and zero at the chemical plant, as in the figure. The river flows with velocity U (meters/second), and has a cross-sectional area A, both of which, for simplicity, are assumed to be constant. Also for simplicity, suppose that c is a function of x only; i.e., it is a constant over each cross section of the stream. This is evidently a poor approximation near the plant, where we expect appreciable across-stream and vertical variations in c, but it should suffice if we are concerned mostly with the concentration variation far upstream and downstream (for $|x|$ greater than several river widths, say). Then it can be shown that $c(x)$ is governed by the differential equation

$$kc'' - Uc' - \beta c = -\frac{Q}{A}\delta(x), \tag{a}$$

where k (meters^2/second) is a diffusion constant, β (grams per second per gram) is a chemical decay constant, and $\delta(x)$ is a delta function. [Physically, (a) expresses a mass balance between the *input* $Q\delta(x)/A$, the transport of pollutant by *diffusion*, kc'', the transport of pollutant by *convection* with the moving stream, Uc', and by disappearance through *chemical decay*, βc.]

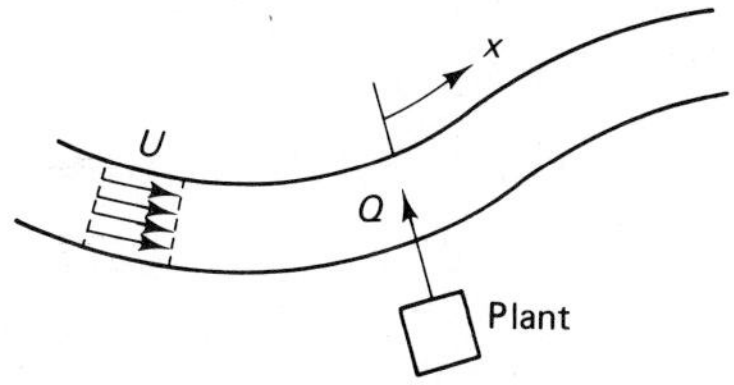

(a) Applying the Fourier transform to (a), show that

$$c(x) = \mathbf{F}^{-1}\left\{\frac{Q}{A}\frac{1}{k\omega^2 + iU\omega + \beta}\right\}. \tag{b}$$

(b) Expanding $1/(k\omega^2 + iU\omega + \beta)$ in partial fractions, and then using Appendix B, show that (b) gives

$$c(x) = \begin{cases} c_0 e^{-\Omega_- x}, & x < 0 \\ c_0 e^{-\Omega_+ x}, & x > 0 \end{cases}, \tag{c}$$

where

$$c_0 = \frac{Q}{A\sqrt{U^2 + 4k\beta}},$$

$$\Omega_\pm = \frac{1}{2k}(\pm\sqrt{U^2 + 4k\beta} - U).$$

(c) Sketch the graph of $c(x)$ and state the qualitative effect of increasing β.

18. (*Fourier sine and cosine transforms*) Beginning with the Fourier integral formula in the form

$$f(x) = \frac{1}{\pi}\int_0^{\infty} d\omega \int_{-\infty}^{\infty} f(\xi)\,(\cos \omega\xi \cos \omega x + \sin \omega\xi \sin \omega x)\, d\xi, \tag{a}$$

show that

(a) If $f(x)$ is an *even* function then (a) is equivalent to the pair of equations

$$\hat{f}_c(\omega) = \int_0^{\infty} f(x) \cos \omega x\, dx, \tag{b}$$

$$f(x) = \frac{2}{\pi}\int_0^{\infty} \hat{f}_c(\omega) \cos \omega x\, d\omega. \tag{c}$$

$\hat{f}_c(\omega)$ is also denoted as $\mathbf{F}_c\{f(x)\}$ and is called the **Fourier cosine transform of f.** The inverse transform is $\mathbf{F}_c^{-1}\{\hat{f}_c(\omega)\} = f(x)$.

(b) If $f(x)$ is an *odd* function, then (a) is equivalent to the pair of equations

$$\hat{f}_s(\omega) = \int_0^{\infty} f(x) \sin \omega x\, dx, \tag{d}$$

$$f(x) = \frac{2}{\pi}\int_0^{\infty} \hat{f}_s(\omega) \sin \omega x\, d\omega. \tag{e}$$

$\hat{f}_s(\omega)$ is also denoted as $\mathbf{F}_s\{f(x)\}$ and is called the **Fourier sine transform of f.** The inverse transform is $\mathbf{F}_s^{-1}\{\hat{f}_s(\omega)\} = f(x)$. *Note:* Observe carefully that (a) holds on $-\infty < x < \infty$, and hence so does (c). If (c) holds on $-\infty < x < \infty$, it certainly holds on $0 \le x < \infty$. Furthermore, (b) only involves values of $f(x)$ on $0 \le x < \infty$. Thus, alternatively, we may regard the x domain in (b) and (c) as only the semi-infinite interval $0 \le x < \infty$. In other words, *(b) and (c) may be used in applications in which the x interval is* $\mathbf{0 \le x < \infty}$. *Similarly, for (d) and (e).*

(c) Show that

$$\mathbf{F}_c\{f''(x)\} = -f'(0) - \omega^2 \hat{f}_c(\omega) \tag{f}$$

if $f(\infty) = f'(\infty) = 0$. [By $f(\infty) = 0$, for example, we mean that $f \to 0$ as $x \to \infty$.]

(d) Show that

$$\mathbf{F}_s\{f''(x)\} = \omega f(0) - \omega^2 \hat{f}_s(\omega) \tag{g}$$

if $f(\infty) = f'(\infty) = 0$.

19. (*Application of Fourier sine and cosine transforms*) (a) Consider the problem

$$\begin{aligned} u'' - k^2 u = f(x), \qquad u(0) = u_0, \\ u(\infty) = u'(\infty) = 0 \end{aligned} \tag{a}$$

on $0 \le x < \infty$. Since the x domain is $0 \le x < \infty$, the Fourier sine and cosine transforms may be applied. Considering the Fourier cosine transform, observe from (f) of Exercise 18 that $\mathbf{F}_c\{u''\} = -u'(0) - \omega^2 \hat{u}_c(\omega)$, but $u'(0)$ is not prescribed. Thus, turning to the Fourier sine transform, observe from (g) of Exercise 18 that $\mathbf{F}_s\{u''\} = u(0) - \omega^2 \hat{u}_s(\omega)$, which looks fine inasmuch as $u(0)$ *is* given. Thus, apply the Fourier sine transform to (a) and show that

$$u(x) = u_0 \mathbf{F}_s^{-1}\left\{\frac{\omega}{\omega^2 + k^2}\right\} - \mathbf{F}_s^{-1}\left\{\frac{\hat{f}_s(\omega)}{\omega^2 + k^2}\right\}. \tag{b}$$

Note: Although you need not evaluate the inverses in (b), we might note that the second one can be evaluated by means of the Fourier sine transform convolution theorem—which we have not given, but which can be found on p. 264 of F. B. Hildebrand, *Advanced Calculus for Applications*, 2nd ed. (Englewood Cliffs, N.J.: Prentice-Hall, 1976).

(b) Given the problem

$$\begin{aligned} u'' - k^2 u = f(x), \qquad u'(0) = u_0', \\ u(\infty) = u'(\infty) = 0, \end{aligned} \tag{c}$$

show that

$$u(x) = -u_0' \mathbf{F}_c^{-1}\left\{\frac{1}{\omega^2 + k^2}\right\} - \mathbf{F}_c^{-1}\left\{\frac{\hat{f}_c(\omega)}{\omega^2 + k^2}\right\}. \tag{d}$$

11.5 DERIVATION OF THE LAPLACE TRANSFORM FROM THE FOURIER INTEGRAL

Recall from Section 11.4 that a restatement of the Fourier integral gave us the *Fourier transform*. Particularly important applications of the Fourier transform involved the solution of linear constant-coefficient ODE (ordinary differential equation) boundary value problems on the doubly infinite interval $-\infty < x < \infty$, problems such as

$$\begin{aligned} u'' - k^2 u = f(x) \qquad (-\infty < x < \infty) \\ u \text{ and } u' \to 0 \text{ as } x \to \pm\infty, \end{aligned} \tag{1}$$

where primes denote d/dx's. We then brought *semi*-infinite boundary value problems, such as

$$\begin{aligned} u'' - k^2 u = f(x) \qquad (0 \le x < \infty) \\ u(0) = u_0, \quad u \text{ and } u' \to 0 \quad \text{as} \quad x \to \infty \end{aligned} \tag{2}$$

within our scope by developing the *Fourier sine and cosine transforms,* although that material was presented only in the exercises.

A third important case, not yet covered, is that of *initial*-value problems, such as

$$\begin{aligned} \ddot{x} - k^2 x = f(t) \qquad (0 \le t < \infty) \\ x(0) = x_0, \quad \dot{x}(0) = \dot{x}_0, \end{aligned} \tag{3}$$

where dots denote d/dt's. Here we have switched to an independent variable t because in problems of initial-value type the independent variable is often the time t, with $t = 0$ marking the "initial time," or starting time. To be able to handle initial value problems, we go back to the Fourier integral once again and develop another integral transform—the *Laplace transform.*

As indicated above, we are concerned here with functions $f(t)$ defined on the semi-infinite interval $0 \le t < \infty$. We can adapt the Fourier integral formula

$$f(t) = \frac{1}{2\pi}\int_{-\infty}^{\infty} e^{i\omega t}\,d\omega \int_{-\infty}^{\infty} f(\tau)e^{-i\omega\tau}\,d\tau \tag{4}$$

to this case by defining $f(t) \equiv 0$ for $t < 0$ in (4). This step gives

$$\frac{1}{2\pi}\int_{-\infty}^{\infty} e^{i\omega t}\,d\omega \int_{0}^{\infty} f(\tau)e^{-i\omega\tau}\,d\tau = \begin{cases} 0, & t < 0 \\ f(t), & t > 0. \end{cases} \tag{5}$$

Limiting our attention to the case $t > 0$ from this point onward, the right-hand side of (5) is $f(t)$, so (5) becomes

$$f(t) = \frac{1}{2\pi}\int_{-\infty}^{\infty} e^{i\omega t}\,d\omega \int_{0}^{\infty} f(\tau)e^{-i\omega\tau}\,d\tau \qquad (t > 0). \tag{6}$$

Unfortunately, this result is of rather limited use since the τ integral, $\int_0^\infty f(\tau)e^{-i\omega\tau}\,d\tau$, is divergent* for many functions of important interest—such as $f(t) = H(t - t_0)$, $\sin t$, t, and e^t.

Nevertheless, suppose that f satisfies the following two rather mild conditions.

1. f is **piecewise continuous**† on $0 \le t \le t_0$ for each finite t_0 (no matter how large).
2. f is **exponential order** as $t \to \infty$; i.e., there exist real constants K, c, and T such that

$$|f(t)| \le Ke^{ct} \tag{7}$$

for all $t > T$.

This class of functions is sufficiently extensive for our purposes, and even includes exponential growth. For example, $f(t) = 1/(t + 3)$, $H(t - 1) - H(t - 3)$, t^2, and e^{8t} all satisfy these conditions.

Now, if $f(t)$ is of exponential order, the τ integral in (6) may very well diverge, so that (6) becomes useless. However, notice that if $f(t)$ satisfies (7), the constructed function $e^{-\gamma t}f(t)$ dies out rapidly as $t \to \infty$ if we choose $\gamma > c$, because $|e^{-\gamma t}f(t)| \le Ke^{-(\gamma - c)t}$ for all $t \ge T$. As verified in Section 12.3, this decay suffices to ensure the convergence of the τ integral in (6). Thus, in place of f in (6) let us put the function $e^{-\gamma t}f$:

$$e^{-\gamma t}f(t) = \frac{1}{2\pi}\int_{-\infty}^{\infty} e^{i\omega t}\,d\omega \int_{0}^{\infty} e^{-\gamma\tau}f(\tau)e^{-i\omega\tau}\,d\tau, \tag{8}$$

for $t > 0$. Realizing that t is a constant insofar as the ω and τ integrations are concerned, we can multiply both sides of (8) by $e^{\gamma t}$ and obtain

$$f(t) = \frac{1}{2\pi}\int_{-\infty}^{\infty} e^{(\gamma + i\omega)t}\,d\omega \int_{0}^{\infty} f(\tau)e^{-(\gamma + i\omega)\tau}\,d\tau, \tag{9}$$

* Convergence and divergence of infinite integrals are discussed in Section 12.2.
† Piecewise continuity was defined on page 460.

the form of which suggests the change of variables $\gamma + i\omega = s$. Then since γ is a constant, $d\omega = ds/i$, so (9) becomes

$$f(t) = \frac{1}{2\pi i}\int_{\gamma-i\infty}^{\gamma+i\infty} e^{st}\, ds \int_0^\infty f(\tau)e^{-s\tau}\, d\tau. \tag{10}$$

Observe that as ω goes from $-\infty$ to ∞ on the real axis, s goes from $\gamma - i\infty$ to $\gamma + i\infty$ in the complex s-plane, as shown in Fig. 11.12. Finally, defining the τ integral in (10) to be the **Laplace transform** of f, say $\bar{f}(s)$, (10) splits into the pair of equations

$$\mathbf{L}\{f(t)\} = \bar{f}(s) = \int_0^\infty f(t)e^{-st}\, dt, \tag{11a}$$

$$\mathbf{L}^{-1}\{\bar{f}(s)\} = f(t) = \frac{1}{2\pi i}\int_{\gamma-i\infty}^{\gamma+i\infty} \bar{f}(s)e^{st}\, ds, \tag{11b}$$

where $\mathbf{L}$ and $\mathbf{L}^{-1}$ denote the transform and inverse transform operators, respectively.

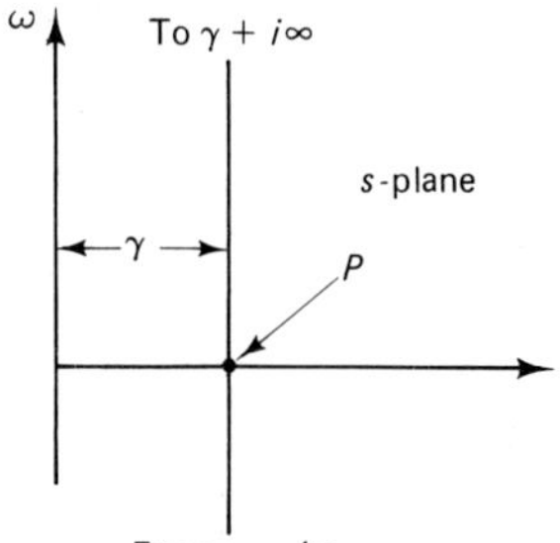

Fig. 11.12 Integration path in s plane.

It would be natural to wonder about the role of γ in the Laplace transform pair, (11a) and (11b). The point is that if f is indeed of exponential order, so that there exists a real constant c in (7), then we merely need γ to be greater than c. If that is the case, it turns out that the value of the inversion integral, on the right-hand side of (11b), is independent of the specific choice of γ; i.e., γ does not show up in the result. This point will become clear in Part V, when we show how to evaluate the complex inversion integral in (11b).

Incidentally, recall that we decided, following (5), to limit our attention to the case $t > 0$. If we *were* to allow for negative t as well, the inversion formula (11b) would read

$$\mathbf{L}^{-1}\{\bar{f}(s)\} = \frac{1}{2\pi i}\int_{\gamma-i\infty}^{\gamma+i\infty} \bar{f}(s)e^{st}\, ds = \begin{cases} 0, & t < 0 \\ f(t), & t > 0. \end{cases} \tag{12}$$

In any case, it will be seen in Chapter 12 that the complex integral inversion formula can be avoided entirely and that, without loss, we can even regard s as real in (11a).

Historically, an integral equation of the form (11a) was considered first by Laplace,* in 1782, although not in terms of what we now call the Laplace transform

* *Pierre-Simon de Laplace* (1749–1827) made numerous important contributions to mathematical physics. Yet his interest was more in the natural phenomena than in the mathematics, and he devoted most of his life to the study of celestial mechanics.

method. The inversion formula (11b) was discovered by Poisson in 1823, and it was not until around 1890 that Oliver Heaviside organized a Laplace transform methodology, or "operational calculus."

Let us close this section by indicating our plan of attack for our main discussion of the Laplace transform, in Chapter 12. Specifically, we plan to render our discussion as simple as possible by discarding the complex integral inversion formula (11b) entirely, relying instead on the use of transform *tables,* together with the use of a number of helpful *properties* of the transform and its inverse. We will return to (11b) eventually, but not until we have developed the powerful complex integral calculus, in Part V.

Having elected to discard (11b), we are able to introduce a second simplification. Specifically, we restrict the constant s in (11a) to be *real*. In other words, s does not need to vary from $\gamma - i\infty$ to $\gamma + i\infty$ because we do not plan to do the integration in (11b), so we can, with no loss, fix s at the point P (Fig. 11.12) on the real axis.

12 Laplace Transform

12.1 INTRODUCTION

First, we note that this chapter is intended to be self-contained, so that the reader need not have studied Chapter 11 first, or even the final section of Chapter 11, in which the Laplace transform was derived from the Fourier integral.

We define the **Laplace transform** $\mathbf{L}\{f(t)\}$, of a function $f(t)$ defined on $0 \le t < \infty$, as

$$\mathbf{L}\{f(t)\} = \int_0^\infty f(t)e^{-st}\,dt, \tag{1}$$

where s is real. Thus the "input" is the function $f(t)$, and the "output" that results from the action of the Laplace transform operator $\mathbf{L}$ is the quantity $\int_0^\infty f(t)e^{-st}\,dt$, which is a function of s and which we denote as $\bar{f}(s)$.

As we shall see, the Laplace transform is a powerful tool in the solution of linear initial-value problems that occur in the form of ordinary or partial differential equations, and it is for this reason that the Laplace transform is routinely included in texts such as this. We consider applications to ordinary differential equations (ODEs) in Section 12.5 and to partial differential equations (PDEs) in Part IV.

Since we will not be ready for applications until Section 12.5, let us at least offer a glimpse of the essential idea right now. The Laplace transform method for solving differential equations is analogous to the simple and familiar "logarithm method" for carrying out arithmetic operations. For suppose that we are given two positive numbers u and v and we wish to compute their product, $y = uv$. Taking the logarithm of both sides gives $\ln y = \ln (uv)$. But $\ln (uv) = \ln u + \ln v$, so we have

$$\ln y = \ln u + \ln v. \tag{2}$$

The idea, then, is a look up $\ln u$ and $\ln v$ in a table of logarithms, and to add these two values. With the sum in hand, we again enter the table and find the antilog. This step gives the solution y. The key point is that in place of the *multiplication* uv, we merely need to do the *addition* $\ln u + \ln v$. Similarly, exponentiation can be reduced to multiplication, since if $y = u^a$ then $\ln y = \ln (u^a) = (a)(\ln u)$, and division can be reduced to subtraction.

Analogously, if we are given a linear *ordinary differential equation* to solve for $x(t)$, say, we begin by taking the Laplace transform of both sides of the equation. Using key properties of the Laplace transform [analogous to the properties $\ln (uv) = \ln u + \ln v$, $\ln (u^a) = a \ln u, \ldots$, of the logarithm] and a transform table, it will turn out that within the transform domain one can solve for $\bar{x}(s)$ by simple *algebra*. Finally, we reenter the table and find the inverse transform $x(t)$.

SINGULAR INTEGRALS 12.2

The Laplace transform integral, $\int_0^\infty f(t)e^{-st}\,dt$, is an example of a "singular" or "improper" integral. Actually, we have managed to work with singular integrals before without even noting their singular nature, especially in Chapter 11. But our discussion of the Laplace transform will be more intensive, and it will prove helpful in the sections to follow if we establish certain basic results regarding such integrals before proceeding.

An integral is said to be **singular,** *or* **improper,** *if one or both integration limits are infinite and/or if the integrand is unbounded at one or more points on the interval.* Otherwise, it is **regular**, or **proper**. Of the integrals

$$\int_3^\infty xe^{-2x}\,dx, \qquad \int_0^5 \frac{e^{-x}}{\sqrt{x}}\,dx, \qquad \int_0^5 \sqrt{x}\,e^x\,dx,$$

for example, the first is singular because of the infinite upper limit, the second is singular because the integrand is unbounded ("blows up") as $x \to 0$, and the third is regular.

Noting that the Laplace transform integral,

$$\bar{f}(s) = \int_0^\infty f(t)e^{-st}\,dt, \tag{1}$$

is singular by virtue of the upper limit, let us consider, first, singular integrals of the type

$$\int_a^\infty F(t)\,dt, \tag{2}$$

where a is finite and $F(t)$ is bounded on $[a, \infty)$. Such integrals are not covered by the classical Riemann definition because the Riemann development presupposes that the interval is finite. Recall that an analogous difficulty is encountered in the calculus in connection with infinite series, for when we write down $\sum_{j=1}^{\infty} a_j$ for the first time, the expression is not meaningful. For example, is $\sum_{j=1}^{\infty} (-1)^{j+1} = 1 - 1 + 1 - 1 + 1 - \cdots = (1-1) + (1-1) + \cdots = 0 + 0 + 0 + \cdots = 0$, or is it $1 - (1-1) - (1-1) - \cdots = 1 - 0 - 0 - \cdots = 1$? And so on. We chose, in the calculus, to *define*

$$\sum_{j=1}^{\infty} a_j \equiv \lim_{n\to\infty} \sum_{j=1}^{n} a_j, \tag{3}$$

so that $\sum_{j=1}^{\infty} a_j = s$ means that to each $\epsilon > 0$ (no matter how small), there corresponds an $N(\epsilon)$ such that $\left|\sum_{j=1}^{n} a_j - s\right| < \epsilon$ for all $n > N(\epsilon)$. If the limit in (3) exists, we say that the series *converges;* otherwise, it *diverges.**

Following that lead, we *define*

$$\int_a^{\infty} F(t)\, dt \equiv \lim_{b\to\infty} \int_a^b F(t)\, dt, \tag{4}$$

so that $\int_a^{\infty} F(t)\, dt = c$ means that to each $\epsilon > 0$ (no matter how small), there corresponds a $B(\epsilon)$ such that $\left|\int_a^b F(t)\, dt - c\right| < \epsilon$ for all $b > B(\epsilon)$. Thus, as so often occurs in mathematics, we define a "new object" as the limit of a sequence of "old objects." If the limit in (4) exists, we say that the integral *converges*, or *exists*; otherwise, it *diverges*, or *fails to exist*.

EXAMPLE 1 Consider $\int_a^{\infty} t^{-p}\, dt$, where $a > 0$. Then

$$\int_a^{\infty} \frac{1}{t^p}\, dt = \lim_{b\to\infty} \int_a^b \frac{1}{t^p}\, dt = \lim_{b\to\infty} \begin{cases} \left.\dfrac{t^{1-p}}{1-p}\right|_a^b & \text{if } p \neq 1 \\ \ln t\big|_a^b & \text{if } p = 1. \end{cases} \tag{5}$$

As $b \to \infty$, $b^{1-p} \to \infty$ for $p < 1$, $b^{1-p} \to 0$ for $p > 1$, and $\ln b \to \infty$. Thus the limit exists only for $p > 1$, so the integral converges for $p > 1$ and diverges for $p \le 1$. Graphically, the idea is that p needs to be positive enough (namely, greater than unity) so that the "tail" (shaded in Fig. 12.1) is squeezed thin enough to be a finite area.

COMMENT This result (convergence for $p > 1$, divergence for $p \le 1$) is reminiscent of, and indeed is closely related to, the well-known result that the so-called p series, $\sum_{n=1}^{\infty} 1/n^p$, converges for $p > 1$ and diverges for $p \le 1$. ◀

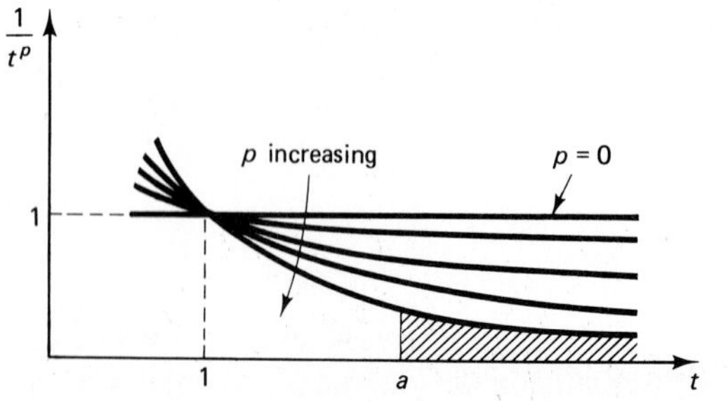

Fig. 12.1 Graph of the integrand, $1/t^p$.

* Accordingly, the series $\sum_{j=1}^{\infty} (-1)^{j+1}$, mentioned above, is divergent because $\sum_{j=1}^{n} a_j = 1, 0, 1, 0, \ldots$ for $n = 1, 2, 3, 4, \ldots$, so that $\lim_{n\to\infty} \sum_{j=1}^{n} a_j$ does not exist.

EXAMPLE 2

$$\int_a^\infty e^{pt}\,dt = \lim_{b\to\infty}\int_a^b e^{pt}\,dt = \lim_{b\to\infty}\begin{cases} \left.\dfrac{e^{pt}}{p}\right|_a^b & \text{if } p \neq 0 \\ t\big|_a^b & \text{if } p = 0. \end{cases} \tag{6}$$

As $b \to \infty$, $e^{pb} \to \infty$ if $p > 0$, $e^{pb} \to 0$ if $p < 0$, and $t\,|_a^b = b - a \to \infty$, so the integral converges for $p < 0$ and diverges for $p \geq 0$. ◀

Unfortunately, to be able to test for convergence/divergence by means of the definition (4), one needs to be able to *evaluate* the integral $\int_a^b F(t)\,dt$. We were able to do that in Examples 1 and 2 since the integrands were simple. More generally, that evaluation may not be feasible, so there have arisen a number of "indirect" tests of convergence, such as comparison tests. [Returning to the analogous case of infinite series, recall from the calculus that in our study of infinite series we were generally unable to implement (3) as a direct test, so we turned to indirect tests such as *comparison tests,* the *ratio test,* and so on.]

***Theorem 1** Comparison Test*
If for the two integrals

$$\int_a^\infty f(t)\,dt \quad \text{and} \quad \int_a^\infty g(t)\,dt$$

with positive integrands over $[a, \infty)$ there exist constants K_1, T_1 such that $f(t) \leq K_1 g(t)$ for all $t \geq T_1$, the convergence of the g integral implies the convergence of the f integral. If there exist constants K_2, T_2 such that $f(t) \geq K_2 g(t)$ for all $t \geq T_2$, the divergence of the g integral implies the divergence of the f integral.

Since the integrand of the integral in question may not be positive, the following theorem is useful.

***Theorem 2** Absolute Convergence*
If $\int_a^\infty |f(t)|\,dt$ converges, so does $\int_a^\infty f(t)\,dt$ (and we then say that the latter converges "absolutely").

EXAMPLE 3 Given the integral

$$\int_0^\infty \frac{e^{-2t}}{t^2+3}\,dt, \tag{7}$$

the integrand of which is positive for all $0 \leq t < \infty$, observe that $e^{-2t}/(t^2+3) \leq \frac{1}{3}e^{-2t}$ for all $t \geq 1$, say. Now $\int_0^\infty e^{-2t}\,dt$ is convergent, according to Example 2, since $p = -2 < 0$. Thus, by the comparison test (Theorem 1), with $g(t) = e^{-2t}$, $K_1 = \frac{1}{3}$, and $T_1 = 1$, the integral (7) is convergent. ◀

EXAMPLE 4 Given the integral

$$\int_0^\infty \frac{e^{-2t}\sin t}{t^2+3}\,dt, \tag{8}$$

the integrand of which is *not* positive over the entire interval $0 \le t < \infty$, observe that

$$\left|\frac{e^{-2t}\sin t}{t^2+3}\right| \le \frac{e^{-2t}}{t^2+3}.$$

Since $\int_0^\infty e^{-2t}dt/(t^2+3)$ converges, according to Example 3, then $\int_0^\infty |e^{-2t}\sin t/(t^2+3)|\,dt$ converges according to Theorem 1. Thus (8) converges according to Theorem 2. ◀

Recall that besides the case where one or both integration limits are infinite, an integral is singular if the integrand becomes unbounded anywhere on the interval. For our purposes it will suffice to consider the case where the integrand becomes unbounded at the left endpoint. If a, b are finite and $|F(t)| \to \infty$ as $t \to a$, we *define*

$$\int_a^b F(t)\,dt \equiv \lim_{\epsilon\to 0}\int_{a+\epsilon}^b F(t)\,dt \qquad (\epsilon > 0). \tag{9}$$

EXAMPLE 5 Consider $\int_0^b t^{-p}\,dt$, where $0 < b < \infty$. Then

$$\int_0^b \frac{1}{t^p}\,dt = \lim_{\epsilon\to 0}\int_\epsilon^b \frac{1}{t^p}\,dt = \lim_{\epsilon\to 0}\begin{cases} \left.\dfrac{t^{1-p}}{1-p}\right|_\epsilon^b & \text{if } p \ne 1 \\ \ln t\,\big|_\epsilon^b & \text{if } p = 1. \end{cases} \tag{10}$$

As $\epsilon \to 0$, $\epsilon^{1-p} \to \infty$ for $p > 1$, $\epsilon^{1-p} \to 0$ for $p < 1$, and $\ln\epsilon \to -\infty$. Thus the limit in (10) exists only for $p < 1$, so the integral converges for $p < 1$ and diverges for $p \ge 1$. Graphically, the idea is that as p increases, the integrand $1/t^p$ "blows up more and more strongly" at $t = 0$, as indicated in Fig. 12.2. Thus p needs to be small enough (namely, less than unity) so that the "vertical column" of area (shaded in Fig. 12.2.) is squeezed thin enough to be finite. ◀

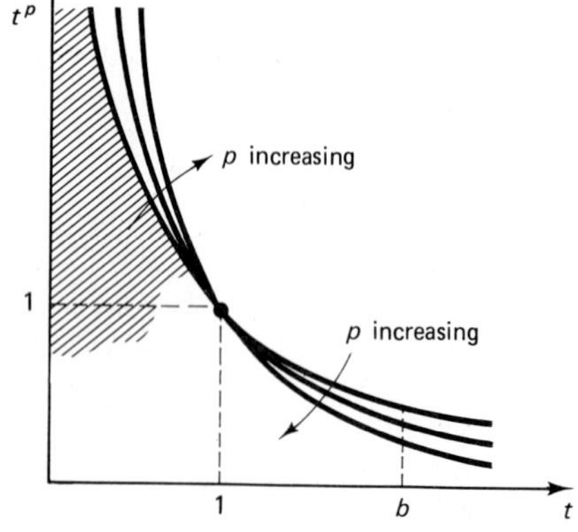

Fig. 12.2 Graph of the integrand, $1/t^p$.

> ***Theorem 3*** *Comparison Test*
> If $0 < b < \infty$ and $f(t) \sim K/t^p$ as $t \to 0$ for some (finite) constants K and p, then $\int_0^b f(t)\,dt$ converges if $p < 1$ and diverges if $p \geq 1$.*

EXAMPLE 6 Test the integral $\int_0^4 [\sin(2t)/t^{3/2}]\,dt$ for convergence/divergence. Evidently, the integrand blows up as $t \to 0$ and needs to be examined there more closely. Recalling the Taylor series $\sin(2t) = (2t) - (2t)^3/3! + (2t)^5/5! - \cdots$, we see that $\sin(2t) \sim 2t$ (as can be verified, if you wish, by applying l'Hospital's rule to the limit $\lim_{t\to 0} [\sin(2t)/2t]$), so

$$\frac{\sin(2t)}{t^{3/2}} \sim \frac{2t}{t^{3/2}} = \frac{2}{t^{1/2}} = \frac{2}{t^p}, \qquad \text{where } p = \frac{1}{2} < 1.$$

Thus, according to Theorem 3, the integral is convergent. ◀

Thus far we have considered only two types of singular integral: first, where the upper integration limit is infinite, and second, where the integrand blows up at the left endpoint. For the combined case, namely, the integral $\int_a^\infty f(t)\,dt$, where $|f(t)| \to \infty$ as $t \to a$, we define

$$\int_a^\infty f(t)\,dt = \lim_{\epsilon\to 0} \int_{a+\epsilon}^b f(t)\,dt + \lim_{c\to\infty} \int_b^c f(t)\,dt \qquad (b > a). \tag{11}$$

Extension to other cases, such as integrals from $-\infty$ to $+\infty$, and integrals the integrands of which blow up at *interior* points on the integration interval will be omitted since those cases will not arise in this chapter.

12.2 EXERCISES

1. Show whether the following integrals converge or diverge.

*(a) $\displaystyle\int_0^\infty \frac{dt}{t^6 + 2}$ (b) $\displaystyle\int_0^\infty \frac{t^3\,dt}{t^5 + 2}$

(c) $\displaystyle\int_0^\infty \frac{t^3\,dt}{t^4 + 6}$ (d) $\displaystyle\int_2^\infty \frac{\cos t\,dt}{t^3}$

*(e) $\displaystyle\int_0^5 \frac{\cos t\,dt}{\sqrt{t}}$

(f) $\displaystyle\int_1^2 \frac{e^t\,dt}{\sqrt{t-1}}$ *Hint*: Set $t - 1 = \tau$ and use Theorem 3.

(g) $\displaystyle\int_1^4 \frac{e^t\,dt}{\sqrt{t^2-1}}$ (h) $\displaystyle\int_0^1 \frac{dt}{t^2 \cos t}$

*(i) $\displaystyle\int_0^\infty \frac{1}{t^2}\,dt$ (j) $\displaystyle\int_0^\infty \frac{1}{\sqrt{t}}\,dt$

(k) $\displaystyle\int_0^\infty \frac{e^{-t}}{\sqrt{t}}\,dt$ (l) $\displaystyle\int_0^\infty \frac{dt}{\sqrt{t}\,(t+1)}$

(m) $\int_0^\infty t^4 e^{-t}\,dt$ *Hint*: $t^4/e^t \leq e^{-t/2}$ for sufficiently large t since $\lim_{t\to 0} [(t^4/e^t)/e^{t/2}] = 0$. If you use this hint, you need to verify the stated limit and show how that limit implies the stated inequality.

(n) $\int_4^\infty \ln t\,dt/t^2$ *Hint*: Show that $\ln t \leq t^\alpha$ for all sufficiently large t, where α is an arbitrarily small positive number, by showing that $\lim_{t\to\infty} (\ln t)/t^\alpha = 0$. Thus $\ln t < t^{1/4}$, for example, for sufficiently large t.

(o) $\int_0^2 \ln t\,dt/\sqrt{t}$ *Hint*: Make the change of variables $t = 1/\tau$ and use the hint given in part (n).

* Recall that $f(t) \sim g(t)$ as $t \to t_0$ means that $\lim_{t\to t_0} f(t)/g(t) = 1$.

***2.** For what p's, if any, does $\int_0^\infty (1/t^p)\, dt$ converge? Explain.

3. Enter the indicated change of variables in the given singular integral, and state whether the resulting integral is singular or not.

(a) $\displaystyle\int_2^\infty \frac{1}{t^2}\, dt,\ t = \frac{1}{\tau}$ (b) $\displaystyle\int_0^3 \frac{1}{\sqrt{t}}\, dt,\ t = \frac{1}{\tau}$

(c) $\displaystyle\int_0^5 \frac{1}{\sqrt{t}} \cos t\, dt,\ t = \tau^2$

(d) $\displaystyle\int_0^5 \frac{1}{\sqrt{t}} \cos t\, dt,\ t = \tau^4$

4. For what range of α's (such as $0 < \alpha < 2$, $\alpha < 0$, no α's, etc.) does each integral converge? Explain.

*(a) $\displaystyle\int_0^\infty \frac{dt}{t^\alpha + 3}$ (b) $\displaystyle\int_0^4 \frac{t^\alpha\, dt}{t^4 + 1}$

*(c) $\displaystyle\int_0^\infty \frac{t^\alpha}{t+1}\, dt$ (d) $\displaystyle\int_0^2 t^\alpha \sin t\, dt$

(e) $\displaystyle\int_1^2 (t^2 - 1)^\alpha\, dt$ (f) $\displaystyle\int_1^\infty \frac{t^\alpha}{\sqrt{t^2 - 1}}\, dt$

5. Show that $\int_0^\infty t^\alpha e^{-t}\, dt$ converges for all $\alpha > -1$.

12.3 CALCULATION OF THE TRANSFORM

If we are to work with the Laplace transform,

$$\mathbf{L}\{f(t)\} = \bar{f}(s) = \int_0^\infty f(t) e^{-st}\, dt, \tag{1}$$

the first question to attend to is whether the transform $\bar{f}(s)$ does indeed exist, i.e., whether or not the integral in (1) is convergent.

Before proving a useful existence theorem, recall from page 535 that *f is of* ***exponential order*** *as $t \to \infty$ if there exist real constants K, c, and T such that*

$$|f(t)| \le Ke^{ct} \tag{2}$$

for all $t \le T$.

The class of functions that are of exponential order as $t \to \infty$ is quite extensive and even includes exponential growth. For example, $f(t) = \sin t$, t^2, and e^{100t} are all of exponential order as $t \to \infty$.

EXAMPLE 1 Verify that t^2 is of exponential order as $t \to \infty$. Application of l'Hospital's rule gives

$$\lim_{t\to\infty} \frac{t^2}{e^{ct}} = \lim_{t\to\infty} \frac{2t}{ce^{ct}} = \lim_{t\to\infty} \frac{2}{c^2 e^{ct}} = 0$$

if $c > 0$. Choose $c = 1$, say. Then, from the definition of limit, there must be a T such that $|t^2/e^t| \le 0.05$, say, for all $t \ge T$. Thus $|t^2| \le 0.05e^t$ for all $t \ge T$, and the verification is complete. ◀

We now state, and prove, a theorem which shows that $\bar{f}(s)$ does indeed exist for a large and useful class of functions $f(t)$.

Theorem 1 *Existence of Transform*

Suppose that (i) f is piecewise continuous on $0 \le t \le t_0$ for every t_0, (ii) f is of exponential order as $t \to \infty$. Then the Laplace transform of f,

$$\bar{f}(s) = \int_0^\infty f(t)e^{-st}\,dt, \tag{3}$$

exists for all $s > c$, where c is the same c as in (2).

Proof We need to show that the singular integral in (3) is convergent. To do so, we first show that it is *absolutely* convergent. Since

$$\int_0^\infty |f(t)e^{-st}|\,dt = \lim_{b\to\infty}\int_0^b |f(t)e^{-st}|\,dt, \tag{4}$$

we wish to show that the limit exists. With $b > T$ we have

$$\int_0^b |f(t)e^{-st}|\,dt = \int_0^T |f(t)|e^{-st}\,dt + \int_T^b |f(t)|e^{-st}\,dt. \tag{5}$$

Now, since f is piecewise continuous on $0 \le t \le T$, there must exist a constant M such that $|f(t)| \le M$ on $0 \le t \le T$. And since f is of exponential order as $t \to \infty$, we have $|f(t)| \le Ke^{ct}$ for all $t \ge T$, so it follows from (5) that

$$\begin{aligned}\int_0^b |f(t)e^{-st}|\,dt &\le M\int_0^T e^{-st}\,dt + K\int_T^b e^{-(s-c)t}\,dt\\ &= \frac{M}{s}(1 - e^{-sT}) + \frac{K}{s-c}e^{-(s-c)T} - \frac{K}{s-c}e^{-(s-c)b}\\ &\le \frac{M}{s}(1 - e^{-sT}) + \frac{K}{s-c}e^{-(s-c)T}\\ &\le \frac{M}{s} + \frac{K}{s-c}.\end{aligned} \tag{6}$$

Surely, $\int_0^b |f(t)e^{-st}|\,dt$ is a monotonically increasing function of b because its integrand is nonnegative. Since the integral is monotonically increasing, and bounded above [by $M/s + K/(s-c)$], it follows that $\lim_{b\to\infty}\int_0^b |f(t)e^{-st}|\,dt$ must exist. Thus $\int_0^\infty f(t)e^{-st}\,dt$ converges absolutely and, from Theorem 2 on page 541, it follows that the integral converges. ■

Being assured, by Theorem 1, that $\bar{f}(s)$ exists for a large and useful class of functions, we proceed to illustrate the evaluation of $\bar{f}$ for several elementary functions, say $f(t) = 1$, e^{at}, and $\sin at$, where a is a real number.

EXAMPLE 2 If $f(t) = 1$, observe that the conditions of Theorem 1 are met, for any $c \ge 0$. Thus $\bar{f}(s)$ should exist for all $s > 0$. Well,

$$\bar{f}(s) = \int_0^\infty e^{-st}\,dt = \lim_{b\to\infty}\left(\frac{e^{-st}}{-s}\bigg|_0^b\right) = \frac{1}{s}, \tag{7}$$

where the limit does indeed exist for all $s > 0$.

COMMENT Whether we write $f(t) = 1$ or $f(t) = H(t)$ will not matter, because $H(t) = 1$ for $t \geq 0$. ◀

EXAMPLE 3 If $f(t) = e^{at}$, the conditions of Theorem 1 are met for any $c \geq a$. Indeed,

$$\bar{f}(s) = \int_0^\infty e^{at}e^{-st}\,dt = \lim_{b\to\infty}\left[\frac{e^{-(s-a)t}}{-(s-a)}\bigg|_0^b\right] = \frac{1}{s-a} \tag{8}$$

for all $s > a$. ◀

EXAMPLE 4 If $f(t) = \sin at$, the conditions of Theorem 1 are met, for any $c \geq 0$. Thus $\bar{f}(s)$ should exist for all $s > 0$. Integrating by parts twice,

$$\begin{aligned}
\bar{f}(s) &= \int_0^\infty \sin at\, e^{-st}\,dt \\
&= \lim_{b\to\infty}\left[\left(\sin at\frac{e^{-st}}{-s}\right)\bigg|_0^b + \frac{a}{s}\int_0^b \cos at\, e^{-st}\,dt\right] \\
&= \lim_{b\to\infty}\frac{a}{s}\int_0^b \cos at\, e^{-st}\,dt \\
&= \lim_{b\to\infty}\frac{a}{s}\left[\left(\cos at\frac{e^{-st}}{-s}\right)\bigg|_0^b - \frac{a}{s}\int_0^b \sin at\, e^{-st}\,dt\right] \\
&= \frac{a}{s}\left[\frac{1}{s} - \frac{a}{s}\bar{f}(s)\right],
\end{aligned} \tag{9}$$

provided that $s > 0$. Solving for $\bar{f}(s)$ gives us

$$\bar{f}(s) = \frac{a}{s^2 + a^2}. \tag{10}$$

COMMENT An appealing alternative to the integration-by-parts derivation of (10), which requires a knowledge of the algebra of complex numbers (Section 18.2), is as follows:

$$\begin{aligned}
\bar{f}(s) &= \int_0^\infty \sin at\, e^{-st}\,dt = \int_0^\infty (\operatorname{Im} e^{iat})e^{-st}\,dt \\
&= \operatorname{Im}\int_0^\infty e^{-(s-ia)t}\,dt = \operatorname{Im}\left[\lim_{b\to\infty}\frac{e^{-(s-ia)t}}{-(s-ia)}\bigg|_0^b\right] \\
&= \operatorname{Im}\frac{1}{s-ia} \qquad (\text{if } s > 0) \\
&= \operatorname{Im}\left(\frac{1}{s-ia}\,\frac{s+ia}{s+ia}\right) = \frac{a}{s^2+a^2},
\end{aligned} \tag{11}$$

as before. In case the steps in (11) are not clear, observe carefully that

$$\left|e^{-(s-ia)b}\right| = \left|e^{-sb}\right|\left|e^{iab}\right| = e^{-sb} \to 0 \tag{12}$$

as $b \to \infty$. ◀

From these three examples, we could begin to construct a Laplace transform *table* (Table 12.1). A longer, but still rather modest Laplace transform table is provided in Appendix C. For a comprehensive table, we refer the reader to Erdèlyi.*

TABLE 12.1 Laplace Transform Mini-table

$f(t)$	$\bar{f}(s)$
1. 1	$\dfrac{1}{s} \quad (s > 0)$
2. e^{at}	$\dfrac{1}{s-a} \quad (s > a)$
3. $\sin at$	$\dfrac{a}{s^2+a^2} \quad (s > 0)$

We promise that the restrictions on s, such as $s > 0$, will cause no difficulty whatsoever in applications.

The table can be used in either direction. For example, just as the Laplace transform of e^{at} is $1/(s-a)$, it is also true that the function whose transform is $1/(s-a)$ is e^{at}. Operationally, we say that

$$\mathbf{L}\{e^{at}\} = \frac{1}{s-a} \quad \text{and} \quad \mathbf{L}^{-1}\left\{\frac{1}{s-a}\right\} = e^{at},$$

where $\mathbf{L}^{-1}$ denotes the *inverse Laplace transform operator*. At this point an important question arises: *Is the inverse transform unique?* For example, if $f(t) = e^{2t}$ and $g(t) = \begin{cases} e^{2t}, & t \neq 5 \\ 4, & t = 5 \end{cases}$, then both $\bar{f}(s)$ and $\bar{g}(s)$ are $1/(s-2)$. Thus $\mathbf{L}^{-1}\{1/(s-2)\} = f(t), g(t)$, and many other such functions as well. Fortunately, it is known from *Lerch's theorem*† that the inverse transform is unique to within an additive *null function*, i.e., a function $N(t)$ such that

$$\int_0^{t_0} N(t)\, dt = 0$$

for every $t_0 > 0$. For example, in the illustration above,

$$N(t) = \begin{cases} 0, & t \neq 5 \\ e^{10} - 4, & t = 5 \end{cases}.$$

* A. Erdèlyi (ed.), *Tables of Integral Transforms*, Vol. 1 (New York: McGraw-Hill, 1954). In addition, most books on the Laplace transform include tables. Besides tables, the inversion of Laplace transforms by numerical integration is an option for especially complicated cases. See, for example, V. Krylov and N. Skoblya, *Handbook of Numerical Inversion of Laplace Transforms*, Israel Program for Scientific Translations (Jerusalem: IPST Press, 1969).

† See Ruel V. Churchill, *Operational Mathematics*, 2nd ed. (New York: McGraw-Hill, 1958), for additional discussion of Lerch's theorem; and D. V. Widder, *The Laplace Transform* (Princeton, N. J.: Princeton University Press, 1941), for proof of the theorem.

Practically speaking, such additional null functions are inconsequential. Thus we plan to ignore them and to regard the inverse transform as unique.

Observe from Table 12.1 that in each case $\bar{f}(s) \to 0$ and $s\bar{f}(s)$ is bounded as $s \to \infty$. These results *always* hold if f satisfies the conditions of Theorem 1, for it follows from (6) that

$$\left| \int_0^b f(t)e^{-st}\,dt \right| \le \int_0^b \left| f(t)e^{-st} \right| dt \le \frac{M}{s} + \frac{K}{s-c}, \tag{13}$$

where the first inequality holds because $|\int_A^B F(t)\,dt|$ is always less than or equal to $\int_A^B |F(t)|\,dt$ if t is real. Letting $b \to \infty$ in (13), and noting that the constants M and K are independent of s, we can deduce from (14) the following result.

Theorem 2 *Large s Behavior of* $\bar{f}$

Let f be piecewise continuous on $0 \le t \le t_0$ for each finite t_0 and of exponential order as $t \to \infty$. Then

(i) $\bar{f}(s) \to 0$ as $s \to \infty$,

(ii) $s\bar{f}(s)$ is bounded as $s \to \infty$.

It is to be emphasized that the functions f that we work with do not necessarily meet the conditions of Theorems 1 and 2. If we refer to piecewise-continuous functions of exponential order as "decent," let us see what might happen if f is *not* decent.

EXAMPLE 5 $f(t) = 1/t^3$ is not piecewise continuous because it is unbounded as $t \to 0$. From our discussion in Section 12.2, we see that

$$\bar{f}(s) = \int_0^\infty \frac{1}{t^3} e^{-st}\,dt \tag{14}$$

does not exist because of the $1/t^p$ type singularity at the origin, with $p = 3 > 1$. ◀

EXAMPLE 6 Similarly, $f(t) = 1/\sqrt{t}$ is not piecewise continuous because it is unbounded as $t \to 0$. However, this time $p = \frac{1}{2} < 1$, so the transform

$$\bar{f}(s) = \int_0^\infty \frac{1}{\sqrt{t}} e^{-st}\,dt \tag{15}$$

does exist and, as will be shown in Example 8, is equal to $\sqrt{\pi/s}$ for $s > 0$. Clearly, then, the conditions in Theorem 1 are sufficient, not necessary. Furthermore, $\bar{f}(s) = \sqrt{\pi/s}$ satisfies Theorem 2(i), but not 2(ii). ◀

EXAMPLE 7 Consider the delta function $f(t) = \delta(t - t_0)$ $(0 < t_0 < \infty)$, which is certainly not "decent." In this case

$$\bar{f}(s) = \int_0^\infty \delta(t - t_0)e^{-st}\, dt = e^{-st_0} \tag{16}$$

does exist, and even satisfies both (i) and (ii) in Theorem 2. ◀

We close this section with a generalization of Example 6.

EXAMPLE 8 *Gamma Function.* Consider the Laplace transform of t^p:

$$\mathbf{L}\{t^p\} = \int_0^\infty t^p e^{-st}\, dt. \tag{17}$$

If p is a positive integer, one finds that repeated integration by parts (each time letting "dv" $= e^{-st}\, dt$) yields the result

$$\mathbf{L}\{t^p\} = \frac{p!}{s^{p+1}} \qquad (s > 0). \tag{18}$$

If p is *not* an integer, the integral in (17) cannot be evaluated in closed from in terms of elementary functions of s. In fact, integrals of the form (17) arise frequently in pure and applied mathematics, not only in connection with the evaluation of $\mathbf{L}\{t^p\}$, but in other settings as well. Thus mathematicians use the integral to introduce a new function, the **gamma function**,*

$$\boxed{\Gamma(x) \equiv \int_0^\infty t^{x-1}e^{-t}\, dt \qquad (x > 0).} \tag{19}$$

Before using the gamma function to evaluate $\mathbf{L}\{t^p\}$ for the case where p is not an integer, let us discuss the essential properties of the gamma function. First, observe that $t^{x-1}e^{-t} \sim t^{x-1}$ as $t \to 0$, so that if $x - 1 < 0$, then the integrand in (19) "blows up" at $t \to 0$. Recalling our discussion of the p integral in Section 12.2, we know that the integrand must not blow up too strongly if the integral is to converge. Specifically, we need $x - 1 > -1$ $(x > 0)$, and this result explains the $x > 0$ condition appended to (19).

An important property of the gamma function can be derived from the definition (19) by integration by parts. With "u" $= t^{x-1}$ and "dv" $= e^{-t}\, dt$,

$$\Gamma(x) = -t^{x-1}e^{-t}\,\Big|_0^\infty + (x - 1)\int_0^\infty t^{x-2}e^{-t}\, dt. \tag{20}$$

The integral in (20) converges [and is $\Gamma(x - 1)$] only if $x > 1$, in which case the boundary term vanishes. Thus (20) becomes

$$\boxed{\Gamma(x) = (x - 1)\Gamma(x - 1) \qquad (x > 1).} \tag{21}$$

Equation (21) is called a *recursion formula* because it gives Γ at one point, recursively, in terms of Γ at another point. In fact, if we compute $\Gamma(x)$, by numerical

* The gamma function was studied extensively by Euler, Legendre, and Gauss.

integration, over $0 < x \le 1$, say, then (21) enables us to compute $\Gamma(x)$ for all $x > 1$. For example,

$$\begin{aligned} \Gamma(3.2) &= 2.2\Gamma(2.2) = (2.2)(1.2)\Gamma(1.2) \\ &= (2.2)(1.2)(0.2)\Gamma(0.2). \end{aligned} \tag{22}$$

Note, in particular, that if x is a positive integer n, then

$$\begin{aligned} \Gamma(n+1) &= n\Gamma(n) = n(n-1)\Gamma(n-1) \\ &= \cdots = n(n-1)(n-2)\cdots(1)\Gamma(1), \end{aligned} \tag{23}$$

or

$$\boxed{\Gamma(n+1) = n!} \tag{24}$$

since

$$\Gamma(1) = \int_0^\infty e^{-t}\, dt = 1.$$

Equation (24) shows that the gamma function may be regarded as a *generalization of the factorial function* for not-necessarily-integer arguments. In fact, it turns out that many formulas involving $p!$, where p is a positive integer, can be extended to cover the case where p is not a positive integer by replacing $p!$ by $\Gamma(p+1)$.

Besides the positive integers, another x for which the gamma function integral can be evaluated is $x = \frac{1}{2}$. The (well known) result is

$$\Gamma(\tfrac{1}{2}) = \sqrt{\pi}, \tag{25}$$

derivation of which is left for the exercises.

Concluding this brief discussion of the gamma function, recall that (19) defines $\Gamma(x)$ only for $x > 0$; for $x < 0$ the integral diverges and (19) is meaningless. What is a reasonable way to extend the definition of $\Gamma(x)$ to negative x? Well, recall that if we know $\Gamma(x)$, we can compute $\Gamma(x+1)$ from the recursion formula $\Gamma(x+1) = x\Gamma(x)$. Instead of using this formula to march to the right, we can turn it around and use it to march to the left. Thus let us *define*

$$\Gamma(x) = \frac{\Gamma(x+1)}{x} \qquad \text{for } x < 0. \tag{26}$$

For example,

$$\Gamma(-2.6) = \frac{\Gamma(-1.6)}{(-2.6)} = \frac{\Gamma(-0.6)}{(-2.6)(-1.6)} = \frac{\Gamma(0.4)}{(-2.6)(-1.6)(-0.6)}, \tag{27}$$

where $\Gamma(0.4)$ is known because its argument is positive. The resulting graph of $\Gamma(x)$ is shown in Fig. 12.3.

In summary, then, $\Gamma(x)$ is defined for all $x \neq 0, -1, -2, \ldots$ by the integral definition (19) together with the "leftward-marching" recursion formula (26). Especially notable is the fact that $\Gamma(x) = (x-1)!$ at $x = 1, 2, 3, \ldots$, and for this reason $\Gamma(x)$ is often referred to as the *generalized factorial function*, as mentioned above.

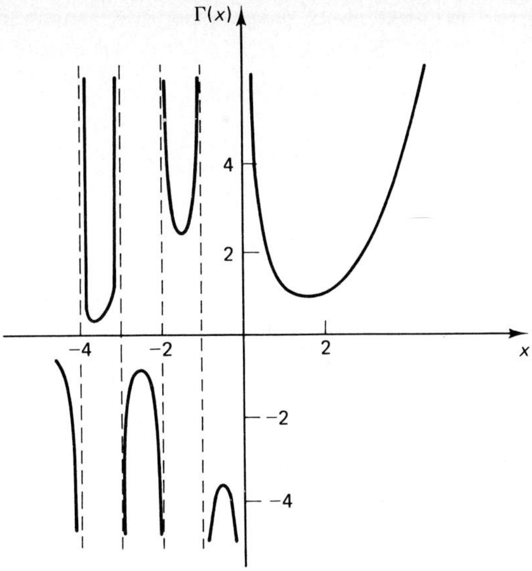

Fig. 12.3 Gamma function.

Some additional results regarding the gamma function are included in the exercises. For further discussion and computational formulas, see, for example, Abramowitz and Stegun.*

Finally, returning to (17) and setting $st = \tau$, with $s > 0$, we obtain

$$\begin{aligned} \mathbf{L}\{t^p\} &= \int_0^\infty t^p e^{-st}\,dt \qquad (p > -1) \\ &= \frac{1}{s^{p+1}} \int_0^\infty \tau^p e^{-\tau}\,d\tau = \frac{\Gamma(p+1)}{s^{p+1}}. \end{aligned} \tag{28}$$ ◀

In this section we have studied the *calculation* of the Laplace transform. In the next we obtain several key *properties* of the transform.

12.3 EXERCISES

1. Show whether or not the given function is of exponential order as $t \to 0$. If it is, determine a suitable set of values of K, c, T in (3).

*(a) $H(t-1) - H(t-3)$ (b) $5e^{4t}$
(c) $\sinh t$ (d) $\cosh 2t$
*(e) $\sin 3t$ (f) $6t$
(g) $e^{-t} \sin t$ (h) e^{t^2}
(i) $H(t-5)$ (j) $\sin (t^2)$

2. If $f(t)$ is of exponential order, does it follow that df/dt is, too? *Hint:* Consider $f(t) = \sin (e^{t^2})$.

3. If $f(t)$ and $g(t)$ are each of exponential order, does it follow that $f(g(t))$ is too? *Hint:* Consider the case $f(t) = e^t$, $g(t) = t^2$, say.

Wherever possible, in Exercises 4 to 11, compare your result with the corresponding entry in Appendix C.

4. Derive $\mathbf{L}\{\cos at\}$ two ways: using integration by parts, and using the fact that $\cos at = \text{Re } e^{iat}$ (see Example 4).

* M. Abramowitz and I. Stegun (eds.), National Bureau of Standards Applied Mathematics Series, 1964.

5. Derive $\mathbf{L}\{e^{at} \sin bt\}$ two ways: using integration by parts, and using $\sin bt = \text{Im } e^{ibt}$.

6. Derive $\mathbf{L}\{e^{at} \cos bt\}$ two ways: using integration by parts, and using $\cos bt = \text{Re } e^{ibt}$.

7. Derive the Laplace transform for each of the following entries in Appendix C.

(a) entry 5 (b) entry 6
(c) entry 11 (d) entry 12
(e) entry 13 (f) entry 14

8. Derive $\mathbf{L}\{t^n\}$, for n a positive integer, using mathematical induction.

9. Derive $\mathbf{L}\{t^n e^{at}\}$, for n a positive integer, using mathematical induction.

10. Derive entry 11 by differentiating both sides of

$$\int_0^\infty \sin at\, e^{st}\, dt = \frac{a}{s^2 + a^2} \tag{a}$$

with respect to s. *Note:* You may formally "differentiate under the integral sign" on the left-hand side; i.e., you may assume the legitimacy of the step

$$\frac{d}{ds}\int_0^\infty \sin at\, e^{-st}\, dt = \int_0^\infty \frac{d}{ds}(\sin at\, e^{-st})\, dt.$$

This step is not covered by our Leibniz rule, on page 346, since the integral is singular (by virtue of the up per limit being ∞). However, sufficiently powerful theorems can be found in Sec. 14-7 of T. M. Apostol's *Mathematical Analysis* (Reading, Mass.: Addison-Wesley, 1957).

11. Use the idea in Exercise 10 to derive

(a) item 12 from item 4 (b) item 7 from item 1
(c) item 13 from item 5 (d) item 14 from item 6
(e) item 15 from item 2 (f) item 21 from item 22

12. Show that $\mathbf{L}\{e^{at}\} = 1/(s - a)$ holds even if $a = \text{Re } a + i \text{ Im } a$ is complex, provided that $s > \text{Re } a$.

13. Show that $\Gamma(\frac{1}{2}) = \sqrt{\pi}$. *Hint:* Show that

$$\Gamma\left(\frac{1}{2}\right) = 2\int_0^\infty e^{-u^2}\, du,$$

so that

$$\left[\Gamma\left(\frac{1}{2}\right)\right]^2 = 4\int_0^\infty e^{-u^2}\, du \int_0^\infty e^{-v^2}\, dv$$
$$= 4\int_0^\infty \int_0^\infty e^{-(u^2+v^2)}\, du\, dv.$$

Regarding the latter as a double integral over the first quadrant of a Cartesian u, v plane, change over to polar coordinates r, θ.

14. Show, by suitable change of variables, that

(a) $\displaystyle\int_0^\infty e^{-t^p}\, dt = \frac{\Gamma(1/p)}{p} \quad (p > 0)$

(b) $\displaystyle\int_0^1 t^m(\ln t)^n\, dt = (-1)^n \frac{n!}{(m+1)^{n+1}}$ (m, n nonnegative integers)

(c) $\displaystyle\int_0^\infty t^2 e^{-t^2}\, dt = \frac{\sqrt{\pi}}{4}$ [Recall, from Exercise 13, that $\Gamma(\frac{1}{2}) = \sqrt{\pi}$.]

(d) $\displaystyle\int_0^\infty t e^{-\sqrt{t}}\, dt = 12$

(e) $\displaystyle\int_0^\infty (t-1)^2 e^{-t^3}\, dt = \tfrac{1}{3}[1 - 2\Gamma(\tfrac{2}{3}) + \Gamma(\tfrac{1}{3})]$

15. Deduce, from the formula given in Exercise 14 (a), that

$$\Gamma(x) \sim \frac{1}{x} \text{ as } x \to 0+. \tag{a}$$

16. (*Beta function*) Derive the result

$$B(p, q) = \int_0^1 t^{p-1}(1-t)^{q-1}\, dt = \frac{\Gamma(p)\Gamma(q)}{\Gamma(p+q)}, \tag{a}$$

for $p > 0$, $q > 0$. $B(p, q)$ is known as the **beta function.** *Hint:* Putting $t = u^2$ in

$$\Gamma(p) = \int_0^\infty t^{p-1}e^{-t}\, dt,$$

show that

$$\Gamma(p)\Gamma(q) = 4\int_0^\infty u^{2p-1}e^{-u^2}\, du \int_0^\infty v^{2q-1}e^{-v^2}\, dv. \tag{b}$$

Regarding the latter as a double integral over the first quadrant of a Cartesian u, v plane, change over to polar coordinates r, θ. Making one more change of variables in each integral, the r integral gives $\Gamma(p+q)$ and the θ integral gives $B(p, q)$.

17. Setting $t = x/(1+x)$, derive from (a) of Exercise 16 the alternative form

$$B(p, q) = \int_0^\infty \frac{x^{p-1}}{(1+x)^{p+q}}\, dx \tag{a}$$
$$(p > 0,\ q > 0).$$

18. By a suitable change of variable, derive from (a) of Exercise 16 the alternative form

$$B(p, q) = 2\int_0^{\pi/2} \cos^{2q-1}\theta \sin^{2p-1}\theta \, d\theta \qquad \text{(a)}$$

$$(p > 0, q > 0).$$

19. Using equation (a) of Exercise 16, 17, or 18, show that

(a) $\int_0^{\pi/2} \cos^q \theta \sin^p \theta \, d\theta = \frac{1}{2}B\left(\frac{p+1}{2}, \frac{q+1}{2}\right)$ for $p > -1, q > -1$

(b) $\int_0^{\pi/2} \sin^p \theta \, d\theta = \int_0^{\pi/2} \cos^p \theta \, d\theta =$

$$\frac{1}{2}B\left(\frac{1}{2}, \frac{p+1}{2}\right) = \frac{\sqrt{\pi}}{2} \frac{\Gamma\left(\frac{p+1}{2}\right)}{\Gamma\left(\frac{p+2}{2}\right)} \qquad \text{for } p > -1$$

(c) $\int_0^{\pi/2} \tan^p \theta \, d\theta = \int_0^{\pi/2} \cot^p \theta \, d\theta =$

$$\frac{1}{2}B\left(\frac{1+p}{2}, \frac{1-p}{2}\right) = \frac{\pi}{2\cos\frac{p\pi}{2}}$$

for $-1 < p < 1$. *Hint:* You may use (a) of Exercise 20 to obtain the final equality.

(d) $$\int_0^{\infty} \frac{t^a \, dt}{(1+t^b)^c} = \frac{1}{b}B\left(\frac{a+1}{b}, \frac{cb-a-1}{b}\right)$$

$$= \frac{1}{b}\frac{\Gamma\left(\frac{a+1}{b}\right)\Gamma\left(\frac{cb-a-1}{2}\right)}{\Gamma(c)} \qquad \text{for } a > -1, \; b > 0, \; bc - a > 1$$

20. It can be shown by the residue theorem (in Part V) that

$$\int_0^{\infty} \frac{x^{\alpha-1}}{1+x} dx = \frac{\pi}{\sin \alpha\pi} \qquad (0 < \alpha < 1).$$

Using this result, (a) of Exercise 17, and (a) of Exercise 16, show that

$$\Gamma(\alpha)\Gamma(1-\alpha) = \frac{\pi}{\sin \alpha\pi} \qquad (0 < \alpha < 1). \qquad \text{(a)}$$

21. (*Period of oscillation of pendulum*) Conservation of energy dictates that the angular displacement $\theta(t)$, of a pendulum of length ℓ and mass m, satisfies the equation

$$\tfrac{1}{2}m(\ell\dot{\theta})^2 + mg(\ell - \ell\cos\theta) = mg(\ell - \ell\cos\theta_0). \qquad \text{(a)}$$

(a) From (a), show that

$$\sqrt{\frac{\ell}{2g}} \int_0^{\theta_0} \frac{d\theta}{\sqrt{\cos\theta - \cos\theta_0}} = \int_0^{T/4} dt, \qquad \text{(b)}$$

where T is the period and θ_0 is the maximum swing. For the case $\theta_0 = \pi/2$, show that

$$T = \sqrt{\frac{2\pi\ell}{g}} \frac{\Gamma(1/4)}{\Gamma(3/4)}.$$

Note: You may use results from Exercises 16 to 19.
(b) At first glance, it appears from (b) that $T(\theta_0) \to 0$ as $\theta_0 \to 0$. Is that assessment correct? Explain.

22. The notion of an "integral representation" of a function, as used in (19) to introduce the gamma function, may be unfamiliar to the reader. If so, it may help to point out that even the elementary functions can be introduced in that manner. For example, one can *define* the logarithm as

$$\ln x \equiv \int_1^x \frac{dt}{t} \qquad (x > 0), \qquad \text{(a)}$$

and all the usual properties of the logarithm can be deduced from (a). For example,

$$\ln x^a = \int_1^{x^a} \frac{dt}{t} = \int_1^x \frac{au^{a-1}}{u^a} du \qquad (t = u^a)$$

$$= a\int_1^x \frac{du}{u} = a \ln x$$

gives the familiar result $\ln x^a = a \ln x$. Derive from (a) the well-known property $\ln(xy) = \ln x + \ln y$. (The author is grateful to Professor J. A. C. Humphrey for helpful comments regarding this exercise.)

PROPERTIES OF THE TRANSFORM AND ITS INVERSE 12.4

Being anxious to get to applications of the Laplace transform in Section 12.5, we limit our discussion in the present section to the handful of key properties that will be needed in those applications. Additional useful properties are then introduced in the final section, Section 12.6.

The first property to emphasize is the linearity of the transform operator.

Theorem 1 *Linearity of the Transform*
If $u(t)$ and $v(t)$ are any two functions such that the transforms $\mathbf{L}\{u(t)\}$ and $\mathbf{L}\{v(t)\}$ both exist, then

$$\boxed{\mathbf{L}\{\alpha u(t) + \beta v(t)\} = \alpha\mathbf{L}\{u(t)\} + \beta\mathbf{L}\{v(t)\}} \tag{1}$$

for any constants α, β.

Proof

$$\begin{aligned}
\mathbf{L}\{\alpha u(t) + \beta v(t)\} &= \int_0^\infty [\alpha u(t) + \beta v(t)]e^{-st}\,dt \\
&= \lim_{b\to\infty}\int_0^b [\alpha u(t) + \beta v(t)]e^{-st}\,dt \\
&= \lim_{b\to\infty} [\alpha\int_0^b u(t)e^{-st}\,dt + \beta\int_0^b v(t)e^{-st}\,dt] \\
&= \alpha\lim_{b\to\infty}\int_0^b u(t)e^{-st}\,dt + \beta\lim_{b\to\infty}\int_0^b v(t)e^{-st}\,dt \\
&= \alpha\mathbf{L}u + \beta\mathbf{L}v,
\end{aligned} \tag{2}$$

where the third equality follows from the elementary theory of Riemann integration, and the fourth equality amounts to the familiar result that $\lim_{b\to b_0}[\alpha f(b) + \beta g(b)] = \alpha \lim_{b\to b_0} f(b) + \beta \lim_{b\to b_0} g(b)$ if the latter two limits exist. This step completes the proof. ■

EXAMPLE 1 $\mathbf{L}\{6 - 5e^{4t}\} = 6\mathbf{L}\{1\} - 5\mathbf{L}\{e^{4t}\}$. Now, $\mathbf{L}\{1\} = 1/s$ for $s > 0$, and $\mathbf{L}\{e^{4t}\} = 1/(s-4)$ for $s > 4$, so

$$\mathbf{L}\{6 - 5e^{4t}\} = 6\frac{1}{s} - 5\frac{1}{s-4} = \frac{s-24}{s(s-4)}$$

for $s > 4$. ◀

Turning to the *inverse*, recall that $\mathbf{L}^{-1}\{\bar{f}(s)\}$ denotes the function $f(t)$ whose Laplace transform is $\bar{f}(s)$.

Theorem 2 *Linearity of the Inverse Transform*
For any $\overline{u}(s)$ and $\overline{v}(s)$ such that the inverse transforms $\mathbf{L}^{-1}\{\overline{u}(s)\}$ and $\mathbf{L}^{-1}\{\overline{v}(s)\}$ both exist,

$$\boxed{\mathbf{L}^{-1}\{\alpha\overline{u}(s) + \beta\overline{v}(s)\} = \alpha\mathbf{L}^{-1}\{\overline{u}(s)\} + \beta\mathbf{L}^{-1}\{\overline{v}(s)\}} \tag{3}$$

for any constants α, β.

Proof Equation (3) follows immediately upon taking $\mathbf{L}^{-1}$ of both sides of (1). ■

EXAMPLE 2 Asked to evaluate the inverse of $\bar{f}(s) = 3s/(s^2 + 3s - 10)$, we turn to Appendix C and notice that this $\bar{f}(s)$ is not to be found in the column of transforms. However, expressing

$$\frac{3s}{s^2 + 3s - 10} = \frac{15/7}{s + 5} + \frac{6/7}{s - 2}, \tag{4}$$

we have, according to Theorem 2,

$$\begin{aligned} \mathbf{L}^{-1}\left\{\frac{3s}{s^2 + 3s - 10}\right\} &= \mathbf{L}^{-1}\left\{\frac{15/7}{s + 5} + \frac{6/7}{s - 2}\right\} \\ &= \frac{15}{7}\mathbf{L}^{-1}\left\{\frac{1}{s + 5}\right\} + \frac{6}{7}\mathbf{L}^{-1}\left\{\frac{1}{s - 2}\right\} \\ &= \frac{15}{7}e^{-5t} + \frac{6}{7}e^{2t}. \quad ◀ \end{aligned} \tag{5}$$

Thus notice how Theorems 1 and 2 (as well as subsequent theorems) serve to "extend" our modest table in Appendix C.

Next, we show that the transform of the derivative $f'(t)$ can be expressed, simply, in terms of the transform of $f(t)$ itself. This result will be indispensible in solving differential equations by the Laplace transform method.

> ***Theorem 3*** *Transform of the Derivative*
> Let $f(t)$ be continuous and $f'(t)$ be piecewise continuous on $0 \le t \le t_0$ for every finite t_0, let $f(t)$ be of exponential order as $t \to \infty$. Then $\mathbf{L}\{f'(t)\}$ exists for all $s > c$, where c is the same c as in (2) on page 544 and
>
> $$\boxed{\mathbf{L}\{f'(t)\} = s\mathbf{L}\{f(t)\} - f(0).} \tag{6}$$

Proof Since

$$\mathbf{L}\{f'(t)\} = \lim_{b\to\infty} \int_0^b f'(t)e^{-st}\,dt, \tag{7}$$

we consider the integral

$$\begin{aligned} I = \int_0^b f'(t)e^{-st}\,dt &= \int_0^{t_1} f'(t)e^{-st}\,dt + \cdots \\ &+ \int_{t_n}^b f'(t)e^{-st}\,dt, \end{aligned} \tag{8}$$

where $t_1, \ldots, t_n$ are the points, in the interval $0 < t < b$, at which f' is discontinuous. Integrating by parts yields

$$
\begin{aligned}
I = f(t)e^{-st}\Big|_0^{t_1} + \cdots + f(t)e^{-st}\Big|_{t_n}^{b} + s\int_0^{t_1} f(t)e^{-st}\,dt \\
+ \cdots + s\int_{t_n}^{b} f(t)e^{-st}\,dt.
\end{aligned}
\tag{9}
$$

By virtue of the continuity of f, the boundary terms at $t_1, \ldots, t_n$ cancel in pairs so that, after recombining the integrals in (9), we have

$$
I = f(b)e^{-sb} - f(0) + s\int_0^b f(t)e^{-st}\,dt. \tag{10}
$$

Now since f is of exponential order as $t \to \infty$, we have $|f(b)e^{-sb}| \le Ke^{-(s-c)b}$ for all $b \ge T$, and this quantity tends to zero (for all $s > c$) as $b \to \infty$. Thus

$$
\begin{aligned}
\mathbf{L}\{f'(t)\} &= \lim_{b\to\infty} [f(b)e^{-sb} - f(0) + s\int_0^b f(t)e^{-st}\,dt] \\
&= 0 - f(0) + s\mathbf{L}\{f(t)\},
\end{aligned}
\tag{11}
$$

as was to be proved. ■

The result above can be used to obtain the transform of higher derivatives as well. For example, if f' satisfies the conditions imposed on f in Theorem 3, replacement of f by f' in (6) gives

$$
\mathbf{L}\{f''(t)\} = s\mathbf{L}\{f'(t)\} - f'(0) = s[s\mathbf{L}\{f(t)\} - f(0)] - f'(0),
$$

so

$$
\boxed{\mathbf{L}\{f''(t)\} = s^2\mathbf{L}\{f(t)\} - sf(0) - f'(0).} \tag{12}
$$

Similarly for the transforms of f''', f'''', and so on. The general result is given in Exercise 1.

The last of the major properties of the Laplace transform that we wish to discuss in this section is the Laplace convolution theorem.

Theorem 4 *Laplace Convolution Theorem*

Suppose that $f(t)$ and $g(t)$ are piecewise continuous on $0 \le t \le t_0$ for each finite t_0, and of exponential order as $t \to \infty$. Then

$$
\boxed{\mathbf{L}^{-1}\{\bar{f}(s)\bar{g}(s)\} = \int_0^t f(\tau)g(t-\tau)\,d\tau} \tag{13}
$$

or, equivalently,

$$
\boxed{\mathbf{L}\left\{\int_0^t f(\tau)g(t-\tau)\,d\tau\right\} = \bar{f}(s)\bar{g}(s)} \tag{14}
$$

for $s > c$.

Proof It suffices to prove (14). By definition,

$$\mathbf{L}\left\{\int_0^t f(\tau)g(t-\tau)\,d\tau\right\} = \int_0^\infty \left\{\int_0^t f(\tau)g(t-\tau)\,d\tau\right\}e^{-st}\,dt. \tag{15}$$

Regarding the latter as an iterated integral over a 45° wedge in a τ, t plane, as sketched in Fig. 12.4, let us invert the order of integration in (15) (see Exercise 9). This step gives

$$\begin{aligned}\mathbf{L}\left\{\int_0^t f(\tau)g(t-\tau)\,dt\right\} &= \int_0^\infty \int_\tau^\infty f(\tau)g(t-\tau)e^{-st}\,dt\,d\tau \\ &= \int_0^\infty f(\tau)\,d\tau \int_\tau^\infty g(t-\tau)e^{-st}\,dt \\ &= \int_0^\infty f(\tau)\,d\tau \int_0^\infty g(\mu)e^{-s(\mu+\tau)}\,d\mu \qquad (t-\tau=\mu) \qquad (16)\\ &= \int_0^\infty f(\tau)e^{-s\tau}\,d\tau \int_0^\infty g(\mu)e^{-s\mu}\,d\mu \\ &= \bar{f}(s)\bar{g}(s),\end{aligned}$$

as asserted. ■

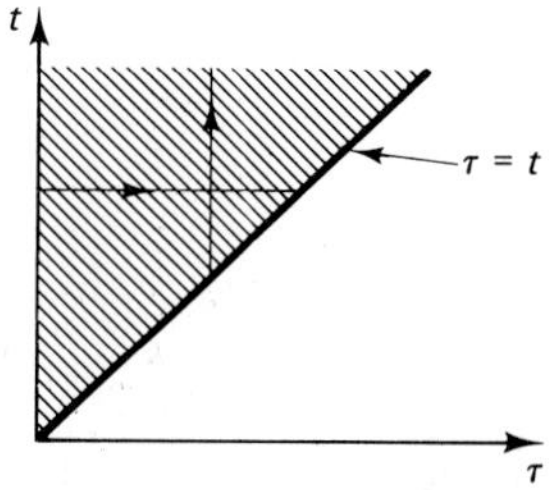

Fig. 12.4 Region of integration in (15).

The integral on the right-hand side of (13) is called the **Laplace convolution** of f and g, and is denoted as $f * g$. It, too, is a function of t:

$$(f * g)(t) \equiv \int_0^t f(\tau)g(t-\tau)\,d\tau. \tag{17}$$

Note the similarity between the Fourier (Section 11.4) and Laplace convolutions.

It is easy to show (Exercise 2) that

$$f * g = g * f, \qquad \text{(commutative)} \qquad (18a)$$

$$f * (g * h) = (f * g) * h, \qquad \text{(associative)} \qquad (18b)$$

$$f * (g + h) = f * g + f * h. \qquad \text{(distributive)} \qquad (18c)$$

The convolution theorem is useful in both directions. Equations containing Laplace convolution integrals sometimes arise, and if we take the Laplace transform of the equation, then (14) is of use. In the "other direction," suppose that we have a transform $\bar{h}(s)$ to invert. It may be possible to facilitate the inversion by factoring $\bar{h}(s)$ as $\bar{h}(s) = \bar{f}(s)\bar{g}(s)$, where the inverses of $\bar{f}$ and $\bar{g}$ are known. If so, the inverse of $\bar{h}$ is the convolution of the inverses of $\bar{f}$ and $\bar{g}$.

EXAMPLE 3 Evaluate $\mathbf{L}^{-1}\{1/s(s-a)\}$. Whereas $1/s(s-a)$ is not to be found in Appendix C, we notice that the factors $1/s$ and $1/(s-a)$ have the inverses

$$\mathbf{L}^{-1}\left\{\frac{1}{s}\right\} = 1 \quad \text{and} \quad \mathbf{L}^{-1}\left\{\frac{1}{s-a}\right\} = e^{at},$$

so that

$$\mathbf{L}^{-1}\left\{\frac{1}{s(s-a)}\right\} = 1 * e^{at}. \tag{19}$$

First, it will be helpful, although not essential, to reexpress $\mathbf{L}^{-1}\{1/s\}$ as $H(t)$ rather than as 1. Then

$$\begin{aligned}\mathbf{L}^{-1}\left\{\frac{1}{s(s-a)}\right\} &= H(t) * e^{at} = \int_0^t H(\tau)e^{a(t-\tau)}\,d\tau \\ &= e^{at}\int_0^t e^{-a\tau}\,d\tau = \frac{e^{at}-1}{a}.\end{aligned} \tag{20}$$

Alternatively [recall (18a)],

$$\begin{aligned}\mathbf{L}^{-1}\left\{\frac{1}{s(s-a)}\right\} &= e^{at} * H(t) = \int_0^t e^{a\tau}H(t-\tau)\,d\tau \\ &= \int_0^t e^{a\tau}\,d\tau = \frac{e^{at}-1}{a},\end{aligned} \tag{21}$$

as above. $H(\tau) = 1$ in (20) and $H(t-\tau) = 1$ in (21), because in each case, the argument of H is positive over the integration interval $0 < \tau < t$.

COMMENT 1 We do not mean to imply that the *only* way to invert $1/s(s-a)$ is by convolution. For example, the method of partial fractions yields

$$\begin{aligned}\mathbf{L}^{-1}\left\{\frac{1}{s(s-a)}\right\} &= \mathbf{L}^{-1}\left\{\frac{1}{a}\frac{1}{s-a} - \frac{1}{a}\frac{1}{s}\right\} \\ &= \frac{1}{a}\mathbf{L}^{-1}\left\{\frac{1}{s-a}\right\} - \frac{1}{a}\mathbf{L}^{-1}\left\{\frac{1}{s}\right\} = \frac{1}{a}e^{at} - \frac{1}{a},\end{aligned}$$

as before.

COMMENT 2 In case (18) has led you to believe that the convolution satisfies all the rules of arithmetic multiplication, note carefully, from (19) and (21), that $1 * e^{at} = (e^{at}-1)/a \neq e^{at}$; i.e., in general, $1 * f(t)$ is *not* equal to $f(t)$, although it *is* always true that $0 * f(t) = 0$. ◀

In this section we have established the linearity of $\mathbf{L}$ and $\mathbf{L}^{-1}$, we have shown how to express the transforms of $f', f'', \ldots,$ in terms of the tranform of f, and we have derived the convolution theorem. With these results, plus our table in Appendix C, we are ready to develop the most important application of the Laplace transform—to the solution of ordinary differential equations.

1. Use (6) together with mathematical induction to verify the general formula

$$\mathbf{L}\{f^{(n)}(t)\} = s^n\bar{f}(s) - s^{n-1}f(0) - s^{n-2}f'(0) - \cdots - f^{(n-1)}(0). \quad \text{(a)}$$

2. (a) Prove (18a).(b) Prove (18b).(c) Prove (18c).

3. Show that $\mathbf{L}\{f * g * h\} = \bar{f}(s)\bar{g}(s)\bar{h}(s)$ or, equivalently, that $\mathbf{L}^{-1}\{\bar{f}\bar{g}\bar{h}\} = f * g * h$. *Note:* According to (18b), it does not matter whether we interpret $f * g * h$ as $(f * g) * h$ or as $f * (g * h)$.

4. To illustrate the results stated in Exercise 3, compute the inverse of $1/s^3$ by writing $\mathbf{L}^{-1}\{1/s^3\} = \mathbf{L}^{-1}\{(1/s)(1/s)(1/s)\} = 1 * 1 * 1 =$ etc., and show that the result agrees with item 7 in Appendix C.

5. Factoring

$$\frac{s}{(s^2 + a^2)^2} = \frac{s}{s^2 + a^2}\frac{1}{s^2 + a^2},$$

it follows from the convolution theorem and entries 3 and 4 of Appendix C that

$$\mathbf{L}^{-1}\left\{\frac{s}{(s^2 + a^2)^2}\right\} = \cos at * \frac{\sin at}{a}.$$

Evaluate the convolution and thus show that

$$\mathbf{L}^{-1}\left\{\frac{s}{(s^2 + a^2)^2}\right\} = \frac{1}{2a}t \sin at,$$

in agreement with item 11 in Appendix C.

6. Evaluate $\mathbf{L}^{-1}\{\bar{f}\}$ using the suggested factoring and following the lines indicated in Example 3 and Exercise 5. In each case, check your answer against the corresponding item in Appendix C.

(a) $\bar{f}(s) = \dfrac{1}{s^2 - a^2} = \dfrac{1}{s - a}\dfrac{1}{s + a}$

(b) $\bar{f}(s) = \dfrac{s}{(s^2 - a^2)^2} = \dfrac{s}{s^2 - a^2}\dfrac{1}{s^2 - a^2}$

(c) $\bar{f}(s) = \dfrac{e^{-as}}{s} = \dfrac{1}{s}e^{-as}$

(d) $\bar{f}(s) = \dfrac{1}{s^2 + a^2} = \dfrac{1}{s - ai}\dfrac{1}{s + ai}$ *Note:* Recall Exercise 12 on page 552.

7. Find the transform of the given function.

*(a) $\displaystyle\int_0^t e^{t-\tau} \sin 2\tau \, d\tau$

(b) $\displaystyle\int_0^t \cos 3(t - \tau) \cos 2\tau \, d\tau$

(c) $\displaystyle\int_0^t \cos 3\tau \cosh 3(t - \tau) \, d\tau$

(d) $\displaystyle\int_0^t (t - \tau)^8 e^{-3\tau} \, d\tau$

*(e) $\displaystyle\int_0^t \frac{\sin \tau}{\sqrt{t - \tau}} \, d\tau$

(f) $\displaystyle\int_0^t \tau^{5.2} \sinh 4(t - \tau) \, d\tau$

8. Occasionally, students misstate the convolution theorem as $\mathbf{L}^{-1}\{\bar{f}\bar{g}\} = f(t)g(t)$. Show that this claim is, in general, incorrect.

9. The interchange

$$\int_0^\infty \int_0^\infty F(t, \tau)\, d\tau\, dt = \int_0^\infty \int_0^\infty F(t, \tau)\, dt\, d\tau$$

is valid if at least one side converges absolutely—that is, if either

$$\int_0^\infty \int_0^\infty |F(t, \tau)|\, d\tau\, dt \quad \text{or} \quad \int_0^\infty \int_0^\infty |F(t, \tau)|\, dt\, d\tau$$

converges. Using this result, verify the legitimacy of the interchange in the order of integration in the proof of the convolution theorem. *Hint:*

$$\int_0^\infty \int_0^t f(\tau)g(t - \tau)e^{-st}\, d\tau\, dt = \int_0^\infty \int_0^\infty f(\tau)g(t - \tau)H(t - \tau)\, d\tau\, dt.$$

APPLICATIONS TO DIFFERENTIAL EQUATIONS 12.5

Finally, some applications.

EXAMPLE 1 *Mass–Spring System.* The displacement $x(t)$ of the mass m shown in Fig. 12.5 is governed by the initial-value problem

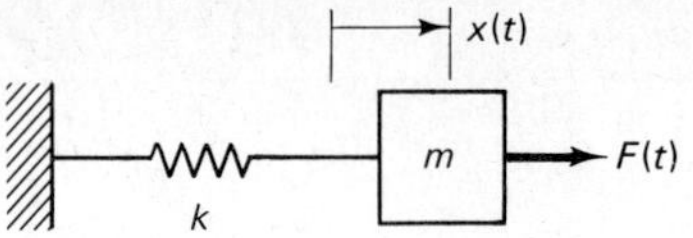

Fig. 12.5 Mass–spring system.

$$m\ddot{x} + kx = F(t) \qquad (0 \le t \le \infty) \tag{1a}$$

$$x(0) = x_0, \quad \dot{x}(0) = \dot{x}_0, \tag{1b}$$

where k is the stiffness of the spring, $F(t)$ is a prescribed applied force, x_0 is the initial displacement, and $\dot{x}_0$ is the initial velocity. (Depending on the context, we sometimes use dots, and sometimes primes, to denote d/dt. Here we use dots.)

To solve (1) by the Laplace transform method, we begin by "transforming (1a)." That is, we operate on both sides of (1a) with the Laplace transform operator $\mathbf{L}$:

$$\mathbf{L}\{m\ddot{x} + kx\} = \mathbf{L}\{F(t)\}. \tag{2}$$

Using the linearity of $\mathbf{L}$ (Theorem 1, page 554), together with the formula $\mathbf{L}\{\ddot{x}\} = s^2\overline{x} - sx(0) - \dot{x}(0) = s^2\overline{x} - sx_0 - \dot{x}_0$ [(12) on page 556 we have for the left-hand side

$$\begin{aligned} \mathbf{L}\{m\ddot{x} + kx\} &= m\mathbf{L}\{\ddot{x}\} + k\mathbf{L}\{x\} \\ &= ms^2\overline{x} - msx_0 - m\dot{x}_0 + k\overline{x}. \end{aligned} \tag{3}$$

so (2) becomes

$$(ms^2 + k)\overline{x} = msx_0 + m\dot{x}_0 + \overline{F}. \tag{4}$$

Observe carefully that *in the "t domain" we were faced with the ODE (1a) on x(t); in the "s domain" the problem (4) is merely a linear algebraic equation on* $\overline{x}(s)$. It is in the s domain that we now do the "solving." That is, solving (4) for $\overline{x}$, we easily obtain

$$\overline{x} = x_0\frac{s}{s^2 + \omega^2} + \dot{x}_0\frac{1}{s^2 + \omega^2} + \frac{1}{m}\frac{\overline{F}}{s^2 + \omega^2}, \tag{5}$$

where $\omega \equiv \sqrt{k/m}$.

Finally, we invert $\overline{x}(s)$ to obtain $x(t)$. Using the linearity of $\mathbf{L}^{-1}$ (Theorem 2, page 554), and items 3 and 4 in Appendix C, we obtain

$$\begin{aligned} x(t) &= \mathbf{L}^{-1}\left\{x_0\frac{s}{s^2 + \omega^2} + \dot{x}_0\frac{1}{s^2 + \omega^2} + \frac{1}{m}\frac{\overline{F}}{s^2 + \omega^2}\right\} \\ &= x_0\mathbf{L}^{-1}\left\{\frac{s}{s^2 + \omega^2}\right\} + \dot{x}_0\mathbf{L}^{-1}\left\{\frac{1}{s^2 + \omega^2}\right\} + \frac{1}{m}\mathbf{L}^{-1}\left\{\frac{\overline{F}(s)}{s^2 + \omega^2}\right\} \\ &= x_0\cos\omega t + \frac{\dot{x}_0}{\omega}\sin\omega t + \frac{1}{m}\mathbf{L}^{-1}\left\{\frac{\overline{F}(s)}{s^2 + \omega^2}\right\}. \end{aligned} \tag{6}$$

To evaluate the last term, we reexpress $\overline{F}(s)/(s^2 + \omega^2)$ as a product and apply the convolution theorem (Theorem 4, page 556):

$$\mathbf{L}^{-1}\left\{\frac{\bar{F}(s)}{s^2+\omega^2}\right\} = \mathbf{L}^{-1}\left\{\frac{1}{s^2+\omega^2}\bar{F}(s)\right\}$$

$$=\mathbf{L}^{-1}\left\{\frac{1}{s^2+\omega^2}\right\} * \mathbf{L}^{-1}\{\bar{F}(s)\} \tag{7}$$

$$=\frac{\sin \omega t}{\omega} * F(t) = \frac{1}{\omega}\int_0^t (\sin \omega\tau)F(t-\tau)\,d\tau,$$

so that

$$x(t) = x_0 \cos \omega t + \frac{\dot{x}_0}{\omega}\sin \omega t + \frac{1}{m\omega}\int_0^t (\sin \omega\tau)F(t-\tau)\,d\tau \tag{8}$$

or, equivalently,

$$x(t) = x_0 \cos \omega t + \frac{\dot{x}_0}{\omega}\sin \omega t + \frac{1}{m\omega}\int_0^t \sin \omega(t-\tau)F(\tau)\,d\tau. \tag{9}$$

COMMENT 1 Observe our implicit assumption that $F(t)$ and $x(t)$ are indeed transformable, i.e., that $\bar{F}(s)$ and $\bar{x}(s)$ exist. In the case of F there is no problem: Since F is prescribed, we simply ask that $\bar{F}$ exist.* Regarding x, however, note that x is not known in advance; it is the unknown. Thus we *tentatively assume* that $x(t)$ is transformable, subject to a posteriori verification. However, rather than carry out that verification, it is more reasonable to merely verify that (9) does satisfy the given ODE (1a) and initial conditions (1b). That step is left for the exercises.

COMMENT 2 Observe that we did *not* find the general solution of (1a) and then impose the initial conditions (1b), as one does in a first course in ODEs. Rather, the initial conditions became incorporated as soon as we wrote $\mathbf{L}\{\ddot{x}\} = s^2\bar{x} - sx_0 - \dot{x}_0$. Thus the result (9) is the particular solution that satisfies those initial conditions.

COMMENT 3 Equation (4) may, after division by $ms^2 + k$, be expressed as

$$\bar{x}(s) = \frac{1}{ms^2+k}[msx_0 + m\dot{x}_0 + \bar{F}(s)]. \tag{10}$$

Since x_0, $\dot{x}_0$, $F(t)$ are inputs and $x(t)$ is the output, we may regard $msx_0 + m\dot{x}_0 + \bar{F}(s)$ as the **input** (in the s domain), $\bar{x}(s)$ as the **output** (in the s domain), and $1/(ms^2 + k)$ as the **transfer function.** The transfer function reflects the nature of the physical system, irrespective of the inputs and outputs. In electrical circuit theory, unity divided by the product of s and the transfer function is known as the *impedance* of the circuit.

COMMENT 4 Rather than transform the ODE (1a), suppose that we integrate it with respect to t, from 0 to t:

$$m\dot{x}(t) - m\dot{x}(0) + k\int_0^t x(\tau)\,d\tau = \int_0^t F(\tau)\,d\tau. \tag{11}$$

* Note that the conditions in Theorem 1 on page 545 are sufficient, not necessary. For example, $\delta(t-t_0)$ is not piecewise continuous, yet $\mathbf{L}\{\delta(t-t_0\} = \int_0^\infty \delta(t-t_0)e^{-st}\,dt = \exp(-st_0)$ does exist.

Integrating again yields

$$mx(t) - mx(0) - m\dot{x}(0)t + k\int_0^t \int_0^{t'} x(\tau)\, d\tau\, dt' = \int_0^t \int_0^{t'} F(\tau)\, d\tau\, dt'. \quad (12)$$

Inverting the order of integration in the double integrals gives the simpler forms (Exercise 2)

$$\int_0^t \int_0^{t'} x(\tau)\, d\tau\, dt' = \int_0^t (t - \tau)x(\tau)\, d\tau, \quad (13a)$$

$$\int_0^t \int_0^{t'} F(\tau)\, d\tau\, dt' = \int_0^t (t - \tau)F(\tau)\, d\tau, \quad (13b)$$

and recalling (1b), (12) becomes

$$x(t) = x_0 + \dot{x}_0 t + \frac{1}{m}\int_0^t (t - \tau)F(\tau)\, d\tau - \omega^2 \int_0^t (t - \tau)x(\tau)\, d\tau. \quad (14)$$

Unfortunately, (14) is not the "solution" of (1) because of the presence of the unknown x in the second integral. Rather, it is an example of an **integral equation**, because of the presence of the unknown within the integral. Beginning with (14), it is possible to reverse our steps (with the help of the Leibniz rule) and recover the original system (1), so that (1) and (14) are equivalent. The study of integral equations is normally reserved for more advanced courses, and our comments here are only introductory. In the present example, the physics (namely, Newton's second law) gave us the differential equation of motion, and it was only by manipulating that equation that we obtained the integral equation (14). In other cases the physics may give us an integral equation directly. In any event, observe that we can solve the *integral* equation (14) by application of the Laplace transform. For the integrals are of convolution type, so we have

$$x(t) = x_0 + \dot{x}_0 t + \frac{1}{m} t * F - \omega^2 t * x, \quad (15)$$

and hence

$$\bar{x}(s) = \frac{x_0}{s} + \frac{\dot{x}_0}{s^2} + \frac{1}{m}\frac{1}{s}\bar{F}(s) - \omega^2 \frac{1}{s^2}\bar{x}(s). \quad (16)$$

Solving (16) for $\bar{x}$ gives us (5), and the solution then proceeds as before. ◀

EXAMPLE 2 *RC Circuit*. The current $I(t)$ in the electrical circuit shown in Fig. 12.6 is [according to (57) on page 896 in Appendix A] governed by the differential equation

$$R\dot{I} + \frac{1}{C}I = \dot{E}(t), \quad (17)$$

where R is the resistance, C the capacitance, and $E(t)$ the applied voltage. Suppose that $I(0) = 0$ and that $E(t)$ is brought from 0 to E_0 almost instantaneously and then held at that value for all subsequent t. In practice, we probably do not know the precise functional form of $E(t)$, except for the fact that it rises almost instanta-

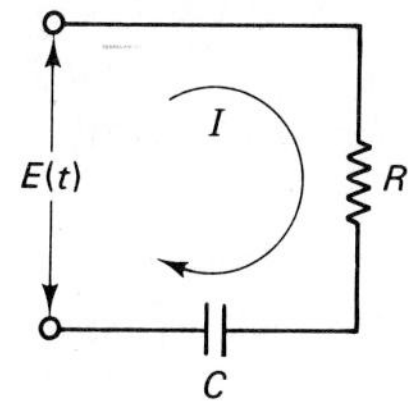

Fig. 12.6 *RC* circuit.

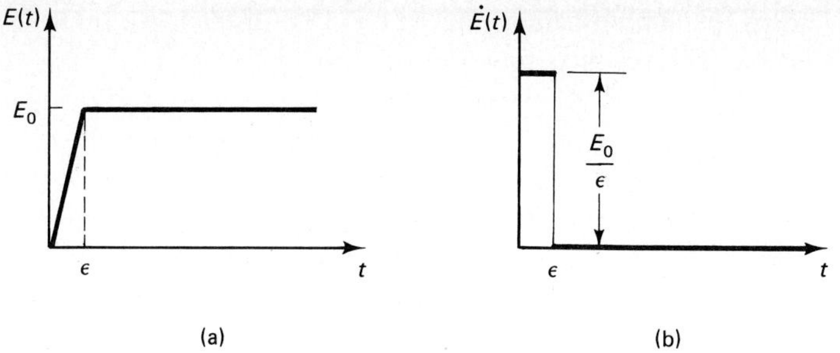

Fig. 12.7 Graphs of E and $\dot{E}$.

neously from 0 to E_0. For definiteness, suppose that $E(t)$ is as shown in Fig. 12.7a. Then $\dot{E}(t)$ is as shown in Fig. 12.7b.

Laplace transforming (17) gives

$$R[s\bar{I} - I(0)] + \frac{1}{C}\bar{I} = \int_0^\epsilon \frac{E_0}{\epsilon} e^{-st}\, dt$$
$$= \frac{E_0}{\epsilon}\frac{1 - e^{-\epsilon s}}{s}. \tag{18}$$

Now we can keep the right-hand side of (18) intact and proceed, but it seems reasonable to use the fact that ϵ is extremely small and let $\epsilon \to 0$. With the help of l'Hospital's rule, that step gives

$$\lim_{\epsilon\to 0} \frac{E_0}{\epsilon}\frac{1 - e^{-\epsilon s}}{s} = E_0, \tag{19}$$

and (18) simplifies to

$$\left(s + \frac{1}{RC}\right)\bar{I} = \frac{E_0}{R} \quad \text{or} \quad \bar{I} = \frac{E_0}{R}\frac{1}{s + RC}. \tag{20}$$

Inverting gives us

$$I(t) = \frac{E_0}{R} e^{-t/RC}, \tag{21}$$

as shown by the solid curve in Fig. 12.8.

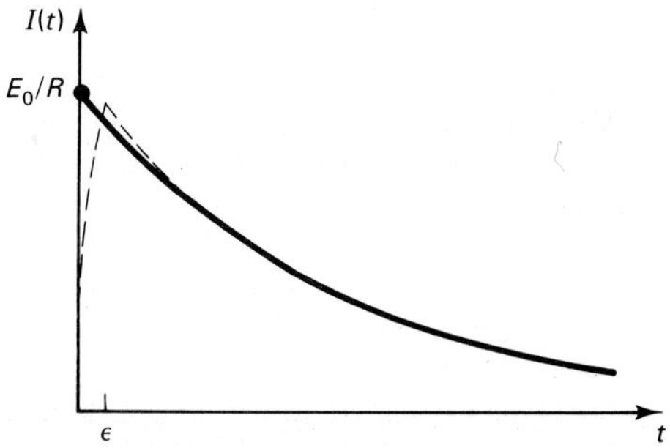

Fig. 12.8 $I(t)$ given by (21) (solid curve); $I(t;\,\epsilon)$ given by (22) (dashed curve).

COMMENT 1 Looking at (21) and its graph, one may be disturbed to find that the condition $I(0) = 0$ seems not to be satisfied. To clarify the situation, let us *not* adopt the simplification offered by (19). Instead, we return to (18), solve for $\bar{I}$, and invert. The result is found to be

$$I(t;\epsilon) = \frac{CE_0}{\epsilon}\{1 - e^{-t/RC} - H(t-\epsilon)[1 - e^{-(t-\epsilon)/RC}]\}, \tag{22}$$

as indicated by the dashed curve in Fig. 12.8. If, in the absence of better information, we agree to accept the piecewise-linear representation of $E(t)$ (Fig. 12.7), then (22) is the exact solution and does satisfy the initial condition $I(0) = 0$. In fact, even if we let $\epsilon \to 0$ in (22), we obtain (Exercise 3)

$$\lim_{\epsilon\to 0} I(t;\epsilon) = \begin{cases} \dfrac{E_0}{R}e^{-t/RC}, & t > 0 \\ 0, & t = 0 \end{cases} \tag{23}$$

which still satisfies the $I(0) = 0$ condition. Thus (21) was *essentially* correct but failed to include the jump discontinuity from 0 to E_0/R at $t = 0$. That loss of information was the price that we paid in letting $\epsilon \to 0$ prematurely in order to simplify the analysis.

COMMENT 2 The source of the difficulty in this problem was the time derivative on E in (17). *If* the right-hand side were $E(t)$ instead, the rapid rise of $E(t)$ would be rather inconsequential, and the representation shown in Fig. 12.7a could be simplified to $E(t) = \text{constant} = E_0$. However, the right-hand side is $\dot{E}(t)$, not $E(t)$, and the "rise portion" of $E(t)$ gives a pulse-like $\dot{E}(t)$ which is (in the limit as $\epsilon \to 0$) equal to $E_0\delta(t)$, where the delta function acts at $t = 0+$. It is this delta function in the input that causes the jump discontinuity in the output I. ◀

EXAMPLE 3 *System of Coupled ODEs.* To illustrate the application of the Laplace transform to systems of coupled ODEs, we consider the following simple case.

$$\begin{aligned} \dot{x} - x - y &= t; \qquad x(0) = 0 \\ \dot{y} - 4x - y &= 0; \qquad y(0) = 2. \end{aligned} \tag{24}$$

Transforming both ODEs yields

$$\begin{aligned} s\bar{x} - x(0) - \bar{x} - \bar{y} &= \frac{1}{s^2} \\ s\bar{y} - y(0) - 4\bar{x} - \bar{y} &= 0 \end{aligned} \tag{25}$$

or

$$\begin{aligned} (s-1)\bar{x} - \bar{y} &= \frac{1}{s^2} \\ 4\bar{x} - (s-1)\bar{y} &= -2. \end{aligned} \tag{26}$$

Solving by algebra, we obtain

$$\bar{x} = \frac{2s^2 + s - 1}{s^2(s^2 - 2s - 3)}, \qquad \bar{y} = 2\frac{s^3 - s^2 + 2}{s^2(s^2 - 2s - 3)}. \tag{27}$$

To invert these forms we expand them in partial fractions, with which method we assume the reader is familiar. (In any case, the method is discussed in the exercises.) Beginning with $\bar{x}$, we express

$$\begin{aligned} \bar{x} &= \frac{2s^2 + s - 1}{s^2(s^2 - 2s - 3)} = \frac{2s^2 + s - 1}{s^2(s+1)(s-3)} \\ &= \frac{As + B}{s^2} + \frac{C}{s+1} + \frac{D}{s-3}. \end{aligned} \tag{28}$$

We wish to determine the constants A, B, C, D so that the last equality holds identically in s (for all $s > 3$). One way to proceed is to combine the terms on the right over a common denominator and then to equate coefficients of like powers of s in the numerator. Thus

$$\frac{2s^2 + s - 1}{s^2(s+1)(s-1)} = \frac{(As + B)(s^2 - 2s - 3) + C(s^3 - 3s^2) + D(s^3 + s^2)}{s^2(s+1)(s-3)} \tag{29}$$

and equating coefficients of s^3, s^2, s, 1 in the numerator gives

$$\begin{aligned} s^3&: \quad 0 = A + C + D \\ s^2&: \quad 2 = -2A + B - 3C + D \\ s&: \quad 1 = -3A - 2B \\ 1&: \quad -1 = -3B. \end{aligned} \tag{30}$$

Solving yields $B = \frac{1}{3}$, $A = -\frac{5}{9}$, $C = 0$, $D = \frac{5}{9}$, so that

$$\begin{aligned} x(t) &= \mathbf{L}^{-1}\left\{-\frac{5}{9}\frac{1}{s} + \frac{1}{3}\frac{1}{s^2} + \frac{5}{9}\frac{1}{s-3}\right\} \\ &= -\frac{5}{9} + \frac{1}{3}t + \frac{5}{9}e^{3t}. \end{aligned} \tag{31}$$

We could solve for $y(t)$ in the same manner, although it is easier merely to solve for $y(t)$ from the first ODE in (24). That step gives $y = \dot{x} - x - t = \frac{8}{9} - \frac{4}{3}t - \frac{10}{9}e^{3t}$. ◀

EXAMPLE 4 *Variable-Coefficient Equation.* As our final application, consider the problem

$$t\ddot{x} + \dot{x} + tx = 0, \tag{32a}$$

$$x(0) = 1, \quad \dot{x}(0) = 0. \tag{32b}$$

This is our first nonconstant-coefficient equation, and we include it not with the pretense that this example will show the reader how to solve variable-coefficient ODEs, but rather to indicate just how heavily the foregoing methodology rests on the presence of constant coefficients. At the same time, (32a) happens to be a rather important ODE, the **Bessel equation of order zero,** which we plan to discuss more deeply in Part IV.

The difficulty imposed by the nonconstant coefficients surfaces immediately, for what is the transform of $t\ddot{x}$? The transform of $\ddot{x}$ is easily expressed in terms of the transform of x, but the t factor complicates matters. However, proceeding formally, observe that

$$
\begin{aligned}
\mathbf{L}\{t\ddot{x}\} &= \int_0^\infty t\ddot{x}e^{-st}\,dt = -\frac{d}{ds}\int_0^\infty \ddot{x}e^{-st}\,dt \\
&= -\frac{d}{ds}[s^2\overline{x}(s) - sx(0) - \dot{x}(0)] = -\frac{d}{ds}[s^2\overline{x}(s) - s].
\end{aligned}
\tag{33}
$$

Similarly for the third term in (32a),

$$
\begin{aligned}
\mathbf{L}\{tx\} &= \int_0^\infty txe^{-st}\,dt = -\frac{d}{ds}\int_0^\infty xe^{-st}\,dt \\
&= -\frac{d}{ds}\overline{x}(s),
\end{aligned}
\tag{34}
$$

so that the transform of (32a) gives

$$
-\frac{d}{ds}[s^2\overline{x}(s) - s] + s\overline{x}(s) - x(0) - \frac{d}{ds}\overline{x}(s) = 0 \tag{35}
$$

or, since $x(0) = 1$,

$$
(s^2 + 1)\frac{d\overline{x}}{ds} + s\overline{x} = 0. \tag{36}
$$

Thus, instead of obtaining an algebraic equation on $\overline{x}$ we are confronted with a first-order ODE on $\overline{x}$, first order because the nonconstant coefficients in (32a) happen to be t's to the first power. Fortunately, (36) is simple. Separating variables and integrating gives

$$
\overline{x}(s) = \frac{C}{\sqrt{s^2 + 1}}. \tag{37}
$$

According to item 23 in Appendix C, it follows that

$$
x(t) = CJ_0(t), \tag{38}
$$

where $J_0(t)$ is the **Bessel function of the first kind and order zero.** It is known from the theory of Bessel functions that $J_0(0) = 1$, so

$$
x(0) = 1 = CJ_0(0) \tag{39}
$$

gives $C = 1$. Thus

$$
x(t) = J_0(t). \tag{40}
$$

However, rather than depend on the theory of Bessel functions, let us do what we can with (37). We could expand

$$
\overline{x}(s) = C(1 + s^2)^{-1/2} = C(1 - \tfrac{1}{2}s^2 + \tfrac{3}{8}s^4 - \cdots) \tag{41}
$$

and seek to invert the series termwise, but this procedure is evidently ill fated because the individual terms do not tend to 0 as $s \to \infty$, so they will not yield "decent" inverses. Instead, try *inverse* powers of s:

$$\bar{x}(s) = \frac{C}{s\sqrt{1 + \dfrac{1}{s^2}}} = \frac{C}{s}\left(1 + \frac{1}{s^2}\right)^{-1/2}$$
$$= C\left(\frac{1}{s} - \frac{1}{2}\frac{1}{s^3} + \frac{3}{8}\frac{1}{s^5} - \cdots\right), \tag{42}$$

for $s > 1$. Formally inverting termwise,

$$x(t) = C\left(1 - \frac{t^2}{4} + \frac{t^4}{64} - \cdots\right), \tag{43}$$

and $x(0) = 1 = C(1 - 0 + 0 - \cdots)$ gives $C = 1$. Thus we have derived the power series representation

$$J_0(t) = 1 - \frac{t^2}{4} + \frac{t^4}{64} - \cdots \tag{44}$$

of the Bessel function $J_0(t)$. It can be shown that the series converges for all finite t and satisfies the ODE (32a). ◀

Reviewing this section, we see that the Laplace transform constitutes a powerful tool in the solution of linear ODEs, especially those having constant coefficients. The power of the method lies in the replacement of a difficult problem in the t domain by a simpler one in the s domain. Since we need to move back and forth, with ease, between the t and s domains, it is efficient to develop a number of theorems and techniques that can be drawn upon repeatedly so that we do not need to reinvent the wheel with each new problem. Some of these theorems and techniques have already been given in Section 12.4. Additional results are presented in the next section, and the method of partial fractions is spelled out in the exercises at the end of the present section.

Finally, we remark that in differential (and integral) equation applications of the Laplace transform the independent variable often happens to be the time t. However, the method in no way depends on the physical significance of the independent and dependent variables. Thus the Laplace transform solution of the problems

$$\ddot{x} + x = f(t) \qquad (0 \le t < \infty)$$
$$x(0) = 1, \quad \dot{x}(0) = 0$$

and

$$y'' + y = f(x) \qquad (0 \le x < \infty)$$
$$y(0) = 1, \quad y'(0) = 0$$

would proceed in identical fashion.

12.5 EXERCISES

1. Verify that (9) does satisfy the initial-value problem. For simplicity, it may be assumed that $F(t)$ is continuous.

2. Derive (13a) and (13b).

3. Derive (23) from (22).

4. Solve the following initial-value problems by means of the Laplace transform. (If necessary, see Exercises 11 to 14 for discussion of partial fraction expansions.)

*(a) $\dot{x} - 4x = e^{2t}$; $x(0) = 5$
(b) $\dot{x} + 2x = t^2 e^{-2t}$; $x(0) = 0$
(c) $\ddot{x} - 4x = 3 + \cosh 2t$; $x(0) = \dot{x}(0) = 0$
(d) $\ddot{x} + 2\dot{x} = H(t - 1)$; $x(0) = 0$, $\dot{x}(0) = 1$
*(e) $\dddot{x} - \ddot{x} - 4\dot{x} + 4x = f(t)$;
$x(0) = \dot{x}(0) = \ddot{x}(0) = 0$
(f) $\ddot{x} - \dot{x} - 2x = 0$; $x(0) = 0$, $\dot{x}(0) = 5$
(g) $y'''' - 16y = 0$; $y(0) = y'(0) = y''(0) = 0$,
$y'''(0) = 3$
(h) $y''' - 2y'' - y' + 2y = H(t - 2)$;
$y(0) = y'(0) = y''(0) = 0$
*(i) $\ddot{x} + 2\dot{x} + x = t^2$; $x(0) = \dot{x}(0) = 0$
(j) $y'''' - 3y'' + 2y = e^x$;
$y(0) = y'(0) = y''(0) = y'''(0) = 0$
(k) $y''' - y = 3x$; $y(0) = y'(0) = 0$, $y''(0) = 1$
(l) $\dot{x} = x + y$; $x(0) = 1$
$\dot{y} = 4x + y$; $y(0) = 0$
(m) $\dot{x} - 2y = e^t - 4t$; $x(0) = 1$
$\dot{y} + x - y = e^t - 2t + 2$; $y(0) = 0$
(n) $\dot{x} + 3\dot{y} + y = 4e^t$; $x(0) = 0$
$\dot{y} - y - x = 0$; $y(0) = 2$
*(o) $\dot{x} = y$; $x(0) = 0$
$\dot{y} = -x$; $y(0) = 1$
(p) $\dot{x} + y + z = 0$; $x(0) = 0$
$x + \dot{y} + z = 0$; $y(0) = 0$
$x + y + \dot{z} = 0$; $z(0) = 1$
(q) $2\dot{x} - y - z = 0$; $x(0) = 0$
$-x + 2\dot{y} - z = 0$; $y(0) = 0$
$-x - y + 2\dot{z} = t$; $z(0) = 0$
(r) $t\dot{x} + x = t$; $x(0) = 0$
(s) $xy'' + y' = 0$; $y(0) = 2$, $y'(0) = 0$

5. *(a)–(s) Reexpress each problem in Exercise 4 as an integral equation, then solve the integral equation by the Laplace transform.

6. Expand $\bar{f}(s)$ in a power series in inverse powers of s, and then invert termwise, as we have done in Example 4. Thus, obtain a power series representation of $f(t)$. Check your result by looking up $\mathbf{L}^{-1}\{\bar{f}(s)\}$ in Appendix C.

(a) $\bar{f}(s) = \dfrac{1}{s - a}$ (b) $\bar{f}(s) = \dfrac{1}{s^2 + a^2}$

(c) $\bar{f}(s) = \dfrac{s}{s^2 + a^2}$ (d) $\bar{f}(s) = \dfrac{1}{s^2 - a^2}$

(e) $\bar{f}(s) = \dfrac{s}{s^2 - a^2}$ (f) $\bar{f}(s) = \dfrac{s}{(s^2 + a^2)^2}$

(g) $\bar{f}(s) = \dfrac{1}{(s - a)^2}$ (h) $\bar{f}(s) = \dfrac{1}{(s - a)^3}$

(i) $\bar{f}(s) = \dfrac{1}{\sqrt{s - a}}$

7. (*Coupled mechanical oscillator*) The displacements $x_1(t)$ and $x_2(t)$ of the masses m_1 and m_2, shown in the figure, are governed by the initial-value problem

$$\begin{aligned} m_1\ddot{x}_1 &= -k_1x_1 - k_{12}(x_1 - x_2); \\ x_1(0) &= x_{10}, \quad \dot{x}_1(0) = \dot{x}_{10} \\ m_2\ddot{x}_2 &= -k_2x_2 - k_{12}(x_2 - x_1); \\ x_2(0) &= x_{20}, \quad \dot{x}_2(0) = \dot{x}_{20}, \end{aligned} \tag{a}$$

where k_1, k_2, k_{12} are the spring stiffnesses. With $m_1 = m_2 = k_1 = k_2 = k_{12}$ and $x_{10} = 1$, $\dot{x}_{10} = x_{20} = \dot{x}_{20} = 0$, solve (a) for $x_1(t)$, $x_2(t)$ by the Laplace transform.

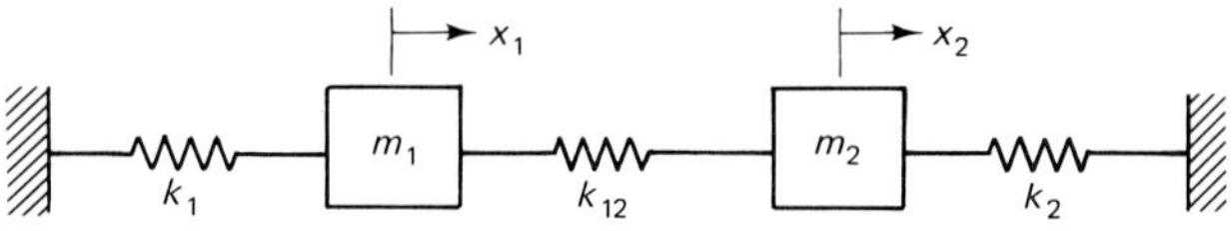

8. (*Coupled RC circuit*) The currents $I_1(t)$ and $I_2(t)$, for the circuit shown in the figure, are governed by the initial-value problem

$$\begin{aligned} R(\dot{I}_1 - \dot{I}_2) + \frac{1}{C}I_1 &= \dot{E}(t); \qquad I_1(0) = 0 \\ \frac{1}{C}I_2 + R(\dot{I}_2 - \dot{I}_1) &= 0; \qquad I_2(0) = 0, \end{aligned} \tag{a}$$

where R is a known resistance, C is a known capacitance, and $E(t)$ is a prescribed applied voltage. Solve (a) for $I_1(t)$ and $I_2(t)$ by the Laplace transform, for the case where $E(t) = Kt$.

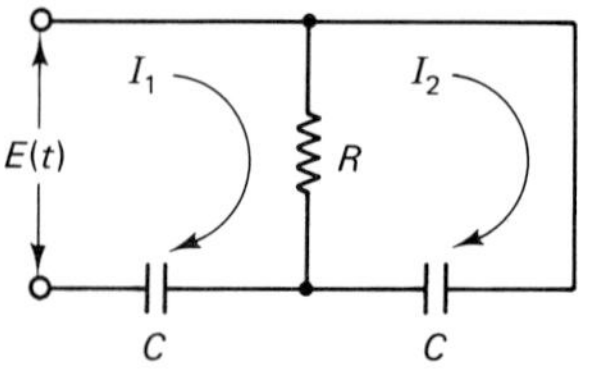

9. It is found that the integral equation

$$C(T) = \int_0^\infty e^{-0.0744\nu^2/T^2}\,\rho(\nu)\,d\nu \tag{a}$$

is an approximate relation between the frequency

spectrum $\rho(\nu)$ and the specific heat $C(T)$ of a crystal. Solve for $\rho(\nu)$ for the cases where

(a) $C(T) = T$ *(b) $C(T) = Te^{-1/T}$

10. (*Finite loaded beam*) According to the classical *Euler beam theory*, the vertical deflection $u(x)$ (measured positive upward) resulting from a load distribution $p(x)$ newtons per unit length (measured positive upward) satisfies the differential equation

$$EIu'''' = p(x), \tag{a}$$

where E and I are physical constants; EI is called the "flexural rigidity" of the beam since u'''', and hence the deflection u, is inversely proportional to EI. Consider such a beam of length L, supported at its ends by knife edges, and loaded at a distance b from one end by a concentrated force P, as shown in Part (a) of the accompanying figure. Considering the beam to be weightless, the loading consists of three point forces, as shown in Part (b): the applied load P, and the two reaction forces at the supports. Since the beam is weightless, we can fictitiously extend it beyond $x = L$, over $0 \le x < \infty$, so that we can apply a Laplace transform on the independent variable x. Representing the point forces by delta functions, (a) becomes

$$EIu'''' = F_1\delta(x) - P\delta(x - b) + F_2\delta(x - L), \tag{b}$$

where $\delta(x)$ is understood to act at $x = 0+$. Turning to the boundary conditions, we have $u(0) = 0$, $u''(0) = 0$ (because u'' is proportional to the local "moment" and there is no moment applied at the free end $x = 0$). Unfortunately, we have only the three initial conditions (i.e., at $x = 0$) $u(0) = u''(0) = u'''(0) = 0$; in applying the Laplace transform we will also need $u'(0)$, but we do not know it in advance.

(a) Solving (b) by the Laplace transform, show that

$$u(x) = u'(0)x + \frac{F_1}{6EI}x^3 - \frac{P}{6EI}(x - b)^3 H(x - b) \quad (0 \le x \le L). \tag{c}$$

(b) To evaluate the unknown $u'(0)$, use the additional known boundary condition $u(L) = 0$. Thus show that

$$u(x) = \frac{1}{6EI}\left\{\left[\frac{P}{L}(L - b)^3 F_1 L^2\right]x + F_1 x^3 - P(x - b)^3 H(x - b)\right\}. \tag{d}$$

Note: This is an interesting problem since it is a *boundary value problem* [note the boundary conditions $u(0) = u''(0) = u'''(0) = 0$, $u(L) = 0$] on a *finite domain*. Nevertheless, we were able to solve by the Laplace transform method. Incidentally, solid mechanicist readers will realize that instead of having the reaction force F_1 at $x = 0+$ and no shear at $x = 0$, we could have deleted the $F_1\delta(x)$ term in $p(x)$ and included F_1 as a shear force at the left end. In that case the $u'''(0) = 0$ boundary condition would be changed to $EIu'''(0) = \text{shear} = F_1$ or $u'''(0) = F_1/EI$. That is,

$$EIu'''' = -P\delta(x - b) + F_2\delta(x - L), \qquad u(0) = u''(0) = 0, \quad u'''(0) = \frac{F_1}{EI}, \quad u(L) = 0. \tag{e}$$

The solution to (e) should, of course, be identical to (d).

11. (*Partial fractions; distinct roots*) Suppose that we wish to invert $\bar{f}(s) = P(s)/Q(s)$, where $P(s)$ is a polynomial of degree p and $Q(s)$ is a polynomial of degree q. Suppose, further, that $p < q$, that the roots $s_1, \ldots, s_q$ of $Q(s) = 0$ are distinct (and possibly complex) and that $P(s)$ does not vanish at $s = s_1, \ldots, s_q$; i.e., any common factors in $P(s)$ and $Q(s)$ are first canceled. Then it is known that we can express $\bar{f}$ in the form

$$\bar{f}(s) = \frac{P(s)}{Q(s)} = \frac{A_1}{s - s_1} + \frac{A_2}{s - s_2} + \cdots + \frac{A_q}{s - s_q}, \tag{a}$$

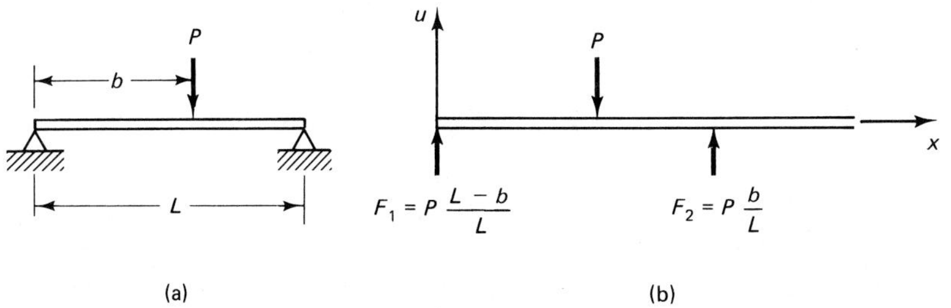

(a) (b)

and that step is usually called "expanding $\bar{f}$ in partial fractions." To calculate the constants $A_1, \ldots, A_q$, one can combine the terms on the right-hand side of (a) and then require the resulting equation to hold identically in s. For example,

$$\bar{f}(s) = \frac{4s+3}{2s^2+s-1}$$

$$= \frac{A_1}{s-\frac{1}{2}} + \frac{A_2}{s+1} + \frac{A_1(s+1)+A_2(s-\frac{1}{2})}{s^2+\frac{1}{2}s-\frac{1}{2}}$$

$$= \frac{(2A_1+2A_2)s+(2A_1-A_2)}{2s^2+s-1},$$

so we need $2A_1 + 2A_2 = 4$ and $2A_1 - A_2 = 3$. These equations give $A_1 = \frac{5}{3}$ and $A_2 = \frac{1}{3}$. Alternatively, one can solve for A_j, for $j = 1, 2, \ldots, q$, in turn, by multiplying both sides of (a) by $s - s_j$ and then letting $s \to s_j$. We now state the problem: In this way, show that

$$A_j = \frac{P(s_j)}{Q'(s_j)} \qquad (j = 1, 2, \ldots, q) \qquad \text{(b)}$$

and that (recall Exercise 12 on page 552)

$$\boxed{f(t) = \mathbf{L}^{-1}\left\{\frac{P(s)}{Q(s)}\right\} = \sum_{j=1}^{q} \frac{P(s_j)}{Q'(s_j)} e^{s_j t}.} \qquad \text{(c)}$$

This result is known as a **Heaviside expansion** formula.

12. Expand $\bar{f}(s)$ in partial fractions two ways: by "combining the terms" (as in the illustration in Exercise 11) and by applying (b) of Exercise 11. Then obtain the inverse $f(t)$.

*(a) $\dfrac{1}{s^2-3s+2}$ (b) $\dfrac{1}{3s^2+2s-1}$

(c) $\dfrac{s-6}{2s^2+s+1}$ (d) $\dfrac{3}{s^2+s+5}$

(e) $\dfrac{s^2-s+4}{s(s^2-1)}$ *(f) $\dfrac{s^2+3}{s(s^2+4)}$

(g) $\dfrac{1}{s^4-1}$

(h) $\dfrac{s^2}{s^3-6s^2+11s-6}$

(i) $\dfrac{2s-5}{s^3-2s^2-s+2}$

13. (*Partial fractions; repeated roots*) As in Exercise 11, we consider $\bar{f}(s) = P(s)/Q(s)$, where the degrees of P and Q are p and q, respectively, and $p < q$. But this time we consider the case where $Q(s) = 0$ has at least one repeated root. If the root s_1, say, is of multiplicity k, the term in (a) of Exercise 11 corresponding to s_1 needs to be changed to the form

$$\frac{A_1}{s-s_1} + \frac{A_2}{(s-s_1)^2} + \cdots + \frac{A_k}{(s-s_1)^k},$$

the inverse of which is

$$\left[A_1 + \frac{A_2}{1!}t + \cdots + \frac{A_k}{(k-1)!}t^{k-1}\right]e^{s_1 t}.$$

For example, if $P(s) = 4s^2 + 5$ and $Q(s)$ can be factored as $(s-2)^3(s+3)$, then

$$\bar{f}(s) = \frac{4s^2+5}{(s-2)^3(s+3)}$$

$$= \frac{A_1}{s-2} + \frac{A_2}{(s-2)^2} + \frac{A_3}{(s-2)^3} + \frac{A_4}{s+3}.$$

This time, of course, formula (b) of Exercise 11 does not apply, so let us use the method of "combining the terms":

$$\frac{4s^2+5}{(s-2)^3(s+3)}$$

$$= [A_1(s-2)^2(s+3) + A_2(s-2)(s+3) + A_3(s+3) + A_4(s-2)^3] \times \frac{1}{(s-2)^3(s+3)}.$$

For

$$4s^2+5$$

$$= A_1(s^3-s^2-8s+12) + A_2(s^2+s-6) + A_3(s+3) + A_4(s^3-6s^2+12s-8)$$

$$= (A_1+A_4)s^3 + (-A_1+A_2-6A_4)s^2 + (-8A_1+A_2+A_3+12A_4)s + (12A_1-6A_2+3A_3-8A_4)$$

to hold identically in s, we equate coefficients of like powers of s:

$$s^3: \quad A_1 + A_4 = 0$$

$$s^2: \quad -A_1 + A_2 - 6A_4 = 4$$

$$s^1: \quad -8A_1 + A_2 + A_3 + 12A_4 = 0$$

$$s^0: \quad 12A_1 - 6A_2 + 3A_3 - 8A_4 = 0,$$

and solve for $A_1, \ldots, A_4$. With the A_j's known, we then have

$$f(t) = \left(A_1 + A_2 t + A_3\frac{t^2}{2}\right)e^{2t} + A_4 e^{-3t}.$$

Apply this method to each of the following cases; i.e., expand the function in partial fractions and obtain the inverse function $f(t)$.

*(a) $\dfrac{1}{s^2(s-1)}$ (b) $\dfrac{2s+7}{s^3(s+2)}$

(c) $\dfrac{1}{s^4(s-1)}$ (d) $\dfrac{1}{(s^2-1)^2}$

(e) $\dfrac{s+2}{s(s-1)^3}$ (f) $\dfrac{1}{s(s+1)^2(s-1)}$

14. (*Partial partial fractions*) If two roots of $Q(s) = 0$ are negatives of each other, the full partial fraction expansion is a bit of overkill since we know, from Appendix C, that

$$\mathbf{L}^{-1}\left\{\frac{1}{s^2+a^2}\right\} = \frac{\sin at}{a}, \quad \mathbf{L}^{-1}\left\{\frac{s}{s^2+a^2}\right\} = \cos at,$$

$$\mathbf{L}^{-1}\left\{\frac{1}{s^2-a^2}\right\} = \frac{\sinh at}{a}, \quad \mathbf{L}^{-1}\left\{\frac{s}{s^2-a^2}\right\} = \cosh at.$$

That is, there is no *need* to break a term like $s/(s^2+9)$ down into $\frac{1}{2}/(s-3i) + \frac{1}{2}/(s+3i)$, the inverse of which is $\frac{1}{2}e^{i3t} + \frac{1}{2}e^{-i3t} = \cos 3t$, since we already know that the inverse of $s/(s^2+9)$ is $\cos 3t$. Thus given $(2s+7)/[s(s^2+9)]$, for example, we suggest doing a "partial partial fraction expansion"

$$\frac{2s+7}{s(s^2+9)} = \frac{A_1}{s} + \frac{A_2 + A_3 s}{s^2+9}$$

instead of the "complete partial fraction expansion"

$$\frac{2s+7}{s(s^2+9)} = \frac{A_1}{s} + \frac{A_2}{s+3i} + \frac{A_3}{s-3i}.$$

Apply the "partial partial fraction expansion" method to each of the following $\bar{f}(s)$'s, and then obtain the inverse function $f(t)$.

*(a) $\dfrac{2s+7}{s(s^2+9)}$ (b) $\dfrac{s-2}{(s-1)(s^2-9)}$

(c) $\dfrac{1}{s^4-1}$ (d) $\dfrac{3s^2+1}{(s^2+1)(s^2-4)}$

(e) $\dfrac{1}{s^2(s^2-1)}$ (f) $\dfrac{1}{s^3(s^2+2)}$

ADDITIONAL PROPERTIES 12.6

In this final section of Chapter 12 we derive a number of additional useful properties of the Laplace transform.

Theorem 1 *Initial-Value Theorem*

Let f be continuous on $0 < t \le t_0$ and f' be piecewise continuous on $0 \le t \le t_0$ for each finite t_0, and let f and f' be exponential order as $t \to \infty$. If $\lim_{t\to 0+} f(t) = f(0+)$ exists, then

$$\boxed{\lim_{s\to\infty} [s\bar{f}(s)] = f(0+).} \tag{1}$$

Proof With the stated assumptions on f and f', it follows from Theorem 3 on page 555 that

$$\mathbf{L}\{f'(t)\} = s\bar{f}(s) - f(0+). \tag{2}$$

Now since f' satisfies the conditions of Theorem 2 on page 548, it follows that $\mathbf{L}\{f'(t)\} \to 0$ as $s \to \infty$. Thus, letting $s \to \infty$ in (2) gives the result stated in (1). ■

Normally, we invert $\bar{f}(s)$ and obtain $f(t)$. If, however, it is only $f(0+)$ that we desire, we do not need to invert $\bar{f}(s)$. All we need to do, according to (1), is to determine the limit of $s\bar{f}(s)$ as $s \to \infty$.

Theorem 2 *s Shift*
If $\mathbf{L}\{f(t)\} = \bar{f}(s)$ exists for $s > s_0$, then for any real constant a,

$$\boxed{\mathbf{L}\{e^{-at}f(t)\} = \bar{f}(s+a)} \tag{3}$$

for $s + a > s_0$, or, equivalently,

$$\boxed{\mathbf{L}^{-1}\{\bar{f}(s+a)\} = e^{-at}f(t).} \tag{4}$$

Proof

$$\begin{aligned}\mathbf{L}\{e^{-at}f(t)\} &= \int_0^{\infty} e^{-at}f(t)e^{-st}\,dt \\ &= \int_0^{\infty} f(t)e^{-(s+a)t}\,dt = \bar{f}(s+a). \quad \blacksquare\end{aligned} \tag{5}$$

EXAMPLE 1 Recalling that $\mathbf{L}\{t^3\} = 6/s^4$, it follows from Theorem 2 that

$$\mathbf{L}\{t^3e^{5t}\} = \frac{6}{(s-5)^4}. \quad \blacktriangleleft \tag{6}$$

EXAMPLE 2 Whereas we can invert $(2s+1)/(s^2+2s+4)$ by partial fractions, it is easier to note that

$$\begin{aligned}\mathbf{L}^{-1}\left\{\frac{2s+1}{s^2+2s+4}\right\} &= \mathbf{L}^{-1}\left\{\frac{2s+1}{(s+1)^2+3}\right\} = \mathbf{L}^{-1}\left\{\frac{2(s+1)-1}{(s+1)^2+3}\right\} \\ &= 2\mathbf{L}^{-1}\left\{\frac{(s+1)}{(s+1)^2+3}\right\} - \mathbf{L}^{-1}\left\{\frac{1}{(s+1)^2+3}\right\} \\ &= 2e^{-t}\cos\sqrt{3}\,t - e^{-t}\frac{\sin\sqrt{3}\,t}{\sqrt{3}},\end{aligned} \tag{7}$$

where the last step is obtained from items 3 and 4 in Appendix C, together with Theorem 2. ◀

Theorem 3 *t Shift*
If $\mathbf{L}\{f(t)\} = \bar{f}(s)$ exists for $s > s_0$, then for any constant $a > 0$,

$$\boxed{\mathbf{L}\{H(t-a)f(t-a)\} = e^{-as}\bar{f}(s)} \tag{8}$$

for $s > s_0$, or, equivalently,

$$\boxed{\mathbf{L}^{-1}\{e^{-as}\bar{f}(s)\} = H(t-a)f(t-a).} \tag{9}$$

Proof

$$\mathbf{L}\{H(t-a)(t-a)\}$$

$$= \int_0^\infty H(t-a)f(t-a)e^{-st}\,dt$$

$$= \int_a^\infty f(t-a)e^{-st}\,dt = \int_0^\infty f(\tau)e^{-s(\tau+a)}\,d\tau \qquad (\tau = t-a) \tag{10}$$

$$= e^{-as}\int_0^\infty f(\tau)e^{-s\tau}\,d\tau = e^{-as}\bar{f}(s). \quad \blacksquare$$

Before illustrating Theorem 3 with an example, observe carefully the significance of $H(t-a)f(t-a)$. Specifically, if the graph of $f(t)$ is as shown in Fig. 12.9a, say, then the graph of $H(t-a)f(t-a)$ is obtained simply by "picking up the graph of $f(t)$ and shifting it to the right a distance a," as shown in Fig. 12.9b—hence the name "t shift."

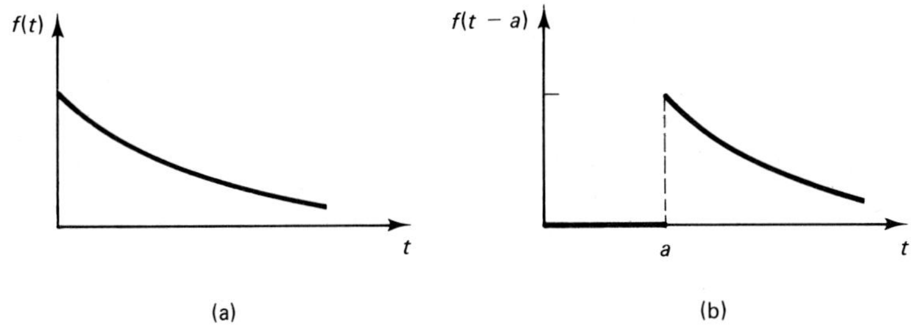

Fig. 12.9 Significance of t shift.

EXAMPLE 3 To solve

$$\dot{x} + 4x = 3H(t-2)e^{-t}; \qquad x(0) = 0 \tag{11}$$

by the Laplace transform, we first rewrite $H(t-2)e^{-t}$ as $e^{-2}H(t-2)e^{-(t-2)}$ to get it into the form $H(t-a)f(t-a)$. Then, transforming (11) gives

$$s\bar{x} + 4\bar{x} = 3e^{-2}\mathbf{L}\{H(t-2)e^{-(t-2)}\}$$

$$= 3e^{-2}e^{-2s}\mathbf{L}\{e^{-t}\} \qquad \text{by (8)}$$

$$= 3e^{-2}\frac{e^{-2s}}{s+1} \qquad \text{by Appendix C,}$$

so

$$\bar{x} = 3e^{-2}\frac{e^{-2s}}{(s+4)(s+1)} = e^{-2}e^{-2s}\left(\frac{1}{s+1} - \frac{1}{s+4}\right). \tag{12}$$

Then, since $\mathbf{L}^{-1}\{1/(s+1)\} = e^{-t}$ and $\mathbf{L}^{-1}\{1/(s+4)\} = e^{-4t}$, it follows from (12) and (9) that

$$x(t) = e^{-2}H(t-2)[e^{-(t-2)} - e^{-4(t-2)}], \tag{13}$$

as displayed in Fig. 12.10. ◀

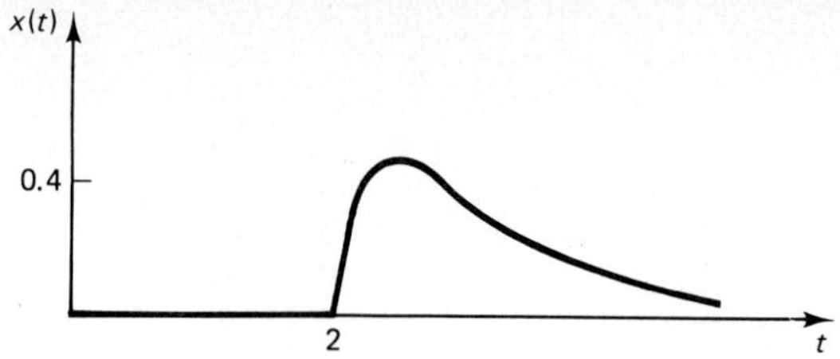

Fig. 12.10 Graph of the solution (13).

***Theorem 4** Multiplication by 1/s*
If $\mathbf{L}\{f(t)\} = \bar{f}(s)$ exists for $s > s_0$, then

$$\mathbf{L}\left\{\int_0^t f(\tau)\,d\tau\right\} = \frac{\bar{f}(s)}{s}, \tag{14}$$

for $s > \max\{0, s_0\}$, or, equivalently,

$$\mathbf{L}^{-1}\left\{\frac{\bar{f}(s)}{s}\right\} = \int_0^t f(\tau)\,d\tau. \tag{15}$$

Proof Actually, this theorem is but an important special case of the convolution theorem. Specifically, $\int_0^t f(\tau)\,d\tau = 1 * f$, so, according to that theorem,

$$\mathbf{L}\left\{\int_0^t f(\tau)\,d\tau\right\} = \mathbf{L}\{1 * f\} = \mathbf{L}\{1\}\mathbf{L}\{f\} = \frac{1}{s}\bar{f}(s), \tag{16}$$

as asserted. ■

EXAMPLE 4 To evaluate $\mathbf{L}^{-1}\{1/s(s^2+1)\}$, for example, we identify $\bar{f}(s)$ as $1/(s^2+1)$. Then, $f(t) = \mathbf{L}^{-1}\{1/(s^2+1)\} = \sin t$, so

$$\mathbf{L}^{-1}\left\{\frac{1}{s(s^2+1)}\right\} = \int_0^t \sin\tau\,d\tau = 1 - \cos t. \tag{17}$$

COMMENT We do not wish to imply that the presented method is the *only* way to proceed. In this example, for instance, we could have used partial fractions instead. ◀

Next, we obtain two useful theorems by differentiating and integrating the equation

$$\bar{f}(s) = \int_0^\infty f(t)e^{-st}\,dt \tag{18}$$

with respect to s. First, we state without proof that *if the integral in (18) converges for $s > s_0$, then*

$$\frac{d\bar{f}(s)}{ds} = \frac{d}{ds}\int_0^\infty f(t)e^{-st}\,dt = \int_0^\infty \frac{\partial}{\partial s}[f(t)e^{-st}]\,dt$$

$$= -\int_0^\infty tf(t)e^{-st}\,dt = -\mathbf{L}\{tf(t)\}, \tag{19}$$

for $s > s_0$, *and*

$$\int_\alpha^\beta \bar{f}(s)\,ds = \int_\alpha^\beta \int_0^\infty f(t)e^{-st}\,dt\,ds = \int_0^\infty f(t)\left(\int_\alpha^\beta e^{-st}\,ds\right)dt \tag{20}$$

for $\beta \geq \alpha \geq s_0$. The key step in (19) is the second equality, where we have inverted the order of the integration with respect to t and the differentiation with respect to s. In (20), the key is again the second equality, where we have inverted the order of the integration with respect to t and the integration with respect to s.

In particular, if $\alpha = s$ and $\beta = \infty$, then (20) becomes

$$\begin{aligned}\int_s^\infty \bar{f}(s')\,ds' &= \int_0^\infty f(t)\left(\int_s^\infty e^{-s't}\,ds'\right)dt \\ &= \int_0^\infty \frac{f(t)}{t}e^{-st}\,dt = \mathbf{L}\left\{\frac{f(t)}{t}\right\},\end{aligned} \tag{21}$$

for all $s > s_0$.

For reference, we state the results (19) and (21) as theorems.

***Theorem 5** Differentiation with Respect to s*

If $\mathbf{L}\{f(t)\} = \bar{f}(s)$ exists for $s > s_0$, then

$$\boxed{\mathbf{L}\{tf(t)\} = -\frac{d\bar{f}(s)}{ds}} \tag{22}$$

for $s > s_0$, or, equivalently,

$$\boxed{\mathbf{L}^{-1}\left\{\frac{d\bar{f}(s)}{ds}\right\} = -tf(t).} \tag{23}$$

EXAMPLE 5 From the known transform

$$\mathbf{L}\{\sin at\} = \frac{a}{s^2 + a^2}, \qquad (s > 0), \tag{24}$$

we may use (22) to infer the additional results

$$\mathbf{L}\{t \sin at\} = -\frac{d}{ds}\left(\frac{a}{s^2 + a^2}\right) = \frac{2as}{(s^2 + a^2)^2} \qquad (s > 0), \tag{25}$$

$$\mathbf{L}\{t^2 \sin at\} = -\frac{d}{ds}\left[\frac{2as}{(s^2 + a^2)^2}\right] = 2a\frac{3s^2 - a^2}{(s^2 + a^2)^3} \qquad (s > 0), \tag{26}$$

and so on. ◀

Theorem 6 *Integration with Respect to s*
If $\mathbf{L}\{f(t)\} = \bar{f}(s)$ exists for $s > s_0$, and $\lim_{t\to 0+} f(t)/t$ exists, then

$$\mathbf{L}\left\{\frac{f(t)}{t}\right\} = \int_s^\infty \bar{f}(s')\,ds' \tag{27}$$

for $s > s_0$, or, equivalently,

$$\mathbf{L}^{-1}\left\{\int_s^\infty \bar{f}(s')\,ds'\right\} = \frac{f(t)}{t}. \tag{28}$$

EXAMPLE 6 To evaluate

$$\mathbf{L}^{-1}\left\{\ln\left(\frac{s-a}{s-b}\right)\right\}, \tag{29}$$

note that

$$\frac{d}{ds}\ln\left(\frac{s-a}{s-b}\right) = \frac{1}{s-a} - \frac{1}{s-b}, \tag{30}$$

so

$$\ln\left(\frac{s-a}{s-b}\right) = -\int_s^\infty \left(\frac{1}{s'-a} - \frac{1}{s'-b}\right) ds'. \tag{31}$$

Thus, identify $\bar{f}(s)$ in Theorem 6 as $-1/(s-a) + 1/(s-b)$ [which exists for $s > \max\{a, b\}$]. Then

$$f(t) = \mathbf{L}^{-1}\left\{-\frac{1}{s-a} + \frac{1}{s-b}\right\} = e^{bt} - e^{at}. \tag{32}$$

Furthermore,

$$\lim_{t\to 0+}\frac{f(t)}{t} = \lim_{t\to 0+}\frac{e^{bt} - e^{at}}{t} = b - a \tag{33}$$

does exist, so (28) gives the desired inverse,

$$\mathbf{L}^{-1}\left\{\ln\left(\frac{s-a}{s-b}\right)\right\} = \frac{e^{bt} - e^{at}}{t}. \quad ◀ \tag{34}$$

As our last item, we consider the task of obtaining the Laplace transform of a *periodic function*. That is, suppose that

$$f(t + T) = f(t) \tag{35}$$

for all $t > 0$, so that f is periodic with period T. How can we determine $\bar{f}(s)$? One obvious possibility would be to expand f in a Fourier series and then to Laplace transform the series. Instead, we prefer the following approach because it will give us $\bar{f}$ in closed form rather than as an infinite series. Beginning with

$$\mathbf{L}\{f(t)\} = \int_0^\infty f(t)e^{-st}\,dt = \int_0^T f(t)e^{-st}\,dt + \int_T^{2T} f(t)e^{-st}\,dt + \cdots, \tag{36}$$

we make the change of variables $\tau = t - T$ in the second integral on the right, $\tau = t - 2T$ in the third integral, and so on. Thus

$$\mathbf{L}\{f(t)\} = \int_0^T f(t)e^{-st}\,dt + \int_0^T f(\tau + T)e^{-s(\tau+T)}\,d\tau + \int_0^T f(\tau + 2T)e^{-s(\tau+2T)}\,d\tau + \cdots. \tag{37}$$

But

$$f(\tau + T) = f(\tau) \qquad \text{by (35)},$$
$$f(\tau + 2T) = f((\tau + T) + T) = f(\tau + T) = f(\tau),$$

and so on, so (37) becomes

$$\begin{aligned}\mathbf{L}\{f(t)\} &= \int_0^T f(t)e^{-st}\,dt + e^{-sT}\int_0^T f(\tau)e^{-s\tau}\,d\tau + e^{-2sT}\int_0^T f(\tau)e^{-s\tau}\,d\tau + \cdots \\ &= (1 + e^{-sT} + e^{-2sT} + \cdots)\int_0^T f(t)e^{-st}\,dt.\end{aligned} \tag{38}$$

Finally, we are able to *sum the series* in parentheses to $1/(1 - e^{-sT})$, because it is a convergent geometric series

$$1 + z + z^2 + \cdots = \frac{1}{1 - z}$$

with "z" $= e^{-sT}$—convergent because $|z| = |e^{-sT}| = e^{-sT} < 1$. If we ask that f be piecewise continuous, say, on one period ($0 \le t \le T$), to ensure the existence of the integral in (38), then we can state the following result.

> ***Theorem 7** Transform of Periodic Function*
> If f is periodic with period T on $0 < t < \infty$ and piecewise continuous on one period, then
>
> $$\boxed{\mathbf{L}\{f(t)\} = \frac{1}{1 - e^{-sT}}\int_0^T f(t)e^{-st}\,dt} \tag{39}$$
>
> for $s > 0$.

The point, of course, is that (39) only requires integration over *one* period, rather than over $0 < t < \infty$.

EXAMPLE 7 If f is the sawtooth wave depicted in Fig. 12.11, $T = 2$, and

$$\int_0^T f(t)e^{-st}\,dt = \int_0^2 2te^{-st}\,dt = 2\frac{1 - (1 + 2s)e^{-2s}}{s^2}, \tag{40}$$

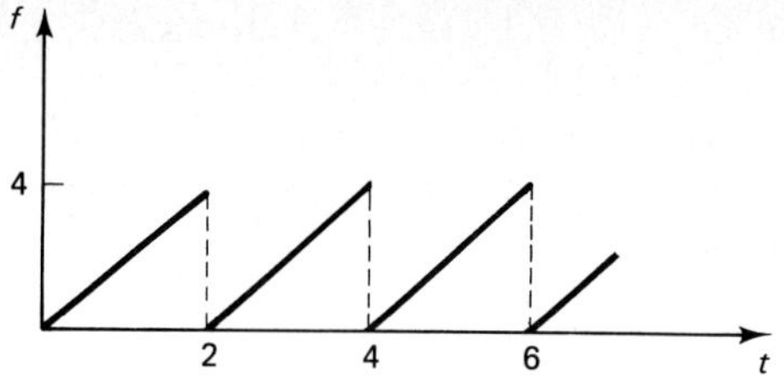

Fig. 12.11 Sawtooth wave.

so

$$\mathbf{L}\{f(t)\} = \frac{1}{1 - e^{-2s}} \frac{2[1 - (1 + 2s)e^{-2s}]}{s^2}$$
$$= \frac{2}{s^2} - \frac{4}{s} \frac{e^{-2s}}{1 - e^{-2s}} \tag{41}$$

for $s > 0$.

A more interesting question is the reverse: What is the inverse of

$$\bar{f}(s) = \frac{2}{s^2} - \frac{4}{s} \frac{e^{-2s}}{1 - e^{-2s}}, \tag{42}$$

where we pretend no advance knowledge of the sawtooth wave in Fig. 12.11 or even the knowledge that $f(t)$ is periodic? The key is to proceed in reverse—i.e., to expand the $1/(1 - e^{-2s})$ in a geometric series in powers of e^{-2s}. Thus

$$\bar{f}(s) = \frac{2}{s^2} - \frac{4}{s} e^{-2s}(1 + e^{-2s} + e^{-4s} + \cdots)$$
$$= \frac{2}{s^2} - \frac{4}{s}(e^{-2s} + e^{-4s} + e^{-6s} + \cdots). \tag{43}$$

Formally inverting termwise,

$$f(t) = 2t - 4[H(t - 2) + H(t - 4) + H(t - 6) + \cdots]. \tag{44}$$

The first few partial sums,

$$f_1(t) = 2t,$$
$$f_2(t) = 2t - 4H(t - 2),$$
$$f_3(t) = 2t - 4H(t - 2) - 4H(t - 4),$$

are sketched in Fig. 12.12, and it is easy to infer that (44) gives the periodic sawtooth wave shown in Fig. 12.11.

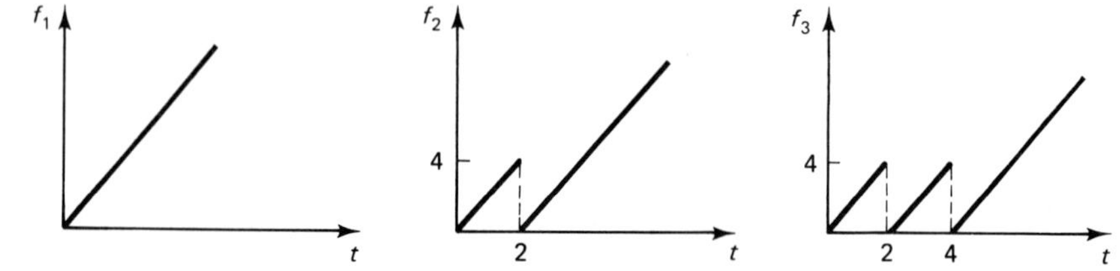

Fig. 12.12 Partial sums of (44).

COMMENT Observe that the mere presence of $1 - e^{-sT}$ in the denominator of a transform does *not* mean that the inverse is periodic. For example, the inverse of $(4/s)e^{-2s}/(1 - e^{-2s})$, in (42), is the *non*periodic "staircase" shown in Fig. 12.13. It is only when this staircase is subtracted from $2t$ that a periodic function is obtained. ◀

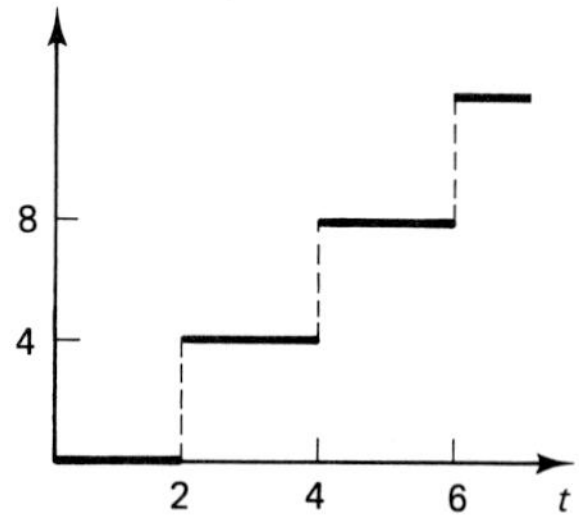

Fig. 12.13 The staircase $4[H(t-2) + H(t-4) + \cdots]$.

This example completes our discussion of the Laplace transform. As a bird's-eye summary, we have tabulated key results, in the order in which they were presented, as items 24 to 34 of Appendix C.

12.6 EXERCISES

1. Invert each of the following. Cite any items from Appendix C and any theorems that you use. If applicable, verify the initial value theorem, namely, that $s\bar{f}(s) \to f(0+)$ as $s \to \infty$.

*(a) $\dfrac{1}{(s^2+a^2)^2}$ (b) $\dfrac{1}{(s^2-a^2)^2}$

(c) $\dfrac{s}{(s-2)^2}$ *(d) $\dfrac{s^2}{(s+1)^3}$

(e) $\dfrac{1}{\sqrt{s+1}}$ (f) $\dfrac{s}{(s-a)^{3/2}}$

*(g) $\dfrac{s}{(s+4)^6}$ (h) $\dfrac{e^{-s}}{s^5}$

(i) $\dfrac{e^{-2s}}{(s+1)^2}$ (j) $\dfrac{e^{-\pi s}}{(s+2)^4}$

(k) $\ln\left(1+\dfrac{a^2}{s^2}\right)$ (l) $\ln\left(1-\dfrac{a^2}{s^2}\right)$

*(m) $\dfrac{e^{-s}}{s(s^2+s+1)}$ (n) $\dfrac{e^{-3s}}{s^2+2s-4}$

(o) $\dfrac{e^{-2s}}{s^2(s^2-2s-2)}$ (p) $\ln\left(\dfrac{s^2+1}{s^2+s}\right)$

(q) $\dfrac{1}{s(1-e^{-s})}$ (r) $\dfrac{1}{s(1+e^{-s})}$

(s) $\dfrac{1}{s}\tanh s$ (t) $\dfrac{1}{s^2(1-e^{-s})}$

(u) $\dfrac{1}{(s+1)(1-e^{-2s})}$ (v) $\dfrac{e^{-s}}{s-8}$

(w) $\dfrac{s}{(s^2+1)^{3/2}}$ (x) $\dfrac{1}{s(1-e^{s})}$

2. (a) Show that if $f(t) = \sin t$, then (39) does indeed give

$$\mathbf{L}\{\sin t\} = \frac{1}{s^2+1}.$$

(b) Show that if $f(t) = \cos t$, then (39) does indeed give

$$\mathbf{L}\{\cos t\} = \frac{s}{s^2+1}.$$

3. (*Scale changes*) Show that if $\mathbf{L}\{f(t)\} = \bar{f}(s)$, then

(a) $\mathbf{L}\{f(at)\} = \dfrac{1}{a}\bar{f}\left(\dfrac{s}{a}\right)$ (b) $\mathbf{L}^{-1}\{\bar{f}(as)\} = \dfrac{1}{a}f\left(\dfrac{t}{a}\right)$

4. Determine the Laplace transform of the function $f(t)$ which is periodic and defined on one period as follows.

*(a) $f(t) = \sin t \quad (0 \le t \le \pi)$

(b) $f(t) = \begin{cases} 1, & 0 \le t < 2 \\ 0, & 2 \le t < 3 \end{cases}$

(c) $f(t) = \sin 2t \quad (0 \le t \le \pi)$

(d) $f(t) = e^{-t} \quad (0 \le t < 2)$

*(e) $f(t) = \begin{cases} t, & 0 \le t \le 1 \\ 0, & 1 < t < 2 \end{cases}$

(f) $f(t) = \begin{cases} t, & 0 \le t < 1 \\ t-2, & 1 \le t \le 2 \end{cases}$

5. (a) Solve $\dot{x} + x = F(t)$ by the Laplace transform, where $x(0) = x_0$ and $F(t)$ is the square wave shown, and show that

$$\begin{aligned} x(t) = x_0 e^{-t} &+ [1 - e^{-(t-0)}]H(t-0) \\ &- [1 - e^{-(t-1)}]H(t-1) \qquad \text{(a)} \\ &+ [1 - e^{-(t-2)}]H(t-2) - \cdots . \end{aligned}$$

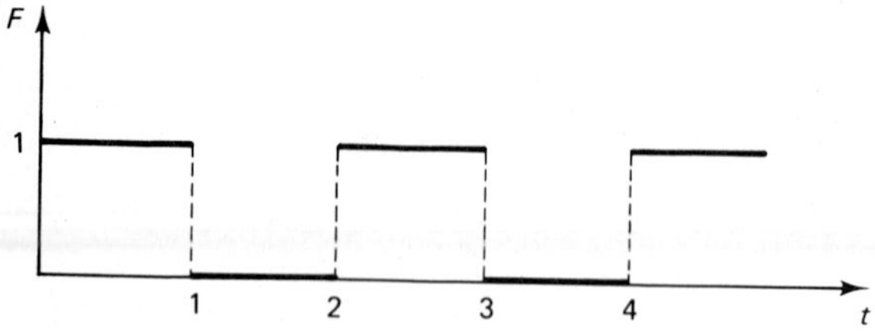

Hint: It would be wasteful to determine $\bar{F}(s)$, because the solution can be expressed as a convolution integral involving $F(t)$ directly. In that integral, express $F(t)$ as an infinite series of Heaviside functions.
(b) Sketch, and label, the graph of $x(t)$, over $0 < t < 3$, say, for the case where $x_0 = 0$. Is $x(t)$ periodic? If not, is there a value of x_0 such that $x(t)$ *is* periodic? Explain.

6. Solve $\dot{x} + x = F(t)$ by the Laplace transform, where $x(0) = x_0$ and $F(t)$ is the periodic function shown. *Hint:* Read Exercise 5.

(a)

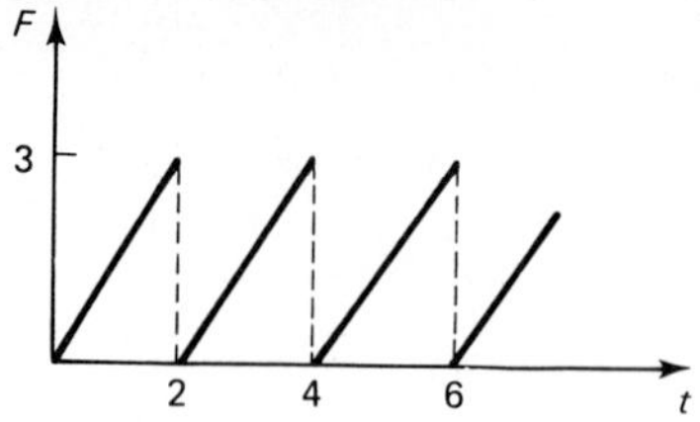

(b)

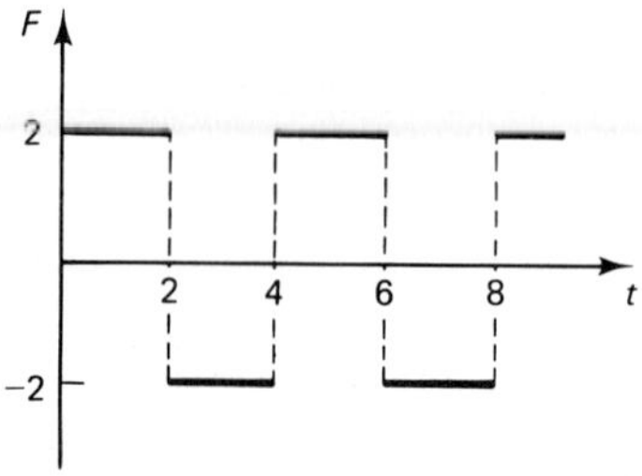

7. Solve $\ddot{x} + x = F(t)$ by the Laplace transform, where $x(0) = x_0$, $\dot{x}(0) = \dot{x}_0$, and $F(t)$ is the square wave shown in Exercise 5. Evaluate $x(1.6)$ if $x_0 = \dot{x}_0 = 1$.

ADDITIONAL REFERENCES FOR PART III

EDWIN F. BECKENBACH (ed.), *Modern Mathematics for the Engineer*. New York: McGraw-Hill, 1961

See Chapter 3, by John W. Miles, for an overview of integral transforms and their applications.

H. S. CARSLAW, *Theory of Fourier Series and Integrals,* 3rd ed. New York: Dover, 1930.

A mathematical treatment, with emphasis on questions of convergence, legitimacy of termwise differentiation and integration of Fourier series, and the Gibbs phenomenon.

H. S. CARSLAW and J. C. JAEGER, *Operational Methods in Applied Mathematics*. New York: Dover, 1963.

More advanced than our treatment, "Carslaw and Jaeger" deals almost exclusively with the Laplace transform. It covers both ODEs and PDEs and contains many applications to problems in electric circuit theory, dynamics and vibrations, heat conduction, hydrodynamics, and so on. Also contained is a historical introduction, a proof of Lerch's theorem, and a chapter on asymptotic solutions for large and small time.

RUEL V. CHURCHILL, *Operational Mathematics,* 2nd ed. New York: McGraw-Hill, 1958.

Extensive treatment of the Laplace transform, with numerous physical applications. Included are several chapters on PDE applications, the inversion integral, and transition to the Fourier transform via the Sturm–Liouville theory.

A. ERDÈLYI (ed.), *Tables of Integral Transforms,* Vol. 1. New York: McGraw-Hill, 1954.

Volume 1 contains a tabulation of Fourier transforms (called "exponential Fourier transforms" therein), Fourier sine and cosine transforms, Laplace transforms, and Mellin transforms.

E. A. GUILLEMIN, *The Mathematics of Circuit Analysis*. New York: Wiley, 1949.

See Chapter VII on Fourier series and integrals.

FRANCIS B. HILDEBRAND, *Advanced Calculus for Applications,* 2nd ed. Englewood Cliffs, N. J.: Prentice-Hall, 1976.

See Chapter 5, and the numerous exercises at the end of that chapter, for its discussion of the Sturm-Liouville problem and eigenfunction expansions.

ATHANASIOS PAPOULIS, *The Fourier Integral and Its Applications*. New York: McGraw-Hill, 1962.

This book covers the Fourier series, Fourier integral and Fourier transform, as well as the Laplace transform. Written from an applied point of view, it contains numerous applications, especially to electrical engineering.

I. N. SNEDDON, *Fourier Transforms*. New York: McGraw-Hill, 1951.

Detailed account of the Fourier integral and Fourier transform.

13 Introductory Concepts

13.1 INTRODUCTION

Engineers and scientists are especially concerned with fields: fluid velocity fields, magnetic fields, salinity fields, temperature fields, and so on. These fields are one-, two-, or three-dimensional, and either steady or time varying. If they depend on two or more space and/or time variables, the governing differential equations are *partial* differential equations (PDEs). Important cases such as the diffusion and Laplace equations were introduced in Part II. Before attempting to solve these PDEs, one needs to understand Fourier series; for a more complete discussion, the Sturm–Liouville theory and the Fourier and Laplace transforms are needed. These subjects were, in fact, studied in Part III, so we are now ready to devote Part IV to the PDEs and their solution.

We knowingly sacrifice some generality, in our treatment, by focusing quickly on three of the most important cases: the diffusion, Laplace, and wave equations, with one chapter devoted to each. If the optional sections are omitted, one studies the solution of these PDEs by the method of *separation of variables* (and for the wave equation, d'Alembert's method), combined with some help from Fourier series. By means of this method, one is able to develop "product solutions," where the individual factors are obtained as solutions of simpler *ODEs*. (Thus the reader may wish to review the ODE material in Appendix A.) Depending on the PDE and the spatial coordinate system used, the ODEs may have elementary solutions, such as trigonometric and exponential functions, or *non*elementary solutions, such as Bessel and Legendre functions. These two important nonelementary cases are treated in *Chapter 17*.

In addition to analytical solution techniques—which involve separation of variables, Fourier series, Sturm–Liouville theory, and Fourier and Laplace transforms—Sections 14.5 and 15.5 are devoted to *numerical* solution techniques. The context of these techniques is matrix algebra, and in these sections we draw heavily on the material in Part I, especially in the exercises.

In the present chapter, Chapter 13, we introduce the notion of a partial differential equation (PDE), then quickly focus on the class of second-order PDEs which form the subject of subsequent chapters, namely, the diffusion, Laplace, and wave equations. These equations are not the only PDEs encountered in applications, but they are regarded as the most important equations of mathematical physics because they model such a wide variety of fundamental physical phenomena.

PRELIMINARY CONCEPTS 13.2

By a **partial differential equation** we mean an equation in which there appear partial derivatives of an unknown function. A PDE is **order** n if it contains partial derivatives of order n, but no higher.

Such equations often arise as mathematical statements describing various physical phenomena. In fact, we have already derived, in Chapter 9, some of the PDEs to be discussed in Part IV. For instance, in Example 3 on page 396 we showed that the PDE

$$\alpha^2\left(\frac{\partial^2 u}{\partial x^2} + \frac{\partial^2 u}{\partial y^2} + \frac{\partial^2 u}{\partial z^2}\right) = \frac{\partial u}{\partial t} \qquad (\alpha^2 = \text{constant}) \tag{1}$$

governs the temperature field $u(x, y, z, t)$,* within a material occupying a three-dimensional region $\mathcal{V}$, wherein heat is transferred by the process of conduction. [Other modes of heat transfer, *not* governed by (1), are convection and radiation.] Equation (1) is of second order since the highest-order partials that appear are of second order.

As additional examples, the equations

$$uu_x + (x + y)u_y = \sin x, \qquad u_{xx} = u_y, \tag{2}$$

where subscripts denote partial derivatives, are PDEs of first and second order, respectively, on the unknown function $u(x, y)$.

By a **solution** of (1), for example, we mean any function $u(x, y, z, t)$ that possesses the derivatives u_{xx}, u_{yy}, u_{zz}, and u_t that appear in (1), and for which (1) reduces to an identity at each point in $\mathcal{V}$ and for each t in the time interval of interest. For example, $4x - 7$, $x^2 - z^2$, and $(\sin 3z)\exp(-9\alpha^2 t)$ are solutions of (1) for all x, y, z, t. Such functions are said to "satisfy" the PDE.

In some problems we will find it fruitful to weaken the foregoing notion of solution so as to allow for the nonexistence of one or more of the relevant partial derivatives along certain curves or surfaces within the region under consideration. We will call attention to this situation when it occurs.

* In Chapter 9 we used the letter T for the temperature. In Part IV we use u instead, since we wish to reserve T for other purposes.

13.3 SECOND-ORDER LINEAR EQUATIONS*

We shall be especially, although not exclusively interested in second-order PDEs of the form†

$$au_{xx} + 2bu_{xy} + cu_{yy} + du_x + eu_y + fu = g, \tag{1}$$

where $a, \ldots, g$ are all prescribed functions of x and y, and where the 2 is included merely for subsequent convenience. Often, $a, \ldots, f$ are constants. If $g = 0$, then (1) is **homogeneous,** and if $g \neq 0$, then (1) is **nonhomogeneous.**

It is useful to express (1) in the more compact form

$$Lu = g, \tag{2}$$

where

$$L = a\frac{\partial^2}{\partial x^2} + 2b\frac{\partial^2}{\partial y\,\partial x} + c\frac{\partial^2}{\partial y^2} + d\frac{\partial}{\partial x} + e\frac{\partial}{\partial y} + f \tag{3}$$

is called the **differential operator.** We say that L, and hence the equation $Lu = g$, is **linear** inasmuch as

$$\boxed{L(c_1u_1 + c_2u_2) = c_1Lu_1 + c_2Lu_2} \tag{4}$$

holds for every choice of the constants c_1, c_2 and for every choice of the functions $u_1(x, y)$, $u_2(x, y)$ (which admit first- and second-order partial derivatives). If an operator does *not* satisfy (4), we say that it is **nonlinear.** Verification that (4) holds for the operator L given by (3) follows essentially the same lines as for the nth-order *ordinary* differential operator in Section A.2 of Appendix A, and is left for the reader. In fact,

$$L(c_1u_1 + c_2u_2 + \cdots + c_ku_k) = c_1Lu_1 + c_2Lu_2 + \cdots + c_kLu_k \tag{5}$$

holds for every finite $k \geq 1$. This important result permits us to build up a linear combination of solutions to $Lu = g$. Specifically, if $u_1, \ldots, u_k$ are *homogeneous solutions* (i.e., they satisfy the associated homogeneous equation $Lu = 0$) and u_p is any *particular solution* (i.e., it satisfies the full equation $Lu = g$), then the linear combination

$$u = u_p + c_1u_1 + \cdots + c_ku_k \tag{6}$$

satisfies the full equation $Lu = g$, since

$$\begin{aligned} Lu &= L(u_p + c_1u_1 + \cdots + c_ku_k) \\ &= Lu_p + c_1Lu_1 + \cdots + c_kLu_k \\ &= g + 0 + \cdots + 0 = g. \end{aligned} \tag{7}$$

* The reader is urged to review Section A.3 in Appendix A before continuing.

† We assume that a, b, c are not all zero, for then (1) would no longer be a second-order equation. Further, we assume that if $a = b = 0$, then $d \neq 0$, for if $a = b = d = 0$, then only y derivatives appear and (1) might best be regarded as an ordinary differential equation rather than as a PDE. Similarly, we assume that if $b = c = 0$, then $e \neq 0$.

It is useful, and standard, to classify (1) as one of three types, depending on the sign of the "discriminant" $b^2 - ac$: (1) is

$$\begin{aligned} &\textbf{elliptic} && \text{if} \quad b^2 - ac < 0, \\ &\textbf{parabolic} && \text{if} \quad b^2 - ac = 0, \\ &\textbf{hyperbolic} && \text{if} \quad b^2 - ac > 0 \end{aligned} \tag{8}$$

in the region under consideration. This terminology is chosen by analogy with the general equation of a conic section, $ax^2 + 2bxy^2 + cy + dx + ey + f = 0$, which equation gives an ellipse, a parabola, or an hyperbola, according to the sign of the discriminant $b^2 - ac$. The significance of these distinctions for PDEs will be made clear in the subsequent chapters.

Prototype examples of these three types are as follows:

1. The **Laplace equation**

$$u_{xx} + u_{yy} = 0 \tag{9}$$

is *elliptic*.

2. The **diffusion equation**

$$\alpha^2 u_{xx} = u_t, \tag{10}$$

where the diffusivity α^2 is a constant and t is the time, is *parabolic*.

3. The **wave equation**

$$c_0^2 u_{xx} = u_{tt}, \tag{11}$$

where c_0^2 is a constant [the subscripted zero is included to avoid confusion with the c in (1)] and t is the time, is *hyperbolic*.

In the case of (9), we identify $a = 1$, $b = 0$, $c = 1$, so that $b^2 - ac = 0 - 1 = -1 < 0$. In (10) we identify $a = \alpha^2$, $b = 0$, $c = 0$ (and $y \equiv t$), so that $b^2 - ac = 0 - 0 = 0$. And in (11) we have $a = c_0^2$, $b = 0$, $c = -1$ (and $y \equiv t$), so $b^2 - ac = 0 + c_0^2 = c_0^2 > 0$.

Of these important equations, we have already met (9) and (10). The diffusion equation $\alpha^2\nabla^2 u = u_t$ was derived in Chapter 9 as governing the temperature field u. In that case the diffusion was the diffusion of heat, and the mode of heat transfer was conduction. In one dimension, $\nabla^2 u$ reduces to u_{xx}, so $\alpha^2\nabla^2 u = u_t$ reduces to (10).

In the case of steady-state conduction, one has $u_t = 0$ by the definition of steady state, so $\alpha^2\nabla^2 u = u_t$ becomes $\alpha^2\nabla^2 u = 0$, or $\nabla^2 u = 0$. In two dimensions, $\nabla^2 u = 0$ is the two-dimensional Laplace equation (9). The Laplace equation also arose in Chapter 9 in connection with irrotational fields. For example, we saw in Example 3 on page 430 that the fluid velocity potential Φ satisfies the Laplace equation. Thus the study of the Laplace equation is often referred to as the realm of *potential theory*. We have not yet met the wave equation (11) and will reserve our discussion of this case for Chapter 16.

Roughly speaking, equations (9), (10), and (11) arise in modeling equilibrium, diffusion, and wave phenomena, respectively. They are so important that we will devote an entire chapter to each. Although one might rank them as the three most important PDEs of mathematical physics, we should stress that there are numerous other important PDEs, not of the form (1), which will not be dealt with in this book. To mention just a few, we note the *Burgers equation*

$$u_t + uu_x = \lambda u_{xx} \tag{12}$$

employed by Burgers in modeling turbulent flow and encountered by others in connection with the theory of shock waves in a real fluid, the *Korteweg–de Vries (KdV) equation*

$$u_t + \alpha uu_x + \beta u_{xxx} = 0, \tag{13}$$

which appears prominently in the theory of nonlinear waves, and the *biharmonic equation*

$$\nabla^4 u = u_{xxxx} + 2u_{xxyy} + u_{yyyy} = 0, \tag{14}$$

which arises in connection with the slow flow of viscous fluids and in structural analysis.

In closing this section, we note that equations of the form (1) may be of "mixed" type if the coefficients a, b, c are not constants. For example, consider the *Tricomi equation*

$$u_{xx} + xu_{yy} = 0. \tag{15}$$

In this case $b^2 - ac = 0 - (1)(x) = -x$, so that the Tricomi equation is elliptic in the right half plane $x > 0$, and hyperbolic in the left half plane $x < 0$! This case, which is central in the theory of transonic flow, is quite complicated and will not be considered here.

13.3 EXERCISES

1. Prove the linearity statement (4). *Hint:* Recall the property

$$\frac{\partial}{\partial x}(c_1 u_1 + c_2 u_2) = c_1 \frac{\partial u_1}{\partial x} + c_2 \frac{\partial u_2}{\partial x},$$

of partial differentiation, and the corresponding properties for $\partial/\partial y$, $\partial^2/\partial y\, \partial x$, $\partial^2/\partial x^2$, and $\partial^2/\partial y^2$.

2. (a) show that (5) follows from (4). Set $k = 4$, for definiteness.
(b) Show that (5) follows from (4) for every finite $k \geq 1$. *Hint:* Use mathematical induction.

3. Use (4) to show whether the following PDEs are linear or nonlinear. *Hint:* Read the discussion of (17) in Section A.2.

*(a) Burgers' equation (12)
(b) *KdV* equation (13)
*(c) biharmonic equation (14)
(d) Tricomi equation (15)
*(e) $u_{xx} + u_{yy} = e^u$
(f) $x^4 u_{xx} = u_y$
(g) $u_{xx} + 5u_{xy} - xu = e^x$
(h) $xu_x + uu_y = 6$

4. Classify the following PDEs, defined over $-\infty < x < \infty$ and $-\infty < y < \infty$, as elliptic, parabolic, or hyperbolic. If the equation is of mixed type, identify the relevant regions and give the classification within each region.

*(a) $u_{xx} + u_{xy} - x^2 u_y = e^{xy}$
(b) $xu_{xx} - u_{xy} + yu_{yy} + 3u_y = 1$
(c) $u_{xy} + u_x - 4u_y = 6u$
*(d) $xu_{xx} - (\sin^2 y + 1)u_{yy} = x^2 u$
(e) $u_{xx} + u_{xy} + u_{yy} + u_x + u_y + u = 1$
(f) $u_{xx} + (\cos x)u_{yy} = 2xy$
*(g) $u_{xx} + u_x + u_y = x^3 u$
(h) $u_{xy} - u_{yy} + e^x u = f(x, y)$

14 *Diffusion Equation*

INTRODUCTION 14.1

We begin our consideration of the *diffusion equation*. In proceeding, we inevitably uncover important aspects of the physics, and the reader is invited to be involved with the physics and phenomenological aspects as well as with the mathematics.

In Section 14.2 we develop the powerful method of separation of variables in conjunction with the Fourier series expansion technique. This method is extended in the optional Section 14.3 by drawing on the more widely applicable Sturm–Liouville theory for the necessary series expansions. In Section 14.4 we use the Fourier and Laplace transforms to solve problems that could not have been handled by separation of variables. Finally, quite a different line of approach is introduced in Section 14.5, a numerical solution technique employing the method of finite differences.

SEPARATION OF VARIABLES 14.2

Separation of variables will be our principal tool for solving PDEs. The essential features of the method are explained in the following introductory example.

EXAMPLE 1 *One-Dimensional Unsteady Heat Conduction.* Beginning our discussion of the diffusion equation

$$\alpha^2 u_{xx} = u_t, \tag{1}$$

we consider the x interval to be finite, say $0 < x < \ell$, and the t interval to be semi-infinite, namely, $0 < t < \infty$. For definiteness, we will consider the diffusion process to be the diffusion of heat by conduction, with α^2 the thermal diffusivity and $u(x, t)$ the temperature. Thus we might be considering unsteady conduction within a rod of length ℓ which is insulated along its lateral surface (as denoted by the cross hatching in Fig. 14.1a), or within a wall or slab of thickness ℓ, a portion of which is sketched in Fig. 14.1b. In any case, the key point is that we assume that the conduction takes place only in the x direction, so that u is a function of x, but not of the other Cartesian coordinates, y and z. [When the diffusion is the diffusion of heat, (1) is referred to as the *heat equation*.]

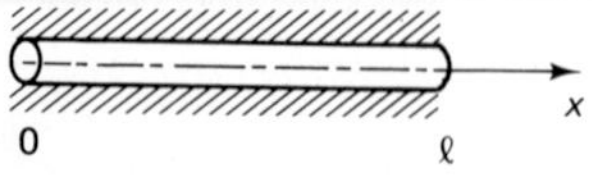

(a)

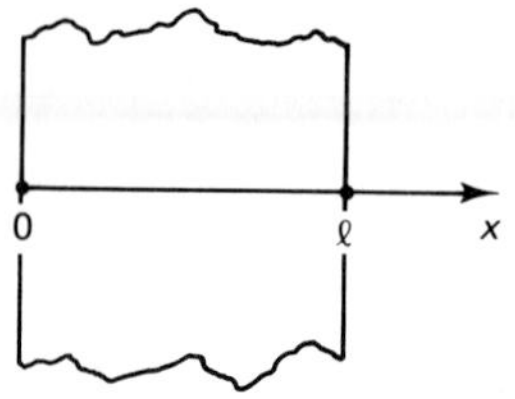

(b)

Fig. 14.1 Conduction in a rod or wall.

Suppose that the boundary conditions are

$$u(0, t) = p(t) \qquad (0 < t < \infty) \tag{2a}$$

$$u(\ell, t) = q(t) \qquad (0 < t < \infty) \tag{2b}$$

and that the initial condition is

$$u(x, 0) = f(x), \qquad (0 < x < \ell) \tag{3}$$

for some prescribed functions p, q, f.

It is convenient to summarize the problem graphically by showing the region under consideration in an x,t plane, the PDE (1) governing $u(x, t)$ in that region, the boundary conditions (2a) and (2b), and the initial condition (3), as we have done in Fig. 14.2.*

In this example we choose $p(t) = q(t) = 0$. Physically, the idea is this. The initial temperature distribution in the rod is known to be $u(x, 0) = f(x)$. Then, both ends of the rod are quenched to $0°\ C$ for all $t > 0$, and we seek to determine

*Observe that it is standard to ask that the PDE $\alpha^2 u_{xx} = u_t$ be satisfied in the *open* region $0 < x < \ell$, $0 < t < \infty$, rather than in $0 \le x \le \ell$, $0 \le t < \infty$. For if the PDE were satisfied in $0 \le t < \infty$, the initial temperature distribution $u(x, 0) = f(x)$ would need to be twice differentiable (because of the presence of the u_{xx} term in the PDE), whereas in applications we may wish to allow f to be merely piecewise continuous, say. Similarly, if the PDE were satisfied in $0 \le x \le \ell$, the boundary temperatures $u(0, t) = p(t)$ and $u(\ell, t) = q(t)$ would need to be once differentiable (because of the u_t term in the PDE), whereas in applications we wish to allow p and q to be discontinuous. Fine, but then our conditions (2) and (3) are evidently carelessly expressed since "$u(0, t)$," "$u(\ell, t)$," and "$u(x, 0)$" make no sense if $u(x, t)$ is only defined in the interior $0 < x < \ell$, $0 < t < \infty$. Thus we should replace (2) and (3) by conditions such as

$$\lim_{x \to 0+} u(x, t) = p(t), \qquad \lim_{x \to \ell-} u(x, t) = q(t), \qquad \lim_{t \to 0+} u(x, t) = f(x),$$

which tie the values of $u(x, t)$ in the *interior* of the region to the boundary and initial data. However, we will continue to use the simpler statements (2) and (3), with the understanding that they are to be replaced by suitable limit statements in the event that p, q, f are not sufficiently well behaved.

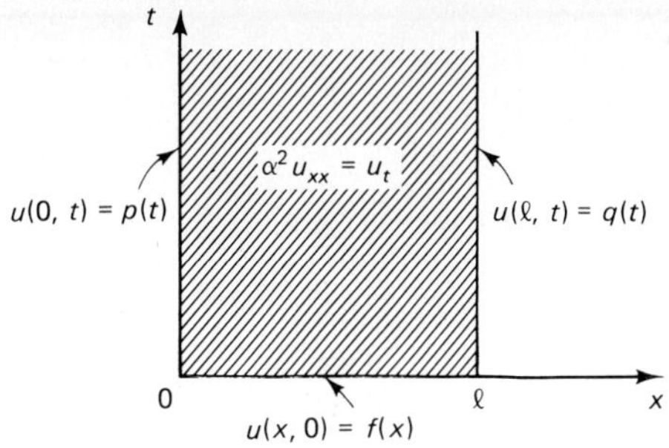

Fig. 14.2 The problem (1)–(3).

the resulting temperature history $u(x, t)$ in the semi-infinite strip $0 < x < \ell$, $0 < t < \infty$.

Before continuing, it is natural to wonder how we know how many boundary and initial conditions to prescribe if we are to have a properly posed problem, for it is not hard to imagine that if these conditions are underprescribed, the solution will be nonunique, and if they are overprescribed, they may be contradictory so that no solution exists. Thus by "properly posed" we shall mean posed such that there does indeed *exist* a solution, and that that solution is *unique*. How do we know that the problem summarized in Fig. 14.2 is properly posed? We handle the existence part by actually *finding* a solution; proof that our solution is unique is then left for Exercise 21. For the time being, it is not unreasonable to get by with the following simple rule of thumb: The PDE is a second-order equation with respect to x, so two x-wise conditions seem appropriate [namely, the boundary conditions (2a) and (2b)], and it is a first-order equation with respect to t, so one t-wise condition seems appropriate [namely, the initial condition (3)].

Beginning our solution of the problem (1) to (3), we adopt a method known as **separation of variables.** Accordingly, we seek solutions to (1) in the product form

$$u(x, t) = X(x)T(t), \tag{4}$$

where the functions X and T are to be determined. Putting the assumed form (4) into (1) gives

$$\alpha^2 X''T = XT', \tag{5}$$

where primes denote ordinary differentiation. To "separate the variables," we divide both sides of (5) by XT and obtain

$$\frac{X''}{X} = \frac{1}{\alpha^2}\frac{T'}{T}. \tag{6}$$

[Actually, we have divided by α^2 as well, but whether we have $1/\alpha^2$ on the right-hand side of (6) or α^2 on the left-hand side will not affect our final results.] Now (6) is of the general form

$$F(x) = G(t), \tag{7}$$

and the only way (7) can be satisfied, if x and t are independent variables, is if $F(x) = G(t) = constant$. For let $t = t_0$ be fixed. Then $G(t) = G(t_0)$ is a constant, so $F(x) = G(t_0) =$ constant. Further, if $F(x) =$ constant and $G(t) = F(x)$, then

$G(t)$ is constant, too, the *same* constant. Thus

$$\frac{X''}{X} = \frac{1}{\alpha^2}\frac{T'}{T} = \text{constant} \equiv -\kappa^2, \tag{8}$$

where we have written κ^2 for convenience, because we will soon need to take the square root of that quantity, and where our defense of the minus sign will be deferred for the moment.

The beauty of the separation procedure is that in place of the *PDE* $\alpha^2 u_{xx} = u_t$, we now have two *ODEs*

$$\frac{X''}{X} = -\kappa^2 \quad \text{and} \quad \frac{1}{\alpha^2}\frac{T'}{T} = -\kappa^2$$

or

$$X'' + \kappa^2 X = 0, \tag{9a}$$

$$T' + \kappa^2\alpha^2 T = 0. \tag{9b}$$

The *separation constant* κ remains to be determined. Solving these ODEs yields

$$X = A\cos\kappa x + B\sin\kappa x, \tag{10a}$$

$$T = Ce^{-\kappa^2\alpha^2 t}. \tag{10b}$$

However, observe that (10a) is the general solution of (9a) only in the event that $\kappa \neq 0$, since if $\kappa = 0$, we lose the sin κx term. We do not know the value(s) of κ yet, so it is best to allow for the possibility that $\kappa = 0$ will be needed. Setting $\kappa = 0$ in (9a) gives $X'' = 0$, with the general solution $X = A + Bx$. Thus we replace (10a) by

$$X = \begin{cases} A + Bx, & \kappa = 0 \\ C\cos\kappa x + D\sin\kappa x, & \kappa \neq 0. \end{cases} \tag{11}$$

Now (10b) gives the general solution of (9b) whether $\kappa \neq 0$ or $\kappa = 0$. However, having already committed ourselves, in (11), to the separate treatment of these two cases, we replace (10b) by the parallel statement

$$T = \begin{cases} E, & \kappa = 0 \\ Fe^{-\kappa^2\alpha^2 t}, & \kappa \neq 0. \end{cases} \tag{12}$$

Thus far we have discovered the "product solutions"

$$u = XT = (A + Bx)E \tag{13}$$

corresponding to $\kappa = 0$, and

$$u = XT = (C\cos\kappa x + D\sin\kappa x)\,Fe^{-\kappa^2\alpha^2 t} \tag{14}$$

for any $\kappa \neq 0$. Since $A, \ldots, F$ are arbitrary constants, we can absorb E into A and B, and F into C and D, and reexpress

$$u = G + Hx \tag{15}$$

for $\kappa = 0$, and

$$u = (I \cos \kappa x + J \sin \kappa x)e^{-\kappa^2 \alpha^2 t} \tag{16}$$

for $\kappa \neq 0$.

Now the PDE $Lu = \alpha^2 u_{xx} - u_t = 0$ is *linear*, so the sum of these solutions,

$$u(x, t) = G + Hx + (I \cos \kappa x + J \sin \kappa x)e^{-\kappa^2 \alpha^2 t}, \tag{17}$$

must also be a solution—for any combination of the constants G, H, I, J, and κ. Note that it is understood, in (17), that $\kappa \neq 0$ since the $G + Hx$ portion already accounts for the contribution from $\kappa = 0$.

In carrying out this superposition of solutions, our aim is to build up as comprehensive a solution as possible so that we increase our chances of successfully coping with the boundary and initial conditions that lie ahead. In fact, we are now ready to apply those conditions to (17). Beginning with the left end condition (2a),

$$u(0, t) = 0 = G + Ie^{-\kappa^2 \alpha^2 t} \qquad (0 < t < \infty) \tag{18}$$

or, putting (18) into a more suggestive form,

$$G(1) + I(e^{-\kappa^2 \alpha^2 t}) = 0 \qquad (0 < t < \infty). \tag{19}$$

Since the functions 1 and $e^{-\kappa^2 \alpha^2 t}$ are LI (linearly independent) over the t interval, it follows from (19) that we need $G = I = 0$.* "Updating" (17) to incorporate these results, we have, thus far,

$$u(x, t) = Hx + J \sin \kappa x \, e^{-\kappa^2 \alpha^2 t} \tag{20}$$

Next, according to (2b) we set

$$u(\ell, t) = 0 = H\ell + J \sin \kappa \ell \, e^{-\kappa^2 \alpha^2 t} \qquad (0 < t < \infty). \tag{21}$$

Reasoning as above, we need

$$H\ell = 0 \tag{22a}$$

and

$$J \sin \kappa \ell = 0. \tag{22b}$$

Equation (22a) gives $H = 0$, so that (20) reduces to

$$u(x, t) = J \sin \kappa x \, e^{-\kappa^2 \alpha^2 t}. \tag{23}$$

Unlike (22a), which unequivocably implies that $H = 0$, equation (22b) offers a choice: Either $J = 0$ or $\sin \kappa \ell = 0$ (or both). Here, and at analogous points in examples to follow, the rule is to *make the less restrictive choice so as to maintain as comprehensive a solution as possible*. In the present case, the choice $J = 0$ would result in the outright loss of the entire $J \sin \kappa x \exp(-\kappa^2 \alpha^2 t)$ term in (23), whereas the choice $\sin \kappa \ell = 0$ merely implies that

$$\kappa \ell = n\pi \quad \text{or} \quad \kappa = \frac{n\pi}{\ell} \tag{24}$$

* As an alternative to the linear-independence reasoning, observe that (19) is equivalent to an *infinite set of linear algebraic equations* in the unknowns G, I, for we can write down (19) for any finite or infinite set of specific t's in $0 < t < \infty$. Doing so, it can be seen that the linear algebraic system admits the unique solution $G = I = 0$.

for $n = 0, \pm 1, \pm 2, \ldots$. Of these values, $n = 0$ can be discarded since it gives $\kappa = 0$, whereas we noted, below (17), that $\kappa \neq 0$ since the $\kappa = 0$ case was already accounted for by the $G + Hx$ part of the solution. Further, $n = -1, -2, \ldots$ can be discarded since the $\sin \kappa x \exp(-\kappa^2 \alpha^2 t) = \sin(n\pi x/\ell) \exp[-(n\pi\alpha/\ell)^2 t]$ combination in (23) is insensitive to the sign of n—to within a factor of ± 1, which factor can be absorbed by J anyhow.

Thus we discard the possible choice $J = 0$ and adopt (24), with $n = 1, 2, 3, \ldots$. Consequently, instead of a single term, in (23), we actually have discovered many such terms,

$$\sin \frac{\pi x}{\ell} e^{-(\pi\alpha/\ell)^2 t}, \quad \sin \frac{2\pi x}{\ell} e^{-(2\pi\alpha/\ell)^2 t}, \quad \sin \frac{3\pi x}{\ell} e^{-(3\pi\alpha/\ell)^2 t}, \quad \ldots,$$

each of which satisfies the PDE $Lu = 0$. Since L is linear, it follows from Section 13.3 that every finite linear combination of such terms also satisfies $Lu = 0$. Thus, with the help of superposition, we can build up the more comprehensive solution

$$u(x, t) = \sum_{n=1}^{N} J_n \sin \frac{n\pi x}{\ell} e^{-(n\pi\alpha/\ell)^2 t}, \tag{25}$$

where N is arbitrarily large and the J_n's are arbitrary constants. Not only does (25) satisfy the PDE, as mentioned, it also satisfies the boundary conditions $u(0, t) = u(\ell, t) = 0$ since each $\sin(n\pi x/\ell)$ term vanishes at $x = 0$ and at $x = \ell$.

Finally, it remains to impose the initial conditions:

$$u(x, 0) = f(x) = \sum_{n=1}^{N} J_n \sin \frac{n\pi x}{\ell}, \qquad (0 < x < \ell). \tag{26}$$

Suppose, for example, that $f(x) = 50 \sin(\pi x/\ell)$. Then (26) is easily satisfied by choosing any $N \geq 1$ and setting $J_1 = 50$, $J_2 = \cdots = J_N = 0$. The desired solution then follows as

$$u(x, t) = 50 \sin \frac{\pi x}{\ell} e^{-(\pi\alpha/\ell)^2 t}, \tag{27}$$

a computer plot of which is shown in Fig. 14.3. Observe the exponential decay of u, as $t \to \infty$. The greater the thermal diffusivity α^2, the faster the decay. Approxi-

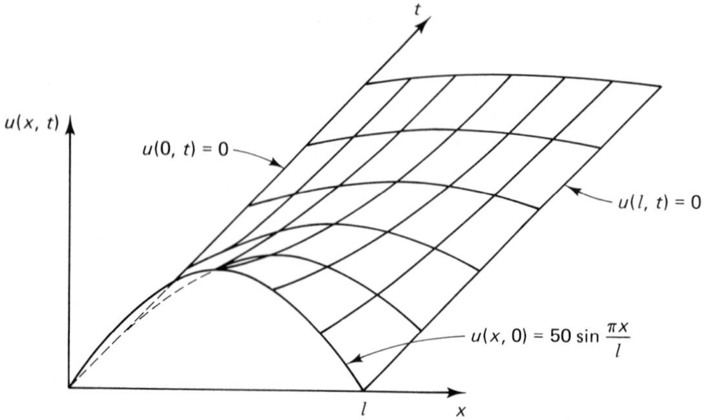

Fig. 14.3 Solution for the case $f(x) = 50\sin\frac{\pi x}{\ell}$.

TABLE 14.1 α^2 for Some Common Materials

	α^2 *(cm²/sec)*
Silver	1.70
Copper	1.14
Aluminum	0.86
Cast iron	0.16
Brick	0.0052
Glass	0.0034
Water	0.0014

mate values of α^2 are tabulated for several common materials, for comparison, in Table 14.1.

If, instead, the initial temperature is prescribed as $f(x) = 20 \sin(\pi x/\ell) - 25 \sin(4\pi x/\ell)$, say then (26) is satisfied by choosing any $N \geq 4$ and setting $J_1 = 20$, $J_2 = J_3 = 0$, $J_4 = -25$, $J_5 = \cdots = J_N = 0$. Then

$$u(x, t) = 20 \sin \frac{\pi x}{\ell} e^{-(\pi\alpha/\ell)^2 t} - 25 \sin \frac{4\pi x}{\ell} e^{-(4\pi\alpha/\ell)^2 t}. \tag{28}$$

More generally, suppose that $f(x)$ is not given as a finite linear combination of $\sin(n\pi x/\ell)$ terms; suppose that it is an essentially arbitrary function defined on $0 < x < \ell$, such as the one depicted in Fig. 14.4. Realizing that N is arbitrarily large, and needing all the help we can get, let $N \to \infty$ in (25) and (26). In particular, (26) becomes

$$f(x) = \sum_{n=1}^{\infty} J_n \sin \frac{n\pi x}{\ell}, \qquad (0 < x < \ell). \tag{29}$$

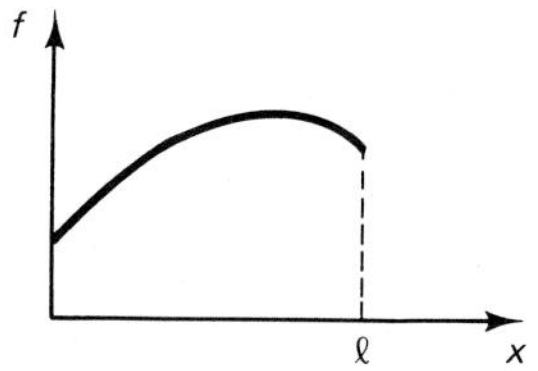

Fig. 14.4 Sample *f*.

Observing that the right-hand side of (29) is of the form of a Fourier series of an odd periodic function, let us *extend the definition of f outside the given interval $0 < x < \ell$* so that the extended function f_{ext} is odd and periodic. First, if f_{ext} is to be odd, we *must* define it over $-\ell < x < 0$, as shown in Fig. 14.5a. Before continuing the extension, observe from the form $\sin(n\pi x/\ell)$ in (29) that the period of f_{ext} is to be 2ℓ. (Recall that the ℓ in the classical Fourier series formula is *half* the period.) Well, the interval in Fig. 14.5a is already of length 2ℓ, so we have, in that figure, one full period. Thus completing the extension over $-\infty < x < \infty$, we have no choice but to create f_{ext} as shown in Fig. 14.5b.

Now, if we regard (29) as a part of the "extended" statement

$$f_{\text{ext}}(x) = \sum_{n=1}^{\infty} J_n \sin \frac{n\pi x}{\ell} \qquad (-\infty < x < \infty), \tag{30}$$

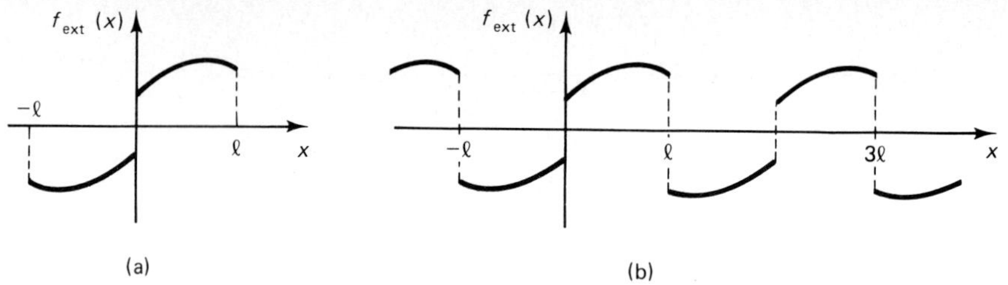

Fig. 14.5 Periodic extension of f.

it follows that we can compute the J_n's in the usual way, as the Fourier sine coefficients of the odd periodic function f_{ext}:

$$J_n = \frac{1}{\ell}\int_{-\ell}^{\ell} f_{ext}(x)\sin\frac{n\pi x}{\ell}\,dx. \tag{31}$$

Since $f_{ext}(x)$ and $\sin(n\pi x/\ell)$ are odd, the integrand is even, so

$$J_n = \frac{2}{\ell}\int_{0}^{\ell} f_{ext}(x)\sin\frac{n\pi x}{\ell}\,dx, \tag{32}$$

or since $f_{ext}(x) = f(x)$ over $0 < x < \ell$,

$$J_n = \frac{2}{\ell}\int_{0}^{\ell} f(x)\sin\frac{n\pi x}{\ell}\,dx. \tag{33}$$

Pulling these results together, we can say that the solution to the problem (1) to (3) is given by

$$u(x, t) = \sum_{n=1}^{\infty} J_n \sin\frac{n\pi x}{\ell}\, e^{-(n\pi\alpha/\ell)^2 t}, \tag{34}$$

where the J_n's are computed according to (33). By (34) being a "solution" we mean that every partial sum of the series in (34) satisfies the PDE $Lu = \alpha^2 u_{xx} - u_t = 0$ in $0 < x < \ell$, $0 < t < \infty$, as well as the two boundary conditions $u(0, t) = u(\ell, t) = 0$.* As to the satisfaction of the initial condition (29), we can say (Theorem 1, page 461) that if f is piecewise continuous, the series on the right-hand side of (29) converges to $f(x)$ at each point where f is continuous, and to the mean value $[f(x+) + f(x-)]/2$ at each point where f is discontinuous.

To illustrate (33) and (34), suppose that

$$f(x) = 100 \qquad (0 < x < \ell). \tag{35}$$

[That is, the rod can be imagined as held in boiling water until its temperature is 100°C throughout. Then, beginning at time $t = 0$, both ends are quenched with ice so that $u(0, t) = u(\ell, t) = 0°$ C for all $t > 0$.] Computing the J_n's from (33), (34) becomes

$$u(x, t) = \frac{400}{\pi}\sum_{n=1, 3, \ldots}^{\infty} \frac{1}{n}\sin\frac{n\pi x}{\ell}\, e^{-(n\pi\alpha/\ell)^2 t}. \tag{36}$$

* Besides the fact that each partial sum (the Nth *partial sum* of a series $\Sigma_{n=1}^{\infty} a_n$ is defined as the sum of the first N terms, $a_1 + a_2 + \cdots + a_n$) satisfies the PDE, one can also show that the *sum* of series satisfies the PDE. In the author's opinion, discussion of this point would involve too much of a digression; we refer the interested reader to Sec. 14 of CHURCHILL AND BROWN.

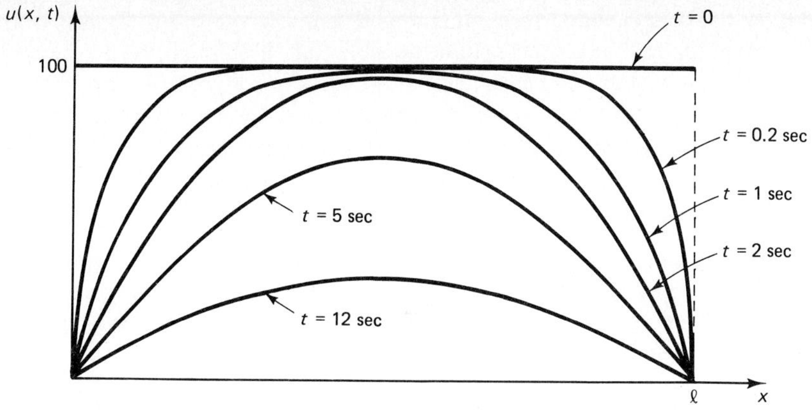

Fig. 14.6 The solution $u(x, t)$ for the case where $u(x, 0) = f(x) = 100$, $\alpha^2 = 1.14$, $\ell = 10$.

Summing the series numerically, at a number of x's and t's, the results are as displayed in Fig. 14.6. For definiteness, we have chosen the material to be copper ($\alpha^2 = 1.14$) and have set $\ell = 10$ cm.

COMMENT 1 Looking at Fig. 14.2 and considering $f(x)$ to be given by (35) often inspires the question: "What is u at the *corners,* namely, at $x = 0$, $t = 0$ and $x = \ell$, $t = 0$? Is it 100? 50?" Perhaps the best answer to that question is that it does not matter. For the solution (34) (in $0 < x < \ell$, $0 < t < \infty$) depends on f only through the integral in (33), and the values of that integral (for $n = 1, 2, \ldots$) are completely insensitive to the values of f at any finite number of points on the interval of integration. For example, if we change (35) to

$$f(x) = \begin{cases} 100, & x \neq \ell/4 \\ 5000, & x = \ell/4, \end{cases}$$

then the J_n's are the same as before and $u(x, t)$ is still given by (36). This dependence of the solution on the *integrated* effect of boundary and initial conditions, not on any handful of values at discrete points, will emerge as a recurrent theme in our study of PDEs, and is in line with Comment 2 on page 466.

COMMENT 2 The conditions $u(0, t) = u(\ell, t) = 0$ implied that $G = H = 0$, so that the $\kappa = 0$ part of (17), namely $G + Hx$, dropped out. In other cases, such as Example 2 to follow, the $\kappa = 0$ part of the solution does not drop out.

COMMENT 3 Let us explain our inclusion of the minus sign in (8). The $-\kappa^2$ led to a negative exponential for T, whereas $+\kappa^2$ would have led to a positive exponential. Since the ends of the rod are held at $u = 0$ for all $t > 0$, exponential decay of u seems far more plausible than unbounded exponential growth. Alternatively, look at X. The $-\kappa^2$ led to $X = C_1 \cos \kappa x + C_2 \sin \kappa x$, whereas $+\kappa^2$ would have led to $X = C_3 \cosh \kappa x + C_4 \sinh \kappa x$. Of these combinations, the former is capable of vanishing (by suitable choice of C_1, C_2, κ) at both $x = 0$ and $x = \ell$, as needed to satisfy the boundary conditions $u(0, t) = u(\ell, t) = 0$, but the latter is not. In any case, *even if we missed these signals and wrote $+\kappa^2$ in (8) we would still, eventually, have arrived at the same solution, for κ would have turned out to be $n\pi i/\ell$, instead of $n\pi/\ell$, and squaring the i would have given us back the minus sign in (8), which we had the foresight to anticipate* (see Exercise 1).

COMMENT 4 We concluded from $\sin \kappa \ell = 0$ that $\kappa \ell = n\pi$. Surely, those are the only roots on the real axis, but is it not possible that there might be additional roots *off* the real axis in the complex plane? If so, those roots would have led to additional terms in (25). The answer is no, the only roots of $\sin z = 0$, in the complex z plane, are $z = n\pi$, as shown in Part V. Even in the absence of that knowledge we could legitimately argue that the roots $\kappa \ell = n\pi$ gave us all the terms that we *needed* to handle the boundary and initial conditions.

COMMENT 5 Could the boundary and initial conditions have been applied in *any* order? No, the initial condition must be saved for last, for it is only after we have built up the linear combination on the right-hand side of (25) that we are prepared to confront the condition $u(x, 0) = f(x)$.

COMMENT 6 If t is not too small, the solution (33) is excellent from a computational point of view because the $\exp[-(n\pi\alpha/\ell)^2 t]$ factor causes rapid convergence of the series. (For example, note that $e^{-n^2} = 0.3679, 0.0183, 0.0001, \ldots$, for $n = 1, 2, 3, \ldots$.) However, the opposite is true as $t \to 0$. In fact, for $t = 0$ the exponentials are all equal to unity and provide no help at all in speeding the convergence. Indeed, with $t = 0$ in (36) the terms drop off merely like $1/n$. Thus, for reasonable accuracy we may need to sum an enormous number of terms if t is small, whereas only one or two terms may suffice if t is large. Just as the series in (36) converges more and more rapidly as t increases, it is possible to derive quite a different series (by a method other than separation of variables) that complements the one in (36) by converging more and more rapidly as $t \to 0$ (see Exercise 13 in Section 14.4).

COMMENT 7 Recall that we inferred, from (18) and the linear independence of 1 and $\exp(-\kappa^2\alpha^2 t)$, that $G = I = 0$. Why did we not, instead, merely solve (18) for G in terms of I (or vice versa) as

$$G = -Ie^{-\kappa^2\alpha^2 t}? \tag{37}$$

This approach can lead to *serious trouble,* for unless we have $G = I = 0$, then (37) will result in one or both of the quantities G and I being nonconstant functions of t. But $A, B, \ldots, I, J$ arose as *constants* of integration; they cannot, in the end, be nonconstant functions of x or t! Similarly for κ.

COMMENT 8 It is interesting to observe that although we began by seeking solutions of *product form,* $X(x)T(t)$, the final result, (36), is not itself of product form; rather, it is a *linear combination* of such terms.

COMMENT 9 Finally, we note that the "periodic extension story" is, in fact, the story behind the half-range sine expansion discussed in Example 6 and Exercise 27 of Section 10.3. In subsequent examples, we will save ourselves some work by turning to the half- and quarter-range sine and cosine formulas, which are reproduced, for convenient reference, on the inside back cover. In the present case, use of those formulas would have proceeded as follows. Comparing (29) with the half- and quarter-range formulas, we see that (29) is of the form of a half-range sine expansion because we have sines (not cosines) and because the summation is over $n = 1, 2, 3, \ldots$ (not $n = 1, 3, \ldots$). Next, comparing $\sin(n\pi x/\ell)$ in (29) with $\sin(n\pi x/L)$ in (HS1) (see the inside back cover), we see that $L = \ell$, so that (HS2) then gives

$$J_n = \frac{2}{\ell} \int_0^\ell f(x) \sin \frac{n\pi x}{\ell} \, dx, \tag{38}$$

as before. ◀

With Example 1 behind us, it is interesting to contrast the solution of ordinary and partial differential equations. To solve an ODE, one usually proceeds by finding a general solution and then applying initial or boundary conditions in order to determine the values of the constants of integration. (The Laplace transform method, on the other hand, is an example of a solution procedure that does *not* involve the determination of a general solution.) For example, a general solution of a second-order linear homogeneous ODE consists of an arbitrary linear combination of two LI solutions. With this idea in mind, it is striking that the solution (34) of the second-order linear homogeneous PDE $\alpha^2 u_{xx} - u_t = 0$ consists of an arbitrary linear combination of an *infinite* number of LI solutions. In fact, even this rather comprehensive-looking result was not billed as a general solution of the PDE, since our solution procedure only allowed for solutions of product form, and there may well be other solutions which are not of that form. Thus the point of the separation of variables method is not to find a *general* solution of the PDE, but to find one that is *comprehensive enough* to be able to cope with the required boundary and initial conditions.

In making a long story out of the preceding example, and in dwelling on so many details, we have shown no mercy. However, most applications of the method of separation of variables follow essentially the lines developed in Example 1, so that a complete understanding of Example 1 will prove to be well worth the effort. We promise that our presentation of subsequent examples will be more streamlined.

EXAMPLE 2 *Different Boundary Conditions.* As a variation on Example 1, suppose that the left end of the rod is insulated and the right end is held at a constant temperature u_0 for all $t > 0$. The problem, then, is as follows:

$$\alpha^2 u_{xx} = u_t \qquad (0 < x < \ell,\ 0 < t < \infty) \tag{39a}$$

$$u_x(0, t) = 0 \qquad (0 < t < \infty) \tag{39b}$$

$$u(\ell, t) = u_0 \qquad (0 < t < \infty) \tag{39c}$$

$$u(x, 0) = f(x) \qquad (0 < x < \ell). \tag{39d}$$

The beginning of the separation-of-variables solution is the same as in Example 1 through (17), so let us pick up at that point:

$$u(x, t) = G + Hx + (I \cos \kappa x + J \sin \kappa x) e^{-\kappa^2 \alpha^2 t}. \tag{40}$$

Applying (39b) yields

$$u_x(0, t) = H + \kappa J e^{-\kappa^2 \alpha^2 t}, \tag{41}$$

so $H = J = 0$. Updating (40) accordingly,

$$u(x, t) = 0 = G + I \cos \kappa x \, e^{-\kappa^2 \alpha^2 t}, \tag{42}$$

Next,

$$u(\ell, t) = u_0 = G + I \cos \kappa\ell \, e^{-\kappa^2\alpha^2 t}, \tag{43}$$

or, equivalently,

$$0 = (G - u_0)(1) + (I \cos \kappa\ell)\,(e^{-\kappa^2\alpha^2 t}), \tag{44}$$

and it follows from the linear independence of 1 and $e^{-\kappa^2\alpha^2 t}$ that

$$G - u_0 = 0$$

and

$$I \cos \kappa\ell = 0.$$

The former gives $G = u_0$, and the latter requires at least one of the two factors I and $\cos \kappa\ell$ to be zero. Rather than set $I = 0$ and lose the entire $I \cos \kappa x \exp(-\kappa^2\alpha^2 t)$ term in (42), we set $\cos \kappa\ell = 0$, so that the allowable values of κ are $n\pi/2\ell$, for $n = \pm 1, \pm 3, \pm 5, \ldots$. Discarding the negative n's, with no loss, and using superposition, we write

$$u(x, t) = u_0 + \sum_{n=1,3,\ldots}^{\infty} I_n \cos \frac{n\pi x}{2\ell}\, e^{-(n\pi\alpha/2\ell)^2 t}. \tag{45}$$

Finally, (39d) requires that

$$f(x) = u_0 + \sum_{n=1,3,\ldots}^{\infty} I_n \cos \frac{n\pi x}{2\ell}. \tag{46}$$

Now, (46) looks like a quarter-range cosine expansion, except for the disconcerting presence of the u_0 on the right-hand side. However, u_0 is a known quantity and can merely be combined with the prescribed function $f(x)$ by subtraction. Thus re-expressing (46) as

$$f(x) - u_0 = \sum_{n=1,3,\ldots}^{\infty} I_n \cos \frac{n\pi x}{2\ell}, \tag{47}$$

it follows from the *quarter-range cosine expansion* formula (QC1) and (QC2) (inside back cover) that

$$I_n = \frac{2}{\ell} \int_0^{\ell} [f(x) - u_0] \cos \frac{n\pi x}{2\ell}\, dx \qquad (n = 1, 3, \ldots). \tag{48}$$

Thus our solution is given by (45), where the I_n expansion coefficients are computed according to (48).

COMMENT Since each exponential tends to zero as $t \to \infty$, we can see from (45) that

$$u(x, t) \sim u_0 \quad \text{as} \quad t \to \infty. \tag{49}$$

We refer to the right-hand side of (49) as the **steady-state** solution, and we denote it as $u_s(x)$. In this case $u_s(x)$ is merely a constant, but that will not always be the case, as we shall see in the exercises. $u_s(x)$ could have been found, at the outset, as the solution to the steady-state problem

$$\alpha^2 u_s'' = 0 \qquad (0 < x < \ell) \tag{50a}$$

$$u_s'(0) = 0, \qquad u_s(\ell) = u_0, \tag{50b}$$

where (50a) is what $\alpha^2 u_{xx} = u_t$ reduces to when we put in $u_s(x)$ for u. Observe that we may consider u as comprising the sum of a steady-state part plus a transient part, where the steady-state part corresponds to the $\kappa = 0$ part of the solution, and the transient part corresponds to the $\kappa \neq 0$ part. In fact, we could have sought a solution in the form

$$u(x, t) = \underbrace{u_s(x)}_{\substack{\text{steady-}\\ \text{state part}}} + \underbrace{X(x)T(t)}_{\substack{\text{transient}\\ \text{part}}} \tag{51}$$

from the outset. The latter form is sometimes more convenient than $u(x, t) = X(x)T(t)$, and is used in Exercises 18 and 19. ◀

In the foregoing examples, we have encountered boundary conditions of the type $u =$ constant. More generally, u may be a prescribed function of t at an endpoint:

$$u(x_0, t) = F(t), \tag{52}$$

where x_0 denotes an endpoint. Such a boundary condition is called a **Dirichlet boundary condition,** or a **boundary condition of the first kind.** In examples 1 and 2 the $F(t)$'s were merely constants; in Exercise 15 we allow them to be nonconstant.

A second possibility is that we do not know u at the boundary, but that we do know the heat flux across that boundary. According to Fourier's law of heat conduction, that flux is proportional to $\partial u/\partial x$, so such a boundary condition is of the form

$$\frac{\partial u}{\partial x}(x_0, t) = F(t) \tag{53}$$

and is called a **Neumann boundary condition** or a **boundary condition of the second kind.** An important special case is that of an *insulated* boundary, i.e., a boundary across which the heat flux is zero: then $\partial u/\partial x(x_0, t) = 0$, as occurred in Example 2 at $x = 0$.

A third important case is that in which some linear combination of u and $\partial u/\partial x$ is prescribed:

$$u(x_0, t) + \beta\frac{\partial u}{\partial x}(x_0, t) = F(t) \tag{54}$$

where $\beta \neq 0$. This "mixed" case is known as a **Robin boundary condition** or a **boundary condition of the third kind.** Within the context of heat transfer, such a condition arises when the boundary is in contact with a fluid, the ambient temperature of which is a known function $u_\infty(t)$. Then according to *Newton's law of cooling* heat is transferred from the fluid to the body at the rate $hA[u_\infty(t) - u(x_0, t)]$, where A is the contact area and h is the convective heat transfer coefficient. That rate must equal the rate at which heat enters the body by conduction, $\kappa A \frac{\partial u}{\partial n}(x_0, t)$, where k is the body's thermal conductivity, so

$$hA[u_\infty(t) - u(x_0, t)] = kA \frac{\partial u}{\partial n}(x_0, t) \tag{55}$$

or, getting (55) into the Robin form (54),

$$u(x_0, t) + \frac{k}{h}\frac{\partial u}{\partial n}(x_0, t) = u_\infty(t), \tag{56}$$

where

$$\frac{\partial u}{\partial n} = \frac{\partial u}{\partial x} \text{ at } x_0 = \ell \quad \text{and} \quad \frac{\partial u}{\partial n} = -\frac{\partial u}{\partial x} \text{ at } x_0 = 0.$$

This case is is more difficult and is discussed in Section 14.3. Practically speaking, however, one can approximate (56) by the Dirichlet condition $u(x_0, t) = u_\infty(t)$ if k/h is sufficiently small, or by the Neumann condition $\frac{\partial u}{\partial n}(x_0, t) = 0$ if h/k is sufficiently small.†

In the exercises that follow, we include Neumann boundary conditions, internal heating (i.e., a nonzero source term F in the PDE $\alpha^2 u_{xx} = u_t - F$), spherical geometry, and additional physical applications such as the flow of electricity in a cable, and the diffusion of one gas into another.

14.2 EXERCISES

1. (a) We argued, in Comment 3 of Example 1, that the separation constant is best expressed as $-\kappa^2$. In this exercise we ask you to prove, in advance, that the separation constant cannot possibly be positive. *Hint:* Rewrite (8) as

$$\frac{X''}{X} = \frac{1}{\alpha^2}\frac{T'}{T} = \beta.$$

Show that $X(x)$ satisfies the problem

$$X'' - \beta X = 0; \qquad X(0) = 0, \quad X(\ell) = 0.$$

Multiply $X'' - \beta X = 0$ through by X, integrate on x from 0 to ℓ, integrate the $\int_0^\ell XX''\,dx$ term by parts, and obtain

$$\beta = -\frac{\int_0^\ell [X'(x)]^2\,dx}{\int_0^\ell [X(x)]^2\,dx}. \tag{a}$$

(b) It was also mentioned in Comment 3, that even if we took the separation constant to be $+\kappa^2$ instead of $-\kappa^2$, the same results would ultimately be obtained. Verify that claim by actually going through the solution again, beginning with

$$\frac{X''}{X} = \frac{1}{\alpha^2}\frac{T'}{T} = +\kappa^2,$$

and eventually reproducing (25). *Hint:* Recall (10) in Section A.5.

2. From (11) and (12) we inferred the solution form (17). Instead, students sometimes conclude that

$$u = (A + Bx + C\cos\kappa x + D\sin\kappa x)(E + Fe^{-\kappa^2\alpha^2 t}).$$

Show that this form is *incorrect*.

3. The solution (36) was for the case where $f(x) = 100°\text{C}$, $\alpha^2 = 1.14\ \text{cm}^2/\text{sec}$, $\ell = 10$ cm.
*(a) Obtain the solution if, instead, $f(x) = 100\cos(\pi x/\ell) = 100\cos(\pi x/10)$.
(b) Sum the series numerically and plot $u(x, t)$ ver-

†More precisely, one is interested in whether the nondimensional *Biot number*, Bi $= h\ell/k$, is sufficiently large or small.

sus t, as we have in Fig. 14.5, for $t = 1$ and 5 sec. *Note:* We suggest that you sketch your best guess of the $u(x, 1)$ and $u(x, 5)$ curves before computing and plotting them.

4. Repeat Exercise 3, but with
$$f(x) = \begin{cases} 100, & 0 < x < 5 \\ 0, & 5 < x < 10. \end{cases}$$

5. Repeat Exercise 3, but with
$$f(x) = \begin{cases} \sin(\pi x/10), & 0 < x < 5 \\ 0, & 5 < x < 10. \end{cases}$$

6. The temperature distribution $u(x, t)$ in a 2 m long brass rod is governed by the problem

$$\alpha^2 u_{xx} = u_t \qquad (0 < x < 2, 0 < t < \infty)$$
$$u(0, t) = u(2, t) = 0 \qquad (t > 0)$$
$$u(x, 0) = \begin{cases} 50x, & 0 < x < 1 \\ 100 - 5x, & 1 < x < 2, \end{cases}$$

where $\alpha^2 = 2.9 \times 10^{-5}$ m²/sec.

(a) Determine the solution for $u(x, t)$.

*(b) Compute (correct to two significant figures) the temperature at the midpoint of the rod at the end of 1 hour.

(c) Compute the time it will take for the temperature at that point to diminish to 10°C.

7. Solve for $u(x, t)$:

$$\alpha^2 u_{xx} = u_t \qquad (0 < x < \ell, 0 < t < \infty)$$
$$u(0, t) = 0 \qquad (0 < t < \infty)$$
$$u(\ell, t) = \begin{cases} 0, & 0 < t < t_0 \\ 100, & t_0 < t < \infty \end{cases}$$
$$u(x, 0) = 0 \qquad (0 < x < \ell).$$

8. Solve $\alpha^2 u_{xx} = u_t$ $(0 < x < \ell, 0 < t < \infty)$ subject to the given boundary and initial conditions. Expansion coefficients should be expressed in integral form, as in (33). Identify the steady-state solution, $u_s(x) = \lim_{t\to\infty} u(x, t)$, if that limit exists.

*(a) $u(0, t) = u_1$, $u(\ell, t) = u_2$, $u(x, 0) = f(x)$

(b) $u_x(0, t) = u_x(\ell, t) = 0$, $u(x, 0) = f(x)$. Show that the steady-state solution is a constant, namely, the average of $f(x)$ over the interval $0 < x < \ell$.

(c) $u(0, t) = u_0$, $u_x(\ell, t) = 0$, $u(x, 0) = f(x)$

9. (*Diffusion of one gas into another*) Consider a cylindrical compressed-gas container of length ℓ divided into two halves by a baffle. On one side of the baffle is one gas, say species A, and on the other side of the baffle is another gas, say species B. At time $t = 0$ the baffle is removed and the gases proceed to mix by diffusion. Considering species A, say, its concentration $c_A(x, t)$ moles/cm³ is governed by the problem

$$D\frac{\partial^2 c_A}{\partial x^2} = \frac{\partial c_A}{\partial t} \qquad (0 < x < \ell, 0 < t < \infty) \quad \text{(a)}$$
$$\frac{\partial c_A}{\partial x}(0, t) = \frac{\partial c_A}{\partial x}(\ell, t) = 0 \qquad (0 < t < \infty) \quad \text{(b)}$$
$$c_A(x, 0) = \begin{cases} c_0 & 0 < x < \ell/2 \\ 0 & \ell/2 < x < \ell, \end{cases} \quad \text{(c)}$$

where D is the diffusion coefficient and D and c_0 are constants.

(a) Solve for $c_A(x, t)$. From $c_A(x, t)$ determine the steady-state solution
$$c_{As}(x) = \lim_{t\to\infty} c_A(x, t). \quad \text{(d)}$$

(b) Integrating equation (a) with respect to x, from 0 to ℓ, show that
$$\int_0^\ell c_A(x, t)\, dx = \text{constant}, \quad \text{(e)}$$

which says that the total amount of A is conserved. This result makes sense physically since the container is sealed [note equation (b)] and the gas is being neither created nor destroyed. (The point here is that it may be possible to learn something about the solution, from the PDE and boundary and initial conditions, without actually obtaining the full solution.)

(c) Solve for $c_{As}(x)$ *directly*, i.e., by solving
$$Dc''_{As}(x) = 0; \qquad c'_{As}(0) = c'_{As}(\ell) = 0$$

and using equation (e). Your result should, of course, be the same as in part (a).

10. Show that the solution (33) and (34) to the problem in Example 1 can be expressed in the form
$$u(x, t) = \int_0^\ell K(\xi; x, t) f(\xi)\, d\xi, \quad \text{(a)}$$

where
$$K(\xi; x, t) = \frac{2}{\ell}\sum_{n=1}^{\infty} \sin\frac{n\pi x}{\ell} \sin\frac{n\pi\xi}{\ell} e^{-(n\pi\alpha/\ell)^2 t}$$

is called the *kernel*. (You need not prove the validity of the interchange in the order of the integration and summation.)

11. (*Periodic boundary conditions*) Consider the conduction of heat in a circular metal ring, the surface of which is insulated. Actually, whether the shape is a circle, or an ellipse, or whatever, is irrelevant insofar as the heat conduction is concerned. If we measure x along the ring, we may regard the ring as a rod of length L with its two ends ($x = 0$ and $x = L$) joined. Although we do not know u or u_x at the two "ends," we do know that

$$u(0, t) = u(L, t), \qquad \text{(a)}$$

$$u_x(0, t) = u_x(L, t), \qquad \text{(b)}$$

for all $0 < t < \infty$. The boundary conditions (a) and (b) are not of the first, second, or third kind; rather, they are known as **periodic boundary conditions.**

*(a) Solve the heat equation $\alpha^2 u_{xx} = u_t$ subject to the boundary conditions (a) and (b) and the initial condition $u(x, 0) = f(x)$ $(0 < x < L)$. Letting $t \to \infty$ in the solution, show that the steady-state solution is a constant temperature that is the average value of the initial distribution f.

(b) ~~Multiplying the PDE by u and~~ integrating THE PDE on x from 0 to L, derive the conservation principle

$$\int_0^L u(x, t)\, dx = \text{constant}. \qquad \text{(c)}$$

(c) Derive the steady-state solution $u_s(x)$ by solving

$$\alpha^2 u_s'' = 0 \qquad (0 < x < L)$$

$$u_s(0) = u_s(L), \quad u_s'(0) = u_s'(L),$$

and using (c). Your result should, of course, be the same as found in part (a).

12. (*Presence of a constant source term*) Consider the problem

$$\alpha^2 u_{xx} = u_t - F \qquad (0 < x < \ell, 0 < t < \infty) \quad \text{(a)}$$

$$u(0, t) = 0, \quad u(\ell, t) = 50 \qquad (0 < t < \infty) \quad \text{(b)}$$

$$u(x, 0) = f(x) \qquad (0 < x < \ell), \quad \text{(c)}$$

where the source term (recall Example 3, page 396) F is assumed to be a constant. Solve for $u(x, t)$. Expansion coefficients may be left in integral form. *Hint:* This is the first problem in which the PDE is *nonhomogeneous,* namely, $Lu = \alpha^2 u_{xx} - u_t = -F$. Observe that if we seek $u(x, t) = X(x)T(t)$, as in the text examples, and attempt to carry out the separation process, we obtain

$$\frac{X''}{X} = \frac{1}{\alpha^2}\frac{T'}{T} - \frac{F}{\alpha^2}\frac{1}{XT}. \qquad \text{(d)}$$

Because of the last term in (d), which contains both x and t dependence, we are unable to complete the separation process successfully. That is, we are unable to get all of the x dependence on one side of the equation and all of the t dependence on the other side. Thus we suggest seeking u, instead, in the form

$$u(x, t) = u_s(x) + X(x)T(t), \qquad \text{(e)}$$

where $u_s(x)$ is the *steady-state solution.* In steady state, $u_t \to 0$ and $u(x, t) \to u_s(x)$, so (a) and (b) yield the problem

$$\alpha^2 u_s''(x) = -F; \qquad u_s(0) = 0, \quad u_s(\ell) = 50 \quad \text{(f)}$$

governing $u_s(x)$. Putting (e) into (a), show that the u_s term cancels the troublesome F term, so that this time the separation can be successfully completed to yield the familiar result

$$\frac{X''}{X} = \frac{1}{\alpha^2}\frac{T'}{T} = \text{constant} = -\kappa^2. \qquad \text{(g)}$$

Then solve (f) for u_s and (g) for X and T, and impose the conditions (b) and (c) on $u(x, t) = u_s(x) + X(x)T(t)$. Regarding the form of (e), observe that, in *physical* terms, u_s is the steady-state solution and XT is a transient quantity needed to match the initial condition $u(x, 0) = f(x)$ with the steady-state solution $u_s(x)$. In *mathematical* terms, u_s is a particular solution (i.e., a particular solution of the full equation $\alpha^2 u_{xx} - u_t = -F$) and XT is a solution of the associated homogeneous equation $\alpha^2 u_{xx} - u_t = 0$.

13. Repeat Exercise 12, but with (b) and (c) changed as follows.

*(a) $u(0, t) = u(\ell, t) = u(x, 0) = 0$
(b) $u_x(0, t) = 0$, $u(\ell, t) = u(x, 0) = 0$

14. (*Presence of a nonconstant source term*) In Exercise 12 we included a source term F that was a constant. More generally, the suggested solution technique would have worked even if F were a nonconstant function of x. In the present exercise we allow for t dependence as well. Thus consider the problem

$$\alpha^2 u_{xx} = u_t - F(x, t) \qquad (0 < x < \ell, 0 < t < \infty)$$

$$u(0, t) = u(\ell, t) = 0 \qquad (0 < t < \infty) \quad \text{(a)}$$

$$u(x, 0) = f(x) \qquad (0 < x < \ell).$$

(a) Solve for $u(x, t)$ by seeking

$$u(x, t) = \sum_{n=1}^{\infty} g_n(t) \sin\frac{n\pi x}{\ell} \qquad \text{(b)}$$

and expanding

$$F(x,t) = \sum_{n=1}^{\infty} F_n(t) \sin \frac{n\pi x}{\ell}, \qquad \text{(c)}$$

where the

$$F_n(t) = \frac{2}{\ell} \int_0^{\ell} F(x,t) \sin \frac{n\pi x}{\ell}\, dx \qquad \text{(d)}$$

coefficients are considered as known (i.e., computable) functions of t. Thus show that

$$u(x,t) = \sum_{n=1}^{\infty} \left[\int_0^t F_n(\tau) e^{(n\pi\alpha/\ell)^2(\tau - t)}\, d\tau + f_n e^{-(n\pi\alpha/\ell)^2 t} \right] \sin \frac{n\pi x}{\ell}, \qquad \text{(e)}$$

where

$$f(x) = \sum_{n=1}^{\infty} f_n \sin \frac{n\pi x}{\ell}, \qquad \text{(f)}$$

so that the f_n's are computed as

$$f_n = \frac{2}{\ell} \int_0^{\ell} f(x) \sin \frac{n\pi x}{\ell}\, dx. \qquad \text{(g)}$$

(b) Work out the solution (e) for the case where $F(x, t) = e^{-t}$, say, and $f(x) = 0$.
(c) Modify the solution procedure described in part (a) if the left end condition is changed from $u(0, t) = 0$ to $u_x(0, t) = 0$.

15. (*Variable end conditions*) Thus far our Dirichlet type boundary conditions have been of constant type, e.g., $u(0, t) = 50$. Here we consider nonconstant conditions. Thus consider the problem

$$\begin{aligned} &\alpha^2 u_{xx} = u_t \qquad (0 < x < \ell,\ 0 < t < \infty) \\ &u(0,t) = p(t), \quad u(\ell, t) = q(t), \quad u(x,0) = f(x), \end{aligned} \qquad \text{(a)}$$

where $p(t)$, $q(t)$, and $f(x)$ are prescribed. Changing dependent variables from $u(x, t)$ to $v(x, t)$ according to

$$u(x,t) = v(x,t) + \left(1 - \frac{x}{\ell}\right) p(t) + \frac{x}{\ell} q(t), \qquad \text{(b)}$$

show that the problem governing v is precisely of the type treated in Exercise 14. *Note:* Observe how an "input" can be moved from the boundary conditions to the PDE. In the present case, the PDE on u was homogeneous and the boundary conditions were nonhomogeneous; following the change of variables (b), you should find that the PDE on v is nonhomogeneous and the boundary conditions are homogeneous.

16. (*Superposition*) Show that the solution to the problem

$$\begin{aligned} &\alpha^2 u_{xx} = u_t + g(x,t) \qquad (0 < x < \ell,\ 0 < t < \infty) \\ &u(0,t) = p(t), \quad u(\ell,t) = q(t), \quad u(x,0) = f(x) \end{aligned} \qquad \text{(a)}$$

can be expressed as $u = u_1 + u_2 + u_3 + u_4$, where $u_1, \ldots, u_4$ are solutions to the four problems

$$\begin{aligned} &\alpha^2 u_{1xx} = u_{1t} + g(x,t) \qquad (0 < x < \ell,\ 0 < t < \infty) \\ &u_1(0,t) = u_1(\ell,t) = u_1(x,0) = 0, \end{aligned} \qquad \text{(b)}$$

$$\begin{aligned} &\alpha^2 u_{2xx} = u_{2t} \qquad (0 < x < \ell,\ 0 < t < \infty) \\ &u_2(0,t) = p(t), \qquad u_2(\ell,t) = u_2(x,0) = 0, \end{aligned} \qquad \text{(c)}$$

$$\begin{aligned} &\alpha^2 u_{3xx} = u_{3t} \qquad (0 < x < \ell,\ 0 < t < \infty) \\ &u_3(0,t) = 0, \quad u_3(\ell,t) = q(t), \quad u_3(x,0) = 0, \end{aligned} \qquad \text{(d)}$$

$$\begin{aligned} &\alpha^2 u_{4xx} = u_{4t} \qquad (0 < x < \ell,\ 0 < t < \infty) \\ &u_4(0,t) = u_4(\ell,t) = 0, \quad u_4(x,0) = f(x). \end{aligned} \qquad \text{(e)}$$

17. (*Nonhomogeneous Neumann conditions*) Solve the conduction problem

$$\begin{aligned} &\alpha^2 u_{xx} = u_t \qquad (0 < x < \ell,\ 0 < t < \infty) \\ &u_x(0,t) = -1, \quad u_x(\ell,t) = 0, \quad u(x,0) = 0 \end{aligned} \qquad \text{(a)}$$

for $u(x, t)$. *Hint:* You should find that the standard separation-of-variables procedure has difficulty coping with the boundary conditions. To proceed successfully, we suggest that you change from $u(x, t)$ to $v(x, t)$ according to

$$u(x,t) = \frac{(x - \ell)^2}{2\ell} + v(x,t), \qquad \text{(b)}$$

then show that v can be split, by superposition, into $v = v_1 + v_2$, where

$$\begin{aligned} &\alpha^2 v_{1xx} = v_{1t} \qquad (0 < x < \ell,\ 0 < t < \infty) \\ &v_{1x}(0,t) = v_{1x}(\ell,t) = 0,\ v_1(x,0) = -\frac{(x-\ell)^2}{2\ell} \end{aligned} \qquad \text{(c)}$$

and

$$\begin{aligned} &\alpha^2 v_{2xx} = v_{2t} - \frac{\alpha^2}{\ell} \qquad (0 < x < \ell,\ 0 < t < \infty) \\ &v_{2x}(0,t) = v_{2x}(\ell,t) = v_2(x,0) = 0. \end{aligned} \qquad \text{(d)}$$

The solution for v_2 can be found easily as a function of t alone. Thus solve for v_2. (You need not solve for v_1.)

18. (*Newton cooling*) Consider the conduction of heat in a rod, the lateral surface of which is *not* insulated. If heat is convected from the rod to the ambient medium, the PDE governing the temperature $u(x, t)$ is

$$\alpha^2 u_{xx} = u_t + h(u - u_\infty), \tag{a}$$

where the constants h and u_∞ are the convective heat transfer coefficient and the ambient temperature, respectively. Our interest in (a) lies in the Newton cooling term $h(u - u_\infty)$. Although it is not essential, one normally begins by eliminating the u_∞ term by setting $v(x, t) = u(x, t) - u_\infty$ and considering, instead, $\alpha^2 v_{xx} = v_t + hv$.

*(a) Solve the Newton cooling problem

$$\begin{aligned} &\alpha^2 v_{xx} = v_t + hv \qquad (0 < x < \ell, 0 < t < \infty) \\ &v(0, t) = v(\ell, t) = 50, \quad v(x, 0) = f(x) \end{aligned} \tag{b}$$

by separation of variables, leaving expansion coefficients in integral form. *Hint:* Seeking $v(x, t) = v_s(x) + X(x)T(t)$, where $v_s(x)$ is the steady-state temperature distribution, show that

$$\frac{X''}{X} = \frac{1}{\alpha^2}\frac{T' + hT}{T} = \text{constant} = -\kappa^2. \tag{c}$$

(b) Solve (b) by omitting the $v_s(x)$ term and seeking $v(x, t) = X(x)T(t)$. [That is, show that the inclusion of the $v_s(x)$ term in the solution form is not really necessary.]

(c) Show that the change of variables $w(x, t) = e^{-ht}v(x, t)$ reduces $\alpha^2 v_{xx} = v_t + hv$ to the more familiar form $\alpha^2 w_{xx} = w_t$.

19. (*Flow of electricity in a cable*) The voltage $v(x, t)$ (volts) and the current $I(x, t)$ (amperes) in a long underground insulated cable are governed by the PDEs

$$v_{xx} = LCv_{tt} + (rC + Lg)v_t + rgv, \tag{a}$$

$$I_{xx} = LCI_{tt} + (rC + Lg)I_t + rgI, \tag{b}$$

where L, C, r, g are positive constants: L is the inductance (henries/kilometer), C is the capacitance to ground (farads/kilometer), r is the resistance (ohms/kilometer), and g is the leakance to ground (mhos/kilometer). These PDEs are called the *telephone equations* and are seen to be of wave (hyperbolic) type. Often, as in telegraph transmission, L and g can be neglected, in which case (a) and (b) reduce to the *telegraph equations*

$$v_{xx} = rCv_t,$$

$$I_{xx} = rCI_t,$$

which are of diffusion type. In the present example we suppose only that $L \approx 0$. Considering only the voltage v, we then have

$$v_{xx} = rCv_t + rgv. \tag{c}$$

[Comparing (c) with the PDE in Exercise 18, we see that the two phenomena are analogous, with the lateral heat loss to the ambient medium corresponding to the voltage loss due to leakage to the ground.] Suppose that the line is of length ℓ, the voltage at $x = 0$ is maintained (for a "long time") at 12 volts, the voltage at $x = \ell$ is maintained (for a "long time") at 6 volts, and then, beginning at $t = 0$, the left end is grounded. Thus

$$v(0, t) = 0 \qquad (0 < t < \infty), \tag{d}$$

$$v(\ell, t) = 6 \qquad (0 < t < \infty). \tag{e}$$

The initial condition $v(x, 0)$ is not given, but can be deduced from (c) together with the information that the ends have been maintained at 12 and 6 volts, respectively, for a long time.

(a) Determine $v(x, 0)$.
(b) Determine the steady-state solution $v_s(x)$.
(c) Solve for $v(x, t)$ by separation of variables. Fourier expansion coefficients may be left in integral form. *Hint:* As in Exercise 18, it will be most convenient to seek $v(x, t) = v_s(x) + X(x)T(t)$.

20. (*Spherical coordinates*) Consider the radial conduction of heat within a solid sphere. If the temperature u is a function only of the spherical polar coordinate ρ and the time t, then $\alpha^2\nabla^2 u = u_t$ becomes

$$\alpha^2\left(u_{\rho\rho} + \frac{2}{\rho}u_\rho\right) = u_t. \tag{a}$$

(a) Setting $u(\rho, t) = (1/\rho)\, v(\rho,t)$, show that v needs to satisfy the more familiar PDE

$$\alpha^2 v_{\rho\rho} = v_t. \tag{b}$$

(b) Noting the idea contained in part (a), solve the problem

$$\alpha^2\left(u_{\rho\rho} + \frac{2}{\rho}u_\rho\right) = u_t \qquad (0 < \rho < a, 0 < t < \infty) \tag{c}$$

$$u(a, t) = 0 \qquad (0 < t < \infty) \tag{d}$$

$$u(\rho, 0) = f(\rho) \qquad (0 < \rho < a). \tag{e}$$

Expansion coefficients may be left in integral form. *Note:* Although we do not specify $u(0, t)$, we do ask that it be *finite*.

21. (*Uniqueness*) (a) Consider the problem

$$\alpha^2 u_{xx} = u_t + f(x,t) \qquad (0 < x < \ell, 0 < t < T) \tag{a}$$

$$u(0,t) = p(t), \quad u(\ell,t) = q(t), \quad u(x,0) = r(x), \tag{b}$$

where T is arbitrarily large. To establish the *uniqueness* of the solution, suppose that $u_1(x,t)$ and $u_2(x,t)$ are two solutions, and define

$$w(x,t) = u_1(x,t) - u_2(x,t). \tag{c}$$

Show that w satisfies the "homogenized" problem

$$\begin{aligned} &\alpha^2 w_{xx} = w_t \qquad (0 < x < \ell, 0 < t < T) \\ &w(0,t) = 0, \quad w(\ell,t) = 0, \quad w(x,0) = 0. \end{aligned} \tag{d}$$

Proceeding formally, show that

$$\frac{d}{dt}\int_0^\ell w^2\,dx = 2\int_0^\ell ww_t\,dx = 2\alpha^2\int_0^\ell ww_{xx}\,dx. \tag{e}$$

Integrating the last integral by parts, and then integrating both sides of the equation on t from 0 to t, show that

$$\int_0^\ell w^2(x,t)\,dx = -\alpha^2\int_0^t\int_0^\ell w_x^2(x,\tau)\,dx\,d\tau. \tag{f}$$

Explain why it follows from (f) that $w(x,t) = 0$ throughout $0 < x < \ell$, $0 < t < T$. Thus it must be true that $u_1(x,t) = u_2(x,t)$ for any solutions u_1 and u_2, so that the solution to (a) and (b) must be unique.
(b) Repeat part (a), but change $u(\ell,t) = q(t)$ in equation (b) to $u_x(\ell,t) = q(t)$.
(c) Establish the uniqueness of the solution to the problem

$$\alpha^2 u_{xx} = u_t + f(x,t) \qquad (0 < x < \ell, 0 < t < T) \tag{g}$$

$$u(0,t) = p(t), \quad u(\ell,t) + \beta u_x(\ell,t) = q(t), \quad u(x,0) = r(x), \tag{h}$$

where T is arbitrarily large and $\beta > 0$, following essentially the same lines as in part (a).

22. (*Existence of steady state*) Having encountered steady-state solutions in the examples and exercises, we wish to stress, here, that *a steady state does not necessarily exist*. To illustrate, consider the problem

$$\alpha^2 u_{xx} = u_t + F(x) \qquad (0 < x < \ell, 0 < t < \infty)$$

$$u_x(0,t) = a, \quad u_x(\ell,t) = b, \quad u(x,0) = f(x).$$

Show that a steady state does not exist unless a certain condition is satisfied by a, b and $F(x)$. Assuming that the condition is satisfied, solve for the steady state $u_s(x)$; do so *directly*, not by solving for $u(x,t)$ and letting t tend to ∞. (A *general* consideration of this point would involve the so-called *Fredholm alternative*.)

14.3 USE OF STURM–LIOUVILLE THEORY PREREQUISITE: SECTION 10.6

[Optional Section]

In Section 14.2 we found that the final step of the separation-of-variables solution involved the expansion of a given function, and in each of the problems encountered we were able to get by by identifying the needed expansion as a classical Fourier series. In the present section we wish to show that the expansion process can be formalized within the Sturm–Liouville theory, and that the Sturm–Liouville approach also enables us to handle problems in which the classical Fourier series is inadequate. These two ideas are developed in the two examples to follow.

EXAMPLE 1 As our first example, we reconsider the conduction problem

$$\alpha^2 u_{xx} = u_t \qquad (0 < x < \ell, 0 < t < \infty) \tag{1a}$$

$$u_x(0,t) = 0 \qquad (0 < t < \infty) \tag{1b}$$

$$u(\ell,t) = u_0 \qquad (0 < t < \infty) \tag{1c}$$

$$u(x,0) = f(x) \qquad (0 < x < \ell), \tag{1d}$$

which was Example 2 in the preceding section. We suggest that you reread that example, especially the comment at the end, in which we draw attention to the solution form

$$u(x, t) = u_s(x) + X(x)T(t). \tag{2}$$

This form will be favored in the present section, over the alternative form $u(x, t) = X(x)T(t)$, for reasons that will be indicated later.

Thus, we begin by seeking the steady-state solution $u_s(x)$, which is to satisfy the problem

$$\alpha^2 u_s''(x) = 0; \qquad u_s'(\ell) = 0, \quad u_s(\ell) = u_0. \tag{3}$$

It is easily found, from (3), that $u_s(x) = u_0$, so that (2) becomes

$$u(x, t) = u_0 + X(x)T(t). \tag{4}$$

Next, we put (4) into (1a) and carry out the usual separation process, obtaining the ODEs

$$X'' + \kappa^2 X = 0, \tag{5a}$$

$$T' + \kappa^2 \alpha^2 T = 0, \tag{5b}$$

on X and T. Solving these yields

$$X = \begin{cases} A \cos \kappa x + B \sin \kappa x, & \kappa \neq 0 \\ C + Dx, & \kappa = 0 \end{cases} \tag{6a}$$

and

$$T(t) = \begin{cases} Ee^{-\kappa^2\alpha^2 t}, & \kappa \neq 0 \\ F, & \kappa = 0. \end{cases} \tag{6b}$$

Actually, the contribution $XT = (C + Dx)F$ from $\kappa = 0$ can be omitted since it is already accounted for by the $u_s(x)$ term. Thus (4) becomes

$$\begin{aligned} u(x, t) &= u_0 + (A \cos \kappa x + B \sin \kappa x)(Ee^{-\kappa^2\alpha^2 t}) \\ &= u_0 + (G \cos \kappa x + H \sin \kappa x)e^{-\kappa^2\alpha^2 t}, \end{aligned} \tag{7}$$

and by imposing (1b) and (1c) we arrive at

$$u(x, t) = u_0 + \sum_{n=1,3,\dots}^{\infty} G_n \cos \frac{n\pi x}{2\ell}\, e^{-(n\pi\alpha/2\ell)^2 t}. \tag{8}$$

Finally, (1d) requires that the G_n's be chosen so that

$$f(x) = u_0 + \sum_{n=1,3,\dots}^{\infty} G_n \cos \frac{n\pi x}{2\ell} \tag{9}$$

or, equivalently,

$$f(x) - u_0 = \sum_{n=1,3,\dots}^{\infty} G_n \cos \frac{n\pi x}{2\ell} \qquad (0 < x < \ell). \tag{10}$$

Two important questions arise. First, given $f(x)$ on $0 < x < \ell$, is (10) *possible*, i.e., can $f(x) - u_0$ be represented by the cosine expansion on the right-hand side? Second, if the representation is possible, how do we compute the G_n's?

Before answering these questions, let us impose the boundary conditions (1b) and (1c) on $u(x, t)$, as given by (4):

$$u_x(0, t) = 0 = u_s'(0) + X'(0)T(t) \qquad (0 < t < \infty), \tag{11a}$$

$$u(\ell, t) = 20 = u_s(\ell) + X(\ell)T(t) \qquad (0 < t < \infty). \tag{11b}$$

Recalling the boundary conditions $u_s'(0) = 0$ and $u_s(\ell) = 20$, given in (3), it follows from (11) that either $X'(0) = X(\ell) = 0$ or $T(t) = 0$. As the less restrictive of these choices, we choose $X'(0) = X(\ell) = 0$. If, in addition, we recall (5a), then the full problem on X is

$$X'' + \kappa^2 X = 0; \qquad X'(0) = 0, \quad X(\ell) = 0, \tag{12}$$

where κ^2 is not yet known and needs to be chosen so that the homogeneous system (12) admits nontrivial solutions. But (12) is precisely a *Sturm–Liouville problem,* as studied in Section 10.6, where "λ" $= \kappa^2$. The eigenfunctions of (12) are

$$\phi_n(x) = \cos\frac{n\pi x}{2\ell} \qquad (n = 1, 3, \ldots). \tag{13}$$

Thus (10) is really an *eigenfunction expansion,* i.e., an expansion of $f(x) - u_0$ in terms of the ϕ_n eigenfunctions of (12). According to Section 10.6, such an expansion is indeed possible if $f(x) - u_0$ and its first derivative are piecewise continuous on $[0, \ell]$ (Theorem 4, page 501). Furthermore, the "weight function $r(x)$" in the inner product is seen, from (12), to be unity, so that

$$G_n = \frac{\langle f(x) - u_0, \cos(n\pi x/2\ell)\rangle}{\langle \cos(n\pi x/2\ell), \cos(n\pi x/2\ell)\rangle} = \frac{\int_0^\ell [f(x) - u_0]\cos(n\pi x/2\ell)\,dx}{\int_0^\ell \cos^2(n\pi x/2\ell)\,dx} \tag{14}$$

or

$$G_n = \frac{2}{\ell}\int_0^\ell [f(x) - u_0]\cos\frac{n\pi x}{2\ell}\,dx. \tag{15}$$

Thus the solution of (1) is given by (8), with the G_n expansion coefficients computed from (15). This solution is in agreement with the corresponding solution to Example 2 in Section 14.2.

COMMENT 1 Observe how the needed Sturm–Liouville problem is "built right in": to cope with the expansion (10) in the x variable, we back up to the $X(x)$ problem and find that it is a Sturm–Liouville problem, the eigenfunctions of which are precisely the $\cos(n\pi x/2\ell)$ functions in (10).

COMMENT 2 Why did we make a point of including the $u_s(x)$ term explicitly in (2)? The purpose of $u_s(x)$ was to handle any nonhomogeneous boundary conditions so that the boundary conditions on $X(x)$ would be homogeneous, as required in the Sturm–Liouville theory. Specifically, whereas u satisfies the nonhomogeneous boundary condition $u(\ell, t) = u_0$, X satisfies the "homogenized" condition $X(\ell) = 0$. ◀

EXAMPLE 2 Consider the problem

$$\alpha^2 u_{xx} = u_t \qquad (0 < x < \ell,\ 0 < t < \infty) \tag{16a}$$

$$u(0, t) = 50 \qquad (0 < t < \infty) \tag{16b}$$

$$u(\ell, t) + 2u_x(\ell, t) = 20 \qquad (0 < t < \infty) \tag{16c}$$

$$u(x, 0) = f(x) \qquad (0 < x < \ell) \tag{16d}$$

in which we call attention to (16c), which is a boundary condition of the third kind (page 599) and which will prove to be a source of difficulty.

As in Example 1, we seek

$$u(x, t) = u_s(x) + X(x)T(t). \tag{17}$$

The steady-state solution $u_s(x)$ satisfies the problem

$$\alpha^2 u_s''(x) = 0; \qquad u_s(0) = 50, \quad u_s(\ell) + 2u_s'(\ell) = 20, \tag{18}$$

and is easily found to be

$$u_s(x) = 50 - \frac{30}{\ell + 2}x. \tag{19}$$

Continuing as in Example 1, we arrive at

$$u(x, t) = 50 - \frac{30}{\ell + 2}x + (G\cos\kappa x + H\sin\kappa x)e^{-\kappa^2\alpha^2 t}. \tag{20}$$

Then (16b) gives $0 = G\exp(-\kappa^2\alpha^2 t)$, so that $G = 0$. Updating (20) accordingly yields

$$u(x, t) = 50 - \frac{30}{\ell + 2}x + H\sin\kappa x\, e^{-\kappa^2\alpha^2 t}. \tag{21}$$

Next, (16c) gives

$$H(\sin\kappa\ell + 2\kappa\cos\kappa\ell)e^{-\kappa^2\alpha^2 t} = 0, \tag{22}$$

so that the characteristic equation on κ is

$$\sin\kappa\ell + 2\kappa\cos\kappa\ell = 0, \tag{23}$$

the solutions of which may be computed numerically and will be denoted as $\kappa = z_1, z_2, \ldots$ (Example 4, page 504). Then, by superposition, we express

$$u(x, t) = 50 - \frac{30}{\ell + 2}x + \sum_{n=1}^{\infty} H_n \sin z_n x\, e^{-z_n^2\alpha^2 t}. \tag{24}$$

Finally, (16d) requires that

$$f(x) = 50 - \frac{30}{\ell + 2}x + \sum_{n=1}^{\infty} H_n \sin z_n x \qquad (0 < x < \ell) \tag{25}$$

or, equivalently,

$$f(x) - 50 + \frac{30}{\ell + 2}x = \sum_{n=1}^{\infty} H_n \sin z_n x \qquad (0 < x < \ell). \tag{26}$$

It is to be stressed that the right-hand side of (26) is *not* of classical Fourier series form because the frequencies z_n in $\sin z_n x$ are not of the form "$n\pi/\ell$" (Fig. 10.18, page 505); i.e., they are not integer multiples of some fundamental frequency. This complication can be traced to (16c), which is a boundary condition of the third kind. Thus, without the Sturm–Liouville theory, we would truly be stuck at this point.

Observing that the expansion (25) is in the x variable, we go back to the X problem, namely,

$$X'' + \kappa^2 X = 0; \qquad X(0) = 0, \quad X(\ell) + 2X'(\ell) = 0. \tag{27}$$

The latter is a Sturm–Liouville problem, the eigenfunctions of which are

$$\phi_n(x) = \sin z_n x \qquad (n = 1, 2, \ldots). \tag{28}$$

Since the weight function is unity, we may therefore compute the H_n's as

$$H_n = \frac{\langle f(x), \sin z_n x\rangle}{\langle \sin z_n x, \sin z_n x\rangle} = \frac{\int_0^\ell \left[f(x) - 50 + \frac{30}{\ell + 2}x\right] \sin z_n x \, dx}{\int_0^\ell \sin^2 z_n x \, dx} \tag{29}$$

or

$$H_n = \frac{4z_n}{2z_n\ell - \sin 2z_n\ell} \int_0^\ell \left[f(x) - 50 + \frac{30}{\ell + 2}x\right] \sin z_n x \, dx. \tag{30}$$

Thus our solution to (16) is given by (24) and (30), where the z_n's are the positive roots of (23). ◀

In summary, the Sturm–Liouville theory is a powerful tool in handling the expansions that arise in solving PDEs by separation of variables. If the needed expansion is of the form

$$F(x) = \sum_{n=1}^{\infty} H_n \phi_n(x) \qquad (a < x < b), \tag{31}$$

say, then one needs to go back to the $X(x)$ problem to be sure that it is indeed of Sturm–Liouville form and to identify the weight function "$r(x)$" needed in the inner product. With this accomplished, one can then compute the desired expansion coefficients in (31) as

$$H_n = \frac{\langle F(x), \phi_n(x)\rangle}{\langle \phi_n(x), \phi_n(x)\rangle} = \frac{\int_a^b F(x)\phi_n(x) r(x)\, dx}{\int_a^b \phi_n^2(x) r(x)\, dx} \tag{32}$$

(where we have assumed here, as usual, that the ϕ_n's are real valued).

The method is by no means limited to the diffusion equation. We will use it for the Laplace and wave equations, as well, in subsequent chapters.

14.3 EXERCISES

Solve the following problems using the method developed in this section. It may be assumed that f and f' are piecewise continuous over the relevant interval. Expansion coefficients may be left in integral form [as in (14) and (29)] when the function to be expanded is not specified. If the characteristic equation is too difficult to solve analytically, merely note that and proceed as though the roots were in hand, as we have done in Example 2.

1. $\alpha^2 u_{xx} = u_t$ $(0 < x < \ell, 0 < t < \infty)$, with these boundary and initial conditions:

(a) $u(0, t) = u_1$, $u(\ell, t) = u_2$, $u(x, 0) = f(x)$
(b) $u_x(0, t) = u_x(\ell, t) = 10$, $u(x, 0) = 0$
(c) $u(0, t) = u_0$, $u_x(\ell, t) = 0$, $u(x, 0) = f(x)$
*(d) $u(0, t) = 50$, $u(\ell, t) + u_x(\ell, t) = 50$, $u(x, 0) = 0$

2. $\alpha^2 u_{xx} = u_t + hu$ $(0 < x < \ell, 0 < t < \infty)$, with these boundary and initial conditions:

*(a) $u(0, t) = 0$, $u(\ell, t) = 200$, $u(x, 0) = f(x)$
(b) $u_x(0, t) = u_x(\ell, t) = 5$, $u(x, 0) = f(x)$
(c) $u(0, t) = 0$, $u(\ell, t) + 2u_x(\ell, t) = 0$, $u(x, 0) = f(x)$
(d) $u(0, t) = 30$, $u_x(\ell, t) = 0$, $u(x, 0) = f(x)$

3. $\alpha^2[u_{\rho\rho} + (2/\rho)u_\rho] = u_t$ $(0 < \rho < a, 0 < t < \infty)$, with these boundary and initial conditions:

*(a) $u(a, t) = u_0$, $u(\rho, 0) = f(\rho)$
(b) $u(a, t) + au_\rho(a, t) = 0$, $u(\rho, 0) = f(\rho)$
(c) $u_\rho(a, t) = 0$, $u(\rho, 0) = f(\rho)$ *Hint:* See Exercise 20 on page 604.

4. $u_{xx} = u_t + 2u_x$ $(0 < x < \ell, 0 < t < \infty)$, with these boundary and initial conditions:

(a) $u(0, t) = 0$, $u(\ell, t) = 0$, $u(x, 0) = f(x)$
(b) $u_x(0, t) = 0$, $u(\ell, t) = 0$, $u(x, 0) = f(x)$
Hint: Recall that in solving the diffusion equation $u_{xx} = u_t$ by separation of variables we have invariably considered the cases $\kappa \neq 0$ and $\kappa = 0$ separately. In this exercise, however, one finds that $\kappa = 1$ needs to be treated separately, rather than $\kappa = 0$.

14.4 INFINITE AND SEMI-INFINITE REGIONS; FOURIER AND LAPLACE TRANSFORMS

[Optional Section]

In Sections 14.2 and 14.3 the x domain was always finite, namely, $0 < x < \ell$. Semi-infinite and infinite domains are also of fundamental interest, and it is these cases that we address in this section.

For definiteness, we will continue to consider the diffusion phenomenon to be the diffusion of heat by conduction.

EXAMPLE 1 *Heat Conduction in an Infinite Rod.* Let us begin with the problem

$$\alpha^2 u_{xx} = u_t \qquad (-\infty < x < \infty, 0 < t < \infty) \tag{1a}$$

$$u(x, 0) = f(x) \qquad (-\infty < x < \infty). \tag{1b}$$

If we regard the infinite rod as the limiting case of a finite rod, on $-\ell < x < \ell$, as $\ell \to \infty$, and recall that boundary conditions are needed for the finite rod, we might well anticipate that some form of boundary conditions may be needed for the infinite rod at $x = \pm\infty$. But since a suitable form for those boundary conditions may not yet be apparent, let us defer that issue for the moment, in the hope that the solution process may provide a clue.

In selecting a solution technique, we observe that our separation-of-variables method will work only if $f(x)$ is periodic with some finite period, so that f can be expanded in a Fourier series. However, our interest in this example is in functions such as $f(x) = e^{-|x|}$, which are not representable by Fourier series but which *are* representable by Fourier integrals. This fact suggests seeking a solution for u in Fourier integral form or, equivalently, using a Fourier transform.

Thus, Fourier transforming (1a) with respect to x,

$$\alpha^2 \int_{-\infty}^{\infty} \frac{\partial^2 u}{\partial x^2} e^{-i\omega x}\, dx = \int_{-\infty}^{\infty} \frac{\partial u}{\partial t} e^{-i\omega x}\, dx \tag{2}$$

or

$$\alpha^2 \left[\frac{\partial u}{\partial x} e^{-i\omega x} \Big|_{-\infty}^{\infty} + i\omega \int_{-\infty}^{\infty} \frac{\partial u}{\partial x} e^{-i\omega x}\, dx \right] = \frac{d}{dt} \int_{-\infty}^{\infty} u(x, t) e^{-i\omega x}\, dx. \tag{3}$$

Noting that $| e^{-i\omega x} | = | \cos \omega x - i \sin \omega x | = \sqrt{\cos^2 \omega x + \sin^2 \omega x} = 1$ for all x, let us require the *boundary condition* $\partial u/\partial x \to 0$ as $x \to \pm\infty$. Then the boundary term drops out, and (3) becomes

$$\alpha^2 i\omega \int_{-\infty}^{\infty} \frac{\partial u}{\partial x} e^{-i\omega x}\, dx = \frac{d}{dt} \hat{u}. \tag{4}$$

Integrating by parts once more gives us

$$\alpha^2 i\omega \left[u e^{-i\omega x} \Big|_{-\infty}^{\infty} + i\omega \int_{-\infty}^{\infty} u e^{-i\omega x}\, dx \right] = \frac{d}{dt} \hat{u}, \tag{5}$$

and if we require the additional *boundary condition* $u \to 0$ as $x \to \pm\infty$, then (5) becomes*

$$\frac{d}{dt} \hat{u} = -\alpha^2 \omega^2 \hat{u}. \tag{6}$$

Notice that the result of Fourier transforming on x has been to eliminate x derivatives from the PDE, leaving an ordinary differential equation with respect to t, namely, equation (6). Solving (6), we obtain

$$\hat{u} = A e^{-\alpha^2 \omega^2 t}. \tag{7}$$

To evaluate the integration constant A, we impose the initial condition (1b) or, rather, the Fourier transform of (1b):

$$\hat{u} \,|_{t=0} = \hat{f}(\omega) = (A e^{-\alpha^2 \omega^2 t}) \,|_{t=0} = A, \tag{8}$$

so $A = \hat{f}(\omega)$, and (7) becomes

$$\hat{u}(\omega, t) = \hat{f}(\omega) e^{-\alpha^2 \omega^2 t}. \tag{9}$$

Finally, using item 9 in Appendix B and the Fourier convolution property (item 20 in appendix B), it follows from (9) that

$$u(x, t) = f(x) * \frac{1}{2\alpha\sqrt{\pi t}} e^{-x^2/(4\alpha^2 t)} \tag{10}$$

or

$$u(x, t) = \frac{1}{2\alpha\sqrt{\pi t}} \int_{-\infty}^{\infty} f(\xi) e^{-(x-\xi)^2/(4\alpha^2 t)}\, d\xi. \tag{11}$$

* Actually, we could have proceeded from (1) to (6) directly by recalling property F2 on page 527, but chose to include the steps for pedagogical reasons.

COMMENT 1 Our derivation of (11) has only been heuristic. Specifically, we have assumed the truth of the statement

$$\int_{-\infty}^{\infty} \frac{\partial}{\partial t} u(x, t)e^{-i\omega x}\, dx = \frac{d}{dt} \int_{-\infty}^{\infty} u(x, t)e^{-i\omega x}\, dx \tag{12}$$

in going from the right-hand side of (2) to the right-hand side of (3), whereas the interchange in the order of differentiation and integration can be rigorously justified only if the integrand $u(x, t)e^{-i\omega x}$ is a sufficiently well-behaved function of x and t. With the tentative solution (11) in hand we could, in principle, now go back to that step and examine $u(x, t)e^{-i\omega x}$ to see if it is indeed sufficiently well behaved. However, we suggest that it is generally best to proceed heuristically until a tentative solution is in hand, as we have done, and then to see under what restrictions that tentative solution satisfies all the requirements—namely, the PDE plus whatever initial and boundary conditions were imposed. In the present example that verification would amount to finding conditions of f such that the right-hand side of (11) satisfies (1a) and (1b).* In fact, we choose to omit the rigorous justification of (11) since that step would lie a bit beyond our present scope. But we can at least check (11) for any simple special cases that are available to us.

The simplest case that comes to mind is

$$f(x) = \text{constant} \equiv F, \tag{13}$$

for then it is obvious that the solution to (1) is simply $u(x, t) = F$. In fact, setting $f(\xi) = F$ in (11) and evaluating the integral, we *do* obtain $u(x, t) = F$ (Exercise 1). Thus observe that (11) turns out to be even more powerful than we had any right to expect, for if $f(x) = F$, then $\hat{f}(\omega)$, in (9), *does not even exist;* also, the solution $u(x, t) = F$ violates the assumption that $u \to 0$ as $x \to \pm\infty$.†

COMMENT 2 As another special case, consider

$$f(x) = \begin{cases} F, & x > 0 \\ 0, & x < 0 \end{cases} = FH(x), \tag{14}$$

where F is a constant and $H(x)$ is the Heaviside function. In this case we find (Exercise 2) that

$$u(x, t) = \frac{F}{2}\left[1 + \operatorname{erf}\left(\frac{x}{2\alpha\sqrt{t}}\right)\right], \tag{15}$$

where

$$\boxed{\operatorname{erf}(z) = \frac{2}{\sqrt{\pi}} \int_0^z e^{-\zeta^2}\, d\zeta} \tag{16}$$

* By the way, regarding (1b), notice that the right-hand side of (11) is not even *defined* for $t = 0$. Thus what we really intended by (1b) was the condition

$$\lim_{t\to 0+} u(x, t) = f(x),$$

as mentioned earlier, in the footnote on page 588.

† The greater-than-expected applicability of (11) can be traced to the Fourier convolution step, and is discussed briefly on p. 535 of M. Greenberg, *Foundations of Applied Mathematics* (Englewood Cliffs, N.J.: Prentice-Hall, 1978).

is an important special function known as the **error function**. That is, the integral in (16) arises frequently in applications, yet it cannot be evaluated in terms of the so-called elementary functions. Thus it is given its own name, the "error function"; its properties, computational formulas, and tabulated values can be found in the literature.* The factor $2/\sqrt{\pi}$ is included in (16) so as to "normalize" the error function, so that [recall Exercise 13 on page 552]

$$\text{erf}\,(\infty) = \frac{2}{\sqrt{\pi}}\int_0^\infty e^{-\zeta^2}\,d\zeta = \frac{2}{\sqrt{\pi}}\left(\frac{\sqrt{\pi}}{2}\right) = 1.$$

The graph of erf (z) is shown in Fig. 14.7 for $z > 0$; for $z < 0$, we rely on the fact that the error function is an odd function (Exercise 5), so that erf $(-z) = -$erf (z).

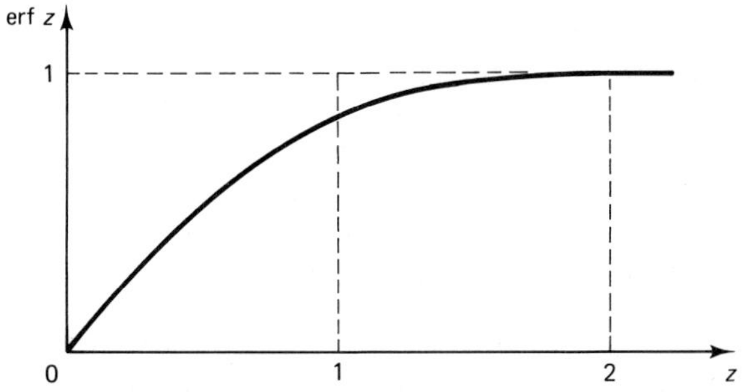

Fig. 14.7 The error function, erf(z).

Besides the integral from 0 to z, in (16), we also encounter the integral from z to ∞ so frequently that we define the **complementary error function** erfc (z) as

$$\begin{aligned}\text{erfc}(z) &= \frac{2}{\sqrt{\pi}}\int_z^\infty e^{-\zeta^2}\,d\zeta = \text{erf}\,(\infty) - \text{erf}\,(z)\\ &= 1 - \text{erf}\,(z).\end{aligned} \tag{17}$$

The solution (15) is sketched in Fig. 14.8. Note carefully that whereas $u(x, 0)$ is discontinuous (at $x = 0$), $u(x, t)$ is continuous for all x, and for all $t > 0$. (In fact, it is an infinitely differentiable function of x for all $t > 0$.) This result illustrates the fact the diffusion is a *smoothing process*.

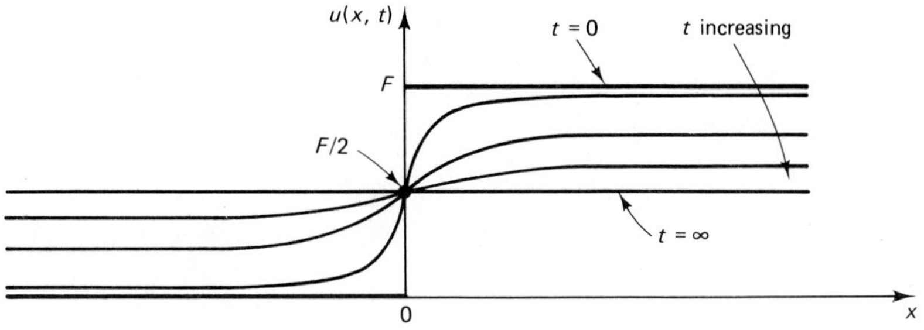

Fig. 14.8 The solution (15), for $u(x, 0) = FH(x)$.

* See, for example, M. Abramowitz and I. Stegun (eds.), National Bureau of Standards Applied Mathematics Series, 1964, or Y. L. Luke, *Mathematical Functions and Their Approximation* (New York: Academic Press, 1975).

COMMENT 3 It is instructive to write (11) in the form

$$u(x, t) = \int_{-\infty}^{\infty} f(\xi) U(\xi - x, t)\, d\xi, \tag{18}$$

where

$$U(\xi - x, t) = \frac{e^{-(\xi - x)^2/(4\alpha^2 t)}}{2\alpha\sqrt{\pi t}} \tag{19}$$

is called the *kernel,* and comprises everything in the integrand other than the input f. $U(\xi - x, t)$ happens to be a so-called *normal* (or *Gaussian*) *distribution* centered at $\xi = x$ (which correctly suggests that diffusion may somehow be an essentially statistical phenomenon). The area between its graph and the ξ axis is unity for all t (Exercise 3), and its graph becomes more and more focused as $t \to \infty$ (Fig. 14.9). In fact, $U(\xi - x, t)$ is a *delta sequence* at x as $t \to 0+$, so that

$$\lim_{t \to 0+} \int_{-\infty}^{\infty} f(\xi) U(\xi - x, t)\, d\xi = f(x), \tag{20}$$

which is precisely the required initial condition. This situation, where the solution is obtained as an integral over boundary or initial data, and where the kernel of that integral can be identified as a delta sequence, is common for PDEs, and will be pointed out for the Laplace equation as well.

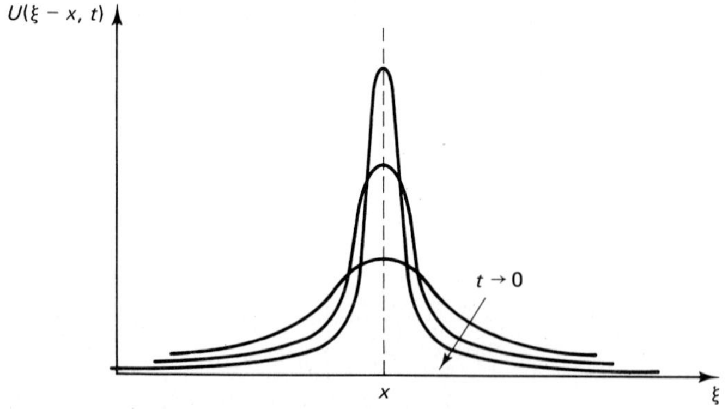

Fig. 14.9 The delta-sequence behavior of $U(\xi - x, t)$ as $t \to 0$.

COMMENT 4 For a more physical interpretation of the kernel U, suppose that we let f be a delta function,

$$f(x) = \delta(x - x_0). \tag{21}$$

In a rough way, this case may be conceptualized as resulting from the application of a welding torch to the rod at x_0 for a brief instant. Then (18) gives

$$\begin{aligned} u(x, t) &= \int_{-\infty}^{\infty} \delta(\xi - x_0) U(\xi - x, t)\, d\xi \\ &= U(x_0 - x, t) = U(x - x_0, t), \end{aligned} \tag{22}$$

where the last equality follows from the fact that U is seen from (19) to be a symmetric function of its first argument. Thus $U(x - x_0, t)$ *may be regarded, physically, as the temperature response to a δ-function input at* $x = x_0$ *and* $t = 0$. Considering that the temperature distribution is a δ-function spike at $t = 0$, we can see from Fig. 14.9 that the solution proceeds to "mellow out," as it is said, as t increases. This mellowing out is a key feature of the diffusion process.

COMMENT 5 As an additional observation about the physics, we note that information spreads, by diffusion, with an *infinite velocity*. For example, in Fig. 14.8 we see that some of the heat initially limited to $0 < x < \infty$ diffuses to $-\infty < x < 0$ for any arbitrarily small time t; this can occur only if the speed of propagation is infinite. Since it is held that energy cannot progagate faster than the speed of light, this result evidently exposes a defect in our diffusion equation model, one that is addressed in the literature,* and which is regarded as inconsequential in practical applications.

COMMENT 6 Finally, we mention that in place of a Fourier transform on x we could have applied a Laplace transform on t to the problem (1). This approach is deferred to Exercise 4. ◀

As promised, our second (and last) example involves conduction in a *semi-infinite* rod.

EXAMPLE 2 *Heat Conduction in a Semi-infinite Rod.* Here we consider the problem

$$\alpha^2 u_{xx} = u_t \qquad (0 < x < \infty,\ 0 < t < \infty) \tag{23a}$$

$$u(0, t) = h(t) \qquad (0 < t < \infty) \tag{23b}$$

$$u(x, 0) = 0 \qquad (0 < x < \infty), \tag{23c}$$

where $h(t)$ is prescribed. Since both the x and t intervals are semi-infinite, we entertain the possibilities of Laplace transforming on x or on t. If we Laplace transform on x, the transform of u_{xx} in (23a) will lead to two boundary terms, one involving $u(0, t)$, the other involving $u_x(0, t)$. Of these, the former is prescribed but the latter is not. Thus we turn to the possibility of transforming on t. In this case, the transform of the u_t term will give rise only to a $u(x, 0)$ term, which data are indeed prescribed by (23c).

Thus, anticipating success, we Laplace transform (23a) on t:

$$\int_0^\infty \alpha^2 u_{xx} e^{-st}\, dt = \int_0^\infty u_t e^{-st}\, dt \tag{24}$$

or

$$\begin{aligned} \alpha^2 \frac{d^2\bar{u}}{dx^2} &= u(x, t)e^{-st}\Big|_{t=0}^{t=\infty} + s\int_0^\infty u e^{-st}\, dt \\ &= s\bar{u} - u(x, 0) = s\bar{u}, \end{aligned} \tag{25}$$

* See, for example, P. M. Morse and H. Feshbach, *Methods of Theoretical Physics,* Part I (New York: McGraw-Hill, 1953), pp. 865–869.

where the step

$$\int_0^\infty \frac{\partial^2 u(x, t)}{\partial x^2} e^{-st}\, dt = \frac{d^2}{dx^2} \int_0^\infty u(x, t) e^{-st}\, dt \tag{26}$$

was undertaken heuristically, in the same spirit as in Example 1. Thus

$$\frac{d^2\overline{u}}{dx^2} - \frac{s}{\alpha^2}\overline{u} = 0,$$

so

$$\overline{u} = Ae^{\sqrt{s}x/\alpha} + Be^{-\sqrt{s}x/\alpha}. \tag{27}$$

We have already used the condition (23c) [in (25)], and have only the left end condition (23b) remaining to determine the two integration constants A and B. It appears that we are in need of a right end condition (at $x = \infty$) as well. In view of the initial condition $u(x, 0) = 0$, it seems reasonable to impose the boundary condition

$$u(x, t) \to 0 \text{ as } x \to \infty \qquad (0 < t < \infty) \tag{28}$$

or, in terms of $\overline{u}$,

$$\begin{aligned} \lim_{x\to\infty} \overline{u} &= \lim_{x\to\infty} \int_0^\infty u(x, t) e^{-st}\, dt \\ &= \int_0^\infty \lim_{x\to\infty} u(x, t) e^{-st}\, dt = \int_0^\infty 0\, dt = 0. \end{aligned} \tag{29}$$

Here the step

$$\lim_{x\to\infty} \int_0^\infty u(x, t) e^{-st}\, dt = \int_0^\infty \lim_{x\to\infty} u(x, t) e^{-st}\, dt \tag{30}$$

was undertaken heuristically.

Imposing (29) (namely, $\overline{u} \to 0$ as $x \to \infty$) on (27) gives $A = 0$, so that

$$\overline{u} = Be^{-\sqrt{s}x/\alpha}. \tag{31}$$

Finally, from the transform of (23b),

$$\overline{u}\,|_{x=0} = \overline{h}(s) = Be^0, \tag{32}$$

so that $B = \overline{h}(s)$ and

$$\overline{u}\,(x, s) = \overline{h}(s) e^{-\sqrt{s}x/\alpha}. \tag{33}$$

To invert, we use item 22 in Appendix C and the Laplace convolution property (item 28 in Appendix C) to obtain

$$\begin{aligned} u(x, t) &= h(t) * \frac{x e^{-x^2/(4\alpha^2 t)}}{2\alpha\sqrt{\pi} t^{3/2}} \\ &= \frac{x}{2\alpha\sqrt{\pi}} \int_0^t h(t - \tau) \frac{e^{-x^2/(4\alpha^2\tau)}}{\tau^{3/2}}\, d\tau \end{aligned} \tag{34}$$

or, equivalently,

$$u(x, t) = \frac{x}{2\alpha\sqrt{\pi}} \int_0^t h(\tau) \frac{e^{-x^2/[4\alpha^2(t-\tau)]}}{(t - \tau)^{3/2}} \, d\tau. \tag{35}$$

COMMENT Observe from (35) how $u(x, t)$ depends on the boundary data $h(\tau)$ only over $0 < \tau < t$, *not* over $0 < \tau < \infty$. This result is entirely reasonable since it would certainly be strange if the temperature distribution today depended, in any way, on the left end condition that will be imposed tomorrow. ◀

In this section we obtained the solution to two important problems: the infinite rod with specified initial temperature [(1a) and (1b)], and the semi-infinite rod with specified left end temperature [(23a) to (23c)]. Their solutions are given by (11) and (35), respectively.

Regarding the physics, we observed that diffusion is a smoothing process and that the propagation speed is infinite. Mathematically, we used these examples to explore the use of the Fourier and Laplace transforms in solving PDEs, and we met the important error function, erf (x). Transform methods will also be used to solve certain Laplace and wave problems in Chapters 15 and 16.

14.4 EXERCISES

1. It was stated, following (13), that if $f(x)$ = constant = F, the solution to (1) is simply $u(x, t) = F$. Verify that our solution (11) does indeed give that result by working out the integral. *Hint:* You may use the known integral

$$\int_{-\infty}^{\infty} e^{-x^2} \, dx = \sqrt{\pi}.$$

2. Show that if $f(x)$ is given by (14), the solution (15) can be obtained by working out the integral in (11).

3. It was stated, following (19), that $\int_{-\infty}^{\infty} U(\xi - x, t) \, d\xi = 1$ for all t. Verify that claim by actually working out the integral. *Hint:* Same hint as in Exercise 1.

4. (a) Integrating (35) for the case where $h(t)$ = constant = u_1, show that

$$u(x, t) = u_1 \operatorname{erfc}\left(\frac{x}{2\alpha\sqrt{t}}\right). \tag{a}$$

(b) If the initial condition (23c) is changed to $u(x, 0)$ = constant = u_0, show that

$$u(x, t) = u_0 + (u_1 - u_0) \operatorname{erfc}\left(\frac{x}{2\alpha\sqrt{t}}\right). \tag{b}$$

5. Show, from (16), that erf $(-z) = -$erf (z).

6. Use (11) to show that if $f(x)$ is

(a) periodic with period τ, then so is $u(x, t)$ a periodic function of x with period τ

(b) an odd function of x, then so is $u(x, t)$ an odd function of x

(c) an even function of x, then so is $u(x, t)$ an even function of x

7. Show that if there exists a function $C(t)$ such that $|u(x, t)| \le C(t)$ for all x in an interval I (such as $0 < x < \infty$ or $-\infty < x < \infty$), then $|\bar{u}(x, s)| \le \bar{C}(s)$ for all x in I. That is, if $u(x, t)$ is a bounded function of x, in I, for each t, then $\bar{u}(x, s)$ is, likewise, a bounded function of x in I.

8. We used a Fourier transform on x to solve the infinite-rod problem (1). Solve it, instead, by using a Laplace transform on t, for the case where

*(a) $f(x) = \sin x$

(b) $f(x) = a_0 + \Sigma_{n=1}^{\infty} \left(a_n \cos \frac{n\pi x}{L} + b_n \sin \frac{n\pi x}{L}\right)$

Hint: By way of boundary conditions at $x = \pm\infty$, ask that $u(x, t)$ be a bounded function of x on $-\infty < x < \infty$, for all $t > 0$, and use the result stated in Exercise 7.

9. (a) Applying the Fourier transform to the problem

$$\alpha^2 u_{xx} = u_t - F(x) \qquad (-\infty < x < \infty, 0 < t < \infty)$$
$$u(x, 0) = f(x) \qquad (-\infty < x < \infty),$$

derive the result

$$u(x, t) = \frac{1}{2\alpha\sqrt{\pi t}} \int_{-\infty}^{\infty} f(x - \xi) e^{-\xi^2/(4\alpha^2 t)} \, d\xi + F(x) * \mathbf{F}^{-1}\left\{\frac{1 - e^{-\alpha^2\omega^2 t}}{\alpha^2\omega^2}\right\}. \tag{a}$$

(b) Show that

$$\mathbf{F}^{-1}\left\{\frac{1 - e^{-\alpha^2\omega^2 t}}{\alpha^2\omega^2}\right\} = \frac{1}{\alpha}\sqrt{\frac{t}{\pi}}\, e^{-x^2/(4\alpha^2 t)} + \frac{x}{2\alpha^2} \operatorname{erfc}\left(\frac{x}{2\alpha\sqrt{t}}\right), \tag{b}$$

so that

$$u(x, t) = \frac{1}{2\alpha\sqrt{\pi t}} \int_{-\infty}^{\infty} f(x - \xi) e^{-\xi^2/(4\alpha^2 t)} \, d\xi + \frac{1}{\alpha}\int_{-\infty}^{\infty} F(x - \xi)\left[\sqrt{\frac{t}{\pi}}\, e^{-\xi^2/(4\alpha^2 t)} + \frac{\xi}{2\alpha}\operatorname{erfc}\left(\frac{\xi}{2\alpha\sqrt{t}}\right)\right] d\xi. \tag{c}$$

Hint: Letting $\hat{g} = (1 - e^{-\alpha^2\omega^2 t})/\alpha^2\omega^2$, show that $\hat{g}_t = e^{-\alpha^2\omega^2 t} = \hat{g}_t$, so that $g_t = \{\exp[-x^2/(4\alpha^2 t)]\}/(2\alpha\sqrt{\pi t})$, with $g|_{t=0} = 0$. Thus

$$g(x, t) = \int_0^t \frac{e^{-x^2/(4\alpha^2\tau)}}{2\alpha\sqrt{\pi\tau}} \, d\tau.$$

Then use change of variables and integration by parts.

10. (a) Applying the Laplace transform to the finite-rod problem,

$$\alpha^2 u_{xx} = u_t \qquad (0 < x < \ell, 0 < t < \infty)$$
$$u(0, t) = u(x, 0) = 0, \quad u(\ell, t) = g(t),$$

derive the result

$$u(x, t) = g(t) * \mathbf{L}^{-1}\left\{\frac{\sinh(\sqrt{s}\, x/\alpha)}{\sinh(\sqrt{s}\, \ell/\alpha)}\right\}. \tag{a}$$

(b) Although the Laplace inverse, needed in equation (a), is not found in Appendix C, let us do the best we can. Specifically, observe that if $g(t) = 1$, the problem is easily solved by separation of variables, as discussed in Section 14.2. Let the solution $u(x, t)$ corresponding to the simple case $g(t) = 1$ be denoted as $h(x, t)$, and regarded as known. (You need not find it.) Then, denoting

$$\mathbf{L}^{-1}\left\{\frac{\sinh(\sqrt{s}\, x/\alpha)}{\sinh(\sqrt{s}\, \ell/\alpha)}\right\} = F(x, t), \tag{b}$$

show from $h(x, t) = 1 * F(x, t)$ that $F(x, t) = h_t(x, t)$, so that

$$u(x, t) = \int_0^t g(t - \tau) h_\tau(x, \tau) \, d\tau. \tag{c}$$

11. (a) Applying the Laplace transform to the problem

$$\alpha^2 u_{xx} = u_t \qquad (0 < x < \infty, 0 < t < \infty)$$
$$u_x(0, t) = -Q, \quad u(x, 0) = 0,$$
$$u(x, t) \to 0 \quad \text{as} \quad x \to \infty,$$

where Q is a prescribed constant, derive the result

$$u(x, t) = \alpha Q \int_0^t \frac{e^{-x^2/(4\alpha^2\tau)}}{\sqrt{\pi\tau}} \, d\tau. \tag{a}$$

(b) Show that equation (a) can be reduced to the form

$$u(x, t) = Q\left[2\alpha\sqrt{\frac{t}{\pi}}\, e^{-x^2/(4\alpha^2 t)} + x \operatorname{erfc}\left(\frac{x}{2\alpha\sqrt{t}}\right)\right], \tag{b}$$

and evaluate the temperature history at the left end, $u(0, t)$.

12. (*Viscous flow due to oscillating plate*) Let a viscous fluid extending over $-\infty < x < \infty$, $0 < y < \infty$, $-\infty < z < \infty$ rest on an infinite horizontal flat plate at $y = 0$, and suppose that the plate is oscillated horizontally with amplitude X_0 and frequency ω. Then the x component of the fluid velocity, $u(y, t)$, satisfies the equation of motion and boundary conditions

$$\nu \frac{\partial^2 u}{\partial y^2} = \frac{\partial u}{\partial t} \qquad (0 < y < \infty, 0 < t < \infty)$$
$$u(y, t) \to 0 \quad \text{as} \quad y \to \infty$$
$$u(0, t) = \omega X_0 \cos \omega t,$$

where the constant ν is the kinematic viscosity of the fluid. (An initial condition is not specified because we seek the steady-state motion.) Derive the solution

$$u(y, t) = \omega X_0 e^{-ry} \cos(\omega t - ry) \qquad \left(r = \sqrt{\frac{\omega}{2\nu}}\right).$$

Hint: Use separation of variables, $u(y, t) = Y(y)T(t)$, or seek $u(y, t) = A(y) \cos \omega t + B(y) \sin \omega t$.

13. (*Small-t solution for finite rod*) In Example 1 of Section 14.2 we obtained, by separation of variables, the solution

$$u(x, t) = \frac{400}{\pi} \sum_{n=1,3,\dots}^{\infty} \frac{1}{n} \sin \frac{n\pi x}{\ell} e^{-(n\pi\alpha/\ell)^2 t} \qquad \text{(a)}$$

to the problem of heat conduction in a rod of length ℓ initially at a uniform temperature $u(x, 0) = 100°$, with both ends held subsequently at 0°. It was pointed out that (a) is very rapidly convergent if t is large and very slowly convergent if t is small. Our object in this exercise is to show how to use the results obtained in this section to obtain the reverse: a series solution that *converges rapidly for small t* (and slowly for large t). First, we recall from the discussion in Section 14.2 that solving the stated finite-rod problem, on $0 < x < \ell$, is equivalent to solving the periodically extended *infinite*-rod problem

$$\alpha^2 u_{xx} = u_t \qquad (-\infty < x < \infty, 0 < t < \infty) \qquad \text{(b)}$$

$$u(x, 0) = f_{\text{ext}}(x), \qquad \text{(c)}$$

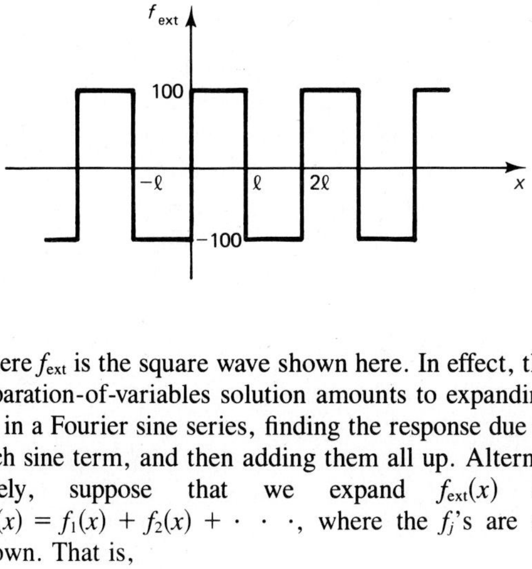

where f_{ext} is the square wave shown here. In effect, the separation-of-variables solution amounts to expanding f_{ext} in a Fourier sine series, finding the response due to each sine term, and then adding them all up. Alternatively, suppose that we expand $f_{\text{ext}}(x)$ as $f_{\text{ext}}(x) = f_1(x) + f_2(x) + \cdots$, where the f_j's are as shown. That is,

$$\begin{aligned} f_{\text{ext}}(x) = {} & \{-100 + 200[H(x) - H(x - \ell)]\} \\ & + 200\{H(x + 2\ell) - H(x + \ell) \\ & + H(x - 2\ell) - H(x - 3\ell)\} \qquad \text{(d)} \\ & + 200\{H(x + 4\ell) - H(x + 3\ell) \\ & + H(x - 4\ell) - H(x - 5\ell)\} + \cdots. \end{aligned}$$

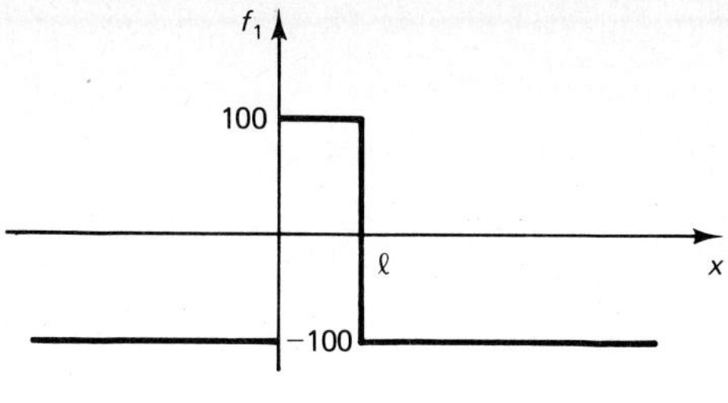

(a)

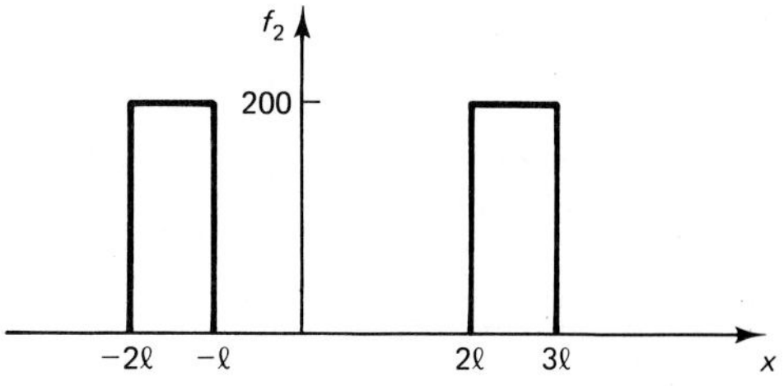

(b)

(a) Recalling (14) and (15), show that the responses to $f_1, f_2, \ldots$ are

$$u_1(x, t) = 100\left[\operatorname{erf}\left(\frac{x}{2\alpha\sqrt{t}}\right) - \operatorname{erf}\left(\frac{x - \ell}{2\alpha\sqrt{t}}\right) - 1\right] \qquad \text{(e)}$$

and

$$\begin{aligned} u_j(x, t) = {} & 100\left\{\operatorname{erf}\left(\frac{x + 2j\ell}{2\alpha\sqrt{t}}\right) - \operatorname{erf}\left[\frac{x + (2j - 1)\ell}{2\alpha\sqrt{t}}\right]\right. \\ & \left. + \operatorname{erf}\left(\frac{x - 2j\ell}{2\alpha\sqrt{t}}\right) - \operatorname{erf}\left[\frac{x - (2j + 1)\ell}{2\alpha\sqrt{t}}\right]\right\}, \qquad \text{(f)} \end{aligned}$$

for $j \geq 2$.

(b) Explain, in simple physical terms, why the series solution

$$u(x, t) = u_1(x, t) + u_2(x, t) + \cdots \qquad \text{(g)}$$

should converge extremely rapidly for small t.

(c) To illustrate, compute $u(x, t)$ at $x = 1$, $t = 0.1$, with $\alpha^2 = 1.14$ and $\ell = 10$, using equation (a), and again, using equation (g). Two-significant-figure accuracy will suffice. *Note:* To compute the error function, we suggest that you use the following approximate formula developed by C. Hastings, Jr.:

$$\operatorname{erf}(x) = 1 - (a_1 q + a_2 q^2 + a_3 q^3)e^{-x^2}$$

$$q = \frac{1}{1 + px}, \qquad p = 0.47047,$$

$$a_1 = 0.3480242, \qquad (h)$$

$$a_2 = -0.0958798, \qquad a_3 = 0.7478556,$$

which is accurate, over $0 \le x < \infty$, to $\pm 2.5 \times 10^{-5}$. Also, recall that erf $(-x) = -\text{erf}\,(x)$. [Formula (h) is called a *rational approximation,* because $e^{x^2}[1 - \text{erf}\,(x)]$ is being approximated by a *rational function* of x, i.e., the ratio of two polynomials, as can be seen by combining the terms in $a_1 q + a_2 q^2 + a_3 q^3$ over a common denominator. Such approximations are now available for many of the functions of practical interest, and many of these have been developed by Hastings. See, for example, M. Abramowitz and I. Stegun (eds.), National Bureau of Standards and Applied Mathematics Series, 1964; or Y. L. Luke, *Mathematical Functions and Their Approximation* (New York: Academic Press, 1975).]

14.5 NUMERICAL SOLUTION

The solution techniques developed thus far—separation of variables and integral transforms—are described as "analytical" since one proceeds to a symbolic solution, such as

$$u(x, t) = \frac{400}{\pi} \sum_{n=1,3,\ldots}^{\infty} \frac{1}{n} \sin \frac{n\pi x}{\ell}\, e^{-(n\pi\alpha/\ell)^2 t}, \qquad (1)$$

without having to do any numerical computation. It is true that a digital computer may be needed in the end, to sum the series in (1), but the overall solution is still predominantly analytical.

Also available are solution techniques which are predominantly *numerical*, and which are normally carried out with the help of high-speed computers. These techniques complement analytical techniques in their ability to cope with problems that may be far too difficult to solve analytically. In fact, the study of the numerical solution of ordinary and partial differential equations has grown with the computer over the past 30 or so years and is now an indispensable tool in science and engineering. Although this text is aimed primarily at analytical solution procedures, it is important to at least introduce the broad domain of numerical methods as well.

In this section we introduce one of the most important techniques for the numerical solution of PDEs, the **finite difference method**. To do so, we consider the representative problem

$$\alpha^2 u_{xx} = u_t \qquad (0 < x < \ell,\ 0 < t < \infty) \qquad (2a)$$

$$u(0, t) = g(t), \quad u(\ell, t) = h(t), \quad u(x, 0) = f(x). \qquad (2b)$$

Our first step is to *discretize* the problem so that we seek $u(x, t)$ not over the entire x, t domain, but only at discrete "grid points" x_j, t_k. That is, we divide ℓ into N equal parts, of dimension $\Delta x = \ell/N$, and define $x_j = j\,\Delta x$, for $j = 0, 1, \ldots, N$. Further, we select a time increment Δt, and define $t_k = k\,\Delta t$, for $k = 0, 1, 2, \ldots$. The resulting grid is shown in Fig. 14.10.

Next, we seek a finite-difference approximation of the PDE (2a) that will relate the values of u at the various grid points. For the u_t term, we use the usual difference quotient approximation

$$\frac{\partial u}{\partial t}(x, t) = \lim_{\Delta t \to 0} \frac{u(x, t + \Delta t) - u(x, t)}{\Delta t} \approx \frac{u(x, t + \Delta t) - u(x, t)}{\Delta t}. \qquad (3)$$

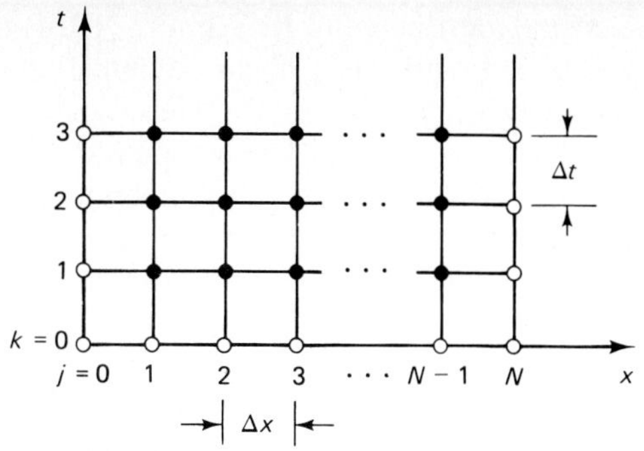

Fig. 14.10 The computational grid.

Treating the u_{xx} term in the same manner, we write

$$\frac{\partial^2 u}{\partial x^2}(x, t) = \frac{\partial}{\partial x}\left(\frac{\partial u}{\partial x}\right) \approx \frac{\dfrac{\partial u}{\partial x}(x + \Delta x, t) - \dfrac{\partial u}{\partial x}(x, t)}{\Delta x}$$

$$\approx \frac{\dfrac{u(x + \Delta x, t) - u(x, t)}{\Delta x} - \dfrac{u(x, t) - u(x - \Delta x, t)}{\Delta x}}{\Delta x}, \tag{4}$$

so

$$\frac{\partial^2 u}{\partial x^2} \approx \frac{u(x + \Delta x, t) - 2u(x, t) + u(x - \Delta x, t)}{(\Delta x)^2}. \tag{5}$$

Putting (3) and (5) into (2a), with $x = x_j$, $x + \Delta x = x_{j+1}$, $x - \Delta x = x_{j-1}$, $t = t_k$, and $t + \Delta t = t_{k+1}$, gives

$$\alpha^2 \frac{u(x_{j+1}, t_k) - 2u(x_j, t_k) + u(x_{j-1}, t_k)}{(\Delta x)^2} \approx \frac{u(x_j, t_{k+1}) - u(x_j, t_k)}{\Delta t}. \tag{6}$$

From (6) and the foregoing discussion, it seems reasonable to adopt the equation

$$\alpha^2 \frac{U_{j-1,k} - 2U_{j,k} + U_{j+1,k}}{(\Delta x)^2} = \frac{U_{j,k+1} - U_{j,k}}{\Delta t} \tag{7}$$

as our *finite-difference approximation* of the original PDE (2a). Solving for $U_{j,k+1}$ yields

$$\boxed{U_{j,k+1} = rU_{j-1,k} + (1 - 2r)U_{j,k} + rU_{j+1,k},} \tag{8}$$

where

$$r \equiv \alpha^2 \frac{\Delta t}{(\Delta x)^2}. \tag{9}$$

Equation (8) provides a "marching scheme" whereby we can march out a solution, one line at a time, subject to the initial and boundary conditions

$$U_{j,0} = f(j\,\Delta x) \equiv f_j \qquad (j = 1, 2, \ldots, N - 1) \tag{10a}$$

$$U_{0,k} = g(k\,\Delta t) \equiv g_k \qquad (k = 1, 2, \ldots) \tag{10b}$$

$$U_{N,k} = h(k\,\Delta t) \equiv h_k \qquad (k = 1, 2, \ldots). \tag{10c}$$

Generally attributed to E. Schmidt (1924) and L. Binder (1911), (8) gives us U, at a given grid point, as a linear combination of U's at the preceding time, as denoted schematically in Fig. 14.11. Thus, beginning at the initial time ($k = 0$), we can use (8) [together with (10)] to compute U all along the line $k = 1$, then along the line $k = 2$, and so on. That is, we "march out" the solution in finite time steps. Furthermore, since the weight factors r, $1 - 2r$, r add up to unity, the right-hand side of (8) evidently amounts to an x-wise averaging of the U values at the preceding time, as seen most clearly for $r = \frac{1}{2}$, in which case the right-hand side is simply $(U_{j+1,k} + U_{j-1,k})/2$. This averaging is at the heart of the diffusion process and is in line with our earlier observation about the "smoothing" nature of diffusion (page 613).

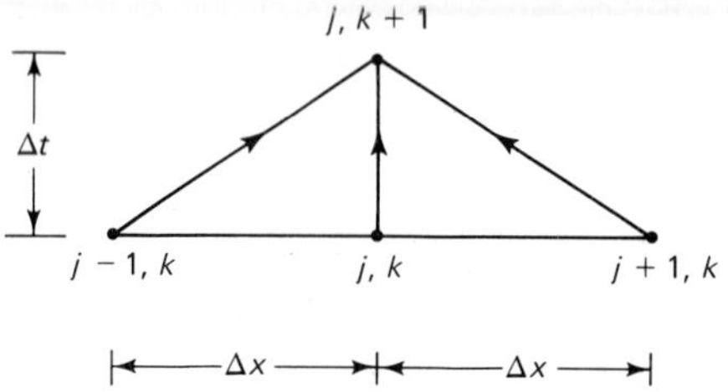

Fig. 14.11 Schematic of (8).

A small problem arises in applying (8). Specifically, in computing $U_{1,1} = rU_{0,0} + (1 - 2r)U_{1,0} + rU_{2,0}$ we need to know the temperature $U_{0,0}$ prescribed at the corner $x = 0$, $t = 0$. If $f(0) = g(0)$, it certainly seems reasonable to set $U_{0,0} = f(0) = g(0)$, but if $f(0) \neq g(0)$, should we set $U_{0,0} = f(0)$? $g(0)$? $[f(0) + g(0)]/2$? Reviewing Comment 1 on page 595, it seems clear that the effect of the corner temperature on the solution should tend to zero as Δx and Δt tend to zero. However, Δx and Δt are *finite* in (8), and $U_{0,0}$ (also the other corner temperature, $U_{N,0}$) *will* affect the generated solution. Thus the question is: What is the *best* way to choose $U_{0,0}$ and $U_{N,0}$? Here we will adopt a simple average,

$$U_{0,0} \equiv \frac{f(0+) + g(0+)}{2}, \tag{11a}$$

$$U_{N,0} = \frac{f(\ell-) + h(0+)}{2}, \tag{11b}$$

although a more accurate choice is given in Exercise 2.

To be sure that the use of (8) is clear, suppose that $g(t) = h(t) = 0$, $f(x) = 100$, $\ell = 1$, $\alpha^2 = 1$, and choose $\Delta x = \frac{1}{4}$, $\Delta t = \frac{1}{80}$, say. Then $r = \alpha^2 \Delta t/(\Delta x)^2 = 0.2$, so we compute, in turn,

$$U_{1,1} = 0.2U_{0,0} + 0.6U_{1,0} + 0.2U_{2,0} = 10 + 60 + 20 = 90, \tag{12a}$$

$$U_{2,1} = 0.2U_{1,0} + 0.6U_{2,0} + 0.2U_{3,0} = 20 + 60 + 20 = 100, \tag{12b}$$

$$U_{3,1} = 0.2U_{2,0} + 0.6U_{3,0} + 0.2U_{4,0} = 20 + 60 + 10 = 90, \tag{12c}$$

$$U_{1,2} = 0.2U_{0,1} + 0.6U_{1,1} + 0.2U_{2,1} = 0 + 54 + 20 = 74, \tag{12d}$$

$$U_{2,2} = 0.2U_{1,1} + 0.6U_{2,1} + 0.2U_{3,1} = 18 + 60 + 18 = 96, \tag{12e}$$

$$U_{3,2} = 0.2U_{2,1} + 0.6U_{3,1} + 0.2U_{4,1} = 20 + 54 + 0 = 74, \tag{12f}$$

and so on. Actually, the calculations (12c) and (12f) were unnecessary because of the obvious symmetry about $x = \ell/2$.

Of course, $\Delta x = \frac{1}{4}$ gives a rather coarse grid, yet the foregoing results are fairly accurate (Exercise 1). If, instead, we divide ℓ into 50 parts, then $\Delta x = 0.02$. Letting $\Delta t = 0.00018$, say, then $r = 0.00018/(0.02)^2 = 0.45$. Turning the calculation over to the computer, the results are shown as dots in Fig. 14.12, and compared with the exact solution (solid curves)

$$u(x, t) = \frac{400}{\pi} \sum_{n=1,3,\dots}^{\infty} \frac{1}{n} \sin n\pi x \, e^{-(n\pi)^2 t}, \tag{13}$$

after 20, 100, and 300 time steps. They are seen to be quite accurate.

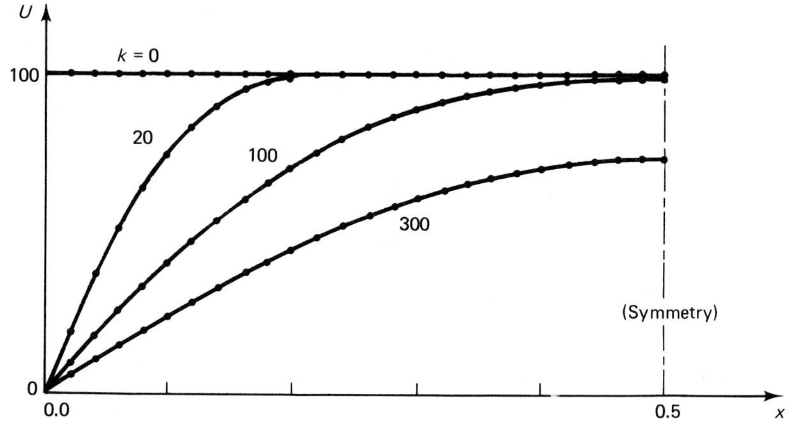

Fig. 14.12 Application of (8), for the case $g(t) = h(t) = 0$, $f(x) = 100$, $\ell = 1$, $\alpha^2 = 1$, $\Delta x = 0.02$, $\Delta t = 0.00018$ $(r = 0.45)$.

Observe that we have used different letters (lowercase and uppercase) in order to distinguish carefully between the exact solution $u(x, t)$ of the PDE (2a) and the approximating solution $U_{j,k}$ generated by the finite-difference equation (8). We call the difference $u(x_j, t_k) - U_{j,k}$ the **discretization error**, at the j, k grid point, since it is the error incurred by virtue of the approximations (3) and (5). As a matter of fact, besides the discretization error there is an additional error incurred because the computer rounds off after a finite number of significant figures. Thus if we further distinguish $U_{j,k}$ as the values computed by a "perfect computer" (i.e., one that maintains an infinite number of significant figures), and $U_{j,k}^*$ as the actual printout of a "real computer," it is fruitful to express the total error as

$$\begin{aligned} \text{total error} &= u(x_j, t_k) - U_{j,k}^* \\ &= [u(x_j, t_k) - U_{j,k}] + [U_{j,k} - U_{j,k}^*] \\ &\equiv \text{discretization error} + \text{round-off error}. \end{aligned} \tag{14}$$

Thus two major concerns come into focus. First, we could like the discretization error, at each fixed x, t point in the domain, to tend to zero as Δx and $\Delta t \to 0$. If it does, we say the finite-difference scheme is **convergent**. Regarding the round-off error, we will be satisfied if it merely remains bounded, i.e., if it does not grow unboundedly. If it does remain bounded, we say the scheme is **stable**.

It is of obvious practical importance to be able to ascertain whether or not a proposed finite-difference scheme—such as (8)—is convergent and stable. There exists a powerful theorem, known as the *Lax equivalence theorem,* which states that under rather broad conditions *convergence is necessary and sufficient for stability.*†
In that case it suffices to examine only one or the other.

Examining (8) for stability, say, as outlined in Exercise 4, it is found that the scheme is *stable* if

$$r \leq \frac{1}{1 - \cos\left(\dfrac{N-1}{N}\pi\right)}, \tag{15}$$

and unstable otherwise. [If N is large, (15) is essentially the condition $r \leq \frac{1}{2}$.] For the calculation displayed in Fig. 14.12 we chose $N = 50$, so for stability (and convergence) we needed $r \leq 0.50049$. Since we had $r = 0.45$, all was well. However, notice that once we decided on $N = 50$ (so that $\Delta x = 0.02$), we then needed Δt to be exceedingly small in order to keep r less than 0.50049. For example, increasing Δt merely to 0.00022 gives $r = 0.55$, which value violates the stability criterion (15). Sure enough, the results are seen (Fig. 14.13) to oscillate wildly and to diverge from the exact solution.

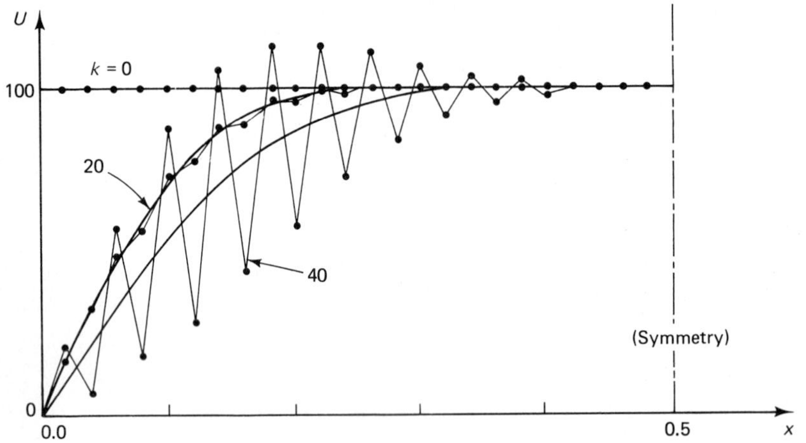

Fig. 14.13 Increasing r above 0.5: $\Delta x = 0.02$, $\Delta t = 0.00022$, and $r = 0.55$.

[Optional]
Thus the restriction (15) may be quite severe, for if Δx is chosen small, for the sake of accuracy, then the allowable Δt may be exceedingly tiny, thereby necessitating a great many time steps and considerable computer time. However, (8) is not the *only* possible finite-difference scheme for the heat equation. For example, observe that the x-wise differencing in (4) and (5) is at the initial time t, whereas we might expect some weighted average over the time interval (t to $t + \Delta t$) to be better, namely,

$$\frac{\partial^2 u}{\partial x^2} \approx (1-\theta)\,\frac{u(x+\Delta x,\ t) - 2u(x,\ t) + u(x-\Delta x,\ t)}{(\Delta x)^2} \tag{16}$$

$$+\ \theta\,\frac{u(x+\Delta x,\ t+\Delta t) - 2u(x,\ t+\Delta t) + u(x-\Delta x,\ t+\Delta t)}{(\Delta x)^2}.$$

† For proof and discussion of the Lax theorem, see R. Richtmeyer and K. Morton, *Difference Methods for Initial-Value Problems,* 2nd ed. (New York: Interscience, 1967).

Thus, in place of (7) we have

$$\alpha^2\left[(1-\theta)\frac{U_{j-1,k}-2U_{j,k}+U_{j+1,k}}{(\Delta x)^2}+\theta\frac{U_{j-1,k+1}-2U_{j,k+1}+U_{j+1,k+1}}{(\Delta x)^2}\right] = \frac{U_{j,k+1}-U_{j,k}}{\Delta t}, \tag{17}$$

which, of course, reduces to (7) if $\theta = 0$. It turns out that the parameter θ gives us the desired control. In particular, it can be shown (Exercise 5) that *if* $\theta \geq \frac{1}{2}$, *then (17) is stable (and convergent) for all* r, i.e., r no longer needs to be restricted by a condition such as (15). The borderline case $\theta = \frac{1}{2}$ yields the especially well-known **Crank-Nicolson** scheme,

$$-rU_{j-1,k+1} + 2(1+r)U_{j,k+1} - rU_{j+1,k+1} = rU_{j-1,k} + 2(1-r)U_{j,k} + rU_{j+1,k} \tag{18}$$

for $j = 1, \ldots, N-1$ and $k = 0, 1, 2, \ldots$, where $r = \alpha^2\,\Delta t/(\Delta x)^2$, as before. Inspecting (18), we see that the price we have paid for achieving stability for all r is that the equations (18) are *coupled* in the neighboring unknowns $U_{j+1,k+1}$, $U_{j,k+1}$, $U_{j-1,k+1}$. Thus we call (18) an **implicit** scheme, whereas (8) was an **explicit** scheme because it gave $U_{j,k+1}$ explicitly. Graphically, the Crank–Nicolson scheme (18) corresponds to the pattern shown in Fig. 14.14, which is to be compared with the one shown in Fig. 14.11.

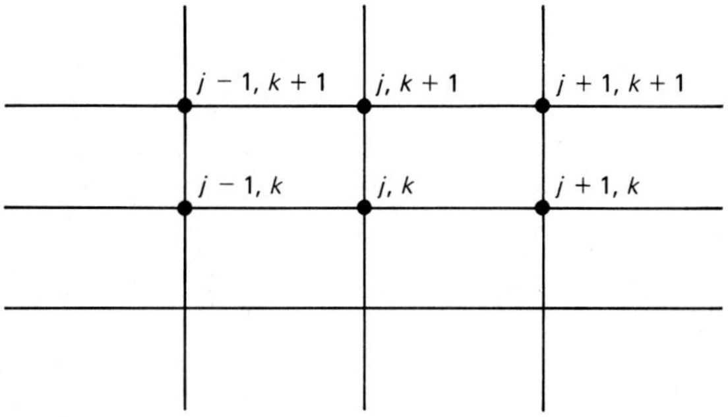

Fig. 14.14 Schematic of (18).

Expressing (18) in matrix form and recalling the boundary conditions $U_{0,k} = g(k\,\Delta t) = g_k$ and $U_{N,k} = h(k\,\Delta t) \equiv h_k$, we have

$$\begin{pmatrix} 2(1+r) & -r & & & \\ -r & 2(1+r) & -r & & \\ & & \ddots & & \\ & & -r & 2(1+r) & -r \\ & & & -r & 2(1+r) \end{pmatrix}\begin{pmatrix} U_{1,k+1} \\ U_{2,k+1} \\ \vdots \\ U_{N-2,k+1} \\ U_{N-1,k+1}\end{pmatrix} = \begin{pmatrix} rg_{k+1} + rg_k + 2(1-r)U_{1,k} + rU_{2,k} \\ rU_{1,k} + 2(1-r)U_{2,k} + rU_{3,k} \\ \vdots \\ rU_{N-3,k} + 2(1-r)U_{N-2,k} + rU_{N-1,k} \\ rh_{k+1} + rU_{N-2,k} + 2(1-r)U_{N-1,k} + rh_k \end{pmatrix}. \tag{19}$$

This system is of the form $\mathbf{AU}_{k+1} = \mathbf{c}$, where $\mathbf{A}$ is *tridiagonal* and *symmetric*. $\mathbf{A}$ and $\mathbf{c}$ are known and $\mathbf{U}_{k+1}$ is the unknown. The idea, then, is to set $k = 0$ and solve (19) for the entire "line" $U_{1,1}, U_{2,1}, \ldots, U_{N-1,1}$, then set $k = 1$ and solve (19) for the entire line $U_{1,2}, U_{2,2}, \ldots, U_{N-1,2}$, and so on.

Numerical implementation of the Crank–Nicolson scheme (19) will be left for the exercises, but there is an important point to be made here. Namely, although (19) can, of course, be solved by the powerful and standard method of Gauss elimination, an interesting and more efficient solution method is available because $\mathbf{A}$ happens to be strongly diagonal. By "strongly diagonal" we mean that all of the off-diagonal terms ($-r$'s and 0's) are small compared to the diagonal terms [$2(1 + r)$'s]. Thus let us split $\mathbf{A}$ into its diagonal part plus the deviation from that,

$$\mathbf{A} = \begin{pmatrix} 2(1+r) & & & & \\ & 2(1+r) & & \bigcirc & \\ & & \ddots & & \\ & \bigcirc & & 2(1+r) & \\ & & & & 2(1+r) \end{pmatrix} + \begin{pmatrix} 0 & -r & 0 & 0 & & \bigcirc \\ -r & 0 & -r & 0 & & \\ & & \ddots & & & \\ & \bigcirc & & -r & 0 & -r \\ & & & 0 & -r & 0 \end{pmatrix}$$

$$\equiv 2(1 + r)\mathbf{I} + \mathbf{A}', \tag{20}$$

say, where $\mathbf{A}'$ is the "deviation." Then $\mathbf{AU}_{k+1} = \mathbf{c}$ becomes

$$[2(1 + r)\mathbf{I} + \mathbf{A}']\mathbf{U}_{k+1} = \mathbf{c} \tag{21}$$

or

$$\mathbf{U}_{k+1} = \frac{1}{2(1 + r)}\mathbf{c} - \frac{1}{2(1 + r)}\mathbf{A}'\mathbf{U}_{k+1}. \tag{22}$$

Since the last term in (22) is small relative to the $\mathbf{U}_{k+1}$ on the left, we could simply neglect it and obtain

$$\mathbf{U}_{k+1} \approx \frac{1}{2(1 + r)}\mathbf{c}.$$

Better yet, we could accept this result as an initial approximation

$$\mathbf{U}_{k+1}^{(0)} = \frac{1}{2(1 + r)}\mathbf{c}, \tag{23}$$

and obtain an improved result as

$$\mathbf{U}_{k+1}^{(1)} = \frac{1}{2(1 + r)}\mathbf{c} - \frac{1}{2(1 + r)}\mathbf{A}'\mathbf{U}_{k+1}^{(0)}. \tag{24}$$

In fact, repeating this procedure, we have the **iterative** algorithm

$$\mathbf{U}_{k+1}^{(n+1)} = \frac{1}{2(1 + r)}[\mathbf{c} - \mathbf{A}'\mathbf{U}_{k+1}^{(n)}], \tag{25}$$

where $\mathbf{U}_{k+1}^{(n+1)}$ is the $(n + 1)$st iterate of $\mathbf{U}_{k+1}$. With k fixed, we carry out (25) for $n = 0, 1, 2, \ldots$ [where $\mathbf{U}_{k+1}^{(0)}$ is given by (23)], until suitable convergence is attained. For example, we might continue the iteration until each element of $\mathbf{U}_{k+1}^{(n+1)}$ and the corresponding element of $\mathbf{U}_{k+1}^{(n)}$ differ in magnitude by less than 10^{-5}, say.

The scheme given by (25) and (23) is called **Jacobi iteration,** and it is shown in Exercise 7 that Jacobi iteration converges to the exact solution of $\mathbf{AU}_{k+1} = \mathbf{c}$ for all finite values of r. In fact, we can improve upon (25), slightly, by using the $(n + 1)$st components as soon as they become available. To elaborate, let us write out the Jacobi scheme (25):

$$U_{1,k+1}^{(n+1)} = \frac{1}{2(1 + r)} [c_1 - a'_{1,1} U_{1,k+1}^{(n)} - \cdots - a'_{1,N-1} U_{N-1,k+1}^{(n)}]$$

$$U_{2,k+1}^{(n+1)} = \frac{1}{2(1 + r)} [c_2 - a'_{2,1} U_{1,k+1}^{(n)} - a'_{2,2} U_{2,k+1}^{(n)} - \cdots - a'_{2,N-1} U_{N-1,k-1}^{(n)}] \tag{26}$$

$$\vdots$$

$$U_{N-1,k+1}^{(n+1)} = \frac{1}{2(1 + r)} [c_{N-1} - a'_{N-1,1} U_{1,k+1}^{(n)} - a'_{N-1,N-2} U_{N-2,k+1}^{(n)} - a'_{N-1,N-1} U_{N-1,k+1}^{(n)}].$$

Having computed $U_{1,k+1}^{(n+1)}$ from the first equation in (26), we might as well use that value in place of the less-up-to-date value $U_{1,k+1}^{(n)}$ that appears in the right-hand side of the second equation. Similarly, we might as well use the already computed values $U_{1,k+1}^{(n+1)}$, $U_{2,k+1}^{(n+1)}$ in place of $U_{1,k+1}^{(n)}$, $U_{2,k+1}^{(n)}$ in the right-hand side of the third equation, and so on. This idea produces the **Gauss–Seidel** scheme

$$\mathbf{U}_{k+1}^{(n+1)} = \frac{1}{2(1 + r)} [\mathbf{c} - \mathbf{L}\mathbf{U}_{k+1}^{(n+1)} - \mathbf{M}\mathbf{U}_{k+1}^{(n)}], \tag{27}$$

where $\mathbf{L}$ and $\mathbf{M}$ are the lower and upper parts, respectively, of $\mathbf{A}'$. That is, $\mathbf{A}' = \mathbf{L} + \mathbf{M}$, where

$$\mathbf{L} = \begin{pmatrix} 0 & & & & \\ -r & 0 & & \bigcirc & \\ 0 & -r & 0 & & \\ & & & \ddots & \\ 0 & \cdot\cdot & 0 & -r & 0 \end{pmatrix} \quad \text{and} \quad \mathbf{M} = \begin{pmatrix} 0 & -r & 0 & 0 & \cdots & 0 & \\ & 0 & -r & 0 & \cdots & 0 & \\ & & 0 & -r & \cdots & 0 & \\ & \bigcirc & & & \ddots & & \\ & & & & & 0 & -r \\ & & & & & & 0 \end{pmatrix}$$

Like the Jacobi scheme, Gauss–Seidel converges to the solution for all finite r, but its *speed* of convergence is roughly twice as great as that of Jacobi.

Finally, there is still another simple improvement available to us that will further increase the speed of convergence. Reexpressing (27) as

$$\begin{aligned} \mathbf{U}_{k+1}^{(n+1)} &= \mathbf{U}_{k+1}^{(n)} + \frac{1}{2(1 + r)} \{\mathbf{c} - \mathbf{L}\mathbf{U}_{k+1}^{(n+1)} - [\mathbf{M} + 2(1 + r)\mathbf{I}]\mathbf{U}_{k+1}^{(n)}\} \\ &\equiv \mathbf{U}_{k+1}^{(n)} + \mathbf{\Delta U}_{k+1}^{(n)}, \end{aligned} \tag{29}$$

we insert a "control parameter" ω:

$$\mathbf{U}_{k+1}^{(n+1)} = \mathbf{U}_{k+1}^{(n)} + \omega \mathbf{\Delta U}_{k+1}^{(n)}. \tag{30}$$

The idea is general and can be applied to any iterative scheme: $\mathbf{\Delta U}_{k+1}^{(n)}$ is a "correction term," and adjusting the size of the correction, by means of ω, may substantially speed the convergence. Often, one chooses ω based on numerical experimentation, but in the present case it can be shown, analytically, that the optimum ω is given by

$$\omega_{\text{opt}} = \frac{2}{1 + \sqrt{1 - \mu^2}}, \quad \text{where} \quad \mu = \frac{r}{1 + r} \cos \frac{\pi}{N}. \tag{31}$$

It is clear, from (31), that ω_{opt} lies somewhere between 1 and 2. Since $\omega_{\text{opt}} > 1$, we call the modified Gauss–Seidel scheme **successive overrelaxation** or, for brevity, **SOR.** Representative Jacobi, Gauss–Seidel, and SOR calculations are included among the exercises.

In summary, we have seen that the *explicit* scheme (8) is simple (and easily programmed), but may require too many time steps to be practicable. The *implicit* Jacobi, Gauss–Seidel, and SOR methods are a bit more unwieldy to implement, but are more powerful in that they are stable for all finite values of r. This fact permits us to choose Δx and Δt based on considerations of accuracy and cost, without worrying about stability.

Since we could not even hint at all of the important applications of matrix theory in Part I, it is to be stressed here that matrix theory is the context within which the many important finite-difference methods exist. The eigenvalue problem, in particular, plays a prominent role, as is seen in several of the exercises to follow.

14.5 EXERCISES

1. (a) Continuing the calculations in (12), compute the $U_{j,k}$'s through $k = 4$.
(b) Compare $U_{1,4}$, $U_{2,4}$, $U_{3,4}$ with the exact values $u(0.25, 0.05)$, $u(0.5, 0.05)$, $u(0.75, 0.05)$, respectively, as computed from (13).

***2.** (*More accurate treatment of corner points*) Recall that to compute $U_{1,1}$ and $U_{3,1}$ by (12a) and (12c), respectively, we needed to know the corner temperatures $U_{0,0}$ and $U_{4,0}$. Although we adopted (11a) and (11b), for simplicity, it should be mentioned that a more rational procedure is available. Specifically, we recommend that in using (8) to solve the problem

$$\alpha^2 u_{xx} = u_t \qquad (0 < x < l, 0 < t < \infty)$$
$$u(0, t) = g(t), \quad u(l, t) = h(t), \quad u(x, 0) = f(x), \tag{a}$$

the temperatures $U_{1,1}$ and $U_{N-1,1}$ be found by solving the local "corner problems." That is, the 1, 1 nodal point is so close to the left-hand corner that the problem (a) might just as well be replaced by the simpler semi-infinite rod problem

$$\alpha^2 u_{xx} = u_t \qquad (0 < x < \infty, 0 < t < \infty)$$
$$u(0, t) = \text{constant} = g(0+), \tag{b}$$
$$u(x, 0) = \text{constant} = f(0+),$$

with the known solution (Exercise 4, page 617)

$$u(x, t) = f(0+) + [g(0+) - f(0+)] \operatorname{erfc}\left(\frac{x}{2\alpha\sqrt{t}}\right). \tag{c}$$

Thus we recommend computing $U_{1,1}$ as

$$U_{1,1} = f(0+) + [g(0+) - f(0+)] \operatorname{erfc}\left(\frac{\Delta x}{2\alpha\sqrt{\Delta t}}\right), \tag{d}$$

and similarly for $U_{N-1,1}$. We now state the problem: Returning to the calculation in (12), compute $U_{2,3}$, say, using (11), and once again using the idea proposed above. Then compare these two results with the exact solution, $u(0.5, 3/80)$, as computed from (13). *Note:* You will need to know the value erfc $(1.118) = 0.1139$.

3. (a) Run the finite-difference calculation displayed in Fig. 14.12 through 300 time steps.
(b) Run the finite-difference calculation displayed in Fig. 14.13 through 40 time steps.

4. (*Stability criterion for the explicit scheme*) Here we wish to derive the stability criterion (15). To begin, show that (8) can be expressed in matrix form as

$$\begin{pmatrix} U_{1,k+1} \\ U_{2,k+1} \\ \vdots \\ U_{N-2,k+1} \\ U_{N-1,k+1} \end{pmatrix} = \begin{pmatrix} 1-2r & r & & & \\ r & 1-2r & r & & 0 \\ & & \ddots & & \\ 0 & & r & 1-2r & r \\ & & & r & 1-2r \end{pmatrix} \begin{pmatrix} U_{1,k} \\ U_{2,k} \\ \vdots \\ U_{N-2,k} \\ U_{N-1,k} \end{pmatrix} + \begin{pmatrix} rU_{0,k} \\ 0 \\ \vdots \\ 0 \\ rU_{N,k} \end{pmatrix}, \tag{a}$$

or, more compactly,

$$\mathbf{U}_{k+1} = \mathbf{A}\mathbf{U}_k + \mathbf{c}_k. \tag{b}$$

Now, in stability analyses it is standard to assume that round-off errors occur only along the first line ($k = 0$), say, and then to see whether the errors remain bounded as k increases. [The idea of limiting the errors to one line seems reasonable since round-off enters randomly. Furthermore, the resulting criterion, (15), is borne out empirically.] Thus, in place of the *exact* values $\mathbf{U}_0$, $\mathbf{c}_0$, the initial round-off errors result in the *actual* values $\mathbf{U}_0^*$, $\mathbf{c}_0^*$. Accordingly, the machine proceeds to compute actual values $\mathbf{U}_{k+1}^*$ according to

$$\mathbf{U}_{k+1}^* = \mathbf{A}\mathbf{U}_k^* + \mathbf{c}_k^*, \tag{c}$$

rather than exact values $\mathbf{U}_{k+1}$ according to (b). Focusing on the round-off error, $\mathbf{e}_k \equiv \mathbf{U}_k - \mathbf{U}_k^*$, show that $\mathbf{e}_k$ propagates according to

$$\mathbf{e}_{k+1} = \mathbf{A}\mathbf{e}_k + \mathbf{b}_k, \tag{d}$$

where $\mathbf{b}_k \equiv \mathbf{c}_k - \mathbf{c}_k^*$. From (d) show that

$$\mathbf{e}_k = \mathbf{A}^k\mathbf{e}_0 + \mathbf{A}^{k-1}\mathbf{b}_0. \tag{e}$$

Show that the $(N-1) \times (N-1)$ matrix $\mathbf{A}$ must have $N-1$ orthogonal eigenvectors, say $\boldsymbol{\phi}_1, \ldots, \boldsymbol{\phi}_{N-1}$, so that $\mathbf{e}_0$ and $\mathbf{b}_0$ can be expressed in the form

$$\mathbf{e}_0 = \alpha_1\boldsymbol{\phi}_1 + \cdots + \alpha_{N-1}\boldsymbol{\phi}_{N-1} \tag{f}$$

$$\mathbf{b}_0 = \beta_1\boldsymbol{\phi}_1 + \cdots + \beta_{N-1}\boldsymbol{\phi}_{N-1}. \tag{g}$$

Thus show that (e) becomes

$$\mathbf{e}_k = (\alpha_1\lambda_1^k + \beta_1\lambda_1^{k-1})\boldsymbol{\phi}_1 + \cdots + (\alpha_{N-1}\lambda_{N-1}^k + \beta_{N-1}\lambda_{N-1}^{k-1})\boldsymbol{\phi}_{N-1}, \tag{h}$$

where $\lambda_1, \ldots, \lambda_{N-1}$ are the eigenvalues of $\mathbf{A}$. Deduce, from (h), that for stability it is necessary and sufficient that $|\lambda_1|, \ldots, |\lambda_{N-1}| \le 1$, and show that (15) follows. *Hint:* It is known that the "tridiagonal" $M \times M$ matrix

$$\begin{pmatrix} b & c & & & \\ a & b & c & & 0 \\ & a & b & c & \\ & & & \ddots & \\ 0 & & a & b & c \\ & & & a & b \end{pmatrix}$$

has eigenvalues

$$\lambda_n = b + 2\sqrt{ac}\cos\frac{n\pi}{M+1} \qquad (n = 1, 2, \ldots, M). \tag{i}$$

5. (*Stability of implicit scheme*) The stability of the implicit scheme (18) for all r (if $\theta \ge \frac{1}{2}$) is quite a striking result. Rather than study the stability of (18), it will suffice—for pedagogical purposes—to consider the simpler case of an *ordinary* differential equation. Specifically, consider the simple *test equation*

$$u_t = -Au, \tag{a}$$

where A is any prescribed positive constant, with the implicit finite-difference approximation

$$\frac{U_{k+1} - U_k}{\Delta t} = -(1-\theta)AU_k - \theta AU_{k+1}. \tag{b}$$

Following the same lines as in Exercise 4, show that the round-off error, $e_k \equiv U_k - U_k^*$, propagates according to

$$e_{k+1} = Ke_k, \qquad \text{(c)}$$

where

$$K = \frac{1 - A(1-\theta)\ \Delta t}{1 + A\theta\ \Delta t}. \qquad \text{(d)}$$

Thus show that the scheme (b) is stable if and only if

$$A(1 - 2\theta)\Delta t \le 2. \qquad \text{(e)}$$

Note: Suppose, first, that $\theta = 0$, so that the scheme is *explicit*. Then (e) tells us that we must choose $\Delta t < 2/A$. In *some* problems, such as occur in the study of the chemical kinetics, A can be enormously large. In that case $\Delta t < 2/A$ is a severe limitation that forces us to use exceedingly small time steps. Such systems are known as **stiff.** However, observe that if we use the *implicit* scheme and choose $\theta \ge \frac{1}{2}$, (e) is satisfied *with no restriction on* Δt.

***6.** Let $g(t) = h(t) = \sin t$, $f(x) = 0$, $\ell = 1$, and $\alpha^2 = 1$, and choose $\Delta x = 0.25$, and $\Delta t = \frac{1}{16}$. Carry out the Crank–Nicolson scheme (19) through $t = \frac{1}{8}$, i.e., through two time steps. *Hint:* Use the symmetry about $x = \ell/2$ to reduce (19) so that **A** is only 2×2, and solve by the inverse matrix method.

7. (*Convergence of Jacobi iteration*) Show that the Jacobi iteration, defined by (25) and (23), converges—for all finite r—to the solution of $\mathbf{AU}_{k+1} = \mathbf{c}$. *Hint:* Read through Exercise 4. Expand

$$\frac{1}{2(1+r)}\mathbf{c} = \sum_{j=1}^{N-1} c_j \boldsymbol{\phi}_j, \qquad \text{(a)}$$

where the $\boldsymbol{\phi}_j$'s are the eigenvectors of $[1/2(1+r)]\mathbf{A}'$. Show that

$$\mathbf{U}^{(n)} \to \sum_{j=1}^{N-1} \frac{c_j}{1+\lambda_j}\boldsymbol{\phi}_j = \sum_{j=1}^{N-1} \frac{c_j}{1 + \dfrac{r}{1+r}\cos\dfrac{j\pi}{N}}\boldsymbol{\phi}_j \qquad \text{(b)}$$

as $n \to \infty$, and verify that the right-hand side of (b) satisfies (21).

8. (*Neumann series*) Recall that the Taylor series

$$\frac{1}{1-t} = 1 + t + t^2 + t^3 + \cdots \qquad \text{(a)}$$

(better known as the *geometric series*) converges to $1/(1-t)$ *if* t is "small"—specifically, if $|t| < 1$. By analogy with this result, it seems reasonable to solve (21) by writing

$$\begin{aligned}\mathbf{U}_{k+1} &= (\mathbf{I} + \mathbf{B})^{-1}\mathbf{d} = (\mathbf{I} - \mathbf{B} + \mathbf{B}^2 - \cdots)\mathbf{d} \\ &= \mathbf{d} - \mathbf{Bd} + \mathbf{B}^2\mathbf{d} - \cdots,\end{aligned} \qquad \text{(b)}$$

where

$$\mathbf{B} \equiv \frac{1}{2(1+r)}\mathbf{A}' \quad \text{and} \quad \mathbf{d} \equiv \frac{1}{2(1+r)}\mathbf{c},$$

for brevity.

(a) Show that (b) is equivalent to the Jacobi iteration

$$\mathbf{U}_{k+1}^{(n+1)} = \mathbf{d} - \mathbf{BU}_{k+1}^{(n)}; \qquad \mathbf{U}_{k+1}^{(0)} = \mathbf{d}. \qquad \text{(c)}$$

(b) The right-hand side of the formula

$$(\mathbf{I} + \mathbf{B})^{-1} = \mathbf{I} - \mathbf{B} + \mathbf{B}^2 - \mathbf{B}^3 + \cdots \qquad \text{(d)}$$

is known as **Neumann series.** Suppose that **B** is real and symmetric (as occurs in this section). Then, show that the Neumann series converges if and only if all of the eigenvalues of **B** are smaller than unity in magnitude. *Hint:* Recall from Section 4.4 that we can write $\mathbf{B} = \mathbf{QDQ}^{-1}$, where **D** is diagonal. Hence $\mathbf{B}^2 = \mathbf{QDQ}^{-1}\mathbf{QDQ}^{-1} = \mathbf{QD}^2\mathbf{Q}^{-1}$, and so on.

9. Solve the problem

$$\begin{pmatrix} 1 & 0.1 & 0.1 \\ 0.1 & 1 & 0.1 \\ 0.1 & 0.1 & 1 \end{pmatrix}\begin{pmatrix} x_1 \\ x_2 \\ x_3 \end{pmatrix} = \begin{pmatrix} 1 \\ 1 \\ 1 \end{pmatrix}$$

by hand, using the Jacobi, Gauss–Seidel, and SOR (with $\omega = 1.2$, say) methods. Stop the iteration when $|x_j^{(n+1)} - x_j^{(n)}| < 0.0005$, say, for all j's ($j = 1, 2, 3$). What would the optimum ω be for the SOR case? (The answer can be seen by inspection.)

10. In (21), let $r = 1$, and for simplicity, let $\mathbf{c} = (1, 1, 1, 1)^{\mathrm{T}}$. (Thus N is 5.) Solve for $\mathbf{U}_{k+1}$ by the Jacobi, Gauss–Seidel, and SOR methods, terminating the iterations when $|U_{j,k+1}^{(n+1)} - U_{j,k+1}^{(n)}| < 0.0001$, say, for all j's ($j = 1, 2, 3, 4$). Tabulate the number of iterations needed for each method. For the SOR method, use $\omega = 1, 1.2, 1.4, 1.6, 1.8, 2$, and compare the optimum ω with that predicted by (31).

11. (*Use of Taylor series*) In deriving the finite-difference approximations (3) and (5), we used the classical difference quotient definition of the derivative, namely,

$$\frac{df}{dx}(x) = \lim_{\Delta x \to 0} \frac{f(x + \Delta x) - f(x)}{\Delta x}$$

$$\approx \frac{f(x + \Delta x) - f(x)}{\Delta x}. \tag{a}$$

In this exercise, we wish to reexamine (3) and (5) using *Taylor series* instead.

(a) Expanding

$$u(x, t + \Delta t) = u(x, t) + u_t(x, t)\,\Delta t + \frac{1}{2!} u_{tt}(x, t)(\Delta t)^2 + \cdots$$

$$\approx u(x, t) + u_t(x, t)\,\Delta t,$$

solve for $u_t(x, t)$ and show that the result is the same as in (3).

(b) Expanding

$$u(x + \Delta x, t)$$

$$= u(x, t) + u_x(x, t)\,\Delta x + \tfrac{1}{2} u_{xx}(x, t)(\Delta x)^2 + \cdots$$

$$\approx u(x, t) + u_x(x, t)\,\Delta x + \tfrac{1}{2} u_{xx}(x, t)(\Delta x)^2 \tag{b}$$

and

$$u(x - \Delta x, t) = u(x, t) + u_x(x, t)(-\Delta x) + \tfrac{1}{2} u_{xx}(x, t)(-\Delta x)^2 + \cdots$$

$$\approx u(x, t) - u_x(x, t)\,\Delta x + \tfrac{1}{2} u_{xx}(x, t)(\Delta x)^2, \tag{c}$$

eliminate $u_x(x, t)$ between (b) and (c), and derive the same result as in (5).

Note: Observe that Δx in equation (a) need not be positive. If it *is* positive, the right-hand member of (a) is known as a *forward difference quotient;* if Δx is negative, the right-hand member of (a) is a *backward difference quotient*. In the latter case one usually replaces Δx by $-\Delta x$, where Δx is then positive. Then the backward difference quotient becomes

$$\frac{df}{dx}(x) \approx \frac{f(x - \Delta x) - f(x)}{-\Delta x} = \frac{f(x) - f(x - \Delta x)}{\Delta x}. \tag{d}$$

In (4), for example, we found it convenient to use a forward difference quotient for $\partial(\partial u/\partial x)/\partial x$ and backward difference quotients for $\frac{\partial u}{\partial x}(x + \Delta x, t)$ and $\frac{\partial u}{\partial x}(x, t)$ since that procedure produced the "centered" formula (5).

15 Laplace Equation

15.1 INTRODUCTION

Having already discussed separation of variables, the Sturm–Liouville theory, and the Fourier and Laplace transforms, in connection with the diffusion equation, we can now proceed a bit more quickly in our treatment of the Laplace and wave equations in this chapter and the next.

First, recall that we have already met the **Laplace equation**

$$\nabla^2 \Phi = 0 \tag{1}$$

in Chapter 9—or, more generally, the nonhomogeneous version

$$\nabla^2 \Phi = f \tag{2}$$

known as the **Poisson equation;** f is a "source" function which is prescribed over the region in question. For example, we found on page 397 that the temperature field u induced by the conduction of heat is

$$\alpha^2 \nabla^2 u = \frac{\partial u}{\partial t} - F, \tag{3}$$

where the constant α^2 is the diffusivity of the material and F is a prescribed heat-source distribution. In steady state $\partial u/\partial t = 0$, so that (3) becomes $\nabla^2 u = -F/\alpha^2$, which equation is indeed of the form (2). In the absence of heat sources within the region, this equation reduces further to the Laplace equation $\nabla^2 u = 0$.

Analogously, we found that the irrotational flow of an incompressible fluid is governed by the Poisson equation (2), where f is a distributed mass source (mass per unit volume per unit time) and Φ is the velocity potential, which is related to the fluid velocity field $\mathbf{q}$ according to $\mathbf{q} = \nabla\Phi$. In the absence of sources, $f = 0$ and the governing PDE reduces to the Laplace equation $\nabla^2\Phi = 0$.

As a final example, this one from the study of electrostatics, we note that the electric potential Φ, which is related to the electric field $\mathbf{E}$ according to $\mathbf{E} = -\nabla\Phi$, is governed by the equation

$$\nabla^2\Phi = -\frac{f}{\epsilon_0}, \tag{4}$$

where f is a distributed charge source (charge per unit volume) and the constant ϵ_0 is the permittivity of free space. In the absence of a charge distribution, (4) reduces to the Laplace equation $\nabla^2\Phi = 0$.

In this chapter we emphasize the homogeneous Laplace equation (1), and defer discussion of the nonhomogeneous case (2) to the exercises.

SEPARATION OF VARIABLES 15.2

We will illustrate the application of the method of separation of variables by means of three examples.

EXAMPLE 1 *Dirichlet Problem for Rectangle*. Consider the boundary value problem

$$\begin{aligned} \nabla^2\Phi = \Phi_{xx} + \Phi_{yy} &= 0 \text{ in } R, \\ \Phi(0, y) &= 0 \qquad (0 < y < b) \\ \Phi(a, y) &= f(y) \qquad (0 < y < b) \\ \Phi(x, 0) = \Phi(x, b) &= 0 \qquad (0 < x < a), \end{aligned} \tag{1}$$

where R is the rectangle shown in Fig. 15.1. Since the governing PDE is a Laplace equation, and the boundary conditions are of Dirichlet type, we call (1) a **Dirichlet problem.**

To solve by separation of variables, we seek

$$\Phi(x, y) = X(x)Y(y). \tag{2}$$

Putting (2) into the PDE gives

$$X''Y + XY'' = 0,$$

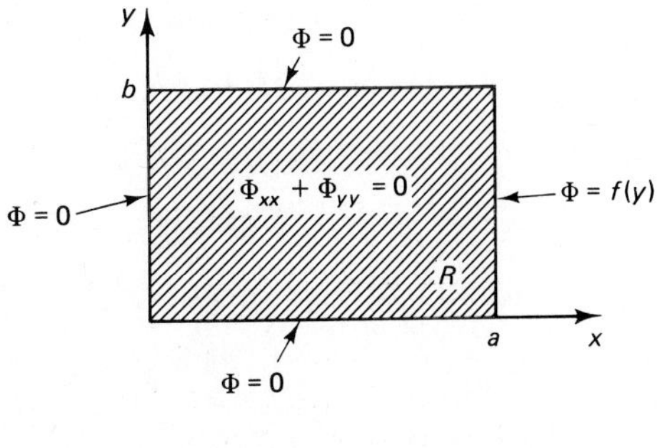

Fig. 15.1 The Dirichlet problem (1).

or, after separating the variables,

$$\frac{X''}{X} = -\frac{Y''}{Y} = \text{constant} = \kappa^2. \tag{3}$$

Thus we have the two ODEs

$$X'' - \kappa^2 X = 0, \tag{4a}$$

$$Y'' + \kappa^2 Y = 0, \tag{4b}$$

so that

$$X = \begin{cases} A + Bx, & \kappa = 0 \\ C \cosh \kappa x + D \sinh \kappa x, & \kappa \neq 0 \end{cases} \tag{5}$$

and

$$Y = \begin{cases} E + Fy, & \kappa = 0 \\ G \cos \kappa y + H \sin \kappa y, & \kappa \neq 0. \end{cases} \tag{6}$$

Why did we write the constant in (3) as $+\kappa^2$ and not as $-\kappa^2$? Because, looking ahead, we anticipated the eventual Fourier series exapansion of $f(y)$, and this expansion involves $\cos \kappa y$ and $\sin \kappa y$ functions. These functions are indeed available, according to (6), thanks to our choice of the constant in (3) as $+\kappa^2$. If we had chosen $-\kappa^2$, then in place of the cosine and sine functions in (6), we would have had the hyperbolic functions $\cosh \kappa y$ and $\sinh \kappa y$.

Thus far we have the product solutions

$$\Phi = XY = (A + Bx)(E + Fy) \tag{7}$$

corresponding to $\kappa = 0$, and

$$\Phi = XY = (C \cosh \kappa x + D \sinh \kappa x)(G \cos \kappa y + H \sin \kappa y) \tag{8}$$

for any $\kappa \neq 0$.

Since the PDE $L\Phi = \Phi_{xx} + \Phi_{yy} = 0$ is *linear*, the sum of these solutions must also be a solution. Thus we can write

$$\Phi = (A + Bx)(E + Fy) + (C \cosh \kappa x + D \sinh \kappa x)(G \cos \kappa y + H \sin \kappa y), \tag{9}$$

where $A, \ldots, H$ are arbitrary constants and κ is an arbitrary nonzero constant.

Next, we apply the boundary conditions, saving $\Phi(a, y) = f(y)$ for last. First,

$$\Phi(0, y) = 0 = A(E + Fy) + C(G \cos \kappa y + H \sin \kappa y), \tag{10}$$

so $A = 0$ and $C = 0$. Updating (9) to incorporate this result,

$$\Phi = x(I + Jy) + \sinh \kappa x (P \cos \kappa y + Q \sin \kappa y), \tag{11}$$

where we have written BE as I, BF as J, DG as P, and DH as Q. Continuing, set

$$\Phi(x, 0) = 0 = Ix + P \sinh \kappa x, \tag{12}$$

from which we conclude that $I = 0$ and $P = 0$. Updating (11) accordingly,

$$\Phi = Jxy + Q \sinh \kappa x \sin \kappa y. \tag{13}$$

Next,

$$\Phi(x, b) = 0 = Jbx + Q \sin \kappa b \sinh \kappa x, \tag{14}$$

so that

$$Jb = 0 \tag{15}$$

and

$$Q \sin \kappa b = 0. \tag{16}$$

Thus $J = 0$ and $\kappa = n\pi/b$ ($n = 1, 2, \ldots$), so that—with the help of superposition—we can express

$$\Phi(x, y) = \sum_{n=1}^{\infty} Q_n \sinh \frac{n\pi x}{b} \sin \frac{n\pi y}{b}. \tag{17}$$

Finally, we are in a position to apply the boundary condition at $x = a$:

$$\Phi(a, y) = f(y) = \sum_{n=1}^{\infty} Q_n \sinh \frac{n\pi a}{b} \sin \frac{n\pi y}{b} \qquad (0 < y < b). \tag{18}$$

Observing that (18) is of precisely the same form as the *half-range sine expansion* (HS1) on the inside back cover, with "L" $= b$ and "b_n" $= Q_n \sinh(n\pi a/b)$, it follows immediately from (HS2) that

$$Q_n \sinh \frac{n\pi a}{b} = \frac{2}{b} \int_0^b f(y) \sin \frac{n\pi y}{b}\, dy. \tag{19}$$

Thus the desired solution is given by (17), with the Q_n's given by

$$Q_n = \frac{2}{b \sinh(n\pi a/b)} \int_0^b f(y) \sin \frac{n\pi y}{b}\, dy. \tag{20}$$

Note that our solution procedure has followed essentially the same lines as in Example 1 on page 587. Thus, if any points remain unclear, we suggest that you reread that example, which was discussed in greater detail.

COMMENT 1 To gain some "feel" for the solution (17), let us consider a particular case. For example, consider the case where $f(y)$ is merely a constant, say 100. Then (20) gives

$$Q_n = \begin{cases} \dfrac{400}{n\pi \sinh(n\pi a/b)}, & n = 1, 3, \ldots \quad (21) \\ 0, & n = 2, 4, \ldots \quad (22) \end{cases}$$

and (17) becomes

$$\Phi(x, y) = \frac{400}{\pi} \sum_{n = 1,3,\ldots}^{\infty} \frac{1}{n} \frac{\sinh(n\pi x/b)}{\sinh(n\pi a/b)} \sin \frac{n\pi y}{b}. \tag{23}$$

We can use (23) to compute Φ at any particular field point (x, y) within the rectangle. Suppose we thus compute Φ at the points $(ja/M, kb/N)$ for $j = 1, 2, \ldots, M - 1$ and $k = 1, 2, \ldots, N - 1$, where M and N are "large" integers. In addition to these points we also know Φ along the boundary. With $M = 5$ and $N = 4$, say, we therefore know Φ at the dotted points in Fig. 15.2a. We can search across each of the three interior rows and down each of the four interior columns to locate, by interpolation, any desired value of Φ. Both the interpolation and the plotting can be accomplished using commonly available computer subroutines. We have done this for the case where $b = a$, and $M = N = 25$, and the results are shown in Fig. 15.2b. Here we have arbitrarily selected the $\Phi = 12.5, 25, 37.5, 50, 62.5, 75, 87.5$ level curves as representative. (Besides "level curves" these curves are also called *equipotential curves* if Φ is a potential, *isothermal curves* if Φ is temperature; and so on.) Notice that $\Phi = 25$ at the center of the square. That particular value could have been predicted in advance by a simple argument, as outlined in Exercise 1(e).

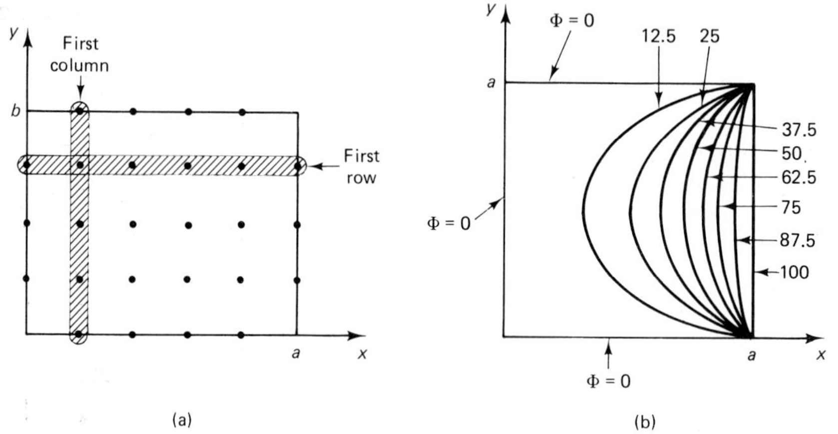

Fig. 15.2 Obtaining equipotential curves.

Besides the case where the region is square, we have also computed Φ [from (23)] and plotted several equipotential curves for the case where $b = 10a$ in Fig. 15.3. (The ratio b/a is often called the *aspect ratio*, so $b/a = 10$ is a large-aspect-ratio case.) Now, before examining the nature of the equipotential curves in Fig. 15.3, notice in advance that except near the ends of the rectangle (i.e., near $y = 0$ and $y = b$) we can expect the problem to be essentially one-dimensional, namely, with a strong variation in x but with very little variation in y. Thus, except near the ends, we tentatively expect that the Φ_{yy} term in the Laplace PDE can be neglected compared with Φ_{xx}, so that we have the *approximate* problem statement

$$\Phi_{xx} \approx 0; \qquad \Phi\,|_{x=0} = 0, \quad \Phi\,|_{x=a} = 100, \tag{24}$$

with the solution $\Phi = 100\, x/a$. Corresponding to this solution, the $\Phi = 25, 50, 75$ equipotentials are the lines $x = a/4, a/2, 3a/4$, respectively, as shown by the dashed lines in Fig. 15.3. Observe that the approximate solution is indeed quite accurate except near the ends of the rectangle, as anticipated.

We mention this approximation not to promote reckless abandon, but to emphasize that typical applications are not nearly as "clean" as we have pretended thus

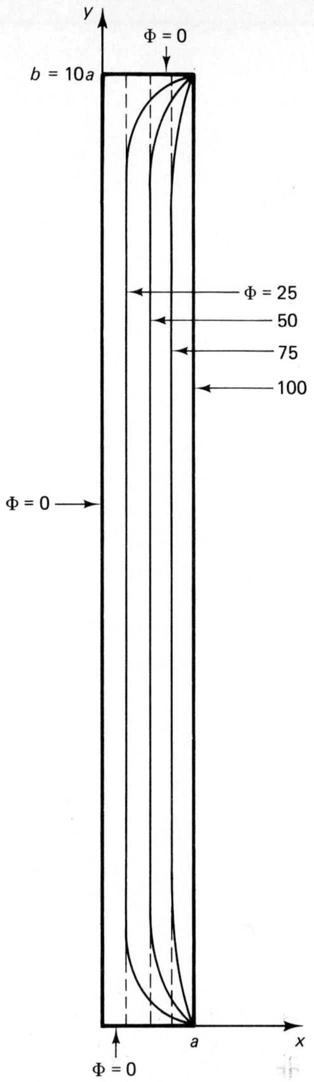

Fig. 15.3 Case of large aspect ratio: $b/a = 10$.

far in this book, and can be rendered mathematically tractable only by adopting approximations of one sort or another.*

COMMENT 2 In case you have studied the optional Section 14.3 on the Sturm–Liouville theory, let us call attention to the Sturm–Liouville problem that is contained within this example. First, observe that the boundary conditions

$$\Phi(x, 0) = X(x)Y(0) = 0, \tag{25a}$$

$$\Phi(x, b) = X(x)Y(b) = 0 \tag{25b}$$

* In recent years it has become increasingly clear that the vast majority of these approximations can be organized systematically within the framework of what is known as *perturbation theory*. The latter lies beyond the scope of this book; for a brief introduction to perturbation methods, and additional references, we refer the interested reader to Chap. 25 of M. Greenberg, *Foundations of Applied Mathematics* (Englewood Cliffs, N.J.: Prentice-Hall, 1978).

on Φ imply the boundary conditions $Y(0) = 0$, $Y(b) = 0$, respectively, on Y. Thus Y is governed by the problem

$$Y'' + \kappa^2 Y = 0; \qquad Y(0) = 0, \quad Y(b) = 0, \tag{26}$$

which is a Sturm–Liouville problem, with eigenfunctions $\sin(n\pi y/b)$. Then (18) is an eigenfunction expansion, so that

$$\begin{aligned} Q_n \sinh \frac{n\pi a}{b} &= \frac{\langle f(y), \sin(n\pi y/b)\rangle}{\langle \sin(n\pi y/b), \sin(n\pi y/b)\rangle} \\ &= \frac{2}{b}\int_0^b f(y)\sin\frac{n\pi y}{b}\,dy, \end{aligned} \tag{27}$$

in agreement with (19).

COMMENT 3 Looking back at (4a), notice that for $\kappa \neq 0$ the general solution can be expressed as a linear combination of $\cosh \kappa x$ and $\sinh \kappa x$ *or* as a linear combination of $e^{\kappa x}$ and $e^{-\kappa x}$. We used the cosh, sinh combination, in (5), as the more *convenient* choice. Specifically, the $\Phi(0, y) = 0$ boundary condition immediately knocked out the $\cosh \kappa x$ term and left us only with the $\sinh \kappa x$. If, instead, we had used $X = Ce^{\kappa x} + De^{-\kappa x}$ in (5), then $\Phi(0, y) = 0$ would have led to the relation $C + D = 0$, so $D = -C$, and $X = C(e^{\kappa x} - e^{-\kappa x})$, which, once again, is a constant times $\sinh \kappa x$. ◀

EXAMPLE 2 *Dirichlet Problem for Semi-infinite Strip.* Let us consider the problem

$$\nabla^2\Phi = \Phi_{xx} + \Phi_{yy} = 0 \qquad (0 < x < a,\ 0 < y < \infty) \tag{28a}$$

$$\Phi(0, y) = 0 \qquad (0 < y < \infty) \tag{28b}$$

$$\Phi(a, y) = 100 \qquad (0 < y < \infty) \tag{28c}$$

$$\Phi(x, 0) = f(x) \qquad (0 < x < a) \tag{28d}$$

summarized in Fig. 15.4. Do we have the appropriate number of boundary conditions? Well, as a rule of thumb, notice that (28a) is a second-order differential equation with respect to x and that there are two x-wise boundary conditions, namely, (28b) and (28c). However, (28a) is also a second-order equation with respect to y, yet we have only the one y-wise boundary condition (28d). If we regard the region as the rectangle $0 < x < a$, $0 < y < b$, as $b \to \infty$, it appears that we should add one more boundary condition at the "upper boundary" $y = \infty$. The sim-

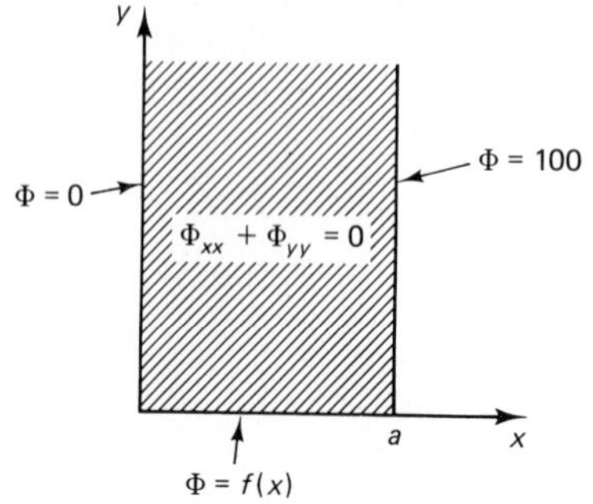

Fig. 15.4 Dirichlet problem for semi-infinite strip.

ple *boundedness*, or *finiteness, condition*

$$\Phi(x, y) \text{ bounded as } y \to \infty \tag{28e}$$

will be seen to suffice, and would appear to be reasonable for most applications which are modeled as in Fig. 15.4.

Again using separation of variables, we seek

$$\Phi(x, y) = X(x)Y(y), \tag{29}$$

and obtain

$$\frac{X''}{X} = -\frac{Y''}{Y} = \text{constant} = -\kappa^2. \tag{30}$$

This time we write $-\kappa^2$ rather than $+\kappa^2$ so as to obtain sines and cosines in the x variable, since we anticipate the eventual Fourier series expansion of $f(x)$. Thus

$$X = \begin{cases} A + Bx, & \kappa = 0 \\ C \cos \kappa x + D \sin \kappa x, & \kappa \neq 0 \end{cases} \tag{31}$$

$$Y = \begin{cases} E + Fy, & \kappa = 0 \\ Ge^{\kappa y} + He^{-\kappa y}, & \kappa \neq 0 \end{cases} \tag{32}$$

and

$$\Phi = (A + Bx)(E + Fy) + (C \cos \kappa x + D \sin \kappa x)(Ge^{\kappa y} + He^{-\kappa y}). \tag{33}$$

Turning to the boundary conditions, let us begin with

$$\Phi(0, y) = 0 = A(E + Fy) + C(Ge^{\kappa y} + He^{-\kappa y}), \tag{34}$$

which implies that $A = C = 0$. Updating (33) accordingly, we obtain

$$\Phi = x(I + Jy) + \sin \kappa x (Pe^{\kappa y} + Qe^{-\kappa y}). \tag{35}$$

Recall that $\kappa \neq 0$ here, since the $(A + Bx)(E + Fy)$ term in (33), and hence the $x(I + Jy)$ term in (35), handles the contribution from $\kappa = 0$. Observe from (35) that there is no harm in further limiting κ to be positive (since a change in the sign of κ still leaves us with a $\sin \kappa x$ multiplied into a linear combination of $e^{-\kappa y}$ and $e^{\kappa y}$ terms). With $\kappa > 0$, it then follows from (28e) that $J = P = 0$, since the y and $e^{\kappa y}$ terms grow unboundedly with y and cannot possibly cancel each other. Thus (35) reduces to

$$\Phi = Ix + Qe^{-\kappa y} \sin \kappa x. \tag{36}$$

Next,

$$\Phi(a, y) = 100 = Ia + Qe^{-\kappa y} \sin \kappa a$$

implies that $I = 100/a$ and $\kappa = n\pi/a$ $(n = 1, 2, \ldots)$, so that

$$\Phi(x, y) = 100\frac{x}{a} + \sum_{n=1}^{\infty} Q_n e^{-n\pi y/a} \sin \frac{n\pi x}{a}. \tag{37}$$

Finally, we impose the condition at $y = 0$:

$$\Phi(x, 0) = f(x) = 100\frac{x}{a} + \sum_{n=1}^{\infty} Q_n \sin \frac{n\pi x}{a}, \tag{38}$$

or, equivalently,

$$f(x) - 100\frac{x}{a} = \sum_{n=1}^{\infty} Q_n \sin\frac{n\pi x}{a}. \tag{39}$$

As in Example 1, the latter is a half-range sine formula, so

$$Q_n = \frac{2}{a}\int_0^a \left[f(x) - 100\frac{x}{a}\right] \sin\frac{n\pi x}{a}\, dx, \tag{40}$$

and the solution is given by (37), with the Q_n's computed according to (40).

COMMENT 1 Note carefully the exponential decay with respect to both y and n, especially with respect to y, which is provided by the $e^{-n\pi y/a}$ factor in (37), as illustrated in Table 15.1. Looking down the columns, we see that the presence of the series in (37) becomes more and suppressed (by the $e^{-n\pi y/a}$ factors) as y increases away from 0. Roughly speaking, we might say that the effect of the end condition $\Phi(x, 0) = f(x)$ is "felt" only near the end, i.e., only over $0 < y < a$ or $0 < y < 2a$, say. Thus conceptually, it is interesting to imagine the region as comprised of two parts: In $0 < y < 2a$, say, the solution is given by (37) and a substantial effect of the end condition $\Phi(x, 0) = f(x)$ is manifested by the infinite series; in $2a < y < \infty$, on the other hand, the series is negligible (for most purposes), and $\Phi(x, y) \approx 100(x/a)$. This comment essentially echoes the discussion in Example 1 corresponding to the large-aspect-ratio case.

TABLE 15.1 Values of $e^{-n\pi y/a}$

	n		
y	1	2	3
0	1	1	1
a	4×10^{-2}	2×10^{-3}	8×10^{-5}
$2a$	2×10^{-3}	3×10^{-6}	7×10^{-9}
$3a$	8×10^{-5}	7×10^{-9}	5×10^{-13}

COMMENT 2 Observe that for the $\kappa \neq 0$ part of (32) we could have written $Ge^{\kappa y} + He^{-\kappa y}$ *or* $G \sinh \kappa y + H \cosh \kappa y$. We chose the exponential form, as the more *convenient*, by virtue of the finiteness condition (28e), for $e^{\kappa y}$ is unbounded as $y \to \infty$ so that (28e) simply gives $G = 0$. If, instead, we had chosen the form $G \sinh \kappa y + H \cosh \kappa y$, the application of (28e) would have been more obtuse. Specifically,

$$G \sinh \kappa y + H \cosh \kappa y = \tfrac{1}{2}\left[(G + H)e^{\kappa y} + (H - G)e^{-\kappa y}\right],$$

so that (28e) implies that $G + H = 0$, or $H = -G$. But then

$$G \sinh \kappa y + H \cosh \kappa y = G(\sinh \kappa y - \cosh \kappa y) = -Ge^{-\kappa y},$$

and, after a more tedious story, we once again end up with the negative exponential form! *Anticipating*, it is best to *start* with the exponential form, as we did in (32). ◀

As our final example, we consider the Laplace equation in *three* dimensions.

EXAMPLE 3 *Dirichlet Problem for Rectangular Prism.* This time we consider the *three*-dimensional problem

$$\nabla^2\Phi = \Phi_{xx} + \Phi_{yy} + \Phi_{zz} = 0 \qquad (0 < x < a,\ 0 < y < b,\ 0 < z < c) \tag{41}$$

where $\Phi = 0$ on each of the six faces of the region except for the face $z = c$, on which Φ is a prescribed function $f(x, y)$,

$$\Phi(x, y, c) = f(x, y) \qquad (0 < x < a,\ 0 < y < b) \tag{42}$$

as depicted in Fig. 15.5. Physically, the situation might, for example, correspond to steady-state heat conduction, with $\Phi(x, y)$ the temperature field; five of the six faces are held with ice water at 0°, and the sixth face is held at a prescribed temperature distribution $f(x, y)$. Or, if the physics corresponds to electrostatics, with Φ the electric potential, then five of the faces are "grounded" and the sixth is held at the potential $f(x, y)$.

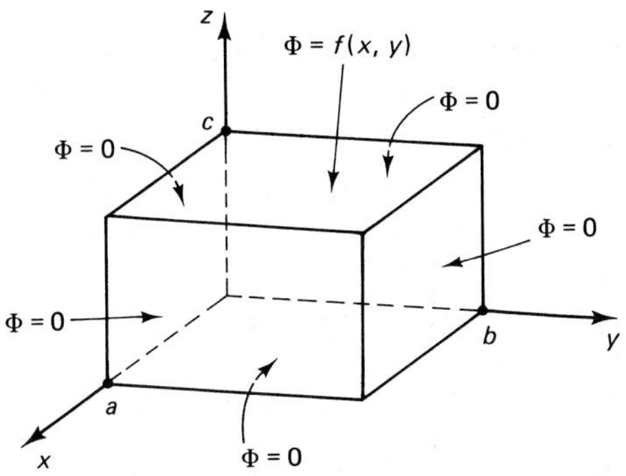

Fig. 15.5 Dirichlet problem for rectangular prism.

This example is the first in which we have more than two independent variables. To solve by separation of variables, we seek

$$\Phi(x, y, z) = X(x)Y(y)Z(z). \tag{43}$$

Putting (43) into (41), dividing by XYZ, and transposing the Z''/Z term, there follows

$$\frac{X''}{X} + \frac{Y''}{Y} = -\frac{Z''}{Z}. \tag{44}$$

The left-hand side of (44) is a function of x and y, the righthand side is a function of z; x, y, z are independent variables, so it follows that

$$\frac{X''}{X} + \frac{Y''}{Y} = -\frac{Z''}{Z} = \text{constant} = -\kappa^2. \tag{45}$$

Why include the minus sign in $-\kappa^2$? Well, looking ahead, we anticipate having to expand $f(x, y)$ in a Fourier series. Thus we expect X and Y to be sine and cosine functions, in which case X''/X and Y''/Y will each be negative. If this reasoning is not entirely clear, we can at least proceed *tentatively* with the constant expressed as $-\kappa^2$, with the understanding that we can always go back and change the sign if we wish.

To complete the separation process, we reexpress $X''/X + Y''/Y = -\kappa^2$ as

$$\frac{X''}{X} = -\frac{Y''}{Y} - \kappa^2 = \text{constant} = -\alpha^2, \tag{46}$$

so that

$$X'' + \alpha^2 X = 0; \qquad X(0) = X(a) = 0 \tag{47}$$

$$Y'' + (\kappa^2 - \alpha^2)Y = 0; \qquad Y(0) = Y(b) = 0 \tag{48}$$

$$Z'' - \kappa^2 Z = 0; \qquad Z(0) = 0, \tag{49}$$

where the boundary conditions on X and Y follow from the fact that $\Phi(0, y, z) = 0 = X(0)Y(y)Z(z)$, $\Phi(a, y, z) = 0 = X(a)Y(y)Z(z)$, $\Phi(x, 0, z) = X(x)Y(0)Z(z)$, and $\Phi(x, b, z) = 0 = X(x)Y(b)Z(z)$. Similarly, $\Phi(x, y, 0) = 0 = X(x)Y(y)Z(0)$ implies that $Z(0) = 0$.* Observe that we have *two* separation constants, κ and α.

Solving $X'' + \alpha^2 X = 0$ subject to the condition $X(0) = 0$ gives $X = A \sin \alpha X$, and $X(a) = 0$ then implies that $\alpha = m\pi/a$, where $m = 1, 2, \ldots$. Thus

$$X(x) = A \sin \frac{m\pi x}{a} \qquad (m = 1, 2, \ldots). \tag{50}$$

Similarly, (48) gives

$$Y(y) = B \sin \frac{n\pi y}{b} \qquad (n = 1, 2, \ldots) \tag{51}$$

where m and n are independent integers, and where

$$\kappa^2 = \pi^2\left(\frac{m^2}{a^2} + \frac{n^2}{b^2}\right). \tag{52}$$

Finally, (49) gives

$$Z(z) = C \sinh\left(\pi\sqrt{\frac{m^2}{a^2} + \frac{n^2}{b^2}}\, z\right), \tag{53}$$

so that, combining ABC as D and using superposition,

$$\Phi(x, y, z) = \sum_{n=1}^{\infty}\sum_{m=1}^{\infty} D_{mn} \sin\frac{m\pi x}{a} \sin\frac{n\pi y}{b} \sinh\left(\pi\sqrt{\frac{m^2}{a^2} + \frac{n^2}{b^2}}\, z\right), \tag{54}$$

where the D_{mn}'s are to be chosen (if possible) so as to satisfy the remaining boundary condition,

$$\begin{aligned}\Phi(x, y, c) &= f(x, y)\\ &= \sum_{n=1}^{\infty}\sum_{m=1}^{\infty} D_{mn} \sinh\left(\pi c\sqrt{\frac{m^2}{a^2} + \frac{n^2}{b^2}}\right) \sin\frac{m\pi x}{a} \sin\frac{n\pi y}{b}.\end{aligned} \tag{55}$$

* This step, of inferring boundary conditions on X, Y, Z from boundary conditions on Φ, works only if the boundary condition under consideration is *homogeneous*. For example, if $\Phi(0, y, z) = 0 = X(0)Y(y)Z(z)$, then $X(0) = 0$ and/or $Y(y) = 0$ and/or $Z(z) = 0$. The latter two choices can be discarded since they would yield $\Phi(x, y, z) = 0$, which solution has no chance of satisfying the nonhomogeneous boundary condition $\Phi(x, y, c) = f(x, y)$, so we conclude that $X(0) = 0$. However, no such argument follows from the *non*homogeneous boundary condition $\Phi(x, y, c) = f(x, y) = X(x)Y(y)Z(c)$.

Here we encounter, for the first time, a "double series." Such series will be discussed briefly following this example. Meanwhile, we proceed formally.

Write

$$E_{mn} = D_{mn} \sinh\left(\pi c\sqrt{\frac{m^2}{a^2} + \frac{n^2}{b^2}}\right), \tag{56}$$

for brevity. The problem is as follows. Given $f(x, y)$, we wish to compute the E_{mn}'s (and hence the D_{mn}'s) such that

$$f(x, y) = \sum_{n=1}^{\infty}\sum_{m=1}^{\infty} E_{mn} \sin\frac{m\pi x}{a} \sin\frac{n\pi y}{b} \tag{57}$$

holds over the given rectangle. To accomplish that goal, we recall the *orthogonality relation* (Section 10.3)

$$\int_0^\ell \sin\frac{m\pi x}{\ell}\sin\frac{n\pi x}{\ell}\,dx = \begin{cases} \ell/2, & m = n \quad (\neq 0) \\ 0, & m \neq n. \end{cases} \tag{58}$$

Thus, multiplying (57) through by $\sin(j\pi x/a)\sin(k\pi y/b)$ and integrating each term on x from 0 to a and also on y from 0 to b, we obtain, with the help of (58),

$$\begin{aligned} &\int_0^b\int_0^a f(x, y) \sin\frac{j\pi x}{a}\sin\frac{k\pi y}{b}\,dx\,dy \\ &\quad = \sum_{n=1}^{\infty}\sum_{m=1}^{\infty} E_{mn}\int_0^a \sin\frac{j\pi x}{a}\sin\frac{m\pi x}{a}\,dx \int_0^b \sin\frac{k\pi y}{b}\sin\frac{n\pi y}{b}\,dy \qquad (59) \\ &\quad = E_{jk}\frac{a}{2}\frac{b}{2} \end{aligned}$$

or, solving for E_{jk} and then changing j to m and k to n,

$$E_{mn} = \frac{4}{ab}\int_0^b\int_0^a f(x, y)\sin\frac{m\pi x}{a}\sin\frac{n\pi y}{b}\,dx\,dy. \tag{60}$$

This completes our solution: given $f(x, y)$, we compute the E_{mn}'s from (60) and hence the D_{mn}'s from (56); the solution is then given by (54). ◀

We do not wish to enter a detailed discussion of double series, but we should at least define them and give a reference for further study since they occurred in Example 3 and will also appear when we study the vibrating membrane problem in Chapter 16.

First, recall that for "single series" we say that the series $\Sigma_{n=1}^{\infty} a_n$ converges to s if to each $\epsilon > 0$ (no matter how small) there corresponds an integer $N_0(\epsilon)$ such that

$$\left| s - \sum_{n=1}^{N} a_n \right| < \epsilon \qquad \text{whenever} \quad N > N_0. \tag{61}$$

Other definitions are sometimes used; *this* one is called *ordinary convergence,* and we say that

$$\sum_{n=1}^{\infty} a_n = s \tag{62}$$

in the sense of ordinary convergence. If, to each $\epsilon > 0$ there does *not* exist such an $N_0(\epsilon)$, the series is said to diverge.

Analogously, the **double series** $\Sigma_{m=1}^{\infty} \Sigma_{n=1}^{\infty} a_{mn}$ is said to converge to s, in the sense of *Pringsheim convergence,* if to each $\epsilon > 0$ (no matter how small) there correspond integers $M_0(\epsilon)$ and $N_0(\epsilon)$ such that

$$\left| s - \sum_{m=1}^{M} \sum_{n=1}^{N} a_{mn} \right| < \epsilon \qquad \text{whenever} \quad M > M_0 \quad \text{and} \quad N > N_0. \tag{63}$$

In that case we write

$$\sum_{m=1}^{\infty} \sum_{n=1}^{\infty} a_{mn} = s; \tag{64}$$

otherwise, the series is said to diverge.

We shall be concerned not so much with double series in general, but with double Fourier series [i.e., of the form (57)] in particular. It should suffice to say that if $f(x, y)$ is well enough behaved, the double Fourier series on the right-hand side of (57), with the E_{mn}'s given by (60), converges to $f(x, y)$ over the given rectangle, and that virtually all functions f of engineering interest are indeed well enough behaved for this to be true. For further discussion of double series, we refer the interested reader to Berg and McGregor.*

15.2 EXERCISES

1. (*Further discussion of Example 1*) (a) There was some question, in (3), as to whether the separation constant would turn out to be positive or negative, and hence whether we should express it as κ^2 or as $-\kappa^2$. Here we ask you to prove, *in advance,* that the κ^2 in (3) cannot be negative. *Hint:* Show that Y satisfies the problem

$$Y'' + \kappa^2 Y = 0; \qquad Y(0) = 0, \quad Y(b) = 0. \tag{a}$$

Multiply $Y'' + \kappa^2 Y = 0$ through by Y, integrate on y from 0 to b, integrate the $\int_0^b YY''\,dy$ term by parts, and obtain

$$\kappa^2 = \frac{\int_0^b [Y'(y)]^2\,dy}{\int_0^b [Y(y)]^2\,dy}. \tag{b}$$

(b) According to the discussion in part (a), the separation constant cannot be negative; hence we expressed it as κ^2 rather than $-\kappa^2$. Nevertheless, it should be emphasized that the choice $-\kappa^2$ would only be less natural, and slightly inconvenient. Thus we ask you to rewrite the separation constant in (3) as $-\kappa^2$ and to show that the same solution form, (17), is nevertheless obtained. *Hint:* To find the roots of $\sinh z = 0$ it is helpful to write $\sinh z = -i \sin iz = 0$, so that $iz = n\pi\,(n = 0, \pm 1, \pm 2, \ldots)$.

(c) For the special case in which $f(y) \equiv f$ is a *constant,* we are no longer forced into carrying out the Fourier series expansion in the y variable. In particular, write $-\kappa^2$ in (3), in place of κ^2, and derive the solution

$$\Phi(x, y) = f\frac{x}{a} + \frac{2f}{\pi} \sum_{n=1}^{\infty} \frac{(-1)^n}{n} \times \frac{\sinh(n\pi y/a) + \sinh[n\pi(b - y)/a]}{\sinh(n\pi b/a)} \sin\frac{n\pi x}{a}, \tag{c}$$

as an alternative to (23). *Hint:* Holding off on the boundary conditions at $y = 0$ and $y = b$, derive the form

$$\Phi(x, y) = f\frac{x}{a} + \sum_{n=1}^{\infty} \left(A_n \sinh\frac{n\pi y}{a} + B_n \cosh\frac{n\pi y}{a}\right) \sin\frac{n\pi x}{a}. \tag{d}$$

Then, applying the conditions $\Phi(x, 0) = 0$ and

*P. W. Berg and J. L. McGregor, *Elementary Partial Differential Equations,* prelim. ed. (San Francisco: Holden-Day, 1964), Sec. 10.3.

$\Phi(x, b) = 0$, and using the identity $\sinh(A - B) = \sinh A \cosh B - \sinh B \cosh A$, obtain (c). *Note:* Since we now have two different (though equivalent) solution forms, (23) and (c) it is natural to wonder if one is, in any way, to be preferred over the other. Along these lines, let us merely note that if $b/a \gg 1$ and we are seeking Φ at points x, y which are not near the ends ($y = 0, y = b$), then (c) is much to be preferred since even the fx/a term by itself gives a good approximation. Keeping, in addition, the first few terms of the series should suffice for excellent accuracy. To achieve comparable accuracy using (23) might well require a great many terms in the series.
(d) Putting (20) into (17), show that the solution can be expressed as an integral over the boundary values, namely, as

$$\Phi(x, y) = \int_0^b K(\eta; x, y) f(\eta)\, d\eta, \tag{e}$$

where the "kernel" K is

$$K(\eta; x, y) = \frac{2}{b} \sum_{n=1}^{\infty} \frac{\sinh(n\pi x/b)}{\sinh(n\pi a/b)} \sin\frac{n\pi y}{b} \sin\frac{n\pi\eta}{b}. \tag{f}$$

(e) Show, by a simple argument, that $\Phi(a/2, a/2) = 25$ for the case where $b = a$ (Fig. 15.2b). *Hint:* Note the superposition indicated in the accompanying figure.
(f) Looking at the level-curve pattern in Fig. 15.2b, and regarding Φ as temperature, where would you say the heat flux is greatest, and where is it least? Explain.

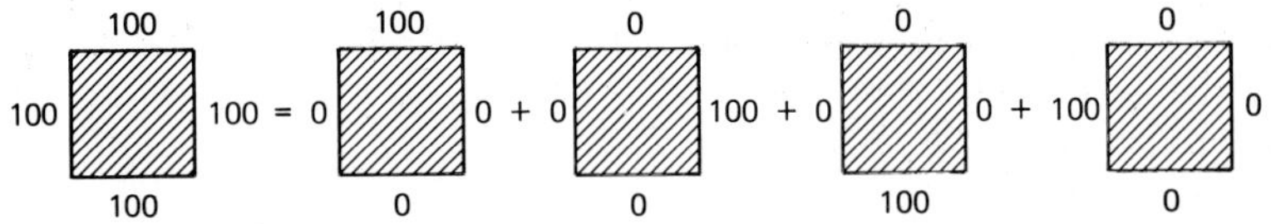

2. (*Superposition applied to boundary conditions*)
(a) Whereas one finds that the problem

$$\begin{aligned} &\nabla^2\Phi = 0 \qquad (0 < x < a,\ 0 < y < b) \\ &\Phi(0, y) = p(y), \quad \Phi(x, b) = q(x), \\ &\Phi(a, y) = r(y), \quad \Phi(x, 0) = s(x) \end{aligned} \tag{a}$$

cannot, in general, be solved by separation of variables, show that we can use superposition, as in the accompanying figure, to reduce the problem to four simpler ones, each of which *can* be solved by separation of variables, with $\Phi = \Phi_1 + \Phi_2 + \Phi_3 + \Phi_4$ (but you need not solve for $\Phi_1, \ldots, \Phi_4$).

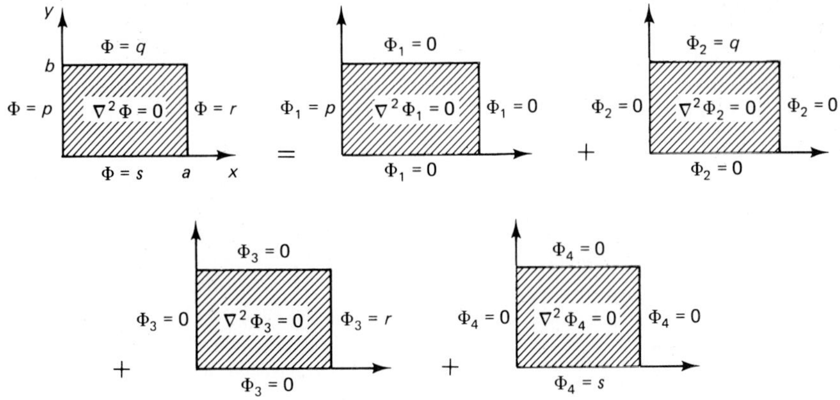

(b) Actually, one does not need to dismantle the problem quite so completely. Rather, one can break problem (a) into *two* problems, as sketched in the figure; in the Φ_1 problem the homogeneous "north" and "south" boundary conditions lead to $\sin(n\pi y/b)$ terms, which permit the Fourier expansion of $p(y)$ and $r(y)$, and in the Φ_2 problem the homogeneous "east" and "west" boundary conditions lead to $\sin(n\pi x/a)$ terms, which permit the expansion of $q(x)$ and $s(x)$. The problem that we pose for you is to calculate Φ_1 and Φ_2, and hence Φ as the sum $\Phi_1 + \Phi_2$.

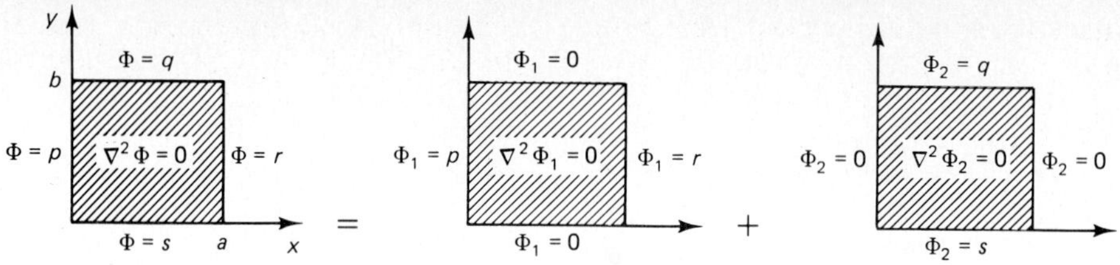

3. Solve the Laplace equation

$$\Phi_{xx} + \Phi_{yy} = 0 \qquad (0 < x < a,\ 0 < y < b) \quad \text{(a)}$$

subject to the given boundary conditions.

(a) $\Phi(0, y) = \Phi(x, 0) = \Phi(a, y) = 0$, $\Phi(x, b) = \begin{cases} 100, & 0 < x < a/2 \\ 0, & a/2 < x < a \end{cases}$

(b) $\Phi(0, y) = \Phi(x, 0) = \Phi(x, b) = 0$, $\Phi_x(a, y) = \begin{cases} 0, & 0 < y < b/2 \\ 50, & b/2 < y < b \end{cases}$

(c) $\Phi(0, y) = \Phi(x, 0) = \Phi(x, b) = \Phi(a, y) = 50$

(d) $\Phi(0, y) = 0$, $\Phi(a, y) = 10$, $\Phi(x, 0) = \Phi(x, b) = 10x/a$

*(e) $\Phi_x(0, y) = \Phi_y(x, 0) = \Phi_y(x, b) = 0$, $\Phi(a, y) = f(y)$

*(f) $\Phi(x, 0) = \Phi_y(x, b) = 0$, $\Phi(0, y) = \Phi(a, y) = \begin{cases} 100, & 0 < y < b/2 \\ 0, & b/2 < y < b \end{cases}$

(g) $\Phi(0, y) = \Phi(a, y) = 0$, $\Phi(x, 0) = 25 \sin \dfrac{\pi x}{a}$, $\Phi(x, b) = 10 \sin \dfrac{\pi x}{a} - 5 \sin \dfrac{3\pi x}{a}$

(h) $\Phi(a, y) = \Phi(x, 0) = \Phi(x, b) = 0$, $\Phi(0, y) = \cos \dfrac{\pi y}{b}$

(i) $\Phi(x, 0) = \Phi(x, b) = \Phi(a, y) = 0$, $\Phi_x(0, y) = 10$

(j) $\Phi_y(x, 0) = \Phi(x, b) = \Phi(0, y) = 0$, $\Phi(a, y) = f(y)$

4. The problem

$$\begin{aligned} &\Phi_{xx} + \Phi_{yy} = 0 \qquad (-\infty < x < \infty,\ 0 < y < b) \\ &\Phi(x, 0) = 0, \quad \Phi(x, b) = 100e^{-(x/10b)^2} \end{aligned} \quad \text{(a)}$$

admits a simple, yet accurate, *approximate* solution, which we ask you to find. *Hint:* Notice that $\exp[-(x/10b)^2]$ is a rather slowly varying function of x.

5. (*Poisson equation*) (a) Show that the solution of the Poisson problem

$$\nabla^2\Phi = f \text{ in } R, \qquad \Phi = g \text{ given on boundary of } R$$

can be written as $\Phi = \Phi_1 + \Phi_2$, where Φ_1 and Φ_2 satisfy the problems

$$\nabla^2\Phi_1 = f \text{ in } R, \qquad \Phi_1 = 0 \text{ on boundary of } R \qquad \text{(a)}$$

and

$$\nabla^2\Phi_2 = 0 \text{ in } R, \qquad \Phi_2 = g \text{ on boundary of } R, \qquad \text{(b)}$$

respectively. [Problem (b) has already been discussed in this section and in the preceding exercises. Thus in the subsequent parts of this exercise we focus on problems of type (a).]

(b) To solve the Poisson problem

$$\begin{aligned} &\Phi_{xx} + \Phi_{yy} = f(x, y) \qquad (0 < x < a,\ 0 < y < b) \\ &\Phi(0, y) = \Phi(a, y) = \Phi(x, 0) = \Phi(x, b) = 0, \end{aligned} \quad \text{(c)}$$

expand the given function f as

$$f(x, y) = \sum_{n=1}^{\infty} f_n(x) \sin \frac{n\pi y}{b}, \qquad \text{(d)}$$

where

$$f_n(x) = \frac{2}{b} \int_0^b f(x, y) \sin \frac{n\pi y}{b}\, dy, \qquad \text{(e)}$$

and seek Φ in the form

$$\Phi(x, y) = \sum_{n=1}^{\infty} \Phi_n(x) \sin \frac{n\pi y}{b}. \qquad \text{(f)}$$

Show that the Φ_n's are found by solving the problems

$$\Phi_n'' - \frac{n^2\pi^2}{b^2}\Phi_n = f_n(x); \qquad \Phi_n(0) = \Phi_n(a) = 0, \quad \text{(g)}$$

for $n = 1, 2, \ldots$. (Naturally, we could have used Fourier series in the x variable instead.)

(c) Use the method outlined in part (b) to solve for Φ for the simple case where $f(x, y) = \text{constant} \equiv f$.

(d) As in part (c), let $f(x, y) = \text{constant} \equiv f$. But instead of using the method outlined in part (b), solve for Φ as follows. Noticing that $fx^2/2$, for example, is a simple particular solution of the Poisson equation $\Phi_{xx} + \Phi_{yy} = f$, seek Φ in the form

$$\Phi(x, y) = \frac{f}{2}x^2 + \Psi(x, y). \qquad \text{(h)}$$

Show that the "complementary solution" Ψ satisfies the problem

$$\Psi_{xx} + \Psi_{yy} = 0 \qquad (0 < x < a, 0 < y < b)$$

$$\Psi(0, y) = 0, \quad \Psi(a, y) = -\frac{fa^2}{2}, \tag{i}$$

$$\Psi(x, 0) = \Psi(x, b) = -\frac{f}{2}x^2,$$

solve for Ψ, and hence for Φ. (Fourier expansion coefficients may be left in integral form.)

6. (*Further discussion of Example 3*) (a) If $a = b = c$ and $f(x, y) = \text{constant} \equiv f$, show that $\Phi(a/2, a/2, a/2) = f/6$. *Hint:* See the hint in Exercise 1(e).
(b) Complete the solution of Φ, for the case where $a = b = c$ and $f(x, y) = \text{constant} \equiv f$, and actually evaluate $\Phi(a/2, a/2, a/2)$ by summing the double series through $m = 5$, $n = 5$, say. Next, sum the series through $m = 11$, $n = 11$, say. Compare your two computed results with the exact value $f/6$ given in part (a).
(c) If

$$\Phi_{xx} + \Phi_{yy} + \Phi_{zz} = 0$$

$$(0 < x < a, 0 < y < a, 0 < z < a)$$

$$\Phi(0, y, z) = 100, \quad \Phi(a, y, z) = 200,$$

$$\Phi(x, 0, z) = 300, \quad \Phi(x, a, z) = 400,$$

$$\Phi(x, y, 0) = 500, \quad \Phi(x, y, a) = 600,$$

determine $\Phi(a/2, a/2, a/2)$. *Hint:* See part (a).

7. Solve the problem

$$\Phi_{xx} + \Phi_{yy} = 0 \qquad (0 < x < \infty, 0 < y < b)$$

$$\Phi(0, y) = f(y), \quad \Phi(x, y) \text{ bounded as } x \to \infty$$

subject to the following additional conditions:
*(a) $\Phi(x, 0) = 100$, $\Phi(x, b) = 50$
(b) $\Phi_y(x, 0) = 0$, $\Phi(x, b) = 100$
(c) $\Phi_y(x, 0) = \Phi_y(x, b) = 0$

8. Delete the boundedness condition (28e), and put forward solutions [different from the solution given by (37) and (40)] that satisfy the other conditions (28a) to (28d).

9. (*Uniqueness*) Suppose that $\Phi(x, y, z)$ is C^2 and satisfies the Poisson equation $\nabla^2\Phi = f(x, y, z)$ throughout some (simply connected) region V, together with the Dirichlet boundary condition $\Phi = g(x, y, z)$ on the (piecewise smooth orientable) surface S of V.
(a) Show that that solution is *unique*. *Hint:* Suppose that there are two such solutions, say Φ_1 and Φ_2. With $\Psi \equiv \Phi_1 - \Phi_2$, show that $\nabla^2\Psi = 0$ in V and $\Psi = 0$ on S. Setting $u = v = \Psi$ in Green's first identity (page 398), show that

$$\int_V (\Psi_x^2 + \Psi_y^2 + \Psi_z^2)\, dV = 0,$$

and conclude that $\Psi_x = \Psi_y = \Psi_z = 0$ throughout V, so that Ψ is at most a constant. Show that that constant must be zero, so that $\Phi_1 = \Phi_2$.
(b) Repeat part (a) with the Dirichlet condition $\Phi = g$ replaced by the Neumann condition $\partial\Phi/\partial n = g$. Show that the solution is unique only to within an arbitrary additive constant.
(c) Repeat part (a) with the Dirichlet condition $\Phi = g$ replaced by a mixed condition, namely, $\Phi = g$ over part of S and $\partial\Phi/\partial n = h$ over the rest of S.

10. (a) Suppose that

$$\nabla^2\Phi = f(x, y, z) \quad \text{in } V, \tag{a}$$

$$\frac{\partial\Phi}{\partial n} = 0 \quad \text{on } S. \tag{b}$$

Show that f *must* be such that $\int_V f\, dV = 0$. *Hint:* Integrate (a) over V and use the divergence theorem to evaluate the $\int_V \nabla^2\Phi\, dV$ term. *Note:* This result surely makes sense physically. For imagine (a) and (b) as governing steady-state conduction, where Φ is the temperature field. According to (b), no heat enters or leaves V through the boundary. Thus, if the net heat source, $\int_V f\, dV$, were *not* zero, the average temperature within V would surely be *changing with time*. But in view of the absence of a $\partial\Phi/\partial t$ term in (a), the field is supposed to be in *steady state*. Hence $\int_V f\, dV$ must be zero.
(b) Suppose that

$$\nabla^2\Phi = 0 \quad \text{in } V, \tag{c}$$

$$\frac{\partial\Phi}{\partial n} = f(x, y, z) \quad \text{on } S. \tag{d}$$

Show that f *must* be such that $\int_S f\, dA = 0$. *Hint:* See the hint in part (a).

15.3 POLAR COORDINATES

Optional Section

Remember that the coordinate system used is a matter of *choice*. If the region under consideration is a rectangle, a semi-infinite strip, or an infinite strip, it is generally most convenient to choose Cartesian coordinates, say x and y, so that the boundary conditions occur on constant-coordinate lines. Similarly, if the region is circular, annular, or a pie-shaped portion thereof, it is generally most convenient to use plane polar coordinates r and θ. In that case, we need to recall from page 386 that the Laplacian is

$$\nabla^2 = \frac{\partial^2}{\partial r^2} + \frac{1}{r}\frac{\partial}{\partial r} + \frac{1}{r^2}\frac{\partial^2}{\partial \theta^2}. \tag{1}$$

EXAMPLE 1 Consider the Dirichlet problem shown in Fig. 15.6 namely,

$$\nabla^2\Phi = \Phi_{rr} + \frac{1}{r}\Phi_r + \frac{1}{r^2}\Phi_{\theta\theta} = 0 \qquad (a < r < b,\ 0 < \theta < \alpha) \tag{2a}$$

$$\Phi(r, 0) = 0 \qquad (a < r < b) \tag{2b}$$

$$\Phi(r, \alpha) = 0 \qquad (a < r < b) \tag{2c}$$

$$\Phi(a, \theta) = 0 \qquad (0 < \theta < \alpha) \tag{2d}$$

$$\Phi(b, \theta) = f(\theta) \qquad (0 < \theta < \alpha). \tag{2e}$$

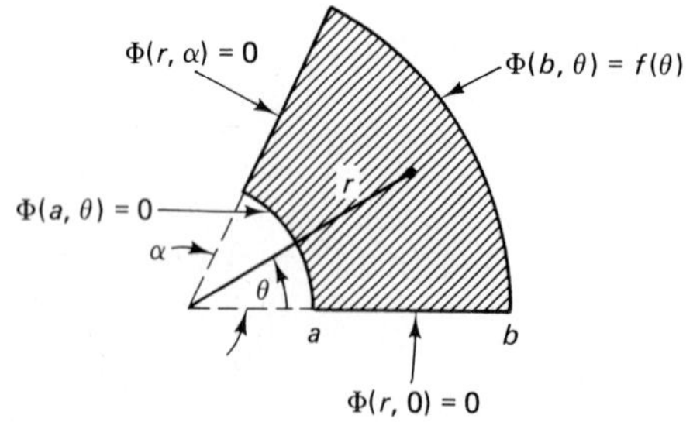

Fig. 15.6 The Dirichlet problem (1).

According to the method of separation of variables, seek $\Phi(r, \theta)$ in the product form

$$\Phi(r, \theta) = R(r)\Theta(\theta). \tag{3}$$

Putting (3) into the PDE gives

$$R''\Theta + \frac{1}{r}R'\Theta + \frac{1}{r^2}R\Theta'' = 0.$$

Multiplying by r^2 and dividing by $R\Theta$ enables us to separate the variables, so that

$$\frac{r^2R'' + rR'}{R} = -\frac{\Theta''}{\Theta} = \text{constant} = \kappa^2. \tag{4}$$

Here we tentatively express the constant as $+\kappa^2$ rather than as $-\kappa^2$, so that we obtain $\cos \kappa\theta$, $\sin \kappa\theta$ terms (rather than $\cosh \kappa\theta$, $\sinh \kappa\theta$) for the eventual Fourier series expansion of $f(\theta)$.

Proceeding, the R and Θ equations are

$$r^2R'' + rR' - \kappa^2 R = 0, \tag{5}$$

$$\Theta'' + \kappa^2\Theta = 0. \tag{6}$$

Although (5) has nonconstant coefficients, it happens to be elementary since it is of Cauchy–Euler form. Thus (see Example 5 in Section 6 of Appendix A).

$$R(r) = \begin{cases} A + B\ln r, & \kappa = 0 \\ Cr^{\kappa} + Dr^{-\kappa}, & \kappa \neq 0 \end{cases} \tag{7}$$

$$\Theta(\theta) = \begin{cases} E + F\theta, & \kappa = 0 \\ G\cos\kappa\theta + H\sin\kappa\theta, & \kappa \neq 0, \end{cases} \tag{8}$$

so that

$$\Phi(r, \theta) = (A + B\ln r)(E + F\theta) + (Cr^{\kappa} + Dr^{-\kappa})(G\cos\kappa\theta + H\sin\kappa\theta). \tag{9}$$

Turning to the boundary conditions, it is essential to invoke (2b) and (2c) before (2e), and it is convenient (although not essential) also to invoke (2d) before (2e). Beginning,

$$\Phi(r, 0) = 0 = (A + B\ln r)E + (Cr^{\kappa} + Dr^{-\kappa})G \tag{10}$$

gives $E = G = 0$, so that

$$\Phi(r, \theta) = (A' + B'\ln r)\theta + (C'r^{\kappa} + D'r^{-\kappa})\sin\kappa\theta. \tag{11}$$

Next

$$\Phi(r, \alpha) = 0 = (A' + B'\ln r)\alpha + (C'r^{\kappa} + D'r^{-\kappa})\sin\kappa\alpha$$

implies that $A' = B' = 0$ and $\sin\kappa\alpha = 0$. Thus $\kappa = n\pi/\alpha$ $(n = 1, 2, \ldots)$, and with the help of superposition, we have

$$\Phi(r, \theta) = \sum_{n=1}^{\infty} (C_n' r^{n\pi/\alpha} + D_n' r^{-n\pi/\alpha}) \sin\frac{n\pi\theta}{\alpha}. \tag{12}$$

Then (2d) gives

$$\Phi(a, \theta) = 0 = \sum_{n=1}^{\infty} (C_n' a^{n\pi/\alpha} + D_n' a^{-n\pi/\alpha}) \sin\frac{n\pi\theta}{\alpha}, \tag{13}$$

so that $C_n' a^{n\pi/\alpha} + D_n' a^{-n\pi/\alpha} = 0$ for each n, or $D_n' = -a^{2n\pi/\alpha}C_n'$. Updating (12) accordingly gives us

$$\Phi(r, \theta) = \sum_{n=1}^{\infty} C_n' (r^{n\pi/\alpha} - a^{2n\pi/\alpha} r^{-n\pi/\alpha}) \sin\frac{n\pi\theta}{\alpha}. \tag{14}$$

Finally,

$$\Phi(b, \theta) = f(\theta) = \sum_{n=1}^{\infty} C_n' \left[b^{n\pi/\alpha} - \left(\frac{a^2}{b}\right)^{n\pi/\alpha} \right] \sin\frac{n\pi\theta}{\alpha}, \tag{15}$$

which is a half-range Fourier sine expansion. Thus

$$C_n' = \frac{1}{b^{n\pi/\alpha} - (a^2/b)^{n\pi/\alpha}} \frac{2}{\alpha} \int_0^\alpha f(\theta) \sin \frac{n\pi\theta}{\alpha}\, d\theta, \tag{16}$$

and the desired solution to (2) is given by (14) and (16).

COMMENT 1 Equivalent to (14), but "prettier," is the form

$$\Phi(r, \theta) = \sum_{n=1}^{\infty} C_n'' \left[\left(\frac{r}{a}\right)^{n\pi/\alpha} - \left(\frac{a}{r}\right)^{n\pi/\alpha} \right] \sin \frac{n\pi\theta}{\alpha}, \tag{17}$$

with

$$C_n'' = \frac{1}{(b/a)^{n\pi/\alpha} - (a/b)^{n\pi/\alpha}} \frac{2}{\alpha} \int_0^\alpha f(\theta) \sin \frac{n\pi\theta}{\alpha}\, d\theta. \tag{18}$$

COMMENT 2 The boundary conditions (2a) to (2d) were of Dirichlet type (Φ prescribed). What if they were of Neumann type ($\partial\Phi/\partial n$ prescribed)? If, for example, (2b) were replaced by the nonhomogeneous Neumann condition

$$\frac{\partial \Phi}{\partial n}(r, 0) = g(r) \qquad (a < r < b) \tag{19}$$

where g is prescribed, what is the $\partial/\partial n$ in terms of r and θ? Well,

$$\frac{\partial \Phi}{\partial n} = \boldsymbol{\nabla}\Phi \cdot \hat{\mathbf{n}} = \left(\frac{\partial \Phi}{\partial r} \hat{\mathbf{e}}_r + \frac{1}{r}\frac{\partial \Phi}{\partial \theta} \hat{\mathbf{e}}_\theta \right) \cdot (-\hat{\mathbf{e}}_\theta) = -\frac{1}{r}\frac{\partial \Phi}{\partial \theta} \tag{20}$$

on the $\theta = 0$ edge, so (19) can be expressed in terms of r, θ as

$$\frac{\partial \Phi}{\partial \theta}(r, 0) = -rg(r) \qquad (a < r < b). \tag{21}$$

Similarly, a Neumann condition

$$\frac{\partial \Phi}{\partial n}(a, \theta) = h(\theta) \qquad (0 < \theta < \alpha) \tag{22}$$

would become

$$\frac{\partial \Phi}{\partial r}(a, \theta) = -h(\theta) \tag{23}$$

because

$$\frac{\partial \Phi}{\partial n} = \boldsymbol{\nabla}\Phi \cdot \hat{\mathbf{n}} = \left(\frac{\partial \Phi}{\partial r} \hat{\mathbf{e}}_r + \frac{1}{r}\frac{\partial \Phi}{\partial \theta} \hat{\mathbf{e}}_\theta \right) \cdot (-\hat{\mathbf{e}}_r) = -\frac{\partial \Phi}{\partial r} \tag{24}$$

on $r = a$. Remember that Neumann conditions are, in physical terms, *flux* conditions. For example, if Φ is a temperature field, then $\partial\Phi/\partial n$ on the boundary is proportional to the *heat flux* across that boundary.

COMMENT 3 The analysis above would have applied equally well if we had, instead, the more general boundary conditions

$$\Phi(r, 0) = \Phi_1, \qquad \Phi(r, \alpha) = \Phi_2,$$

$$\Phi(a, \theta) = f(\theta), \qquad \Phi(b, \theta) = g(\theta),$$

where Φ_1, Φ_2 are constants. In other words, the $A(E + F\theta)$ term in (9) could easily handle the $\Phi(r, 0) = \Phi_1$, $\Phi(r, \alpha) = \Phi_2$ boundary conditions, while the cos $(n\pi\theta/\alpha)$ and sin $(n\pi\theta/\alpha)$ terms could handle whatever Fourier series expansions of $f(\theta)$ and $g(\theta)$ are necessary. However, if instead Φ_1 and/or Φ_2 were *nonconstant* functions of r, these functions would need to be expanded. Unfortunately, the functions available for those expansions, the $r^{n\pi\alpha}$'s and $r^{-n\pi\alpha}$'s, are not sines and cosines, so that classical Fourier series theory would not suffice. The more powerful *Sturm–Liouville* theory would, however, and this story is left for Exercise 12. ◀

EXAMPLE 2 *Dirichlet Problem for Circular Disk.* In this second and final example, we consider the Dirichlet problem shown in Fig. 15.7, namely,

$$\nabla^2\Phi = \Phi_{rr} + \frac{1}{r}\Phi_r + \frac{1}{r^2}\Phi_{\theta\theta} = 0 \qquad (0 \le r < b) \tag{25a}$$

$$\Phi(b, \theta) = f(\theta). \tag{25b}$$

Recalling (9), we can immediately write

$$\Phi(r, \theta) = (A + B \ln r)(E + F\theta) + (Cr^{\kappa} + Dr^{-\kappa})(G \cos \kappa\theta + H \sin \kappa\theta), \tag{26}$$

but comparing (25) with (2), we seem to be missing some boundary conditions. After all, the PDE is second order in both r and θ, so that we expect to need two r boundary conditions and two θ boundary conditions, as were present in Example 1. For insight, it is useful to imagine obtaining the disk in Fig. 15.7 as a limiting case of the region in Fig. 15.6, namely, as $a \to 0$ and $\alpha \to 2\pi$. As $a \to 0$, the $r = a$ circular arc boundary shrinks to a *point,* and we lose that particular boundary curve and corresponding boundary condition. Next, let $\alpha \to 2\pi$. The moment α becomes 2π, we lose the two boundary conditions on the straight edges $\theta = 0$ and $\theta = \alpha$, because those edges disappear as boundary edges and become interior to the region.

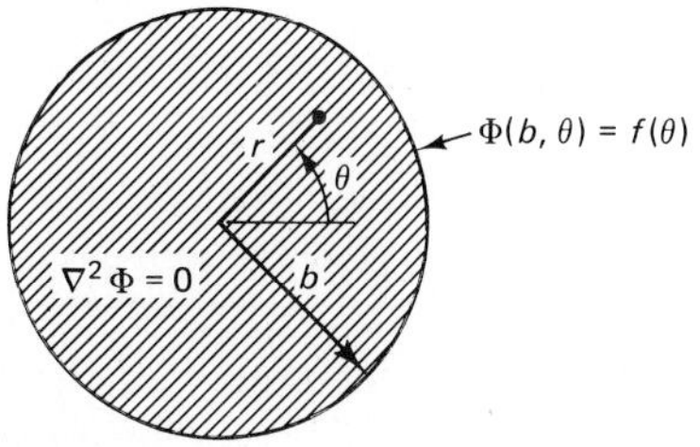

Fig. 15.7 The Dirichlet problem (25).

To compensate for these losses, we do the following. First, we adjoin to (25), as our missing r condition, a *boundedness condition* at $r = 0$, namely,*

$$\Phi(r, \theta) \text{ bounded as } r \to 0. \tag{27}$$

To apply this condition, observe that in (26) both the $\ln r$ and $r^{-\kappa}$ terms "blow up" as $r \to 0$; i.e., $\ln r \to -\infty$ and $r^{-\kappa} \to \infty$ as $r \to 0$. Thus, according to (27),

* Boundedness is generally an appropriate requirement, but not always (see, for example, Exercise 10).

we knock those terms out by setting $B = D = 0$. Then (26) reduces to the form

$$\Phi(r, \theta) = E' + F'\theta + r^{\kappa}(G' \cos \kappa\theta + H' \sin \kappa\theta). \tag{28}$$

Next, we call attention to an important difference between Example 1 and the present example. Namely, the θ domain in Example 1 was finite ($0 < \theta < \alpha$), whereas here it is infinite ($-\infty < \theta < \infty$). For in Example 1 (Fig. 15.6) the representative point can move about as much as it likes but θ can never become less than 0 nor more than α. In the present example (Fig. 15.7), on the other hand, there is nothing to prevent repeated encirclements of the origin, clockwise *or* counterclockwise. Now, if Φ is to be single valued and hence uniquely determined at each point within the disk, it needs to be 2π *periodic in* θ, that is,

$$\Phi(r, \theta + 2\pi) = \Phi(r, \theta), \tag{29}$$

and this periodicity condition will compensate for our two missing θ boundary conditions. Thus the full problem is given by (25), (27), and (29).

To impose (29), look at each term, in turn, in (28). First, E' is a constant and is therefore certainly a 2π-periodic function of θ. Next, $F'\theta$ is a linear function of θ; it is not 2π-periodic, so we set $F' = 0$. Finally, we come to the $\cos \kappa\theta$ and $\sin \kappa\theta$ terms. Surely, these are periodic functions of θ, but we need to find the allowable κ's such that they are 2π periodic. That is, we need

$$\cos \kappa(\theta + 2\pi) = \cos \kappa\theta, \qquad \sin \kappa(\theta + 2\pi) = \sin \kappa\theta \tag{30}$$

for all θ. It follows (Exercise 1) from (30) that κ can take on only integer values: $\kappa = n$ ($n = 1, 2, 3, \ldots$).

Thus

$$\Phi(r, \theta) = E' + \sum_{n=1}^{\infty} r^n(G_n' \cos n\theta + H_n' \sin n\theta), \tag{31}$$

and we are ready for (25b):

$$\Phi(b, \theta) = f(\theta) = E' + \sum_{n=1}^{\infty} b^n(G_n' \cos n\theta + H_n' \sin n\theta). \tag{32}$$

How to solve for E', G_n', and H_n'? We do *not* appeal to the half- and quarter-range formulas this time. Those formulas were used in cases where the function to be expanded was defined on a *finite* interval, such as $0 < x < \ell$. Thus we needed to provide a periodic extension in order to have a periodic function. In the present example, however, the θ domain is $-\infty < \theta < \infty$, and $f(\theta)$ in (32) is *already* a 2π-periodic function. Thus (32) is to be seen as *a classical Fourier series expansion of the* 2π*-periodic function* $f(\theta)$, and the usual formulas for the calculation of the Fourier coefficients give

$$E' = \frac{1}{2\pi}\int_{-\pi}^{\pi} f(\theta)\, d\theta, \qquad G_n' = \frac{1}{\pi b^n}\int_{-\pi}^{\pi} f(\theta) \cos n\theta\, d\theta,$$
$$H_n' = \frac{1}{\pi b^n}\int_{-\pi}^{\pi} f(\theta) \sin n\theta\, d\theta. \tag{33}$$

The desired solution is given by (31) and (33). If, for example, f is 100 on the upper half of the circle and 0 on the lower half (in which case f is really the 2π-peri-

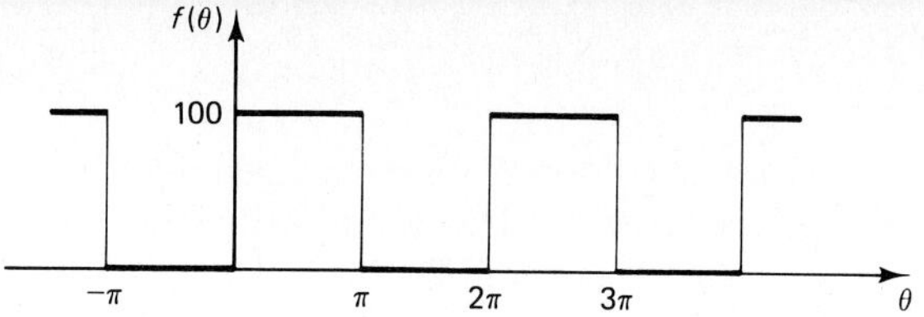

Fig. 15.8 Illustration of f.

odic function depicted in Fig. 15.8), we obtain the result

$$\Phi(r, \theta) = 50 + \frac{200}{\pi} \sum_{n=1,3,\ldots}^{\infty} \left(\frac{r}{b}\right)^n \frac{\sin n\theta}{n}. \tag{34}$$

Representative equipotentials are sketched in Fig. 15.9.

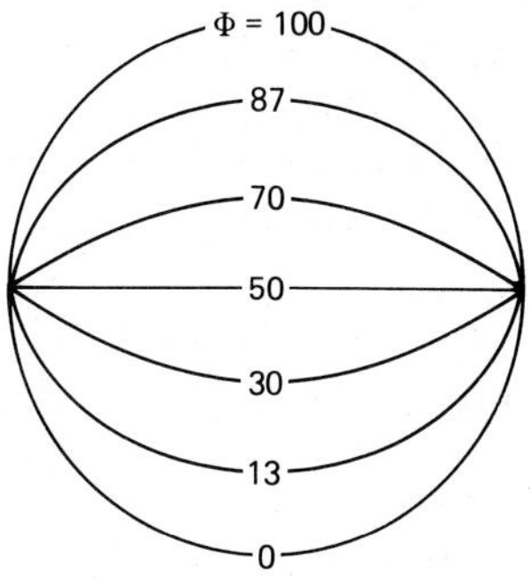

Fig. 15.9 Representative equipotentials.

COMMENT 1 Setting $r = 0$ in (31), observe that *the potential Φ at the center of the disk equals E', which is the average of f around the circumference,* as is seen to hold for the example shown in Fig. 15.9. This result bears a significant generalization. For suppose that the function Φ_0 is any solution of $\nabla^2\Phi = 0$ within any two-dimensional region $\mathscr{R}$, not necessarily a circular disk. Consider any point P in $\mathscr{R}$, and let $\mathscr{C}$ be any circle, centered at P and lying entirely within $\mathscr{R}$. Define the disk within $\mathscr{C}$ as $\mathscr{D}$ (Fig.15.10). Then $\nabla^2\Phi = 0$ within $\mathscr{D}$, subject to the Dirichlet boundary condition $\Phi = \Phi_0$ on $\mathscr{C}$, so the italicized result above can be applied: *The potential Φ at P is the average of the Φ values around $\mathscr{C}$.* Known as the **average value theorem,** this result is of importance in two-dimensional potential theory, and an analogous result holds in three dimensions as well.

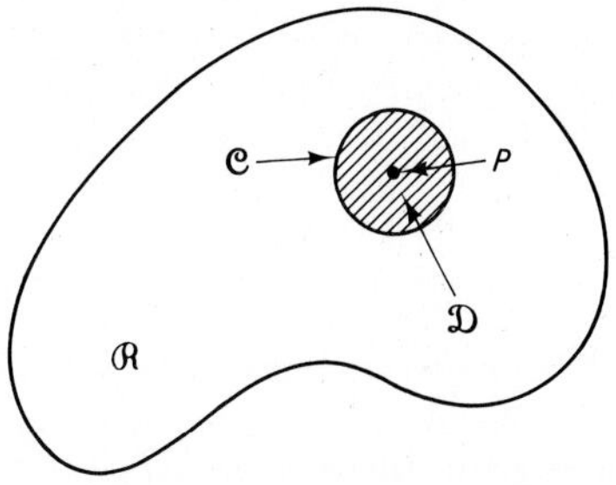

Fig. 15.10 The disk $\mathscr{D}$.

COMMENT 2 Let us put (33) into (31). First changing the dummy variable of integration to ϑ, say, to avoid confusion with the θ's in (31), the result is

$$\Phi(r, \theta) = \frac{1}{\pi}\int_{-\pi}^{\pi}\left[\frac{1}{2} + \sum_{n=1}^{\infty}\left(\frac{r}{b}\right)^n \cos n(\vartheta - \theta)\right] f(\vartheta)\, d\vartheta, \tag{35}$$

where we have formally interchanged the order of integration and summation. It is a striking fact that the infinite series in (35) can be summed, i.e., gotten into closed form. The result (Exercise 4),

$$\begin{aligned}\Phi(r, \theta) &= \frac{1}{2\pi}\int_{-\pi}^{\pi}\frac{b^2 - r^2}{b^2 - 2br\cos(\vartheta - \theta) + r^2} f(\vartheta)\, d\vartheta \\ &\equiv \int_{-\pi}^{\pi} P(r, \vartheta - \theta) f(\vartheta)\, d\vartheta,\end{aligned} \tag{36}$$

is known as the **Poisson integral formula,** and $P(r, \vartheta - \theta)$ is known as the **Poisson kernel.** It is clear, by inspection, that if the boundary temperature is a constant, say $f(\theta) = 1$, then the solution Φ will be a constant, too, $\Phi(r, \theta) = 1$. Putting these values into (36) yields the following property of the Poisson kernel:

$$\int_{-\pi}^{\pi} P(r, \vartheta - \theta)\, d\vartheta = 1, \tag{37}$$

for all values of r and θ ($0 \le r < b$, $-\infty < \theta < \infty$). This property will be drawn on in the exercises. ◀

In summary, our discussion of the two-dimensional Laplace equation in polar coordinates turned up a number of interesting features and results: the nonconstant coefficient Cauchy–Euler equation on R, the possible loss of boundary conditions and the need for boundedness and periodicity conditions, the average value theorem, and the Poisson integral formula. Be careful regarding 2π periodicity. Sometimes it applies, and sometimes it does not. For example, in Example 1 it would have been absurd to talk about 2π periodicity of $\Phi(r, \theta)$, because Φ was defined only on the finite θ interval $0 < \theta < \alpha$.

15.3 EXERCISES

1. Show that equations (30) hold, for all θ, if and only if $\kappa = n = 1, 2, 3, \ldots$. [It can be seen, from (26), that negative integer values contribute nothing new, and $\kappa = 0$ was disallowed because the $(A + B \ln r)(E + F\theta)$ term already accounted for the $\kappa = 0$ case.]

2. In example 2 we noted that $-\infty < \theta < \infty$ and imposed the periodicity condition (29). Alternatively, we can consider that $0 < \theta < 2\pi$, in which case the lines $\theta = 0$ and $\theta = 2\pi$ now show up as *boundary edges.* Since $0 < \theta < 2\pi$, 2π periodicity is *not* germane, but we now have the two artificially created boundaries $\theta = 0$ and $\theta = 2\pi$ along which to specify boundary conditions. In particular, we impose the two conditions

$$\Phi(r, 0) = \Phi(r, 2\pi), \tag{a}$$

$$\Phi_\theta(r, 0) = \Phi_\theta(r, 2\pi), \tag{b}$$

over $0 < r < b$, so that both the temperature and the heat flux are continuous along the two abutting edges $\theta = 0$ and $\theta = 2\pi$. With this reformulation of the problem [namely, regarding the θ domain as $0 < \theta < 2\pi$, and imposing the continuity conditions (a) and (b)], solve for $\Phi(r, \theta)$ and show that the solution obtained is the same as was obtained in Example 2.

3. In Comment 1 of Example 2 we obtained the *average value theorem* for the *two*-dimensional Laplace equation, and asserted its truth for the *three*-dimensional case. Prove the average value theorem for the *one*-dimensional potential equation $\Phi_{xx} = 0$.

4. Derive the result

$$\frac{1}{2} + \sum_{n=1}^{\infty} \left(\frac{r}{b}\right)^n \cos n(\vartheta - \theta) = \frac{1}{2} \frac{b^2 - r^2}{b^2 - 2\,br\cos(\vartheta - \theta) + r^2}, \tag{a}$$

stated in Example 2. *Hint:* Write

$$\sum_{n=1}^{\infty} \left(\frac{r}{b}\right)^n \cos n(\vartheta - \theta) = \text{Re} \sum_{n=1}^{\infty} \left(\frac{r}{b}\right)^n e^{in(\vartheta - \theta)}, \tag{b}$$

and use the *geometric series*

$$\sum_{n=0}^{\infty} z^n = \frac{1}{1 - z}, \tag{c}$$

which holds even if z is complex, provided that $|z| < 1$. As usual, Re denotes the real part of the quantity; thus

$$\text{Re}\left(\frac{r}{b}\right)^n e^{in(\vartheta-\theta)} = \text{Re}\left[\left(\frac{r}{b}\right)^n \cos n(\vartheta - \theta) + i\left(\frac{r}{b}\right)^n \sin n(\vartheta - \theta)\right] = \left(\frac{r}{b}\right)^n \cos n(\vartheta - \theta).$$

5. (*Maximum principle*) Show, from the Poisson integral formula (36), that if $f(\theta) \le M\,(-\pi \le \theta \le \pi)$ for some constant M, then $u(r, \theta) \le M$ everywhere inside the disk. Thus the maximum value of u occurs on the boundary. This result is known as the **maximum principle** of potential theory. More completely, show that if $m \le f(\theta) \le M$, then $m \le u(r, \theta) \le M$. *Note:* Here the region was a two-dimensional circular disk. Proof that the same result holds for *any* bounded two- or three-dimensional region can be found in I. S. Sokolnikoff and R. M. Redheffer, *Mathematics of Physics and Modern Engineering,* 2nd ed. (New York: McGraw-Hill, 1966), p. 512.

***6.** Solve the *half*-disk problem

$$\nabla^2\Phi = 0 \quad \text{in} \quad 0 < r < a,\, 0 < \theta < \pi;$$

$$\Phi(r, 0) = \Phi(r, \pi) = 0, \quad \Phi(a, \theta) = 100.$$

You may use any results that you wish from Example 2.

7. As a sort of "inverse" of Example 2, consider the region to be the whole plane, with a circular *hole* of radius b:

$$\begin{aligned} &\nabla^2\Phi = 0 \qquad (b < r < \infty) \\ &\Phi(b, \theta) = f(\theta), \qquad \Phi \text{ bounded as } r \to \infty. \end{aligned} \tag{a}$$

(a) Derive the solution forms

$$\begin{aligned} \Phi(r, \theta) &= E + \sum_{n=1}^{\infty} \left(\frac{b}{r}\right)^n (G_n \cos n\theta + H_n \sin n\theta), \\ E &= \frac{1}{2\pi} \int_{-\pi}^{\pi} f(\theta)\, d\theta, \\ G_n &= \frac{1}{\pi} \int_{-\pi}^{\pi} f(\theta) \cos n\theta\, d\theta, \\ H_n &= \frac{1}{\pi} \int_{-\pi}^{\pi} f(\theta) \sin n\theta\, d\theta \end{aligned} \tag{b}$$

and

$$\Phi(r, \theta) = \frac{1}{2\pi} \int_{-\pi}^{\pi} \frac{r^2 - b^2}{r^2 - 2\,br\cos(\vartheta - \theta) + b^2} f(\vartheta)\, d\vartheta. \tag{c}$$

(b) Find $\Phi(r, \theta)$ for the case where $f(\theta) = 20 + 10 \sin 2\theta$, and sketch enough (labeled) level curves to reveal the overall level-curve pattern.

8. Consider a thin flat circular plate of radius b, which is thermally insulated on its two flat faces. With a hacksaw we make a radial cut, along $\theta = 0$, say, from $r = b$ to $r = 0$. The small gap, due to the cut, may be approximated as a thermal insulator, so that $\partial\Phi/\partial n = 0$ on both edges, namely $\theta = 0$ and $\theta = 2\pi$. If the circumference of the plate is held at the temperature $50(1 + \sin\theta)$ for a long time, the steady-state temperature field $\Phi(r, \theta)$ is governed by the boundary value problem

$$\nabla^2\Phi = 0 \qquad (0 < r < b,\, 0 < \theta < 2\pi)$$

$$\frac{\partial\Phi}{\partial n}(r, 0) = \frac{\partial\Phi}{\partial n}(r, 2\pi) = 0,$$

$$\Phi(b, \theta) = 50(1 + \sin\theta).$$

Solve for, and plot, the temperature distributions $\Phi(r, 0)$ and $\Phi(r, 2\pi)$ along the two edges of the cut. Does the answer depend in any way on whether the plate is steel, or brass, or whatever? Explain.

9. Solve the following potential problems: $\nabla^2\Phi = 0$

*(a) in $a < r < b,\ 0 < \theta < \alpha$; $\Phi(r, 0) = \Phi_1$, $\Phi(r, \alpha) = \Phi_2$, $\Phi(a, \theta) = f(\theta)$, $\Phi(b, \theta) = g(\theta)$

(b) in $a < r < b,\ 0 < \theta < \alpha;\ \Phi(r, \alpha) = \Phi_1$, $\partial\Phi/\partial n = 0$ on remainder of boundary

(c) in $0 < r < b$, $0 < \theta < \pi$; $\Phi(b, \theta) = 100$ over $0 < \theta < \pi/2$, and 0 on remainder of boundary

(d) in $a < r < b$, $-\infty < \theta < \infty$; $\Phi(a, \theta) = f(\theta)$, $\Phi(b, \theta) = g(\theta)$

(e) in $a < r < b$, $-\infty < \theta < \infty$; $\dfrac{\partial\Phi}{\partial n}(a, \theta) = 0$, $\dfrac{\partial\Phi}{\partial n}(b, \theta) = 50 \sin 4\theta$

*(f) in $a < r < \infty$, $0 < \theta < \pi$; $\Phi(r, 0) = \Phi(r, \pi) = 0$, $\Phi(a, \theta) = \Phi_1$

(g) in $a < r < b$, $0 < \theta < \pi$; $\Phi(r, 0) = 0$, $\Phi(b, \theta) = \Phi_1$, $\Phi(r, \pi) = \Phi_1$, $\dfrac{\partial\Phi}{\partial n}(a, \theta) = 0$ (Expansion coefficients may be left in integral form.)

(h) in $a < r < \infty$, $0 < \theta < 2\pi$; $\Phi(r, 0) = \Phi(r, 2\pi) = 0$, $\Phi(a, \theta) = \Phi_1$ (We have an infinite sheet with a hole of radius a and a radial slit along $\theta = 0$. The edge of the hole is held at a voltage Φ_1, and the edges of the slit are "grounded.")

(i) in $0 < r < b$, $0 < \theta < 3\pi/2$; $\Phi(r, 0) = \Phi(r, 3\pi/2) = 100$, $\Phi(b, \theta) = 0$

(j) in $a < r < b$, $-\infty < \theta < \infty$; $\Phi(a, \theta) = \Phi_1$, $\Phi(b, \theta) = \Phi_2$

(k) in $a < r < b$, $-\infty < \theta < \infty$; $\dfrac{\partial\Phi}{\partial n}(a, \theta) = 0$, $\Phi(b, \theta) = \Phi_1$

(l) in $0 < r < b$, $0 < \theta < \pi/2$; $\Phi(r, 0) = 0$, $(\partial\Phi/\partial n)(r, \pi/2) = 0$, $(\partial\Phi/\partial n)(b, \theta) = \sin 2\theta$

10. (*Flow over a circular bump*) We are interested in the disturbance in an otherwise-uniform plane flow of speed U, of an inviscid incompressible fluid, induced by a semicircular bump of radius a, as sketched in the accompanying figure. (That is, the bump is a half-cylinder which is infinitely long normal to the plane of the paper.) Reviewing Example 3 on page 430, we see that the fluid velocity field $\mathbf{q}$, which is sought, can be expressed as $\mathbf{q} = \nabla\Phi$, where the "velocity potential" Φ satisfies the boundary value problem

$$\nabla^2\Phi = \Phi_{rr} + \frac{1}{r}\Phi_r + \frac{1}{r^2}\Phi_{\theta\theta} = 0$$

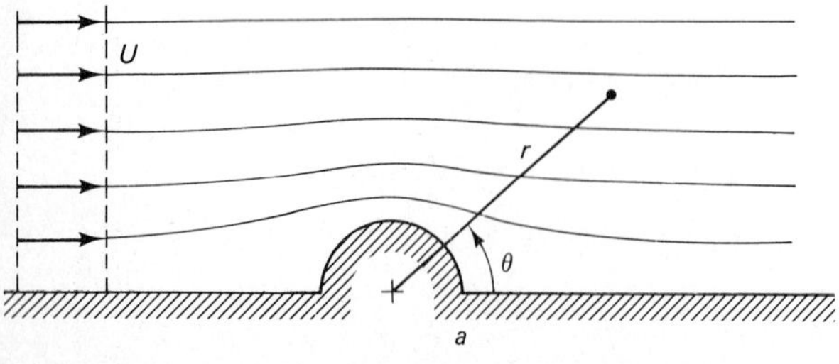

$$(a < r < \infty,\ 0 < \theta < \pi) \tag{a}$$

$$\Phi_n(r, 0) = \Phi_n(a, \theta) = \Phi_n(r, \pi) = 0,$$

$$\Phi(r, \theta) \sim Ur \cos\theta \text{ as } r \to \infty$$

(i.e., $\Phi \sim Ux$ as $r \to \infty$, so that $\mathbf{q} = \nabla\Phi \sim U\hat{\mathbf{i}}$). Derive the solution

$$\Phi(r, \theta) = U\left(r + \frac{a^2}{r}\right)\cos\theta + \text{arbitrary constant.} \tag{b}$$

Note 1: The velocity field is then available as $\mathbf{q} = \nabla\Phi$. Knowing $\mathbf{q}$, one could use the Bernoulli equation of fluid mechanics to deduce the pressure field and, in particular, the resulting aerodynamic force on the semicircular bump (which might, for example, be the roof of a building).

Note 2: Observe that *in this problem a boundedness condition on Φ would be inappropriate* since $\Phi \sim Ur\cos\theta$ as $r \to \infty$. Nevertheless, the *physical* quantity $\mathbf{q} = \nabla\Phi$ *is* bounded: $\mathbf{q} \sim U\hat{\mathbf{i}}$ as $r \to \infty$. Finally, observe that (b) can be expressed as $\Phi = \Phi_1 + \Phi_2$, where $\Phi_1 = Ur \cos\theta = Ux$ is the potential of the "free stream" and $\Phi_2 = U(a^2/r)\cos\theta$ accounts for the disturbance induced by the bump.

11. (*Flow over a circular cylinder; nonuniqueness*) In Exercise 10 we considered the flow of a "free stream" past a wall with a semicircular bump. Here, we consider the flow of a free stream past a circular cylinder. The boundary value problem may be posed as follows:

$$\nabla^2\Phi = \Phi_{rr} + \frac{1}{r}\Phi_r + \frac{1}{r^2}\Phi_{\theta\theta} = 0 \tag{a}$$

$$(a < r < \infty,\ 0 < \theta < 2\pi)$$

$$\Phi_n(a, \theta) = 0 \tag{b}$$

$$\nabla\Phi|_{\theta=0} = \nabla\Phi|_{\theta=2\pi} \text{ over } a < r < \infty \tag{c}$$

$$\Phi \sim Ur\cos\theta \text{ as } r \to \infty. \tag{d}$$

That is, if we specify that $0 < \theta < 2\pi$, the radial lines $\theta = 0$ and $\theta = 2\pi\,(a < r < \infty)$ become part of the boundary (see the accompanying sketch), so that boundary conditions are needed along these lines. The appropriate boundary condition is that the physical velocity $\mathbf{q}$ be the same at $\theta = 0$ and $\theta = 2\pi$ (for all $a < r < \infty$). Hence condition (c) or, equivalently,

$$\Phi_r(r, 0) = \Phi_r(r, 2\pi) \qquad (a < r < \infty), \tag{e}$$

$$\frac{1}{r}\Phi_\theta(r, 0) = \frac{1}{r}\Phi_\theta(r, 2\pi) \qquad (a < r < \infty). \tag{f}$$

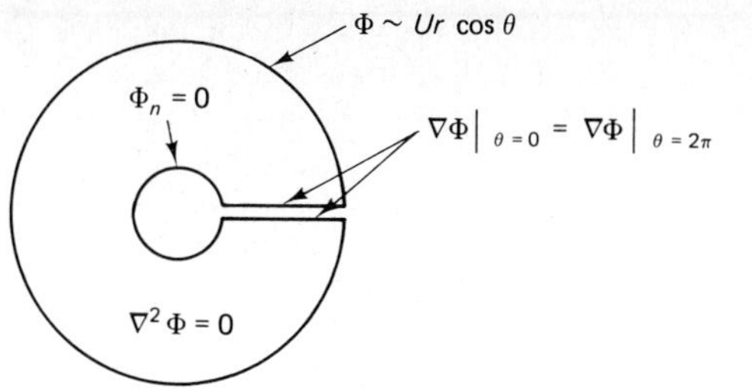

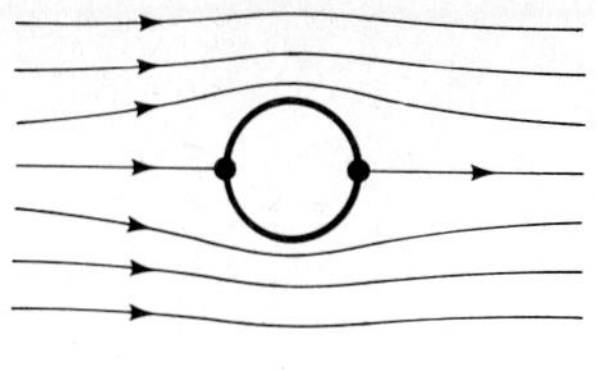

(a)

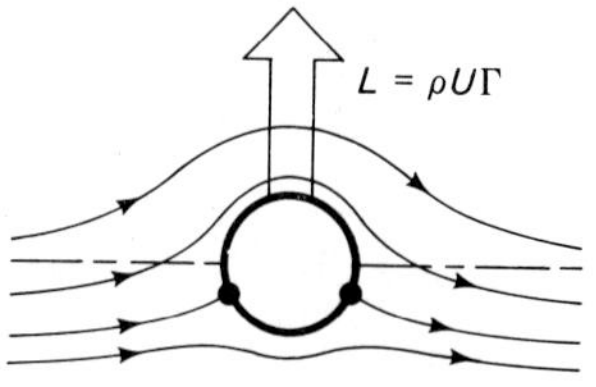

(c)

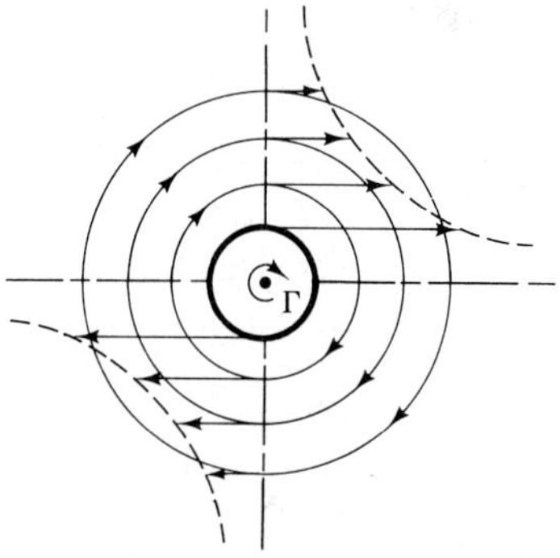

(b)

Integrating (e) with respect to r, and canceling r's in (f), we obtain

$$\Phi(r, 0) = \Phi(r, 2\pi) + \Gamma \qquad (a < r < \infty) \quad \text{(g)}$$

$$\Phi_\theta(r, 0) = \Phi_\theta(r, 2\pi) \qquad (a < r < \infty), \quad \text{(h)}$$

where Γ is an arbitrary constant.

(a) Solve the resulting boundary value problem (a), (b), (g), (h), (d), and show that

$$\Phi(r, \theta) = U\left(r + \frac{a^2}{r}\right)\cos\theta - \frac{\Gamma}{2\pi}\theta. \quad \text{(i)}$$

Note: In physical terms, the $U(r + a^2r^{-1})\cos\theta$ term in (i) corresponds to a flow that is symmetric about the x axis, and which has *stagnation points* (where $\mathbf{q} = \mathbf{0}$) at $r = a$, $\theta = 0$, and π [part (a) of the accompanying figure]. The $-(\Gamma/2\pi)\theta$ term gives

$$\mathbf{q} = \nabla\left(-\frac{\Gamma}{2\pi}\theta\right) = -\frac{\Gamma}{2\pi r}\hat{\mathbf{e}}_\theta,$$

which is the circular flow sketched in Fig. (b), and which can be regarded as generated by a fictitious clockwise *vortex* (see Exercise 3, page 378) at the origin—"fictitious" because there is no fluid inside the cylinder. The superposition of the two flows gives a flow somewhat as sketched in Fig. (c), namely, the symmetric flow plus some clockwise "swirl" proportional to Γ. Observe from Figs. (a) and (b) that the two flows *add* on the upper half of the cylinder and *subtract* on the lower half. Thus, in Fig. (c) we find higher velocities on the upper half than on the lower half and hence (since Bernoulli's equation $\rho q^2/2 + p =$ constant, where p is pressure and ρ is fluid mass density, says, "the higher the velocity the lower the pressure") lower pressures on the top than on the bottom. Thus, integrating, it is not surprising to find that the net pressure force on the cylinder is a *lift force* $L = \rho U\Gamma$ per unit length of the cylinder (i.e., per unit z length). In summary, the solution (i) is nonunique because of the arbitrary constant Γ. (To eliminate the nonuniqueness, one would be drawn into considering *real-fluid* effects, specifically, the inevitably nonzero viscosity.) In fact, the Γ term is extremely important since it alone contributes to an aerodynamic force on the cylinder.

(b) Show that the two stagnation points, in part (c) of the figure are located by the equation $\sin\theta = -\Gamma/(4\pi Ua)$. For example, if $\Gamma = 0$, then $\theta = \pi$ and 2π, as in Fig. (a). What happens if $\Gamma > 4\pi Ua$?

12. (*Sturm–Liouville to the rescue*) The problem

$$\nabla^2\Phi = 0 \qquad \left(a < r < b,\ 0 < \theta < \frac{\pi}{2}\right)$$

$$\Phi(r, 0) = \Phi(a, \theta) = \Phi(b, \theta) = 0 \quad \text{(a)}$$

$$\Phi\left(r, \frac{\pi}{2}\right) = f(r),$$

illustrated in the figure, involves an expansion of $f(r)$ in a series which is not of classical Fourier series form.

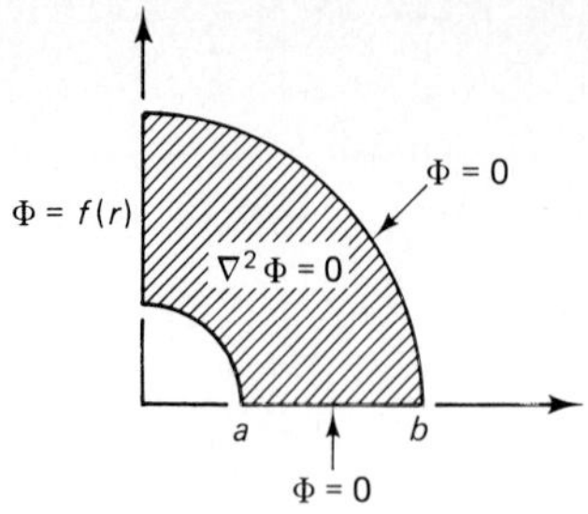

*(a) Separating according to

$$\frac{r^2R'' + rR'}{R} = -\frac{\Theta''}{\Theta} = -\kappa^2, \qquad \text{(b)}$$

solve for $\Phi(r, \theta)$ with the help of the Sturm–Liouville theory.

(b) The correct choice of $-\kappa^2$ as the separation constant in equation (b) was not critical, for if we chose $+\kappa^2$, we would merely have found that the κ's are purely imaginary. Nonetheless, it is more convenient to choose the correct sign to begin with. Thus, show, in advance, that the separation constant must be negative. *Hint:* Write $(r^2R'' + rR')/R = \alpha$ or $r^2R'' + rR' = \alpha R$. Multiply through by R/r and integrate from a to b.

13. (*Three-dimensional case*) The electric potential (voltage) Φ in a spherical shell $a < \rho < b$ (ρ, ϕ, θ are spherical polar coordinates) is governed by the boundary value problem

$$\nabla^2\Phi = 0 \qquad (a < \rho < b)$$

$$\Phi = \Phi_1 \text{ on } \rho = a, \quad \Phi = 0 \text{ on } \rho = b.$$

That is, the outer surface is "grounded." Solve for Φ. *Hint:* Evidently, $\Phi(\rho, \phi, \theta)$ does not vary with ϕ or θ.

15.4. FOURIER TRANSFORM

[Optional Section]

Recall, about Fourier series, that the period is necessarily finite. Thus, our Fourier series expansions, in the preceding section, were always of functions defined along edges of finite extent. If, instead, the edge is doubly infinite in extent, we can imagine the Fourier series giving way to the Fourier integral. And since the Fourier integral formula is equivalent to the Fourier transform and inverse, it seems reasonable to bypass the separation-of-variables approach altogether and to apply the Fourier transform from the start.

Let us illustrate with an example.

EXAMPLE 1 *Dirichlet Problem for Half Plane.* We consider the half-plane problem

$$\nabla^2\Phi = \Phi_{xx} + \Phi_{yy} = 0 \qquad (-\infty < x < \infty, 0 < y < \infty) \qquad \text{(1a)}$$

$$\Phi(x, 0) = f(x) \qquad (-\infty < x < \infty) \qquad \text{(1b)}$$

depicted in Fig. 15.11, realizing that we may be stipulating additional boundary conditions on Φ, and conditions on f, as the solution proceeds.

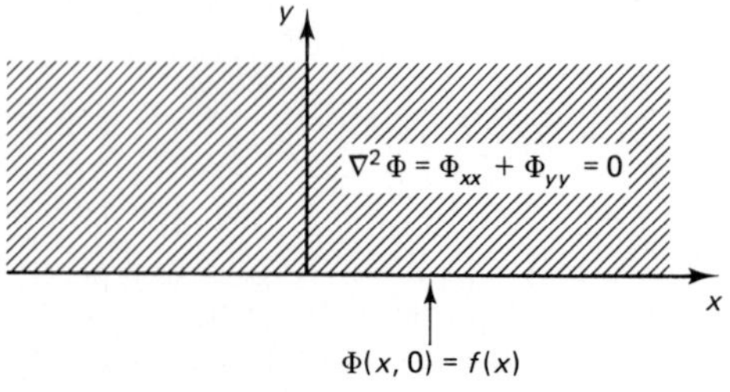

Fig. 15.11 Dirichlet problem for upper half plane.

Fourier transforming (1a), recall from Section 11.4 that $\mathbf{F}\{\Phi_{xx}\} = (i\omega)^2\hat{\Phi}(\omega, y)$ if Φ and $\Phi_x \to 0$ as $x \to \pm\infty$. Then

$$-\omega^2\hat{\Phi} + \frac{d^2\hat{\Phi}}{dy^2} = 0, \tag{2}$$

so that

$$\hat{\Phi} = Ae^{|\omega| y} + Be^{-|\omega| y}. \tag{3}$$

[Do not worry about the absolute value signs in (3); we discuss that point later.]

Now the Fourier transform of (1b), namely,

$$\hat{\Phi}|_{y=0} = \hat{f}(\omega) \tag{4}$$

gives us a boundary condition to apply to (3). However, that step will give but one equation in the two unknowns A and B. As the needed second condition, suppose that $\Phi(x, y) \to 0$ as $y \to \infty$, as is reasonable since we have already assumed that Φ and $\Phi_x \to 0$ as $x \to \pm\infty$. Then we formally obtain

$$\begin{aligned}\lim_{y\to\infty} \hat{\Phi}(\omega, y) &= \lim_{y\to\infty} \int_{-\infty}^{\infty} \Phi(x, y)e^{-i\omega x}\,dx \\ &= \int_{-\infty}^{\infty} \lim_{y\to\infty} \Phi(x, y)e^{-i\omega x}\,dx = \int_{-\infty}^{\infty} 0\,dx = 0,\end{aligned} \tag{5}$$

so that the condition $\Phi(x, y) \to 0$ as $y \to \infty$ on Φ implies the analogous condition

$$\hat{\Phi}(\omega, y) \to 0 \quad \text{as} \quad y \to \infty, \tag{6}$$

on $\hat{\Phi}$. Applying (6) to (3) gives $A = 0$, so

$$\hat{\Phi} = Be^{-|\omega| y}, \tag{7}$$

and then (4) gives $B(\omega) = \hat{f}(\omega)$, so that

$$\hat{\Phi}(\omega, y) = \hat{f}(\omega)e^{-|\omega| y}. \tag{8}$$

If we then use item 4 in Appendix B, together with the Fourier convolution theorem, to invert (8), we obtain the final result

$$\begin{aligned}\Phi(x, y) &= f(x) * \frac{y}{\pi}\frac{1}{x^2 + y^2} \\ &= \frac{y}{\pi}\int_{-\infty}^{\infty} \frac{f(\xi)}{(x - \xi)^2 + y^2}\,d\xi,\end{aligned} \tag{9}$$

which is known as the **Poisson integral formula for the half plane.**

COMMENT 1 Returning to (2), it would be natural to wonder why we included absolute value signs in the solution (3). Could we not have written

$$\Phi = Ce^{\omega y} + De^{-\omega y} \tag{10}$$

instead? The answer is yes, (10) is fine. But (3) is more convenient, for if we use (3), then (6) gives the simple result $A = 0$, whereas if we use (10), then (6) gives the equivalent but more unwieldy result that $C(\omega) = 0$ for $\omega > 0$ and $D(\omega) = 0$

for $\omega < 0$. (Recall that ω ranges from $-\infty$ to $+\infty$ in the Fourier inversion formula.)

COMMENT 2 Expressing (9) as

$$\Phi(x, y) = \int_{-\infty}^{\infty} K(x - \xi, y) f(\xi)\, d\xi, \tag{11}$$

where the kernel K is

$$K(x - \xi, y) = \frac{y}{\pi} \frac{1}{(x - \xi)^2 + y^2}, \tag{12}$$

observe that K has unit area for each $y > 0$, since (Exercise 1)

$$\frac{y}{\pi} \int_{-\infty}^{\infty} \frac{1}{(x - \xi)^2 + y^2}\, d\xi = 1, \tag{13}$$

and its graph become more and more sharply focused (at $\xi = x$) as $y \to 0+$, as seen from Fig. 15.12. These are the classic symptoms of delta sequences (see Exercise 2, page 517), and we assert that K is indeed a delta sequence, as $y \to 0+$. Then

$$\lim_{y \to 0+} \int_{-\infty}^{\infty} K(\xi - x, y) f(\xi)\, d\xi = f(x), \tag{14}$$

which is precisely the required boundary condition! ◀

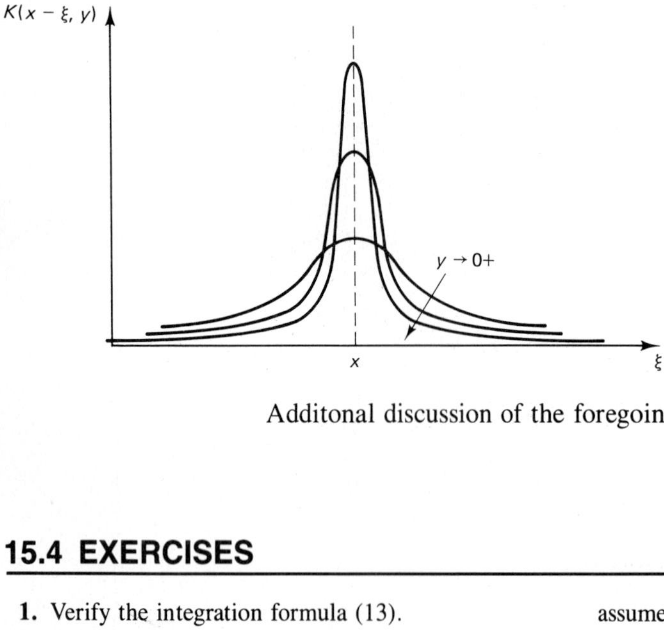

Fig. 15.12 Delta-sequence behavior of $K(x - \xi, y)$ as $y \to 0+$.

Additonal discussion of the foregoing example is reserved for the exercises.

15.4 EXERCISES

1. Verify the integration formula (13).

2. For each given f, evaluate $\Phi(x, y)$ from (9), and verify, a posteriori, that $\Phi(x, y)$ does satisfy the Laplace equation in the upper half plane (although it may not, in addition, satisfy the conditions that Φ and $\Phi_x \to 0$ as $x \to \pm\infty$ and that $\Phi \to 0$ as $y \to \infty$, as was assumed, if f does not die out fast enough, as $x \to \pm\infty$, to be Fourier transformable, as was also assumed).

(a) $f(x) = \text{constant} = f_0$.
*(b) $f(x) = H(x)$, where H is the Heaviside function. Plot Φ versus x at $y = 0$, 1, and 3, say.

(c) $f(x) = H(x + x_0) - H(x - x_0)$. Plot Φ versus x at $y = 0$ and at $y = 2x_0$, say. Show that $\Phi(x, y) \sim 2x_0/\pi y$ as $y \to \infty$. *Hint:* Note that

$$\tan^{-1} x = x - \frac{x^3}{3} + \frac{x^5}{5} - \frac{x^7}{7} + \cdots \qquad \text{(a)}$$

for $|x| < 1$, and

$$\tan^{-1} x = \frac{\pi}{2} - \frac{1}{x} + \frac{1}{3x^3} - \frac{1}{5x^5} + \cdots \qquad \text{(b)}$$

for $|x| > 1$, where, in each case, $\tan^{-1}$ denotes the "principal value," lying in the range from $-\pi/2$ to $\pi/2$.

(d) $f(x) = x[H(x + x_0) - H(x - x_0)]$. Plot Φ versus x at $y = 0$, and at $y = 2x_0$, say. Show that

$$\Phi(x, y) \sim \frac{2}{\pi} \frac{x_0 x^3 + x_0^3 x}{y^3}$$

as $y \to \infty$. *Hint:* Besides equations (a) and (b), note that

$$\ln(1 + x) = x - \frac{x^2}{2} + \frac{x^3}{3} - \frac{x^4}{4} + \cdots \qquad \text{(c)}$$

for $-1 < x \leq 1$. *Note:* Observe that for fixed x, $\Phi(x, y)$ dies out proportional to $1/y$ (as $y \to \infty$) in part (c), and proportional to $1/y^3$ in part (d). The more rapid decay in the latter case is no doubt due to the fact that $\int_{-\infty}^{\infty} f(x)\, dx = 0$ in part (d), whereas $\int_{-\infty}^{\infty} f(x)\, dx \neq 0$ in part (c).

(e) $f(x) = \delta(x)$. Plot Φ versus x at $y = 1$ and 2, say.

3. (a) Show, from (9), that if f is an even function of x, so is $\Phi(x, y)$.
(b) Show that if f is an odd function of x, so is $\Phi(x, y)$.

4. For the infinite-strip problem

$$\nabla^2 \Phi = 0 \qquad (-\infty < x < \infty,\ 0 < y < a)$$

$$\Phi(x, 0) = f(x), \quad \Phi(x, a) = g(x),$$

show that

$$\Phi(x, y) = \mathbf{F}^{-1}\left\{ \hat{f}(\omega) \frac{\sinh \omega(a - y)}{\sinh \omega a} + \hat{g}(\omega) \frac{\sinh \omega y}{\sinh \omega a} \right\}.$$

NUMERICAL SOLUTION 15.5

Following the same general lines as in Section 14.5, where we developed finite-difference solution techniques for the diffusion equation, here we do the same for the Laplace equation or, more generally and with no additonal difficulty, for the *Poisson equation* $\nabla^2 u = f$. This PDE governs numerous important physical phenomena, as has already been mentioned. For example, within the context of steady-state heat conduction, u is the temperature field and (give or take a multiplicative physical constant) f is a heat source distibution; in electrostatics, u is the electric potential (voltage) field and f is a charge distribution; in connection with the irrotational motion of an inviscid fluid, u is the velocity potential and f is a mass source distribution; and so on.

Limiting our development to the two-dimensional case, let us begin with the problem

$$u_{xx} + u_{yy} = f(x, y) \qquad (0 < x < a,\ 0 < y < b) \tag{1}$$

$$u(0, y) = p(y), \quad u(x, 0) = q(x), \quad u(a, y) = r(y), \quad u(x, a) = s(x), \tag{2}$$

depicted in Fig. 15.13a. Seeking an approximate numerical solution, we *discretize* the problem by dividing a into M equal parts of dimension $\Delta x = a/M$, dividing b into N equal parts of dimension $\Delta y = b/N$, and defining *nodal points* $P_{jk} = (x_j, y_k) = (j\Delta x, k\Delta y)$ for $j = 0, 1, 2, \ldots, M$ and $k = 0, 1, 2, \ldots, N$. Accordingly, we seek u not everywhere in the region, but only at nodal points—more

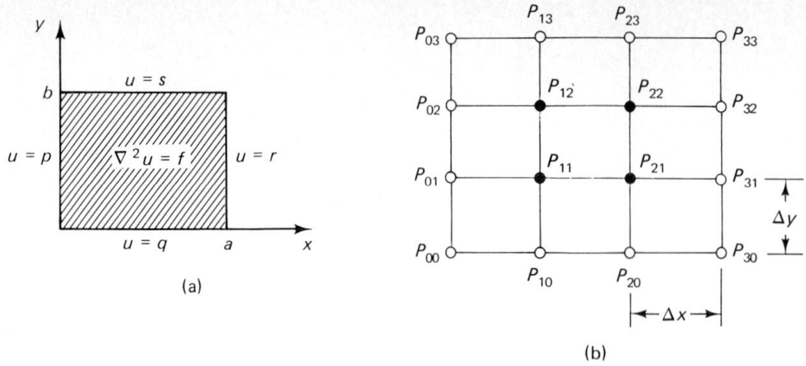

Fig. 15.13 The problem (1), and the finite-difference mesh.

specifically, at the interior nodal points, since u is prescribed at the boundary nodal points. The grid is shown in Fig. 15.13b for the choice $M = N = 3$.

Next, we replace the PDE (1) by a finite-difference approximation that will lead to a set of linear algebraic equations in the unknown nodal values of u. As in Section 14.5, we adopt the approximations

$$\frac{\partial^2 u}{\partial x^2}(x, y) \approx \frac{u(x - \Delta x, y) - 2u(x, y) + u(x + \Delta x, y)}{(\Delta x)^2}, \tag{3}$$

$$\frac{\partial^2 u}{\partial y^2}(x, y) \approx \frac{u(x, y - \Delta y) - 2u(x, y) + u(x, y + \Delta y)}{(\Delta y)^2}. \tag{4}$$

Putting (3) and (4) into the PDE, with $x = x_j$, $x - \Delta x = x_{j-1}$, $x + \Delta x = x_{j+1}$ (and similarly for y) gives

$$\frac{u(x_{j-1}, y_k) - 2u(x_j, y_k) + u(x_{j+1}, y_k)}{(\Delta x)^2} + \frac{u(x_j, y_{k-1}) - 2u(x_j, y_k) + u(x_j, y_{k+1})}{(\Delta y)^2} \approx f(x_j, y_k). \tag{5}$$

From (5) it seems reasonable to adopt the equation

$$\frac{U_{j-1,k} - 2U_{j,k} + U_{j+1,k}}{(\Delta x)^2} + \frac{U_{j,k-1} - 2U_{j,k} + U_{j,k+1}}{(\Delta y)^2} = f(x_j, y_k) \tag{6}$$

[where $f_{j,k} = f(x_j,y_k)$] as our *finite-difference approximation* of the PDE (1).

As in Section 14.5, we have used different letters (lowercase and uppercase) in order to distinguish between the exact solution $u(x, y)$ of the PDE (1) and the approximating solution $U_{j,k}$ generated by the finite-difference equation (6). We call $u(x_j, y_k) - U_{j,k}$ the **discretization error,** at P_{jk}, namely, the error incurred by virtue of the approximations (3) and (4). Clearly, a critical question is whether or not the discretization error tends to zero as Δx and $\Delta y \to 0$. If it does, we classify the finite-difference scheme as **convergent.** This sophisticated issue lies well beyond our present scope and will not be addressed here.*

* Incidentally, recall that in our study of the *diffusion* equation (Section 14.5) we paid comparable attention to the companion questions of convergence and stability. The difference scheme was said to be *stable* if round-off error did not grow unboundedly with time. For the Poisson and Laplace equations, however, we do not "march out" a solution in time, so the question of stability is not germane. Further, round-off error is probably quite negligible compared with the discretization error for the methods considered in this section.

If we choose $\Delta x = \Delta y \equiv h$, (6) becomes

$$\boxed{U_{j-1,k} + U_{j,k-1} + U_{j+1,k} + U_{j,k+1} - 4U_{j,k} = h^2 f_{j,k},} \tag{7}$$

which is often expressed, schematically, in the form

$$\begin{bmatrix} & 1 & \\ 1 & -4 & 1 \\ & 1 & \end{bmatrix} U = h^2 f. \tag{8}$$

If, in addition, $f(x, y) = 0$, so that (1) reduces to the Laplace equation, then (7) gives

$$U_{j,k} = \tfrac{1}{4}(U_{j-1,k} + U_{j,k-1} + U_{j+1,k} + U_{j,k+1}), \tag{9}$$

and it is striking that this result is a discrete version of the average value theorem given on page 653.

To illustrate the implementation of these results, let us make (1) and (2) more specific. Let $a = b = 1$ and choose $f(x, y) = p(y) = q(x) = s(x) = 0$ and $r(y) = 100 \sin \pi y$, so that we have the simple exact solution

$$u(x, y) = 100 \frac{\sinh \pi x}{\sinh \pi} \sin \pi y \tag{10}$$

available for comparison with our computed approximate solution.

As the simplest possible case, choose $M = N = 2$ (Fig. 15.14). Then $\Delta x = \Delta y = 0.5$, and (7) applies with $f_{j,k} = 0$. We have only one internal node, P_{11}, so we write out (7) only for that point, i.e., with $j = k = 1$:

$$U_{0,1} + U_{1,0} + U_{2,1} + U_{1,2} - 4U_{1,1} = 0, \tag{11}$$

or, recalling the given boundary conditions, $0 + 0 + 100 \sin(\pi/2) - 4U_{1,1} = 0$.

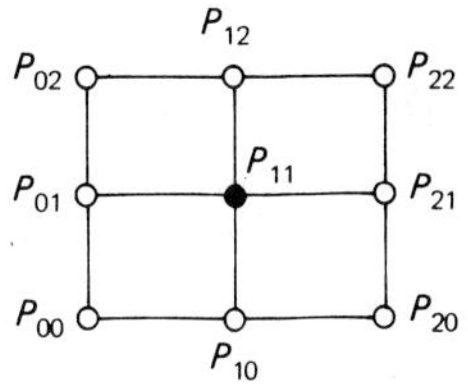

Fig. 15.14 The choice $M = N = 2$.

Solving, $U_{1,1} = 25$, and we have the comparison:

$$\begin{aligned} &\text{Computed:} \quad U_{1,1} = 25 \\ &\text{Exact:} \qquad u_{1,1} = 100 \frac{\sinh(\pi/2)}{\sinh \pi} \sin \frac{\pi}{2} = 19.93, \end{aligned} \tag{12}$$

where $u_{j,k}$ *means* $u(x, y)$ evaluated at P_{jk}.

Next, choose $M = N = 3$ (Fig. 15.13b), Writing out (7) for the internal nodes P_{11}, P_{21}, P_{12}, P_{22}, in turn, gives

$$P_{11}\text{:} \quad U_{0,1} + U_{1,0} + U_{2,1} + U_{1,2} - 4U_{1,1} = 0 \tag{13a}$$

$$P_{21}\text{:} \quad U_{1,1} + U_{2,0} + U_{3,1} + U_{2,2} - 4U_{2,1} = 0 \tag{13b}$$

$$P_{12}: \quad U_{0,2} + U_{1,1} + U_{2,2} + U_{1,3} - 4U_{1,2} = 0 \tag{13c}$$

$$P_{22}: \quad U_{1,2} + U_{2,1} + U_{3,2} + U_{2,3} - 4U_{2,2} = 0. \tag{13d}$$

Roughly speaking, (13a) ensures the approximate satisfaction of the Laplace equation in the neighborhood of P_{11}, (13b) ensures the approximate satisfaction of the Laplace equation in the neighborhood of P_{21}, and so on, so that the satisfaction of (13) is equivalent to the approximate satisfaction of the Laplace equation in the entire rectangular domain.

Recalling the boundary values $U_{01} = U_{02} = U_{10} = U_{20} = U_{13} = U_{23} = 0$ and $U_{31} = 100 \sin(\pi/3)$, $U_{32} = 100 \sin(2\pi/3)$, and rewriting (13) in matrix form, we have

$$\left(\begin{array}{cc|cc} -4 & 1 & 1 & 0 \\ 1 & -4 & 0 & 1 \\ \hline 1 & 0 & -4 & 1 \\ 0 & 1 & 1 & -4 \end{array}\right)\left(\begin{array}{c} U_{1,1} \\ U_{2,1} \\ \hline U_{1,2} \\ U_{2,2} \end{array}\right) = \left(\begin{array}{c} 0 \\ -100 \sin \frac{\pi}{3} \\ \hline 0 \\ -100 \sin \frac{2\pi}{3} \end{array}\right), \tag{14}$$

where the dashed lines are to be ignored for the moment. Solving (14) and comparing with the corresponding exact values, we have:

$$\begin{aligned} &\text{Computed:} \quad U_{1,1} = U_{1,2} = 10.83,\ U_{2,1} = U_{2,2} = 32.48 \\ &\text{Exact:} \quad u_{1,1} = u_{1,2} = 9.37,\ u_{2,1} = u_{2,2} = 29.99. \end{aligned} \tag{15}$$

Naturally, $M = N = 3$ is still quite crude, and sure enough, the results are seen from (15) to be only rough approximations.

It will prove useful to increase M and N one more time, to $M = N = 4$. Then (Exercise 1) we obtain the system

$$\left(\begin{array}{ccc|ccc|ccc} -4 & 1 & 0 & 1 & & & & & \\ 1 & -4 & 1 & 0 & 1 & & & & \\ 0 & 1 & -4 & 0 & 0 & 1 & & & \\ \hline 1 & 0 & 0 & -4 & 1 & 0 & 1 & & \\ & 1 & 0 & 1 & -4 & 1 & 0 & 1 & \\ & & 1 & 0 & 1 & -4 & 0 & 0 & 1 \\ \hline & & & 1 & 0 & 0 & -4 & 1 & 0 \\ & & & & 1 & 0 & 1 & -4 & 1 \\ & & & & & 1 & 0 & 1 & -4 \end{array}\right)\left(\begin{array}{c} U_{1,1} \\ U_{2,1} \\ U_{3,1} \\ U_{1,2} \\ U_{2,2} \\ U_{3,2} \\ U_{1,3} \\ U_{2,3} \\ U_{3,3} \end{array}\right) = \left(\begin{array}{c} 0 \\ 0 \\ -100 \sin \frac{\pi}{4} \\ \hline 0 \\ 0 \\ -100 \sin \frac{\pi}{2} \\ \hline 0 \\ 0 \\ -100 \sin \frac{3\pi}{4} \end{array}\right). \tag{16}$$

Solving (16) and comparing with the exact solution, we have

$$\text{Computed:}\quad U_{1,1} = U_{1,3} = 5.9,\ U_{2,1} = U_{2,3} = 15.2,\ U_{3,1} = U_{3,3} = 33.2$$
$$U_{1,2} = 8.3,\ U_{2,2} = 21.4,\ U_{3,2} = 47.0$$
$$\text{Exact:}\quad u_{1,1} = u_{1,3} = 5.32,\ u_{2,1} = u_{2,3} = 14.09,\ u_{3,1} = u_{3,3} = 32.01 \tag{17}$$
$$u_{1,2} = 7.52,\ u_{2,2} = 19.93,\ u_{3,2} = 45.27,$$

and these results show continued improvement over (15) and (12).

In some problems, *symmetries* are available which permit a considerable reduction in the computation. In the problem just considered, for example, in (15), we found that $U_{1,1} = U_{1,2}$ and $U_{2,1} = U_{2,2}$, and in (17) we found that $U_{1,1} = U_{1,3}$, $U_{2,1} = U_{2,3}$, and $U_{3,1} = U_{3,3}$. In other words, the solution was found to be symmetric about the midline $y = \frac{1}{2}$. That symmetry could have been noticed in advance, because the boundary conditions and the region itself were all symmetric about that line and could have been used to reduce the computation. With the choice $M = N = 3$, for example, observe from Fig. 15.15 that we need only deal with the nodal points P_{11} and P_{21} (or, equivalently, with P_{12} and P_{22}):

$$P_{11}:\quad 0 + 0 + U_{2,1} + U_{1,1} - 4U_{1,1} = 0, \tag{18a}$$

$$P_{21}:\quad U_{1,1} + 0 + 100 \sin\frac{\pi}{3} + U_{2,1} - 4U_{2,1} = 0, \tag{18b}$$

which are only two equations in two unknowns, whereas the comparable system (13) comprised four equations in four unknowns.

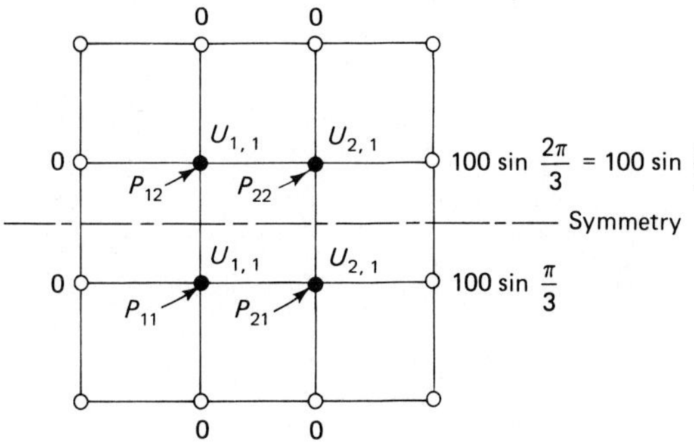

Fig. 15.15 Use of symmetry.

[Optional]

The systems (14) and (16) are of the form $\mathbf{AU} = \mathbf{c}$, where $\mathbf{A}$ is $(N-1)^2 \times (N-1)^2$.* (All elements *not* shown, in $\mathbf{A}$, are zero.) Even if N is a relatively modest 20, then $\mathbf{A}$ is 361×361. Consequently, considerable attention attaches to *efficient* means of solution. Before discussing solution techniques, observe that $\mathbf{A}$ is "strongly diagonal" inasmuch as its largest elements occur on the main diagonal. This feature should prove useful (since if $\mathbf{A}$ *is* diagonal, then $\mathbf{AU} = \mathbf{c}$ is as simple as possible), and is no accident; it results from our arranging the elements of $\mathbf{U}$ in "row sequence." That is, the first three elements of $\mathbf{U}$ $(U_{1,1}, U_{2,1}, U_{3,1})$ correspond to the first row of nodal points, the second three elements of $\mathbf{U}$ correspond to the second

* Proof that $\mathbf{A}$ is nonsingular is left for Exercise 14.

row of nodal points, and so on. For example, if we disturb the row sequence by interchanging the $U_{1,3}$ and $U_{3,2}$ elements in $\mathbf{U}$, in (16), the third and eighth columns of $\mathbf{A}$ interchange as well (also the third and eighth rows of $\mathbf{c}$), and the resulting $\mathbf{A}$ is no longer strongly diagonal.

Besides being strongly diagonal, $\mathbf{A}$ is said to be "banded." (A matrix is **banded** if all of its elements are zero outside a diagonal band centered on the main diagonal.) In fact, it can be partitioned [see dashed lines in (14) and (16)] as

$$\mathbf{A} = \begin{pmatrix} \mathbf{B} & \mathbf{I} & & & & \\ \mathbf{I} & \mathbf{B} & \mathbf{I} & & 0 & \\ & & \cdot & & & \\ & & & \cdot & & \\ & 0 & & \mathbf{I} & \mathbf{B} & \mathbf{I} \\ & & & & \mathbf{I} & \mathbf{B} \end{pmatrix}, \tag{19}$$

where $\mathbf{I}$ is an identity matrix of order $N - 1$ and $\mathbf{B}$ is the $(N - 1)$st-order matrix

$$\mathbf{B} = \begin{pmatrix} -4 & 1 & & & & \\ 1 & -4 & 1 & & 0 & \\ & & \cdot & & & \\ & & & \cdot & & \\ & 0 & & 1 & -4 & 1 \\ & & & & 1 & -4 \end{pmatrix}. \tag{20}$$

Although $\mathbf{A}$ is not tridiagonal, it is *block* tridiagonal.

Turning to solution techniques, we note first that the elementary Gauss elimination is not so bad, because $\mathbf{A}$ is banded. It is not hard to see that in the course of the elimination process the zeros outside the original band will remain zeros.

More commonly, however, iterative methods such as SOR (successive overrelaxation) are employed. The idea is essentially the same as developed in Section 14.5 for the implicit finite-difference solution of the diffusion equation. Basing our discussion on (7), the **Jacobi method** consists of the iterative scheme

$$U_{j,k}^{(n+1)} = \frac{1}{4}[U_{j-1,k}^{(n)} + U_{j,k-1}^{(n)} + U_{j+1,k}^{(n)} + U_{j,k+1}^{(n)} - h^2 f_{j,k}] \tag{21}$$

(for the interior nodes) for $n = 0, 1, 2, \ldots$, where $U_{p,q}^{(m)}$ denotes the mth iterate of $U_{p,q}$. The starting values are arbitrary; for example, we could use $U_{j,k}^{(0)} = 0$ for all interior points P_{jk}. This method is simple and of theoretical interest, but is not often used in practice. For we can easily improve on (21) by using the latest iterates as soon as they become available, and moving systematically across the first row (left to right), then the second, and so on. Known as the **Gauss–Seidel** or **Liebmann** method, the latter idea produces the scheme

$$U_{j,k}^{(n+1)} = \frac{1}{4}[U_{j-1,k}^{(n+1)} + U_{j,k-1}^{(n+1)} + U_{j+1,k}^{(n)} + U_{j,k+1}^{(n)} - h^2 f_{j,k}]. \tag{22}$$

Reexpressing (22) as

$$U_{j,k}^{(n+1)} = U_{j,k}^{(n)} + \frac{1}{4}[U_{j-1,k}^{(n+1)} + U_{j,k-1}^{(n+1)} + U_{j+1,k}^{(n)}$$

$$+ U_{j,k+1}^{(n)} - h^2 f_{j,k} - 4U_{j,k}^{(n)}] \quad (23)$$

$$\equiv U_{j,k}^{(n)} + \Delta U_{j,k}^{(n)},$$

we can insert a control parameter ω as follows,

$$U_{j,k}^{(n+1)} = U_{j,k,}^{(n)} + \omega \Delta U_{j,k}^{(n)} \quad (24)$$

and choose ω so as to speed the convergence. It has been shown* that the optimum ω is

$$\omega_{\text{opt}} = 2\frac{1 - \sin(\pi/N)}{\cos^2(\pi/N)}. \quad (25)$$

For large N, $\omega_{\text{opt}} \sim 2$. Since this amounts to an overcorrection, in (24), the method is usually called **successive overrelaxation (SOR),** although it is also known as the **extrapolated Liebmann method.**

Thus far we have dealt with cases where the boundary is rectilinear, such that all intersections of the grid lines and the boundary curve occur at nodal points. What if that is not the case, as illustrated in Fig. 15.16 for the case of a curved boundary? Then (7) cannot be applied at a node such as O (Fig. 15.16), so we need to modify (7) accordingly. We begin with the Taylor series expansions

$$u|_E = u|_O + u_x|_O \alpha h + \frac{1}{2} u_{xx}|_O (\alpha h)^2 + \cdots \quad (26a)$$

$$u|_W = u|_O - u_x|_O h + \frac{1}{2} u_{xx}|_O h^2 - \cdots. \quad (26b)$$

Multiplying (26b) by α and adding the result to (26a) gives

$$u|_E + \alpha u|_W = u|_O + \alpha u|_O + \frac{1}{2}(\alpha^2 + \alpha) h^2 u_{xx}|_O + \cdots, \quad (27)$$

so that if we neglect terms of order h^3 and higher in (27), we obtain

$$u_{xx}|_O \approx \frac{2}{h^2}\left[\frac{1}{\alpha(1+\alpha)} u|_E + \frac{1}{1+\alpha} u|_W - \frac{1}{\alpha} u|_O\right]. \quad (28)$$

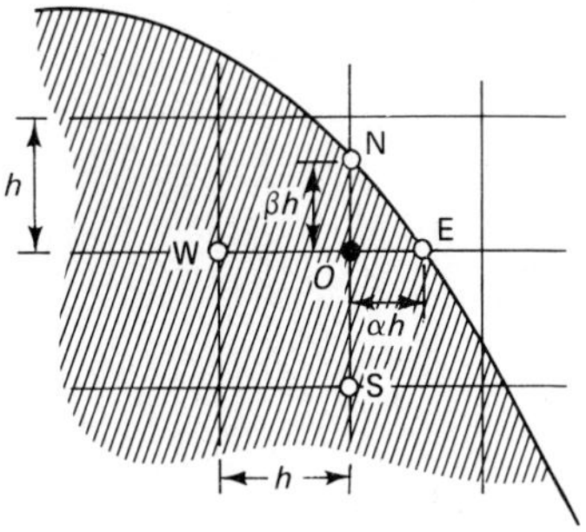

Fig. 15.16 Curved boundary; $0 < \alpha < 1$, $0 < \beta < 1$.

* S. P. Frankel, "Convergence Rates of Iterative Treatments of Partial Differential Equations," *Mathematical Tables and other Aids to Computation,* Vol. 4, 1950, pp. 65–75.

Similarly,

$$u_{yy}|_O \approx \frac{2}{h^2}\left[\frac{1}{\beta(1+\beta)}u|_N + \frac{1}{1+\beta}u|_S - \frac{1}{\beta}u|_O\right]. \tag{29}$$

Using (28) and (29), our finite-difference approximation to the Poisson equation $u_{xx} + u_{yy} = f(x, y)$, at O, becomes

$$\frac{1}{1+\alpha}U_W + \frac{1}{1+\beta}U_S + \frac{1}{\alpha(1+\alpha)}U_E + \frac{1}{\beta(1+\beta)}U_N - \frac{\alpha+\beta}{\alpha\beta}U_O = \frac{h^2}{2}f_O. \tag{30}$$

Naturally, if $\alpha = \beta = 1$, then (30) reduces to (7).

EXAMPLE 1 To illustrate (30), consider the Poisson problem shown in Fig. 15.17a. Unlike our introductory problem (1) and (2), which could have been solved analytically by methods discussed in Section 15.2, the present problem cannot be solved by those means because of the more complicated boundary shape. Wishing to illustrate (30), without worrying about accuracy, let us use the rather coarse grid shown in Fig. 15.17b. Applying (7) at P_{11}, (30) at P_{21} (with $\alpha = \frac{1}{2}$ and $\beta = 1$), (7) at P_{12}, and (30) at P_{13} (with $\alpha = \frac{1}{2}$ and $\beta = 1$) yields the four equations

$$50 + 100 + U_{2,1} + U_{1,2} - 4U_{1,1} = 20 \tag{31a}$$

$$\tfrac{2}{3}U_{1,1} + \tfrac{1}{2}(100) + \tfrac{4}{3}(100) + \tfrac{1}{2}(100) - 3U_{2,1} = \tfrac{1}{2}(80) \tag{31b}$$

$$50 + U_{1,1} + 100 + U_{1,3} - 4U_{1,2} = 40 \tag{31c}$$

$$\tfrac{2}{3}(50) + \tfrac{1}{2}U_{1,2} + \tfrac{4}{3}(100) + \tfrac{1}{2}(75) - 3U_{1,3} = \tfrac{1}{2}(60), \tag{31d}$$

respectively, where in (31d) we used the average value 75 at the corner $x = 1$, $y = 4$. ◀

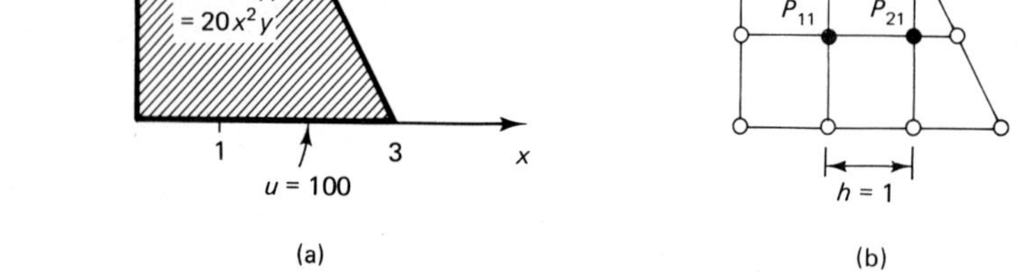

Fig. 15.17 Irregular boundary.

In this section we have endeavored to introduce the finite-difference approach to the solution of the Poisson and Laplace equations, at about the same level of completeness as in Section 14.5 on the diffusion equation. We derived the difference equations (6) and (7), and the modification of (7) in the event of more complicated boundaries. We illustrated their implementation using coarse grids, for simplicity, and discussed more efficient solution techniques for fine grids. In all cases, boundary conditions were of Dirichlet type, although Neumann and Robin boundary conditions are treated in the exercises.

15.5 EXERCISES

1. Setting $M = N = 4$, derive the system (16).

2. Corresponding to the choice $M = N = 4$, the system (16) consists of nine equations in nine unknowns. Keeping $M = N = 4$, use the symmetry about $y = \frac{1}{2}$ to obtain, in place of (16), a system of only six equations in six unknowns.

3. (*More general curved boundary formula*) Equation (30) applies when the north and east grid points need to be moved so as to fall on the curved boundary, as in Fig. 15.16. Most generally, consider the case shown in the accompanying figure, and show that in place of (30) we obtain the most general formula

$$\frac{1}{\gamma(\gamma+\alpha)}U_W + \frac{1}{\delta(\delta+\beta)}U_S + \frac{1}{\alpha(\alpha+\gamma)}U_E + \frac{1}{\beta(\beta+\delta)}U_N - \frac{\alpha\gamma+\beta\delta}{\alpha\beta\gamma\delta}U_O = \frac{h^2}{2}f_O. \tag{a}$$

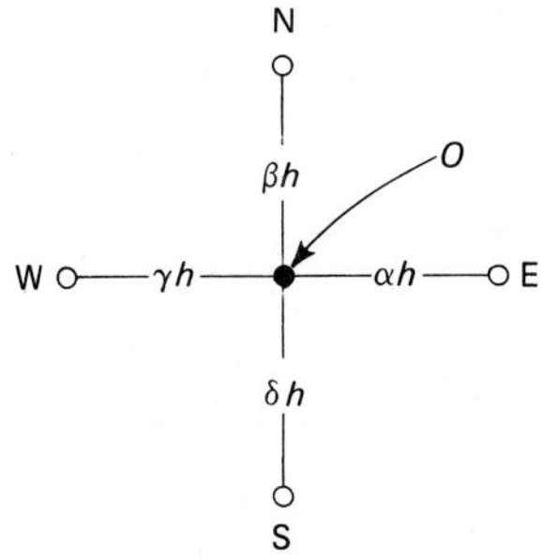

4. (*Dirichlet problems*) Solve the Dirichlet problems shown in the figures. In part (d) the PDE is $\nabla^2 u = f$, where f is a constant; in parts (a), (b), and (c), $\nabla^2 u = 0$. Use (7) [or, if necessary, equation (a) in Exercise 3], and solve by Gauss elimination. Use symmetry insofar as possible. (For simplicity, we denote nodes as $a, b, \ldots$ rather than as $P_{11}, P_{21}, \ldots$.)

*(a)

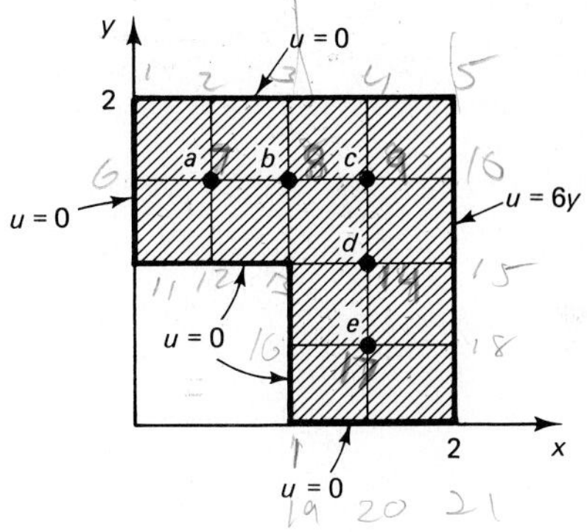

(b)

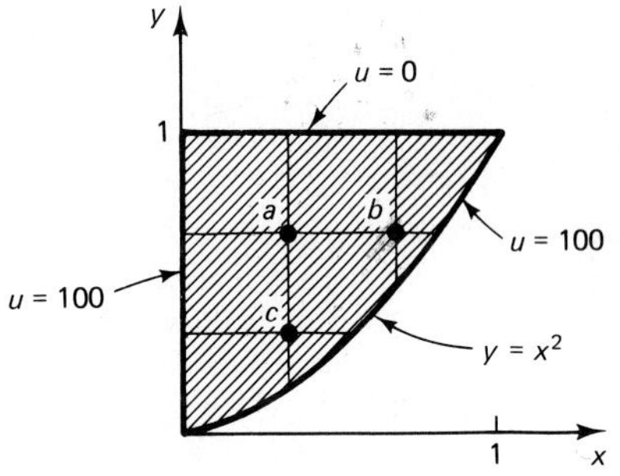

(c)

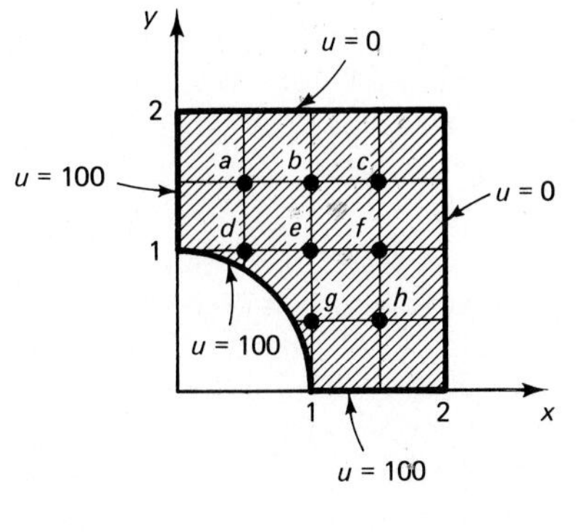

(d)

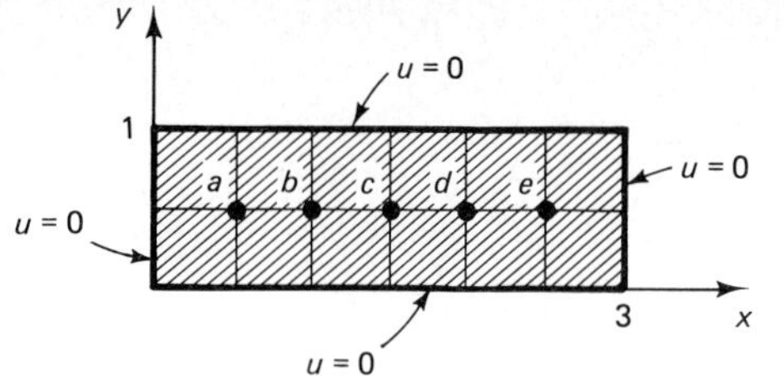

5. Is it possible for the finite-difference method to give the *exact* solution? If so, under what circumstances? If not, why not?

6. Let f and its first three derivatives be continuous in some neighborhood of x. Using Taylor's formula, with Lagrange remainder, derive the **forward, backward,** and **central difference approximations**

$$f'(x) \approx \frac{f(x+h) - f(x)}{h} \qquad \text{(forward)}, \qquad \text{(a)}$$

$$f'(x) \approx \frac{f(x) - f(x-h)}{h} \qquad \text{(backward)}, \qquad \text{(b)}$$

$$f'(x) \approx \frac{f(x+h) - f(x-h)}{2h} \qquad \text{(central)}, \qquad \text{(c)}$$

respectively, where $h > 0$, and show that the errors incurred in (a) to (c) are $O(h)$, $O(h)$, and $O(h^2)$, respectively, as $h \to 0$. [A function $A(h)$ is said to be **of order B(h) as h → h₀** if $A(h)/B(h)$ is *bounded* as $h \to h_0$. If so, we write $A(h) = O(B(h))$ as $h \to h_0$. Thus $A(h) = O(h)$ as $h \to 0$, for example, means that $A(h)/h$ is *bounded* as $h \to 0$. This "big oh" notation is widely used in pure and applied mathematics.] Observe that if h is small, then h^2 is an order of magnitude smaller than h, so that the central difference formula (c) is an order of magnitude more accurate than the forward and backward difference formulas (a) and (b). To illustrate (a) to (c), let $f(x) = e^x$ and compute $f'(1)$ using (a) to (c), for $h = 0.1$ and 0.01, and compare these values with the *exact* value.

7. (*Neumann condition*) Heretofore in this section we have considered only Dirichlet boundary conditions. To see how to handle a Neumann condition, consider the representative problem shown in the figure.

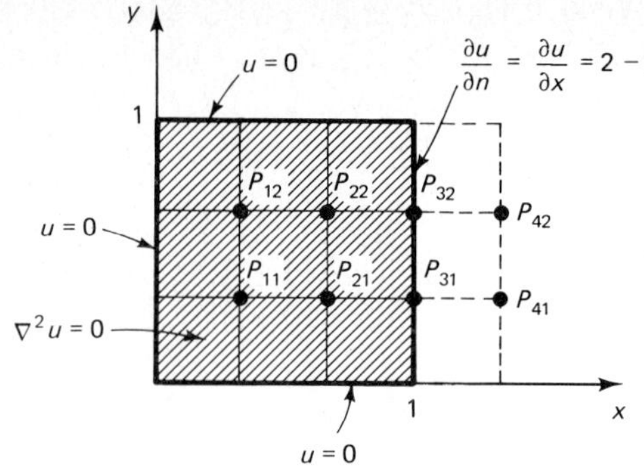

(a) Apply (7) at P_{11}, P_{21}, P_{12}, P_{22}, thus obtaining four equations in the six unknowns $U_{1,1}$, $U_{2,1}$, $U_{3,1}$, $U_{1,2}$, $U_{2,2}$, $U_{3,2}$. Next, apply the Neumann condition $\partial u/\partial x = 2 - y$ at P_{31} and P_{32}, using backward difference quotients [(b) in Exercise 6] for $\partial u/\partial x$. This step gives one equation relating $U_{3,1}$ and $U_{2,1}$, and one equation relating $U_{3,2}$ and $U_{2,2}$. Using these equations to solve for $U_{3,1}$ in terms of $U_{2,1}$, and for $U_{3,2}$ in terms of $U_{2,2}$, derive (but you need not solve) the resulting system

$$\begin{pmatrix} -4 & 1 & 1 & 0 \\ 1 & -3 & 0 & 1 \\ 1 & 0 & -4 & 1 \\ 0 & 1 & 1 & -3 \end{pmatrix} \begin{pmatrix} U_{1,1} \\ U_{2,1} \\ U_{1,2} \\ U_{2,2} \end{pmatrix} = \begin{pmatrix} 0 \\ -\frac{5}{9} \\ 0 \\ -\frac{4}{9} \end{pmatrix}.$$

(b) To use the more accurate central difference formula (c) in Exercise 6, in place of the backward difference formula (b), imagine the region extended as indicated by the dashed lines. Apply (7) at P_{11}, P_{21}, P_{31}, P_{12}, P_{22}, P_{32}, and then apply the Neumann condition $\partial u/\partial x = 2 - y$ at P_{31} and P_{32}, using the central difference formula (c). Using the two Neumann-condition equations to eliminate $U_{4,1}$ and $U_{4,2}$, derive six equations in the six unknowns $U_{1,1}$, $U_{2,1}$, $U_{3,1}$, $U_{1,2}$, $U_{2,2}$, $U_{3,2}$. You need not solve these equations.

8. (*Neumann and Robin boundary conditions*) Derive the governing difference equations on the U's at the heavy-dotted nodal points, using central difference quotients (see Exercises 6 and 7) for the $\partial u/\partial n$'s. Use whatever symmetries are available, to reduce the problem. In each case, $\nabla^2 u = 0$. (For simplicity, we denote nodes as $a, b, \ldots$ rather than as $P_{11}, P_{21}, \ldots$.) You need not solve for the U's.

(a)

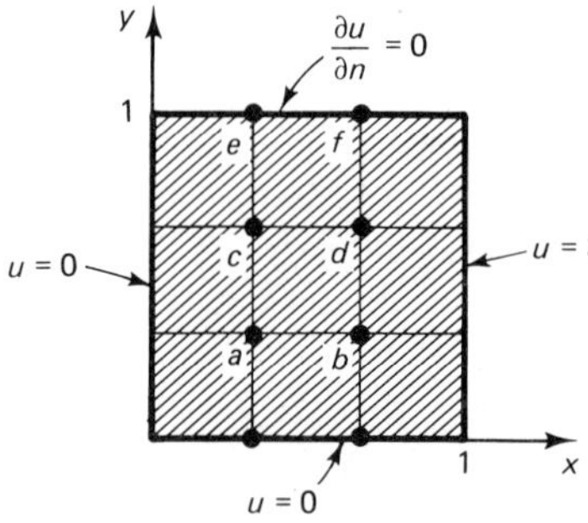

*(b)

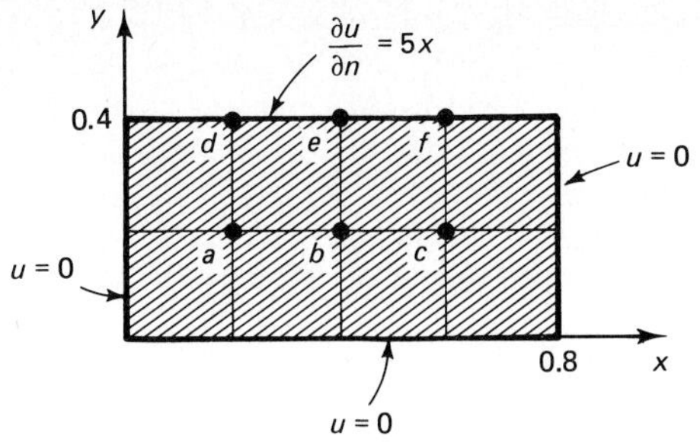

(c)

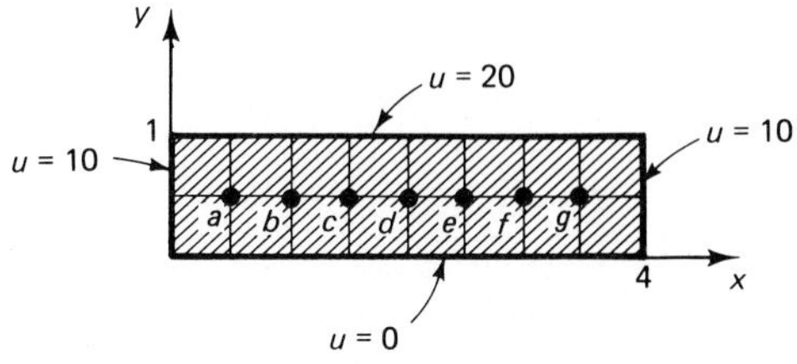

Hint: The problem in part (c) is equivalent, by symmetry about $x = 2$, to the problem $\nabla^2 u = 0$ in $0 < x < 2$, $0 < y < 1$; $u(0, y) = 10$, $u(x, 0) = 0$, $u(x, 1) = 20$, and $\frac{\partial u}{\partial n}(2, y) = 0$.

(d)

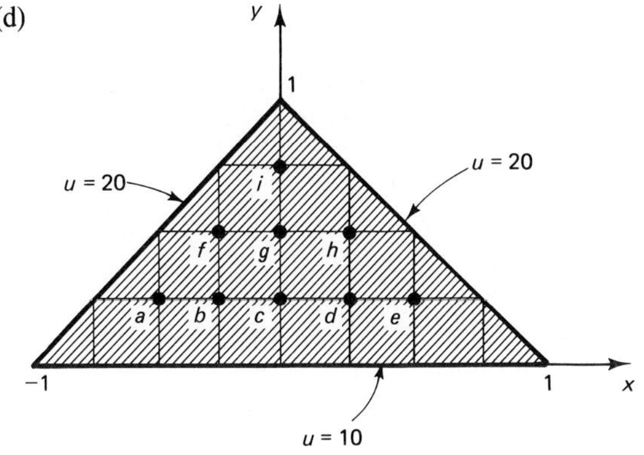

Hint: See the hint in part (c).

(e)

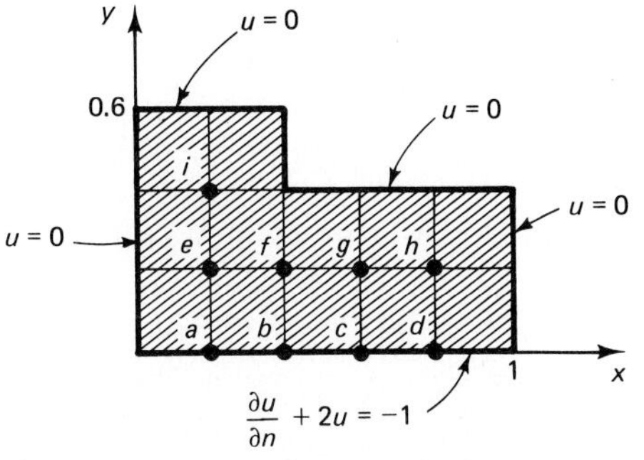

(f)

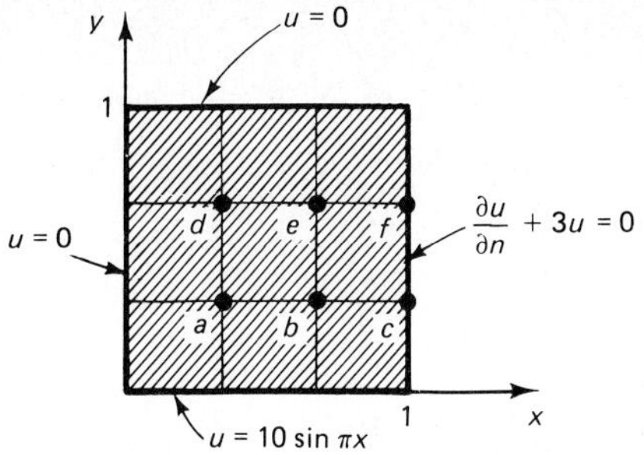

9. *(a) Letting all of the $U_{j,k}^{(0)}$'s $= 0$, solve for the $U_{j,k}^{(1)}$'s and $U_{j,k}^{(2)}$'s by hand, for the system (14), using the Jacobi, Liebmann, and SOR methods. For SOR, use the optimum ω.
(b) Continue the iterations on a computer, for each of the three methods, until $|U_{j,k}^{(n)} - U_{j,k}^{(n-1)}| \le 0.01$ at each of the four nodes. Compare the number of iterations needed by the three methods.

10. (*Other elliptic PDEs*) The Laplace and Poisson equations are *elliptic,* and the methods developed in this section are applicable to other elliptic equations as well. In each case, first verify that the PDE is elliptic. Then derive a finite-difference equation analogous to (7), using (3), (4), and central differences for first-order derivatives (see Exercise 6). (Let $\Delta x = \Delta y = h$.) Finally, apply the difference equation at each interior node for the case where the domain is $0 < x < 1$, $0 < y < 1$, where $u(0, y) = u(x, 0) = u(x, 1) = 0$ and $u(1, y) = \sin \pi y$, and where $\Delta x = \Delta y = \frac{1}{3}$. (You need not solve the resulting system of equations for the $U_{j,k}$'s.)

(a) $(1 + x^2)u_{xx} + u_{yy} = 0$
*(b) $u_{xx} + 2u_{yy} - u_x = 4$
(c) $u_{xx} + u_{yy} - u = 0$
(d) $u_{xx} + (1 + x^2 + y^2)u_{yy} + 2u_y = 1$

11. Derive the analog of (7) for the three-dimensional case, $u_{xx} + u_{yy} + u_{zz} = f(x, y, z)$.

12. (*Polar coordinates*) Regions bounded by constant-r and constant-θ curves are best treated using *polar* coordinates. Using the polar coordinate grid shown, show that the Poisson equation

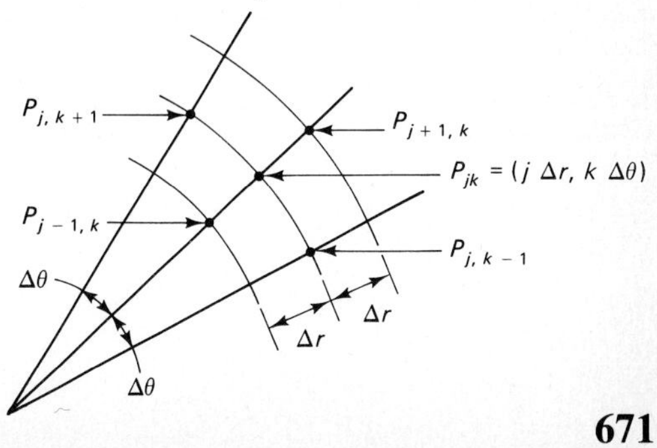

$$\nabla^2 u = u_{rr} + \frac{1}{r} u_r + \frac{1}{r^2} u_{\theta\theta} = f(r, \theta) \qquad \text{(a)}$$

admits the finite-difference approximation

$$\left(1 - \frac{1}{2j}\right) U_{j-1,k} + \frac{1}{(j\,\Delta\theta)^2} U_{j,k-1} + \left(1 + \frac{1}{2j}\right) U_{j+1,k}$$
$$+ \frac{1}{(j\,\Delta\theta)^2} U_{j,k+1} - 2\left[1 + \frac{1}{(j\,\Delta\theta)^2}\right] U_{j,k} \qquad \text{(b)}$$
$$= (\Delta r)^2 f_{j,k}$$

as the polar coordinate analog of (6). Use the central difference formula given in Exercise 6 for the u_r term in (a).

***13.** Use (b) in Exercise 12 to solve for U at the nodes a, b, c, d. Suppose that $f(r, \theta) = \text{constant} \equiv f$.

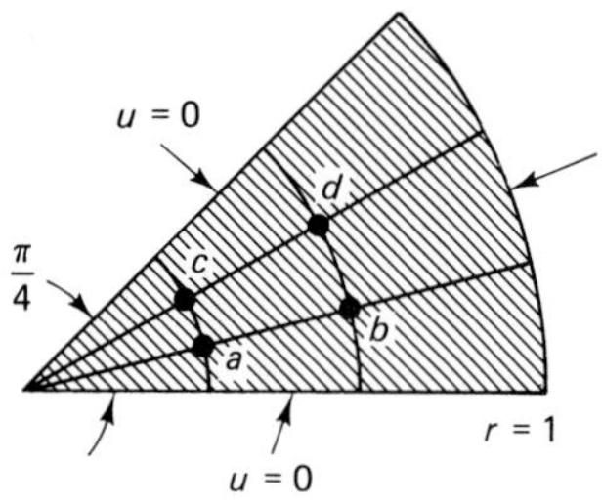

14. (*Discrete Maximum Principle*) (a) Let $U_{j,k}$ satisfy (7) with $f = 0$ (the Laplace case), at each interior nodal point of a given grid, and let $U_{\max}$ be the maximum value of $U_{j,k}$ over the set of all boundary nodal points. Show that $U_{j,k} \le U_{\max}$ *at each interior nodal point, so that* $U_{j,k}$ *achieves its maximum on the boundary*. This result is the discrete (finite difference) analog of the maximum principle for solutions of the Laplace PDE (see page 655).

(b) Let $U_{\min}$ be the minimum value of $U_{j,k}$ over the set of all boundary nodal points. Applying the maximum principle above to the function $-U_{j,k}$, show that $U_{\min} \le U_{j,k}$ *at each interior nodal point, so that* $U_{j,k}$ *achieves its minimum on the boundary*. Thus $U_{\min} \le U_{j,k} \le U_{\max}$ at all interior nodes.

15. (*Existence and uniqueness for the finite-difference system*) Use the maximum principle above to prove both the uniqueness and existence of the solution to the finite-difference problem (7). *Hint:* Consider the problem (7) on the $U_{j,k}$'s at the interior nodes, subject to prescribed boundary values at the boundary nodes. Show that if there are *two* solutions to the problem, their difference satisfies (7) and is *zero* at all boundary nodes. Then apply the results of Exercise 13 to show that the difference must, similarly, vanish at all interior nodes as well, so that the solution must, in fact, be unique. Since the problem is of the form $\mathbf{AU} = \mathbf{c}$, where $\mathbf{A}$ is square, show that uniqueness then implies existence.

Wave Equation 16

INTRODUCTION 16.1

In Chapters 14 and 15 we did not need to present derivations of the diffusion and Laplace equations because those derivations were given in Chapter 9, in our discussion of the divergence theorem. However, such a derivation of the wave equation, from the physics, has not yet been given, and we plan to devote this introduction to showing where the wave equation "comes from." Actually, the equation arises in many different contexts, such as electromagnetics, water-wave mechanics, supersonic flow, pulsatile blood flow, acoustics, elastic waves in solids, and vibrating strings and membranes. Thus we need to be selective, and we choose to begin with the theory of the *vibrating string,* since that case requires only a knowledge of the familiar Newton's second law of motion, and also because that case is of classic historical importance, as it was studied extensively by the great mathematicians *Jean Le Rond d'Alembert* (1717–1783), *Leonhard Euler* (1707–1783), *Daniel Bernoulli* (1700–1782), and *Joseph-Louis Lagrange* (1736–1813). It might be mentioned that nowadays new domains of mathematics are born, identified by name (such as "perturbation theory," "catastrophe theory," and so on), and developed. As late as the eighteenth century, however, interest tended to attach, instead, to specific problems, and the vibrating string was one that attracted a great deal of attention. Discussion of the vibrating string was not seen as the birth of a new domain, "partial differential equations," although in effect it was. For example, it was in his study of the vibrating string that d'Alembert introduced the method of *separation of variables,* which (as we have seen) is now a standard and powerful tool in the solution of partial differential equations. Using that technique, d'Alembert needed to represent the initial shape of the string by what we now call a "Fourier series." Whether that representation was, in fact, possible for any given initial shape of the string was a subject of heated debate, a debate that continued well into the nineteenth century. For an interesting historical account, we recommend the book by Kline.*

Beginning our derivation, consider a flexible string stretched under tension τ between fixed endpoints at $x = 0$ and $x = \ell$ on an x axis, as shown in Fig. 16.1. Let the mass per unit length of the string be ρ, a constant, and suppose that the string supports a distributed load $f(x, t)$ newtons per unit x length (Fig. 16.1). Considering the plane motion of the string (i.e., in the x, y plane), the desired unknown is the displacement $y(x, t)$.

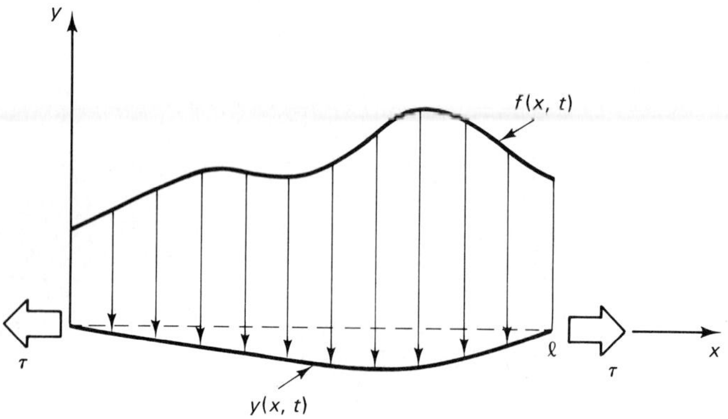

Fig. 16.1 Vibrating string.

We begin with two (not unrelated) assumptions, namely that

1. *The slope $\partial y/\partial x$ (and hence y) is uniformly small over the length of the string.*
2. *The horizontal motion of any point on the string can be neglected relative to its vertical motion.*

These assumptions seem quite reasonable if, for example, the string is a violin string. In addition, we assume:

3. *The string is perfectly flexible, so that at each point along its length it carries the tangential tension force τ, but no shear force or bending moment.*

The relevant physical principle is Newton's second law of motion, and we proceed to apply this law to the vertical part of the motion of an element of the string between x and $x + \Delta x$ (Fig. 16.2). This step gives

$$\tau \sin \theta(x + \Delta x, t) - \tau \sin \theta(x, t) - f(x + \beta \Delta x, t)\, \Delta x = (\rho \Delta s) \frac{\partial^2 y}{\partial t^2}(x + \alpha \Delta x, t). \tag{1}$$

That is, the sum of the vertical forces on the element is equal to the mass $\rho \Delta s$ times the vertical acceleration of the mass center (at $x + \alpha\, \Delta x$, for some α between 0 and 1). Here we have assumed that f is a continuous function of x (although that condition could easily be relaxed), so that there is a point $x + \beta\, \Delta x$ $(0 < \beta < 1)$ at which f takes on its average value over the $(x, x + \Delta x)$ interval.

* Morris Kline, *Mathematical Thought from Ancient to Modern Times* (New York: Oxford University Press, 1972), e.g., pp. 503–518.

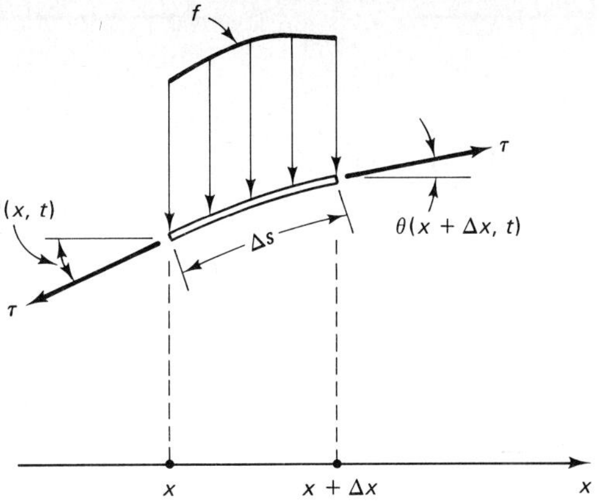

Fig. 16.2 String element.

According to assumption 1, $\sin\theta \approx \theta \approx \tan\theta = \partial y/\partial x$ and $\Delta s \approx \Delta x$, so (1) becomes

$$\tau \frac{\dfrac{\partial y}{\partial x}(x + \Delta x,\ t) - \dfrac{\partial y}{\partial x}(x,\ t)}{\Delta x} - f(x + \beta\,\Delta x, t) = \rho \frac{\partial^2 y}{\partial t^2}(x + \alpha\,\Delta x, t). \tag{2}$$

Finally, letting $\Delta x \to 0$ in (2) yields the partial differential equation

$$\tau \frac{\partial^2 y}{\partial x^2}(x, t) - f(x, t) = \rho \frac{\partial^2 y}{\partial t^2}(x, t). \tag{3}$$

If f is simply the gravitational force on the string (i.e., the *weight* force per unit length of the string), $f(x, t) = \rho g =$ constant, where g is the acceleration due to gravity, and (3) becomes

$$\tau \frac{\partial^2 y}{\partial x^2} = \rho \frac{\partial^2 y}{\partial t^2} + \rho g. \tag{4}$$

If the gravitational term is negligible, as is surely the case for a violin string, then (4) reduces to

$$\tau \frac{\partial^2 y}{\partial x^2} = \rho \frac{\partial^2 y}{\partial t^2} \tag{5}$$

or, with $c \equiv \sqrt{\tau/\rho}$,

$$\boxed{c^2 \frac{\partial^2 y}{\partial x^2} = \frac{\partial^2 y}{\partial t^2};} \tag{6}$$

Equation (6) is known as the one-dimensional **wave equation,** "one-dimensional" because the spatial dependence is only one-dimensional. The constant c has units of velocity and will soon be seen to bear an important physical significance.

In the next section we discuss the *solution* of (6), subject to various initial conditions and end conditions. For the present we close this section with an introduction to the *two*-dimensional wave equation. Thus let us consider the two-dimensional version of a vibrating string, namely, a vibrating *membrane* such as a drumhead.

First, we consider that the membrane is stretched *uniformly,* under a tension τ per unit length; i.e., at each point of the membrane the tension per unit length along any straight line through that point, independent of the orientation of the line, is τ. If, for example, we stretch a rectangular membrane as shown in Fig. 16.3, and then clamp the edges, the membrane would *not* be stretched uniformly, for the tension per unit length on any *vertical* line would be τ, but the tension per unit length on any *horizontal* line would be 0. A musical drumhead, however, *is* stretched uniformly, as we have assumed.

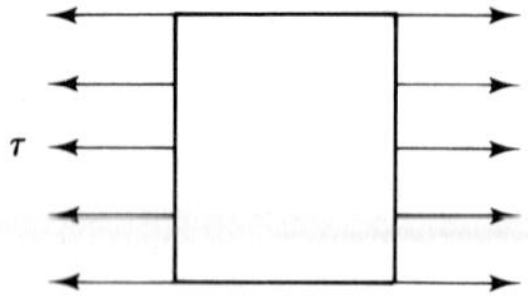

Fig. 16.3 *Non*uniformly stretched membrane.

Denoting the displacement of the membrane, relative to the x, y plane, as $w(x, y)$, we proceed essentially as before. Thus we assume that the slopes $\partial w/\partial x$ and $\partial w/\partial y$ are uniformly small over the domain, that the x and y motion of any point on the membrane can be neglected relative to its motion perpendicular to the x, y plane, and that the membrane is perfectly flexible so that only the tangential tensile force τ need be considered. Then, applying Newton's second law to a membrane element lying between x and $x + \Delta x$, y and $y + \Delta y$ (Fig. 16.4), we have

$$\tau\,\Delta y \sin\theta\big|_{x+\Delta x} - \tau\,\Delta y \sin\theta\big|_{x} + \tau\,\Delta x \sin\phi\big|_{y+\Delta y} - \tau\,\Delta x \sin\phi\big|_{y} - f\,\Delta x\,\Delta y = \rho\,\Delta A\frac{\partial^2 w}{\partial t^2}, \qquad (7)$$

where ρ is the mass per unit area of the membrane and ΔA is the surface area of the element under consideration. By virtue of the stated assumptions, $\sin\theta \approx \theta \approx$

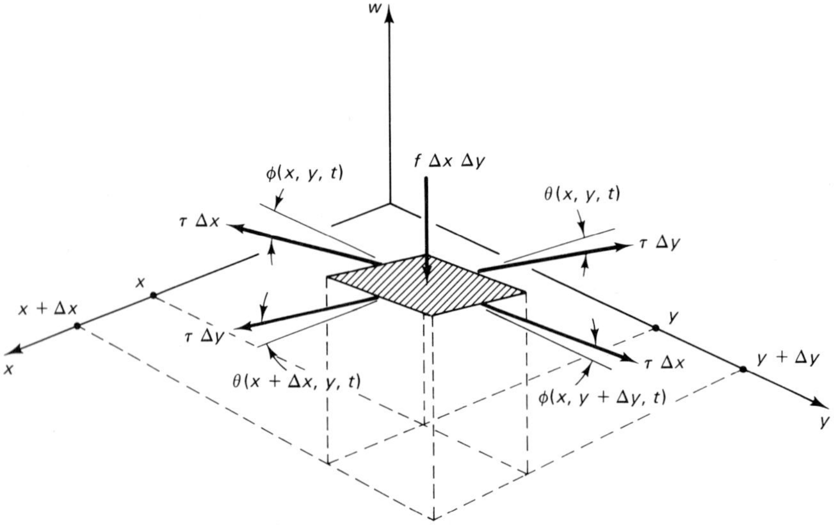

Fig. 16.4 Membrane element.

$\tan\theta = \partial w/\partial x$, $\sin\phi \approx \phi \approx \tan\phi = \partial w/\partial y$, and $\Delta A \approx \Delta x\,\Delta y$, so (7) becomes

$$\tau \frac{\left.\frac{\partial w}{\partial x}\right|_{x+\Delta x} - \left.\frac{\partial w}{\partial x}\right|_{x}}{\Delta x} + \tau \frac{\left.\frac{\partial w}{\partial y}\right|_{y+\Delta y} - \left.\frac{\partial w}{\partial y}\right|_{y}}{\Delta y} - f = \rho \frac{\partial^2 w}{\partial t^2}, \tag{8}$$

and letting Δx and $\Delta y \to 0$ gives the partial differential equation

$$\tau\left(\frac{\partial^2 w}{\partial x^2} + \frac{\partial^2 w}{\partial y^2}\right) - f(x, y, t) = \rho \frac{\partial^2 w}{\partial t^2}. \tag{9}$$

In particular, if $f = 0$ and we define $c = \sqrt{\tau/\rho}$, then (9) becomes the classical *two-dimensional wave equation**

$$c^2\left(\frac{\partial^2 w}{\partial x^2} + \frac{\partial^2 w}{\partial y^2}\right) = \frac{\partial^2 w}{\partial t^2}. \tag{10}$$

Still more generally, the wave equation can be expressed as

$$c^2\,\nabla^2 w = \frac{\partial^2 w}{\partial t^2},$$

where ∇^2 is $\partial^2/\partial x^2$ in one dimension, $\partial^2/\partial x^2 + \partial^2/\partial y^2$ in two dimensions, and $\partial^2/\partial x^2 + \partial^2/\partial y^2 + \partial^2/\partial z^2$ in three dimensions.

Thus far we have only derived the governing field equation. In the next section we complete the formulation by specifying appropriate boundary and initial conditions, and obtaining solutions. Additional physical applications appear in the exercises and in the sections to follow.

16.1 EXERCISES

1. (*Static loaded string with lateral spring*) From (3) we see that the *static* deflection of a string subjected to a steady load $f(x)$ is governed by the ODE $\tau y''(x) = f(x)$. As an interesting variation of this case, suppose that the string is restrained, laterally, by a distributed spring of stiffness k (newtons per meter per meter), as in Exercise 5 on page 524. Then show that the governing ODE becomes

$$y'' - \frac{k}{\tau} y = \frac{f(x)}{\tau}. \tag{a}$$

[This ODE appeared, with slight differences in notation, in connection with the Leibniz rule (Example 2, page 346) and the Fourier transform (Exercises 16 on page 532 and 19 on page 534.)]

2. (*String with bead*) Returning to our modeling of the vibrating string, suppose that we add to the string, at $x = x_0$, a small bead of mass m. Then (3) can be revised, to account for the bead, as

$$\tau y_{xx} - f = [\rho + m\delta(x - x_0)]\,y_{tt}, \tag{a}$$

where δ is the Dirac delta function. Alternatively, show that we can avoid the delta function by "staying away from the bead," i.e., by treating the x domains $x < x_0$ and $x > x_0$ separately. Specifically, show that

*Another interesting special case, which relates back to Chapter 15, is the steady case where $f = f(x, y)$ and $w = w(x, y)$. In that case, (9) becomes the *Poisson equation*

$$\frac{\partial^2 w}{\partial x^2} + \frac{\partial^2 w}{\partial y^2} = \frac{1}{\tau} f(x, y).$$

we then have $\tau y_{xx} - f = \rho y_{tt}$ in each of the two domains. Denoting $y_L(x, t)$ and $y_R(x, t)$ as the solutions in $x < x_0$ and $x > x_0$, respectively, show that y_L and y_R need to be fitted together according to the two conditions

$$y_R(x_0, t) = y_L(x_0, t), \tag{b}$$

$$\tau\left[\frac{\partial y_R}{\partial x}(x_0, t) - \frac{\partial y_L}{\partial x}(x_0, t)\right] = m\frac{\partial^2 y}{\partial t^2}(x_0, t). \tag{c}$$

3. (*Current and magnetic field*) Suppose that the "string" is actually a flexible wire of mass per unit length ρ, under tension τ, carrying a current I in the presence of a uniform magnetic field of magnetic flux density $\mathbf{B} = B_1\hat{\mathbf{i}} + B_2\hat{\mathbf{j}} + B_3\hat{\mathbf{k}}$. Since a charge Q moving with velocity $\mathbf{U}$ in such a field experiences a force $\mathbf{F} = Q\mathbf{U} \times \mathbf{B}$, we may need to revise the vibrating string equation to include lateral magnetic forcing terms.

(a) Show that within the usual vibrating-string approximations, the magnetic force exerted on an element of the wire is

$$\Delta\mathbf{F} \approx qA\,\Delta x[U\hat{\mathbf{i}} + (Uy_x + y_t)\hat{\mathbf{j}} + (Uz_x + z_t)\hat{\mathbf{k}}] \times \mathbf{B} \tag{a}$$

where the constants q, A, U are the charge per unit volume within the wire, cross-sectional area of the wire, and velocity of the charges within the wire, respectively.

(b) Working out the cross product in (a) and noting that qAU is the current I, show that the equations of (the not-necessarily-planar) motion of the wire are

$$\begin{aligned}\tau y_{xx} - IB_3 + (Iz_x + qAz_t)B_1 &= \rho y_{tt}\\ \tau z_{xx} + IB_2 - (Iy_x + qAy_t)B_1 &= \rho z_{tt},\end{aligned} \tag{b}$$

where x, y, z are right-handed Cartesian coordinates. Notice that these equations are *coupled* due to the z_x, z_t, y_x, and y_t terms. Naturally, in a particular application one or more of the additional magnetic-field terms may be negligible.

4. (*Electromagnetic waves*) Electromagnetic fields in free space are governed by the Maxwell equations

$$\nabla \times \mathbf{H} = \epsilon_0\frac{\partial \mathbf{E}}{\partial t} \tag{a}$$

$$\nabla \times \mathbf{E} = -\mu_0\frac{\partial \mathbf{H}}{\partial t} \tag{b}$$

$$\nabla \cdot \mathbf{H} = 0 \tag{c}$$

$$\nabla \cdot \mathbf{E} = 0, \tag{d}$$

where $\mathbf{E}$, $\mathbf{H}$ are the electric and magnetic field intensities, respectively, and ϵ_0, μ_0 are the permittivity and permeability of free space, respectively. Show that $\mathbf{E}$ and $\mathbf{H}$ satisfy the wave equations

$$\frac{1}{\epsilon_0\mu_0}\nabla^2\mathbf{H} = \frac{\partial^2\mathbf{H}}{\partial t^2} \quad\text{and}\quad \frac{1}{\epsilon_0\mu_0}\nabla^2\mathbf{E} = \frac{\partial^2\mathbf{E}}{\partial t^2} \tag{e}$$

Hint: Recall the identity $\nabla \times (\nabla \times \mathbf{v}) = \nabla(\nabla \cdot \mathbf{v}) - \nabla^2\mathbf{v}$.

5. (*Water waves*) Consider plane water waves in water of depth $h(x)$. If the wavelength is much greater than h (as is true for ocean tides and for various waves in shallow water), the governing equations are found to be

$$u_t + uu_x = -g\eta_x \tag{a}$$

$$[u(\eta + h)]_x = -\eta_t, \tag{b}$$

where u is the x velocity [which is approximately constant with respect to y; hence $u = u(x, t)$], $\eta(x, t)$ is the free-surface displacement relative to the undisturbed water level, g is the acceleration due to gravity, and subscripts denote partial derivatives. If, in addition, we restrict our attention to *small amplitude* motions—so that the "second-order" term uu_x can be neglected relative to the "first-order" terms u_t and $g\eta_x$, and η can be neglected relative to h—then show that η satisfies the equation $g(h\eta_x)_x = \eta_{tt}$ or, if $h(x)$ is a constant,

$$c^2\eta_{xx} = \eta_{tt}; \qquad c = \sqrt{gh}. \tag{c}$$

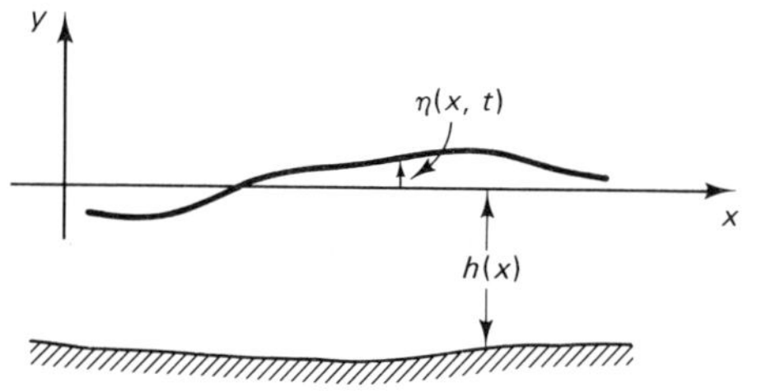

6. (*Acoustic waves*) Consider an inviscid gas initially at rest, subjected to a small disturbance. The equations governing the resulting flow are

$$\mathbf{q}_t + \mathbf{q}\cdot\nabla\mathbf{q} = -\frac{1}{\rho}\nabla p \qquad \text{(equation of motion)} \quad \text{(a)}$$

$$\rho_t + \nabla\cdot(\rho\mathbf{q}) = 0 \qquad \text{(continuity)} \quad \text{(b)}$$

$$p\rho^{-\gamma} = \text{constant} = p_\infty\rho_\infty^{-\gamma} \quad \text{(isentropic flow)}, \quad \text{(c)}$$

where $\mathbf{q}$, p, ρ are the velocity, pressure, and density fields, respectively, and $\gamma = c_p/c_v$ is the ratio of the specific heats at constant pressure and constant volume. The pressure–density relation (c) is based on an assumption that the flow is isentropic (constant and uniform entropy). Since the disturbance is small, we assume further that ρ, p differ only slightly from the initial values ρ_∞, p_∞ in the undisturbed state. Thus we express $\rho = \rho_\infty + \rho'$, $p = p_\infty + p'$, where ρ', p' and their derivatives are small compared to ρ_∞, p_∞, respectively. Finally, $\boldsymbol{\nabla} \times \mathbf{q} = \boldsymbol{\nabla} \times \mathbf{0} = \mathbf{0}$ initially, so the fluid particles have no "spin" initially. Since the gas is assumed to be inviscid, there are no shear stresses to impart spin, so the flow remains irrotational for all $t > 0$. Thus there exists a velocity potential ϕ such that $\mathbf{q} = \boldsymbol{\nabla}\phi$.

(a) Show that the assumptions above permit us to approximate (a) to (c) by the simpler system

$$\mathbf{q}_t = -\frac{1}{\rho_\infty}\boldsymbol{\nabla} p' \tag{d}$$

$$\rho_t' + \rho_\infty \boldsymbol{\nabla}\cdot\mathbf{q} = 0 \tag{e}$$

$$p' = \frac{\gamma p_\infty}{\rho_\infty}\rho'. \tag{f}$$

Hint: To obtain (f), recall the Taylor expansion $(1 + x)^\alpha = 1 + \alpha x + \cdots \approx 1 + \alpha x$, for small x.

(b) Putting $\mathbf{q} = \boldsymbol{\nabla}\phi$ into (d) and (e), show that ϕ is governed by the wave equation

$$a_\infty^2 \nabla^2 \phi = \frac{\partial^2 \phi}{\partial t^2}; \qquad a_\infty = \sqrt{\gamma \frac{p_\infty}{\rho_\infty}}. \tag{g}$$

7. (*Longitudinal waves in a rod*) Consider a uniform metal bar, of cross-sectional area A and mass per unit length ρ, with a stress distribution $\sigma(x, t)$ and a resulting longitudinal displacement $u(x, t)$. Applying Newton's second law to an element of the rod between x and $x + \Delta x$, shown in the figure, show that

$$A\frac{\partial \sigma}{\partial x} = \rho \frac{\partial^2 u}{\partial t^2}. \tag{a}$$

Suppose that the material admits a linear stress-strain relationship $\sigma = E\epsilon$, where the constant of proportionality E is Young's modulus, and the strain ϵ is defined as the "stretch per unit length," so that $\epsilon = \dfrac{u(x + \Delta x, t) - u(x, t)}{\Delta x}$. From these relations, show that σ and u both satisfy one-dimensional wave equations,

$$c^2\frac{\partial^2 u}{\partial x^2} = \frac{\partial^2 u}{\partial t^2}, \qquad c^2\frac{\partial^2 \sigma}{\partial x^2} = \frac{\partial^2 \sigma}{\partial t^2}; \qquad c = \sqrt{\frac{EA}{\rho}}. \tag{b}$$

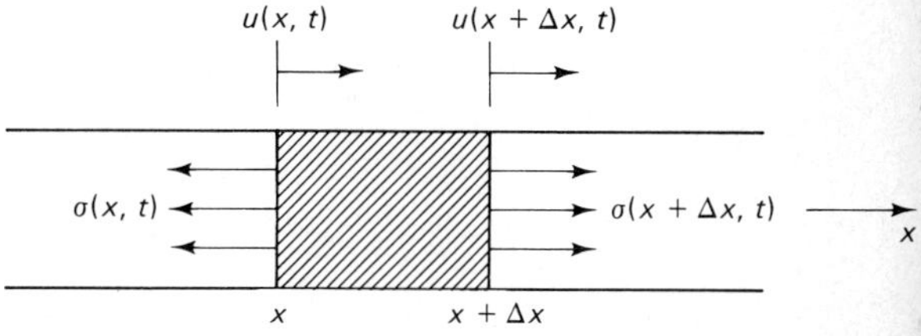

SEPARATION OF VARIABLES 16.2

In Section 16.1 we derived the wave equation as the governing PDE for the motion of a vibrating string. Here we complete the formulation, for a specific case, by appending boundary and initial conditions and solving by the method of separation of variables.

Specifically, we consider a *finite string,* extending over $0 < x < \ell$, tied at its two ends, and having initial vertical displacements and velocities of $f(x)$ and 0, respectively. Thus the complete problem statement is as follows:

$$c^2 y_{xx} = y_{tt} \qquad (0 < x < \ell,\ 0 < t < \infty) \tag{1a}$$

$$y(0, t) = y(\ell, t) = 0 \qquad (0 < t < \infty) \tag{1b}$$

$$y(x, 0) = F(x), \quad y_t(x, 0) = 0 \qquad (0 < x < \ell), \tag{1c}$$

as summarized in Fig. 16.5.

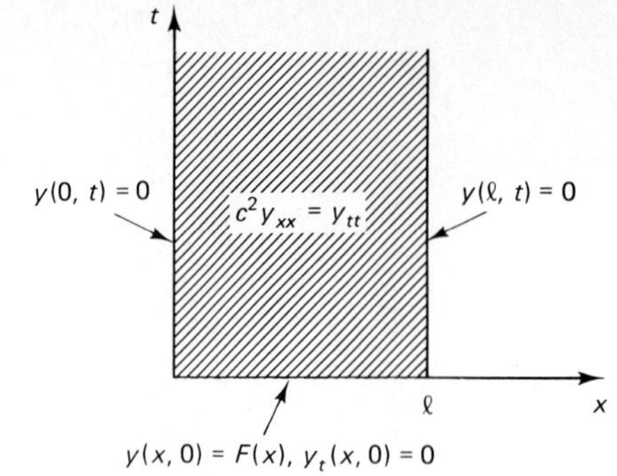

Fig. 16.5 Finite string problem.

Notice that in contrast with the diffusion equation $\alpha^2 u_{xx} = u_t$, where only u was specified initially, here we have specified both y *and* y_t. On an intuitive basis, it certainly seems reasonable that both of these quantities need to be specified; mathematically, we are guided by the fact that the wave equation is a *second*-order equation with respect to t (whereas the diffusion equation was *first* order). Verification that the problem statement (1) *uniquely* determines $y(x, t)$ is left for Exercise 13. Here we limit our attention to *finding* the solution.

Using separation of variables, we seek

$$y(x, t) = X(x)T(t). \tag{2}$$

Putting (2) into (1a) and separating the variables gives

$$\frac{X''}{X} = \frac{1}{c^2}\frac{T''}{T} = \text{constant} = -\kappa^2. \tag{3}$$

Thus

$$X'' + \kappa^2 X = 0, \tag{4a}$$

$$T'' + \kappa^2 c^2 T = 0, \tag{4b}$$

and

$$X = \begin{cases} A + Bx, & \kappa = 0 \\ D\cos\kappa x + E\sin\kappa x, & \kappa \neq 0 \end{cases} \tag{5}$$

$$T = \begin{cases} F + Gt, & \kappa = 0 \\ H\cos\kappa ct + I\sin\kappa ct, & \kappa \neq 0. \end{cases} \tag{6}$$

Here $-\kappa^2$ was used as the separation constant because it led to $\cos\kappa ct$ and $\sin\kappa ct$ solutions for T, as seem reasonable since we anticipate a vibratory motion.

With the help of superposition, we can write

$$y(x, t) = (A + Bx)(F + Gt) + (D\cos\kappa x + E\sin\kappa x)(H\cos\kappa ct + I\sin\kappa ct). \tag{7}$$

Applying the boundary conditions,

$$y(0, t) = 0 = A(F + Gt) + D(H\cos\kappa ct + I\sin\kappa ct), \tag{8}$$

gives $A = D = 0$, so

$$y(x, t) = x(F' + G't) + \sin \kappa x(H' \cos \kappa ct + I' \sin \kappa ct), \tag{9}$$

and then

$$y(\ell, t) = 0 = \ell(F' + G't) + \sin \kappa\ell(H' \cos \kappa ct + I' \sin \kappa ct) \tag{10}$$

gives $F' = G' = 0$ and $\sin \kappa\ell = 0$. Thus $\kappa\ell = n\pi$, and we can express

$$y(x, t) = \sum_{n=1}^{\infty} \sin \frac{n\pi x}{\ell}\left(H_n' \cos \frac{n\pi ct}{\ell} + I_n' \sin \frac{n\pi ct}{\ell}\right). \tag{11}$$

Saving the nonhomogeneous initial condition for last, set

$$y_t(x, 0) = 0 = \sum_{n=1}^{\infty} \frac{n\pi c}{\ell} I_n' \sin \frac{n\pi x}{\ell},$$

from which it follows that $I_n' = 0$ for each n. Thus far, then,

$$y(x, t) = \sum_{n=1}^{\infty} H_n' \sin \frac{n\pi x}{\ell} \cos \frac{n\pi ct}{\ell}. \tag{12}$$

Finally, we require that

$$y(x, 0) = F(x) = \sum_{n=1}^{\infty} H_n' \sin \frac{n\pi x}{\ell} \qquad (0 < x < \ell) \tag{13}$$

and the by-now-familiar half-range sine formula gives

$$H_n' = \frac{2}{\ell} \int_0^{\ell} F(x) \sin \frac{n\pi x}{\ell}\, dx \qquad (n = 1, 2, \ldots). \tag{14}$$

Thus the solution to (1) is given by (12), with the H_n' coefficients computed according to (14). The right-hand side of (12) represents a superposition of distinct *modes* of vibration,* each of which is a *standing wave* of spatial frequency $n\pi/\ell$ and temporal frequency $n\pi c/\ell$. The first three modes are depicted in Fig. 16.6. Points

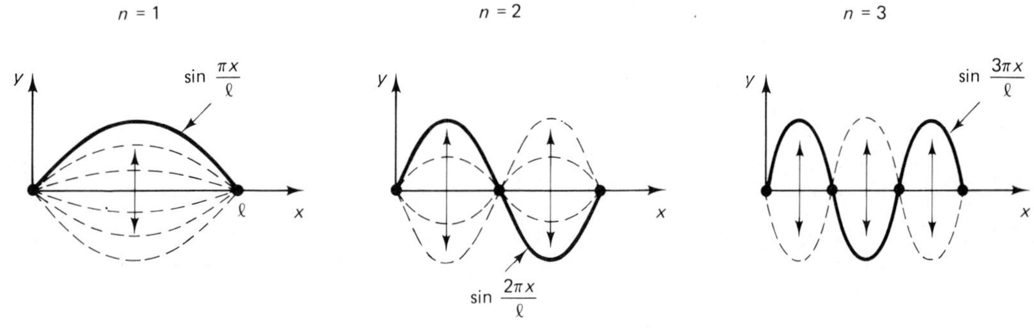

Fig. 16.6 First three modes.

* These modes are said to be *orthogonal* inasmuch as their shapes satisfy the orthogonality relation

$$\int_0^{\ell} \sin \frac{m\pi x}{\ell} \sin \frac{n\pi x}{\ell}\, dx = 0$$

for any pair of integers m and n ($m \neq n$).

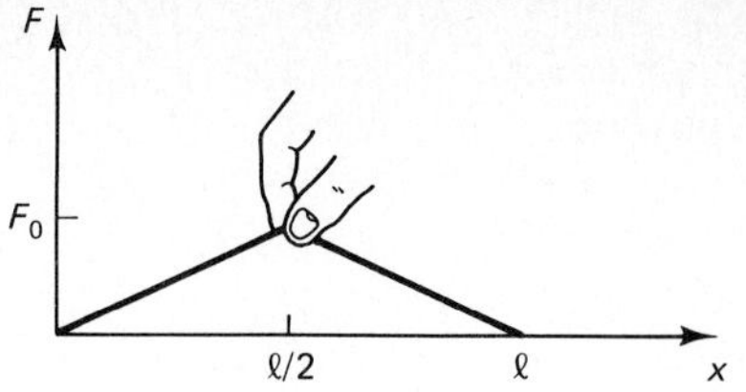

Fig. 16.7 Plucked string.

on the string at which $y = 0$ for all t are called *nodal points,* and these are shown in the figure by heavy dots.

To illustrate, suppose that the initial shape $F(x)$ is as shown in Fig. 16.7. That is, we pull the string up at its midpoint and then release it from rest. Computing H_n' from (14) gives (Exercise 2)

$$H_n' = \frac{8F_0}{n^2\pi^2}\sin\frac{n\pi}{2}, \tag{15}$$

so

$$y(x, t) = \frac{8F_0}{\pi^2}\sum_{n=1}^{\infty}\frac{1}{n^2}\sin\frac{n\pi}{2}\sin\frac{n\pi x}{\ell}\cos\frac{n\pi c t}{\ell}. \tag{16}$$

It is interesting to see what (16) can tell us about the musical quality of a violin string plucked in the manner shown in Fig. 16.7. For reference, let us write out some of the notes on a piano, beginning with the lowest, together with their frequencies (in cycles per second):

A_0,	$A_0^\#$,	B_0,	C_1,	$C_1^\#$,	D_1,
27.500	29.135	30.868	32.703	34.648	36.708
$D_1^\#$,	E_1,	F_1,	$F_1^\#$,	G_1,	$G_1^\#$,
38.891	41.203	43.654	46.249	48.999	51.913
A_1,	$A_1^\#$,	B_1,	C_2,	$C_2^\#$,	D_2,
55.000	58.270	61.735	65.406	69.296	73.416
$D_2^\#$,	E_2,	F_2,	$F_2^\#$,	G_2,	$G_2^\#$,
77.782	82.407	87.307	92.499	97.999	103.83
A_2,	$A_2^\#$,	B_2,	C_3,	$C_3^\#$,	D_3,
110.00	116.51	123.47	130.81	138.59	146.83
$D_3^\#$,	E_3,	F_3,	$F_3^\#$,	G_3,	. . .
155.56	164.81	174.61	185.00	196.00	

where #'s denote sharps. Suppose, for definiteness, that we tune the string so that its fundamental frequency $\pi c/\ell$ corresponds to A_0. (Recall that $c = \sqrt{\tau/\rho}$.) That is, we adjust the tension τ so that

$$\frac{\pi}{\ell}\sqrt{\frac{\tau}{\rho}}\,\frac{\text{rad}}{\text{sec}} = \left(27.5\,\frac{\text{cycles}}{\text{sec}}\right)\left(\frac{2\pi\ \text{rad}}{\text{cycle}}\right)$$

or

$$\tau = (55\ell)^2\rho. \tag{17}$$

Then the first several terms in (16) correspond to the combination of notes shown in Table 16.1. Observe that the overtones (with nonzero amplitude) E_2, $C_3^{\#}$, . . . do not occur at octaves above A_0, and that their amplitudes are quite small compared to that of A_0. Thus the sound is not a pristine A_0 with octave overtones, but is, nonetheless, fairly "clean" because of the relatively small amplitudes of the higher notes. The mix of frequencies and amplitudes is different for different instruments, and an A_0 played on a violin certainly sounds different from an A_0 played on a tuba.*

TABLE 16.1 Musical Content of (16)

n	$n\frac{\pi c}{\ell}$ Frequency (cycles/sec)	Relative Amplitude $\frac{1}{n^2}\left\|\sin\frac{n\pi}{2}\right\|$	Musical Note
1	27.5	1	A_0
2	55.0	0	A_1
3	82.5	$\frac{1}{9}$	$\approx E_2$
4	110.0	0	A_2
5	137.5	$\frac{1}{25}$	$\approx C_3^{\#}$

Returning to (12), it appears that if we are to determine the *shape* of the string, as it varies with t, we actually need to sum the series numerically at a number of different x's and t's However, it is striking that we can do much better, as follows. Using the trigonometric identity

$$\sin A \cos B = \tfrac{1}{2}[\sin(A - B) + \sin(A + B)], \tag{18}$$

we can reexpress (12) as

$$y(x, t) = \frac{1}{2}\sum_{n=1}^{\infty} H_n'\left[\sin\frac{n\pi}{\ell}(x - ct) + \sin\frac{n\pi}{\ell}(x + ct)\right]. \tag{19}$$

Finally, comparing the form of (19) with that of (13), we see that (19) can be expressed simply, in terms of the prescribed function F, as

$$y(x, t) = \frac{F(x - ct) + F(x + ct)}{2}. \tag{20}$$

One problem with (20): For a given x in the x interval $(0, \ell)$, and a given t in the t interval $(0, \infty)$, one or both of the arguments $x - ct$ and $x + ct$, of F, may lie outside the domain of definition of F, namely $(0, \ell)$, so that (20) is then meaningless.

* Actually, the sound of a violin is due very little to the air being set in motion by the vibrating string. Rather, the string drives the sounding board, through its connection at the bridge, and it is the vibrating sounding board that sets the adjacent air in motion and creates an audible sound. Thus a serious investigation of violin mechanics would lead immediately to the much more difficult problem of the vibrating sounding board.

However, observe that the half-range sine series idea, used in deriving (14) from (13), really amounts to extending F outside the given interval $(0, \ell)$ so that the extended function $F_{ext}(x)$ is an odd periodic function, of period 2ℓ, defined on the interval $-\infty < x < \infty$. Thus we can rewrite (20) in the form

$$y(x, t) = \frac{F_{ext}(x - ct) + F_{ext}(x + ct)}{2}, \tag{21}$$

which can be used for *any* values of $x - ct$ and $x + ct$.

To illustrate (21) numerically, let $\ell = 10$ and $c = 12$, let F be the shape shown in Fig. 16.7. with $F_0 = 1$, and let us compute y at $x = 2$ and $t = 3$, say. Using (21) and the fact that F_{ext} is periodic with period $2\ell = 20$, and odd, we have

$$\begin{aligned}
y(2, 3) &= \tfrac{1}{2}\,[F_{ext}(2 + 36) + F_{ext}(2 - 36)] \\
&= \tfrac{1}{2}\,[F_{ext}(38) + F_{ext}(-34)] \\
&= \tfrac{1}{2}\,[F_{ext}(18) + F_{ext}(-14)] && \text{(periodicity of } F_{ext}) \\
&= \tfrac{1}{2}\,[F_{ext}(-2) + F_{ext}(6)] && \text{(periodicity of } F_{ext}) \\
&= \tfrac{1}{2}\,[-F(2) + F(6)] && (F_{ext} \text{ is odd, and } F_{ext} = F \\
& && \text{on the interval from 0 to 10)} \\
&= \tfrac{1}{2}(-\tfrac{2}{5} + \tfrac{4}{5}) && \text{(definition of } F \text{ in Fig. 16.7)} \\
&= \tfrac{1}{5}.
\end{aligned}$$

Beyond using (21) to compute y at any given x and t, we can use it to obtain the graph of $y(x, t)$, over the entire interval $(0, \ell)$, at any given t, by observing that the graph of $F_{ext}(x - ct)$, plotted as a function of x, is simply the graph of $F_{ext}(x)$ translated to the *right* through a distance ct. Similarly, the graph of $F_{ext}(x + ct)$ is simply the graph of $F_{ext}(x)$ translated to the *left* through a distance ct. Thus if F is as shown in Fig. 16.7, say, then $F_{ext}(x)$ is as shown in Fig. 16.8a, $F_{ext}(x - ct)$ and $F_{ext}(x + ct)$ are as shown in Fig. 16.8b, and $y(x, t) = \frac{1}{2}[F_{ext}(x - ct) + F_{ext}(x + ct)]$ is (by direct addition of the two graphs in Fig. 16.8b, and scaling by $\frac{1}{2}$) as shown in Fig. 16.8c. Carrying out the solution in this manner, at a number of different times, over one complete cycle, yields the solution sequence shown in Fig. 16.9 (Exercise 4). The results depicted in Fig. 16.9 are evidently consistent with the physics. Beginning at $t = 0$ we see that the string segments AB and BC are straight. Thus there is no interaction of tension and curvature to produce a net force on the string elements (as discussed in Section 16.1), except at the single point B, which is driven downward. The resulting plateau DE moves downward at a *constant velocity*. Thus string elements between D and E have no vertical acceleration, since they are in *uniform* vertical motion, and this result fits together nicely with the fact that neither is there any net vertical *force* on those elements. (Recall that we have neglected the effects of gravity.)

Until now, we have been speaking of the "wave equation" but have not addressed the wave nature of the solution. Well, referring to the solution form (12), we see that y is thereby expressed as a superposition of **standing waves,** of shape sin $(n\pi x/\ell)$ and frequency (i.e., temporal frequency) $n\pi c/\ell$. In fact, the sum of the series is also a standing wave, of frequency $\pi c/\ell$. Alternatively, (19) expresses y as a superposition of **traveling waves,** of sinusoidal shape, some of which travel to the

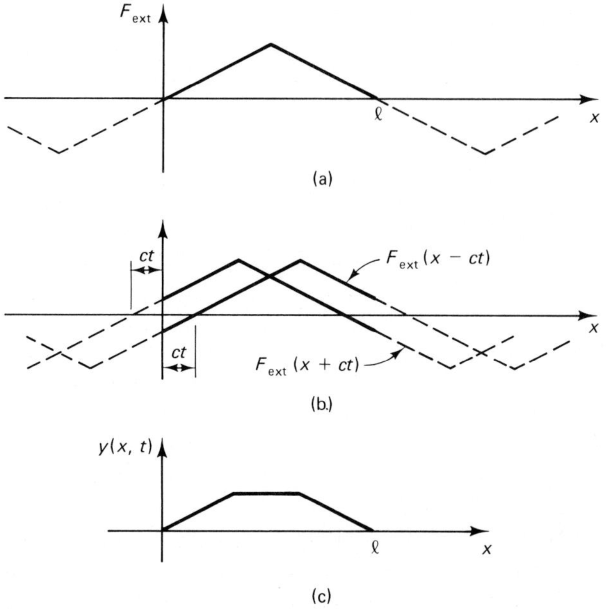

Fig. 16.8 Obtaining $y(x, t)$ from (21).

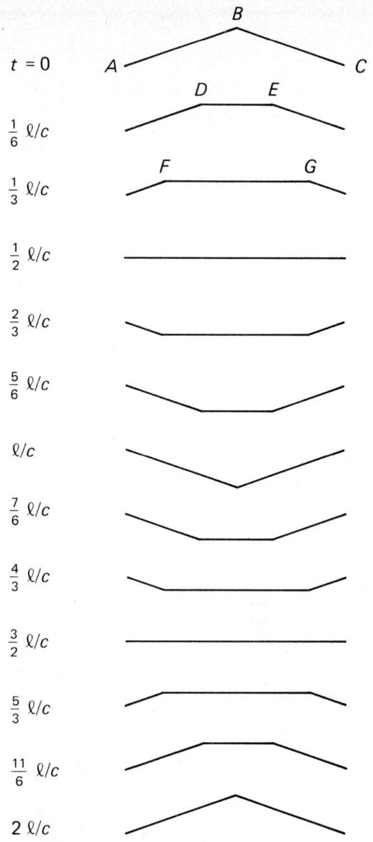

Fig. 16.9 Solution sequence over one cycle.

right and some of which travel to the left, with speed c. *Thus the parameter c in the wave equation $c^2 y_{xx} = y_{tt}$ is now seen to be the speed of the traveling waves.* Recalling that $c = \sqrt{\tau/\rho}$, it does seem reasonable, physically, that the wave speed should increase with the tension τ and decrease with the lineal mass density ρ. To repeat, (19) expresses y as the superposition of sinusoidal waves crisscrossing leftward and rightward with speed c. Over the physical interval $(0, \ell)$, these waves add up to a standing wave with nodes at the ends $x = 0$ and $x = \ell$, as illustrated in Fig. 16.9 for the case where $y(x, 0) = F(x)$ is the function graphed in Fig. 16.7.

To close our discussion of this example, observe an important difference between wave and diffusion phenomena. If the triangular function ABC in Fig. 16.9 were the initial temperature in a rod of length ℓ, the "kink" at B would smooth out immediately, so that the ensuing temperature $u(x, t)$ would be an infinitely differentiable function of x for all $t > 0$. *This smoothing out property of the diffusion phenomenon is not shared by wave phenomena.* For example, in Fig. 16.9 we see that the kink at B propagates to D and E, then to F and G, and so on; there is no smoothing out. In fact, although we have billed the results shown in the figure as the "solution," it should be confessed that the displayed $y(x, t)$ does not satisfy the wave equation $c^2 y_{xx} = y_{tt}$ *at* the kinks because y_{xx} does not exist at those points. (Indeed, even the first derivative y_x does not exist there.) This shortcoming is not regarded as important in applications (Exercise 12).

Summarizing this section, we solved the wave equation $c^2 y_{xx} = y_{tt}$ governing the vibration of a finite string, by separation of variables, and interpreted the resulting motion both in terms of standing waves and traveling waves—with passage from one to the other accomplished easily by applying the trigonometric identity (18). The parameter c in the wave equation was found to be the speed of the traveling waves. Finally, we were able to get the infinite series solution into a simple "closed form," in terms of the initial deflection. That important step, the reduction to closed form, had no counterpart in our study of the diffusion and Laplace equations.

16.2 EXERCISES

1. Solve the vibrating-string problem

$$c^2 y_{xx} = y_{tt} \qquad (0 < x < \ell, 0 < t < \infty)$$

$$y(0, t) = y(\ell, t) = 0, \quad y(x, 0) = F(x),$$

$$y_t(x, 0) = G(x)$$

by separation of variables, leaving the Fourier expansion coefficients in integral form.

2. Derive (15) by carrying out the integration called for in (14).

3. Letting $\ell = 10$, $c = 25$, and $F(x) = 0.03x(10 - x)$, use (21) to compute

*(a) $y(5, 3)$ (b) $y(4, 2)$
(c) $y(4, 1)$ (d) $y(2, 6)$
(e) $y(3, 0.1)$ (f) $y(6, 1)$
(g) $y(6, 1.8)$ *(h) $y(7.5, 2.1)$
(i) $y(2.5, 7.3)$ (j) $y(8.6, 76.3)$

4. Using the solution technique illustrated in Fig. 16.8, obtain the graphs shown in Fig. 16.9, for

(a) $t = \frac{1}{6}\frac{\ell}{c}$ and $\frac{1}{3}\frac{\ell}{c}$ (b) $t = \frac{1}{2}\frac{\ell}{c}$ and $\frac{2}{3}\frac{\ell}{c}$
(c) $t = \frac{5}{6}\frac{\ell}{c}$ and $\frac{\ell}{c}$ (d) $t = \frac{7}{6}\frac{\ell}{c}$ and $\frac{4}{3}\frac{\ell}{c}$
(e) $t = \frac{3}{2}\frac{\ell}{c}$ and $\frac{5}{3}\frac{\ell}{c}$ (f) $t = \frac{11}{6}\frac{\ell}{c}$ and $2\frac{\ell}{c}$

***5.** (*Inclusion of damping*) Unless the string vibrates in a vacuum, there will be some damping due to the movement of the string through the fluid (be it air, water, or whatever). If the damping force is proportional to the velocity y_t, the modified equation of motion becomes

$$c^2 y_{xx} = y_{tt} + a y_t, \tag{a}$$

where a is a known constant. (For definiteness, suppose that $0 < a < 2\pi c/\ell$.) Solve (a) by separation of variables, for a finite string of length ℓ, subject to the conditions

$$y(0, t) = y(\ell, t) = 0, \quad y(x, 0) = F(x), \quad y_t(x, 0) = 0, \tag{b}$$

leaving expansion coefficients in integral form. Summarize, in words, the effect(s) of the damping term ay_t.

6. (*Inclusion of lateral spring*) If, as shown in the figure, a lateral spring is included, the modified equation of motion for the vibrating string becomes $\tau y_{xx} - ky = \rho y_{tt}$, where k is the stiffness of the spring (newtons per meter per meter), or

$$c^2 y_{xx} - by = y_{tt} \qquad (c^2 = \tau/\rho,\ b = k/\rho > 0). \tag{a}$$

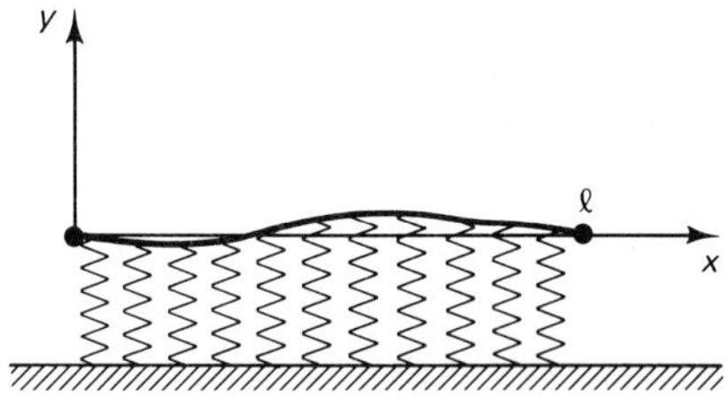

Solve (a) by separation of variables, for a finite string of length ℓ, subject to the conditions

$$y(0, t) = y(\ell, t) = 0, \quad y(x, 0) = F(x), \quad y_t(x, 0) = G(x), \tag{b}$$

leaving expansion coefficients in integral form. Summarize, in words, the effect(s) of the spring term by.

7. (*Nonhomogeneous wave equation*) We saw on page 675 that if the effects of gravity are included, the governing PDE for the vibrating string is

$$c^2 y_{xx} = y_{tt} + g \qquad (0 < x < \ell, 0 < t < \infty). \tag{a}$$

Solve (a) subject to the boundary and initial conditions

$$y(0, t) = y(\ell, t) = 0, \quad y(x, 0) = F(x), \quad y_t(x, 0) = 0. \tag{b}$$

Expansion coefficients may be left in integral form. *Hint:* Observe that if we seek $y(x, t) = X(x)T(t)$ and attempt to separate variables, we obtain

$$\frac{X''}{X} = \frac{1}{c^2}\frac{T''}{T} + \frac{g}{c^2 XT}. \tag{c}$$

Because of the last term in (c), which contains both x and t dependence, we are unable to successfully complete the separation process; i.e., we are unable to get all of the x dependence on one side of the equation and all of the t dependence on the other. Thus we suggest seeking y, instead, in the form

$$y(x, t) = y_p(x) + X(x)T(t), \tag{d}$$

where $y_p(x)$ is simply the "static sag" of the string due to gravity, i.e., y_p satisfies the problem $c^2 y_p'' = g$, with $y_p(0) = y_p(\ell) = 0$. [In mathematical terms, $y_p(x)$ is a particular solution of the nonhomogeneous equation $c^2 y_{xx} - y_{tt} = g$, and XT is a solution of the associated homogeneous equation $c^2 y_{xx} - y_{tt} = 0$. Incidentally, the static sag $y_p(x)$ is by no means the only possible particular solution. For example, one can obtain particular solutions that are functions of t alone. We suggest that you think about why the form $y_p(t)$ would *not* be a promising choice.]

8. (*Nonconstant forcing function*) In Exercise 7 we included a forcing term that was a constant. The suggested solution technique would have worked even if the forcing term were a nonconstant function of x. In this exercise we allow for t dependence as well. Thus consider the problem

$$\begin{aligned} &c^2 y_{xx} = y_{tt} + F(x, t) \qquad (0 < x < \ell, 0 < t < \infty) \\ &y(0, t) = y(\ell, t) = 0, \qquad y(x, 0) = f(x), \\ &y_t(x, 0) = g(x). \end{aligned} \tag{a}$$

(a) Solve for $y(x, t)$ by seeking

$$y(x, t) = \sum_{n=1}^{\infty} h_n(t) \sin \frac{n\pi x}{\ell} \tag{b}$$

and expanding

$$F(x, t) = \sum_{n=1}^{\infty} F_n(t) \sin \frac{n\pi x}{\ell}, \tag{c}$$

where the

$$F_n(t) = \frac{2}{\ell}\int_0^{\ell} F(x, t) \sin \frac{n\pi x}{\ell}\, dx \tag{d}$$

coefficients are considered as known (i.e., computable) functions of t. Thus show that

$$\begin{aligned} y(x, t) = \sum_{n=1}^{\infty} \Bigg[f_n \cos \omega_n t + \frac{g_n}{\omega_n} \sin \omega_n t \\ + \frac{1}{\omega_n}\int_0^t F_n(\tau) \sin \omega_n(\tau - t)\, d\tau \Bigg] \sin \frac{n\pi x}{\ell}, \end{aligned} \tag{e}$$

where $\omega_n = n\pi c/\ell$ and

$$f(x) = \sum_{n=1}^{\infty} f_n \sin \frac{n\pi x}{\ell}, \qquad g(x) = \sum_{n=1}^{\infty} g_n \sin \frac{n\pi x}{\ell}, \tag{f}$$

so that the f_n's and g_n's are computed as

$$\begin{aligned} f_n &= \frac{2}{\ell}\int_0^{\ell} f(x) \sin \frac{n\pi x}{\ell}\, dx, \\ g_n &= \frac{2}{\ell}\int_0^{\ell} g(x) \sin \frac{n\pi x}{\ell}\, dx. \end{aligned} \tag{g}$$

(b) Work out the solution (e) for the case where $F(x, t) = F_0 \sin \Omega t$ and $f(x) = g(x) = 0$, being careful to distinguish the case where the driving frequency Ω does *not* coincide with any of the natural frequencies ω_n from the case where Ω is *equal* to one of the ω_n's, say ω_k.
(c) Repeat part (b), with $F(x) = \delta(x - \ell/2) \sin \Omega t$, where δ is the delta function.

9. (*Variable end conditions*) Thus far our Dirichlet-type boundary conditions have been of constant type, e.g., $y(0, t) = 0$. Here we consider nonconstant conditions. Thus consider the problem

$$\begin{aligned} &c^2 y_{xx} = y_{tt} \qquad (0 < x < \ell, 0 < t < \infty) \\ &y(0, t) = p(t), \quad y(\ell, t) = q(t), \\ &y(x, 0) = f(x), \\ &y_t(x, 0) = g(x). \end{aligned} \tag{a}$$

Changing dependent variables from $y(x, t)$ to $z(x, t)$ according to

$$y(x, t) = z(x, t) + \left(1 - \frac{x}{\ell}\right)p(t) + \frac{x}{\ell} q(t), \tag{b}$$

show that the problem governing z is precisely of the type treated in Exercise 8. *Note:* Observe how an "input" can be moved from the boundary conditions to the PDE. In the present case, the PDE on y was homogeneous and the boundary conditions were nonhomogeneous; following the change of variables you should find that the PDE on z is nonhomogeneous and the boundary conditions are homogeneous.

10. Recall from Exercise 19 on page 604 that the voltage $v(x, t)$ [also the current $I(x, t)$] in a long underground cable is governed by the PDE

$$v_{xx} = LCv_{tt} + (rC + Lg)v_t + rgv. \qquad \text{(a)}$$

(a) Observe that (a) in Exercise 5 corresponds to a special case of equation (a), namely, where either r or g is zero. Does (a) in Exercise 6 correspond to a special case of (a)? Explain.
(b) Express (a) as $v_{xx} = Av_{tt} + Bv_t + Cv$, for simplicity. It is proposed that if v_1 is a solution of $v_{xx} = Av_{tt} + Bv_t$, and v_2 is a solution of $v_{xx} = Av_{tt} + Cv$, then, by superposition, $v = v_1 + v_2$ is a solution of $v_{xx} = Av_{tt} + Bv_t + Cv$. Give a critical assessment of that proposal.

11. (*Longitudinal waves in a rod*) First, read Exercise 7 on page 679. Now, consider a rod of length ℓ, cross-sectional area A, Young's modulus E, and mass per unit length ρ. At one end ($x = 0$) the rod is- attached to a wall that can be assumed to be rigid, and at the other end ($x = \ell$) the rod is free. Prior to time $t = 0$ we pull on the free end with a force F_0 (hence a stress $\sigma_0 = F_0/A$) and the rod is in static equilibrium. At $t = 0$ we abruptly remove the force.

(a) Show that the problem governing the displacement $u(x, t)$ is

$$c^2 u_{xx} = u_{tt} \qquad (0 < x < \ell, 0 < t < \infty) \qquad \text{(a)}$$

$$u(0, t) = 0, \quad u_x(\ell, t) = 0 \qquad \text{(b)}$$

$$u(x, 0) = \frac{\sigma_0}{E}x, \quad u_t(x, 0) = 0. \qquad \text{(c)}$$

(You may use any equations contained in Exercise 7 on page 679.)
(b) Solve for $u(x, t)$.
*(c) Determine the stress at the wall, $\sigma(0, t)$.

12. (*On breakdowns at kinks*) On page 685 it was pointed out that the wave equation is not satisfied at points at which the graph of y has a "kink" (discontinuous slope), and it was asserted that this shortcoming is not significant in applications. The purpose of this exercise is to support that assertion, and to do that we consider, for example, the initial shape $F(x)$ shown in Fig. 16.7, with a kink at $x = \ell/2$. In reality, we expect the string to have a small, but nonzero, radius of curvature at that point. Let $F^*(x)$ be an initial shape that is identical to $F(x)$ except over some small interval $|x - \ell/2| \leq \delta$, where F is "rounded off." Specifically, on that interval let F^* be a fifth-degree polynomial that matches F, F' and F'' at $x = (\ell/2) \pm \delta$, so that F^* is twice differentiable on $0 \leq x \leq \ell$. Whereas the solution $y(x, t)$ corresponding to the initial shape $F(x)$ fails to satisfy the PDE at points where it has kinks (Fig. 16.9), show that the solution $y^*(x, t)$ corresponding to the initial shape $F^*(x)$ is a twice-differentiable function of x for all $t \geq 0$, and thus suffers no such breakdowns. Further, show that for any $\epsilon > 0$, no matter how small, we can have $|y(x, t) - y^*(x, t)| < \epsilon$ for all $0 \leq x \leq \ell$ and $t \geq 0$ by sufficiently reducing δ. In view of these results, it seems unreasonable to fault $y(x, t)$ for the above-mentioned breakdowns at kinks.

13. (*Uniqueness*) In preceding exercises we have discussed solution techniques for the problem

$$c^2 y_{xx} = y_{tt} + F(x, t) \qquad (0 < x < \ell, 0 < t < \infty)$$

$$y(0, t) = p(t), \quad y(\ell, t) = q(t), \qquad \text{(a)}$$

$$y(x, 0) = f(x), \quad y_t(x, 0) = g(x).$$

In this exercise we ask you to show that the solution to (a) is *unique*. *Hint:* As usual, in uniqueness proofs, let $y_1(x, t)$ and $y_2(x, t)$ be two solutions and consider the difference $w(x, t) = y_1(x, t) - y_2(x, t)$. Show that w satisfies the "homogenized" problem

$$c^2 w_{xx} = w_{tt} \qquad (0 < x < \ell, 0 < t < \infty) \qquad \text{(b)}$$

$$w(0, t) = w(\ell, t) = 0, \qquad \text{(c)}$$

$$w(x, 0) = w_t(x, 0) = 0. \qquad \text{(d)}$$

Considering the integral

$$E(t) = \int_0^\ell (w_t^2 + c^2 w_x^2)\, dx, \qquad \text{(e)}$$

show—with the help of Leibniz differentiation, (b) and (c)—that $dE/dt = 0$. Show, with the help of (d) that it follows that $E(t) = 0$ for all $t \geq 0$, and hence that $w(x, t) = 0$ for all $0 < x < \ell$ and $t > 0$. That is, $y_1(x, t) - y_2(x, t) = 0$, so y_1 and y_2 are necessarily identical. Thus there exists at most *one* solution to (a).

14. (*Lumped-parameter model*) It is sometimes useful to model a *continuous* system, such as our string in the vibrating string problem, approximately, by a *discrete* system. To illustrate, let us divide the string into four

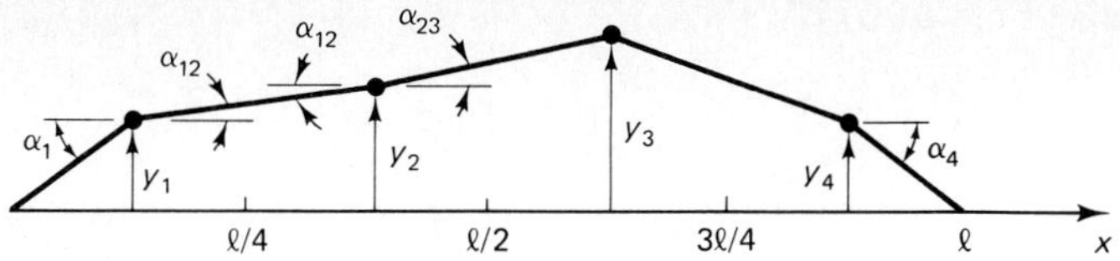

equal parts and focus the mass $\rho\ell/4$ of each segment at the center of that segment. (Such a system is often called a "lumped-parameter" system.) Thus we have four "beads" of mass $\rho\ell/4$ connected by massless string under tension τ, as shown in the figure.

(a) Applying Newton's second law of motion to the first mass, show that

$$\frac{\rho\ell}{4}\ddot{y}_1 \approx \tau\left(\frac{y_2 - y_1}{\ell/4} - \frac{y_1}{\ell/8}\right). \tag{a}$$

Doing the same for the remaining three masses, show that the resulting equations can be expressed in matrix form as

$$\ddot{\mathbf{y}} + \mathbf{A}\mathbf{y} = \mathbf{0}, \tag{b}$$

where

$$\mathbf{y} = \begin{pmatrix} y_1 \\ \vdots \\ y_4 \end{pmatrix} \text{ and } \mathbf{A} = \frac{16\tau}{\rho\ell^2}\begin{pmatrix} 3 & -1 & 0 & 0 \\ -1 & 2 & -1 & 0 \\ 0 & -1 & 2 & -1 \\ 0 & 0 & -1 & 3 \end{pmatrix}. \tag{c}$$

(b) More generally, with N beads one obtains (you need not derive this result)

$$\ddot{\mathbf{y}} + \mathbf{A}\mathbf{y} = \mathbf{0}, \tag{d}$$

where

$$\mathbf{y} = \begin{pmatrix} y_1 \\ \vdots \\ y_N \end{pmatrix} \quad \text{and}$$

$$\mathbf{A} = \left(\frac{N}{\ell}\right)^2 \frac{\tau}{\rho}\begin{pmatrix} 3 & -1 & & & & \\ -1 & 2 & -1 & & 0 & \\ & -1 & 2 & -1 & & \\ & & & \ddots & & \\ & 0 & & -1 & 2 & -1 \\ & & & & -1 & 3 \end{pmatrix}. \tag{e}$$

Seeking a solution of (d) in the form

$$\begin{aligned} y_1 &= \eta_1 \sin(\omega t + \phi) \\ &\vdots \\ y_N &= \eta_N \sin(\omega t + \phi) \end{aligned} \quad \text{or} \quad \mathbf{y} = \boldsymbol{\eta}\sin(\omega t + \phi),$$

show that

$$\mathbf{B}\boldsymbol{\eta} = \lambda\boldsymbol{\eta}, \tag{f}$$

where

$$\mathbf{B} = \begin{pmatrix} 3 & -1 & & & & \\ -1 & 2 & -1 & & 0 & \\ & -1 & 2 & -1 & & \\ & & & \ddots & & \\ & 0 & & -1 & 2 & -1 \\ & & & & -1 & 3 \end{pmatrix}$$

and $\lambda = (\rho/\tau)(\ell/N)^2\omega^2$.

(c) If, for a given N, one solves the eigenvalue problem (f), one obtains approximations to the first N orthogonal mode shapes and eigenfrequencies of the continuous string. Specifically, the eigenvectors $\boldsymbol{\eta}_1, \dots, \boldsymbol{\eta}_N$ give the approximate mode shapes [the corresponding *exact* mode shapes, for the continuous string, are $\sin(\pi x/\ell), \dots, \sin(N\pi x/\ell)$], and the eigenvalues $\lambda_1, \dots, \lambda_N$ give the approximate eigenfrequencies $\omega_1 = (N/\ell)\sqrt{\tau/\rho}\sqrt{\lambda_1}, \dots, \omega_N = (N/\ell)\sqrt{\tau/\rho}\sqrt{\lambda_N}$ [the corresponding *exact* eigenfrequencies are $\omega_1 = \pi c/\ell = (\pi/\ell)\sqrt{\tau/\rho}, \dots, \omega_N = N\pi c/\ell = (N\pi/\ell)\sqrt{\tau/\rho}$]. We now state the problem: Use available computer software to solve (f) for the case where $N = 10$. Compare the resulting 10 eigenfrequences with the exact values, and compare the first two mode shapes with their exact counterparts.

***15.** (*Vibrating membrane*) Solve the vibrating rectangular membrane problem

$$c^2(w_{xx} + w_{yy}) = w_{tt} \qquad (0 < x < a,\ 0 < y < b,\ 0 < t < \infty)$$

$$w(0, y, t) = w(a, y, t) = 0$$

$$w(x, 0, t) = w(x, b, t) = 0$$

$$w(x, y, 0) = f(x, y), \quad w_t(x, y, 0) = 0$$

for $w(x, y, t)$ by separation of variables, leaving expansion coefficients in integral form. *Hint:* It may help to review Example 3 on page 641.

16. (*Vibrating beam*) It is known from mechanics* that the free vibration of a uniform beam is governed by the fourth-order PDE

$$y_{xxxx} + \frac{\rho}{EI} y_{tt} = 0, \tag{a}$$

where $y(x, t)$ is the deflection, ρ is the mass per unit length, E is Young's modulus of the material, and I is the moment of inertia of the cross section about its neutral axis.

(a) If the beam is "cantilevered" (see the accompanying figure), the relevent boundary conditions are

$$\begin{aligned} &y(0, t) = y_x(0, t) = 0 \\ &y_{xx}(\ell, t) = 0 \quad \text{(no bending moment)} \\ &y_{xxx}(\ell, t) = 0 \quad \text{(no shear force).} \end{aligned} \tag{b}$$

In addition, suppose that the beam is initially at rest, so that $y_t(x, 0) = 0$. Seeking $y(x, t) = X(x)T(t)$, derive the solution form

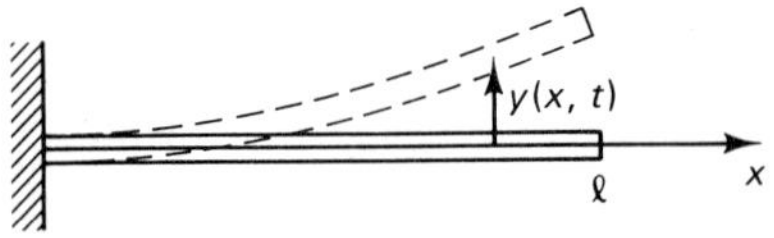

$$y(x, t) = \sum_{n=1}^{\infty} A_n X_n(x) \cos \omega_n t, \tag{c}$$

where the mode shapes are given by

$$X_n(x) = \sin \frac{z_n x}{\ell} - \sinh \frac{z_n x}{\ell} + \left(\frac{\cos z_n + \cosh z_n}{\sin z_n - \sinh z_n} \right) \left(\cos \frac{z_n x}{\ell} - \cosh \frac{z_n x}{\ell} \right),$$

the frequencies are

$$\omega_n = \sqrt{\frac{EI}{\rho}} \left(\frac{z_n}{\ell} \right)^2,$$

and where the z_n's are the solutions of the transcendental equation $\cos z \cosh z + 1 = 0$.

(b) If instead of being cantilevered, the beam is pinned at both ends, the boundary conditions (b) are to be replaced by

$$\begin{aligned} &y(0, t) = y(\ell, t) = 0, \\ &y_{xx}(0, t) = y_{xx}(\ell, t) = 0 \quad \text{(no bending moment).} \end{aligned} \tag{d}$$

Find the solution form, analogous to the one cited in part (a), corresponding to the boundary conditions (d).

16.3 D'ALEMBERT'S SOLUTION

For the wave equation

$$c^2 y_{xx} = y_{tt}, \tag{1}$$

there exists a remarkable alternative approach known as d'Alembert's method. The method is based on a change in independent variables, from x, y to ξ, η, say, where the new variables are defined in terms of the old ones by the relations

$$\xi = x - ct, \tag{2a}$$

$$\eta = x + ct. \tag{2b}$$

(If this change of variables appears to be "out of the blue," recall that the combinations $x - ct$, $x + ct$ began to appear prominently in Section 16.2.)

To reexpress (1) in terms of ξ, η, note that the needed "building blocks" are the $\partial/\partial x$ and $\partial/\partial t$ operators. According to the chain rule,

$$\frac{\partial}{\partial x} = \frac{\partial}{\partial \xi}\frac{\partial \xi}{\partial x} + \frac{\partial}{\partial \eta}\frac{\partial \eta}{\partial x} = \frac{\partial}{\partial \xi} + \frac{\partial}{\partial \eta} \tag{3}$$

*See, for example, William T. Thomson, *Theory of Vibration with Applications*, 2nd ed. (Englewood Cliffs, N.J.: Prentice-Hall, 1981).

and

$$\frac{\partial}{\partial t} = \frac{\partial}{\partial \xi}\frac{\partial \xi}{\partial t} + \frac{\partial}{\partial \eta}\frac{\partial \eta}{\partial t} = -c\frac{\partial}{\partial \xi} + c\frac{\partial}{\partial \eta}, \tag{4}$$

so (1) becomes

$$c^2\left(\frac{\partial}{\partial \xi} + \frac{\partial}{\partial \eta}\right)\left(\frac{\partial}{\partial \xi} + \frac{\partial}{\partial \eta}\right)y = \left(c\frac{\partial}{\partial \xi} - c\frac{\partial}{\partial \eta}\right)\left(c\frac{\partial}{\partial \xi} - c\frac{\partial}{\partial \eta}\right)y$$

or

$$\left(\frac{\partial}{\partial \xi} + \frac{\partial}{\partial \eta}\right)(y_\xi + y_\eta) = \left(\frac{\partial}{\partial \xi} - \frac{\partial}{\partial \eta}\right)(y_\xi - y_\eta)$$

or

$$y_{\xi\xi} + y_{\xi\eta} + y_{\eta\xi} + y_{\eta\eta} = y_{\xi\xi} - y_{\xi\eta} - y_{\eta\xi} + y_{\eta\eta}. \tag{5}$$

Assuming that y is well-enough behaved so that $y_{\xi\eta} = y_{\eta\xi}$, (5) simplifies to $4y_{\xi\eta} = 0$, or

$$y_{\xi\eta} = 0. \tag{6}$$

The point, then, is that when expressed in terms of the ξ, η variables, the wave equation simplifies dramatically. In fact, (6) can actually be solved by quadrature (i.e., by direct integration). First integrating with respect to η gives

$$y_\xi = \int 0\,\partial\eta = 0 + f(\xi) = f(\xi) \tag{7}$$

where the "constant of integration" f is allowed to be an arbitrary function of ξ since ξ was held fixed during the integration on η. Next, integration of (7) with respect to ξ gives $y = \int f(\xi)\,\partial\xi$ plus an arbitrary function of η, say $G(\eta)$. Now, since f is arbitrary, we may as well simply write $F(\xi)$ in place of $\int f(\xi)\,\partial\xi$. Thus we have

$$y = F(\xi) + G(\eta), \tag{8}$$

or, returning to the original variables,

$$\boxed{y = F(x - ct) + G(x + ct),} \tag{9}$$

where F and G are arbitrary [although twice differentiable if (9) is to satisfy (1)] functions.

Since it follows from the sequence (6) to (9) that y is *necessarily* of the form (9), we say that (9) is the **general solution of the wave equation** (1). In contrast, observe that we did *not* obtain a general solution of the diffusion equation in Chapter 14, nor did we obtain a general solution of the Laplace equation in Chapter 15. Thus, obtaining (9) is a noteworthy event in our study of PDEs.

To illustrate the use of (9), consider the infinite-string problem

$$c^2 y_{xx} = y_{tt} \qquad (-\infty < x < \infty,\ 0 < t < \infty) \tag{10a}$$

$$y(x, 0) = p(x), \quad y_t(x, 0) = q(x). \tag{10b}$$

Since we already have the general solution (9) of the wave equation (10a), we can bypass (10a) and immediately impose the initial conditions (10b) in order to determine the functions F and G in (9). Thus writing

$$y(x, 0) = p(x) = F(x) + G(x) \tag{11}$$

$$y_t(x, 0) = q(x) = -cF'(x) + cG'(x), \tag{12}$$

we have two equations in the two unknowns F and G. Integrating (12) from any fixed point, say 0, to x gives

$$\int_0^x q(x')\,dx' = -cF(x) + cF(0) + cG(x) - cG(0), \tag{13}$$

and solving (11) and (13) by simple algebra gives

$$F(x) = \frac{p(x)}{2} - \frac{1}{2c}\int_0^x q(x')\,dx' + \frac{F(0) - G(0)}{2}, \tag{14a}$$

$$G(x) = \frac{p(x)}{2} + \frac{1}{2c}\int_0^x q(x')\,dx' - \frac{F(0) - G(0)}{2}. \tag{14b}$$

Having thus determined the functional form of F and of G, (9) gives the desired solution,

$$\begin{aligned} y(x, t) &= F(x - ct) + G(x + ct) \\ &= \frac{p(x - ct)}{2} - \frac{1}{2c}\int_0^{x-ct} q(x')\,dx' + \frac{F(0) - G(0)}{2} \\ &\quad + \frac{p(x + ct)}{2} + \frac{1}{2c}\int_0^{x+ct} q(x')\,dx' - \frac{F(0) - G(0)}{2}, \end{aligned}$$

or, after simplification,

$$y(x, t) = \frac{p(x - ct) + p(x + ct)}{2} + \frac{1}{2c}\int_{x-ct}^{x+ct} q(x')\,dx'. \tag{15}$$

This result is important and warrants further discussion. To begin, consider the x, t domain ($-\infty < x < \infty$, $0 < t < \infty$), as shown in Fig. 16.10. Equation (15) gives the solution at any point x, t in the upper half plane, so let us mark the x, t point in the figure and then use dummy variables x', t' for the coordinate axes.

Note carefully, from (15), that $y(x, t)$ depends on initial data only on the closed interval $[A, B]$; specifically, it depends on p at A, p at B, and on the integral of q from A to B. In fact, the initial data on the interval $[A, B]$ suffice to determine the solution *everywhere* within the triangle ABC. [For example, $y(x_0, t_0)$ depends only

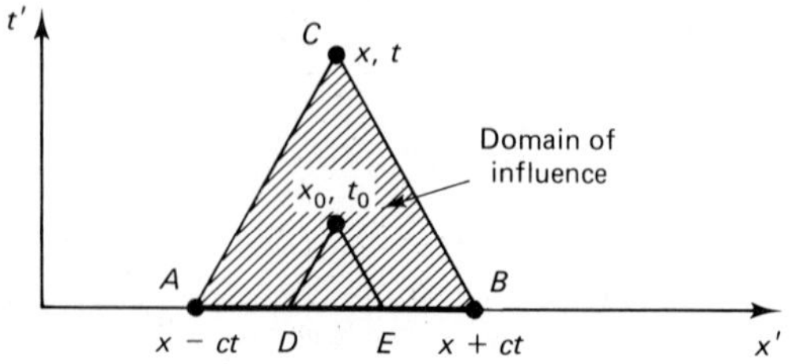

Fig. 16.10 Domain of influence.

on data from D to E.] Hence the triangle ABC is known as the **domain of influence** of the interval $[A, B]$.

This limited dependence on the initial data is a striking feature of the wave equation, for recall from Chapters 14 and 15 that if the governing PDE were, instead, the diffusion or Laplace equation, the solution at each point in the upper half plane domain would depend on data *along the entire axis,* not just on some finite segment such as A, B.

EXAMPLE 1 For illustrative purposes, suppose that $q(x) = 0$ and that $p(x)$ is the triangular pulse shown in Fig. 16.11. Since $q(x) = 0$, (15) gives

$$y(x, t) = \frac{p(x - ct) + p(x + ct)}{2}. \tag{16}$$

At $t = 0$, (16) becomes $y(x, 0) = p(x)/2 + p(x)/2$, so that we may regard the initial triangular pulse as the sum of two "half-pulses," $p(x)/2$ and $p(x)/2$. Subsequently, $y(x, t) = p(x - ct)/2 + p(x + ct)/2$. The first term, $p(x - ct)/2$, amounts to the original half-pulse *translated to the right* through a distance ct, and the second term, $p(x + ct)/2$, amounts to the original half-pulse *translated to the left* through a distance ct, as depicted in Fig. 16.12. Clearly, the *speed* of these rightward- and leftward-running waves is c.

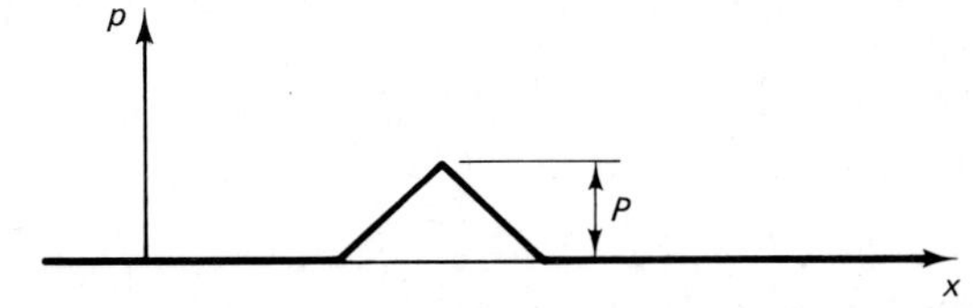

Fig. 16.11 Triangular pulse as initial shape.

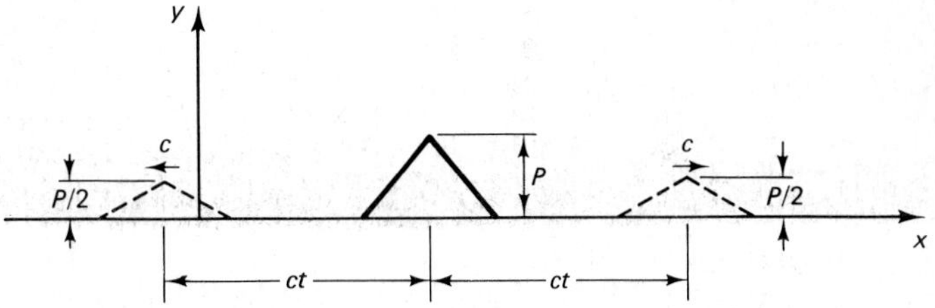

Fig. 16.12 Breakup of initial pulse into rightward- and leftward running traveling waves.

It is also useful to display these results on an x, t plane, as we have in Fig. 16.13. Naturally, plotting $y(x, t)$ above the x, t plane calls for three-dimensional graphics, but it should suffice to merely "lay the y solution curves down" in the plane of the paper, as we have in the figure. Notice that the $p(x - ct)/2$ term in (16) is constant along $x - ct =$ constant lines, so that the values of $p(x - ct)/2$ propagate along these lines, without change.

Similarly, the $p(x + ct)/2$ term in (16) is constant along $x + ct =$ constant lines, so the values of $p(x + ct)/2$ propagate along those lines. These special families of curves, the lines $x - ct =$ constant and $x + ct =$ constant, are known as **characteristics**. In Fig. 16.13 we have drawn only a handful of characteristics—those which define the two "channels" (I and II) in which the half pulses propagate. So that the reader will not be misled into believing that these are the *only* charac-

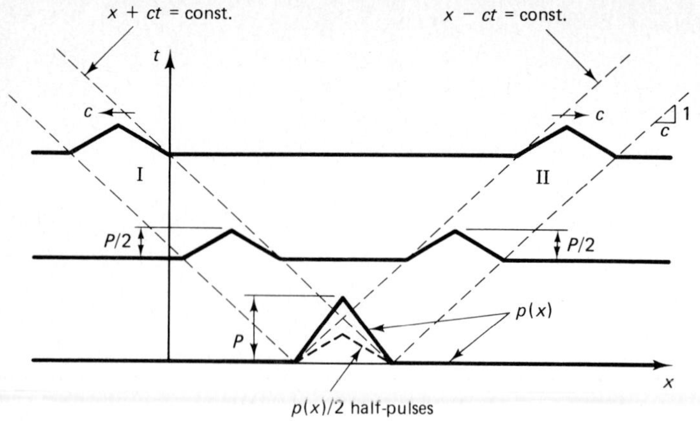

Fig. 16.13 Solution shown in x, t plane.

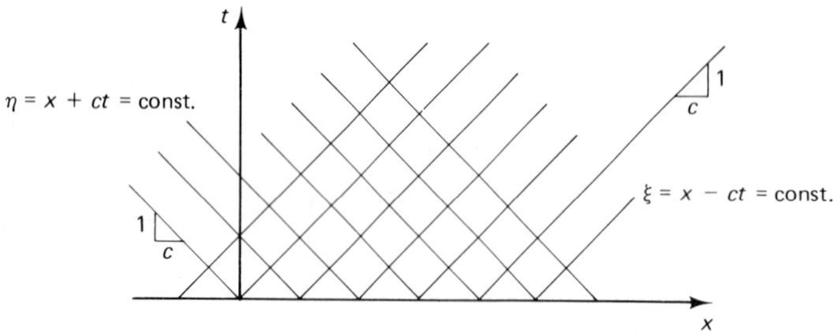

Fig. 16.14 The two families of characteristics.

teristics, we should emphasize that $\xi = x - ct =$ constant and $\eta = x + ct =$ constant are two *families* of curves, as is made more evident in Fig. 16.14. ◀

EXAMPLE 2 In Example 1 we took $q(x)$ to be zero and $p(x)$ to be a simple triangular pulse in order to gain some understanding of the $[p(x - ct) + p(x + ct)]/2$ term in (15). To study the *integral* term in (15), suppose that $p(x) = 0$ and that $q(x) = \delta(x - x_0)$, say. (This delta function velocity input might, for example, serve as a first approximation to the initial condition imposed on a piano wire by the impact of the hammer.) Then (15) gives

$$
\begin{aligned}
y(x, t) &= 0 + \frac{1}{2c}\int_{x-ct}^{x+ct} \delta(x' - x_0)\, dx' \\
&= \begin{cases} 0, & x_0 < x - ct \\ \dfrac{1}{2c}, & x - ct < x_0 < x + ct, \\ 0, & x_0 > x + ct \end{cases}
\end{aligned}
\tag{17}
$$

as depicted in Fig. 16.15.

The integration in (17) was carried out using equation (12) on page 514. More graphically, note that y at P (Fig. 16.15) is $1/2c$ times the integral of $\delta(x - x_0)$ over the interval from Q to R. Since the delta function acts at x_0, and x_0 is outside the Q, R interval, the integral is zero and y is zero at P. If we now imagine sliding P to the right, along the $t =$ constant line, then only when P lies between S and T

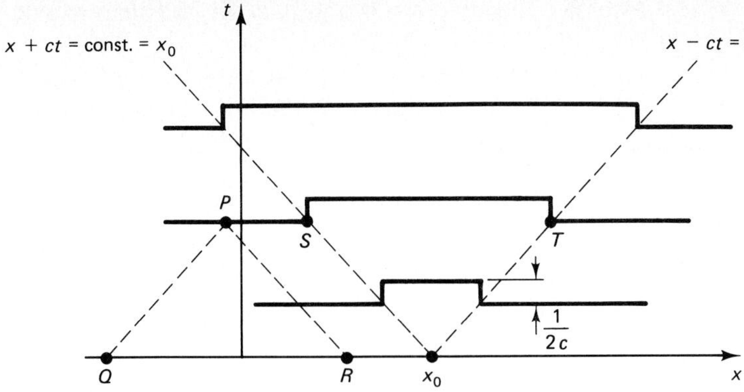

Fig. 16.15 Solution due to hammer blow input.

does x_0 fall between Q and R. In that event the integral of the delta function is unity and $y = (1/2c)(1) = 1/2c$, as shown in the figure. ◀

In this section we introduced the change of independent variable $\xi = x - ct$, $\eta = x + ct$, and derived the general solution $y = F(x - ct) + G(x + ct)$ of the wave equation. To illustrate the use of this general solution, we solved an infinite-string problem with prescribed initial conditions and derived the solution (15).

In fact, the story presented in this section is a special case of a more general *theory of characteristics* for hyperbolic partial differential equations. Besides illuminating the essential structure associated with hyperbolic PDEs, that theory leads to a powerful numerical solution technique known as the *method of characteristics.**

Besides the method of characteristics, one can apply the *finite difference method* to solve hyperbolic PDEs such as the wave equation. That method was discussed in Section 14.5 in regard to the diffusion equation, and in Section 15.5 in regard to the Laplace equation. In our opinion a similar section for the wave equation is not necessary, and we therefore close our discussion of the wave equation with the present section.

16.3 EXERCISES

1. Verify, by direct substitution, that the right-hand side of (9) does indeed satisfy the wave equation (1).

2. Verify that the right-hand side of (15) satisfies the wave equation and the two initial conditions.

3. (a) Obtain the general solution for the nonhomogeneous wave equation $c^2 y_{xx} = y_{tt} - K$, where K is a constant.
(b) Use the general solution obtained in part (a) to find the solution to the problem

$$c^2 y_{xx} = y_{tt} - K \qquad (-\infty < x < \infty,\ 0 < t < \infty)$$

$$y(x, 0) = p(x), \quad y_t(x, 0) = q(x).$$

4. Find the general solution of the given PDE by introducing the suggested change of variables. Verify that, like the wave equation, the PDE is hyperbolic.
*(a) $u_{xx} + 4u_{xy} + 3u_{yy} = 0;\ \xi = x - y,\ \eta = 3x - y$

* See, for example, M. Greenberg, *Foundations of Applied Mathematics*, (Englewood Cliffs, N.J.: Prentice-Hall, 1978); or, for a more complete discussion, E. Zauderer, *Partial Differential Equations of Applied Mathematics* (New York: Wiley, 1983).

(b) $u_{xx} + 4u_{xy} - 5u_{yy} = 0; \xi = x - y, \eta = 5x + y$
(c) $u_{xx} + 6u_{xy} + 8u_{yy} = 0; \xi = 4x - y,$
$\eta = 2x - y$
(d) $u_{xx} + 4u_{xy} - 5u_{yy} = 0; \xi = x + y,$
$\eta = 5x - y$

5. Find the general solution of the given PDE by introducing a suitable change of variables of the form $\xi = ax + by$, $\eta = cx + dy$. Verify that, like the wave equation, the PDE is hyperbolic.

*(a) $u_{xx} + 8u_{xy} + 12u_{yy} = 0$
(b) $u_{xx} - 2u_{xy} - 3u_{yy} = 0$
(c) $u_{xx} - 10u_{xy} + 9u_{yy} = 0$

6. Find the general solution of the *first*-order PDE $u_t + cu_x = 0$, where c is a constant, by introducing the change of variables $\xi = x - ct$, $\eta = t$, and then use that general solution to solve the problem

$$u_t + cu_x = 0 \qquad (-\infty < x < \infty, 0 < t < \infty)$$
$$u(x, 0) = f(x).$$

7. In Figs. 16.12 and 16.13 we showed $y(x, t)$ at times t which were large enough so that the two half pulses had completely separated; i.e., they did not overlap. In this exercise we examine the case in which they do overlap. Letting

$$p(x) = \begin{cases} 0, & x < 1 \\ 2x - 2, & 1 < x < 1.5 \\ 4 - 2x, & 1.5 < x < 2 \\ 0, & x > 2, \end{cases}$$

$q(x) = 0$, and $c = 20$, show labeled graphs of $y(x, t)$ at $t = 0.005$ and at $t = 0.02$.

8. With $c = 100$, sketch the solution to (10) at $t = 0.02$ and $t = 0.04$, using an x, t plane display as in Figs. 16.13 and 16.15, and labeling all key values. H denotes the Heaviside step function and δ is the Dirac delta function.

(a) $p(x) = H(x + 1) - H(x - 1), q(x) = 0$
(b) $p(x) = H(x), q(x) = 0$
(c) $p(x) = 0, q(x) = H(x + 1) - H(x - 1)$
(d) $p(x) = H(x), q(x) = \delta(x)$

9. *(a) Use (10) to solve the problem

$$c^2 y_{xx} = y_{tt} \qquad (0 < x < \infty, 0 < t < \infty) \qquad \text{(a)}$$
$$y(x, 0) = y_t(x, 0) = 0 \qquad (0 < x < \infty) \qquad \text{(b)}$$
$$y(0, t) = h(t) \qquad (0 < t < \infty), \qquad \text{(c)}$$

where $h(t)$ is prescribed. [We can imagine taking the left end of the string between two fingers and, beginning at $t = 0$, "jiggling" it according to $y(0, t) = h(t)$.]

(b) Solve (a) to (c) by means of the Laplace transform, instead. *Note:* You may assume the truth of the statement:

$$\lim_{x\to\infty} \bar{y}(x, s) = \lim_{x\to\infty} \int_0^\infty y(x, t)e^{-st}\, dt$$
$$= \int_0^\infty \lim_{x\to\infty} y(x, t)e^{-st}\, dt = \int_0^\infty 0\, dt = 0.$$

10. (*Use of Fourier transform*) Solve the problem

$$c^2 y_{xx} = y_{tt} \qquad (-\infty < x < \infty, 0 < t < \infty)$$

subject to the given initial conditions, using a Fourier transform on the x variable.

(a) $y(x, 0) = p(x), y_t(x, 0) = 0$
(b) $y(x, 0) = 0, y_t(x, 0) = \delta(x)$

11. (*Image system*) (a) Use (15) to show that *the solution to (10) is an even function of x, for all t, if p(x) and q(x) are even functions of x,* and that *it is an odd function of x, for all t, if p(x) and q(x) are odd functions of x.*
(b) Use the results noted in part (a) to show that the *semi*-infinite string problem

$$c^2 y_{xx} = y_{tt} \qquad (0 < x < \infty, 0 < t < \infty)$$
$$y(x, 0) = p(x), \quad y_t(x, 0) = 0, \quad y(0, t) = 0 \qquad \text{(a)}$$

can be solved by treating instead the "extended" problem

$$c^2 Y_{xx} = Y_{tt} \qquad (-\infty < x < \infty, 0 < t < \infty)$$
$$Y(x, 0) = \begin{cases} p(x), & x > 0 \\ -p(-x), & x < 0 \end{cases}, \qquad Y_t(x, 0) = 0. \qquad \text{(b)}$$

That is, within the *actual* domain $(0 < x < \infty, 0 < t < \infty)$ we have $y(x, t) = Y(x, t)$, where the solution for Y has already been derived in Example 1. With $c = 2$ and

$$p(x) = \begin{cases} 0, & x < 6 \\ x - 6, & 6 < x < 7 \\ 8 - x, & 7 < x < 8 \\ 0, & x > 8, \end{cases}$$

sketch the solution at $t = 2$ and $t = 6$, using an x, t plane display as in Figs. 16.13 and 16.15. (The solution in the second quadrant of the x,t plane is "fictitious"; it is merely the result of the mathematical extension, and is known as the **image system**.)

Bessel and Legendre Functions (Optional) 17

INTRODUCTION 17.1

In Chapters 14 to 16 our separation-of-variables solution of the diffusion, Laplace, and wave equations led to ordinary differential equations that were elementary, i.e., they admitted general solutions expressible in terms of elementary functions. For example, for the Laplace equation in plane polar coordinates,

$$\nabla^2 u = u_{rr} + \frac{1}{r} u_r + \frac{1}{r^2} u_{\theta\theta} = 0, \tag{1}$$

the assumed solution form $u(r, \theta) = R(r)\Theta(\theta)$ led to the ODEs

$$r^2R'' + rR' - \kappa^2 R = 0, \qquad \text{(Cauchy–Euler equation)} \tag{2}$$

$$\Theta'' + \kappa^2\Theta = 0, \tag{3}$$

with elementary solutions

$$R(r) = \begin{cases} Ar^{\kappa} + Br^{-\kappa}, & \kappa \neq 0 \\ C + D \ln r, & \kappa = 0 \end{cases} \tag{4}$$

and

$$\Theta(\theta) = \begin{cases} E \sin \kappa\theta + F \cos \kappa\theta, & \kappa \neq 0 \\ G + H\theta, & \kappa = 0. \end{cases} \tag{5}$$

In other important cases, not yet considered here, the resulting ODEs are *not* elementary. For example, consider the Laplace equation in cylindrical coordinates, where u varies with r and z. Then, in place of (1) we have

$$\nabla^2 u = u_{rr} + \frac{1}{r} u_r + u_{zz} = 0, \tag{6}$$

and $u(r, z) = R(r)Z(z)$ gives the ODEs

$$rR'' + R' + \kappa^2 rR = 0, \tag{7}$$

$$Z'' - \kappa^2 Z = 0. \tag{8}$$

This time, the R equation is *not* a Cauchy–Euler equation; it is nonelementary, and its solutions are *Bessel functions*, as discussed in the next section.

Or, consider the Laplace equation in spherical polars. If there is symmetry about the z axis, u is independent of θ, so

$$\nabla^2 u = u_{\rho\rho} + \frac{2}{\rho} u_\rho + \frac{1}{\rho^2} u_{\phi\phi} + \frac{\cot\phi}{\rho^2} u_\phi = 0, \tag{9}$$

and $u = R(\rho)\Phi(\phi)$ gives

$$\rho^2 R'' + 2\rho R' - \kappa^2 R = 0, \tag{10}$$

$$\Phi'' + \cot\phi\,\Phi' + \kappa^2 \Phi = 0. \tag{11}$$

Of these, (11) is nonelementary, and its solutions are *Legendre functions,* as discussed in Section 17.3.

In fact, if other non-Cartesian coordinates (such as elliptic-cylinder, parabolic-cylinder, or conical coordinates) are used, then still other nonelementary functions, or "special functions," are encountered. However, we will continue to limit our attention in this text to the Cartesian, cylindrical, and spherical polar coordinate systems since these are the most important in engineering and science. Furthermore, the Bessel and Legendre function stories are quite representative, so that a study of these two cases should provide a base for futher study in more advanced or specialized texts. *

17.2 BESSEL FUNCTIONS

The differential equation

$$\boxed{x^2 y'' + xy' + (x^2 - \nu^2)y = 0,} \tag{1}$$

where ν is a constant, is known as **Bessel's equation of order ν,** and its solutions are known as **Bessel functions of order ν.** This equation was studied systematically by Friedrich Wilhelm Bessel (1784–1846), director of the astronomical observatory at Königsberg, in connection with his work on planetary motion. Outside the realm of planetary motion, the equation appears prominently in a wide range of applica-

*For a detailed study of the solution of the diffusion, Laplace, and wave equations by the method of separation of variables, in a variety of orthogonal curvilinear coordinate systems, we recommend P. Moon and D. E. Spencer, *Field Theory for Engineers* (Princeton, N.J.: D. Van Nostrand, 1961).

tions, such as steady and unsteady diffusion in cylindrical domains, and one-dimensional wave propagation and diffusion in variable-cross-section media.

The equation is said to be nonelementary in the sense that its solutions are not (except for certain values of ν) expressible in closed form in terms of the so-called elementary functions. There exists a vast body of results regarding series, integral, and approximate representation of the various Bessel functions, and in this brief section we need to be rather selective. *In a shorter course, one may wish to omit the last two parts of this section, on modified Bessel functions and Bessel function solutions to other differential equations.*

We consider the parameter ν to be any real number. In fact, since only the quantity ν^2 occurs in (1), positive and negative values of ν are indistinguishable, and we can consider ν to be nonnegative without loss of generality.

Preparing to apply the method of Frobenius (which is reviewed in Appendix A), we observe first that all points x are regular points of (1) except for $x = 0$, which is a regular singular point. We could avoid the singular point and expand about some other point, say x_0, to obtain two LI (linearly independent) solutions of the form $\sum_{n=0}^{\infty} a_n(x - x_0)^n$, but it is best to jump in right *at* the singular point $x = 0$ because then the singular behavior of the solution, at $x = 0$, will come into explicit view. Thus we seek a Frobenius-type expansion about $x = 0$,

$$y(x) = x^c \sum_{k=0}^{\infty} a_k x^k = \sum_{k=0}^{\infty} a_k x^{k+c} \qquad (a_0 \neq 0). \tag{2}$$

Putting (2) into (1) gives, after simplification,

$$\sum_{k=0}^{\infty} [(k + c)^2 - \nu^2] a_k x^{k+c} + \sum_{k=0}^{\infty} a_k x^{k+c+2} = 0, \tag{3}$$

or, equivalently,

$$\sum_{k=0}^{\infty} \{[(k + c)^2 - \nu^2] a_k + a_{k-2}\} x^{k+c} = 0, \tag{4}$$

where $a_{-1} = a_{-2} \equiv 0$. Equating to zero the coefficients in braces in (4), for each k, gives

$$k = 0: \quad (c^2 - \nu^2) a_0 = 0, \tag{5a}$$

$$k = 1: \quad [(c + 1)^2 - \nu^2] a_1 = 0, \tag{5b}$$

$$k \geq 2: \quad [(c + k)^2 - \nu^2] a_k = -a_{k-2}. \tag{5c}$$

Since $a_0 \neq 0$, (5a) gives the indicial equation $c^2 - \nu^2 = 0$, with the two roots $c = +\nu, -\nu$. First let $c = +\nu$. Then (5b) gives $a_1 = 0$ and (5c) gives the recursion relation

$$a_k = -\frac{a_{k-2}}{k(k + 2\nu)}. \tag{6}$$

From (6), together with the fact that $a_1 = 0$, it follows that $a_1 = a_3 = a_5 = \cdots = 0$ and that

$$a_{2k} = \frac{(-1)^k}{2^{2k} k! (\nu + k)(\nu + k - 1) \cdots (\nu + 1)} a_0. \tag{7}$$

It will be preferable to get the ever-growing $(\nu + k)(\nu + k - 1)\cdots(\nu + 1)$ into closed form. This step can be accomplished if we recall (from page 549) the gamma function recursion formula $\Gamma(x) = (x-1)\Gamma(x-1)$, for then $\Gamma(\nu + k + 1) = (\nu + k)\Gamma(\nu + k) = (\nu + k)(\nu + k - 1)\Gamma(\nu + k - 1) = \cdots = (\nu + k) \times (\nu + k - 1)\cdots(\nu + 1)\Gamma(\nu + 1)$ gives $(\nu + k)(\nu + k - 1)\cdots(\nu + 1) = \Gamma(\nu + k + 1)/\Gamma(\nu + 1)$. With this replacement, we have

$$\begin{aligned} y(x) &= \sum_{k=0}^{\infty} a_{2k} x^{2k+\nu} = a_0 \sum_{k=0}^{\infty} \frac{(-1)^k \Gamma(\nu + 1)}{2^{2k} k! \Gamma(\nu + k + 1)} x^{2k+\nu} \\ &= 2^{\nu}\Gamma(\nu + 1) a_0 \sum_{k=0}^{\infty} \frac{(-1)^k}{k! \Gamma(\nu + k + 1)} \left(\frac{x}{2}\right)^{2k+\nu}. \end{aligned} \tag{8}$$

Dropping the constant factor $2^{\nu}\Gamma(\nu + 1)a_0$, we call the resulting solution the **Bessel function of the first kind, of order ν,** and denote it as $J_\nu(x)$:

$$J_\nu(x) = \sum_{k=0}^{\infty} \frac{(-1)^k}{k! \Gamma(\nu + k + 1)} \left(\frac{x}{2}\right)^{2k+\nu}. \tag{9}$$

As representative, we have displayed the graphs of J_0, J_1, and J_2 in Fig. 17.1.

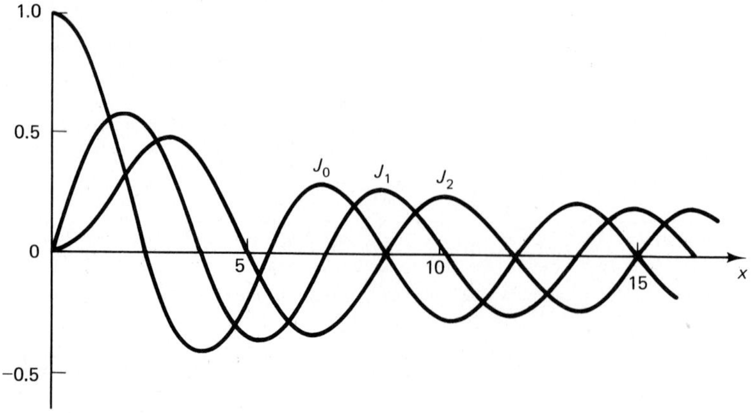

Fig. 17.1 Bessel functions of the first kind.

To obtain a second LI solution, we turn to the other indicial root, $c = -\nu$. There is no need to retrace all of our steps; all we need to do is change ν to $-\nu$ everywhere in the right-hand side of (9). Denoting the result as $J_{-\nu}(x)$, the **Bessel function of the first kind, of order $-\nu$,** we have

$$J_{-\nu}(x) = \sum_{k=0}^{\infty} \frac{(-1)^k}{k! \Gamma(k - \nu + 1)} \left(\frac{x}{2}\right)^{2k-\nu}. \tag{10}$$

Here we need to distinguish two cases. If ν is *not an integer*, then $J_{-\nu}(x)$ and $J_\nu(x)$ are LI and we can express the *general solution* of (1) as

$$y(x) = AJ_\nu(x) + BJ_{-\nu}(x). \tag{11}$$

However, if ν is *an integer*, say n, it can be shown (Exercise 1) that $J_{-n}(x) =$

$(-1)^n J_n(x)$, so that $J_{-n}(x)$ and $J_n(x)$ are not LI. Thus all we have is the one solution

$$J_n(x) = \sum_{k=0}^{\infty} \frac{(-1)^k}{k!(n+k)!} \left(\frac{x}{2}\right)^{2k+n}, \tag{12}$$

obtained from (9) by setting $\nu = n$ and recalling that $\Gamma(n + k + 1) = (n + k)!$. Nonetheless, a second LI solution can be found by the method of variation of parameters. Leaving the details (for the case $n = 0$) to Exercise 2, here we merely state that the result is the **Bessel function of the second kind, of order n,**

$$Y_n(x) = \frac{2}{\pi}\left\{\left(\ln\frac{x}{2} + \gamma\right)J_n(x) - \frac{1}{2}\sum_{k=0}^{n-1}\frac{(n-k-1)!}{k!}\left(\frac{x}{2}\right)^{2k-n} - \frac{1}{2}\sum_{k=0}^{\infty}\frac{(-1)^k[\phi(k) + \phi(k+n)]}{k!(k+n)!}\left(\frac{x}{2}\right)^{2k+n}\right\}, \tag{13}$$

where $\phi(k) \equiv 1 + \frac{1}{2} + \cdots + 1/k$ for $k \geq 1$, $\phi(0) \equiv 0$, and $\gamma \equiv \lim_{n\to\infty}[\phi(k) - \ln k] = 0.5772157\ldots$ is *Euler's constant*. The first few Y_n's are shown in Fig. 17.2.

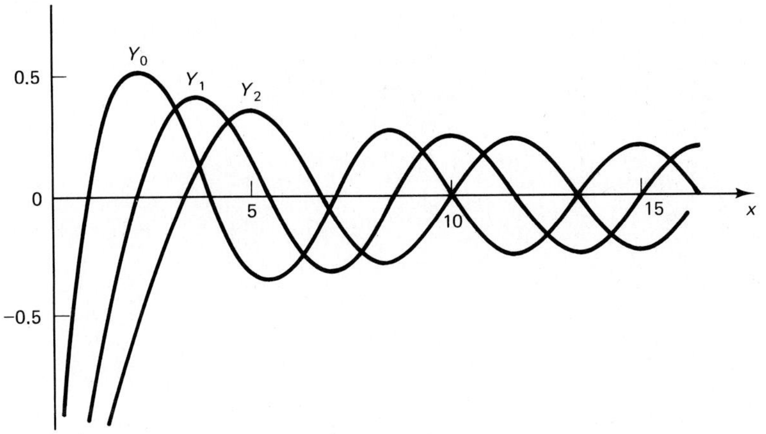

Fig. 17.2 Bessel functions of the second kind.

Thus the general solution of the Bessel equation (1) can now be stated as

$$y(x) = \begin{cases} AJ_\nu(x) + BJ_{-\nu}(x), & \nu \neq \text{integer}, \\ CJ_n(x) + DY_n(x), & \nu = n = \text{integer}. \end{cases} \tag{14}$$

For reference, let us write out the first couple of J_n's and Y_n's:

$$J_0(x) = 1 - \frac{x^2}{2^2} + \frac{x^4}{2^4(2!)^2} - \frac{x^6}{2^6(3!)^2} + \cdots, \tag{15}$$

$$J_1(x) = \frac{x}{2} - \frac{x^3}{2^3 1!2!} + \frac{x^5}{2^5 2!3!} - \frac{x^7}{2^7 3!4!} + \cdots, \tag{16}$$

$$Y_0(x) = \frac{2}{\pi}\left[\left(\ln\frac{x}{2} + \gamma\right)J_0(x) + \frac{x^2}{2^2} - \frac{x^4}{2^4(2!)^2}\left(1 + \frac{1}{2}\right) + \frac{x^6}{2^6(3!)^2}\left(1 + \frac{1}{2} + \frac{1}{3}\right) - \cdots\right], \tag{17}$$

$$Y_1(x) = \frac{2}{\pi}\left[\left(\ln\frac{x}{2} + \gamma\right)J_1(x) - \frac{1}{x} - \frac{x}{4} + \frac{x^3}{2^3 2!}\frac{1 + (1 + \frac{1}{2})}{2} - \frac{x^5}{2^5 2!3!}\frac{(1 + \frac{1}{2}) + (1 + \frac{1}{2} + \frac{1}{3})}{2} - \cdots\right]. \tag{18}$$

A few observations and remarks about the J_n's and Y_n's before proceeding to a physical application:

1. Consider the solution pair J_0, Y_0. These are displayed together in Fig. 17.3 and are seen to bear some resemblance to the cos x, sin x solutions of the simpler ODE $y'' + y = 0$. However, unlike sin x, Y_0 is singular at $x = 0$. Specifically, it "blows up" according to

$$Y_0(x) \sim \frac{2}{\pi}\ln x \tag{19}$$

as $x \to 0$, and this singular behavior is the result of the fact that $x = 0$ is a singular point of the Bessel equation. Second, unlike cos x, sin x, the solutions J_0, Y_0 decay as $x \to \infty$. In fact, it can be shown (see Exercise 3) that

$$J_0(x) \sim \sqrt{\frac{2}{\pi x}}\cos\left(x - \frac{\pi}{4}\right), \tag{20a}$$

$$Y_0(x) \sim \sqrt{\frac{2}{\pi x}}\sin\left(x - \frac{\pi}{4}\right), \tag{20b}$$

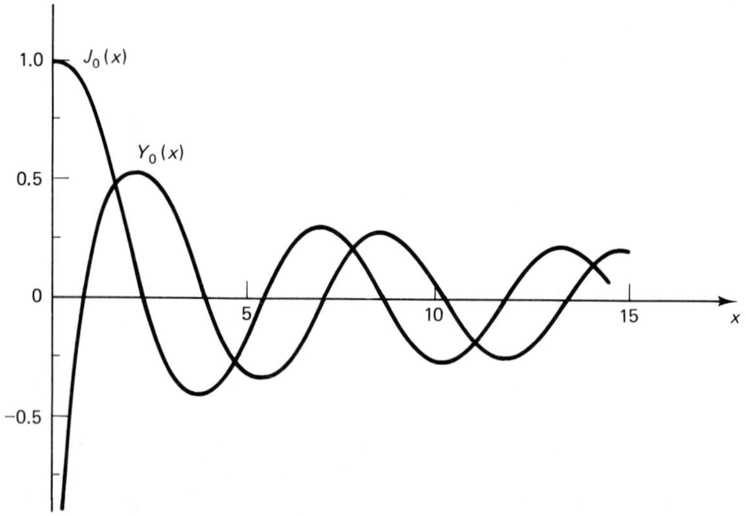

Fig. 17.3 J_0 and Y_0.

as $x \to \infty$. Third, whereas the zeros of $\cos x$, $\sin x$ are equally spaced, those of J_0, Y_0 are not quite. For example, denoting the zeros of J_0 [i.e., the roots of $J_0(x) = 0$] as $z_{01}, z_{02}, \ldots$, the first five z_{0n}'s are listed in Table 17.1. Although the spacing is not quite constant, it does *tend* to a constant (namely, π) as $n \to \infty$, in accordance with the asymptotic behavior (20). The zeros of the various Bessel functions will be important to us, in the solution of PDEs by separation of variables, just as the zeros of the cosine and sine functions were important to us in Chapters 14 to 16. They are tabulated in standard reference works* and we will regard then as known numbers.

TABLE 17.1 Zeros of J_0

n	z_{0n}	*Difference*
1	2.405	
		3.115
2	5.520	
		3.134
3	8.654	
		3.138
4	11.792	
		3.139
5	14.931	

2. Besides J_0, Y_0, how do the other J_n's and Y_n's behave, as $x \to 0$ and as $x \to \infty$? From (12) and (13), we can see that

$$J_n(x) \sim \frac{1}{2^n n!} x^n \qquad (n = 0, 1, 2, \ldots) \tag{21a}$$

$$Y_n(x) \sim \begin{cases} \dfrac{2}{\pi} \ln x & (n = 0) \\ -\dfrac{2^n(n-1)!}{\pi} \dfrac{1}{x^n} & (n = 1, 2, \ldots) \end{cases} \tag{21b}$$

as $x \to 0$. Thus, while J_n develops a stronger and stronger *zero* at $x = 0$, as n increases, Y_n develops a stronger and stronger *singularity* there. Whereas (12) and (13) yield the asymptotic behavior of J_n, Y_n as $x \to 0$, because the expansions are *about* $x = 0$, they do *not* yield the behavior of J_n, Y_n as $x \to \infty$. However, it turns out (Exercise 3) that

$$J_n(x) \sim \sqrt{\frac{2}{\pi x}} \cos(x - \psi_n), \tag{22a}$$

$$Y_n(x) \sim \sqrt{\frac{2}{\pi x}} \sin(x - \psi_n), \tag{22b}$$

as $x \to \infty$, where $\psi_n = (2n + 1)\pi/4$.

3. Finally, we state one more result that will be useful in the examples and exercises to follow. If κ is any positive root of the equation $J_n(\kappa c) = 0$, where c is a

* See, for example, M. Abramowitz and I. Stegun (eds.), *Handbook of Mathematical Functions with Formulas, Graphs, and Mathematical Tables* (New York: Dover, 1965); E. Jahnke, F. Emde, and F. Lösch, *Tables of Higher Functions,* 6th ed. (New York; McGraw-Hill, 1960): and A. Gray and G. Mathews, *A Treatise on Bessel Functions and Their Applications to Physics,* 2nd ed. (with T. MacRobert) (New York: Dover, 1966).

given positive number, then (Exercise 5)

$$\int_0^c [J_n(\kappa x)]^2 x\,dx = \frac{c^2}{2}[J_{n+1}(\kappa c)]^2. \tag{23}$$

EXAMPLE 1 *Unsteady Diffusion in a Disk*. Consider the unsteady conduction of heat in a circular disk such as a coin of radius c, the flat faces of which are insulated. Specifically, suppose that the temperature u is governed by the problem

$$\begin{aligned} &\alpha^2\nabla^2 u = \alpha^2\left(u_{rr} + \frac{1}{r}u_r\right) = u_t \qquad (0 \le r < c,\ 0 < t < \infty) \\ &u(c, t) = 0, \quad u(r, 0) = f(r), \end{aligned} \tag{24}$$

where α is the diffusivity constant. That is, the disk is initially at a prescribed temperature $f(r)$, and we quench the outer edge (with ice water, for example) to 0°C for all $t > 0$. We have not bothered to include the $(1/r^2)u_{\theta\theta}$ term in $\nabla^2 u$ because it is evident, from the circular shape of the region and the fact that f is a function of r only, that u will not vary with θ.

Solving by separation of variables, we seek

$$u(r, t) = R(r)T(t). \tag{25}$$

Then the separated equations are

$$rR'' + R' + \kappa^2 rR = 0, \tag{26a}$$

$$T' + \kappa^2\alpha^2 T = 0. \tag{26b}$$

Except for the presence of the κ^2, (26a) is a Bessel equation of order 0. If we scale r according to $r = b\rho$, where b is a constant (to be determined), (26a) becomes

$$\rho\frac{d^2R}{d\rho^2} + \frac{dR}{d\rho} + \kappa^2 b^2\rho R = 0. \tag{27}$$

Thus, if we set $b = 1/\kappa$, then (27) *is* a Bessel equation, and $R = AJ_0(\rho) + BY_0(\rho) = AJ_0(\kappa r) + BY_0(\kappa r)$. The case $\kappa = 0$ needs to be treated separately because $Y_0(0)$ does not exist. Doing so, we have

$$R(r) = \begin{cases} AJ_0(\kappa r) + BY_0(\kappa r), & \kappa \ne 0 \\ C + D\ln r, & \kappa = 0 \end{cases} \tag{28}$$

and, of course,

$$T(t) = \begin{cases} Ee^{-\kappa^2\alpha^2 t}, & \kappa \ne 0 \\ F, & \kappa = 0. \end{cases} \tag{29}$$

Thus far,

$$u(r, t) = (C + D\ln r)F + [AJ_0(\kappa r) + BY_0(\kappa r)]Ee^{-\kappa^2\alpha^2 t}. \tag{30}$$

Although not explicitly stated in (24), we need to impose a boundedness condition on u. Since $\ln r$ and $Y_0(\kappa r)$ blow up as $r \to 0$, we set $D = B = 0$ and obtain

$$u(r, t) = C' + A'J_0(\kappa r)e^{-\kappa^2\alpha^2 t}, \tag{31}$$

where $C' \equiv CF$ and $A' \equiv AE$. Next,

$$u(c, t) = 0 = C' + A'J_0(\kappa c)e^{-\kappa^2\alpha^2 t} \tag{32}$$

gives $C' = 0$ and $J_0(\kappa c) = 0$, so that $\kappa c = z_{0n}$ $(n = 1, 2, \ldots)$, where the z_{0n}'s are the positive zeros of $J_0(z)$. With the help of superposition, we can build up the more comprehensive solution

$$u(r, t) = \sum_{n=1}^{\infty} A_n' \, J_0\left(z_{0n} \frac{r}{c}\right) e^{-(z_{0n}\alpha/c)^2 t}. \tag{33}$$

Finally, we are ready to handle the initial condition,

$$u(r, 0) = f(r) = \sum_{n=1}^{\infty} A_n' \, J_0\left(z_{0n} \frac{r}{c}\right). \tag{34}$$

Since (34) involves an expansion in the r variable, let us examine the boundary value problem on R, namely,

$$\begin{aligned} &(rR')' + \kappa^2 rR = 0 \qquad (0 < r < c) \\ &R(0) \text{ finite}, \quad R(c) = 0. \end{aligned} \tag{35}$$

Comparing (35) with the Sturm–Liouville problem (13) on page 497, we see that (35) is *not quite* of standard (or *regular*) Sturm–Liouville form for these reasons: The coefficient r in $(rR')'$ is not strictly positive on the interval $[0, c]$ because it is zero at the left endpoint; similarly for the coefficient r in $\kappa^2 rR$; finally, the finiteness condition on $R(0)$ is not of standard Sturm–Liouville form. Thus we call (35) a *singular* Sturm–Liouville problem. Nonetheless, it is easily shown that Theorem 1 (real eigenvalues), Theorem 2 (orthogonality of eigenfunctions), and Theorem 5 (nonnegative eigenvalues) in Section 10.6 still apply. Also true, but not easily shown, is Theorem 4 on the pointwise convergence of eigenfunction expansions.*

Thus we see that (34) amounts to an expansion (a *Fourier–Bessel expansion*) of the given function $f(r)$ in terms of the orthogonal eigenfunctions $J_0(z_{0n}r/c)$, so that

$$\begin{aligned} A_n' &= \frac{\left\langle f(r), \, J_0\left(z_{0n}\frac{r}{c}\right)\right\rangle}{\left\langle J_0\left(z_{0n}\frac{r}{c}\right), \, J_0\left(z_{0n}\frac{r}{c}\right)\right\rangle} = \frac{\displaystyle\int_0^c f(r) J_0\left(z_{0n}\frac{r}{c}\right) r \, dr}{\displaystyle\int_0^c \left[J_0\left(z_{0n}\frac{r}{c}\right)\right]^2 r \, dr} \\ &= \frac{2}{c^2[J_1(z_{0n})]^2} \int_0^c f(r) J_0\left(z_{0n}\frac{r}{c}\right) r \, dr, \end{aligned} \tag{36}$$

where the last equality follows from (23).

Thus the desired solution is given by (33) and (36).

COMMENT 1 The singular nature of the Sturm–Liouville problem (35) is *not* intrinsically tied to the fact that the ODE is a Bessel equation. For example, if the disk $0 \le r < c$ were instead an annulus $c_1 < r < c_2$, with $u(c_1, t) = u(c_2,$

* For more detailed discussion and further references, see Churchill and Brown.

$t) = 0$, the R problem

$$(rR')' + \kappa^2 rR = 0 \qquad (c_1 < r < c_2)$$
$$R(c_1) = 0 \qquad R(c_2) = 0$$

would be a *regular* Sturm–Liouville problem [see Exercise 10(b)].

COMMENT 2 We described the body as a "coin," insulated on its two flat faces. Alternatively, it could be a long cylinder, of radius c, with no variation in u in the axial direction. ◀

MODIFIED BESSEL FUNCTIONS

Besides the Bessel equation of order ν,

$$x^2y'' + xy' + (x^2 - \nu^2)y = 0, \tag{37}$$

with general solution

$$y(x) = \begin{cases} AJ_\nu(x) + BJ_{-\nu}(x), & \nu \neq \text{integer} \\ CJ_n(x) + DY_n(x), & \nu = n = \text{integer}, \end{cases} \tag{38}$$

one also encounters the **modified Bessel equation of order ν,**

$$\boxed{x^2y'' + xy' + (-x^2 - \nu^2)y = 0.} \tag{39}$$

For heuristic purposes, it is useful to note that (39) resembles the simpler equation $y'' - y = 0$ in much the same way that (37) resembles the simpler equation $y'' + y = 0$. Thus, just as (37) has oscillatory solutions, we can expect that (39) has *non*oscillatory solutions. In fact, the modified Bessel equation (39) is transformed, by the change of variables $ix = t$, to the Bessel equation

$$t^2\frac{d^2y}{dt^2} + t\frac{dy}{dt} + (t^2 - \nu^2)y = 0. \tag{40}$$

If we denote any solution to (40) as $Z_\nu(t)$, a solution of (39) is $Z_\nu(ix)$. Although we can now state the general solution to (39) as

$$y(x) = \begin{cases} AJ_\nu(ix) + BJ_{-\nu}(ix), & \nu \neq \text{integer} \\ CJ_n(ix) + DY_n(ix), & \nu = n = \text{integer}, \end{cases} \tag{41}$$

it is more standard to introduce new functions—with real arguments. Considering $J_\nu(ix)$ first, changing x to ix in (9) gives

$$J_\nu(ix) = i^\nu \sum_{k=0}^{\infty} \frac{1}{k!\Gamma(\nu + k + 1)}\left(\frac{x}{2}\right)^{2k+\nu}, \tag{42}$$

so if we define

$$I_\nu(x) \equiv i^{-\nu}J_\nu(ix), \tag{43}$$

then

$$I_\nu(x) = \sum_{k=0}^{\infty} \frac{1}{k!\Gamma(\nu + k + 1)}\left(\frac{x}{2}\right)^{2k+\nu} \tag{44}$$

is a *real-valued* solution of the modified Bessel equation (39) and is known as the **modified Bessel function of the first kind and order ν.*** Similarly, we define

$$I_{-\nu}(x) \equiv i^{\nu} J_{-\nu}(ix) = \sum_{k=0}^{\infty} \frac{1}{k!\Gamma(k - \nu + 1)} \left(\frac{x}{2}\right)^{2k-\nu} \tag{45}$$

and

$$I_n(x) \equiv i^{-n} J_n(ix) = \sum_{k=0}^{\infty} \frac{1}{k!(n + k)!} \left(\frac{x}{2}\right)^{2k+n}. \tag{46}$$

Looking back at (41), then, the idea is to replace $J_\nu(ix)$, $J_{-\nu}(ix)$, $J_n(ix)$ by $I_\nu(x)$, $I_{-\nu}(x)$, and $I_n(x)$, respectively. For $Y_n(ix)$, we state, without discussion, that it is standard to introduce the real-valued function

$$K_n(x) \equiv \frac{\pi}{2} i^{n+1}[J_n(ix) + iY_n(ix)], \tag{47}$$

the **modified Bessel function of the second kind, and order n.**

Thus the general solution of the modified Bessel function (39) can be stated as

$$y(x) = \begin{cases} AI_\nu(x) + BI_{-\nu}(x), & \nu \neq \text{integer} \\ CI_n(x) + DK_n(x), & \nu = n = \text{integer}. \end{cases} \tag{48}$$

Key asymptotic behavior of the I_n's and K_n's is as follows (Exercise 12):

$$I_n(x) \sim \frac{1}{n!}\left(\frac{x}{2}\right)^n \qquad (n = 0, 1, 2, \ldots) \tag{49a}$$

$$K_n(x) \sim \begin{cases} -\ln x & (n = 0) \\ \dfrac{(n-1)!}{2}\left(\dfrac{2}{x}\right)^n & (n = 1, 2, \ldots) \end{cases} \tag{49b}$$

as $x \to 0$, and

$$I_n(x) \sim \frac{1}{\sqrt{2\pi x}} e^x \qquad (n = 0, 1, 2, \ldots) \tag{50a}$$

$$K_n(x) \sim \sqrt{\frac{\pi}{2x}} e^{-x} \qquad (n = 0, 1, 2, \ldots) \tag{50b}$$

as $x \to \infty$. Thus, while I_n develops a stronger and stronger *zero* at $x = 0$, as n increases, K_n develops a stronger and stronger *singularity* there. As $x \to \infty$, on the other hand, the I_n's grow unboundedly and the K_n's tend to zero. The graphs of I_0 and K_0 and shown in Fig. 17.4.

* Analogously, and in a more familiar setting, observe that the ODEs $y'' + y = 0$ and $y'' - y = 0$ admit the solutions $\sin x$ and $\sin(ix)$, respectively. In place of $\sin(ix)$, however, we use the real-valued solution $\sinh x$, where $\sinh x = i^{-1} \sin(ix)$.

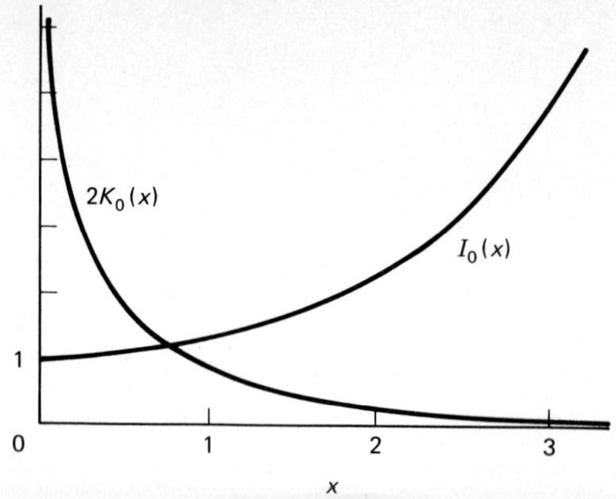

Fig. 17.4 I_0 and K_0.

EXAMPLE 2 *Steady-State Temperature in an Infinite Cylinder*. Here we seek the temperature distribution $u(r, z)$ in an infinitely long cylinder of radius c, subjected to a boundary temperature that is a periodic function of z:

$$\begin{aligned} \nabla^2 u &= u_{rr} + \frac{1}{r} u_r + u_{zz} = 0 \qquad (0 \le r < c,\ -\infty < z < \infty) \\ u(c, z) &= f(z), \end{aligned} \tag{51}$$

where $f(z)$ is the square wave of period $2b$ shown in Fig 17.5.

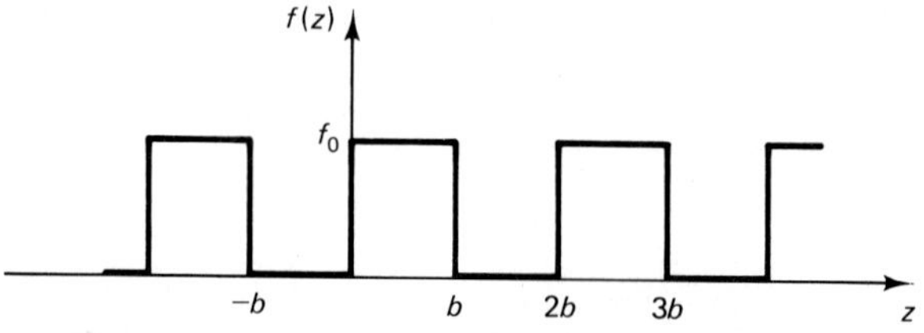

Fig. 17.5 Boundary temperature $f(z)$.

With $u(r, z) = R(r)Z(z)$, separating variables gives

$$\frac{R'' + (1/r)R'}{R} = -\frac{Z''}{Z} = \kappa^2, \tag{52}$$

where we choose $+\kappa^2$ rather than $-\kappa^2$ since the applied boundary temperature $f(z)$ is a periodic function of z, so $\cos \kappa z$, $\sin \kappa z$ look more promising than $e^{\kappa z}$, $e^{-\kappa z}$.

This time the R equation is (after scaling r so as to absorb the κ^2) a *modified* Bessel equation, and we have

$$R(r) = \begin{cases} AI_0(\kappa r) + BK_0(\kappa r), & \kappa \neq 0 \\ C + D \ln r, & \kappa = 0 \end{cases} \tag{53a}$$

$$Z(z) = \begin{cases} E \cos \kappa z + F \sin \kappa z, & \kappa \neq 0 \\ G + Hz, & \kappa = 0. \end{cases} \tag{53b}$$

If u is to be a bounded function of r and z, we need to set $B = D = H = 0$, so that

$$u(r, z) = C' + I_0(\kappa r)(E' \cos \kappa z + F' \sin \kappa z) \tag{54}$$

or, using superposition,

$$u(r, z) = C' + \sum_{n=1}^{\infty} I_0(\kappa_n r)(E_n' \cos \kappa_n z + F_n' \sin \kappa_n z). \tag{55}$$

Finally, the boundary condition on $r = c$ gives

$$\begin{aligned} u(r, z) = f(z) &= \frac{1}{2}f_0 + \frac{2}{\pi}f_0 \sum_{n=1,3,\ldots}^{\infty} \frac{1}{n} \sin \frac{n\pi z}{b} \\ &= C' + \sum_{n=1}^{\infty} I_0(\kappa_n c)(E_n' \cos \kappa_n z + F_n' \sin \kappa_n z), \end{aligned} \tag{56}$$

so

$$C' = \tfrac{1}{2} f_0, \quad E_n' = 0, \quad \kappa_n = \frac{n\pi}{b},$$

$$F_n' = \begin{cases} \dfrac{2f_0}{\pi n} \dfrac{1}{I_0(n\pi c/b)} & n = 1, 3, \ldots \\ 0 & n = 0, 2, 4, \ldots. \end{cases}$$

Hence the desired solution is

$$u(r, z) = \frac{1}{2}f_0 + \frac{2f_0}{\pi} \sum_{n=1,3,\ldots}^{\infty} \frac{1}{n} \frac{I_0(n\pi r/b)}{I_0(n\pi c/b)} \sin \frac{n\pi z}{b}. \tag{57}$$

In this example modified Bessel functions entered in the r variable, but the eventual series expansion took place on the z variable. ◀

BESSEL FUNCTION SOLUTIONS TO OTHER DIFFERENTIAL EQUATIONS

We have already noted that although the ODE $xy'' + y' + \kappa^2 xy = 0$ is not itself a Bessel equation, it can be transformed to the Bessel equation $t(d^2y/dt^2) + dy/dt + ty = 0$ by the change of variables $\kappa x = t$. Thus $y = AJ_0(t) + BY_0(t) = AJ_0(\kappa x) + BY_0(\kappa x)$, so that the solution of the original ODE can be expressed *in terms of* Bessel functions.

More generally, the equation

$$\frac{d}{dx}\left(x^a \frac{dy}{dx}\right) + bx^c y = 0, \tag{58}$$

where a, b, c are real numbers, can be transformed to a Bessel equation by transforming both independent *and* dependent variables: with

$$\alpha\sqrt{b}x^{1/\alpha} = t \quad \text{and} \quad x^{-\nu/\alpha}y = u, \tag{59}$$

it is found that (58) becomes the Bessel equation of order ν,

$$t^2 \frac{d^2u}{dt^2} + t\frac{du}{dt} + (t^2 - \nu^2)u = 0, \tag{60}$$

where

$$\alpha = \frac{2}{c - a + 2} \quad \text{and} \quad \nu = \frac{1 - a}{c - a + 2}. \tag{61}$$

[The latter is meaningless if $c - a + 2 = 0$, but in that event (58) is merely a Cauchy–Euler equation.] Thus, if Z_ν denotes any Bessel function solution of (60), then putting (59) into $u(t) = Z_\nu(t)$ gives the solution

$$y(x) = x^{\nu/\alpha} Z_\nu(\alpha \sqrt{b}\, x^{1/\alpha}) \tag{62}$$

of (58).

EXAMPLE 3 Revisiting the equation

$$xy'' + y' + \kappa^2 y = (xy')' + \kappa^2 y = 0, \tag{63}$$

we have $a = c = 1$ and $b = \kappa^2$, so $\alpha = 1$ and $\nu = 0$. Then (62) gives

$$y(x) = Z_0(\kappa x),$$

and since two LI solutions Z_0 are J_0, Y_0, we have the general solution

$$y(x) = AJ_0(\kappa x) + BY_0(\kappa x) \tag{64}$$

of (63), as noted in Example 1. ◀

More generally, Z_ν gives two LI solutions, as listed in Table 17.2.

TABLE 17.2 LI Z_ν's

	$\nu = n = integer$	$\nu = integer$
$b > 0$	$J_{\lvert n\rvert}$, $Y_{\lvert n\rvert}$	$J_{\lvert \nu\rvert}$, $J_{-\lvert \nu\rvert}$
$b < 0$	$I_{\lvert n\rvert}$, $K_{\lvert n\rvert}$	$I_{\lvert \nu\rvert}$, $I_{-\lvert \nu\rvert}$

EXAMPLE 4 Consider the equation

$$x^3 y'' - x^2 y' + y = 0. \tag{65}$$

Is (65) really of the form (58) and, if so, what are a, b, c? To answer these questions, write out (58) as

$$x^a y'' + a x^{a-1} y' + b x^c y = 0, \tag{66}$$

and compare its form with that of (65). To do so, first divide (65) by x^3 and (66) by x^a. Then, comparing the coefficients of the y' and y terms, we see that $a = -1$, $b = 1$, and $c = -4$. Thus $\alpha = -2$ and $\nu = -2$, so that the general solution of (65) can be expressed as

$$y(x) = x[AJ_2(-2x^{-1/2}) + BY_2(-2x^{-1/2})]. \tag{67}$$

Looking back at the formulas for J_2 and Y_2, we see that J_2 and Y_2 are even functions (once we realize that the $\ln x$ in Y_2 is really $\ln |x|$), so the minus signs in (67) can be omitted. Finally,

$$y(x) = x\left[AJ_2\left(\frac{2}{\sqrt{x}}\right) + BY_2\left(\frac{2}{\sqrt{x}}\right)\right]. \quad \blacktriangleleft$$

Examples 3 and 4 were merely illustrations of the use of (62) in solving equations of the form (58). *Physical* applications, wherein ODEs of the form (58) arise in the separation-of-variables solution of PDEs, are given in Exercises 15 and 16.

In conclusion, in this section we have studied the Bessel and modified Bessel equations and their solutions. Considerable additional information is contained in the exercises to follow. Problems in which *double* series are encountered have been omitted for brevity, but the essential ideas are outlined in Exercise 9(d).

17.2 EXERCISES

1. (a) Verify that if ν is not an integer, then $J_{-\nu}(x)$ and $J_\nu(x)$ are LI, as stated just before equation (11).
(b) Verify that $J_{-n}(x) = (-1)^n J_n(x)$. *Hint:* Rather than return to (5), it is easier to use (10) (with $\nu = n$), and the fact that $\Gamma(0) = \Gamma(-1) = \Gamma(-2) = \cdots = \infty$.

2. (*Derivation of Y_0*) Having found the solution $y_1(x) = J_0(x)$, of the Bessel equation of order zero, seek a second LI solution by the method of variation of parameters as follows: Seeking $y_2(x) = A(x)J_0(x)$, show that A satisfies the equation

$$xA''J_0 + 2xA'J_0' + A'J_0 = 0. \tag{a}$$

Solving (a), show that

$$A(x) = \int^x \frac{dt}{t[J_0(t)]^2}, \tag{b}$$

and hence that

$$\begin{aligned} A(x) &= \int^x \left(\frac{1}{t} + \frac{t}{2} + \frac{5t^3}{32} + \cdots\right) dt \\ &= \ln x + \frac{1}{4}x^2 + \frac{5}{128}x^4 + \cdots. \end{aligned} \tag{c}$$

Thus show that

$$\begin{aligned} y_2(x) &= A(x)J_0(x) \\ &= J_0(x)\ln x + \frac{1}{4}x^2 - \frac{3}{128}x^4 + \cdots. \end{aligned} \tag{d}$$

The right-hand side of (d) is called the **Neumann function of order zero,** $\mathbf{Y}_0(x)$. Rather than adopt $y_2(x) = \mathbf{Y}_0(x)$, it is standard to form the linear combination

$$y_2(x) = \frac{2}{\pi}[\mathbf{Y}_0(x) + (\gamma - \ln 2)J_0(x)] \equiv Y_0(x), \tag{e}$$

where γ is Euler's constant and $Y_0(x)$ is the Bessel function of the second kind and order zero. [Why favor Y_0 over $\mathbf{Y}_0$? The answer lies in the large-x behavior

$$J_0(x) \sim \sqrt{\frac{2}{\pi x}}\cos\left(x - \frac{\pi}{4}\right),$$

$$\mathbf{Y}_0(x) \sim \sqrt{\frac{\pi}{2x}}\sin\left(x - \frac{\pi}{4}\right) - (\gamma - \ln 2)\sqrt{\frac{2}{\pi x}}\cos\left(x - \frac{\pi}{4}\right),$$

$$Y_0(x) \sim \sqrt{\frac{2}{\pi x}}\sin\left(x - \frac{\pi}{4}\right).$$

Don't J_0, Y_0 make a handsome couple? J_0, $\mathbf{Y}_0$, on the other hand, are as natural a pair as quiche and bubble gum.] Show, from (d) and (e), that

$$Y_0(x) = \frac{2}{\pi}\left[\left(\ln\frac{x}{2} + \gamma\right)J_0(x) + \frac{1}{4}x^2 - \frac{3}{128}x^4 + \cdots\right],$$

as in (17). *Note:* Alternatively, noting that $[J_0(t)]^{-2}$ is analytic at $t = 0$, one can use (b) to deduce the *form* of A as $\ln x$ plus a power series in x, and hence the form of y_2 as

$$y_2(x) = J_0(x)\ln x + \sum_{k=0}^{\infty} B_k x^k. \tag{f}$$

Putting (f) into the Bessel equation, one can determine the B_k's. (You need not do that.)

3. (*Large-x behavior*) (a) Entering the change of variables $y(x) = \sigma(x)v(x)$, from y to v, in $y'' + p(x)y' + q(x)y = 0$, show that the first derivative term can be knocked out by choosing σ so that $2\sigma' + p\sigma = 0$. Show that the result is the "normal form"

$$v'' + \left(\frac{\sigma'' + p\sigma' + q\sigma}{\sigma}\right)v = 0, \tag{a}$$

where

$$\sigma(x) = e^{-(1/2)\int^x p(t)dt}. \tag{b}$$

(b) For the Bessel equation (1), show that $\sigma(x) = 1/\sqrt{x}$ and that equation (a) is

$$v'' + \left(1 - \frac{\nu^2 - 1/4}{x^2}\right)v = 0. \tag{c}$$

If we write $1 - (\nu^2 - 1/4)/x^2 \approx 1$ for large x, then $v'' + v \approx 0$, so we expect that $v(x) \approx A \cos(x + \phi)$, or

$$y(x) \approx \frac{A}{\sqrt{x}\cos(x + \phi)} \tag{d}$$

as $x \to \infty$. That is, we expect that every solution of (1) behaves according to (d) as $x \to \infty$. Evaluating the A, ϕ constants corresponding to a particular solution, such as $J_0(x)$ or $Y_0(x)$, is more complicated and will not be discussed here.

4. Let Z_ν denote J_ν or $J_{-\nu}$ if $\nu \neq$ integer and J_n or Y_n if $\nu = n =$ integer.

(a) The formulas

$$\frac{d}{dx}[x^\nu Z_\nu(\alpha x)] = \alpha x^\nu Z_{\nu-1}(\alpha x), \tag{a}$$

$$\frac{d}{dx}[x^{-\nu} Z_\nu(\alpha x)] = -\alpha x^{-\nu} Z_{\nu+1}(\alpha x), \tag{b}$$

are useful. Verify them for the case where Z_ν is J_ν. *Hint:* Use (9). *Note:* A special case of (b) is the well-known formula $J_0'(x) = -J_1(x)$.

(b) From equations (a) and (b), show that

$$2\frac{d}{dx}Z_\nu(\alpha x) = \alpha[Z_{\nu-1}(\alpha x) - Z_{\nu+1}(\alpha x)] \tag{c}$$

and

$$Z_{\nu+1}(\alpha x) = \frac{2\nu}{\alpha x}Z_\nu(\alpha x) - Z_{\nu-1}(\alpha x). \tag{d}$$

(c) Show that

$$J_{1/2}(x) = \sqrt{\frac{2}{\pi x}}\sin x \tag{e}$$

and

$$J_{-1/2}(x) = \sqrt{\frac{2}{\pi x}}\cos x. \tag{f}$$

(d) Derive, from equations (e) and (f), together with the relation between J_ν and I_ν, the analogous results

$$I_{1/2}(x) = \sqrt{\frac{2}{\pi x}}\sinh x \tag{g}$$

and

$$I_{-1/2}(x) = \sqrt{\frac{2}{\pi x}}\cosh x. \tag{h}$$

(e) Derive, from equation (b), the recursion formula

$$J_{n+1/2}(x) = \frac{2n-1}{x}J_{n-1/2}(x) - J_{n-3/2}(x). \tag{i}$$

From (i), (e), and (f) it follows that *all* $J_{n+1/2}$'s are expressible in closed form in terms of $\sin x$, $\cos x$, and powers of x. For example, derive such expressions for $J_{3/2}(x)$ and $J_{-3/2}(x)$.

5. Recall that $J_n(\kappa x)$ satisfies the equation

$$(xy')' + \left(\kappa^2 x - \frac{n^2}{x}\right)y = 0 \quad (n = 0, 1, 2, \ldots). \tag{a}$$

Multiplying through by $2xy'$ and integrating from $x = 0$ to $x = c$, obtain

$$[(xy')^2 + (\kappa^2x^2 - n^2)y^2]\Big|_0^c - 2\kappa^2\int_0^c xy^2\,dx = 0 \tag{b}$$

for any $c > 0$. Show that the bracketed quantity vanishes at $x = 0$, so that

$$2\kappa^2\int_0^c x[J_n(\kappa x)]^2\,dx = \kappa^2c^2[J_n'(\kappa c)]^2 + (\kappa^2c^2 - n^2)[J_n(\kappa c)]^2, \tag{c}$$

where $J_n'(\kappa c)$ means (in accordance with usual notation) $J_n'(t)\,|_{t=\kappa c}$. If $J_n(\kappa c) = 0$, show (with the help of results given in Exercise 4) that (c) yields (23).

6. (*Generating function for J_n*) It can be shown that

$$e^{(x/2)(t-1/t)} = \sum_{n=-\infty}^{\infty} J_n(x)t^n, \tag{a}$$

and the left-hand side is known as the **generating function** for the J_n's.

(a) Rather than ask for complete verification of (a), we ask only that the $n = 0$ term be verified. That is, expanding exp $(xt/2)$ and exp $(-x/2t)$ in Maclaurin series (one in ascending powers of t, one in descending powers) and multiplying these series together, show that the coefficient of t^0 is $J_0(x)$.

(b) Equation (a) is useful for deriving various properties of the J_n's. For example, taking $\partial/\partial x$ of both sides, show that

$$\frac{d}{dx} J_n(x) = \tfrac{1}{2} [J_{n-1}(x) - J_{n+1}(x)].$$

(c) Similarly, taking $\partial/\partial t$ of both sides, show that

$$J_{n+1}(x) = \frac{x}{2(n+1)} [J_n(x) + J_{n+2}(x)].$$

7. (*Integral representation of* J_n) Besides the generating function (Exercise 6), another source of information about the J_n's is the integral representation

$$J_n(x) = \frac{1}{\pi} \int_0^{\pi} \cos (n\theta - x \sin \theta)\, d\theta. \qquad \text{(a)}$$

Verify (a) for the case $n = 0$ by using the Taylor series $\cos t = \sum_{j=0}^{\infty} [(-1)^j/(2j)!]t^{2j}$ and integrating the series termwise. *Hint:* See Exercise 19(b) in Section 12.3.

8. Let $f(x) = \sqrt{\ell^2 - x^2}$ on $-\ell \le x \le \ell$ (the graph of which is a semicircle), and let it be periodic with period 2ℓ. Show that its Fourier series is

$$f(x) = \frac{\pi\ell}{4} + \frac{\pi\ell}{2} \sum_{n=1}^{\infty} [J_0(n\pi) + J_2(n\pi)] \cos \frac{n\pi x}{\ell}.$$

Hint: Use the formula

$$\cos (x \cos \theta) = J_0(x) - 2J_2(x) \cos 2\theta + 2J_4(x) \cos 4\theta - \cdots. \qquad \text{(a)}$$

[Analogous formulas exist for $\cos (x \sin \theta)$, $\sin (x \cos \theta)$, and $\sin (x \sin \theta)$.]

9. Solve the following boundary value problems, leaving expansion coefficients in integral form. In each case, u is to be bounded in the given region.

*(a) $\nabla^2 u = u_{rr} + \frac{1}{r} u_r + u_{zz} = 0$

$(0 \le r < c,\ 0 < z < \infty)$

$u(c, z) = 0, \quad u(r, 0) = f(r)$

(b) $\nabla^2 u = u_{rr} + \frac{1}{r} u_r + u_{zz} = 0$

$(0 \le r < c,\ 0 < z < \ell)$

$u(r, 0) = u(c, z) = 0, \quad u(r, \ell) = f(r)$

(c) $\nabla^2 u = u_{rr} + \frac{1}{r} u_r + u_{zz} = 0$

$(0 \le r < c,\ 0 < z < \ell)$

$u(r, 0) = u_1, \quad u(r, \ell) = u_2, \quad u(c, z) = u_3$

(d) $\nabla^2 u = u_{rr} + \frac{1}{r} u_r + \frac{1}{r^2} u_{\theta\theta} + u_{zz} = 0$

$(0 \le r < c,\ 0 < z < \infty)$

$u(c, \theta, z) = 0, \quad u(r, \theta, 0) = f(r, \theta)$ *Hint:* Seeking $u = R(r)\Theta(\theta)Z(z)$, show that

$$r^2R'' + rR' + (\alpha^2 r^2 - \beta^2)R = 0, \qquad \text{(a)}$$

$$\Theta'' + \beta^2\Theta = 0, \qquad \text{(b)}$$

$$Z'' - \alpha^2 Z = 0, \qquad \text{(c)}$$

where α, β are separation constants. Solving (a) to (c), we find it tempting to write

$$u(r, \theta, z) = [AJ_\beta(\alpha r) + BJ_{-\beta}(\alpha r)](C \cos \beta\theta + D \sin \beta\theta) \times (Ee^{\alpha z} + Fe^{-\alpha z}), \qquad \text{(d)}$$

where $J_{-\beta}$ is understood to mean Y_β if β turns out to be an integer. But be careful about possibly missing out on needed terms. For example, if $\beta = 0$ (and $\alpha \neq 0$) in (a) to (c),

$$u(r, \theta, z) = [AJ_0(\alpha r) + BY_0(\alpha r)](C + D\theta)(E^{\alpha z} + Fe^{-\alpha z}). \qquad \text{(e)}$$

Observe that the θ term in (e) was not represented in (d). Furthermore, if $\alpha = 0$ (and $\beta \neq 0$) in (a) to (c),

$$u(r, \theta, z) = (Ar^\beta + Br^{-\beta})(C \cos \beta\theta + D \sin \beta\theta)(E + Fz). \qquad \text{(f)}$$

Finally, if both α *and* β are zero in (a) to (c), then

$$u(r, \theta, z) = (A + B \ln r)(C + D\theta)(E + Fz). \qquad \text{(g)}$$

If we want to be sure not to have missed any needed terms, we should take u to be a linear combination of products of the form given in (d) to (g). Doing so, and noting that u is to be bounded, and a 2π-periodic function of θ, obtain

$$u(r, \theta, z) = A + r^m(B \cos m\theta + C \sin m\theta) + DJ_0(\alpha r)e^{-\alpha z} + J_n(\gamma r)(E \cos n\theta + F \sin n\theta)e^{-\gamma z}, \qquad \text{(h)}$$

where α, γ are yet-to-be-determined nonzero constants and m, n are positive integers. Invoking $u(c, \theta, z) = 0$, obtain from (h) the form

$$u(r, \theta, z) = \sum_{j=1}^{\infty} D_j J_0(\alpha_j r) e^{-\alpha_j z} + \sum_{j=1}^{\infty} \sum_{n=1}^{\infty} J_n(\gamma_{nj} r)(E_{nj} \cos n\theta + F_{nj} \sin n\theta) e^{-\gamma_{nj} z}, \tag{i}$$

where $\alpha_j c = z_{0j}$ is the jth zero of J_0 and $\gamma_{nj} c = z_{nj}$ is the jth zero of J_n. Imposing $u(r, \theta, 0) = f(r, \theta)$ and attending first to the θ variable, show that

$$\frac{1}{2\pi} \int_0^{2\pi} f(r, \theta)\, d\theta = \sum_{j=1}^{\infty} D_j J_0(\alpha_j r),$$

$$\frac{1}{\pi} \int_0^{2\pi} f(r, \theta) \cos n\theta\, d\theta = \sum_{j=1}^{\infty} E_{nj} J_n(\gamma_{nj} r) \quad (n = 1, 2, \ldots) \tag{j}$$

$$\frac{1}{\pi} \int_0^{2\pi} f(r, \theta) \sin n\theta\, d\theta = \sum_{j=1}^{\infty} F_{nj} J_n(\gamma_{nj} r) \quad (n = 1, 2, \ldots).$$

Finally, infer from (j) that

$$D_j = \frac{1}{\pi c^2 [J_1(z_{0j})]^2} \int_0^{2\pi} \int_0^c f(r, \theta) J_0(\alpha_j r) r\, dr\, d\theta,$$

$$E_{nj} = \frac{2}{\pi c^2 [J_{n+1}(z_{nj})]^2} \int_0^{2\pi} \int_0^c f(r, \theta) \times \cos n\theta J_n(\gamma_{nj} r) r\, dr\, d\theta, \tag{k}$$

and similarly for F_{nj}.

10. (*Variations on Example 1*) Solve for the temperature u, leaving expansion coefficients in integral form. u is to be bounded in the given region, for all t.

(a) $\alpha^2\left(u_{rr} + \frac{1}{r} u_r\right) = u_t \quad (0 \le r < c, 0 < t < \infty)$

$u_r(c, t) = 0, \quad u(r, 0) = f(r)$

Hint: Recall, from Exercise 4(a), that $J_0'(x) = -J_1(x)$. Also, (c) in Exercise 5 should be useful.

*(b) $\alpha^2\left(u_{rr} + \frac{1}{r} u_r\right) = u_t$

$(a \le r \le b, \ 0 < t < \infty)$

$u(a, t) = 0, \quad u(b, t) = u_0, \quad u(r, 0) = 0$

(c) $\alpha^2\left(u_{rr} + \frac{1}{r} u_r + \frac{1}{r^2} u_{\theta\theta}\right) = u_t$

$(0 \le r < c, 0 < t < \infty)$

$u(c, \theta, t) = 0, \quad u(r, \theta, 0) = f(r, \theta)$

Hint: The essential ideas are the same as in Exercise 9(d).

11. (*Vibrating membrane*) As derived on page 676, the displacement w of a vibrating membrane, such as a drumhead, is the two-dimensional wave equation $c^2\nabla^2 w = w_{tt}$. Considering the symmetric (θ-independent) motion of a circular drum, we have

$$c^2\left(w_{rr} + \frac{1}{r} w_r\right) = w_{tt} \qquad (0 \le r < a, 0 < t < \infty)$$

$$w(a, t) = 0.$$

Show that the lowest vibrational frequency is $0.383c/a$ cycles/second.

12. Derive the results (49a) and (49b).

13. (*Variations on Example 2*) Solve for the temperature u. u is to be bounded in the given region.

(a) $u_{rr} + \frac{1}{r} u_r + u_{zz} = 0$

$(c < r < \infty, -\infty < z < \infty)$

$u(c, z) = f(z)$, as given in Fig. 17.5

(b) $u_{rr} + \frac{1}{r} u_r + u_{zz} = 0 \quad (c < r < \infty, 0 < z < \infty)$

$u(r, 0) = 0, \quad u(c, z) = u_0 \sin(3z/2)$

*(c) $u_{rr} + \frac{1}{r} u_r + u_{zz} = 0 \quad (c < r < \infty, 0 < z < \ell)$

$u(r, 0) = u_1, \quad u(r, \ell) = u_2, \quad u(c, z) = u_3$

14. Using (62), obtain general solutions to the following equations.

*(a) $y'' + xy = 0$ (b) $y'' - xy = 0$
(c) $x^5 y'' + 2y = 0$ (d) $xy'' + 2y' + 3y = 0$
*(e) $xy'' + 2y' - y = 0$
(f) $2xy'' + 3y' + 5y = 0$ *Hint:* To simplify the result, see Exercise 4.
(g) $y'' + k^2 y = 0$ That is, show that (62) (with some help from Exercise 4) does yield the elementary and well-known solution $A \sin kx + B \cos kx$.

***15.** Let ρ, ϕ, θ be spherical polar coordinates, and let $u(\rho, t)$ be the spherically symmetric temperature field within a sphere of radius c, where t is the time. Solve the problem

$$\alpha^2\nabla^2 u = \alpha^2\left(u_{\rho\rho} + \frac{2}{\rho} u_\rho\right) = u_t$$

$$(0 \le \rho < c, 0 < t < \infty)$$

$$u(\rho, 0) = f(\rho), \quad u(c, t) = 0.$$

Hint: The result can be simplified with the help of Exercise 4.

16. (*Vibration of hanging chain*) A hanging chain (see the accompanying figure) differs from the classical vi-

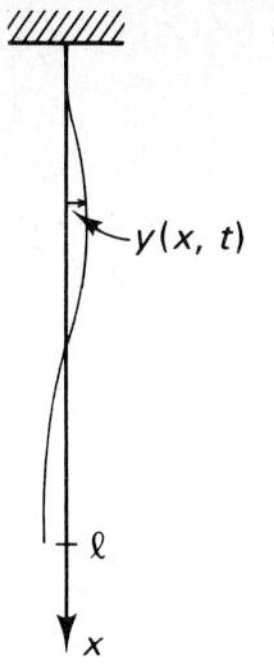

brating string in that the tension τ is not a constant. Rather, $\tau = \rho g(\ell - x)$, where ρ is the mass per unit length of the chain and g is the acceleration of gravity, and the equation of motion becomes

$$(\tau y_x)_x = \rho y_{tt}$$

or

$$g((\ell - x)y_x)_x = \rho y_{tt}. \tag{a}$$

Solve (a) subject to the conditions that $y(0, t) = 0$, $y(x, 0) = f(x)$, $y_t(x, 0) = 0$, and that y is a bounded function of x for all $t \geq 0$.

LEGENDRE FUNCTIONS 17.3

The differential equation

$$\boxed{(1 - x^2)y'' - 2xy' + \lambda y = 0,} \tag{1}$$

where λ is a constant, is known as **Legendre's equation,** after the French mathematician Adrien-Marie Legendre (1752–1833).

Looking ahead to applications, we shall be particularly interested in the Legendre equation in the context of the eigenvalue problem

$$((1 - x^2)y')' + \lambda y = 0 \qquad (-1 \leq x \leq 1) \tag{2a}$$

$$y(-1) \text{ and } y(1) \text{ finite.} \tag{2b}$$

That is, we shall be interested in nontrivial solutions of (2a) which are finite at both endpoints $x = \pm 1$. In fact, (2) is a singular Sturm–Liouville system, singular because the $1 - x^2$ coefficient vanishes at both endpoints and hence is not strictly positive on the closed interval.

Toward solving (2), we note, first, that the Legendre equation is nonelementary, and second, that $x = \pm 1$ are regular singular points of the equation. To expose the singular behavior of y at those points we could seek Frobenius-type expansions about those points. However, in view of the finiteness conditions (2b), we are not now interested in solutions that are singular at $x = \pm 1$. Rather, we are after well-behaved solutions, so it seems more promising to seek power series solutions about the ordinary point $x = 0$:

$$y(x) = \sum_{k=0}^{\infty} a_k x^k. \tag{3}$$

Doing so leads to the recursion relation

$$a_{k+2} = \frac{k(k+1) - \lambda}{(k+1)(k+2)} a_k \qquad (k = 0, 1, 2, \ldots). \tag{4}$$

Setting $k = 0, 1, 2, \ldots$ in (4) shows that a_0 and a_1 remain arbitrary, and that subsequent a_k's can be expressed, alternately, in terms of a_0 and a_1. Specifically,

$$a_2 = -\frac{\lambda}{2} a_0,$$

$$a_3 = \frac{2 - \lambda}{6} a_1,$$

$$a_4 = -\frac{(6 - \lambda)\lambda}{24} a_0,$$

and so on, so we can express

$$y(x) = a_0\left[1 - \frac{\lambda}{2} x^2 - \frac{(6 - \lambda)\lambda}{24} x^4 - \cdots\right] + a_1\left[x + \frac{2 - \lambda}{6} x^3 + \frac{(12 - \lambda)(2 - \lambda)}{120} x^5 + \cdots\right]. \tag{5}$$

It can be shown that the even- and odd-powered infinite series in (5) converge on $|x| < 1$, but not on $|x| \leq 1$ because of singularities present at $x = \pm 1$. However, if λ happens to be such that

$$\lambda = n(n + 1), \tag{6}$$

for any integer $n = 0, 1, 2, \ldots$, then one of those two series *terminates* at $k = n$, as can be seen from (4). Specifically, if $\lambda = n(n + 1)$, where n is *even* (*odd*), then the even-powered (odd-powered) series terminates at n (i.e., $a_{n+2} = a_{n+4} = \cdots = 0$). For example, if $n = 2$ and $\lambda = 2(2 + 1) = 6$, then (5) gives

$$y(x) = a_0[1 - 3x^2] + a_1[\text{nonterminating odd-powered series}].$$

Thus the choice $a_1 = 0$ gives the solution

$$y(x) = a_0(1 - 3x^2),$$

which is, as desired, finite for all $|x| \leq 1$, including the endpoints $x = \pm 1$. Or, if $n = 3$ and $\lambda = 3(4) = 12$, then (5) gives

$$y(x) = a_0\,[\text{nonterminating even-powered series}] + a_1\left[x - \frac{5}{3} x^3\right].$$

This time setting $a_0 = 0$, we have the solution

$$y(x) = a_1\left(x - \frac{5}{3} x^3\right).$$

Normalizing these polynomial solutions by suitable choice of a_0 or a_1 so that $y(1) = 1$, we denote the nth one as $P_n(x)$ and call it the **Legendre polynomial of degree n.** The first several are as follows:

$$P_0(x) = 1,$$

$$P_1(x) = x,$$

$$P_2(x) = \tfrac{1}{2}(3x^2 - 1),$$
$$P_3(x) = \tfrac{1}{2}(5x^3 - 3x), \tag{7}$$
$$P_4(x) = \tfrac{1}{8}(35x^4 - 30x^2 + 3),$$
$$\vdots$$

To summarize, we have found that the eigenvalues λ_n of (2) are $\lambda_n = n(n+1)$ $(n = 0, 1, 2, \ldots)$, and that the corresponding eigenfunctions $\phi_n(x)$ are the Legendre polynomials $\phi_n(x) = P_n(x)$.

In spite of the singular nature of (2), it is nevertheless true that the $P_n(x)$ eigenfunctions comprise an orthogonal set, and it can also be shown that our pointwise expansion Theorem 4 (page 501) still holds (see, for example, Churchill and Brown). Thus, if a given function $f(x)$ satisfies the conditions of that theorem (as will virtually always be the case in applications), we can expand f in a **Fourier–Legendre series,**

$$f(x) = \sum_{n=0}^{\infty} a_n P_n(x) \qquad (-1 < x < 1), \tag{8}$$

where

$$a_n = \frac{\langle f(x), P_n(x)\rangle}{\langle P_n(x), P_n(x)\rangle} = \frac{\int_{-1}^{1} f(x)P_n(x)\,dx}{\int_{-1}^{1} [P_n(x)]^2\,dx}. \tag{9}$$

Here we have used the fact that the weight function in the inner product is unity, as follows from the form of (2a). Further, it can be shown [Exercise 4(e)] that

$$\int_{-1}^{1} [P_n(x)]^2\,dx = \frac{2}{2n+1} \qquad (n = 0, 1, 2, \ldots), \tag{10}$$

so that (9) becomes

$$a_n = \frac{2n+1}{2}\int_{-1}^{1} f(x)\,P_n(x)\,dx. \tag{11}$$

EXAMPLE 1 To illustrate (8), suppose that $f(x) = xH(x)$, where H is the Heaviside function. Then

$$a_0 = \tfrac{1}{2}\int_{-1}^{1} f(x)\,dx = \tfrac{1}{2}\int_{0}^{1} x\,dx = \tfrac{1}{4}. \tag{12}$$

Computing several more a_n's, from (11), we obtain

$$f(x) = \tfrac{1}{4}P_0(x) + \tfrac{1}{2}P_1(x) + \tfrac{5}{16}P_2(x) - \tfrac{3}{32}P_4(x) + \cdots. \tag{13}$$

For comparison, we have plotted the graphs of f and the partial sums $s_1(x) = \frac{1}{4}P_0(x), \ldots, s_3(x) = \frac{1}{4}P_0(x) + \frac{1}{2}P_1(x) + \frac{5}{16}P_2(x)$ in Fig. 17.6. ◀

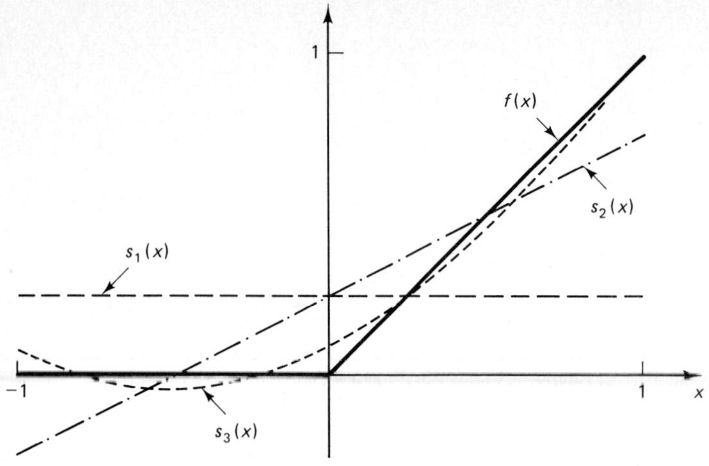

Fig. 17.6 Convergence of the series to *f*.

We are now ready for our principal application, namely, to three-dimensional potential theory.

EXAMPLE 2 *Laplace Equation in Spherical Polars.* We consider the Dirichlet problem

$$\nabla^2 u = u_{\rho\rho} + \frac{2}{\rho} u_{\rho\rho} + \frac{1}{\rho^2} u_{\phi\phi} + \frac{\cot\phi}{\rho^2} u_\phi = 0 \tag{14}$$

in the sphere $0 \le \rho < c$, with the boundary condition

$$u(c, \phi) = f(\phi) \qquad (0 \le \phi \le \pi) \tag{15}$$

and the stipulation that u be bounded in the given domain. The spherical polar coordinates ρ, ϕ, θ are shown in Fig. 17.7. Since both the region and the boundary condition are symmetric about the z axis, we anticipate that u will be too; i.e., u will be independent of θ, so $u = u(\rho, \phi)$. Accordingly, θ-derivative terms have been omitted in (14).

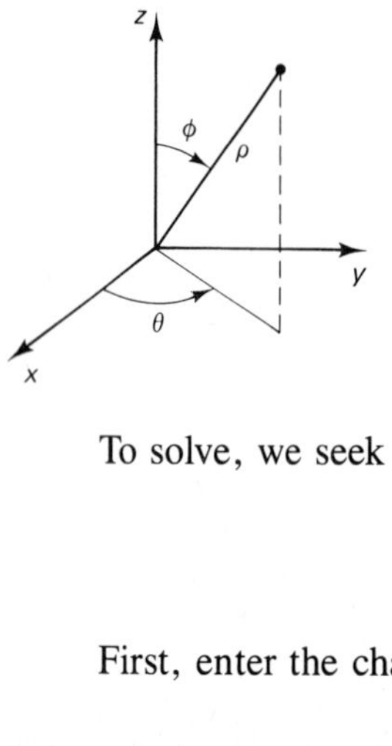

Fig. 17.7 Spherical polar coordinates.

To solve, we seek $u(\rho, \phi) = R(\rho)\Phi(\phi)$ and obtain, by separation, the ODEs

$$\rho^2 R'' + 2\rho R' - \kappa^2 R = 0, \tag{16a}$$

$$\Phi'' + \cot\phi\,\Phi' + \kappa^2\Phi = 0. \tag{16b}$$

First, enter the change of variables $\mu = \cos\phi$ in (16b), and (Exercise 1) obtain the new equation

$$(1 - \mu^2)\frac{d^2\Phi}{d\mu^2} - 2\mu\frac{d\Phi}{d\mu} + \kappa^2\Phi = 0. \tag{17}$$

Since (17) is a Legendre equation, we see that the allowable values of the separation constant κ are such that

$$\kappa^2 = n(n + 1) \qquad (n = 0, 1, 2, \ldots) \tag{18}$$

if Φ is to be bounded on $-1 \le \mu \le 1$. (In terms of the physical spherical domain, $\mu = 1$ corresponds to $\phi = 0$, so that unboundedness of Φ at $\mu = 1$ would mean unboundedness of the solution u along the z axis, from the origin to the "north pole." Similarly, unboundedness of Φ at $\mu = -1$ would mean unboundedness of u along the z axis, from the origin to the "south pole.") The corresponding bounded solutions are arbitrary scalar multiples of

$$\Phi = P_n(\mu) = P_n(\cos\phi). \tag{19}$$

Turning to the R equation, with $\kappa^2 = n(n + 1)$, the solution of (16a) is

$$R(\rho) = A\rho^n + \frac{B}{\rho^{n+1}} \qquad (n = 0, 1, 2, \ldots). \tag{20}$$

Here the required boundedness of u requires that $B = 0$. Putting (19) and (20) together and using the principle of superposition, we have, thus far,

$$u(\rho, \phi) = \sum_{n=0}^{\infty} A_n\rho^n P_n(\cos\phi). \tag{21}$$

Finally, the boundary condition (15) requires that

$$u(c, \phi) = f(\phi) = \sum_{n=0}^{\infty} A_n c^n P_n(\cos\phi). \tag{22}$$

Since (22) involves an expansion in the ϕ variable, let us examine the boundary value problem on Φ, namely,

$$\begin{gathered} ((1 - \mu^2)\Phi)' + \kappa^2\Phi = 0 \qquad (-1 \le \mu \le 1) \\ \Phi(-1) \text{ and } \Phi(1) \text{ finite.} \end{gathered} \tag{23}$$

Thus we see that (23) amounts to a Fourier–Legendre expansion of the given function f in terms of the orthogonal eigenfunctions $P_n(\mu)$, or $P_n(\cos\phi)$. Accordingly,

$$A_n c^n = \frac{2n + 1}{2}\int_{-1}^{1} fP_n\, d\mu = \frac{2n + 1}{2}\int_{\pi}^{0} f(\phi)P_n(\cos\phi)(-\sin\phi\, d\phi),$$

so

$$A_n = \frac{2n + 1}{2c^n}\int_0^{\pi} f(\phi)P_n(\cos\phi)\sin\phi\, d\phi. \tag{24}$$

In conclusion, the desired solution is given by (21), with the A_n's computed according to (24). ◀

In Example 2 we limited our attention to the axisymmetric case, where u is independent of θ, and we encountered Legendre's equation and the Legendre polynomials. The *other* solutions of Legendre's equation, known as *Legendre functions of the second kind,* were excluded by the boundedness condition on u, so they were not studied. These solutions are discussed in Exercise 6. More generally, if the boundary condition in Example 2 were *not* θ-independent, we would need the full Laplace equation

$$\nabla^2 u = \frac{1}{\rho^2}\left[\frac{\partial}{\partial \rho}\left(\rho^2 \frac{\partial u}{\partial \rho}\right) + \frac{1}{\sin\phi}\frac{\partial}{\partial \phi}\left(\sin\phi \frac{\partial u}{\partial \phi}\right) + \frac{1}{\sin^2\phi}\frac{\partial^2 u}{\partial \theta^2}\right] = 0, \quad (25)$$

and would encounter the so-called *associated Legendre functions* (Exercise 13).

17.3 EXERCISES

1. Setting $\mu = \cos\phi$ in (16b), show that (17) follows.

2. We derived $P_0(x)$ through $P_4(x)$ using the recursion formula (4) and the normalization $P_n(1) = 1$. Continuing that process, show that $P_5(x) = \frac{1}{8}(63x^5 - 70x^3 + 15x)$ and $P_6(x) = \frac{1}{48}(693x^6 - 945x^4 + 315x^2 - 15)$.

3. (*Rodrigues' foumula*) It can be shown that

$$P_n(x) = \frac{1}{2^n n!}\frac{d^n}{dx^n}[(x^2 - 1)^n], \quad \text{(a)}$$

and this result is known as **Rodrigues' formula.** This formula is useful for deriving the P_n's and also for deducing their various properties. Using (a), derive $P_0(x)$ through $P_4(x)$.

4. (*Generating function for P_n*) It can be shown that

$$(1 - 2rx + r^2)^{-1/2} = \sum_{n=0}^{\infty} P_n(x) r^n, \quad (|x| \le 1, |r| < 1) \quad \text{(a)}$$

and the left-hand side is known as the **generating function** for the P_n's. This result is useful for deriving various properties of the P_n's.

(a) Expanding the left-hand side in powers of r, through r^3, say, verify that the coefficients of $r^0, \dots, r^3$ are indeed $P_0(x), \dots, P_3(x)$, respectively.

(b) Use equation (a) to show that $P_n(-x) = (-1)^n P_n(x)$, so that if n is an even (odd) integer, then $P_n(x)$ is an even (odd) function of x.

(c) By taking $\partial/\partial r$ of equation (a), show that

$$nP_n(x) = (2n - 1)xP_{n-1}(x) - (n - 1)P_{n-2}(x) \quad (n = 2, 3, \dots). \quad \text{(b)}$$

[It can be shown that (b) holds for the Q_n's (Exercise 6) as well.]

(d) By taking $\partial/\partial x$ of (a), show that

$$P_n'(x) - 2xP_{n-1}'(x) + P_{n-2}'(x) = P_{n-1}(x) \quad (n = 2, 3, \dots). \quad \text{(c)}$$

(e) Squaring both sides of (a) and integrating on x from -1 to $+1$, show that

$$\int_{-1}^{1} \frac{dx}{1 - 2rx + r^2} = \int_{-1}^{1} \sum_{m=0}^{\infty} r^m P_m(x) \sum_{n=0}^{\infty} r^n P_n(x)\, dx.$$

Recalling that the P_n's are orthogonal, show that the latter becomes

$$\frac{1}{r}\ln\left(\frac{1 + r}{1 - r}\right) = \sum_{n=0}^{\infty}\left\{\int_{-1}^{1} [P_n(x)]^2\, dx\right\} r^{2n}. \quad \text{(d)}$$

Finally, expanding $\ln[(1 + r)/(1 - r)]$ in powers of r, show that

$$\int_{-1}^{1} [P_n(x)]^2\, dx = \frac{2}{2n + 1} \quad (n = 0, 1, 2, \dots). \quad \text{(e)}$$

5. (*Integral representation of P_n*) It can be shown that

$$P_n(x) = \frac{1}{\pi}\int_0^{\pi} (x + \sqrt{x^2 - 1}\cos t)^n\, dt \quad (n = 0, 1, 2, \dots) \quad \text{(a)}$$

and the right-hand side of (a) is called *Laplace's integral form for $P_n(x)$*. Here we ask you to verify (a) for the cases $n = 0$, 1, and 2, by working out the integral.

6. (*Legendre functions of second kind*) For the Legendre equation

$$(1 - x^2)y'' - 2xy' + n(n + 1)y = 0, \quad \text{(a)}$$

on the interval $-1 \leq x \leq 1$, we obtained the bounded solution $y(x) = P_n(x)$ and stated that a second LI (linearly independent) solution to (a) is inevitably unbounded in the neighborhood of each endpoint ($x = -1$ and 1). The chosen second LI solution is denoted as $Q_n(x)$ and is called the **Legendre function of the second kind.** Thus the general solution of (a) can be expressed as

$$y(x) = AP_n(x) + BQ_n(x). \tag{b}$$

In this exercise we examine the Q_n's.

(a) For the special case $n = 0$, solve (a) by reduction of order, and show that a second LI solution is $\ln [(1 + x)/(1 - x)]$. Scaling this solution by $\frac{1}{2}$, we define

$$Q_0(x) = \frac{1}{2} \ln \left(\frac{1 + x}{1 - x}\right). \tag{c}$$

Sketch the graph of $Q_0(x)$ on $-1 < x < 1$, and notice that $|Q_0(x)| \to \infty$ as $x \to \pm 1$.

(b) More generally, consider any nonnegative integer n. With only $P_n(x)$ in hand, seek a second solution (by the method of variation of parameters) in the form $y(x) = A(x)P_n(x)$, and show that $Q_n(x)$ is necessarily of the form

$$Q_n(x) = C_nP_n(x) \int^x \frac{dt}{(1 - t^2)[P_n(t)]^2} + D_nP_n(x). \tag{d}$$

(c) Evaluating the integral in (d) show that the first couple of Q_n's are of the form

$$\begin{aligned} Q_0(x) &= \frac{1}{2} C_0 \ln \left(\frac{1 + x}{1 - x}\right) + D_0, \\ Q_1(x) &= C_1\left[\frac{x}{2} \ln \left(\frac{1 + x}{1 - x}\right) - 1\right] + D_1x. \end{aligned} \tag{e}$$

By convention, $C_0 = 1$, $D_0 = 0$ and $C_1 = 1$, $D_1 = 0$, so that

$$\begin{aligned} Q_0(x) &= \frac{1}{2} \ln \left(\frac{1 + x}{1 - x}\right), \\ Q_1(x) &= \frac{x}{2} \ln \left(\frac{1 + x}{1 - x}\right) - 1. \end{aligned} \tag{f}$$

(d) With Q_0 and Q_1 in hand, we can obtain Q_2, Q_3, . . . by means of the recursion formula given in Exercise 4(c). For example, show that

$$Q_2(x) = \frac{3x^2 - 1}{4} \ln \left(\frac{1 + x}{1 - x}\right) - \frac{3}{2}x. \tag{g}$$

7. In the Fourier–Legendre expansion (8), show that (a) a_0 is the average value of f on the interval

(b) if f is an even function of x, then $a_1 = a_3 = a_5 = \cdots = 0$

(c) If f is an odd function of x, then $a_0 = a_2 = a_4 = \cdots = 0$ *Hint:* See Exercise 4(b).

8. (a) Expanding the function $f(x) = H(x)$ (Heaviside function) in a Fourier–Legendre series, show that

$$\begin{aligned} &f(x) \\ &= \tfrac{1}{2} P_0(x) + \tfrac{3}{4} P_1(x) - \tfrac{7}{16} P_3(x) + \tfrac{11}{32} P_5(x) - \cdots \end{aligned} \tag{a}$$

on $-1 < x < 1$.

(b) Plot, together, the graphs of $f(x)$ and the fourth partial sum $s_4(x) = \frac{1}{2} P_0(x) + \cdots + \frac{11}{32} P_5(x)$. *Note:* $P_5(x)$ is given in Exercise 2.

9. (a) Expanding the function $f(x) = |x|$ in a Fourier–Legendre series, show that

$$f(x) = \tfrac{1}{2} P_0(x) + \tfrac{5}{8} P_2(x) - \tfrac{9}{48} P_4(x) + \cdots \tag{a}$$

on $-1 < x < 1$.

(b) Plot, together, the graphs of $f(x)$ and the first three partial sums $s_1(x) = \frac{1}{2} P_0(x), \ldots, s_3(x) = \frac{1}{2} P_0(x) + \frac{5}{8} P_2(x) - \frac{9}{48} P_4(x)$.

10. (*Further discussion of Example 2*) (a) Show that the value of u at the center of the sphere ($\rho = 0$) is equal to the average value of f on the spherical surface $\rho = c$.

(b) Show that if f is 0 on the upper half of the sphere ($0 < \phi < \pi/2$) and 1 on the lower half ($\pi/2 < \phi < \pi$), then (21) and (24) give

$$\begin{aligned} u(\rho, \phi) &= \frac{1}{2} P_0(\cos \phi) - \frac{3}{4}\left(\frac{\rho}{c}\right)P_1(\cos \phi) \\ &\quad + \frac{7}{16}\left(\frac{\rho}{c}\right)^3 P_3(\cos \phi) + \cdots. \end{aligned} \tag{a}$$

11. (a) Solve the problem in Example 2 again, but this time let the domain be the region *out*side the surface $\rho = c$, i.e., $c < \rho < \infty$.

(b) Does $\lim_{\rho\to\infty} u(\rho, \phi)$ equal the average value of f on the boundary surface $\rho = c$?

(c) What is u if $f(\phi) = \text{constant} = 1$?

12. (*Electric field induced by two charges*) Given a positive charge Q and a negative charge $-Q$, a distance $2a$ apart, let us locate a spherical polar coordinate system as shown in the accompanying figure. Since the charges fall on the z axis, it follows that the induced field will be symmetric about that axis.

(a) The electric potential (i.e., the voltage Φ induced by a charge q is $\Phi = (1/4\pi\epsilon_0)(q/r)$, where the constant ϵ_0 is the permittivity of free space and r is the

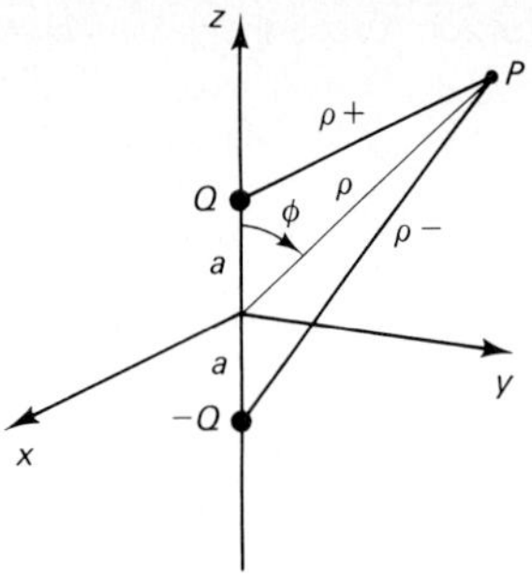

distance from the charge to the field point. Thus the potential induced at the field point P shown in the figure is

$$\Phi = \frac{1}{4\pi\epsilon_0}\left(\frac{Q}{\rho_+} - \frac{Q}{\rho_-}\right). \tag{a}$$

Show that (a) gives

$$\Phi(\rho, \phi) = \frac{Q}{4\pi\epsilon_0}\left(\frac{1}{\sqrt{a^2 + \rho^2 - 2a\rho\cos\phi}} - \frac{1}{\sqrt{a^2 + \rho^2 + 2a\rho\cos\phi}}\right)$$

$$= \begin{cases} \dfrac{1}{4\pi\epsilon_0}\dfrac{2Q}{\rho}\displaystyle\sum_{n=1,3,\ldots}^{\infty}\left(\frac{a}{\rho}\right)^n P_n(\cos\phi) & (\rho > a) \\ \dfrac{1}{4\pi\epsilon_0}\dfrac{2Q}{a}\displaystyle\sum_{n=1,3,\ldots}^{\infty}\left(\frac{\rho}{a}\right)^n P_n(\cos\phi) & (\rho < a). \end{cases} \tag{b}$$

Hint: See Exercise 4.

(b) With the point P fixed, imagine letting a become arbitrarily *small*. Show, from (b) that we obtain

$$\Phi(\rho, \phi) \sim \frac{1}{4\pi\epsilon_0} 2Qa \frac{\cos\phi}{\rho^2} \tag{c}$$

as $a \to 0$. Observe that if, as a decreases, Q increases so that the product Qa is constant, then (c) becomes

$$\Phi(\rho, \phi) \sim \frac{\mu}{4\pi\epsilon_0}\frac{\cos\phi}{\rho^2}, \tag{d}$$

where $\mu = 2Qa$ is called the *dipole moment*, and the charge configuration is said to constitute an electric *dipole*.

(c) With the point P fixed, imagine letting a become arbitrarily *large*. Show, from equation (b), that we obtain

$$\Phi(\rho, \phi) \sim \frac{1}{4\pi\epsilon_0}\frac{2Q}{a^2}\rho\cos\phi = \frac{1}{4\pi\epsilon_0}\frac{2Q}{a^2} z \tag{e}$$

as $a \to \infty$. Observe that if, as a increases, Q increases so that Q/a^2 is constant, the electric field intensity becomes

$$\mathbf{E} = -\boldsymbol{\nabla}\Phi \sim -\boldsymbol{\nabla}\left(\frac{\delta}{4\pi\epsilon_0} z\right) \qquad \left(\delta = \frac{2Q}{a^2}\right)$$
$$= -\frac{\delta}{4\pi\epsilon_0}\hat{\mathbf{k}}. \tag{f}$$

That is, we may regard a uniform $\mathbf{E}$ field as induced by equal and opposite powerful charges a great distance apart, as shown schematically in the accompanying sketch.

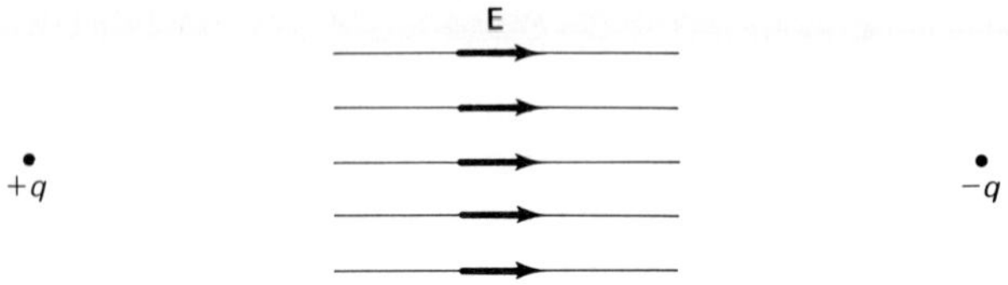

13. (*Associated Legendre functions*) If, in Example 2, the prescribed function $f(\phi)$ is changed to $f(\phi, \theta)$, then in place of (14) we need the full Laplace equation (25) (which allows for ρ, ϕ, *and* θ dependence of u).

(a) Seeking $u = R(\rho)\Phi(\phi)\Theta(\theta)$, obtain the separated equations

$$\rho^2 R'' + 2\rho R' - \kappa^2 R = 0, \tag{a}$$

$$\Phi'' + \cot\phi\,\Phi' + \left(\kappa^2 - \frac{\alpha^2}{\sin^2\phi}\right)\Phi = 0, \tag{b}$$

$$\Theta'' + \alpha^2\Theta = 0, \tag{c}$$

where κ, α are separation constants. Notice that (b) differs from (16b) only by the presence of the α^2 term. Notice that α needs to be an integer if Θ, and hence u, is to be 2π periodic in θ. Thus set $\alpha = m\,(m = 0, 1, 2, \ldots)$. Also, we state without proof that we need $\kappa^2 = n(n+1)\,(n = 0, 1, 2, \ldots)$, as in Example 2, if Φ is to be bounded on $0 \le \phi \le \pi$. Thus we may rewrite (b) as

$$\Phi'' + \cot\phi\,\Phi' + \left[n(n+1) - \frac{m^2}{\sin^2\phi}\right]\Phi = 0. \tag{d}$$

(b) Letting $\mu = \cos\phi$ in (d), show that (d) becomes

$$\frac{d}{d\mu}\left[(1 - \mu^2)\frac{d\Phi}{d\mu}\right] + \left[n(n+1) - \frac{m^2}{1 - \mu^2}\right]\Phi = 0. \tag{e}$$

The latter admits bounded solutions $\Phi = P_n^m(\mu)$, which are called **associated Legendre functions**, and which are related to the Legendre polynomials according to

$$P_n^m(\mu) = (1 - \mu^2)^{m/2} \frac{d^m}{d\mu^m} P_n(\mu) \qquad (m, n = 0, 1, 2, \ldots). \tag{f}$$

Like the P_n's, the P_n^m's are orthogonal on the interval $(-1, 1)$, with weight function 1, and can be used to expand given functions on that interval.

ADDITIONAL REFERENCES FOR PART IV

P. W. BERG and J. L. MCGREGOR, *Elementary Partial Differential Equations,* prelim. ed. San Francisco: Holden-Day, 1964.

A general reference for Chapters 13 to 16.

FRANCIS B. HILDEBRAND, *Advanced Calculus for Applications,* 2nd ed. Englewood Cliffs, N. J.: Prentice-Hall, 1976.

A compact and comprehensive text, for graduate or advanced undergraduate students.

D. E. JOHNSON and J. R. JOHNSON, *Mathematical Methods in Engineering and Physics.* Englewood Cliffs, N.J.: Prentice-Hall, 1982.

Deals primarily with the various special functions of mathematical physics, and is recommended here in connection with our Chapter 17 on Bessel and Legendre functions. Even short of a careful study of the other special functions—such as those associated with the names Hermite, Laguerre, Chebyshev, and Mathieu—we recommend "browsing" through a book like Johnson and Johnson so as to at least become aware of these functions and the circumstances under which they arise.

A. N. TYCHONOV and A. A. SAMARSKI, *Partial Differential Equations of Mathematical Physics,* Vols. I and II. San Francisco: Holden-Day, 1967.

A classical treatment of PDEs suitable for a one- or two- semester course on the subject, either for graduate students or advanced undergraduates in engineering, physics, chemistry, or mathematics. Volumes I and II cover two- and three-dimensional problems, respectively.

ERICH ZAUDERER, *Partial Differential Equations of Applied Mathematics.* New York: Wiley, 1983.

This graduate-level text includes nonlinear problems, and perturbation and asymptotic methods. Of special note is the discussion of the *method of characteristics.*

18 Functions of a Complex Variable

18.1 INTRODUCTION

There is much to recommend the study of complex variable theory. In this text on applied mathematics, we should state first that the subject is of great importance in applications. For example, it may be recalled from our discussion of the Laplace transform that the inverse Laplace transformation is given as a contour integral in a complex s plane. Not yet having studied complex variable theory, we were forced to avoid the inversion formula and to rely, instead, on the use of transform tables. More generally, the evaluation of a wide class of definite integrals (even along the real axis) is facilitated by use of the complex integral calculus. Another particularly important application is in the use of conformal mapping to solve boundary value problems in two-dimensional potential theory.

Equally important about complex variable theory is that it serves to "complete" our understanding, from the calculus, of real-valued functions of a single real variable. For example, in studying Taylor series one finds that the expansion

$$\frac{1}{1 + x^2} = 1 - x^2 + x^4 - x^6 + \cdots$$

holds only $|x| < 1$. Yet the function $1/(1 + x^2)$ is infinitely differentiable for *all* x, and offers no clue as to why the interval of convergence should be anything less than infinite. It is only when we consider instead the function $1/(1 + z^2)$, where $z = x + iy$, that the source of the difficulty comes into view, namely, singularities at $z = \pm i$, off of the real axis, in the complex z plane.

Finally, complex variable theory is elegant.

The format of Part V echoes the standard format of the real-variable calculus. Beginning, in *Chapter 18,* with a discussion of *complex numbers* and the "complex plane," we next introduce the notion of a complex-valued *function* of a (single) complex variable, and then define and discuss a number of *elementary functions,* such as the exponential, trigonometric, and hyperbolic functions. Defining a *limit concept,* and *continuity,* we are able, in the final section, to define a particularly important limit, namely, the *derivative*. Thus, in this chapter, we get as far as the differential calculus of functions of a complex variable.

The complex integral calculus and series expansions are then developed in *Chapters 20* and *21*. In between is *Chapter 19* on conformal mapping. That chapter is marked OPTIONAL merely to indicate that it is not a prerequisite for Chapters 20 or 21. Thus, in a shorter course one might cover only Chapters 18 and 19, or, instead, Chapters 18, 20, and 21.

COMPLEX NUMBERS AND THE COMPLEX PLANE 18.2

Historically, complex numbers were created, several hundred years ago, within the context of the theory of equations. For if one allowed only real numbers, then equations such as $x^2 + 1 = 0$ and $x^2 + 2x + 4 = 0$ had no solution. Thus, in a step that was slow to gain general acceptance, a broader number system was devised so that the equations given above, and indeed *every* polynomial equation, possess solutions within that number system. Eventually named *complex numbers* by Gauss (1777–1855), these new numbers were of the form $a + ib$, where a and b are real and where i satisfies the equation $i^2 = -1$.

The (real) numbers a, b are called the *real* and *imaginary parts* of $a + ib$, respectively:

$$\text{Re}\,(a + ib) \equiv a, \qquad \text{Im}(a + ib) \equiv b \;\; (\text{not } ib). \tag{1}$$

We do not distinguish between $a + ib$ and $a + bi$, and we generally write $a + i0$ as a, and $0 + ib$ as ib, for brevity. The former complex number is said to be *purely real* and the latter is said to be *purely imaginary*. Finally, two complex numbers are said to be *equal* if their real and imaginary parts, respectively, are the same; i.e.;

$$a_1 + ib_1 = a_2 + ib_2 \tag{2}$$

holds if and only if $a_1 = a_2$ and $b_1 = b_2$.

Beyond introducing complex numbers, we will need an algebra for their manipulation. Here the idea will be to stay as close as possible to the rules of ordinary arithmetic (i.e., governing real numbers). For example, the rules of ordinary arithmetic would seem to dictate that

$$(a_1 + ib_1) + (a_2 + ib_2) = (a_1 + a_2) + i(b_1 + b_2)$$

and that

$$\begin{aligned}(a_1 + ib_1)(a_2 + ib_2) &= a_1a_2 + ia_1b_2 + ib_1a_2 + i^2b_1b_2 \\ &= (a_1a_2 - b_1b_2) + i(a_1b_2 + b_1a_2).\end{aligned}$$

But, be sure to see that these equalities have no logical support since $a_1 + ib_1$ is a single complex number, not $a_1 + i$ times b_1; similarly for $a_2 + ib_2$. Rather, we have merely been trying to motivate reasonable definitions for the addition and multiplication of complex numbers. Accordingly, we now *define*

$$(a_1 + ib_1) + (a_2 + ib_2) \equiv (a_1 + a_2) + i(b_1 + b_2) \tag{3}$$

and

$$(a_1 + ib_1)(a_2 + ib_2) = (a_1a_2 - b_1b_2) + i(a_1b_2 + b_1a_2). \tag{4}$$

For instance, $(3 - 2i) + (5 + i) = 8 - i$, and $(3 - 2i)(5 + i) = 17 - 7i$.

Before proceeding, let us agree to denote complex numbers by a single letter, usually z, for brevity. Thus, we write $z = a + ib$. Now, with the above definitions, it is easily verified that the familiar rules of algebra hold for complex numbers. For instance, if we denote any three complex numbers as $z_1 = a_1 + ib_1$, $z_2 = a_2 + ib_2$, and $z_3 = a_3 + ib_3$, then

$$z_1 + z_2 = z_2 + z_1, \quad z_1z_2 = z_2z_1 \qquad \text{(commutative)} \tag{5}$$

$$(z_1 + z_2) + z_3 = z_1 + (z_2 + z_3), \quad (z_1z_2)z_3 = z_1(z_2z_3) \qquad \text{(associative)} \tag{6}$$

$$z_1(z_2 + z_3) = z_1z_2 + z_1z_3 \qquad \text{(distributive).} \tag{7}$$

Further, there are zero and unit numbers since, from (3),

$$z + (0 + i0) = z$$

and, from (4),

$$(1 + i0)z = z$$

for all z. Thus, for brevity, we write $0 + i0 = 0$ and $1 + i0 = 1$. Finally, $-z \equiv (-1)z$, so that the *subtraction* of complex numbers is defined by $z_1 - z_2 = z_1 + (-1)z_2$.

It is to be stressed that mathematical notation is important, and that the foregoing discussion can be reorganized by introducing complex numbers as **ordered pairs** of real numbers. Thus, in place of $z = a + ib$ we write

$$z = (a, b)$$

where a and b are called the real and imaginary parts, respectively, of the complex number z. If $z_1 = (a_1, b_1)$ and $z_2 = (a_2, b_2)$ are any two complex numbers, we define their sum and product as

$$z_1 + z_2 = (a_1, b_2) + (a_2, b_2) \equiv (a_1 + a_2, b_1 + b_2) \tag{8}$$

and

$$z_1z_2 = (a_1, b_1)(a_2, b_2) \equiv (a_1a_2 - b_1b_2, a_1b_2 + a_2b_1), \tag{9}$$

respectively. These definitions are seen to be equivalent to (3) and (4). Although the form $z = a + ib$ is more convenient, and will be used almost exclusively in the remainder of Part V, the ordered-pair approach, created by the great Irish mathematician *William R. Hamilton* (1805–1865), is important to us. First, it is based entirely on real numbers and completely avoids the mysterious "imaginary" number $i = \sqrt{-1}$. Since the forms $z = a + ib$ and $z = (a, b)$ are found to be equivalent, we can thus put to rest apprehensions about the quantity i and accept it—partly as a historical fact and partly as a computational convenience. Second, the ordered-pair format $z = (a, b)$ suggests a graphical representation of z as a point in a Cartesian a, b plane. Since Cartesian axes are more usually denoted by x and y rather than by a and b, let us write $z = x + iy = (x, y)$ and represent z as a point in a so-called **complex z plane,** as shown in Fig. 18.1.* The x axis is called the **real axis,** and the y axis is called the **imaginary axis.** One may be concerned that we have labeled the point on the y axis as "y"; should it not be "iy"? The answer is that either the real or the complex label is correct, depending on whether we are designating the point as a point on the real y axis or as a point z in the complex z plane.

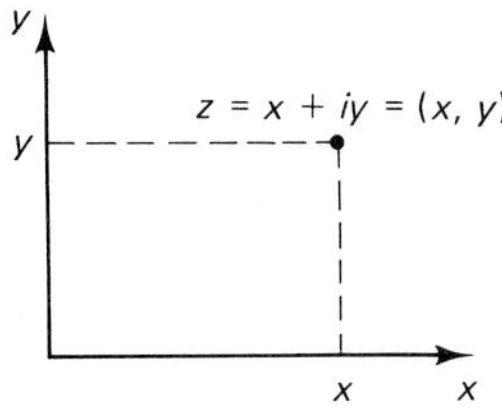

Fig. 18.1 Complex z plane.

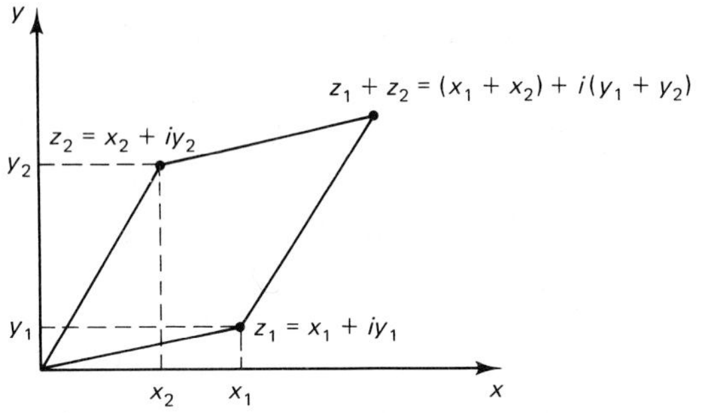

Fig. 18.2 Addition in the z plane.

Observe from Fig. 18.2 that the addition of complex numbers defined by (3) [or, equivalently, by (8)] satisfies the parallelogram law, so that one may think of complex numbers as vectors; i.e., a z vector is the vector from the origin to the point z.

The *distance* from the origin to the point z (i.e., the "length of the z vector") is called the **absolute value** or **modulus** of z and, by analogy with the absolute value of a real number, is denoted as $|z|$, or as mod (z). Clearly (Fig. 18.1),

$$|z| = \sqrt{x^2 + y^2}. \tag{10}$$

For example, $|2 - i| = \sqrt{5}$. It is easy to verify (Exercise 2) that

$$|z_1 z_2| = |z_1|\,|z_2|; \tag{11}$$

i.e., the absolute value of a product equals the product of the absolute values of the factors. Further (Fig. 18.3), the inequality

$$|z_1 + z_2| \leq |z_1| + |z_2| \tag{12}$$

follows from the Euclidean proposition that the length of any one side of a triangle is less than or equal to the sum of the lengths of the other two sides. Hence (12) is known as the **triangle inequality.**

Note carefully that the complex numbers are not ordered as real numbers are. For example, whereas $-6 < 2$, $10 > 7$, and so on, analogous statements such as $z < 0$, $z > 3$, and $4 + 3i > 1 + 2i$ are not meaningful. Of course, statements such as Re $z < 6$, Im $z < 6$, $|z| > 4$, and $|1 - i| < |3 - i|$ *do* make sense because Re z, Im z, and $|z|$ are all real numbers.

* The complex plane is sometimes called the *Argand diagram* after the French mathematician *Jean Robert Argand* (1768–1822), who was one of the first to propose such representation of complex numbers. Argand, a bookkeeper by profession, was a self-taught mathematician.

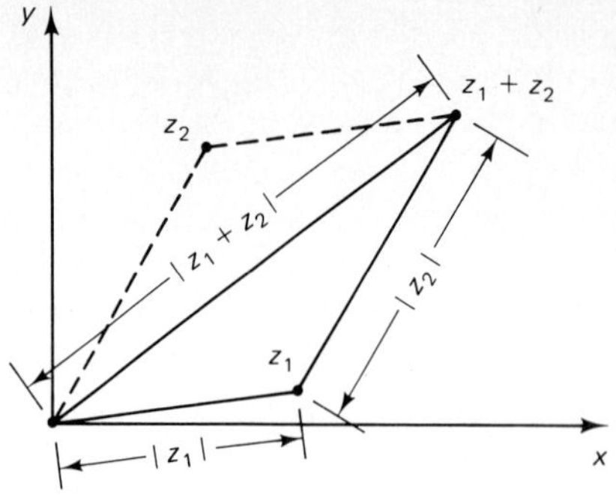

Fig. 18.3 Triangle inequality.

Besides $z = x + iy$, it is useful to define the **complex conjugate** of z as

$$\bar{z} \equiv x - iy. \tag{13}$$

Thus, if $z_1 = 8 + 3i$ and $z_2 = -4i$, then $\bar{z}_1 = 8 - 3i$ and $\bar{z}_2 = 4i$. It is easily shown (Exercise 3) that

$$\overline{z_1 + z_2} = \bar{z}_1 + \bar{z}_2, \tag{14a}$$

$$\overline{z_1 z_2} = \bar{z}_1 \bar{z}_2, \tag{14b}$$

and that

$$|z| = \sqrt{z\bar{z}}. \tag{15}$$

Graphically, $\bar{z}$ is simply the reflection of z about the real axis (Fig. 18.4).

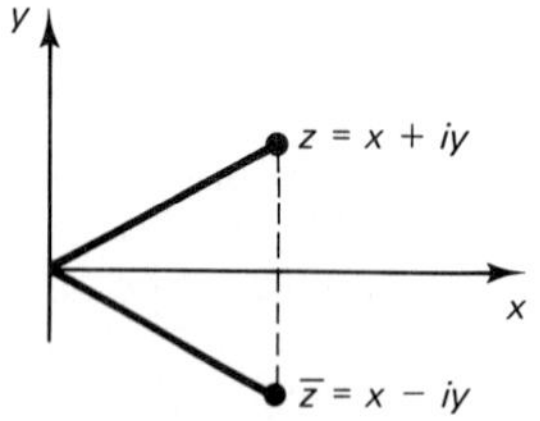

Fig. 18.4 Complex conjugate.

Finally, the complex conjugate is useful in defining the *division* of two complex numbers. Division is defined as the inverse of multiplication. That is, the quotient $z = z_1/z_2$ is the complex number $z = x + iy$ such that $z_2 z = z_1$. Writing out the latter as

$$(x_2 + iy_2)(x + iy) = x_1 + iy_1, \tag{16}$$

expanding the left-hand side, and equating real and imaginary parts on the left-and right-hand sides, we obtain

$$x = \frac{x_1 x_2 + y_1 y_2}{x_2^2 + y_2^2}, \qquad y = \frac{x_2 y_1 - x_1 y_2}{x_2^2 + y_2^2}. \tag{17}$$

Practically speaking, however, it is simpler to multiply numerator and denominator by the complex conjugate of the denominator,

$$z = \frac{z_1}{z_2} = \frac{z_1 \bar{z}_2}{z_2 \bar{z}_2}, \tag{18}$$

because the denominator $z_2\bar{z}_2 = |z|^2$ is now *real*. Writing out (18), we find

$$z = \frac{z_1}{z_2} = \frac{z_1\bar{z}_2}{z_2\bar{z}_2} = \frac{(x_1 + iy_1)(x_2 - iy_2)}{x_2^2 + y_2^2}$$
$$= \frac{x_1x_2 + y_1\,y_2}{x_2^2 + y_2^2} + i\,\frac{x_2\,y_1 - x_1\,y_2}{x_2^2 + y_2^2}, \tag{19}$$

which agrees with (17).

EXAMPLE 1

$$\frac{2+i}{3-4i} = \frac{2+i}{3-4i}\,\frac{3+4i}{3+4i} = \frac{(6-4)+(8+3)i}{9+16} = \frac{2}{25} + \frac{11}{25}i,$$

which result can be checked by showing that $3 - 4i$ times $\frac{2}{25} + \frac{11}{25}i$ gives $2 + i$. ◀

In closing this section, we note that besides the *Cartesian* notation $z = x + iy$, for complex numbers, there is also a *polar* notation "$z = re^{i\theta}$," which is often convenient. However, because it contains the complex exponential $e^{i\theta}$, we delay our introduction of the polar notation until we have discussed the complex exponential function.

18.2 EXERCISES

1. Using the definitions (3) and (4), verify
(a) the commutative properties (5)
(b) the associative properties (6)
(c) the distributive property (7)

2. Verify (11).

3. Verify (14a), (14b), and (15).

4. Recall that the definitions of addition and multiplication, (3) and (4), were rigged so that the familiar commutative, associative, and distributive rules hold. Thus one can manipulate complex numbers easily and with little fuss. Nevertheless, it may be valuable to work an example or two, paying careful attention to the definitions and properties (3) to (7). In this spirit we ask you to solve the following equations for z and then to verify, carefully, that the root(s) do indeed satisfy the given equation. In each step of the verification, identify the definition or property [(3) to (7)] being used. Naturally, z^2 means zz.

(a) $z^2 - 2z + 2 = 0$
(b) $2z^2 + 2z + 1 = 0$
(c) $3z^2 + 2z + 1 = 0$
(d) $z^2 + 2iz + 1 = 0$
(e) $10z^2 - 6z + 1 = 0$
(f) $z^2 - 3iz - 2 = 0$

5. Show that
(a) $|z^3| = |z|^3$
(b) $|z^n| = |z|^n \quad (n = 1, 2, \dots)$
(c) $|z_1z_2z_3| = |z_1|\,|z_2|\,|z_3|$
(d) $|z_1z_2\cdots z_n| = |z_1|\,|z_2|\cdots|z_n| \, (n = 1, 2, \dots)$
(e) $|z_1 + z_2 + z_3| \le |z_1| + |z_2| + |z_3|$
(f) $|z_1 + z_2 + \cdots + z_n| \le |z_1| + |z_2| + \cdots + |z_n| \, (n = 1, 2, \dots)$

6. Show that
(a) $\bar{\bar{z}} = z$
(b) $\overline{\left(\frac{1}{z}\right)} = \frac{1}{\bar{z}}$
(c) z is real if and only if $z = \bar{z}$
(d) $\overline{z^3} = \bar{z}^3$
(e) $\overline{z^n} = \bar{z}^n \, (n = 1, 2, \dots)$

7. Show that if $z = x + iy$, then $x = (z + \bar{z})/2$ and $y = (z - \bar{z})/2i$.

8. Show that if $z_iz_2 = 0$, then at least one of the two factors must be zero.

9. Evaluate each of the following. That is, express each in standard Cartesian form $x + iy$.

*(a) $(2 - i)^3$

(b) $\frac{1}{1 - 2i}$

(c) $\frac{i}{2 + 5i}$

(d) $\frac{1 + i}{1 - i}$

*(e) $\left(\frac{1 + i}{2 - i}\right)^3$

(f) $\text{Re}\,\frac{2 + 3i}{4 + 5i}$

(g) $\text{Im}\,(1 + i)^3$

(h) $\left(\text{Re}\,\frac{1}{1 + i}\right)^3$

(i) $\text{Re}\left(\frac{1}{a + ib} + \frac{1}{c + id}\right)$

(j) $\text{Im}\left(\frac{a + ib}{c + id}\right)$

10. Evaluate

(a) $\left|\frac{1 - i}{1 + i}\right|$

(b) $\left|\frac{(2 - i)^3}{(1 + 3i)^2}\right|$

(c) $|(1 - 2i)^2 + (1 + i)^2|$

11. Verify the triangle inequality for each of the following cases.

(a) $z_1 = 2 + 3i$, $z_2 = 1 - i$
(b) $z_1 = 1 + i$, $z_2 = 7i$
(c) $z_1 = 5$, $z_2 = 4i$
(d) $z_1 = 3 + 4i$, $z_2 = 2 + i$

18.3 ELEMENTARY FUNCTIONS

Having introduced complex numbers $z = x + iy$, we next introduce *functions* of a complex variable. Since functions will be defined on sets of complex numbers, we will need to distinugish various topological features of these sets. In fact, the needed discussion can be found back in Section 6.2. Thus here we merely review the key ideas.

First, we define the **distance** between any two points $z_1 = x_1 + iy_1$ and $z_2 = x_2 + iy_2$ as

$$d(z_1, z_2) \equiv |z_1 - z_2| = \sqrt{(x_1 - x_2)^2 + (y_1 - y_2)^2}. \tag{1}$$

Next, we define a **neighborhood** $N(z_0; r)$ of a point z_0 in the z plane as the set of points z closer to z_0 than r, i.e., such that

$$|z - z_0| < r \qquad (r > 0). \tag{2}$$

A set S is **connected** if each pair of points in S can be joined by an unbroken line consisting of a finite number of straight segments, each contained entirely within S. A point P is a **boundary point** of S if *every* neighborhood of P (no matter how small) contains points in S as well as points not in S, and a point P in S is an **interior point** of S if there exists some neighborhood of P lying entirely within S. Finally, a connected set S is a **region;** S is an **open region** or **domain** if it contains *none* of its boundary points, and is a **closed region** if it contains *all* of its boundary points.

To illustrate, $|z - z_0| < r$ defines an open region (Fig. 18.5a), $|z - z_0| \leq r$ defines a closed region (Fig. 18.5b), and Re $z > 2$ defines an open region.

Turning now to functions, recall from the elementary calculus that a function f of a real variable x is a rule that assigns a unique value $f(x)$ to each point x in some set on an x-axis, as illustrated in Fig. 18.6. One also calls f a *mapping*. Following Descartes (1596–1650), a useful graphical display of f (the "graph" of f) can be obtained by arranging the x and f axes at right angles to each other and plotting the set of points $x, f(x)$, as illustrated in Fig. 18.7. Analogously, we define a **function w of**

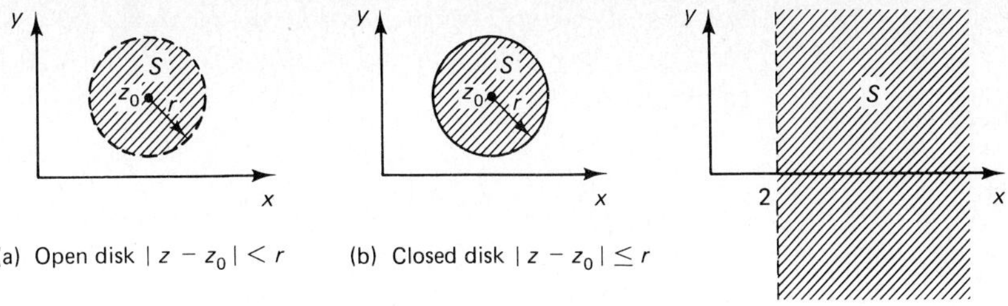

(a) Open disk $|z - z_0| < r$ (b) Closed disk $|z - z_0| \leq r$ (c) Open half-plane Re $z > 2$

Fig. 18.5 The regions $|z - z_0| < r$, $|z - z_0| \leqq r$, Re $z > 2$.

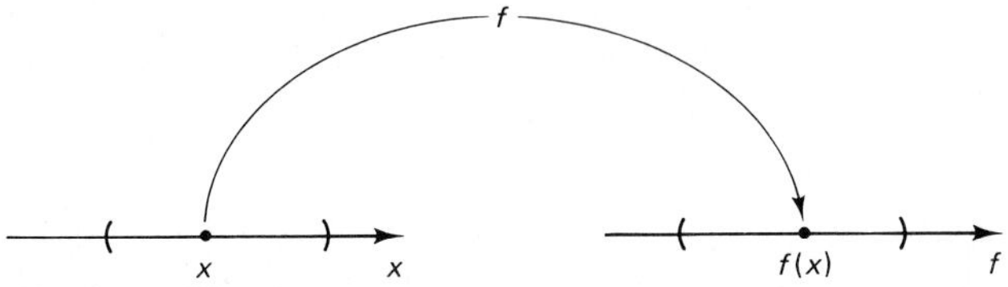

Fig. 18.6 The mapping *f*.

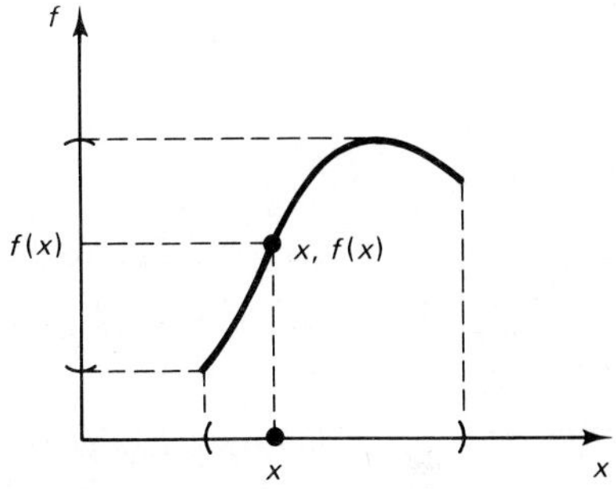

Fig. 18.7 Graph of *f*.

a complex variable z as a rule that assigns a unique value $w(z)$ to each point z in some set D in the complex plane.*

In general, $w(z)$ is complex, so the mapping is as depicted in Fig. 18.8 from the z plane to a w plane. The set D on which w is defined is called the *domain of definition*† of w, and the set R of $w(z)$ values is called the *range of values* of w. Strictly speaking, one distinguishes between the *function* (or mapping) and the *values* of the function by using the notation w for the former and $w(z)$ for the latter. However, we plead guilty, in this book, of occasionally speaking of "the function $w(z)$."

Notice carefully that Descartes' method of graphical display (Fig. 18.7) is not available to us in the complex case because both D and R are two-dimensional, so that the "graph of w" would require a plot in four dimensions. *Thus graphs like the*

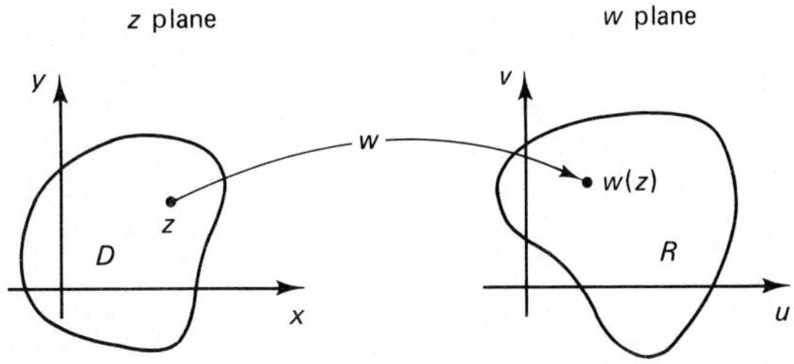

Fig. 18.8 The mapping *w*.

* Just as the letter f is traditionally, although by no means exclusively, used for functions of a real variable, it is traditional to use either w or f for functions of a complex variable. We plan to use both extensively.

† The domain of definition of a function is not necessarily an open set, and is thus not necessarily a domain in the sense defined on page 730. This inconsistency in terminology is unfortunate, but is too deeply entrenched to tamper with.

one shown in Fig. 18.7 will not be possible in Part V! Of course, the real and imaginary parts of $f(z)$, say u and v, respectively, must be functions of x and y. Thus we can express

$$w(z) = u(x, y) + iv(x, y), \tag{3}$$

and although we cannot plot "the graph of w," we *can* plot, separately, the surfaces $u(x, y)$ and $v(x, y)$. However, this form of display is seldom used, although that situation may change with the proliferation of computer graphics.

EXAMPLE 1 To illustrate some of these ideas, consider $w(z) = z^2$, defined on the first quadrant of the z plane: $0 < x < \infty$, $0 < y < \infty$. Then $w(z) = (x + iy)^2 = x^2 - y^2 + i2xy$, so that $u(x, y) = x^2 - y^2$ and $v(x, y) = 2xy$. Since $0 < x < \infty$ and $0 < y < \infty$, it follows from the form of u and v that $-\infty < u < \infty$ and $0 < v < \infty$, so that the range of w is the entire upper halfplane $v > 0$, as shown in Fig. 18.9. If, for example, $z = 1 + 2i$, then $w(z) = (1 - 4) + i2(1)(2) = -3 + 4i$, as shown in the figure.

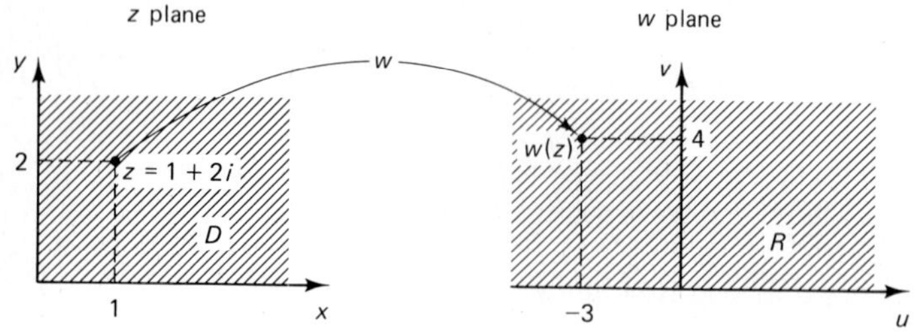

Fig. 18.9 Mapping defined in Example 1.

Since we cannot draw a graph of $w(z) = z^2$ [as we could for the real function $w(x) = x^2$], and we do not wish to plot the surfaces $u(x, y) = x^2 - y^2$, $v(x, y) = 2xy$ (although this could be done using computer graphics), the question remains: What *can* be done, easily, to provide some form of graphical display of w? We could, of course, select a number of points in D and display each, together with its image in R, as we have done in Fig. 18.9 for the single point $z = 1 + 2i$. However, this seems hardly an attractive idea. A more appealing, and commonly used device, is to display the images of representative *curves*. For instance, the straight line $y = 1$, $0 < x < \infty$ gives $u = x^2 - 1$, $v = 2x$ or, eliminating x, $u = v^2/4 - 1$. Similarly, the image curve corresponding to the curve $y = y_0$, $0 < x < \infty$ is the parabola $u = v^2/4y_0^2 - y_0^2$, and the image curve corresponding to the curve $x = x_0$, $0 < y < \infty$ is the parabola $u = -v^2/4x_0^2 + x_0^2$, as displayed in Fig. 18.10 for $x_0 = 1, 2, \ldots$ and $y_0 = 1, 2, \ldots$. This type of display will be especially important in Chapter 19 when we study conformal mapping. ◀

Next, we introduce the important elementary functions e^z, $\sin z$, $\cos z$, $\sinh z$, and $\cosh z$.

EXPONENTIAL FUNCTION

Beginning with the **exponential function** e^z [also written as $\exp(z)$], it is essential to see, first, that we cannot "figure out" how to compute $e^z = e^{x+iy}$; the latter is a new quantity for us, and we render it meaningful by *defining* it. As a rule of thumb,

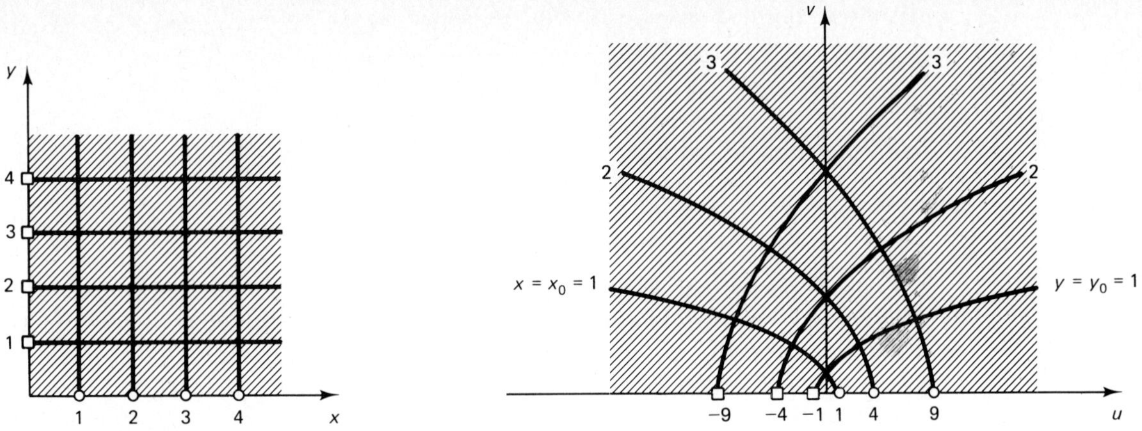

Fig. 18.10 Representative curves and their image curves.

it is generally fruitful to define new objects in terms of, or as extensions of, old ones. For example, in the present case we could recall that for *real* x we have the familiar Taylor series

$$e^x = 1 + x + \frac{x^2}{2!} + \frac{x^3}{3!} + \cdots \qquad (|\,x\,| < \infty). \tag{4}$$

Thus it seems reasonable to *define*

$$e^z \equiv 1 + z + \frac{z^2}{2!} + \frac{z^3}{3!} + \cdots, \tag{5}$$

since (5) reduces to (4) in the event that z is purely real. In fact, this series approach was adopted by *Karl Weierstrass* (1815–1897) in his development of the complex variable theory. This approach would be awkward here since it would confront us with complex infinite series at a rather early point in our development of the subject. Thus we prefer the more traditional approach, wherein the introduction of series is delayed until after we have developed both the differential and integral calculus of functions of a complex variable.

Recalling the real-variable formula $e^{x_1+x_2} = e^{x_1}e^{x_2}$, let us tentatively write

$$e^z = e^x e^{iy}. \tag{6}$$

The latter falls short of defining e^z because e^{iy} is still undefined. At this point we do turn to Taylor series, but only to motivate our final definition of e^z. For if we treat iy as real, then

$$\begin{aligned} e^{iy} &= 1 + (iy) + \frac{1}{2!}(iy)^2 + \frac{1}{3!}(iy)^3 + \frac{1}{4!}(iy)^4 + \cdots \\ &= \left(1 - \frac{y^2}{2!} + \frac{y^4}{4!} - \cdots\right) + i\left(y - \frac{y^3}{3!} + \frac{y^5}{5!} - \cdots\right) \\ &= \cos y + i \sin y. \end{aligned}$$

From this result it seems reasonable to *define*

$$\boxed{e^{iy} \equiv \cos y + i \sin y,} \tag{7}$$

and combining (7) with (6), to *define*

$$\boxed{e^{z} \equiv e^{x}(\cos y + i \sin y).} \tag{8}$$

Due to Euler, and known as **Euler's formula,** (7) is only a special case of (8) (for $z = iy$), but it is so important in the history of mathematics that we have framed it, together with (8). It (almost) goes without saying that the name of the variable in (7) is immaterial; thus it is equally true that $e^{i\theta} = \cos\theta + i\sin\theta$, $e^{it} = \cos t + i\sin t$, and so on.

Notice carefully from (7) that

$$|e^{iy}| = |\cos y + i \sin y| = \sqrt{\cos^2 y + \sin^2 y} = 1 \tag{9}$$

for all y, and from (8) that

$$|e^{z}| = |e^{x}(\cos y + i \sin y)| = |e^{x}|\,|\cos y + i \sin y| = e^{x} \tag{10}$$

for all z. For example, $|e^{3-5i}| = e^3$ and $|e^{-4+i}| = e^{-4}$. Finally, observe from (8) that $e^z \neq 0$ for all (finite) z's, because $e^x \neq 0$ for all (finite) x's, and $\cos y$ and $\sin y$ do not simultaneously vanish for any value of y.

TRIGONOMETRIC AND HYPERBOLIC FUNCTIONS

Changing y to $-y$ in (7), and recalling that the cosine is even and the sine is odd, we obtain the companion formula

$$e^{-iy} = \cos y - i \sin y \tag{11}$$

and solving (7) and (11) for $\cos y$, $\sin y$, we obtain

$$\cos y = \frac{e^{iy} + e^{-iy}}{2}, \tag{12}$$

$$\sin y = \frac{e^{iy} - e^{-iy}}{2i}. \tag{13}$$

Equations (12) and (13) suggest that we now define the **cosine** and **sine functions** as

$$\boxed{\cos z \equiv \frac{e^{iz} + e^{-iz}}{2},} \tag{14}$$

$$\boxed{\sin z \equiv \frac{e^{iz} - e^{-iz}}{2i}.} \tag{15}$$

The right-hand sides are meaningful by virtue of (8). For example, $e^{iz} = e^{i(x+iy)} = e^{-y+ix} = e^{-y}(\cos x + i \sin x)$.

Furthermore, the formulas

$$\cosh x = \frac{e^x + e^{-x}}{2}, \tag{16}$$

$$\sinh x = \frac{e^x - e^{-x}}{2}, \tag{17}$$

suggest that we define the **hyperbolic cosine** and **hyperbolic sine functions** as

$$\cosh z \equiv \frac{e^z + e^{-z}}{2}, \tag{18}$$

$$\sinh z \equiv \frac{e^z - e^{-z}}{2}, \tag{19}$$

From (14), (15), (18), and (19) follow the connections

$$\cos(iz) = \cosh z, \tag{20a}$$

$$\sin(iz) = i \sinh z, \tag{20b}$$

$$\cosh(iz) = \cos z, \tag{20c}$$

$$\sinh(iz) = i \sin z, \tag{20d}$$

between the trigonometric and hyperbolic functions.

Out of habit, it is natural to want to know what $\cos z$, $\sin z$, $\cosh z$, $\sinh z$ "look like." But whereas the *real* functions $\cos x$, $\sin x$, $\cosh x$, $\sinh x$ admit the familiar graphs shown in Fig. 18.11, recall that we cannot draw analogous graphs for the complex functions $\cos z$, $\sin z$, $\cosh z$, and $\sinh z$ because we would need four dimensions to do so. Nevertheless, a limited visual image of these functions is readily available by looking only along the real and imaginary axes. Considering $\sin z$, for example, observe that on the real axis, $\sin z = \sin x$ is the familiar oscillatory function whose graph is shown in Fig. 18.11. On the imaginary axis, however, $\sin z = \sin iy = i \sinh y$ is not oscillatory, and it is not even bounded!

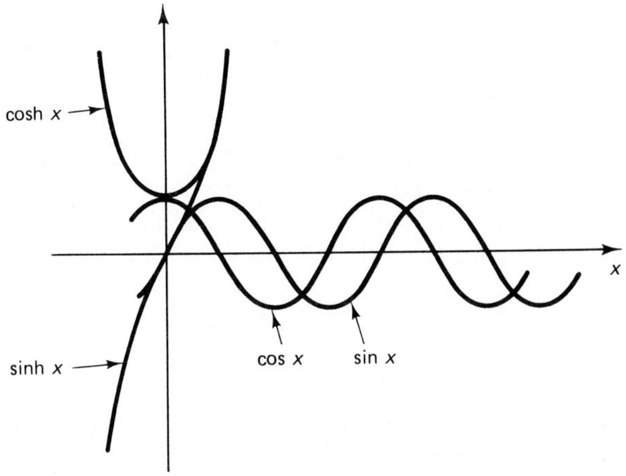

Fig. 18.11 Graphs of $\cos x$, $\sin x$, $\cosh x$, $\sinh x$.

Because we have based our definitions of e^z, $\cos z$, $\sin z$, $\cosh z$, and $\sinh z$ on real-variable formulas [for example, compare (18) and (19) with (16) and (17)], *it now turns out that the familiar formulas for real exponential, trigonometric, and hyperbolic functions are true for the complex functions as well.* For example,

$$\sin^2 z + \cos^2 z = 1, \qquad \sin(-z) = -\sin z, \qquad \cos(-z) = \cos z \tag{21a}$$

hold for any z, and

$$\cos(z_1 + z_2) = \cos z_1 \cos z_2 - \sin z_1 \sin z_2 \tag{21b}$$

$$\sin(z_1 + z_2) = \sin z_1 \cos z_2 + \sin z_2 \cos z_1 \tag{21c}$$

hold for any z_1, z_2.

EXAMPLE 2 As representative, let us prove that $\sin^2 z + \cos^2 z = 1$:

$$\begin{aligned} \sin^2 z + \cos^2 z &= -\tfrac{1}{4}(e^{iz} - e^{-iz})^2 + \tfrac{1}{4}(e^{iz} + e^{-iz})^2 \\ &= \tfrac{1}{4}(-e^{i2z} + 2 - e^{-i2z} + e^{i2z} + 2 + e^{-i2z}) \\ &= 1. \quad ◀ \end{aligned} \tag{22}$$

Additional identities are listed in the exercises.

Finally, besides $\sin z$, $\cos z$, $\sinh z$, $\cosh z$, we define

$$\tan z \equiv \frac{\sin z}{\cos z}, \qquad \cot z \equiv \frac{\cos z}{\sin z}, \tag{23a}$$

$$\sec z \equiv \frac{1}{\cos z}, \qquad \csc z \equiv \frac{1}{\sin z}, \tag{23b}$$

$$\tanh z \equiv \frac{\sinh z}{\cosh z}, \qquad \coth z \equiv \frac{\cosh z}{\sinh z}, \tag{23c}$$

$$\operatorname{sech} z \equiv \frac{1}{\cosh z}, \qquad \operatorname{csch} z \equiv \frac{1}{\sinh z}. \tag{23d}$$

In this section we have introduced the notion of a function w of a single complex variable z in general, and a number of elementary functions in particular. Additional elementary functions are presented in Sections 18.4 and 18.5. It would be reasonable to expect that we will subsequently turn to functions of *several* complex variables $w(z_1, \ldots, z_n)$, as one does in studying *real*-variable theory. Yet it is curious and interesting that virtually the entire body of complex variable theory deals only with functions of a single complex variable. To be sure, functions of several complex variables have been considered,* but this case is relatively obscure both in theory and applications.

* See, for example, V. Vladimirov's *Methods of the Theory of Functions of Many Complex Variables* (Cambridge, Mass.: MIT Press, 1966), which includes applications to quantum field theory, function theory, and the theory of differential equations with constant coefficients.

1. What point sets are defined by the following?

(a) $|z - 1| \le 4$ (b) $|z + 1| < 3$
(c) $|z + 2 - i| < 2$ (d) $|z + 2 - i| = 2$
(e) $|z| < |z - 4|$ (f) $|z + 1| \le |z|$
(g) $|z - z_1| < |z - z_2|$
(h) $|z + 1| = |z| + 1$ (i) $\text{Re}\,(z - i) > 3$
(j) $\text{Im}\,(z - i) > 1$

2. Determine the range R for the given function. Include sketches of both the domain D and the range R, and give the equations of any curved parts of the boundary of R.

*(a) $w(z) = z + 2 + i$ on $0 < x < 1, 0 < y < 1$
(b) $w(z) = 2iz$ on $0 < x < 1, 0 < y < \infty$
(c) $w(z) = iz + 3$ on $0 < x < \infty, 0 < y < \infty$
(d) $w(z) = z^2$ on $-\infty < x < 0, 0 < y < \infty$
(e) $w(z) = z^2$ on $1 < x < 2, 1 < y < 3$
*(f) $w(z) = iz^2$ on $0 < x < 1, 0 < y < 1$
(g) $w(z) = z^3$ on $0 < x < \infty, 0 < y < \infty$

3. Show whether or not $|e^z| = e^{|z|}$. More generally, is $|w(z)| = w(|z|)$?

4. Show whether or not $\overline{e^z} = e^{\bar{z}}$. More generally, is $\overline{w(z)} = w(\bar{z})$?

5. Show that (20a) to (20d) follow from (14), (15), (18), and (19).

6. Show that

(a) $e^{z_1}e^{z_2} = e^{z_1+z_2}$
(b) $(e^z)^n = e^{nz}$ for any integer n [More generally, it is true that $(e^{z_1})^{z_2} = e^{z_1 z_2}$, but proof of that fact needs to await our introduction of the logarithmic function in Section 18.4.]

7. Show that

(a) $\sin(-z) = -\sin z$ and $\cos(-z) = \cos z$
(b) $\cos(z_1 + z_2) = \cos z_1 \cos z_2 - \sin z_1 \sin z_2$
(c) $\sin(z_1 + z_2) = \sin z_1 \cos z_2 + \sin z_2 \cos z_1$
(d) $\cos(z + 2\pi) = \cos z$ and $\sin(z + 2\pi) = \sin z$
(e) $\cos(x + iy) = \cos x \cosh y - i \sin x \sinh y$
(f) $\sin(x + iy) = \sin x \cosh y + i \cos x \sinh y$

8. Show that

(a) $\sinh(-z) = -\sinh z$ and $\cosh(-z) = \cosh z$
(b) $\cosh(z_1 + z_2) = \cosh z_1 \cosh z_2 + \sinh z_1 \sinh z_2$
(c) $\sinh(z_1 + z_2) = \sinh z_1 \cosh z_2 + \cosh z_1 \sinh z_2$
(d) $\cosh(z + 2\pi i) = \cosh z$ and $\sinh(z + 2\pi i) = \sinh z$
(e) $\cosh(x + iy) = \cosh x \cos y + i \sinh x \sin y$
(f) $\sinh(x + iy) = \sinh x \cos y + i \cosh x \sin y$
(g) $\cosh^2 z - \sinh^2 z = 1$

9. Evaluate each of the following in standard Cartesian form.

*(a) $e^{2+\pi i}$ (b) e^{1-i}
(c) $e^{-\pi i/4}$ *(d) $\sin(3 + \pi i)$
(e) $\cos(-2 + 3\pi i)$ (f) $\sec(1 + i)$
*(g) $\csc(1 - i)$ (h) $\tan\left(-\dfrac{3\pi}{4} i\right)$
(i) $\cot\left(\dfrac{\pi i}{4}\right)$ (j) $\sinh(3 + \pi i)$
(k) $\cosh(1 - \pi i)$ (l) $\tanh(2 + 4\pi i)$

10. Show that the range R of the function e^z on the rectangular domain $a < x < b$, $0 < y < \pi/2$ is as shown in the accompanying figure. *Hint:* At first glance it is tempting to take a number of points on the boundary of D [such as a, $(a + b)/2$, b, $b + (\pi/4)i$, $b + (\pi/2)i$, etc.] and find their images in the f plane. That procedure can only give *points* on the boundary of R, not the boundary *curve*. Thus one should find the image of the entire line segment C_1, then C_2, C_3, and C_4.

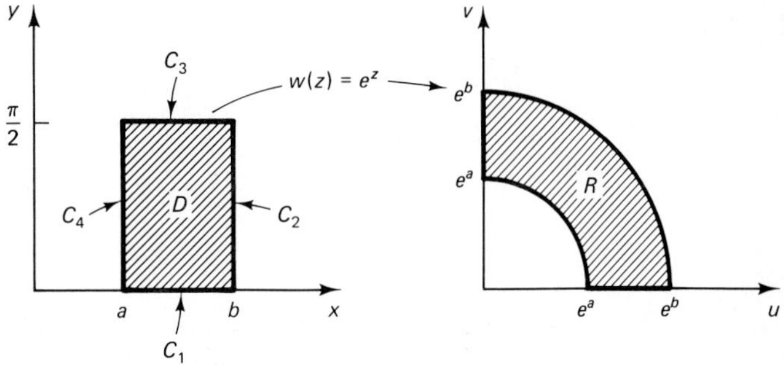

11. Show that the range R of the function $\sin z$ on the semi-infinite strip $-\pi/2 < x < \pi/2$, $0 < y < \infty$ is shown in the accompanying figure. (See the hint in Exercise 10.)

12. Prove that

(a) $e^z = 1$ if and only if $z = 2n\pi i$, where n is any integer

(b) $e^{z_1} = e^{z_2}$ if and only if $z_1 = z_2 + 2n\pi i$ where n is any integer

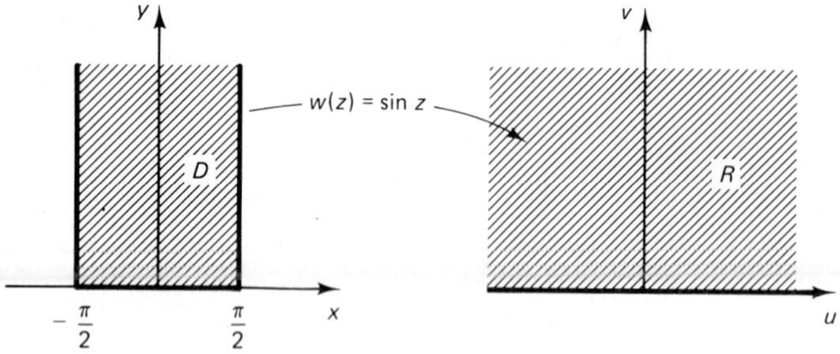

18.4 POLAR FORM, ADDITIONAL ELEMENTARY FUNCTIONS, AND MULTIVALUEDNESS

Having introduced the complex exponential function in the preceding section, we can now present the polar representation of complex numbers. This representation will be especially useful when, later in this section, we discuss powers of z and the logarithmic function.

POLAR FORM

If r, θ are the usual polar coordinates with $r \geq 0$ and θ measured in radians counterclockwise from the positive x axis), then (Fig. 18.12)

$$z = x + iy = r\cos\theta + ir\sin\theta = r(\cos\theta + i\sin\theta). \tag{1}$$

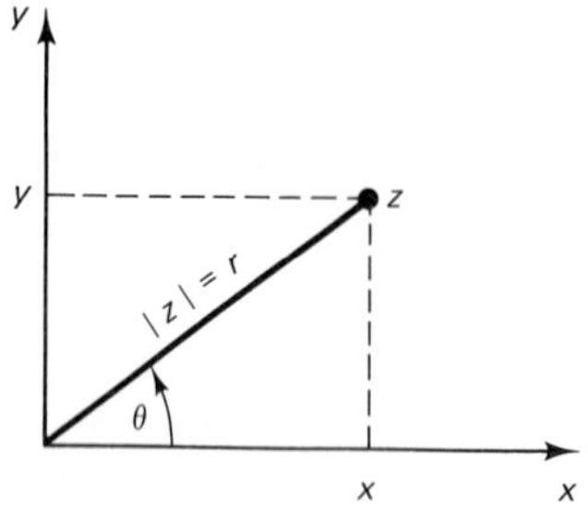

Fig. 18.12 Polar coordinates.

Recalling Euler's formula $e^{i\theta} = \cos\theta + i\sin\theta$, we see that (1) can be reexpressed as

$$z = re^{i\theta}, \tag{2}$$

which is the **polar** form of the complex number z. Since

$$|z| = \sqrt{x^2 + y^2} = r,$$

we see that r is the **absolute value** or **modulus** of z:

$$r = \text{mod}\,(z) = \sqrt{x^2 + y^2}. \tag{3}$$

The angle θ, called the **argument** of z and denoted as arg (z), can be determined from the formula

$$\theta = \arg\,(z) = \tan^{-1}\frac{y}{x} \tag{4}$$

for $z \neq 0$; for $z = 0$ the angle θ is undefined. (Subsequently, we will omit the parentheses around z and will write mod z and arg z.)

Observe, from Fig. 18.12, that given any point $z(\neq 0)$ the angle θ can be determined only to within an arbitrary integer multiple of 2π. As a useful reference, the value of θ satisfying of $0 \leq \theta < 2\pi$ will be called the **principal argument** of z and will be written as Arg z. Denoting the value of Arg z as θ_0, we have

$$\theta = \arg z = \text{Arg}\, z + 2k\pi = \theta_0 + 2k\pi, \tag{5}$$

for $k = 0, \pm 1, \pm 2, \ldots$. *This infinite set of θ values is indeed obtained from (4) because $\tan^{-1}$ ( ) is multivalued. However, (4) yields spurious values as well, and these spurious values need to be discarded.* We illustrate these ideas with an example.

EXAMPLE 1 Let $z = 1 + i$, so that $x = 1$ and $y = 1$. Then (3) gives $r = \sqrt{2}$, and (4) gives $\theta = \tan^{-1}(1/1) = \tan^{-1} 1$. Now $\tan^{-1} 1$ gives the values $\pi/4$ plus any integer multiple of 2π, and it *also* gives the values $5\pi/4$ plus any integer multiple of 2π. Since $z = 1 + i$ lies in the first quadrant of the z plane, the former set of values is correct. The latter values, however, are incorrect and must be discarded. Thus we conclude that $\theta_0 = \pi/4$, and

$$\arg\,(1 + i) = \frac{\pi}{4} + 2k\pi,$$

for any $k = 0, \pm 1, \pm 2, \ldots$. ◀

Observe that whereas the Cartesian form $x + iy$ is especially convenient for the addition and subtraction of complex numbers, the polar form is especially convenient for their multiplication and division. Specifically,

$$z_1 z_2 = (r_1 e^{i\theta_1})(r_2 e^{i\theta_2}) = r_1 r_2 e^{i(\theta_1 + \theta_2)}, \tag{6}$$

so that *the modulus of the product is the product of the moduli,* and the *argument of the product is the sum of the arguments.* Further, for nonzero complex numbers z_1 and z_2,

$$\frac{z_1}{z_2} = \frac{r_1 e^{i\theta_1}}{r_2 e^{i\theta_2}} = \frac{r_1}{r_2}\, e^{i(\theta_1 - \theta_2)}, \tag{7}$$

so *the modulus of the quotient is the quotient of the moduli,* and *the argument of the quotient is the difference of the arguments* (see Exercise 3).

Similarly, it is convenient to use the polar form for computing *integral powers of z* since

$$z^n = (re^{i\theta})^n = r^n e^{in\theta} \tag{8}$$

for any integer n (positive, negative, or zero). That is, mod (z^n) = (mod $z)^n$ and arg $(z^n) = n(\arg z)$. Expressing (8) in the equivalent Cartesian form* gives the well-known **de Moivre formula,**

$$z^n = r^n (\cos n\theta + i \sin n\theta). \tag{9}$$

To appreciate the value of (8) and (9), consider the task of computing $(2 - 3i)^{473}$. Although we could work out this quantity in Cartesian form, it is easier to reexpress $2 - 3i$ in the form $re^{i\theta}$, for then it follows immediately, that $(2 - 3i)^{473} = r^{473}e^{i473\theta}$. Finally, that result can be reexpressed in Cartesian form as $r^{473}(\cos 473\theta + i \sin 473\theta)$.

EXAMPLE 2 As a simple detailed illustration, consider the calculation of $(1 + i)^3$ using polar representation. First, observe that z^n is a single-valued function in spite of the multivaluedness of θ. To see why that is true, put (5) into (8):

$$z^n = r^n e^{in(\theta_0 + 2k\pi)} = r^n e^{in\theta_0} e^{i2nk\pi}, \tag{10}$$

which gives the unique value $r^n e^{in\theta_0}$ because $e^{i2nk\pi} = 1$ for all possible choices of $k(=0, \pm 1, \pm 2, \ldots)$. Thus with no loss we can regard θ in (8) and (9) as θ_0. In the present case, $r = \sqrt{2}$ and $\theta_0 = \pi/4$, so

$$(1 + i)^3 = (\sqrt{2}\, e^{i(\pi/4)})^3 = 2\sqrt{2}\, e^{i(3\pi/4)}, \tag{11}$$

as shown in Fig. 18.13; observe that the modulus of $z = 1 + i$ has been cubed and its argument has been tripled. If desired, we can now return to Cartesian form and write

$$(1 + i)^3 = 2\sqrt{2} \left(\cos \frac{3\pi}{4} + i \sin \frac{3\pi}{4} \right) = -2 + 2i. \qquad ◀$$

If $w = z^n$, then $z = w^{1/n}$ is called the *n*th *root* of w. Thus let us consider next

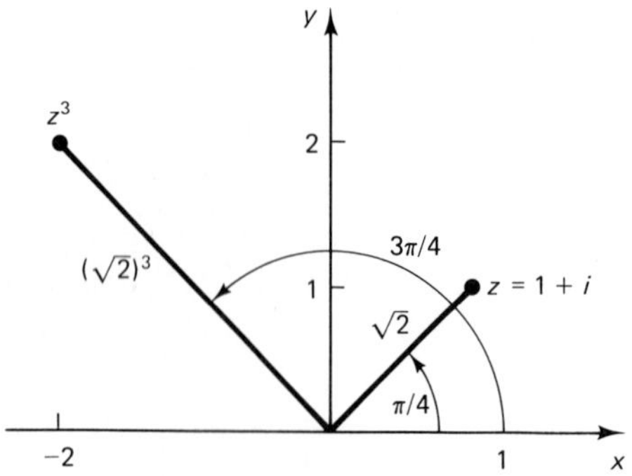

Fig. 18.13 $1 + i$ and $(1 + i)^3$.

*Some authors would say that the right-hand side of (9) is in polar form because the variables present are r and θ. However, in this text we will call ae^{ib} and $a + ib$ polar and Cartesian forms, respectively. Thus the right-hand side of (9) is in *Cartesian* form even though $a = r^n \cos n\theta$ and $b = r^n \sin n\theta$ involve the polar variables r, θ.

the nth root $z^{1/n}$ (where we have changed the independent variable from w back to z). Proceeding as above, we obtain

$$z^{1/n} = (re^{i(\theta_0+2k\pi)})^{1/n} = r^{1/n}e^{i(\theta_0/n)}e^{i(2k\pi/n)} \tag{12}$$

for $k = 0, \pm 1, \pm 2, \ldots$. Now, whereas z^n was found to be single valued, $z^{1/n}$ is seen to be *multivalued* because the $e^{i2k\pi/n}$ factor in (12) takes on *different* values for different values of k. Specifically, as k is indexed, the complex number $e^{i2k\pi/n}$ cycles among n distinct values. Those values are equally spaced on the unit circle, as illustrated in Fig. 18.14 for the case where $n = 6$. Thus, calling the values of $z^{1/n}$ the nth *roots of* z, we see that there are exactly n nth roots of z and that they are given by

$$z^{1/n} = \begin{cases} \sqrt[n]{r}\, e^{i[(\theta_0+2k\pi)/n]} & \text{(polar)} \\ \sqrt[n]{r}\left[\cos\left(\dfrac{\theta_0 + 2k\pi}{n}\right) + i \sin\left(\dfrac{\theta_0 + 2k\pi}{n}\right)\right] & \text{(Cartesian)} \end{cases} \tag{13}$$

for $k = 0, 1, \ldots, n - 1$. To interpret this result geometrically, suppose that we are given z with mod $z = r$ and Arg $z = \theta_0$. Then the n nth roots of z lie on a circle of radius $\sqrt[n]{r}$, centered at the origin. They are equally spaced on that circle, with the argument of the "first" one (corresponding to $k = 0$) being θ_0/n.

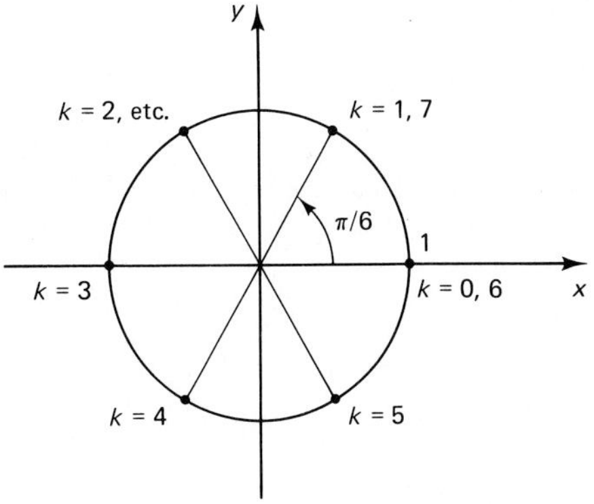

Fig. 18.14 Values of $e^{i2k\pi/n}$ for $n = 6$.

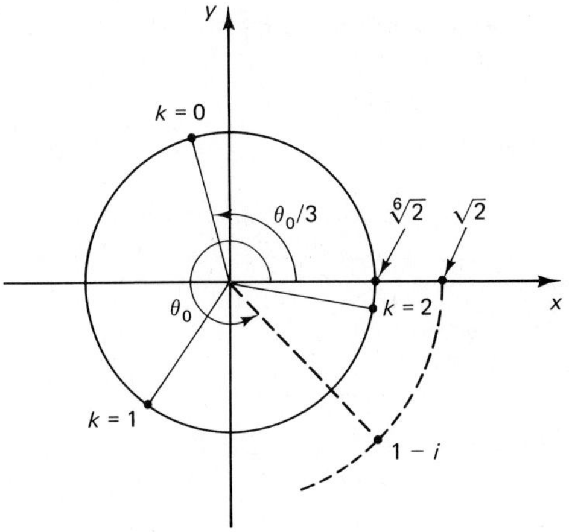

Fig. 18.15 The three cube roots of $1 - i$.

EXAMPLE 3 Evaluate $(1 - i)^{1/3}$. That is, compute the three cube roots of $z = 1 - i$. In this case $r = \sqrt{2}$ and $\theta_0 = 7\pi/4$, so

$$(1 - i)^{1/3} = \sqrt[6]{2}\, e^{i7\pi/12}, \quad \sqrt[6]{2}\, e^{i15\pi/12}, \quad \sqrt[6]{2}\, e^{i23\pi/12}, \tag{14}$$

as displayed in Fig. 18.15. ◀

THE LOGARITHM OF Z

The quantity log z denotes the natural (i.e., with respect to the base $e \approx 2.71828$) logarithm of z, and is defined as the inverse of the exponential function. Thus, if $e^w = z$, then

$$w = \log z. \tag{15}$$

Since e^w cannot be zero for any (finite) value of w, it is to be understood that $z \neq 0$ in (15); i.e., $z = 0$ is to be excluded from the domain of definition of $\log z$. To obtain a formula for the values of $\log z$, note that if we express $w = u + iv$ and $z = re^{i\theta}$ then $e^w = z$ becomes

$$e^u e^{iv} = re^{i\theta}, \tag{16}$$

from which it follows (Exercise 7) that

$$\begin{aligned} e^u &= r, \\ v &= \theta + \text{arbitrary integer multiple of } 2\pi. \end{aligned} \tag{17}$$

Equivalently, $u = \ln r$ and $v = \theta_0 + 2k\pi$, where *we will use the "ln" notation to denote the usual natural logarithmic function of real variables;* for example, $\ln 2 \approx 0.693$. Since $\log z = u + iv$, it follows that

$$\boxed{\log z = \ln r + i(\theta_0 + 2k\pi) \qquad (z \neq 0)} \tag{18}$$

for any $k = 0, \pm 1, \pm 2, \ldots$. Each such value of k yields a distinct value of $\log z$, so that $\log z$ has an *infinite* number of values for each z; hence we say that it is *infinite*-valued.

EXAMPLE 4 Compute $\log(1 - i)$. Here $z = 1 - i$, so $r = \sqrt{2}$ and $\theta_0 = 7\pi/4$. Thus (18) gives

$$\begin{aligned} \log(1 - \mathrm{i}) &= \ln \sqrt{2} + i\left(\frac{7\pi}{4} + 2k\pi\right) \\ &= \ln \sqrt{2} + i\frac{7\pi}{4}, \quad \ln \sqrt{2} + i\frac{15\pi}{4}, \quad \ln \sqrt{2} - i\frac{\pi}{4}, \quad \ldots, \end{aligned} \tag{19}$$

for $k = 0, +1, -1, \ldots$. ◀

GENERAL POWERS OF Z

Having studied z^n and $z^{1/n}$ earlier in this section, here we consider *general* powers of z, namely,

$$w(z) = z^c, \tag{20}$$

where c is any given number—real or complex. If we try to evaluate z^c by expressing z in polar form and proceeding as we did with z^n and $z^{1/n}$, we run into trouble if c is complex. For example, suppose that $c = i$. Then

$$z^i = (re^{i\theta})^i = r^i e^{-\theta} = r^i e^{-(\theta_0 + 2k\pi)},$$

but the r^i is, as yet, an undefined quantity. Instead, let us deal with z^c by mimicking the real-variable formula $x^a = e^{\ln x^a} = e^{a \ln x}$. Thus let us define z^c in terms of the already defined quantity $\log z$ as

$$\boxed{z^c \equiv e^{c \log z} = e^{c[\ln r + i(\theta_0 + 2k\pi)]},} \tag{21}$$

for $k = 0, \pm 1, \pm 2, \ldots$.

If c is an *integer* n, then (21) gives

$$z^n = e^{n(\ln r + i\theta_0)} = e^{\ln r^n} e^{in\theta_0} = r^n e^{in\theta_0} \tag{22}$$

because $e^{i2nk\pi} = 1$ for all k's, and (22) is, of course, identical to our earlier result for z^n. Similarly, if $c = 1/n$ then (21) produces the same result as was stated earlier in (13).

As a modest generalization of the case $c = 1/n$, let c be any *rational* number $c = m/n$, where m/n is reduced to simplest form (e.g., 3/2 rather than 12/8). Then (21) gives the result, analogous to (13), that

$$z^{m/n} = \begin{cases} r^{m/n} e^{i(m/n)(\theta_0 + 2k\pi)} & \text{(polar)} \\ r^{m/n}\left[\cos \dfrac{m}{n}(\theta_0 + 2k\pi) + i \sin \dfrac{m}{n}(\theta_0 + 2k\pi)\right] & \text{(Cartesian)} \end{cases} \tag{23}$$

for $k = 0, 1, \ldots, n - 1$. The interesting point about this result is not so much the easily obtained right-hand side of (23), but the fact that $z^{m/n}$, just like $z^{1/n}$, is n-valued, independent of m. To see why that is so, observe that the factor $\exp\,[i(m/n)2k\pi]$ in (23) is 1 when $k = 0$, takes on different values as k increases through integer values, and returns to 1 when $(m/n)2k\pi$ becomes an integer multiple of 2π for the first time. That occurs when $k = n$. Thus $z^{m/n}$ *is* n*-valued*, as stated.

If, on the other hand, c is an *irrational* real number (i.e., not expressible in the form m/n), then z^c is *infinite* valued and its values are given by

$$z^c = \begin{cases} r^c e^{ic(\theta_0 + 2k\pi)} & \text{(polar)} \\ r^c[\cos c(\theta_0 + 2k\pi) + i \sin c(\theta_0 + 2k\pi)] & \text{(Cartesian)} \end{cases} \tag{24}$$

for $k = 0, \pm 1, \pm 2, \ldots$. For suppose that the factor $\exp\,(ic\,2k\pi)$ does repeat itself as k increases from some value k_1 to some other value k_2. Then $\exp\,(ic2k_1\pi) = \exp\,(ic2k_2\pi)$, so it must be true that $2ck_1\pi = 2ck_2\pi + 2N\pi$ for some integer N. But then $c = N/(k_1 - k_2)$ would be rational, contrary to our assumption that c is irrational. Thus each value of $k(= 0, \pm 1, \pm 2, \ldots)$ leads to a distinct value of z^c, so z^c is infinite valued, as asserted.

Finally, suppose that c is *complex;* i.e., $c = a + ib$ where $b \neq 0$. Again, z^c is *infinite* valued, and its values are, according to (21),

$$z^c = e^{(a+ib)[\ln r + i(\theta_0 + 2k\pi)]}$$

$$z^c = \begin{cases} e^{a\ln r - b(\theta_0 + 2k\pi)} e^{i[b\ln r + a(\theta_0 + 2k\pi)]} & \text{(polar)} \\ e^{a\ln r - b(\theta_0 + 2k\pi)}\{\cos\,[b \ln r + a(\theta_0 + 2k\pi)] \\ \quad + i \sin\,[b \ln r + a(\theta_0 + 2k\pi)]\} & \text{(Cartesian)} \end{cases} \tag{25}$$

for $k = 0, \pm 1, \pm 2, \ldots$. Notice that the $e^{-2bk\pi}$ factor takes on a distinct value for each integer value of k.

EXAMPLE 5 Find all possible values of 1^i. Since $z = 1$ and $c = i$, we have $r = 1$, $\theta_0 = 0$, $a = 0$, and $b = 1$ to put into (25). Instead of merely putting these values into (25), let us fall back on the definition (21) and write

$$1^i = e^{i \log 1} = e^{i[\ln 1 + i(0 + 2k\pi)]} = e^{-2k\pi} \tag{26}$$

for $k = 0, \pm 1, \pm 2, \ldots$. Perhaps surprisingly, $|\,1^i\,| = e^{-2k\pi}$ is *not* unity, except for $k = 0$. In fact, arbitrarily large values of $| 1^i |$ can be obtained by letting k be sufficiently negative. ◀

As a partial summary, we have seen that z^c is single valued if c is an integer, n-valued if $c = 1/n$, n-valued if $c = m/n$ (reduced to simplest form), infinite valued if c is real and irrational, and infinite valued if Im $c \neq 0$.

OBTAINING SINGLE-VALUED FUNCTIONS

In the foregoing discussion we considered the multivalued quantities log z and z^c ($c \neq$ integer). The inverses of trigonometric and hyperbolic functions are multivalued as well, and these cases are dealt with in the exercises.

The pattern that emerges is that *inverses of single-valued functions that are not one-to-one are necessarily multivalued.* For example, z^2, is single valued, but not one-to-one; it is two-to-one (e.g., both $+1$ and -1 are sent into 1). Thus the inverse $\sqrt{z}$ is one-to-two, and hence double valued.

Observe that in some circumstances multivaluedness is perfectly acceptable. For example, in integrating $\int dx/(x^4 + 1)$ by partial fractions, we need to know all possible roots of the equation $x^4 + 1 = 0$, i.e., all possible values of $z^{1/4}$ for $z = -1$. If, however, a quantity is to be considered as a *function,* then multivaluedness is unacceptable; functions are to be single valued. (Thus notice that in the foregoing discussion of log z and noninteger powers of z we avoided calling these quantities functions.)

Nonetheless, *such multivalued quantities can be rendered single valued by suitably restricting their domains of definition.* For log z, for example, that step can be accomplished by specifying the integer k in (18). If, for example, we choose $k = 0$, that decision amounts to restricting θ (i.e., arg z) so that $0 \leq \theta < 2\pi$. Graphically, we can imagine a "slit" or "cut" in the z plane, along the positive real axis, from infinity all the way in to the origin, as depicted in Fig. 18.16a. One calls the slit a **branch cut.** The point is that in the cut plane log z is single valued and is thus a legitimate function. The particular single-valued function corresponding to the cut domain shown in Fig. 18.16 is called the **principal value** of log z because it corresponds to the choice of the principal argument θ_0 for arg z. If, instead, we set $k = 1$ in (18), that choice amounts to using the branch cut shown in Fig. 18.16b. Like branches on a tree, we call these two single-valued functions *branches* of the multivalued quantity log z.

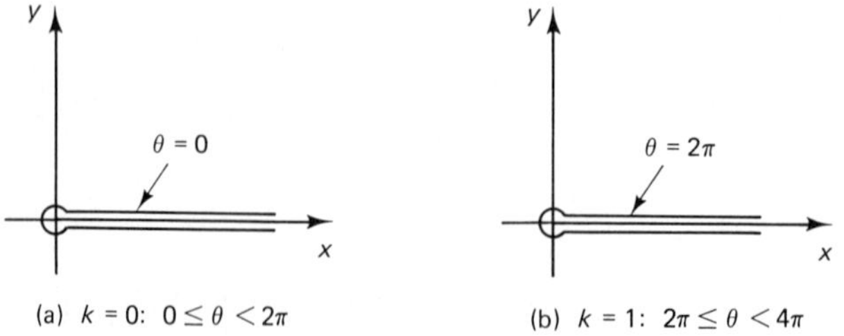

Fig. 18.16 Two possible branch cuts for log z.

EXAMPLE 6 Compute log $(-2i)$ using the two different branch cuts shown in Fig. 18.16. The key step is the conversion of $-2i$ to polar form such that θ is consistent with the specified branch cut. For the cut shown in Fig. 18.16a we have

$-2i = 2e^{3\pi i/2}$, so that

$$\log(-2i) = \log(2e^{3\pi i/2}) = \ln 2 + i\frac{3\pi}{2},$$

and for the cut shown in Fig. 18.16b, $-2i = 2e^{7\pi i/2}$, so

$$\log(-2i) = \log(2e^{7\pi i/2}) = \ln 2 + i\frac{7\pi}{2}. \blacktriangleleft$$

Now that we have seen how to render $\log z$ single valued, we can complete our discussion of the logarithmic function by stating that the familiar properties of the real logarithmic function do carry over to the complex case. For example (Exercise 12),

$$\log(z_1 z_2) = \log z_1 + \log z_2, \tag{27}$$

$$\log\left(\frac{z_1}{z_2}\right) = \log z_1 - \log z_2, \tag{28}$$

and

$$\log z^c = c \log z \qquad (c \text{ real or complex}), \tag{29}$$

provided that all of the log functions in the equation are defined by the same branch cut. For example,(29) is correct if we use the principal-value definition of both log functions, provided that $\arg z = \theta$ satisfies $0 \le \theta < 2\pi$ and $\arg(z^c) = c\theta$ satisfies $0 \le c\theta < 2\pi$.

The other multivalued quantity that we have discussed, z^c, can be rendered single valued in exactly the same manner as $\log z$. For example, the branch cut shown in Fig. 18.16a yields the so-called principal-value branch of z^c.

In this section we have introduced the polar form of complex numbers, the concept of multivaluedness in general and the quantities $\log z$ and z^c in particular, and have shown how to render them single valued. In Section 18.5 we continue with the differential calculus of functions of a complex variable.

18.4 EXERCISES

1. Determine r and the principal argument θ_0 for each of the following values of z.

*(a) $-3i$ (b) $8i$ (c) -6
(d) $1 + 5i$ (e) $-4 - 3i$ *(f) $2 - 12i$
(g) $-1 + i$ (h) $-1 - i$ (i) $0.2 + i$
(j) $\sqrt{3} - i$

2. Express Re $(re^{i\theta})$ and Im $(re^{i\theta})$ in terms of r and θ.

3. Consider formulas (6) and (7) for the product and quotient $z_1 z_2$ and z_1/z_2. Show that these quantities are uniquely determined even though $\arg z_1$ and $\arg z_2$ are, according to (5), multivalued.

4. Obtain z^{10} and z^{20}, in both polar and Cartesian form, for each given z.

*(a) $-1 + i$ (b) $1 + i$ (c) $1 + 2i$
(d) $2 - i$ (e) $3 - i$ (f) $3 + 4i$
(g) $5 - 12i$ (h) $12 + 5i$

5. Find all values of $z^{1/2}$ and $z^{1/5}$ for each given z. Express those values in polar form, and show their location in the z plane, as we have done in Fig. 18.15.

*(a) i (b) 1 (c) 2
(d) $-i$ (e) $3 - 2i$
(f) $-1 + 2i$ (g) $3 + 4i$ (h) $1 - 4i$

6. Obtain, in Cartesian form, all values of $\log z$ for each given z.

*(a) -2	(b) 1	(c) i
(d) $-5i$	(e) $2 - i$	(f) $3 - 4i$
(g) $13 - 5i$	(h) $1 + 6i$	

7. Recall that, by *definition,* two complex numbers $z_1 = x_1 + iy_1$ and $z_2 = x_2 + iy_2$ are equal if $x_1 = x_2$ and $y_1 = y_2$. Show that it follows from this definition that $r_1 e^{i\theta_1} = r_2 e^{i\theta_2}$ (where $r_1 \neq 0$ and $r_2 \neq 0$) if $r_1 = r_2$ and $\theta_1 = \theta_2 +$ arbitrary integer multiple of 2π.

8. Obtain, in polar form, all values of $z^{2/3}$, $z^{3/2}$ and $z^{''}$, for each given z.

*(a) $2i$	(b) 3	(c) -4
(d) $-6i$	(e) $1 - i$	(f) $2 + i$
(g) $1 - 4i$	(h) $2 + 2i$	

9. *(a)–(h) Obtain, in Cartesian form, all values of z^i and z^{1-i} for each z given in Exercise 8.

10. Let c be any real or complex number other than 0. Then for each integer value of k,

$$c^z = e^{z \log c} = e^{z[\ln|c| + i(\mathrm{Arg}c + 2k\pi)]} \tag{a}$$

defines a distinct single-valued function of z. Suppose that we set $k = 0$, because then if c is real and equal to e, c^z reduces to the familiar exponential function e^z. Thus let us define

$$c^z \equiv e^{z(\ln|c| + i\mathrm{Arg}c)}. \tag{b}$$

We call it the **generalized exponential function** because it allows for any value of $c\,(\neq 0)$ and reduces to the exponential function e^z for the case where $c = e$. We now state the problem: With c^z defined by (b), evaluate c^z for $c = 1 + \sqrt{3}i$ and $z = 2 - 5i$.

11. Obtain, in Cartesian form, the principal values of $\log z$ and $\sqrt{z}$ for each given z.

*(a) $-3i$	(b) 2	(c) -4
(d) $2 - i$	(e) $1 + \sqrt{3}i$	(f) $-1 - i$
(g) $-5i$	(h) $4 - 2i$	

12. (a) Derive (27). (b) Derive (28).
(c) Derive (29).

13. (*Inverse of sine function*) We define the inverse of the sine function

$$w(z) = \sin^{-1} z \tag{a}$$

such that $z = \sin w$.

(a) Writing the latter as

$$z = \frac{e^{iw} - e^{-iw}}{2i},$$

show that $e^{iw} = iz + (1 - z^2)^{1/2}$, and hence that

$$\sin^{-1} z = -i \log\,[iz + (1 - z^2)^{1/2}]. \tag{b}$$

(b) Observe that $\sin^{-1} z$ is multivalued because of the $(1 - z^2)^{1/2}$ *and* because of the log. Specifically, for each value of $z\,(\neq \pm 1)$, the $(1 - z^2)^{1/2}$ gives two values; then, for each of these values, the log gives an infinite set of values. To illustrate this point, show that

$$\sin^{-1}\left(\frac{1}{2}\right) = \frac{\pi}{6} + 2k\pi \quad \text{or} \quad \frac{5\pi}{6} + 2k\pi$$

for $k = 0, \pm 1, \pm 2, \ldots$.
(c) Determine all possible values of $\sin^{-1} 2$.
(d) Determine all possible values of $\sin^{-1}(2i)$.

14. (*Inverses of other trigonometric functions*) Proceeding as in Exercise 13, derive the following formulas.

(a) $\cos^{-1} z = -i \log\,[z + (z^2 - 1)^{1/2}]$

(b) $\tan^{-1} z = -\dfrac{i}{2} \log \dfrac{i - z}{i + z}$

(c) $\cot^{-1} z = -\dfrac{i}{2} \log \dfrac{z + i}{z - i}$

15. (*Inverses of hyperbolic functions*) Proceeding as in Exercise 13, derive the following formulas.

(a) $\sinh^{-1} z = \log\,[z + (1 + z^2)^{1/2}]$

(b) $\cosh^{-1} z = \log\,[z + (z^2 - 1)^{1/2}]$

(c) $\tanh^{-1} z = \dfrac{1}{2} \log \dfrac{1 + z}{1 - z}$

(d) $\coth^{-1} z = \dfrac{1}{2} \log \dfrac{z + 1}{z - 1}$

16. If $f(x)$ is a complex-valued function of x (such as e^{ix}), then

$$\begin{aligned} \int f(x)\,dx &= \int [\mathrm{Re}\,f(x) + i\,\mathrm{Im}\,f(x)]\,dx \\ &= \int \mathrm{Re}\,f(x)\,dx + i \int \mathrm{Im}\,f(x)\,dx, \end{aligned} \tag{a}$$

where the second equality follows from the *linearity* of integration. Next, it can be seen from (a) that

$$\mathrm{Re} \int f(x)\,dx = \int \mathrm{Re}\,f(x)\,dx, \tag{b}$$

$$\mathrm{Im} \int f(x)\,dx = \int \mathrm{Im}\,f(x)\,dx. \tag{c}$$

These results can be used to simplify the evaluation of certain integrals.

(a) Evaluate $\int_0^\infty e^{-x} \cos ax\, dx$ by writing

$$\int_0^\infty e^{-x} \cos ax\, dx = \text{Re} \int_0^\infty e^{-(1-ia)x}\, dx,$$

evaluating the (simpler) integral on the right-hand side, and then taking its real part.

(b) Evaluate $\int_0^\infty e^{-x} \sin ax\, dx$ using the same idea as in part (a).

(c) As a warning against being too cavalier in using Re and Im, we ask you to show that the statement $\int_a^b \sin mx \sin nx\, dx = \text{Im} \int_a^b e^{i(m+n)x}\, dx$ is *incorrect*.

17. A method sometimes used to obtain a particular solution $x_p(t)$ of the differential equation

$$\ddot{x} + c\dot{x} + kx = F \cos \omega t, \tag{a}$$

where c, k, F, ω are constants and dots denote d/dt, is to consider instead the equation

$$\ddot{v} + c\dot{v} + kv = Fe^{i\omega t}, \tag{b}$$

to solve for a particular solution $v_p(t)$ by the method of undetermined coefficients, and then to obtain $x_p(t)$ from

$$x_p(t) = \text{Re } v_p(t). \tag{c}$$

(a) Show why the method is valid. *Hint:* It may be more convenient to express (a) in operator form as $Lx = F \cos \omega t$.

(b) Use the proposed method to solve for $x_p(t)$.

(c) To see the advantage of the proposed method, solve (a) for $x_p(t)$ directly, again using undetermined coefficients.

(d) Obtain a particular solution $x_p(t)$ of

$$\ddot{x} + c\dot{x} + kx = F \sin \omega t$$

by considering instead

$$\ddot{v} + c\dot{v} + kv = Fe^{i\omega t}.$$

DIFFERENTIAL CALCULUS AND ANALYTIC FUNCTIONS 18.5

As in the development of the real-variable theory, we next define the *limit* of a function, *continuity,* and the *derivative*. In fact, differentiability (more precisely, the closely related concept of *analyticity*) lies at the heart of complex variable theory and will be crucial throughout our subsequent study of conformal mapping, the complex integral calculus, and series expansions.

Let z_0 be an interior point in the domain of definition of $f(z)$. We say that *the* ***limit*** *of $f(z)$, as z approaches z_0, is L,*

$$\lim_{z \to z_0} f(z) = L \tag{1}$$

[or, equivalently, we write $f(z) \to L$ as $z \to z_0$] if to each $\epsilon > 0$ (no matter how small) there corresponds a $\delta > 0$ such that

$$|f(z) - L| < \epsilon \tag{2}$$

for all z's satisfying $0 < |z - z_0| < \delta$. That is (Fig. 18.17), we can keep the function values $f(z)$ arbitrarily close to L (namely, within the ϵ-disk "bull's-eye") by keeping z sufficiently close to z_0 (namely, within $0 < |z - z_0| < \delta$). Observe carefully that because $\mathbf{0} < |z - z_0| < \delta$, the value of f *at* $z = z_0$ is not at all germane. Specifically, it need *not* be true that $f(z_0) = L$ for (1) to hold; (1) merely states that $f(z)$ *approaches* L as z *approaches* z_0. However, if in addition to having $\lim_{z \to z_0} f(z) = L$ we also have $f(z_0) = L$, we say that the function $f(z)$ is **continuous** at z_0.

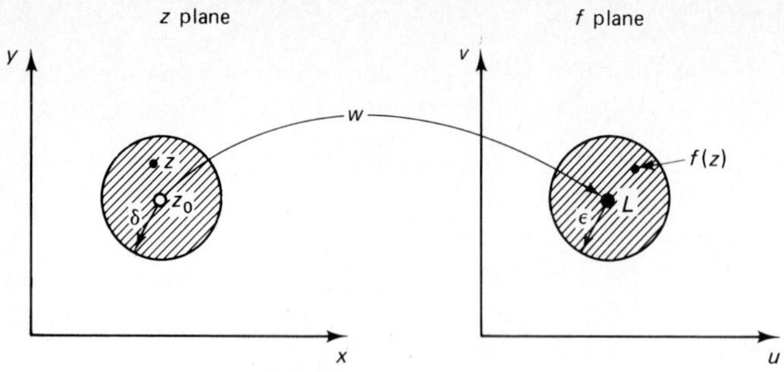

Fig. 18.17 Limit of $f(z)$ as $z \to z_0$.

EXAMPLE 1 Show that

$$\lim_{z \to i} (z^2 + iz) = -2. \tag{3}$$

To do so, we need to show that to each $\epsilon > 0$ (no matter how small) there corresponds a $\delta > 0$ such that $|(z^2 + iz) - (-2)| < \epsilon$ for all z's in $0 < |z - i| < \delta$. No doubt, the smaller we choose, ϵ, the smaller δ will need to be. Thus $\delta = \delta(\epsilon)$, and our objective is to put forward a suitable $\delta(\epsilon)$ in order to verify (3). Since

$$\begin{aligned} |z^2 + iz + 2| &= |(z - i)(z + 2i)| = |z - i|\,|z + 2i| \\ &= |z - i|\,|(z - i) + 3i| \le |z - i|(|z - i| + 3), \end{aligned} \tag{4}$$

where the last step follows from the triangle inequality, $|z^2 + iz + 2| < \epsilon$ will be satisfied if

$$|z - i|(|z - i| + 3) < \epsilon. \tag{5}$$

Now, solving $x(x + 3) = \epsilon$ we obtain the positive solution $x = (-3 + \sqrt{9 + 4\epsilon})/2$, so evidently (5) will be satisfied if

$$|z - i| < \frac{-3 + \sqrt{9 + 4\epsilon}}{2}. \tag{6}$$

In summary, we have shown that given any $\epsilon > 0$, we will have $|(z^2 + iz) - (-2)| < \epsilon$ for all z's in $0 < |z - i| < \delta(\epsilon)$ if we choose

$$\delta(\epsilon) = \frac{-3 + \sqrt{9 + 4\epsilon}}{2}, \tag{7}$$

or smaller; hence the truth of (3) is established. In fact, it is also true that the value of $z^2 + iz$ *at* $z = i$ is -2, so the function $z^2 + iz$ is continuous at $z = i$. Similarly, one can show that it is continuous *everywhere* in the z plane. ◀

We do not wish to dwell on limits and continuity too long, since the focus of this section is differentiability. Thus, let us merely note that the functions z^n ($n = 0, 1, 2, \ldots$), e^z, $\sin z$, $\cos z$, $\sinh z$, and $\cosh z$, for example, are continuous everywhere in the z plane; the function $1/z$, for instance, is continuous for all z except $z = 0$, because $\lim_{z \to 0} 1/z$ does not exist. We are now in a position to define the derivative df/dz. In doing so, we stay as close as possible to the real-variable definition. Thus, if z_0 is an interior point of the domain of definition of f, we define the **derivative** of f, at z_0, as

$$f'(z_0) \equiv \lim_{\Delta z \to 0} \frac{f(z_0 + \Delta z) - f(z_0)}{\Delta z}, \tag{8}$$

provided, of course, that the limit exists. Equivalently, and sometimes more conveniently,

$$f'(z_0) \equiv \lim_{z \to z_0} \frac{f(z) - f(z_0)}{z - z_0}. \tag{9}$$

Now, recall that in the real-variable case, where

$$f'(x_0) \equiv \lim_{x \to x_0} \frac{f(x) - f(x_0)}{x - x_0}, \tag{10}$$

the limit value needs to be independent of the way in which x approaches x_0. For example, for the case shown in Fig. 18.18, $f'(x_0)$ does not exist for $x_0 = 1$ because the limiting value obtained when $x \to x_0$ from the left (namely, 1) is different from the limiting value obtained when $x \to x_0$ from the right (namely, -1). In fact, x does not need to approach x_0 from one side or the other. For example, the sequence $x_n = x_0 + (-1)^n e^{-n}$ $(n = 0, 1, 2, \ldots)$ approaches x_0 as $n \to \infty$, but not "one-sidedly."

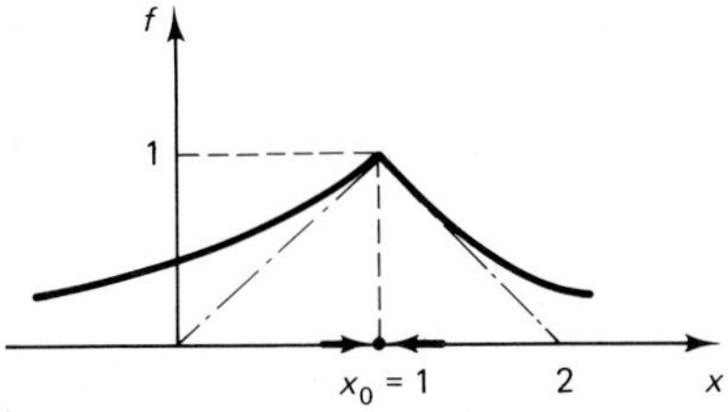

Fig. 18.18 Approach to x_0.

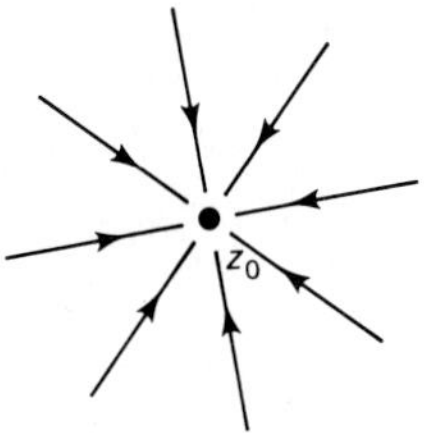

(a)

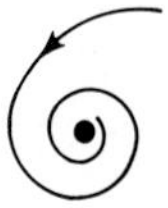

(b)

Fig. 18.19 Approach to z_0.

Analogously, in the complex case (9), we insist that the limit exist uniquely, independent of the way in which z approaches z_0. (Note that we avoid saying "independent of the direction of approach" because that wording seems to limit the mode of approach to linear, as in Fig. 18.19a, whereas it may be spiral, for example, as in Fig. 18.19b. Even more so, we avoid saying "as z approaches z_0 from all directions." If this point is unclear, it should suffice to imagine Stephen Leacock's Lord Ronald, who ". . . said nothing; he flung himself from the room, flung himself upon his horse and rode madly off in all directions."

Let us illustrate the definition (8).

EXAMPLE 2 If $f(z) = z^2$, then [dropping the subscripted zero in (8)]

$$f'(z) = \lim_{\Delta z \to 0} \frac{(z + \Delta z)^2 - z^2}{\Delta z} = \lim_{\Delta z \to 0} (2z + \Delta z) = 2z \tag{11}$$

so that $f(z) = z^2$ is differentiable for *all* z, and $f'(z) = 2z$. [The last step, in (11), should be quite clear even if we do not go to the trouble of putting forward a $\delta(\epsilon)$ relation, as we did in Example 1.] ◀

Recalling the real-variable result $(d/dx)(x^2) = 2x$, and the similarity between (9) and (10), it is not surprising that $(d/dz)(z^2)$ turned out to be $2z$. Similarly, one finds that $(d/dz)(e^z) = e^z$, $(d/dz)(\sin z) = \cos z$, and so on (Exercise 10). Furthermore, the various familiar rules of differentiation carry over to the complex case. For example, we have

$$[f(z) + g(z)]' = f'(z) + g'(z), \tag{12}$$

$$[f(z)g(z)]' = f'(z)g(z) + f(z)g'(z), \tag{13}$$

and the chain rule

$$\frac{d}{dz} f(g(z)) = f'(g(z))g'(z), \tag{14}$$

where $f'(g(z))$ is df/dg. Furthermore, differentiability implies continuity, and l'Hospital's rule holds, as in the real case (Exercises 7 and 8).

From the examples cited above, one may wonder how $f(z)$ can *fail* to be differentiable.

EXAMPLE 3 $f(z) = 1/z$ is not differentiable at $z = 0$ because it is not continuous there. That is, since differentiability implies continuity, continuity is a *necessary* condition for differentiability. For all $z \neq 0$, however, $f'(z)$ exists (i.e., f *is* differentiable) and equals $-1/z^2$. ◀

EXAMPLE 4 Whereas $f(z) = 1/z$ fails to be differentiable only at a single point,

$$f(z) = \bar{z}$$

is not differentiable *anywhere*. For observe that

$$\frac{f(z + \Delta z) - f(z)}{\Delta z} = \frac{\overline{z + \Delta z} - \bar{z}}{\Delta z} = \frac{\overline{\Delta z}}{\Delta z} = \frac{\Delta x - i\Delta y}{\Delta x + i\Delta y}. \tag{15}$$

For a horizontal approach to z we have $\Delta y = 0$, and the limit of the difference quotient (15), as $\Delta x \to 0$, is $+1$. For a vertical approach, on the other hand, $\Delta x = 0$, and the limit of the difference quotient (15), as $\Delta y \to 0$, is -1. Since a unique limit (of $[f(z + \Delta z) - f(z)]/\Delta z$, as $\Delta z \to 0$) does not exist, it follows that $f(z) = \bar{z}$ is not differentiable anywhere in the z plane.* ◀

Because differentiability turns out to be crucial in the study of functions of a complex variable, it will be important to find a test that can be applied to a given function $f(z) = u(x, y) + iv(x, y)$ to see if it is differentiable. Toward that end, let us first set $\Delta y = 0$ in $\Delta z = \Delta x + i\Delta y$, so that $\Delta z = \Delta x$. That is, let $z_0 + \Delta z$ approach z_0 parallel to the x axis. Then the limit of the difference quotient in (8) becomes

$$\lim_{\Delta x \to 0} \frac{[u(x_0 + \Delta x, y_0) + iv(x_0 + \Delta x, y_0)] - [u(x_0, y_0) + iv(x_0, y_0)]}{\Delta x}$$

* Generalizing this example, Saff and Snider show that in $f(z) = u(x, y) + iv(x, y)$ it is critical that the x's and y's on the right-hand side occur in the combination $x + iy$, so that $f(z)$ can be expressed in terms of z alone without involving $\bar{z}$, if $f(z)$ is to be differentiable.

$$= \lim_{\Delta x\to 0} \frac{[u(x_0 + \Delta x, y_0) - u(x_0, y_0)}{\Delta x} + i \lim_{\Delta x\to 0} \frac{v(x_0 + \Delta x, y_0) - v(x_0, y_0)}{\Delta x} \tag{16}$$

$$= \frac{\partial u}{\partial x} + i\frac{\partial y}{\partial x}.$$

Alternatively, let us set $\Delta x = 0$ in $\Delta z = \Delta x + i\,\Delta y$, so that $\Delta z = i\,\Delta y$. That is, let $z_0 + \Delta z$ approach z_0 parallel to the y axis. This time, the limit of the difference quotient in (8) becomes

$$\lim_{\Delta y\to 0} \frac{[u(x_0, y_0 + \Delta y) + iv(x_0, y_0 + \Delta y)] - [u(x_0, y_0) + iv(x_0, y_0)]}{i\,\Delta y}$$
$$= \frac{1}{i}\frac{\partial u}{\partial y} + \frac{\partial v}{\partial y} = \frac{\partial v}{\partial y} - i\frac{\partial u}{\partial y}. \tag{17}$$

Since the value of the limit in (8) is to be independent of the path of approach, as emphasized above, the results in (16) and (17) must agree if f is to be differentiable at z_0, i.e., if $f'(z_0)$ is to exist. Thus, equating the right-hand sides of (16) and (17) shows that $u(x, y)$ and $v(x, y)$ must satisfy the relations

$$\boxed{\frac{\partial u}{\partial x} = \frac{\partial v}{\partial y}, \qquad \frac{\partial u}{\partial y} = -\frac{\partial v}{\partial x}} \tag{18}$$

at the point in question. The latter are known as the **Cauchy–Riemann equations.*** Clearly, satisfaction of these equations is *necessary* for differentiability, but may not be sufficient since they have been obtained by considering only two possible paths of approach to the point z_0. (In fact, they are *not* sufficient, as follows from the example in Exercise 9.) However, let us suppose, further, that u, v, and the four partial derivatives in (18) are *continuous* in some neighborhood of z_0.† Consider an arbitrary approach to the point z_0, as indicated schematically in Fig. 18.20 by the curve C, and let us denote (x_0, y_0) and (x, y) as P_0 and P, respectively, for brevity. From (8),

$$f'(z_0) = \lim_{\Delta z\to 0} \frac{[u(P) + iv(P)] - [u(P_0) + iv(P_0)]}{\Delta z}. \tag{19}$$

Now, since u and v have been assumed to be C^1 in some neighborhood of P_0, we can use the mean value theorem (page 233) to express

$$u(P) - u(P_0) = u_x(Q_1)\,\Delta x + u_y(Q_1)\,\Delta y \tag{20a}$$
$$v(P) - v(P_0) = v_x(Q_2)\,\Delta x + v_y(Q_2)\,\Delta y, \tag{20b}$$

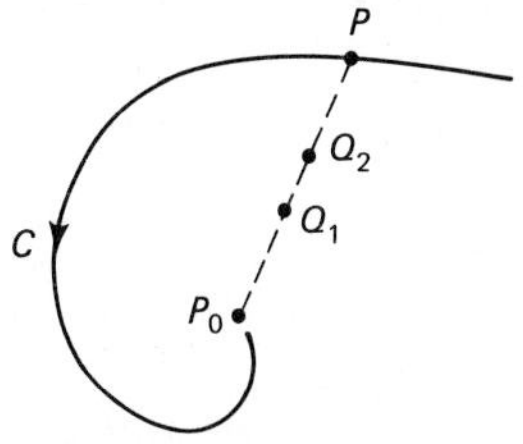

Fig. 18.20 Arbitrary approach to z_0.

* Cauchy is pronounced Kōshē.

† In terms or the C^n notation defined on page 233, we say that u and v are C^1 in some neighborhood of z_0.

where the points Q_1, Q_2 lie somewhere on the straight line between P_0 and P—for example, as we have shown in Fig. 18.20. Using (20), we may restate (19) as

$$f'(z_0) = \lim_{\Delta z \to 0} \frac{u_x(Q_1)\,\Delta x + u_y(Q_1)\,\Delta y + i[v_x(Q_2)\,\Delta x + v_y(Q_2)\,\Delta y]}{\Delta z}.$$

Finally, using the fact that Q_1 and Q_2 approach P_0 as $\Delta z \to 0$, let us rewrite the last result as

$$\begin{aligned} f'(z_0) &= \lim_{\Delta z \to 0} \left\{ \frac{u_x(P_0)\,\Delta x + u_y(P_0)\,\Delta y + i[v_x(P_0)\,\Delta x + v_y(P_0)\,\Delta y]}{\Delta z} + \delta \right\} \\ &= \lim_{\Delta z \to 0} \left\{ \frac{u_x(P_0)(\Delta x + i\,\Delta y) - iu_y(P_0)(\Delta x + i\,\Delta y)}{\Delta z} + \delta \right\} \\ &= u_x(P_0) - iu_y(P_0) + \lim_{\Delta z \to 0} \delta, \end{aligned} \tag{21}$$

where we have used the Cauchy–Riemann relations to obtain the second equality, and where

$$\begin{aligned} \delta = {} & [u_x(Q_1) - u_x(P_0)]\frac{\Delta x}{\Delta z} + [u_y(Q_1) - u_y(P_0)]\frac{\Delta y}{\Delta z} \\ & + i[v_x(Q_2) - v_x(P_0)]\frac{\Delta x}{\Delta z} + i[v_y(Q_2) - v_y(P_0)]\frac{\Delta y}{\Delta z}. \end{aligned} \tag{22}$$

From the continuity of the four partial derivatives, it follows that each bracketed quantity in (22) tends to zero as $\Delta z \to 0$. Furthermore, $|\Delta x| \le |\Delta z|$ and $|\Delta y| \le |\Delta z|$ give $|\Delta x/\Delta z| \le 1$ and $|\Delta y/\Delta z| \le 1$. Thus $\lim_{\Delta z \to 0} \delta = 0$, and (21) gives the result

$$f'(z_0) = u_x(P_0) - iu_y(P_0) = u_x(x_0, y_0) - iu_y(x_0, y_0), \tag{23}$$

independent of the manner of approach of P to P_0. From the foregoing results we extract the following:

> ***Theorem 1*** *Necessary, Sufficient Conditions for Differentiability*
> Let $f(z) = u(x, y) + iv(x, y)$ be defined throughout some neighborhood of a point $z_0 = x_0 + iy_0$. For f to be differentiable at z_0
>
> **(i)** it is **necessary** that the Cauchy–Riemann equations (18) be satisfied at x_0, y_0,
> **(ii)** it is **sufficient** that u and v be C^1 in some neighborhood of z_0 and that the Cauchy–Riemann equations (18) be satisfied at z_0.
>
> If f is differentiable, then f' is given by any of these four equivalent expressions:
>
> $$f' = u_x + iv_x = v_y - iu_y = u_x - iu_y = v_y + iv_x. \tag{24}$$

Now suppose that $f(z)$ is differentiable at z_0. If, in addition, it is differentiable throughout some neighborhood of z_0, we say that it is **analytic** at z_0; if it is not analytic at z_0, it is **singular** there; and if f is analytic at each point of a region D, we say that f is analytic in D. (The terms *regular* and *holomorphic* are also used in place of analytic.)

How can a function $f(z)$ be differentiable at a point and yet *fail* to be differentiable in some neighborhood of the point? Well, consider the following example.

EXAMPLE 5. Consider

$$f(z) = |z|^2 = z\bar{z}. \tag{25}$$

Then $f = (x^2 + y^2) + 0i$, so $u = x^2 + y^2$ and $v = 0$. Since

$$u_x = 2x, \qquad u_y = 2y,$$

$$v_x = 0, \qquad v_y = 0,$$

we see that u, v, u_x, u_y, v_x, v_y are continuous everywhere. Moreover, $u_x = v_y$ is satisfied at all points on $x = 0$ (the y axis) and $u_y = -v_x$ is satisfied at all points on $y = 0$ (the x axis), so both Cauchy–Riemann equations are satisfied *only* at the origin. Thus $f(z) = |z|^2$ is differentiable *only* at $z = 0$ and hence it is analytic *nowhere*. ◀

Such behavior, however, is hardly typical of the functions that we are apt to encounter, most of which are either analytic everywhere or almost everywhere. Functions that are analytic everywhere (i.e., at each point z in the z plane) are said to be **entire.**

EXAMPLE 6 Consider

$$f(z) = \sin z = \sin x \cosh y + i \cos x \sinh y. \tag{26}$$

Then

$$u_x = \cos x \cosh y, \qquad u_y = \sin x \sinh y,$$

$$v_x = -\sin x \sinh y, \qquad v_y = \cos x \cosh y.$$

Clearly, u, v, u_x, u_y, v_x, v_y are continuous everywhere, and $u_x = v_y$ and $u_y = -v_x$ everywhere, so that, according to Theorem 1, $f(z) = \sin z$ is analytic everywhere, i.e., it is an entire function. From (24),

$$f'(z) = \cos x \cosh y - i \sin x \sinh y. \tag{27}$$

To reexpress the latter in terms of z we could substitute $x = (z + \bar{z})/2$ and $y = (z - \bar{z})/2i$ and simplify. The $\bar{z}$'s would cancel and we would obtain $f'(z) = \cos z$. However, in the present case it is simpler to notice, from (27), that

$$f'(z) = \cos x \cosh y - \sin x \sin (iy) = \cos (x + iy) = \cos z. \tag{28}$$

In fact, practically speaking, we could have depended on the familiar real-variable result $(d/dx) \sin x = \cos x$ to tell us that $(d/dz) \sin z = \cos z$, but the point of this example was to illustrate Theorem 1 and the concept of analyticity. ◀

Similarly, $\cos z$, e^z, $\sinh z$, $\cosh z$, and polynomial functions of z, for example, are entire functions. More complicated cases can be built from these as composite functions. Consider, for example, $f(z) = e^{\sin z}$. Recalling that

$$\frac{d}{dz} f(g(z)) = \frac{df}{dg}\frac{dg}{dz}, \quad \text{we have} \quad \frac{d}{dz} f = \left(\frac{d}{dg} e^{g}\right)\left(\frac{d}{dz} \sin z\right).$$

Each derivative on the right-hand side exists because the exponential and sine functions are known to be entire; thus $f(z) = e^{\sin z}$ is entire, too, and $(d/dz)e^{\sin z} = e^{\sin z} \cos z$.

The function $1/z$ is analytic for all $z \neq 0$. At $z = 0$ the derivative

$$\frac{d}{dz}\frac{1}{z} = -\frac{1}{z^2}$$

fails to exist, so $z = 0$ is a singular point of $f(z) = 1/z$. Alternatively, $z = 0$ is necessarily a singular point of $1/z$ because the latter is not continuous there.

In some cases f is expressed more conveniently in terms of the polar variables r, θ as

$$f(z) = u(r, \theta) + iv(r, \theta). \tag{29}$$

The Cauchy–Riemann equations are then found (Exercise 12) to be

$$\frac{\partial u}{\partial r} = \frac{1}{r}\frac{\partial y}{\partial \theta}, \qquad \frac{\partial v}{\partial r} = -\frac{1}{r}\frac{\partial u}{\partial \theta}, \tag{30}$$

and the derivative of f is

$$\begin{aligned} f'(z) &= e^{-i\theta}(u_r + iv_r) = \frac{e^{-i\theta}}{r}(v_\theta - iu_\theta) \\ &= e^{-i\theta}\left(u_r - \frac{i}{r}u_\theta\right) = e^{-i\theta}\left(\frac{1}{r}v_\theta + iv_r\right). \end{aligned} \tag{31}$$

EXAMPLE 7. Consider the principal value of $\log z$, defined by

$$\log z = \ln r + i\theta, \tag{32}$$

where $0 < r < \infty$ and $0 \leq \theta < 2\pi$. That is, the domain of definition of $\log z$ is the cut plane shown in Fig. 18.21. In this case,

$$\begin{gathered} u(r, \theta) = \ln r, \qquad v(r, \theta) = \theta, \\ u_r = \frac{1}{r}, \quad u_\theta = 0, \quad v_r = 0, \quad v_\theta = 1, \end{gathered} \tag{33}$$

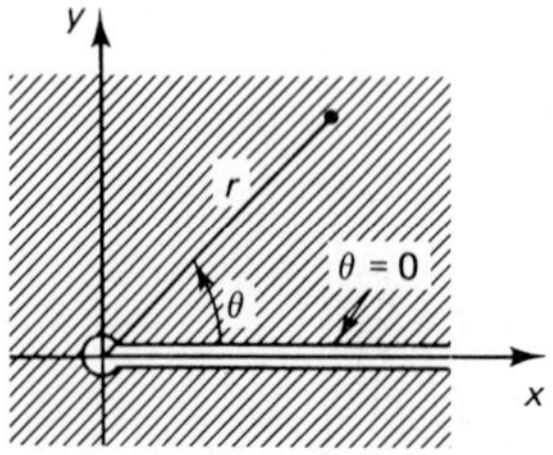

Fig. 18.21 Domain of definition of principal value of log z.

so we see that u, v, u_r, u_θ, v_r, v_θ are all continuous in the cut plane, and that the Cauchy–Riemann equations (30) are satisfied everywhere in the cut plane (which does *not* include the origin). Thus $f(z)$ is analytic everywhere in the cut plane, and (31) gives

$$f'(z) = e^{-i\theta}\left(\frac{1}{r} + i0\right) = \frac{1}{re^{i\theta}} = \frac{1}{z}. \quad ◀$$

As the final item in this section, we establish an important and interesting link between analytic function theory and partial differential equations—specifically, the Laplace equation in two dimensions. If $f(z) = u(x, y) + iv(x, y)$ is analytic in some domain D, then

$$u_x = v_y \quad \text{and} \quad u_y = -v_x \tag{34}$$

in D. Taking $\partial/\partial x$ of the first and $\partial/\partial y$ of the second,

$$u_{xx} = v_{yx} \quad \text{and} \quad u_{yy} = -v_{xy}. \tag{35}$$

Now, we will find, in Section 20.5, that if f is analytic in D, the partial derivatives of u and v of *all* orders exists and are continuous in D. It then follows from Theorem 1 on page 220 that $v_{yx} = v_{xy}$, so that (35) gives $u_{xx} + u_{yy} = 0$ in D. Similarly, taking $\partial/\partial y$ of the first equation in (34), and $\partial/\partial x$ of the second, leads to $v_{xx} + v_{yy} = 0$. Functions that satisfy Laplace's equation and are C^2 are called **harmonic functions,** so we have the following result.

***Theorem 2** Harmonic Functions*

If $f(z) = u(x, y) + iv(x, y)$ is analytic in a domain D, then u and v are harmonic in D; i.e., they are C^2 and they satisfy the Laplace equations

$$\nabla^2 u = u_{xx} + u_{yy} = 0, \tag{36a}$$

$$\nabla^2 v = v_{xx} + v_{yy} = 0 \tag{36b}$$

in D.

Observe that if $f(z) = u(x, y) + iv(x, y)$ is analytic, the harmonic functions u and v are a related pair since they are related through the Cauchy–Riemann equations. To call attention to this relationship, we refer to them as *conjugate* harmonic functions. Given one harmonic function, conjugate harmonic functions can be inferred from the Cauchy–Riemann equations.

EXAMPLE 8 It is easily verified that the function

$$u(x, y) = 3xy^2 - x^3 \tag{37}$$

is harmonic in the entire z plane. To find a conjugate harmonic function $v(x, y)$ we rely on the relations $u_x = v_y$ and $u_y = -v_x$. Thus

$$v_x = -6xy, \tag{38a}$$

$$v_y = 3y^2 - 3x^2. \tag{38b}$$

Integrating (38a) partially, with respect to x, we obtain

$$v(x, y) = \int -6xy\, \partial x = -3x^2y + A(y), \tag{39}$$

where $A(y)$ is (thus far) arbitrary. Then, by putting (39) into (38b), we obtain

$$-3x^2 + A'(y) = 3y^2 - 3x^2,$$

whence $A(y) = y^3 + c$ for any constant c. Thus conjugate harmonic functions corresponding to the given u are

$$v(x, y) = y^3 - 3x^2y + c \qquad (c \text{ arbitrary}). \tag{40}$$

Further, one finds that the analytic function

$$f(z) = u + iv = (3xy^2 - x^3) + i(y^3 - 3x^2y + c) \tag{41}$$

is actually $f(z) = -z^3 + ic$ [as one might suspect by noting that for $y = 0$ (41) gives $f(x) = -x^3 + ic$.]. ◀

More generally, it can be shown (Exercise 17) that given one harmonic function (u or v), a conjugate harmonic function (v or u) can always be determined (to within an arbitrary additive constant) so that $f = u + iv$ is analytic.

In summary, we began this section by defining and discussing the differentiability of a function $f(z)$. However, differentiability at a single point will prove to be much less significant than differentiability throughout a whole region, so we proceeded to introduce the notion of analyticity. In a sense, all the rest of Part V amounts to a study of the consequences of a function's analyticity or its lack of analyticity. Finally, in our closing discussion of harmonic functions we discovered an important and useful link between analytic function theory and the two-dimensional Laplace equation, i.e., the realm of potential theory, studied earlier in Chapter 15.

18.5 EXERCISES

1. Show that $\lim_{z\to 1} 3iz = 3i$, by referring to our definition of *limit* and actually putting forth a suitable δ. Specifically, show that $\delta = \epsilon/3$ at *most*. Further, show that $f(z) = 3iz$ is continuous at $z = 1$.

2. (a) Show that $\lim_{z\to 0} z^2 = 0$ by referring to our definition of *limit* and actually putting forth a suitable δ. Further, show that $f(z) = z^2$ is continuous at $z = 0$.
(b) Similarly, show that $\lim_{z\to z_0} z^2 = z_0^2$, and show that $f(z) = z^2$ is continuous for all z.

3. Prove that if $\lim_{z\to z_0} f(z) = A$ and $\lim_{z\to z_0} g(z) = B$, then
(a) $\lim_{z\to z_0} [f(z) + g(z)] = A + B$
(b) $\lim_{z\to z_0} f(z)g(z) = AB$
(c) $\lim_{z\to z_0} \dfrac{f(z)}{g(z)} = \dfrac{A}{B}$ if $B \neq 0$

4. If $f(x)$ is continuous for all (real) x, does it follow that $f(z)$ is continuous everywhere in the z plane? Explain.

5. Use the difference quotient formula (8) to evaluate $f'(z)$, as we did in Example 2.
(a) $f(z) = z^3$
(b) $f(z) = 1/z \ (z \neq 0)$
(c) $f(z) = 1/z^2 \quad (z \neq 0)$
(d) $f(z) = 1/(z + 1) \quad (z \neq -1)$

6. Use the difference quotient formula (8) to prove
(a) equation (12)
(b) equation (13)
(c) equation (14)

7. Prove that if $f(z)$ is differentiable at z_0, it must be continuous there. *Hint:* Write

$$f(z) = \frac{f(z) - f(z_0)}{z - z_0}(z - z_0) + f(z_0).$$

8. (*l'Hospital's rule*) Prove l'Hospital's rule, namely, that if $f(z)$ and $g(z)$ are differentiable at z_0, with $f(z_0) = g(z_0) = 0$ and $g'(z_0) \neq 0$, then

$$\lim_{z \to z_0} \frac{f(z)}{g(z)} = \frac{f'(z_0)}{g'(z_0)}. \tag{a}$$

9. (*Insufficiency of Cauchy–Riemann conditions*) We have seen that the Cauchy–Riemann conditions are necessary for differentiability. The example

$$f(z) = \begin{cases} \dfrac{(x^3 - y^3) + i(x^3 + y^3)}{x^2 + y^2}, & z \neq 0 \\ 0, & z = 0, \end{cases}$$

due to S. Pollard (1928), shows that they are *not*, however, sufficient. Verify that statement by showing that the Cauchy–Riemann conditions are satisfied at $z = 0$ but that f is not differentiable at that point.

10. Given $f(z)$, use (24) to obtain $f'(z)$. Express the answer in terms of z.

*(a) $\cos z$ (b) e^z
(c) $\sinh z$ (d) $\cosh z$
(e) $\dfrac{1}{z}$ $(z \neq 0)$ (f) $\dfrac{1}{z+2}$ $(z \neq -2)$
(g) $\dfrac{z+1}{z-1}$ $(z \neq 1)$

11. Given $f(z)$, determine $f'(z)$, where it exists, and state where f is analytic and where it is not.

(a) $(1 - 2z^3)^5$ (b) $\dfrac{x + iy}{x^2 + y^2}$
(c) $|z| \sin z$ *(d) $\dfrac{1}{z^2 + 3iz - 2}$
(e) $\dfrac{1}{z^3 + 1}$ (f) $x + i \sin y$

12. (*Cauchy–Riemann equations in polar coordinates*) Derive the Cauchy–Riemann equations (30)
(a) by carrying out the limit in (8) *Hint:* First let $\Delta z \to 0$ along the constant-θ line through z_0, and then let $\Delta z \to 0$ along the constant-r line through z_0.
(b) by entering the change of variables $x = r \cos \theta$, $y = r \sin \theta$ in (18)

13. Determine where these functions are differentiable and where they are analytic, by checking for satisfaction of the Cauchy–Riemann equations and for continuity of u, v and their first-order partial derivatives.

(a) $f(z) = z^{100}$
(b) $f(z) = \sqrt{z}$, defined by the branch cut shown in Fig. 18.21
(c) $f(z) = 1/\sqrt{z}$, where the $\sqrt{z}$ is defined by the branch cut shown in Fig. 18.21

14. Prove that
(a) $f(z)$ and $\overline{f(z)}$ can both be analytic, in a given region, if and only if $f(z)$ is a constant
(b) if $f(z)$ is analytic in a region D, and $f'(z) = 0$ in D, then $f(z)$ is a constant

15. Determine whether or not the given function u is harmonic and, if so, in what region. If it is, find the most general conjugate function v and corresponding analytic function $f(z)$. Express f in terms of z.

*(a) $e^x \cos y$ (b) $e^{2x} \sin 2y$
(c) $x^3 - 3xy^2$ (d) $r^3 \sin 3\theta$
(e) $r^2 \cos 2\theta + 4$ (f) r
(g) $x \cos 2x \cosh 2y + y \sin 2x \sinh 2y$

16. (*Orthogonality of u = constant and v = constant curves*) (a) Prove that if $f(z) = u + iv$ is analytic in a region D, then the two families of level curves u = constant and v = constant are mutually orthogonal at all points in D at which $f'(z) \neq 0$.
(b) Illustrate the idea contained in part (a) by sketching the u and v level curves for the case $f(z) = z = x + iy$.
(c) Repeat part (b), for the case $f(z) = z^2 = (x^2 - y^2) + i2xy$.
(d) Repeat part (b), for the case

$$f(z) = \frac{1}{z} = \frac{x}{x^2 + y^2} - i\frac{v}{x^2 + y^2}.$$

17. (*Existence of conjugate harmonic function*) Let $u(x, y)$ be a given function that is harmonic in the rectangle $x_1 \leq x \leq x_2$, $y_1 \leq y \leq y_2$. Prove that there exists a conjugate harmonic function $v(x, y)$ in the rectangle $x_1 < x < x_2$, $y_1 < y < y_2$, say D, such that $f = u + iv$ is analytic in D. Show, further, that $v(x, y)$ is uniquely determined, to within an arbitrary additive constant. *Hint:* Infer from the Cauchy–Riemann equation $\partial u/\partial x = \partial v/\partial y$ that

$$v(x, y) = \int_{y_0}^{y} \frac{\partial u}{\partial x}(x, y')\partial y' + A(x)$$

and use the second Cauchy–Riemann equation and the fact that u is harmonic to obtain

$$A(x) = -\int_{x_0}^{x} \frac{\partial u}{\partial y}(x', y_0)\, dx',$$

where (x_0, y_0) is any point in D. Verify, with the help of the Leibniz rule (Theorem 1, page 346), that

$$v(x, y) = \int_{y_0}^{y} \frac{\partial u}{\partial x}(x, y')\, \partial y' - \int_{x_0}^{x} \frac{\partial u}{\partial y}(x', y_0)\, dx' \quad \text{(a)}$$

does indeed satisfy the Cauchy–Riemann equation and is harmonic in D. Next, show that (a) is equivalent to the line integral representation

$$v(x, y) = \int_{(x_0, y_0)}^{(x,y)} \left[-\frac{\partial u}{\partial y}(x', y')\, dx' + \frac{\partial u}{\partial y}(x', y')\, dy' \right] \quad \text{(b)}$$

over any path in D, and conclude from (b) that v is determined only to within an arbitrary additive constant. *Note:* Similarly, one can show that given a harmonic function v, there exists a conjugate harmonic function u which can be determined to within an arbitrary additive constant.

Conformal Mapping (Optional) 19

This chapter is listed as OPTIONAL because it is not a prerequisite for any of the material to follow.

INTRODUCTION 19.1

In Chapter 18 we noted that a function $w = f(z)$ is actually a mapping, from a given region in the z plane to a corresponding one in the w plane. However, we paid little attention to the geometrical aspects of the mapping and concentrated instead on analytical aspects such as the values of the function, differentiability, and analyticity. In the present chapter we complement that discussion by turning to the geometrical issues. Besides completing our introduction to functions of a complex variable, i.e., functions as mappings, the concept of conformal mapping will provide us with a powerful solution technique for problems in two-dimensional potential theory.

In Section 19.2 we lay the groundwork, and in Section 19.3 we examine a particular important mapping—the *bilinear* transformation—in detail, and illustrate its use in solving certain two-dimensional boundary value problems. In the final section, 19.4, we survey a number of other mappings and consider more general boundary conditions as well.

CONFORMAL MAPS 19.2

Suppose that we wish to solve the two-dimensional Laplace equation

$$\nabla^2 \psi = \psi_{xx} + \psi_{yy} = 0 \tag{1}$$

in some domain D of the x, y plane. We ask ψ to be C^2 in D, and to satisfy prescribed boundary conditions as well. For example, ψ might be the steady-state temperature distribution within D due to the maintaining of a certain temperature distribution along the boundary of D.

The degree of difficulty in solving for ψ varies considerably with the shape of the domain D, and the methods developed in Part IV fail if the shape is not sufficiently simple, such as rectangular or circular. Thus there is interest in seeking a change of variables

$$u = u(x, y), \qquad v = v(x, y), \tag{2}$$

from x, y to u, v, in the hope that the new region (in the u, v plane), say D', will be simpler than D. Our plan, then, is to solve the new (and presumably simpler) problem in the u, v plane, and to then "return to the x, y plane" using the relations (2). Evidently, we will want a one-to-one correspondence between points in D and points in D', so that we can move back and forth unambiguously. Thus, besides asking $u(x, y)$ and $v(x, y)$ to be single-valued in D, we also want single-valued *inverse* functions

$$x = x(u, v), \qquad y = y(u, v) \tag{3}$$

to exist in D'. Recalling the implicit function theorem (page 241), we can ensure the existence of the desired inverse functions by requiring that u and v be C^1 in D and that the Jacobian be nonzero in D:

$$\frac{\partial(u, v)}{\partial(x, y)} = \begin{vmatrix} u_x & u_y \\ v_x & v_y \end{vmatrix} = u_x v_y - u_y v_x \neq 0. \tag{4}$$

With these assumptions, we proceed to enter the change of variables into (1). Denoting $\psi(x(u, v), y(u, v)) \equiv \Psi(u, v)$, we obtain

$$\psi_x = \Psi_u u_x + \Psi_v v_x$$

and

$$\psi_{xx} = (\Psi_{uu} u_x + \Psi_{uv} v_x) u_x + \Psi_u u_{xx} + (\Psi_{vu} u_x + \Psi_{vv} v_x) v_x + \Psi_v v_{xx}. \tag{5}$$

Similarly,

$$\psi_{yy} = (\Psi_{uu} u_y + \Psi_{uv} v_y) u_y + \Psi_u u_{yy} + (\Psi_{vu} u_y + \Psi_{vv} v_y) v_y + \Psi_v v_{yy}, \tag{6}$$

so equation (1) becomes

$$\begin{aligned}(u_x^2 + u_y^2)\Psi_{uu} &+ (u_x v_x + u_y v_y)(\Psi_{uv} + \Psi_{vu}) \\ &+ (v_x^2 + v_y^2)\Psi_{vv} + (u_{xx} + u_{yy})\Psi_u + (v_{xx} + v_{yy})\Psi_v = 0.\end{aligned} \tag{7}$$

Thus, in making the change of variables (2) in order to simplify the domain, we inadvertently render the governing PDE much more complicated, for in place of the familiar Laplace equation (1) we have the evidently more difficult equation (7).

However, if we restrict the change of variables (2) so that

$$u_x = v_y \quad \text{and} \quad u_y = -v_x \tag{8}$$

in D, and ask u and v to be C^2 so that $u_{xy} = u_{yx}$ and $v_{xy} = v_{yx}$ in D, then (8) gives

$u_{xx} + u_{yy} = 0$ and $v_{xx} + v_{yy} = 0$, and (7) reduces to

$$(u_x^2 + u_y^2)(\Psi_{uu} + \Psi_{vv}) = 0. \tag{9}$$

Using (8) again, we can write $u_x^2 + u_y^2 = u_x v_y - u_y v_x$, which has already been assumed nonzero in D. Then it follows from (9) that

$$\Psi_{uu} + \Psi_{vv} = 0 \tag{10}$$

everywhere in D'; i.e., the Laplace equation is "preserved" under the change of variables.

Thus far there has been no mention, or use, of complex variable theory. However, the fact that (8) coincides with the Cauchy–Riemann equations suggests that it might be helpful (although not essential) to regard the x, y and u, v planes as complex z and w planes, where $z = x + iy$ and $w = f(z) = u(x, y) + iv(x, y)$. Then $u_x v_y - u_y v_x = u_x^2 + v_x^2 = |f'(z)|^2$, so the nonvanishing-Jacobian condition (4) can be stated more crisply as $f'(z) \neq 0$ in D, and we have estabished the following important result.

Theorem 1 *Preservation of Laplace Equation*

Let $w = f(z) = u(x, y) + iv(x, y)$ be analytic everywhere in a domain D, with $f'(z) \neq 0$ everywhere in D.* Denote the image of D as D', and let the mapping be one-to-one. If $\psi(x, y)$ is harmonic in D, then $\psi(x(u, v), y(u, v)) \equiv \Psi(u, v)$ is harmonic in D'.

EXAMPLE 1 *Application of Theorem 1.* Consider the Dirichlet problem shown in Fig. 19.1a: the Laplace equation on $\psi(x, y)$ together with Dirichlet boundary conditions whereby $\psi = 50$ on the circular part of the boundary and $\psi = 10$ on the straight part. Physically, $\psi(x, y)$ might be the steady-state temperature distribution in a large plate with a circular cutout near one edge.

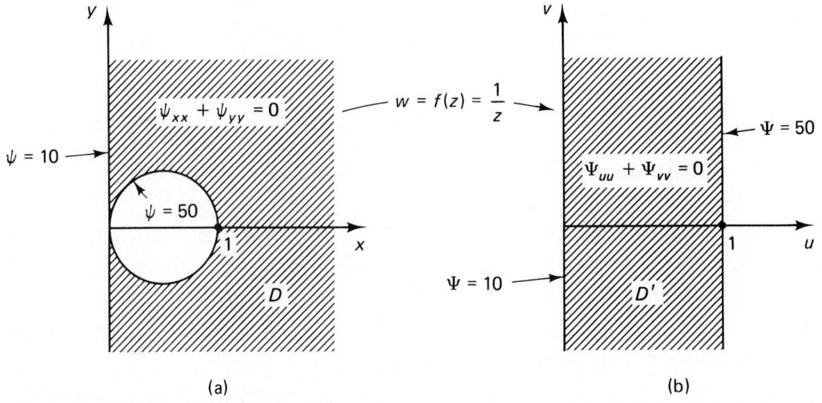

Fig. 19.1 Steady-state temperature problem.

* Recall that D is open because it is a domain. Thus $f' \neq 0$ in D means at all *interior* points of D; f' does not need to be nonzero on the *boundary* of D.

First, observe that the given problem cannot be solved by separation of variables in Cartesian coordinates (because the boundary is not comprised of constant-x and constant-y curves), nor in plane polar coordinates (because no matter where the origin is located the boundary is not comprised of constant-r and constant-θ curves). Nor do the Laplace and Fourier transforms provide any help.

Turning to Theorem 1, suppose we notice that the mapping $f(z) = 1/z$ sends the given domain D into the simpler strip D' shown in Fig. 19.1b (Exercise 1). Furthermore, $f(z) = 1/z$ is analytic for all $z \neq 0$, and hence everywhere inside D; $f'(z) = -1/z^2 \neq 0$ everywhere in D; and the mapping is one-to-one since both $f(z) = 1/z$ and the inverse function $z(f) = 1/f$ are obviously single valued. Thus it follows from Theorem 1 that

$$\nabla^2\Psi = \Psi_{uu} + \Psi_{vv} = 0 \tag{11}$$

in D'. Finally, the images of the boundary curves $x = 0$ and $(x - \frac{1}{2})^2 + y^2 = \frac{1}{4}$ are $u = 0$ and $u = 1$, so that $\Psi(0, v) = 10$ and $\Psi(1, v) = 50$, as indicated in Fig. 19.1b.

Now, the Ψ problem is simple because Ψ is evidently independent of v. Thus the Laplace equation simplifies to $d^2\Psi/du^2 = 0$, so $\Psi = Au + B$. The boundary conditions $\Psi(0, v) = 10$ and $\Psi(1, v) = 50$ permit us to solve for A and B, and we obtain the solution

$$\Psi(u, v) = 10 + 40u \tag{12}$$

in D'. To obtain the solution for $\psi(x, y)$ in D, we merely substitute $u = u(x, y)$ and $v = v(x, y)$ into the right-hand side of (12). (In this case there happen to be no v's.)

Since $f(z) = 1/z = u + iv$, we have

$$u + iv = \frac{1}{x + iy}\frac{x - iy}{x - iy} = \frac{x}{x^2 + y^2} - i\frac{y}{x^2 + y^2},$$

so

$$u = \frac{x}{x^2 + y^2}, \qquad v = -\frac{y}{x^2 + y^2}. \tag{13}$$

Thus

$$\psi(x, y) = \Psi(u(x, y), v(x, y)) = 10 + \frac{40x}{x^2 + y^2}. \tag{14}$$

COMMENT 1 Where did the mapping $f(z) = 1/z$ come from? How did we know to choose it? We do not have a constructive method to offer for the selection of a suitable mapping function. That choice will involve some combination of experience with a variety of standard mapping functions, and the use of tables, as will be discussed in the next two sections.

COMMENT 2 In case it was not clear that $\Psi(u, v)$ is independent of v, observe, a posteriori, that $\Psi = 10 + 40u$ does indeed satisfy the *full* equation (11) as well as the boundary conditions.

COMMENT 3 We stated, without discussion, that the constant boundary conditions "carry over" to the w plane. The reasoning is as follows. Suppose that a curve C in the z plane is parametrized by $x = x(\tau)$, $y = y(\tau)$ for $\tau_1 < \tau < \tau_2$. Then $\psi(x, y) = \text{constant} = \psi_0$ on C becomes

$$\psi(x(\tau), y(\tau)) = \Psi(u(x(\tau), y(\tau)), v(x(\tau), y(\tau))) = \psi_0$$

for $\tau_1 < \tau < \tau_2$. That is, $\psi = \psi_0$ on C carries over to $\Psi = \psi_0$ on the image C' of C, which is parametrized by

$$u = u(x(\tau), y(\tau)), \qquad v = v(x(\tau), y(\tau)) \qquad \text{for } \tau_1 < \tau < \tau_2. \quad \blacktriangleleft$$

Before continuing, let us return to Theorem 1 with the following question: If the condition $f'(z) \neq 0$ ensures the existence of single-valued inverse functions $x = x(u, v)$ and $y = y(u, v)$, and the "forward" mapping $f(z)$ is of course single valued, why do we bother including the additional condition that "the mapping be one-to-one" in the theorem? Let us answer this question by means of an example.

Consider the mapping $f(z) = z^2 = (x^2 - y^2) + i2xy$ on the domain D shown in Fig. 19.2. Clearly, f is analytic in D and $f'(z) = 2z \neq 0$ in D, yet the mapping is not one-to-one. For example, both $1 + i$ and $-1 - i$ are sent into $2i$. Yet the implicit function theorem (page 241), on which we have relied, has not let us down, for it asserts that if

$$\begin{aligned} F(x, y, u, v) &= u - x^2 + y^2 = 0 \\ G(x, y, u, v) &= v - 2xy = 0 \end{aligned} \tag{15}$$

for $x = 1$, $y = 1$, $u = 0$, $v = 2$, then (15) uniquely implies the existence of single-valued functions $x = x(u, v)$, $y = y(u, v)$, in some neighborhood of $(u, v) = (0, 2)$, **such that x(0, 2) = 1 and y(0, 2) = 1.** By virtue of the boldface condition, there is no contradiction. Thus the conditions that $f'(z) \neq 0$ and that the mapping be one-to-one, in Theorem 1, are not redundant.

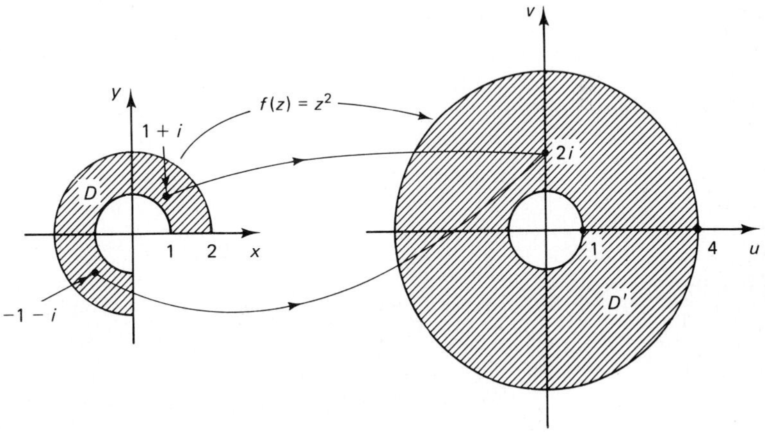

Fig. 19.2 Lack of one-to-oneness.

Recall that Theorem 1 requires that $f(z)$ be analytic and that $f'(z) \neq 0$ in the given domain. As we shall prove below, such mappings are "conformal"; i.e., they preserve angles in both magnitude and sense. To make this claim precise, consider two oriented smooth curves C_1 and C_2 that intersect at z_0 (Fig. 19.3). Let C_1 and C_2 be parametrized by $z_1(\tau) = x_1(\tau) + iy_1(\tau)$ and $z_2(\tau) = x_2(\tau) + iy_2(\tau)$, respectively, where x_1, y_1, x_2, y_2 are differentiable functions of the real parameter τ, where

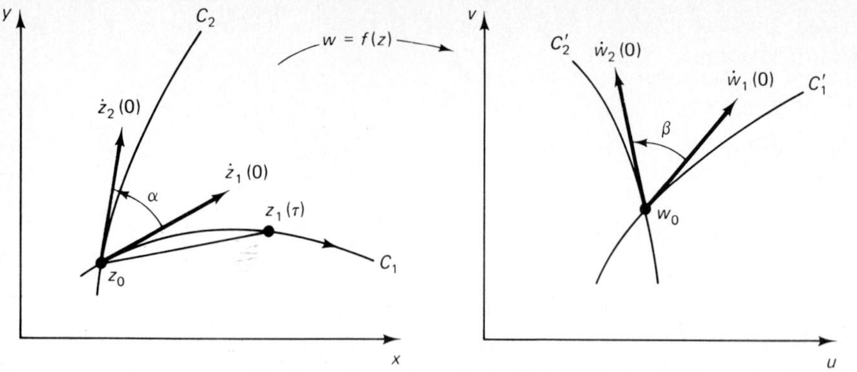

Fig. 19.3 Conformality.

$z_1(0) = z_2(0) = z_0$, and where $\dot{z}_1(0)$ and $\dot{z}_2(0)$ are both nonzero. (Dots will be used to denote $d/d\tau$.) Then the complex number

$$\dot{z}_1(0) = \lim_{\tau \to 0} \frac{z_1(\tau) - z_1(0)}{\tau} = \dot{x}_1(0) + i\dot{y}_1(0) \tag{16}$$

is a tangent "vector" to C_1 at z_0, and similarly for $\dot{z}_2(0)$. Let the angle measured counterclockwise from $\dot{z}_1(0)$ to $\dot{z}_2(0)$ be denoted as α.

Now consider a mapping $w = f(z)$ which is a nonconstant analytic function. Under this mapping, z_0 is sent into $w_0 = f(z_0)$ and the curves C_1, C_2 are sent into curves C_1', C_2' which are parametrized by $w_1(\tau) = f(z_1(\tau))$, $w_2(\tau) = f(z_2(\tau))$, respectively. By chain differentiation,

$$\dot{w}_1(0) = f'(z_0)\dot{z}_1(0), \qquad \dot{w}_2(0) = f'(z_0)\dot{z}_2(0), \tag{17}$$

so that if (and only if) $f'(z_0) \neq 0$, there exist unique tangent vectors $\dot{w}_1(0)$, $\dot{w}_2(0)$, at w_0, given by (17) and depicted in Fig. 19.3. From (17) it follows that

$$\begin{aligned} \arg \dot{w}_1(0) &= \arg f'(z_0) + \arg \dot{z}_1(0), \\ \arg \dot{w}_2(0) &= \arg f'(z_0) + \arg \dot{z}_2(0), \end{aligned} \tag{18}$$

and subtraction gives

$$\arg \dot{w}_1(0) - \arg \dot{w}_2(0) = \arg \dot{z}_1(0) - \arg \dot{z}_2(0). \tag{19}$$

If we denote the angle $\arg \dot{w}_1(0) - \arg \dot{w}_2(0)$ as β (Fig. 19.3), (19) tells us that

$$\beta = \alpha, \tag{20}$$

and this result is the promised conformality. Observe that the result (20) holds for *any* two oriented smooth curves C_1, C_2 intersecting at z_0. Let us pull these results together now by defining conformality and then giving conditions which ensure that a mapping is conformal.

We say that a mapping $w = f(z)$ is **conformal** at z_0 if it preserves, both in magnitude and in sense, the angle between every pair of oriented smooth curves that intersect at z_0.

> ***Theorem 2*** *Conformality; Preservation of Angles*
> If $f(z)$ is analytic, the mapping $w = f(z)$ is conformal, except at points where $f'(z) = 0$.

EXAMPLE 2 To emphasize the *local* nature of conformality, consider the mapping $w = z^2$. If the domain of definition D is the first quadrant $0 < x < \infty$, $0 < y < \infty$, the range of values D' is the upper half plane $v > 0$, as shown in Fig. 19.4. In this case f is analytic everywhere, and $f'(z) = 2z = 0$ only at the origin. Thus the mapping $w = z^2$ is conformal everywhere in D. If angles are preserved, we may well wonder how the quarter plane manages to open out into the upper half plane. Thus consider, as representative, the curve ABC and its image $A'B'C'$. The angle of intersection at B, namely $\pi/2$, is indeed preserved, although *away from the neighborhood of* B the curve ABC opens out like the pages of a book (Fig. 19.4). At $z = 0$, the only point at which conformality breaks down, the angle $\pi/2$ is *not* preserved; it is doubled. ◀

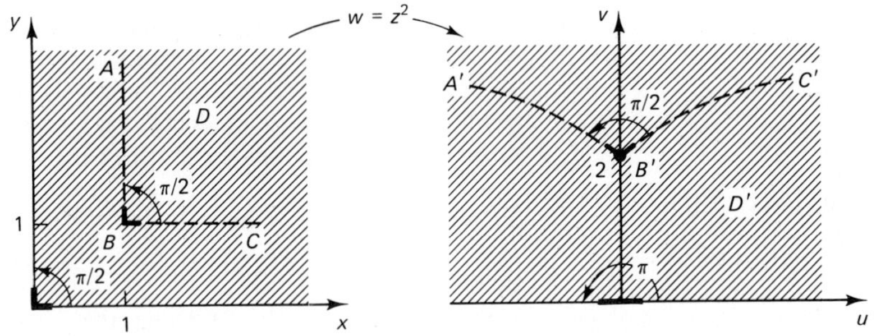

Fig. 19.4 The mapping $w = z^2$.

Reviewing this section, we showed first that under mappings $w = f(z)$, where f is analytic and $f'(z) \neq 0$, the Laplace equation is preserved. This fact is of great importance in two-dimensional potential theory, for it implies that given a particular problem in two-dimensional potential theory, one may be able to effect a simplification in the shape of the domain without disturbing the governing Laplace equation. We illustrated this line of approach in Example 1, and plan to develop it more fully in the two sections to follow. Furthermore, we showed that the above-noted conditions on f guarantee conformality of the map.

Some additional results are included in the exercises, but an important question remains: For a given domain D and a desired image D', does a one-to-one conformal map *exist?* If so, is it *unique*? These questions are answered, for simply connected domains (other than the entire z plane), by the **Riemann mapping theorem.***

The existence part of the theorem states, in effect, that any simply connected domain D (not the entire plane) *can* be mapped one-to-one and conformally onto any other simply connected domain D' (not the entire plane).† For a complete statement of the theorem, some discussion, and further references, the reader is referred to Saff and Snider.

* *Bernhard Riemann* (1826–1866) was a student of Gauss and Weber and became a professor of mathematics at Göttingen in 1859. His celebrated mapping theorem appears near the end of his doctoral dissertation.

† Connectedness was defined on page 215. A domain D is said to be *simply* connected if every closed curve in D can be continuously deformed, within D, to a point. For example, a disk is simply connected, an annulus is not. Further, we say that D is mapped *onto* D' if every point in D' is the image of one or more points in D.

1. Show that the image of the domain D shown in Fig. 19.1a, under the mapping $w = f(z) = 1/z$, is the infinite strip shown in Fig. 19.1b.

2. (*Analyticity of inverse mapping*) If $w = f(z)$ is a one-to-one mapping, there exists a single-valued inverse function, say $z = f^{-1}(w)$. Show that if f is an analytic function of z, then f^{-1} (i.e., the inverse function, *not* the numerical inverse $1/f$) is an analytic function of w, and

$$\frac{df^{-1}(w)}{dw} = \frac{1}{df(z)/dz}$$

or, equivalently,

$$\frac{dz}{dw} = \frac{1}{dw/dz}. \tag{a}$$

Hint: Show that if $\Delta z \to 0$, then $\Delta w \to 0$, too.

3. Give a shorter proof of Theorem 1 using the fact that the inverse mapping $z(w)$ is analytic, too, as noted in the preceding exercise. *Hint:* There exists a conjugate harmonic function corresponding to $\psi(x, y)$, say $\zeta(x, y)$, such that

$$F(z) = \psi(x, y) + i\zeta(x, y) \tag{a}$$

is an analytic function of z. Thus

$$\begin{aligned} F(z(w)) &= \psi(x(u, v), y(u, v)) \\ &\quad + i\zeta(x(u, v), y(u, v)) \\ &= \Psi(u, v) + iZ(u, v). \end{aligned} \tag{b}$$

Show why it follows from (b) that $\Psi(u, v)$ is harmonic.

4. (*Local magnification*) Let $w = f(z)$ be analytic at z_0, with $f'(z_0) \neq 0$. Denoting $\lim_{\Delta z \to 0} |\Delta w/\Delta z|$ as the *local magnification,* show that the local magnification is equal to $|f'(z_0)|$.

5. Are the following mappings conformal at $z = 0$? If not, why not?

*(a) e^z (b) ze^z
(c) $iz + 3$ *(d) iz^2
(e) $\sin z$ (f) $1/(z - 1)$
(g) $z^2 + z$ (h) $z^3 - 1 + 2i$

6. (a) In Example 2 we observed that the mapping $w = z^2$ is conformal for all z except $z = 0$. At $z = 0$ we noted that the "corner angle" $\pi/2$ gets doubled to π. Show that *all* angles are doubled at $z = 0$ (i.e., between every pair of oriented smooth curves that intersect at $z = 0$).
(b) More generally, show that for the mapping $w = z^n$ for any integer $n = 2, 3, 4, \ldots$, angles are multiplied by n at $z = 0$.
(c) Still more generally, suppose that $w = f(z) = (z - z_0)^n g(z)$, where $g(z)$ is analytic, $g(z_0) \neq 0$, $g'(z_0) \neq 0$, and n is any positive integer greater than 1. Show that angles are multiplied by n at z_0; i.e., in place of (20) we have $\beta = n\alpha$.

7. Let $w = f(z) = u(x, y) + iv(x, y)$ be analytic everywhere in a domain D, with $f'(z) \neq 0$ everywhere in D. Denote the image of D as D', and let the mapping be one-to-one. If $\psi(x, y)$ satisfies the *Poisson equation*

$$\psi_{xx} + \psi_{yy} = Q(x, y),$$

where Q is prescribed, what equation does $\psi(x(u, v), y(u, v)) = \Psi(u, v)$ satisfy in D'?

19.3 BILINEAR TRANSFORMATION

One of the most useful conformal mappings, or transformations, is the **bilinear transformation***

$$w = \frac{az + b}{cz + d} \qquad (ad - bc \neq 0), \tag{1}$$

which is also known as the *Möbius transformation* or *linear fractional transforma-*

* Cleared of fractions, (1) becomes $czw + dw - az = b$, which is linear in z and linear in w; hence it is *bilinear* in z and w.

tion. The constants a, b, c, d are allowed to be complex, and the condition $ad - bc \neq 0$ ensures that $w(z)$ is not merely a constant.

Since

$$w'(z) = \frac{ad - bc}{(cz + d)^2} \tag{2}$$

exists for all z except $z = -d/c$ (at which point w is undefined as well), and is nonzero (since $ad - bc \neq 0$ by assumption), we see that *the bilinear transformation is conformal everywhere except at* $z = -d/c$, which point is called the *pole* of the transformation. Although w is undefined at $z = -d/c$, it will be convenient to regard the image of that point as the **point at infinity** in the w plane, denoted as $w = \infty$. To indicate that the w plane has been augmented by the point at infinity, we call the result the **extended complex plane.** In contrast, the "usual" complex plane (i.e., not augmented by the point at infinity) will be called the **finite complex plane.** Observe that if we are to allow the values $z = \infty$ and $w = \infty$, we need to decide how to interpret $(az + b)/(cz + d)$, say, for $z = \infty$. We will define the latter as a/c if $c \neq 0$, and as ∞ if $c = 0$.

Besides being conformal, the bilinear transformation is also *one-to-one* on the extended z and w planes, for (1) gives a unique w for each z, and the inverse mapping

$$z = -\frac{dw - b}{cw - a} \tag{3}$$

[obtained by solving (1) for z] gives a unique z for each w.

Observe that the transformation $w = 1/z$, used in Example 1 in Section 19.2, was an example of a bilinear transformation. In fact, if we call the transformations

$$w = Az \qquad \text{(scaling and rotation)} \tag{4}$$

$$w = z + B, \qquad \text{(translation)} \tag{5}$$

$$w = \frac{1}{z} \qquad \text{(inversion)} \tag{6}$$

scaling and rotation, translation, and *inversion transformations,* respectively, the general bilinear transformation (1) amounts to a composition of these three simpler transformations. For if $c \neq 0$, it is easily verified (by successive substitution) that

$$\begin{gathered} w_1 = cz, \qquad w_2 = w_1 + d, \qquad w_3 = \frac{1}{w_2}, \\ w_4 = \frac{bc - ad}{c} w_3, \qquad w = w_4 + \frac{a}{c} \end{gathered} \tag{7}$$

takes us from z to w_1 to w_2 to w_3 to w_4 to w by a finite sequence of scaling and rotation, translation, and inversion transformations; and similarly if $c = 0$, for then

$$w_1 = \frac{a}{d} z, \qquad w = w_1 + \frac{b}{d}. \tag{8}$$

Thus, to study the bilinear transformation, we begin by examining the simpler transformations (4) to (6). Considering the scaling and rotation transformation (4) first, it is helpful to express (4) in polar form, with $z = re^{i\theta}$ and $w = \rho e^{i\phi}$, as

$$\rho e^{i\phi} = (|A|e^{i \arg A})(re^{i\theta}). \tag{9}$$

Thus

$$\rho = |A|r \tag{10a}$$

and

$$\phi = \theta + \arg A; \tag{10b}$$

that is, the modulus of w is the modulus of z scaled by $|A|$, and the argument of w is the argument of z plus arg A: hence the name "scaling and rotation."

EXAMPLE 1 *Scaling and Rotation.* To illustrate, observe that the transformation

$$w = (1 + i)z \tag{11}$$

maps the domain D onto the domain D', as shown in Fig. 19.5. Since $1 + i = \sqrt{2}e^{i\pi/4}$, D' is obtained from D as a result of scaling by $\sqrt{2}$ and rotating by $+\pi/4$.

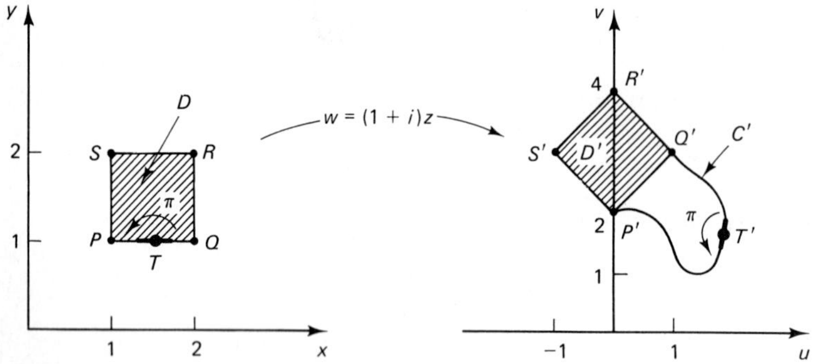

Fig. 19.5 The mapping (11).

COMMENT Be sure to see that it is *not* correct to infer the image domain D' by locating the corner point images P', Q', R', S' and then noting that the mapping is conformal, "so a straight line connecting P and Q must go into a straight line connecting P' and Q'." For conformality would still be satisfied if the image of PQ were the curve C from P' to Q'. For example, the angle π at T is the same as the angle π at T'. Rather, we obtain the correct image curve $P'Q'$ by noting from

$$w = u + iv = (1 + i)(x + iy) = (x - y) + i(x + y)$$

that

$$u = x - y, \qquad v = x + y. \tag{12}$$

Now, the equation of PQ is $y = 1$, and putting $y = 1$ into (12), we obtain the image curve $P'Q'$ in the parametric form $u = x - 1$, $v = x + 1$ for $1 \le x \le 2$. Or, eliminating the "parameter" x, we obtain the straight line $v = u + 2$. ◀

Next, the translation transformation (5) is quite simple: All points z simply translate by B.

EXAMPLE 2 *Translation.* The transformation

$$w = z + 1 - i \tag{13}$$

maps the reference domain D onto D', shown in Fig. 19.6. ◀

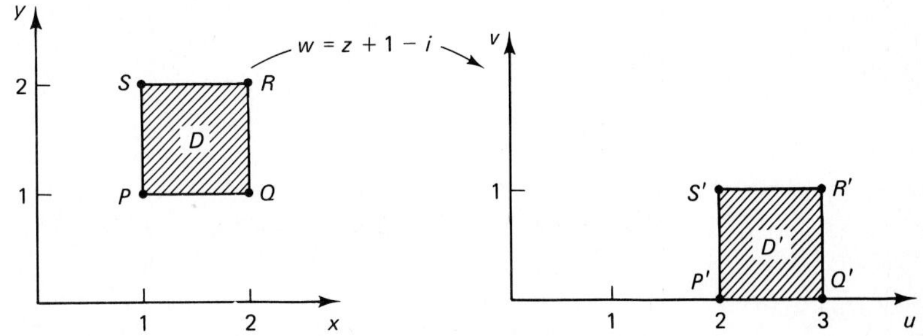

Fig. 19.6 The mapping (13).

Finally, consider the inversion transformation (6). With $z = re^{i\theta}$ and $w = \rho e^{i\phi}$, (6) becomes

$$\rho e^{i\phi} = \frac{1}{r} e^{-i\theta}, \tag{14}$$

so that $\rho = 1/r$ and $\phi = -\theta$. Since the radius suffers an inversion about the unit circle (for example, $r = 3$ gives $\rho = \frac{1}{3}$ and $r = \frac{1}{4}$ gives $\rho = 4$), we call (6) an inversion transformation. The mapping of some representative points is shown in Fig. 19.7. Besides the mapping of individual points, observe that $w = 1/z$ sends the circle $|z| = r$ onto the circle $|w| = 1/r$ $(r \neq 0)$, as illustrated in Fig. 19.8. for $r < 1$.

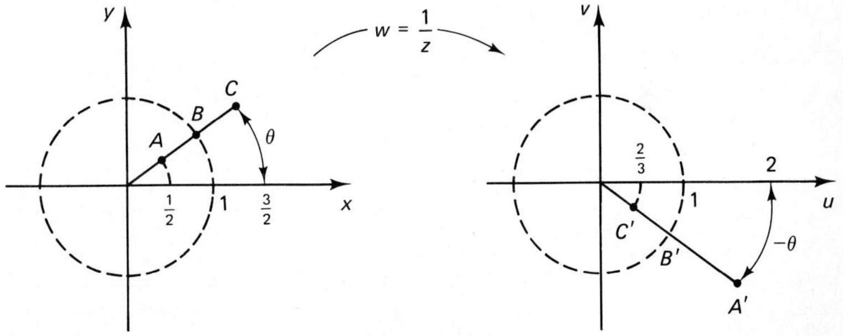

Fig. 19.7 The mapping $1/z$.

That $w = 1/z$ sends the circle $|z| = r$, centered at the origin of the z plane into the circle $|w| = 1/r$ centered at the origin of the w plane is, of course, rather obvious. What is striking and not at all obvious, however, is the fact that $w = 1/z$ sends *every* circle in the z plane into a circle (or perhaps a straight line). To prove this claim, consider any circle

$$(x - a)^2 + (y - b)^2 = c^2 \tag{15}$$

in the z plane, centered at (a, b) and having radius c (>0). If we set $x = (z + \bar{z})/2$

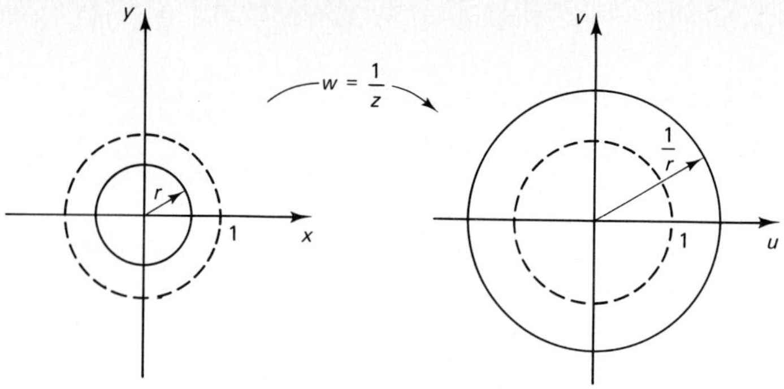

Fig. 19.8 Inversion of circles centered at the origin.

and $y = (z - \bar{z})/2i$, (15) becomes

$$z\bar{z} + Az + \overline{A}\bar{z} + B = 0, \tag{16}$$

where $A = -a + bi$ and $B = a^2 + b^2 - c^2$. From $w = 1/z$ it follows that $z = 1/w$ and $\bar{z} = 1/\bar{w}$, so that the image in the w plane of the circle (16) is given by the equation

$$\frac{1}{w\bar{w}} + A\frac{1}{w} + \overline{A}\frac{1}{\bar{w}} + B = 0. \tag{17}$$

At this point we distinguish two cases: $B \neq 0$ and $B = 0$. Geometrically speaking, $B = 0$ corresponds to the case where the circle (15) passes through the origin ($z = 0$), and $B \neq 0$ corresponds to the case where it does *not*.

1. **B ≠ 0** *(circles not through $z = 0$):* If $B \neq 0$ we can reexpress (17) as

$$w\bar{w} + \frac{\overline{A}}{B}w + \frac{A}{B}\bar{w} + \frac{1}{B} = 0, \tag{18}$$

which equation is of precisely the same form as (16) because $1/B$ is real and the coefficient A/B is the complex conjugate of the coefficient $\overline{A}/B$. Thus the image curve is a circle.

2. **B = 0** *(circles through $z = 0$):* If $B = 0$, we can reexpress (17) as

$$1 + A\bar{w} + \overline{A}w = 0 \tag{19}$$

or, in terms of u and v,

$$bv - au + \tfrac{1}{2} = 0, \tag{20}$$

which is the equation of a straight line.

Thus the inversion transformation (6) sends every circle into either a circle or a straight line. Furthermore, it is easy to show (Exercise 1) that it sends every *straight line* into either a circle or a straight line. This property, of sending every circle or straight line into a circle or a straight line, is shared by the transformations (4) and (5) (Exercise 2). Then, since the bilinear transformation (1) is a composition of a finite sequence of the transformations (4), (5), and (6), it follows that the bilinear transformation inherits that interesting and useful property.

> ***Theorem 1** Circles and Straight Lines*
> The bilinear transformation (1) sends every circle or straight line into either a circle or a straight line.

How can we tell if the image is a circle or a straight line? The key point is that the image curve will be unbounded (hence a straight line, not a circle) if and only if the circle or straight line in the z plane happens to pass through the pole $z = -d/c$, the image of which is $w = \infty$.

Having in hand the property enunciated in Theorem 1, we turn to the "design" question: How do we design a bilinear transformation (1) (i.e., how do we choose a, b, c, d) so as to send a particular circle or straight line into a particular circle or straight line? Since three distinct points uniquely determine a circle or straight line, the issue amounts to sending three distinct points in the z plane into three distinct points in the w plane.

EXAMPLE 3 *Upper Half Plane into Unit Disk.* Suppose we wish to conformally map the upper half plane $y \geq 0$ onto the unit disk $|w| \leq 1$ (Fig. 19.9). Since the boundaries of D and D' are a straight line and a circle, respectively, we turn to the bilinear transformation. Three distinct points determine a straight line or circle, so it will suffice to determine a, b, c, d in (1) so as to send any three distinct points on the boundary curve $y = 0$ into any three distinct points on the boundary curve $|w| = 1$. For example, suppose that we map $z = -1$ into $w = -1$, $z = 0$ into $w = -i$, and $z = 1$ into $w = 1$. Putting these z, w pairs into (1) and cross-multiplying, we obtain the equations

$$\begin{aligned} a - b + c - d &= 0 \\ b \qquad + id &= 0 \\ a + b - c - d &= 0. \end{aligned} \tag{21}$$

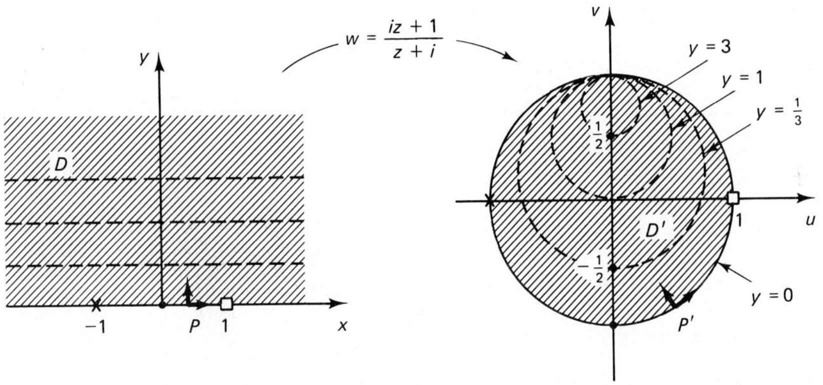

Fig. 19.9 Upper half plane onto unit disk.

Solving (21) and putting the results into (1), we obtain the bilinear transformation

$$w = \frac{iz + 1}{z + i}. \tag{22}$$

Since the pole $z = -i$ lies outside D, the mapping (22) is conformal in D, as desired. And since the boundary of D is mapped into $|w| = 1$, it seems reasonable that the image of D under the mapping (22) will be either the interior $|w| \leq 1$ (as desired) *or* the exterior $|w| \geq 1$ (*not* as desired). At the least, we can check a single interior point in D. For example, we see that $z = i$ is sent into $w = 0$, which *is* in $|w| \leq 1$. However, how can we be sure that (22) maps D *onto* the unit disk?* Might not the image D' be the disk $|w| \leq 1$ but with one or more holes in it? Or might not some of D' lie inside the unit disk and some of it lie outside? In the absence of theorems that would answer such topological questions,† let us determine the images of the lines $y =$ constant (>0), since the totality of such lines covers all of D. Furthermore, their images are easily determined: $y = c > 0$ is a straight line, not passing through the pole $-i$, so its image is a circle. And since each such line contains the point $z = \infty$, which maps into $w = i$, all of the image circles pass through $w = i$. The result is as shown in Fig. 19.9, from which we can see that $y \geq 0$ does indeed map onto $|w| \leq 1$, as desired.

COMMENT Another way to see that $y > 0$ maps onto the *interior* of the unit disk, not the exterior, is to use the conformality of the mapping. For suppose that we walk along the boundary curve $y = 0$ in the positive x direction, pointing our right hand straight ahead and our left hand to the left, as indicated by the little arrows at P in Fig. 19.9. By conformality, the image arrows at P' are oriented as shown. Thus, if we walk along the boundary of D with D at our left, our image walks along the boundary of D' with D' at its left. With this idea in mind, we see that if, instead, we wish to map $y \geq 0$ onto the *exterior* of the unit disk, we can accomplish that by reversing the order of the three points. For example, sending $z = -1$ into $w = 1$, $z = 0$ into $w = -i$, and $z = 1$ into $w = -1$ produces the mapping shown in Fig. 19.10. ◀

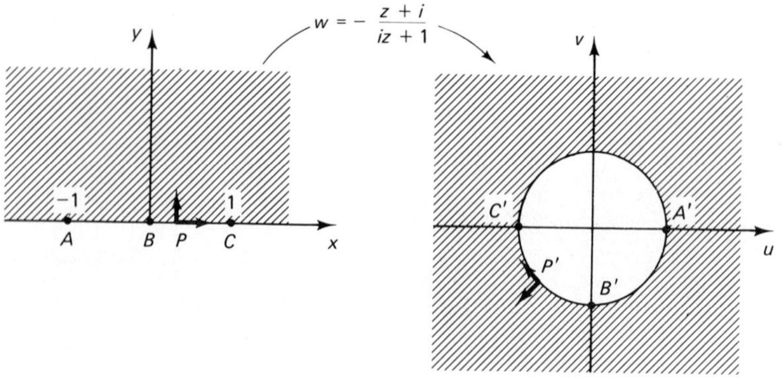

Fig. 19.10 Exterior mapping.

* "Onto" was defined on page 765.
† Such theorems are to be found in Saff and Snider.

Notice, in Example 3, that once we specified three distinct points on the boundary $y = 0$ of D and three distinct image points on the boundary $|w| = 1$ of D', the bilinear transformation was uniquely determined [see also Exercise 6(b)]. However, there are an infinite number of ways of choosing the three image points given any three z points, so there are evidently an infinite number of distinct bilinear transformations that map $y \geq 0$ onto $|w| \leq 1$; (22) is merely one such transformation. The reason we mention this fact is to observe that the bilinear transformation is *more* than powerful enough, by virtue of the several available "design parameters" a, b, c, d, to send one specified circle or straight line into a specified image circle or straight line. In fact, the bilinear transformation can be used to map regions bounded by *two* circles (Fig. 19.11a and b) into an annulus between *concentric* circles, say. These and other mappings are tabulated, for reference, in Appendix D.

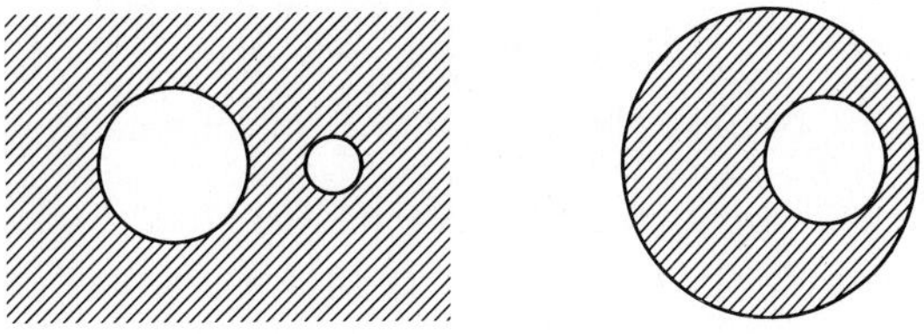

Fig. 19.11 More complicated regions. (a) (b)

EXAMPLE 4 Solve the steady-state temperature problem shown in Fig. 19.12. Referring to the tabulation in Appendix D, we see that item 3 is suitable, with $x_1 = 2$ and $x_2 = 3$. Thus, with $a = (7 + 2\sqrt{6})/5$, we have

$$w = \frac{z - a}{az - 1} \tag{23}$$

maps D onto the annulus shown in Fig. 19.13. (Observe that the pole $z = 1/a \approx 0.42$ does *not* lie in D.)

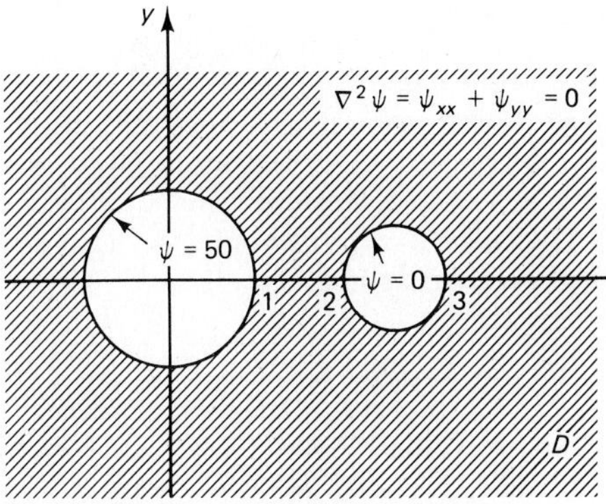

Fig. 19.12 Dirichlet problem on $\psi(x, y)$.

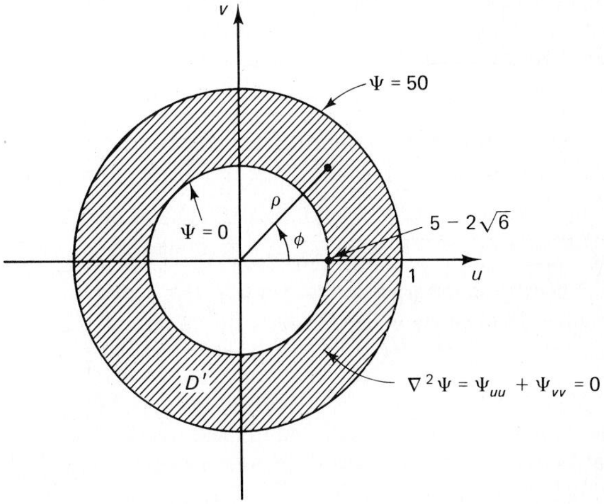

Fig. 19.13 Image of D.

The resulting problem on Ψ (Fig. 19.13) is solved easily using polar coordinates ρ, ϕ $(w = u + iv = \rho e^{i\phi})$ because Ψ is evidently independent of ϕ. Thus

$$\nabla^2\Psi = \Psi_{\rho\rho} + \frac{1}{\rho}\Psi_\rho + \frac{1}{\rho^2}\Psi_{\phi\phi} = 0 \tag{24}$$

reduces to the ordinary differential equation

$$\frac{d^2}{d\rho^2}\Psi + \frac{1}{\rho}\frac{d}{d\rho}\Psi = 0, \tag{25}$$

with general solution $\Psi = A \ln \rho + B$. Then, applying the boundary conditions and setting $b = 5 - 2\sqrt{6}$ for brevity, we have

$$\Psi(\rho) = 50\left(1 - \frac{\ln \rho}{\ln b}\right). \tag{26}$$

Finally, obtaining ρ in terms of x and y (Exercise 11), we have

$$\begin{aligned}\psi(x, y) &= \Psi(\rho(x, y)) \\ &= \frac{50}{\ln b}\left[\ln b - \ln\sqrt{\frac{(x-a)^2 + y^2}{(ax-1)^2 + a^2y^2}}\right]\end{aligned} \tag{27}$$

as the desired solution. ◀

In this section we have studied only the bilinear transformation (1). The property that it sends every circle or straight line into either a circle or a straight line makes this transformation especially useful in applications, and was discussed in some detail. Additional aspects are explored in the exercises.

19.3 EXERCISES

1. Show that the inversion transformation $w = 1/z$ sends straight lines that do *not* pass through $z = 0$ into circles, and straight lines that *do* pass through $z = 0$ into straight lines.

2. Show that the following transformations send every circle or straight line into a circle or a straight line.

(a) the scaling and rotation (4): $w = Pz$ (P complex)

(b) the translation (5): $w = z + Q$ (Q complex)

***3.** What are the u, v coordinates of the center of the circle defined by (18)? What is the radius of the circle?

4. (*Composition of two bilinear transformations*) Show that the composition of two bilinear transformations is also a bilinear transformation. That is, show that if $f(z)$ and $g(z)$ are bilinear transformations, so is $f(g(z))$.

5. (*Fixed points*) A **fixed point** of a mapping $w = f(z)$ is a point z_0 that is "mapped into itself"; i.e., z_0 is a fixed point of $w = f(z)$ if $f(z_0) = z_0$. Prove that a *bilinear transformation* $w = (az + b)/(cz + d)$ *has at most two fixed points, unless it is simply the identity* transformation $w = z$.

6. (*Three points into three points*) (a) Prove that *any three given distinct points z_1, z_2, z_3 in the extended z plane can be mapped into any three given distinct points w_1, w_2, w_3, respectively, in the extended w plane by a bilinear transformation $w = f(z)$ which is given, implicitly, by the* relation

$$\frac{w - w_1}{w - w_3}\frac{w_2 - w_3}{w_2 - w_1} = \frac{z - z_1}{z - z_3}\frac{z_2 - z_3}{z_2 - z_1}. \tag{a}$$

Hint: Show first that the transformation $w = f(z)$ implied by (a) is indeed bilinear. Then verify that (a) guarantees that $f(z_1) = w_1$, $f(z_2) = w_2$, and $f(z_3) = w_3$.

(b) Prove that the bilinear transformation $w = f(z)$ in part (a) is unique. *Hint:* Suppose that $w = g(z)$ is another bilinear transformation which maps the three given z points into the three given w points. With the help of the results stated in Exercises 4 and 5, show that the composite transformation $g^{-1}(f(z))$ has three fixed points, so it must be the identity transformation.

7. Rederive the mapping (22) using (a) in Exercise 6, with $z_1 = -1$, $z_2 = 0$, $z_3 = 1$, $w_1 = -1$, $w_2 = -i$, $w_3 = 1$.

8. The mapping (22) is not the only bilinear transformation that maps $y \geq 0$ onto $|w| \leq 1$. Using either (a) in Exercise 6 or the method chosen in Example 3, determine a bilinear transformation that sends

*(a) $z_1 = 0$, $z_2 = 1$, $z_3 = 2$ into $w_1 = -1$, $w_2 = -i$, $w_3 = 1$

(b) $z_1 = -1$, $z_2 = 0$, $z_3 = \infty$ into $w_1 = -1$, $w_2 = -i$, $w_3 = 1$

(c) $z_1 = 0$, $z_2 = 1$, $z_3 = \infty$ into $w_1 = 1$, $w_2 = i$, $w_3 = -1$

9. For the mapping (22), determine the image of

(a) the strip $-1 \leq y \leq 0$

(b) the half plane $-\infty < y \leq -1$

***10.** Find two distinct bilinear transformations that map $x \leq 0$ onto $|w| \geq 2$.

11. In Example 4, determine $\rho(x, y)$ and show that (27) does follow from (26).

12. Determine the image of the given region under the mapping $w = (z + 1)/(z - i)$.

(a) $y \leq 0$ (b) $0 \leq y \leq 1$

(c) $y \geq 1$ (d) $x \geq 0$

(e) the wedge $0 \leq \arg z \leq \pi/4$

(f) the quadrant $0 \leq \arg z \leq \pi/2$

(g) the annulus $1 \leq |z| \leq 2$

13. Solve the given Dirichlet problem (shown in the figure) for $\psi(x, y)$, with the help of the mappings tabulated in Appendix D, if applicable.

*(a)

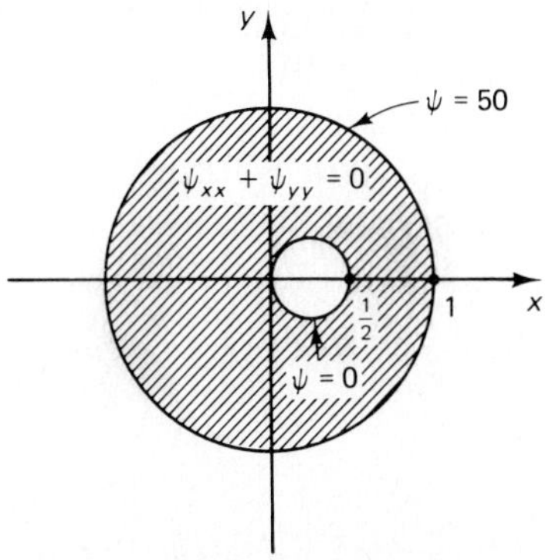

(b) *Hint:* The desired mapping can be obtained as a limiting case of the mapping given in item 3.

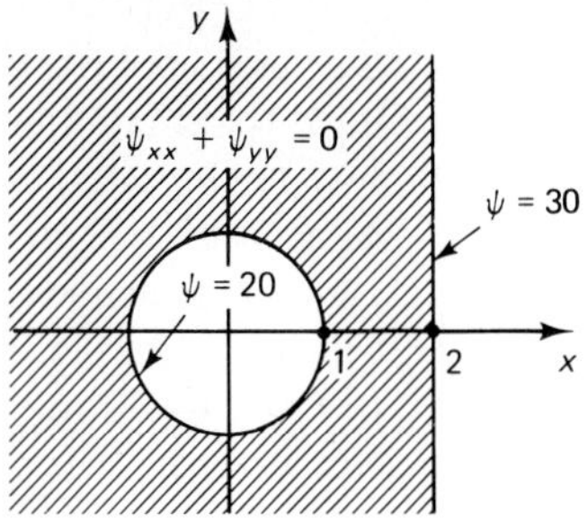

(c) *Hint:* Map $z = 3$ into $w = \infty$.

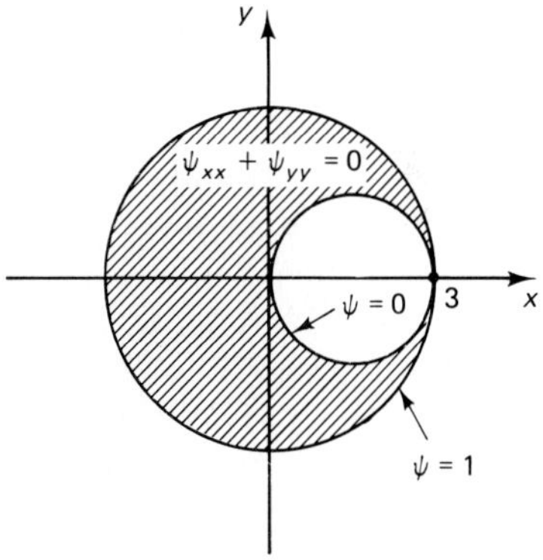

*(d) In particular, solve for $\psi(0, 4)$. *Hint:* Evidently, the bilinear transformation cannot map the given region onto either an infinite strip or the region between concentric circles. (Why not?) Instead, map the region onto a *wedge*. For example, send $z = 3$ to $w = \infty$ and $z = -3$ to $w = 0$.

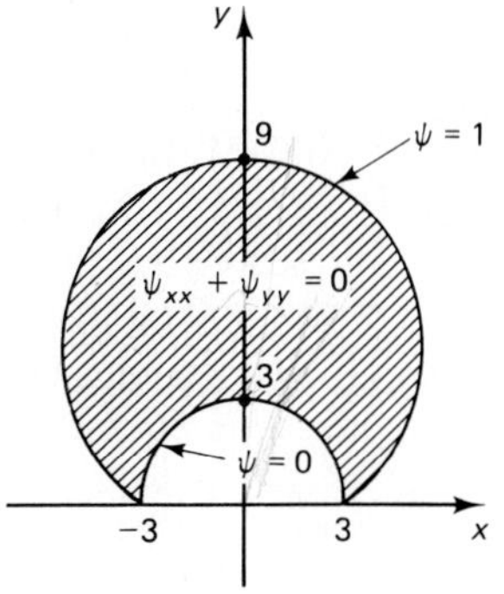

19.4 APPLICATIONS AND ADDITIONAL MAPPINGS

Our principal reason for including a chapter on conformal mapping is that it provides us with an additional and powerful method for solving boundary value problems in two-dimensional potential theory. Although examples of that method were included in each of the preceding two sections, our emphasis in those sections was on the general principles behind conformal mapping (Section 19.2) and on the bilinear transformation in particular (Section 19.3). In a more complete treatment of the subject we would follow our discussion of the bilinear transformation with similar discussions of the mappings provided by the various other elementary functions (e^z, $\log z$, $\sin z$, etc.) as well as the important Schwarz–Christoffel and Joukowski transformations. However, in this final section we plan to emphasize applications. Thus additional mappings will be introduced, from the tabulation in Appendix D, but only to solve the particular problem at hand. Development of the key properties of these mappings will be left for the exercises.

Having thus far considered only constant Dirichlet boundary conditions (ψ = constant), our first step is to allow for more general boundary conditions, specifically, nonconstant Dirichlet and Neumann conditions.

Consider a curve C in the z plane which is all or part of the boundary of the region D under consideration, and let C be parametrized by $x = x(\tau)$, $y = y(\tau)$, for $\tau_1 < \tau < \tau_2$. The image curve C', under the conformal transformation $w = u + iv = f(z)$, is then given parametrically by $u = u(x(\tau), y(\tau)) \equiv U(\tau)$, $v = v(x(\tau), y(\tau)) \equiv V(\tau)$ for $\tau_1 < \tau < \tau_2$.

With these parametrizations in mind, *the Dirichlet condition*

$$\psi(x, y) = \psi(x(\tau), y(\tau)) = F(\tau) \qquad (\tau_1 < \tau < \tau_2) \tag{1}$$

on C is seen to transform into

$$\psi(x, y) = \Psi(U(\tau), V(\tau)) = F(\tau) \qquad (\tau_1 < \tau < \tau_2) \tag{2}$$

on C'. In the event that $F(\tau)$ is merely a constant, the boundary condition $\psi = F_0$ on C merely carries over into the boundary condition $\Psi_0 = F_0$ on C'. Notationally, (2) may be more transparent in the form

$$\boxed{\psi\,|_z = \Psi\,|_w = F(\tau).} \tag{2'}$$

EXAMPLE 1 The Dirichlet problem shown in Fig. 19.14 is the same as in Example 1 in Section 19.2 (page 761) except for the boundary conditions. First, observe that the y axis maps onto the v axis and the constant boundary condition $\psi = 0$ on the y axis carries over to $\Psi = 0$ on the v axis. We are more interested in determining the fate of the nonconstant boundary condition on the circle C. If we parametrize C by

$$x = \tfrac{1}{2} + \tfrac{1}{2}\cos\tau, \qquad y = \tfrac{1}{2}\sin\tau \quad \text{for} \quad 0 \le \tau < 2\pi, \tag{3}$$

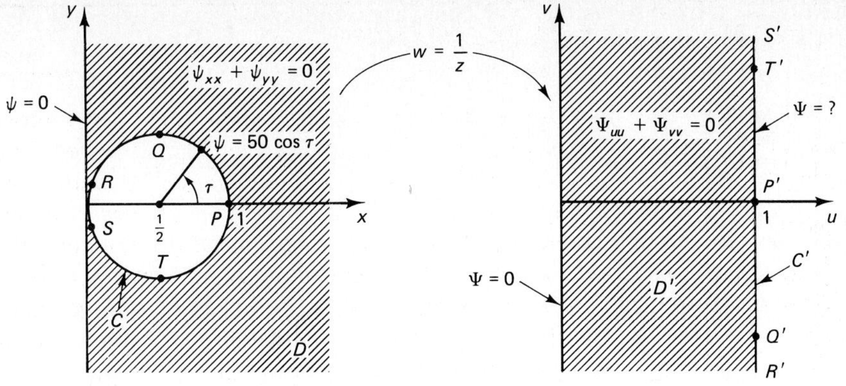

Fig. 19.14 Nonconstant Dirichlet boundary conditions.

and observe that

$$w = u + iv = \frac{1}{z} = \frac{1}{x + iy} = \frac{x}{x^2 + y^2} - i\frac{y}{x^2 + y^2}$$

$$= 1 - i\frac{\sin\tau}{1 + \cos\tau},$$

we see that the image C' is parametrized by

$$u = 1, \qquad v = -\frac{\sin\tau}{1 + \cos\tau} \quad \text{for} \quad 0 \le \tau < 2\pi, \tag{4}$$

and is therefore as shown in Fig. 19.14. Thus the transformed boundary condition is $\Psi = 50\cos\tau$ on the curve C' given by (4). Actually, it may be more natural to express that condition in terms of v. The v, τ relation in (4) gives

$$\cos\tau = \frac{1 - v^2}{1 + v^2},$$

so the transformed boundary condition is

$$\Psi(1, v) = 50\frac{1 - v^2}{1 + v^2} \quad (-\infty < v < \infty). \tag{5}$$

COMMENT 1 We will not try to solve the transformed problem for Ψ since our purpose was only to show how to handle the boundary conditions. However, we might note the resulting problem on Ψ is more difficult than in Example 1 in Section 19.2 because the boundary condition (5) is *not* independent of v as it was in Section 19.2. The present problem can be solved by a Fourier transform on v, but that story is left for Exercise 1.

COMMENT 2 In case it is not yet clear, notice that the idea behind the transformation of nonconstant Dirichlet conditions is quite simple in *principle*: If ψ at any point z on C is ψ_0, then the value of Ψ at the image point w on C' is Ψ_0, too, as can be seen from (2′). ◀

Next, we turn to *Neumann*-type boundary conditions, namely, whereby the normal derivative $\partial\psi/\partial n$ is prescribed on the boundary C of D. If C is again parametrized by $x = x(\tau)$, $y = y(\tau)$ for $\tau_1 < \tau < \tau_2$, the Neumann condition is of the form

$$\frac{\partial \psi}{\partial n} = F(\tau) \qquad (\tau_1 < \tau < \tau_2) \tag{6}$$

on C. Thus the question is: How does the quantity $\partial\psi/\partial n$ transform under the conformal map $w = f(z)$? Let z be any point on C, and let z_0 lie within D on a line L which is normal to C at z, as shown in Fig. 19.15. The image L' of L will, in general, be curved, but by conformality it will be perpendicular to C' (the image of C) at w (the image of z). Then, with $\Delta z = z - z_0$ and $\Delta w = w - w_0$, we have

$$\left.\frac{\partial \psi}{\partial n}\right|_z = \lim_{\Delta z \to 0} \frac{\psi|_z - \psi|_{z_0}}{|\Delta z|}. \tag{7}$$

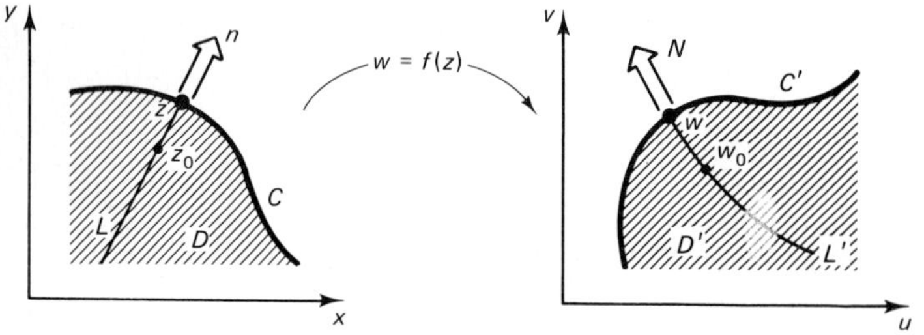

Fig. 19.15 Neumann boundary condition.

But $\psi|_z = \Psi|_w$, $\psi|_{z_0} = \Psi|_{w_0}$, and $\lim_{\Delta z \to 0} \Delta w/\Delta z = f'(z)$, so that

$$\left.\frac{\partial \psi}{\partial n}\right|_z = \lim_{\Delta z \to 0} \frac{\Psi|_w - \Psi|_{w_0}}{|\Delta w|}\left|\frac{\Delta w}{\Delta z}\right| = \left.\frac{\partial \Psi}{\partial N}\right|_w |f'(z)|, \tag{8}$$

where $\partial/\partial n$ and $\partial/\partial N$ denote the outward normal derivatives at z and w, respectively. In the final equality we used the fact that $\Delta z \to 0$ implies that $\Delta w \to 0$, for if $w = f(z)$ is a differentiable function of z, it must surely be a *continuous* function of z. We conclude, from (8), that *the Neumann condition* (6) *transforms according to*

$$\boxed{\left.\frac{\partial \Psi}{\partial N}\right|_w = \frac{1}{|f'(z)|}\left.\frac{\partial \Psi}{\partial n}\right|_z = \frac{1}{|f'(z(\tau))|}F(\tau), \quad (\tau_1 < \tau < \tau_2),} \tag{9}$$

where $f'(z) \neq 0$ *by the assumed conformality. As an important special case, we see from* (9) *that if* $\partial\psi/\partial n = 0$ *on* C, *then* $\partial\Psi/\partial N = 0$ *on* C'. To remember (9), observe, heuristically, that $dN = |f'(z)|\, dn$ because $|f'(z)|$ is the local magnification (Exercise 4, page 766).

The homogeneous case $F = 0$ is quite simple and does not require an immediate illustrative example (although it will occur in Examples 3 and 4). The nonhomogeneous case arises less frequently in applications, so illustrative examples will be relegated to the exercises. Thus, in the remainder of this section we consider a sequence of additional applications that are intended to acquaint the reader with some additional mappings and generally, to solidify the conformal mapping technique with regard to the solution of problems in two-dimensional potential theory.

EXAMPLE 2 *Steady-state Temperature in Semi-infinite Strip.* Consider the Dirichlet problem

$$\begin{aligned} \psi_{xx} + \psi_{yy} &= 0, \qquad (0 < x < 1, 0 < y < \infty) \\ \psi(0, y) = \psi(1, y) &= 0, \quad \psi(x, 0) = 100, \end{aligned} \tag{10}$$

governing the steady-state temperature $\psi(x, y)$ in a semi-infinite strip. Looking through the table of mappings in Appendix D, our object is to find a mapping, or sequence of mappings, that will map the semi-infinite strip onto the *upper half plane*, the *unit disk*, or *something even simpler*. Let us explain. Mapping onto the upper half plane or unit disk would be desirable because the solution of the Dirichlet problem is *known* for those regions. Specifically, they were found in Chapter 15 (pages 659 and 654, respectively). And by "something even simpler" we mean any region that renders the problem especially simple. For example, an infinite strip with constant boundary conditions (Fig. 19.16) would be excellent because the problem on Ψ is essentially *one*-dimensional: Ψ varies only with v, so that $\Psi_{uu} + \Psi_{vv} = 0$ reduces to $\Psi_{vv} = 0$, which easily gives $\Psi = A + Bv = \Psi_1 + (\Psi_2 - \Psi_1)v/a$.

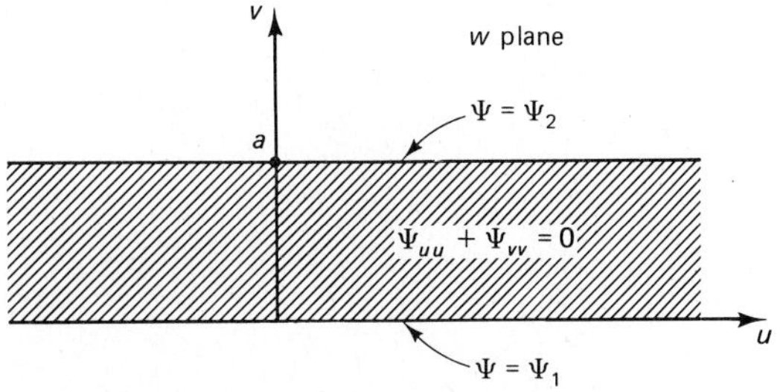

Fig. 19.16 Something simple.

Item 9 in Appendix D provides the mapping shown in Fig. 19.17, which is conformal throughout the interior of D. (Conformality does break down at the corner points F and G, since $(d/dz)(-\cos \pi z) = \pi \sin \pi z = 0$ there, but that breakdown is of no concern because F and G are *boundary* points of D, not interior points.)

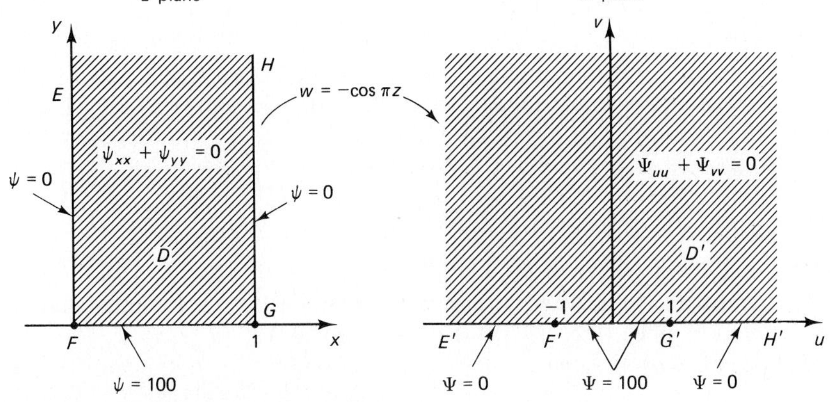

Fig. 19.17 Mapping onto upper half plane.

At this point we could use the above-mentioned solution to the Dirichlet half-plane problem [(9) on page 659] to solve for $\Psi(x, y)$:

$$\begin{aligned}\Psi(x, y) &= \frac{v}{\pi}\int_{-\infty}^{\infty} \frac{\Psi(u', 0)\, du'}{(u' - u)^2 + v^2} \\ &= \frac{100v}{\pi}\int_{-1}^{1} \frac{du'}{(u' - u)^2 + v^2} \\ &= \frac{100}{\pi}\left(\tan^{-1}\frac{1-u}{v} + \tan^{-1}\frac{1+u}{v}\right).\end{aligned} \tag{11}$$

However, it may be more instructive to bypass (11) and to carry out one more mapping, from the w plane to a $\zeta = \xi + i\eta$ plane, using item 7 in Appendix D. Denoting $\Psi(u(\xi, \eta), v(\xi, \eta)) = \tilde{\Psi}(\xi, \eta)$, this second mapping is indicated in Fig. 19.18. Finally, the problem in the ζ plane is quite simple and gives the solution

$$\tilde{\Psi}(\xi, \eta) = \frac{100}{\pi}\eta. \tag{12}$$

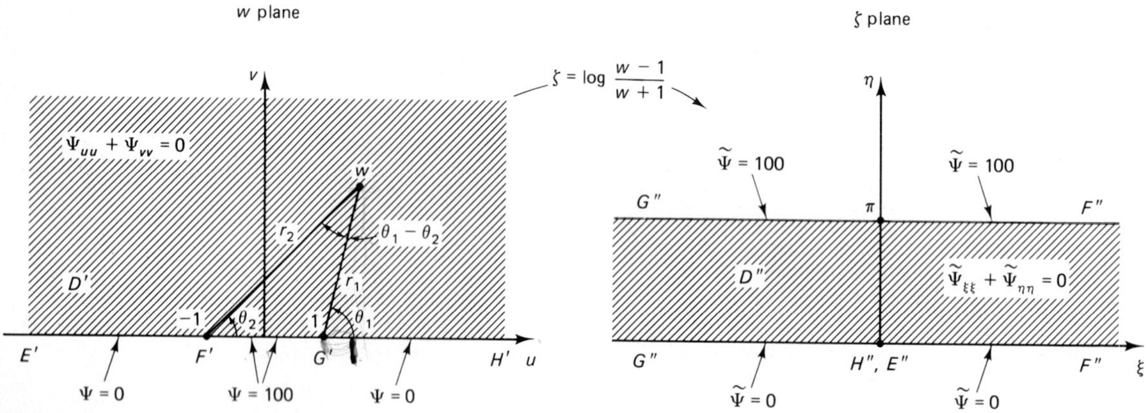

Fig. 19.18 One more mapping.

Retracing our steps, we need to express η in terms of u and v, and then u and v in terms of x and y. First, we express $w - 1 = r_1 e^{i\theta_1}$ and $w + 1 = r_2 e^{i\theta_2}$ (Fig. 19.18), so that

$$\zeta = \xi + i\eta = \log\left(\frac{r_1}{r_2}e^{i(\theta_1 - \theta_2)}\right) = \ln\frac{r_1}{r_2} + i(\theta_1 - \theta_2). \tag{13}$$

Thus $\eta = \theta_1 - \theta_2$, so

$$\Psi(u, v) = \frac{100}{\pi}(\theta_1 - \theta_2) = \frac{100}{\pi}\left(\tan^{-1}\frac{u+1}{v} - \tan^{-1}\frac{u-1}{v}\right) \tag{14}$$

[in agreement with (11)], where the values of both $\tan^{-1}$ ( )'s are understood to lie between 0 and π since (Fig. 19.18) $0 < \theta_1 < \pi$ and $0 < \theta_2 < \pi$.

Next, $w = -\cos \pi z$ gives

$$u = -\cos \pi x \cosh \pi y, \qquad v = \sin \pi x \sinh \pi y, \tag{15}$$

so, from (14) and (15), the desired solution is

$$\psi(x, y) = \frac{100}{\pi}\left[\tan^{-1}\left(\frac{1 - \cos \pi x \cosh \pi y}{\sin \pi x \sinh \pi y}\right) + \tan^{-1}\left(\frac{1 + \cos \pi x \cosh \pi y}{\sin \pi x \sinh \pi y}\right)\right], \tag{16}$$

where, as mentioned above, the $\tan^{-1}$ ( )'s are understood to lie between 0 and π.

COMMENT 1 In this example, the original semi-infinite strip problem could have been solved by separation of variables, which method yields (Exercise 3)

$$\psi(x, y) = \frac{400}{\pi} \sum_{n=1,3,\dots}^{\infty} \frac{\sin n\pi x}{n} e^{-n\pi y}. \tag{17}$$

Thus it is noteworthy that even though the problem could be solved by separation of variables, the conformal mapping approach proves superior (at least in this case) inasmuch as it gives the solution in *closed form* rather than as an infinite series. No doubt, suitable series expansion of the right-hand side of (16) should produce the right-hand side of (17), but we will not pursue this point.

COMMENT 2 Naturally, the two successive transformations (from z to w to ζ) are equivalent to the single transformation

$$\zeta = \log \frac{1 + \cos \pi z}{1 - \cos \pi z}, \tag{18}$$

but it is easier to proceed by a sequence of smaller and simpler steps, as we have. ◀

EXAMPLE 3 *Flow in Corner.* Recall from Section 9.12 that the plane, irrotational, incompressible flow of an inviscid fluid is governed by the Laplace equation

$$\nabla^2\phi = \phi_{xx} + \phi_{yy} = 0,$$

where ϕ is the velocity potential, which is related to the velocity $\mathbf{q} = u(x, y)\hat{\mathbf{i}} + v(x, y)\hat{\mathbf{j}}$ according to $\mathbf{q} = \nabla\phi$. Now, consider the plane flow in a 90° corner, bounded by walls along the x and y axes, as sketched in Fig. 19.19a. The boundary condition is that $\mathbf{q} \cdot \hat{\mathbf{n}} = \nabla\phi \cdot \hat{\mathbf{n}} = \partial\phi/\partial n = 0$ all along the walls. The mapping $\zeta = \xi + i\eta = z^2$* maps the first quadrant of the z plane, conformally, onto the upper half of the w plane, and [as noted, in italics, following (9)] the homogeneous Neumann condition on ϕ carries over to Φ.

Now, a simple Φ that is harmonic in D' and satisfies the $\partial\Phi/\partial N = 0$ boundary condition is $\Phi = U\xi$, corresponding to the uniform flow with velocity $\nabla\Phi = U\hat{\mathbf{i}}$, shown in Fig. 19.19b. Since $\zeta = \xi + i\eta = (x^2 - y^2) + i2xy$ gives $\xi = x^2 - y^2$ and $\eta = 2xy$, it follows from

$$\Phi(\xi, \eta) = U\xi \tag{19}$$

* We use ξ, η in place of the usual u, v because, following standard fluid mechanics notation, we are using u, v to designate the x, y velocity components.

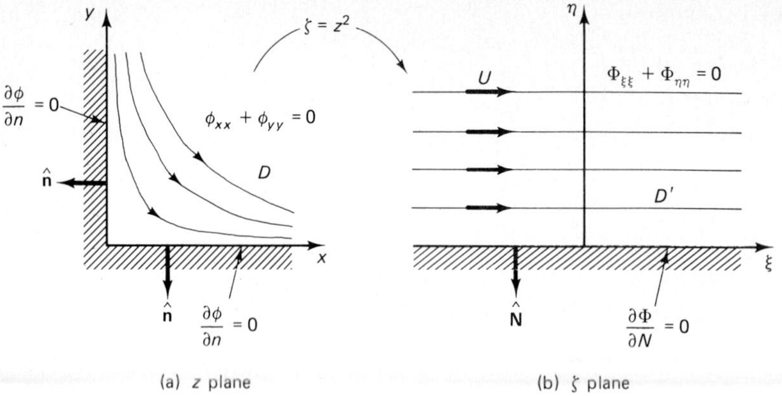

Fig. 19.19 Corner flow.

that

$$\phi(x, y) = U(x^2 - y^2) \tag{20}$$

and that the desired velocity field in the x, y plane is

$$\mathbf{q} = \nabla\phi = 2U(x\hat{\mathbf{i}} - y\hat{\mathbf{j}}). \tag{21}$$

Although (21) is the desired flow field, let us carry the discussion a bit further. Recall from our study of the gradient in Section 9.5 that at each point in the field the vector $\nabla\phi$ is normal to the ϕ = constant curve through that point. It is also true that if $\psi(x, y)$ is the conjugate harmonic function corresponding to $\phi(x, y)$, so that $w(z) = \phi(x, y) + i\psi(x, y)$ is an analytic function of z, then the ψ = constant curves are orthogonal to the ϕ = constant curves. Thus the fluid particles move along ψ = constant curves. These curves are called *streamlines*, and $\psi(x, y)$ is called the *stream function.** Corresponding to $\phi(x, y) = U(x^2 - y^2)$, the conjugate harmonic function $\psi(x, y)$ is easily found (Exercise 4) to be

$$\psi(x, y) = 2Uxy, \tag{22}$$

so the streamlines $\psi(x, y) = 2Uxy$ = constant are the hyperbolas xy = constant (Fig. 19.20).

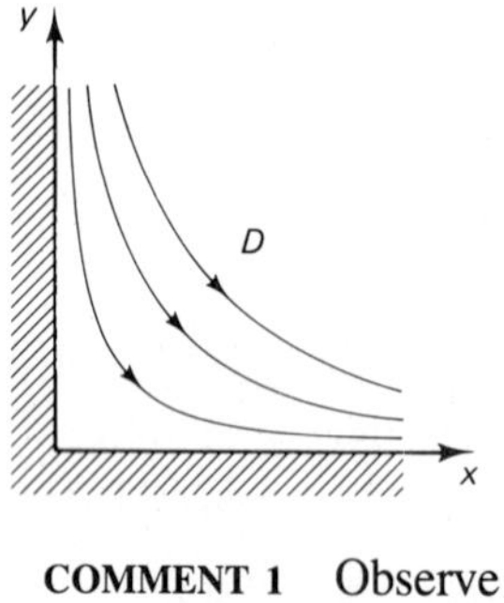

Fig. 19.20 Streamlines for the corner flow.

COMMENT 1 Observe that our introduction of the stream function ψ was not essential since the desired velocity field had already been completely determined by (21), although it was convenient for obtaining the streamline pattern. However, it is fairly standard in the fluid mechanics literature to work with the *complex velocity*

* For additional discussion of the stream function, see Exercise 7 on page 433.

potential

$$w(z) = \phi(x, y) + i\psi(x, y) \tag{23}$$

from the outset [or, in the ζ plane, $W(\zeta) = \Phi(\xi, \eta) + i\Psi(\xi, \eta)$]. The velocity is derivable from w by differentiation since

$$\begin{aligned} \frac{dw}{dz} &= \phi_x + i\psi_x \qquad \text{(since } w \text{ is analytic)} \\ &= \phi_x - i\phi_y \qquad \text{(since } \phi \text{ and } \psi \text{ are related by the Cauchy–Riemann equations)} \\ &= u - iv. \end{aligned} \tag{24}$$

Thus the x and y velocity components are $u = \operatorname{Re} w'(z)$ and $v = -\operatorname{Im} w'(z)$, respectively.

To illustrate how one works with the complex potential w, let us rework the present example using w. In the ζ plane we have

$$\frac{dW}{d\zeta} = U - i0, \tag{25}$$

so $W = U\zeta$ (plus an arbitrary constant, which can be set equal to zero without loss). Returning to the z plane via $\zeta = z^2$, we have

$$w = Uz^2 = U(x^2 - y^2) + i2Uxy \tag{26}$$

and

$$\frac{dw}{dz} = 2Uz = 2Ux + i2Uy, \tag{27}$$

so the quantities of interest are $\phi(x, y) = U(x^2 - y^2)$, $\psi(x, y) = 2Uxy$, $u(x, y) = 2Ux$, and $v(x, y) = -2Uy$, as found above. Notice in particular that $u = v = 0$ at the corner ($x = y = 0$), which is therefore a *stagnation point*.

COMMENT 2 We do *not* claim that the corner flow that we have found is the *only* one possible (see Exercise 4).

COMMENT 3 Finally, a word of caution. A possible source of difficulty in this example (and the one to follow) is in keeping the notation straight. For example, $w(z)$ is the complex potential that we seek; the conformal mapping is given by $\zeta(z)$, not $w(z)$. ◀

Our final example is another fluid-flow problem, in which we again use the complex potential $w(z)$. Besides helping to solidify our ability to use the complex potential, the example is intended to introduce the important Joukowski transformation.

EXAMPLE 4 *Flow Past a Circular Cylinder*. This time we wish to find the plane, irrotational, incompressible flow of an inviscid fluid over a semicircular bump, where the flow tends to a uniform stream $\mathbf{q} = U\hat{\mathbf{i}}$ as we move away from the

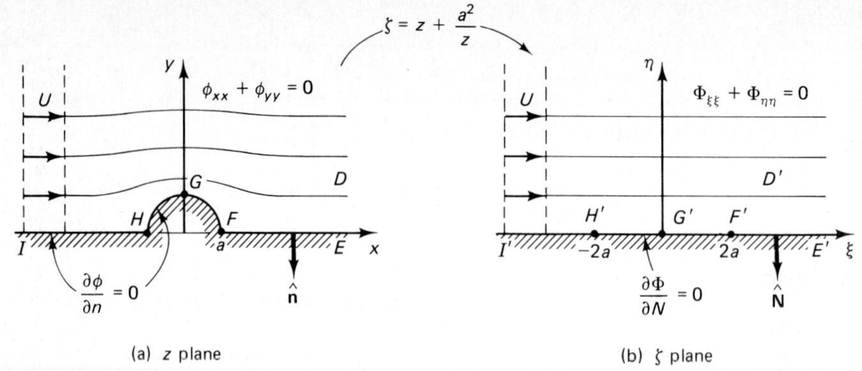

Fig. 19.21 Flow over semicircular bump.

bump, as sketched in Fig. 19.21a. Physically, the boundary condition is that the velocity component normal to the solid boundary *EFGHI* is zero.

From Appendix D we find that the **Joukowski transformation**

$$\zeta = z + \frac{a^2}{z} \tag{28}$$

maps the flow region D, conformally, onto the upper half of the ζ plane (Fig. 19.21b). Besides preserving the homogeneous Neumann boundary condition, the Joukowski transformation also preserves the "boundary condition at infinity,"

$$\frac{dw}{dz} = u(x, y) - iv(x, y) \sim U \qquad \text{as} \quad z \to \infty, \tag{29}$$

because

$$\frac{dw}{dz} = \frac{dW}{d\zeta}\frac{d\zeta}{dz} \tag{30}$$

and $d\zeta/dz \to 1$ as $z \to \infty$. Thus the boundary condition at infinity in the ζ plane is

$$\frac{dW}{d\zeta} \sim U \qquad \text{as} \quad \zeta \to \infty. \tag{31}$$

In fact, the complex potential $W = U\zeta = U(\xi + i\eta)$ satisfies all three requirements; W is analytic in D',

$$\frac{\partial\Phi}{\partial N} = -\frac{\partial\Phi}{\partial\eta} = -\frac{\partial}{\partial\eta}(U\xi) = 0 \quad \text{on} \quad \eta = 0,$$

and $dW/d\zeta = U \sim U$ as $z \to \infty$. Thus $W = U\zeta$, so it follows from (28) that

$$w = U\left(z + \frac{a^2}{z}\right). \tag{32}$$

With $z = re^{i\theta}$, (32) becomes

$$w = U\left(r + \frac{a^2}{r}\right)\cos\theta + iU\left(r - \frac{a^2}{r}\right)\sin\theta, \tag{33}$$

so

$$\phi(r, \theta) = U\left(r + \frac{a^2}{r}\right) \cos \theta \tag{34a}$$

and

$$\psi(r, \theta) = U\left(r - \frac{a^2}{r}\right) \sin \theta. \tag{34b}$$

In addition,

$$\frac{dw}{dz} = u - iv = U\left(1 - \frac{a^2}{z^2}\right) = U\left(1 - \frac{a^2}{r^2} \cos 2\theta\right) + iU\frac{a^2}{r^2} \sin 2\theta, \tag{35}$$

so the velocity components are

$$u(r, \theta) = U\left(1 - \frac{a^2}{r^2} \cos 2\theta\right), \tag{36a}$$

$$v(r, \theta) = -U\frac{a^2}{r^2} \sin 2\theta. \tag{36b}$$

COMMENT 1 Observe that (36) does satisfy the boundary condition at infinity: $u \sim U$ and $v \to 0$ as $r \to \infty$. And from (34b) we see that the solid boundary $EFGH$ (Fig. 19.21a) is a streamline, namely, $\psi = 0$: on EF and HI the $\sin \theta$ factor is zero, and on FGH the $r - a^2/r$ factor is zero.

COMMENT 2 The boundary value problem on ϕ, which is indicated in Fig. 19.21a, was also solved earlier (Exercise 10, page 656) by separation of variables. ◀

In this section we have worked through a sequence of examples of the solution of problems in two-dimensional potential theory using conformal mapping. In Examples 1 and 3 a single mapping sufficed, whereas in Example 2 a composition of two successive mappings was employed. Rather than develop or discuss the mappings, we treated them as off-the-shelf items from Appendix D so that we could focus on the overall solution technique. However, additional attention is paid to the mappings themselves in the exercises to follow: mappings by elementary functions, by the Schwarz–Christoffel transformation [of which the mapping $w(z) = -\cos \pi z$ in Example 1 was an example], by the Joukowski transformation, and by compositions of these mappings.

19.4 EXERCISES

1. Solve the problem

$$\Psi_{uu} + \Psi_{vv} = 0 \qquad (0 < u < 1, -\infty < v < \infty)$$

$$\Psi(0, v) = 0, \quad \Psi(1, v) = \frac{1 - v^2}{1 + v^2},$$

which occurred in Example 1, by applying a Fourier transform on the v variable. Show that the solution is given by the Fourier convolution

$$\Psi(u, v) = \frac{1 - v^2}{1 + v^2} * \mathbf{F}^{-1}\left\{\frac{\sinh \omega u}{\sinh \omega}\right\}.$$

(The inverse $\mathbf{F}^{-1}\{\sinh \omega u/\sinh \omega\}$ can be evaluated using the residue theorem, but that theorem will not be derived until Chapter 21.)

2. In each case, ψ satisfies the Laplace equation $\psi_{xx} + \psi_{yy} = 0$ in the given region D, as well as the given boundary conditions. Given the mapping $w = f(z)$, determine the image D' of D as well as the transformed boundary conditions on the boundary of D'. [You need *not* solve for $\Psi(u, v)$.]

*(a) On AB: $\psi = 0$
On BC: $\psi = 1$
On CE: $\psi = 1 + x$
On EF: $\dfrac{\partial \psi}{\partial n} = 0$
$w = \dfrac{z + 1}{z - 1}$

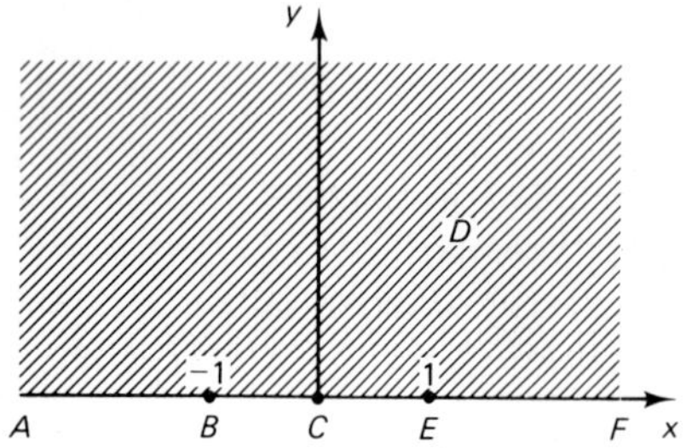

(b) Same region D as in part (a). On AB and EF $\partial\psi/\partial n = 0$, on BE $\partial\psi/\partial n = x$. $w = (1 + z)/(1 - z)$.
(c) Same region D as in part (a). On AB, BC, CE, and EF $\psi = 0$, 10, 20, and 30, respectively $w = (i - z)/(i + z)$.
(d) Same region D as in part (a). On AB $\partial\psi/\partial n = 0$, on BCE $\partial\psi/\partial n = x^3$, and on EF $\psi = e^{-x}$ $w = (i - z)/(i + z)$.
*(e) On ABC: $\psi = 50 \sin \theta$
On CEA: $\dfrac{\partial \psi}{\partial n} = 1$
$w = i\dfrac{1 - z}{1 + z}$

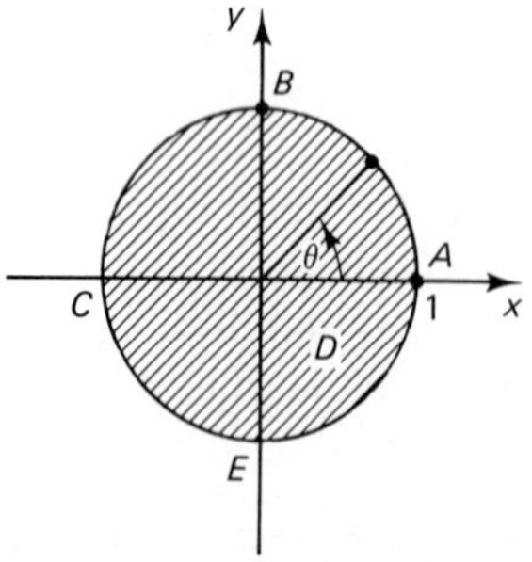

(f) On AB: $\psi = 0$
On BC: $\dfrac{\partial \psi}{\partial n} = \sin x$
On CE: $\psi = e^{-y}$
$w = \sin z$

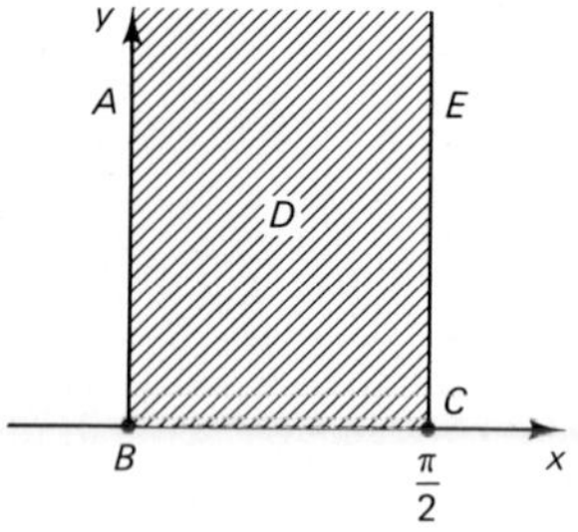

(g) On AB: $\psi = \psi_1$
On BC: $\psi = \psi_2$
On CEA: $\psi = \psi_3$
$w = \log z$ (principal value)

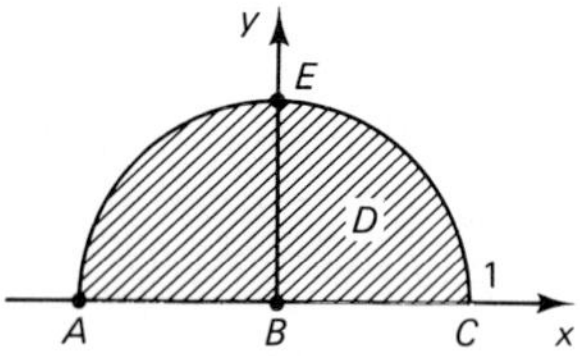

3. (*Example 2*) (a) Verify that the solution given by (16) does satisfy the given boundary conditions. (b) Derive, by using separation of variables, the alternative solution form (17). Verify that (16) and (17) agree, numerically, at $x = \frac{1}{2}$, $y = 1$, say.

4. (*Example 3*) (a) Derive the conjugate harmonic function given by (22) (to within an arbitrary additive constant).
(b) The corner flow found in Example 3 and depicted in Fig. 19.20 is not the only possible one. Determine a corner flow of the type sketched in the accompanying figure.

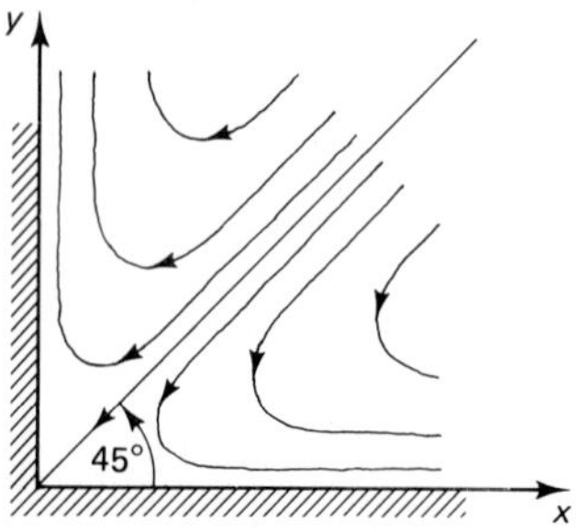

(c) Sketch still another possible corner flow.

5. (*Appendix D*) Verify the image of the region and selected boundary points for the following mappings tabulated in Appendix D.

(a) item 1 (b) item 2 (c) item 3
(d) item 4 (e) item 5 (f) item 6
(g) item 7 (h) item 8 (i) item 9
(j) item 10 (k) item 11 (l) item 12

6. Solve the following boundary value problems using the mapping $w = z^2$.

(a)

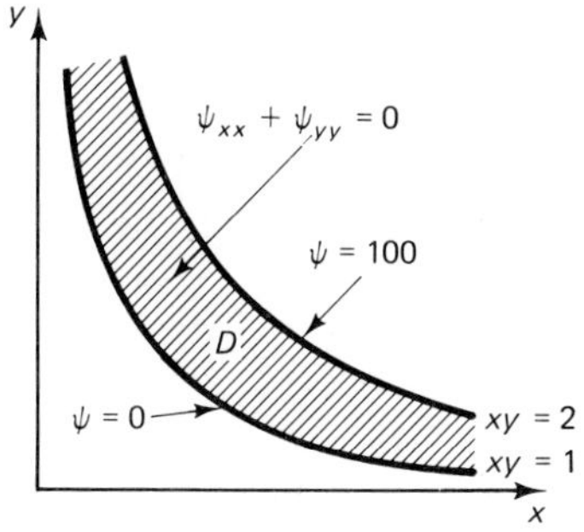

(b)

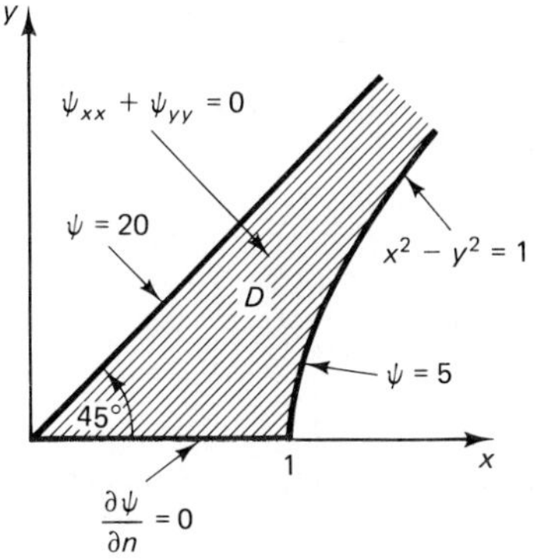

***7.** Solve the boundary value problem shown in the accompanying figure, with the help of Appendix D.

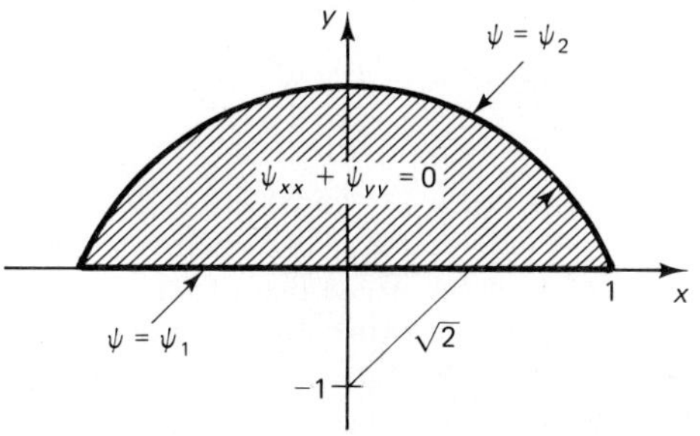

8. (*Flow over outside corner*) Consider the plane, irrotational, incompressible flow of an inviscid fluid over an *outside* corner, as sketched in the figure.

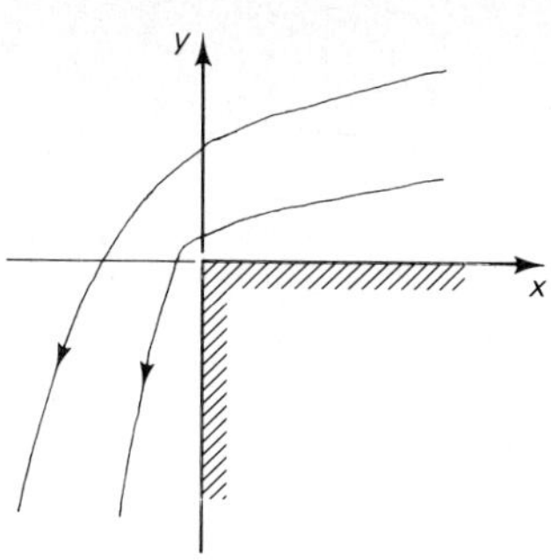

Mapping the flow region onto the upper half plane, derive the complex velocity potential $w = -Uz^{2/3}$. Determine the velocity along the wall [$u(x, 0)$ for $0 < x < \infty$, $v(0, y)$ for $-\infty < y < 0$]. Is the corner a stagnation point as it was for the *inside* corner flow in Example 3?

9. (*Branch cut for* $\sqrt{z^2 - 4a^2}$) The function $f(z) = \sqrt{z^2 - 4a^2}$ occurs in obtaining the inverse of the Joukowski transformation (Exercise 10), and requires some preliminary discussion. Specifically, the function is double valued for all z's except $z = \pm 2a$, and our object in this exercise is to explore suitable branch cuts that will render the function single valued. First, factor $z^2 - 4a^2 = (z - 2a)(z + 2a)$, and then express $z - 2a = r_1 e^{i\theta_1}$, $z + 2a = r_2 e^{i\theta_2}$.
(a) One suitable branch cut consists of two separate cuts, one to the point $+2a$ and the other to the point $-2a$, as shown in the first figure, with θ_1 and θ_2 both defined to be zero, say, at any point P on top of the right-hand cut. [Alternatively, one could define $\theta_1 = 2\pi$, $\theta_2 = 0$ for example, at P. That definition would give a different branch of the function $f(z)$.] Then θ_1 and θ_2 are uniquely determined at every point in the cut plane; hence so is the function

$$\sqrt{z^2 - 4a^2} = \sqrt{r_1 r_2}\, e^{i(\theta_1 + \theta_2)/2}. \tag{a}$$

To illustrate, let us evaluate $f(z)$ at the point Q, which is at $x = 4a$, $y = 0$, on the bottom edge of the cut. Clearly, $r_1 = 2a$ and $r_2 = 6a$. To determine θ_1 and θ_2 at Q we begin at P, where $\theta_1 = \theta_2 = 0$ are known, and follow a legitimate path from P to Q, such as C. (That is, *the path is to remain within the cut plane,* as does C. The path C', on the other hand, crosses the cut and is therefore not "legitimate." Following C, we see that θ_1 increases from 0 at P to 2π at Q; θ_2 increases, then decreases, then increases, such that its net change is nil. Thus (a) gives

$$f\,\big|_{z=Q} = \sqrt{(2a)(6a)}\; e^{i(2\pi+0)/2} = -2\sqrt{3}\,a.$$

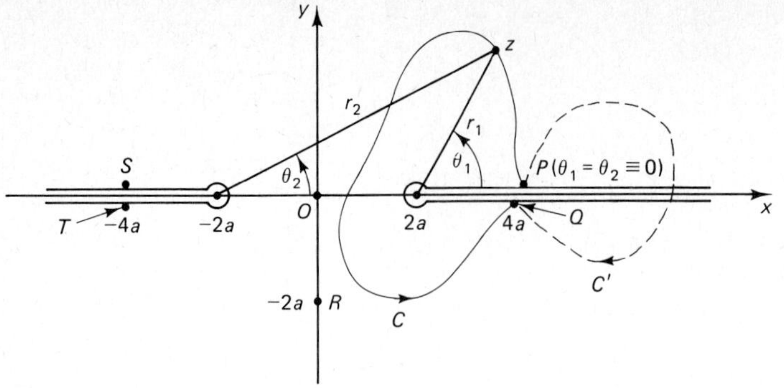

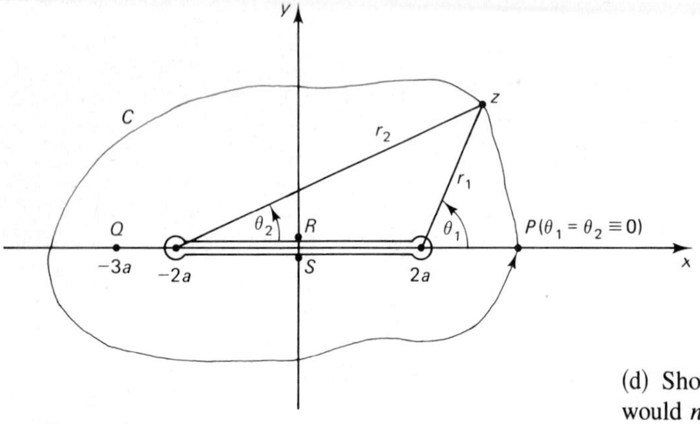

We now state the problem: Evaluate $f(z)$ at points R, S, T, and O.

(b) Another suitable branch cut is the *finite* cut from $-2a$ to $+2a$, with $\theta_1 = \theta_2 \equiv 0$ at any point P on the x axis to the right of $2a$, as shown in the second figure. Observe carefully that this cut does not render θ_1 and θ_2 single valued, but it *does* render the *function* single valued, which is all we ask. To illustrate, suppose we begin at a point P such that $x = 4a$, $y = 0$, with $\theta_1 = \theta_2 = 0$. Then $f|_P = \sqrt{(2a)(6a)}\, e^{i(0+0)/2} = 2\sqrt{3}a$. If we then make the (legitimate) trip C, we find that upon arriving at P we have $\theta_1 = \theta_2 = 2\pi$! Nevertheless, $f|_P = \sqrt{(2a)(6a)}\, e^{i(2\pi+2\pi)/2} = 2\sqrt{3}\, a$, as before. The essential idea behind the success of the finite cut is that a complete encirclement of $z = 2a$ causes a sign change in the value of f, and similarly for a complete encirclement of $z = -2a$. Since the cut forces encirclements of *both* points, an even number of sign changes results, so the function value is uniquely determined by the cut. We now state the problem: Use this branch cut to evaluate f at Q, R, and S.

(c) Modify the branch cut defined in part (b) by defining $\theta_1 \equiv 2\pi$, $\theta_2 \equiv 0$ at P. Using this branch cut, evaluate f at Q, R, and S.

(d) Show that the cuts defined in parts (b) and (c) would *not* be suitable cuts for $f(z) = (z^2 - 4a^2)^{1/3}$.

Note: An alternative approach to handling multivalued functions is the method of **Riemann surfaces.** See, for example, R. V. Churchill, *Complex Variables and Applications,* 2nd ed. (New York: McGraw-Hill, 1960).

10. (*Joukowski transformation*) Show that the **Joukowski transformation**

$$\zeta = \xi + i\eta = z + \frac{a^2}{z} \qquad (a > 0) \tag{a}$$

maps the circles $x^2 + y^2 = c^2$ onto the confocal ellipses

$$\frac{\xi^2}{(c + a^2/c)^2} + \frac{\eta^2}{(c - a^2/c)^2} = 1 \tag{b}$$

with foci at $\zeta = \pm 2a$, as shown in the figure. Thus show that the circle $|z| = a$ maps onto the line segment $\eta = 0$, $|\xi| \le 2a$. Show that the exterior region $|z| > a$ maps onto the entire ζ plane minus that line segment, and that the interior $|z| < a$ does, too. Hence the inverse transformation is double valued. In fact, show that

$$z = \frac{\zeta + \sqrt{\zeta^2 - 4a^2}}{2}, \tag{c}$$

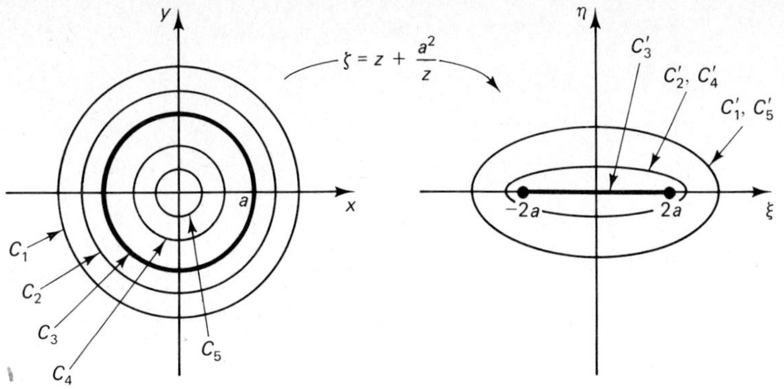

where the branch cut in Exercise 9(b) corresponds to the mapping of the slit ζ plane onto $|z| > a$, and the branch cut in Exercise 9(c) corresponds to the mapping of the slit ζ plane onto $|z| < a$.

11. (*Flow perpendicular to flat plate*) Determine the plane, irrotational, incompressible, inviscid velocity field around a thin flat plate that is perpendicular to a uniform stream V; i.e., $dw/dz = u - iv \sim iV$ as $z \to \infty$. In particular, show that on top of the plate $u = Vx/\sqrt{4a^2 - x^2}$ and $v = 0$, and on the bottom of the plate $u = -Vx/\sqrt{4a^2 - x^2}$ and $v = 0$. *Hint:* Use the mapping sequence shown in the figure, and see Exercises 9 and 10.

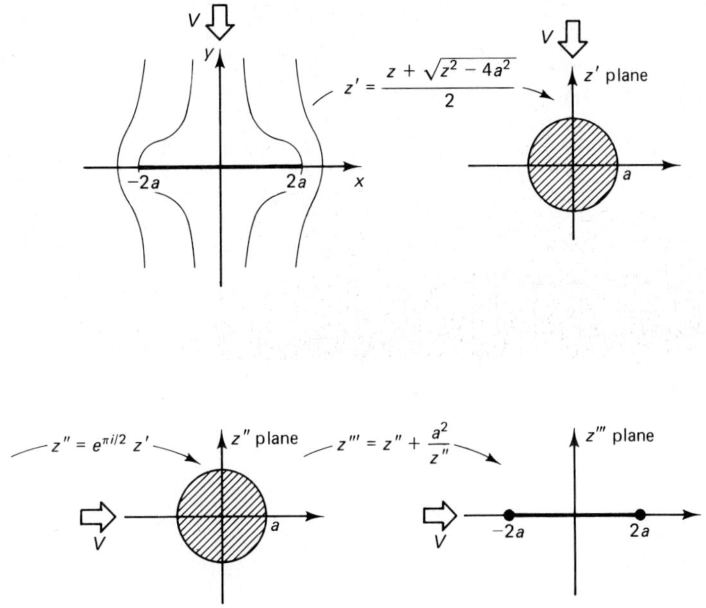

12. (*Schwarz–Christoffel transformation*) The Schwarz–Christoffel transformation enables us to map the upper *half plane* onto a given *polygon* (or vice versa using the inverse transformation). To see how it works, consider the mapping of the upper half plane by a transformation $w = f(z)$ such that

$$\frac{df}{dz} = A(z - a)^b, \qquad \text{(a)}$$

where a is a point on the x axis, b is a real number such that $-1 < b < 1$, A is allowed to be complex, and where $(z - a)^b$ is defined by the downward branch cut shown in the figure, with $-\pi/2 < \arg(z - a) < 3\pi/2$. [The branch cut is taken downward in order to keep it out of the region under consideration, the upper half plane. Thus $(z - a)^b$ is defined *throughout* the upper half plane.] To obtain the image D' of D we consider the boundary curve C of

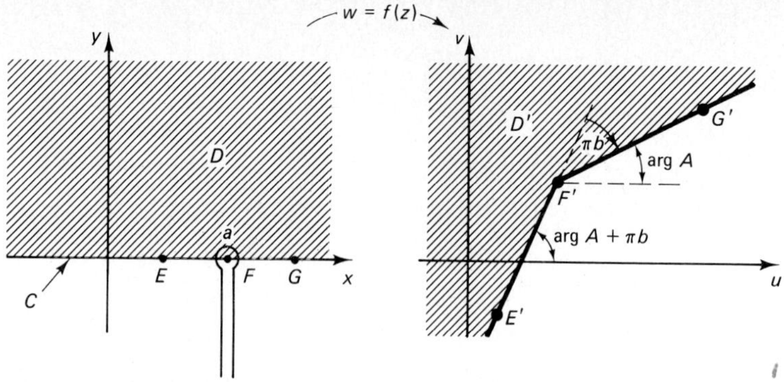

D. Parametrize that curve by $x = \tau - a$, $y = 0$ for $-\infty < \tau < \infty$. Then the image curve is parametrized by $w(\tau) = f(z(\tau))$, so

$$\frac{dw}{d\tau} = f'(z)\frac{dz}{d\tau}. \tag{b}$$

With dots denoting $d/d\tau$, it follows that

$$\arg \dot{w} = \arg f' + \arg \dot{z}. \tag{c}$$

As noted in Section 19.2, $\dot{z}$ is a tangent vector to C and $\dot{w}$ is a tangent vector to the image C' of C, so (c) indicates that the tangent vector $\dot{w}$ is rotated counterclockwise, relative to the tangent vector $\dot{z}$, through the angle $\arg f'$.

(a) Show that the image domain D' is as shown in the figure.
(b) To illustrate, consider $f(z)$ to be such that

$$\frac{df}{dz} = A(z-1)^{-1/2}(z+1)^{-1/2} = \frac{A}{\sqrt{z^2-1}}. \tag{d}$$

If we had already studied the complex *integral* calculus, we could infer from (d) that

$$f(z) = A\int \frac{dz}{\sqrt{z^2-1}} = A \sin^{-1} z + B. \tag{e}$$

Not having studied the complex integral calculus, we only ask you to verify that d/dz of $A \sin^{-1} z + B$ does give (d). Next, with $A = 1$ and $B = 0$, say, show that $w = f(z) = \sin^{-1} z$ maps the upper half plane onto the semi-infinite strips $-\pi/2 + k\pi < u < \pi/2 + k\pi$, $0 < v < \infty$ $(k = 0, \pm 1, \pm 2, \ldots)$. Choosing the branch (of the multivalued function $\sin^{-1} z$) corresponding to $k = 0$, the result is as depicted in the figure, and is in agreement with item 10 in Appendix D.

The Complex Integral Calculus 20

INTRODUCTION 20.1

In Chapter 18 we got as far as the differential calculus of functions of a complex variable, with special emphasis on the concept of analyticity. After applying the analytic function theory to conformal mapping in Chapter 19, we now pick up where we left off in Chapter 18 and turn to the complex *integral* calculus. We begin by defining the complex integral $\int_C f(z)\,dz$, and then proceed to derive the *Cauchy theorem*, the *fundamental theorem of the complex integral calculus*, and the *Cauchy integral formula*.

Beyond helping us to evaluate integrals, these results will permit us to further develop complex function theory on a broad front. For example, the Cauchy integral formula will enable us to show that an analytic function possesses derivatives of *all* orders, a striking result with no analog in real-variable theory. The Cauchy integral formula will also enable us to develop *Taylor series* for functions of a complex variable, and a significant generalization of the latter known as *Laurent series*. Laurent series, in turn, will clarify the nature of *singularities*.

COMPLEX INTEGRATION 20.2

We now introduce the **complex integral**

$$\int_C f(z)\,dz \tag{1}$$

of a given function f along a given oriented curve C in the complex z plane; f may or may not be analytic, and C may be either a closed curve or an arc, but in either case we shall assume that it is piecewise smooth and simple.* The curve C is called the *path of integration*, or *contour*. To define the integral (1), we stay as close as possible to the definition of line integrals developed in Section 9.10.

Suppose that C has initial and final points $z = A$ and $z = B$, respectively; if C is closed, then $B = A$. Divide C into n arcs by specifying points $z_0 = A, z_1, z_2, \ldots, z_{n-1}, z_n = B$ along C. Let the division be chosen arbitrarily, provided that the points z_j are spaced and numbered so that the arc length from A to z_j is less than the arc length from A to z_k if $j < k$ (Fig. 20.1). Denote the n arcs as $C_1, C_2, \ldots, C_n$, where the endpoints of C_j are z_{j-1} and z_j. On each C_j choose some point Q_j that is anywhere between the endpoints of C_j or at one of the endpoints, and form the sum

$$J_n = \sum_{j=1}^{n} f(Q_j)\Delta z_j, \tag{2}$$

where $\Delta z_j = z_j - z_{j-1}$. The choice of the z_j's and Q_j's defines a *partition* of C, and we call the largest $|\Delta z_j|$ the *norm* of the partition. We introduce not just one partition, but a sequence of them such that the norm of the nth partition tends to zero as $n \to \infty$. If the corresponding sequence of sums $J_1, J_2, \ldots$ converges to a limit, we call that limit the integral $\int_C f(z)\,dz$. We then say that the integral *exists*, i.e., that it is *convergent*.

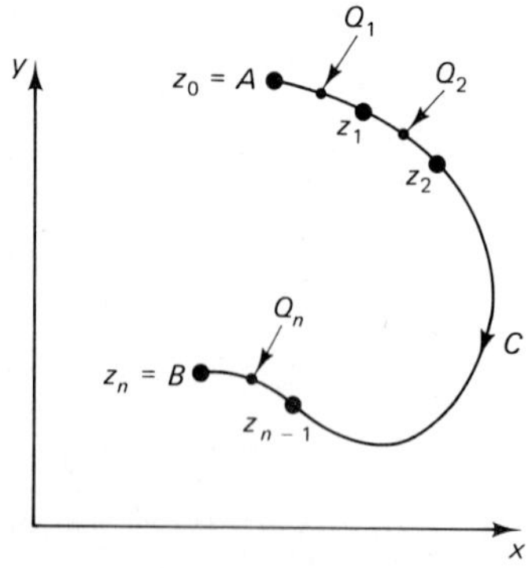

Fig. 20.1 Partition of C.

From this definition it is easy to show that complex integration is *linear*, i.e.,

$$\int_C [\alpha f(z) + \beta g(z)]\,dz = \alpha \int_C f(z)\,dz + \beta \int_C g(z)\,dz \tag{3}$$

for any scalars α and β and for any functions f and g for which the three integrals exist, and that if we break C into two parts, C_1 and C_2 (Fig. 20.2), then

$$\int_C f(z)\,dz = \int_{C_1} f(z)\,dz + \int_{C_2} f(z)\,dz. \tag{4}$$

Finally, if we reverse the orientation of C and call the reverse path "$-C$," we have

$$\int_{-C} f(z)\,dz = -\int_C f(z)\,dz. \tag{5}$$

* These terms were defined in Section 9.10 on line integrals.

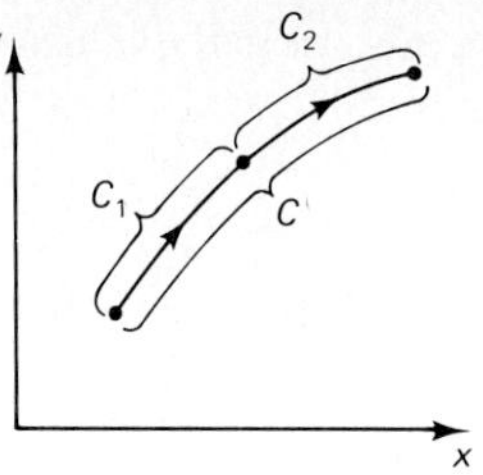

Fig. 20.2 Breaking up the path.

EXAMPLE 1 *Using the Limit Definition to Evaluate Integrals.* To illustrate the limit definition of the complex integral, consider the simple case where $f(z) = 1$. To use (2), let us first note that the points Q_j and z_j are different for each n, so that it would be better to rewrite (2) as

$$J_n = \sum_{j=1}^{n} f(Q_{jn})\Delta z_{jn}, \tag{6}$$

where the subscript n refers to the nth partition. Now, with $f(z) = 1$, (6) gives

$$\begin{aligned} J_n = \sum_{j=1}^{n} \Delta z_{jn} &= (z_{1n} - A) + (z_{2n} - z_{1n}) \\ &\quad + \cdot \cdot \cdot + (z_{n-1,n} - z_{n-2,n}) + (B - z_{n-1,n}) \\ &= B - A \end{aligned} \tag{7}$$

terms. Since $J_n = B - A$ holds for *each* $n = 1, 2, \ldots$, it is clear that $\lim_{n\to\infty} J_n = \lim_{n\to\infty} (B - A) = B - A$. Thus

$$\int_C dz = B - A, \tag{8}$$

where A, B are the initial and final points, respectively, of the path C. ◀

It is not much more difficult to show (Exercise 1) that

$$\int_C z\, dz = \frac{B^2}{2} - \frac{A^2}{2}. \tag{9}$$

Why all the fuss? Doesn't $\int_C z\, dz = (z^2/2)|_A^B$ follow immediately from the fact that $(d/dz)(z^2/2) = z$? Yes it does, but we have not yet developed the fundamental theorem of the complex integral calculus, on which result that claim would be based; all we have, thus far, is the limit definition.

Of course, the limit definition is too unwieldy to prove useful in evaluating more complicated integrals, so we proceed to develop other lines of approach. In this regard it will be illuminating to distinguish two basically different strategies.

One strategy is to reduce $\int_C f(z)\, dz$ to one or more *real* integrals. To do so, one merely needs to reexpress

$$\begin{aligned} \int_C f(z)\, dz &= \int_C (u + iv)(dx + i\, dy) \\ &= \int_C (u\, dx - v\, dy) + i \int_C (v\, dx + u\, dy). \end{aligned} \tag{10}$$

Thus we can evaluate $\int_C f(z)\,dz$ by evaluating the two real line integrals

$$\int_C [u(x, y)\,dx - v(x, y)\,dy] \quad \text{and} \quad \int_C [v(x, y)\,dx + u(x, y)\,dy]$$

by methods developed earlier in Chapter 9. Let us illustrate with two examples.

EXAMPLE 2 Evaluate

$$I = \int_C z^2\,dz, \tag{11}$$

where C is the parabolic arc shown in Fig. 20.3. Parametrizing C according to $y = \tau$, $x = 4 - \tau^2$, as τ goes from $+2$ to -2, we have

$$\begin{aligned} I &= \int_C [(x^2 - y^2)\,dx - 2xy\,dy] + i\int_C [2xy\,dx + (x^2 - y^2)\,dy] \\ &= \int_2^{-2} \left[(x^2 - y^2)\frac{dx}{d\tau} - 2xy\frac{dy}{d\tau}\right] d\tau + i\int_2^{-2} \left[2xy\frac{dx}{d\tau} + (x^2 - y^2)\frac{dy}{d\tau}\right] d\tau \\ &= \int_2^{-2} [((4 - \tau^2)^2 - \tau^2)(-2\tau) - 2(4 - \tau^2)\tau]\,d\tau \\ &\qquad + i\int_2^{-2} [2(4 - \tau^2)\tau(-2\tau) + ((4 - \tau^2)^2 - \tau^2)]\,d\tau \\ &= 0 + i\frac{16}{3} = \frac{16}{3}i. \end{aligned} \tag{12}$$

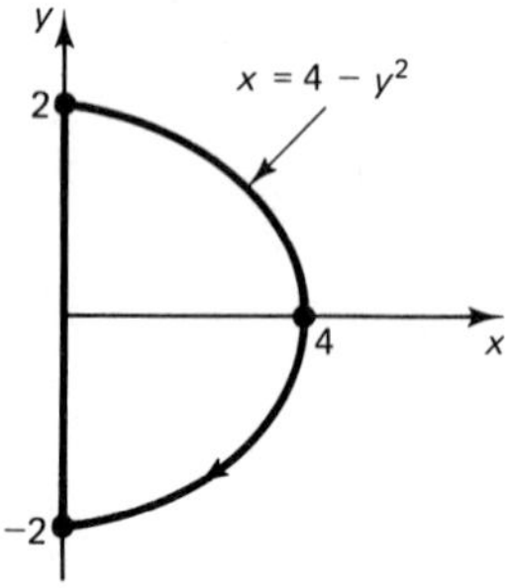

Fig. 20.3 The path C in (11).

COMMENT It is natural to wonder whether we could have simplified the evaluation of I by deforming C into a simpler shape, such as a straight line from the initial point $2i$ to the final point $-2i$. This same important question arose in Chapter 9 when we studied line integrals, and we found that path deformation (between fixed endpoints) was permissible if the given vector field was sufficiently well behaved. In view of the connection between $\int_C f(z)\,dz$ and real line integrals, displayed in (10), we expect that the same is true for the complex integral $\int_C f(z)\,dz$: The path C can be deformed if $f(z)$ is suffcently well behaved. We defer discussion of this question to Section 20.3. ◀

EXAMPLE 3 Evaluate

$$I = \oint_C (z - a)^n \, dz, \tag{13}$$

where a is a given complex number, n is any integer (positive, negative, or zero), and C is a circle of radius R, centered at $z = a$ and oriented counterclockwise (Fig. 20.4). In this case C is *closed*. Generally, we will use the $\oint_C$ notation when the contour C is closed.

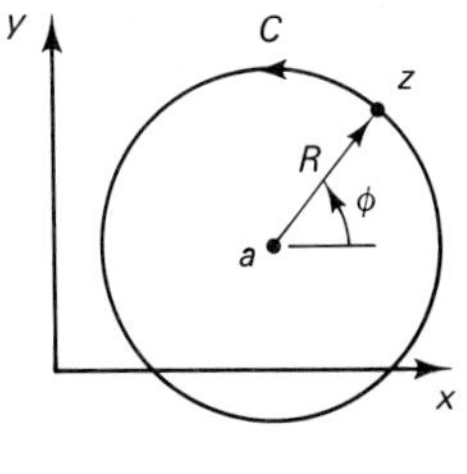

Fig. 20.4 The closed contour C in (13).

It will be convenient to use the polar angle ϕ to parametrize C, by setting

$$z - a = Re^{i\phi}. \tag{14}$$

Then

$$I = \int_0^{2\pi} (Re^{i\phi})^n (Rie^{i\phi} \, d\phi) = iR^{n+1} \int_0^{2\pi} e^{i(n+1)\phi} \, d\phi$$

$$= \frac{R^{n+1}}{n+1} e^{i(n+1)\phi} \Big|_0^{2\pi} = 0,$$

provided that $n \neq -1$ (in which case the latter yields the indeterminate form $0/0$). Treating $n = -1$ separately,

$$I = iR^0 \int_0^{2\pi} e^{i0\phi} \, d\phi = i \int_0^{2\pi} d\phi = 2\pi i.$$

Thus

$$\oint_C (z - a)^n \, dz = \begin{cases} 2\pi i & (n = -1) \\ 0 & (n \neq -1). \end{cases} \tag{15}$$ ◀

The other possible strategy is to keep the complex integral intact and to develop theorems that will enable us to work with $\int_C f(z) \, dz$ directly. It will be found that this approach is the more fruitful and will be pursued exclusively in the remainder of Part V. Looking ahead, we shall obtain Cauchy's theorem, the fundamental theorem of the integral calculus, Cauchy's integral formula, and the residue theorem, in that order. These integral theorems will prove powerful indeed, and will also yield additional important results regarding function theory in general.

In that development we will often need to be able to "bound" complex integrals, i.e., to obtain bounds on their absolute magnitude (modulus). Thus, in the remainder of this section we consider a rather simple upper bound that will suffice for almost all of our needs. First, observe that

$$\begin{aligned} |J_n| &= \left| \sum_{j=1}^{n} f(Q_j)\Delta z_j \right| \le \sum_{j=1}^{n} |f(Q_j)\Delta z_j| \\ &\le \sum_{j=1}^{n} |f(Q_j)|\,|\Delta z_j|, \end{aligned} \tag{16}$$

where both inequalities follow from Exercise 5 on page 729. Now, if there exists a real constant M such that $|f(z)| \le M$ everywhere on C, then $|f(Q_j)| \le M$ for each j, and (16) gives

$$|J_n| \le M \sum_{j=1}^{n} |\Delta z_j|. \tag{17}$$

Thus

$$\begin{aligned} \left| \int_C f(z)\,dz \right| &= \left| \lim_{n\to\infty} J_n \right| = \lim_{n\to\infty} |J_n| \\ &\le M \lim_{n\to\infty} \sum_{j=1}^{n} |\Delta z_j| = ML, \end{aligned} \tag{18}$$

where L is the length of (the presumably rectifiable curve) C. The second equality in (18) amounts to the fact that the modulus of the limit of a sequence of complex numbers equals the limit of the moduli of those numbers (Exercise 4), and the final equality follows from the definition of arc length (Section 7.7). Let us frame the result, for emphasis:

$$\boxed{\left| \int_C f(z)\,dz \right| \le ML,} \tag{19}$$

where $|f(z)| \le M$ on C and L is the length of C. Subsequently, we shall refer to this result as the *ML bound.*

EXAMPLE 4 Use (19) to bound the integral

$$\int_C \sin z\,dz, \tag{20}$$

where C is the path shown in Fig. 20.5. Well,

$$\begin{aligned} |f(z)| &= |\sin z| = |\sin(x+iy)| \\ &= |\sin x \cosh y + i \cos x \sinh y| \\ &= \sqrt{\sin^2 x \cosh^2 y + \cos^2 x \sinh^2 y} \\ &\le \sqrt{\cosh^2 y + \sinh^2 y} \le \sqrt{\cosh^2 2 + \sinh^2 2} \end{aligned} \tag{21}$$

on C, and $L = \sqrt{13}$, so (19) gives

$$\left| \int_C \sin z\,dz \right| \le \sqrt{13(\cosh^2 2 + \sinh^2 2)} = \sqrt{13 \cosh 4}. \tag{22}$$

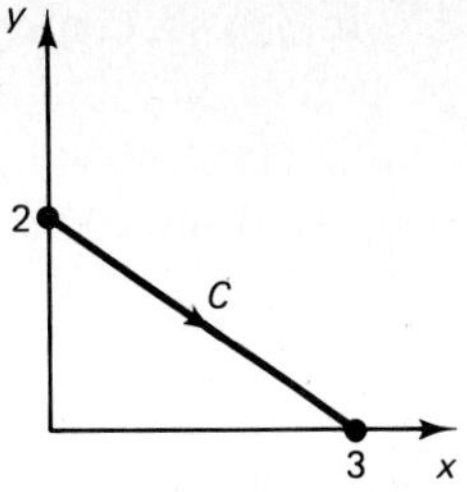

Fig. 20.5 The path C in (20).

COMMENT If tempted to use the (incorrect) inequality $|\sin z| \le 1$ in place of (21), one should review the properties of the sine function in Section 18.3. ◀

One more example.

EXAMPLE 5 Use (19) to bound the integral

$$I = \oint_C \frac{dz}{z(z-2)^3}, \tag{23}$$

where C is the circular contour shown in Fig. 20.6. On C we have

$$|z| = 5$$

and

$$|z-2| \ge 5 - 2 = 3.$$

That is, the $z - 2$ vector is shortest (as z traverses C) when z is at P; there, $|z-2| = 3$. Thus

$$\left| \frac{1}{z(z-2)^3} \right| \le \frac{1}{(5)(3^3)}$$

and

$$\left| \oint_C \frac{dz}{z(z-2)^3} \right| \le \frac{1}{(5)(27)} 2\pi(5) = \frac{2\pi}{27}. \quad ◀$$

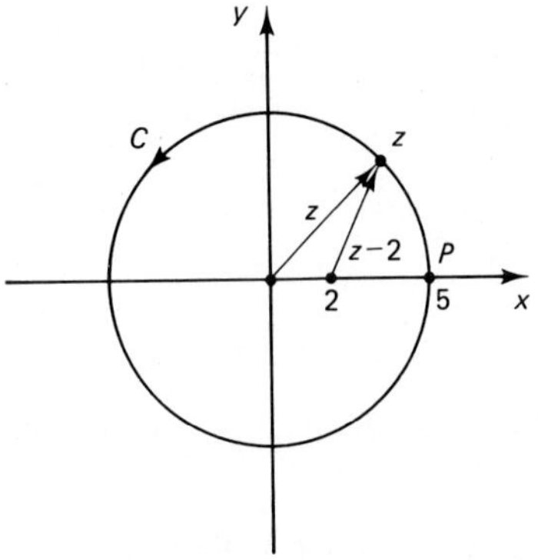

Fig. 20.6 The contour C in (23).

In this section we defined the complex integral $\int_C f(z)\, dz$, indicated its principal properties, showed how to express it in terms of real line integrals, and derived the simple upper bound given by (19). In the sections to follow we continue our development of the complex integral calculus.

20.2 EXERCISES

1. (a) Use the limit definition to derive the result

$$\int_C z\, dz = \frac{B^2}{2} - \frac{A^2}{2}$$

stated in (9). *Hint:* Choose Q_{jn} first at one end of C_{jn} and then at the other. Specifically, with $Q_{jn} = z_{jn}$ obtain the sum

$$J_n^a = z_{1n}(z_{1n} - A) + z_{2n}(z_{2n} - z_{1n}) + \cdots + B(B - z_{n-1,n})$$

and with $Q_{jn} = z_{j-1,n}$ obtain the sum

$$J_n^r = A(z_{1n} - A) + z_{1n}(z_{2n} - z_{1n}) + \cdots + z_{n-1,n}(B - z_{n-1,n}),$$

where the superscripted a and r denote "advanced" and "retarded," respectively. Add these results and let $n \to \infty$.
(b) Derive (9), instead, by expressing $\int_C z\, dz$ in terms of real line integrals and then evaluating those integrals.

2. Evaluate the following by expressing them in terms of real line integrals and then evaluating those integrals.
*(a) $\int_C |z|^2\, dz$, where C is a straight line from $z = 0$ to $z = 1 + i$
(b) $\int_C \bar{z}\, dz$, where C is the same as in part (a)
(c) $\int_C \bar{z}\, dz$, where C is a clockwise semicircle from $z = 2$ to $z = -2$, centered at $z = 0$
*(d) $\int_C dz/z$, where C consists of three straight-line segments: from $z = 1$ to $z = 1 - i$, from $z = 1 - i$ to $z = -1 - i$, and then from $z = -1 - i$ to $z = -1$
(e) $\int_C e^z\, dz$, where C consists of two straight-line segments: from $z = i$ to $z = 1 + i$, and then from $z = 1 + i$ to $z = 1 - 2i$
(f) $\int_C (\text{Re } z)\, dz$, where C is a clockwise quarter circle from $z = 3i$ to $z = 3$, centered at $z = 0$
(g) $\int_C (\text{Im } z)\, dz$, where C is a straight line from $z = i$ to $z = 2 + 2i$

3. Consider $I = \int_C \bar{z}\, dz$, where the initial and final points of C are $z = 0$ and $z = 1 + i$, respectively. Show that the integral is *path dependent* by choosing two different paths and obtaining different values for I.

4. Let $z_1, z_2, \ldots$ be a convergent sequence of complex numbers. Show that $|\lim_{n\to\infty} z_n| = \lim_{n\to\infty} |z_n|$. [This result was used in (18).]

5. Use (19) to obtain upper bounds on the absolute magnitude of each of the following integrals.
*(a) $\int_C z^5\, dz$, where C is a straight line from $z = i$ to $z = 2 + 2i$
(b) $\int_C e^z\, dz$, where C is a straight line from $z = -2$ to $z = 1 + 3i$
(c) $\int_C e^{-z}\, dz$, where C is the same as in part (b)
*(d) $\int_C dz/z$, where C is a circle of radius 4 centered at $z = 2 + i$
(e) $\int_C dz/(z^2 + 1)$, where C is a circle of radius 3 centered at $z = 0$
(f) $\int_C (z^2 + 1)dz/(z^2 - 1)$, where C is a circle of radius 1 centered at $z = 1$
(g) $\int_C dz/z(z + i)$, where C is a quarter circle from $z = i$ to $z = 1$, centered at $z = 0$

6. (a) If C is a straight line from $z = 2$ to $z = 2 + (\pi/2)i$, show that

$$\left| \int_C \frac{dz}{e^z + 1} \right| \le \frac{\pi}{2} \frac{1}{\sqrt{e^4 + 1}}.$$

(b) If C is a straight line from $z = 2i$ to $z = 3$, show that

$$\left| \int_C \frac{\cos z}{z}\, dz \right| \le \frac{13}{6} \cosh 2.$$

7. In our subsequent work we will sometimes need an upper bound on the absolute magnitude of a given integral, and (19) will generally suffice. A corresponding *lower* bound was not developed in this section because it will not be needed. Nevertheless, suppose that $|f(z)| \ge m$ on C. It is tempting to conjecture, by analogy with (19), that

$$\left| \int_C f(z)\, dz \right| \ge mL \qquad \text{(a)}$$

provides a lower bound on the magnitude of the integral. Prove that (a) is *not correct*.

8. (*A sharper upper bound*) (a) As an alternative to (19), derive the upper bound

$$\left| \int_C f(z)\, dz \right| \le \int_C |f(z)|\, |dz| \tag{a}$$

and show that (a) is sharper than (19) inasmuch as

$$\left| \int_C f(z)\, dz \right| \le \int_C |f(z)|\, |dz| \le ML. \tag{b}$$

[The price that we pay for this improvement is that (a) is generally more difficult to apply than (19) because it requires the evaluation of the integral $\int_C |f(z)|\,|dz|$.] (b) To better understand these two bounds, apply each of them to the integral $I = \int_0^2 (x^3 - x)\, dx$; i.e., $\int_C (z^3 - z)\, dz$, where C is a straight line from $z = 0$ to $z = 2$. Compare the two results with the *exact* value of I. Further, show the graphical significance of each of the three members of (b), by suitable sketches.

CAUCHY'S THEOREM 20.3

Cauchy's theorem, which we are about to consider, is a cornerstone of the entire analytic function theory, and is related to a similar theorem on irrotational fields (Theorem 1, page 424).

Considering $\oint_C f(z)\, dz$, where C is a piecewise-smooth simple closed curve, we begin by expressing

$$\oint_C f(z)\, dz = \oint_C (u\, dx - v\, dy) + i \oint_C (u\, dy + v\, dx). \tag{1}$$

Suppose that $f(z)$ is analytic and that $f'(z)$ is continuous in a simply connected domain D containing the path C. If we write the first integral on the right-hand side of (1) as

$$\oint_C (u\, dx - v\, dy) = \oint_C \mathbf{w} \cdot d\mathbf{R}, \tag{2}$$

where $\mathbf{w} = u(x, y)\hat{\mathbf{i}} - v(x, y)\hat{\mathbf{j}}$, then

$$\nabla \times \mathbf{w} = 0\hat{\mathbf{i}} - 0\hat{\mathbf{j}} + \left(-\frac{\partial v}{\partial x} - \frac{\partial u}{\partial y} \right)\hat{\mathbf{k}} \tag{3}$$

vanishes everywhere in D by virtue of the Cauchy–Riemann equation $\partial u/\partial y = -\partial v/\partial x$ (which holds because f has been assumed analytic in D). Then it follows from Theorem 1 on page 424 that

$$\oint_C (u\, dx - v\, dy) = 0. \tag{4}$$

Similarly, if we write the second integral on the right-hand side of (1) as

$$\oint_C (u\, dy + v\, dx) = \oint_C \mathbf{w} \cdot d\mathbf{R}, \tag{5}$$

where, this time, $\mathbf{w} = v(x, y)\hat{\mathbf{i}} + u(x, y)\hat{\mathbf{j}}$, then

$$\nabla \times \mathbf{w} = 0\hat{\mathbf{i}} - 0\hat{\mathbf{j}} + \left(\frac{\partial u}{\partial x} - \frac{\partial v}{\partial y} \right)\hat{\mathbf{k}} \tag{6}$$

vanishes everywhere in D by virtue of the other Cauchy–Riemann equation, $\partial u/\partial x = \partial v/\partial y$. Then it follows that

$$\oint_C (u\,dy + v\,dx) = 0. \tag{7}$$

Thus we have shown that *if $f(z)$ is analytic and $f'(z)$ is continuous in a simply connected domain D, then*

$$\oint_C f(z)\,dz = 0 \tag{8}$$

for every piecewise-smooth simple closed curve C in D.

This result was published by Cauchy in 1825. Seventy-five years later it was shown by Edouard Goursat (1858–1936) that the stated result holds even if one does not assume the continuity of $f'(z)$(i.e., of u_x, u_y, v_x, v_y).* Indeed, we will show (in Section 20.5) that if f is analytic in D (i.e., once differentiable), then f possesses derivatives of *all* orders in D. In particular, since f' is differentiable in D, it follows that f' must be continuous there.

Thus, deleting the assumption that $f'(z)$ is continuous, we have the so-called "strong version" of Cauchy's theorem, also known as the Cauchy–Goursat theorem, in recognition of Goursat's important contribution:

> ***Theorem 1*** *Cauchy's Theorem*
>
> If $f(z)$ is analytic in a simply connected domain D, then
>
> $$\boxed{\oint_C f(z)\,dz = 0} \tag{9}$$
>
> for every piecewise-smooth simple closed curve C in D.

EXAMPLE 1 Consider

$$I = \oint_C \frac{dz}{z^2 - 5z + 6} = \oint_C \frac{dz}{(z-2)(z-3)}, \tag{10}$$

where C is the unit circle, traversed counterclockwise (Fig. 20.7). The integrand $f(z) = 1/(z-2)(z-3)$ is analytic everywhere except at $z = 2$ and $z = 3$. Thus it is analytic in the simply connected domain D (Fig. 20.7) containing C, so $I = 0$ by Cauchy's theorem. ◀

We have already mentioned the connection between the complex integral $\int_C f(z)\,dz$ of an analytic function f and the real line integral $\int_C \mathbf{w}\cdot d\mathbf{R}$ of an irrotational field $\mathbf{w}$. Take one more look at the irrotational field theorem on page 424, and notice the equivalence between the vanishing of $\int_C \mathbf{w}\cdot d\mathbf{R}$ for every closed loop C

*For proof, see, for example, R. V. Churchill, *Complex Variables and Applications*, 2nd ed. (New York: McGraw-Hill, 1960), Chap. 5; or Konrad Knopp, *Theory of Functions*, Part I (New York: Dover, 1945), Chap. 4.

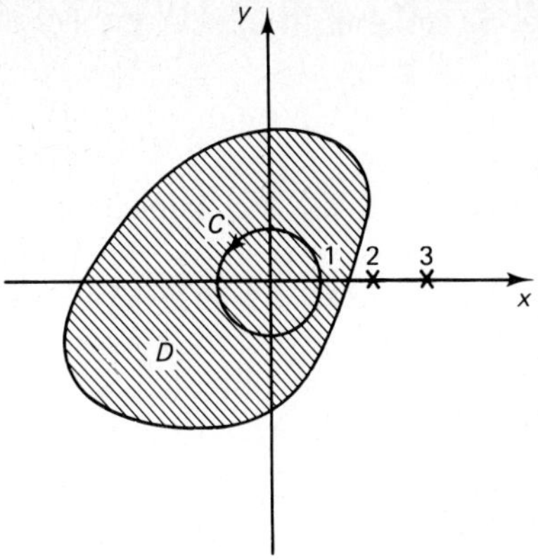

Fig. 20.7 *C* and *D* for Example 1.

and the path independence of integrals $\int_C \mathbf{w} \cdot d\mathbf{R}$ between fixed endpoints. Thus we might well anticipate such equivalence for complex integrals as well. In fact, we have the following:

> ***Theorem 2*** *Path Independence*
> If $f(z)$ is analytic in a simply connected domain D, then $\int_C f(z)\,dz$ is independent of path in D. That is, given any initial point P in D and any final point Q in D, the value of $\int_C f(z)\,dz$ is the same for every piecewise smooth path C, lying entirely within D, from P to Q.

Partial Proof Let C_1 and C_2 be any two piecewise-smooth paths from P to Q. Suppose that C_1 and C_2 are both simple curves and that they intersect each other only at the endpoints P and Q (Fig. 20.8a). (The additional argument needed for the case where intersections do occur, possibly an infinite number of them, will be omitted here.) Then $C_1 + (-C_2)$ is a piecewise-smooth simple closed curve in D (Fig. 20.8b), so, according to Cauchy's theorem,

$$\oint_{C_1+(-C_2)} f(z)\,dz = 0. \tag{11}$$

But

$$\begin{aligned}\oint_{C_1+(-C_2)} f(z)\,dz &= \int_{C_1} f(z)\,dz + \int_{-C_2} f(z)\,dz \\ &= \int_{C_1} f(z)\,dz - \int_{C_2} f(z)\,dz,\end{aligned} \tag{12}$$

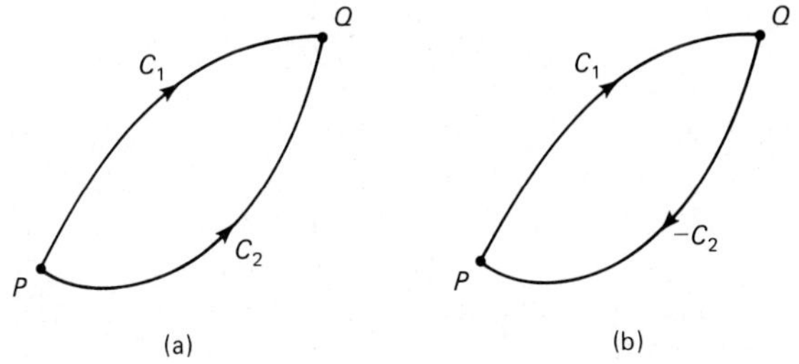

Fig. 20.8 You take the high road, I'll take the low.

and it follows from (11) and (12) that

$$\int_{C_1} f(z)\,dz = \int_{C_2} f(z)\,dz,$$

as claimed. This step completes the proof, except for the omission noted above. ■

It is useful to interpret path independence in terms of a process of *path deformation*. That is, we can imagine deforming C_1, continuously, into C_2 (Fig. 20.8a), keeping the endpoints fixed. If f is analytic on C_1 and C_2 and we cross no singular points in the process (thus f is analytic on and between C_1 and C_2), then $\int_{C_1} f(z)\,dz$ is equal to $\int_{C_2} f(z)\,dz$. The point, of course, is that we may be able to *simplify* the path by such deformation in the sense that $\int_{C_2} f(z)\,dz$ may be more easily evaluated than $\int_{C_1} f(z)\,dz$.

In fact, path deformation can be applied to *closed* paths as well. For example, suppose that f is analytic on and between the closed paths C_1 and C_2 shown in Fig. 20.9a. Let us "slit" the region by introducing a piecewise-smooth curve connecting a point A on C_1 with a point B on C_2 (with this curve intersecting C_1 only at A and C_2 only at B). Denote this curve as C' when it is oriented from A to B and as $-C'$ when it is oriented from B to A, as shown in Fig. 20.9b. (Actually, C' and $-C'$ are coincident, but we have separated them in the figure for clarity.) Since $C = C_1 + C' + (-C_2) + (-C')$ is a piecewise-smooth simple closed curve and f is analytic inside and on C, it follows from Cauchy's theorem that $\oint_C f(z)\,dz = 0$ (see Exercise 3). Thus

$$\begin{aligned}\oint_C f(z)\,dz &= \oint_{C_1+C'+(-C_2)+(-C')} f(z)\,dz\\ &= \oint_{C_1} f(z)\,dz + \int_{C'} f(z)\,dz + \oint_{-C_2} f(z)\,dz + \int_{-C'} f(z)\,dz\\ &= \oint_{C_1} f(z)\,dz + \int_{C'} f(z)\,dz - \oint_{C_2} f(z)\,dz - \int_{C'} f(z)\,dz\\ &= 0,\end{aligned} \tag{13}$$

so

$$\oint_{C_1} f(z)\,dz = \oint_{C_2} f(z)\,dz. \tag{14}$$

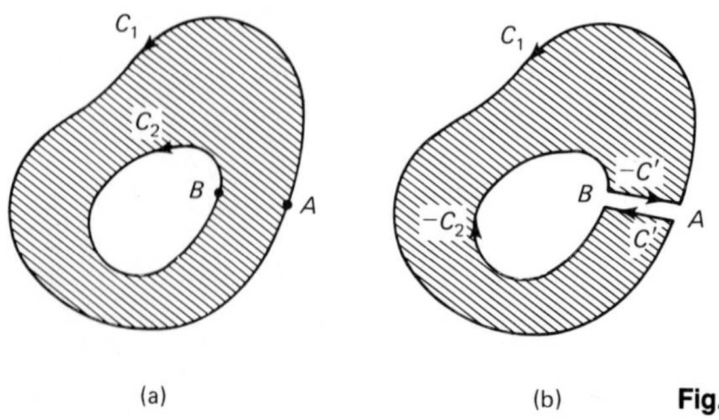

Fig. 20.9 Path deformation for closed path.

That is, deforming C_1 into C_2, (14) will hold if f is analytic between and on C_1 and C_2.

EXAMPLE 2 *An Important Little Integral.* Consider

$$I = \oint_C (z - a)^n \, dz, \tag{15}$$

where C is any piecewise-smooth simple closed curve, oriented counterclockwise, such as the curve C shown in Fig. 20.10; n is any integer (positive, negative, or zero), and a is any given complex number lying inside C. According to the discussion preceding this example, we can deform the contour C to a *circular* contour C', lying wholly within C, as depicted in Fig. 20.10, since $(z - a)^n$ is analytic on and between C and C'. The resulting integral, $\oint_{C'} (z - a)^n \, dz$, was evaluated in Example 3 on page 795. Recalling the result of that evaluation, we have

$$\boxed{\oint_C (z - a)^n \, dz = \begin{cases} 2\pi i & (n = -1) \\ 0 & (n \neq -1). \end{cases}} \tag{16}$$

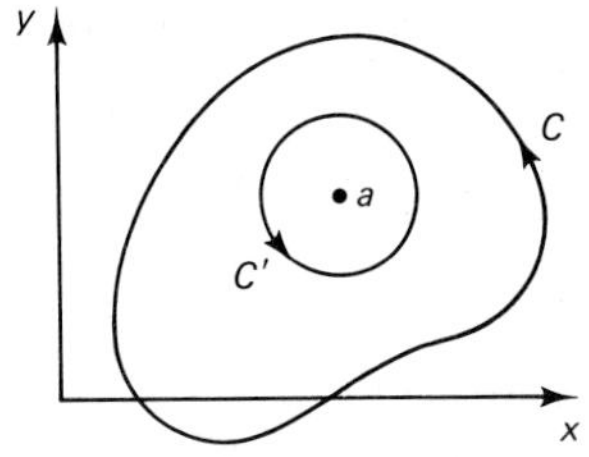

Fig. 20.10 Deformation of C to a circle C'.

That is, the result obtained on page 795 holds even if C is not a circle centered at a. Although rather specific, formula (16) will be used frequently, and is worth remembering. ◀

EXAMPLE 3 Evaluate

$$I = \oint_C \frac{dz}{z^2(z - 2)(z - 4)}, \tag{17}$$

where C is given in Fig. 20.11. Expanding the integrand in partial fractions yields

$$I = \frac{3}{32} \oint_C \frac{dz}{z} + \frac{1}{8} \oint_C \frac{dz}{z^2} - \frac{1}{8} \oint_C \frac{dz}{z - 2} + \frac{1}{32} \oint_C \frac{dz}{z - 4}. \tag{18}$$

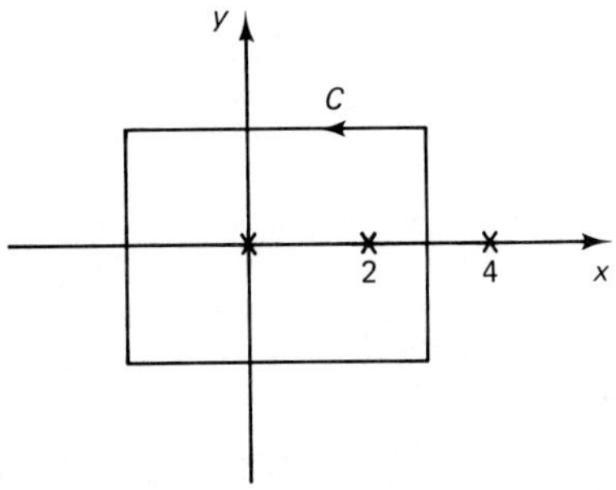

Fig. 20.11 The contour C.

The last integral is zero by Cauchy's theorem, and the first three are covered by the "important little integral" (16). Thus

$$I = \frac{3}{32}(2\pi i) + \frac{1}{8}(0) - \frac{1}{8}(2\pi i) + \frac{1}{32}(0) = -\frac{\pi i}{16}. \qquad (19)$$ ◀

This example ends our consideration of Cauchy's theorem. The value of this theorem will become more and more evident as we proceed through the remainder of Part V.

20.3 EXERCISES

1. According to Example 3 on page 795,

$$\oint_C \frac{dz}{z^2} = 0,$$

where C is a counterclockwise circle of radius R, centered at the origin. Yet $f(z) = 1/z^2$ is not analytic within C; it is singular at $z = 0$. Explain why this result does *not* violate Cauchy's theorem.

2. Consider $I = \oint_C dz/z$, where C is the counterclockwise unit circle, and the assertion that $I = 0$, from Cauchy's theorem, because $f(z) = 1/z$ is analytic in the domain D containing C. (See the accompanying figure.) Yet we showed (Example 3 on page 795) that $I = 2\pi i$. Explain the apparent contradiction.

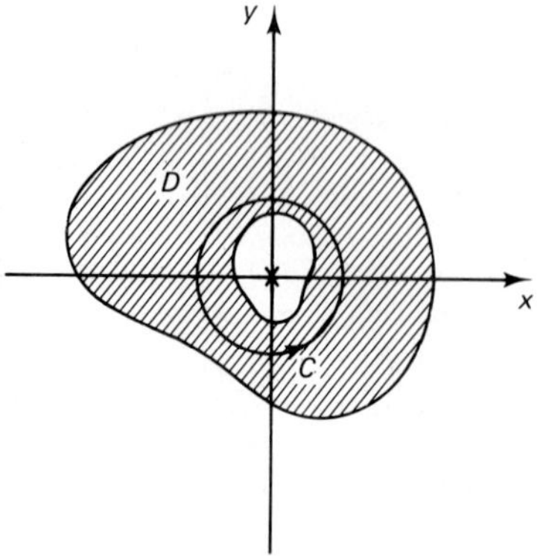

3. Prove that *if C is a piecewise-smooth simple closed curve and $f(z)$ is analytic inside and on C, then $\oint_C f(z)\, dz = 0$.* *Hint:* The idea is to show that if f is analytic inside and on C, then there exists a domain D (see the figure) containing C, such that f is analytic within D. The desired result follows immediately from Cauchy's theorem. If needed, you may draw on the fact that C is necessarily rectifiable (i.e., of finite length) because it is piecewise smooth. Also, if $F(x)$ is continuous on a closed interval $a \le x \le b$, it has an absolute maximum and an absolute minimum on that interval.

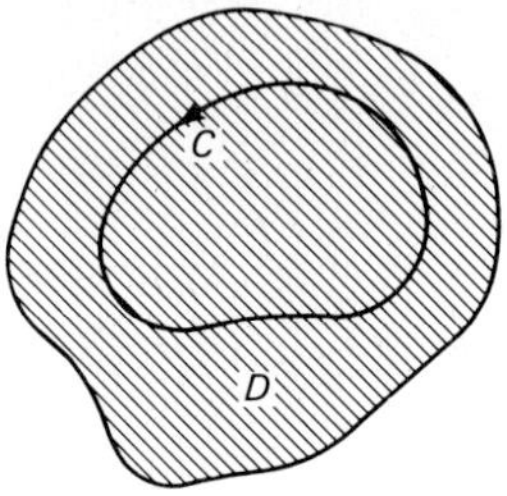

4. Let C_1, C_2, C_3 be the following simple closed curves:

C_1: $|z| = 1$, counterclockwise

C_2: $|z| = 1$, clockwise

C_3: the square with vertices at $1 - i$, $1 + i$, $-1 + i$, $-1 - i$, counterclockwise.

Evaluate each of the following integrals, using Cauchy's theorem if applicable and partial fractions if necessary.

*(a) $\oint_{C_1} \operatorname{Re} z\, dz$ (b) $\oint_{C_1} \operatorname{Im} z\, dz$

(c) $\oint_{C_3} \operatorname{Im} z\, dz$ *(d) $\oint_{C_3} \frac{dz}{z^2 - 3}$

(e) $\oint_{C_1} \frac{dz}{z^4}$ (f) $\oint_{C_1} \frac{dz}{z(z-2)}$

*(g) $\oint_{C_2} \frac{dz}{z(z+5)}$ (h) $\oint_{C_1} e^{\sin z} dz$

(i) $\oint_{C_2} \sin(\cos z)\, dz$ (j) $\oint_{C_3} \frac{dz}{|z|}$

(k) $\oint_{C_1} \bar{z}\, dz$ (l) $\oint_{C_3} \bar{z}\, dz$

5. Can we use path deformation to obtain

$$\oint_{C_3} \bar{z}\, dz = \oint_{C_1} \bar{z}\, dz, \qquad \text{(a)}$$

where C_1 and C_3 are defined in Exercise 4? Explain.

6. Evaluate $\int_C z^{20} dz$, where C is the path
*(a) $y = x - x^3$, from $x = 0$ to $x = 1$
(b) $y = x - x^3$, from $x = 0$ to $x = -1$
(c) $x = y - y^5$, from $y = 0$ to $y = 1$

7. Evaluate $\int_C \bar{z}\, dz$, where C is a straight line from $z = 0$ to $z = 1 + i$, where C is the parabola $y = x^2$ from $z = 0$ to $z = 1 + i$, and where C is the rectilinear path from $z = 0$ to $z = 1$ to $z = 1 + i$.

8. (*Path deformation in multiply connected domain*) Show that if $f(z)$ is analytic in the shaded region between and on the contours C_1, C_2, C_3 (see the accompanying figure), then

$$\oint_{C_1} f(z) dz = \oint_{C_2} f(z)\, dz + \oint_{C_3} f(z)\, dz. \qquad \text{(a)}$$

You may use the result stated in Exercise 3. *Note:*

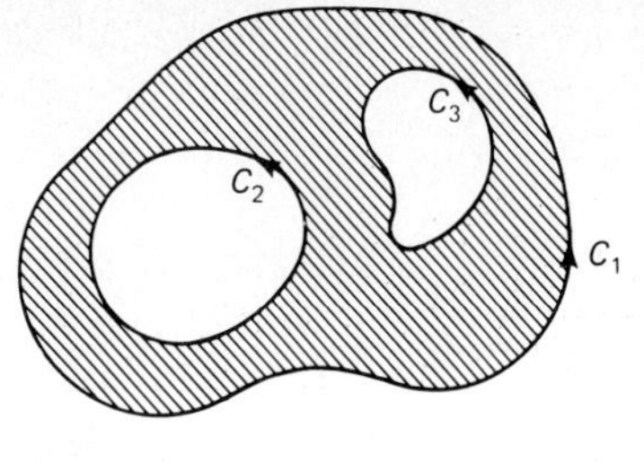

More generally,

$$\oint_{C_1} f(z)\, dz = \oint_{C_2} f(z)\, dz + \cdots + \oint_{C_n} f(z)\, dz$$

if $C_2, \ldots, C_n$ are nonintersecting counterclockwise closed contours within C_1 and f is analytic between and on $C_1, \ldots, C_n$.

9. Evaluate the following integrals, where in each case, C is the circle $|z| = 3$, counterclockwise.

*(a) $\oint_C \dfrac{dz}{z(z-1)}$ (b) $\oint_C \dfrac{dz}{z(z-5)}$

(c) $\oint_C \dfrac{z\, dz}{z^2+1}$ *(d) $\oint_C \dfrac{z\, dz}{z^2 - 3z + 2}$

(e) $\oint_C \dfrac{dz}{z^3(z^2-1)}$ (f) $\oint_C \dfrac{z\, dz}{z^3 - 1}$

FUNDAMENTAL THEOREM OF THE COMPLEX INTEGRAL CALCULUS 20.4

Before obtaining the fundamental theorem of the complex integral calculus, let us, for the sake of comparison and motivation, recall the *fundamental theorem of the real integral calculus:* Let $f(x)$ be continuous on the interval $x_0 \le x \le x_1$. Then the function

$$G(x) = \int_{x_0}^{x} f(\xi)\, d\xi \qquad (x_0 \le x \le x_1) \tag{1}$$

is differentiable on $x_0 \le x \le x_1$ and is a *primitive* or *indefinite integral* of f; i.e.,

$$G'(x) = f(x) \tag{2}$$

on the closed interval. In fact, the primitive of f is unique to within an arbitrary additive constant. If $F(x)$ is any particular primitive of f, then

$$\int_{x_0}^{x} f(\xi)\, d\xi = F(x) - F(x_0). \tag{3}$$

The foregoing result was found, in the elementary calculus, to be especially valuable for evaluating integrals for which a primitive could be found by inspection. For example, to evaluate $\int_2^5 x^2\, dx$ one notices that $x^3/3$ is a primitive of x^2 [because

$(d/dx)(x^3/3) = x^2$], so

$$\int_2^5 x^2\,dx = \frac{x^3}{3}\bigg|_2^5 = \frac{125-8}{3} = \frac{117}{3}.$$

Of course, the primitive $(x^3/3) + 4$, say, would have produced the same result.

Turning now to the complex case, let $f(z)$ be analytic in a simply connected domain D. If z_0 is a fixed point in D, then $\int_{z_0}^{z} f(\zeta)\,d\zeta$ is (Theorem 2, page 801) path independent and hence defines a single-valued function of z, which we denote as $G(z)$:

$$G(z) = \int_{z_0}^{z} f(\zeta)\,d\zeta. \tag{4}$$

(Before continuing, notice that in the complex case we have asked f to be analytic, for the integral to define a single-valued function, whereas in the real case it sufficed to ask f to be continuous.)

Next, we show that $G'(z) = f(z)$ in D. Consider the difference quotient

$$\begin{aligned}\frac{G(z+\Delta z) - G(z)}{\Delta z} &= \frac{1}{\Delta z}\left[\int_{z_0}^{z+\Delta z} f(\zeta)\,d\zeta - \int_{z_0}^{z} f(\zeta)\,d\zeta\right] \\ &= \frac{1}{\Delta z}\int_{z}^{z+\Delta z} f(\zeta)\,d\zeta \\ &= \frac{1}{\Delta z}\int_{z}^{z+\Delta z} f(z)\,d\zeta + \frac{1}{\Delta z}\int_{z}^{z+\Delta z} [f(\zeta) - f(z)]\,d\zeta \\ &= f(z) + \frac{1}{\Delta z}\int_{z}^{z+\Delta z} [f(\zeta) - f(z)]\,d\zeta,\end{aligned} \tag{5}$$

where z_0, z, and $z + \Delta z$ are displayed in Fig. 20.12. By the above-noted path independence, there is no loss in taking the path from z to $z + \Delta z$ to be straight (although the path from z_0 to z may need to be curved in order to remain within D). Using the "ML bound" on the last integral in (5), we have

$$\left|\frac{1}{\Delta z}\int_{z}^{z+\Delta z} [f(\zeta) - f(z)]\,d\zeta\right| \le \frac{1}{|\Delta z|} M|\Delta z| = M, \tag{6}$$

where $M = \max|f(\zeta) - f(z)|$ on the line from z to $z + \Delta z$. But since f is continu-

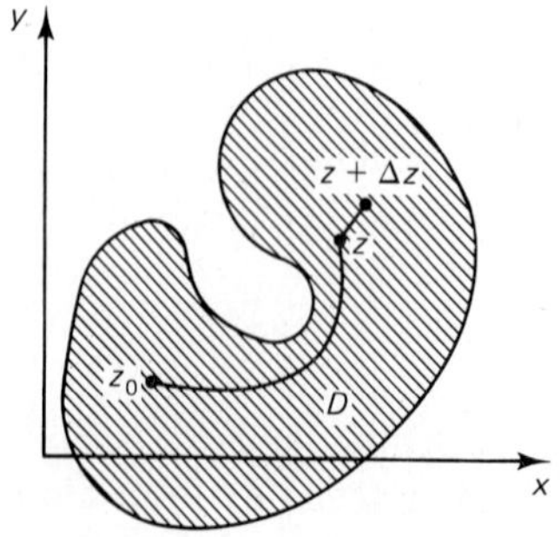

Fig. 20.12 z_0, z, and $z + \nabla z$.

ous (because it is analytic), $M \to 0$ as $\Delta z \to 0$. Thus, letting $\Delta z \to 0$ in (5) gives

$$G'(z) = f(z), \tag{7}$$

as claimed.

Any function $F(z)$ satisfying $F'(z) = f(z)$ is called a **primitive** or **indefinite integral of f.** It is easy to show (Exercise 1) that any two primitives corresponding to a given f differ at most by an arbitrary additive constant. Thus if $F(z)$ is any particular primitive of $f(z)$, it follows that

$$G(z) = \int_{z_0}^{z} f(\zeta)\, d\zeta = F(z) + C, \tag{8}$$

where C is a constant. To evaluate C, set $z = z_0$. Then

$$0 = F(z_0) + C \tag{9}$$

gives $C = -F(z_0)$, so

$$\int_{z_0}^{z} f(\zeta)\, d\zeta = F(z) - F(z_0). \tag{10}$$

Pulling these results together, we have:

Theorem 1 *Fundamental Theorem of the Complex Integral Calculus*
Let $f(z)$ be analytic in a simply connected domain D, and let z_0 be any fixed point in D. Then

(i) $G(z) = \int_{z_0}^{z} f(\zeta)\, d\zeta$ is analytic in D and $G'(z) = f(z)$.
(ii) If $F(z)$ is any primitive of $f(z)$ [i.e., $F'(z) = f(z)$], then

$$\boxed{\int_{z_0}^{z} f(\zeta)\, d\zeta = F(z) - F(z_0).} \tag{11}$$

As in the analogous case of real integrals, (11) is especially useful for evaluating integrals for which a primitive can be found by inspection.

EXAMPLE 1 To evaluate $\int_{2i}^{3} \sin z\, dz$, observe that $F(z) = -\cos z$ (plus any constant) is a primitive of $\sin z$. Then

$$\int_{2i}^{3} \sin z\, dz = -\cos z \Big|_{z=2i}^{z=3} = -\cos 3 + \cos 2i = \cosh 2 - \cos 3. \tag{12}$$

COMMENT Notice that the notation $\int_{2i}^{3}$ suffices. That is, we do not need to specify the path to be followed, from $2i$ to 3, because $\sin z$ is analytic in the whole plane, and hence line integrals of $\sin z$ are path independent; they depend only on the endpoints. ◀

EXAMPLE 2 Evaluate

$$I = \int_{1+i}^{-i} \frac{dz}{z}. \tag{13}$$

With the foregoing comment in mind, we observe, first, that the problem is not clearly posed because the integral is *not* single valued. Specifically, the integrand $1/z$ is analytic for all $z \neq 0$, and the whole plane with $z = 0$ deleted is a multiply connected region (due to the hole at $z = 0$). Thus our path independence theorem (on page 801) does not guarantee that I will have the same values for paths such as C_1 and C_2 in Fig. 20.13. In fact,

$$\int_{C_1} \frac{dz}{z} - \int_{C_2} \frac{dz}{z} = \int_{C_1+(-C_2)} \frac{dz}{z} = 2\pi i,$$

according to the "important little integral" (16) on page 803, so

$$\int_{C_1} \frac{dz}{z} \neq \int_{C_2} \frac{dz}{z}. \tag{14}$$

Sure enough, this multivaluedness of the integral shows up if we write

$$I = \int_{1+i}^{-i} \frac{dz}{z} = \log z \Big|_{1+i}^{-i}, \tag{15}$$

because $\log z$ is multivalued!

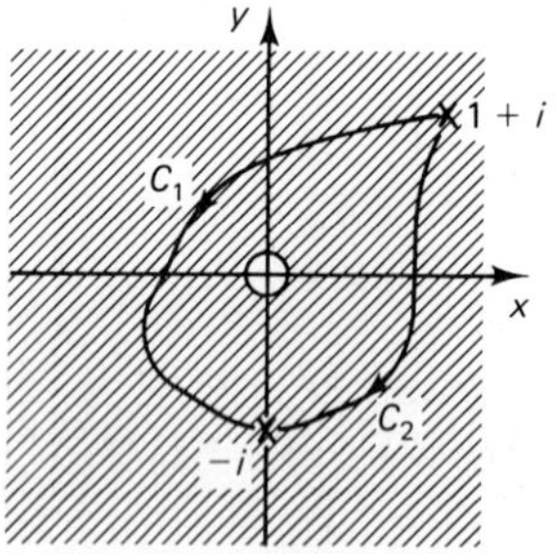

Fig. 20.13 Alternative paths.

With this background in mind we see that we can pose the problem carefully in different ways. One way would be to ask for all possible values of I. To answer that question, use (15):

$$\begin{aligned} I &= \log z \Big|_{1+i}^{-i} = \log(-i) - \log(1+i) \\ &= \left[\ln 1 + i\left(-\frac{\pi}{2} + 2m\pi\right)\right] - \left[\ln\sqrt{2} + i\left(\frac{\pi}{4} + 2n\pi\right)\right], \end{aligned} \tag{16}$$

where m and n are arbitrary integers (0, ±1, ±2, . . .). Thus

$$I = -\frac{\ln 2}{2} + i\left[-\frac{3\pi}{4} + 2(m-n)\pi\right] \tag{17}$$

or, since m and n are independent integers,

$$I = -\frac{\ln 2}{2} + i\left(2p - \frac{3}{4}\right)\pi \tag{18}$$

for any $p = 0, \pm 1, \pm 2, \ldots$.

Alternatively, we could seek the unique value of I where the path C from $1 + i$ to $-i$ is confined to a particular *simply* connected domain or, equivalently, where $\log z$ is made single valued by specifying a particular branch. Indeed, the branch cut for $\log z$ will serve to render the domain simply connected.

For example, for every path (such as C_1 or C_2) within the simply connected cut domain shown in Fig. 20.14a, we have the unique value

$$\begin{aligned} I &= \int_{1+i}^{-i} \frac{dz}{z} = \log(-i) - \log(1+i) \\ &= \ln 1 + i\frac{3\pi}{2} - \left(\ln\sqrt{2} + i\frac{\pi}{4}\right) = -\frac{\ln 2}{2} + i\frac{5\pi}{4}, \end{aligned} \tag{19}$$

whereas for every path within the simply connected cut domain shown in Fig. 20.14b we have the unique value

$$\begin{aligned} I &= \int_{1+i}^{-i} \frac{dz}{z} = \log(-i) - \log(1+i) \\ &= \ln 1 - i\frac{\pi}{2} - \left(\ln\sqrt{2} + i\frac{\pi}{4}\right) = -\frac{\ln 2}{2} - i\frac{3\pi}{4}. \end{aligned} \tag{20}$$

◀

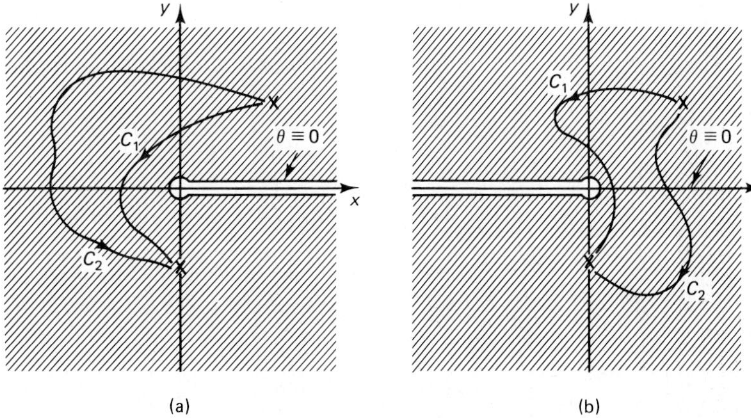

Fig. 20.14 Two possible simply connected domains; two possible branch cuts for log z.

As important as the fundamental theorem is, observe that we have no systematic procedure for determining a primitive for a given integrand. And if a primitive is not available, the fundamental theorem is of no help.

Thus we continue our development of additional theorems for the complex integral calculus. In particular, we are aiming at the Cauchy integral formula (in the section to follow) and the residue theorem (in the final section of Part V).

1. It was stated below equation (7) that "any two primitives corresponding to a given f differ at most by an arbitrary additive constant." Prove that assertion. *Hint:* Let $F_1(z)$ and $F_2(z)$ be primitives of $f(z)$, so that $F_1'(z) = f(z)$ and $F_2'(z) = f(z)$. Subtract the latter two equations.

2. Give three different primitives for each of the following functions.

*(a) z (b) z^5 (c) $e^{2z} - z$ (d) $\cos(z-2)$

3. Use the fundamental theorem to evaluate each of the following.

*(a) $\int_0^i z\,dz$ (b) $\int_{-i}^{i} z^4 dz$
(c) $\int_4^{-1-2i} (e^{-z} - 3z^2)dz$
*(d) $\int_i^0 \cos 3z\,dz$ (e) $\int_{1-i}^{1+i} ze^z dz$
(f) $\int_4^{-i} z\sin z\,dz$ (g) $\int_0^{3i} ze^{z^2} dz$
(h) $\int_0^{1+2i} \sin^2 z\,dz$ (i) $\int_{-2i}^{3} z\cos 2z\,dz$
(j) $\int_i^{2+i} \cosh 3z\,dz$ (k) $\int_0^i \cos^3 z\,dz$
(l) $\int_i^1 z^2 e^{2z^3} dz$

4. Determine I, in Example 2, using the given cut domain. What is the value of p, in (18), corresponding to your result?

*(a)

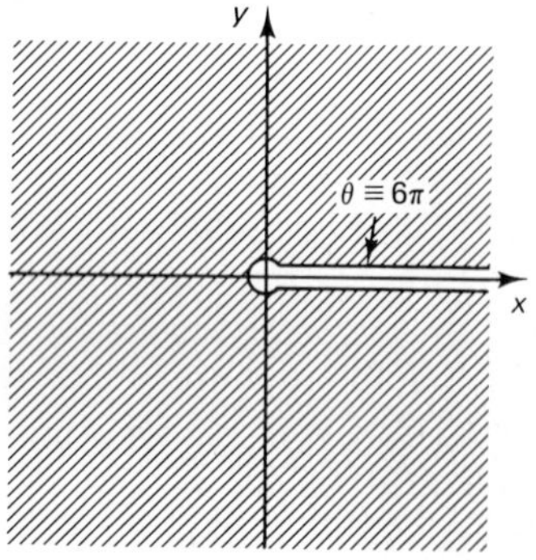

(b)

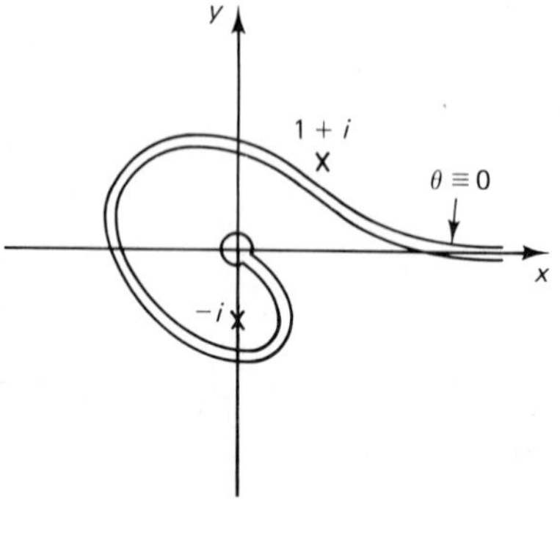

5. Determine all possible values of

$$I = \int_{1-i}^{1+i} \frac{dz}{z(z-1)}.$$

6. Determine the (unique) value of I, in Exercise 5, if the path from $1-i$ to $1+i$ is restricted to lie in the simply connected domain given below.

(a)

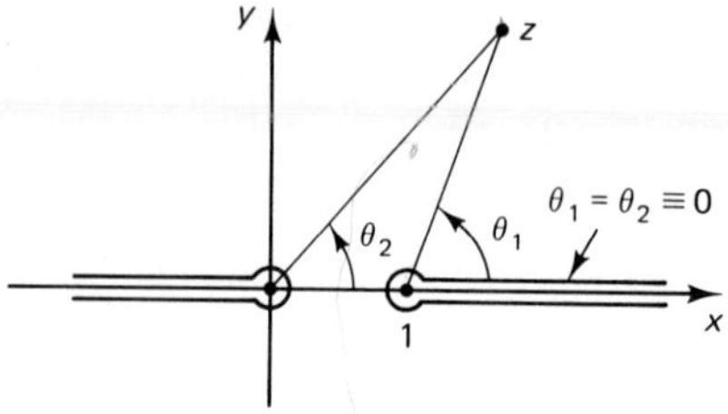

(b)

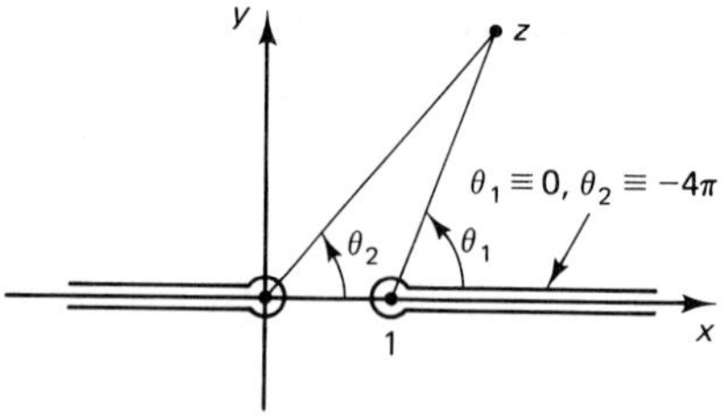

7. At some point in the calculus one is likely to encounter the calculation

$$I = \int_{-\infty}^{\infty} \frac{dx}{x^2+1} = \lim_{\substack{A\to\infty \\ B\to\infty}} \tan^{-1} x \Big|_{x=-A}^{x=B} = \pi. \tag{a}$$

Surely the integral is uniquely determined, so it is interesting that the multivalued $\tan^{-1}(\ )$ enters the picture. However, no matter which continuous branch of $\tan^{-1}(\ )$ is chosen [e.g., $-\pi/2 < \tan^{-1}(\ ) < \pi/2$, $\pi/2 < \tan^{-1}(\ ) < 3\pi/2$, etc.] the unique result, π, is indeed obtained. For study purposes, it may be useful to reexamine this evaluation in the light of complex variable theory. Then

$$I = \int_C \frac{dz}{z^2+1} = \lim_{\substack{A\to\infty \\ B\to\infty}} \tan^{-1} z \Big|_{z=-A}^{z=B}, \tag{b}$$

where C is a straight line path from $-A$ to B along the real axis. To evaluate the right hand member of (b), show that

$$\tan^{-1} z = \frac{1}{2i} \log \frac{z-i}{z+i}, \tag{c}$$

so that

$$I = \int_C \frac{dz}{z^2 + 1} = \lim_{\substack{A\to\infty \\ B\to\infty}} \log \frac{z - i}{z + i} \bigg|_{z=-A}^{z=B} \tag{d}$$

[or, equivalently, derive (d) by applying the method of partial fractions to the integral]. Finally, evaluate the right hand member of (d) by introducing any suitable branch cuts for the log $(z - i)$ and log $(z + i)$ functions.

CAUCHY INTEGRAL FORMULA 20.5

Cauchy's theorem is based on analyticity of the integrand. What if the integrand is *not* analytic? Well, suppose that $f(z)$ is analytic in a simply connected domain D, let C be any piecewise-smooth simple closed curve in D, oriented counterclockwise, and consider the integral

$$I = \oint_C \frac{f(z)}{z - a}\, dz, \tag{1}$$

where a is any fixed point within C (Fig. 20.15a). Cauchy's theorem does not apply to I because the integrand $f(z)/(z - a)$ is not analytic everywhere within and on C; it is analytic everywhere except at $z = a$. Before proceeding, notice that rather than consider $\oint_C f(z)\, dz$, where $f(z)$ is not everywhere analytic within and on C, we have narrowed our scope considerably by specifying a particular form for the integrand, in (1), with a single singular point put clearly in evidence. Nevertheless, even though the form of the integrand in (1) is somewhat specific, the results that we obtain will be quite powerful.

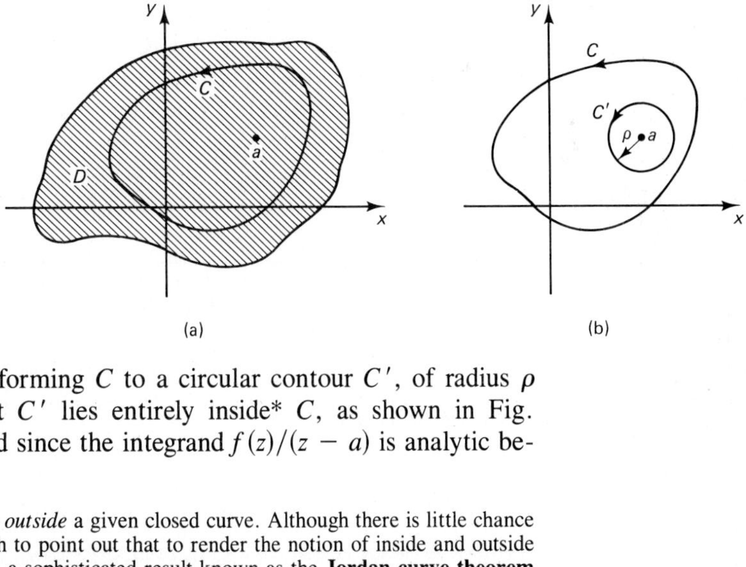

Fig. 20.15 *C* and *a* in (1).

To evaluate I, we begin by deforming C to a circular contour C', of radius ρ which is sufficiently small so that C' lies entirely inside* C, as shown in Fig. 20.15b. The deformation is justified since the integrand $f(z)/(z - a)$ is analytic between and on C and C'.

* We often speak of the region *inside* or *outside* a given closed curve. Although there is little chance of misunderstanding in this regard, we wish to point out that to render the notion of inside and outside precise is not at all simple, and there exists a sophisticated result known as the **Jordan curve theorem** which clarifies the matter in a rigorous way. Discussion of this theorem lies well outside our present scope and can be found in R. N. Pederson, "The Jordan Curve Theorem for Piecewise Smooth Curves," *American Mathematical Monthly*, Vol. 76, 1969, pp. 605–610, or in G. N. Watson, *Complex Integration and Cauchy's Theorem*, Cambridge Tracts No. 15, 1914, Chap. 1.

Proceeding heuristically for a moment, observe that we can make ρ as small as we wish. If we imagine ρ as infinitesimal, all of C' lies quite close to the point a, so $f(z) \approx f(a)$ everywhere on C', and we expect that

$$I = \oint_{C'} \frac{f(z)}{z-a}\,dz \;\to\; f(a)\oint_{C'} \frac{dz}{z-a} = 2\pi i\, f(a). \tag{2}$$

This argument suggests that we write

$$\begin{aligned} I &= \oint_{C'} \frac{f(a)}{z-a}\,dz + \oint_{C'} \frac{f(z)-f(a)}{z-a}\,dz \\ &= f(a)\oint_{C'} \frac{dz}{z-a} + \oint_{C'} \frac{f(z)-f(a)}{z-a}\,dz \\ &= 2\pi i f(a) + \oint_{C'} \frac{f(z)-f(a)}{z-a}\,dz, \end{aligned} \tag{3}$$

and then show that the last integral in (3) is zero by letting ρ become arbitrarily small. Using the ML bound, we have

$$\left| \oint_{C'} \frac{f(z)-f(a)}{z-a}\,dz \right| \le \frac{M}{\rho} 2\pi\rho = M, \tag{4}$$

where $M = \max |f(z) - f(a)|$ on C'. But since f is continuous (because it is analytic), $M \to 0$ as $\rho \to 0$, and we conclude from (3) that $I = 2\pi i\, f(a)$. This result is known as the **Cauchy integral formula**.

> ***Theorem 1*** *Cauchy Integral Formula*
>
> Let $f(z)$ be analytic in a simply connected domain D, let C be a piecewise-smooth simple closed curve in D oriented counterclockwise, and let a be a fixed point lying inside C. Then (the Cauchy integral formula states that)
>
> $$\oint_{C} \frac{f(z)}{z-a}\,dz = 2\pi i f(a). \tag{5}$$

From a *computational* point of view, the Cauchy integral formula is a valuable tool in evaluating integrals.

EXAMPLE 1 Evaluate

$$I_j = \oint_{C_j} \frac{\sin z}{z^2 - iz + 2}\,dz \tag{6}$$

where C_j is C_1, C_2, and C_3, in turn, as shown in Fig. 20.16.

We first examine the integrand to see where (if anywhere) it is singular. In the present case it should be evident that $\sin z/(z^2 - iz + 2)$ is singular only at the zeros of $z^2 - iz + 2$, namely, the points $z = 2i$ and $z = -i$. Since the singular points fall outside C_1, it follows from Cauchy's theorem that $I_1 = 0$.

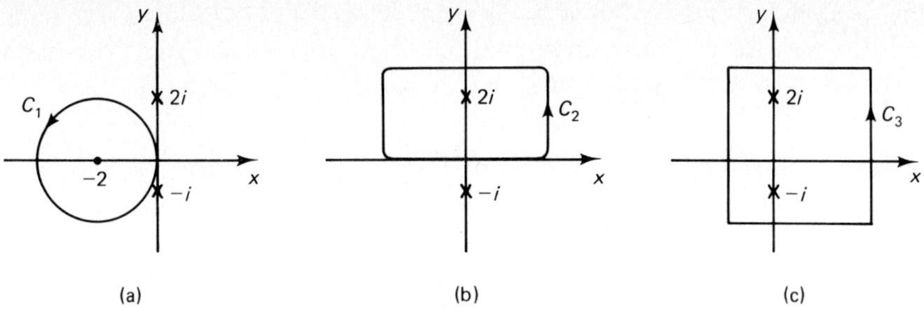

Fig. 20.16 Contours to be considered in (6).

Turning to I_2, we cannot invoke Cauchy's theorem because the singular point $2i$ falls inside the contour. Rather, we rewrite (6) in the more suggestive form

$$I_2 = \oint_{C_2} \left(\frac{\sin z}{z + i}\right) \frac{dz}{z - 2i}. \tag{7}$$

Comparing (7) with (5), we identify $f(z) = \sin z/(z + i)$ and $a = 2i$. Then (5) gives

$$I_2 = 2\pi i \left(\frac{\sin z}{z + i}\right)\bigg|_{z=2i} = \frac{2\pi}{3} \sin 2i = i\frac{2\pi}{3} \sinh 2. \tag{8}$$

Last, consider I_3. In this case there are *two* singular points ($2i$ and $-i$) within C_3, whereas the Cauchy integral formula allows for only *one*. Thus, to be able to use the Cauchy integral formula, let us first use path deformation (Exercise 3) to obtain

$$I_3 = \oint_{C_3} \frac{\sin z}{z^2 - iz + 2}\, dz = \oint_{C_3'} \frac{\sin z}{z^2 - iz + 2}\, dz + \oint_{C_3''} \frac{\sin z}{z^2 - iz + 2}\, dz, \tag{9}$$

where C_3' and C_3'' are as shown in Fig. 20.17. Then

$$\oint_{C_3'} \left(\frac{\sin z}{z + i}\right) \frac{dz}{z - 2i} = 2\pi i \left(\frac{\sin z}{z + i}\right)\bigg|_{z=2i} = i\frac{2\pi}{3} \sinh 2 \tag{10a}$$

and

$$\oint_{C_3''} \left(\frac{\sin z}{z - 2i}\right) \frac{dz}{z + i} = 2\pi i \left(\frac{\sin z}{z - 2i}\right)\bigg|_{z=-i} = i\frac{2\pi}{3} \sinh 1, \tag{10b}$$

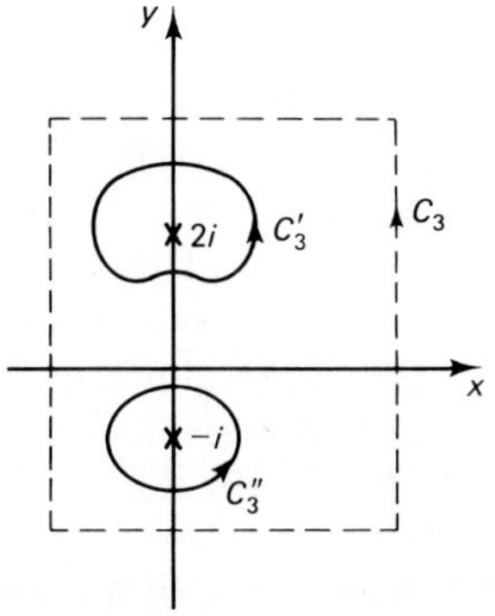

Fig. 20.17 Isolating the singular points.

so (9) gives

$$I_3 = i\frac{2\pi}{3}\sinh 2 + i\frac{2\pi}{3}\sinh 1 = i\frac{2\pi}{3}(\sinh 2 + \sinh 1). \tag{11}$$

COMMENT We used path deformation (Fig. 20.17) to isolate the two singular points. Alternatively, we could have kept C_3 intact and used partial fractions, whereby

$$I_3 = \oint_{C_3} \frac{\sin z}{z^2 - iz + 2}\,dz = \frac{i}{3}\oint_{C_3} \frac{\sin z}{z + i}\,dz - \frac{i}{3}\oint_{C_3} \frac{\sin z}{z - 2i}\,dz.$$

Since each of the two integrals on the right-hand side has only one singular point, they can each be evaluated using the Cauchy integral formula. ◀

From a *theoretical* point of view, the Cauchy integral formula is important in a number of ways, which we develop in the remainder of this section and in Chapter 21.

Used in the "computational mode," as in Example 1, point a in (5) is truly a constant. In computing I_2 in Example 1, for instance, $a = 2i$. Shifting our viewpoint a bit, it is useful to realize that (5) holds for *any* point a inside C. If we emphasize the allowed variability of a by using the letter z in its place, and use a dummy integration variable ζ in place of z, we can reexpress (5) as

$$f(z) = \frac{1}{2\pi i}\oint_C \frac{f(\zeta)}{\zeta - z}\,d\zeta. \tag{12}$$

This slight shift enables us to see, more easily, that *if $f(z)$ is analytic inside C, then it is completely determined by its boundary values on C;* specifically, the value $f(z)$ at any point z interior to C is given by an integration over its boundary values on C, namely,

$$f(z) = \oint_C K(\zeta, z) f(\zeta)\,d\zeta, \tag{13}$$

where

$$K(\zeta, z) = \frac{1}{2\pi i}\frac{1}{\zeta - z}$$

is the "kernel." Since both the real and imaginary parts of the analytic function $f(z) = u(x, y) + iv(x, y)$ are harmonic, we see that (12) is very close to providing the solution to the classical *Dirichlet problem*, namely, $\nabla^2 u = 0$ in the interior of C, together with a Dirichlet boundary condition on u (u given on C). Thus, as in Chapter 19, we see once again the close connection between analytic function theory and two-dimensional potential theory. Rather than expand on this point, let us defer it to the exercises and return to (12) with a different idea in mind.

Specifically, let us derive, from (12), an analogous formula for $f'(z)$. Not having a complex version of the Leibniz rule for differentiation under the integral sign, we fall back on taking the limit of the difference quotient,

$$\frac{f(z+\Delta z)-f(z)}{\Delta z}=\frac{1}{2\pi i\,\Delta z}\oint_C\left[\frac{1}{\zeta-z-\Delta z}-\frac{1}{\zeta-z}\right]f(\zeta)\,d\zeta$$
$$=\frac{1}{2\pi i}\oint_C\frac{f(\zeta)\,d\zeta}{(\zeta-z)(\zeta-z-\Delta z)}. \tag{14}$$

If, for heuristic purposes, we formally pass the limit across the integral sign, we obtain

$$\lim_{\Delta z\to 0}\frac{1}{2\pi i}\oint_C\frac{f(\zeta)\,d\zeta}{(\zeta-z)(\zeta-z-\Delta z)}=\frac{1}{2\pi i}\oint_C\lim_{\Delta z\to 0}\frac{f(\zeta)\,d\zeta}{(\zeta-z)(\zeta-z-\Delta z)}$$
$$=\frac{1}{2\pi i}\oint_C\frac{f(\zeta)\,d\zeta}{(\zeta-z)^2}. \tag{15}$$

(Equivalently, we could have simply taken d/dz across the integral sign.)

This result suggests reexpressing (14) in the form

$$\frac{f(z+\Delta z)-f(z)}{\Delta z}=\frac{1}{2\pi i}\oint_C\frac{f(\zeta)\,d\zeta}{(\zeta-z)^2}+\Delta I, \tag{16}$$

where the "deviation term" is, by simple algebra,

$$\Delta I=\frac{1}{2\pi i}\oint_C\frac{f(\zeta)\,d\zeta}{(\zeta-z)(\zeta-z-\Delta z)}-\frac{1}{2\pi i}\oint_C\frac{f(\zeta)\,d\zeta}{(\zeta-z)^2}$$

or

$$\Delta I=\frac{\Delta z}{2\pi i}\oint_C\frac{f(\zeta)\,d\zeta}{(\zeta-z)^2(\zeta-z-\Delta z)}. \tag{17}$$

Then, letting $\Delta z\to 0$ in (16), we obtain

$$f'(z)=\frac{1}{2\pi i}\oint_C\frac{f(\zeta)\,d\zeta}{(\zeta-z)^2}+\lim_{\Delta z\to 0}\Delta I, \tag{18}$$

so we need to consider $\lim_{\Delta z\to 0}\Delta I$. To do so, let us deform C, in (17), to a circle C' with its center at z and its radius ρ small enough so that C' lies entirely inside C (Fig. 20.18). Choosing $|\Delta z|<\rho/5$, say, it must be true that $|\zeta-z-\Delta z|>4\rho/5$ for all ζ on C'. Moreover, there must certainly exist some finite constant M such that $|f(\zeta)|\le M$ on C', since f is analytic on C'. Therefore, the ML bound gives

$$|\Delta I|\le\frac{|\Delta z|}{2\pi}\frac{M}{\rho^2(4\rho/5)}2\pi\rho. \tag{19}$$

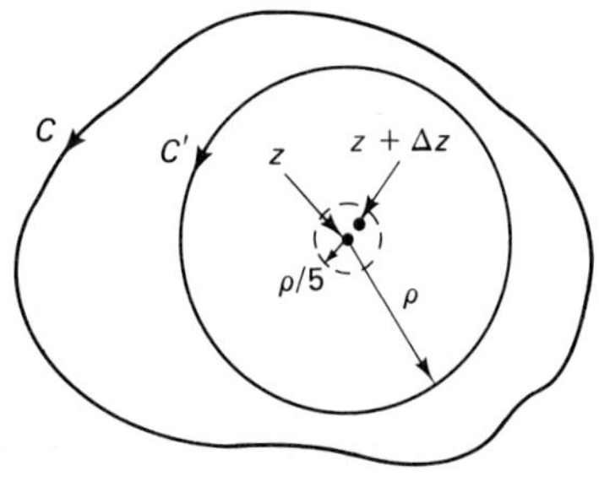

Fig. 20.18 Bounding ΔI.

It follows from (19) that if $\Delta z \to 0$ with C' fixed (and hence M and ρ fixed), then $\Delta I \to 0$. Thus (18) gives the result

$$f'(z) = \frac{1}{2\pi i} \oint_C \frac{f(\zeta)\, d\zeta}{(\zeta - z)^2}. \tag{20}$$

Similarly, if we form the difference quotient $[f'(z + \Delta z) - f'(z)]/\Delta z$, we can, with no further assumptions on f, show that

$$f''(z) = \frac{2}{2\pi i} \oint_C \frac{f(\zeta)\, d\zeta}{(\zeta - z)^3} \tag{21}$$

(Exercise 4) and, in fact, that for *all* $n = 0, 1, 2, \ldots,$

$$\boxed{f^{(n)}(z) = \frac{n!}{2\pi i} \oint_C \frac{f(\zeta)}{(\zeta - z)^{n+1}}\, d\zeta.} \tag{22}$$

Observe carefully that having assumed only that $f(z)$ is once differentiable (analytic within C), we have demonstrated that it possesses derivatives of all *orders!** This remarkable result has no analog in real-variable theory. For example, observe that $f(z) = x^2 H(x)$ (where H is the Heaviside function) is once differentiable for all x (sketch the graphs of f and f'), but the second derivative fails to exist at $x = 0$ due to the "kink" in the graph of f' at that point. Similarly, $f(x) = x^3 H(x)$ is twice differentiable for all x, but not thrice.

For reference, let us distinguish (5) as the Cauchy integral formula, and (22) as the *extended* Cauchy integral formula; this terminology is not standard, but will be helpful.

Besides the important theoretical consequences of (22), the latter is more powerful than (5) for evaluating integrals because it allows for any nonnegative integer power of $\zeta - z$ in the denominator of the integrand. Let us illustrate.

EXAMPLE 2 To evaluate

$$I = \oint_C \frac{e^z}{z^3}\, dz, \tag{23}$$

where C is the counterclockwise unit circle $|z| = 1$, rewrite (23) in the form

$$I = \oint_C \frac{e^\zeta}{(\zeta - 0)^3}\, d\zeta, \tag{24}$$

which is more convenient for comparison with (22). Thus we see that $n = 2$, $z = 0$, and $f(\zeta) = e^\zeta$, so (22) gives

$$I = \frac{2\pi i}{2!}\left(\frac{d^2}{dz^2} e^z\right)\bigg|_{z=0} = \pi i. \quad ◀ \tag{25}$$

*With this result in hand, we suggest reviewing the text between equations (7) and (9) on page 800. Incidentally, we might also note that (22) opens up the interesting possibility of defining noninteger derivatives of a function, for if we interpret $n!$ as $\Gamma(n + 1)$ and define the intended branch of $(\zeta - z)^{n+1}$, the right-hand side of (22) is defined for *noninteger* values of n as well.

EXAMPLE 3 Evaluate

$$I = \oint_C \frac{\sin 2z}{(z + 3)(z + 1)^2}\, dz, \tag{26}$$

where C is a clockwise rectangular contour with vertices at $3 + i$, $-2 + i$, $-2 - i$, $3 - i$. The only singular point within C is $z = -1$, and comparison of (26) with (22) shows that

$$I = -\frac{2\pi i}{1!} \frac{d}{dz}\left(\frac{\sin 2z}{z + 3}\right)\Bigg|_{z=-1}, \tag{27}$$

where the minus sign in (27) is due to the fact that C is clockwise, not counterclockwise, as assumed in (22). Thus $I = -(\pi i/2)(4 \cos 2 + \sin 2)$. ◀

Beyond the Cauchy integral formula and its extension, it is tempting to include such important results as Liouville's theorem and Morera's theorem, which now follow easily from already established results. However, we do not want this section to ramble, and we want to retain a clear emphasis on the Cauchy integral formula. Thus the above-mentioned theorem, and other results as well, will be reserved for the exercises.

20.5 EXERCISES

1. Evaluate each integral, where C is the counterclockwise circle $|z| = 3$. Use Cauchy's integral formula or its extension.

*(a) $\oint_C \frac{\cos z}{z}\, dz$ (b) $\oint_C \frac{\sin z}{z}\, dz$

(c) $\oint_C \frac{dz}{z^2 - 5z}$ *(d) $\oint_C \frac{z^2 - 1}{z^2 + 1} e^z\, dz$

(e) $\oint_C \frac{e^{2z}}{z^5}\, dz$

(f) $\oint_C \frac{z + 1}{(z - 1)(z + 2)^3}\, dz$

*(g) $\oint_C \frac{\sinh 3z}{(z^2 + 1)^2}\, dz$ (h) $\oint_C \frac{z + 2}{z^4 - 1}\, dz$

(i) $\oint_C \frac{e^{z^2}}{z \cos (z/2)}\, dz$ (j) $\oint_C \frac{z\, dz}{(z + i)(z^2 + 1)}$

(k) $\oint_C \frac{z^3}{z^2 + i}\, dz$ (l) $\oint_C \frac{dz}{z(z - 2)(z - 4)}$

2. (*Important little integral*) Earlier, on page 803, we indicated that

$$\oint_C (z - a)^n\, dz = \begin{cases} 2\pi i & (n = -1) \\ 0, & (n \neq -1), \end{cases} \tag{a}$$

where C is a counterclockwise piecewise-smooth simple closed curve, a is any point inside C, and n is any integer. Derive (a) using Cauchy's theorem and Cauchy's integral formula or its extension.

3. Justify the path deformation shown in Fig. 20.17.

4. Derive (21) by carrying out essentially the same steps as in our derivation of (20).

5. (a) Show from (22) that if C is a circle of radius ρ, with center at z, if $f(z)$ is analytic inside and on C, and if M is the maximum value of $|f(z)|$ on C, then

$$|f^{(n)}(z)| \leq \frac{n!M}{\rho^n}. \tag{a}$$

(b) (**Liouville's theorem**) Use (a) to prove Liouville's theorem: *If f is entire (i.e., analytic for all finite z) and bounded for all z, then f is a constant.*
(c) Since $f(z) = \sin z$ is entire and not a constant, it must not (according to Liouville's theorem) be bounded. Demonstrate that, in fact, it is *not* bounded.
(d) (**Fundamental theorem of algebra**) Use Liouville's theorem to prove the fundamental theorem of algebra: *If $P(z)$ is a polynomial function of z, of degree 1 or greater,*

$$P(z) = a_n z^n + a_{n-1} z^{n-1} + \cdots + a_0 \qquad (a_n \neq 0)$$

then $P(z) = 0$ has at least one root. Hint: Suppose that $P(z)$ is nonzero everywhere. Then $f(z) = 1/P(z)$ is analytic everywhere and is bounded.

6. (*Morera's theorem*) Prove **Morera's theorem**: *If $f(z)$ is continuous in a simply connected domain D and $\oint_C f(z)\, dz = 0$ for every piecewise-smooth simple closed curve C in D, then $f(z)$ is analytic in D. Hint:* Review our derivation of the fundamental theorem of the complex integral calculus in Section 20.4, and notice that although we asked f to be analytic in D, all we actually used was the continuity of f together with path independence of the integral between endpoints in D (equivalently, the vanishing of $\oint_C f(z)\, dz$ for every closed loop C in D).

7. (*Dirichlet problems*) As mentioned in the text, just as the Cauchy integral formula

$$f(z) = \frac{1}{2\pi i} \oint_C \frac{f(\zeta)}{\zeta - z}\, d\zeta \tag{a}$$

expresses an analytic function $f(z) = u + iv$ in terms of its boundary values, we would expect there to be a similar integral formula expressing a harmonic function $u(x, y)$ in terms of its boundary values. In this exercise we seek such a formula for two important cases: the case where the domain is a circular disk, and the case where the domain is the upper half plane.

(a) (*Circular disk*) Let C be the counterclockwise circle $|\zeta| = R$. If we seek the desired expression for u by equating real parts of the left- and right-hand sides of (a), we find that the right-hand side involves both u *and* v, whereas v is not welcome. The reason that v enters is that $1/(\zeta - z)$ is not purely real. With $\zeta = Re^{i\phi}$, show that we can reexpress (a) as

$$\begin{aligned} f(z) &= \frac{1}{2\pi i} \oint_C \left(\frac{1}{\zeta - z} - \frac{1}{\zeta - R^2/\bar{z}} \right) f(\zeta)\, d\zeta \\ &= \frac{1}{2\pi} \int_0^{2\pi} \left[\frac{\zeta}{\zeta - z} + \frac{\bar{z}}{\bar{\zeta} - \bar{z}} \right] f(\zeta)\, d\phi, \end{aligned} \tag{b}$$

where the bracketed quantity is real. In particular, show that

$$\frac{\zeta}{\zeta - z} + \frac{\bar{z}}{\bar{\zeta} - \bar{z}} = \frac{R^2 - r^2}{|\zeta - z|^2} \tag{c}$$

and hence that

$$u(r, \theta) = \frac{1}{2\pi} \int_0^{2\pi} \frac{(R^2 - r^2) u(R, \phi)}{R^2 - 2Rr\cos(\phi - \theta) + r^2}\, d\phi, \tag{d}$$

where $z = re^{i\theta}$ and $\zeta = Re^{i\phi}$. This result was also derived by separation of variables, in Section 15.3, and is known as the **Poisson integral formula for the circular disk.**

(b) (*Upper half plane*) This time let C be the contour shown here. Show that (a) can be reexpressed as

$$f(z) = \frac{1}{2\pi i} \oint_C \left(\frac{1}{\zeta - z} - \frac{1}{\zeta - \bar{z}} \right) f(\zeta)\, d\zeta \tag{e}$$

for all $R > |z|$. Suppose that, as our boundary condition at infinity, $f(z) \to 0$ as $z \to \infty$. Letting $R \to \infty$ in (e), show that the semicircle integral tends to zero, leaving us with

$$f(z) = \frac{1}{2\pi i} \int_{-\infty}^{\infty} \left(\frac{1}{\xi - z} - \frac{1}{\xi - \bar{z}} \right) f(\xi)\, d\xi. \tag{f}$$

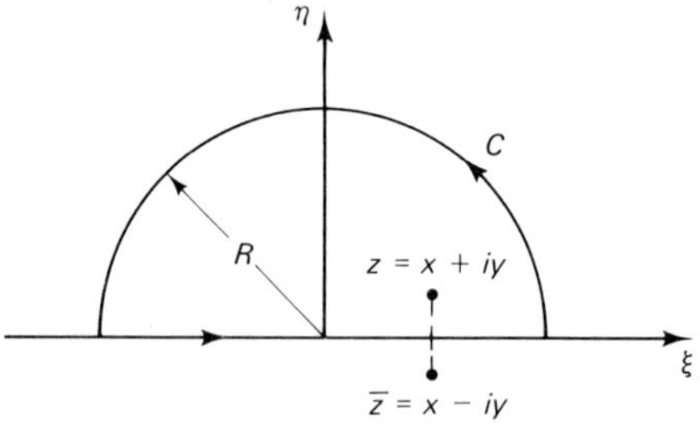

Finally, equating real parts in (f), show that

$$u(x, y) = \frac{y}{\pi} \int_{-\infty}^{\infty} \frac{u(\xi, 0)}{(\xi - x)^2 + y^2}\, d\xi \tag{g}$$

is the solution to the Dirichlet problem for the upper half plane, with the boundary condition $u(x, y) \to 0$ as $r = \sqrt{x^2 + y^2} \to \infty$. This result was also derived by means of the Fourier transform in Section 15.4, and is the **Poisson integral formula for the upper half plane**.

Note: The Dirichlet problems considered here in parts (a) and (b) can also be solved by an elegant technique known as the method of *Green's functions*. For the reader who subsequently studies that method and comes back to this exercise to compare the two approaches, it may be helpful for us to note that the mysterious point $\zeta = R^2/\bar{z}$ that shows up in (b) and the mysterious point $\zeta = \bar{z}$ that shows up in (e) are (in the terminology of the method of Green's functions) the *image points*.

Series Expansion and the Residue Theorem 21

INTRODUCTION 21.1

Looking back for a moment, recall that one can reexpress a complex integral $\int_C f(z)\, dz$ in terms of two *real* integrals according to the formula

$$\int_C f(z)\, dz = \int_C (u\, dx - v\, dy) + i \int_C (v\, dx + u\, dy). \tag{1}$$

Consequently, there was the temptation, in Chapter 20, to stop right there and to rely on the theory of real line integrals, which was studied in Chapter 9. However, we promised that it would prove more fruitful to keep $\int_C f(z)\, dz$ intact and to develop a distinct complex integral calculus. We began that development in Chapter 20 and got as far as Cauchy's theorem and the Cauchy integral formula. Those results will now enable us to derive the Taylor and Laurent series expansions of functions of a complex variable (Sections 21.4 and 21.5), which, in turn, will permit us to clarify the notion of singularities (Section 21.6), and finally, to complete our development of the complex integral calculus by deriving the powerful residue theorem (Section 21.7).

COMPLEX SERIES 21.2

We begin by studying complex series. Our development closely parallels that of real infinite series but is more focused and concise because in subsequent sections we deal only with *power series*. Although it is presumed that the reader has already studied real infinite series in the calculus, our discussion in this and subsequent sections will be almost entirely self-contained.

By a *complex infinite series* we mean any sum of the form

$$\sum_{n=0}^{\infty} c_n = c_0 + c_1 + c_2 + c_3 + \cdots, \tag{1}$$

where the c_n's are complex numbers. Before continuing, recall that *finite* series are uniquely determined, no matter how we sequence the addition operations. For example, it does not matter whether we compute the finite series $c_0 + c_1 + c_2$ as $(c_0 + c_1) + c_2$ or $(c_1 + c_2) + c_0$, or $(c_0 + c_2) + c_1$, because of the associative property of addition. However, the associative property does not hold, in general, for *infinite* series, so it remains to clarify what is intended by the infinite series written in (1). Denoting the sum of the first N terms as the Nth *partial sum*,

$$s_N = c_0 + c_1 + \cdots + c_{N-1} = \sum_{n=0}^{N-1} c_n, \tag{2}$$

we hereby define the infinite series in (1) as the limit of the sequence of partial sums,

$$\sum_{n=0}^{\infty} c_n = \lim_{N\to\infty} s_N. \tag{3}$$

That is, as occurs so often in mathematics, we define the "new object" (the infinite complex series) as the limit of a sequence of "old objects" (finite complex series). Although other definitions are sometimes used (Exercise 2), the one given in (3) is the most common and is known as *ordinary convergence*.

If the limit exists and is some complex number s, we say that the series is **convergent** and converges to s. That is, given any $\epsilon > 0$ (no matter how small), there corresponds an integer $N_0(\epsilon)$ such that $|s - s_N| < \epsilon$ for all $N > N_0$.* We have written "$N_0(\epsilon)$" because N_0 will, in general, depend on ϵ: The smaller we choose ϵ, the larger we expect N_0 to be.

If the limit does *not* exist, we say that the series is **divergent,** or diverges. Be sure to see that for a series to diverge the sequence of partial sums does *not* necessarily grow unboundedly (Exercise 3, for the case $c = 1$), it merely fails to approach a unique limit.

EXAMPLE 1 *Geometric Series.* To illustrate the limit definition (3), consider the especially useful **geometric series**

$$\sum_{n=0}^{\infty} c^n = 1 + c + c^2 + \cdots, \tag{4}$$

where c is any complex number. Writing

$$s_N = 1 + c + c^2 + \cdots + c^{N-1} \tag{5}$$

and

$$cs_N = c + c^2 + \cdots + c^{N-1} + c^N, \tag{6}$$

* It (almost) goes without saying that ϵ is a real number because it is stated that "$\epsilon > 0$"; *complex* numbers are not ordered, so $\epsilon > 0$ would make no sense if ϵ were complex.

we obtain, by subtraction, $(1 - c)s_N = 1 - c^N$. Thus provided that $c \neq 1$, we have

$$s_N = \frac{1 - c^N}{1 - c} \qquad (c \neq 1). \tag{7}$$

For $c = 1$ we see from (7) that $s_N = N$, so

$$s_N = \begin{cases} \dfrac{1 - c^N}{1 - c} & (c \neq 1) \\ N & (c = 1). \end{cases} \tag{8}$$

The beauty of (8) is that it gives us s_N in *closed form*. Letting $N \to \infty$ in (8), we see that $\lim_{N\to\infty} s_N$ fails to exist if $|c| \geq 1$, and equals $1/(1 - c)$ if $|c| < 1$ (Exercise 3). That is, the geometric series (6) converges to $1/(1 - c)$ if $|c| < 1$ and it diverges if $|c| \geq 1$. ◀

Example 1 is exceptional inasmuch as we were able to get s_N into closed form. That step not only permitted a direct assessment of the convergence or divergence of the series (i.e., by actually taking the limit of s_N as $N \to \infty$), it even enabled us to determine the sum [namely, $1/(1 - c)$]. Unfortunately, getting s_N into closed form is not feasible in general, so we desire a theorem, or theorems, which will enable us to determine the convergence or divergence of a given series in a less direct manner.

Before proceeding along those lines we should mention that we can reexpress the complex series (1) in terms of two *real* series, for if Re $c_n = a_n$ and Im $c_n = b_n$, then by *linearity* (Exercise 4)

$$\sum_{n=0}^{\infty} c_n = \sum_{n=0}^{\infty} a_n + i \sum_{n=0}^{\infty} b_n, \tag{9}$$

which formula is analogous to equation (1) in Section 21.1. However, we shall be better advised to keep the c_n's intact and to develop an independent theory of complex series.

In the remainder of this section we present three theorems which carry over virtually intact from the theory of real series and which will be used in the section to follow.

> ***Theorem 1*** *Cauchy Criterion*
> The series $\Sigma_{n=0}^{\infty} c_n$ converges if and only if to each $\epsilon > 0$ (no matter how small) there corresponds an integer $N_0(\epsilon)$ such that $|s_M - s_N| < \epsilon$ for all integers M and N greater than N_0.

Proof Suppose that the series converges to s. From the definition of convergence it follows that to each $\epsilon > 0$ there corresponds an integer $N_0(\epsilon)$ such that $|s_k - s| < \epsilon/2$ for all $k > N_0$. Then for all M and N greater than N_0, we have

$$|s_M - s_N| = |(s_M - s) + (s - s_N)| \leq |s_M - s| + |s_N - s| < \frac{\epsilon}{2} + \frac{\epsilon}{2}, \tag{10}$$

or, $|s_M - s_N| < \epsilon$. Proof of the converse, that the stated condition implies convergence, is a longer and more difficult story and will be omitted.* ■

The Cauchy criterion is fundamental in analysis because it provides a *necessary and sufficient* condition for convergence. On the other hand, as a *test* for convergence it is generally difficult to apply. Thus one develops a number of more easily applied theorems, providing various *sufficient* conditions, or *necessary* conditions, for convergence. Two such theorems follow.

> ***Theorem 2*** *Comparison Test*
> If the series $\Sigma_{n=0}^{\infty} M_n$ converges, where the M_n's are positive constants and $|c_n| \leq M_n$ for each n greater than some integer J, the series $\Sigma_{n=0}^{\infty} c_n$ converges too.

terms

Proof According to the Cauchy criterion, the assumed convergence of $\Sigma_{n=0}^{\infty} M_n$ implies that to each $\epsilon > 0$ there corresponds an N_0 such that $M_p + M_{p+1} + \cdots + M_{p+q} < \epsilon$ for all $p > N_0$ and for all $q \geq 0$. Then

$$\begin{aligned}|c_p + c_{p+1} + \cdots + c_{p+q}| &\leq |c_p| + |c_{p+1}| + \cdots + |c_{p+q}| \\ &\leq M_p + M_{p+1} + \cdots + M_{p+q} < \epsilon\end{aligned} \tag{11}$$

for all $p > N_0$ and for all $q \geq 0$, so $\Sigma_{n=0}^{\infty} c_n$ converges, too. ■

EXAMPLE 2 Determine the convergence or divergence of the series

$$\sum_{n=0}^{\infty} \frac{i^n}{n!} = 1 + i + \frac{i^2}{2!} + \frac{i^3}{3!} + \cdots \qquad (i = \sqrt{-1}, \text{ as usual}). \tag{12}$$

Since

$$\left|\frac{i^n}{n!}\right| = \frac{1}{n!} < \frac{1}{2^n} \tag{13}$$

for all $n \geq 4$ and $\Sigma_{n=0}^{\infty} 1/2^n = \Sigma_{n=0}^{\infty} (\frac{1}{2})^n$ is a convergent geometric series, it follows from the comparison test that the series (12) is convergent. We say that the terms $1/2^n$ *dominate* those in (12). ◀

> ***Theorem 3*** *Ratio Test*
> If $\lim_{n\to\infty} |c_{n+1}/c_n| = L$, then $\Sigma_{n=0}^{\infty} c_n$ converges if $L < 1$ and diverges if $L > 1$. (No information is obtained if $L = 1$ or if the limit does not exist.)

Proof Suppose that $L < 1$. Choose any number q such that $L < q < 1$. Then it must be true that $|c_{n+1}/c_n| < q$ for all sufficiently large n's, say for all $n \geq J$. Thus

$$|c_{J+1}| < q|c_J|,$$

* See, for example, T. M. Apostol, *Mathematical Analysis* (Reading, Mass.: Addison-Wesley, 1957).

$$|c_{J+2}| < q|c_{J+1}| < q^2|c_J|,$$
$$|c_{J+3}| < q|c_{J+2}| < q^3|c_J|,$$

and so on. According to the comparison test, the series $\Sigma_{n=0}^{\infty} c_n$ converges by comparison with the series $\Sigma_{n=0}^{\infty} q^n|c_J|$, which is $|c_J|$ times the convergent geometric series $\Sigma_{n=0}^{\infty} q^n$. The case where $L > 1$ is left for the exercises. ■

EXAMPLE 3 Determine the convergence or divergence of the series

$$\sum_{n=0}^{\infty} \frac{(1+i)^n}{n!}. \tag{14}$$

In this case,

$$\lim_{n\to\infty} \left|\frac{c_{n+1}}{c_n}\right| = \lim_{n\to\infty} \left|\frac{1+i}{n+1}\right| = \sqrt{2} \lim_{n\to\infty} \frac{1}{n+1} = 0,$$

so $L = 0$ and, according to the ratio test, the series is convergent. ◀

EXAMPLE 4 Determine the convergence or divergence of the series

$$\sum_{n=2}^{\infty} e^{-(2+3i)n}. \tag{15}$$

Again applying the ratio test,

$$\begin{aligned}\lim_{n\to\infty} \left|\frac{c_{n+1}}{c_n}\right| &= \lim_{n\to\infty} \left|e^{-(2+3i)}\right| = \left|e^{-(2+3i)}\right| \\ &= \left|e^{-2}e^{-3i}\right| = e^{-2}\left|e^{-3i}\right| = e^{-2},\end{aligned}$$

so $L = e^{-2} < 1$ and the series is convergent.

COMMENT Whether the sum begins at $n = 2$ or $n = 0$ is immaterial insofar as the convergence or divergence of the series is concerned, although it is, of course, important insofar as the *value* of the series. ◀

In this section we have not aimed at a complete discussion of complex series. Rather, we have limited our scope to fundamentals together with specific results that will be needed for our subsequent study of *power series*.

21.2 EXERCISES

1. (*Necessary condition for convergence*) Prove that for a series $\Sigma_{n=0}^{\infty} c_n$ to converge it is *necessary*, although not sufficient, that $c_n \to 0$ as $n \to \infty$. *Hint:* To prove necessity, let $M = N + 1$ in the Cauchy criterion (Theorem 1). To prove that the condition is not sufficient, recall the well-known divergent harmonic series (Exercise 6).

2. Although (3) is the commonly used definition of an infinite series $\Sigma_{n=0}^{\infty} c_n$, it is not the only one possible. Various "summability methods" are sometimes employed, of which (3) (often called *ordinary convergence*) is only one. [For an interesting account of various summability theories, see G. H. Hardy, *Divergent Series* (Oxford: Oxford University Press, 1949).] For example, according to *Cesàro summability,* which is especially useful in the theory of Fourier series,

$$\sum_{n=0}^{\infty} c_n = \lim_{N\to\infty} \left(\frac{s_1 + s_2 + \cdots + s_N}{N} \right), \tag{a}$$

that is, the limit of the arithmetic mean of the partial sums. It can be shown that if a series converges to s in the ordinary sense, it will also be Cesàro summable, and to the same value s. Further, there are series that diverge in the ordinary sense that are, nevertheless, Cesàro summable. Show that the series $1 - 1 + 1 - 1 + \cdots$ diverges in the ordinary sense (see Exercise 1), yet is Cesàro summable to the value $\frac{1}{2}$.

3. Using (8), show that $\lim_{N\to\infty} s_N$ fails to exist if $|c| \geq 1$. Further, show that the s_N's grow unboundedly if $|c| > 1$, but remain bounded if $|c| = 1$ and $c \neq 1$. (Recall that c is, in general, complex.)

4. (*Linearity*) Prove that if $\Sigma_{n=0}^{\infty} p_n$ and $\Sigma_{n=0}^{\infty} q_n$ are convergent complex series and α, β are arbitrary constants, then

$$\sum_{n=0}^{\infty} (\alpha p_n + \beta q_n) = \alpha \sum_{n=0}^{\infty} p_n + \beta \sum_{n=0}^{\infty} q_n. \tag{a}$$

5. Complete the proof of Theorem 3, i.e., for the case $L > 1$. *Hint:* Use the necessary condition given in Exercise 1.

6. (*Application of Cauchy criterion to harmonic series*) Use the Cauchy criterion to show that the well-known **harmonic series**

$$\sum_{n=1}^{\infty} \frac{1}{n} = 1 + \frac{1}{2} + \frac{1}{3} + \cdots \tag{a}$$

is divergent. *Hint:* Observe that

$$\begin{aligned} |s_{2N} - s_N| &= \frac{1}{N+1} + \frac{1}{N+2} + \cdots + \frac{1}{N+N} \\ &> \frac{1}{N+N} + \frac{1}{N+N} + \cdots + \frac{1}{N+N} \\ &= \frac{1}{2}. \end{aligned}$$

7. Use any of Theorems 1 to 3 or the necessary condition given in Exercise 1 to determine the convergence or divergence of the following series.

*(a) $\displaystyle\sum_{n=1}^{\infty} \frac{n}{(2+i)^n}$ (b) $\displaystyle\sum_{n=5}^{\infty} \frac{n^5}{3^n}$

(c) $\displaystyle\sum_{n=2}^{\infty} \frac{1}{(2i)^n \ln n}$ *(d) $\displaystyle\sum_{n=0}^{\infty} \left(\frac{1+n}{2+n}\right)^3$

(e) $\displaystyle\sum_{n=1}^{\infty} \frac{(1+3i)^n}{n^{100}}$ (f) $\displaystyle\sum_{n=1}^{\infty} n^4 e^{-(5-i)n}$

(g) $\displaystyle\sum_{n=1}^{\infty} e^{-in}$ *(h) $\displaystyle\sum_{n=1}^{\infty} (\sin n)\left(\frac{1+i}{2-i}\right)^n$

21.3 POWER SERIES

In Section 21.2 we dealt with series of *constants*. More generally, let us allow the terms to be functions of z:

$$\sum_{n=0}^{\infty} f_n(z) = f_0(z) + f_1(z) + \cdots. \tag{1}$$

Of course, at any particular z point (within the domain of definition of all of the f_n's) convergence and divergence are defined and established as indicated in Section 21.2. The set of all z points for which the series converges is called the *region of convergence* of the series.

Since we are leading up to complex Taylor series we shall not consider the general case (1). Rather, we suppose that $f_n(z)$ is of the form $c_n(z-a)^n$, where the c_n's and a are, in general, complex numbers. The resulting form,

$$\sum_{n=0}^{\infty} c_n(z-a)^n = c_0 + c_1(z-a) + c_2(z-a)^2 + \cdots, \tag{2}$$

is called a **power series**. If, to determine the region of convergence of (2), we apply the ratio test, we find (Exercise 1) that:

Theorem 1 *Power Series Convergence by Ratio Test*

If

$$\lim_{n\to\infty}\left|\frac{c_{n+1}}{c_n}\right| = L, \tag{3}$$

then the power series (2) converges in the disk $|z - a| < 1/L$ and diverges in $|z - a| > 1/L$. If $L = \infty$, the series converges only at the point $z = a$, and if $L = 0$, it converges for all z, i.e., in $|z - a| < \infty$.

EXAMPLE 1 *Geometric Series.* The geometric series

$$\sum_{n=0}^{\infty} z^n = 1 + z + z^2 + \cdot\cdot\cdot \tag{4}$$

is the same as encountered in Example 1 in Section 21.2 except that the terms are z^n instead of constants. Since $c_n = 1$ ($n = 0, 1, 2, \ldots$) in (2), (3) gives

$$\lim_{n\to\infty}\left|\frac{c_{n+1}}{c_n}\right| = L = 1, \tag{5}$$

so the geometric series converges in the disk $|z| < 1$ and diverges in $|z| > 1$. Observe that Theorem 1 gives no information regarding convergence or divergence for points on the circle $|z| = 1$. ◀

At first glance, it is tempting to conclude from Theorem 1 that a power series inevitably converges in a *circular disk* centered at a (that disk being the single point $z = a$ if $L = \infty$ and the whole z plane if $L = 0$). However, notice carefully that Theorem 1 yields no information at all if $\lim_{n\to\infty}|c_{n+1}/c_n|$ does not exist (as occurs if, for example, $c_n = \sin n$), and in that event it is conceivable that a noncircular region of convergence may exist. Toward clarifying this point, we first present the following lemma.*

Lemma 1 *Power Series Convergence*

If the power series (2) converges at a point z_0, then it converges everywhere in the open disk $|z - a| < |z_0 - a|$ (Fig. 21.1).

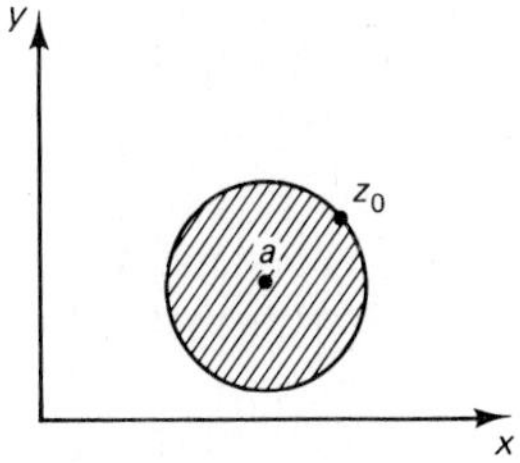

Fig. 21.1 The disk $|z - a| < |z_0 - a|$.

* Not an end in itself, a lemma is normally developed to help prove a subsequent theorem.

Proof Since the series converges for $z = z_0$, it follows (Exercise 1 on page 823) that $c_n(z_0 - a)^n \to 0$ as $n \to \infty$. Thus there must certainly exist a constant K such that $|c_n(z_0 - a)^n| < K$ for all $n = 0, 1, 2, \ldots$, and from this result we infer that $|c_n| < K/|z_0 - a|^n$ $(n = 0, 1, 2, \ldots)$. Then, for any z such that $|z - a| < |z_0 - a|$, we have

$$|c_n(z - a)^n| < K\left|\frac{z - a}{z_0 - a}\right|^n. \tag{6}$$

Observing that $|(z - a)/(z_0 - a)| < 1$, we see that $K|(z - a)/(z_0 - a)|^n$ is the nth term of a convergent geometric series (scaled by K). Thus it follows from (6) and the comparison test that (2) is convergent, as stated. ■

With the help of this lemma we can now show that the region of convergence of a power series is inevitably a circular disk.

Theorem 2 *Power Series Convergence in a Disk*
For a power series

$$\sum_{n=0}^{\infty} c_n(z - a)^n = c_0 + c_1(z - a) + c_2(z - a)^2 + \cdots \tag{7}$$

there exist three distinct possibilities regarding its region of convergence:

(i) The series converges only at the point $z = a$.
(ii) The series converges in the whole z plane.
(iii) There exists a constant $R > 0$, called the **radius of convergence** of (7), such that (7) converges everywhere in $|z - a| < R$ and diverges everywhere in $|z - a| > R$.

Proof The possibilities (i) and (ii) are easily accounted for by putting forward a specific example for each case (Exercise 4), so we turn to (iii). If (i) does *not* apply, there must be a point $z_1 \neq a$ at which (7) converges, and if (ii) does *not* apply, there must be a point z_2 at which (7) diverges. From the lemma it is evident that $|z_2 - a| \geq |z_1 - a|$. If $|z_2 - a| = |z_1 - a|$, it follows from the lemma that (7) converges everywhere in $|z - a| < |z_1 - a|$. Furthermore, the lemma also implies that (7) diverges everywhere in $|z - a| > |z_1 - a|$, for if it converged anywhere in that region, it could not diverge at z_2 as assumed. Thus if $|z_2 - a| = |z_1 - a|$, then $R = |z_2 - a| = |z_1 - a|$ is the radius of convergence referred to in (iii), and it remains to consider the case where $|z_2 - a| > |z_1 - a|$, as depicted in Fig. 21.2. Let S be the set of values ρ such that (7) converges for all $|z - a| < \rho$. From the lemma it follows that if some value ρ_0 belongs to S, so do all ρ's satisfying $0 \leq \rho \leq \rho_0$. Thus S is necessarily an interval (on a ρ axis), either $0 \leq \rho < R$ or $0 \leq \rho \leq R$ for some R such that $|z_1 - a| \leq R \leq |z_2 - a|$. Furthermore, (7) must diverge everywhere in $|z - a| > R$ because if it converged anywhere in that region, the right endpoint of the S interval would be greater than R. Then R is the radius of convergence referred to in (iii), and the proof is complete. ■

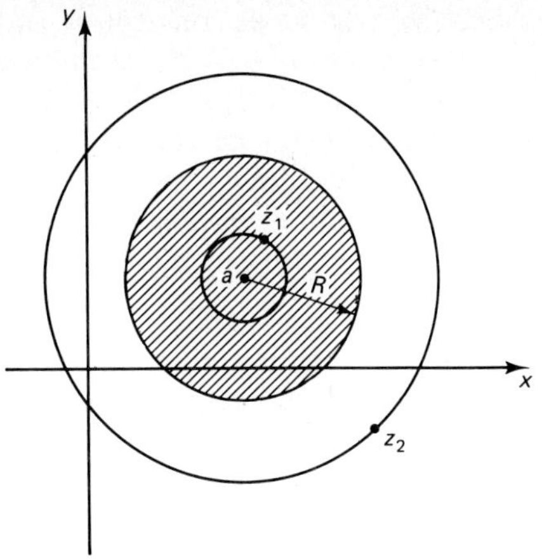

Fig. 21.2 Disk of convergence.

Repeating the essence of Theorem 2, for emphasis, we have learned that the region of convergence of a complex power series $\Sigma_n c_n(z - a)^n$ is necessarily a circular disk (possibly of zero or infinite radius) centered at the point a. Before continuing, let us tie this result together with the corresponding result for *real* power series, as studied in an introductory course on the calculus. Specifically, let the c_n's and the number a all be real. If $0 < R < \infty$, say, the region of convergence in the z plane is as shown in Fig. 21.3. And if we consider only real values of z, $z = x$, the region of convergence on the x axis is the *interval* $|x - a| < R$ centered at a: The series $\Sigma_n c_n(x - a)^n$ converges everywhere in $|x - a| < R$, and diverges everywhere in $|x - a| > R$. This result should be familiar to the reader from the calculus.

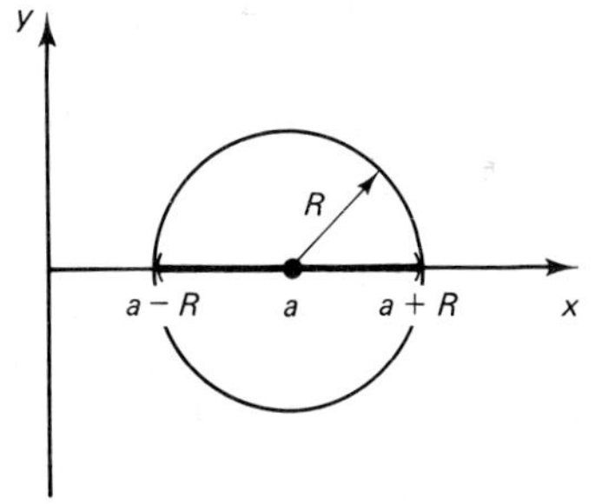

Fig. 21.3 If a is real.

To proceed further, it will be helpful to extend the concept of *uniform* convergence from real-variable theory to complex variable theory. First, recall that the series

$$\sum_{n=0}^{\infty} f_n(z) = f_0(z) + f_1(z) + f_2(z) + \cdots \tag{8}$$

converges to $s(z)$, at a given point z, if to each $\epsilon > 0$ (no matter how small) there corresponds an integer N_0 such that $|s(z) - s_N(z)| < \epsilon$ for all $N > N_0$, where $s_N(z) = \Sigma_{n=0}^{N-1} f_n(z)$ is the Nth partial sum of the series. If the series converges at each point z in a region G, we say that the series *converges in G*. In that event we expect that N_0 will depend not only on ϵ, but will, in general, also vary from point to point within G: $N_0 = N_0(\epsilon, z)$. However, *if to each* $\epsilon > 0$ *(no matter how small) there* *corresponds an integer $N_0(\epsilon)$ (i.e.,* ***independent of z****) such that* $|s(z) - s_N(z)| < \epsilon$ *for all* $N > N_0$ *and for all z in a region G, we say that the series (8) converges* ***uniformly*** *to s(z) in G.* [Dropping back to real-variable theory, one merely needs to change the z's to x's and to change the word "region" to interval (on the x axis).]

The key point is, as we shall soon see, that uniformly convergent series can be manipulated with considerable impunity. Thus it is important to be able to test a given series for uniform convergence. For this purpose the **Weierstrass *M*-test** often suffices.*

Theorem 3 *Weierstrass M-Test*

If $M_0, M_1, M_2, \ldots$ are positive constants such that $|f_n(z)| \leq M_n$ for all z in a region G and for all $n = 0, 1, 2, \ldots$, and if

$$\sum_{n=0}^{\infty} M_n = M_0 + M_1 + M_2 + \cdots \tag{9}$$

is convergent, then the series

$$\sum_{n=0}^{\infty} f_n(z) = f_0(z) + f_1(z) + f_2(z) + \cdots \tag{10}$$

converges uniformly in G.

Proof First, observe that it follows immediately from the comparison test that (10) converges in G, say to $s(z)$, so it remains to prove that the convergence is uniform. Since (9) converges, say to S, it follows that to each $\epsilon > 0$ there corresponds an N_0 such that

$$\left| S - \sum_{n=0}^{N-1} M_n \right| = |M_n + M_{N+1} + \cdots| = M_N + M_{N+1} + \cdots < \epsilon \tag{11}$$

for all $N > N_0$. Then

$$\begin{aligned} \left| s(z) - \sum_{n=0}^{N-1} f_n(z) \right| &= |f_N(z) + f_{N+1}(z) + \cdots| \\ &\leq |f_N(z)| + |f_{N+1}(z)| + \cdots \\ &\leq M_N + M_{N+1} + \cdots < \epsilon \end{aligned} \tag{12}$$

for all $N > N_0$, so the convergence of (10) is indeed uniform. ■

EXAMPLE 2 The series

$$\sum_{n=1}^{\infty} \frac{1}{n^2 + |z|^2}$$

* *Karl Weierstrass* (1815–1897) and *Augustin-Louis Cauchy* (1789–1857) are perhaps the two names most closely associated with the introduction of rigorous analysis in mathematics. Cauchy's development of complex variable theory is essentially the one followed here (and in most other texts as well), whereas Weierstrass built his theory on the power series representation of complex functions. In particular, the concept of uniform convergence is generally attributed to Weierstrass and the British mathematical physicist *Sir G. G. Stokes* (1819–1903).

converges uniformly in the whole z plane, by the Weierstrass M-test, because

$$\left|\frac{1}{n^2 + |z|^2}\right| \leq \frac{1}{n^2} \tag{13}$$

for all z and for all $n = 1, 2, \ldots$, and $\sum_{n=1}^{\infty} 1/n^2$ is a convergent p series.* ◀

With the concept of uniform convergence in hand, we return to power series and close this section with a sequence of interesting results.

Theorem 4 *Uniform Convergence of Power Series*
If the power series

$$\sum_{n=0}^{\infty} c_n(z-a)^n = c_0 + c_1(z-a) + \cdots \tag{14}$$

has a radius of convergence $R > 0$, the series converges uniformly in $|z - a| \leq R_0$ for every $R_0 < R$.

Proof of Theorem 4 is left to the exercises.

By virtue of the uniformity of convergence, we now show the following.

Lemma 2 *Continuity of Sum Function*
If the power series (14) converges in $|z - a| < R$, the sum function $s(z)$ is continuous there.

Proof Let z_0 be any point in $|z - a| < R$. We wish to show that $|s(z) - s(z_0)|$ can be made arbitrarily small by keeping z sufficiently close to z_0. With the Nth partial sum $s_N(z)$ and Nth remainder $R_N(z)$ defined as

$$s_N(z) = \sum_{n=0}^{N-1} c_n(z-a)^n, \qquad R_N(z) = \sum_{n=N}^{\infty} c_n(z-a)^n, \tag{15}$$

we have

$$\begin{aligned} |s(z) - s(z_0)| &= |s_N(z) + R_N(z) - s_N(z_0) - R_N(z_0)| \\ &\leq |s_N(z) - s_N(z_0)| + |R_N(z)| + |R_N(z_0)|. \end{aligned} \tag{16}$$

From the uniform convergence of (14), noted in Theorem 4, it follows that to each $\epsilon' > 0$ there corresponds an N_0 such that $|R_N(z)| < \epsilon'$ for all $N > N_0$ and for all z in $|z - a| < R'$ for any R' such that $|z_0 - a| < R' < R$ (Fig. 21.4). Furthermore, $s_N(z) - s_N(z_0)$ is a continuous function of z (because it is a finite-degree polynomial)

*Recall, from the calculus, that the **p series,**

$$\sum_{n=1}^{\infty} \frac{1}{n^p} = 1 + \frac{1}{2^p} + \frac{1}{3^p} + \cdots \qquad (p \text{ real})$$

converges for $p > 1$ and diverges for $p \leq 1$. For the borderline divergent case $p = 1$, the p series is known as the **harmonic series**. The harmonic series was the subject of Exercise 6 on page 824.

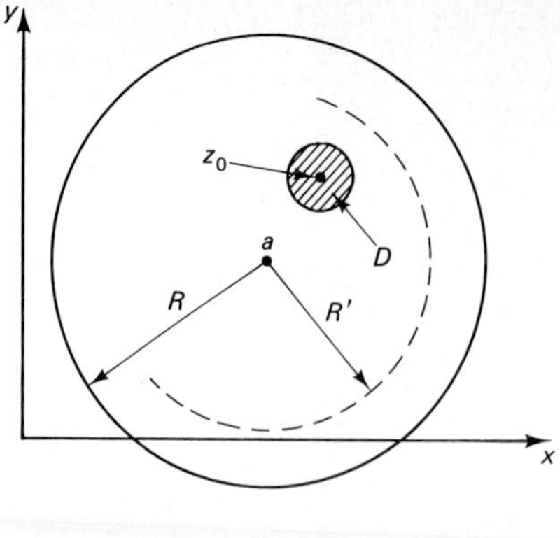

Fig. 21.4 Geometry for Lemma 2.

which is zero at z_0, so it must be possible to find a sufficiently small neighborhood D of z_0 (Fig. 21.4), lying within $|z - a| < R'$, so that $|s_N(z) - s(z_0)| < \epsilon'$ for all z in D. Thus (16) gives

$$|s(z) - s(z_0)| < \epsilon' + \epsilon' + \epsilon' = 3\epsilon' \tag{17}$$

for all z in D. Letting $\epsilon = 3\epsilon'$, we have, for arbitrarily small ϵ, $|s(z) - s(z_0)| < \epsilon$ for all z in D, so $s(z)$ is continuous at z_0, as was to be proved. ■

The idea behind Lemma 2 is as follows. For a power series, each term is a continuous function of z. Similarly, each partial sum $s_N(z)$ is continuous because it is a finite sum of continuous functions. The point, then, is that the uniformity of the convergence ensures that the continuity of the sequence of partial sums is passed on to the sum function. To clarify this point further, it may be helpful to consider an example from *real*-variable theory, so that we can use graphical illustration. Specifically, consider the function sequence

$$s_N(z) = \begin{cases} e^{Nx}, & x \le 0 \\ 2 - e^{-Nx}, & x > 0 \end{cases} \tag{18}$$

for $N = 0, 1, 2, \ldots$, the graph of which is shown in Fig. 21.5a. (Whether s_N arises as the Nth partial sum of a series or as a sequence independent of any series is

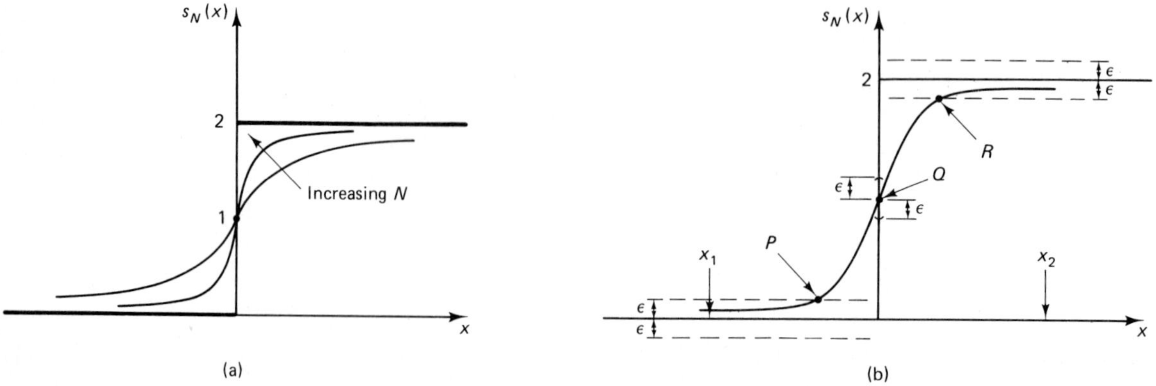

Fig. 21.5 The sequence (18).

not important.) Clearly, the limit function is

$$s(x) = \lim_{N\to\infty} s_N(x) = \begin{cases} 2, & x > 0 \\ 1, & x = 0, \\ 0, & x < 0 \end{cases} \tag{19}$$

as shown with heavy lines in Fig. 21.5a. Now, each $s_N(x)$ is continuous for all x, yet the limit function $s(x)$ is discontinuous at $x = 0$. Evidently, then, the convergence of $s_N(x)$ to $s(x)$ cannot have been uniform over any x-interval containing $x = 0$. The truth of this claim is plainly illustrated in Fig. 21.5b, for if the convergence were uniform (over $x_1 \le x \le x_2$, say), then given an arbitrarily narrow "ϵ band" about the limit function $s(x)$ we should be able to force the graph of $s_N(x)$ into that band for all N's greater than some sufficiently large N_0. As is evident from the figure, however, the graph of $s_N(x)$ inevitably "leaks out" between Q and some point R, and between Q and some point P (see Exercise 7).

Finally, we note that we have designated the foregoing result as a lemma, rather than a theorem, because we will be able to make a stronger statement in Theorem 6.

Theorem 5 *Termwise Integration of Power Series*
If the power series (14) converges in $|z - a| < R$, then the integral of the sum function $s(z)$ over any piecewise smooth curve C within that disk is equal to the sum of the integrals of the individual terms:

$$\int_C \underbrace{\sum_{n=0}^{\infty} c_n(z-a)^n}_{s(z)}\, dz = \sum_{n=0}^{\infty} c_n \int_C (z-a)^n\, dz. \tag{20}$$

Proof First $s(z)$ is (according to Lemma 2) continuous, so the integral on the left-hand side of (20) does indeed exist. Writing

$$\int_C s(z)\, dz = \int_C [s_N(z) + R_N(z)]\, dz = \int_C s_N(z)\, dz + \int_C R_N(z)\, dz, \tag{21}$$

we have

$$\left| \int_C s(z)\, dz - \int_C s_N(z)\, dz \right| = \left| \int_C R_N(z)\, dz \right|. \tag{22}$$

Since (14) converges *uniformly* in $|z - a| < R$ (and hence all along C), it follows that to each $\epsilon > 0$ there corresponds an N_0 such that $|R_N(z)| < \epsilon$ for all $N > N_0$ and for all z on C. Thus if the length of C is L, then (22) gives

$$\left| \int_C s(z)\, dz - \int_C s_N(z)\, dz \right| \le \epsilon L \tag{23}$$

for all $N > N_0$, from which (20) follows. ■

EXAMPLE 3 Evaluate the integral of the series

$$\sum_{n=0}^{\infty} z^n = 1 + z + z^2 + \cdots \tag{24}$$

along a straight-line path from $z = 0$ to $z = (1 + i)/2$. Of course, *if* we are able to sum the series [i.e., to determine the sum function $s(z)$ in closed form], we need merely integrate $s(z)$ over the given path. If we can*not* obtain $s(z)$ in closed form (as is usually the case), we can fall back on Theorem 5 and integrate termwise. Proceeding along those lines in the present example, we first ascertain, by the ratio test, that the series converges in $|z| < 1$, and then we observe that C does lie entirely within that disk. Then, according to Theorem 5, we have

$$\begin{aligned}\int_C \sum_{n=0}^{\infty} z^n \, dz &= \sum_{n=0}^{\infty} \int_0^{(1+i)/2} z^n \, dz \\ &= \left(\frac{1+i}{2}\right) + \frac{1}{2}\left(\frac{1+i}{2}\right)^2 + \frac{1}{3}\left(\frac{1+i}{2}\right)^3 + \cdots .\end{aligned} \tag{25}$$

COMMENT Actually, in the present case we *can* sum the series (24) because it is simply a geometric series, with $s(z) = 1/(1 - z)$. Thus we could have computed

$$\int_C \sum_{n=0}^{\infty} z^n \, dz = \int_0^{(1+i)/2} \frac{dz}{1 - z} = -\log(1 - z) \Big|_{z=0}^{z=(1+i)/2} \tag{26}$$

directly. That (25) and (26) are in agreement is left for an exercise in Section 21.4. ◀

We close this section with the following important theorem.

> ***Theorem 6*** *Analyticity of Sum Function*
> If the power series (14) converges in $|z - a| < R$, then the sum function $s(z)$ is **analytic** within that disk.

Proof If C is any piecewise-smooth simple closed curve in $|z - a| < R$, then, according to Theorem 5,

$$\oint_C s(z) \, dz = \sum_{n=0}^{\infty} \oint_C (z - a)^n \, dz. \tag{27}$$

But each integral on the right-hand side of (27) is zero, so $\oint_C s(z)\, dz = 0$. Then, from Morera's theorem (page 818), it follows that $s(z)$ is analytic in $|z - a| < R$. ■

Highlighting the principal results in this section, we found that the region of convergence of a power series $\Sigma_n c_n(z - a)^n$ is necessarily a circular disk (possibly of zero or infinite radius) centered at point a. Introducing the notion of uniform continuity, we then found that power series converge uniformly within every disk concentric with, and smaller than, the disk of convergence. This uniformity was shown to render convergent power series very nice indeed: They can be integrated termwise within their disk of convergence (they can be differentiated termwise too, but we have not yet come to that), and they sum to a function that is analytic in the disk of convergence. With this final result (Theorem 6), we establish a strong link between the analytic function theory and the theory of power series.

Although our interest, in this section, has been in power series, we should mention that results such as Lemma 2, Theorem 5, and Theorem 6 can be generalized to series of the form $\Sigma_n\, a_n(z)$. In particular, let us merely state, for reference, a useful generalized version of Theorem 5.*

> ***Theorem 5′*** *Termwise Integration of Series*
> Let C be a piecewise-smooth curve, let $a_0(z), a_1(z), \ldots$ be continuous along C, and let $\Sigma_{n=0}^{\infty}\, a_n(z)$ converge uniformly along C. Then the integral of the sum function $s(z)$, along C, is equal to the sum of the integrals of the individual terms:
>
> $$\int_C \underbrace{\sum_{n=0}^{\infty} a_n(z)}_{s(z)}\, dz = \sum_{n=0}^{\infty} \int_C a_n(z)\, dz. \tag{28}$$

21.3 EXERCISES

1. Prove Theorem 1.

2. Apply Theorem 1 in each case to determine, insofar as possible, the regions of convergence and divergence.

*(a) $\Sigma_{n=0}^{\infty}\, z^{2n}$ (b) $\Sigma_{n=2}^{\infty}\, n^2(z-3)^n$
(c) $\Sigma_{n=0}^{\infty}\, n!(z+5)^n$ *(d) $\Sigma_{n=4}^{\infty}\, e^n(z+i)^n$
(e) $\Sigma_{n=1}^{\infty}\, e^{-n}z^n$ (f) $\Sigma_{n=0}^{\infty}\, (n^{100}/n!)z^n$
*(g) $\Sigma_{n=0}^{\infty}\, e^{in}z^n$ (h) $\Sigma_{n=0}^{\infty}\, \dfrac{\cos n}{n^2+1}z^n$
(i) $\Sigma_{n=1}^{\infty}\, [(2-i)z]^n$

3. (*Lemma 1*) The following alternative proof is proposed for Lemma 1: For any z closer to a than z_0 we have $|c_n(z-a)^n| < |c_n(z-a)^n|$ and since the series $\Sigma_{n=0}^{\infty}\, c_n(z_0-a)^n$ converges by assumption, then, by the comparison test, so must the series $\Sigma_{n=0}^{\infty}\, c_n(z-a)^n$. Show why the proposed reasoning is incorrect.

4. (*Theorem 2*) (a) Show that "the series converges only at the point $z = a$" is a possibility by putting forward a series for which that is the case.
(b) Show that "the series converges in the whole z plane" is a possibility by putting forward a series for which that is the case.

5. Using the Weierstrass M-test, show that the given series converges uniformly in the given region.

(a) $\Sigma_{n=1}^{\infty}\, 1/(n^2+z)$ in $\operatorname{Re} z \geq 0$
(b) $\Sigma_{n=0}^{\infty}\, e^{nz}$ in $\operatorname{Re} z \leq K$ for any $K < 0$
(c) $\Sigma_{n=0}^{\infty}\, e^{-n}/(n+|z|)$ in the whole z plane
(d) $\Sigma_{n=0}^{\infty}\, 1/(n^2|z|+1)$ in $K \leq |z| < \infty$ for any $K > 0$
(e) $\Sigma_{n=1}^{\infty}\, (n+z)/n!$ in $|z| < K$ for any $K < \infty$
(f) $\Sigma_{n=2}^{\infty}\, e^{nz}/n!$ in $\operatorname{Re} z \leq K$ for any finite K

6. (*Theorem 4*) Prove Theorem 4. *Hint:* From the necessary condition given in Exercise 1 on page 823, show that there exists a finite constant K such that $|c_n||z-a|^n < K$ for all n and for all z in $|z-a| < R$. Thus show that $|c_n(z-a)^n| < K(R_0/R)^n$ in $|z-a| < R_0$, for all n, and apply the Weierstrass M-test.

7. Observe, in our discussion of the sequence (18), that we did *not* claim that if the limit function is discontinuous, the convergence has to be nonuniform. Indeed, show that the function sequence $s_N(x) = [N/(N+1)]\, H(x)$ converges uniformly on the interval $-10 \leq x \leq 10$, say, even though the limit function $s(x) = H(x)$ is discontinuous at $x = 0$. Here

$$H(x) = \begin{cases} 1, & x > 0 \\ \frac{1}{2}, & x = 0 \\ 0, & x < 0 \end{cases}$$

is the Heaviside step function.

* For proof, see Konrad Knopp, *Theory of Functions,* Part I (New York: Dover, 1945), Theorem 4, p.76

8. Evaluate the given integral, justifying your steps. In each case C is a straight line from $z = 1$ to $z = 2$.

*(a) $\int_C \sum_{n=1}^{\infty} ((z+1)^n/n^5 6^n)\, dz$
(b) $\int_C \sum_{n=1}^{\infty} [(z-1)/(2-i)]^n\, dz$

9. (*Addition and multiplication of power series*) Suppose that $\sum_{n=0}^{\infty} a_n(z-a)^n$ converges to $f(z)$ in $|z-a| < R_1$ and that $\sum_{n=0}^{\infty} b_n(z-a)^n$ converges to $g(z)$ in $|z-a| < R_2$. Let $R = \min(R_1, R_2)$. Then, by linearity (Exercise 4, page 824),

$$\sum_{n=0}^{\infty} a_n(z-a)^n + \sum_{n=0}^{\infty} b_n(z-a)^n = \sum_{n=0}^{\infty} (a_n + b_n)(z-a)^n \qquad \text{(a)}$$

in $|z-a| < R$; the series on the right-hand side of (a) converges to $f(z) + g(z)$ in that disk. Turning to the *product* of the two series, suppose that we multiply them term by term and then group the resulting terms in ascending degree. It can be shown that the resulting series, called the **Cauchy product** of the two series, converges to $f(z)g(z)$ in $|z-a| < R$.

(a) Show that the Cauchy product is given by

$$\left(\sum_{m=0}^{\infty} a_m(z-a)^m\right)\left(\sum_{n=0}^{\infty} b_n(z-a)^n\right) = \sum_{p=0}^{\infty} c_p(z-a)^p \qquad \text{(b)}$$

where

$$c_p = \sum_{q=0}^{p} a_q b_{p-q} = a_0 b_p + a_1 b_{p-1} + \cdots + a_{p-1}b_1 + a_p b_0. \qquad \text{(c)}$$

(b) To illustrate, work out the Cauchy product of the series

$$\sum_{n=0}^{\infty} \left(\frac{z-1}{2}\right)^n \text{ and } \sum_{n=0}^{\infty} (z-1)^n,$$

through the third-degree term, and give its region of convergence. Give, in closed form, the function to which it converges.

10. (*Uniqueness theorem for power series*) Prove the following theorem: *If two power series,*

$$\sum_{n=0}^{\infty} a_n(z-a)^n \quad \text{and} \quad \sum_{n=0}^{\infty} b_n(z-a)^n,$$

converge to the same function within some disk $|z-a| < R$, *i.e., if*

$$\sum_{n=0}^{\infty} a_n(z-a)^n = \sum_{n=0}^{\infty} b_n(z-a)^n \qquad \text{(a)}$$

in $|z| < R$, *then it must be true that* $a_n = b_n$ *for each* $n = 0, 1, 2, \ldots$. *Hint:* Use induction.

21.4 TAYLOR SERIES

We have seen (Section 20.5) that if a function $f(z)$ is analytic at $z = a$, it admits derivatives of all orders there. Thus it is possible to formally define the **Taylor series**

$$\sum_{n=0}^{\infty} \frac{f^{(n)}(a)}{n!}(z-a)^n \qquad (1)$$

of $f(z)$ about the point a. However, whether or not the Taylor series is *useful* depends on the answers to these questions: (1) Does the series converge? (2) If it does converge, in some disk $|z-a| < R$, does it converge to $f(z)$; i.e., does (1) *represent* $f(z)$ in the disk? (3) Finally, if (1) does represent $f(z)$, might there exist power series representations of $f(z)$ *other than* the Taylor series (1)? These questions are answered by the following major theorem.

Theorem 1 *Taylor Series*

Let $f(z)$ be analytic in a domain D. If a lies within D, and $|z - a| < R$ is any disk centered at a and lying entirely within D, then $f(z)$ admits precisely one power series representation in $|z - a| < R$, namely, its Taylor series (1):

$$f(z) = \sum_{n=0}^{\infty} \frac{f^{(n)}(a)}{n!}(z - a)^n = f(a) + f'(a)(z - a) + \cdots. \tag{2}$$

Proof Let C be the circle $|z - a| = R$ (Fig. 21.6), taken counterclockwise. For any point z inside C we have, according to the Cauchy integral formula,

$$f(z) = \frac{1}{2\pi i}\oint_C \frac{f(\zeta)}{\zeta - z}\,d\zeta. \tag{3}$$

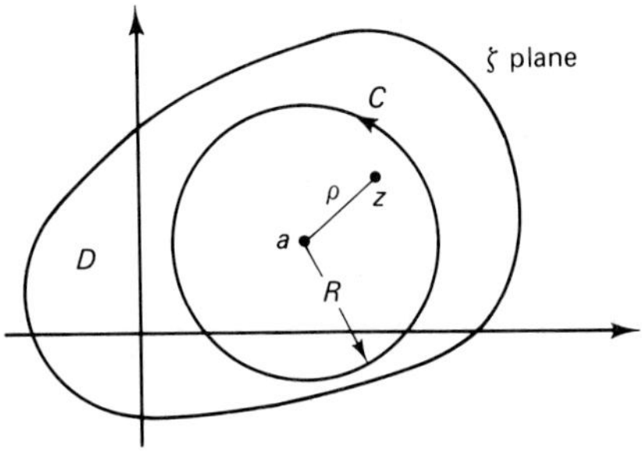

Fig. 21.6 Getting ready to derive Taylor series.

Let us reexpress

$$\frac{1}{\zeta - z} = \frac{1}{\zeta - a}\,\frac{1}{1 - (z - a)/(\zeta - a)} \tag{4}$$

in the integrand, and then apply the algebraic identity

$$\frac{1}{1 - t} = 1 + t + t^2 + \cdots + t^{n-1} + \frac{t^n}{1 - t} \qquad (t \neq 1) \tag{5}$$

with $t = (z - a)/(\zeta - a)$. These steps give

$$f(z) = \frac{1}{2\pi i}\left\{\oint_C \frac{f(\zeta)}{\zeta - a}\,d\zeta + (z - a)\oint_C \frac{f(\zeta)}{(\zeta - a)^2}\,d\zeta + \cdots \right.$$
$$\left. + (z - a)^{n-1}\oint_C \frac{f(\zeta)}{(\zeta - a)^n}\,d\zeta\right\} + R_n(z), \tag{6}$$

where the *remainder term* is

$$R_n(z) = \frac{(z - a)^n}{2\pi i}\oint_C \frac{f(\zeta)}{(\zeta - a)^n(\zeta - z)}\,d\zeta. \tag{7}$$

(Note that there is no question as to the termwise integration of an infinite series here because $1 + t + \cdots + t^{n-1}$ is not an infinite series; it is only a finite sum.) Then, recalling the *extended* Cauchy integral formula

$$f^{(n)}(a) = \frac{n!}{2\pi i} \oint_C \frac{f(\zeta)}{(\zeta - a)^{n+1}} \, d\zeta, \tag{8}$$

we see that (6a) becomes

$$f(z) = f(a) + f'(a)(z - a) + \cdots + \frac{f^{(n-1)}(a)}{(n-1)!}(z - a)^{n-1} + R_n, \tag{9}$$

which is the complex version of Taylor's formula with remainder, studied in the calculus.

Finally, we would like to show that $R_n \to 0$ as $n \to \infty$. We have high hopes that the latter is true since R_n comes from the $t^n/(1 - t)$ term in (5), and t^n does tend to zero as $n \to \infty$ because $|t| = |(z - a)/(\zeta - a)| = \rho/R < 1$ for all points ζ on C (Fig. 21.6).

Since $f(z)$ is analytic on C it must be bounded on C. Thus suppose that $|f(z)| < m$ on C. Noting further, from Fig. 21.6, that $|z - a| = \rho$, that $|\zeta - a| = R$, and that $|\zeta - z| \geq R - \rho$ for all ζ on C, we have

$$|R_n(z)| = \frac{\rho^n}{2\pi} \left| \oint_C \frac{f(\zeta)}{(\zeta - a)^n(\zeta - z)} \, d\zeta \right|$$

$$\leq \frac{\rho^n}{2\pi} \frac{m}{R^n(R - \rho)} 2\pi R \qquad \text{(by ML bound)} \tag{10}$$

$$= \frac{mR}{R - \rho}\left(\frac{\rho}{R}\right)^n,$$

which tends to zero as $n \to \infty$ for all z in $|z - a| < R$. Then, by the definition of series convergence, letting $n \to \infty$ in (9) gives the resulting Taylor series representation

$$f(z) = f(a) + f'(a)(z - a) + \frac{f''(a)}{2!}(z - a)^2 + \cdots \tag{11}$$

of $f(z)$ in $|z - a| < R$.

It remains to prove uniqueness, i.e., that (11) is the *only* representation of $f(z)$ of the form $\Sigma_{n=0}^{\infty} a_n(z - a)^n$. That step follows immediately from the power series uniqueness theorem in Exercise 10 on page 834, and the proof is complete.* ■

Recall from Section 21.3 that *every convergent power series represents an analytic function*. From Theorem 1 we now see that the converse is true as well: *Every analytic function is representable by a convergent power series*!

* Actually, the proof could have been shortened a bit by using Theorem 5′ on page 833, thereby avoiding having to deal with the remainder term R_n, but the longer version is more instructive.

EXAMPLE 1 To obtain the Taylor series expansion of $f(z) = e^z$ about $z = 0$, say, we could work out the coefficients $f(0), f'(0), f''(0)/2!$, and so on, but it is easier to note that (2) is of exactly the same form as in real-variable theory, so we need merely change the x's to z's in the familiar formula

$$e^x = 1 + x + \frac{x^2}{2!} + \frac{x^3}{3!} + \cdots. \tag{12}$$

Observing also that e^z is analytic in the whole plane, we see from Theorem 1 that the Taylor series representation

$$e^z = 1 + z + \frac{z^2}{2!} + \frac{z^3}{3!} + \cdots \tag{13}$$

holds in $|z| < \infty$. As in real-variable theory, we call the Taylor expansion of $f(z)$ about $z = 0$ the *Maclaurin expansion* of $f(z)$.

If, however, we wish to expand e^z about some point other than the origin, say $z = i$, then the remembered formula (12) is of no help, and we need to work out the $f^{(n)}(a)/n!$ coefficients in (2). Doing so, we obtain

$$e^z = e^i + e^i(z - i) + \frac{e^i}{2!}(z - i)^2 + \cdots \tag{14}$$

which, again, holds in the whole plane, $|z - i| < \infty$. ◀

EXAMPLE 2 *Presence of a Singular Point*. Consider the Taylor series expansion of

$$f(z) = \frac{1}{1 - z} \tag{15}$$

about $z = 0$, namely, the geometric series

$$\frac{1}{1 - z} = 1 + z + z^2 + \cdots. \tag{16}$$

Clearly, f is singular only at $z = 1$, so (Theorem 1) the representation (16) must be valid in $|z| < 1$, as depicted in Fig. 21.7. (This simple result is in agreement with the results of our earlier discussion of the geometric series in Section 20.3.)

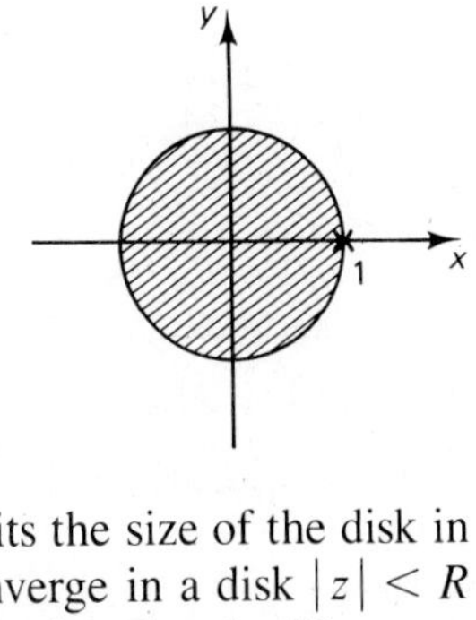

Fig. 21.7 Taylor series representation of $1/(1 - z)$.

COMMENT 1 Observe carefully how the singular point limits the size of the disk in which (16) is valid. For if $1 + z + z^2 + \cdots$ were to converge in a disk $|z| < R$ for $R > 1$, it would necessarily converge to an analytic function therein (Theorem 6, page 832), which would be impossible by virtue of the singularity at $z = 1$.

COMMENT 2 Whereas $1/(1 - z)$ is meaningful everywhere except at the point $z = 1$, the series $1 + z + z^2 + \cdots$ is meaningful only inside the disk $|z| < 1$ and is therefore only a *partial representation* of the original function. It is interesting to imagine being handed the series $1 + z + z^2 + \cdots$ and not knowing that the sum function is $1/(1 - z)$. Applying the ratio test to the series, we ascertain that it converges only in $|z| < 1$. Nevertheless, if we wish to compute values of the mysterious function (of which the series is a partial representation) *outside* of $|z| < 1$, we can (at least in principle) proceed as follows. Denote the function, of which $1 + z + z^2 + \cdots$ is a partial representation, as $f(z)$. Then (Exercise 1) we can compute

$$f(z) = 1 + z + z^2 + z^3 + \cdots, \tag{17}$$

$$f'(z) = 1 + 2z + 3z^2 + \cdots, \tag{18}$$

$$f''(z) = 2 + 6z + \cdots, \tag{19}$$

and so on, at some point P_1, of our choosing, within $|z| < 1$ (Fig. 21.8). With these values in hand, we can expand f in Taylor series about P_1, obtaining

$$f(z) = f(P_1) + f'(P_1)(z - P_1) + \frac{f''(P_1)}{2!}(z - P_1)^2 + \cdots. \tag{20}$$

Then, applying the ratio test (or some other convergence test) to this new Taylor series, we would find that it converges inside the circle C_1. [Since we are pretending not to know that f happens to be $1/(1 - z)$, we do not know about the singular point at $z = 1$.] Similarly, we can use the representation (20) to compute f, f', f'', . . . at some other point P_2 (Fig. 21.8) and thus derive still another Taylor series representation of f, this time valid inside C_2, and so on. This "stepping-stone" process is an example of **analytic continuation.** We choose not to develop any theorems or detailed discussion of analytic continuation and, instead, refer the reader to SAFF AND SNIDER and Knopp.* Incidentally, the best we could possibly do, in this example, given the series $1 + z + \cdots$, is to obtain $f(z) = 1/(1 - z)$, which is the most complete possible analytic continuation of this particular series. ◀

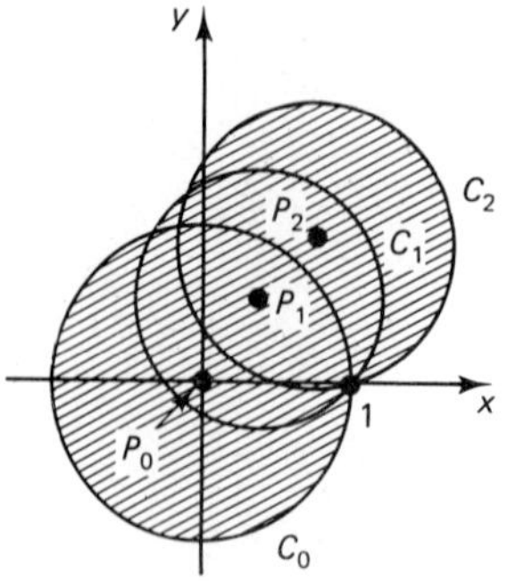

Fig. 21.8 Analytic continuation.

* Konrad Knopp, *Theory of Functions*, Part I (New York: Dover, 1945).

EXAMPLE 3 Consider the function

$$f(z) = \log z, \tag{21}$$

defined according to the principal-value branch cut shown in Fig. 21.9; i.e., $\log z = \log(re^{i\theta}) = \ln r + i\theta$, where $0 \le \theta \le 2\pi$. Its Taylor series about $z = 1 + i$, namely,

$$\ln \sqrt{2} + i\frac{\pi}{4} + \frac{1-i}{2}(z - 1 - i) + \frac{i}{4}(z - 1 - i)^2 + \cdots, \tag{22}$$

can be shown (Exercise 3) to converge in the disk $|z - 1 - i| < \sqrt{2}$ since $f'(z) = 1/z$ fails to exist only at $z = 0$, which point is the distance $\sqrt{2}$ from the point $1 + i$ about which we have expanded the function. However, it is to be understood that the Taylor series (22) represents f not in the entire disk $|z - 1 - i| < \sqrt{2}$ but only in the shaded portion of it (Fig. 21.9). For example, at the point $z = 1$ on the bottom of the cut, denoted by P in the figure, the series converges to $\log(1e^{i0}) = 0$, whereas f at P is actually equal to $\log(1e^{i2\pi}) = i2\pi$. ◀

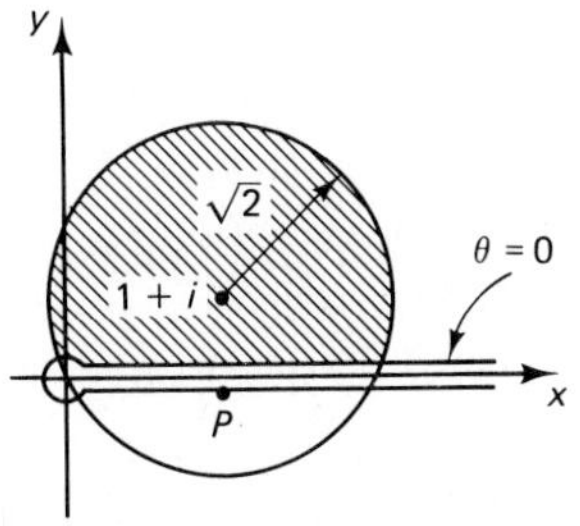

Fig. 21.9 Taylor expansion of log z about $1 + i$.

EXAMPLE 4 The Taylor expansion of the function

$$f(z) = \frac{1}{1 + z^2} \tag{23}$$

about $z = 0$ yields the representation

$$\frac{1}{1 + z^2} = 1 - z^2 + z^4 - z^6 + \cdots \qquad (|z| < 1) \tag{24}$$

valid in the disk of convergence, which is limited to $|z| < 1$ by the presence of the singular points at $z = \pm i$ (where the denominator $1 + z^2$ vanishes), as shown in Fig. 21.10.

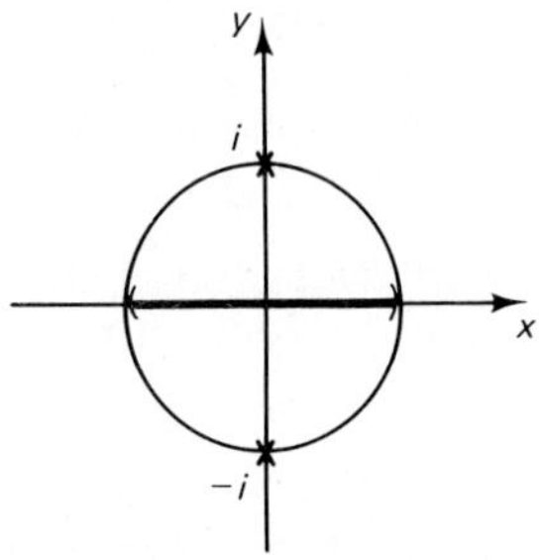

Fig. 21.10 Taylor expansion of $1/(1 + z^2)$ about $z = 0$.

COMMENT 1 To derive (24), it is a bit simpler to use the familiar geometric series $1/(1 - t) = 1 + t + t^2 + \cdots$, with $t = -z^2$, than to work out the coefficients "$f^{(n)}(a)/n!$" in the Taylor series formula (2).

COMMENT 2 If we restrict z to lie on the real axis, then (24) becomes the real Taylor series

$$\frac{1}{1 + x^2} = 1 - x^2 + x^4 - x^6 + \cdots \qquad (|x| < 1). \tag{25}$$

If one encounters (25) in studying the real-variable calculus, the limitation $|x| < 1$ must surely seem paradoxical. For why should the series diverge outside $|x| < 1$ if the function $1/(1 + x^2)$ is so beautifully behaved (e.g., infinitely differentiable) for *all* x? However, our study of complex function theory now renders the situation transparent: The restriction $|x| < 1$ in (25) occurs because the function $1/(1 + z^2)$ has singularities *off the real axis,* at $z = +i$ and $z = -i$. ◀

EXAMPLE 5 As a second example in which the results of real-variable theory appear paradoxical, consider the function

$$f(x) = \begin{cases} e^{-1/x^2}, & x \neq 0 \\ 0, & x = 0, \end{cases} \tag{26}$$

the graph of which is shown in Fig. 21.11. Besides $f(0) = 0$, it is easy to show that $f'(0) = f''(0) = f'''(0) = \cdots = 0$ (Exercise 4), so the Taylor series of f, about $x = 0$, is simply $0 + 0 + 0 + \cdots$. Surely, the latter converges for *all* x (namely, to zero), but it does not represent the given f anywhere except at $x = 0$. Why this striking failure of the Taylor series? After all, f is infinitely differentiable for all x and hence seems quite well behaved.

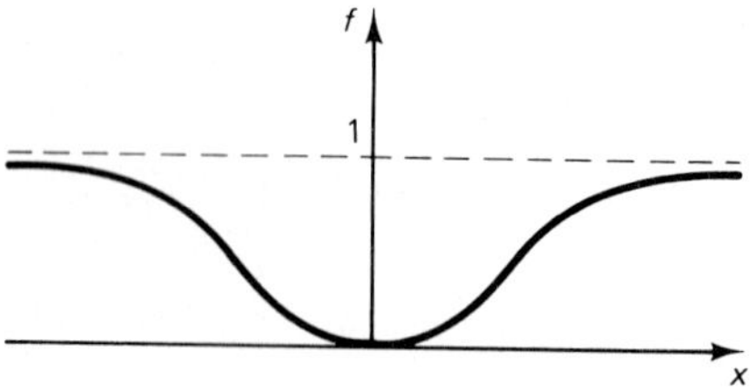

Fig. 21.11 Graph of f given by (26).

Again the "paradox" is resolved by examining the behavior of

$$f(z) = \begin{cases} e^{-1/z^2}, & z \neq 0 \\ 0, & z = 0 \end{cases} \tag{27}$$

in the complex plane. Specifically, observe that if $z \to 0$ along the real axis, then $f(z) = e^{-1/x^2} \to 0$ as $x \to 0$, but if $z \to 0$ along the *imaginary axis,* then $f(z) = e^{-1/(iy)^2} = e^{1/y^2} \to \infty$ as $y \to 0$. Thus $f(z)$ is not even *continuous* at $z = 0$, let alone analytic. Hence its Taylor series expansion about $z = 0$ is doomed to converge to f only at the expansion point $z = 0$. ◀

EXAMPLE 6 *Undetermined Coeffficients.* In this final example we emphasize the practical matter of how to generate the Taylor series of a given function in a convenient manner. To illustrate, suppose that we wish to determine the first few terms of the Taylor expansion of

$$f(z) = \frac{e^z}{\cos z} \tag{28}$$

about $z = 0$. Naturally, we can work out $f(0), f'(0), \ldots$ and use the Taylor series formula. However, the repeated differentiations grow increasingly tedious and we wonder whether we might, instead, benefit from the fact that the expansions of e^z and $\cos z$ are known (i.e., remembered or easily derived). Thus proceed as follows. First, express

$$\frac{e^z}{\cos z} = a_0 + a_1 z + a_2 z^2 + \cdots, \tag{29}$$

where the a_j's are to be determined. Multiplying both sides of (29) by $\cos z$ and then recalling the expansions of e^z and $\cos z$, write

$$1 + z + \frac{z^2}{2} + \frac{z^3}{6} + \cdots = (a_0 + a_1 z + a_2 z^2 + a_3 z^3 + \cdots) \times \left(1 - \frac{z^2}{2} + \frac{z^4}{24} - \cdots\right). \tag{30}$$

Now, the first series on the right converges in $|z| < \pi/2$ [because $f(z) = e^z/\cos z$ is singular at $z = \pm\pi/2, \pm 3\pi/2, \ldots$, where $\cos z = 0$] and the second (i.e., the cosine series) converges in $|z| < \infty$, so it is justified to multiply them term by term and to rearrange the result in ascending powers of z (see the discussion of the Cauchy product in Exercise 9, page 834). That step gives

$$1 + z + \frac{z^2}{2} + \frac{z^3}{6} + \cdots = a_0 + a_1 z + \left(a_2 - \frac{1}{2}a_0\right)z^2 + \left(a_3 - \frac{1}{2}a_1\right)z^3 + \cdots. \tag{31}$$

Finally, equating coefficients of like powers of z (see Exercise 10, page 834), we obtain $a_0 = 1$, $a_1 = 1$, $a_2 = 1$, and $a_3 = \frac{2}{3}$, so

$$\frac{e^z}{\cos z} = 1 + z + z^2 + \frac{2}{3}z^3 + \cdots \tag{32}$$

in $|z| < \pi/2$.

Subsequently, we shall refer to this method as the *method of undetermined coefficients.* ◀

In retrospect, this section has focused on one major result, the Taylor series expansion theorem (Theorem 1). Prior to this section we knew that every convergent power series sums to (i.e., represents) an analytic function. Conversely, Theorem 1 tells us that every analytic function admits a convergent power series (namely, a Taylor series) representation.

21.4 EXERCISES

1. (*Termwise differentiation of Taylor series*) Prove that a Taylor series can be differentiated termwise any number of times within its disk of convergence; i.e., if

$$f(z) = \sum_{n=0}^{\infty} \frac{f^{(n)}(a)}{n!}(z-a)^n$$

in $|z-a| < R$, then

$$f'(z) = \frac{d}{dz}\sum_{n=0}^{\infty} \frac{f^{(n)}(a)}{n!}(z-a)^n = \sum_{n=0}^{\infty} \frac{d}{dz}\left[\frac{f^{(n)}(a)}{n!}(z-a)^n\right]$$

in $|z-a| < R$, and similarly for f'', f''', and so on.

2. Differentiating the geometric series termwise (see Exercise 1), derive the result

$$\frac{1}{(1-z)^3} = \frac{1}{2}\sum_{n=0}^{\infty}(n+1)(n+2)z^n.$$

3. (a) Derive the Taylor series (22).
(b) In particular, obtain an expression for the nth term of the series, and use the ratio test to show that the series converges in $|z-1-i| < \sqrt{2}$ and diverges in $|z-1-i| > \sqrt{2}$.

4. For the function $f(x)$ defined by (26), show that $f'(0) = 0$ and $f''(0) = 0$, say, as claimed in Example 5.

5. Is the following power series the Taylor series of some function? If so, in what region does the series represent the function; if not, why not?

*(a) $\sum_{n=1}^{\infty}(-1)^{n+1}n(z-1)^n$ (b) $\sum_{n=0}^{\infty}\frac{z^{n-1}}{4^{n+1}}$
(c) $\sum_{n=4}^{\infty}\left(\frac{z+i}{1+i}\right)^{2n}$ (d) $1+z^3$

6. What is the radius of convergence of the Taylor series of $1/(z^2-3z+2)$ about
(a) $z = 0$ *(b) $z = 3i$
(c) $z = 1-5i$ (d) $z = 5-i$

7. What is the radius of convergence of the Taylor series of $(z^2-3z+2)/(z^2-2z+3i+1)$ about
*(a) $z = 0$ (b) $z = 10i$
(c) $z = 2-5i$ (d) $z = 20$

8. Obtain the Taylor series of the given function, about $z = a$, and give its radius of convergence R.

(a) $\sin z$, $a = 0$ (b) $\sin z$, $a = 2-i$
*(c) $\cos 2z$, $a = 3i$ (d) e^{z^6}, $a = 0$
*(e) $\frac{1}{i+z}$, $a = 0$ (f) $\frac{z^3}{2-iz}$, $a = 0$
(g) $\sin z^8$, $a = 0$ (h) $\cos(z+i)$, $a = -i$
(i) $\operatorname{erf} z = (2/\sqrt{\pi})\int_0^z e^{-t^2}\,dt$, $a = 0$

9. (*Binomial series*) (a) Derive the **binomial series**

$$\frac{1}{(1-z)^m} = 1 + mz + \frac{m(m+1)}{2!}z^2 + \frac{m(m+1)(m+2)}{3!}z^3 + \cdots = \sum_{n=0}^{\infty}\frac{(m+n-1)!}{(m-1)!\,n!}z^n \quad (|z|<1) \tag{a}$$

for any positive integer m.
(b) Use (a) to obtain the Taylor series of $1/(3-z)^2$ about $z = i$. Identify its disk of convergence. *Hint:* Write

$$\frac{1}{(3-z)^2} = \frac{1}{[3-(z-i)-i]^2} = \frac{1}{(3-i)^2\left[1-\left(\frac{z-i}{3-i}\right)\right]^2} \tag{b}$$

and use $(z-i)/(3-i)$ in place of z in (a).

10. Use (a) in exercise 9 to obtain the Taylor expansions

$$\text{(a)}\ \frac{1}{(2z+1)^3} = \frac{1}{2}\sum_{n=0}^{\infty}(-1)^n(n+1)(n+2)2^n z^n \quad \left(|z| < \frac{1}{2}\right) \tag{a}$$

$$\text{(b)}\ \frac{1}{(2z+1)^3} = \frac{1}{250}\sum_{n=0}^{\infty}(-1)^n(n+1)(n+2)\left(\frac{2}{5}\right)^n \times (z-2)^n \quad \left(|z-2| < \frac{5}{2}\right) \tag{b}$$

$$\text{(c)}\ \frac{1}{z^2-z-6} = \frac{1}{20}\sum_{n=0}^{\infty}\frac{(-4)^{n+1}-1}{4^n}(z+1)^n \quad (|z+1| < 1) \tag{c}$$

11. Using the method of undetermined coefficients, obtain the first several terms (through the z^5 term, say) of the Taylor expansion of f about $z = 0$. Indicate the disk of convergence.

(a) $f(z) = \tan z = \dfrac{\sin z}{\cos z}$

(b) $f(z) = \sec z = \dfrac{1}{\cos z}$

12. Let $\sqrt{z}$ be defined according to a principal-value branch cut. Work out the first several terms of the Taylor series of $\sqrt{z}$, about the given point and indicate the region of validity of the Taylor series representation.

*(a) $z = -1$
(b) $z = -i$
(c) $z = 1 - i$
(d) $z = 2 - i$

13. Verify that the results expressed in (25) and (26) on page 832 are in agreement, as claimed there, by expanding $\log(1 - z)$ in a Taylor series.

LAURENT SERIES 21.5

Consider the function

$$f(z) = \frac{1}{(z-1)(z-2i)}, \tag{1}$$

which is analytic for all z except the two (singular) points $z = 1$ and $z = 2i$. If we develop a Taylor expansion about $z = 0$, that expansion will be valid [i.e., will converge to $f(z)$] in the disk $|z| < 1$. Thus, expanding about $z = 0$, the region $|z| \geq 1$ is evidently inaccessible to us. However, there exists a more general representation known as a *Laurent series,* which includes the Taylor series as a special case and which permits expansions in any *annulus* throughout which f is analytic. Thus, for the f given above, there would be *three* possible Laurent expansions about $z = 0$: one in $2 < |z| < \infty$, one in $1 < |z| < 2$, and one in $|z| < 1$ (Fig. 21.12a). (The latter would simply be the *Taylor series.*) In fact, with the Laurent series one is even able to expand about a singular point! For the function f given above, for example, we can expand about $z = 1$ in $0 < |z - 1| < \sqrt{5}$ or in $\sqrt{5} < |z - 1| < \infty$ (Fig. 21.12b); similarly, we could expand about the other singular point $z = 2i$.

With this introduction, we are ready for Laurent's theorem.

***Theorem 1** Laurent Series*

Let D be the closed region between, and including, concentric circles C_i, C_o, with their centers at $z = a$. If $f(z)$ is analytic in D, then it admits the **Laurent series** representation

$$f(z) = \sum_{n=-\infty}^{\infty} c_n (z-a)^n \tag{2}$$

in D, with the c_n's given uniquely by

$$c_n = \frac{1}{2\pi i} \oint_C \frac{f(\zeta)}{(\zeta - a)^{n+1}}\, d\zeta \tag{3}$$

where C is any piecewise-smooth simple closed counterclockwise path lying entirely in D.

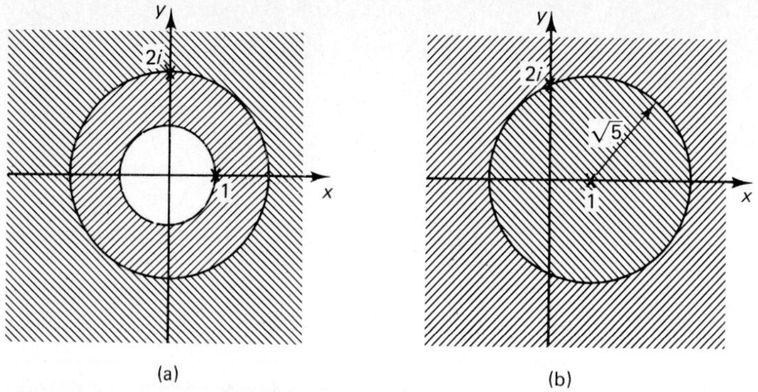

Fig. 21.12 Laurent expansion regions for f given by (1).

Proof The circles C_i, C_0 are shown in Fig. 21.13a. Consider the closed contour $C_1 + C_2 + C_3 + C_4$, where C_1 is the circle C_0 taken counterclockwise, C_3 is the circle C_i taken clockwise, and C_2, C_4 are abutting and oppositely oriented, as shown in Fig. 21.13b (where C_2 and C_4 are separated slightly for clarity). Then Cauchy's integral formula gives

$$\begin{aligned} f(z) &= \frac{1}{2\pi i}\oint_{C_1+C_2+C_3+C_4} \frac{f(\zeta)}{\zeta - z}\,d\zeta \\ &= \frac{1}{2\pi i}\oint_{C_1} \frac{f(\zeta)}{\zeta - z}\,d\zeta + \frac{1}{2\pi i}\oint_{C_3} \frac{f(\zeta)}{\zeta - z}\,d\zeta, \end{aligned} \tag{4}$$

where the second equality in (4) holds because the contributions from C_2 and C_4 are equal and opposite and hence cancel.

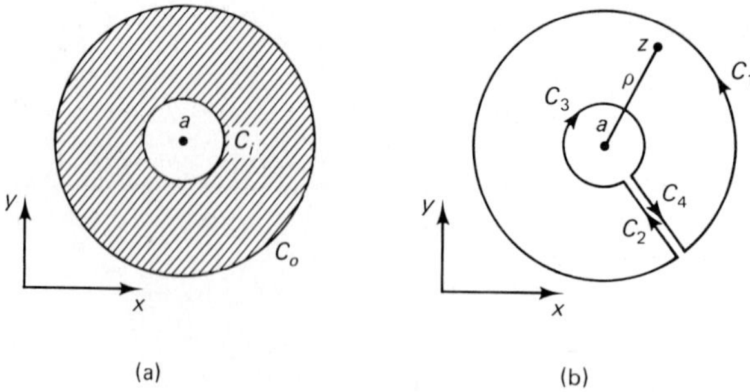

Fig. 21.13 Laurent series.

Considering the C_1 integral first, express

$$\frac{1}{\zeta - z} = \frac{1}{\zeta - a}\,\frac{1}{1 - \dfrac{z - a}{\zeta - a}} = \frac{1}{\zeta - a}\sum_{n=0}^{\infty}\left(\frac{z - a}{\zeta - a}\right)^n. \tag{5}$$

The latter series converges uniformly in ζ on C_1, so (Theorem 5′ on page 833)

$$\begin{aligned} \frac{1}{2\pi i}\oint_{C_1} \frac{f(\zeta)}{\zeta - z}\,d\zeta &= \frac{1}{2\pi i}\oint_{C_1} \frac{f(\zeta)}{\zeta - a}\sum_{n=0}^{\infty}\left(\frac{z - a}{\zeta - a}\right)^n d\zeta \\ &= \sum_{n=0}^{\infty}\left[\frac{1}{2\pi i}\oint_{C_1} \frac{f(\zeta)}{(\zeta - a)^{n+1}}\,d\zeta\right](z - a)^n = \sum_{n=0}^{\infty} c_n (z - a)^n, \end{aligned} \tag{6}$$

where

$$c_n = \frac{1}{2\pi i} \oint_{C_1} \frac{f(\zeta)}{(\zeta - a)^{n+1}} \, d\zeta \tag{7}$$

(see Exercise 1). The path C_1 can be deformed to any piecewise-smooth simple closed counterclockwise path C lying entirely in D because the integrand is analytic between and on C_1 and C.

Next, consider the C_3 integral in (4). This time, express

$$\frac{1}{\zeta - z} = -\frac{1}{z - a} \frac{1}{1 - \dfrac{\zeta - a}{z - a}} = -\frac{1}{z - a} \sum_{n=0}^{\infty} \left(\frac{\zeta - a}{z - a} \right)^n, \tag{8}$$

which converges uniformly in ζ on C_3. Thus

$$\begin{aligned}
\frac{1}{2\pi i} \oint_{C_3} \frac{f(\zeta)}{\zeta - z} \, d\zeta &= -\frac{1}{2\pi i} \oint_{C_3} \frac{f(\zeta)}{z - a} \sum_{n=0}^{\infty} \left(\frac{\zeta - a}{z - a} \right)^n d\zeta \\
&= \sum_{n=0}^{\infty} \left[-\frac{1}{2\pi i} \oint_{C_3} f(\zeta)(\zeta - a)^n \, d\zeta \right] (z - a)^{-(n+1)} \\
&= \sum_{n=-1}^{-\infty} \left[\frac{1}{2\pi i} \oint_{-C_3} \frac{f(\zeta)}{(\zeta - a)^{n+1}} \, d\zeta \right] (z - a)^n \\
&= \sum_{n=-1}^{-\infty} \left[\frac{1}{2\pi i} \oint_{C} \frac{f(\zeta)}{(\zeta - a)^{n+1}} \, d\zeta \right] (z - a)^n \\
&= \sum_{n=-1}^{-\infty} c_n (z - a)^n,
\end{aligned} \tag{9}$$

where, in the next-to-last equality we deformed $-C_3$ (i.e., the contour C_3 with its direction reversed so as to be counterclockwise) to C.

Proof of the uniqueness of the Laurent series is deferred to the exercises. ■

Before continuing, observe that the sum in (2) is a "new object" for us because it runs from $n = -\infty$ to $n = +\infty$. However, looking back at the proof, we can see that (2) is to be understood as the sum of two "ordinary" series:

$$\sum_{n=-\infty}^{\infty} c_n (z - a)^n = \sum_{n=0}^{\infty} c_n (z - a)^n + \sum_{n=-1}^{-\infty} c_n (z - a)^n \tag{10}$$

or, equivalently,

$$\sum_{n=-\infty}^{\infty} c_n (z - a)^n = \sum_{n=0}^{\infty} c_n (z - a)^n + \sum_{n=1}^{\infty} c_{-n} (z - a)^{-n}. \tag{11}$$

Note also that $f(z)$ has been assumed analytic only in the annulus; Theorem 1 allows for singular points inside C_i and outside C_o. If, in fact, there are *no* singular points inside C_i, *then* application of the extended Cauchy integral formula and Cauchy's theorem to (3) gives

$$c_n = \begin{cases} \dfrac{f^{(n)}(a)}{n!}, & n = 0, 1, 2, \ldots \text{ (by Cauchy integral formula)} \quad (12) \\ 0, & n = -1, -2, \ldots \text{ (by Cauchy theorem)} \quad (13) \end{cases}$$

and the Laurent series (2) reduces to the Taylor series

$$f(z) = \sum_{n=0}^{\infty} \frac{f^{(n)}(a)}{n!}(z - a)^n. \tag{14}$$

However, if $f(z)$ *does* have singular points inside C_i (which is the case of interest in this section), then (12) and (13) do not apply, and we are simply "stuck" with the integral expression of the c_n's that is given in (3). Thus, whereas Taylor series coefficients are the easily computed quantities $f^{(n)}(a)/n!$, Laurent series coefficients are given by the evidently unwieldy integral expression in (3). *Practically speaking, however, we shall be able to avoid (3) in developing Laurent series, as demonstrated in the examples to follow.*

EXAMPLE 1 We have already met the Taylor series expansion of

$$f(z) = \frac{1}{1 - z} \tag{15}$$

about $z = 0$, namely

$$f(z) = \frac{1}{1 - z} = 1 + z + z^2 + \cdots, \tag{16}$$

which holds in the disk $|z| < 1$, the radius of which is dictated by the presence of the singular point at $z = 1$. To determine the *Laurent* expansion of f about $z = 0$, in the *outer* annulus $1 < |z| < \infty$ (Fig. 21.14), write

$$\frac{1}{1 - z} = \frac{1}{z}\frac{1}{1/z - 1} = -\frac{1}{z}\frac{1}{1 - 1/z}. \tag{17}$$

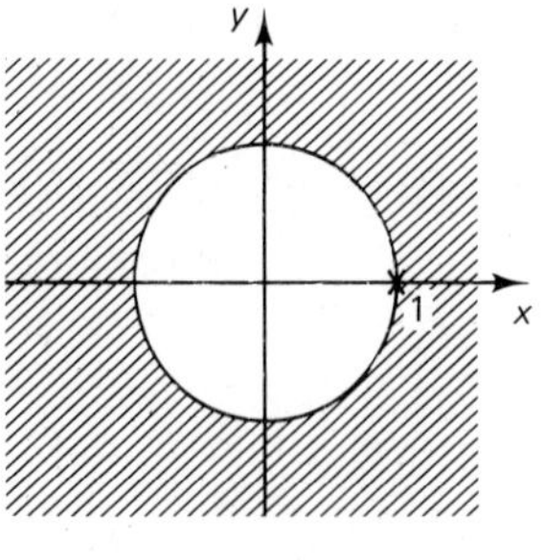

Fig. 21.14 Laurent expansion annulus.

Now, the first factor, $1/z$, is *already* in powers of z, so leave it intact. In the second factor, set $1/z = t$ and observe that $|t| < 1$ because $|z| > 1$, so we can write the *Taylor* expansion

$$\frac{1}{1 - 1/z} = \frac{1}{1 - t} = 1 + t + t^2 + \cdots \qquad (|t| < 1) \tag{18}$$

in the variable t. With the latter expression completed, we revert to the z variable by setting $t = 1/z$. Thus

$$\frac{1}{1 - 1/z} = 1 + \frac{1}{z} + \frac{1}{z^2} + \cdots \qquad (1 < |z| < \infty) \tag{19}$$

so

$$f(z) = \frac{1}{1-z} = \underbrace{-\left(\frac{1}{z}\right)}_{0<|z|<\infty} \underbrace{\left(1 + \frac{1}{z} + \frac{1}{z^2} + \cdots\right)}_{1<|z|<\infty}. \tag{20}$$

The first factor, $1/z$, is a rather short (namely, one term) Laurent series which converges in the annulus $0 < |z| < \infty$. The second converges in the annulus $1 < |z| < \infty$, so the product converges in the *overlap* annulus $1 < |z| < \infty$:

$$f(z) = \frac{1}{1-z} = -\frac{1}{z} - \frac{1}{z^2} - \frac{1}{z^3} - \cdots \qquad (1 < |z| < \infty). \tag{21}$$

The expansions (16) and (21) are both about the point $z = 0$, and they are different from each other. Does that fact violate the uniqueness results stated earlier? No, because the expansions are valid in different annuli: (16) in $|z| < 1$, and (21) in $1 < |z| < \infty$. ◀

Observe carefully that we did *not* use (3) to evaluate the c_n coefficients in (21). Rather, the rearrangement accomplished in (17) enabled us to recast the problem in terms of a Taylor series expansion in a suitably defined t variable [namely, (18)]. That idea, recasting the problem in terms of Taylor series, will be relied on exclusively in our derivations of Laurent series.

EXAMPLE 2 Expand

$$f(z) = \frac{1}{z(z-2)} \tag{22}$$

about $z = i$, in the annulus $\sqrt{5} < |z - i| < \infty$ (Fig. 21.15). It is convenient, though by no means necessary, to shift our origin to the point of expansion by setting $\zeta = z - i$. Doing so, and using the same approach as adopted in Example 1, write

$$\frac{1}{z(z-2)} = \frac{1}{(\zeta + i)(\zeta + i - 2)} = \frac{1}{\zeta^2} \frac{1}{1 + i/\zeta} \frac{1}{1 + (i-2)/\zeta}. \tag{23}$$

Then, with $i/\zeta = t_1$ and $(i-2)/\zeta = t_2$, we have the Taylor expansions

$$\frac{1}{1 + i/\zeta} = \frac{1}{1 + t_1} = 1 - t_1 + t_1^2 - \cdots \qquad (|t_1| < 1)$$

$$= 1 - \frac{i}{\zeta} + \frac{i^2}{\zeta^2} - \cdots \qquad \left(\left|\frac{i}{\zeta}\right| < 1 \text{ or } |\zeta| > 1\right)$$

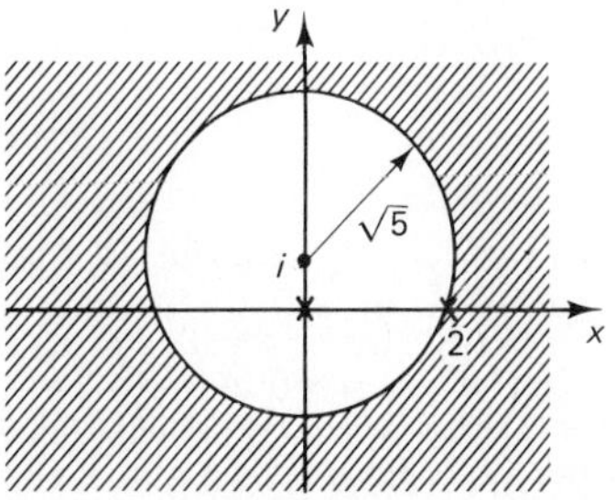

Fig. 21.15 Laurent expansion annulus.

and

$$\frac{1}{1+(i-2)/\zeta} = \frac{1}{1+t_2} = 1 - t_2 + t_2^2 - \cdots \qquad (|t_2| < 1)$$

$$= 1 - \frac{i-2}{\zeta} + \frac{(i-2)^2}{\zeta^2} - \cdots$$

$$\left(\left|\frac{i-2}{\zeta}\right| < 1 \text{ or } |\zeta| > \sqrt{5}\right)$$

Combining these results gives us

$$\begin{aligned} \frac{1}{z(z-2)} &= \frac{1}{\zeta^2}\left(1 - \frac{i}{\zeta} - \frac{1}{\zeta^2} - \cdots\right)\left(1 - \frac{i-2}{\zeta} + \frac{3-4i}{\zeta^2} - \cdots\right) \\ &= \frac{1}{\zeta^2} + (-i-i+2)\frac{1}{\zeta^3} + [-1 + i(i-2) + (3-4i)]\frac{1}{\zeta^4} + \cdots \\ &= \frac{1}{\zeta^2} + (2-2i)\frac{1}{\zeta^3} + (1-6i)\frac{1}{\zeta^4} + \cdots \\ &= \frac{1}{(z-i)^2} + (2-2i)\frac{1}{(z-i)^3} + (1-6i)\frac{1}{(z-i)^4} + \cdots \end{aligned} \tag{24}$$

holds in the overlap annulus $\sqrt{5} < |z - i| < \infty$, and is the desired Laurent series. That is, $c_{-1} = c_0 = c_1 = c_2 = \cdots = 0$, $c_{-2} = 1$, $c_{-3} = 2 - 2i$, $c_{-4} = 1 - 6i$. and so on. ◀

EXAMPLE 3 The function

$$f(z) = \frac{1}{\sin z} \tag{25}$$

is singular at $z = 0, \pm\pi, \pm 2\pi, \ldots$, where $\sin z = 0$. Expand $f(z)$ about $z = 0$ in the annulus $0 < |z| < \pi$.

Since $\sin z = z - z^3/3! + \cdots$ tends to z as $z \to 0$ (l'Hospital's rule verifies the fact that $z/\sin z \to 1$ as $z \to 0$) it will be fruitful to reexpress f as

$$f(z) = \frac{1}{z}\frac{z}{\sin z}, \tag{26}$$

for then the first factor, $1/z$, is *already* a (rather short) Laurent expansion which converges in $0 < |z| < \infty$, and the second factor, $z/\sin z$, is *analytic* in $|z| < \pi$ (and singular at $z = \pm\pi, \pm 2\pi, \pm 3\pi, \ldots$) and admits the *Taylor* expansion (Exercise 4)

$$\frac{z}{\sin z} = 1 + \frac{1}{6}z^2 + \frac{7}{360}z^4 + \cdots \tag{27}$$

in $|z| < \pi$.* Combining these results yields

*Notice that at $z = 0$ the ratio $z/\sin z$ is $0/0$, which is not defined. However, if we *define* $z/\sin z \equiv 1$ at $z = 0$, then $z/\sin z$ is indeed analytic in $|z| < \pi$, as stated. If assigning the value 1 at $z = 0$ seems arbitrary and unjustified, observe that $f(z) = (1/z)(z/\sin z)$ is undefined at $z = 0$ *in any event*, so defining $z/\sin z \equiv 1$ at $z = 0$ is merely a matter of convenience.

$$\frac{1}{\sin z} = \frac{1}{z} + \frac{1}{6}z + \frac{7}{360}z^3 + \cdots \tag{28}$$

in the overlap annulus $0 < |z| < \pi$. ◀

EXAMPLE 4 Expand

$$f(z) = e^{1/z} \tag{29}$$

about $z = 0$.

Evidently, f is analytic for all $z \neq 0$ and singular for $z = 0$, so the expansion of f about $z = 0$ will be a Laurent expansion valid in the annulus $0 < |z| < \infty$. To obtain that expansion, let $1/z = t$ and observe that $e^{1/z} = e^t$ admits the *Taylor* expansion

$$e^{1/z} = e^t = 1 + t + \frac{t^2}{2!} + \frac{t^3}{3!} + \cdots \tag{30}$$

in $|t| < \infty$. Since $|t| < \infty$ corresponds to $|z| > 0$, it follows [by setting $t = 1/z$ in (30)] that the desired expansion is

$$e^{1/z} = 1 + \frac{1}{z} + \frac{1}{2!}\frac{1}{z^2} + \frac{1}{3!}\frac{1}{z^3} + \cdots \tag{31}$$

in the annulus $0 < |z| < \infty$. ◀

EXAMPLE 5 As our final example, consider

$$f(z) = \log z, \tag{32}$$

where $\log z$ is defined according to the principal-value cut shown in Fig. 21.16. Does $f(z)$ admit a Laurent expansion about $z = 0$? Well, $f(z) = \log z = \log(re^{i\theta}) = \ln r + i\theta$ is *discontinuous* across the branch cut since $\theta = 0$ on the top of the cut and $\theta = 2\pi$ on the bottom. Since the cut extends from the origin to infinity, it follows that there exists no annulus, centered at $z = 0$, throughout which f is analytic. Thus f *does not admit* a Laurent expansion about $z = 0$. ◀

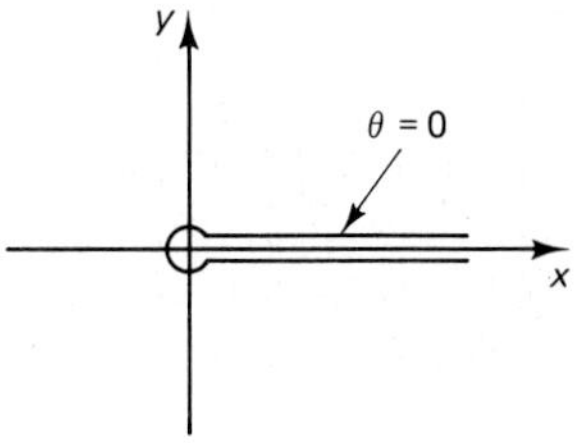

Fig. 21.16 Principal-value branch cut.

In closing this section we wish to stress, again, that our Laurent expansions (in Examples 1 to 4) were obtained without using the integral expression (3) for the c_n coefficients. We recommend a review of those examples with special attention paid to the heavy reliance on Taylor series.

25.5 EXERCISES

1. (*Theorem 1*) Some details, in the proof of Theorem 1, were left to the exercises. They are as follows.
(a) It was stated that the series in (5) is uniformly convergent in ζ on C_1. Verify that claim.
(b) Similarly, verify that the series in (8) converges uniformly in ζ on C_3.
(c) We proved that (under the conditions stated in the theorem) $f(z)$ can be represented by the Laurent series

$$f(z) = \sum_{n=0}^{\infty} c_n (z-a)^n + \sum_{n=-1}^{-\infty} c_n (z-a)^n, \qquad \text{(a)}$$

with the c_n's given by (3). Prove that the representation is unique. *Hint:* Assume that $f(z)$ admits any representation of the same form,

$$f(z) = \sum_{n=0}^{\infty} c'_n (z-a)^n + \sum_{n=-1}^{-\infty} c'_n (z-a)^n, \qquad \text{(b)}$$

in the same annulus D. Multiply equation (b) through by $(z-a)^k$ and integrate around a counterclockwise circle C, lying entirely within D, with its center at $z = a$. Show that the two series in (b) converge uniformly on C, so that the series can be integrated termwise. Doing so, show that

$$\oint_C f(z)(z-a)^k dz = 2\pi i c'_{-k-1}$$

$$(k = 0, \pm 1, \pm 2, \dots)$$

and hence that

$$c'_k = \frac{1}{2\pi i}\oint_C \frac{f(z)}{(z-a)^{k+1}} dz = c_k.$$

2. Let R_o, R_i be the radii of the circles C_o, C_i in Fig. 21.13. Show that the first series on the right-hand side of (11) converges in $|z-a| < R_o$, and that the second series converges in $|z-a| > R_i$. [Hence the Laurent series representation (2) is valid in the overlap region $R_i < |z-a| < R_o$.]

3. Show that the same final result is obtained in Example 2 if we begin by expanding $1/z(z-2)$ in partial fractions.

4. Derive the Taylor expansion (27) using the method of undetermined coefficients.

5. Obtain the first few terms of the Laurent expansion of each of the following. *Hint:* In part (d), for example, use the same line of approach as was employed in Example 3.

*(a) $\dfrac{1}{z}$ in $1 < |z-i| < \infty$

(b) $\dfrac{1}{z^2+1}$ in $1 < |z| < \infty$

(c) $\dfrac{z^2+3}{z}$ in $0 < |z| < \infty$

*(d) $\dfrac{1}{e^z-1}$ in $0 < |z| < 2\pi$

(e) $\dfrac{1}{z(z^3+2)}$ in $0 < |z| < \sqrt[3]{2}$

(f) $\dfrac{1}{z} + \dfrac{z}{z+i}$ in $1 < |z| < \infty$

(g) $\dfrac{1}{z^3}$ in $2 < |z-2| < \infty$

*(h) $\dfrac{1}{z^2}$ in $1 < |z+i| < \infty$

(i) $\dfrac{1}{\sin z}$ in $0 < |z-\pi| < \pi$

6. Determine all possible Taylor and Laurent expansions, about the given point $z = a$, and state their regions of validity.

*(a) $\sin\dfrac{1}{z}$, $a = 0$ *(b) $\dfrac{1}{z}$, $a = -2$

(c) e^{-1/z^3}, $a = 0$ (d) $\dfrac{z^2+5}{z^2+4}$, $a = -1$

(e) $\dfrac{1+z}{2+z}$, $a = -i$ (f) $\dfrac{\sin z}{z^4}$, $a = 0$

(g) $\dfrac{\cos 2z}{(z+i)^2}$, $a = -i$ (h) e^{-z^2}, $a = 0$

***7.** A certain function $f(z)$ is represented by the expansion

$$\frac{1}{z^2} + \frac{1}{z^3} + \frac{1}{z^4} + \cdots$$

in $1 < |z| < \infty$. Determine the value of $f(z)$ at $z = \frac{1}{2}$.

8. Obtain the Laurent expansion of

$$\frac{1}{(z-1)(z-2)} \quad \text{in} \quad 1 < |z| < 2$$

as follows. First, show that

$$\frac{1}{(z-1)(z-2)} = -\frac{1}{2z}\sum_{n=0}^{\infty}\sum_{m=0}^{\infty} \frac{1}{2^m} z^{m-n}, \qquad \text{(a)}$$

then make a change of summation indices from m, n to p, q according to $p = m - n$, $q = m$. Show that the m, n and p, q "domains of summation" are as

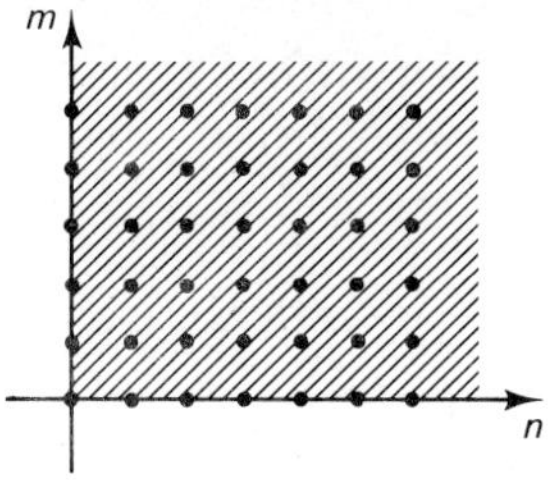

(a)

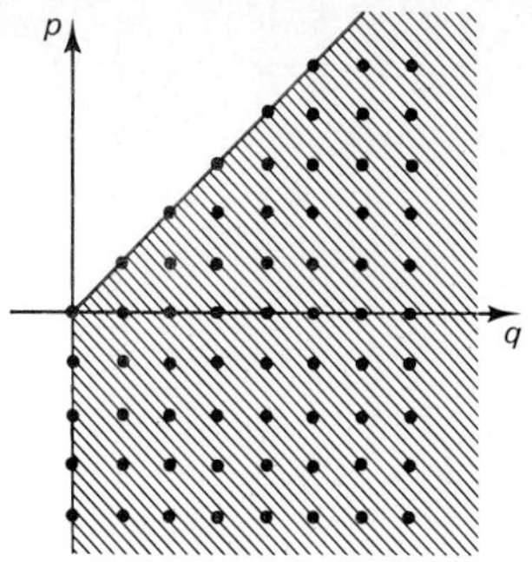

(b)

shown in the accompanying figure, so that

$$\frac{1}{(z-1)(z-2)} = -\frac{1}{2z}\left[\sum_{p=1}^{\infty}\left(\sum_{q=p}^{\infty}\frac{1}{2^q}\right)z^p + \sum_{p=0}^{-\infty}\left(\sum_{q=0}^{\infty}\frac{1}{2^q}\right)z^p\right]. \quad \text{(b)}$$

Hence show that the desired expansion is

$$\frac{1}{(z-1)(z-2)} = -\frac{1}{2}\sum_{n=0}^{\infty}\left(\frac{z}{2}\right)^n - \sum_{n=-1}^{-\infty} z^n. \quad \text{(c)}$$

Although the preceding derivation is of pedagogical interest, (c) can be derived much more simply. In particular, expand $1/(z-1)(z-2)$ in partial fractions, then expand one of the terms in $|z| < 2$ and the other in $|z| > 1$.

9. Expand

*(a) $\dfrac{1}{z(z^2+1)}$ in $1 < |z-1| < \sqrt{2}$

(b) $\dfrac{1}{z(z^2+iz+2)}$ in $1 < |z-i| < 3$

10. (*Bessel functions*) In an exercise in Chapter 17 we noted that $e^{(x/2)(z-1/z)}$ is the *generating function* for the Bessel functions $J_n(x)$ inasmuch as

$$e^{(x/2)(z-1/z)} = \sum_{n=-\infty}^{\infty} J_n(x)z^n. \quad \text{(a)}$$

(Here x is an independent real variable, *not* Re z.)

(a) By considering the analytic nature of the generating function on the left-hand side, show that the Laurent representation (a) is valid in $0 < |z| < \infty$.

(b) Use (3), with C taken to be the unit circle, to derive the formula

$$J_n(x) = \frac{1}{\pi}\int_0^{\pi} \cos(n\theta - x\sin\theta)\, d\theta. \quad \text{(b)}$$

We call (b) an *integral representation* of $J_n(x)$.

21.6 SINGULARITIES AND RESIDUES

Recall that if $f(z)$ is *analytic* at $z = a$, then f admits a Taylor series representation

$$f(z) = f(a) + f'(a)(z-a) + \frac{f''(a)}{2!}(z-a)^2 + \cdots \quad (1)$$

in some neighborhood of point a. It will be useful to characterize the behavior of f at a in a bit more detail. Specifically, if $f(a) = 0$, we say that f has a **zero** at a. Furthermore, if $f(a) = f'(a) = \cdots = f^{(k-1)}(a) = 0$ and $f^{(k)}(a) \neq 0$, we say that the zero is of order k. Thus f has a ***k*th-order zero** at a if

$$f(z) = \frac{f^{(k)}(a)}{k!}(z-a)^k + \frac{f^{(k+1)}(a)}{(k+1)!}(z-a)^{k+1} + \cdots, \quad (2)$$

where $f^{(k)}(a) \neq 0$. For example, $\sin z$ has a first-order zero at $z = 0$, $\sin(z^3)$ has a third-order zero there, and $1 - \cos z$ has a second-order zero there. If $f(a) \neq 0$ in (1), so that f does not have a zero at $z = a$, it will nevertheless be convenient to say that f has a *zeroth-order* zero there, although we warn the reader that this terminology is not standard.

Recall further that $f(z)$ is *not* analytic at $z = a$, it is *singular* there. Now that we have studied Laurent series, we will be able to examine the nature of singularities more closely, and such examination is the focus of this section.

First, suppose that $f(z)$ is singular at $z = a$ but analytic in an annulus $0 < |z - a| < \rho$ (for some $\rho > 0$).* Then $z = a$ is said to be an **isolated singular point** of f. For example, $1/z(z + 2)$ is singular only at $z = 0$ and $z = -2$, both of which singular points are isolated; $1/\sin z$ is singular only at $z = 0, \pm\pi, \pm 2\pi, \ldots$, all of which are isolated.

EXAMPLE 1 The function

$$f(z) = \frac{1}{\sin(1/z)} \tag{3}$$

is singular at the points $z = 1/k\pi$ ($k = \pm 1, \pm 2, \ldots$) and at $z = 0$ (Fig. 21.17). Each of the former is isolated, but the singular point $z = 0$ is *not* because every annulus $0 < |z| < \rho$ inevitably contains at least one singular point (in fact, an infinite number of them) no matter how small we choose ρ (Exercise 1). ◀

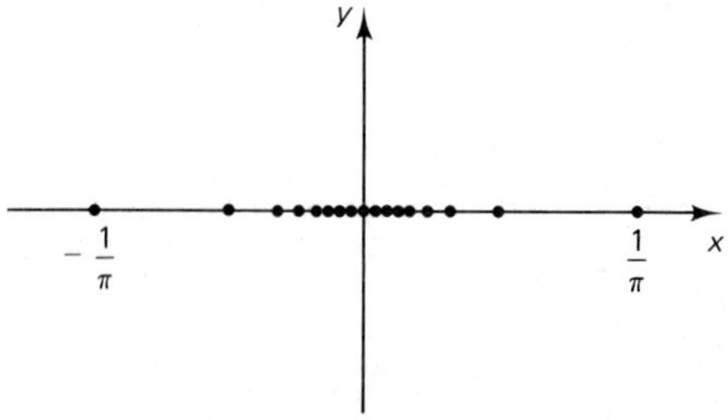

Fig. 21.17 Singular points of $1/\sin(1/z)$.

EXAMPLE 2 The function $f(z) = \log z$, made single valued by a principal-value branch cut (sketch the cut), is singular only at $z = 0$. The latter is not an isolated singular point because there is no annulus $0 < |z| < \rho$ throughout which f is continuous, let alone analytic, for $\log z = \ln x$ on top of the cut and $\log z = \ln x + 2\pi i$ on the bottom of the cut. ◀

In the remainder of this section we consider only isolated singular points. Now, if $f(z)$ has an isolated singularity at $z = a$, there necessarily exists some annulus $0 < |z - a| < \rho$ in which f admits the Laurent series representation

$$f(z) = \sum_{n=0}^{\infty} c_n(z - a)^n + \sum_{n=-1}^{-\infty} c_n(z - a)^n$$

*Recall that a region $|z - a| < \rho$ is called a *neighborhood* of point a. Thus SAFF AND SNIDER call the region $0 < |z - a| < \rho$ a *punctured neighborhood* of the point a.

$$= \sum_{n=-\infty}^{\infty} c_n(z-a)^n \tag{4}$$

$$= \cdots + c_{-2}\frac{1}{(z-a)^2} + c_{-1}\frac{1}{z-a} + c_0 + c_1(z-a) + c_2(z-a)^2 + \cdots.$$

If the expansion terminates on the left, so that it is of the form

$$f(z) = c_{-N}\frac{1}{(z-a)^N} + c_{-N+1}\frac{1}{(z-a)^{N-1}} + \cdots, \tag{5}$$

we categorize the singularity of f at $z = a$ as an **Nth-order pole.** (A *first*-order pole is sometimes called a *simple* pole.) If not (i.e., if there are an infinite number of negative powers of $z - a$ present), we categorize the singularity as an **essential singularity**.

In either case, we define the coefficient c_{-1} as the **residue** of $f(z)$ at $z = a$. The significance of residues, and why they are called "residues," will be seen in the next section. There we will find that to evaluate an integral $\oint_C f(z)\,dz$ it is important to be able to determine the residues of f at its singular points which lie within the contour C. Thus toward obtaining a general formula for c_{-1}, first suppose that $f(z)$ has a *simple* pole at $z = a$, so that

$$f(z) = c_{-1}\frac{1}{z-a} + c_0 + c_1(z-a) + \cdots. \tag{6}$$

Then

$$(z-a)f(z) = c_{-1} + c_0(z-a) + c_1(z-a)^2 + \cdots, \tag{7}$$

and letting $z \to a$ in both sides gives

$$c_{-1} = \lim_{z\to a}\,[(z-a)f(z)]. \tag{8}$$

Next, suppose that $f(z)$ has an Nth-order pole at $z = a$, so that

$$f(z) = c_{-N}\frac{1}{(z-a)^N} + c_{-N+1}\frac{1}{(z-a)^{N-1}} + \cdots. \tag{9}$$

Then

$$(z-a)^N f(z) = c_{-N} + c_{-N+1}(z-a) + c_{-N+2}(z-a)^2 + \cdots \tag{10}$$

and letting $z \to a$ gives c_{-N} rather than c_{-1}. However, if we notice that the right side is the Taylor series of $(z-a)^N f(z)$, and that c_{-N+j} is c_{-1} when $j = N - 1$, it follows from the form of the coefficients in the Taylor series that

$$\boxed{c_{-1} = \frac{1}{(N-1)!}\lim_{z\to a}\left\{\frac{d^{N-1}}{dz^{N-1}}[(z-a)^N f(z)]\right\}.} \tag{11}$$

Of course, (11) reduces to (8) in the event that the pole is a simple pole, that is, if $N = 1$.

Observe that if we are to apply (11) we need to know N; i.e., we need to know that $f(z)$ has an Nth-order pole at $z = a$. In this regard, we state the following result (Exercise 2).

> ***Theorem 1** Nth-Order Pole*
> If $p(z)$ and $q(z)$ have zeros of order P and Q, respectively, at $z = a$, then $p(z)/q(z)$ has a pole of order $N = Q - P$ there if $Q > P$, and is analytic there if $Q \leq P$.

EXAMPLE 3 Classify the singularities and determine the residues of

$$f(z) = \frac{1}{z^3(2-z)}. \tag{12}$$

Clearly, f is singular at $z = 0$ and $z = 2$. Expanding the denominator in Taylor series about those points gives

$$z^3(2-z) = 2z^3 - z^4 \tag{13}$$

and

$$z^3(2-z) = -8(z-2) - 12(z-2)^2 - 6(z-2)^3 - (z-2)^4, \tag{14}$$

respectively. (In each case the Taylor series happens to terminate.) Thus the denominator has a third-order zero at $z = 0$ and a first-order zero at $z = 2$. The numerator, unity, has a zeroth-order zero at both points so, according to Theorem 1, f has a third-order pole at $z = 0$ and a first-order pole at $z = 2$.

To compute the residue of f at $z = 0$, apply (11) with $N = 3$:

$$\begin{aligned}\operatorname*{Res}_{z=0} f(z) &= c_{-1} = \frac{1}{2!}\lim_{z\to 0}\left\{\frac{d^2}{dz^2}\left[z^3\frac{1}{z^3(2-z)}\right]\right\} \\ &= \frac{1}{2}\lim_{z\to 0}\frac{d^2}{dz^2}\left(\frac{1}{2-z}\right) = \frac{1}{8}.\end{aligned} \tag{15}$$

To compute the residue of f at $z = 2$, apply (11) with $N = 1$ [i.e., use (8)]:

$$\operatorname*{Res}_{z=2} f(z) = c_{-1} = \lim_{z\to 2}\left[(z-2)\frac{1}{z^3(2-z)}\right] = -\frac{1}{8}. \tag{16}$$

Alternatively, we could have derived the Laurent expansions

$$\begin{aligned}\frac{1}{z^3(2-z)} &= \frac{1}{2z^3(1-z/2)} = \frac{1}{2z^3}\left(1 + \frac{z}{2} + \frac{z^2}{4} + \frac{z^3}{8} + \cdots\right) \\ &= \frac{1}{2z^3} + \frac{1}{4z^2} + \frac{1}{8z} + \frac{1}{16} + \frac{z}{32} + \cdots\end{aligned} \tag{17}$$

in $0 < |z| < 2$, and (Exercise 4)

$$\frac{1}{z^3(2-z)} = -\frac{1}{8}\frac{1}{z-2} + \frac{3}{16} - \cdots \tag{18}$$

in $0 < |z-2| < 2$, and from these representations we can see that f has a third-order pole at $z = 0$, with residue $\frac{1}{8}$, and a first-order pole at $z = 2$, with residue $-\frac{1}{8}$. ◀

EXAMPLE 4 Classify the singularities and determine the residues of

$$f(z) = \frac{z}{\sin z}. \tag{19}$$

Since $\sin z$ vanishes only at $z = n\pi$ $(n = 0, \pm 1, \pm 2, \dots)$, let us expand it about $n\pi$:

$$\begin{aligned}\sin z &= \sin n\pi + \cos n\pi (z - n\pi) - \frac{\sin n\pi}{2!}(z - n\pi)^2 - \frac{\cos n\pi}{3!}(z - n\pi)^3 \\ &\quad + \cdots \\ &= (-1)^n(z - n\pi) - \frac{(-1)^n}{3!}(z - n\pi)^3 + \cdots.\end{aligned} \tag{20}$$

Thus $\sin z$ has *first*-order zeros at each of the points $z = n\pi$. The numerator, z, has a *first*-order zero at $z = 0$ and *zeroth*-order zeros at $z = \pm\pi, \pm 2\pi, \dots$, so, according to Theorem 1, f has first-order poles at $z = \pm\pi, \pm 2\pi, \dots$ (and is analytic at $z = 0$).

To compute the residues of f at those points, use (8):

$$\begin{aligned}\operatorname*{Res}_{z=n\pi} f(z) &= c_{-1} = \lim_{z\to n\pi} \frac{(z - n\pi)z}{\sin z} \\ &= n\pi \lim_{z\to n\pi} \frac{z - n\pi}{\sin z} = n\pi \lim_{z\to n\pi} \frac{1}{\cos z} \\ &= (-1)^n n\pi,\end{aligned} \tag{21}$$

where the fourth equality follows from l'Hospital's rule. ◀

EXAMPLE 5 Classify the singularities and determine the residues of

$$f(z) = \cos \frac{1}{z}. \tag{22}$$

Since the derivative

$$f'(z) = -\frac{1}{z^2} \sin \frac{1}{z}$$

exists for all $z \neq 0$, f is analytic for all $z \neq 0$. To examine the behavior of f at $z = 0$, observe carefully that the known Taylor expansion

$$\cos t = 1 - \frac{t^2}{2!} + \frac{t^4}{4!} - \cdots \tag{23}$$

in $0 \le |t| < \infty$ gives [by setting $t = 1/z$ in (23)]

$$f(z) = \cos \frac{1}{z} = 1 - \frac{1}{2!}\frac{1}{z^2} + \frac{1}{4!}\frac{1}{z^4} - \cdots \tag{24}$$

in $0 < |z| < \infty$. Thus f has an essential singularity at $z = 0$, with residue $c_{-1} = 0$ [because there is no $1/z$ term in (24)].

COMMENT Be sure to see that the residue could *not* have been determined using (11) since that formula applies only when the singularity is an Nth-order pole; in this case the singularity is an essential singularity. ◀

Now that we have distinguished isolated singularities as poles or essential singularities, it is of interest to examine the *behavior* of $f(z)$ as z approaches such a singular point.*

First, suppose that $f(z)$ has a pole at $z = a$, say a second-order pole for definiteness. Then

$$f(z) = \frac{c_{-2}}{(z-a)^2} + \frac{c_{-1}}{z-a} + c_0 + c_1(z-a) + \cdots \qquad (c_{-2} \neq 0) \tag{25}$$

holds in some annulus $0 < |z - a| < \rho$. Since $c_0 + c_1(z - a) + \cdots$ is a convergent power series in $|z - a| < \rho$, its sum, say $g(z)$, is analytic in $|z - a| < \rho$, and we can express (25) more compactly as

$$f(z) = \frac{c_{-2}}{(z-a)^2} + \frac{c_{-1}}{z-a} + g(z). \tag{26}$$

Since $g(z)$ is analytic at $z = a$ it is surely continuous there, so

$$(z-a)^2 f(z) = c_{-2} + c_{-1}(z-a) + g(z)(z-a)^2 \to c_{-2} \tag{27}$$

as $z \to a$. Hence $|(z - a)^2 f(z)| = |z - a|^2 |f(z)| \to |c_{-2}| \neq 0$, and since $|z - a|^2 \to 0$ as $z \to a$ it must be true that $|f(z)| \to \infty$ as $z \to a$.† Similarly for a pole of *any* order, so we can state the following.

> ***Theorem 2** Behavior near Pole*
> If $f(z)$ has a pole at $z = a$, then $|f(z)| \to \infty$ as $z \to a$.

Thus the graph of $|f(z)|$, plotted above the z plane, exhibits a "pole"-like shape somewhat as sketched in Fig. 21.18. However, the behavior of $f(z)$ as z approaches

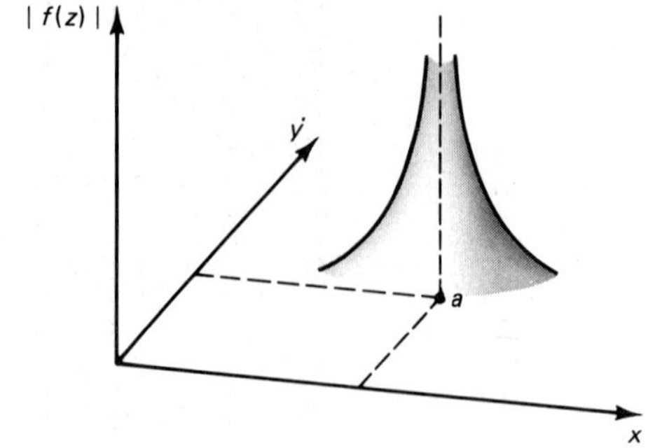

Fig. 21.18 Pole-like growth.

* Strictly speaking, calling a point z_0 a "singular point" (or a "zero") leaves something to be desired, for the *point* is not singular, the *function* is. Nevertheless, it is accepted terminology to say that *f(z) has a singularity at* z_0 and also that z_0 *is a singular point of f(z)*.

† "$|f(z)| \to \infty$ as $z \to a$" means that to each constant $M > 0$ (i.e., no matter how large) there corresponds a constant $\delta > 0$ such that $|f(z)| > M$ for all $|z - a| < \delta$.

an *essential* singularity is much more subtle. To illustrate, consider $f(z) = e^{-1/z^2}$, which has an essential singularity at $z = 0$, as is evident from the Laurent expansion

$$e^{-1/z^2} = 1 - \frac{1}{z^2} + \frac{1}{2!}\frac{1}{z^4} - \frac{1}{3!}\frac{1}{z^6} + \cdots, \tag{28}$$

which is valid in $0 < |z| < \infty$. Now, if $z \to 0$ along the real axis, then $e^{-1/z^2} = e^{-1/x^2} \to 0$ as $x \to 0$, but if $z \to 0$ along the imaginary axis, then $e^{-1/z^2} = e^{-1/(iy)^2} = e^{1/y^2} \to \infty$ as $y \to 0$. In fact, *Emile Picard* (1856–1941) proved the following.

> ***Theorem 3*** *Behavior near Essential Singularity; Picard's Theorem*
> Let $f(z)$ have an essential singularity at $z = a$. Then $f(z)$ takes on *every* complex number as a value, with at most one exception, and it does so an infinite number of times within any given neighborhood of a.

Although a proof of this remarkable theorem lies well beyond our present scope, it may be illuminating to at least illustrate the stated result with an example.*

EXAMPLE 6 Recall [from the form of (31) on page 849] that $e^{1/z}$ has an essential singularity at $z = 0$. Now, $e^{1/z}$ does not equal 0 for any z, so 0 is the "exceptional value" referred to in the theorem. Suppose that c is any given complex number other than this exceptional value; i.e., $c \neq 0$. Then $e^{1/z} = c$ gives $1/z = \log c = \ln|c| + i(\theta_0 + 2n\pi)$, where θ_0 is the principal argument of c. Thus, $e^{1/z}$ takes on the value c at the points

$$z_n = \frac{1}{\ln|c| + i(\theta_0 + 2n\pi)} \tag{29}$$

for $n = 0, \pm 1, \pm 2, \ldots$, and it should be evident that an infinite number of these points are to be found in every neighborhood $|z| < \rho$, no matter how small we choose ρ (Exercise 5). ◀

One last point. Recall from Section 19.3 that when we wish to include the *point at infinity* in the z plane we speak of the *extended* z plane. Thus, when we say that $f(z) = e^z$, say, is analytic everywhere in the z plane, it is to be understood that we are not including the point at infinity. If we *do* wish to examine e^z in the extended z plane, we also need to examine it at infinity. To do so, we make the change of variables $z = 1/t$, so $z = \infty$ corresponds to $t = 0$, and then examine $e^z = e^{1/t}$ at $t = 0$. In this case $e^{1/t}$ has an essential singularity at $t = 0$, so we say that e^z has an essential singularity at $z = \infty$. Thus e^z is analytic everywhere in the extended z plane except at $z = \infty$, where it has an essential singularity. Similarly,

$$f(z) = \frac{1}{z^2} + 3 + z - 4z^3 \tag{30}$$

* For proof of Picard's Theorem, see E. C. Titchmarsh, *Theory of Functions*, 2nd ed. (London: Oxford University Press, 1939).

has a second-order pole at $z = 0$ and a third-order pole at infinity, because

$$f\left(\frac{1}{t}\right) = t^2 + 3 + \frac{1}{t} - \frac{4}{t^3} \tag{31}$$

has a third-order pole at $t = 0$.

Reviewing the material in this section, we first distinguished between isolated singularities and nonisolated ones, and then turned exclusively to the former, further distinguishing them as poles or essential singularities. We defined the residue of a function at an isolated singular point and indicated how to calculate residues, as will be necessary in Section 21.7 (on the residue theorem).

21.6 EXERCISES

1. In case it is not clear that $f(z)$ given by (3) is singular at $z = 0$, we ask you to show that it is not even continuous at that point (let alone analytic). Specifically, consider $\lim_{z\to 0}\,[1/\sin(1/z)]$ as $z \to 0$ along the real axis, and then again as $z \to 0$ along the imaginary axis.

2. Prove that if $p(z)$ and $q(z)$ have zeros of order P and Q, respectively, at $z = a$, then $p(z)/q(z)$ has a pole of order $N = Q - P$ there if $Q > P$.

3. Prove that if $f(z)$ has an Nth-order zero at $z = a$, then $1/f(z)$ has an Nth-order pole there.

4. Derive the Laurent expansion (18).

5. Verify the claim made in the last sentence of Example 6.

6. Determine the location of the zeros (if any) of order 1 or higher, and their order, for each given function.

*(a) $z^2 - z$ (b) $e^z - 1$
(c) $z \sin z$ *(d) $z \cos^2 z$
(e) $(z^2 + 1)^3$ (f) $2 + e^z$
(g) $z^2 + z + 1$ (h) $1 - z^4$

7. Determine all singular points, in the finite z plane, of the following functions. If isolated, classify them further as Nth-order poles or essential singularities and evaluate the corresponding residues.

*(a) $\dfrac{e^z - 1}{z^3}$ (b) $\dfrac{z^2}{e^z - 1}$
(c) $\dfrac{1}{z^3 - 1}$ *(d) $\dfrac{1}{1 + 1/(1 + z)}$
(e) $\dfrac{1}{\sinh z}$ (f) $\dfrac{1}{\cosh z}$
(g) $\dfrac{z}{\sin^3 z}$ (h) $\sin\dfrac{1}{z}$
*(i) $\cos\dfrac{1}{z}$ (j) $\sinh\dfrac{1}{z}$
(k) $\cosh\dfrac{1}{z}$ (l) $\sin\dfrac{1}{z^3}$
(m) e^{1/z^3} (n) $4 - \dfrac{z}{(z - 1)^2}$
*(o) $\dfrac{1}{e^z}$ (p) $\tan(z^2)$
(q) $\tan\dfrac{1}{z^2}$ (r) $\dfrac{1}{e^{z^2}}$
(s) $\dfrac{1}{\sin(z - 2)}$ (t) $\dfrac{z}{\cos(z + 1)}$

8. (a) Given the representation

$$f(z) = \frac{1}{z} + \frac{1}{z^2} + \frac{1}{z^3} + \cdots, \tag{a}$$

does it follow that f has an essential singularity at $z = 0$, with a residue of unity? Explain.
(b) Given the representation

$$f(z) = \frac{1}{z^2}\left[1 - \frac{2}{z} + \left(\frac{2}{z}\right)^2 - \cdots\right], \tag{b}$$

does it follow that f has an essential singularity at $z = 0$, with a residue of zero? Explain.

The last major event in Part V is the residue theorem, which will provide an extremely powerful technique for the evaluation of complex integrals—and real integrals as well. With the groundwork that has been laid in these last two chapters, the residue theorem can now be obtained quite easily.

We consider the closed contour integral

$$I = \oint_C f(z)\, dz, \tag{1}$$

where f has a finite number of singularities within C, each of them isolated. For definiteness, suppose that f has two such points, z_1 and z_2, as shown in Fig. 21.19a. (Whether or not f has singular points *outside* C as well will not be germane.)

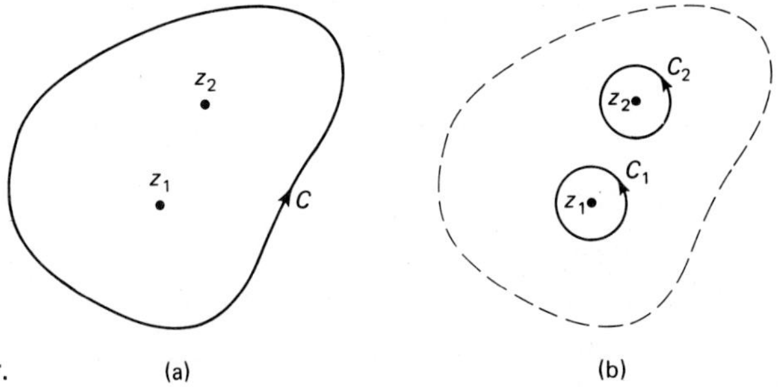

Fig. 21.19 Deformation of contour.

Using Cauchy's theorem to deform the contour, as shown in Fig. 21.19b, we have

$$I = \oint_C f(z)\, dz = \oint_{C_1} f(z)\, dz + \oint_{C_2} f(z)\, dz. \tag{2}$$

Denote the integrals on the right-hand side as I_1 and I_2, respectively. To evaluate these integrals, expand f in Laurent series in annuli $0 < |z - z_1| < \rho_1$ and $0 < |z - z_2| < \rho_2$, as is possible beause the singular points z_1 and z_2 are isolated:

$$f(z) = \sum_{n=-\infty}^{\infty} c_n^{(1)}(z - z_1)^n \quad \text{in} \quad 0 < |z - z_1| < \rho_1 \tag{3a}$$

and

$$f(z) = \sum_{n=-\infty}^{\infty} c_n^{(2)}(z - z_2)^n \quad \text{in} \quad 0 < |z - z_2| < \rho_2. \tag{3b}$$

Then, being sure to locate C_1 and C_2 entirely within these respective annuli, and recalling the "important little integral" (16) on page 803, we obtain

$$I = \oint_{C_1} \sum_{n=-\infty}^{\infty} c_n^{(1)}(z - z_1)^n\, dz + \oint_{C_2} \sum_{n=-\infty}^{\infty} c_n^{(2)}(z - z_2)^n\, dz$$

$$= \sum_{n=-\infty}^{\infty} c_n^{(1)} \oint_{C_1} (z - z_1)^n \, dz + \sum_{n=-\infty}^{\infty} c_n^{(2)} \oint_{C_2} (z - z_2)^n \, dz \tag{4}$$

$$= 2\pi i c_{-1}^{(1)} + 2\pi i c_{-1}^{(2)}.$$

That is, I is equal to $2\pi i$ times the sum of the residues (at the singular points located within C). Incidentally, now we can see why the c_{-1}'s are called the "residues"—because they are the only coefficients that survive the integration in (4).

The derivation above is attractive heuristically in its directness, although it does beg justification of the termwise integration used in obtaining the second equality in (4). This step can indeed be justified by the fact that the two series converge *uniformly* on the respective contours C_1 and C_2. However, the termwise integration procedure can be sidestepped altogether simply by using equation (3) on page 843, with $n = -1$. That step gives, immediately,

$$\oint_{C_1} f(z) \, dz = 2\pi i c_{-1}^{(1)} \tag{5a}$$

and

$$\oint_{C_2} f(z) \, dz = 2\pi i c_{-1}^{(2)} \tag{5b}$$

which agrees with the result obtained in (4).

Surely the same method applies if C contains *any* finite number of isolated singular points, so we can now state the celebrated residue theorem.

***Theorem 1** Residue Theorem*

Let C be a piecewise-smooth simple closed curve oriented counterclockwise, and let $f(z)$ be analytic inside and on C except at finitely many isolated singular points $z_1, \ldots, z_k$ within C. If $c_{-1}^{(j)}$ denotes the residue of f at z_j, then

$$\boxed{\oint_C f(z) \, dz = 2\pi i \sum_{j=1}^{k} c_{-1}^{(j)};} \tag{6}$$

i.e., the integral equals $2\pi i$ times the sum of the residues (within C).

Naturally, if C is *clockwise,* the integral equals $-2\pi i$ times the sum of the residues.

EXAMPLE 1 Evaluate

$$I = \oint_C \frac{\cos z}{z^3(z^2 + 4)} \, dz, \tag{7}$$

where C is the rectangular contour drawn in Fig. 21.20, with vertices at $-2 - i$, $2 - i$, $2 + 3i$, and $-2 + 3i$. The integrand $f(z)$ has a third-order pole at $z = 0$ and first-order poles at $z = \pm 2i$. Of these singular points (all of which are isolated)

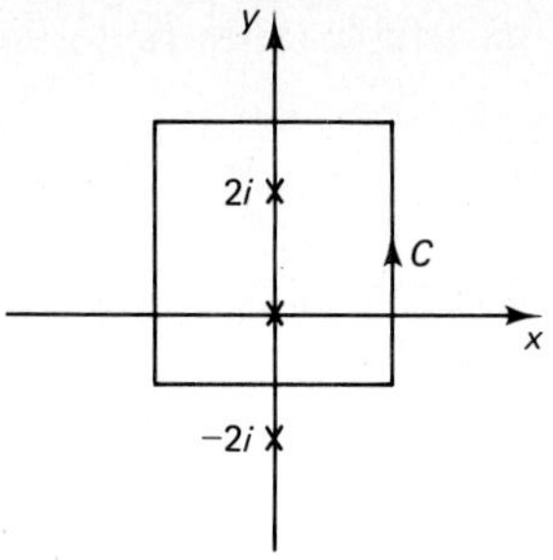

Fig. 21.20 The contour C in (7).

only the two within C are relevant. Computing

$$\operatorname*{Res}_{z=0} f(z) = \frac{1}{2!}\lim_{z\to 0}\frac{d^2}{dz^2}\left[z^3\frac{\cos z}{z^3(z^2+4)}\right] = \frac{1}{2}\lim_{z\to 0}\frac{d^2}{dz^2}\frac{\cos z}{z^2+4} = -3/16 \tag{8}$$

and

$$\operatorname*{Res}_{z=2i} f(z) = \lim_{z\to 2i}\left[(z-2i)\frac{\cos z}{z^3(z^2+4)}\right] = \lim_{z\to 2i}\frac{\cos z}{z^3(z+2i)} = \frac{\cosh 2}{32}, \tag{9}$$

we have

$$I = 2\pi i\left(\operatorname*{Res}_{z=0} f + \operatorname*{Res}_{z=2i} f\right) = 2\pi i\left(-\frac{3}{16}+\frac{\cosh 2}{32}\right) = \frac{\pi i}{16}(\cosh 2 - 6). \tag{10}$$

COMMENT Even with this first example, the power of the residue theorem becomes evident, for the integrand did not look especially simple, yet the evaluation of the integral merely required the rather straightforward calculation of two residues. Furthermore, the detailed shape of C was not relevant except insofar as it enclosed certain singular points (and satisfied the rather mild requirements stated in Theorem 1). ◀

Practically speaking, the residue theorem is of special importance in the evaluation of *real* integrals, as will be evident from the examples to follow.

Consider, first, the class of real integrals of the form

$$I = \int_0^{2\pi} F(\cos\theta, \sin\theta)\, d\theta, \tag{11}$$

where F is a rational function of each of its two arguments. A *rational function* is the ratio of two finite-degree polynomials, so $F(x, y)$ is a rational function of each of its two arguments if it is a finite linear combination of terms of the form $x^m y^n$ divided by another such finite linear combination. For example,

$$F_1(x, y) = \frac{5 - x^4 + xy^3}{x + 4y^2}$$

is a rational function of both x and y, and

$$F_2(\cos\theta, \sin\theta) = \frac{2 - \cos^2\theta \sin\theta}{1 + \cos\theta}$$

and

$$F_3(\cos\theta, \sin\theta) = \frac{\sin 4\theta}{(1 + \cos\theta)^2}$$

are rational functions of $\cos\theta$ and $\sin\theta$. [In the case of F_3, we need to recall the trigonometric identity

$$\sin 4\theta = \cos\theta\,(4\sin\theta - 8\sin^3\theta);$$

similar identities exist for $\cos k\theta$ and $\sin k\theta$ for $k = 2, 3, 4, \ldots$.]

Integrals of the form shown in (11) arise, for example, in evaluating the coefficients in Fourier series. To evaluate I, we enter the change of variables

$$z = e^{i\theta}. \tag{12}$$

This change of variables converts I from an integral on a real θ axis to a contour integral in a complex z plane, for as θ varies from 0 to 2π, z undergoes one complete counterclockwise trip around the unit circle (the unit circle because $z = e^{i\theta}$ is of the form $z = re^{i\theta}$ with $r = 1$).

From (12), $dz = ie^{i\theta}\,d\theta = iz\,d\theta$, so $d\theta = dz/iz$, and

$$\begin{aligned} \cos\theta &= \frac{e^{i\theta} + e^{-i\theta}}{2} = \frac{z + z^{-1}}{2} = \frac{z^2 + 1}{2z}, \\ \sin\theta &= \frac{e^{i\theta} - e^{-i\theta}}{2i} = \frac{z - z^{-1}}{2i} = \frac{z^2 - 1}{2iz}, \end{aligned} \tag{13}$$

so

$$I = 3\int_C F\left(\frac{z + z^{-1}}{2}, \frac{z - z^{-1}}{2i}\right)\frac{dz}{iz}. \tag{14}$$

Now, $\cos\theta$ and $\sin\theta$ are seen to be rational functions of z. In turn, F is a rational function of $\cos\theta$ and $\sin\theta$, so F (and hence the new integrand F/iz) is a rational function of z. Thus the integrand in (14) is analytic everywhere except at those zeros of the denominator that lie within the contour C, i.e., within the unit circle. Let us illustrate.

EXAMPLE 2 Evaluate

$$I = \int_0^{2\pi} \frac{d\theta}{2 - \sin\theta}. \tag{15}$$

With the change of variables $z = e^{i\theta}$, we obtain

$$I = \oint_C \frac{1}{2 - \dfrac{z^2 - 1}{2iz}} \frac{dz}{iz} = -2 \oint_C \frac{dz}{z^2 - 4iz - 1}$$

$$= -2 \oint_C \frac{dz}{(z - z_+)(z - z_-)} \equiv \oint_C f(z)\, dz, \tag{16}$$

where $z_+ = (2 + \sqrt{3})i$ and $z_- = (2 - \sqrt{3})i$. Since z_+ lies outside C and z_- lies inside (Fig. 21.21), the residue theorem gives

$$I = 2\pi i \operatorname*{Res}_{z=z_-} f = 2\pi i \lim_{z \to z_-} \left[(z - z_-) \frac{-2}{(z - z_+)(z - z_-)} \right]$$

$$= 2\pi i \left(\frac{-2}{z_- - z_+} \right) = \frac{2\pi}{\sqrt{3}}. \tag{17}$$

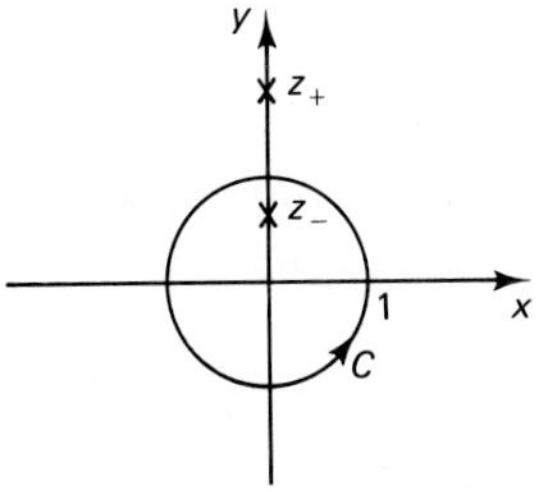

Fig. 21.21 Contour and singular points.

COMMENT 1 It is to be emphasized that *the residue theorem does not apply if there are one or more singular points* ***on*** *C,* for the theorem requires that $f(z)$ is to be analytic on C. For example if we generalize (15) to the form

$$I = \int_0^{2\pi} \frac{d\theta}{a - \sin\theta}, \tag{18}$$

where a is real, we find that the residue theorem does not apply if $-1 \le a \le 1$ because in that case the singular points $\pm\sqrt{1 - a^2} + ai$ fall right on the contour C (Exercise 1).

COMMENT 2 It is also to be noted that if the integral limits in (15) were 0 to π, say, the residue theorem could not have been applied because the corresponding contour C in the z plane would not have been closed; it would only have been a semicircle. ◀

Moving on, let us examine some other applications of the residue theorem to the evaluation of real integrals.

EXAMPLE 3 Consider the evaluation of the real integral

$$I = \int_{-\infty}^{\infty} \frac{dx}{x^2 + 1}. \tag{19}$$

Toward this end, we consider, instead, the contour integral

$$J = \oint_C \frac{dz}{z^2 + 1}, \tag{20}$$

where C is the closed semicircle contour shown in Fig. 21.22. Clearly, the integrand $f(z)$ has first-order poles at $z = +i, -i$ and is analytic elsewhere. Thus, on the one hand, application of the residue theorem gives

$$J = 2\pi i \operatorname*{Res}_{z=i} f = 2\pi i \lim_{z \to i} \left[(z - i) \frac{1}{(z + i)(z - i)} \right] = \pi \tag{21}$$

(for all $R > 1$, so that the point $z = i$ falls within C). On the other hand,

$$J = \int_{-R}^{R} \frac{dx}{x^2 + 1} + \int_{C_R} \frac{dz}{z^2 + 1}, \tag{22}$$

where C_R denotes the semicircular portion of C. Equating these two results gives

$$\pi = \int_{-R}^{R} \frac{dx}{x^2 + 1} + \int_{C_R} \frac{dz}{z^2 + 1}, \tag{23}$$

Now, (23) holds for *all* R's (greater than unity), so it must be true as $R \to \infty$. Taking that limit, (23) becomes

$$\pi = \int_{-\infty}^{\infty} \frac{dx}{x^2 + 1} + \lim_{R \to \infty} \int_{C_R} \frac{dz}{z^2 + 1}. \tag{24}$$

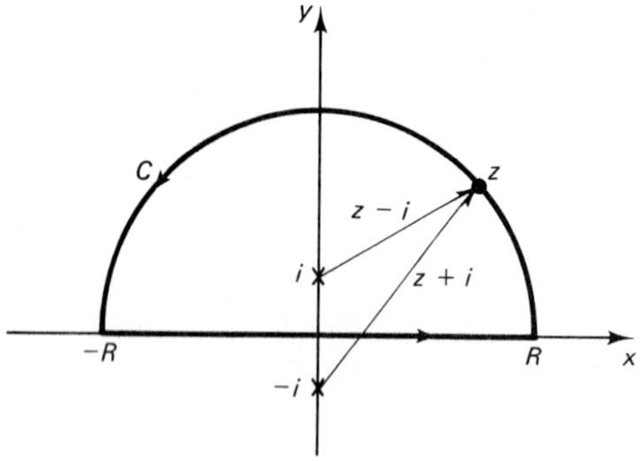

Fig. 21.22 The contour C.

To evaluate the last term in (24), we apply the ML bound. To obtain an upper bound M on the magnitude of the integrand, it suffices to get a lower bound on the magnitude of the denominator $z^2 + 1$. Well, as z traverses the C_R contour, $|z - i|$ is smallest when z is at Ri, namely $R - 1$, and $|z + 1|$ is smallest when z is at R, namely $\sqrt{R^2 + 1}$, Thus

$$\left| \frac{1}{z^2 + 1} \right| = \frac{1}{|z - i||z + i|} \leq \frac{1}{(R - 1)\sqrt{R^2 + 1}} \tag{25}$$

for all z on C_R. Furthermore, the length of C_R is πR, so the ML bound gives

$$\left| \int_{C_R} \frac{dz}{z^2 + 1} \right| \leq \frac{\pi R}{(R - 1)\sqrt{R^2 + 1}}, \tag{26}$$

which tends to zero as $R \to \infty$. Thus (24) becomes $\pi = I + 0$, so the answer is

$$I = \pi. \tag{27}$$

COMMENT 1 Recall from Section 12.2 that an integral is singular if one or both integration limits are infinite and/or if the integrand grows unboundedly anywhere on the interval. There we considered singular integrals of the type $\int_a^\infty F(t)\,dt$, and defined

$$\int_a^\infty F(t)\,dt \equiv \lim_{b\to\infty} \int_a^b F(t)\,dt; \tag{28}$$

the integral on the left *exists,* or *converges,* if the limit on the right exists.

In (19) we met a singular integral in which *both* integration limits were infinite. Such an integral is defined as

$$\int_{-\infty}^\infty F(t)\,dt \equiv \lim_{\substack{a\to\infty \\ b\to\infty}} \int_{-a}^b F(t)\,dt, \tag{29}$$

where a and b tend to ∞ independently.* Observe that the definition in (29) seems to be at odds with our claim above that

$$\lim_{R\to\infty} \int_{-R}^{R} \frac{dx}{x^2+1} = \int_{-\infty}^{\infty} \frac{dx}{x^2+1}, \tag{30}$$

because here $a = b = R$, so a and b tend to ∞ together. However, *if the integral in (29) does exist,* its value is independent of the manner in which a and b tend to infinity, so it is permissible to take $a = b$. In the present case the integral in (19) does indeed exist, so (30) is correct.

COMMENT 2 The method employed in this example is fairly general, so let us review it. Given an integral I from $-\infty$ to ∞ on a real axis, we considered instead a contour integral J on a closed contour in a z plane. On the one hand, we could evaluate J by the residue theorem (because the contour was closed) and, on the other hand, J could be expressed as the desired integral I plus a computable integral; specifically, the upper semicircle contribution was shown to tend to zero as $R \to \infty$.

If we are asked to evaluate the *semi*-infinite integral

$$I_1 = \int_0^\infty \frac{dx}{x^2+1} \tag{31}$$

instead, we can use the fact that the integrand $1/(x^2+1)$ is an even function, so that

$$I_1 = \int_0^\infty \frac{dx}{x^2+1} = \frac{1}{2}\int_{-\infty}^{\infty} \frac{dx}{x^2+1}. \tag{32}$$

* This definition is equivalent to the statement

$$\int_{-\infty}^\infty F(t)\,dt \equiv \int_{-\infty}^0 F(t)\,dt + \int_0^\infty F(t)\,dt,$$

where the integrals on the right-hand side are, in turn, defined according to (28).

Then we can proceed as before. However, if asked to evaluate

$$I_2 = \int_0^\infty \frac{dx}{x^2 + x + 1}, \tag{33}$$

we can*not* use that line of approach to move the lower integration limit to $-\infty$ because the integrand $1/(x^2 + x + 1)$ is not an even function of x. In this case we suggest proceeding as indicated in Exercise 7.

COMMENT 3 Finally, observe that in this example we could have "closed the contour" below, rather than above, as depicted in Fig. 21.23. Doing so, we have

$$J = -2\pi i \operatorname*{Res}_{z=-i} f \qquad \text{(the minus sign because } C \text{ is } \textit{clockwise}\text{)}$$

$$= -2\pi i \lim_{z \to -i} \left[(z + i) \frac{1}{(z + i)(z - i)} \right] = \frac{-2\pi i}{-2i} = \pi,$$

so we obtain (24) again, but this time C_R is the *lower* semicircle. In essentially the same manner as above, we can show that the C_R integral tends to zero as $R \to \infty$, so we obtain the same final result, $I = \pi$. ◀

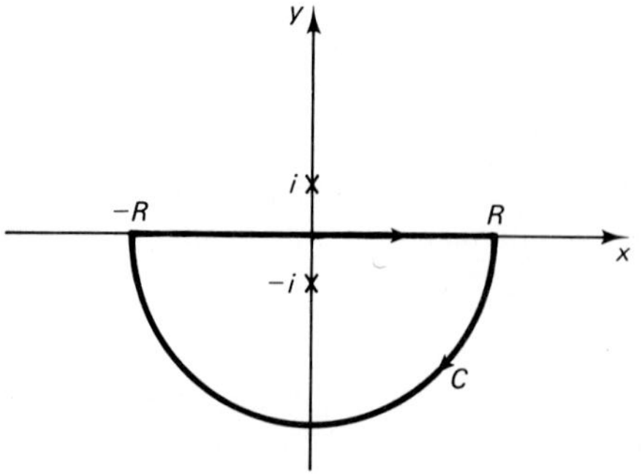

Fig. 21.23 A different contour C.

It is true that the integral in (11) was not especially imposing and could have been evaluated by a trigonometric change of variables, giving $I = \tan^{-1} x \big|_{-\infty}^{\infty} = \pi$. However, our chief concern was developing the relevant contour integral method. That method applies equally well to *any* integral of the form

$$I = \int_{-\infty}^\infty \frac{p(x)}{q(x)}\, dx, \tag{34}$$

where $p(x)$ and $q(x)$ are finite-degree polynomials, of degree P and Q, respectively, provided that $Q - P \geq 2$ and that $q(x)$ has no real zeros (Exercise 9).

EXAMPLE 4 Evaluate

$$I = \int_0^\infty \frac{\cos ax}{x^2 + 1}\, dx \qquad (a > 0) \tag{35}$$

First, extend the lower integration limit back to $-\infty$ by noting that the integrand is an even function of x, so that

$$I = \frac{1}{2} \int_{-\infty}^\infty \frac{\cos ax}{x^2 + 1}\, dx. \tag{36}$$

Next, consider the contour integral

$$J = \oint_C \frac{\cos az}{z^2 + 1}\, dz, \tag{37}$$

where C is shown in Fig. 21.22. Looking ahead, we will wish to show that the C_R integral tends to zero as $R \to \infty$. Does that step appear to be feasible? Well,

$$\cos az = \frac{e^{iaz} + e^{-iaz}}{2},$$

and if we consider the single point $z = Ri$ on C_R, we see that the e^{-iaz} term in $\cos az$ is $e^{-ia(Ri)} = e^{aR}$ there. This exponential growth (as $R \to \infty$) makes it appear highly unlikely that the C_R integral tends to zero as $R \to \infty$. Furthermore, if we try closing the contour below instead, as in Fig. 21.23, at the point $z = -Ri$ on C_R the e^{+iaz} term in $\cos az$ is $e^{ia(-Ri)} = e^{aR}$. Thus if the e^{-iaz} term does not kill us, the e^{+iaz} term does!

To surmount this difficulty, let us consider a *single* exponential in place of $\cos az$. Specifically, consider

$$J = \oint_C \frac{e^{iaz}}{z^2 + 1}\, dz \tag{38}$$

in place of (37), with C as shown in Fig. 21.22. The integrand $f(z)$ is analytic everywhere except at $z = \pm i$, where it has first-order poles. Thus, on the one hand,

$$J = 2\pi i \operatorname*{Res}_{z=i} f(z) = (2\pi i)\left(\frac{e^{ia(i)}}{2i}\right) = \pi e^{-a}, \tag{39}$$

and on the other hand,

$$J = \int_{-R}^{R} \frac{e^{iax}}{x^2 + 1}\, dx + \int_{C_R} \frac{e^{iaz}}{z^2 + 1}\, dz \tag{40}$$

or, with $R \to \infty$,

$$J = \int_{-\infty}^{\infty} \frac{\cos ax + i \sin ax}{x^2 + 1}\, dx + \lim_{R\to\infty} \int_{C_R} \frac{e^{iaz}}{z^2 + 1}\, dz. \tag{41}$$

Now, since $|e^{iaz}| = |e^{ia(x+iy)}| = |e^{iax}||e^{-ay}| = e^{-ay} \le 1$ on C_R, it follows that

$$\left|\frac{e^{iaz}}{z^2 + 1}\right| \le \left|\frac{1}{z^2 + 1}\right| \le \frac{1}{(R-1)\sqrt{R^2 + 1}}, \tag{42}$$

everywhere on C_R, where the last inequality follows from (25). Furthermore, the length of C_R is πR, so the ML bound gives

$$\left|\int_{C_R} \frac{e^{iaz}}{z^2 + 1}\, dz\right| \le \frac{\pi R}{(R-1)\sqrt{R^2 + 1}}, \tag{43}$$

which does tend to zero as $R \to \infty$. With this result, comparison of (39) and (41) gives

$$\pi e^{-a} = \int_{-\infty}^{\infty} \frac{\cos ax}{x^2 + 1}\, dx + i \int_{-\infty}^{\infty} \frac{\sin ax}{x^2 + 1}\, dx. \tag{44}$$

Finally, equating real parts in (44) gives

$$\int_{-\infty}^{\infty} \frac{\cos ax}{x^2 + 1}\, dx = \pi e^{-a}, \tag{45}$$

and hence the answer

$$I = \frac{1}{2}\int_{-\infty}^{\infty} \frac{\cos ax}{x^2 + 1}\, dx = \frac{\pi}{2} e^{-a}. \tag{46}$$

Of course, we can also equate imaginary parts in (44), and that step gives the "bonus" result

$$\int_{-\infty}^{\infty} \frac{\sin ax}{x^2 + 1}\, dx = 0. \tag{47}$$

COMMENT As a partial check, notice that for the case $a = 0$, (46) does reduce to the same result as was found in Example 3. ◀

EXAMPLE 5 Evaluate

$$I = \int_{0}^{\infty} \frac{x^{1/3}}{(x + 1)^2}\, dx. \tag{48}$$

To do so, we consider the contour integral

$$J = \oint_C \frac{z^{1/3}}{(z + 1)^2}\, dz, \tag{49}$$

where C is to be a suitably chosen closed contour. Before selecting C it is important to notice that although the $x^{1/3}$ appearing in (48) is single valued (e.g., $8^{1/3} = 2$), the $z^{1/3}$ in (49) is *multi*valued (e.g., $8^{1/3} = 2, 2e^{i2\pi/3}$, and $2e^{i4\pi/3}$). Thus it is important to specify the meaning of $z^{1/3}$ (that is, to render it single valued) before proceeding. Let us do so by introducing the principal-value branch cut shown in Fig. 21.24a.

Next, let us select the contour C shown in Fig. 21.24b, where the outer circle is of radius R and the inner circle is of radius ϵ. (We plan to let $R \to \infty$ and $\epsilon \to 0$.) Breaking C into four parts, denote PQ as C_U, QS as C_R, ST as C_L, and TP as C_ϵ.

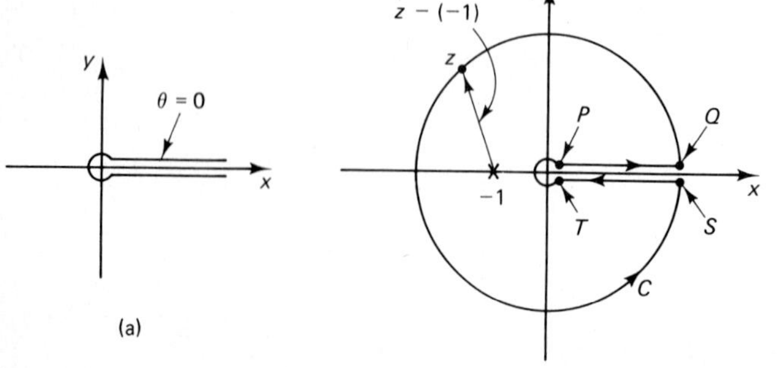

Fig. 21.24 Branch cut in contour.

Observe carefully that on C_U we have $z = xe^{i0}$, so

$$z^{1/3} = x^{1/3}e^{i0/3} = x^{1/3}, \tag{50a}$$

whereas on C_L we have $z = xe^{2\pi i}$, so

$$z^{1/3} = x^{1/3}e^{2\pi i/3}. \tag{50b}$$

And since the integrand $f(z)$ is analytic inside and on C, except for a second-order pole at $z = -1$, we have

$$\begin{aligned} 2\pi i \operatorname*{Res}_{z=-1} f(z) &= \int_\epsilon^R \frac{x^{1/3}}{(x+1)^2}\,dx + \int_{C_R} \frac{z^{1/3}}{(z+1)^2}\,dz \\ &+ \int_R^\epsilon \frac{x^{1/3}e^{2\pi i/3}}{(x+1)^2}\,dx + \int_{C_\epsilon} \frac{z^{1/3}}{(z+1)^2}\,dz. \end{aligned} \tag{51}$$

Applying the ML bound to the C_R integral, observe that

$$\left|\frac{z^{1/3}}{(z+1)^2}\right| = \frac{|R^{1/3}e^{i\theta/3}|}{|z+1|^2} = \frac{R^{1/3}}{|z-(-1)|^2} \le \frac{R^{1/3}}{(R-1)^2} \tag{52}$$

on C_R and that the length of C_R is $2\pi R$, so that

$$\left|\int_{C_R} \frac{z^{1/3}}{(z+1)^2}\,dz\right| \le \frac{R^{1/3}}{(R-1)^2}2\pi R, \tag{53}$$

which tends to zero as $R \to \infty$. Similarly (Exercise 10),

$$\left|\int_{C_\epsilon} \frac{z^{1/3}}{(z+1)^2}\,dz\right| \le \frac{\epsilon^{1/3}}{(1-\epsilon)^2}2\pi\epsilon, \tag{54}$$

which tends to zero as $\epsilon \to 0$.

Furthermore,

$$\begin{aligned} \operatorname*{Res}_{z=-1} f(z) &= \frac{1}{1!}\lim_{z\to -1}\frac{d}{dz}\left[(z+1)^2\frac{z^{1/3}}{(z+1)^2}\right] = \frac{1}{3}(-1)^{-2/3} \\ &= \frac{1}{3}(1e^{\pi i})^{-2/3} = \frac{e^{-2\pi i/3}}{3}, \end{aligned} \tag{55}$$

where, in evaluating $(-1)^{-2/3}$, we have expressed $-1 = 1e^{\pi i}$, in accordance with the branch cut shown in Fig. 21.24a.

Thus, letting $R \to \infty$ and $\epsilon \to 0$ in (51) gives

$$\begin{aligned} 2\pi i\frac{e^{-2\pi i/3}}{3} &= \int_0^\infty \frac{x^{1/3}}{(x+1)^2}\,dx + \int_\infty^0 \frac{x^{1/3}e^{2\pi i/3}}{(x+1)^2}\,dx \\ &= (1 - e^{2\pi i/3})\int_0^\infty \frac{x^{1/3}}{(x+1)^2}\,dx, \end{aligned} \tag{56}$$

or

$$\int_0^\infty \frac{x^{1/3}}{(x+1)^2}\,dx = \frac{2\pi i}{3}\frac{e^{-2\pi i/3}}{1-e^{2\pi i/3}} = \frac{2\pi}{3\sqrt{3}}. \tag{57}$$

COMMENT The final result is *not* dependent on the choice of branch cut for $z^{1/3}$.

We leave it as an exercise to show that the same result is obtained if we define θ as $2\pi k$, on the upper edge of the cut, for *any* integer k. ◀

As our final example, we illustrate the use of the residue theorem in working out inverse Laplace transforms by the Laplace inversion formula. Before doing that it will be useful to review certain aspects of the Laplace transform.

Recall that the Fourier integral formula (and hence the Fourier transform) applies to functions that are defined on the infinite interval $(-\infty, \infty)$ and that need to be restricted so as to ensure convergence. For example, the Fourier transform of the function $f(x) = \sin x$ does not exist because the integral

$$\hat{f}(\omega) = \int_{-\infty}^{\infty} \sin x \, e^{-i\omega x} \, dx$$

is divergent. However, in many applications the domain is the *semi*-infinite interval $(0, \infty)$, as occurs, for example, in initial-value problems, where the independent variable is the time t. Furthermore, we often wish to work with a wider range of functions than would be permissible within the context of the Fourier transform, including such functions as $\sin t$, t^2, and e^{3t}.

In Section 11.5 (which we urge the reader to review before continuing) we adapted the Fourier integral formula to meet these two needs by applying that formula to the function

$$F(t) = \begin{cases} e^{-\gamma t} f(t), & t > 0 \\ 0, & t < 0. \end{cases} \tag{58}$$

Here the real constant γ is chosen to be positive enough so that the combination $e^{-\gamma t} f(t)$ dies out (exponentially) as $t \to \infty$, so as to ensure the needed convergence. Thanks to the inclusion of the $e^{-\gamma t}$ factor we can then tolerate such f's as $f(t) = \sin t$, t^2, and e^{3t}. (In these cases we would need $\gamma > 0$, $\gamma > 0$, and $\gamma > 3$, respectively.)

The upshot is that in the resulting Laplace transform pair

$$\bar{f}(s) = \int_0^{\infty} f(t) e^{-st} \, dt, \tag{59a}$$

$$f(t) = \frac{1}{2\pi i} \int_{\gamma - i\infty}^{\gamma + i\infty} \bar{f}(s) e^{st} \, ds, \tag{59b}$$

the constant γ (see Fig. 21.25) needs to be sufficiently positive so that $e^{-\gamma t} f(t) \to 0$ as $t \to \infty$.

EXAMPLE 6 *Laplace Transform Inversion.* Given the Laplace transform

$$\bar{f}(s) = \frac{1}{(s-2)^3}, \tag{60}$$

determine the Laplace inverse $f(t)$ by evaluating the inversion integral in (59b):

$$f(t) = \frac{1}{2\pi i} \int_{\gamma - i\infty}^{\gamma + i\infty} \frac{e^{st}}{(s-2)^3} \, ds. \tag{61}$$

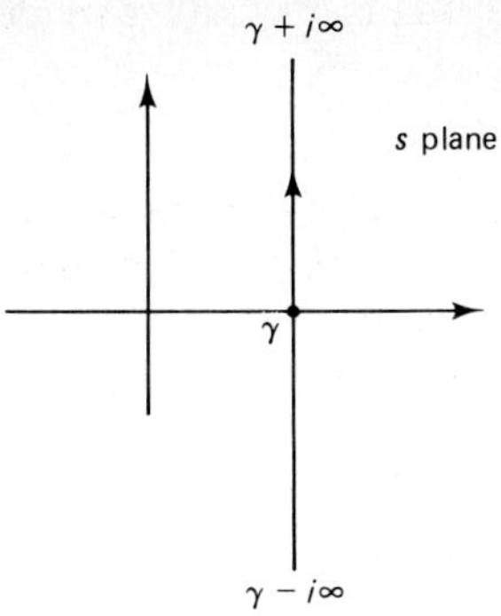

Fig. 21.25 The contour in (59b).

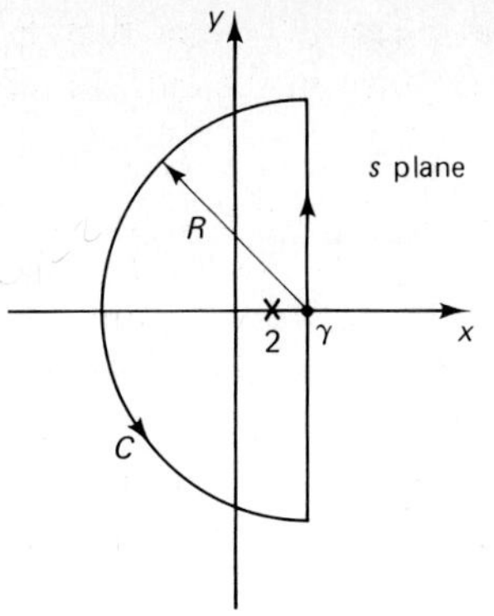

Fig. 21.26 Laplace inversion contour C.

The only singularity of the integrand is the third-order pole at $s = 2$. Now, recalling that γ needs to be sufficiently positive so that $e^{-\gamma t}f(t) \to 0$ as $t \to \infty$, how are we to determine γ if we do not yet know the inverse $f(t)$? We assert that γ *will be sufficiently positive if the integration contour ($\gamma - i\infty$ to $\gamma + i\infty$) is placed to the right of all singularities of* $\bar{f}(s)$. This rule will ensure that $e^{-\gamma t}f(t) \to \infty$ as $t \to \infty$ as desired and as can be *verified* a posteriori once $f(t)$ is in hand.

Thus in the present case we need $\gamma > 2$. Furthermore, let us tentatively close the contour on the left with a semicircle of radius R centered at $s = \gamma$, as depicted in Fig. 21.26. Thus consider

$$J = \frac{1}{2\pi i}\oint_C \frac{e^{st}}{(s-2)^3}\,ds, \tag{62}$$

where C is the indicated closed contour.

On the one hand,

$$J = 2\pi i \operatorname*{Res}_{s=2} \frac{e^{st}}{2\pi i(s-2)^3} = \frac{1}{2}t^2e^{2t}, \tag{63}$$

and on the other hand,

$$J = \frac{1}{2\pi i}\int_{\gamma-iR}^{\gamma+iR} \frac{e^{st}}{(s-2)^3}\,ds + \frac{1}{2\pi i}\int_{C_R} \frac{e^{st}}{(s-2)^3}\,ds, \tag{64}$$

where C_R is the semicircular part of C. Equating these results, letting $R \to \infty$, and recalling (61) gives

$$\frac{1}{2}t^2e^{2t} = f(t) + \frac{1}{2\pi i}\lim_{R\to\infty}\int_{C_R} \frac{e^{st}}{(s-2)^3}\,ds. \tag{65}$$

Now

$$|e^{st}| = |e^{(x+iy)t}| = |e^{xt}||e^{iyt}| = e^{xt} \le e^{\gamma t} \tag{66a}$$

and

$$|s - 2| \le R - 2 \tag{66b}$$

for all points s on C_R, so

$$\left| \frac{e^{st}}{(s-2)^3} \right| \leq \frac{e^{\gamma t}}{(R-2)^3} \tag{67}$$

on C_R. Hence the ML bound gives

$$\left| \int_{C_R} \frac{e^{st}}{(s-2)^3} \, ds \right| \leq \frac{e^{\gamma t}}{(R-2)^3} \pi R, \tag{68}$$

which tends to zero as $R \to \infty$. Thus (65) gives

$$f(t) = \tfrac{1}{2} t^2 e^{2t}, \tag{69}$$

which result agrees with item 15 in Appendix C.

COMMENT 1 With (69) in hand, we can see that we need $\gamma > 2$, and this value is consistent with the choice made in the solution above.

COMMENT 2 The result (69) holds only for $t > 0$, for observe that the $e^{xt} \leq e^{\gamma t}$ inequality in (66a) holds (on C_R) only if $t > 0$. If $t < 0$, the foregoing analysis breaks down and we need to close the contour on the *right* instead, as in Fig. 21.27. We leave it as an exercise (Exercise 17) to show that with this contour used in (62) we obtain $f(t) = 0$ for $t < 0$, as is consistent with (58). ◀

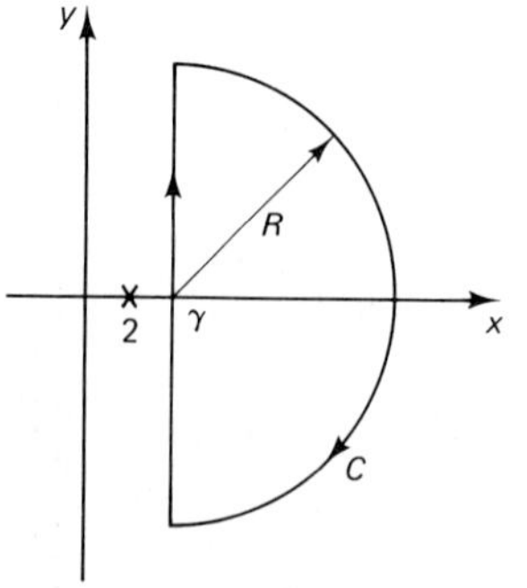

Fig. 21.27 Laplace inversion contour for $t < 0$.

Reviewing the foregoing examples, it becomes apparent that a key step is in setting up the "J integral"—i.e., in choosing its integrand and the closed contour C. The integrand is often, although not always, the same as the original integrand but with the original real variable replaced by the complex variable z. As an example of this rule, compare (48) with (47); as an example of an exception to the rule, compare (38) with (35). If the contour in the complex plane is not closed, we need to close it so that we can apply the residue theorem.

In studying the exercises that follow, it should become clear that the six examples in this section are representative of broad classes of integrals, and that the residue theorem is quite a powerful tool in the complex integral calculus.

1. Setting $z = e^{i\theta}$ in (18), with $-1 \le a \le 1$, show that the integrand has singular points at $z = \pm\sqrt{1 - a^2} + ai$, and that both of these singular points fall on the contour C.

2. Let C_1 be a closed rectangular contour, traversed counterclockwise, with vertices at $-1 - i$, $3 - i$, $3 + 3i$, $-1 + 3i$. Let C_2 be a closed triangular contour, traversed clockwise, with vertices at -2, 2, and $-2 + 3i$. Evaluate the given integral by means of the residue theorem.

*(a) $\displaystyle\oint_{C_1} \frac{dz}{\sin 2z}$ (b) $\displaystyle\oint_{C_1} \frac{dz}{z^2 e^z}$

(c) $\displaystyle\oint_{C_1} \frac{z^2\,dz}{\sinh 2z}$ *(d) $\displaystyle\oint_{C_1} \left(\frac{z+1}{z-1}\right)^3 dz$

(e) $\displaystyle\oint_{C_2} \frac{dz}{z^2 - 2iz - 2}$ (f) $\displaystyle\oint_{C_2} \frac{dz}{(\cosh \pi z/2)^2}$

3. Evaluate by means of contour integration and the residue theorem. *Hint:* $\int_0^A f(x)\,dx = \frac{1}{2}\int_{-A}^A f(x)\,dx$ if $f(x)$ is even.

*(a) $\displaystyle\int_0^{\pi} \sin^2 x\,dx$ (b) $\displaystyle\int_0^{\pi} \cos^2 x\,dx$

(c) $\displaystyle\int_0^{\pi} \cos^4 x\,dx$ (d) $\displaystyle\int_0^{\pi} \cos^6 x\,dx$

*(e) $\displaystyle\int_0^{\pi/2} \sin^6 x\,dx$ (f) $\displaystyle\int_{-\pi}^{\pi} \frac{d\theta}{7 + \cos\theta}$

(g) $\displaystyle\int_0^{\pi} \frac{d\theta}{1 + \cos^2\theta}$ (h) $\displaystyle\int_0^{\pi} \frac{d\theta}{1 + \sin^2\theta}$

*(i) $\displaystyle\int_0^{2\pi} \frac{d\theta}{2 + \sin 2\theta}$

4. Using contour integration and the residue theorem, show that

$$\int_0^{\pi} \frac{\cos t\,dt}{1 - 2a\cos t + a^2} = \frac{\pi a}{1 - a^2} \qquad (-1 < a < 1)$$

5. Does the integral $\int_{-\infty}^{\infty} x\,dx$ exist? Explain. (See Comment 1 in Example 3.)

6. Evaluate by means of the residue theorem; a and b are real and positive.

*(a) $\displaystyle\int_0^{\infty} \frac{dx}{x^4 + a^4}$

(b) $\displaystyle\int_0^{\infty} \frac{dx}{x^{2n} + 1}$ $(n = 1, 2, \ldots)$

(c) $\displaystyle\int_0^{\infty} \frac{dx}{(x^2 + a^2)(x^2 + b^2)}$

(d) $\displaystyle\int_0^{\infty} \frac{x^2}{x^4 + 1}\,dx$ *(e) $\displaystyle\int_0^{\infty} \frac{dx}{(x^2 + 1)^2}$

(f) $\displaystyle\int_{-\infty}^{\infty} \frac{dx}{4x^2 + 2x + 1}$ (g) $\displaystyle\int_0^{\infty} \frac{x^2}{x^6 + 1}\,dx$

*(h) $\displaystyle\int_0^{\infty} \frac{\cos x}{(x^2 + 1)^2}\,dx$

7. We wish to evaluate

$$I = \int_0^{\infty} \frac{dx}{x^2 + x + 1} \tag{a}$$

by the residue theorem.

(a) Show that considering

$$J = \oint_C \frac{dz}{z^2 + z + 1}, \tag{b}$$

where C is the contour shown in Fig. 21.22 does *not* work.

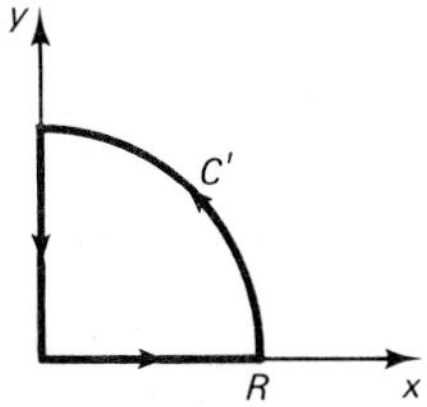

(b) Show that considering

$$J = \oint_{C'} \frac{dz}{z^2 + z + 1}, \tag{c}$$

where C' is the contour shown here, does not work either.

(c) Show that I *can* be evaluated by considering

$$J = \oint_C \frac{\log z}{z^2 + z + 1}\,dz, \tag{d}$$

where C is the contour shown in Fig. 21.24b. (The inner radius is ϵ and the outer radius is R. As in Example 5, let $\epsilon \to 0$ and $R \to \infty$.)

8. Use the same method as put forward in Exercise 7(c) to evaluate

*(a) $\displaystyle\int_0^{\infty} \frac{dx}{x^3 + 1}$ (b) $\displaystyle\int_0^{\infty} \frac{dx}{(x^2 + 2x + 10)^2}$

(c) $\displaystyle\int_0^{\infty} \frac{x}{x^3 + 1}\,dx$ (d) $\displaystyle\int_0^{1} \frac{dx}{x^2 + 1}$

Hint: First set $t = \dfrac{1}{x} - 1$.

9. Consider

$$I = \int_{-\infty}^{\infty} \frac{p(x)}{q(x)}\, dx, \tag{a}$$

where $p(x)$ and $q(x)$ are finite-degree polynomials, of degree P and Q, respectively, with $Q - P \geq 2$, and where $q(x)$ has no real zeros. To evaluate I by the residue theorem we consider, instead,

$$J = \oint_C \frac{p(z)}{q(z)}\, dz,$$

where C is the contour shown in Fig. 21.22. If C_R denotes the upper semicircle portion of C, show that

$$\lim_{R\to\infty} \int_{C_R} \frac{p(z)}{q(z)}\, dz = 0,$$

as claimed immediately before Example 4.

10. (*Example 5*) (a) Derive the inequality (54). (b) Verify the claim made in the comment at the end of Example 5.

11. Evaluate

*(a) $\int_0^{\infty} \frac{x^{a-1}}{x+1}\, dx \quad (0 < a < 1)$

(b) $\int_0^{\infty} \frac{\sqrt{x}}{x^3+1}\, dx$ (c) $\int_0^{\infty} \frac{dx}{\sqrt{x}(x^2+1)^2}$

(d) $\int_0^{\infty} \frac{\ln x}{x^2+1}\, dx$

12. Show that

$$\int_0^{\infty} e^{-x^2} \cos 2ax\, dx = \frac{\sqrt{\pi}}{2} e^{-a^2}$$

by integrating e^{-z^2} around a rectangle with vertices at $0, R, R + ia$, and ia, and recalling (Exercise 13, page 552) the known integral

$$\int_0^{\infty} e^{-x^2}\, dx = \frac{\sqrt{\pi}}{2}.$$

13. Use the inversion formula (59b) and the residue theorem to evaluate the following inverse Laplace transforms; a, b are real.

(a) $\mathbf{L}^{-1}\left\{\frac{1}{s^2}\right\}$ (b) $\mathbf{L}^{-1}\left\{\frac{1}{s^6}\right\}$ (c) $\mathbf{L}^{-1}\left\{\frac{1}{s^2+a^2}\right\}$

(d) $\mathbf{L}^{-1}\left\{\frac{1}{s^2-a^2}\right\}$ (e) $\mathbf{L}^{-1}\left\{\frac{1}{(s-a)^4}\right\}$

(f) $\mathbf{L}^{-1}\left\{\frac{s}{(s^2+a^2)^2}\right\}$ (g) $\mathbf{L}^{-1}\left\{\frac{1}{(s-a)^2+b^2}\right\}$

(h) $\mathbf{L}^{-1}\left\{\frac{e^{-as}}{s^3}\right\}$ (i) $\mathbf{L}^{-1}\left\{\frac{e^{-as}}{(s-b)^2}\right\}$

14. (*Cauchy principal value*) If $|f(x)| \to \infty$ as $x \to b$, where $a < b < c$, the integral $\int_a^c f(x)\, dx$ is said to be *singular* and is defined as

$$\int_a^c f(x)\, dx = \lim_{\substack{\epsilon_1\to 0\\ \epsilon_2\to 0}} \left\{ \int_a^{b-\epsilon_1} f(x)\, dx + \int_{b+\epsilon_2}^{c} f(x)\, dx \right\}, \tag{a}$$

where ϵ_1 and ϵ_2 tend to zero independently. If the limit on the right-hand side of (a) exists, we say that $\int_a^c f(x)\, dx$ *exists* or *converges*; otherwise, it *does not exist* or *diverges*. Now it is possible that the stated limit fails to exist but *does* exist if we choose $\epsilon_1 = \epsilon_2 (= \epsilon$, say); i.e., ϵ_1 and ϵ_2 tend to zero together. In that case we write

$$⨍_a^c f(x)\, dx = \lim_{\epsilon\to 0} \left\{ \int_a^{b-\epsilon} f(x)\, dx + \int_{b+\epsilon}^{c} f(x)\, dx \right\} \tag{b}$$

and call $⨍_a^c f(x)\, dx$ the **Cauchy principal value** (hence the C through the integral sign) of the integral.

(a) Show that

$$\int_{-1}^{3} \frac{dx}{x}$$

is divergent [i.e., in the sense of (a)], although it is convergent in the Cauchy principal-value sense (b).
(b) Repeat part (a) for the integral $\int_1^4 dx/x(x-2)$.

15. Use the residue theorem to show that

$$\int_0^{\infty} \frac{\sin x}{x}\, dx = \frac{\pi}{2}.$$

Hint: Consider $\int_C (e^{iz}/z)\, dz$, where C is the "indented" semicircular contour shown in the accompanying figure. The indentation at $z = 0$ is needed because e^{iz}/z is singular (has a first-order pole) at $z = 0$, and we do not want the contour passing through a singular point if we are to be able to apply the residue theo-

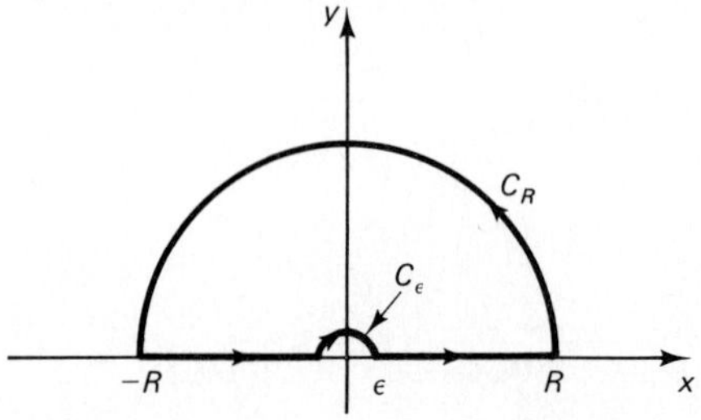

rem. Then, show that

$$\int_C \frac{e^{iz}}{z}\,dz = 0 = \oint_{-\infty}^{\infty} \frac{\cos x + i \sin x}{x}\,dx + \lim_{R\to\infty}\int_{C_R}\frac{e^{iz}}{z}\,dz + \lim_{\epsilon\to 0}\int_{C_\epsilon}\frac{e^{iz}}{z}\,dz, \tag{a}$$

where C_R and C_ϵ are the semicircular contours of radius R and ϵ, respectively. To show that the C_R integral tends to zero, show that

$$\left|\int_{C_R}\frac{e^{iz}}{z}\,dz\right| \le \int_0^{\pi}\left|\frac{e^{iz}}{z}\right| R\,d\theta$$

by (a) in Exercise 8 on page 799

$$= \int_0^{\pi} e^{-R\sin\theta}\,d\theta = 2\int_0^{\pi/2} e^{-R\sin\theta}\,d\theta < 2\int_0^{\pi/2} e^{-2R\theta/\pi}\,d\theta = \frac{\pi}{R}(1 - e^{-R}) \to 0 \tag{b}$$

as $R \to \infty$. [Notice carefully that if in place of the sharper bound (a) on page 799, we use the usual ML bound, we obtain the result

$$\left|\int_{C_R}\frac{e^{iz}}{z}\,dz\right| \le \pi, \tag{c}$$

which is true, but not sharp enough to show that the integral actually tends to zero as $R \to \infty$. This is the first instance in which the ML bound has not sufficed.] To show that the C_ϵ integral tends to zero, show that

$$\frac{e^{iz}}{z} = \frac{1}{z} + i - \frac{z}{2} + \cdots \qquad (0 < |z| < \infty) = \frac{1}{z} + g(z), \tag{d}$$

where $g(z)$ is analytic for all z (and hence bounded on C_ϵ), so that

$$\lim_{\epsilon\to 0}\int_{C_\epsilon}\frac{e^{iz}}{z}\,dz = \lim_{\epsilon\to 0}\left[\int_{C_\epsilon}\frac{1}{z}\,dz + \int_{C_\epsilon} g(z)\,dz\right] = -\pi i + \lim_{\epsilon\to 0}\int_{C_\epsilon} g(z)\,dz = -\pi i. \tag{e}$$

Finally, note that

$$\oint_{-\infty}^{\infty}\frac{\cos x + i\sin x}{x}\,dx = \oint_{-\infty}^{\infty}\frac{\cos x}{x}\,dx + i\int_{-\infty}^{\infty}\frac{\sin x}{x}\,dx. \tag{f}$$

[The latter integral does not need the Cauchy principal-value sign because $(\sin x)/x$ is finite for all x—in particular, at $x = 0$.]

16. Use the inversion formula (59b) and the residue theorem to show that

$$\mathbf{L}^{-1}\left\{\frac{1}{s}\right\} = 1 \qquad (t > 0).$$

Hint: Showing that the value of the C_R integral tends to zero as $R \to \infty$ will involve a bounding process similar to the one indicated in (b) in Exercise 15.

17. It was stated in Comment 2 on page 872 that one obtains $f(t) = 0$ for $t < 0$ by closing the contour on the right, as shown in Fig. 21.27. Verify that claim. And have a pleasant aftermath.

ADDITIONAL REFERENCES FOR PART V

L. V. AHLFORS, *Complex Analysis,* 2nd ed. New York: McGraw-Hill, 1966.
A more advanced treatment than in this text.

R. V. CHURCHILL, *Complex Variables and Applications,* 2nd ed. New York: McGraw-Hill, 1960.
About the same level as this text, although more complete. Numerous physical applications of conformal mapping.

KONRAD KNOPP, *Theory of Functions,* Part I. New York: Dover, 1945.

A clear, concise, and rigorous development of the theory of functions of a complex variable.

E. G. PHILLIPS, *Functions of a Complex Variable,* Edinburgh: Oliver & Boyd, 1957.

Like Knopp, this book is rather small. It contains a great many worked examples, especially on contour integration.

Appendix: Ordinary Differential Equations Review

A

INTRODUCTION A.1

As mentioned in the Preface, it is assumed that the reader has studied the differential and integral calculus and has had the equivalent of a first course in ordinary differential equations (ODEs). In principle, then, this appendix is redundant. In practice, however, there appear to be useful purposes to be served by its inclusion. First, there are numerous points in the text where we need to draw upon a theorem or formula from such a course in ODEs, and it seems to work best to organize those theorems and results in an appendix for convenient reference. Second, ODE solution skills are essential, particularly in Part IV, and this appendix should suffice for review purposes. The treatment is more than a skeletal listing of theorems and formulas, but is limited to those topics that are needed in this book.

PRELIMINARIES AND LINEARITY A.2

By an **ordinary differential equation** we mean an equation that involves at least one derivative of an unspecified function y of x, say, and possibly various specified functions of x as well, and which holds on some specified interval (finite or infinite) on a real x axis. (More generally, one may fruitfully allow the independent variable to be complex, but we choose not to do that here.) For example, each of the equations

$$xy' - y = 6 \qquad (0 < x < \infty) \tag{1}$$

and

$$y''' + x^2y' \sin y + 3y = e^x \qquad (2 < x < 5), \tag{2}$$

where primes denote derivatives with respect to x are ODEs.

A differential equation is said to be of **order** n if the highest derivative appearing in the equation is of order n. Thus (1) is a first-order equation, and (2) is a third-order equation. Further, we say that a function $y = Y(x)$ is a **solution** of the ODE if substituting for y and its various derivatives in the ODE the quantity $Y(x)$ and its corresponding derivatives reduces the ODE to an identity over the specified x interval. For example, $y = 5x - 6$ is a solution of (1), although by no means the only one.

We shall be especially interested in ODEs of the form

$$y^{(n)} + p_1(x)y^{(n-1)} + \cdots + p_{n-1}(x)y' + p_n(x)y = f(x), \tag{3}$$

where $y^{(n)}$ is short for d^ny/dx^n. For example, $y'' + x^3y' - 2y = 5 \sin x + 3$ is of the form (3). Equation (3) can be expressed more compactly in the form

$$Ly = f(x), \tag{4}$$

where

$$L = \frac{d^n}{dx^n} + p_1(x)\frac{d^{n-1}}{dx^{n-1}} + \cdots + p_{n-1}(x)\frac{d}{dx} + p_n(x) \tag{5}$$

is called the **differential operator**; thus Ly (i.e., the result of the action of L upon y) is understood to mean

$$\begin{aligned} Ly &= \left[\frac{d^n}{dx^n} + p_1(x)\frac{d^{n-1}}{dx^{n-1}} + \cdots + p_{n-1}(x)\frac{d}{dx} + p_n(x)\right]y \\ &= y^{(n)} + p_1(x)y^{(n-1)} + \cdots + p_{n-1}(x)y' + p_n(x)y. \end{aligned} \tag{6}$$

A fundamental property of the operator L, given by (5), is "linearity." The operator L, given by (5), is **linear** inasmuch as

$$\boxed{L(c_1y_1 + c_2y_2) = c_1Ly_1 + c_2Ly_2} \tag{7}$$

holds over the x interval of interest for every choice of the constants c_1, c_2 and for every choice of the (n times differentiable) functions $y_1(x)$, $y_2(x)$. To verify this claim, we recall the familiar result from the calculus,

$$\frac{d^k}{dx^k}(c_1y_1 + c_2y_2) = c_1\frac{d^k}{dx^k}y_1 + c_2\frac{d^k}{dx^k}y_2 = c_1y_1^{(k)} + c_2y_2^{(k)}.$$

Using this result yields

$$\begin{aligned} L(c_1y_1 + c_2y_2) &= \frac{d^n}{dx^n}(c_1y_1 + c_2y_2) + p_1(x)\frac{d^{n-1}}{dx^{n-1}}(c_1y_1 + c_2y_2) \\ &\quad + \cdots + p_n(x)(c_1y_1 + c_2y_2) \\ &= c_1y_1^{(n)} + c_2y_2^{(n)} + p_1(x)(c_1y_1^{(n-1)} + c_2y_2^{(n-1)}) \\ &\quad + \cdots + p_n(x)(c_1y_1 + c_2y_2) \\ &= c_1[y_1^{(n)} + p_1(x)y_1^{(n-1)} + \cdots + p_n(x)y_1] \end{aligned}$$

$$+ c_2[y_2^{(n)} + p_1(x)y_2^{(n-1)} + \cdots + p_n(x)y_2]$$
$$= c_1Ly_1 + c_2Ly_2,$$

as claimed. In fact,

$$L(c_1y_1 + c_2y_2 + \cdots + c_ky_k) = c_1Ly_1 + c_2Ly_2 + \cdots + c_kLy_k \tag{8}$$

holds for *every* finite $k \geq 1$. For if $k = 3$, say, then

$$\begin{aligned} L(c_1y_1 + c_2y_2 + c_3y_3) &= L(c_1y_1 + 1(c_2y_2 + c_3y_3)) \\ &= c_1Ly_1 + 1L(c_2y_2 + c_3y_3) \quad \text{from (7)} \\ &= c_1Ly_1 + c_2Ly_2 + c_3Ly_3 \quad \text{from (7)}. \end{aligned}$$

Similarly for $k = 4, 5, \ldots$.

If L is linear, we say that the differential equation $Ly = f$ is linear, too. The importance of linearity cannot be overstated, as we shall appreciate in a moment. First, some more terminology. If $f = 0$ we say that the differential equation (4) is **homogeneous**, and if $f \neq 0$ we say the differential equation is **nonhomogeneous**.

Consider the homogeneous case

$$Ly = 0. \tag{9}$$

If each of $y_1, \ldots, y_k$ are solutions of (9)(i.e., $Ly_1 = 0, \ldots, Ly_k = 0$), so is $c_1y_1 + \cdots + c_ky_k$ a solution, for any choice of the constants $c_1, \ldots, c_k$, since

$$\begin{aligned} L(c_1y_1 + \cdots + c_ky_k) &= c_1Ly_1 + \cdots + c_kLy_k \quad \text{from (8)} \\ &= (c_1)(0) + \cdots + (c_k)(0) \quad \text{by assumption} \\ &= 0. \end{aligned} \tag{10}$$

The important process of building up a more comprehensive solution as a linear combination of individual solutions is known as **superposition**. As we have seen in (10), the validity of superposition rests on the linearity of L.

Next, consider the nonhomogeneous case

$$Ly = f. \tag{11}$$

Suppose that y_p is any particular solution of $Ly = f$ and that $y_1, \ldots, y_k$ are "homogeneous solutions," i.e., solutions of the "associated homogeneous equation" $Ly = 0$. Then

$$y(x) = y_p(x) + c_1y_1(x) + \cdots + c_ky_k(x) \tag{12}$$

is a solution to (11) for any choice of the constants $c_1, \ldots, c_k$, since

$$\begin{aligned} Ly &= L(y_p + c_1y_1 + \cdots + c_ky_k) \\ &= Ly_p + c_1Ly_1 + \cdots + c_kLy_k \\ &= f + 0 + \cdots + 0 = f. \end{aligned} \tag{13}$$

This result will be used in Section A.3 when we develop the so-called "general solution" of (3).

Finally, we mention that it is often useful to regard f as the sum of a number of parts,

$$f = f_1 + \cdots + f_\ell. \tag{14}$$

In that case, if $y_{p1}, \ldots, y_{p\ell}$ *are particular solutions of* $Ly = f_1, \ldots, Ly = f_\ell$, *respectively, then*

$$y_p = y_{p1} + \cdots + y_{p\ell} \tag{15}$$

is a particular solution of $Ly = f_1 + \cdots + f_\ell = f$, since

$$\begin{aligned} L(y_{p1} + \cdots + y_{p\ell}) &= Ly_{p1} + \cdots + Ly_{p\ell} \\ &= f_1 + \cdots + f_\ell = f. \end{aligned} \tag{16}$$

Before continuing with our discussion of the linear equation (3), it may be possible to clarify further the idea of linearity by looking at the other side of the coin. *If an operator L is not linear* [i.e., if (7) does not hold for every choice of constants c_1, c_2 and sufficiently differentiable functions y_1, y_2], *it is* ***nonlinear***. To illustrate, consider the operator L such that

$$Ly = y'' + 3xy^2; \tag{17}$$

i.e.,

$$L(\;) = \frac{d^2}{dx^2}(\;) + 3x(\;)^2. \tag{18}$$

Then

$$\begin{aligned} L(c_1y_1 + c_2y_2) - c_1Ly_1 - c_2Ly_2 \\ &= c_1y_1'' + c_2y_2'' + 3x(c_1y_1 + c_2y_2)^2 \\ &\quad - c_1(y_1'' + 3xy_1^2) - c_2(y_2'' + 3xy_2^2) \\ &= 3x[(c_1^2 - c_1)y_1^2 + (c_2^2 - c_2)y_2^2 + 2c_1c_2y_1y_2], \end{aligned} \tag{19}$$

which is *not* identically zero for all possible choices of c_1, c_2, $y_1(x)$, $y_2(x)$, as is required by (7) for L to be linear. For example, if $c_1 = c_2 = 1$, $y_1(x) = 1$, and $y_2(x) = x$, the right-hand side of (19) is $6x^2$. Thus this operator L is not linear; it is nonlinear.

With this brief example of a nonlinear operator behind us, *we confine our attention in the remainder of this appendix, except for Section A.9, exclusively to the linear operator (5) and the corresponding linear differential equation (3).*

A.3 LINEAR INDEPENDENCE AND THE GENERAL SOLUTION OF $Ly = f$

Besides asking that y satisfy (i.e., be a solution of) the differential equation $Ly = f$, over some interval, we may also ask that $y, y', \ldots, y^{(n-1)}$ take on a set of prescribed values at some given point x_0 in the interval. Then the complete problem on y looks like this:

$$y^{(n)} + p_1(x)y^{(n-1)} + \cdots + p_{n-1}(x)y' + p_n(x)y = f(x); \tag{1a}$$

$$y(x_0) = k_1, \quad y'(x_0) = k_2, \quad \ldots, \quad y^{(n-1)}(x_0) = k_n. \tag{1b}$$

We will refer to (1b) as **initial conditions** since we may imagine knowing all of that data at the "starting point" or "initial point" x_0, and wishing to generate a solution $y(x)$ of (1a), as a function of x, as x departs from that point.

At least three significant questions come to mind regarding the **initial-value problem** (1). First, *are* there any solutions? This is the question of "existence" (Do any solutions exist?). Second, *how many* solutions are there? This is the question of "uniqueness" (Is the solution unique?). Third, how do we *find* the solution(s)? We return to the third question in subsequent sections. Here we focus on existence and uniqueness.

***Theorem 1** Existence, Uniqueness*

Let the functions $p_1(x), \ldots, p_n(x)$, and $f(x)$ be continuous on an interval $a \leq x \leq b$ containing the point $x = x_0$. Then there **exists** a solution $y(x)$ of the differential equation (1a), over $a \leq x \leq b$, which satisfies the initial conditions (1b), for any given values of the constants $k_1, \ldots, k_n$. Furthermore, that solution is **unique**.

Normally, x_0 will be at one of the endpoints of the interval.

Next, we introduce a notion of linear dependence, for functions, which is analogous to that introduced in Chapter 2 for vectors. *A finite set of functions $\{u_1(x), \ldots, u_n(x)\}$ is **linearly dependent** (LD for short) on a given x interval if at least one of the functions can be expressed as a linear combination of the others over that interval. If none of the functions can be so expressed, the set is **linearly independent** (LI for short)*. Following the same lines as in Chapter 2, we can show that it follows from this definition that *a finite set of functions $\{u_1(x), \ldots, u_n(x)\}$ is LD on a given x interval if and only if there exist constants α_j, not all zero, such that*

$$\alpha_1 u_1(x) + \cdots + \alpha_n u_n(x) = 0 \tag{2}$$

on the interval; otherwise, the set is LI.

***Theorem 2** Necessary Condition for Linear Dependence*

For a finite set of functions $\{u_1(x), \ldots, u_n(x)\}$, at least $n - 1$ times differentiable, to be LD over a given x interval I, it is necessary (although not sufficient) that $W(x) = 0$ over I, where $W(x)$ is the **Wronskian determinant**

$$W(x) \equiv \begin{vmatrix} u_1(x) & \cdots & u_n(x) \\ u_1'(x) & & u_n'(x) \\ \vdots & & \vdots \\ u_1^{(n-1)}(x) & \cdots & u_n^{(n-1)}(x) \end{vmatrix}. \tag{3}$$

Proof If the set is to be LD, then (2) holds, over the given interval, with α_j's not all zero. Differentiating that equation repeatedly, we have

$$\begin{aligned} \alpha_1 u_1(x) + \cdots + \quad & \alpha_n u_n(x) = 0 \\ \alpha_1 u_1'(x) + \cdots + \quad & \alpha_n u_n'(x) = 0 \\ & \vdots \\ \alpha_1 u_1^{(n-1)}(x) + \cdots + & \alpha_n u_n^{(n-1)}(x) = 0. \end{aligned} \tag{4}$$

Regarding x as fixed, we must have the determinant $W(x)$ be zero for (4) to admit a nontrivial solution for the α_j's (Theorem 6, page 100). Since this condition must hold for *each* x in the interval I, it follows that we need $W(x) = 0$ on I. ■

We reiterate that $W(x) = 0$ over I is necessary, not sufficient. To establish that the condition is not, in fact, sufficient, consider the case where $n = 2$ and

$$u_1(x) = \begin{cases} x^2, & -1 \le x \le 0 \\ 0, & 0 \le x \le 1 \end{cases}, \qquad u_2(x) = \begin{cases} 0, & -1 \le x \le 0 \\ x^2, & 0 \le x \le 1 \end{cases} \tag{5}$$

over $-1 \le x \le 1$. Then

$$W(x) = \begin{cases} \begin{vmatrix} x^2 & 0 \\ 2x & 0 \end{vmatrix} = 0 & \text{for } -1 \le x \le 0 \\ \begin{vmatrix} 0 & x^2 \\ 0 & 2x \end{vmatrix} = 0 & \text{for } 0 \le x \le 1, \end{cases}$$

so that $W(x) = 0$ over I. Yet $\{u_1, u_2\}$ is *not* LD since $\alpha_1 u_1(x) + \alpha_2 u_2(x) = 0$ becomes

$$\begin{aligned} \alpha_1 x^2 + 0 = 0 \qquad & \text{for } -1 \le x \le 0 \\ 0 + \alpha_2 x^2 = 0 \qquad & \text{for } 0 \le x \le 1, \end{aligned}$$

which implies that $\alpha_1 = \alpha_2 = 0$, so that $\{u_1, u_2\}$ is LI over I. However:

> ***Theorem 3*** *Linear Dependence of* $\{u_1,\ldots,u_n\}$
> If $\{u_1, \ldots, u_n\}$ happen to be solutions of an nth-order differential equation (3), where $p_1(x), \ldots, p_n(x)$, and $f(x)$ are continuous over the interval I under consideration, then $W(x) = 0$ over I is both necessary and sufficient for the linear dependence of $\{u_1, \ldots, u_n\}$.

By the way, it is sometimes difficult to remember whether $W = 0$ corresponds to linear dependence or linear independence. Look at it this way: Given an arbitrarily selected handful of functions $u_1, \ldots, u_n$ the odds are that the functions are essentially "unrelated," i.e., that they are LI. Similarly, the odds are that their Wronskian determinant $W(x)$ will not happen to work out to be identically zero. Thus W *not* vanishing identically corresponds to linear independence. It takes the exceptional circumstance that $W(x) = 0$ to result in the exceptional circumstance that the set is LD.

We are now in a position to establish the *number* of LI solutions that exist for the homogeneous equation $Ly = 0$. Proof of the theorem is included because it may help tie together some of the foregoing concepts.

Theorem 4 *Number of LI Solutions of Ly = 0*
The homogeneous equation

$$Ly = y^{(n)} + p_1(x)y^{(n-1)} + \cdots + p_n(x)y = 0 \tag{6}$$

over an interval I, where $p_1(x), \ldots, p_n(x)$ are continuous on I, admits exactly n LI solutions.

Proof Suppose that $u_1(x), \ldots, u_{n+1}(x)$ are solutions of (6). Let ξ be any point in I. The n equations

$$\begin{aligned} c_1u_1(\xi) + \cdots + \; c_{n+1}u_{n+1}(\xi) &= 0 \\ c_1u_1^{(n-1)}(\xi) + \cdots + c_{n+1}u_{n+1}^{(n-1)}(\xi) &= 0 \end{aligned} \tag{7}$$

in the $n + 1$ unknowns $c_1, \ldots, c_{n+1}$ necessarily have nontrivial solutions [see item (iv) of Theorem 5, page 100]. Choosing such a set of c_j's, use them to define

$$v(x) \equiv c_1u_1(x) + \cdots + c_{n+1}u_{n+1}(x) \tag{8}$$

and observe first that

$$\begin{aligned} Lv &= L(c_1u_1 + \cdots + c_{n+1}u_{n+1}) \\ &= c_1Lu_1 + \cdots + c_{n+1}Lu_{n+1} = 0 + \cdots + 0 = 0 \end{aligned}$$

and second that $v(\xi) = \cdots = v^{(n-1)}(\xi) = 0$ by virtue of (7). Now, one function $v(x)$ that satisfies $Ly = 0$ and the initial conditions $v(\xi) = \cdots = v^{(n-1)}(\xi) = 0$ is simply $v(x) = 0$. By the uniqueness part of Theorem 1, $v(x) = 0$ is the *only* possible $v(x)$, so that (8) becomes

$$c_1u_1(x) + \cdots + c_{n+1}u_{n+1}(x) = 0. \tag{9}$$

Recalling that the c_j's in (9) are not all zero, it follows that $\{u_1, \ldots, u_{n+1}\}$ must be LD. Thus $Ly = 0$ cannot have $n + 1$ LI solutions, and hence it *cannot have more than n* LI solutions.

To show that there are *no less than n* LI solutions of $Ly = 0$, let us simply put forward n such solutions. According to the existence part of Theorem 1, there must be solutions $Y_1(x), \ldots, Y_n(x)$ of $Ly = 0$ satisfying the initial conditions

$$\begin{aligned} &Y_1(x_0) = 1, \quad Y_1'(x_0) = 0, \ldots, Y_1^{(n-1)}(x_0) = 0 \\ &Y_2(x_0) = 0, \quad Y_2'(x_0) = 1, Y_2''(x_0) = 0, \ldots, Y_2^{(n-1)}(x_0) = 0 \\ &\quad\vdots \\ &Y_n(x_0) = 0, \ldots, Y_n^{(n-2)}(x_0) = 0, Y_n^{(n-1)}(x_0) = 1, \end{aligned}$$

where x_0 is any point in I. We call $\{Y_1(x), \ldots, Y_n(x)\}$ a **fundamental set** of solutions. That the set is LI follows from the fact that

$$W(x_0) = \begin{vmatrix} 1 & & \bigcirc \\ & 1 & \\ & \ddots & \\ \bigcirc & & 1 \end{vmatrix} = 1 \neq 0,$$

together with Theorem 3. This step completes our proof. ■

The foregoing discussion brings us to the idea of the "general solution" of the nth-order equation $Ly = f$. If $u_1, \ldots, u_n$ are LI solutions of the associated homogeneous equation $Ly = 0$, and y_p is any particular solution of the full equation $Ly = f$, then by linearity,

$$\boxed{y = c_1u_1(x) + \cdots + c_nu_n(x) + y_p(x)}$$

is also a solution of $Ly = f$, a **general solution**, in fact, *inasmuch as the c_j's can be chosen so that $y(x)$ given by (10) satisfies any prescribed set of initial conditions* $y(x_0), y'(x_0), \ldots, y^{(n-1)}(x_0)$. That is, the equations

$$\begin{aligned} c_1u_1(x_0) + \cdots + \quad c_nu_n(x_0) &= y(x_0) - y_p(x_0) \\ c_1u_1'(x_0) + \cdots + \quad c_nu_n'(x_0) &= y'(x_0) - y_p'(x_0) \\ &\vdots \\ c_1u_1^{(n-1)}(x_0) + \cdots + c_nu_n^{(n-1)}(x_0) &= y^{(n+1)}(x_0) - y_p^{(n-1)}(x_0) \end{aligned} \tag{11}$$

can be solved (uniquely) for $c_1, \ldots, c_n$ since the determinant of the coefficient matrix is the Wronskian of $u_1, \ldots, u_n$ at x_0, which cannot vanish because the u_j's are LI.

The c_j's in (10) are referred to as the *constants of integration*.

A.4 ABEL'S FORMULA FOR THE WRONSKIAN

Let $y_1, \ldots, y_n$ be any n solutions (LI or not) of the homogeneous equation

$$y^{(n)} + p_1(x)y^{(n-1)} + \cdots + p_{n-1}(x)y' + p_n(x)y = 0. \tag{1}$$

A useful formula involving the Wronskian W of $y, \ldots, y_n$ is obtained as follows. For simplicity, let $n = 3$. Then

$$\begin{aligned} \frac{dW}{dx} &= \frac{d}{dx}\begin{vmatrix} y_1 & y_2 & y_3 \\ y_1' & y_2' & y_3' \\ y_1'' & y_2'' & y_3'' \end{vmatrix} \\ &= \begin{vmatrix} y_1' & y_2' & y_3' \\ y_1' & y_2' & y_3' \\ y_1'' & y_2'' & y_3'' \end{vmatrix} + \begin{vmatrix} y_1 & y_2 & y_3 \\ y_1'' & y_2'' & y_3'' \\ y_1'' & y_2'' & y_3'' \end{vmatrix} + \begin{vmatrix} y_1 & y_2 & y_3 \\ y_1' & y_2' & y_3' \\ y_1''' & y_2''' & y_3''' \end{vmatrix}, \end{aligned} \tag{2}$$

from (c) in Exercise 20 on page 92. The first two determinants on the right-hand side of (2) vanish by virtue of having two identical rows. In the third determinant substitute, from (1), $y_1''' = -p_3y_1 - p_2y_1' - p_1y_1''$, $y_2''' = -p_3y_2 - p_2y_2' - p_1y_2''$, and $y_3''' = -p_3y_3 - p_2y_3' - p_1y_3''$, so that

$$\frac{dW}{dx} = \begin{vmatrix} y_1 & y_2 & y_3 \\ y_1' & y_2' & y_3' \\ -p_3y_1 - p_2y_1' - p_1y_1'' & -p_3y_2 - p_2y_2' - p_1y_2'' & -p_3y_3 - p_2y_3' - p_1y_3'' \end{vmatrix}$$

$$= -p_3\begin{vmatrix} y_1 & y_2 & y_3 \\ y_1' & y_2' & y_3' \\ y_1 & y_2 & y_3 \end{vmatrix} - p_2\begin{vmatrix} y_1 & y_2 & y_3 \\ y_1' & y_2' & y_3' \\ y_1' & y_2' & y_3' \end{vmatrix} - p_1\begin{vmatrix} y_1 & y_2 & y_3 \\ y_1' & y_2' & y_3' \\ y_1'' & y_2'' & y_3'' \end{vmatrix} \tag{3}$$

$$= 0 + 0 - p_1 W$$

or

$$\frac{dW}{dx} + p_1(x)W = 0. \tag{4}$$

Although we have chosen $n = 3$, this same result is obtained for *any* finite $n \geq 1$. Rewriting (4) in the form $dW/W + p_1(x)\,dx = 0$ and integrating from any point a to x, we obtain

$$\boxed{W(x) = W(a)e^{-\int_a^x p_1(t)\,dt},} \tag{5}$$

which is known as **Abel's formula*** and which is used in Part III in our discussion of the Sturm–Liouville theory. Since the exponential function in (5) is never zero, it follows from (5) that $W(x)$ is either identically zero for all x (if $W(a) = 0$), or nonzero for all x (if $W(a) \neq 0$).

SOLUTION OF HOMOGENEOUS EQUATION $Ly = 0$; CONSTANT COEFFICIENTS — A.5

In this section we meet the *complex exponential function* e^z, where $z = a + ib$ is complex. It is essential to realize that we cannot "figure out" how to compute this quantity; e^z is a new object for us, and it is up to us to render e^z meaningful by defining it. To motivate the definition, recall that if the exponent is *real*, say x, then we have the well-known Taylor series

$$e^x = \sum_{n=0}^{\infty} \frac{x^n}{n!} \qquad (-\infty < x < \infty). \tag{1}$$

It seems reasonable to use this formula to lend meaning to the complex exponential e^z. Thus let us agree that (1) holds, by definition, even when the exponent x is changed to the purely complex quantity ix:

$$\begin{aligned} e^{ix} &= 1 + \frac{ix}{1!} + \frac{i^2x^2}{2!} + \frac{i^3x^3}{3!} + \frac{i^4x^4}{4!} + \frac{i^5x^5}{5!} + \cdots \\ &= \left(1 - \frac{x^2}{2!} + \frac{x^4}{4!} - \cdots\right) + i\left(x - \frac{x^3}{3!} + \frac{x^5}{5!} - \cdots\right) \qquad (2) \\ &= \cos x + i \sin x. \end{aligned}$$

Thus, let us define

* *Neils Henrik Abel* was born in Norway in 1802 and died of tuberculosis at the age of 27. His most important work was on the subject of elliptic functions.

$$e^{ix} = \cos x + i \sin x \tag{3a}$$

for all finite x. Replacing x by $-x$ and recalling the properties $\cos(-x) = \cos x$ and $\sin(-x) = -\sin x$ of the cosine and sine functions, there follows the companion result

$$e^{-ix} = \cos x - i \sin x; \tag{3b}$$

Equations (3a) and (3b) are known as **Euler's formulas**. [Naturally, there is nothing special about choosing the letter x; (3a) and (3b) hold if x is replaced by 0, or t, or whatever.]

Adding and subtracting (3a) and (3b) yields the reverse relations

$$\cos x = \frac{e^{ix} + e^{-ix}}{2}, \tag{4a}$$

$$\sin x = \frac{e^{ix} - e^{-ix}}{2i}. \tag{4b}$$

More generally, what if z in e^z is neither purely real nor purely imaginary but is of the form $z = x + iy$? It seems reasonable to expect that

$$e^z = e^{x+iy} = e^x e^{iy} = e^x(\cos y + i \sin y). \tag{5}$$

However, observe that there is no logical support for the second equality in (5). It is true, we admit, that

$$e^{a+b} = e^a e^b \tag{6}$$

when a and b are both real, but iy in (5) is not real! Nevertheless, it is after all up to us to define the quantity e^{x+iy} and, mimicking the familiar real-variable formula (6), we choose to set

$$e^{x+iy} = e^x e^{iy} \tag{7}$$

by definition, from which the truth of (5) then follows.

It is also useful to note some simple connections between the trigonometric functions $\cos x$, $\sin x$ and the hyperbolic functions $\cosh x$, $\sinh x$. Recalling the definitions (see Fig. A.1)

$$\cosh x = \frac{e^x + e^{-x}}{2} \tag{8a}$$

$$\sinh x = \frac{e^x - e^{-x}}{2}, \tag{8b}$$

or equivalently,

$$e^x = \cosh x + \sinh x \tag{9a}$$

$$e^{-x} = \cosh x - \sinh x, \tag{9b}$$

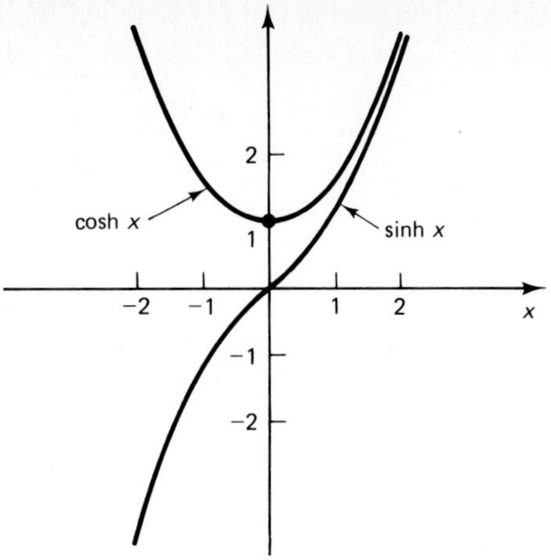

Fig. A.1 Cosh x and sinh x.

it is easy to show that

$$\boxed{\begin{aligned} \cos ix &= \cosh x, \\ \sin ix &= i \sinh x, \\ \cosh ix &= \cos x, \\ \sinh ix &= i \sin x. \end{aligned}} \qquad \begin{aligned} &(10a) \\ &(10b) \\ &(10c) \\ &(10d) \end{aligned}$$

For example,

$$\cos ix = \frac{e^{i(ix)} + e^{-i(ix)}}{2} = \frac{e^{-x} + e^{x}}{2} = \cosh x$$

gives (9a).

We are now ready to consider the solution of the homogeneous equation with constant coefficients, i.e.,

$$y^{(n)} + p_1 y^{(n-1)} + \cdots + p_{n-1} y' + p_n y = 0, \tag{11}$$

where the p_j's are constants. It is promising to seek solutions of (11) in the form

$$y = e^{\lambda x}, \tag{12}$$

where λ is a constant to be determined, because then each term in (11) will be of the same form, namely, some constant times $e^{\lambda x}$, and it is possible that by choosing λ suitably we can get these terms to cancel to zero. Specifically, $y' = e^{\lambda x}$, $y'' = \lambda^2 e^{\lambda x}$, and so on, so that (11) becomes

$$(\lambda^n + p_1 \lambda^{n-1} + \cdots + p_{n-1}\lambda + p_n) e^{\lambda x} = 0. \tag{13}$$

Now we need (13) to hold over the entire x interval under consideration. The $e^{\lambda x}$ factor is not zero for *any* (finite) x,* let alone over an entire interval, so our only hope is to choose λ such that

$$\lambda^n + p_1 \lambda^{n-1} + \cdots + p_{n-1}\lambda + p_n = 0. \tag{14}$$

* Do you agree? Sketch the graph of $e^{\lambda x}$, over $-\infty < x < \infty$, for the cases $\lambda < 0$, $\lambda = 0$, $\lambda > 0$.

The left-hand side of (14) is called the **characteristic polynomial** corresponding to the ODE (11), and (14) is called the **characteristic equation**. Factoring (14),

$$(\lambda - \lambda_1)(\lambda - \lambda_2) \cdots (\lambda - \lambda_n) = 0,$$

so $\lambda = \lambda_1, \lambda_2, \ldots, \lambda_n$. According to (12), we therefore have the n solutions $y = e^{\lambda_1 x}, \ldots, e^{\lambda_n x}$ of (11), or, by superposition,

$$y = c_1 e^{\lambda_1 x} + c_2 e^{\lambda_2 x} + \cdots + c_n e^{\lambda_n x}. \tag{15}$$

This result is the *general* solution of (11) if and only if $e^{\lambda_1 x}, \ldots, e^{\lambda_n x}$ are LI. Surely they are *not* LI if any of the λ_j roots are repeated, so for the moment let us suppose that the n roots are distinct. To see if $e^{\lambda_1 x}, \ldots, e^{\lambda_n x}$ are then LI, suppose, for simplicity, that $n = 3$ and consider the equation

$$\alpha_1 e^{\lambda_1 x} + \alpha_2 e^{\lambda_2 x} + \alpha_3 e^{\lambda_3 x} = 0. \tag{16}$$

If the truth of (16) requires that $\alpha_1 = \alpha_2 = \alpha_3 = 0$, then $e^{\lambda_1 x}, e^{\lambda_2 x}, e^{\lambda_3 x}$ are LI. Multiplying (16) by $e^{-\lambda_1 x}$ and then taking d/dx of the result gives

$$0 + \alpha_2(\lambda_2 - \lambda_1)e^{(\lambda_2 - \lambda_1)x} + \alpha_3(\lambda_3 - \lambda_1)e^{(\lambda_3 - \lambda_1)x} = 0. \tag{17}$$

Next, multiply (17) by $e^{-(\lambda_2 - \lambda_1)x}$ and take d/dx of the result. This step gives

$$0 + 0 + \alpha_3(\lambda_3 - \lambda_1)(\lambda_3 - \lambda_2)e^{(\lambda_3 - \lambda_2)x} = 0. \tag{18}$$

Now, $e^{(\lambda_3 - \lambda_2)x}$ is surely not zero for any (finite) x. Also, $\lambda_3 \neq \lambda_1$ and $\lambda_3 \neq \lambda_2$, by assumption, so that (18) implies that $\alpha_3 = 0$. With $\alpha_3 = 0$, (17) then implies that $\alpha_2 = 0$. And with $\alpha_3 = \alpha_2 = 0$, (16) then implies that $\alpha_1 = 0$ too, so that $e^{\lambda_1 x}$, $e^{\lambda_2 x}$, $e^{\lambda_3 x}$ are LI (over any given x interval) if the λ_j's are distinct. Although we considered $n = 3$, extension to the general case should be obvious.

Alternatively, the linear dependence of the set $\{e^{\lambda_1 x}, \ldots, e^{\lambda_n x}\}$, where the λ_j's are distinct, can be established using Theorem 3 in Section A.3, together with the results given in Exercise 21 on page 93. We leave this line of approach as an exercise.

The upshot is that if the λ_j roots are distinct, then (15) is the general solution of (11).

EXAMPLE 1 Consider the initial-value problem

$$y'' + y' - 6y = 0, \qquad (0 \leq x < \infty) \tag{19a}$$

$$y(0) = 1, \quad y'(0) = -8. \tag{19b}$$

Seeking $y = e^{\lambda x}$ gives the characteristic equation $\lambda^2 + \lambda - 6 = 0$, with the distinct roots $\lambda = 2, -3$, so the general solution of (19a) is

$$y = c_1 e^{2x} + c_2 e^{-3x}. \tag{20}$$

The foregoing theory guarantees that (20) is capable of meeting the initial conditions (19b). Thus when we set

$$\begin{aligned} y(0) &= 1 = c_1 + c_2 \\ y'(0) &= -8 = 2c_1 - 3c_2, \end{aligned} \tag{21}$$

the determinant of the coefficient matrix $\begin{pmatrix} 1 & 1 \\ 2 & -3 \end{pmatrix}$ in (21) must be nonzero, as is seen to be true. Then (21) can be solved uniquely for c_1, c_2 to give $c_1 = -1$, $c_2 = 2$, so that the unique solution to (19) is $y = -e^{2x} + 2e^{-3x}$.

COMMENT More accurately, we should have called (20) *a* general solution of (19a), not *the* general solution. For example, another general solution is $y = c_1 e^{2x} + c_2(4e^{2x} + 25e^{-3x})$, since e^{2x} and $4e^{2x} + 25e^{-3x}$ satisfy (19a) and are LI. ◀

EXAMPLE 2 Consider the ODE

$$y'' - 9y = 0 \qquad (-\infty < x < \infty). \tag{22}$$

This time, $y = e^{\lambda x}$ gives $\lambda^2 - 9 = 0$, so $\lambda = +3, -3$, and we have the general solution

$$y = c_1 e^{3x} + c_2 e^{-3x}. \tag{23}$$

Alternatively, we can express the general solution in the form

$$y = c_3 \cosh 3x + c_4 \sinh 3x \tag{24}$$

since (23) gives

$$\begin{aligned} y &= c_1(\cosh 3x + \sinh 3x) + c_2(\cosh 3x - \sinh 3x) \\ &= (c_1 + c_2)\cosh 3x + (c_1 - c_2)\sinh 3x \\ &= c_3 \cosh 3x + c_4 \sinh 3x. \end{aligned} \tag{25}$$

It is easily verified that cosh 3*x*, sinh 3*x* are indeed LI. Observe that whereas (23) and (24) are equivalent, one form may be a bit more *convenient* than the other. For example, if we have initial conditions

$$y(0) = 0, \quad y'(0) = 5 \tag{26}$$

attached to (22), the form (24) is more convenient since $y(0) = 0 = c_3 + 0$ gives $c_3 = 0$, and $y'(0) = 5 = 3c_4 \cosh 0 = 3c_4$ gives $c_4 = \frac{5}{3}$, so that $y(x) = \frac{5}{3}\sinh 3x$. That is, the condition $y(0) = 0$ immediately "selects" the sinh. If, instead, we use the form (23), then, a bit more circuitously, we have

$$\begin{aligned} y(0) &= 0 = c_1 + c_2 \\ y'(0) &= 5 = 3c_1 - 3c_2, \end{aligned} \tag{27}$$

so $c_1 = \frac{5}{6}$, $c_2 = -\frac{5}{6}$, and

$$y = \frac{5}{6}e^{3x} - \frac{5}{6}e^{-3x} = \frac{5}{3}\left(\frac{e^{3x} - e^{-3x}}{2}\right) = \frac{5}{3}\sinh 3x,$$

as before. ◀

EXAMPLE 3 *Repeated Roots*. Consider

$$y'' - 6y' + 9y = 0. \tag{28}$$

Seeking $y = e^{\lambda x}$ gives the characteristic equation

$$\lambda^2 - 6\lambda + 9 = 0 \tag{29}$$

or

$$(\lambda - 3)(\lambda - 3) = 0. \tag{30}$$

Unfortunately, the root $\lambda = 3$ is repeated (we say it is of *multiplicity* 2), so that we obtain only the one solution e^{3x}. Thus far we have

$$y = ce^{3x},$$

but this expression falls short of being the desired general solution of (28) because the general solution of the second-order equation (28) should be of the form $c_1u_1(x) + c_2u_2(x)$, where c_1, c_2 are arbitrary constants and u_1, u_2 are LI solutions of (28). To find the missing solution we use the method of **reduction of order**, attributed to d'Alembert.* That is, we take the solution ce^{3x} corresponding to the repeated root and "let c vary"; specifically, we seek y in the form

$$y = c(x)e^{3x}. \tag{31}$$

(Because we vary the parameter c, the method is also referred to, by some authors, as **variation of parameters**.) It is interesting that this form proves fruitful, for it is entirely noncommittal. That is, *all* functions $f(x)$ are of the form (31) since *any* given function $f(x)$ can be expressed as $c(x)e^{3x}$ by choosing $c(x)$ to be $f(x)e^{-3x}$. Proceeding nevertheless, differentiation of (31) gives $y' = c'e^{3x} + 3ce^{3x}$, and $y'' = c''e^{3x} + 6c'e^{3x} + 9ce^{3x}$, so that (28) becomes

$$(c'' + 6c' + 9c - 6c' - 18c + 9c)e^{3x} = 0. \tag{32}$$

Notice in advance that the ce^{3x} terms *must* cancel (as they do), since if $c(x)$ were a *constant* (in which case the c', c'' terms would be zero), then putting ce^{3x} into the left-hand side of (28), the resulting terms had *better* cancel to zero because e^{3x} is known to be a solution of (28)! Thus canceling the c terms and the e^{3x} factor in (32) leaves us with a second-order equation in c, in which no undifferentiated c terms appear. Setting $c' = q$, say, will therefore accomplish a reduction of order to a first-order equation in q. In fact, the c' terms cancel as well, so that $c'' = 0$. Integrating, $c(x) = c_1 + c_2x$, and (31) becomes

$$y = c_1e^{3x} + c_2xe^{3x} = (c_1 + c_2x)e^{3x}, \tag{33}$$

which is a general solution of (28).

Observe that the "missing solution," xe^{3x}, did not show up when we looked for solutions of the form $e^{\lambda x}$ because it is not of that form. ◀

More generally, suppose that $Ly = 0$ is any linear ODE with constant coefficients, and that λ_k is a root, of multiplicity ℓ, of the characteristic equation. The d'Alembert method will lead us to the "missing solutions" $xe^{\lambda_k x}, x^2e^{\lambda_k x}, \ldots, x^{\ell-1}e^{\lambda_k x}$. For example, if the roots of the characteristic equation of some seventh-order differential equation are $\lambda = 0, 0, -1, 4, 5, 5, 5$, the general solution can be written, without further ado, as

* *Jean d'Alembert* (1717–1783) is well known for his work on Fourier Series, partial differential equations, mechanics, and hydrodynamics.

$$
\begin{aligned}
y &= (c_1 + c_2 x)e^{0x} + c_3 e^{-x} + c_4 e^{4x} + (c_5 + c_6 x + c_7 x^2)e^{5x} \\
&= c_1 + c_2 x + c_3 e^{-x} + c_4 e^{4x} + (c_5 + c_6 x + c_7 x^2)e^{5x}.
\end{aligned} \tag{34}
$$

More about d'Alembert's method in Section A.6, when we look at differential equations with variable coefficients.

EXAMPLE 4 *Damped Oscillator; Free Vibration.* Here we consider a mechanical oscillator (Fig. A.2a) consisting of a mass m which slides on a lubricated horizontal surface subject to a restraining spring of stiffness k, and an applied "driving force" $f(t)$, where t is the time. We measure the displacement x as positive to the right, with $x = 0$ corresponding to the position at which the spring is neither stretched nor compressed. We consider three horizontal forces to act on m (Fig. A.2b). First, the force exerted on the mass by the spring, F_{spring}, is kx in magnitude and opposes the displacement, so that

$$F_{\text{spring}} = -kx. \tag{35a}$$

Thus, if $x > 0$, the spring force is negative (i.e., it is directed to the left, the negative x direction), and if $x < 0$, it is positive (i.e., it is directed to the right). Second, the force exerted on the mass by virtue of its contact with the oil film, F_{film}, is proportional to the velocity $\dot{x}$ and opposes the velocity, so that

$$F_{\text{film}} = -c\dot{x}, \tag{35b}$$

which is leftward if the velocity is rightward, and conversely; c will depend on the viscosity of the oil, the thickness of the film, and the contact area of the mass with the oil film. Finally, we allow for the presence of an applied force,

$$F_{\text{applied}} = f(t), \tag{35c}$$

which is some prescribed function of t.

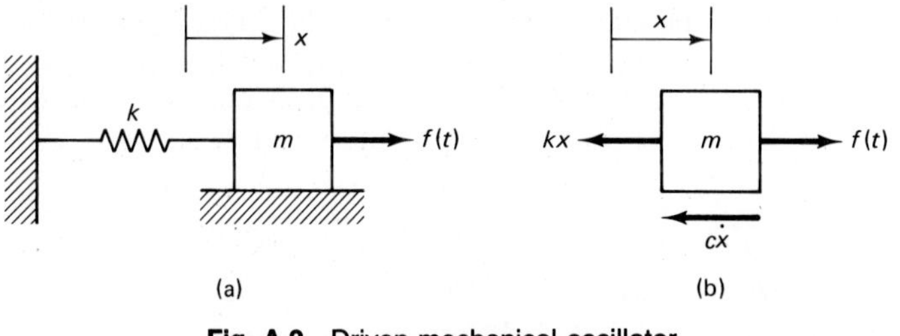

Fig. A.2 Driven mechanical oscillator.

These three forces are shown in Fig. A.2b at an instant when $x > 0$ and $\dot{x} > 0$ (so that the spring and oil film forces are both toward the left).

We assume m, k, c to be known constants, with $m > 0$, $k > 0$, and $c > 0$. Then Newton's second law gives

$$
\begin{aligned}
m\ddot{x} &= F_{\text{spring}} + F_{\text{film}} + F_{\text{applied}} \\
&= -kx - c\dot{x} + f(t),
\end{aligned} \tag{36}
$$

so we have the linear nonhomogeneous second-order ordinary differential equation

$$m\ddot{x} + c\dot{x} + kx = f(t) \tag{37}$$

governing the motion $x(t)$. Normally, we consider the t interval $0 \le t < \infty$, and we may wish to append initial conditions

$$x(0) = x_0, \quad \dot{x}(0) = \dot{x}_0, \tag{38}$$

where x_0 and $\dot{x}_0$ are prescribed constants.

In this section we have limited our attention to homogeneous equations, so in the remainder of this example we set $f(t) = 0$ and consider the so-called "free" or "undriven" vibration governed by

$$m\ddot{x} + c\dot{x} + kx = 0. \tag{39}$$

To solve (39) we seek $x = e^{\lambda t}$ and obtain the characteristic equation

$$m\lambda^2 + c\lambda + k = 0. \tag{40}$$

We distinguish four cases:

Case 1: $c = 0$ Then (40) gives $\lambda = \pm i\sqrt{k/m}$. As is customary, we set $\omega \equiv \sqrt{k/m}$, where ω will turn out to be the frequency of vibration (in radians per unit time), the so-called *natural frequency* since it is the frequency of the undriven motion (i.e., for $f = 0$). Thus we have the general solution

$$x = c_1 e^{i\omega t} + c_2 e^{-i\omega t}. \tag{41}$$

However, anticipating that x will be real valued, it seems reasonable to suppress the complex exponentials and to express the general solution, equivalently, as

$$x = c_3 \cos \omega t + c_4 \sin \omega t. \tag{42}$$

In fact, it is interesting and useful to go one step further and to reexpress x in the form

$$x = A \sin(\omega t + \phi), \tag{43}$$

where A is easily identified as the *amplitude* of the motion and ϕ is a *phase angle* (Fig. A.3). To establish the equivalence of (43) and (42), we use the trigonometric identity $\sin(a + b) = \sin a \cos b + \sin b \cos a$ to expand $\sin(\omega t + \phi)$ in (43).

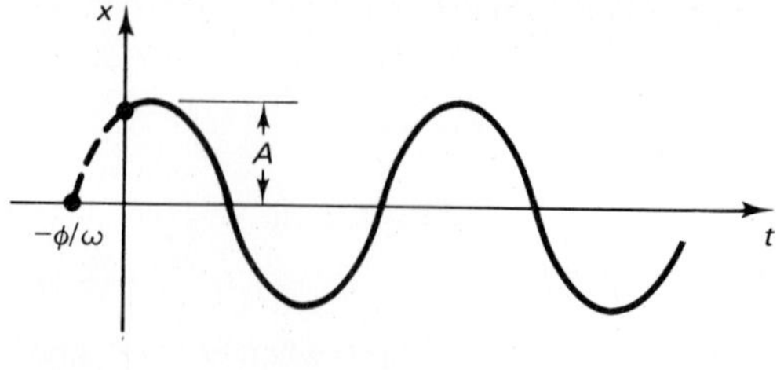

Fig. A.3 Case 1: c = 0.

Thus

$$A \sin \omega t \cos \phi + A \sin \phi \cos \omega t = c_3 \cos \omega t + c_4 \sin \omega t. \tag{44}$$

Since $\sin \omega t$, $\cos \omega t$ are LI (why?), it follows from (44) that

$$A \cos \phi = c_3, \tag{45a}$$

$$A \sin \phi = c_4. \tag{45b}$$

Squaring and adding these two equations reveals that

$$A = \sqrt{c_3^2 + c_4^2}. \tag{46}$$

Next it is tempting to divide the two equations and conclude that

$$\phi = \tan^{-1}\frac{c_3}{c_4} \tag{47}$$

(and indeed one often sees this done). However, whereas the formulas

$$\cos\phi = \frac{c_3}{\sqrt{c_3^2 + c_4^2}}, \tag{48a}$$

$$\sin\phi = \frac{c_4}{\sqrt{c_3^2 + c_4^2}} \tag{48b}$$

determine a unique angle ϕ such that $-\pi < \phi \leq \pi$, the formula (47) determines two ϕ's in that interval, one correct and one spurious. [For example, if $c_3 = c_4 = -1$, then (48a) gives $\phi = -3\pi/4$ and $+3\pi/4$, and (48b) gives $\phi = -3\pi/4$ and $-\pi/4$. Together, they imply the unique value $\phi = -3\pi/4$. However, (47) gives the *two* possible values $\phi = -3\pi/4$ and $+\pi/4$, of which the latter is spurious.] Thus if we do use (47), some additional logic is needed in order to identify the correct ϕ.

In summary, the equivalence of (42) and (43) is thus established. That equivalence is, in the author's opinion, striking—for if we imagine adding the graphs of $c_3 \cos \omega t$ and $c_4 \sin \omega t$, it is not at all obvious that what inevitably results is a single sine wave. In closing, notice of course that c_3, c_4 in (42) and A, ϕ in (43) are the "integration constants" and will be uniquely determined if we impose the initial conditions (38).

Case 2: $0 < c < \sqrt{4mk}$ Solving (39), we have

$$\lambda = \frac{-c \pm \sqrt{c^2 - 4mk}}{2m}. \tag{49}$$

The square root is imaginary, zero, or real, according to whether $c^2 - 4mk$ happens to be negative, zero, or positive, respectively. In case 2 we have assumed that $c < \sqrt{4mk}$, so that the square root is imaginary. It is therefore reasonable to rewrite (49) as

$$\lambda = \frac{-c \pm i\sqrt{4mk - c^2}}{2m} \equiv -\frac{c}{2m} \pm i\Omega, \tag{50}$$

where $\Omega \equiv \sqrt{4km - c^2}/2m$. Thus

$$\begin{aligned} x &= c_1 e^{(-c/2m + i\Omega)t} + c_2 e^{(-c/2m - i\Omega)t} \\ &= e^{-(c/2m)t}(c_1 e^{i\Omega t} + c_2 e^{-i\Omega t}) \end{aligned}$$

or, equivalently,

$$x = Ae^{-(c/2m)t} \sin(\Omega t + \phi), \tag{51}$$

where A, ϕ are constants and $A \geq 0$. It is clear from (51) that the graph of $x(t)$ is essentially as shown in Fig. A.4. Clearly, $x(t) \to 0$ as $t \to \infty$ no matter how large are the initial conditions x_0 and $\dot{x}_0$. Thus we say that $x(t)$ "damps out," and we call

c the *damping coefficient*. In contrast, the motion displayed in Fig. A.3 is "undamped."

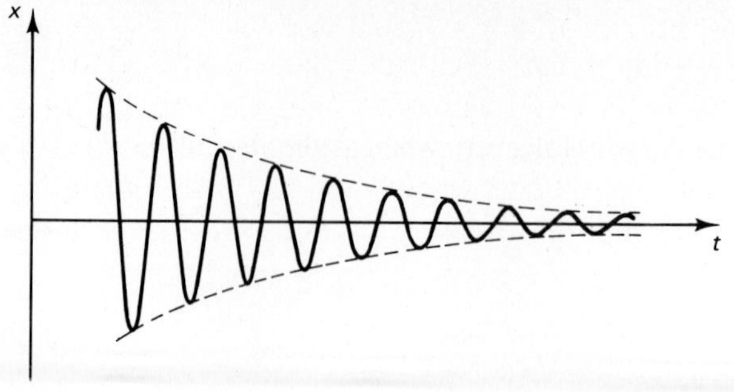

Fig. A.4 Case 2: $0 < c \leq \sqrt{4mk}$.

Case 3: $c = \sqrt{4mk}$ In this case we have $\lambda = -c/2m$, which root is of multiplicity 2. Thus

$$x = (c_1 + c_2 t)e^{-(c/2m)t}, \tag{52}$$

the graph of which is some linear combination of the two graphs shown in Fig. A.5.

Case 4: $c > \sqrt{4mk}$ This time the square root in (49) is real, and we can see that the two λ roots are distinct (and negative). Thus

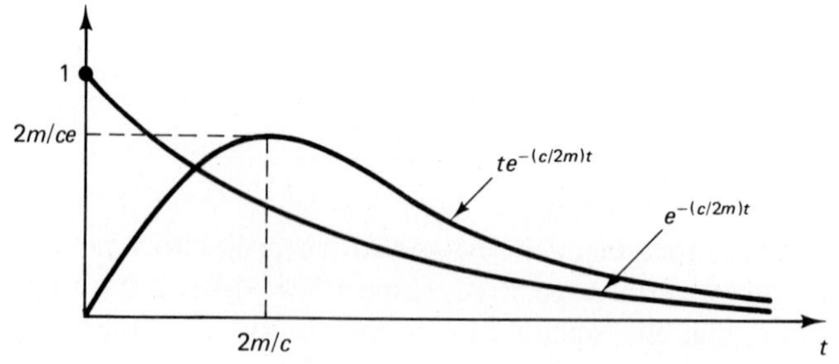

Fig. A.5 Case 3: $c = \sqrt{4mk}$.

$$x = e^{-(c/2m)t}\left(c_1 e^{(\sqrt{c^2-4mk}/2m)t} + c_2 e^{-(\sqrt{c^2-4mk}/2m)t}\right). \tag{53}$$

It is not difficult to show that the graph of (53) is one of the four types shown in Fig. A.6, depending on the values of the parameters m, c, k and the initial conditions x_0, $\dot{x}_0$.

Fig. A.6 Case 4: $c > \sqrt{4mk}$.

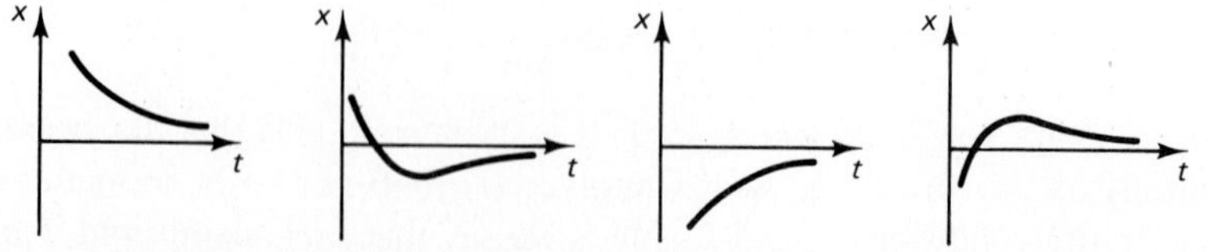

COMMENT 1 Reviewing these four cases, we see that for $c = 0$ the solution (43) is purely oscillatory and oscillates at the natural frequency $\Omega = \omega = \sqrt{k/m}$. As c increases, within the range $0 < c < \sqrt{4mk}$, two changes occur, as can be seen from (51). First, there appears an $e^{-(c/2m)t}$ factor that damps the oscillation, and second, the frequency $\Omega = \sqrt{4km - c^2}/2m$ decreases from ω and approaches zero as $c \to \sqrt{4km}$ (Fig. A.7). The decrease in Ω with increasing c makes sense physically since it seems natural to expect the system to become more "sluggish" as the damping is increased. For all $c > \sqrt{4km}$ the solution is nonoscillatory and exhibits monotone exponential decay as $t \to \infty$. The transitional value $c = \sqrt{4mk}$ is called the *critical damping* and is denoted as

$$c_{cr} = \sqrt{4mk}.$$

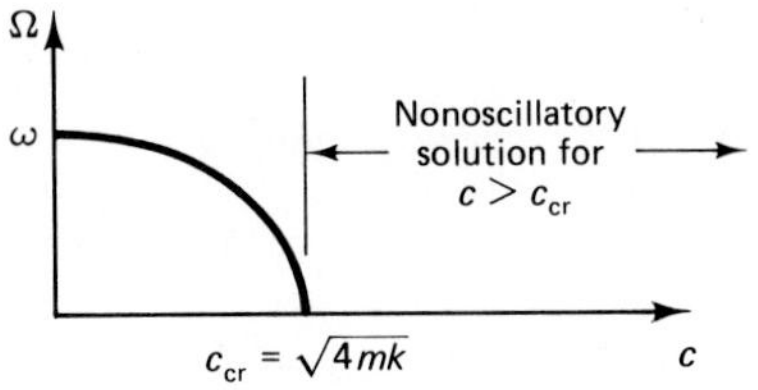

Fig. A.7 Effect of damping on frequency.

COMMENT 2 There exists an electrical analog of the mechanical system studied in this example. For consider the electrical circuit shown in Fig. A.8. We regard the impressed voltage $E(t)$ (volts) as input, and the current $I(t)$ (amperes) that results as the output. The *inductor* (coil) has an *inductance* L (henrys), the *capacitor* (condenser) has a capacitance C (farads), and the *resistor* has a resistance R (ohms), where L, C, R are assumed to be positive constants. If we denote the charge on the capacitor as $Q(t)$, then $Q(t)$ and $I(t)$ are related by

$$\frac{dQ}{dt} = I, \tag{54}$$

where Q is measured in coulombs. No current flows through the capacitor. Rather, the two horizontal lines of the capacitor may be regarded as "storage tanks" for charge, and E may be regarded as a "pump" that pumps charge from one tank to the other.

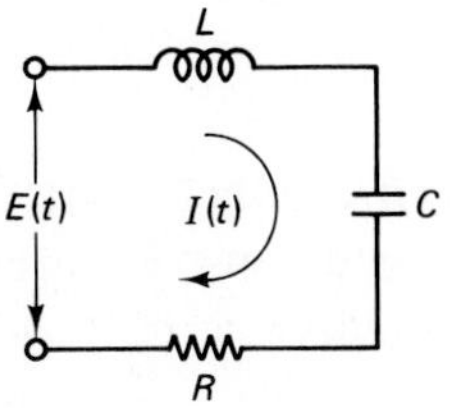

Fig. A.8 Electrical circuit analog.

The governing physical principle is *Kirchhoff's second law,* namely that *the impressed voltage must equal the sum of the voltage drops around the circuit,* where it is known from circuit theory that the voltage drops across the inductor, capacitor, and resistor are $L(dI/dt)$, $(1/C)Q$, IR, respectively. Thus

$$L\frac{dI}{dt} + RI + \frac{1}{C}Q = E(t) \tag{55}$$

or, from (54),

$$L\frac{d^2Q}{dt^2} + R\frac{dQ}{dt} + \frac{1}{C}Q = E(t). \tag{56}$$

This is precisely the same differential equation as (37a), under the following correspondence, or *analog*:

Mechanical	$x(t)$	$f(t)$	m	c	k
Electrical	$Q(t)$	$E(t)$	L	R	$1/C$

Or, if we take d/dt of (55),

$$L\frac{d^2I}{dt^2} + R\frac{dI}{dt} + \frac{1}{C}I = \dot{E}(t), \tag{57}$$

with the correspondence

Mechanical	$x(t)$	$f(t)$	m	c	k
Electrical	$I(t)$	$\dot{E}(t)$	L	R	$1/C$

The existence of such analogs is the rule rather than the exception. In the present example we mention the mechanical/electrical analog merely to show that the second-order linear differential equation with constant coefficients is of basic interest to both mechanical and electrical engineers. Beyond that purpose, however, analogs are of great interest in science and engineering for at least two reasons: first, whatever knowledge or understanding we have of a given phenomenon may be immediately carried forward to any analogous phenomenon, and second, if we wish to investigate a phenomenon experimentally, it may be simpler to carry out the experiments on an analogous phenomenon. For example, it is not hard to imagine that the electrical circuit in Fig. A.8 would be simpler, less expensive, and more precise to work with than the analogous mechanical system. ◀

EXAMPLE 5 *A Boundary Value Problem; Nonuniqueness*. As our final example in this section, consider the problem

$$y'' + y = 0 \qquad (0 \le x \le \pi) \tag{58a}$$

$$y(0) = 0 \qquad y(\pi) = 0. \tag{58b}$$

Obviously, $y(x) = 0$ satisfies both the differential equation and the boundary conditions. Is this solution unique? Well, the general solution of (58a) is $y = c_1 \cos x + c_2 \sin x$, and (58b) gives the system

$$\begin{aligned} y(0) &= 0 = c_1 + 0c_2 \\ y(\pi) &= 0 = -c_1 + 0c_2 \end{aligned} \tag{59}$$

on c_1, c_2 with solution $c_1 = 0$, $c_2 =$ arbitrary. Thus the trivial solution $y(x) = 0$ is but one solution out of the infinite set of solutions $y(x) = c_2 \sin x$ (c_2 arbitrary).

The point of this example is that this result—nonuniqueness—in no way violates the uniqueness part of Theorem 1 on page 914 since that theorem governs *initial*-value problems, where the conditions "$y(x_0) = k_1,\ y'(x_0) = k_2, \ldots,$

$y^{(n-1)}(x_0) = k_n$" are all applied at the same point x_0, which is regarded as an initial point or starting point. In the present example, however, the conditions (58b) are not all at the same point x_0; one is at the left endpoint, and the other is at the right endpoint. Thus, (58) is classified not as an initial-value problem but as a **boundary value problem**.

We do not, however, wish to imply that the solutions to boundary value problems are necessarily nonunique. For example, if (58a) is changed to $y'' + \omega^2 y = 0$, we find that the solution $y(x) = 0$ *is* unique unless the constant ω happens to be a nonzero integer. Thus our intention, in this example, is merely to emphasize that Theorem 1 is for initial-value problems only, and provides no information at all for boundary value problems. Not only may uniqueness break down, for boundary value problems, but existence may fail as well. For example, if $y(\pi) = 0$ is changed to $y(\pi) = 1$, in (58b), equations (59) are inconsistent and there exists no solution to (58). ◀

SOLUTION OF HOMOGENEOUS EQUATION $Ly = 0$; NONCONSTANT COEFFICIENTS — A.6

In this section we discuss methods of solution of differential equations of the form

$$y^{(n)} + p_1(x)y^{(n-1)} + \cdots + p_{n-1}(x)y' + p_n(x)y = 0, \tag{1}$$

i.e., where the coefficients are not necessarily constants. In general, this case is substantially more difficult than the constant-coefficient case insofar as obtaining solutions is concerned.

Occasionally, one solution can be found by inspection, with additional solutions then obtained by reduction of order.

EXAMPLE 1 *Reduction of Order*. Consider

$$xy'' + xy' - y = 0 \qquad (0 < x < \infty) \tag{2}$$

or, if we normalize the leading coefficient, as in (1),

$$y'' + y' - \frac{1}{x}y = 0.$$

In the event that we notice that $y_1(x) = x$ is a solution of (1), we can seek the missing solution in the form

$$y(x) = c(x)x. \tag{3}$$

Then $y' = c'x + c$ and $y'' = c''x + 2c'$, so (2) becomes

$$x^2c'' + 2xc' + x^2c' + xc - xc = 0 \tag{4}$$

or

$$xc'' + (x + 2)c' = 0. \tag{5}$$

Setting $c' = q$ gives us

$$\frac{dq}{q} + \left(1 + \frac{2}{x}\right) dx = 0, \tag{6}$$

so

$$\ln q + x + 2 \ln x = A, \tag{7}$$

or, more conveniently,

$$\ln q + \ln e^x + \ln x^2 = \ln B. \tag{8}$$

Then

$$\ln(qx^2e^x) = \ln B, \tag{9}$$

$$qx^2e^x = B, \tag{10}$$

$$c' = q = B\frac{e^{-x}}{x^2}. \tag{11}$$

Integrating once more, we have

$$c(x) = B \int^x \frac{e^{-t}}{t^2} dt \tag{12}$$

or, equivalently,*

$$c(x) = B \int_1^x \frac{e^{-t}}{t^2} dt + D. \tag{13}$$

Thus

$$y = c(x)x = Bx \int_1^x \frac{e^{-t}}{t^2} dt + Dx, \tag{14}$$

which is a general solution to (2).† It turns out that the integral in (14) cannot be evaluated in terms of the so-called elementary functions, so we will leave it intact.

COMMENT 1 Note that the Dx term in (14) is merely (an arbitrary constant times) the solution $y_1(x) = x$ that we discovered by inspection. Thus the "missing solution" has now been found as $y_2(x) = \int_1^x e^{-t}\, dt/t^2$.

COMMENT 2 It needs to be emphasized that the solution form $y = e^{\lambda x}$, which works so well for constant-coefficient equations, does *not* work in the variable-coefficient case. To illustrate, suppose that we seek solutions of (2) in the form $y = e^{\lambda x}$. Then (since λ is a constant)

$$y' = \lambda e^{\lambda x}, \tag{15a}$$

$$y'' = \lambda^2 e^{\lambda x}, \tag{15b}$$

so (2) becomes

* The lower integration limit can be chosen as *any* positive constant; we have arbitrarily selected 1. If we had chosen 2, instead, the result would be equivalent to (13), for the difference between the integral from 1 to x and the integral from 2 to x is the integral from 1 to 2, which is a constant. That constant, times B, can be absorbed by D. But we do avoid setting the lower limit equal to 0 because the integral would then be divergent.

† We leave it to the reader, in this and subsequent cases, to verify that the final result is indeed a general solution of the given differential equation.

$$(\lambda^2 x + \lambda x - 1)e^{\lambda x} = 0. \tag{16}$$

A *common (and serious) error* is to conclude from (16) that $\lambda^2 x + \lambda x - 1 = 0$, and then to solve this equation for λ. This step would give λ as a function of x, whereas it was assumed, in (15), that λ is a constant! Thus let us reiterate that the solution form $y = e^{\lambda x}$ is to be reserved for constant-coefficient equations. ◀

There is a class of nonconstant-coefficient equations which is of frequent occurrence in applications, and which can always be solved in terms of elementary functions, namely, equations of the form

$$x^n y^{(n)} + a_1 x^{n-1} y^{(n-1)} + \cdots + a_{n-1} x y' + a_n y = 0, \tag{17}$$

where the a_j's are constants. In other words, each coefficient is a power of x, where the power is the same as the order of the derivative that it multiplies. In view of this correspondence, such equations are sometimes called *equidimensional* equations. However, we choose to refer to equations of the form (17) as **Cauchy–Euler equations**.*

Recall that $y = e^{\lambda x}$ was a promising solution form for constant-coefficient equations because each term in the equation ($y = e^{\lambda x}$, $y' = \lambda e^{\lambda x}$, $y'' = \lambda^2 e^{\lambda x}, \ldots$) was of the same form, to within a scale factor. Thus, by suitable choice(s) of λ, the terms could exactly cancel to zero, thereby satisfying the differential equation. Similarly, there exists such a solution form for Cauchy–Euler equations, namely

$$y = x^\lambda,$$

for then the terms $y = x^\lambda$, $xy' = \lambda x^\lambda$, $x^2 y'' = \lambda(\lambda - 1)x^\lambda, \ldots$ are linearly dependent, and can cancel to zero, in (16), by suitable choice(s) of λ.

It will suffice, for our purposes, to limit our attention to the second-order case

$$x^2 y'' + a_1 x y' + a_2 y = 0 \tag{18}$$

over any positive x interval. Using (17), (18) becomes

$$\lambda(\lambda - 1)x^\lambda + a_1 \lambda x^\lambda + a_2 x^\lambda = 0,$$

so that we need

$$\lambda^2 + (a_1 - 1)\lambda + a_2 = 0. \tag{19}$$

Thus

$$\lambda = \frac{1 - a_1 \pm \sqrt{(a_1 - 1)^2 - 4a_2}}{2}. \tag{20}$$

If a_1, a_2 are both real, then (20) provides distinct real roots if $(a_1 - 1)^2 - 4a_2 > 0$, repeated roots if $(a_1 - 1)^2 - 4a_2 = 0$, and distinct complex roots if $(a_1 - 1)^2 - 4a_2 < 0$. Consider these cases separately.

* *Augustin-Louis Cauchy* (1789–1857) studied engineering at the Ecole Polytechnique but turned to mathematics, upon the advice of Lagrange and Laplace, because of poor health. Only *Leonhard Euler* (1707–1783) was more prolific. Blind during the last 17 years of his life, Euler's productivity never faltered, partly because of his phenomenal memory. He knew, from memory, the innumerable formulas of trigonometry and analysis, the first six powers of the first 100 prime numbers, numerous poems, and the epic Aeneid in Latin. His collected works comprise more than 70 volumes.

Case 1: $(a_1 - 1)^2 - 4a_2 > 0$. Denoting the two roots as λ_+, λ_-, we have the general solution

$$y = c_1 x^{\lambda_+} + c_2 x^{\lambda_-} \tag{21}$$

of (18).

EXAMPLE 2 If

$$x^2 y'' + 2xy' - y = 0, \tag{22}$$

then $\lambda_+ = (-1 + \sqrt{5})/2$, $\lambda_- = (-1 - \sqrt{5})/2$, so we have the general solution

$$y = c_1 x^{(-1+\sqrt{5})/2} + c_2 x^{(-1-\sqrt{5})/2} \tag{23}$$

of (22). ◀

Case 2: $(a_1 - 1)^2 - 4a_2 = 0$. In this case the roots coalesce so that $\lambda_+ = \lambda_- = (1 - a_1)/2 \equiv \lambda$. Thus we have found but one solution, $y = c_1 x^\lambda$. By reduction of order, we seek the missing solution as $y = c(x)x^\lambda$. Putting this form into (18) and recalling that $\lambda = (1 - a_1)/2$ and that $(a_1 - 1)^2 - 4a_2 = 0$, we find that

$$xc'' + c' = 0 \tag{24}$$

or, with $c' = q$,

$$\frac{dq}{q} + \frac{dx}{x} = 0,$$

$$\ln q + \ln x = \text{constant} \equiv \ln B,$$

say, so that $qx = B$, $c' = q = B/x$, and $c(x) = B \ln x + A$. Thus we have the general solution

$$y = (A + B \ln x)x^\lambda, \tag{25}$$

where the $x^\lambda \ln x$ part is the "missing solution" which has now been found by the process of reduction of order.

EXAMPLE 3 Given the equation

$$x^2 y'' + 3xy' + y = 0, \tag{26}$$

we have the repeated root $\lambda = -1$, so that

$$y = (A + B \ln x)x^{-1}. \quad ◀ \tag{27}$$

Case 3: $(a_1 - 1)^2 - 4a_2 < 0$. In this case the radical in (20) is purely imaginary, so it is reasonable to rewrite

$$\lambda = \frac{1 - a_1}{2} \pm i\frac{\sqrt{4a_2 - (a_1 - 1)^2}}{2} \equiv \alpha \pm i\beta. \tag{28}$$

Thus

$$\begin{aligned} y &= c_1 x^{\alpha+i\beta} + c_2 x^{\alpha-i\beta} \\ &= x^{\alpha}(c_1 x^{i\beta} + c_2 x^{-i\beta}) \\ &= x^{\alpha}(c_1 e^{i\beta \ln x} + c_2 e^{-i\beta \ln x}). \end{aligned} \tag{29}$$

Preferring real-valued functions, we may express the general solution, alternatively, as

$$y = x^{\alpha}[c_3 \cos(\beta \ln x) + c_4 \sin(\beta \ln x)]. \tag{30}$$

EXAMPLE 4 Considering

$$x^2 y'' - xy' + 3y = 0, \tag{31}$$

we have $\alpha = 1$, $\beta = \sqrt{2}$, so that

$$y = x[c_1 \cos(\sqrt{2} \ln x) + c_2 \sin(\sqrt{2} \ln x)]. \quad ◀ \tag{32}$$

EXAMPLE 5 As a final example of the Cauchy–Euler equation, consider the equation

$$r^2 R'' + rR' - \kappa^2 R = 0 \qquad (\kappa \geq 0) \tag{33}$$

on $R(r)$, because precisely this equation arises in Section 15.3. Seeking $R = r^{\lambda}$, (33) becomes $[\lambda(\lambda - 1) + \lambda - \kappa^2]r^{\lambda} = 0$. Thus $\lambda^2 - \kappa^2 = 0$, so $\lambda = \pm\kappa$, and the general solution of (33) is

$$R = Ar^{\kappa} + Br^{-\kappa}, \tag{34}$$

unless $\kappa = 0$, for if $\kappa = 0$, then the two terms on the right-hand side of (34) coalesce into a single constant. Let us solve (33) specifically for the case $\kappa = 0$. Setting $R' = p$, to reduce the order, we have $r^2 p' + rp = 0$, or

$$\frac{dp}{p} + \frac{dr}{r} = 0. \tag{35}$$

Thus $\ln p + \ln r = \text{constant} = \ln C$, so $\ln(pr) = \ln C$ and hence $pr = C$. Since $p = R'$, we have $R' = C/r$, so that

$$R = C \ln r + D \qquad (\kappa = 0), \tag{36}$$

which is the desired general solution of (33) for the case $k = 0$. [Or we could have obtained (36) directly from (25), with $\lambda = 0$.] ◀

The foregoing discussion of the Cauchy–Euler equation will suffice for our needs in this book, but there is an additional result that is too interesting not to mention. Namely, it turns out that *the change of variables*

$$x = e^t \tag{37}$$

reduces the Cauchy–Euler equation (16) to a constant-coefficient equation. Let us demonstrate this line of approach for the second-order case (18). By chain differentiation,

$$\frac{d(\,)}{dx} = \frac{d(\,)}{dt}\frac{dt}{dx} = \frac{d(\,)}{dt}\left(\frac{dx}{dt}\right)^{-1} = e^{-t}\frac{d(\,)}{dt}. \tag{38}$$

Thus, if we express $y(x(t)) = Y(t)$, then (18) becomes

$$e^{2t}e^{-t}\frac{d}{dt}\left(e^{-t}\frac{dY}{dt}\right) + a_1 e^t e^{-t}\frac{dY}{dt} + a_2 Y = 0.$$

Upon simplification, we have the constant-coefficient equation

$$\frac{d^2Y}{dt^2} + (a_1 - 1)\frac{dY}{dt} + a_2 Y = 0. \tag{39}$$

Solving (39) by seeking $Y = e^{\lambda t}$ then leads to the same results as given in (21), (27), and (30). For example, consider the case of repeated roots, where

$$\lambda = \frac{1 - a_1 \pm \sqrt{(a_1 - 1)^2 - 4a_2}}{2} = \frac{1 - a_1}{2} \tag{40}$$

Then

$$Y(t) = (A + Bt)e^{\lambda t}. \tag{41}$$

But $t = \ln x$ and $e^{\lambda t} = (e^t)^\lambda = x^\lambda$, so

$$y(x) = (A + B\ln x)x^\lambda, \tag{42}$$

in agreement with (27).

In closing this section we emphasize that except for special cases, such as Cauchy–Euler equations, we are generally unable to get closed-form solutions to variable-coefficient equations in terms of elementary functions. Thus we often settle for *power series solutions* of such equations. The power series method is not discussed in this appendix, but is presented in Part IV so that we can handle two especially important variable-coefficient equations: Bessel's equation and Legendre's equation.

A.7 SOLUTION OF NONHOMOGENEOUS EQUATION $Ly = f$ BY UNDETERMINED COEFFICIENTS

Having thus far limited our attention to the homogeneous equation $Ly = 0$, we now consider the nonhomogeneous case $Ly = f$. Recall from Section A.3 that the general solution of $Ly = f$ may be expressed as

$$y = c_1u_1(x) + \cdots + c_nu_n(x) + y_p(x), \tag{1}$$

where $u_1, \ldots, u_n$ are LI solutions of the associated homogeneous equation $Ly = 0$, and y_p is any **particular solution** of the full equation $Ly = f$. The $c_1u_1(x) + \cdots + c_nu_n(x)$ portion of (1) is the general solution of the homogeneous equation $Ly = 0$ and is referred to as the **complementary solution** $y_c(x)$. Thus the right-hand side of (1) is the sum of the complementary and particular solutions,

$$y = y_c(x) + y_p(x). \tag{2}$$

What's new for us, in this section, is the additional term $y_p(x)$. In this section and the next we discuss two useful methods for determining $y_p(x)$: the method of undetermined coefficients and the method of variation of parameters.

Let us introduce the method of undetermined coefficients through an example before formulating some general comments about the method.

EXAMPLE 1 Consider the differential equation

$$y'''' - y'' = 3x^2 - e^{2x}. \tag{3}$$

Following the method developed in Section A.5, the associated homogeneous equation $y'''' - y'' = 0$ admits the general solution

$$y_c = c_1 + c_2x + c_3e^x + c_4e^{-x}. \tag{4}$$

To determine $y_p(x)$ by the method of undetermined coefficients, we proceed as follows. Write down each term on the right-hand side of (3) together with its derivatives. Thus

$$\begin{aligned} 3x^2 &\longrightarrow 3x^2, 6x, 6, 0, 0, \ldots \\ e^{2x} &\longrightarrow e^{2x}, 2e^{2x}, 4e^{2x}, \ldots . \end{aligned} \tag{5}$$

Ignoring multiplicative constants, we see that $3x^2$ and e^{2x} generate the following finite sets of LI functions:

$$\begin{aligned} 3x^2 &\longrightarrow x^2, x, 1 \\ e^{2x} &\longrightarrow e^{2x}. \end{aligned} \tag{6}$$

Tentatively, seek y_p as linear combination of these terms:

$$y_p(x) = (Ax^2 + Bx + C) + (De^{2x}), \tag{7}$$

where it will be useful to enclose each "family" of terms within parentheses. Next, check each term in y_p for duplication with terms in y_c. Doing so, we find that the Bx and C terms in (7) duplicate similar terms in (4). The method then calls for multiplying the entire family, involved in the duplication, by the lowest positive integer power of x needed to eliminate all such duplication. Trying

$$\begin{aligned} y_p(x) &= x(Ax^2 + Bx + C) + (De^{2x}) \\ &= (Ax^3 + Bx^2 + Cx) + (De^{2x}), \end{aligned} \tag{8}$$

we see that the Bx^2 term is now okay, but that the Cx term is guilty of duplication. Thus try

$$\begin{aligned} y_p(x) &= x^2(Ax^2 + Bx + C) + (De^{2x}) \\ &= Ax^4 + Bx^3 + Cx^2 + De^{2x}. \end{aligned} \tag{9}$$

This time we are done, since all duplication has now been eliminated. Having settled on the form (9), we put (9) into (3) and obtain

$$24A + 16De^{2x} - 12Ax^2 - 6Bx - 2C - 4De^{2x} = 3x^2 - e^{2x}. \tag{10}$$

Finally, equating coefficients of like terms,

$$
\begin{aligned}
x^2:&\quad -12A = 3\\
x:&\quad -6B = 0\\
1:&\quad 24A - 2C = 0\\
e^{2x}:&\quad 12D = -1,
\end{aligned}
\tag{11}
$$

so that $A = -\frac{1}{4}$, $B = 0$, $C = -3$, $D = -\frac{1}{12}$. Thus

$$y_p(x) = -\tfrac{1}{4}x^4 - 3x^2 - \tfrac{1}{12}e^{2x}, \tag{12}$$

and a general solution of (3) is

$$y = y_c + y_p = c_1 + c_2x + c_3e^x + c_4e^{-x} - \tfrac{1}{4}x^4 - 3x^2 - \tfrac{1}{12}e^{2x}. \tag{13}$$

COMMENT 1 When we say "equating coefficients of like terms" in (10), what we really mean is that if we rewrite (10) as

$$(-12A - 3)x^2 + (-6B)x + (24A - 2C)1 + (12D + 1)e^{2x} = 0 \tag{14}$$

and observe that $x^2, x, 1, e^{2x}$ are LI, it follows that each coefficient in (14) must be zero. That result gives (11) and is equivalent to "equating coefficients of like terms" in (10).

COMMENT 2 The key point in the analysis above is the system (11). The success of the choice (9) shows up in that (11) is *consistent*. By comparison, suppose that we had used (7) or (8). Consider (7). Putting (7) into (3) gives

$$16De^{2x} - 2A - 4De^{2x} = 3x^2 - e^{2x}, \tag{15}$$

which cannot be satisfied by *any* choice of the constants A, B, C, D, because equating coefficients of x^2 terms gives $0 = 3$. ◀

What is the extent of applicability of the method? The method works for any linear differential equation $Ly = f$ with constant coefficients, provided that f has only a finite number of LI derivatives. For example, $f = x^2e^x$ produces the finite family x^2e^x, xe^x, e^x, whereas $f = 1/x$ produces the infinite family $1/x, 1/x^2, 1/x^3, \ldots$. Thus undetermined coefficients would work for $f = x^2e^x$, but would not work for $f = 1/x$. More generally, if f is to have a finite number of LI derivatives, that means that there exists a finite integer N, and constants $a_1, \ldots, a_{N+1}$ such that

$$a_1f^{(N)} + a_2f^{(N-1)} + \cdots + a_Nf' + a_{N+1}f = 0 \tag{16}$$

over the x interval under consideration. From our discussion of the solution to such equations we know that f must be of one or more of the forms

$$Cx^me^{\alpha x}\cos\beta x,\ Cx^me^{\alpha x}\sin\beta x, \tag{17}$$

where m is a nonnegative integer, α and β are real constants, and C is any constant. Thus we can conclude that undetermined coefficients will work for a linear constant-coefficient equation if f is of the form (17), or if it is a linear combination of such forms.

EXAMPLE 2 *Forced Harmonic Oscillator*. Here we return to the mechanical oscillator studied in Example 4 of Section A.5, but this time we consider the "forced vibration," i.e., where $f \neq 0$. In particular, we consider the important special case $f(t) = F \sin \omega_0 t$, where F and ω_0 are constants. For simplicity, we consider the damping c to be zero. Thus the governing equation becomes

$$m\ddot{x} + kx = F \sin \omega_0 t$$

or

$$\ddot{x} + \omega^2 x = \frac{F}{m} \sin \omega_0 t, \tag{18}$$

where $\omega = \sqrt{k/m}$ is the natural frequency, i.e., the frequency of the *free* vibration.

Seeking to obtain the general solution of (18) in the form $x = x_c(t) + x_p(t)$, we recall (or notice by inspection) that

$$x_c = c_1 \cos \omega t + c_2 \sin \omega t. \tag{19}$$

Turning to the particular solution, we see that the sin $\omega_0 t$ term in (18) generates the family $\sin \omega_0 t$, $\cos \omega_0 t$, so we tentatively express

$$x_p = A \sin \omega_0 t + B \cos \omega_0 t. \tag{20}$$

We need to distinguish two cases:

Case 1: $\omega_0 \neq \omega$ If the driving frequency ω_0 is different from the natural frequency ω, each of the terms in (20) is different from (i.e., is not a linear combination of) the terms in (19), so we accept (20) without modification. Putting (20) into (18) and equating coefficients of like terms gives

$$\sin \omega_0 t: \quad -\omega_0^2 A + \omega^2 A = \frac{F}{m} \tag{21a}$$

$$\cos \omega_0 t: \quad -\omega_0^2 B + \omega^2 B = 0, \tag{21b}$$

so that

$$A = \frac{F/m}{\omega^2 - \omega_0^2}, \qquad B = 0. \tag{22}$$

Thus

$$x = \underbrace{c_1 \cos \omega t + c_2 \sin \omega t}_{x_c(t)} + \underbrace{\frac{F/m}{\omega^2 - \omega_0^2} \sin \omega_0 t}_{x_p(t)}, \tag{23}$$

where c_1, c_2 can be found so as to satisfy any initial conditions

$$x(0) = x_0, \quad \dot{x}(0) = \dot{x}_0, \tag{24}$$

where x_0 and $\dot{x}_0$ are constants.

A question of special interest is: What form does the solution, or "response," approach as $t \to \infty$?. From a practical point of view, it is important to realize that the neglect of the damping c is generally only a useful approximation, and that for large time even a tiny amount of damping may have a prominent effect. Thus let us look at the general solution in the event that $c \neq 0$. Setting $c/m = 2\epsilon$, where the 2 is merely for convenience, we can (but will omit the steps) derive the general solution of

$$\ddot{x} + 2\epsilon\dot{x} + \omega^2 x = \frac{F}{m}\sin\omega_0 t \tag{25}$$

as

$$\begin{aligned} x = {} & e^{-\epsilon t}(c_1 \cos\sqrt{\omega^2 - \epsilon^2}\,t + c_2 \sin\sqrt{\omega^2 - \epsilon^2}\,t) \\ & + \frac{F/m}{(\omega^2 - \omega_0^2)^2 + 4\epsilon^2\omega_0^2}[(\omega^2 - \omega_0^2)\sin\omega_0 t - 2\epsilon\omega_0\cos\omega_0 t], \end{aligned} \tag{26}$$

where c_1, c_2 may be found by imposing the initial conditions (24). Observe that as $t \to \infty$ the complementary solution decays to zero due to the $e^{-\epsilon t}$ factor, even if ϵ is quite small, so that (26) gives

$$x \approx \frac{F/m}{(\omega^2 - \omega_0^2)^2 + 4\epsilon^2\omega_0^2}[(\omega^2 - \omega_0^2)\sin\omega_0 t - 2\epsilon\omega_0\cos\omega_0 t] \tag{27}$$

as $t \to \infty$. Finally, if the damping c is sufficiently small, we may set $\epsilon \to 0$ in (27) and obtain

$$x \approx \frac{F/m}{\omega^2 - \omega_0^2}\sin\omega_0 t \tag{28}$$

for large t. This result is often called the *steady state*, or *driven response*. Comparing (28) with (23), we see that the last term in (23) (namely, the particular solution x_p) is the so-called steady-state response.

Thus even if an engineer neglects the damping, so that the system is modeled by (18), he or she will realize that the steady-state response corresponds only to the x_p part of (23) since the actual presence of any damping at all will cause the complementary solution to die out as $t \to \infty$. Finally, notice that the steady-state response is completely independent of the initial conditions, since the initial conditions affect only the constants c_1, c_2 in the complementary solution.

Since the steady-state response is of important interest, it may be useful to carry the story just a bit further. It is tempting to identify the coefficient $(F/m)/(\omega^2 - \omega_0^2)$ as the amplitude. However, amplitude is understood to be positive, whereas that coefficient will be positive *or* negative depending on whether $\omega > \omega_0$ or $\omega < \omega_0$. Thus let us reexpress (28) as

$$x \approx \left|\frac{F/m}{\omega_0^2 - \omega^2}\right| \sin(\omega_0 t + \phi), \tag{29a}$$

where

$$\phi = \begin{cases} 0, & \omega < \omega_0 \\ \pi, & \omega > \omega_0. \end{cases} \tag{29b}$$

The amplitude and phase are plotted versus the driving frequency in Fig. A.9a and b, respectively. These figures are called "response curves." It is tempting to come away from Fig. A.9a with the idea that the amplitude is infinite at $\omega_0 = \omega$. However, recall that we are considering $\omega_0 \neq \omega$ in case 1 for if ω_0 were to equal ω, then (21a) would become $(0)(A) = F/m$, which has no solution. Thus we need to consider the case $\omega_0 = \omega$ separately.

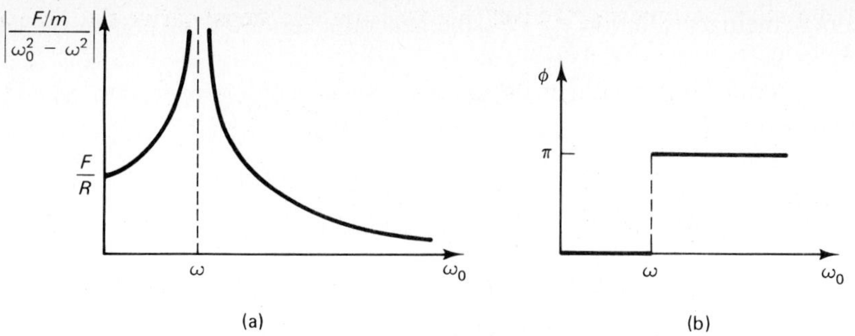

Fig. A.9 Response curves.

Case 2: $\omega_0 = \omega$ The underlying difficulty in this case is that if $\omega_0 = \omega$, the terms in (20) duplicate those in (19), so that we need to modify (20) to the form

$$x_p = t(A \sin \omega t + B \cos \omega t). \tag{30}$$

Putting (30) into $\ddot{x} + \omega^2 x = (F/m) \sin \omega t$ and solving for A and B, we obtain the particular solution

$$x_p = -\frac{F}{2m\omega} t \cos \omega t, \tag{31}$$

and the general solution

$$x = c_1 \cos \omega t + c_2 \sin \omega t - \frac{F}{2m\omega} t \cos \omega t. \tag{32}$$

The $t \cos \omega t$ term grows unboundedly, as sketched in Fig. A.10, and this unbounded growth is referred to as *resonance*. ◀

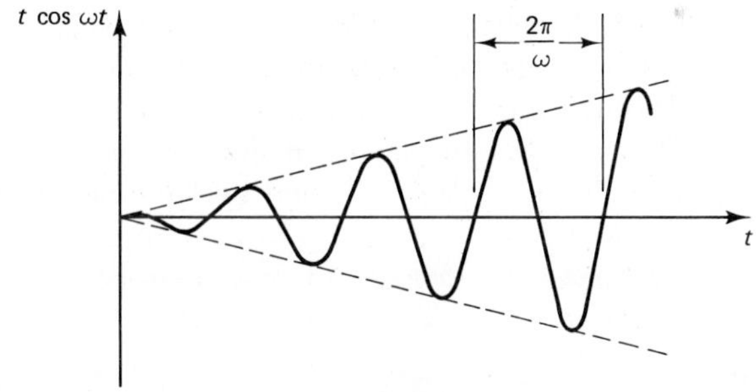

Fig. A.10 Resonant growth.

SOLUTION OF NONHOMOGENEOUS EQUATION $Ly = f$ BY VARIATION OF PARAMETERS — A.8

Besides the method of undetermined coefficients, there is also a method due to Lagrange* for obtaining particular solutions to the linear nonhomogeneous equation $Ly = f$. Known as **variation of parameters**, the method presupposes that we know

* *J. L. Lagrange* (1736–1813), one of the all-time great mathematicians, used the method in 1774. The elegant simplicity of the method is characteristic of Lagrange's work.

the complementary solution y_c, i.e., the general solution of the homogeneous equation $Ly = 0$.

For definiteness, consider the general linear nonhomogeneous *second*-order equation

$$y'' + p_1(x)y' + p_2(x)y = f(x). \tag{1}$$

As mentioned above, we suppose that the complementary solution

$$y_c = c_1 y_1(x) + c_2 y_2(x) \tag{2}$$

is known. According to variation of parameters, we seek y_p in the form

$$y_p = c_1(x)y_1(x) + c_2(x)y_2(x), \tag{3}$$

i.e., we "vary the parameters" c_1 and c_2 in (2). Notice that this idea is essentially the same as the idea behind the method of reduction of order, which was discussed in Section A.5 in connection with repeated roots of the characteristic equation. And just as we remarked about reduction of order, we remark here that (3) shows little promise, inasmuch as it is completely noncommittal: *Any* given function can be expressed in the form (3). For example, if $y_1(x) = \sin x$ and $y_2(x) = \cos x$, the function x^3, say, can be expressed as

$$x^3 = c_1(x) \sin x + c_2(x) \cos x \tag{4}$$

by suitable choice of c_1 and c_2. In fact, that choice is nonunique: we could choose $c_1(x) = x^3/\sin x$ and $c_2(x) = 0$, or $c_1(x) = 0$ and $c_2(x) = x^3 \cos x$, or $c_1(x) = e^x$ and $c_2(x) = (x^3 - e^x \sin x)/\cos x$, and so on. Nevertheless, let us proceed.

Needing y' and y'' to put into (1), we differentiate (3):

$$y_p' = c_1 y_1' + c_2 y_2' + c_1' y_1 + c_2' y_2. \tag{5}$$

Looking ahead, y_p'' will include $c_1, c_2, c_1', c_2', c_1'', c_2''$ terms, so that (1) will become a nonhomogeneous second-order differential equation in c_1 and c_2, hardly an improvement over the original equation (1)! However, since it is only one equation in the two unknowns (c_1, c_2), we wonder if we might not be free to append another condition on c_1, c_2 to complete—and simplify—the system. The flexibility to append another condition is also supported by the nonuniqueness illustrated in the paragraph above.

An especially convenient condition to append will be

$$c_1' y_1 + c_2' y_2 = 0, \tag{6}$$

for this condition knocks the c_1', c_2' terms out of (5) so that y_p'' will contain only *first*-order derivatives of c_1 and c_2. Thus

$$y_p'' = c_1 y_1'' + c_2 y_2'' + c_1' y_1' + c_2' y_2', \tag{7}$$

and (1) becomes

$$c_1(y_1'' + p_1 y_1' + p_2 y_1) + c_2(y_2'' + p_1 y_2' + p_2 y_2) + c_1' y_1' + c_2' y_2' = f. \tag{8}$$

Since $y_1'' + p_1 y_1' + p_2 y_1 = 0$ and $y_2'' + p_1 y_2' + p_2 y_2 = 0$ by assumption, (8) simplifies to

$$c_1' y_1' + c_2' y_2' = f. \tag{9}$$

In (6) and (9) we have two equations in the two unknowns c_1', c_2', namely,

$$\begin{aligned} y_1 c_1' + y_2 c_2' &= 0, \\ y_1' c_1' + y_2' c_2' &= f. \end{aligned} \tag{10}$$

Now, the determinant of the coefficient matrix is the Wronskian

$$W(x) = \begin{vmatrix} y_1 & y_2 \\ y_1' & y_2' \end{vmatrix} \tag{11}$$

of y_1, y_2, and since y_1, y_2 are LI, then $W(x) \neq 0$ over the x interval of interest (as follows from the material in Sections A.3 and A.4). Thus (10) can indeed be solved (uniquely) for c_1', c_2' over the entire x interval. This step gives

$$c_1'(x) = -\frac{f(x)y_2(x)}{W(x)}, \qquad c_2'(x) = \frac{f(x)y_1(x)}{W(x)}. \tag{12}$$

Integrating (12), the particular solution (3) becomes

$$y_p(x) = \int_{x_0}^{x} \frac{y_1(\xi)y_2(x) - y_1(x)y_2(\xi)}{W(\xi)} f(\xi)d\xi, \tag{13}$$

where x_0 is any point in the x interval. [Choosing a different value of x_0 will merely alter $c_1(x)$ and $c_2(x)$ by additive constants. Those constants times $y_1(x)$ and $y_2(x)$, respectively, can be absorbed by the complementary solution. Thus any convenient choice of x_0 in (13) will do.] Of course, the general solution of (1) is then

$$\boxed{y(x) = c_1 y_1(x) + c_2 y_2(x) + \int_{x_0}^{x} \frac{y_1(\xi)y_2(x) - y_1(x)y_2(\xi)}{W(\xi)} f(\xi)\, d\xi,} \tag{14}$$

where c_1, c_2 are arbitrary constants.

Before looking at an example, observe how perfect and elegant the choice of (6) was as a second condition on $c_1(x)$ and $c_2(x)$, for it suppressed the second-order derivatives c_1'', c_2'', and it also caused the determinant of the coefficient matrix in (10) to be the Wronskian, which is guaranteed not to vanish by virtue of the linear independence of y_1, y_2. This nonvanishing was critical to the success of the method since it assured that (10) could indeed be solved for c_1', c_2'.

Finally, let us pause to compare the two methods —undetermined coefficients and variation of parameters—for obtaining particular solutions. Undetermined coefficients was reliable only if the differential equation was of constant-coefficient type and if the "forcing term" f (in $Ly = f$) had a finite number of LI derivatives. However, neither of these restrictions apply for variation of parameters. Of course, if the coefficients are nonconstant, the complementary solution may not be easy to find, but once it is found, the particular solution can then be found by variation of parameters.

EXAMPLE 1 Consider the undamped, forced harmonic oscillator

$$\ddot{x} + \omega^2 x = f(t) \qquad (0 \leq t < \infty) \tag{15}$$

where ω is a constant. Then

$$x_c(t) = c_1 \cos \omega t + c_2 \sin \omega t, \tag{16}$$

so $x_1(t) = \cos \omega t$ and $x_2(t) = \sin \omega t$. Also,

$$W(t) = \begin{vmatrix} x_1 & x_2 \\ \dot{x}_1 & \dot{x}_2 \end{vmatrix} = \begin{vmatrix} \cos \omega t & \sin \omega t \\ -\omega \sin \omega t & \omega \cos \omega t \end{vmatrix} = \omega, \tag{17}$$

so (14) gives

$$\begin{aligned} x(t) &= c_1 \cos \omega t + c_2 \sin \omega t + \int_0^t \frac{\cos \omega\tau \sin \omega t - \cos \omega t \sin \omega\tau}{\omega} f(\tau)\, d\tau \\ &= c_1 \cos \omega t + c_2 \sin \omega t + \frac{1}{\omega} \int_0^t \sin \omega(t - \tau) f(\tau) d\tau, \end{aligned} \tag{18}$$

where we have chosen $t_0 = 0$, say, as the lower integration limit. For example, if $f(t) = (F/m) \sin \omega t$, if we carry out the integration in (18), we obtain

$$\begin{aligned} x(t) &= c_1 \cos \omega t + c_2 \sin \omega t + \frac{F}{2m\omega^2}(\sin \omega t - \omega t \cos \omega t) \\ &= c_1 \cos \omega t + \tilde{c}_2 \sin \omega t - \frac{F}{2m\omega} t \cos \omega t, \end{aligned} \tag{19}$$

where c_1, $\tilde{c}_2$ are arbitrary constants, in agreement with our earlier result (32) obtained by undetermined coefficients.

COMMENT Be sure to see that undetermined coefficients could not have been applied, in any case, to (15) since the functional form of $f(t)$ was not prescribed. Nevertheless, we were able to obtain the solution (18), in integral form at least, by variation of parameters. That solution could also have been obtained by the powerful Laplace transform method, but that method is studied in Part III and will therefore be omitted here. ◀

Next, consider the *first-order linear differential equation*

$$\boxed{y' + P(x)y = Q(x).} \tag{20}$$

First, obtain y_c:

$$y_c' + P(x)y_c = 0, \tag{21}$$

$$\int \frac{dy_c}{y_c} + \int P(x)\, dx = 0, \tag{22}$$

$$\ln y_c + \int_{x_0}^x P(\xi)\, d\xi = \text{constant}, \tag{23}$$

where x_0 is any point in the x interval. It will be convenient to express the constant on the right-hand side as $\ln c$, for then (23) gives

$$y_c(x) = e^{\ln c - \int_{x_0}^x P(\xi)\, d\xi} = c e^{-\int_{x_0}^x P(\xi)\, d\xi} = cR(x), \tag{24}$$

where

$$R(x) \equiv e^{-\int_{x_0}^{x} P(\xi)\, d\xi}. \tag{25}$$

Varying the parameter c in (24), we seek

$$y_p(x) = c(x)R(x). \tag{26}$$

Then $y_p' = c'R + cR' = c'R - cPR$, so (20) becomes

$$c'R - \cancel{cPR} + \cancel{cPR} = Q. \tag{27}$$

Thus

$$c(x) = \int_{x_0}^{x} Q(\xi)R^{-1}(\xi)\, d\xi, \tag{28}$$

where x_0 is any convenient point in the interval.

Therefore, we have the general solution

$$y(x) = y_c(x) + y_p(x),$$

$$\boxed{y(x) = cR(x) + R(x)\int_{x_0}^{x} Q(\xi)R^{-1}(\xi)\, d\xi.} \tag{29}$$

This result is also derived, in the traditional course in ordinary differential equations, by multiplying the terms in (20) by a suitable "integrating factor."

Notice that the solution (29) contains two arbitrary constants, c and x_0, whereas (20) was only first order, so its solution should contain but one arbitrary constant of integration. In fact, the solution (29) does contain but one arbitrary constant since x_0 and c are not independent. This fact can be seen most easily from (23), for observe that a change in x_0 changes the $\int_{x_0}^{x} P(\xi)\, d\xi$ term by an additive constant, which can be absorbed by the constant on the right-hand side. Indeed, we could have omitted the x_0's entirely and worked with indefinite integrals, but their inclusion is convenient because then (29) gives $y(x_0) = c$. Thus, if an initial condition is prescribed, say $y(x_0) = y_0$, c is simply equal to y_0.

EXAMPLE 2 To illustrate (29), consider

$$y' + 2xy = \sin x \qquad (0 \le x < \infty) \tag{30a}$$

$$y(0) = 5. \tag{30b}$$

With $x_0 = 0$,

$$R(x) = e^{-\int_0^x 2\xi d\xi} = e^{-x^2},$$

so that the general solution of (30a) is

$$y(x) = ce^{-x^2} + e^{-x^2}\int_0^x e^{\xi^2} \sin \xi\, d\xi. \tag{31}$$

Finally, imposing (30b) yields

$$y(0) = 5 = c + 0, \tag{32}$$

so that $c = 5$. Hence

$$y(x) = 5e^{-x^2} + e^{-x^2} \int_0^x e^{\xi^2} \sin \xi \, d\xi. \tag{33}$$

COMMENT As noted in the paragraph preceding this example, observe that by choosing x_0 to be the point at which the condition (30b) is imposed, we got the integral term in (32) to be zero, thus simplifying the calculation of the integration constant c. ◀

Having discussed the application of variation of parameters to first- and second-order equations, let us briefly indicate the extension to the equation

$$y^{(n)} + p_1(x)y^{(n-1)} + \cdots + p_{n-1}(x)y' + p_n(x)y = f(x) \tag{34}$$

of order n for any $n > 1$. Assuming that the complementary solution

$$y_c(x) = c_1y_1(x) + \cdots + c_ny_n(x) \tag{35}$$

is in hand, we seek

$$y_p(x) = c_1(x)y_1(x) + \cdots + c_n(x)y_n(x). \tag{36}$$

Looking ahead, we can see that putting (36) into (34) will give one equation in the n unkown $c_j(x)$'s, so that we have an opportunity to impose $n - 1$ additional conditions.

To put (36) in (34) we need $y_p', y_p'', \ldots, y_p^{(n)}$. From (36),

$$y_p'(x) = c_1y_1' + \cdots + c_ny_n' + c_1'y_1 + \cdots + c_n'y_n. \tag{37}$$

To suppress the order of the derivatives on the $c_j(x)$'s, we choose, as the first of our $n - 1$ additional conditions, to get the last n terms in (37) equal to zero:

$$c_1'y_1 + \cdots + c_n'y_n = 0. \tag{38}$$

Thus (37) reduces to

$$y_p'(x) = c_1y_1' + \cdots + c_ny_n'. \tag{39}$$

Next,

$$y_p''(x) = c_1y_1'' + \cdots + c_ny_n'' + c_1'y_1' + \cdots + c_n'y_n', \tag{40}$$

and in the same spirit, we set

$$c_1'y_1' + \cdots + c_n'y_n' = 0. \tag{41}$$

Continuing in this manner, we obtain the system

$$\begin{aligned} y_1c_1' + \cdots + \quad y_nc_n' &= 0 \\ y_1'c_1' + \cdots + \quad y_n'c_n' &= 0 \\ &\vdots \\ y_1^{(n-2)}c_1' + \cdots + y_n^{(n-2)}c_n' &= 0 \\ y_1^{(n-1)}c_1' + \cdots + y_n^{(n-1)}c_n' &= f \end{aligned} \tag{42}$$

of n equations in the n unknowns $c_1', \ldots, c_n'$. This system can be solved (uniquely) for $c_1', \ldots, c_n'$ since the determinant of the coefficient matrix is the Wronskian W of $y_1, \ldots, y_n$, where the solutions $y_1, \ldots, y_n$ of the homogeneous equation are LI, so that $W(x) \neq 0$ over the interval. Thus we can solve (42) for $c_1', \ldots, c_n'$ and integrate to obtain the desired $c_1(x), \ldots, c_n(x)$ in (36).

Having considered the methods of undetermined coefficients and variation of parameters, recall that the latter method is the more powerful inasmuch as it is not limited to constant-coefficient equations, nor does it require f to have only a finite number of LI derivatives. However, the price of that power is that the method is generally more tedious to apply since it involves integrations, whereas undetermined coefficients involves only differentiations. Thus as a rule of thumb, we suggest favoring undetermined coefficients, unless the method does not apply.

EXISTENCE AND UNIQUENESS FOR LINEAR SYSTEMS — A.9

In preceding sections we have emphasized the nth-order linear initial-value problem

$$y^{(n)} + p_1(x)y^{(n-1)} + \cdots + p_{n-1}(x)y' + p_n(x)y = f(x) \tag{1a}$$

$$y(x_0) = k_1, \quad y'(x_0) = k_2, \quad \ldots, \quad y^{(n-1)}(x_0) = k_n. \tag{1b}$$

Also of great importance, both in theory and application, are problems of the form

$$\begin{aligned} y_1' &= a_{11}(x)y_1 + \cdots + a_{1n}(x)y_n + f_1(x); \qquad y_1(x_0) = b_1 \\ y_2' &= a_{21}(x)y_1 + \cdots + a_{2n}(x)y_n + f_2(x); \qquad y_2(x_0) = b_2 \\ &\vdots \\ y_n' &= a_{n1}(x)y_1 + \cdots + a_{nn}(x)y_n + f_n(x); \qquad y_n(x_0) = b_n, \end{aligned} \tag{2}$$

i.e., linear first-order systems; for instance, see the example on chemical kinetics on page 163.

In this section we show that (2) *includes* problems of the form (1), and we give a useful existence/uniqueness theorem for (2).

Considering (1), let us define

$$y_1 \equiv y \tag{3a}$$

$$y_2 \equiv y' = y_1' \tag{3b}$$

$$y_3 \equiv y'' = y_2' \tag{3c}$$

$$\vdots$$

$$y_n \equiv y^{(n-1)} = y_{n-1}'. \tag{3d}$$

Then (1a) becomes

$$y_n' + p_1(x)y_n + \cdots + p_{n-1}(x)y_2 + p_n(x)y_1 = f(x). \tag{4}$$

Pulling (3) and (4) together and expressing the initial conditions (1b) in terms of $y_1, \ldots, y_n$, we have the system

$$
\begin{aligned}
y_1' &= y_2; & y_1(x_0) &= k_1 \\
y_2' &= y_3; & y_2(x_0) &= k_2 \\
&\vdots & &\vdots \\
y_{n-1}' &= y_n; & y_{n-1}(x_0) &= k_{n-1} \\
y_n' &= -p_n(x)y_1 - p_{n-1}(x)y_2 - \cdots - p_1(x)y_n + f(x); & y_n(x_0) &= k_n,
\end{aligned}
\tag{5}
$$

which is indeed of the form (2).

We close with the following theorem, which is needed in the text.

> ***Theorem 1*** *Existence, Uniqueness*
> Let the functions $a_{ij}(x)$ $(1 \leq i \leq n,\ 1 \leq j \leq n)$ and $f_i(x)$ $(1 \leq i \leq n)$ be continuous on an interval $a \leq x \leq b$ containing the point x_0. Then there **exist** solutions $y_1(x), \ldots, y_n(x)$ of (2), over $a \leq x \leq b$, which satisfy the stated initial conditions, for any given values of the constants $b_1, \ldots, b_n$. Furthermore, that solution is **unique**.

A.10 CLOSURE

In closing, we feel obliged to reiterate that this appendix has not been intended as a course in ordinary differential equations. Rather, we have reviewed ideas, theorems, formulas, and techniques which are drawn upon in the text. We have emphasized linear equations, especially those of second order. Thus we have included none of the rich results concerning nonlinear equations, for example, and very little concerning first-order equations. For additional reading, the following texts are recommended.

ADDITIONAL REFERENCES

W. E. Boyce and R. C. DiPrima, *Elementary Differential Equations and Boundary Value Problems*, 3rd ed. New York: Wiley, 1977.

R. L. Borrelli and C. S. Coleman, *Differential Equations: A Modeling Approach*. Englewood Cliffs, N.J.: Prentice-Hall, 1987

Appendix: Short Table of Fourier Transforms B

$f(x) = \frac{1}{2\pi}\int_{-\infty}^{\infty} \hat{f}(\omega)e^{i\omega x}\,d\omega$	$\hat{f}(\omega) = \int_{-\infty}^{\infty} f(x)e^{-i\omega x}\,dx$
1. $\begin{cases} 0, & x < 0 \\ e^{-ax}, & x > 0 \end{cases}$ (Re $a > 0$)	$\frac{1}{a + i\omega}$
2. $\begin{cases} e^{ax}, & x < 0 \\ 0, & x > 0 \end{cases}$ (Re $a > 0$)	$\frac{1}{a - i\omega}$
3. $e^{-a\|x\|}$ $(a > 0)$	$\frac{2a}{\omega^2 + a^2}$
4. $\frac{1}{x^2 + a^2}$ $(a > 0)$	$\frac{\pi}{a}e^{-a\|\omega\|}$
5. $e^{-a\|x\|/\sqrt{2}} \sin\left(\frac{a}{\sqrt{2}}\|x\| + \frac{\pi}{4}\right)$ $(a > 0)$	$\frac{2a^3}{\omega^4 + a^4}$
6. $\begin{cases} 1, & \|x\| < a \\ 0, & \|x\| > a \end{cases}$ $(a > 0)$	$\frac{2 \sin a\omega}{\omega}$
7. $\frac{1}{\sqrt{\|x\|}}$	$\sqrt{\frac{2\pi}{\|\omega\|}}$
8. $\begin{cases} 2a - \|x\|, & \|x\| < 2a \\ 0, & \|x\| > 2a \end{cases}$ $(a > 0)$	$\frac{4 \sin^2 a\omega}{\omega^2}$
9. $e^{-x^2/4a}$ $(a > 0)$	$2\sqrt{\pi a}\, e^{-a\omega^2}$
10. $g(ax + b)e^{icx}$ $(a > 0$, c real$)$	$\frac{1}{a}e^{ib(\omega - c)/a}\,\hat{g}\left(\frac{\omega - c}{a}\right)$
11. $g(ax) \cos cx$ $(a > 0$, c real$)$	$\frac{1}{2a}\left[\hat{g}\left(\frac{\omega - c}{a}\right) + \hat{g}\left(\frac{\omega + c}{a}\right)\right]$

$f(x) = \frac{1}{2\pi}\int_{-\infty}^{\infty} \hat{f}(\omega)e^{i\omega x}\,d\omega$	$\hat{f}(\omega) = \int_{-\infty}^{\infty} f(x)e^{-i\omega x}\,dx$
12. $g(ax)\sin cx \quad (a > 0,\ c \text{ real})$	$\frac{1}{2ai}\left[\hat{g}\left(\frac{\omega - c}{a}\right) - \hat{g}\left(\frac{\omega + c}{a}\right)\right]$
13. $g(x + c) \quad (c \text{ real})$	$e^{i\omega c}\hat{g}(\omega)$
14. $\frac{g(x + c) + g(x - c)}{2} \quad (c \text{ real})$	$\cos \omega c\, \hat{g}(\omega)$
15. $\frac{g(x + c) - g(x - c)}{2i} \quad (c \text{ real})$	$\sin \omega c\, \hat{g}(\omega)$
16. $x^n g(x) \quad (n = \text{positive integer})$	$i^n \frac{d^n}{d\omega^n}\hat{g}(\omega)$
17. $\alpha g(x) + \beta h(x)$	$\alpha\hat{g}(\omega) + \beta\hat{h}(\omega)$
18. $g^{(n)}(x)$	$(i\omega)^n\hat{g}(\omega)$
19. $f(x) = \int_{-\infty}^{x} g(\xi)\,d\xi$, where $f(x) \to 0$ as $x \to \infty$	$\hat{f}(\omega) = \frac{1}{i\omega}\hat{g}(\omega)$
20. $(g * h)(x) = \int_{-\infty}^{\infty} g(x - \xi)h(\xi)\,d\xi$	$\hat{g}(\omega)\hat{h}(\omega)$

Appendix: Short Table of Laplace Transforms C

$f(t)$	$\bar{f}(s) = \int_0^\infty f(t)e^{-st}dt$
Note: a, b, p are real constants, and s is regarded as real.	
1. 1	$\frac{1}{s}$ $(s > 0)$
2. e^{at}	$\frac{1}{s-a}$ $(s > a)$
3. $\sin at$	$\frac{a}{s^2 + a^2}$ $(s > 0)$
4. $\cos at$	$\frac{s}{s^2 + a^2}$ $(s > 0)$
5. $\sinh at$	$\frac{a}{s^2 - a^2}$ $(s > \|a\|)$
6. $\cosh at$	$\frac{s}{s^2 - a^2}$ $(s > \|a\|)$
7. t^n $(n =$ positive integer$)$	$\frac{n!}{s^{n+1}}$ $(s > 0)$
8. t^p $(p > -1)$	$\frac{\Gamma(p+1)}{s^{p+1}}$ $(s > 0)$
9. $e^{at} \sin bt$	$\frac{b}{(s-a)^2 + b^2}$ $(s > a)$
10. $e^{at} \cos bt$	$\frac{s-a}{(s-a)^2 + b^2}$ $(s > a)$
11. $t \sin at$	$\frac{2as}{(s^2 + a^2)^2}$ $(s > 0)$

	$f(t)$	$\bar{f}(s) = \int_0^\infty f(t)e^{-st}\,dt$
12.	$t \cos at$	$\dfrac{s^2 - a^2}{(s^2 + a^2)^2} \quad (s > 0)$
13.	$t \sinh at$	$\dfrac{2as}{(s^2 - a^2)^2} \quad (s > a)$
14.	$t \cosh at$	$\dfrac{s^2 + a^2}{(s^2 - a^2)^2} \quad (s > a)$
15.	$t^n e^{at} \quad (n = \text{positive integer})$	$\dfrac{n!}{(s - a)^{n+1}} \quad (s > a)$
16.	$t^p e^{at} \quad (p > -1)$	$\dfrac{\Gamma(p + 1)}{(s - a)^{p+1}} \quad (s > a)$
17.	$\ln t$	$-\dfrac{\gamma + \ln s}{s} \quad (s > 0)$ (γ = Euler's constant ≈ 0.577215665)
18.	$H(t - a) \quad (a \geqq 0)$	$\dfrac{e^{-as}}{s} \quad (s > 0)$
19.	$\delta(t - a) \quad (a > 0)$	e^{-as}
20.	$\delta'(t - a) \quad (a > 0)$	se^{-as}
21.	$\dfrac{e^{-a^2/t}}{\sqrt{t}} \quad (a \geqq 0)$	$\sqrt{\dfrac{\pi}{s}}\, e^{-2a\sqrt{s}} \quad (s > 0)$
22.	$\dfrac{e^{-a^2/t}}{t^{3/2}} \quad (a > 0)$	$\dfrac{\sqrt{\pi}}{a} e^{-2a\sqrt{s}} \quad (s > 0)$
23.	$J_0(t)$	$\dfrac{1}{\sqrt{s^2 + 1}} \quad (s > 0)$
24.	$\alpha u(t) + \beta v(t)$	$\alpha\bar{u}(s) + \beta\bar{v}(s)$ (Section 12.5)
25.	$f'(t)$	$s\bar{f}(s) - f(0)$ (Section 12.5)
26.	$f''(t)$	$s^2\bar{f}(s) - sf(0) - f'(0)$ (Section 12.5)
27.	$f^{(n)}(t)$	$s^n\bar{f}(s) - s^{n-1}f(0) - s^{n-2}f'(0) - \cdots - f^{(n-1)}(0)$ (Section 12.5)
28.	$(f * g)(t) = \int_0^t f(\tau)g(t - \tau)\,d\tau$	$\bar{f}(s)\bar{g}(s)$ (Section 12.5)
29.	$e^{-at}f(t)$	$\bar{f}(s + a)$ (Section 12.7)
30.	$H(t - a)f(t - a)$	$e^{-as}\bar{f}(s)$ (Section 12.7)
31.	$\int_0^t f(\tau)\,d\tau$	$\dfrac{\bar{f}(s)}{s}$ (Section 12.7)
32.	$tf(t)$	$-\dfrac{d\bar{f}(s)}{ds}$ (Section 12.7)
33.	$\dfrac{f(t)}{t}$	$\int_s^\infty \bar{f}(s')\,ds'$ (Section 12.7)
34.	$f(t) \quad [f(t + T) = f(t)]$	$\dfrac{1}{1 - e^{-sT}} \int_0^T f(t)e^{-st}\,dt$ (Section 12.7)

Appendix: Conformal Mapping of Regions

D

Note: Image points denoted by primes.

1.

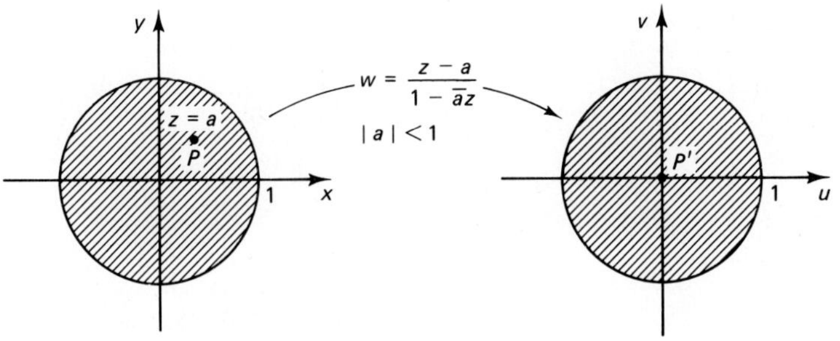

2.

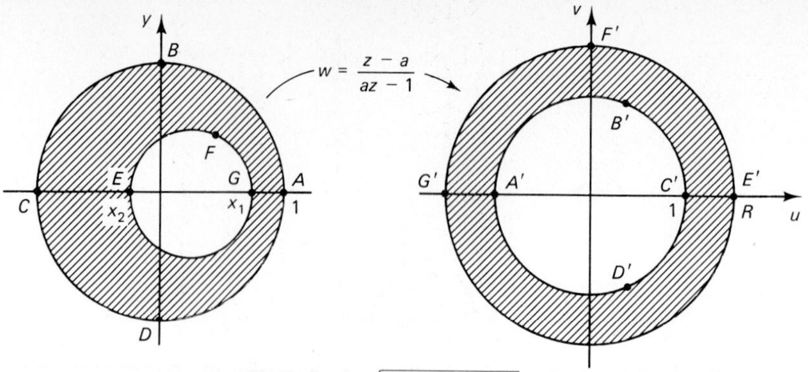

$$a = \frac{1 + x_1x_2 + \sqrt{(1 - x_1^2)(1 - x_2^2)}}{x_1 + x_2}$$

$$R = \frac{1 - x_1x_2 + \sqrt{(1 - x_1^2)(1 - x_2^2)}}{x_1 - x_2}$$

$$-1 < x_2 < x_1 < 1$$

3.

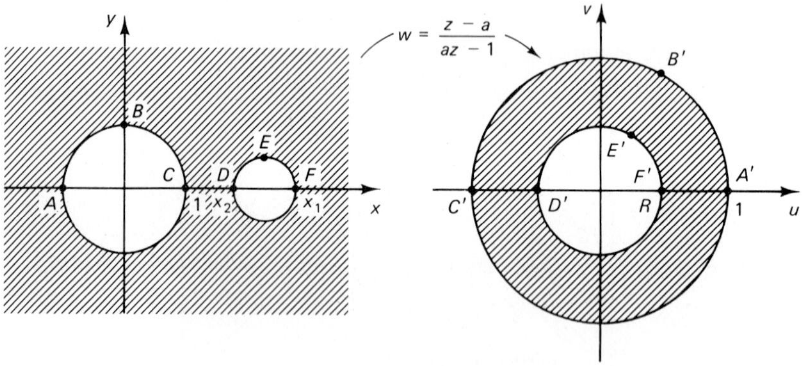

$$a = \frac{x_1x_2 + 1 + \sqrt{(x_1^2 - 1)(x_2^2 - 1)}}{x_1 + x_2}$$

$$R = \frac{x_1x_2 - 1 - \sqrt{(x_1^2 - 1)(x_2^2 - 1)}}{x_1 - x_2}$$

$$1 < x_2 < x_1$$

4.

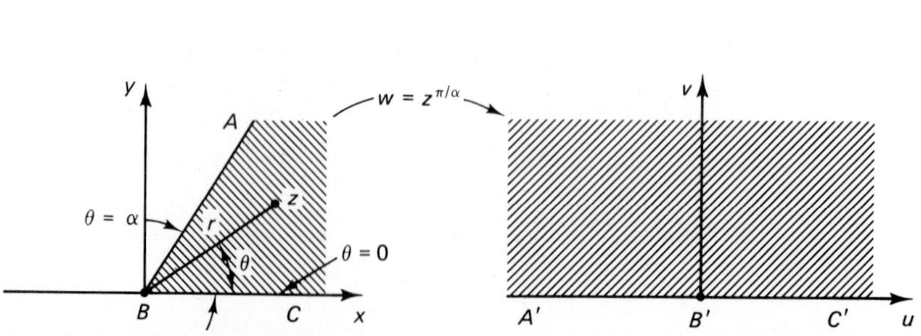

5.

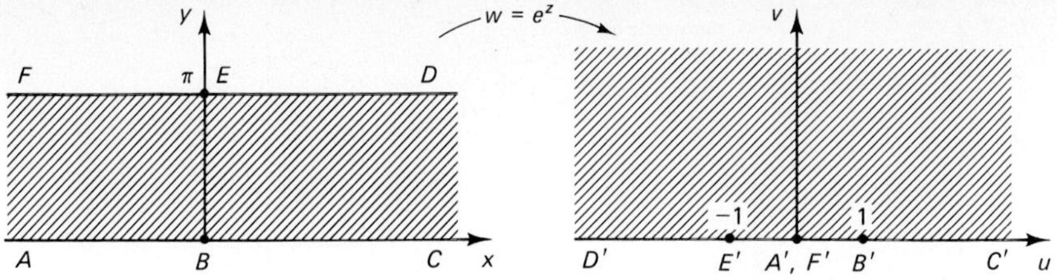
w = e^z
y
F
π
E
D
A
B
C
x
v
−1
1
D′
E′
A′, F′
B′
C′
u

6.

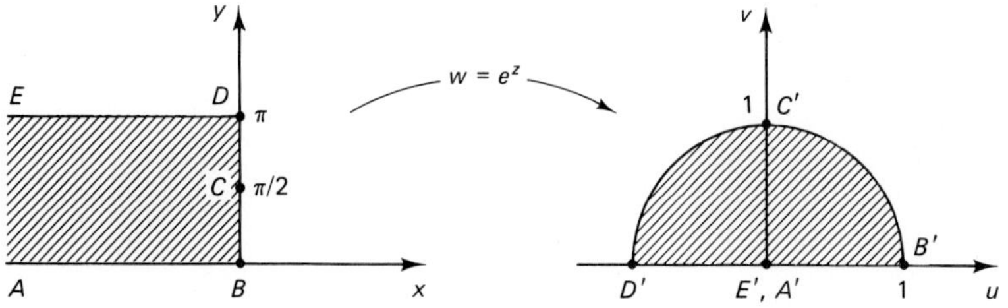
w = e^z
y
E
D
π
C
π/2
A
B
x
v
1
C′
B′
D′
E′, A′
1
u

7.

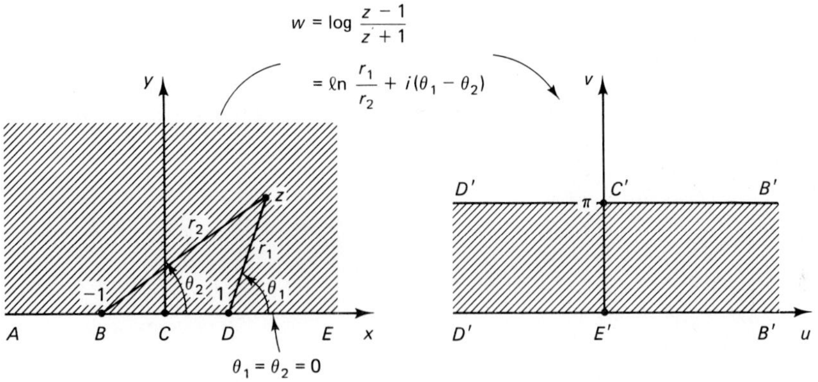
w = log (z − 1)/(z + 1)
= ℓn r₁/r₂ + i(θ₁ − θ₂)
y
z
r₂
r₁
θ₂
θ₁
−1
1
A
B
C
D
E
x
θ₁ = θ₂ = 0
v
D′
π
C′
B′
D′
E′
B′
u

8.

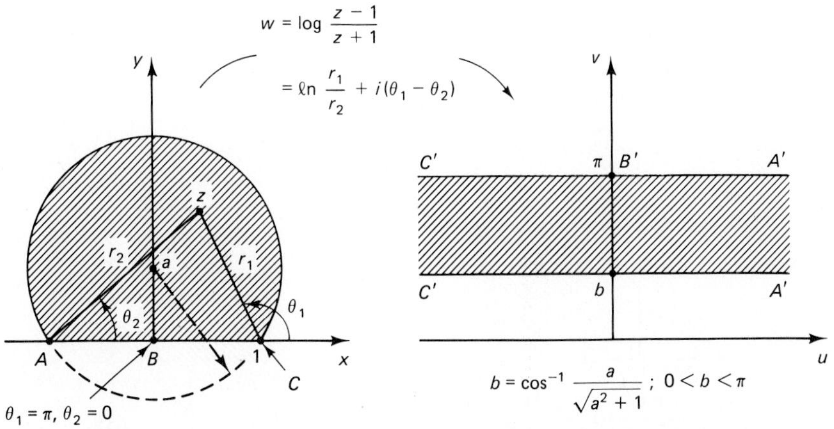
w = log (z − 1)/(z + 1)
= ℓn r₁/r₂ + i(θ₁ − θ₂)
y
z
r₂
a
r₁
θ₂
θ₁
A
B
1
x
C
θ₁ = π, θ₂ = 0
v
C′
π
B′
A′
C′
b
A′
u
b = cos⁻¹ a/√(a² + 1) ; 0 < b < π

9.

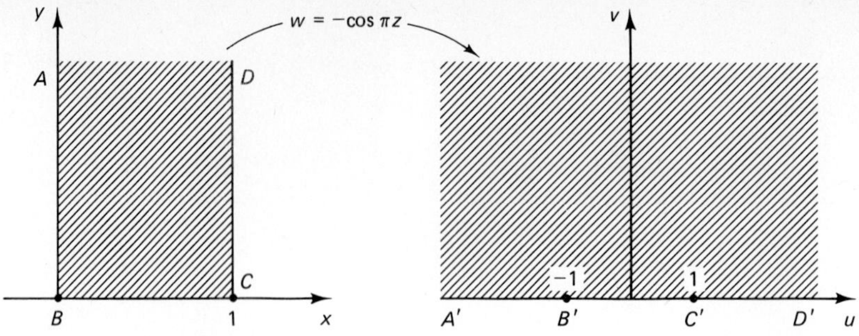
w = −cos πz
y
A
D
C
B
1
x
v
−1
1
A′
B′
C′
D′
u

10.

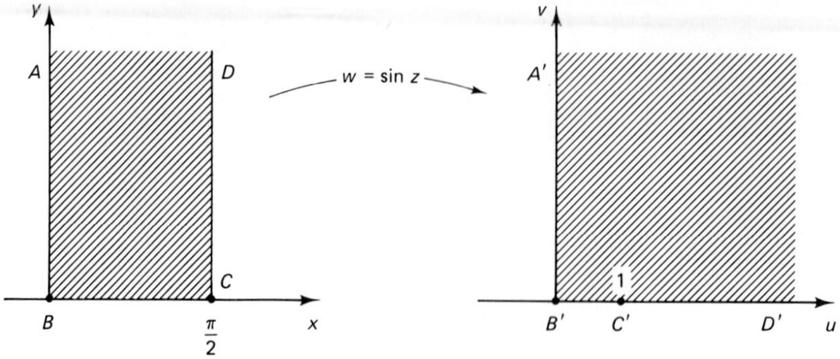
w = sin z
y
A
D
C
B
π/2
x
v
A′
1
B′
C′
D′
u

11.

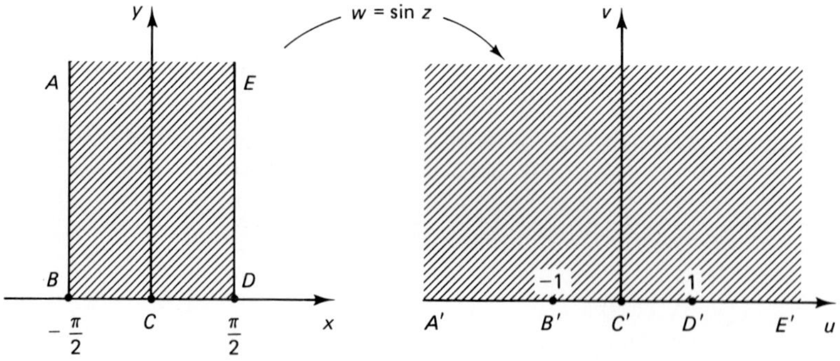
w = sin z
y
A
E
B
D
−π/2
C
π/2
x
v
−1
1
A′
B′
C′
D′
E′
u

12.

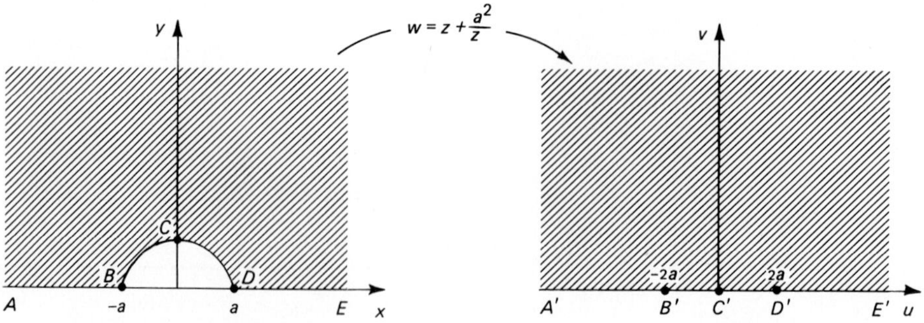
w = z + a²/z
y
C
B
D
A
−a
a
E
x
v
−2a
2a
A′
B′
C′
D′
E′
u

Answers to Selected Exercises

CHAPTER 1

SECTION 1.3

2 (a) $x_4 = \alpha_1$, $x_3 = \alpha_2$, $x_2 = -4 + 3\alpha_1 + 9\alpha_2$, $x_1 = -2 + 3\alpha_1 + 5\alpha_2$
(e) $x_4 = \alpha_1$, $x_3 = \alpha_2$, $x_2 = 2 + \alpha_1 + \alpha_2$, $x_1 = 1 - \alpha_2$ (i) $z = \frac{15}{4}$, $y = -\frac{3}{4}$, $x = \frac{7}{2}$
3 (a) $i_3 = i_2 = \dfrac{E}{3R}$, $i_1 = \dfrac{2E}{3R}$ **6** (a) $x_1 = \pm 3$, $x_2 = \pm\sqrt{10}$, $x_3 = 0$ (four solutions)
7 (a) $\lambda = 1$ gives $y = \alpha$, $x = -\alpha$; $\lambda = 3$ gives $y = x = \alpha$; no nontrivial solutions for $\lambda \neq 3$ or 1

CHAPTER 2

SECTION 2.3

4 (a) 1 (d) -1 (g) $-\frac{1}{2}$ **5** (a) 48.19° (g) 70.53°

SECTION 2.5

1 (a) $\|\mathbf{u}\| = 5$, $\|\mathbf{v}\| = \sqrt{5}$, $\theta = 1.11$ rad $= 63.4°$ (g) $\|\mathbf{u}\| = \sqrt{15}$, $\|\mathbf{v}\| = 3\sqrt{5}$, $\theta = 2.09$ rad $= 120.0°$
3 (c) $ABC = 108.4°$, $BCD = 90°$, $CDE = 116.6°$, $DEA = 90°$, $EAB = 135°$; sum $= 540°$ (correct for every pentagon) **6** (a) $\mathbf{u}_1 = \mathbf{u} = (1, 3, 0)$, $\mathbf{u}_2 = \mathbf{u} - \frac{10}{11}\mathbf{v} = (-\frac{9}{11}, \frac{3}{11}, 0)$, $\mathbf{u}_3 = \mathbf{u} - \frac{5}{4}\mathbf{v} + \frac{3}{4}\mathbf{w} = (0, 0, -\frac{9}{4})$
7 (a) $3\sqrt{3}$ **9** (a) $(\alpha, \beta, 3\alpha)$; α, β arbitrary **10** (c) $\mathbf{u}_1 = (0, \frac{18}{13}, \frac{27}{13})$, $\mathbf{u}_2 = (2, \frac{21}{13}, -\frac{14}{13})$
12 (b) $l_1 = \dfrac{2}{\sqrt{30}}$, $l_2 = -\dfrac{1}{\sqrt{30}}$, $l_3 = \dfrac{5}{\sqrt{30}}$ **14** (a) Yes **15** (a) $\pm\left(-\dfrac{1}{\sqrt{14}}, \dfrac{2}{\sqrt{14}}, \dfrac{3}{\sqrt{14}}\right)$

SECTION 2.6

1 (a) No, (6) is not satisfied. (b) Yes **2** Yes; (2), (6), and (iii)

SECTION 2.7

1 (a) Yes (d) No (h) Yes

3 (a) No, there is no negative inverse. That is, if $\mathbf{u} = (x_1, x_2)$ is in L then, if L is to be a vector space, we need $(-x_1, -x_2)$ to be in L—but it is not. **5** (a) span $\{(-4, 0, 1), (1, 1, 0)\}$ **6** (a) $(-4, 0, 1)$ and $(2, 1, 0)$, say

SECTION 2.8

1 (a) LD (g) LI (m) LI

SECTION 2.9

1 (a) No (g) Yes (p) No **2** (a) $\mathbf{u} = \frac{1}{7}\mathbf{e}_1 + \frac{1}{5}\mathbf{e}_2 + \frac{3}{35}\mathbf{e}_3$ **3** (a) $\mathbf{u} = \dfrac{2}{\sqrt{14}}\hat{\mathbf{e}}_1 + \dfrac{1}{\sqrt{5}}\hat{\mathbf{e}}_2 + \dfrac{6}{\sqrt{70}}\hat{\mathbf{e}}_3$

4 (a) $\mathbf{u} = \frac{1}{15}\mathbf{e}_1 + \frac{1}{3}\mathbf{e}_2 + \frac{1}{5}\mathbf{e}_4$ **9** (b) $\hat{\mathbf{n}} = \pm\left(\dfrac{2}{\sqrt{14}}\hat{\mathbf{i}} + \dfrac{3}{\sqrt{14}}\hat{\mathbf{j}} - \dfrac{1}{\sqrt{14}}\hat{\mathbf{k}}\right)$, $c = \dfrac{5}{\sqrt{14}}$

12 (a) $\hat{\mathbf{e}}_1 = (1, 0)$, $\hat{\mathbf{e}}_2 = (0, 1)$

(d) $\hat{\mathbf{e}}_1 = \left(\dfrac{1}{\sqrt{2}}, \dfrac{1}{\sqrt{2}}, 0\right)$, $\hat{\mathbf{e}}_2 = \left(\dfrac{3}{\sqrt{22}}, -\dfrac{3}{\sqrt{22}}, \dfrac{2}{\sqrt{22}}\right)$, $\hat{\mathbf{e}}_3 = \left(-\dfrac{1}{\sqrt{11}}, \dfrac{1}{\sqrt{11}}, \dfrac{3}{\sqrt{11}}\right)$

13 (e) $\mathbf{e}_1^* = (1, -1, 0)$, $\mathbf{e}_2^* = (0, 1, -1)$, $\mathbf{e}_3^* = (0, 0, 1)$

SECTION 2.10

1 (a) 1 (d) 3 **2** (a) 3 (d) 1 **3** (a) 2 (e) 1 **8** (a) 3

CHAPTER 3

SECTION 3.2

2 (a) Not defined (d) 6×1 **5** (a) Only if $\mathbf{AB} = \mathbf{BA}$ **8** (a) $\begin{pmatrix} 2^{99} & 2^{99} \\ 2^{99} & 2^{99} \end{pmatrix}$ (e) $\mathbf{0}$ **10** (a) $\begin{pmatrix} 0 & 0 & 0 & 0 \\ 1 & 0 & 0 & 0 \\ 0 & 1 & 0 & 0 \end{pmatrix}$

16 (b) $\begin{pmatrix} 1 & 1 \\ 0 & -1 \end{pmatrix}$, say **20** (a) $\mathbf{0}$ (c) $\begin{pmatrix} 0 & 0 \\ \alpha & \beta \end{pmatrix}$; α, β arbitrary

22 Probability that A is bankrupt after three matches, starting with \$1, is $p_{21}^{(3)} = \frac{5}{8}$.

SECTION 3.3

1 (a) -3 and $\begin{pmatrix} 3 & 6 \\ -3 & -6 \end{pmatrix}$, respectively **5** (b) $\begin{pmatrix} 1 & 3 & \frac{5}{2} \\ 3 & 4 & 0 \\ \frac{5}{2} & 0 & 7 \end{pmatrix}$ **6** (a) $\begin{pmatrix} 0 & 5 \\ 5 & 0 \end{pmatrix} + \begin{pmatrix} 0 & 2 \\ -2 & 0 \end{pmatrix}$

SECTION 3.4

2 (g) -40 **3** (a) 0 (g) -24 (m) 5 **10** (a) 232

18 (a) $a_4 = 0$, so unstable (b) $\Delta_2 = 0$, so unstable (c) Stable

24 (a) $\det \mathbf{A}' = -\det \mathbf{A}$ (d) $\det \mathbf{A}' = 2 \det \mathbf{A}$

SECTION 3.5

1 (a) 1 (g) 2 (m) 3 **2** (a) 4 **7** (a) $x_1 = \frac{2}{5}$, $x_2 = \frac{9}{5}$

10 (c) $r(\mathbf{A}) = 1$. If $c \neq 6$, then $r(\mathbf{A}|\mathbf{c}) = 2$, and there are no solutions. If $c = -6$, then $r(\mathbf{A}|\mathbf{c}) = 1$ and there is a three-parameter family of solutions. **11** (a) $\lambda = 1, 3$ **14** (a) $r = 2$, so the set is LD.

15 $H_2 + O_2 = 2OH$, $O_2 + 2H_2O = 4OH$, $2H_2O + O = H + 3OH$, $H + O = OH$

SECTION 3.6

1 (a) $\mathbf{A}^{-1} = \dfrac{1}{ad - bc}\begin{pmatrix} d & -b \\ -c & a \end{pmatrix}$ (g) $\mathbf{A}^{-1} = \begin{pmatrix} 1 & -1 & 0 \\ 0 & 1 & -1 \\ 0 & 0 & 1 \end{pmatrix}$ **3** (a) $x_1 = \frac{-24}{-13} = \frac{24}{13}$, $x_2 = \frac{6}{-13} = -\frac{6}{13}$

6 (a) $\mathbf{A}^{-1} = \begin{pmatrix} -2 & 7 \\ 1 & -3 \end{pmatrix}$ (d) $\mathbf{A}^{-1} = \begin{pmatrix} \frac{5}{2} & \frac{1}{2} & -2 \\ 4 & 0 & -3 \\ -1 & 0 & 1 \end{pmatrix}$

10 An $n \times n$ matrix $\mathbf{A}$ is invertible if and only if det $\mathbf{A} = n$ (Theorem 1). But then $r(\mathbf{A}) = n$ and (by Theorem 2 of Section 3.5) that implies that $\mathbf{A}$ has n LI rows (columns).
13 Only if $\mathbf{A}^{-1}$ and $\mathbf{B}$ happen to commute, for then $\mathbf{A}^{-1}\mathbf{BA} = \mathbf{BA}^{-1}\mathbf{A} = \mathbf{BI} = \mathbf{B}$.
15 $(\mathbf{A}^{-1})^{\mathrm{T}} = (\mathbf{A}^{\mathrm{T}})^{-1}$ by property I5. This $= \mathbf{A}^{-1}$ since $\mathbf{A}^{\mathrm{T}} = \mathbf{A}$ by assumption. Thus $\mathbf{A}^{-1}$ is symmetric.

16 (c) $\mathbf{x} = \dfrac{1}{8k}\begin{pmatrix} 5 & 4 & 3 \\ 4 & 8 & 4 \\ 3 & 4 & 5 \end{pmatrix}\begin{pmatrix} f_1 \\ f_2 \\ f_3 \end{pmatrix}$

SECTION 3.7

1 $\mathbf{Q} = \begin{pmatrix} 1 & 2 \\ 1 & -1 \end{pmatrix}$. Not orthogonal because column vectors are not ON. $[\mathbf{x}]_{B'} = \begin{pmatrix} 3 \\ 6 \end{pmatrix}$, $[\mathbf{x}]_B = \begin{pmatrix} \frac{8}{3} \\ -\frac{1}{3} \end{pmatrix}$

3 (a) $\mathbf{Q} = \begin{pmatrix} 2/\sqrt{5} & 1/\sqrt{5} \\ 1/\sqrt{5} & -2/\sqrt{5} \end{pmatrix}$, which is orthogonal. **4** (b) $[\mathbf{x}]_{B'} = (\sqrt{2}, 2, 5/\sqrt{3}, -10/\sqrt{6})^{\mathrm{T}}$

5 (a) No (d) Yes **9** $\mathbf{Q}^n = \begin{pmatrix} \cos n\theta & \sin n\theta \\ -\sin n\theta & \cos n\theta \end{pmatrix}$

SECTION 3.8

2 (a) Nonlinear (d) Linear **4** (b) The nth-order identity matrix $\mathbf{I}$
6 (a) dim $R = 2$, dim $K = 1$, dim $V = 3$. $\mathbf{F}$ is onto, is not one-to-one and is not invertible. A basis for K is $(0, -1, 1)^{\mathrm{T}}$, and a basis for R is $\begin{pmatrix} 1 \\ 0 \end{pmatrix}$, $\begin{pmatrix} 0 \\ 1 \end{pmatrix}$.
(d) dim $R = 2$, dim $K = 0$, dim $V = 2$. $\mathbf{F}$ is not onto, is one-to-one, and is not invertible. A basis for R is $(4, 3, 0)^{\mathrm{T}}$, $(0, 5, -4)^{\mathrm{T}}$, and K has no basis.
7 (a) $\begin{pmatrix} 1 & 0 \\ 0 & 0 \end{pmatrix}$ is one-to-one but not onto. There exists none that is onto but not one-to-one. $\begin{pmatrix} 0 & 0 \\ 0 & 0 \end{pmatrix}$ is neither onto nor one-to-one. $\begin{pmatrix} 1 & 2 \\ 1 & 1 \end{pmatrix}$ is onto and one-to-one.

9 $\mathbf{A} = \begin{pmatrix} v_1^2 & v_1v_2 & v_1v_3 \\ v_2v_1 & v_2^2 & v_2v_3 \\ v_3v_1 & v_3v_2 & v_3^2 \end{pmatrix}$ **12** (b) $\mathbf{A} = \begin{pmatrix} 2L_1^2 - 1 & 2L_2L_1 \\ 2L_1L_2 & 2L_2^2 - 1 \end{pmatrix}$

13 (a) $(\mathbf{GF})(\mathbf{x}) = \begin{pmatrix} -20 \\ -40 \end{pmatrix}$. $\mathbf{GF}$ transformation matrix $= \begin{pmatrix} 2 & 10 & 6 & -4 \\ 4 & 20 & 12 & -8 \end{pmatrix}$
15 (c) $\mathbf{F}(\mathbf{X}) = (2, 1, \sqrt{2} - 3, 1)^{\mathrm{T}}$
(d) $\mathbf{F}(\mathbf{X}_p) = (1.2439, 3.5859, 2.2637, 1)^{\mathrm{T}}$, $\mathbf{F}(\mathbf{X}_e) = (1.5394, 3.7757, 1.3275, 1)^{\mathrm{T}}$

CHAPTER 4

SECTION 4.2

1 (a) $\lambda = 0$. A basis for eigenspace corresponding to $\lambda = 0$ is $(1, 0, 0)^{\mathrm{T}}$, $(0, 1, 0)^{\mathrm{T}}$, $(0, 0, 1)^{\mathrm{T}}$, say.
(g) $\lambda = 0$; basis is $(c, 0, -a)^{\mathrm{T}}$, $(b, -a, 0)^{\mathrm{T}}$, say. $\lambda = a + b + c$; basis is $(1, 1, 1)^{\mathrm{T}}$, say.
(m) $\lambda = 1$; basis is $(0, 1, 0)^{\mathrm{T}}$.
7 (a) $\lambda = 1$, with $\mathbf{e} = \alpha(1, 0, 0)^{\mathrm{T}} + \beta(1, -2, 0)^{\mathrm{T}}$; $\lambda = 2$, with $\mathbf{e} = \alpha(8, 2, 3)^{\mathrm{T}}$.
10 No. For example $\mathbf{A} = \begin{pmatrix} 1 & 2 \\ 0 & 3 \end{pmatrix}$ and $\mathbf{B} = \begin{pmatrix} 1 & 0 \\ 6 & 3 \end{pmatrix}$ both have $\lambda = 1, 3$. **14** (c) $\mathbf{p}_{\mathrm{eq}} = \dfrac{x_0 + y_0}{4}\begin{pmatrix} 1 \\ 3 \end{pmatrix}$

16 (a) $\lambda = \frac{3}{2}$, $\mathbf{e} = \alpha\begin{pmatrix} 1 \\ 1 \end{pmatrix}$; $\lambda = \frac{1}{3}$, $\mathbf{e} = \beta\begin{pmatrix} 1 \\ -1 \end{pmatrix}$

SECTION 4.3

1 (a) $(1, 0, 0, 0)^{\mathrm{T}}, \left(0, \frac{1}{\sqrt{2}}, \frac{1}{\sqrt{2}}, 0\right)^{\mathrm{T}}, (0, 0, 0, 1)^{\mathrm{T}}, \left(0, \frac{1}{\sqrt{2}}, -\frac{1}{\sqrt{2}}, 0\right)^{\mathrm{T}}$, say.

2 (a) $\mathbf{e}$'s $= \alpha\begin{pmatrix}1\\0\end{pmatrix}$ and $\beta\begin{pmatrix}1\\-1\end{pmatrix}$, which are LI but not orthogonal.

5 (a) High mode has $\omega = 4.588$, $\mathbf{e} = \begin{pmatrix}1\\-19.05\end{pmatrix}$; low mode has $\omega = 1.396$, $\mathbf{e} = \begin{pmatrix}1\\0.0525\end{pmatrix}$.

6 (b) For low mode, need $a = b$ and $c = d$.

8 $\mathbf{x} = A_1\begin{pmatrix}\sin(t + \phi_1)\\ \sin(t + \phi_1)\end{pmatrix} + A_2\begin{pmatrix}4\sin(\sqrt{6}t + \phi_2)\\ -\sin(\sqrt{6}t + \phi_2)\end{pmatrix}$. Eigenfrequencies are $1, \sqrt{6}$. Modes not orthogonal.

12 (b) $\lambda \approx 6.99$ (exact $\lambda = 7$), $\mathbf{e} \approx \begin{pmatrix}0.02\\1\\0.98\end{pmatrix}$ (exact $\mathbf{e} = \begin{pmatrix}0\\1\\1\end{pmatrix}$). (d) $\lambda \approx -6.9955$, $\mathbf{e} \approx \begin{pmatrix}0.0013\\0.9975\\1\end{pmatrix}$

(i) $\lambda = 3$, $\mathbf{e} = \alpha\begin{pmatrix}1\\1\\0\end{pmatrix} + \beta\begin{pmatrix}0\\0\\1\end{pmatrix}$

SECTION 4.4

1 (a) $\mathbf{Q} = \begin{pmatrix}1 & 3\\0 & 2\end{pmatrix}$, $\mathbf{D} = \begin{pmatrix}2 & 0\\0 & 0\end{pmatrix}$ (d) $\mathbf{Q} = \begin{pmatrix}1/\sqrt{2} & 1/\sqrt{3} & 1/\sqrt{6}\\ -1/\sqrt{2} & 1/\sqrt{3} & 1/\sqrt{6}\\ 0 & -1/\sqrt{3} & 2/\sqrt{6}\end{pmatrix}$, $\mathbf{D} = \begin{pmatrix}0 & 0 & 0\\0 & -1 & 0\\0 & 0 & 2\end{pmatrix}$

3 (a) $x = Ae^{2t} + B$, $y = Ae^{2t} - B$
(e) $x = Ae^{2t} + Be^{7t} + Ce^{-t}$, $y = Ae^{2t} - 2Ce^{-t}$, $z = -Ae^{2t} + Be^{7t} - Ce^{-t}$

4 Yes. For example, if $\mathbf{A}$ has n distinct λ's, one of which is zero, then, $\det \mathbf{A} = 0$ (so $\mathbf{A}$ is singular), yet $\mathbf{A}$ is diagonalizable per Theorem 3.

7 (a) $x \approx 0.9990A_1 \sin(0.4799t + \phi_1) + 0.0455A_2 \sin(3.126t + \phi_2)$,
$y \approx 0.0455A_1 \sin(0.4799t + \phi_1) - 0.9990A_2 \sin(3.126t + \phi_2)$ Low mode: frequency ≈ 0.4799, mode shape $\approx \begin{pmatrix}0.9990\\0.0455\end{pmatrix}$ High mode: frequency ≈ 3.126, mode shape $\approx \begin{pmatrix}0.0455\\-0.9990\end{pmatrix}$

8 (d) $\mathbf{I}' = \begin{pmatrix}I_{x'x'} & 0 & 0\\0 & I_{y'y'} & 0\\0 & 0 & I_{z'z'}\end{pmatrix} = \begin{pmatrix}\frac{127\sigma}{12} & 0 & 0\\0 & \frac{121\sigma}{12} & 0\\0 & 0 & \frac{62\sigma}{3}\end{pmatrix}$, where the x', y', z', axes are defined by the eigenvectors $\frac{1}{\sqrt{2}}\begin{pmatrix}1\\-1\\0\end{pmatrix}, \frac{1}{\sqrt{2}}\begin{pmatrix}1\\1\\0\end{pmatrix}, \begin{pmatrix}0\\0\\1\end{pmatrix}$, respectively.

SECTION 4.5

2 (a) $\mathbf{P} = \begin{pmatrix}1 & 0\\0 & \frac{1}{4}\end{pmatrix}$, $\mathbf{J} = \begin{pmatrix}1 & 1\\0 & 1\end{pmatrix}$ (g) $\mathbf{P} = \begin{pmatrix}2 & 1\\1 & 0\end{pmatrix}$, $\mathbf{J} = \begin{pmatrix}0 & 1\\0 & 0\end{pmatrix}$

(m) $\mathbf{P} = \begin{pmatrix}1 & 0 & 0 & 0\\0 & -1 & -1 & 2\\0 & 1 & 0 & -1\\0 & 1 & 1 & -1\end{pmatrix}$, $\mathbf{J} = \begin{pmatrix}-1 & 1 & 0 & 0\\0 & -1 & 1 & 0\\0 & 0 & -1 & 1\\0 & 0 & 0 & -1\end{pmatrix}$

3 (a) $x = (At + B)e^t$, $y = [-2At + (A - 2B)]e^t$
(f) $x = [(C_2 + C_3) + C_2t]e^{3t} + C_1e^{-t}$, $y = [(C_2 + 2C_3) + 2C_2t]e^{3t} + C_1e^{-t}$, $z = 2C_2e^{3t} + C_1e^{-t}$.

SECTION 4.6

1 (a) With $x_1 \equiv x$ and $\dot{x}_1 = \dot{x} \equiv x_2$, we have $\dot{x}_1 = x_2$; $x_1(0) = 5$ and $\dot{x}_2 = -6x_1 + 2\sin t$; $x_2(0) = -4$, so
$\mathbf{A} = \begin{pmatrix} 0 & 1 \\ -6 & 0 \end{pmatrix}$, $\mathbf{f} = \begin{pmatrix} 0 \\ 2\sin t \end{pmatrix}$, $\mathbf{c} = \begin{pmatrix} 5 \\ -4 \end{pmatrix}$.

2 (a) $\mathbf{A} = \begin{pmatrix} 1 & 1 \\ 1 & 1 \end{pmatrix}$, $\mathbf{f} = \begin{pmatrix} 0 \\ e^{3t} \end{pmatrix}$, $\mathbf{c} = \begin{pmatrix} 0 \\ 0 \end{pmatrix}$. $\mathbf{Q} = \begin{pmatrix} 1 & 1 \\ 1 & -1 \end{pmatrix}$, $\mathbf{Q}^{-1} = \frac{1}{2}\begin{pmatrix} 1 & 1 \\ 1 & -1 \end{pmatrix}$, $\mathbf{D} = \begin{pmatrix} 2 & 0 \\ 0 & 0 \end{pmatrix}$,
$x = \frac{1}{3}e^{3t} - \frac{1}{2}e^{2t} + \frac{1}{6}$, $y = \frac{2}{3}e^{3t} - \frac{1}{2}e^{2t} - \frac{1}{6}$.

4 (a) $e^{\mathbf{A}} = \begin{pmatrix} e & e^3 - e \\ 0 & e^3 \end{pmatrix}$ (f) $e^{\mathbf{A}} = \begin{pmatrix} 1 & 5 \\ 0 & 1 \end{pmatrix}$ (i) $e^{\mathbf{A}} = \frac{e}{2}\begin{pmatrix} -3 & 2 & -7 \\ 3 & 0 & 5 \\ 5 & -2 & 9 \end{pmatrix}$

SECTION 4.7

1 (a) $\begin{pmatrix} 2 & \frac{1}{2} \\ \frac{1}{2} & 4 \end{pmatrix}$ (j) $\begin{pmatrix} 0 & \frac{1}{2} & \frac{1}{2} \\ \frac{1}{2} & 0 & \frac{1}{2} \\ \frac{1}{2} & \frac{1}{2} & 1 \end{pmatrix}$

2 (a) $2x_1^2 + 4x_2^2 + x_1x_2 = \dfrac{3 + \sqrt{5}}{2}x_1'^2 + \dfrac{3 - \sqrt{5}}{2}x_2'^2$. Positive definite. $\mathbf{Q} = \begin{pmatrix} \dfrac{1}{a} & \dfrac{1}{b} \\ \dfrac{2 + \sqrt{5}}{a} & \dfrac{2 - \sqrt{5}}{b} \end{pmatrix}$,
where $a = \sqrt{10 + 4\sqrt{5}}$, $b = \sqrt{10 - 4\sqrt{5}}$ (g) $3x_1x_2 = \frac{3}{2}x_1'^2 - \frac{3}{2}x_2'^2$, $\mathbf{Q} = \dfrac{1}{\sqrt{2}}\begin{pmatrix} 1 & 1 \\ 1 & -1 \end{pmatrix}$

4 (a) $\mathbf{x} = \mathbf{Q}\mathbf{x}'$, so $\mathbf{x}' = \mathbf{Q}^{-1}\mathbf{x} = \mathbf{Q}^{\mathrm{T}}\mathbf{x}$ (if $\mathbf{Q}$ *is* a modal matrix), so we identify $\mathbf{Q} = \begin{pmatrix} 1 & 0 \\ \frac{1}{2} & 1 \end{pmatrix}$. But the columns are not ON.
(e) $x_3^2 + 2x_1x_3 = (x_3^2 + 2x_1x_3 + x_1^2) - x_1^2 = (x_3 + x_1)^2 - x_1^2 = x_1'^2 - x_2'^2$, where $x_1' = x_1 + x_3$, $x_2' = x_1$, $x_3' = \alpha x_1 + \beta x_2 + \gamma x_3$ (α, β, γ arbitrary)

6 $V \sim \frac{1}{2}kx^2 + \frac{1}{2}ky^2 - \dfrac{P}{l}(x^2 - xy + y^2)$
$\mathbf{A} = \begin{pmatrix} \dfrac{k}{2} - \dfrac{P}{l} & \dfrac{P}{2l} \\ \dfrac{P}{2l} & \dfrac{k}{2} - \dfrac{P}{l} \end{pmatrix}$, $\lambda_1 = \dfrac{1}{2}\left(k - \dfrac{P}{l}\right)$, $\lambda_2 = \dfrac{1}{2}\left(k - \dfrac{3P}{l}\right)$, and $\lambda_1 > 0$, $\lambda_2 > 0$ gives $P < \dfrac{kl}{3}$, so $P_{cr} = \dfrac{kl}{3}$.

CHAPTER 5

SECTION 5.2

1 (a) $\hat{\mathbf{u}} = \left(\dfrac{1}{\sqrt{2}}, \dfrac{i}{\sqrt{2}}\right)$ **2** (a) The set is a basis for $\mathbb{C}^3$. **4** (a) $\mathbf{u} = \dfrac{4 - 5i}{2}\mathbf{e}_1 + \dfrac{8i}{9}\mathbf{e}_2 - \dfrac{9 - 4i}{18}\mathbf{e}_3$
5 $(\alpha\mathbf{x} \cdot \mathbf{y}) = \Sigma_{j=1}^n \alpha x_j\bar{y}_j = \alpha\, \Sigma_{j=1}^n x_j\bar{y}_j = \alpha(\mathbf{x} \cdot \mathbf{y})$, $\mathbf{x} \cdot (\alpha\mathbf{y}) = \Sigma_{j=1}^n x_j\overline{\alpha y_j} = \bar{\alpha}\, \Sigma_{j=1}^n x_j\bar{y}_j = \bar{\alpha}(\mathbf{x} \cdot \mathbf{y})$

SECTION 5.3

1 (a) $\mathbf{A}^{-1} = \dfrac{8 + i}{65}\begin{pmatrix} 4 & -i \\ -1 & 2 \end{pmatrix}$

2 (a) $\lambda_1 = 3 + \sqrt[4]{2}\, e^{\pi i/8}$, $\mathbf{e}_1 = \alpha\left(1, \sqrt[4]{2}\sin\dfrac{\pi}{8} - \left(1 + \sqrt[4]{2}\cos\dfrac{\pi}{8}\right)i\right)^{\mathrm{T}}$, $\lambda_2 = 3 - \sqrt[4]{2}\, e^{\pi i/8}$,
$\mathbf{e}_2 = \beta\left(1, -\sqrt[4]{2}\sin\dfrac{\pi}{8} + \left(-1 + \sqrt[4]{2}\cos\dfrac{\pi}{8}\right)i\right)^{\mathrm{T}}$, α, β arbitrary.

3 (b) $\lambda_1 = 2 + i$, $\mathbf{e}_1 = \alpha\begin{pmatrix}1\\ i\end{pmatrix}$; $\lambda_2 = 2 - i$, $\mathbf{e}_2 = \beta\begin{pmatrix}1\\ -i\end{pmatrix}$, α, β arbitrary **4** $(a - d)^2 + 4bc < 0$

5 (a) $\mathbf{A} = \begin{pmatrix}2 & 1+i\\ 1-i & 3\end{pmatrix}$, $\lambda_1 = 1$, $\mathbf{e}_1 = \alpha\begin{pmatrix}1+i\\ -1\end{pmatrix}$, $\lambda_2 = 4$, $\mathbf{e}_2 = \beta\begin{pmatrix}1\\ 1-i\end{pmatrix}$ so $F = |x_1'|^2 + 4|x_2'|^2$, where

$\mathbf{x} = \mathbf{U}\mathbf{x}' = \dfrac{1}{\sqrt{3}}\begin{pmatrix}1+i & 1\\ -1 & 1-i\end{pmatrix}\mathbf{x}'$, and $\mathbf{x}' = \mathbf{U}^{-1}\mathbf{x} = \mathbf{U}^*\mathbf{x} = \dfrac{1}{\sqrt{3}}\begin{pmatrix}1-i & -1\\ 1 & 1+i\end{pmatrix}\mathbf{x}$

6 (b) $\mathbf{A}^{1000} = \dfrac{1}{5}\begin{pmatrix}4+6^{1000} & 2i(1-6^{1000})\\ 2i(6^{1000}-1) & 4(6^{1000})+1\end{pmatrix}$ **10** Neither. **13** (a) $c_2 = c_1$ (b) None

CHAPTER 6

SECTION 6.2

1 (a) $\sqrt{21}$ (d) $5\sqrt{2}$ **2** No **6** (a) Boundary points are $x = 0$, $x = 1$. Connected. Neither.
(f) The set is $\{x \mid x = n\pi,\ n = 0, \pm 1, \pm 2, \ldots\}$. Not connected. Closed. Each point of the set is a boundary point.
(k) Boundary points are the origin and the circle $\{(x_1, x_2) \mid x_1^2 + x_2^2 = 1\}$. Connected. Open.
(n) Boundary points are $\{(x_1, x_2, x_3, x_4) \mid x_1^2 + x_2^2 + x_3^2 + x_4^2 = 3\}$. Connected. Open.

SECTION 6.3

1 (a) $f_x = 3x^2y^5$, $f_y = 5x^3y^4$, $f_{xy} = 15x^2y^4$, $f_{yx} = 15x^2y^4$, $f_{xx} = 6xy^5$, $f_{yy} = 20x^3y^3$, $f_{xy} = f_{yx}$ for all x, y
5 (a) $f_x(0, 0) = 1$ (e) $f_y(6, 0)$ does not exist (i) $f_{xy}(0, 0)$ does not exist

SECTION 6.4

1 $(2500t^3 + 6t)\cos(625t^4 + 3t^2 + 3)$ **3** (a) $(\sin s \cos s - 3\sin 6s)/\sqrt{\sin^2 s + \cos 6s}$

4 (a) $[t + t\sin t(\sin t + t\cos t)]/\sqrt{t^2(\sin^2 t + 1) + 16}$ **5** (a) $\dfrac{126}{25e}$ **9** (a) $y(x) = AJ_0(kx) + BY_0(kx)$

SECTION 6.5

1 (a) $e^{-2x} = 1 - 2x + 2x^2 - \frac{4}{3}x^3 + \cdots$ (f) $\dfrac{1}{1 + x^2} = \frac{1}{2} + \frac{1}{2}(x + 1) + \frac{1}{4}(x + 1)^2 + 0(x + 1)^3 + \cdots$

3 (a) $|\sin x - x| = \left|\dfrac{\cos\mu}{6}x^3\right| < \dfrac{\cos 0}{6}(0.5)^3 = 0.0208$

SECTION 6.6

1 (a) Conditions not met because $f_y(2, 1) = 0$. (d) $y(x) = 1 + \dfrac{3}{2}(x + 2) + \dfrac{48 - 9\pi^2}{32}(x + 2)^2 + \cdots$

(h) $y(x) = 1 + \dfrac{2}{e}(x - 1) + \dfrac{e - 4}{e^2}(x - 1)^2 + \cdots$ **2** (a) $y' = \dfrac{y}{3y^2 - x}$, $y'' = -\dfrac{2xy}{(3y^2 - x)^3}$

4 (a) $y_x = \dfrac{1}{2ye^{-y} - x}$ **5** (a) Conditions not met, because $\dfrac{\partial(f, g)}{\partial(u, v)} = 0$ at $(0, 0, 0, 0)$; no conclusion.

6 (a) $J(u, v) = -16uv$

SECTION 6.7

1 (a) $x_u = x_v = 1$, $y_u = 2v$, $y_v = 2u$ and, if $v \neq u$, $u_x = \dfrac{u}{u - v}$, $u_y = \dfrac{1}{v - u}$, $v_x = \dfrac{2v}{v - u}$, $v_y = \dfrac{1}{u - v}$

(e) $x_u = x_v = 1$, $y_u = 3u^2$, $y_v = -3v^2$ and, if $u^2 + v^2 \neq 0$, $u_x = \dfrac{v^2}{u^2 + v^2}$, $u_y = \dfrac{1}{3(u^2 + v^2)}$, $v_x = \dfrac{u^2}{u^2 + v^2}$,

$v_y = -\dfrac{1}{3(u^2 + v^2)}$ **2** (d) $\nabla^2 f = f_{uu} - 2f_{uv} + 2f_{vv}$ (assuming $f_{uv} = f_{vu}$)

4 (a) $u_x = \dfrac{vw(w-v)}{vw(w-v) - uw(w-u) + uv(v-u)}$

5 (b) $\rho_x = \sin\phi\cos\theta$, $\phi_x = \dfrac{1}{\rho}\cos\phi\cos\theta$, $\theta_x = -\dfrac{1}{\rho}\dfrac{\sin\theta}{\sin\phi}$

SECTION 6.8

1 (a) Only $x = 0$; horizontal inflection point (e) Only $x = 1$; local minimum
2 (a) Only (0, 0); saddle (f) Only (1, −2); local maximum (m) *All* points on x and y axes; minima
3 (a) Only (0, 0, 0); Theorem 4 gives no information (d) Only (0, 0, 0); all λ's positive, so local minimum
6 (a) No information (b) Local minimum
8 Consider $f(x, y, z) = -x^2 - y^2 + z^4$, say. One finds that **A**'s eigenvalues are all ≤ 0. Yet f does not have a local maximum at (0, 0, 0) since $f(0, 0, z) = z^4 > 0$ in every neighborhood of (0, 0, 0).

SECTION 6.9

1 (a) $\left(\dfrac{2}{5}, \dfrac{4}{5}\right)$ **3** (c) Closest point is $\left(2 - \dfrac{2\sqrt{35}}{5}, -1 + \dfrac{\sqrt{35}}{5}\right)$, farthest is $\left(2 + \dfrac{2\sqrt{35}}{5}, -1 - \dfrac{\sqrt{35}}{5}\right)$

4 (a) $\left(\dfrac{13}{5}, -\dfrac{6}{5}\right)$ **5** (a) (3, 1, 0)

CHAPTER 7

SECTION 7.2

8 No. For example, if **u** and **v** point east and **w** points north, then $(\mathbf{u} \times \mathbf{v}) \times \mathbf{w} = \mathbf{0} \times \mathbf{w} = \mathbf{0}$, whereas $\mathbf{u} \times (\mathbf{v} \times \mathbf{w})$ is nonzero and points south.

SECTION 7.3

1 (h) Can use $\mathbf{u} \times \mathbf{v} = 4\hat{\mathbf{i}} - \hat{\mathbf{j}} + 3\hat{\mathbf{k}}$
(k) Area $= \dfrac{\sqrt{122}}{2}$; perpendicular vector is $\alpha(-8\hat{\mathbf{i}} - 7\hat{\mathbf{j}} + 3\hat{\mathbf{k}})$ for any $\alpha \neq 0$.
2 (a) $\mathbf{M} = -3\hat{\mathbf{i}} - 3\hat{\mathbf{j}} + \hat{\mathbf{k}}$ **3** (a) Not on a straight line **4** (a) $\sqrt{161}$ **5** (a) $\pm\dfrac{1}{\sqrt{6}}(\hat{\mathbf{i}} + 2\hat{\mathbf{j}} - \hat{\mathbf{k}})$

7 (b) Shortest distance $= \dfrac{4}{\sqrt{14}}$; unit normal $= \pm\dfrac{1}{\sqrt{14}}(2\hat{\mathbf{i}} + \hat{\mathbf{j}} - 3\hat{\mathbf{k}})$

SECTION 7.4

1 (a) Both = −6 **4** (d) 30 **12** (a) Not coplanar

SECTION 7.5

1 (a) $\mathbf{u}' = 2\tau\mathbf{B}$, $\mathbf{u}'' = 2\mathbf{B}$, $\|\mathbf{u}'\| = 2|\tau|\|\mathbf{B}\|$ (d) $\mathbf{u}' = -\sin\tau\hat{\mathbf{i}} + \cos\tau\hat{\mathbf{j}}$, $\mathbf{u}'' = -\cos\tau\hat{\mathbf{i}} - \sin\tau\hat{\mathbf{j}}$, $\|\mathbf{u}'\| = 1$
7 (a) $(\mathbf{u}\cdot\mathbf{v})'' = \mathbf{u}''\cdot\mathbf{v} + 2\mathbf{u}'\cdot\mathbf{v}' + \mathbf{u}\cdot\mathbf{v}''$

SECTION 7.6

1 (a) $r = 2\sqrt{2}$, $\theta = \dfrac{\pi}{4}$ rad $= 45°$, $z = 0$ (e) $r = \sqrt{37}$, $\theta = 6.118$ rad $= 350.5°$, $z = 3$

2 (a) $\rho = 2$, $\phi = \dfrac{\pi}{2}$ rad $= 90°$, $\theta = 0$ rad $= 0°$
(e) $\rho = \sqrt{46}$, $\phi = 1.423$ rad $= 81.52°$, $\theta = 5.820$ rad $= 333.4°$
3 (a) $\dot{\mathbf{A}} = (3\cos 3t + 27t^4)\hat{\mathbf{e}}_r + (3\sin 3t - 36t^3)\hat{\mathbf{e}}_\theta + 2t\hat{\mathbf{e}}_z$
8 (c) $\mathbf{v} = V\hat{\mathbf{e}}_\rho + \dfrac{V}{\sqrt{2}}\Omega t\,\hat{\mathbf{e}}_\theta$, $\mathbf{a} = -\dfrac{1}{2}V\Omega^2 t(\hat{\mathbf{e}}_\rho + \hat{\mathbf{e}}_\phi) + \sqrt{2}V\Omega\hat{\mathbf{e}}_\theta$ **9** $\|\mathbf{v}\| = \rho\sqrt{\Omega_1^2 + \Omega_2^2}$, $\|\mathbf{a}\| = \rho(\Omega_1^2 + \Omega_2^2)$

SECTION 7.7

1 (a) $z = \tau$, $y = (3\tau - 8)/5$, $x = (\tau + 4)/5$ $(-\infty < \tau < \infty)$, for example
(f) $x = 2\cos\tau$, $y = 2\sin\tau$, $z = \frac{5}{2} - \cos\tau - \sin\tau$ $(0 \le \tau < 2\pi)$, for example

3 (a) $\hat{\mathbf{T}} = \dfrac{\hat{\mathbf{j}} + 2\tau\hat{\mathbf{k}}}{\sqrt{1 + 4\tau^2}}$, $\hat{\mathbf{N}} = \dfrac{-2\tau\hat{\mathbf{j}} + \hat{\mathbf{k}}}{\sqrt{1 + 4\tau^2}}$, $\hat{\mathbf{B}} = \hat{\mathbf{i}}$, $\rho = \dfrac{1}{\kappa} = \dfrac{1}{2}(1 + 4\tau^2)^{3/2}$, $\nu = 0$ **4** $s = 2\pi\sqrt{a^2 + b^2}$

6 (a) $\dfrac{dv}{dt} = \dfrac{4t}{\sqrt{1 + 4t^2}}$, $\kappa v^2 = \dfrac{2}{\sqrt{1 + 4t^2}}$

CHAPTER 8

SECTION 8.2

1 (a) $\frac{1}{4}$ (d) $\sin 2 - \sin 1 - 1$ **4** (a) $x_c = \frac{2}{3}a$, $y_c = \frac{1}{3}b$ (d) $x_c = 1$, $y_c = \dfrac{56}{25}$ **5** (a) $I_x = \dfrac{3\sigma}{4}$, $I_y = \dfrac{65\sigma}{12}$

SECTION 8.3

1 (a) -14 (d) $-\frac{244}{5}$ **4** (a) $\frac{1}{4}$ **5** (a) $\dfrac{\sigma}{6}$ **6** (a) $\displaystyle\int_0^1 \int_y^1 \int_0^z f\,dx\,dz\,dy$ (d) $\displaystyle\int_0^2 \int_0^x \int_0^z f\,dy\,dz\,dx$

SECTION 8.4

3 (c) $\hat{\mathbf{n}} = -\dfrac{1}{\sqrt{3}}(\hat{\mathbf{i}} + \hat{\mathbf{j}} + \hat{\mathbf{k}})$ **4** (c) $\hat{\mathbf{n}} = \hat{\mathbf{k}}$ for $u \ne 0$. For $u = 0$, $\mathbf{R}_u \times \mathbf{R}_v = \mathbf{0}$ and $\hat{\mathbf{n}} = \dfrac{0}{0}\hat{\mathbf{k}}$ is undefined. However, S is flat (lying in x, y plane), so $\hat{\mathbf{n}} = \hat{\mathbf{k}}$ at $u = 0$ as well.
6 (c) $\mathbf{R}_u \times \mathbf{R}_v = -(1 - u)\cos v\hat{\mathbf{i}} - (1 - u)\sin v\hat{\mathbf{j}} - (1 - u)\hat{\mathbf{k}} = \mathbf{0}$ only at $u = 1$, i.e., at the point of the cone, where a unique normal does not exist. Away from that point, $\hat{\mathbf{n}} = -\dfrac{1}{\sqrt{2}}(\cos v\hat{\mathbf{i}} + \sin v\hat{\mathbf{j}} + \hat{\mathbf{k}})$
(d) $x + z = 1$
7 (d) $cx + az = \sqrt{2}ac$ **9** (a) One: $x = u$, $y = v$; $-\infty < u < \infty$, $-\infty < v < \infty$
Another: $x = u\cos v$, $y = u\sin v$; $0 \le u < \infty$, $0 \le v < 2\pi$ (e) One: $x = u\cos v$, $y = u\sin v$, $z = \sqrt{u^2 - 1}$; $1 \le u < \infty$, $0 \le v < 2\pi$
Another: $x = u^2\sin v$, $y = u^2\cos v$, $z = \sqrt{u^4 - 1}$; $1 \le u < \infty$, $0 < v \le 2\pi$
11 (a) $4x + 2y - z = 5$ (d) $2x - 2y - z = -3$

SECTION 8.5

1 (a) $A = 2\pi h$. Either of the other two parametrizations would work as well. (d) $A = \sqrt{2}\pi h^2$
6 (a) $A = \dfrac{\pi}{4}$

SECTION 8.6

1 (a) $\dfrac{3}{\sqrt{2}}$ (d) 2π **2** (a) $\dfrac{1}{3}$ (d) $\dfrac{4}{5}$ **3** (a) $\dfrac{4\sigma_o}{\sqrt{6}}$ (d) $\dfrac{8\pi c^4}{3}$ **4** (a) $\dfrac{3}{4}\ln 2$

SECTION 8.7

3 (a) $\mathbf{F}(0, 0, 0) = \pi\sigma GR\hat{\mathbf{k}}$ **4** (a) $z_c = \dfrac{3}{4}h$ (c) $z_c = \dfrac{3}{4}\dfrac{R^4 - 2R^2a^2 + a^4}{2R^3 - 3aR^2 + a^3}$ **8** (a) $\mathbf{F}(0, 0, 0) = 2\pi\sigma Gh\hat{\mathbf{k}}$

SECTION 8.8

1 (a) $x^2 \int_0^{t^2} \cos(tx^2)\,dx + 2t\sin(t^5)$ (d) $\int_{-2}^{-\alpha} x^3 e^{\alpha x^3}\,dx - e^{-\alpha^4}$ **2** (a) $f(x) = x - \dfrac{1}{3}x^3 + \cdots$
10 (a) $\int_0^2 \int_1^4 x^2\cos(tx^2 + y^3)\,dx\,dy$

CHAPTER 9

SECTION 9.3

4 (b) $\|\mathbf{v}\|$ = constant on circles centered at the origin. Yes

5 (a) $x = \tau,\ y = \frac{3}{2}\tau,\ z = -\frac{1}{2}\tau$ (e) $x = 2,\ y = \tau,\ z = -\dfrac{3}{\tau}$

SECTION 9.4

1 (a) div $\mathbf{v} = 0$ everywhere (e) div $\mathbf{v} = y - 4z = -17$ at $(3, -1, 4)$

3 (a) $\mathbf{v} = 6\hat{\mathbf{i}} + 2x\hat{\mathbf{j}} + y \sin x\hat{\mathbf{k}}$, say (e) $\mathbf{v} = \left(\dfrac{x^3}{3} - x\right)\hat{\mathbf{i}}$, say

SECTION 9.5

1 (a) $\nabla u = 6\hat{\mathbf{i}}$ everywhere **2** (a) $\dfrac{du}{ds} = 4$ (e) $\dfrac{du}{ds} = \dfrac{4}{\sqrt{5}}$ **3** (b) $180\hat{\mathbf{i}} + 140\hat{\mathbf{j}}$ **4** (a) $-400k$ (b) $-400k$

5 (c) $\hat{\mathbf{n}} = [(2x - 1)\hat{\mathbf{i}} + 4y\hat{\mathbf{j}} + 2z\hat{\mathbf{k}}]/\sqrt{(2x-1)^2 + 16y^2 + 4z^2}$; $\hat{\mathbf{n}} = \dfrac{\hat{\mathbf{i}} + 2\sqrt{5}\,\hat{\mathbf{k}}}{\sqrt{21}}$ at $(0, 0\ \sqrt{5})$

6 (a) $\hat{\mathbf{n}} = \dfrac{1}{\sqrt{8}}(x\hat{\mathbf{i}} + y\hat{\mathbf{j}})$; $\hat{\mathbf{n}} = \hat{\mathbf{i}}$ at $(\sqrt{8}, 0)$ **7** (a) $x + y - z = 1$; $\hat{\mathbf{n}} = \pm\dfrac{1}{\sqrt{3}}(\hat{\mathbf{i}} + \hat{\mathbf{j}} - \hat{\mathbf{k}})$

8 (c) $x - y = 3$; $\hat{\mathbf{n}} = \pm\dfrac{1}{\sqrt{2}}(\hat{\mathbf{i}} - \hat{\mathbf{j}})$ **9** (a) In the direction $-37\hat{\mathbf{i}} - 12\hat{\mathbf{j}} + 2\hat{\mathbf{k}}$ **11** (a) 280

SECTION 9.6

1 (a) $\nabla \times \mathbf{v} = \mathbf{0}$ everywhere (e) $\nabla \times \mathbf{v} = 4x\hat{\mathbf{j}} - x\hat{\mathbf{k}} = 12\hat{\mathbf{j}} - 3\hat{\mathbf{k}}$ at $(3, 4, -1)$

SECTION 9.7

2 (a) 0 and $\mathbf{0}$

SECTION 9.8

1 (a) $\nabla u = \hat{\mathbf{e}}_r$, $\nabla^2 u = \dfrac{1}{r}$, $\nabla \cdot \mathbf{v} = 3$, $\nabla \times \mathbf{v} = \mathbf{0}$ **5** (c) $\nabla^2 \mathbf{v} = -\dfrac{1}{r^2}\hat{\mathbf{e}}_\theta$

8 No, $d\theta$ is not an arc length "ds." What *is* true is that $\nabla u \cdot \hat{\mathbf{e}}_\theta = \dfrac{1}{r}\dfrac{\partial u}{\partial \theta}$.

14 (a) $\nabla u = \hat{\mathbf{e}}_\rho$, $\nabla^2 u = \dfrac{2}{\rho}$, $\nabla \cdot \mathbf{v} = 3$, $\nabla \times \mathbf{v} = \mathbf{0}$

SECTION 9.9

1 (d) $\frac{1}{3}$ (g) $\frac{1}{2}$ **3** (a) Both sides equal $\frac{1104}{5}$ **4** (a) Both integrals equal $2ab$

SECTION 9.10

1 (a) $\frac{45}{2}$ (e) $\frac{326}{3}$ **2** (a) 0 (e) -4 **3** (a) $2(\sin 1 - \cos 1 - \sin 3 + 3\cos 3)$ (e) $-\frac{8502}{45}$ **4** (a) 0 (c) 1
5 (b) $2\pi ab$

SECTION 9.11

1 (d) Both integrals equal $-\frac{1}{6}$. **2** (a) Both integrals equal $\frac{1}{2}$. **3** (a) Both integrals equal 0.
5 (a) Both results equal -63. **10** (a) 20 (e) 8π **11** (a) $-\frac{289}{90}$

SECTION 9.12

1 (a) $\Phi = x - 2y - 8z$ + constant (e) $\Phi = x^2 z + \dfrac{3}{2}y^2$ + constant

2 (a) No, because no choice of f can eliminate the $\hat{\mathbf{k}}$ term in $\nabla \times \mathbf{v} = (f_y + 1)\hat{\mathbf{i}} - f_x\hat{\mathbf{j}} - x\hat{\mathbf{k}}$.

4 (c) $-\frac{10}{3}$ 5 (a) $\frac{\pi^2}{2}(\pi^2 + 9)$

10 (a) $\mathbf{w} = cx\hat{\mathbf{j}} + (ay - bx)\hat{\mathbf{k}}$ (with $x_0 = y_0 = f = 0$, say) (d) $\mathbf{w} = -xyz\hat{\mathbf{j}}$ (with $x_0 = y_0 = f = 0$, say)

SECTION 9.13

1 (a) Both integrals equal 120π. (d) Both integrals equal $\frac{8\pi}{3}$. (o) Both integrals equal -2π.

2 (a) $\int_0^\pi 4\,d\tau$ (b) $\int_0^1 e^{-3\tau}(\sin 2\tau)\sqrt{9 + 9\tau^2 + e^{-2\tau}}\,d\tau$ 3 (a) $2 + \sqrt{8} + 2\ln(1 + \sqrt{2})$

4 (a) $\mathbf{F} = 2\sin\theta\,\hat{\mathbf{e}}_r - rz\,\hat{\mathbf{e}}_\theta + 5\hat{\mathbf{e}}_z$ (e) $\mathbf{F} = \rho^2\hat{\mathbf{e}}_\rho + \frac{\sin\theta}{\rho}\hat{\mathbf{e}}_\phi - \frac{1}{\rho\sin\theta}\hat{\mathbf{e}}_\theta$ 6 (a) $-\frac{3}{2}\pi a^2$

7 (a) Both integrals equal $2\pi\omega a^2$. 8 (a) Rotational (c) $\Phi = \frac{1}{6}\rho^6 +$ constant

9 (a) -12π (e) $\frac{1}{3}[(1 + 4\pi^2)^{3/2} - 1]$

CHAPTER 10

SECTION 10.2

5 (a) $f_e(x) = 2, f_o(x) = -5x$; neither (e) $f_e(x) = 0, f_o(x) = x/(x^4 + 2)$; odd

12 (a) Not periodic (g) Periodic; period π (m) Periodic; period π 13 (a) 2π (e) 2π

SECTION 10.3

3 (a) Yes (d) No; right hand limit does not exist at $x = 0$

4 (a) $f(x) = 2\sum_{n=1}^{\infty}\frac{(-1)^{n+1}}{n}\sin nx$ for all x except $\pm\pi, \pm 3\pi, \pm 5\pi, \ldots$

(d) $f(x) = \pi - \frac{8}{\pi}\sum_{n=1,3,\ldots}^{\infty}\frac{1}{n^2}\cos\frac{nx}{2}$ for all x (g) $f(x) = \frac{2}{\pi} - \frac{4}{\pi}\sum_{n=1}^{\infty}\frac{1}{4n^2 - 1}\cos 2nx$ for all x

5 $A_0 = a_0$, $A_n = a_n\cos\frac{n\pi a}{\ell} - b_n\sin\frac{n\pi a}{\ell}$, $B_n = a_n\sin\frac{n\pi a}{\ell} + b_n\cos\frac{n\pi a}{\ell}$

18 (a) $f(x) = \frac{F}{2} - \frac{iF}{\pi}\sum_{n=-\infty}^{\infty}\frac{e^{i(2n-1)x}}{2n - 1}$

20 (a) $f(x) = \frac{2\ell}{\pi}\sum_{n=1}^{\infty}\frac{(-1)^{n+1}}{n}\sin\frac{n\pi x}{\ell}$ (d) $f(x) = -\frac{112}{15} + \frac{768}{\pi^4}\sum_{n=1}^{\infty}\frac{(-1)^{n+1}}{n^4}\cos\frac{n\pi x}{2}$

24 (c) $q(t) = CV\left\{\frac{2\ln 2 - 1}{2\ln 2} - \sum_{n=1}^{\infty}\left[\frac{\ln 2}{4n^2\pi^2 + (\ln 2)^2}\cos\left(\frac{2n\pi t}{RC\ln 2}\right) + \frac{2n\pi}{4n^2\pi^2 + (\ln 2)^2}\sin\left(\frac{2n\pi t}{RC\ln 2}\right)\right]\right\}$

28 (a) Half-range cosine: $f(x) = 100$; half-range sine: $f(x) = \frac{400}{\pi}\sum_{n=1,3,\ldots}^{\infty}\frac{1}{n}\sin\frac{n\pi x}{\ell}$;

quarter-range cosine: $f(x) = \frac{400}{\pi}\sum_{n=1,3,\ldots}^{\infty}\frac{(-1)^{(n-1)/2}}{n}\cos\frac{n\pi x}{2\ell}$

SECTION 10.4

6 Can see, from its graph, that f is periodic with period 2π, continuous on $(-\infty, \infty)$, and that f' is piecewise continuous on $[-\pi, \pi]$. Thus, according to Theorem 3, termwise differentiation is permissible.

SECTION 10.5

2 $\|\mathbf{E}\| = \frac{\sqrt{70{,}602}}{42}$ 3 (a) $\mathbf{u} \approx \frac{3}{\sqrt{5}}\hat{\mathbf{e}}_1 + \frac{11}{\sqrt{6}}\hat{\mathbf{e}}_2$, $\|\mathbf{E}\| = \frac{\sqrt{14{,}430}}{30}$

5 (a) In span $\{\hat{\mathbf{e}}_1\}$, $\mathbf{u} \approx \frac{6}{\sqrt{3}}\hat{\mathbf{e}}_1$, $\|\mathbf{E}\| = \sqrt{6} \approx 2.45$. In span $\{\hat{\mathbf{e}}_1, \hat{\mathbf{e}}_2\}$, $\mathbf{u} \approx \frac{6}{\sqrt{3}}\hat{\mathbf{e}}_1 + \sqrt{3}\,\hat{\mathbf{e}}_2$, $\|\mathbf{E}\| = \sqrt{3} \approx 1.73$. In span $\{\hat{\mathbf{e}}_1, \hat{\mathbf{e}}_2, \hat{\mathbf{e}}_3\}$, $\mathbf{u} \approx \frac{6}{\sqrt{3}}\hat{\mathbf{e}}_1 + \sqrt{3}\,\hat{\mathbf{e}}_2 + \sqrt{3}\,\hat{\mathbf{e}}_3$, $\|\mathbf{E}\| = 0$. In span $\{\hat{\mathbf{e}}_1, \hat{\mathbf{e}}_2, \hat{\mathbf{e}}_3, \hat{\mathbf{e}}_4\}$, $\mathbf{u} \approx \frac{6}{\sqrt{3}}\hat{\mathbf{e}}_1 + \sqrt{3}\,\hat{\mathbf{e}}_2 + \sqrt{3}\,\hat{\mathbf{e}}_3$, $\|\mathbf{E}\| = 0$. That is, $\mathbf{u}$ happens to lie in the subspace span $\{\hat{\mathbf{e}}_1, \hat{\mathbf{e}}_2, \hat{\mathbf{e}}_3\}$ of $\mathbb{R}^4$.

7 (a) For $k = 1, 2$, $\|\mathbf{E}\| = 0.0491\ell^{3/2}$; for $k = 3, 4$, $\|\mathbf{E}\| = 0.0195\ell^{3/2}$; for $k = 5, 6$, $\|\mathbf{E}\| = 0.0110\ell^{3/2}$.

12 (c) $|x| \approx \frac{1}{2} + \frac{5}{16}(3x^2 - 1)$

SECTION 10.6

1 (a) $\lambda_n = \left(\frac{2n-1}{2\ell}\pi\right)^2$, $\phi_n(x) = \sin\left(\frac{2n-1}{2\ell}\pi x\right)$, $n = 1, 2, \ldots$, $100 = \frac{400}{\pi}\sum_{n=1}^{\infty}\frac{1}{2n-1}\sin\left(\frac{2n-1}{2\ell}\pi x\right)$

(d) $\lambda_n = z_n^2$, where the z_n's are the positive roots of $\tan(z\ell) = \frac{1}{z}$; $\phi_n(x) = \cos(z_n x)$ $(n = 1, 2, \ldots)$,

$50 = 200\sum_{n=1}^{\infty}\frac{\sin(z_n\ell)}{2z_n\ell + \sin(2z_n\ell)}\cos(z_n x)$ **7** (a) $(x^5y')' + \lambda x^5 y = 0$; $p = x^5$, $q = 0$, $r = x^5$

9 $f(x) = 120e^x\sum_{n=1}^{\infty}\frac{n\pi - e^{-2}\left(3\sin\frac{2n\pi}{3} + n\pi\cos\frac{2n\pi}{3}\right)}{9 + n^2\pi^2}\sin\frac{n\pi x}{3}$ **13** (b) $P_{cr} = \left(\frac{\pi}{2\ell}\right)^2 EI$

CHAPTER 11

SECTION 11.2

1 (a) $2[H(x+1) - H(x-3)]$ **3** (a) $x(t) = 3e^{-2t} + H(t - t_0)e^{-2(t-t_0)}$

SECTION 11.3

1 (a) $f(x) = \frac{100}{\pi}\int_0^{\infty}[\sin(2-x)\omega + \sin\omega x]\frac{d\omega}{\omega}$ for all $x \neq 0, 2$.
At the points $x = 0$ and $x = 2$, $f(x)$ equals 100, whereas the integral converges to the average value 50.

(g) $f(x) = \frac{1}{\pi}\int_0^{\infty}\frac{\cos\omega x + \omega\sin\omega x}{1+\omega^2}\,d\omega$ for all $x \neq 0$.
For $x = 0$, $f(x)$ equals 1, whereas the integral converges to the average value 1/2.

4 $u(x) = \frac{1}{\pi}\int_0^{\infty}\frac{\cos\omega x}{EI\omega^4 + k}\,d\omega$

SECTION 11.4

1 (e) $\hat{f}(\omega) = \frac{(1+i\omega)e^{-i\omega} - 1}{\omega^2}$ **2** (b) $f(x) = \frac{\sin ax}{\pi x}$

15 (a) $144\frac{3-\omega^2}{(\omega^2+9)^3}$ (b) $-i\frac{\sqrt{\pi}}{16}\omega e^{-\omega^2/16}$ (g) $2[H(x+1) - H(x-1)] - \frac{1}{\sqrt{2\pi}|x|}$ (h) $\frac{2}{\pi}\frac{e^{i3x}}{x^2+4}$

CHAPTER 12

SECTION 12.2

1 (a) Convergent (e) Convergent (i) Divergent
2 None; need $p > 1$ for "convergence at ∞," and need $p < 1$ for "convergence at 0."
4 (a) $\alpha > 1$ (c) $-1 < \alpha < 0$

SECTION 12.3

1 (a) Yes. $K = 1$, $c = 0$, $T = 5$, say. (e) Yes. $K = 2$, $c = 0$, $T = 1$, say.

SECTION 12.4

7 (a) $\frac{2}{(s-1)(s^2+4)}$ for $s > 1$ (e) $\sqrt{\frac{\pi}{s}}\frac{1}{s^2+1}$ for $s > 0$

SECTION 12.5

4 (a) $x(t) = \frac{11}{2}e^{4t} - \frac{1}{2}e^{2t}$ (e) $x(t) = \frac{1}{6}\int_0^t (2\cosh 2\tau + \sinh 2\tau - 2e^{\tau})f(t-\tau)\,d\tau$
(i) $x(t) = t^2 - 4t + 6 - 2(t+3)e^{-t}$ (o) $x(t) = \sin t,\ y(t) = \cos t$

5 (a) $x(t) - 5 - 4\int_0^t x(\tau)\,d\tau = \dfrac{e^{2t}-1}{2}$ (g) $y(x) - \dfrac{1}{2}x^3 - \dfrac{8}{3}\int_0^x (x-\xi)^3 y(\xi)\,d\xi = 0$

9 (b) $\rho(\nu) = 2\sqrt{\dfrac{0.0744}{\pi}}\, e^{-1/(0.2976\nu^2)}$

12 (a) $\bar{f}(s) = \dfrac{1}{s-2} - \dfrac{1}{s-1},\ f(t) = e^{2t} - e^t$ (f) $\bar{f}(s) = \dfrac{3}{4}\dfrac{1}{s} + \dfrac{1}{8}\dfrac{1}{s+2i} + \dfrac{1}{8}\dfrac{1}{s-2i},\ f(t) = \dfrac{3}{4} + \dfrac{\cos 2t}{4}$

13 (a) $\bar{f}(s) = -\dfrac{1}{s} - \dfrac{1}{s^2} + \dfrac{1}{s-1},\ f(t) = e^t - t - 1$

14 (a) $\bar{f}(s) = \dfrac{7}{9}\dfrac{1}{s} + \dfrac{2 - \frac{7}{9}s}{s^2+9},\ f(t) = \dfrac{7}{9} + 2\dfrac{\sin 3t}{3} - \dfrac{7}{9}\cos 3t$

SECTION 12.6

1 (a) $f(t) = \dfrac{1}{2a}t\sin at$ (d) $f(t) = (1 - 2t + \frac{1}{2}t^2)e^{-t}$ (g) $f(t) = \frac{1}{24}t^4e^{-4t}(1 - \frac{4}{5}t)$

(m) $f(t) = H(t-1)\left[1 - \left(\dfrac{\sin(t-1)}{\sqrt{3}} + \cos(t-1)\right)e^{-(t-1)/\sqrt{3}}\right]$

4 (a) $\bar{f}(s) = \dfrac{\cosh(\pi s/2)}{s^2+1}$ (e) $\bar{f}(s) = \dfrac{1}{s^2(1+e^{-s})} - \dfrac{e^{-s}}{s(1-e^{-2s})}$

CHAPTER 13

SECTION 13.2

3 (a) Nonlinear (c) Linear (e) Nonlinear
4 (a) Hyperbolic everywhere (d) Elliptic in $x < 0$, hyperbolic in $x > 0$ (g) Parabolic everywhere

CHAPTER 14

SECTION 14.2

3 (a) $u(x,t) = \dfrac{400}{\pi}\sum_{n=2,4,\ldots}^{\infty} \dfrac{n}{n^2-1}\sin\dfrac{n\pi x}{\ell}e^{-(n\pi\alpha/\ell)^2 t}$ **6** (b) 60°C

8 (a) $u(x,t) = u_1 + (u_2 - u_1)\dfrac{x}{\ell} + \sum_{n=1}^{\infty} J_n \sin\dfrac{n\pi x}{\ell}e^{-(n\pi\alpha/\ell)^2 t}$,
where $J_n = \dfrac{2}{\ell}\int_0^{\ell}\left[f(x) - u_1 - (u_2-u_1)\dfrac{x}{\ell}\right]\sin\dfrac{n\pi x}{\ell}\,dx;\ u_s(x) = u_1 + (u_2-u_1)\dfrac{x}{\ell}$

11 (a) $u(x,t) = G + \sum_{n=1}^{\infty}\left[I_n\cos\dfrac{2n\pi x}{L} + J_n\sin\dfrac{2n\pi x}{L}\right)e^{-(2n\pi\alpha/L)^2 t}$,
where $G = \dfrac{1}{L}\int_0^L f(x)\,dx,\ I_n = \dfrac{2}{L}\int_0^L f(x)\cos\dfrac{2n\pi x}{L}\,dx,\ J_n = \dfrac{2}{L}\int_0^L f(x)\sin\dfrac{2n\pi x}{L}\,dx$

13 (a) $u(x,t) = \dfrac{Fx}{2\alpha^2}(\ell - x) + \sum_{n=1}^{\infty} J_n\sin\dfrac{n\pi x}{\ell}e^{-(n\pi\alpha/\ell)^2 t}$, where $J_n = -\dfrac{2}{\ell}\int_0^{\ell}\dfrac{Fx}{2\alpha^2}(\ell - x)\sin\dfrac{n\pi x}{\ell}\,dx$

18 (a) $v(x,t) = v_s(x) + \sum_{n=1}^{\infty} J_n\sin\dfrac{n\pi x}{\ell}e^{-[(n\pi\alpha/\ell)^2+h]t}$, where $J_n = \dfrac{2}{\ell}\int_0^{\ell}[f(x) - v_s(x)]\sin\dfrac{n\pi x}{\ell}\,dx$,
and $v_s(x) = \dfrac{50}{\sinh(\sqrt{h}/\alpha)\ell}\left[\sinh\dfrac{\sqrt{h}}{\alpha}x + \sinh\dfrac{\sqrt{h}}{\alpha}(\ell - x)\right]$

SECTION 14.3

1 (d) $u(x, t) = 50 + \sum_{n=1}^{\infty} C_n \sin z_n x \, e^{-(z_n\alpha)^2 t}$, where $C_n = \dfrac{200[\cos(z_n\ell) - 1]}{2z_n\ell - \sin(2z_n\ell)}$, and the z_n's are the positive roots of $\tan z\ell - z$

2 (a) $u(x, t) = u_s(x) + \sum_{n=1}^{\infty} C_n \sin \dfrac{n\pi x}{\ell} e^{-[(n\pi\alpha/\ell)^2 + h]t}$, where $C_n = \dfrac{2}{\ell}\int_0^{\ell} [f(x) - u_s(x)] \sin \dfrac{n\pi x}{\ell}\, dx$ and $u_s(x) = 200 \dfrac{\sinh(\sqrt{h}/\alpha)x}{\sinh(\sqrt{h}/\alpha)\ell}$

3 (a) $u(\rho, t) = u_0 + \dfrac{1}{\rho}\sum_{n=1}^{\infty} C_n \sin \dfrac{n\pi\rho}{a} e^{-(n\pi\alpha/a)^2 t}$, where $C_n = \dfrac{2}{a}\int_0^{a} [\rho f(\rho) - u_0\rho] \sin \dfrac{n\pi\rho}{a}\, d\rho$

SECTION 14.4

8 (a) $u(x, t) = \mathbf{L}^{-1}\left\{\dfrac{\sin x}{s^2 + \alpha^2}\right\} = e^{-\alpha^2 t} \sin x$

SECTION 14.5

2 Using (11), $U_{2,3} = 87.2$; using proposed idea, $U_{2,3} = 86.53$; exact $u(0.5, \frac{3}{80}) = 86.42$.
6 $U_{1,1} = U_{2,1} = U_{3,1} = 0.0312$, $U_{1,2} = U_{3,2} = 0.1248$, $U_{2,2} = 0.1404$

CHAPTER 15

SECTION 15.2

3 (e) $\Phi(x, y) = C + \sum_{n=1}^{\infty} G_n \cosh \dfrac{n\pi x}{b} \cos \dfrac{n\pi y}{b}$, where $C = \dfrac{1}{b}\int_0^{b} f(y)\, dy$, and $G_n = \dfrac{2}{b \cosh(n\pi a/b)}\int_0^{b} f(y) \cos \dfrac{n\pi y}{b}\, dy$

(f) $\Phi(x, y) = \dfrac{400}{\pi}\sum_{n=1,3,\ldots}^{\infty} \dfrac{1}{n}\left(1 - \cos \dfrac{n\pi}{4}\right)\left[\cosh \dfrac{n\pi x}{2b} + \dfrac{1 - \cosh(n\pi a/b)}{\sinh(n\pi a/b)} \sinh \dfrac{n\pi x}{2b}\right] \sin \dfrac{n\pi y}{2b}$

7 (a) $\Phi(x, y) = 100 - 50\dfrac{y}{b} + \sum_{n=1}^{\infty} H_n e^{-n\pi x/b} \sin \dfrac{n\pi y}{b}$, where $H_n = \dfrac{2}{b}\int_0^{b} \left[f(y) - 100 + 50\dfrac{y}{b}\right] \sin \dfrac{n\pi y}{b}\, dy$

SECTION 15.3

6 Denoting the solution (34) as $\psi(r, \theta)$, we have $\phi(r, \theta) = 2[\psi(r, \theta) - 50] = \dfrac{400}{\pi}\sum_{n=1,3,\ldots}^{\infty} \left(\dfrac{r}{b}\right)^n \dfrac{\sin n\theta}{n}$.

9 (a) $\Phi(r, \theta) = \Phi_1 + (\Phi_2 - \Phi_1)\dfrac{\theta}{\alpha} + \sum_{n=1}^{\infty} (A_n r^{n\pi/\alpha} + B_n r^{-n\pi/\alpha}) \sin \dfrac{n\pi\theta}{\alpha}$, where A_n, B_n are the solution of the equations $A_n a^{n\pi/\alpha} + B_n a^{-n\pi/\alpha} = \dfrac{2}{\alpha}\int_0^{\alpha} \left[f(\theta) - \Phi_1 - (\Phi_2 - \Phi_1)\dfrac{\theta}{\alpha}\right] \sin \dfrac{n\pi\theta}{\alpha}\, d\theta$
$A_n b^{n\pi/\alpha} + B_n b^{-n\pi/\alpha} = \dfrac{2}{\alpha}\int_0^{\alpha} \left[g(\theta) - \Phi_1 - (\Phi_2 - \Phi_1)\dfrac{\theta}{\alpha}\right] \sin \dfrac{n\pi\theta}{\alpha}\, d\theta$ (f) $\Phi(r, \theta) = \dfrac{400}{\pi}\sum_{n=1,3,\ldots}^{\infty} \dfrac{1}{n}\left(\dfrac{a}{r}\right)^n \sin n\theta$

12 (a) $\Phi(r, \theta) = \sum_{n=1}^{\infty} G_n \psi_n(r) \sinh \kappa_n \theta$, where $\kappa_n = \dfrac{n\pi}{\ln(b/a)}$, $G_n = \dfrac{1}{\sinh(\pi\kappa_n/2)} \dfrac{\int_a^b f(r)\psi_n(r)\frac{1}{r}\,dr}{\int_a^b \psi_n^2(r)(1/r)\,dr}$, and $\psi_n(r) = \sin(\kappa_n \ln r) - \tan(\kappa_n \ln a) \cos(\kappa_n \ln r)$

SECTION 15.4

2 (b) $\Phi(x, y) = \dfrac{1}{2} + \dfrac{1}{\pi}\tan^{-1}\dfrac{x}{y}$, where $-\dfrac{\pi}{2} \le \tan^{-1}\dfrac{x}{y} \le \dfrac{\pi}{2}$

SECTION 15.5

4 (a) $U_e = 1.4077$

8 (b) $$\begin{pmatrix} -4 & 1 & 0 & 1 & 0 & 0 \\ 1 & -4 & 1 & 0 & 1 & 0 \\ 0 & 1 & -4 & 0 & 0 & 1 \\ 2 & 0 & 0 & -4 & 1 & 0 \\ 0 & 2 & 0 & 1 & -4 & 1 \\ 0 & 0 & 2 & 0 & 1 & -4 \end{pmatrix}\begin{pmatrix} U_a \\ U_b \\ U_c \\ U_d \\ U_e \\ U_f \end{pmatrix} = \begin{pmatrix} 0 \\ 0 \\ 0 \\ -0.4 \\ -0.8 \\ -1.2 \end{pmatrix}$$

9 (a)

	Jacobi	Liebmann	SOR
$U_{1,1}^{(2)}$	$3.125\sqrt{3}$	$3.125\sqrt{3}$	$3.578\sqrt{3}$
$U_{2,1}^{(2)}$	$15.625\sqrt{3}$	$17.19\sqrt{3}$	$17.931\sqrt{3}$
$U_{1,2}^{(2)}$	$3.125\sqrt{3}$	$4.69\sqrt{3}$	$5.492\sqrt{3}$
$U_{2,2}^{(2)}$	$15.625\sqrt{3}$	$17.97\sqrt{3}$	$18.454\sqrt{3}$

10 (b) $(2 + h)U_{j-i,k} + 4U_{j,k-1} + (2 - h)U_{j+1,k} + 4U_{j,k+1} - 12U_{j,k} = 8h^2$

$$\begin{pmatrix} -12 & \frac{5}{3} & 4 & 0 \\ \frac{7}{3} & -12 & 0 & 4 \\ 4 & 0 & -12 & \frac{5}{3} \\ 0 & 4 & \frac{7}{3} & -12 \end{pmatrix}\begin{pmatrix} U_{1,1} \\ U_{2,1} \\ U_{1,2} \\ U_{2,2} \end{pmatrix} = \begin{pmatrix} \frac{8}{9} \\ \frac{8}{9} - \frac{5\sqrt{3}}{6} \\ \frac{8}{9} \\ \frac{8}{9} - \frac{5\sqrt{3}}{6} \end{pmatrix}$$

13 $U_a = -0.00858f$

CHAPTER 16

SECTION 16.2

3 (a) $y(5, 3) = 0$ (h) $y(7.5, 2.1) = -0.375$

5 $y(x, t) = e^{-at/2} \sum_{n=1}^{\infty} E_n \sin \frac{n\pi x}{\ell}\left(\frac{a}{2\omega_n} \sin \omega_n t + \cos \omega_n t\right)$, $E_n = \frac{2}{\ell}\int_0^{\ell} F(x) \sin \frac{n\pi x}{\ell}\, dx$, $\omega_n = \sqrt{\left(\frac{n\pi c}{\ell}\right)^2 - \left(\frac{a}{2}\right)^2}$

11 (c) $\sigma(0, t) = \frac{4\sigma_0}{\pi} \sum_{n=1,3,\ldots}^{\infty} \frac{1}{n} \sin \frac{n\pi}{2} \cos \frac{n\pi ct}{2\ell}$

15 $w(x, y, t) = \sum_{m=1}^{\infty} \sum_{n=1}^{\infty} E_{mn} \sin \frac{m\pi x}{a} \sin \frac{n\pi y}{b} \cos \pi c \sqrt{\left(\frac{m}{a}\right)^2 + \left(\frac{n}{a}\right)^2}\, t$,

$E_{mn} = \frac{4}{ab}\int_0^b \int_0^a f(x, y) \sin \frac{m\pi x}{a} \sin \frac{n\pi y}{b}\, dx\, dy$

SECTION 16.3

4 (a) $u(x, y) = F(x - y) + G(3x - y)$ **5** (a) $u(x, y) = F(2x - y) + G(6x - y)$

9 (a) $y(x, t) = \begin{cases} 0, & x > ct \\ h\left(t - \frac{x}{c}\right), & x < ct \end{cases}$

CHAPTER 17

SECTION 17.2

9 (a) $u(r, z) = \sum_{n=1}^{\infty} A_n J_0(k_n r) e^{-k_n z}$, where $A_n = \dfrac{2}{c^2[J_1(k_n c)]^2} \int_0^c f(r) J_0(k_n r) r \, dr$, and k_n is the nth root of $J_0(kc) = 0$

10 (b) $u(r, t) = u_0 \dfrac{\ln (r/a)}{\ln (b/a)} + \sum_{n=1}^{\infty} A_n \Psi_n(r) e^{-k_n^2 \alpha^2 t}$, where $\Psi_n(r) = Y_0(k_n a) J_0(k_n r) - J_0(k_n a) Y_0(k_n r)$, and k_n is the nth root of $J_0(ka)Y_0(kb) - J_0(kb)Y_0(ka) = 0$

13 (c) $u(r, z) = u_1 + (u_2 - u_1)\dfrac{z}{\ell} + \sum_{n=1}^{\infty} A_n I_0\left(\dfrac{n\pi c}{\ell}\right) \sin \dfrac{n\pi z}{\ell}$,

where $A_n = \dfrac{2}{\ell I_0(n\pi c/\ell)} \int_0^{\ell} \left[u_3 - u_1 - (u_2 - u_1)\dfrac{z}{\ell}\right] \sin \dfrac{n\pi z}{\ell} \, dz$

14 (a) $y(x) = \sqrt{x}[AJ_{1/3}(\tfrac{2}{3} x^{3/2}) + BJ_{-1/3}(\tfrac{2}{3} x^{3/2})]$ (e) $y(x) = \dfrac{1}{\sqrt{x}}[AI_1(2\sqrt{x}) + BK_1(2\sqrt{x})]$

15 $u(\rho, t) = \dfrac{1}{\rho} \sum_{n=1}^{\infty} A_n \sin \dfrac{n\pi\rho}{c} e^{-(n\pi\alpha/c)^2 t}$, where $A_n = \dfrac{2}{c} \int_0^c f(\rho) \sin \dfrac{n\pi\rho}{c} \rho \, d\rho$

CHAPTER 18

SECTION 18.2

9 (a) $2 - 11i$ (e) $-\frac{26}{125} - \frac{18}{125} i$

SECTION 18.3

2 (a) $2 < u < 3,\ 1 < v < 2$ (f) $\dfrac{u^2}{4} - 1 < v < 1 - \dfrac{u^2}{4},\ -2 < u < 0$

9 (a) $-e^2$ (d) $\sin 3 \cosh \pi + i \cos 3 \sinh \pi$ (g) $\dfrac{2 \cosh 1 \sin 1}{\cosh 2 - \cos 2} + i \dfrac{2 \cos 1 \sinh 1}{\cosh 2 - \cos 2}$

SECTION 18.4

1 (a) $r = 3,\ \theta_0 = 3\pi/2$ (f) $\pi = 2\sqrt{37},\ \theta_0 = 4.878$

4 (a) $(-1 + i)^{10} = \begin{cases} 32e^{i3\pi/2} & \text{(polar)} \\ -32i & \text{(Cartesian)} \end{cases}$ $\quad (-1 + i)^{20} = \begin{cases} 1024e^{15\pi i} & \text{(polar)} \\ -1024 & \text{(Cartesian)} \end{cases}$

5 (a) $i^{1/2} = e^{i\pi/4}, e^{i5\pi/4}$ $\quad i^{1/5} = e^{i\pi/10}, e^{i\pi/2}, e^{i9\pi/10}, e^{i13\pi/10}, e^{i17\pi/10}$

6 (a) $\log(-2) = \ln 2 + (2k + 1)\pi i \quad (k = 0, \pm 1, \pm 2, \ldots)$

8 (a) $(2i)^{2/3} = \sqrt[3]{4}\, e^{\pi i/3}, \sqrt[3]{4}\, e^{\pi i}, \sqrt[3]{4}\, e^{5\pi i/3}$ $\quad (2i)^{3/2} = \sqrt{8}\, e^{3\pi i/4}, \sqrt{8}\, e^{7\pi i/4}$

$(2i)^{\pi} = e^{\pi \ln 2} e^{i(1+4k)\pi^2/2} \quad (k = 0, \pm 1, \pm 2, \ldots)$

9 (a) $(2i)^i = e^{-(\pi/2 + 2k\pi)}[\cos(\ln 2) + i \sin(\ln 2)]$

$(2i)^{1-i} = e^{\ln 2 + \pi/2 + 2k\pi}\left[\cos\left(\dfrac{\pi}{2} + 2k\pi - \ln 2\right) + i \sin\left(\dfrac{\pi}{2} + 2k\pi - \ln 2\right)\right],\ k = 0, \pm 1, \pm 2, \ldots$

11 (a) $\log(-3i) = \ln 3 + i\dfrac{3\pi}{2},\ \sqrt{-3i} = -\sqrt{\dfrac{3}{2}} + \sqrt{\dfrac{3}{2}}\, i$

SECTION 18.5

10 (a) $f'(z) = -\sin z$

11 (d) $f'(z) = -\dfrac{2z + 3i}{(z^2 + 3iz - 2)^2}$ for all $z \neq -i, -2i$ $\quad f(z)$ analytic for all $z \neq -i, -2i$

15 (a) Harmonic for all z; $v(x, y) = e^x \sin y + c$; $f(z) = e^z + \text{constant}$

CHAPTER 19

SECTION 19.2

5 (a) e^z analytic at $z = 0$ and $\frac{d}{dz} e^z = e^z \neq 0$ there, so yes, conformal at $z = 0$

(d) iz^2 analytic at $z = 0$, but $\frac{d}{dz}(iz^2) = 2iz = 0$ there, so no, not conformal at $z = 0$

SECTION 19.3

3 $u = a/(a^2 + b^2 - c^2)$, $v = -b/(a^2 + b^2 - c^2)$, radius $= c/(a^2 + b^2 - c^2)$ 8 (a) $w = \frac{iz - (i - 1)}{z + (i - 1)}$

10 Using (a) in Exercise 6, we can use $z_1 = 0$, $z_2 = i$, $z_3 = \infty$, $w_1 = 2$, $w_2 = -2i$, $w_3 = -2$ say, or $z_1 = -i$, $z_2 = 0$, $z_3 = i$, $w_1 = 2i$, $w_2 = 2$, $w_3 = -2i$. These give $w = (2 - 2z)/(1 + z)$ and $w = (2z - 2)/(z + 1)$, respectively.

13 (a) $\psi(x, y) = \frac{50}{\ln R}\left(\ln R - \ln \sqrt{\frac{(x - a)^2 + y^2}{(ax - 1)^2 + a^2y^2}}\right)$, $R = 2 + \sqrt{3}$ (d) $\psi(0, 4) = 0.3060$

SECTION 19.4

2 (a) D' is lower half plane: $-\infty < u < \infty$, $-\infty < v < 0$. On $E'C'$ $(-\infty < u < -1)$, $\Psi = \frac{2u}{u - 1}$; on $C'B'(-1 < u < 0)$, $\Psi = 1$; on $B'A'(0 < u < 1)$, $\Psi = 0$; on $F'E'(1 < u < \infty)$, $\frac{\partial \Psi}{\partial v} = 0$

(e) D' is upper half plane: $-\infty < u < \infty$, $0 < v < \infty$. On $C'E'A'(-\infty < u < 0)$, $\frac{\partial \Psi}{\partial v} = -\frac{2}{1 + u^2}$; on $A'B'C'(0 < u < \infty)$, $\Psi = \frac{100u}{1 + u^2}$.

7 $\psi(x, y) = \psi_2 + \frac{4}{\pi}(\psi_1 - \psi_2)\left\{\cos^{-1}\left(\frac{x^2 + y^2 - 1}{\sqrt{[(x - 1)^2 + y^2][(x + 1)^2 + y^2]}}\right) - \frac{3\pi}{4}\right\}$, where $0 \leq \cos^{-1}(\ ) \leq \pi$

CHAPTER 20

SECTION 20.2

2 (a) $\frac{2}{3}(1 + i)$ (d) $-\pi i$ 5 (a) $|\int_C z^5\, dz| \leq 128\sqrt{10}$ (d) $\left|\int_C \frac{dz}{z}\right| \leq \frac{8\pi}{4 - \sqrt{5}}$

SECTION 20.3

4 (a) πi (d) 0 (g) $-\frac{2\pi i}{5}$ 6 (a) $\frac{1}{21}$ 9 (a) 0 (d) $2\pi i$

SECTION 20.4

2 (a) $\frac{z^2}{2}, \frac{z^2}{2} + 6, \frac{z^2}{2} - 1 + 2i$ 3 (a) $-\frac{1}{2}$ (d) $-\frac{i}{3}\sinh 3$ 4 (a) $-\frac{\ln 2}{2} + i\frac{5\pi}{4}$

SECTION 20.5

1 (a) $2\pi i$ (d) $-4\pi i \sin 1$ (g) $\pi i(\sin 3 - 3\cos 3)$

CHAPTER 21

SECTION 21.2

7 (a) Converges (d) Diverges (h) Converges

SECTION 21.3

2 (a) Converges in $|z| < 1$, diverges in $|z| \geq 1$ (d) Converges in $|z + i| < \frac{1}{e}$, diverges in $|z + i| \geq \frac{1}{e}$
(g) Converges for all z **8** (a) $\sum_{n=1}^{\infty} \frac{3^{n+1} - 2^{n+1}}{n^5 6^n (n + 1)}$

SECTION 21.4

5 (a) Yes, in $|z - 1| < 1$ **6** (b) $\sqrt{10}$ **7** (a) $\sqrt{4 - \sqrt{6}}$
8 (c) $\cos 2z = \cosh 6 - 2i \sinh 6(z - 3i) - 2 \cosh 6(z - 3i)^2 + \cdots ; R = \infty$
(e) $\frac{1}{i + z} = -i + z + iz^2 - z^3 + \cdots ; R = 1$ (i) $\operatorname{erf} z = \frac{2}{\sqrt{\pi}} z - \frac{4}{3!\sqrt{\pi}} z^3 + \cdots ; R = \infty$
12 (a) $\sqrt{z} = i - \frac{i}{2}(z + 1) - \frac{i}{8}(z + 1)^2 + \cdots$ in $|z + 1| < 1$

SECTION 21.5

5 (a) $\frac{1}{z} = \sum_{n=0}^{\infty} \frac{(-i)^n}{(z - i)^{n+1}}$ (d) $\frac{1}{e^z - 1} = \frac{1}{z} - \frac{1}{2} + \frac{1}{12} z + \cdots$ (h) $\frac{1}{z^2} = \sum_{n=0}^{\infty} \frac{(n + 1)i^n}{(z + 1)^{n+2}}$
6 (a) $\sin \frac{1}{z} = \sum_{n=0}^{\infty} \frac{(-1)^n}{(2n + 1)!} \frac{1}{z^{2n+1}}$ in $0 < |z| < \infty$
(b) T.S. in $|z + 2| < 2$: $\frac{1}{z} = -\frac{1}{2} \sum_{n=0}^{\infty} \left(\frac{z + 2}{2}\right)^n$, L.S. in $2 + |z + 2| < \infty$: $\frac{1}{z} = \sum_{n=0}^{\infty} \frac{2^n}{(z + 2)^{n+1}}$ **7** $f(\frac{1}{2}) = 8$
9 (a) $\frac{1}{z(z^2 + 1)} = \sum_{n=0}^{\infty} \frac{(-1)^n}{(z - 1)^{n+1}} + \sum_{n=0}^{\infty} \frac{(i - 1)^{n+1} + (-i - 1)^{n+1}}{2^{n+2}} (z - 1)^n$

SECTION 21.6

6 (a) First-order zeros at $z = 0$, $z = 1$
(d) First-order zero at $z = 0$, second-order zeros at $z = (2n + 1)\frac{\pi}{2}$ $(n = 0, \pm 1, \pm 2, \ldots)$
7 (a) Second-order pole at $z = 0$; residue $= \frac{1}{2}$ (d) First-order pole at $z = -2$; residue $= -1$
(i) Essential singularity at $z = 0$; residue $= 0$ (o) No singular points

SECTION 21.7

2 (a) 0 (d) $12\pi i$ **3** (a) $\frac{\pi}{2}$ (e) $\frac{5\pi}{32}$ (i) $2\pi/(4 - \sqrt{6})$ **6** (a) $\frac{\pi}{2\sqrt{2}}$ (e) $\frac{\pi}{4}$ (h) $\frac{\pi}{2e}$ **8** (a) $\frac{2\pi}{3\sqrt{3}}$
11 (a) $\frac{\pi}{\sin \pi a}$

Selected Mathematical Notation

Index

SELECTED FORMULAS

FOURIER SERIES

(a) $f(x)$ $2l$-periodic on $-\infty < x < \infty$:

$$f(x) = a_0 + \sum_{n=1}^{\infty} \left(a_n \cos \frac{n\pi x}{l} + b_n \sin \frac{n\pi x}{l} \right)$$

$$a_0 = \frac{1}{2l} \int_{-l}^{l} f(x)\, dx$$

$$a_n = \frac{1}{l} \int_{-l}^{l} f(x) \cos \frac{n\pi x}{l}\, dx, \quad n \geq 1$$

$$b_n = \frac{1}{l} \int_{-l}^{l} f(x) \sin \frac{n\pi x}{l}\, dx, \quad n \geq 1$$

(b) $f(x)$ defined only on $0 < x < L$:

Half-range sine: $f(x) = \sum_{n=1}^{\infty} b_n \sin \frac{n\pi x}{L}$ (HS1)

$$b_n = \frac{2}{L} \int_0^L f(x) \sin \frac{n\pi x}{L}\, dx \qquad \text{(HS2)}$$

Half-range cosine: $f(x) = a_0 + \sum_{n=1}^{\infty} a_n \cos \frac{n\pi x}{L}$ (HC1)

$$a_0 = \frac{1}{L} \int_0^L f(x)\, dx \qquad \text{(HC2)}$$

$$a_n = \frac{2}{L} \int_0^L f(x) \cos \frac{n\pi x}{L}\, dx \qquad \text{(HC3)}$$

Quarter-range sine: $f(x) = \sum_{n=1,3,\ldots}^{\infty} b_n \sin \frac{n\pi x}{2L}$ (QS1)

$$b_n = \frac{2}{L} \int_0^L f(x) \sin \frac{n\pi x}{2L}\, dx \qquad \text{(QS2)}$$

Quarter-range cosine: $f(x) = \sum_{n=1,3,\ldots}^{\infty} a_n \cos \frac{n\pi x}{2L}$ (QC1)

$$a_n = \frac{2}{L} \int_0^L f(x) \cos \frac{n\pi x}{2L}\, dx \qquad \text{(QC2)}$$

FOURIER INTEGRAL: $f(x) = \int_0^{\infty} [a(\omega) \cos \omega x + b(\omega) \sin \omega x]\, d\omega$

$$a(\omega) = \frac{1}{\pi} \int_{-\infty}^{\infty} f(x) \cos \omega x\, dx, \quad b(\omega) = \frac{1}{\pi} \int_{-\infty}^{\infty} f(x) \sin \omega x\, dx$$